BRITISH MUSEUM Dept. of printed books

GENERAL CATALOGUE OF PRINTED BOOKS

Photolithographic edition to 1955

Volume 11

BAR-BARS

PUBLISHED BY
THE TRUSTEES OF THE BRITISH MUSEUM
LONDON 1965

Printed in England by
Balding + Mansell, London and Wisbech

BAR.

—— The Bar . . . A poem, with notes. pp. vi. 160. *Hurst, Robinson & Co.: London*, 1825. 8°. **11630. bb. 49.**

—— The Bar, with sketches of eminent judges, barristers, &c. &c. A poem, with notes. pp. vi. 160. *Hurst, Robinson & Co.: London*, 1825. 8°. **11630. bb. 49.**

—— Second edition, improved. pp. vi. 160. *Hurst & Robinson: London*, 1826. 8°. **11648. dd. 18.**

—— The Bar and Legal World. *See* PERIODICAL PUBLICATIONS.—*London*.

—— The Bar and the Public. A collection of letters and articles, showing the present bar system to be the cause of the block in the courts of law . . . Reprinted from . . . letters of correspondents . . . and editorial articles appearing . . . in the Echo, *etc.* pp. 47. *E. W. Allen: London*, 1878. 8°. **6146. bbb. 7. (9.)**

—— The Bar Sinister. A social study. pp. vi. 354. *Cassell & Co.: New York*, 1885. 8°. **12706. k. 10.**

—— The Bar Sinister, or Memoirs of an Illegitimate, *etc.* [Signed: C. E. L., i.e. Hon. Camden E. Lambert.] 1836. 12°. *See* L., C. E. **N. 1346.**

—— "Crossing the Bar," and a few other translations. By H. M. B. [i.e. Henry Montagu Butler.] 1890. 8°. *See* B., H. M. **11408. d. 58.**

—— A Golden Bar. By the author of 'Christina North' [i.e. Eleanor A. Towle], *etc.* [A novel.] 3 vol. *Hurst & Blackett: London*, 1882. 8°. **12642. dd. 6.**

BAR. *See* also LORRAINE AND BAR.

——, *Counts of*. *See* GROSDIDIER DE MATONS (M.) Catalogue des actes des comtes de Bar de 1022 à 1239. 1922. 8°. **10167. g. 4.**

—— *See* GROSDIDIER DE MATONS (M.) Le Comté de Bar des origines au Traité de Bruges, *etc.* 1922. 8°. **10167. g. 5.**

——, *Dukes of*. *See* BAUDOT (J.) Les Princesses Yolande et les ducs de Bar de la famille des Valois. 1900. 8°. **9902. bb. 32.**

——, *House of*. *See* LORRAINE, *House of*.

BAR, IOLANDE, *Countess de*. *See* YOLANDA, *of Flanders, Countess de Bar*.

BAR, *in Poland, Confederacy of*.

—— *See* KONOPCZYŃSKI (W.) Polityka i ustrój Generalności Konfederacji Barskiej. Dwa nieznane przyczynki [i.e. "Krótkie zebranie okoliczności, jakiemi rozpoczęta, w postępach swoich pomnożona i dotąd utrzymana Generalna Konfederacja," here attributed to Jacek Antoni Puttkammer, and a part of the "Sancita" of the Generalność]. Wydał W. Konopczyński. 1930. 8°. [*Polska Akademia Umiejętności.—Archiwum Komisji Historycznej*. ser. 2. tom. 2.] **Ac. 750/16.**

—— Książeczka do nabożeństwa w czasach Konfederacyi Barskiej ułożona, a teraz na nowo przejrzana, poprawiona, uzupełniona. pp. 218. *Lipsk*, 1865. 16°. **3355. a. 3.**

—— Manifest der neuen Confoderation zu Bar, nebst Anmerkungen eines vornehmen Polen. pp. 135. 1768. 4°. **4695. e. 9. (2.)**

—— Wiadomości o Konfederacyi Barskiéj. [By S. Kaczkowski.] pp. xvi. 266. *Poznań*, 1843. 8°. **9475. bb. 27.**

BAR, *Dominus*. *See* BARTOLUS, *de Saxoferrato*.

BAR ASSOCIATION. Bar Association of St. Louis. *See* SAINT LOUIS, *Missouri*.

—— Bar Association of the State of New Hampshire. *See* NEW HAMPSHIRE.

BAR COMMITTEE. *See* ENGLAND.

BAR EXAMINATION ANNUAL. *See* PERIODICAL PUBLICATIONS.—*London*. The Bar Examination Journal, *etc.*

BAR EXAMINATION JOURNAL. *See* PERIODICAL PUBLICATIONS.—*London*.

BAR HARBOR. Souvenir Programme of a Meeting held at Bar Harbor, Maine, on August fourth, nineteen hundred and eighteen, to commemorate the fourth anniversary of Great Britain's entry into the war. *The Pilgrims: New York*, 1919. 8°. **09082. c. 37.**

BAR HEBRAEUS. *See* GRĪGHŌR (Abu al-Faraj) called BAR HEBRAEUS.

BAR-LE-DUC. Coutume de Bar-le-Duc, commentée par feu M. le Paige . . . alliée à celle de Saint-Mihiel. Troisieme édition, augmentée d'une notion des loix civiles ou romaines, de leur origine . . . Par M. de Maillet. 3 pt. *Toul*, 1783. 8°. **5424. aa. 3.**

—— Les Citoyens de Bar-sur-Ornin . . . assemblés en sections, a leurs frères les Citoyens de Paris. [Assuring them of support.] pp. 4. *Bar-sur-Ornin*, [1793.] 4°. **F. 17*. (33.)**

—— Les Citoyens de la Commune de Bar-sur-Ornin, reunis en société populaire. Aux représentans du peuple composant le Comité de Sureté générale à la Convention Nationale. [On the arrest of F. Robinot-Garnier, in reply to a pamphlet by C. X. Garnier-Anthoine.] pp. 24. *Bar-sur-Ornin*, [1774.] 4°. **F. 17*. (11.)**

—— Département de la Meuse. Observations de la commune de Bar-sur-Ornin, chef-lieu du département de la Meuse, sur les réclamations de la Commune de Verdun contre la fixation actuelle des principaux établissemens publics. pp. 8. [*Paris*, 1800?] 8°. **F.R. 110. (5.)**

—— Études sur le budget de la ville de Bar-le-Duc, Meuse. 1837–1846. pp. 253. *Bar-le-Duc*, 1849. 8°. **10170. d. 12.**

—— Exposé des persécutions exercées dans la commune de Bar-sur-Ornin. pp. 54. *Bar-sur-Ornin*, [1795?] 4°. **R. 675. (11.)**

—— Secret Memoirs of Barleduc, from the death of Queen Anne, to the present time. With an account of the late conspiracies for an invasion and rebellion in Great Britain. [With special reference to the court of Prince James Edward Francis Stuart.] pp. 95. *P. Campbell: Dublin*, 1716. 16°. **12314. aaa. 1. (12.)**

—— [Another copy.] **G. 5029.**

ARCHIVES DE LA MEUSE.

—— Collection Cloüet-Buvignier sur l'histoire du Verdunois . . . Inventaire publié par Paul Marichal. pp. 96. *Paris*, 1923. 8°. [*Mettensia*. no. 8.] **Ac. 5331/4.**

BIBLIOTHÈQUE.

—— Manuscrits de la Bibliothèque de Bar-le-Duc. [By H. Dannreuther.] 1894. 8°. *See* FRANCE.—*Ministère de l'Instruction Publique*. Catalogue général des manuscrits, *etc.* [New Series.] Départements. tom. 24. 1886, *etc.* 8°.

BAR-LE-DUC.

SOCIÉTÉ DES LETTRES, SCIENCES ET ARTS DE BAR-LE-DUC.

—— Mémoires de la Société des Lettres, Sciences et Arts de Bar-le-Duc. 10 tom. *Bar-le-Duc*, 1871–81. 8°.

—— Deuxième série. 10 tom. *Bar-le-Duc*, 1882–91. 8°.

—— Troisième série. 10 tom. *Bar-le-Duc*, 1892–1901. 8°.

—— Quatrième série. 10 tom. *Bar-le-Duc*, 1902–12. 8°.

—— Index général des matières . . . 1871–1890, *etc.* pp. 44. *Bar-le-Duc*, 1893. 8°. Ac. **271.**

BAR-LE-DUC, *Bailliage de.*

—— Motion sur l'échange de Sancerre, présentée à l'Assemblée nationale . . . par MM. les députés du bailliage de Blois, Valenciennes et Bar-le-Duc. pp. 45. [1789.] 8°. *See* BLOIS, *Bailliage de.* R. **242.** (**3.**)

BAR MUSICAL SOCIETY. *See* LONDON.—III.

BAR POINT, *pseud.*

—— Backgammon up to Date . . . By "Bar Point." pp. 51. *T. De la Rue & Co.: London*, 1931. 8°. **07912.** ee. **94.**

BAR REPORTS. *See* PERIODICAL PUBLICATIONS.—London.—*Law Times.*

BAR-SUR-ORNIN. *See* BAR-LE-DUC.

BAR-SUR-SEINE.

—— Inventaire-sommaire des archives communales antérieures à 1790, rédigé par M. d'Arbois de Jubainville . . . Bar-sur-Seine. *Paris*, 1864. 4°. [*Collection des inventaires-sommaires, etc.*] S. **148.** b. **7.**

—— Le noble et gentil jeu de l'arbaleste à Bar-sur-Seine. pp. 8. *Troyes*, 1853. 8°. K.T.C. **28.** a. **17.** (**3.**)
One of an edition of 17 copies.

BAR-SUR-SEINE, *Bailliage de.*

—— Cahiers de doléances du bailliage de Bar-sur-Seine. 1911. *See* TROYES, *Bailliage de.* Département de l'Aube. Cahiers de doléances du bailliage de Troyes . . . pour les États Généraux de 1789, *etc.* 1909, *etc.* 8°. **9231.** s. **20.**

Clergé.

—— Cahier de doléances de la Chambre du Clergé du bailliage et comté de Bar-sur-Seine. pp. 29. 1789. 8°. F.R. **22.** (**33.**)

Conseillers honoraires.

—— Sentence de MM. les Conseillers honoraires en titre au bailliage de Bar-sur-Seine, exerçans la justice sur le fait des Aides . . . qui ordonne que l'Avis au Public sera lacéré & brûlé au pied de l'escalier du Palais : suivie des lettres écrites à cette occasion, aux officiers de cette jurisdiction, par quelques magistrats. pp. 16. 1788. 8°. F.R. **6.** (**19.**)

Noblesse.

—— Cahier de la Noblesse du comté de Bar-sur-Seine. pp. 19. [1789.] 8°. F.R. **22.** (**32.**)

—— [Another copy.] Cahier de la Noblesse du comté de Bar-sur-Seine. [1789.] 8°. R. **37.** (**7.**)

BÄR ( ) [For the German surname of this form :] *See* BAER.

BAR * * * (DE) *Chevalier.* La Morale des Sens . . Extrait des mémoires de Mr le Chevalier De Bar * * * (Barville), *etc.* *See* BARVILLE (de) *Chevalier.*

BAR (DE) *Duke.*

—— Coutumes et droits successoraux de la classe paysanne et l'indivision des propriétés rurales en Autriche. pp. 358. [1935.] 8°. *See* LOUVAIN.—*Academia Lovaniensis.*—*École des Sciences Politiques et Sociales.* **05551.** i. **23.**

BAR (DE) *Mademoiselle.* *See* PIRON (A.) Œuvres inédites de Piron. Prose et vers accompagnées de lettres également inédites adressées à Piron par MMlles Quinault et de Bar. 1859. 8°. **12236.** c. **9.**

BAR (ADAM)

—— *See* CRACOW.—*Uniwersytet Jagielloński.*—*Biblioteka.* Katalog wystawy czasopism polskich od w. XVI do r. 1830. [With an introduction by A. Bar.] 1938. 8°. Ac. **749.** c/**6.**

—— *See* GRABOWSKI (M.) Michała Grabowskiego listy literackie. Wydał A. Bar. 1934. 8°. [*Archiwum do Dziejów Literatury i Oświaty w Polsce.* ser. 2. tom 2.] Ac. **750**/**22.**

—— Charakterystyka i źródła powieści Kraszewskiego w latach 1830–1850. pp. xi. 229. *Warszawa*, [1924.] 8°. **011840.** bb. **20.**
No. 21 *of "Prace historyczno-literackie."*

—— Jan Kochanowski w obcych językach. Próba bibljografji. pp. 29. *Kraków*, 1930. 4°. **11913.** b. **6.**

—— Słownik pseudonimów i kryptonimów pisarzy polskich oraz Polski dotyczących. Opracował A. Bar przy współudziale Wł. Tad. Wisłockiego i Tad. Godłowskiego. 3 tom. *Kraków*, 1936, 38. 8°. **2038.** e.

—— [Another copy.] Słownik pseudonimów i kryptonimów pisarzy polskich, *etc.* 3 tom. 1936–38. 8°.
See POLAND.—*Związek Bibliotekarzy i Archiwistów Polskich.*—*Krakowskie Koło.* **11900.** s. **28.**

—— Teatr krakowski pod dyrekcją Koźmiana. [Containing an article by S. Koźmian.] pp. 91. *we Lwowie*, [1939.] 8°. **11796.** b. **33.**

—— Zapomniany powieściopisarz lwowski [i.e. Walery Hilary Łoziński.] pp. viii. 105. 1931. 8°. *See* LEOPOL.—*Zakład Naukowy Imienia Ossolińskich.* Ac. **7215**/**68.**

BAR (ADELAÏDE DE) *Princess.*

—— La Tanya hongroise. [With a map.] pp. 262. [1937.] 8°. *See* LOUVAIN.—*Academia Lovaniensis.*—*École des Sciences Politiques et Sociales.* Ac. **2646.** g/**8.**

BAR (ALEXANDRE DE) *See* LAMARTINE DE PRAT (M. L. A. de) Le Lac. (Compositions et eaux-fortes par A. de Bar.) 1860. fol. **1750.** b. **17.**

—— *See* LEFÈVRE (André P.E.) Les Parcs et les jardins . . . Ouvrage illustré de 29 vignettes par A. de Bar. 1867. 12°. **7055.** b. **56.**

BAR (ALEXIS GUILLAUME HENRI COLLIN DE) *See* COLLIN DE BAR.

BAR (ARTHUR)

—— De la gastrostomie. Thèse, *etc.* pp. 24. *Strasbourg*, 1865. 4°. [*Collection générale des dissertations de la Faculté de Médecine de Strasbourg.* sér. 2. tom. 38.] **7381*.** e.

BAR (Augustin Henri)

—— Des adhérences du péricarde au cœur. Thèse, *etc.* pp. 35. *Strasbourg*, 1865. 4°. [*Collection générale des dissertations de la Faculté de Médecine de Strasbourg.* sér. 2. tom. 38.] **7381.***e.

BAR (Bonaventure de)

—— *See* Alvin-Beaumont (V.) Autour de Watteau. Réfutation des thèses sur . . . B. Debar, *etc.* [1932.] 4°. **7863.** v. **9.**

BAR (Carl Ludwig von) *See* Jonge (M. de) Retourbillets und kein Ende. Erwiderung gegen Professor L. von Bar, *etc.* [In answer to a contribution by von Bar to "Das Gerichtssaal."] 1889. 8° **5607.bb.4.**

—— *See* Rachel (Samuel) Samuelis Rachelii . . . De jure naturae et gentium dissertationes . . . Edited by L. von Bar, *etc.* 1916. 4°. Ac. **1866**/3. (**3.**)

—— *See* Textor (Johannes W.) *the Elder.* Joh. Wolfgangi Textoris . . . Synopsis juris gentium. Edited by L. von Bar. 1916. 4°. Ac. **1866**/3. (**8.**)

—— *See* Zurich.—*Universität Zürich.—Rechts- und Staatswissenschaftliche Fakultät.* Festschrift dem Herrn geheimen Justizrat Dr. L. v. Bar . . . gewidmet, *etc.* 1908. 8°. **6916.** b. **27.**

—— Die Ausscheidung von Domainen für Seine Majestät den König von Hannover. pp. 87. *Hannover*, 1862. 8°. **8226.** bb. **64.** (**3.**)

—— *See* Miquèl (J.) Die Ausscheidung des Hannoverschen Domanialguts . . . Eine Erwiederung. [A reply to the work by C. L. von Bar.] 1863. 8°. **5605.** aa. **62.** (**3.**)

—— Der Burenkrieg, die Russificirung Finnlands, die Haager Friedensconferenz, und die Errichtung einer internationalen Academie zur Ausgleichung von Streitigkeiten der Staaten. pp. vii. 61. *Hannover*, 1900. 8°. **06955.** f. **10.**

—— Das deutsche Reichsgericht. pp. 62. *Berlin*, 1875. 8°. [*Deutsche Zeit- und Streit-Fragen.* Jahrg. 4. Hft. 60.] **12209.** f.

—— Das Fremdenrecht und seine volkswirthschaftliche Bedeutung. pp. 30. *Berlin*, 1892. 8°. [*Volkswirthschaftliche Zeitfragen.* Hft. 113.] **8207.i.32/113.**

—— [Geschichte des deutschen Strafrechts.] A History of Continental Criminal Law. By C. L. von Bar . . . and others [i.e. with additional matter by various authors]. Translated by Thomas S. Bell . . . and others. With an editorial preface by John H. Wigmore, *etc.* pp. lvi. 561. *John Murray: London*, 1916. 8°. [*Continental Legal History Series.* vol. 6.] Ac. **2185**

—— Geschichte und Reform der deutschen Civiljustiz. Ein gemeinverständlicher Vortrag. pp. 43. *Leipzig*, 1871. 8°. **5656.** f. **9.**

—— Das Gesetz über das Telegraphenwesen des Deutschen Reiches. pp. 35. *Berlin*, [1892.] 8°. **5604.** e. **1.** (**5.**)

—— Gesetz und Schuld im Strafrecht. Fragen des geltenden deutschen Strafrechts und seiner Reform. 3 Bd. *Berlin*, 1906–09. 8°. **6055.** dd. **27.**

—— Die Grundlagen des Strafrechts. Eine Einleitung in die Theorie des Strafrechts. pp. 93. *Leipzig*, 1869. 8°. **6055.** cc. **15.**

—— Das internationale Privat- und Strafrecht. pp. xviii. 616. *Hannover*, 1862. 8°. **6955.** bb. **11.**

BAR (Carl Ludwig von)

—— Theorie und Praxis des internationalen Privatrechts . . . Zweite umgearbeitete Auflage des internationalen Privat- und Strafrechts. 2 Bd. *Hannover*, 1889. 8°. **6955.** g. **9.**

—— International Law: private and criminal . . . Translated, with notes, by G. R. Gillespie. pp. xxxii. 766. *W. Green: Edinburgh*, 1883. 8°. **6916.** b. **4.**

—— [Another copy, with a different titlepage.] *Soule & Bugbee: Boston, Edinburgh* [printed], 1883. 8°. **6955.** e. **7.**

—— The Theory and Practice of Private International Law . . . Second edition, revised and enlarged. Translated by G. R. Gillespie. pp. xlvi. 1162. *W. Green & Sons: Edinburgh*, 1892. 8°. **06955.** ee. **10.**

—— Teoria e pratica del diritto internazionale privato. Traduzione . . . a cura del Prof. Giulio Cesare Buzzati. pp. viii. 662. *Torino*, 1915. 8°. [*Biblioteca di scienze politiche ed amministrative.* ser. 3. vol. 11. pt. 1.] **8005.** K.

—— Internationales Handelsrecht. 1913. *See* Ehrenberg (V.) [Professor of Law at ... Leipzig.] Handbuch des gesamten Handelsrechts, *etc.* Bd. 1. 1913, *etc.* 8°. **05605.ee.28.**

—— Internationales Privatrecht. 1906. *See* Hinneberg (P.) Die Kultur der Gegenwart, *etc.* Tl. 2. Abt. 8. 1905, *etc.* 8°. **11313.** p.

—— Lehrbuch des internationalen Privat- und Strafrechts. pp. xvi. 360. *Stuttgart*, 1892. 8°. **6916.** aaa. **20.**

—— [Another copy.] **6916.** aaa. **23.**

—— Die Lehre vom Causalzusammenhange im Rechte, besonders im Strafrechte. pp. 155. *Leipzig*, 1871. 8°. **6057.** c. **2.** (**10.**)

—— Medizinische Forschung und Strafrecht. *See* Regelsberger (F.) Festgabe, *etc.* 1901. 8°. **6005.** e. **16.**

—— Recht und Beweis im Civilprocesse. Ein Beitrag zur Kritik und Reform des deutschen Civilprocesses. pp. xviii. 270. *Leipzig*, 1867. 8°. **5656.** f. **8.**

—— *See* Meyer (K. G. L.) Bemerkungen zur Civil-Processgesetzgebung. Mit Rücksicht auf die Schrift des Prof. v. Bar: "Recht und Beweis in Civilprocesse," *etc.* 1867. 8°. **5655.** df. **32.**

—— Recht und Beweis im Geschworenengericht. Ein Beitrag zur Kritik der Praxis und Gesetzgebung auf dem Gebiete des Strafverfahrens. pp. xvi. 368. *Hannover*, 1865. 8°. **6025.** cc. 3.

—— Staat und katholische Kirche in Preussen. pp. iv. 130. *Berlin*, 1883. 8°. **8074.** e. **17.** (**2.**)

—— Zur Frage der Geschworenen- und Schöffengerichte. pp. 31. *Berlin*, 1873. 8°. **5511.** h. **1.** (**8.**)

—— Zur Lehre von Versuch und Theilnahme am Verbrechen. pp. x. 100. *Hannover*, 1859. 8°. **5605.** bb. **7.**

BAR (Catherine de) *See* Mathilde, *du Saint Sacrement.*

BAR (Elvire D.) Dictionnaire des épithètes et qualificatifs. pp. vi. 552. *Paris*, 1930. 8°. **12951.** de. **12.**

BAR (F.) *Writer on Agriculture.*

—— Коренное преобразованіе крестьянскаго хозяйства и общиннаго землевладѣнія. pp. 128. *Москва*, 1894. 8°. **08277.** g. **42.**

BAR (Francis)

—— Les Épîtres latines de Raoul le Tourtier, 1065 ?–1141 ? Étude de sources. La légende d'Ami et Amile. pp. 288. *Paris*, 1937. 8°. **11859.** d. **2.**

BAR (FRANCIS)

—— Les Routes de l'autre monde. Descentes aux enfers et voyages dans l'au-delà. pp. 159. *Paris*, 1946. 8°. [*Mythes et religions*. vol. 17.] W.P. **13335/17**.

BAR (GASTON DE)

—— *See* PARIS.—*Comité des Travaux Historiques et Scientifiques*. Tables générales des Bulletins du Comité, *etc*. (II [*etc*.]. Par G. de Bar.) 1923, *etc*. 8°. Ac. **437/8**.

BAR (GEORG LUDWIG VON) *Baron*. *See* BAAR (Georges L. de)

BAR (GERMAN) *See* BAHR (Hermann)

BAR (HENRI) *See* BAR (Augustin H.)

BAR (JEAN ÉTIENNE) Convention Nationale. Motifs des dispositions du titre III du livre premier du Code civil, sur les droits des époux, *etc*. pp. 14. [*Paris*, 1793.] 8°. F.R. **206**. (**13**.)

—— Convention Nationale. Projet de décret pour accélérer l'expédition des affaires au Tribunal de Cassation, présenté le 15 août, *etc*. pp. 2. [1795?] 8°. F.R. **182**. (**8**.)

—— Convention nationale. Projet de décret relatif aux mesures répressives à prendre contre les corps administratifs, les municipalités et les particuliers qui tenteroient directement ou indirectement de dissoudre des sociétés populaires, *etc*. pp. 3. [*Paris*, 1791?] 8°. R. **155**. (**14**.)

—— Convention Nationale. Rapport et projet de décret sur la pétition du citoyen Roger fils, marchand à Rouen, et celle des citoyens Dupont, Martine, et Bornainville, *etc*. pp. 8. *Paris*, an III [1795]. 8°. F. **1257**. (**7**.)

—— Convention Nationale. Rapport et projet de décret, sur le référé du Tribunal du sixième arrondissement de Paris, présentant la question: si les contestations . . . entre les époux divorcés . . . doivent être portées devant un Tribunal de famille *etc*. pp. 3. [*Paris*, 1793?] 8°. F.R. **208**. (**9**.)

—— [Another copy.] F. **535**. (**5**.)

—— Convention Nationale. Rapport et projet de décret, sur un jugement du tribunal criminel du département de la Charente-Inférieure, *etc*. pp. 10. [*Paris*, 1795?] 8°. F. **1232**. (**8**.)

—— Corps Législatif. Conseil des Anciens. Opinion de J.-E. Bar . . . sur la résolution du 13 fructidor an 7, relative à l'entrée et au sejour de la force armée dans le cercle determiné par l'article 69 de la constitution. Séance du 28 fructidor an 7. pp. 11. *Paris*, [1799.] 8°. F.R. **280**. (**24**.)

—— Corps Législatif. Conseil des Anciens. Opinion de J.-E. Bar . . . sur la résolution relative aux émigrés naufragés à Calais. pp. 11. *Paris*, an 7 [1799]. 8°. F. **739**. (**1**.)

—— Corps Législatif. Conseil des Anciens. Rapport fait par J.-E. Bar . . . sur la résolution du 18 thermidor dernier, relative aux secours à délivrer aux parens des accusés contumax. Séance du 14 vendémiaire an 8. pp. 18. *Paris*, [1799.] 8°. F.R. **219**. (**3**.)

—— Corps Législatif. Conseil des Anciens. Rapport fait par Bar sur la résolution du 13 ventôse an 7, qui annulle un arrêté du représentant du peuple Mallarmé portant circonscription de canton dans le département de la Moselle. pp. 10. *Paris*, fructidor, an 7 [1790]. 8°. F.R. **108**. (**83**.)

BAR (JOACHIM ROMANUS)

—— Relationes inter religiosos et Episcopum iuxta constitutiones Polonarum synodorum usque ad 1420 annum. Dissertatio, *etc*. pp. 95. *Cracoviae*, 1940. 8°. **04784**. h. **49**.

BAR (JOACHIM ROMANUS) and **ZMARZ** (WOJCIECH)

—— Polska bibliografia prawa kanonicznego od wynalezienia druku do 1940 roku. Tom II za lata 1800–1940. (Bibliographia polonica iuris canonici, *etc*.) pp. 355. *Lublin*, 1947. 8°. [*Towarzystwo Naukowe Katolickiego Uniwersytetu Lubelskiego. Rozprawy wydziału kanoniczno-teologicznego*. no. 4.] Ac. **2652**. 1/**3**.

BAR (KARL LUDWIG VON) *See* BAR (C. L. von)

BAR (KATARZYNA MECHTYLDA DE) *See* MATHILDE, *du Saint Sacrement*.

BAR (LUDWIG VON) *Jurist*. *See* BAR (C. L. von)

BAR (LUDWIG VON) *Regierungsassessor*. Die kriegswirt schaftliche Regelung der Eierversorgung im Deutsche-Reich, unter besonderer Berücksichtigung der Organisation in Preussen. pp. 59. *Berlin*, 1919. 8°. [*Beiträge zur Kriegswirtschaft*. Hft. 49.] **8226**. pp. **35**.

BAR (OTTO VON) Die Noth der Productivstände. pp. 29. *Osnabrück*, 1883. 8°. **8229**. de. **29**. (**6**.)

BAR (PAUL)

—— *See* HEGAR (A.) and KALTENBACH (R.) Traité de gynécologie opératoire . . . Traduit . . . par . . . P. Bar, *etc*. 1885. 8°. **07580**. k. **25**.

—— *See* INTERNATIONAL MEDICAL CONGRESS. [Paris, 1900.] XIIIe Congrès international de médecine . . . Comptes rendus, *etc*. (vol. 15. Section d'obstétrique. Comptes rendus publiés par MM. Bar et Champetier de Ribes.) [1901.] 8°. Ac. **3699/12**.

—— Recherches expérimentales et cliniques pour servir à l'histoire de l'embryotomie céphalique. pp. vi. 313. *Paris*, 1889. 8°. **7580**. dd. **6**.

BAR (R. N.) *See* NETHERLANDS.—*Kingdom of the Netherlands*.—*Colonies*.—*East Indies*. Militair Wetboek voor het Nederlandsch Oost-Indisch Leger . . . Bewerkt door W. A. van Rees . . . en R. N. Bar. 1864. 8°. **6875**. aa. **59**.

BÄR (RAIMOND) *See* KLOOT (M. A. van R. van der) and BÄR (R.) Genealogische Kwartierstaten van nederlandsche geslachten, *etc*. 1887, *etc*. fol. **1861**. a. **8**.

BARA (CHARLES) Le Général Washington. Constitution de la République des États-Unis. pp. iii. 43. *Valenciennes*, 1889. 8°. **9004**. l. **28**. (**7**.)

BARA (HIEROME DE) Le Blason des armoiries, auquel est monstree la maniere de laquelle les anciens & modernes ont vsé en icelles . . . Reueu, corrigé, amplifié par l'auteur, *etc*. pp. 247. MS. NOTES. *Pour B. Vincent: [Lyons,]* 1581. 4°. **605**. f. **1**.

—— Le Blason des armoiries, *etc*. *I. de Gabiano & S. Girard: Lyon*, 1604. 4°. **C.22.f.12.**
A duplicate of the preceding, omitting the colophon, and with a different titlepage.

—— [Another edition.] Reueu, corrigé, & augmenté en ceste derniere edition, par B. R. D. E. L. R. pp. 197. *R. Boutonné: Paris*, 1628. fol. **9903**. l. **7**.

BARA (JAN) *See* BENJAMIN BEN JONAH, *of Tudela*. De Reysen van R. Benjamin Jonasz Tudelens . . . In't Nederduyts overgeschreven door J. Bara. 1666. 12°. **1936**. a. **14**.

—— *See* BOSSE (A.) Algemeene manier van de Hr. Desargues, tot de praktyk der perspectiven . . . Uit het Frans vertaalt van J. Bara. 1686. 8°. **1041**. c. **33**.

BARA (Jan)

—— Galteno en Alimene, of Verdoemde ontrouw. [A play. In verse.] pp. 59. *J. van Duisberg: Amsterdam,* 1656. 8°. **11556.** b. **42.** (**2.**)

—— Godvruchtige Verklikker, vertoonende de losse en dwalende wegen der menschen, met de waare paden, om alle dartelheyd te mijden; met andere nijp-dichten, kusjes en minne-vaarzen, *etc.* pp. 154. *J. van Duisbergh: Amsterdam,* 1657. 8°. **11556.** b. **42.** (**1.**)
With an additional titlepage, engraved.

—— Herstelde Vorst, ofte Geluckigh ongeluck. [A play. In verse.] *L. Spillebout: Amsterdam,* 1650. 4°. **11755.** e. **22.**

—— Huwelycks Sang up de bruyloft van . . . Peter van Beeck, ende . . . Johanna de Petain, *etc. L. Spillebout: Amsterdam,* 1650. *obl.* 16°. **11556.** aa. **1.** (**4.**)

—— Huwelycks-Schaekel-Dicht over het vereenigen van . . . Dirck Block, met . . . Angnita Leeuw, *etc. I. Lescaille: Amsterdam,* [1648.] *obl.* 16°. **11556.** aa. **1.** (**1.**)

—— Trou-Strick, tusschen . . . Antonius van Hoek de Jonge, ende . . . Johanna Mol, *etc. J. Rieuwertsz.: Amsterdam,* 1649. *obl.* 16°. **11556.** aa. **1.** (**2.**)

—— Zege-dicht, op d' echtes-verening van . . . Sr. David Leeuw, met . . . Juffr. Kornelia Hooft, *etc.* [Signed: J. B., i.e. Jan Bara.] [1651.] *obl.* 16°. *See* B., J. **11556.** aa. **1.** (**5.**)

BARA (Jean Baptiste) Corps Législatif. Conseil des Cinq Cents. Opinion . . . sur le projet de la commission des hypothèques, relatif à l'organisation de l'administration & des bureaux des hypothèques, & sur la réformation du tarif du 9 messidor an 3. Séance du 14 fructidor an 6. pp. 6. *Paris,* fructidor an 6 [1798]. 8°. F.R. **255.** (**13.**)

—— Corps Législatif. Conseil des Cinq Cents. Rapport fait . . . au nom d'une commission spéciale, chargée d'examiner la demande d'une pension, pour la citoyenne Collardeau, veuve du général Moreau, mort devant Luxembourg . . . le 23 pluviose an 3. pp. 4. *Paris,* an 7 [1799]. 8°. F. **204.** (**13.**)

—— Corps Législatif. Conseil des Cinq Cents. Rapport fait . . . sur la question de savoir si le Directoire exécutif ne doit pas être autorisé à faire continuer les travaux préparatoires qui ont pour objet de donner aux cantons les limites constitutionnelles dont ils sont susceptibles. Séance du premier brumaire an 7. pp. 10. *Paris,* brumaire an 7 [1798]. 8°. F.R. **108.** (**71.**)

—— Tribunat. Opinion . . . sur le projet de loi concernant l'organisation des justices de paix. Séance du 12 frimaire an 9. pp. 4. [*Paris,* 1800.] 8°. F.R. **185.** (**31.**)

—— Tribunat. Rapport fait . . . sur le projet de loi tendant à autoriser la commune de Dijon à acquérir deux édifices nationaux. Séance du 22 ventose an 9. pp. 4. *Paris,* ventose an 9 [1801]. 8°. R. **645.** (**25.**)

—— Tribunat. Rapport fait . . . sur un projet de loi tendant à autoriser la commune de Saint-Meuge . . . à vendre aux citoyens Jadot et Aubry un terrain communal. Séance du 9 frimaire an 10. *Paris,* frimaire an 10 [1801]. 8°. R. **643.** (**5.**)

BARA (Louis) La Science de la paix. Programme . . . Mémoire couronné, à Paris, en 1849, par le Congrès des sociétés anglo-américaines des amis de la paix. [Edited, with an introduction, by C. Potvin.] pp. xv. 251. *Bruxelles, Paris,* 1872. 8°. **8425.** i. **16.**

BARABAN (Léopold) À travers la Tunisie. Études sur les oasis, les dunes, les forêts, la flore, et la géologie . . . Ouvrage avec carte et vignettes. pp. viii. 227. *Paris,* 1887. 8°. **10097.** bb. **32.**

BARABAN (Victor) Du traitement des fractures de la rotule, *etc.* pp. 24. *Paris,* 1852. 4°. [*Collection des thèses soutenues à la Faculté de Médecine de Paris.* An 1852. tom. 1.] **7372.** e. **5.**

BARABANOV (A. M.)

—— *See* Muhammad Ṭāhir, *al-Ḳarākhī.* Хроника Мухаммеда Тахира ал-Карахи о дагестанских войнах . . . Арабский текст, подготовленный А. М. Барабановым, *etc.* 1946. 8°. [*Труды Института Востоковедения.* no. 37.] Ac. **1125.** ik/**2.**

—— *See* Muhammed Ṭāhir, *al Karkhī.* Хроника . . . о дагестанских войнах в период Шамиля. Перевод . . . А. М. Барабанова, *etc.* 1941. 8°. [*Труды Института Востоковедения.* no. 35.] Ac. **1125.** ik/**2.**

BARABÁS (Ábel) Goethes Wirkung in der Weltlitteratur. Goethe, Byron und Madách. pp. 70. *Leipzig,* 1903. 8°. **011840.** k. **78.**

—— A jövő évtized regénye. pp. 227. *Budapest,* 1910. 8°. **12590.** f. **16.**

—— Petőfi. pp. 286. *Budapest,* 1907. 8°. **010790.** df. **50.**

—— Renaissance a dalköltészetben. pp. xiii. 133. *Budapest,* 1904. 8°. **11826.** m. **10.**

—— Vas Gereben. pp. 219. *Budapest,* 1903. [*Vas Gereben munkáinak együttes képes kiadása.* Potkötet.] **012589.** g. **1.**

BARABÁS (Andreas) *See* Barabás (Endre)

BARABAS (Endre)

—— *See* Papp (József) *Dr.* Epizódok a románság történetéből a magyar uralom alatt. Barabas E. adatgyüjteménye és feldolgozása alapján közzéteszi: Papp. J. 1931. 8°. **09314.** e. **41.**

—— Das erste Dezennium des ungarischen Unterrichtswesens in Rumänien von 1918–1928 . . . Sonderabdruck aus der Zeitschrift: "Die Stimme der Minderheiten," *etc.* pp. 131. *Lugos,* 1929. 8°. **8358.** dd. **8.**

—— Kolozs vármegye közgazdasági leirása, *etc.* pp. 58. *Budapest,* 1910. 8°. [*Megyei monografiák.*] Ac. **825/110.**

—— Románia közoktatásügye. pp. 91. *Kolozsvárt,* 1908. 8°. **8307.** i. **23.** (**2.**)

—— Udvarhely vármegye közgazdasági leirása, *etc.* pp. 57. *Budapest,* 1904. 8°. [*Megyei monografiák.*] Ac. **825/110.**

BARABÁS (Gyula)

—— Ég az erdő. Regény. pp. 159. *Budapest,* [1936.] 8°. **12593.k.22.**

—— Székely erdők alján. Regény. pp. 313. *Budapest,* [1932.] 8°. **12590.** pp. **2.**

BARABÁS (Miklós)

—— *See* Hoffmann (Edith) Barabás Miklós. 77 képmelléklettel. 1950. 8°. **7871.** bb. **7.**

—— *See* Prónay (G.) *Baron, the Elder.* Skizzen aus dem Volksleben in Ungarn . . . Mit . . . bildlichen Darstellungen von Barabás, *etc.* 1855. fol. **1781.** b. **30.**

BARABÁS (MIKLÓS)

—— *See* VAJDA (J.) Magyar képek albuma. Barabás M. rajzai után, *etc.* 1859. 8º. **12354. g. 13.**

BARABÁS (SAMU) *See* BLAGAY, *Family of.* Codex diplomaticus Comitum de Blagay. A Blagay-család oklevéltára . . . Szerkesztették Thallóczy L. és Barabás S., *etc.* 1897. 8º. [*Monumenta Hungariae historica.* osztály 1. köt. 28.] Ac. **825.**

—— *See* FRANGEPÁN, *Family of.* Codex diplomaticus Comitum de Frangepanibus . . . Kiadják Dr. Thallóczi L., Barabás S. 1910, *etc.* 8º. [*Monumenta Hungariae historica.* osztály 1. köt. 35, 38.] Ac. **825.**

—— *See* GEORGE I. [Rákóczy], *Prince of Transylvania.* I. Rákóczy Gy. és a Porta. Levelek és okiratok . . . Szerkesztették Beke A. és Barabás S. 1888. 8º. Ac. **825/79.**

—— Székely oklevéltár 1219–1776. Közzéteszi Barabás S. [köt. 8.] pp. xxiii. 490. 1934. 8º. [*Magyar Történelmi Tár.* köt. 28.] Ac. **825/27.**
Köt. 1, 2, *were published by Magyar Történelmi Társulat.—Kolozsvári Bizottság ; köt* 3–7 *were published by the Székely Történelmi Pályadij-alapra Felügyelő Bizottság. They are placed at* Ac. 7311/4.

—— Zrinyi Miklós a szigetvári hős életére vonatkozó levelek és okiratok. A Magyar Tud. Akadémia történelmi bizottsága megbizásából közrebocsájtja Barabás Samu. 2 pt. *Budapest,* 1898, 99. 8º. [*Monumenta Hungariae historica.* osztály 1. köt. 29, 30.] Ac. **825.**

BARABAS (STEVEN)

—— So Great Salvation. The history and message of the Keswick Convention, *etc.* pp. 207. *Marshall, Morgan & Scott: London, Edinburgh,* 1952. 8º. **4708.** bb. **27.**

BARABÁS (TIBOR)

—— Magyar Jakobinusok. Színmű 3 felvonásban. pp. 79. *Budapest,* [1950.] 8º. **11758.** pp. **47.**

BARABASH (E.) Спиритизмъ въ исторіи, *etc.* pp. 141. *С.-Петербургъ,* 1886. 8º. **8632.** bb. **47.**

BARABASHEV (NIKOLAI PAVLOVICH)

—— Борьба с идеализмом в области космогонических и космологических гипотез. [With plates.] pp. 118. *Издательство Харьковского Государственного Университета имени А. М. Горького: Харьков,* 1952. 8º. **8565.** aaa. **33.**

BARABASZ (STANISŁAW) Ornament płaski na pomnikach krakowskich z XV i XVI wieku zebrał S. Barabasz, *etc.* (Flachornamente, *etc.*) *Pol. & Ger.* 3 cz. pl. LXXV. *Kraków,* [1894–1900.] fol. **1708.** d. **1.**

BARABBAS. The Quaker's Sermon: or, a Holding-forth concerning Barabbas [i.e. Dr. Sacheverel]. pp. 24. *A. Baldwin: London,* 1711. 8º. **8132.** aa. **13.** (**3.**)

—— The Release of Barabbas; or, the Causes of popular clamour and discontent considered, in a discourse on St. John, ch. XVIII. ver. 40. [By Thomas Hunter, Vicar of Weverham.] pp. vi. 16. *R. Baldwin: London,* 1770. 4º. **4474.** g. **4.**

—— The Vision of Barabbas, and other poems. [By John Joseph Brown.] pp. 103. *Henry Frowde: London,* 1891. 8º. **11651.** g. **41.**

BARABÉ (ALEXANDRE THÉODORE) Recherches historiques sur le tabellionage royal, principalement en Normandie, et sur les divers modes de contracter à l'époque du moyen-âge d'après de nombreuses pièces M.SS., et sigillographie normande en XXIV. planches . . . avec fac-simile d'une belle charte ducale du XI. siècle commentée par Dom Tassin en 1758 en deux lettres inédits. pp. viii. 577. *Rouen,* 1863. 8º. **9904.** k. 16.

BARABÉ (PAUL HENRI)

—— Quelques figures de notre histoire . . . (Marie de l'Incarnation, Mgr. de Laval, Marguerite Bourgeoys, Marie-Catherine de Saint Augustin, Madame d'Youville, Mgr. Taché, Mgr. Grandin, Mgr. Langevin.) Deuxième édition. [With portraits.] pp. 149. *Hull, Canada; Ottawa,* 1941. 8º. **10655.** v. **44.**

BARABESI (RAFFAELLO) Bibliografia della provincia di Grosseto. pp. x. 573. *Siena,* 1930. 8º. **11901.** pp. **15.**

BARABIN (G. DE)

—— Hommes & choses de la Révolution—Saint-Sulpice-en-Pareds. pp. 116. *Fontenay,* [1938.] 8º. **09226.** g. **34.**

BARABINO (NICOLÒ) *See* DELOGU (G.) Nicolò Barabino, *etc.* [With plates and a portrait.] 1928. 8º. **7859.** p. **30.**

—— *See* SAPORI (F.) I Maestri dell'arte, *etc.* (no. 4. Nicolo Barabino.) [1919, *etc.*] 16º. **07806.de.18/4.**

BARABINO (PIETRO) Tiri radenti e curvi nella difesa fissa da costa e più specialmente dei tiri curvi. pp. 79. *Roma,* 1881. 8º. **8831.** b. **17.** (**4.**)

BARABINO (SANTIAGO E.)

—— *See* CONGRESO CIENTÍFICO INTERNACIONAL AMERICANO. [Buenos Ayres, 1910.] Congreso Científico Internacional Americano . . . Publicación dirigida por . . . S. E. Barabino, *etc.* 1910, *etc.* 8º. Ac. **3083/2.**

BARAC (ANTUN)

—— *See* ŠENOA (A.) Djela. (Uredio A. Barac.) 1951, *etc.* 8º. W.P. c. **316.**

—— *See* ZAGREB.—*Sveučilište u Zagrebu.—Filozofski Fakultet.* Zbornik radova. (Urednički odbot Dr. A. Barac, *etc.*) 1951. 8º. Ac. **742.** d/**2.**

—— August Šenoa. Studija. [With a bibliography.] pp. 152. *Zagreb,* 1926. 8º. **11859.** ee. **3.**

—— Bjelinski u hrvatskoj književnosti. (Poseban otisak iz 272. knjige Rada Jugoslavenske akademije.) pp. 35. 1948. 8º. *See* ZAGREB.—*Jugoslavenska Akademija Znanosti i Umjetnosti.* **011850.** k. **81.**

—— Hrvatska književna kritika. pp. 330. *u Zagrebu,* 1938. 8º. [*Djela Jugoslavenske Akademije Znanosti i Umjetnosti.* knj. 34.] Ac. **741/16.**

—— Mažuranić. pp. 388. 1945. 8º. *See* ZAGREB.—*Matica Hrvatska.* **11868.** c. **11.**

—— Veličina malenih. Sastavci o književnosti i književicima. pp. 311. *Zagreb,* 1947. 8º. **11868.** c. **8.**

BARAC (FRANJO) Croats and Slovenes friends of the Entente in the World War: a few official documents derived from the archives of the Imperial and Royal Military Commands. Published [with a preface] by F. Barac. pp. 128. *Lang, Blanchong & Co.: Paris,* 1919. 8º. **08026.** d. **37.**

BARAC (IOAN)

—— *See* BOGDAN-DUICĂ (G.) Ioan Barac. Studii, *etc.* 1933. 8º. [*Academia Română. Studii și cercetări.* no. 22.] Ac. **743/43.**

BARACA (GIOVANNI) Tigellio. Scene storiche in un prologo, 2 parti e 5 atti, in versi. pp. 147. *Sassari,* 1885. 8º. **11715.** bb. **12.**

BARACCHI (FRANCESCO) Lutti e glorie di Milano dal settembre 1847 al marzo 1848. Cronaca storica. pp. 108. *Milano,* 1848. 12º. **8033.** b. **1.** (**2.**)

BARACCO (GIOVANNI) *See* PERIODICAL PUBLICATIONS.—*Turin.* Il Propagatore religioso. [Edited by G. Baracco.] 1836, *etc.* 8º. P.P. 23. e.

BARACCO (Giovanni)

—— Lettere . . . a Vincenzo Gioberti, 1834–1851. Pubblicate con proemio e note a cura di Luigi Màdaro. pp. xviii. 227. *Roma*, 1936. 8°. [*Regio Istituto per la Storia del Risorgimento Italiano. Biblioteca scientifica.* ser. 2. *Fonti.* vol. 13. *Carteggi di Vincenzo Gioberti.* vol. 3.] Ac. **2801**. b/4. (a.)

BARACCO (Michele) *See* Amoretti (C.) Descrizione di due macchine per la pasta immaginate da M. Baracco. [1809?] *s. sh.* 4°. B. **480**. (8.)

BARACCONI (Giuseppe) Menandro. Commedia storica in cinque atti, in versi. pp. 197. *Roma*, 1877. 8°. **11715**. f. **6**.

—— I Rioni di Roma. pp. ix. 718. *Città di Castello*, 1889. 8°. **7706**. aa. **50**.

—— Terza ristampa interamente rifatta. pp. 606. *Torino, Roma*, 1905. 8°. **07707**. h. **23**.

—— Rivista aneddotica del teatro romano antico. pp. xvi. 207. *Roma*, 1882. 8°. **11794**. b. **47**.

—— Venere. (Con 43 illustrazioni fuori testo.) pp. 386. *Torino, Roma*, 1907. 8°. **07808**. g. **20**.
No. 4 *of the* "*Biblioteca d'Arte.*"

BARACÉ (Alexandre de la Motte) *Viscount de Senonnes.* *See* La Motte Baracé.

BARACH (Alvan Leroy)

—— Physiologic Therapy in Respiratory Diseases . . . Second edition [of "Principles and Practices of Inhalational Therapy."] pp. xv. 408. *J. B. Lippincott Co.: Philadelphia*, [1948.] 8°. **7617**. d. **20**.

—— Principles and Practices of Inhalational Therapy, *etc.* pp. xvi. 315. *J. B. Lippincott Co.: Philadelphia*, [1944.] 8°. **7462**. r. 44.

—— [A reissue.] Principles and Practices of Inhalational Therapy, *etc.* *Blackwell Scientific Publications: Oxford; printed in U.S.A.*, 1945. 8°. **7462**. ppp. **27**.

BARACH (Carl Sigmund) *See* Alfredus, *Anglicus.* Excerpta e libro Alfredi Anglici De motu cordis, item Costa-Ben-Lucae De differentia animae et spiritus liber . . . Als Beitraege zur Geschichte der Anthropologie und Psychologie des Mittelalters . . . herausgegeben und mit . . . Anmerkungen versehen von Dr. C. S. Barach. [*Bibliotheca philosophorum mediae aetatis.* vol. 2.] **8463**. d. **8**.

—— *See* Descartes (R.) René Descartes' Meditationes de prima philosophia . . . Herausgegeben . . . von Dr. C. S. Barach. 1866. 8°. **8465**. cc. **42**. (**5**.)

—— Kleine philosophische Schriften . . . Neue Gesammtausgabe. 3 pt. *Wien*, 1878. 8°. **8468**. i. **10**.

—— Bibliotheca philosophorum mediae aetatis. Herausgegeben von Dr. C. S. Barach. vol. 1, 2. *Innsbruck*, 1876, 78. 8°. **8463**. d. **8**.
No more published.

—— Die gegenwärtige Aufgabe der Philosophie, aus der bisherigen Stellung der Philosophie zum Leben und den Forderungen des Lebens entwickelt. pp. 248. *Wien*, 1858. 8°. **8465**. f. **1**.

—— Hieronymus Hirnhaim. Ein Beitrag zur Geschichte der philosophisch-theologischen Cultur im siebzehnten Jahrhundert. pp. 72. *Wien*, 1864. 8°. **10705**. dd. **31**. (**8**.)

—— Pierre Daniel Huet als Philosoph. Ein Beitrag zur Geschichte der geistigen Bewegung im siebzehnten Jahrhundert. pp. 62. *Wien & Leipzig*, 1862. 8°. **8464**. e. **44**. (**4**.)

BARACH (Carl Sigmund)

—— Die Wissenschaft als Freiheitsthat. Philosophische Principlehre. pp. ii. 83. *Wien*, 1869. 8°. **8466**. f. **27**. (**7**.)

BARACH (Joseph Hayem)

—— Diabetes and its Treatment. pp. xviii. 326. *Oxford University Press: New York*, 1949. 8°. [*Oxford Medical Publications.*] **20036**. a. **1/765**.

BARACH (Moritz) *See* also Maerzroth (Jacob) *pseud.* [i.e. M. Barach.]

—— Glühende Kohlen. Novelle von Moritz Barach (Jakob Märzroth). 1844. *See* Ephemerides. Kalender und Jahrbuch für Israeliten, *etc.* Jahrg. 3. 1842, *etc.* 12°. P.P. **2377**. g.

BARACH (Rosa) and **MURAU** (Caroline) Aus Österreichs Herzen! Eine Auswahl der besten Poesien, welche zur Vermählungsfeier . . . des . . . Erzherzogs Kronprinz Rudolf mit . . . der . . . Prinzessin Stefanie verfasst wurden. Gesammelt und herausgegeben von R. Barach und K. Murau. pp. 100. *Wien*, [1882.] 8°. **11528**. h. **18**. (**2**.)

BARACHISIUS, *Saint.* *See* Jonas, *Saint.* SS. Jonae et Barachisii martyrum in Perside acta graeca. [Edited by H. Delehaye.] 1903. 8°. **4824**. de. **22**. (**11**.)

BARACHOVICH (Giurgije) *See* Baraković (Juraj)

BARACK (Carl August) *See* Ezzo, *Scholasticus Babenbergensis.* Ezzos Gesang von den Wundern Christi und Notkers Memento Mori . . . Herausgegeben von K. A. Barack. 1879. 4°. **1897**. b. **32**.

—— *See* Hass (K.) Ein Lobgedicht auf Nürnberg . . . Ein Beitrag zur deutschen Kulturgeschichte von K. A. Barack. 1858. 8°. **11511**. d. **33**. (**4**.)

—— *See* Heitz (P.) Elsässische Büchermarken . . . Mit Vorbemerkungen und Nachrichten über die Drucker von Dr. K. A. Barack. 1892. 4°. **N.L.1.d.**

—— *See* Oheim (G.) Gallus Oheims Chronik von Reichenau. Herausgegeben von . . . K. A. Barack. 1866. 8°. [*Bibliothek des Litterarischen Vereins in Stuttgart.* Bd. 84.] Ac. **8963**.

—— *See* Roswitha. Die Werke der Hrotsvitha. Herausgegeben von Dr. K. A. Barack. 1858. 8°. **11712**. c. **64**.

—— *See* Schricker (A.) Kunstschätze in Elsass-Lothringen. [By A. Schricker, assisted by C. A. Barack.] 1896. fol. **1754**. e. **2**.

—— *See* Singer (F. X.) Zum 100. Geburtstag von Karl August Barack, *etc.* [With a portrait.] [1927.] 4°. **010703**. g. **34**.

—— *See* Teufel. Des Teufels Netz . . . Herausgegeben von . . . K. A. Barack. 1863. 8°. [*Bibliothek des Litterarischen Vereins in Stuttgart.* Bd. 70.] Ac. **8963**.

—— *See* Zimmern Chronicle. Zimmerische Chronik. Herausgegeben von . . . K. A. Barack. 1869. 8°. [*Bibliothek des Litterarischen Vereins in Stuttgart.* Bd. 91–94.] Ac. 8963.

—— Elsass-lothringische Handschriften und Handzeichnungen. Bearbeitet von K. A. Barack. pp. v. 227. *Strassburg*, 1895. 4°. [*Katalog der Kaiserlichen Universitäts- und Landesbibliothek in Strassburg.*] **11905**. m. **24**.

BARACK (Carl August)

—— Die Handschriften der Fürstlich-Fürstenbergischen Hofbibliothek zu Donaueschingen. Geordnet und beschrieben von Dr. K. A. Barack. pp. xii. 666. 1865. 8°. *See* Donaueschingen. — *Fürstlich - Fürstenbergische Hofbibliothek.* **11907.** f. **6.**

—— Hans Böhm und die Wallfahrt nach Niklashausen im Jahre 1476, ein Vorspiel des grossen Bauernkrieges. Nach Urkunden und Chroniken bearbeitet. Besonderer Abdruck aus dem xiv. Bande des Archivs des histor. Vereins von Unterfranken. pp. 108. *Würzburg,* 1858. 8°. **9325.** eee. **5.** (**3.**)

BARACK (Karl August) *See* Barack (Carl A.)

BARACK (Max) Der Drumbeder vun Wallstadt. Eine Sammlung heiterer Gedichte in Pfälzer Mundart. pp. 87. *Heidelberg,* 1875. 8°. **11528.** b. **13.**

—— Pälzer Duwak. Schnurrige Erzählungen in Pfälzer Mundart, *etc.* pp. 127. *Kaiserslautern,* 1923. 8°. **012554.** bb. **19.**

BARACLOUGH (W. H.) Every Inventor his own Patent Agent. A handy book of the principles of the patent law, *etc.* pp. xxvii. 418. *Effingham Wilson: London,* 1928. 8°. **6376.** ppp. **29.**

—— Profit by Patents. pp. 34. *Cornish Bros.: Birmingham,* 1897. 8°. **8228.** aaaa. **32.** (**3.**)

BARACOA. Baracoa. [A historical account.] 1876. *See* Cuba. Los Tres primeros Historiadores de la Isla de Cuba, *etc.* tom. 2. 1876, *etc.* 4°. **9551.** l. **1.**

BARACS-DELTOUR ( ) *Dr.* Pariser Selbsterlebnisse während des Krieges. pp. 336. *München,* [1917.] 12°. **9084.** e. **2.**

BARĄCZ (Sadok) Archiwum . . . Dominikanów w Jarosławiu. Skreślił Ks. S. Barącz. Wydanie drugie. pp. 270. *Kraków,* 1887. 8°. **4784.** d. **51.**

—— Bajki, fraszki, podania, przysłowia i pieśni na Rusi . . . Drugie wydanie. pp. 271. *Lwów,* 1886. 8°. **12430.** g. **36.**

—— Dzieje klasztoru WW. OO. Dominikanów w Podkamieniu. pp. 348. *Tarnopol,* 1870. 8°. **4784.** ee. **9.**

—— Pamiątki Jazłowieckie. Zebrał S. Barącz. pp. 230. *Lwów,* 1862. 8°. **10291.** bb. **22.**

—— Pamiątki miasta Stanisławowa. Zebrał X. S. Barącz. pp. 191. *Lwów,* 1858. 8°. **10290.** d. **24.**

—— Pamiątki miasta Żółkwi. Zebrał Ks. S. Barącz. pp. 139. *Lwów,* 1852. 8°. **10215.** c. **8.**

—— Pamiętnik dziejów Polskich. Z aktów urzędowych lwowskich i z rękopismów zebrał X. S. Barącz. pp. 310. *we Lwowie,* 1855. 8°. **9475.** c. **24.**

—— Pamiętnik szlachetnego Ledochowskich domu. pp. 220. *Lwów,* 1879. 8°. **9904.** k. **1.**

—— Rys dziejów Zakonu Kaznodziejskiego w Polsce. 2 tom. *we Lwowie,* 1861. 8°. **4784.** dd. **8.**

—— Wolne miasto handlowe Brody. pp. 197. *Lwów,* 1865. 8°. **10291.** dd. **14.**

—— Żywoty sławnych ormian w Polsce. pp. viii. 485. *we Lwowie,* 1856. 8°. **10790.** dd. **23.**

BARAD (Muljibhai B.) *See* Mulji-bhāi B. Varada.

BARADA (Miho)

—— *See* Trogir. Trogirski spomenici . . . Prepisao i uredio Dr. M. Barada. 1948, *etc.* 8°. [*Monumenta spectantia historiam slavorum meridionalium.* knj. 44, *etc.*] Ac. **741**/3.

BARADA (Miho)

—— Dalmatia Superior. (Poseban otisak iz 270. knjige Rada Jugoslavenske akademije znanosti i umjetnosti.) pp. 25. *Zagreb,* 1949. 8°. **9134.** l. **17.**

—— Hrvatski vlasteoski feudalizam po Vinodolskom zakonu. [With the text of the law and a modern Croatian version.] pp. 133. *Zagreb,* 1952. 8°. [*Djela Jugoslavenske Akademije Znanosti i Umjetnosti.* knj. 44.] Ac. **741/16.**

—— Monumenta catarensia. (Kotorski spomenici.—Urednik M. Barada.) 1951– . 8°. *See* Zagreb.—*Jugoslavenska Akademija Znanosti i Umjetnosti.—Historijski Institut.* Ac. **741.** bb.

BARADAEUS (Jacobus) *Bishop of Edessa.* *See* Jacob, *Bishop of Edessa,* called Būrdě'ānā.

BARADAT (Ernest) Faculté de Droit de Paris. Thèse pour la licence. (Jus romanum. Depositi vel contra.—Droit français. Du prêt.) pp. 59. *Paris,* 1860. 8°. **5406.** c. **2.** (**1.**)

BARADELLE ( ) Liberté, Egalité. Municipalité du ixe arrondissement. Discours prononcé . . . le 23 thermidor de l'an 7 . . . pour la fête du dix août, *etc.* pp. 14. *Paris,* [1799.] 8°. **F. 1059.** (**18.**)

BARADÈRE (H.) Antiquités mexicaines. Relation des trois expéditions du capitaine Dupaix, ordonnées en 1805, 1806, et 1807, pour la recherche des antiquités du pays, notamment celles de Mitla et de Palenque ; accompagnée des dessins de Castañeda . . . et d'une carte du pays exploré ; suivie d'un parallèle de ces monuments avec ceux de l'Égypte, de l'Indostan, et du reste de l'ancien monde, par M. Alexandre Lenoir . . . d'une dissertation sur l'origine de l'ancienne population des deux Amériques, et sur les diverses antiquités de ce continent, par M. Warden . . . avec un discours préliminaire par M. Charles Farcy . . . et des notes explicatives, et autres documents, par M.M. Baradère, De St. Priest, et plusieurs voyageurs qui ont parcouru l'Amérique. [Edited by H. Baradère.] 2 tom. *Paris,* 1834. fol. **762.** i. **2.**

BARADEZ (Jean)

—— Fossatum Africae. Recherches aériennes sur l'organisation des confins sahariens à l'époque romaine, *etc.* [With plates and a map.] pp. x. 361. *Paris,* 1949. 8°. **07704.** b. **22.**

—— Tipasa. Ville antique de Maurétanie, *etc.* [With illustrations, and a plan.] pp. 78. *Alger,* 1952. 8°. **07705.** ee. **8.**

—— Vue aérienne de l'organisation romaine dans le sud-algérien Fossatum Africae. [With maps.] pp. x. 369. *Paris,* 1949. 8°. **07708.** d. **18.**

BARADI (Mauro)

—— *See* Osias (C.) and Baradi (M.) The Philippine Charter of Liberty. [1933.] 8°. **20018.** h. **34.**

BARADIIN (Badzar) *See* Zhal-Kan-Bo Dag-Ba Zhal-Tsan. Статуя Майтреи в золотом храме в Лавране. [Translated from the Tibetan, with an introduction by B. Baradiin.] 1924 [1912–24]. 8°. [*Bibliotheca Buddhica.* no. 22.] **14003.** dd. **22.**

BARADLAI (János) A magyarországi gyógyszerészet története az ősidőktől a mai napig. Irták: Dr. Baradlai J. és Bársony Elemér. [With plates, including portraits.] 2 köt. 1930. 8°. *See* Hungary.—*Magyarországi Gyógyszerész-Egyesület.* **8901.** dd. **18.**

BAR-ADON (Dorothy) *See* Kahn, afterwards Bar-Adon.

BAR-ADON (Pessach)

—— *See* Kahn, afterwards Bar-Adon (Dorothy R.) and Bar-Adon (P.) Seven who fell. [1947.] 8°. **4035.** a. **12.**

BARADOU (Jean Marie Victor) Reflexions sur la méthode d'étudier les sciences naturelles et leurs liaisons avec la médecine, sur la médecine proprement dite, et sur les devoirs du médecin, *etc.* pp. 31. *Montpellier*, 1814. 4°. **1180. g. 16. (23.)**

BARADOU (Octave) Considérations . . . sur la syphilis et quelques-uns de ses symptomes. Thèse, *etc.* pp. 62. *Montpellier*, 1846. 4°. **1182. d. 17. (5.)**

—— De l'emploi thérapeutique des eaux thermo-minérales de Vichy dans les maladies du foie et de la rate, *etc.* pp. 68. *Vichy*, 1865. 12°. **7470. aaa. 73. (5.)**

BARADO Y FONT (Francisco) *See* García Llansó (A.) Armas y armaduras . . . Prólogo de D. F. Barado, *etc.* 1895. 8°. **8825. ee. 25.**

—— D. Luis de Requesens y la política española en los Países Bajos. Discursos leídos [by F. Barado y Font and J. Suárez Inclán] ante la Real Academia de la Historia en la recepción pública del Señor D. F. Barado y Font, *etc.* pp. 155. *Madrid*, 1906. 8°. **9195. i. 4.**

—— Literatura militar española en el siglo xix. Bosquejo histórico-bibliográfico. pp. lxxx[v]iii. 336. *Madrid*, 1889. 8°. **11840. aaa. 20.**

—— Mis Estudios históricos, *etc.* pp. 148. *Madrid*, 1893. 8°. **9181. b. 14.**

—— Sitio de Amberes en 1584, 1585; con el principio y fin que tuvo la dominación española en los Estados Bajos. pp. 484. *Madrid*, 1895. 8°. **09078. aa. 3.**

—— La Vida militar en España. Cuadros y dibujos de José Cusachs . . . Texto de F. Barado. pp. xi. 343. *Barcelona*, 1888. fol. **1860. b. 11.**

BARADO Y FONT (Francisco) and **GÉNOVA** (Juan)

—— Armas portátiles de fuego. El moderno armamento de la infantería y su influencia en el combate. pp. 831. *Barcelona*, 1881. 8°. **8829. a. 59.**

BARADUC ( ) Essai critique sur le traitement de la pneumonie franche. pp. 52. *Paris*, 1874. 4°. [*Collection des thèses soutenues à la Faculté de Médecine de Paris.* An 1874. tom. 1.] **7374. a. 6.**

BARADUC (A.) Dissertation sur les hernies de l'estomac. Thèse, *etc.* pp. 24. *Paris*, 1837. 4°. **1184. h. 13. (24.)**

BARADUC (Hippolyte André Ponthion) Des causes de la mort à la suite des brûlures superficielles, des moyens de l'éviter. pp. 47. *Paris*, 1862. 8°. **7440. cc. 5.**

—— Études théorique et pratique des affections nerveuses considérées sous le rapport des modifications qu'opèrent sur elles la lumière et la chaleur; théorie de l'inflammation; des ventouses vésicantes. pp. 289. *Paris*, 1850. 8°. **7440. cc. 4.**

—— Relation de quelques faits de chirurgie pratique, *etc.* pp. 76. *Paris*, 1842. 4°. [*Collection des thèses soutenues à la Faculté de Médecine de Paris.* An 1842. tom. 1.] **7371. c. 15.**

BARADUC (Hippolyte Ferdinand) L'Âme humaine, ses mouvements, ses lumières, et l'iconographie de l'invisible fluidique. [With plates.] pp. 299. *Paris*, 1896. 8°. **08464. h. 13.**

—— The Human Soul, its movements, its lights, and the iconography of the fluidic invisible. [With illustrations.] pp. 188. *G. A. Mann: Paris*, 1913. 8°. **8467. df. 21.**

—— Les Vibrations de la vitalité humaine. Méthode biométrique appliquée aux sensitifs et aux névrosés. pp. viii. 280. *Paris*, 1904. 8°. **7405. cc. 9.**

BARADUC (Jacques Joseph Léon) Considérations sur la glaucome et son traitement chirurgical. pp. 43. *Paris*, 1865. 4°. [*Collection des thèses soutenues à la Faculté de Médecine de Paris.* An 1865. tom. 1.] **7373. f. 7.**

BARAENUS (Justus) Epistola Justi Baræni . . . ad theologum regium . . . Dn. Abrahamum Scultetum, &c. In qua dissensus ille sui causas modeste amiceque exponit et rogat, ut Regiæ Maiestati fides Lutheranorum candidè commendetur. pp. 19. *Antwerpiæ*, 1620. 4°. **3907. aa. 23. (3.)**

BARAFIN (Pierre Paul Joseph) Durville, ou les coups du sort, drame en deux actes, en prose. pp. 34. *Bruxelles*, [1801.] 8°. **11738. aa. 15. (3.)**

BARAFORT (François) Des partages d'ascendants et des modifications à introduire dans la loi sur cette matière à propos de l'enquête agricole. pp. 184. *Lyon*, 1869. 8°. **5423. b. 18.**

—— Traité théorique et pratique de la séparation des patrimoines. pp. 456. *Paris*, 1866. 8°. **5405. aaa. 6.**

BARAG (T. Ya.)

—— Караганда. [With plates.] pp. 33. *Москва*, 1950. 8°. [*Архитектура городов СССР.*] **W.P. 14081/14.**

BARAGA (Frédéric) Abrégé de l'histoire des Indiens de l'Amérique septentrionale . . . Traduit de l'allemand. pp. 296. *Paris*, [1837.] 12°. **9555. a. 7.**

—— A Dictionary of the Otchipwe Language, explained in English . . . A new edition, by a Missionary of the Oblates. 2 pt. *Beauchemin & Valois: Montreal*, 1878. 8°. **12910. c. 4.**

—— A Theoretical and Practical Grammar of the Otchipwe Language . . . A second edition, by a Missionary of the Oblates. pp. xi. 422. *Beauchemin & Valois: Montreal*, 1878. 8°. **12910. c. 3.**

BARAGAÑA (Eugenio García) *See* García Baragaña.

BARAGIN (D. D.)

—— Калинин. pp. 74. *Москва*, 1952. 8°. [*Архитектура городов СССР.*] **W.P. 14081/15.**

BARAGIOLA (Aristide)

—— *See* Goldoni (C.) [*Single Plays.—Le Bourru bienfaisant.*] Il Búrbero benèfico ossía il Bisbètico di buòn cuòre . . . Edizione scolástica con accènti ortofònici, curata dal Dr. A. Baragiola. 1883. 8°. **11716. aa. 23.**

—— *See* Hildebrand. Dall' antico Tedesco. Das Hildebrandslied. L'Inno d'Ildebrando. Versione con introduzione . . . di A. Baragiola. 1882. 8°. **3455. g. 11.**

—— *See* Muspilli. Dall' antico alto Tedesco. Muspilli ovvero l'Incendio universale. Versione con introduzione ed appendice del dottore A. Baragioli. 1882. 8°. **11427. ee. 3.**

—— Il Canto popolare a Bosco o Gurin, colonia tedesca nel cantone Ticino. pp. 175. *Cividale*, 1891. 8°. **11528. l. 21.**

—— Crestomazia italiana ortofonica . . . Prosa, *etc.* pp. xxiv. 494. *Strasburgo*, 1881. 8°. **12941. d. 5.**

—— Giacomo Leopardi, filosofo, poeta, e prosatore. Dissertazione dottorale, *etc.* pp. xv. 65. *Strasburgo*, 1876. 8°. **11840. i. 35.**

BARAGIOLA (Carlo)

—— Il Segreto dell'Africa Equatoriale. [Impressions of a journey made in 1930. With illustrations.] pp. 294. *Milano*, 1933. 8°. **10094. p. 24.**

BARAGIOLA (W. I.) *See* LIEBIG (J. von) *Baron.* Justus von Liebig und Friedrich Mohr in ihren Briefen von 1834–1870 . . . Herausgegeben . . . in Gemeinschaft mit . . . W. I. Baragiola von G. W. A. Kahlbaum. 1904. 8°. [*Monographien aus der Geschichte der Chemie.* Hft. 8.] **08909.** bb. **20.**

BARAGNON (JULES) Faculté de Droit de Paris. Thèse pour la licence. (Jus romanum. De captivis et postliminio reversis.—Droit français. Des absents.) pp. 59. *Paris,* 1860. 8°. **5406.** c. **2.** (**2.**)

BARAGNON (LOUIS NUMA) Examen de la brochure de M. Hubaine [entitled: "Le Gouvernement temporel des papes jugé par la diplomatie française"]. pp. 48. *Nîmes,* 1862. 8°. **8051.** de. **3.** (**1.**)

BARAGNON (PIERRE LOUIS) *See* MÉNARD (L.) Abrégé de l'histoire de Nismes de Ménard, continué . . . par P. L. Baragnon. 1831, *etc.* 8°. **795.** h. **25.**

BARAGUE (   ) Aphos, comédie en un acte et en vers, *etc.* [By —— Baragué.] pp. 51. 1748. 8°. *See* APHOS. **164.** f. **25.**

—— [Another issue.] **11738.** a. **28.** (**4.**)

BARAGUEY D'HILLIERS (ACHILLE) *Count.* *See* CASTELLANE (E. V. E. B. de) *Count.* Campagnes de Crimée, d'Italie, d'Afrique . . . Lettres adressées au maréchal de Castellane par les maréchaux Baraguey d'Hilliers, Niel, *etc.* 1898. 8°. **09078.** b. **25.**

BARAGUEY D'HILLIERS (LOUIS) *See* BOURDON (F. M. P.) Discours prononcés à l'occasion de la fête de la victoire . . . à Alençon [by Bourdon, Baraguey d'Hilliers and others]. [1796.] 4°. **F. 69*.** (**27.**)

—— *See* CUSTINE (A. P. de) *Count.* Mémoires posthumes du général françois Comte de Custine: rédigés par un de ses aides de camp [i.e. L. Baraguey d'Hilliers]. 1794. 8°. **113.** c. **16.**

BARAGURA (   )

—— [For the Ruthenian surname in this form:] *See* BARAHURA.

BARAGWANATH (JOHN)

—— Pay Streak. [Autobiographical reminiscences.] pp. 274. *Doubleday, Doran & Co.: Garden City, N.Y.,* 1936. 8°. **010885.** ff. 38.

BARAGWANATH (WILLIAM) The Beringa Gold-Field, *etc.* pp. 17. pl. XIII. *Melbourne,* 1907. fol. [*Memoirs of the Geological Survey of Victoria.* no. 5.]

C.S.G.356/4.

BARAHONA.

—— Memoria del Honorable Ayuntamiento de la Común de Barahona correspondiente a su ejercicio administrativo del año 1946–1947 [*etc.*]. *Barahona,* 1947– . 8°. L.A.S. **436/50.**

BARAHONA (DIEGO) Glosa a la obra de don Jorge Manrrique. Hecha por D. Barahona . . . M.D.XLI. (Printed in facsimile.) G.L. 1902. 8°. *See* MANRIQUE (J.) **011451.** eee. **14.**

BARAHONA (FERNANDO DE)

—— *See* HERNÁNDEZ DÍAZ (J.) Papeletas para la Historia del Retablo en Sevilla durante la segunda mitad del siglo XVII. F. D. de Ribas . . . F. de Barahona. [1935.] 8°. **7876.** c. **22.**

BARAHONA (FRANCISCO GALAZ Y) *See* GALAZ Y BARAHONA.

BARAHONA (JOSÉ ANTONIO) Aventuras de un Chileno en la Argentina i en el Desierto de Atacama. Obra escrita por J. A. B. [i.e. J. A. Barahona.] pp. 220. 1895. 8°. *See* B., J. A. **10481.** aa. **43.**

BARAHONA (JUAN DE VILLEGAS) *See* VILLEGAS BARAHONA.

BARAHONA DE SOTO (LUIS) *See* RAMÍREZ DE LUQUE (F.) Lucena desagraviada. Disertacion apologetica sobre el verdadero autor de la Prision del Rey Chico de Granada. Anadida una breve apologia del verdadero autor [i.e. L. Barahona de Soto] del poema Lagrimas de Angelica, *etc.* [1782.] 8°. **833.** e. **28.**

—— *See* RODRÍGUEZ MARÍN (F.) Luis Barahona de Soto. Estudio biográfico, bibliográfico y crítico, *etc.* 1903. 8°. **10632.** h. **28.**

—— Poesias. 1778. *See* LÓPEZ DE SEDANO (J. J.) Parnaso Español, *etc.* tom. 9. 1768, *etc.* 8°. **242.** k. **36.**

—— Poesías líricas. *See* RODRÍGUEZ MARÍN (F.) Luis Barahona de Soto, *etc.* 1903. 8°. **10632.** h. **28.**

—— Primera parte de la Angelica de L. Barahona de Soto . . . con aduertimientos . . . y breues summarios . . . por . . . Pedro Verdugo de Sarria. ff. 251. *H. de Mena; a costa de I. Diaz: Granada,* 1586. 4°. G. **11310.**

—— [A facsimile of the edition of 1586.] 1904. 8°. *See* NEW YORK, *City of.—Hispanic Society of America.* K.T.C. **6.** a. **4.**

—— Egloga. *See* QUINTANA (M. J.) Poesias selectas Castellanas, *etc.* tom. 1. 1830. 8°. **1464.** b. **18.**

BARAHONA JIMÉNEZ (LUIS)

—— Glosas del Quijote. pp. 124. *San José, Costa Rica,* 1953. 8°. **11870.** ee. **24.**

—— El Gran incógnito. Visión interna del campesino costarricense. pp. 164. *San José, Costa Rica,* 1953. 8°. **10483.** b. **10.**
Universidad de Costa Rica. Sección Tesis de grado y ensayos. no. 3.

BARAHONA STREBER (OSCAR) and **ZURCHER ACUÑA** (HARRY)

—— Aspectos teóricos y prácticos de los riesgos profesionales. Explicación de las reformas que introdujo el Código de Trabajo vigente a la ley no. 53 de 31 de enero de 1925 sobre reparación por accidentes de trabajo, *etc.* pp. 152. *San José, Costa Rica,* 1943. 8°. **08286.** k. **67.**

BARAHONA VEGA (CLEMENTE) Cervantes en el Folklore Chileno. Un proyecto para la celebración del centenario . . . De la Revista Iberia. pp. 16. *Santiago de Chile,* 1915. 8°. **11825.** aa. **29.**

—— Trovas i modinhas populares del Brasil traducidas i parafraseadas por C. Barahona Vega . . . Coleccion folklorista, *etc.* pp. 49. *Santiago de Chile,* 1903. 16°. **011451.** de. **6.**

—— Corona fúnebre a la memoria de D. Clemente Barahona Vega, 1863–1918. Publicada por Leonardo Eliz. [With portraits.] pp. 199. *Valparaiso,* 1919. 8°. **10883.** e. **11.**

BARAHURA (VOLODIMIR)

—— Микола Хвильовий. Літературна сильветка. pp. 62. *Львів,* 1933. 8°. **11856.** eee. **1.**

BARAIBAR (CARLOS DE)

—— Las Falsas "Posiciones Socialistas" de Indalecio Prieto. pp. 203. *Madrid,* 1935. 8°. **8042.** k. 34.

BARÁIBAR (FEDERICO) *See* BARÁIBAR Y ZUMÁRRAGA.

BARÁIBAR Y ZUMÁRRAGA (FEDERICO) *See* ANACREON. [*Spanish.*] Odas de Anacreonte. (Epigramas.) [Translated into Spanish verse, with a sketch of the life and works of Anacreon, and bibliographical notes, by F. Baráibar y Zumárraga.] 1884. 8°. **11335**. bbb. **26**.

—— *See* ARISTOPHANES, *the Poet.* [*Works.—Spanish.*] Comedias . . . Traducidas . . . por D. F. Baráibar y Zumárraga. 1880, *etc.* 8°. **11705**. de. **2**.

—— *See* ARRIANUS (F.) [*Anabasis.—Spanish.*] Historia de las expediciones de Alejandro . . . traducida . . . por D. F. Baráibar y Zumárraga. 1883. 8°. **9026**. b. **20**.

—— *See* HOMER. [*Odyssey.—Spanish.*] La Odisea. Traducida . . . por . . . F. Baráibar y Zumárraga. 1886. 8°. **11315**. bbb. **22**.

—— Vocabulario de palabras usadas en Alava y no incluídas en el Diccionario de la Real Academia Española (decimotercia edición), o que lo están en otras acepciones ó como anticuadas. 1903. *See* MADRID.—*Real Academia Española.* Memorias. tom. 9. 1870, *etc.* 8°. Ac. **144/10**.

—— [Another edition.] pp. 325. *Madrid,* 1903. 8°. **12941**. l. **12**.

BARAILLER-LAPLANTE (P. CONSTANTIN) Dissertation sur les anévrismes externes, *etc.* pp. 23. *Paris,* 1818. 4°. **1183**. d. **15**. (**28**.)

BARAILLER-LAPLANTE (PIERRE) Dissertation sur le cancer de l'uterus; thèse, *etc.* pp. 26. *Paris,* 1812. 4°. **1182**. i. **4**. (**8**.)

BARAILLON (JEAN FRANÇOIS) *See* BARAILON.

BARAILON (JEAN FRANÇOIS) La Batue générale des brigands et des fripons; discours prononcé et projet de decret proposé à la Convention Nationale, dans sa séance du 22 fructidor de l'an troisième de la République, *etc.* pp. 12. [*Paris,* 1795.] 8°. **F. 356**. (**12**.)

—— Convention Nationale. Compte rendu . . . par J.-F. Barailon . . . envoyé en mission dans dix-sept départemens . . . pour l'etablissement des écoles primaires, des écoles centrales, & pour assurer l'exécution des lois relatives à l'instruction publique. pp. 3. *Paris,* brumaire IV [1795]. 8°. **F. 1552**. (**52**.)

—— Convention Nationale. Considérations sur la nécessité d'ajourner le jugement de Louis Capet & de sa femme. pp. 16. [*Paris,* 1792.] 8°. **F. 912**. (**12**.)

—— Convention Nationale. Motifs du décret presenté à la Convention Nationale, et lu à sa tribune le 30 avril, par J.-F. Barailon. pp. 6. [*Paris,* 1793.] 8°. **F. 1265**. (**10**.)

—— Convention Nationale. Organisation et tableau des fêtes décadaires. pp. 30. *Paris,* nivose an 3 [1795]. 8°. **F. 1068**. (**9**.)

—— [Another copy.] Convention Nationale. Organisation et tableau des fêtes décadaires, *etc.* *Paris,* an III [1795]. 8°. R. **182**. (**12**.)

—— Convention Nationale. Projet de constitution présenté à la Convention Nationale, le premier juin 1793, *etc.* pp. 97. *Paris,* 1793. 8°. **F.R. 86**. (**3**.)

—— Convention Nationale. Projet de décret sur les subsistances, *etc.* pp. 6. [*Paris,* 1793.] 8°. **F.R. 261**. (**8**.)

—— Convention Nationale. Quelques réflexions relatives à Louis Capet. pp. 14. [*Paris,*] 1792. 8°. **F. 912**. (**11**.)

—— Corps Législatif. Conseil des Anciens. Ce que Barailon faisoit à la Convention les 31 mai, premier et 2 juin 1793, et avant le 9 thermidor an 2. Séance du 14 thermidor an 7. pp. 4. *Paris,* an 7 [1799]. 8°. R. **174**. (**8**.)

BARAILON (JEAN FRANÇOIS)

—— Corps Législatif. Conseil des Anciens. Opinion . . . sur la résolution du 13 fructidor an 7, qui rapporte la loi du 18 fructidor an 5, relative à l'entrée des troupes dans le rayon fixé par l'article 69 de la constitution. Séance du premier jour complémentaire an 7. pp. 11. [*Paris,*] [1799.] 8°. **F.R. 280**. (**25**.)

—— [Another copy.] Corps législatif. Conseil des Anciens. Opinion . . . sur la résolution du 13 fructidor an 7, *etc.* [*Paris,*] an 7 [1799]. 8°. R. **116**. (**45**.)

—— Corps Législatif. Conseil des Cinq-Cents. Opinion . . . sur l'accumulation de places & de traitemens, ayant pour objet les arts, les sciences & l'instruction publique. Séance du premier germinal, an V. pp. 6. *Paris,* [1797.] 8°. **F.R. 235**. (**11**.)

—— Corps Législatif. Conseil des Cinq-Cents. Opinion . . . sur la loi du 10 juin 1793 relative au mode de partage des communaux. Séance du 26 fructidor, an IV. pp. 7. *Paris,* [1796.] 8°. **F.R. 248**. (**1**.)

—— Corps Législatif. Conseil des Cinq-Cents. Opinion . . . sur les trois projets de résolution, relatifs aux Écoles primaires, secondaires & centrales . . . Séance du 27 brumaire an 6. pp. 16. [*Paris,* 1797.] 8°. **F.P. 235**. (**16**.)

—— Corps Législatif. Conseil des Cinq-Cents. Rapport . . . sur la question de savoir si un militaire peut être appelé à des fonctions publiques . . . Séance du 17 floréal, an V. pp. 14. *Paris,* [1797.] 8°. **F.R. 235**. (**12**.)

—— [Another copy.] **F.R. 280**. (**4**.)

—— Corps Législatif. Conseil des Cinq-Cents. Rapport et projet des résolution . . . sur le costume du Corps Législatif et de tous les fonctionnaires. Au nom d'une Commission spéciale . . . Séance du 12 nivôse. pp. 11. *Paris,* an V [1797]. 8°. **F.R. 68**. (**22**.)

—— Corps Législatif. Opinion . . . sur le rapport et le projet d'arrêté de la commission administrative du Corps Législatif. Comité général du 25 floréal an 10. pp. 10. *Paris,* an 10 [1802]. 8°. **F.R. 72**. (**20**.)

—— Opinion . . . sur le jugement de Louis Capet . . . & de sa famille. pp. 6. [*Paris,* 1792.] 8°. **F. 912**. (**13**.)

—— Opinion . . . sur les fêtes civiques à établir dans la République Française. pp. 8. [*Paris,* 1792.] 8°. **F. 1065**. (**3**.)

—— Projet sur le costume particulier à donner à chacun des deux conseils législatifs, et à tous les fonctionnaires publics de la République Française, présenté à la Convention Nationale. pp. 31. *Paris,* 13 fructidor de l'an 3e [1795]. 4°. **936**. c. **15**.

—— Rapport . . . au nom d'une commission spéciale . . . sur les voies de fait, violences et meurtres qui ont eu lieu dans l'assemblée primaire de la commune de Mortagne . . . dans ses séances des 3 et 4 de ce mois, et sur la validité des opérations de cette même. Séance du 18 germinal, an cinq. pp. 12. *Paris,* [1797.] 8°. **F.R. 106**. (**24**.)

—— Recherches sur les peuples Cambiovicenses de la carte Théodosienne, dite de Peutinger; sur l'ancienne ville romaine de Néris, département de l'Allier; sur les ruines de plusieurs autres villes romaines de l'ancien Berry, *etc.* pp. 444. *Paris,* 1806. 8°. **7705**. aaa. **38**.

—— Votation . . . dans les séances des 15, 16–17, et 19 janvier 1793. pp. 7. *Paris,* 1793. 8°. **F. 912**. (**14**.)

BARAIZE (E.) Plan des nécropoles thébaines. *Le Caire,* 1904–13. *obl.* fol. [*Service des Antiquités de l'Égypte. Catalogue général des antiquités égyptiennes.*] **1710**. c. **8**.

BARAJAS. Saynete, intitulado El Hidalgo de Barajas. pp. 12. *Madrid*, 1792. 4º. **1342**. f. **5**. (**62**.)

—— [Another copy.] **11726**. h. **2**. (**13**.)

—— [Another issue.] *See* Coleccion. Coleccion de Saynetes, *etc.* tom. 2. 1791, *etc.* 4º. **11725**. c. **21**.

BARAJAS (Carlos) Leyendas y Paisajes Guanajuatenses . . . Ilustraciones, *etc.* pp. xi. 176. *Mexico*, 1916. 8º. **12450**. p. **1**.

BARAJAS (Pedro) *Bishop of San Luis Potosí.* *See* Garza y Ballesteros (L. de la) successively *Bishop of Sonora* and *Archbishop of Mexico.* Manifestacion que hacen . . . los Illmos. Señores Arzobispo de Mexico y Obispos de Michoacan . . . y Potosí . . . con ocasion del manifiesto y de los decretos expedidos por . . . D. B. Juarez, *etc.* 1859. 8º. **4183**. aaa. **87**. (**7**.)

—— Carta Pastoral que el Illmo. . . . D. P. Barajas . . . dirige al venerable Clero . . . y á todos los Fieles de su diócesis, con motivo de la Encíclica que Su Santidad . . . Pio IX dirigió al orbe Católico, el 19 de Enero del corriente año. pp. 32. *México*, 1860. 4º. **4183**. aaa. **7**. (**13**.)

—— Segunda Carta Pastoral que el Illmo . . . D. P. Barajas dirige á todos sus diocesanos, con motivo de la protesta que con fecha 5 del corriente elevó al Supremo Gobierno de la Nacion, contra los artículos 42, 44 y 4º. de los transitorios de la ley sobre administracion de justicia, que versan sobre el fuero eclesiástico. pp. 11. *San Luis Potosí*, 1855. 4º. **4183**. aaa. **7**. (**12**.)

BARAJONA (Juan de) *See* Villegas Barahona.

BARÁK (Josef) *See* Osvěta. Osvěta Lidu. Bibliotéka prostonárodních přednášek . . . Pořádá [číslo 1–13] J. Barák. 1871, *etc.* 8º. **012208**. e. **18–21**.

—— Vzpomínky J. Baráka. [With some of his poems.] pp. 160. *v Praze*, [1904.] 8º. **010790**. de. **51**.

BARAKAN (S. L.)

—— Библиография произведений А. С. Пушкина и литературы о нем. 1949—юбилейный год. (Составители: С. Л. Баракан, Х. В. Беляева, Б. М. Богатырь, Л. Г. Гринберг, Б. В. Злочевская. Под редакцией Л. Г. Гринберг.) pp. 566. 1951. *See* Russia.—*Академия Наук СССР.* *Институт Литературы (Пушкинский Дом).* **2783.as.5/4.**

BARAKAN (S. L.) and **LEVKOVICH** (Ya. L.)

—— Библиография произведений А. С. Пушкина и литературы о нем. 1950. (Составители С. Л. Баракан и Я. Л. Левкович.) pp. 172. 1952. 8º. *See* Russia.—*Академия Наук СССР.* —*Институт Литературы (Пушкинский Дом).*

2783.as.5/5.

BARAKAT (Bahi ed Dine) *See* Bahī al-Dīn Barakāt.

BARAKAT ALLĀH (Muḣammad) *See* Thimm (C. A.) Hindūstānī Self-Taught . . . Second edition (revised by Maulave Mohammad Barakatullah). 1904. 8º. [*Marlborough's Self-Taught Library.* no. 15.] **012902**. eee. **33/20**.

—— The Khilafet. [With a portrait.] pp. 96. *Luzac & Co.: London; Zurich* [printed], 1924. 8º. **9058**. b. **15**.

BARAKAT RĀM, *Kakrejā.* A Golden Present for the Lovers of Curios, Researchers and Budhists. Rare Art. 300 years old. [A circular, offering for sale two Moortis.] [*Lyallpur*, 1906.] fol. **1887**. a. **9**. (**12**.)

BARAKATULLAH (Mohammad) *See* Barakat Allāh (Muḣammad)

BARAKBAH (Syed Sheh) *See* Sheh Barakbah, *Saiyid.*

BARAKHOVSKY (A.)

—— Бригадный хозрасчет в совхозы. pp. 28. *Москва*, 1932. 8º. **07077**. e. **66**.

BARAKONYI (Ferencz) Barakonyi Barakonyi Ferencz költeményei. Sajtó alá rendezte Erdélyi P. pp. 184. *Kolozsvár*, 1907. 8º. **011586**. g. **100**.

BARAKOVIĆ (Juraj) Djela J. Barakovića . . . Priredili za štampu P. Budmani i M. Valavac. pp. xiii. 390. *u Zagrebu*, 1889. 8º. [*Stari pisci hrvatski.* knj. 17.] Ac. **741/14**.

—— Giarulla uressena zuityem od scest uichof uita, sloxena u'slouinschi giazich. [In verse. With woodcuts.] pp. 168. *A. Turrini: Venetia*, 1620. 8º. **242**. a. **31**.

BARALÂM, *Saint.* *See* Barlaam.

BARALDI (Giovanni) *See* Garbiglietti (A.) Ulteriori considerazioni anatomico-fisiologiche intorno all' osso malare, ossia zigomatico, ed al suo sviluppo, coll' aggiunta di note ed appunti al libro del Prof. G. Baraldi sulla craniogenesi dei mammiferi. Memoria, *etc.* 1874. 8º. **07305**. g. **36**. (**3**.)

—— Alcune ricerche contribuenti alla conoscenza della tavola triturante o macinante dei denti mascellari negli equidi. [1887.] *See* Pisa.—*Società Toscana di Scienze Naturali.* Atti, *etc.* vol. 8. 1875, *etc.* 8º. Ac. **2817**.

BARALDI (Giuseppe) *See* Fabriani (S.) Vita di Monsignore Giuseppe Baraldi, *etc.* 1834. 8º. **490**. g. **20**.

—— *See* Riva (Giuseppe) Discorso intorno la vita e le opere di . . . G. Baraldi, *etc.* 1832. 8º. **4867**. bb. **5**.

—— Compendio storico della città e provincia di Modena dai tempi della Romana repubblica sino al MDCCXCVI. pp. 340. *Modena*, 1846. 16º. **9166**. b. **2**.

—— Leone duodecimo e Pio ottavo. (Memorie.) pp. 33. *Venezia*, 1829. 8º. **1370**. d. **5**.

—— Necrologia della contessina Maria Riccini. pp. 38. *Modena*, 1831. 8º. T. **2483**. (**3**.)

—— Notizia biografica di Stefano Antonio Morcelli. pp. viii. 134. *Modena*, 1825. 8º. **10630**. d. **22**.

—— Notizia biografica su Teresa Franzoni. pp. 48. [*Modena*, 1820.] 8º. **4867**. aaaa. **37**.

—— Notizia biografica sul cardinale Ferdinando Maria Saluzzo . . . e cenno storico-genealogico de' marchesi Saluzzo del P. G. A. Borghi. pp. 158. *Napoli*, 1845. 8º. **4856**. c. **3**.

—— Notizia biografica sul marchese Ettore d'Yenne governatore di Genova. pp. viii. 80. *Modena*, 1831. 8º. T. **2486**. (**4**.)

—— Relazione della traslazione delle reliquie de' santi Francesco di Sales e Giovanna di Chantal col panegirico del santo di monsignor Rey vescovo di Pinerolo. pp. xii. 83. *Modena*, 1827. 8º. T. **2485**. (**1**.)

BARALDI (Michele) La Nascita di Lodovico Ariosto. Poemetto. pp. 64. *Ferrara*, 1802. 8º. **899**. c. **7**. (**1**.)

BARALDI (P. V.) La Fisica e la meccanica applicate all' industria conformemente allo stato attuale della scienza e dell'arte, *etc.* pp. xviii. 643. *Milano*, 1850. 8º. **8705**. c. **21**.

BARALDI (Paolo) Vita del servo di Dio padre Paolo Baraldi, *etc.* [With a portrait.] pp. 95. *Mantova*, 1765. 4º. **4866**. ee. **14**.

BARALDI (Paolo Giuseppe) *See* Gray (Thomas) *the Poet.* [*Elegy written in a Country Churchyard.—Translations.*] Elegia . . . sopra un cimitero di campagna tradotta . . . in più lingue, *etc.* [One Italian version by P. G. Baraldi.] 1817. 8°. **11632**. cc. **4**.

—— —— 1843. 8°. **1465**. k. **23**.

BARALÈRE (Y.) *pseud.* [i.e. Jean Baptiste Moïse Jollivet.] *See* Chol (E.) and Lerouge ( ) Les Citoyens Chol et Lerouge . . . à Y. Baralère redacteur du journal intitulé; l'Ami de la Convention . . . en réponse à un paragraphe de son no. 3. [1794.] 8°. F. **982**. (**24**.)

—— *See* Periodical Publications.—*Paris.* L'Ami de la Convention et le défenseur du peuple. Par Y. Baralère. [1795.] 8°. F. **1495**. (**2**.)

—— Acte d'accusation contre Carrier, présenté aux Comités réunis, à la Convention Nationale, et au peuple français. pp. 16. [*Paris,* 1794.] 8°. F. **1050**. (**2**.)

—— Apothéose des Jacobins: suite de la fête du 2 pluviôse. pp. 4. [*Paris,* 1795?] 8°. **935**. b. **12**. (**35**.)

—— [Another copy.] F. **350**. (**7**.)

—— Le Coup de grace des Jacobins. pp. 8. [*Paris,* 1795?] 8°. F. **349**. (**14**.)

—— [Another copy.] F. **354**. (**11**.)

—— Coupons lui la queue. [An attack on the remnant of the Robespierre faction.] pp. 7. [*Paris,* 1794?] 8°. F. **350**. (**14**.)

—— [Another copy.] **935**. b. **17**. (**14**.)

—— Grande colère du médecin Duhem, de voir qu'il ne peut sauver son ami Carrier et que l'avant garde des égorgeurs va défiler sans trompette sur la place de la Révolution. pp. 16. [*Paris,* 1794.] 8°. F. **352**. (**11**.)

—— [Another copy.] Grande colère du médecin Duhem, de voir qu'il ne peut sauver son ami Carrier, *etc.* [*Paris,* 1794.] 8°. R. **98**. (**24**.)

—— Les Jacobins convaincus d'imposture. pp. 8. [*Paris,* 1794.] 8°. F. **355**. (**27**.)

—— [Another copy.] Les Jacobins convaincus d'imposture. [*Paris,* 1794.] 8°. R. **158**. (**25**.)

—— Rappellez [*sic*] vos collègues. pp. 30. *Paris,* an III [1795]. 8°. F. **843**. (**14**.)

BAR ALI. *See* Yēshū' bar 'Alī.

BARALIS (Bartholomaeus) *Praes.* *See* Rousseau (Nicolaus) Quæstio medica, *etc.* (An pesti sola manifesta?) 1647. 4°. **1182**. e. **8**. (**44**.)

BARALIS (Carolus) *Resp.* *See* Patin (R.) Quæstio medica, *etc.* (An fortes creantur fortibus?) [1651.] 4°. **1182**. e. **8**. (**41**.)

BARALLAT Y FALGUERA (Celestino) Principios de Botánica funeraria. pp. 102. *Barcelona,* 1885. 8°. **7032**. e. **10**.

—— Shakespeare y Moratín ante la fosa, y traducción catalana de un cuadro de Shakespeare [i.e. Hamlet v, i.], *etc.* pp. 23. *Barcelona,* 1896. 8°. **11764**. m. **24**.

BARALLE (de) *Procureur Général.* *See* Flanders.—*Parlement.* Recueil d'arrêts du Parlement de Flandres. Par MM. Dubois d'Hermaville . . . de Baralle, *etc.* 1773. 4°. **5402**. b. **2**.

BARALLI DA CASTEL (Liberio) *See* Magazzini (V.) Coltivazione toscana . . . Data in luce dal molto R. P. D. L. Baralli da Castel. 1634. 8°. **967**. b. **19**. (**2**.)

BARALT (Blanca Z. de)

—— El Martí que yo conocí, *etc.* [With a portrait.] pp. 211. *La Habana,* 1945. 8°. **10899**. aa. **6**.

BARALT (José Ignacio Lares) *See* Lares Baralt.

BARALT (Luis A.) Harmonic Method for learning Spanish . . . First Spanish book, *etc.* pp. xxxii. 227. *D. Appleton & Co.: New York,* 1899. 8°. **12943**. aa. **51**.

BARALT (Rafael Maria) *See* Codazzi (A.) Resumen de la geografía de Venezuela. (Toda obra revisada por R. M. Baralt y R. Diaz.) 1841. 8°. **1304**. e. **19**.

—— *See* Fernández San Román (E.) *Marquis de San Román.* Causa formada al brigadier E. Fernandez San Roman, publicada . . . por R. M. Baralt y N. Fernandez Cuesta. 1849. 8°. **8042**. g. **40**. (**5**.)

—— *See* Periodical Publications.—*Madrid.* Antologia Española. Revista de ciencias, literatura y critica bajo la direccion de Don S. Santos Lerin y Don R. M. Baralt. 1848, *etc.* 8°. P.P. **4087**.

—— *See* Villanueva Estengo (J. L.) Las Angelicas fuentes ó el Tomista en las Cortes . . . Nueva edicion, precedida de unos apuntes biográficos acerca del autor, por R. M. Baralt y N. Fernandez Cuesta. 1849. 8°. **8042**. g. **40**. (**4**.)

—— [Poems.] *See* Rójas (J. M.) Biblioteca de Escritores Venezolanos contemporáneos, *etc.* 1875. 8°. **12230**. f. **6**.

—— D. Rafael Maria Baralt. [Selected poems. With an introduction by V. A. Zerpa.] pp. 87. *Curazao,* 1888. 8°. [*Parnaso Venezolano.* ser. 1. tom. 2.] **11450**. ccc. **38**.

—— Diccionario de Galicismos, ó sea de las voces, locuciones y frases de la lengua Francesa que se han introducido en el habla Castellana moderna, con el juicio crítico de las que deben adoptarse, y la equivalencia Castiza de las que no se hallan en este caso . . . Con un prólogo de Don J. E. Hartzenbusch. pp. xxiii. 709. *Madrid,* 1855. 8°. **12943**. b. **30**.

—— Segunda edicion. pp. xxi. 626. *Madrid, Caracas,* 1874. 8°. **12941**. d. **10**.

—— Letras Españolas: primera mitad del siglo xix. Prólogo de D. Rufino Blanco-Fombona. pp. 188. *Madrid,* [1918.] 8°. **12230**. cc. **14**.

—— Libertad de imprenta . . . Precedida de una introduccion por D. Nemesio Fernandez Cuesta. pp. xvi. 123. *Madrid,* 1849. 8°. **8042**. g. **40**. (**6**.)

—— Oda a Cristóbal Colon. pp. 21. *Madrid,* 1850. 4°. **11450**. dd. **23**.

BARALT (Rafael María) and **DÍAZ** (Ramón)

—— Resúmen de la Historia de Venezuela, desde el descubrimiento de su territorio por los Castellanos en el siglo xv, hasta el año de 1797 . . . Ha cooperado á el en la parte relativa á las guerras de la conquista de la Costa-Firme el señor Ramon Diaz. pp. 448. *Paris,* 1841. 8°. **1446**. i. **7**. (**1**.)

—— Resumen de la historia de Venezuela desde el descubrimiento de su territorio . . . en el siglo xv, hasta el año de 1797, *etc.* (Desde el año de 1797 hasta él de 1830. Tiene al fin un breve bosquejo histórico que comprende los años de 1831 hasta 1837.) 3 tom. *Curazao,* 1887. 8°. **2398**. e. **10**.

BARALT (RAFAEL MARÍA) and **DÍAZ** (RAMÓN)

—— Resúmen de la Historia de Venezuela, desde el año de 1797 hasta el de 1830 . . . Tiene al fin un breve bosquejo historico que comprende los años de 1831 hasta 1837. 2 tom. *Paris*, 1841. 8°. **1446**. i. **7**. (**2**.)

—— Resumen de la Historia de Venezuela desde el año de 1797 hasta el de 1830 . . . Con notas de Vicente Lecuna. Tiene al fin un breve bosquejo histórico que comprende los años de 1831 hasta 1837. [With plates.] 2 tom. Brujas, Paris, 1939. 8°. Ac. 8590/8.

—— Resumen de la Historia de Venezuela desde el descubrimiento de su territorio por los castellanos en el siglo xv, hasta el año de 1797. Ordenado y compuesto . . . por Rafael María Baralt. Ha cooperado a él en la parte relativa a las guerras de la conquista de la Costa Firme el señor Ramón Díaz, el cual le ha añadido los apéndices, *etc.* [With plates, including a portrait.] pp. xi. 503. Brujas, Paris, 1939. 8°. Ac. 8590/9.

—— *See* BRICEÑO-IRAGORRY (M.) Pasión y triunfo de dos grandes libros . . . Homenaje a Codazzi y a Baralt en el centenario de la Geografía y de la Historia [i.e. the "Resúmen de la Historia de Venezuela" by R. M. Baralt and R. Díaz]. 1941. 4°. **10481**. y. **36**.

—— *See* CASAS (P. de las) Defensa documentada de la conducta del . . . Sr. M. M. de Las Casas, en la prision del general Miranda . . . contra las . . . imputaciones que le han hecho los autores del "Resumen de la historia de Venezuela" (R. M. Baralt y R. Diaz), *etc.* 1843. 8°. **9781**. d. **26**.

BARALT (RAFAEL MARÍA) and **FERNANDEZ CUESTA** (NEMESIO)

—— Historia de las Córtes de 1848 á 1849. pp. 100. *Madrid*, 1849. 8°. **8042**. g. **40**. (**2**.)

—— Lo Pasado y lo Presente. pp. 135. *Madrid*, 1849. 8°. **8042**. g. **40**. (**3**.)

—— Programas políticos. Cuestiones preliminares al examen histórico y científico de los prospectos o programas políticos que han visto la luz en España desde Enero de 1848 hasta principios de 1849. 2 pt. *Madrid*, 1849. 8°. **8042**. g. **40**. (**1**.)

BARALY, *pseud.* [i.e. JEAN BAPTISTE MOÏSE JOLLIVET.]

—— Le Front de Robespierre et de sa clique, ou la necessité de la liberté de la presse. pp. 8. [*Paris*, 1794?] 8°. **F**. **852**. (**5**.)

—— [Another copy.] **F**. **356**. (**5**.)

—— Les Jacobins démasqués, suite au Front de Robespierre et de sa clique, ou la necessité de la liberté de la presse. pp. 8. [*Paris*, 1794?] 8°. **935**. b. **12**. (**28**.)

—— [Another copy.] **F**. **354**. (**18**.)

—— [Another copy.] **935**. b. **17**. (**16**.)

—— Les Jacobins démasqués, *etc.* pp. 8. [*Paris*, 1794?] 8°. **R**. **158**. (**19**.)

—— *See* B., L., *ardent Ami de la Liberté*. Réponse de plusieurs Jacobins patriotes à la feuille intitulée, les Jacobins démasqués. [1794?] 8°. **R**. **158**. (**21**.)

—— *See* CALBEN (M. L.) Réponse à un écrit [by — Baraly] intitulé, Les Jacobins démasqués. [1794.] 8°. F. 349. (5.)

BARALY, *pseud.* [i.e. JEAN BAPTISTE MOÏSE JOLLIVET.]

—— L'Agonie des Jacobins; suite aux Jacobins démasqués. pp. 8. [*Paris*, 1795?] 8°. **F**. **349**. (**8**.)

—— [Another copy.] **F**. **349**. (**8***.)

—— [Another copy.] **F**. **355**. (**2**.)

—— Les Jacobins aristocrates, fédéralistes, et contre-révolutionnaires. pp. 8. [*Paris*, 1794?] 8°. **935**. b. **12**. (**24**.)

—— [Another copy.] **F**. **355**. (**5**.)

BARAMIDZE (ALEKSANDR GEORGIEVICH)

—— *See* TIFLIS.—*Академия Наук Грузинской ССР.—Институт Истории Грузинской Литературы имени Руставели.* История грузинской литературы, *etc.* [By A. Baramidze, Sh. Radiani and V. Zhgenti.] 1952. 8°. **11871**. bb. **21**.

BAR AMITHAI, *pseud.* [i.e. JOSEPH JOHLSON.] Ueber die Beschneidung in historischer und dogmatischer Hinsicht . . . Den Denkenden in Israel . . . vorgelegt von Bar Amithai. pp. 20. *Frankfurt*, 1843. 8°. **4033**. cc. **19**.

BARAMKI (DIMITRY C.)

—— *See* SELLERS (Ovid R.) and BARAMKI (D. C.) A Roman-Byzantine Burial Cave in Northern Palestine, *etc.* 1953. 8°. [*Bulletin of the American Schools of Oriental Research. Supplementary Studies.* no. 15/16.] Ac. **8824**. c. (**1**.)

—— Guide to the Umayyad Palace at Khirbat al Mafjar. [With illustrations.] pp. 15. 1947. 8°. *See* PALESTINE.—*Department of Antiquities for Palestine.* **07702.de.10.**

BARAN (ANTON) Geschichte der alten lateinischen Stadtschule und des Gymnasiums in Krems, *etc.* pp. vii. 226. *Krems*, 1896. 8°. **8357**. f. **32**.

BARAN (STEPAN)

—— Земельні справи в Галичині. (Відбитка з "Господарсько-кооперативного життя.") pp. 20. *Авґсбурґ*, 1948. 8°. **08282**. de. **35**. *Видання "Об'єднання Українських Кооператорів на еміграції."* ч. 2.

BARAN (WŁADYSŁAW) Henryk Bukowski, wielki bibljofil polski. [With a portrait.] pp. 18. *Warszawa, Kraków*, 1926. 4°. **010790**. e. **51**.

BARANAUCKAS (ANTANAS) *Titular Bishop of Thespiae.* *See* BARANOWSKI (Anton)

BARANCY (A. P.) L'Archange et les vampires. Choses vues. 1933. *See* PERIODICAL PUBLICATIONS.—*Paris.* Les Œuvres libres, *etc.* no. 139. 1921, *etc.* 8°. **12208**. ee. **139**.

—— Les Grandes fantasias. Choses vues. 1936. *See* PERIODICAL PUBLICATIONS.—*Paris.* Les Œuvres libres. no. 180. 1921, *etc.* 8°. **12208**. ee. **180**.

BARANCY (FRANÇOIS DE) Examen de la response du Sieur J. B. Morin . . . à la lettre d'un faux amy de Monsieur Gauttier, *etc.* *See* MORIN (J. B.) Recueil de lettres . . . en suite de l'Apologie du Sieur Gassend touchant la question De motu impresso a motore translato, *etc.* 1650. 4°. **718**. g. **17**.

BARANDA (JOAQUÍN) [For official documents issued by J. Baranda as Minister of Justice and Public Instruction of the Republic of Mexico:] *See* MEXICO.—*Ministerio de Justicia é Instrucción Pública.*

—— Obras. pp. xxxi. 415. *México*, 1900. 8°. **12231**. c. **9**.

BARANDA (JOAQUÍN)

—— Recordaciones históricas. [Completed by Perfecto Baranda Mac-Gregor.] 2 tom. *México*, [1907, 13.] 8º. **9772.** t. **5.**

BARANDA (JULIÁN GARCÍA SÁINZ DE) *See* GARCÍA SÁINZ DE BARANDA.

BARANDA (MANUEL) [For official documents issued by M. Baranda as Governor of the State of Guanajuato:] *See* GUANAJUATO, *State of.*—Baranda (M.) *Governor.*

—— [For official documents issued by M. Baranda as Minister of Justice and Public Instruction of the Republic of Mexico:] *See* MEXICO.—*Ministerio de Justicia é Instrucción Pública.*

—— Parte official de la derrota de Arista, toma de los minerales del Marfil, Valenciana, *etc.* [A despatch from M. Baranda.] *México*, 1833. *s. sh.* fol. **9770.** k. **11.** (**189.**)

BARANDA (MARIANO RIPOLLÉS Y) *See* RIPOLLÉS Y BARANDA.

BARANDA (PEDRO SÁINZ DE) *See* SÁINZ DE BARANDA.

BARANDA DE ESTRADA (MANUEL PORRES) *See* PORRES BARANDA DE ESTRADA.

BARANDA MAC-GREGOR (PERFECTO) *See* BARANDA (Joaquín) Recordaciones históricas. [Completed by P. Baranda Mac-Gregor.] [1907, *etc.*] 8º. **9772.** t. **5.**

BARANDEGUY-DUPONT ( ) A Bayonne sur ses courses de taureaux. [In verse.] pp. 12. *Paris*, 1865. 12º. **11481.** aaa. **19.**

—— Béranger devant ses accusateurs. [In verse.] pp. 7. *Paris*, 1860. 8º. **11826.** bbb. **11.**

—— Bucoliques du moulin des Cressonnières, *etc.* pp. 35. *Paris*, 1864. 12º. **11481.** aaa. **17.**

—— Le Dernier âne de Montmartre. [In verse.] pp. 10. *Paris*, 1865. 12º. **11481.** aaa. **18.**

—— Les Nouveaux bourgeois-gentilshommes. Satire. pp. 12. *Paris*, 1858. 12º. **11482.** c. **52.** (**2.**)

—— O ma maison des Batignolles! [In verse.] pp. 8. *Paris*, 1862. 8º. **11481.** bbb. **2.**

—— La Tableaumanie. [In verse.] pp. 11. *Paris*, 1858. 12º. **7854.** c. **41.** (**8.**)

—— Une Voix des Pyrénées. [Poems.] pp. 84. *Paris*, 1854. 8º. **11481.** bb. **43.** (**1.**)

BARANDIARÁN (JOSÉ MIGUEL DE) *See* ARANZADI Y UNAMUNO (T. de) Exploración de seis Dólmenes de la Sierra de Urbasa, Navarra. Memoria presentada . . . por D. T. de Aranzadi . . . D. J. M. de Barandiarán, *etc.* 1923. 8º. Ac. **154**/3. (**8.**)

—— *See* ARANZADI Y UNAMUNO (T. de) Grutas artificiales de Alava. Memoria presentada . . . por D. Telesforo de Aranzadi . . . D. J. M. de Barandiarán, *etc.* 1923. 8º. Ac. **154**/3. (**9.**)

—— *See* ARANZADI Y UNAMUNO (T. de) Los Nuevos Dolmenes de la Sierra de Encia . . . Por D. T. de Aranzadi . . . D. J. M. de Barandiarán, *etc.* [1921.] 8º. **7707.** df. **48.**

—— El Hombre prehistórico en el país vasco, *etc.* pp. 267. *Buenos Aires*, 1953. 8º. W.P. **714 42.** *Biblioteca de cultura vasca.* vol. 42.

BARANDIARÁN (JOSÉ MIGUEL DE)

—— El Mundo Subterráneo. Las Grutas. [Reprinted from "Eusko-Folklore."] 4 pt. [*San Sebastián*, 1921.] 8º. **07708.** g. **86.**

BARANDIARÁN (MARTÍN JOSÉ DE) Ensayo sobre el orígen y remedio de nuestros males. pp. 26. *México*, 1812. 4º. **9770.** aaa. **14.** (**15.**)

BARANDIARÁN (TOMÁS ROYO) *See* ROYO BARANDIARÁN.

BARANDIERY MONTMAYEUR (JEAN FRANÇOIS) *Count d'Essuile.* Adresse à Messieurs les officiers municipaux et notables composant le Conseil général de la Commune de Paris. [Containing observations on M. Brulé's project of a canal for the navigation of the Seine.] pp. 8. [*Paris*, 1791?] 4º. F. **7*.** (**22.**)

BARANDON (FÉLIX) Considérations sur quelques cas de fractures . . . Thèse, *etc.* pp. 51. *Montpellier*, 1864. 4º. **7379.** f. **5.** (**1.**)

BARANDON (PAUL)

—— Das Kriegsverhütungsrecht des Völkerbundes. pp. xi. 406. *Berlin*, 1933. 8º. **08425.** g. **24.**

—— Das System der politischen Staatsverträge seit 1918. pp. xii. 250. *Stuttgart*, 1937. 8º. [*Handbuch des Völkerrechts.* Bd. 4. Abt. 2.] **W.P.2876/4.(2.)**

BARANDUN (JOHANNES) Fablas, Siemis a Wilhelm Tell. pp. 248. *Cuera*, 1860. 16º. **12304.** aaa. **15.**

—— La Giuvantegna dilg Johannes Barandun, Mral dals 1847 dilg cuming d'Ortenstein am berg. pp. 296. *Cuera*, 1864. 8º. **885.** d. **25.**

BARANEK (F. M.)

—— Czechoslovak-Polish Relations. pp. 97. *Czechoslovak Societies in Calcutta, Bombay, Secunderabad and Lahore: Batanagar*, 1942. 8º. **8029.** d. **43.**

BARANEK (JOSEF)

—— Die Materie und die Prinzipien ihrer Veränderung. Untersuchungen zum Weltbilde Newtons. pp. 50. *Breslau*, 1937. 8º. [*Jahresbericht der Schlesischen Gesellschaft für vaterländische Cultur.* no. 110. Naturw.-med. Reihe. no. 4.] Ac. **866**/2.

BARANERA (FRANCISCO XAVIER) Handbook of the Philippine Islands. Translated from the Compendio de Geografía of P. F. X. Baranera . . . With an historical sketch by Alexander Laist. pp. 152. *W. Partier: Manila*, 1899. 8º. **10055.** aaa. **13.**

BARANETSKY (IOSIF VASIL'EVICH) Die kreisförmige Nutation und das Winden der Stengel. pp. 73. *St. Pétersbourg*, 1883. 4º. [*Mémoires de l'Académie Impériale des Sciences de St. Pétersbourg.* sér. 7. tom. 31. no. 8.] Ac. **1125**/3.

—— Die stärkeumbildenden Fermente in den Pflanzen. Mit 1 Tafel. pp. 64. *Leipzig*, 1878. 8º. **7033.** g. **6.** (**10.**)

—— Die tägliche Periodicität im Längenwachsthum der Stengel . . . Avec 5 planches. pp. 91. *St.-Pétersbourg*, 1879. 4º. [*Mémoires de l'Académie Impériale des Sciences de St. Pétersbourg.* sér. 7. tom. 27. no. 2.] Ac. **1125**/3.

—— Ueber die Ursachen, welche die Richtung der Aeste der Baum- und Straucharten bedingen. 1901. *See* RATISBON.—*Regensburgische Botanische Gesellschaft.* Flora, *etc.* Neue Reihe. Bd. 89. 1818, *etc.* 8º. Ac. **3258**/3.

BARANETSKY (Iosif Vasil'evich)

—— Untersuchungen über die Periodicität des Blutens der krautartigen Pflanzen . . . Mit 6 Tafeln. 1877. *See* Halle.—*Naturforschende Gesellschaft zu Halle.* Abhandlungen, *etc.* Bd. 13. 1854, *etc.* 4°. Ac. **2944/6.**

BARANETZKY (Josef) *See* Baranetsky (Iosif Vasil'evich)

BARANGA (Aurel)

—— Teatru: Iarbă rea. Pentru fericirea poporului, în colaborare cu N. Moraru. Bulevardul împăcării. Intr'o noapte de vară... Cântecul libertății. Mielul turbat. [With a portrait.] pp. 393. *București,* 1953. 8°. **11759.** b. **31.**

—— Iarbă rea. Piesă, *etc.* pp. 85. [*Bucharest,*] 1949. *obl.* 8°. **11759.** a. **6.**

BARANGÉ (N.) Thèse pour le doctorat en médecine. (Questions sur diverses branches des sciences médicales.) pp. 24. *Paris,* 1840. 4°. [*Collection des thèses soutenues à la Faculté de Médecine de Paris.* An 1840. tom. 1.] **7371.** b. **2.**

BARANGER (Émile Charles) Études sur les lésions phlegmasiques du col de la matrice. pp. 94. *Paris,* 1858. 4°. [*Collection des thèses soutenues à la Faculté de Médecine de Paris.* An 1858. tom. 1.] **7373.** a. **15.**

BARANGER (Léon) and **SIMON** (André Louis)

—— Almanach du franc buveur pour 1926, *etc.* [With illustrations.] pp. 145. 1926. 8°. *See* Ephemerides. P.P. **2397.** dac.

BARANGER (Pierre Germain) Pages d'histoire militaire. Campagnes modernes traitées dans les conditions fixées par le programme d'admission a l'École supérieure de Guerre. I. De 1796 à 1878, exposé sommaire. II. Guerre de 1870–71, étude raisonnée. pp. 398. *Paris,* 1913. 8°. **9231.** cc. **14.**

BARANGER (René)

—— Un An de gardianage en Camargue, *etc.* (Nouvelle édition.) [With illustrations.] pp. 134. [*Clichy,* 1955.] 8°. **07295.** k. **128.**

BARANGÓ-SOLÍS (Fernando) Un Movimiento Revolucionario: de los sucesos de Ciudad Real al proceso Sánchez Guerra, *etc.* pp. 207. *Barcelona,* [1929.] 8°. **10634.** de. **29.**

BARANIECKI (Adryan)

—— Miejskie Muzeum Przemysłowe im. Dra Adryana Baranieckiego. *See* Cracow.—*Muzeum Techniczno-Przemysłowe, etc.*

—— Notice sur le petit-lait en général, et en particulier sur les bains de petit-lait en Bessarabie, *etc.* pp. 23. *Paris,* 1858. 8°. **7461.** cc. **48.** (4.)

BARANIECKI (Łukasz) *Archbishop of Leopol.* Kazanie przy rozpoczęciu uroczystego obchodu pamiątki kanonizacyi Świętego Franciszka de Hieronimo, kapłana Towarzystwa Jezusowego, *etc.* pp. 16. *we Lwowie,* 1840. 8°. **10292.** g. **1.** (4.)

BARANIECKI (Maryjan Aleksander) *See* Kłos (T.) Algoritmus, to jest nauka liczby polską rzeczą wydana przez . . . T. Kłosa 1538. Wydał . . . M. A. Baraniecki. 1889. 8°. [*Biblijoteka Pisarzów Polskich.* no. 6.] Ac. **750/45.**

—— Arytmetyka, kurs teoretyczny . . . Z przypiskami Dra A. Żbikowskiego i Prof. J. N. Frankego. pp. lviii. 375. *Warszawa,* 1884. 8°. **8535.** g. **13.**

BARANIECKI (Maryjan Aleksander)

—— Początkowy wykład syntetyczny własności przecięć stożkowych na podstawie ich pokrewieństwa harmonicznego z kołem. pp. xvi. 131. *Warszawa,* 1885. 8°. **8535.** g. **16.**

—— Teorya wyznaczników, determinantów. Kurs uniwersytecki. pp. xxii. 600. 1879. 8°. *See* Paris.—*Towarzystwo Nauk Ścisłych.* **8533.** h. **21.**

BARANIUS (August Wilhelm) Versuch einer Biographie der Frau Gräfin von Lichtenau, einer berühmten Dame des vorigen Jahrhunderts. [With a portrait.] pp. 132. *Zürich & Lindau,* 1800. 12°. **10706.** b. **27.**

BARANIV (O.)

—— Римське право. *Мюнхен,* 1947– fol. W.P. **14327.**

Reproduced from typewriting.

BARANKEVICH (Ivan) Старый Нил. Рассказ. pp. 31. *Москва,* 1920. 8°. [*Красная Книжка.* no. 2.] **012265.aaa.21/2.**

BARANKIN (Edward William)

—— On System of Linear Equations, with applications to linear programming and the theory of tests of statistical hypotheses. *University of California Press: Berkeley & Los Angeles,* 1951. 8°. [*University of California Publications in Statistics.* vol. 1. no. 8.] Ac. **2689.** g/**61.**

BARANKIN (Edward William) and **GURLAND** (John)

—— On Asymptotically Normal, Efficient Estimators, *etc.* *University of California Press: Berkeley & Los Angeles,* 1951– . 8°. [*University of California Publications in Statistics.* vol. 1. no. 6, *etc.*] Ac. **2689.** g/**61.**

BARANKOVICS (István)

—— *See* Pethő (S.) A magunk utján. [Edited by I. Barankovics.] [1937.] 8°. **08073.** dd. **25.**

BARANNIKOV (Aleksei Petrovich)

—— *See* Beskrovnuy (V. M.) Хинди-русский словарь . . . Под редакцией . . . А. П. Баранникова . . . С приложением грамматического очерка составленного . . . А. П. Баранниковым. 1953. 8°. **12908.** cc. **28.**

—— *See* Beskrovnuy (V. M.) and Krasnodembsky (V. E.) Урду-русский словарь. Под редакцией . . . А. П. Баранникова. 1951. 8°. **14119.** a. **77.**

—— *See* Chaturbhuja Miśra. Прем Сагар. Перевод с хинди, вступительная статья и примечания А. П. Баранникова. 1937. 8°. [*Академия Наук СССР. Труды Института Востоковедения.* no. 25.] Ac. **1125.** ik 2.

—— *See* Rudenko (B. T.) Грамматика грузинского языка. (Ответственный редактор А. П. Баранников.) 1940. 8°. [*Труды Института Востоковедения.* no. 32.] Ac. **1125.** ik/2.

—— *See* Russia.—*Академия Наук СССР.*—*Институтъ Востоковѣдѣнія.* Советское Востоковедение. (А. П. Баранников ответственный редактор.) 1940, *etc.* 8°. Ac. **1125.** ik/**7.**

—— *See* Sergievsky (M. V.) and Barannikov (A. P.) Цыганско-русский словарь, *etc.* 1938. 8°. **12975.** cc. **21.**

—— *See* Tulasīdāsa. Рамаяна, или Рамачаританаманаса . . . Перевод . . . комментарии и вступительная статья . . . А. П. Баранникова. 1948. 8°. **14154.** ddd. **22*.**

—— Українські цигани. [With texts and an Ukrainian translation, and with plates. And with a summary in German.] pp. 60. 1931. 8°. *See* Kiev.—*Українська Академія Наук.—Етнографічна Комісія.—Кабінет Нацмен.* Ac. **1101.** gb.

BARANNIKOV (Oleksy Petrovich) *See* Barannikov (Aleksyei P.)

BARANOFF (Wladimir) *See* Baranov (V.)

BARANOFFSKI (Stefan I.) *See* Baranovsky (Stepan I.)

BARANOV (A. M.)

—— *See* Dul'nev (O. B.) Результати дослідів організації східчастих маршрутів на лінії Коростень—Одеса, *etc.* [By O. B. Dul'nev, A. M. Baranov, and others.] 1936. 8°. Ac. **1101**. ch/4.

BARANOV (A. N.)

—— *See* Russia.—*Народный Комиссариат Внутренних Дел, etc.—Главное Управление Геодезии и Картографии.* Атлас мира. [Edited by A. N. Baranov and others.] 1954. fol. **2060**. cc.

BARANOV (Aleksandr Andreevich)

—— *See* Chevigny (Hector) Lord of Alaska. Baranov and the Russian adventure. 1946. 8°. **010460**. l. **21**.

—— *See* Khlyebnikov (K. T.) Жизнеописаніе А. А. Баранова, *etc.* 1835. 8°. **10795**. cc. **19**.

BARANOV (F. I.)

—— Теория и расчет орудий рыболовства . . . Издание 2-е, исправленное и дополненное. pp. 435. *Москва*, 1948. 8°. **8808**. df. **40**.

BARANOV (Ip. G.)

—— *See* Liu (Ta-chün) Китайская музыка . . . Переводъ съ примѣчаніями и дополненіями И. Г. Баранова, *etc.* 1924. 8°. **7895**. ff. **33**.

—— Организація внутренней торговли въ Китаѣ. Краткій очеркъ. 2-е изданіе, измѣненное и дополненное. pp. 53. *Харбин*, 1920. 8°. **08229**. s. **37**.

BARANOV (Ivan Petrovich) Леонидъ Андреевъ, какъ художникъ-психологъ и мыслитель. pp. ii. 85. *Кіевъ*, 1907. 8°. **8460**. i. **4**.

—— М. Арцыбашевъ, какъ художникъ-психологъ и импрессіонистъ и какъ пѣвецъ смерти стараго и жизни новаго человѣка. pp. 76. *Кіевъ*, 1908. 8°. **11851**. v. **25**.

BARANOV (Kharlampy Karpovich)

—— Арабско-русский словарь (современного литературного языка). Под редакцией и с предисловием . . . И. Ю. Крачковского. вып. 4. 1946. 8°. *See* Russia.—*Академия Наук СССР.* —*Институтъ Востоковѣдѣнія.* Ac. **1125**. ik/8.

BARANOV (Koz'ma) Ночь на Рождество Христово. Русская повѣсть девятнадцатаго столѣтія. 3 част. *Москва*, 1834. 12°. **12591**. d. **4**.

BARANOV (N. P.) Не виновенъ. Драма изъ современной жизни въ 4-хъ дѣйствіяхъ, *etc.* pp. 48. *С.-Петербургъ*, 1912. 8°. **11758**. a. **27**. (3.)

BARANOV (N. V.)

—— Ленинград. (Архитектурно-планироворочный обзор развития города. Ответственный редактор: Баранов, Н. В. . . . Художник издания: Каменский, В. А.) pp. 402. 1943. fol. *See* Leningrad. —*Петроградскій Совѣтъ Рабочихъ и красноармейскихъ Депутатовъ*, afterwards *Ленинградскій Городской Совѣтъ Депутатовъ Трудящихся.—Исполнительный комитетъ.* L.R. **295**. c. 23.

BARANOV (Pavel Aleksandrovich)

—— *See* Frolov-Bagreev (A. M.) Ампелография СССР, *etc.* (Составители первого тома: П. А. Баранов, А. М. Негруль [and others].) 1946, *etc.* fol. S. n. **10/7**.

—— *See* Tashkend.—*Средне-Азіатскій Государственный Университетъ.* Бюллетень . . . Под редакцией В. Г. Мухина и П. А. Баранова. 1923, *etc.* 8°. Ac. **1163**.

—— Выдающийся русский ботаник Андрей Николаевич Бекетов. К 50-летию со дня смерти. [With portraits and a bibliography.] pp. 37. *Москва*, 1952. 8°. [*Московское Общество Испытателей Природы. Историческая серия.* no. 47.] Ac. **2988/15**.

BARANOV (Platon Ivanovich) Архивъ Правительствующаго Сената . . . Опись именнымъ Высочайшимъ Указамъ и Повеленіямъ . . . 1704–1725 (1725–1740, 1740–1762). Составилъ П. Барановъ. (Указатели къ III тому.) 3 том. 1872–78. 8°. *See* Russia.—*Правительствующій Сенатъ.* **9455**. g. **2**.

BARANOV (S. S.)

—— Атлас спектров пропускания прозрачных окрашенных пленок. [By S. S. Baranov, S. V. Khludov and E. V. Shpol'sky.] pp. 146. *Издательство Академии Наук СССР: Москва, Ленинград*, 1948. 8°. **8716**. g. **55**.

BARANOV (V. V.)

—— *See* Polezhaev (A. I.) Стихотворения. Редакция, биографический очерк и примечания В. В. Баранова, *etc.* 1933. 8°. **20002**. ee. **17**

BARANOV (Vladimir) Life and Happiness. pp. 51. *Trübner & Co.: London*, 1883. 8°. **8463**. f. **15**. (**6**.)

BARANOVICH (A. I.)

—— Магнатское хозяйство на юге Волыни в XVIII в. [With folding plates, including a map.] pp. 182. *Москва*, 1955. 8°. **09456**. df. **69**.
The titlepage headed: Академия Наук СССР. Институт Истории.

BARANOVICH (Lazar) *Bishop of Chernigov.* *See* Lazar, successively *Bishop* and *Archbishop of Chernigov and Novgorod Syeversk.*

BARANOVICH (M.) Рязанская Губернія. [Its geography, statistics, produce, etc. With a map and plans.] pp. iii. iv. 551. 1860. *See* Russia.—*Army.—Генеральный Штабъ.* Матеріалы для географіи и статистики Россіи, *etc.* 1860, *etc.* 8°. **10291**. g.

BARANOVICH (Ol.)

—— Залюднення Волинського воєводства в першій половині XVII ст. (Залюднення України перед хмельниччиною. I.) pp. 155. *у Києві*, 1930. 8°. Ac. **1101**. gc.
The titlepage headed: Всеукраїнська академія наук. Соціяльно-економічний відділ. Комісія історично-географічна.

BARANOVSKY (Antony) *Bishop.* *See* Baranowski (A.) *Titular Bishop of Thespiae.*

BARANOVSKY (Mikhail Ivanovich Tugan) *See* Tugan-Baranovsky.

BARANOVSKY (Stepan Ivanovich) Bråttmåls-statistik i Finland. [With a table.] pp. 52. *Helsingfors*, 1850. 12°. **08282**. e. **61**. (**2**.)

—— Folkmängds-förhållanden i Finland. pp. 68. *Helsingfors*, 1850. 12°. **08282**. e. **61**. (**1**.)

BARANOWSKI (ALBERTUS) *Archbishop of Gnesen. See* GNESEN, *Synod of.* Concilium prouinciale Regni Poloniæ, quod . . . B. Macieiowski . . . habuit Petricouiæ. Anno Domini, M.DCVII. [Issued by A. Baranowski.] 1609. 4°. **5015.** b. **12.**

BARANOWSKI (ANTON) *Titular Bishop of Thespiae.* Gabija. Rinktinė knyga, paaukuota lietuvos dainiaus Vyskupo Antano Baranaucko atminimui. pp. 77. *Krokuvoje,* 1907. 8°. **11852.** v. **11.**

—— Замѣтки о литовскомъ языкѣ и словарѣ. I–VIII. (Отдѣльный оттискъ изъ Сборника отдѣленія русскаго языка и словесности Императорской Академіи Наукъ.) pp. 80. iii. *Санктпетербургъ,* 1898. 8°. **12976.** s. **18.**

BARANOWSKI (ANTON) *Titular Bishop of Thespiae,* and **WEBER** (HUGO ERNST BARTHOLD)

—— Ostlitauische Texte mit Einleitungen und Anmerkungen herausgegeben von A. Baranowski und H. Weber. Hft. 1. pp. xxxv. 23. *Weimar,* 1882. 8°. **12264.** k. **6.**

BARANOWSKI (BOHDAN)

—— Dzieje wojskowości polskiej, do roku 1831. Wypisy źródłowe. [By B. Baranowski, W. Bortnowski and W. Lewandowski. With plates.] (Pod redakcją W. Bortnowskiego.) pp. 291. *w Jeleniej Górze,* 1949. 8°. **8836.** d. **11.**

—— Położenie chłopów u schyłku Rzeczypospolitej szlacheckiej. Wybór tekstów źródłowych. Opracowali R. [*sic*] Baranowski, Z. Libiszowska, R. Rosin. pp. xxxi. 260. *Warszawa,* 1953. **09475.** e. **45.**

—— Polska a Tatarszczyzna w latach 1624–1629. (La Pologne et la Tartarie dans les années 1624–29.) [With a summary in French.] pp. 134. *Łódź,* 1948. 8°. [*Łódzkie Towarzystwo Naukowe.* wydział 2. no. 1.] Ac. **1141/2.**

—— Powstania chłopskie na ziemiach dawnej Rzeczypospolitej. pp. 157. *Warszawa,* 1952. 8°. **09525.** ee. **30.**

—— Procesy czarownic w Polsce w XVII i XVIII wieku. (Les Procès des sorcières en Pologne aux XVII-ème et XVIII-ème siècles. Résumé.) pp. 181. *Łódź,* 1952. 8°. [*Łódzkie Towarzystwo Naukowe.* wydział 2. no. 13.] Ac. **1141/2.**

—— Sprawy obyczajowe w sądownictwie wiejskim w Polsce wieku XVII i XVIII. (Le problème du système des peines réservées au [*sic*] délits sexuels dans le village polonais aux XVII-ème et XVIII-ème siècles. Résumé) pp. 117. *Łódź,* 1955. 8°. [*Łódzkie Towarzystwo Naukowe.* wydział 2. no. 16.] Ac. **1146/2.**

—— Upadek kultury w Polsce w dobie reakcji katolickiej XVII–XVIII w. Wypisy źródłowe. [By B. Baranowski, W. Lewandowski and J. St. Piątkowski.] pp. 224. *Warszawa,* 1950. 8°. **09456.** k. **36.**

—— Znajomość wschodu w dawnej Polsce do XVIII wieku. La Connaissance de l'Orient en Pologne avant le XVIII-ème s. (Résumé.) pp. 256. *Łódź,* 1950. 8°. [*Łódzkie Towarzystwo Naukowe.* wydział 2. no. 3.] Ac. **1141/2.**

BARANOWSKI (BOHDAN) and **LEWANDOWSKI** (W.)

—— Nietolerancja i zabobon w Polsce w wieku XVII i XVIII. Wypisy źródłowe. pp. 223. *Warszawa,* 1950. 8°. **9501.** c. **4.**

BARANOWSKI (BOLESŁAW) J. I. Kraszewski, jego życie i zasługi. pp. 72. 1879. 8°. *See* LEOPOL.—*Towarzystwo Pedagogiczne.* **10795.** h. **9.**

BARANOWSKI (IGNACY) Pamiętniki Ignacego Baranowskiego, 1840–1862. [With a portrait.] Wydał Adam Wrzosek. pp. lv. 463. *Poznań,* 1923. 8°. [*Roczniki Poznańskiego Towarzystwa Przyjaciół Nauk.* tom 49.] Ac. **915.**

BARANOWSKI (IGNACY TADEUSZ) *See* POLAND. [*Collections of Laws, etc.*] Księgi Referendarskie . . . 1582–1602 [*etc.*]. Wydał I. T. Baranowski. 1910, *etc.* 8°. [*Wydawnictwa Towarzystwa Naukowego Warszawskiego.* no. 4, *etc.*] Ac. **1150/2.**

—— Komisye porządkowe, 1765–1788. (Osobne odbicie z tomu XLIX. Rozpraw Wydziału histor.-filozof. Akademii Umiejętności, *etc.*) pp. 46. *w Krakowie,* 1907. 8°. **8716.** g. **34.** (**5.**)

—— Materyały do dziejów wsi Polskiej. Zesz. I. pp. 57. *Warszawa,* 1909. 8°. [*Prace Towarzystwa Naukowego Warszawskiego.* II. Wydział. no. 2.] Ac. **1150/2.**

—— Prusy Królewskie. Część I. Wydał I. T. Baranowski. (Polska XVI wieku pod względem geograficzno-statystycznym. tom XII.) [With a preface by A. Jabłonowski.] pp. xiii. 314. xlii. *Warszawa,* 1911. [*Wydawnictwa Towarzystwa Naukowego Warszawskiego.* Wydział II. Komisya historyczna.] *See* ŹRÓDŁA. Źródła dziejowe. tom 23. 1876, *etc.* 8°. Ac. **1150/3.**

—— Przemysł Polski w XVI wieku. Z pośmiertnego rękopisu wydał K. Tymieniecki. pp. 192. *w Warszawie,* 1919. 8°. **08229.** c. **19.**

BARANOWSKI (JAN) *Director of the Astronomical Observatory at Warsaw.*

—— *See* COPERNICUS (N.) Nicolai Copernici . . . De revolutionibus orbium coelestium libri sex, *etc.* [Edited by J. Baranowski.] 1854. fol. **8560.** k. **8.**

BARANOWSKI (JAN JÓZEF)

—— Anglo-Polish Lexicon. 2 pt. *Warsaw,* 1883. 8°. **012977.** a. **54.**

—— Inventions mécaniques et travaux littéraires de J. J. Baranowski, *etc. Paris,* 1886. 4°. **8706.** h. **14.** (**7.**)

—— Nouveau système de voter au moyen d'un appareil dit scrutateur mécanique, *etc.* [With a plate.] pp. 24. *Paris,* 1849. 8°. **8008.** c. **37.** (**2.**)

—— Słownik polsko-angielski. pp. iii. 402. *Warszawa,* 1884. 8°. **012977.** a. **53.**

—— Vade-mecum de la langue française rédigé d'après les dictionnaires classiques, avec les exemples de bonnes locutions que donne l'Académie Française, *etc.* pp. 223. *E. Leroux : Paris ; Trübner & Cie: Londres ; Édimbourg* [printed], 1879. 16°. **12954.** a. **43.**

—— Biography of John Joseph Baranowski translated from the illustrated Polish journal "Klosy" . . . with his portrait . . . and observation upon his work to be shortly published under the title of "Anglo-Polish Lexicon." pp. 8. *Paris,* 1881. 8°. **10601.** b. **28.** (**2.**)

BARANOWSKI (KAZIMIERZ) Na Wawel. (Zbiory Heleny Dąbczańskiej.) pp. 30. *Lwów,* 1906. 8°. **07707.** h. **33.** (**2.**)

BARANOWSKI (R.) *See* BARANOWSKI (B.)

BARANOWSKI (STEFAN) *See* BARANOVSKY (Stepan I.)

BARANOWSKI (SZYMON) *See* CATULLUS (C. V.) [*Works.—Latin and Polish.*] Q. Valerii Catulli . . . Liber . . . Poezye przełożone . . . przez Sz. Baranowskiego. 1839. 8°. [*Biblioteka klassyków łacińskich na polski język przełożona.* tom 4.] **11304.** dd. **1/2.**

—— Przygody starego żołnierza z dziewiątego pułku Księztwa Warszawskiego, według ustnego opowiadania zebrał i skreślił S. Baranowski. pp. x. 107. *Lipsk,* 1857. 8°. **12590.** b. **2.**

BARANOWSKI (Walerian)

—— Dokąd ludzkość dąży? pp. 152. *Hamburg, Bruksela,* 1946. 8°. **8009**. k. **31**.

BARANOWSKI (Zdzislaw)

—— The International Horseman's Dictionary. English-French-German. Lexique international du cavalier . . . Internationales Pferde-Lexikon, *etc.* [With plates.] pp. xxii. 176. *Museum Press: London,* 1955. *obl.* 8°. Cup. **1247**. k. **36**.

BARANOWSKI (Zygmunt) and **KOWALSKI** (Seweryn)

—— Nauka wiary i obyczajów dla klasy II gimnazjalnej. Wydanie II. pp. 134. 1942. 8°. *See* Poland.—*Urząd Wychowania Narodowego, etc.* **4381**. bb. **18**.

BARANSHCHIKOV (Vasily) Нещастныя приключенія Василья Баранщикова мѣщанина Нижняго Новагорода . . . въ Америкѣ, Азїи и Европѣ съ 1780 по 1787 годъ. С. К. Р. (Печатано съ дозволенія указнаго въ типографіи г. Вильковскаго и Галченкова.) pp. 72. *въ Санктпетербургѣ,* 1787. 8°. **1424**. c. **1**. (**1**.)

BARAŃSKA (Marcelina) Odwrót kawaleryi. Krotochwila w jednym akcie. pp. 47. *Warszawa,* 1894. 16°. **11758**. a. **21**. (**3**.)

BARANSKI (Anton) Die altnordische Geschichte. I. Das nordische Pferd. pp. vii. 73. *Wien,* 1911. 8°. **7295**. ee. **36**.

—— Geschichte der Ägyptischen Kaukasusprovinz im Lichte der tiergeographischen Untersuchungsmethode. pp. iv. 93. *Wien,* 1910. 8°. **09055**. b. **33**.

—— Geschichte der Thierzucht und Thiermedicin im Alterthum. pp. viii. 245. *Wien,* 1886. 8°. **7293**. l. **14**.

—— Praktische Anleitung zur Vieh- und Fleischschau für Stadt- und Bezirksärzte, Thierärzte, Sanitätsbeamte, sowie besonders zum Gebrauche für Physikats-Candidaten. pp. viii. 168. *Wien,* 1880. 8°. **7291**. b. **12**.

—— Thierproduction . . . Mit vielen Holzschnitten. 3 Tl. *Wien,* 1890, 91. 8°. **7291**. d. **6**.

—— Die vorgeschichtliche Zeit im Lichte der Hausthiercultur. pp. iv. 296. *Wien,* 1896. 8°. **7293**. l. **23**.

—— Wo lag Troie? Im Lichte der tiergeographischen Untersuchungsmethode. pp. iv. 64. *Wien,* 1910 [1909]. 8°. **7707**. df. **30**. (**8**.)

—— Zähmung und Abstammung des Pferdes. pp. 75. *Leipzig,* 1884. 8°. [*Vorträge für Thierärzte.* ser. 7. Hft. 1/2.] **7291**. ee.

—— Die Zähmung unserer Hausthiere. pp. 67. *Leipzig,* 1884. 8°. [*Vorträge für Thierärzte.* ser. 6. Hft. 9/10.] **7291**. ee.

BARAŃSKI (Franciszek) Jeszcze Polska nie zginęła! Pieśni patryotyczne i narodowe zebrał F. Barański. I. Muzyka. (II. Słowa.) Wydanie drugie pomnożone. 2 pt. *Lwów,* [1897.] *obl.* 8°. MA. **1146**. a.

—— Koleżeństwo szkolne. Dramat w pięciu aktach. pp. 62. *Żytomiérz,* 1860. 8°. **11758**. h. **10**.

—— Śpiewnik sokoli. [Songs, with musical notes.] Zebrał i ułożył F. Barański. pp. 85. 96. *Kraków,* 1896. 16°. MA. **1146**.

—— W dzień Bożego Narodzenia. Kolędy zebrał F. Barański. Część I: Słowa. (Część II: Muzyka.) 2 część. *Lwów,* [1899.] *obl.* 8°. MA. **1146**. b.

BARAŃSKI (Kazimierz Ostaszewski) *See* Ostaszewski-Barański.

BARANSKY (Nikolai Nikolaevich)

—— Экономическая география СССР. Учебник для 8-го класса средней школы, *etc.* [With maps.] pp. 408. *Москва,* 1936. 8°. **010005**. m. **20**.

—— Экономическая география СССР. Учебник для 8 класса средней школы. Издание десятое, *etc.* [With maps and illustrations.] pp. 415. *Москва,* 1949. 8°. **010005**. k. **4**.

—— Экономическая география СССР . . . Издание двенадцатое, *etc.* [With maps.] pp. 423. *Москва,* 1951. 8°. **010005**. s. **5**.

—— Экономическая география СССР . . . Издание четырнадцатое, *etc.* [With maps.] pp. 407. *Москва,* 1953. 8°. **010005**. s. **21**.

—— Очерки по школьной методике экономической географии. pp. 225. *Москва,* 1946. 8°. **010007**. f. **78**.

BARANSKY (Nikolai Nikolaevich) and **KAMINSKY** (B.)

—— Социалистическая реконструкция областей, краев и республик СССР. в постановлениях партийных и советских органов. Пособие для проработки районного курса экономической географии СССР. Составлено . . . Н. Баранским и Б. Каминским, под ред. Н. Баранского. 2 ч. 1932. 8°. *See* Moscow.—*Императорскій Московскій Университетъ.—Географическое Отдѣленіе.—Каѳедра Экономической Географіи.* Ac. **1105**. f.

BARANTE ( ) *Baron.* *See* Guignard (F. E. de) *Count de Saint-Priest.* Mémoires . . . Publiés par le baron de Barante. 1929, *etc.* 8°. **10655**. bbb. **6**.

BARANTE (Amable Guillaume Prosper Brugière de) *Baron.* *See* Brugière de Barante.

BARANTE (Césarine Brugière de) *Baroness.* *See* Brugière de Barante.

BARANTE (Claude Antoine Prosper Félix Brugière de) *Baron.* *See* Brugière de Barante.

BARANTE (Claude Ignace Brugière de) *See* Brugière de Barante.

BARANTE (P. de)

—— Jeanne d'Arc . . . Avec seize gravures, *etc.* pp. 238. *Paris,* 1935. 8°. **20003**. i. **45**.

BARANTSEVICH (E. M.) Чума. Появленіе и распространеніе ея у человѣка, *etc.* pp. 104. *Москва,* 1898. 8°. **07561**. h. **12**.

BARANTSEVICH (Kazimir Stanislavovich) *See* Smirnov (A. Pl.) Осада Казани . . . Съ предисловіемъ К. С. Баранцевича, *etc.* [1911.] 8°. **12590**. f. **31**.

—— *See* Tolstoi (A. K.) *Count.* Опричина. Драма . . . Передѣланная стихами изъ романа "Князь Серебряный" гр. А. Толстаго К. С. Баранцевичемъ. 1890. 8°. **11758**. f. **46**. (**6**.)

—— Порванныя струны, и другіе разсказы. pp. 360. *С.-Петербургъ и Москва,* [1902.] 8°. **012590**. d. **28**.

—— Родныя картинки. 17 разсказовъ. pp. 368. *Москва,* 1895. 8°. **012590**. g. **87**.

—— Скитанія Егорки. pp. 92. *С.-Петербургъ,* 1901. 8°. **012590**. ccc. **46**.

BARANTSOV (Aleksandr Alekseevich) *Count.*

—— *See* Weil (M. H.) Les Progrès de l'artillerie russe. Analyse du rapport du Général Baranzoff. 1873. 8°. [*Publications de la Réunion des Officiers. Mélanges militaires.* sér. 2. no. 6.] **8832**. h. **30**. (**4**.)

BÁRÁNY (ÁGOSTON) Torontálvármegye' hajdana. Emlegette Bárány Á. 2 rész. *Budán*, 1845. 8°. **10210**. cc. **20**.

BÁRÁNY (ERNST HERBERT)

—— *See* UPSALA.—*Regia Academia Upsaliensis*. Inbjudningsskrift till åhörande av de offentliga föreläsningar (med vilka E. Bárány [and others] tillträda sina ämbeten), *etc.* 1902, *etc.* 8°. Ac. **1077/10**. (**77**.)

—— A Contribution to the Physiology of Bone Conduction. Inaugural-Dissertation, *etc.* pp. viii. 223. *Uppsala*, 1938. 8°. **7407**. ppp. **29**.

BÁRÁNY (FRANZ R.)

—— Abnormal Vascular Reactions in Diabetes Mellitus. A clinical physiological study. [Translated by Marcia Skogh.] pp. 129. *Lund*, 1955. 8°. [*Acta medica scandinavica*. suppl. 304.] P.P. **3081**. b. (**2**.)

BÁRÁNY (GYÖRGY) *See* BIBLE.—*New Testament*. [*Hungarian*.] A' mi Urunk Jesus Kristusnak Uj Testamentoma most Görög nyelvböl . . . fordittatott, *etc.* [Translated by G. Bárány and others.] 1754, *etc.* 8°. **3061**. b. **13**.

BÁRÁNY (IGNÁC) Magyar nyelvkönyv . . . Hetedik . . . kiadás. 3 füz. *Budapest*, 1875, 76, 74. 8°. **12975**. i. **3**. *Füz*. 1 *is of the seventh, füz*. 2 *of the sixth, and füz*. 3 *of the third edition*.

—— Nyelvgyakorlatok . . . Hatodik . . . kiadás. 3 folyam. *Budapest*, 1875, 73, 76. 8°. **12975**. i. **2**. *Foly*. 1 *is of the sixth, foly*. 2 *of the fifth, and foly*. 3 *of the third edition*.

BÁRÁNY (JÁNOS) *See* BIBLE.—*New Testament*. [*Hungarian*.] A' mi Urunk Jesus Kristusnak Uj Testamentoma most Görög nyelvböl . . . fordittatott, *etc.* [Translated by J. Bárány and others.] 1754, *etc.* 8°. **3061**. b. **13**.

BÁRÁNY (MAGDA OBERSCHALL) *See* OBERSCHALL (Magda) *Báránynė*.

BÁRÁNY (PÉTER)

—— A' magyar anyáknak az országgyűlésére egybe-gyűltt ország' nagyjai', 's magyar atyák' elejéke terjesztett. alázatos kéréssek. [By P. Bárány.] pp. 32. 1790. 12° *See* HUNGARY.—*Országgyülés*.

BÁRÁNY (ROBERT)

—— *See* UPSALA.—*Regia Academia Upsaliensis*. Inbjudningsskrift till åhörande av den offentliga föreläsning (med vilken R. Bárány tillträder sitt ämbete), *etc.* 1902, *etc.* 8°. Ac. **1077/10**. (**29**.)

BARANYAI (ERZSÉBET)

—— *See* MUNKA. Nevelő munka az általános iskolában. Irták: Baranyai E., Barra Gy. [and others], *etc.* 1947. 8°. [*A köznevelés könyvtára*. no. 1.] S. **270/2**.

—— A magasabbrendű értelmesség meghatározása és vizsgálatának módszere. (Superior Intelligence and its Examination. Extract.) pp. 302. *Szeged*, 1938. 8°. [*Acta litterarum ac scientiarum Reg. Universitatis Hung. Francisco-Iosephinae*. sectio philosoph. tom. 9.] Ac. **833**. (**3**.)

—— A neveléslélektani kutatás magyar feladatai a tanítás lélektana körében. Vázlat egy magyar neveléslélektani kutató intézet munkatervéhez. (Hungarian problems of educational psychology, in the range of the psychology of teaching.) [With an English summary.] *Szeged*, 1931. 8°. [*Acta litterarum ac scientiarum Reg. Universitatis Hung. Francisco-Josephinae*. Sectio philosophica. tom. 3. fasc. 2.] Ac. **833**. (**3**.)

BARANYAI (PÁL) Aȝtékozló fiúról, *etc.* 1880. *See* PEST.—*Magyar Tudományos Akadémia*. Régi magyar költők tára. köt. 2. 1877, *etc.* 8°. Ac. **825/39**.

BARANYAI (ZOLTÁN)

—— *See* HUNGARY.—*Magyar Királyi Külügyminisztérium*, afterwards *Magyar Külügyminisztérium*. Hungary and the Conference of Paris. (vol. 2, 4. Edited by Z. Baranyai.) 1947. 4°. S. **275/4**.

—— *See* HUNGARY.—*Magyar Királyi Külügyminisztérium*, afterwards *Magyar Külügyminisztérium*. La Hongrie et la Conférence de Paris. [tom. 2 and 4 edited by Z. Baranyai.] 1947. 4°. S. **275/5**.

—— Ungarn. Das Antlitz einer Nation. (Herausgegeben von Zoltan Baranyai.) [By various authors. With plates and maps.] pp. viii. 869. *Budapest*, 1940. 8°. **10215**. m. **9**.

—— Visages de la Hongrie. Ouvrage orné de 257 illustrations. [By various authors.] (Rédigé par Z. Baranyai avec l'assistance de Jean Győry et de Gyula Ember.) [With a map.] pp. 621. *Paris; Budapest* [printed], 1938. 8°. **10215.r.5.**

BARANYAY (FERENC)

—— Disquisitio notitiarum antiquarum liberæ regiæque civitatis Strigoniensis et arcis archi-episcopalis nominis ejusdem. [With a plate.] pp. 74. *Pesthini*, 1820. 8°. **9315**. bbb. **7**.

BARANYI (PÁL LÁSZLO) *Begin*. Gаѡвеле Глакизне, *etc.* [The Cyrillic alphabet as used by the Wallachians, followed by syllabaries, prayers, creeds, a catechism, etc., i.e. P. L. Baranyi's Pânea Pruncilor of 1702?] [1700?] 8°. *See* WALLACHIAN ALPHABET. **12976**. aaa. **16**.

BÁRÁNY-OBERSCHALL (MAGDA VON) *See* OBERSCHALL (M.) *Báránynė*.

BARANZANUS (JOANNES ANTONIUS) *See* BARANZANUS (Redemptus)

BARANZANUS (REDEMPTUS) Campus philosophicus, in quo omnes dialecticæ quæstiones . . . agitantur . . . Præmissa est introductio breuis ad dialecticam. 2 pt. *Apud B. Vincentium: Lugduni*, 1620. 8°. **8468**. aa. **6**.

—— Vranoscopia, seu de cœlo; in qua vniuersa cœlorum doctrina clarè, dilucidè, & breuiter traditur, *etc.* [With prefaces by J. B. Murator and L. des Hayes.] 2 pt. *P. & I. Chouet*: [*Geneva*,] 1617. 4°. **533**. h. **2**.

BARANZOFF ( ) [For the Russian surname in this form:] *See* BARANTSOV.

BARANZONE (FRANCESCO MARIA) [For official documents issued by F. M. Baranzone as Governor of Rome:] *See* ROME.—*The City*.—*Official Documents issued by the Governors of the City*.

BARAONA (FRANCISCO DE VITORIA) *See* VITORIA BARAONA.

BARAONA (SANCHO DE) *See* VARAONA.

BARAONA DE SOTO (LUIS) *See* BARAHONA DE SOTO.

BARAS (ALEXANDRE) *See* MARSEILLES.—*Société artistique des Bouches-du-Rhône*. Tribune artistique et littéraire du Midi. (Directeur A. Baras. tom. 8, *etc.*) 1857, *etc.* 8°. P.P. **1909**. d.

BARAS (E.) *Dr.*

—— La Circoncision. Son historique et son importance au point de vue hygiénique. Avec la traduction intégrale de la prière de Maimonide. pp. 56. *Paris*, 1936. 8°. **7580**. r. **28**.

BARAS (ÉMILE) *See* KOWNACKI (A.) Émile Baras. L'homme et l'œuvre. 1889. 12°. **10603**. i. **20**. (**16**.)

BARAS (GUILLAUME) Considérations physiologiques sur la menstruation, *etc.* pp. 18. *Montpellier,* an VII [1797]. 4°. **1180**. d. **5**. (**4**.)

BARAS (LÉON PAUL) Considérations sur quelques points de pathologie générale; thèse, *etc.* pp. 23. *Paris,* 1833. 4°. **1184**. e. **16**. (**10**.)

BARAŞ (MARCU I.) Le Socialisme juridique et son influence sur l'évolution du droit civil en France à la fin du XIXe siècle et au XXe siècle, *etc.* [With a bibliography.] pp. 134. *Paris,* 1923. 8°. **5406**. f. **20**.

BARAS (MARIE MARC ANTOINE)

—— Au peuple français et à ses ennemis sur le projet d'une contre-révolution . . . Seconde édition. pp. 54. *Toulouse: Paris,* 1791. 8°. R. **207**. (**1**.)

—— Avis très-important aux bons citoyens, sur les assemblées primaires. [A criticism of the pamphlet entitled "Réflexions sur les assemblées primaires." With the text.] pp. 12. [1791.] 8°. R. **93**. (**2**.)

—— Compte moral, rendu par M. M. A. Baras, ancien administrateur du district de Toulouse à ses concitoyens. pp. 11. [1795?] 8°. F. **981**. (**2**.)

BARASC (C.) Ma technique apicole. Nouveau manuel d'apiculture, *etc.* pp. 304. *Paris,* 1932. 8°. **07299**. de. **33**.

BARASCH (MARCO I.) *See* BARAŞ.

BARASCUD (ALPHONSE CLÉMENT) Campagne de Chine, 1900–1901. Service vétérinaire du corps expéditionnaire français et dans les armées alliées. Illustré de nombreuses gravures. pp. 269. *Vannes,* 1903. 8°. **09055**. cc. **7**.

BARASCUD (J. G. ÉMILE) Essai sur l'erysipèle. Tribut académique, *etc.* pp. 21. *Montpellier,* [1834.] 4°. **1181**. g. **7**. (**14**.)

BARASCUT (J. P. M.) Essai sur l'emploi du nitrate d'argent contre certaines phlegmasies des membranes muqueuses . . . Thèse, *etc.* pp. 32. *Paris,* 1837. 4°. **1184**. h. **17**. (**1**.)

BARAS DELSHENS (J. PAUL) Considérations physiologiques et pathologiques sur la menstruation, *etc.* pp. 53. *Montpellier,* 1809. 4°. **1180**. f. **14**. (**18**.)

BARASHKOV (I. M.)

—— Высокие урожаи льна-долгунца. Колхоз "Ударник," Грязовецкого района, Вологодской области. Издание второе. [With illustrations.] pp. 31. *Москва,* 1954. 8°. **7081**. ee. **14**.

Part of a series entitled "Передовой опыт в сельском хозяйстве."

BARASSI (CARLO) *See* KONINCK (L. de) Francesco . . . Traduzione di C. Barassi, *etc.* [1905.] 8°. [*Breitkopf & Härtels Textbibliothek.* no. 293.] **11747**. ccc. **1**/**293**.

BARASSI (LUDOVICO) Il Contratto di lavoro nel diritto positivo italiano. pp. xx. 914. *Milano,* 1901. 8°. **5359**. eee. **12**.

—— Istituzioni di diritto civile. pp. xv. 664. *Milano,* 1914. 8°. **5373**. de. **3**.

—— Teoria della ratifica del contratto annullabile. pp. xiv. 437. *Milano,* 1898. 8°. **5373**. dd. **2**.

—— La Teoria generale delle obbligazioni. 3 vol. *Milano,* 1946. 8°. **5373**. l. **2**.

BARASSINUS (ROBERTUS)

—— Disputatio de astrorum in medicina observatione. Quam . . . sub præsidio . . . M. Ægidii Gaudini . . . Publicè tuebatur Robertus Barassinus, *etc.* pp. 8. *Ex Typographiâ Michaelis Yvon: Cadomi,* 1642. 4°. **1830**. c. **1**. (**148**.)

BARÁT (BÉLA)

—— *See* LÓSY-SCHMIDT (E.) and BARÁT (B.) Technikai lexikon . . . Szerkesztették Dr. Lósy-Schmidt E., Dr. Barát B., *etc.* 1928. 8°. **12224**. e. **5**.

BARAT (ÉMILE) De l'angine couenneuse épidémique. Thèse, *etc.* pp. 38. *Montpellier,* 1857. 4°. **7379**. d. **11**. (**12**.)

BARAT (EMMANUEL) Le Style poétique et la révolution romantique. pp. vii. 316. *Paris,* 1904. 8°. **011853**. bb. **14**.

BARÁT (ENDRE)

—— Rabszolgák voltunk. Napló 1942–43. pp. 160. *Budapest,* 1948. 8°. **9101**. de. **117**.

BARAT (ÉTIENNE) L'Association, son emploi rationnel. Examen théorique du principe: ses propriétés, ses effets, *etc.* pp. 244. *Paris,* 1867. 8°. **8205**. aaa. **14**.

BARAT (JOAN)

—— Diari del captaire. [Reminiscences of Paris.] pp. 167. *Palma de Mallorca,* 1955. 16°. [*Raixa.* vol. 3.] W.P. D. **71**/**3**.

BARAT (JOSEPH ALEXANDRE) Notre-Dame de l'Épine et son pélerinage. pp. 191. *Châlons-sur-Marne,* 1860. 12°. **4629**. a. **20**.

—— [Another edition.] pp. 181. *Châlons-sur-Marne,* 1877. 8°. **3902**. c. **12**.

BARAT (MADELEINE SOPHIE LOUISE) *See* MAGDALEN SOPHIA [Barat], *Saint.*

BARAT (NICOLAS) *See* THOMASSIN (L.) Glossarium universale hebraicum, *etc.* [Edited by N. Barat and Charles Bordes.] 1697. fol. **67**. i. **6**.

—— Nouvelle bibliothèque choisie, où l'on fait connoître les bons livres en divers genres de literature, *etc.* 2 tom. *Amsterdam,* 1714. 12°. **261**. b. **29, 30**.

BARAT (S. B. F.) *See* MORELLET (J. N.) Le Nivernais . . . Publié par MM. Morellet, Barat, *etc.* 1838, *etc.* fol. **1300**. m. **10**.

BARATA (ANTONIO FRANCISCO) *See* BRITO BOTELHO (B. de) Historia breve de Coimbra . . . Segunda edição annotada por A. F. Barata. 1873. 8°. **10027**. ccc. **10**.

—— Cancioneiro geral. Continuação ao de Garcia de Resende compilado por A. F. Barata e avaliado pelo Doutor T. Braga. pp. xxv. 271. *Evora,* 1902. 8°. **11450**. f. **39**.

—— Cancionero Portuguez . . . Segunda edição melhorada e accrescentada. [With prefatory notices by T. Ribeiro and E. A. Vidal.] pp. xxxviii. 226. *Coimbra,* 1878. 8°. **11452**. e. **2**.

—— Homenagem do Infante D. Henrique no quingentesimo anniversario de seu nascimento no Porto, *etc.* pp. 39. *Lisboa,* 1894. 8°. **10601**. ee. **21**. (**13**.)

—— O Rancho da Carqueja, tentativa de romance historico, *etc.* pp. xi. 195. *Coimbra,* 1864. 8°. **12490**. c. **1**.

—— Synaxaria Fernando Martins de Bulhões—Santo Antonio—com uma carta do Santo. pp. 61. *Minerva Eborense,* 1895. 4°. **4827**. h. **18**.

—— Vasco da Gama em Evora, *etc.* pp. 53. *Lisboa,* 1898. 8°. **10601**. ff. **16**. (**4**.)

BARATA DA SILVA (José) Reflexões sobre os arrozaes e as commissões em Portugal . . . Primeira parte. pp. 76. *Lisboa*, 1861. 8°. **7073**. aaa. **11**.

BARATAEV (Mikhail) *Prince*. Нумизматическiе факты грузинскаго царства. (Монеты царства грузинскаго . . . Monnaies du Royaume de Géorgie, *etc*.—Documens numismatiques du Royaume de Géorgie, *etc*.—Сборникъ приложенiя и думы къ разряду третьему, *etc*.) *Russ. & Fr*. *Санктпетербургъ*, 1844. 8°. **813**. h. **27**.

BARATARIAN ANTICIPATION. Baratarian Anticipation: or, a true and genuine account of the speech that will be delivered from the throne of Barataria [Ireland]; and the debates that will take place upon the same in both ——s of ——t, in that Kingdom, on the 18th day of January next, *etc*. pp. 56. *T. Butler: Dublin*, 1787. 8°. **8145**. c. **3**.

BARATARIANA. Baratariana. A select collection of fugitive political pieces, published during the administration of Lord Townshend in Ireland. The second edition corrected and enlarged. [By Henry Grattan, Henry Flood, Sir Hercules Langrishe, H. M. Boyd and the Rev. — Simpson. Edited by Simpson.] pp. x. 354. *Dublin*, 1773. 12°. **712**. d. **22**.

—— [Another copy.] G. **4797**.

—— The third edition, corrected and enlarged. pp. xviii. 328. MS. NOTE [by Lord Macaulay]. *Dublin*, 1777. 12°. **8145**. aa. **6**.

—— *See* Brutus, *pseud*., and Search (H.) *pseud*. Essays historical, political and moral; being a proper supplement to Baratariana. [1774?] 12°. **712**. d. **23**.

BARATASHVILI (M.)

—— Стрекоза. Комедия . . . Перевод с грузинского и сценическая редакция Г. Штайна. pp. 107. *Москва*, 1953. 8°. **17075**. d. **29**.

BARATASHVILI (Nikolai)

—— Стихотворения. Перевод . . . Бориса Пастернака. Редакция В. В. Гольцева. pp. 78. *Москва*, 1948. 8°. **011586**. df. **91**.

BARATA Y QUEMAZÓN (Cándido) Cancion inglesa al soldado tan manso como bravo. *México*, 1824. *s. sh*. fol. **9770**. k. **8**. (**78**.)

BARATCIART (André) Guiristinoqui bicitceco eta hiltceco moldea, *etc*. [By A. Baratciart.] pp. 311. 1787. 12°. *See* Molde. **886**. c. **19**.

—— Guiristinoqui bicitceco eta hilteco moldea, *etc*. [By A. Baratciart.] pp. 267. [1827.] 12°. *See* Molde. **872**. c. **22**.

—— [Another edition.] pp. 256. 1841. 12°. *See* Molde. **4406**. df. **33**.

BARAT DULAURIER (J. Adrien) Études sur les hémorrhagies de la moelle ou hématomyélie. pp. 39. *Paris*, 1859. 4°. [*Collection des thèses soutenues à la Faculté de Médecine de Paris*. An 1859. tom. 1.] **7373**. b. **13**.

BARATECH (Carlos E. Corona) *See* Corona Baratech.

BARATELLA (Antonio) *See* Segarizzi (A. A. C.) Antonio Baratella e i suoi corrispondenti. 1916. 8°. [*Miscellanea di storia veneta*. ser. 3. tom. 10.] **Ac.6580/2.(6.)**

BARATERIO (Francesco) Oratio . . . ad principem Hieronymum Priolum. *See* Sansovino (F.) Delle orationi a principi di Venetia . . . libro primo. 1562. 4°. **1090**. l. **7**. (**1**.)

BARATERIUS (Bartholomaeus) Nova compilatio juris feudal. communis. *See* Germany. [*Laws, etc*.—i.] Joh. Schilteri Codex juris Alemannici feudalis, *etc*. 1728. fol. **503**. h. **10**.

BARÁTH (Ferencz) *See* Carlyle (Thomas) [*The French Revolution*.] A Franczia Forradalom . . . fordította Baráth F. 1875, *etc*. 8°. Ac. **825/35**.

—— Dömötör János életrajza. pp. 18. *See* Dömötör (J.) Dömötör J. munkái, *etc*. 1878. 8°. **12264**. ee. **3**.

BARÁTH (Miklós) Tokai támadás. Költői beszély. pp. 119. *Győrött*, 1849. 8°. **11585**. d. **6**.

BARATHIEU (Victor Louis) De l'hépatite aiguë. Thèse, *etc*. pp. 20. *Paris*, 1837. 4°. **1184**. h. **5**. (**17**.)

BARATIER (Albert Ernest Augustin) A travers l'Afrique. Édition définitive ornée de huit portraits et de six cartes. pp. v. 350. *Paris*, 1912. 8°. **010097**. k. **40**.

—— Au Congo. Souvenirs de la Mission Marchand. De Loango à Brazzaville . . . Illustrations, *etc*. pp. 126. *Paris*, [1914.] 8°. **10095**. e. **7**.

—— [Another edition.] pp. 284. *Paris*, [1921.] 8°. **010094**. e. **18**.

—— Épopées africaines. Édition definitive, ornée de sept portraits et de deux cartes. pp. 338. *Paris*, 1913. 8°. **09061**. aaaa. **52**.

—— Souvenirs de la mission Marchand. Fachoda. [With plates, including a portrait.] pp. 228. *Paris*, 1942. 8°. **9062**. aaa. **35**.

BARATIER (Anatole) L'Administration militaire au Tonkin. [With maps.] pp. 241. *Paris*, 1889. 8°. **8824**. ccc. **10**.

—— L'Intendance militaire pendant la guerre de 1870–1871. Justification.—Réorganisation. pp. viii. 155. *Paris*, 1871. 8°. **8830**. e. **8**.

—— L'Intendance prussienne comparée à l'intendance française. pp. 36. *Paris*, 1873. 8°. [*Publications de la Réunion des Officiers*. sér. 2. no. 45–47.] **8832**. h. **33**. (**3**.)

—— Principes rationnels de la marche des impedimenta dans les grandes armées, *etc*. pp. 46. *Paris*, 1872. 12°. **8824**. bb. **3**.

—— Les Réquisitions en temps de guerre. pp. 52. *Paris*, 1873. 8°. [*Publications de la Réunion des Officiers*. sér. 2. no. 72–75.] **8832**. h. **34**. (**5**.)

BARATIER (Charles) Les Étangs de la Dombes. Histoire —dessèchement—remise en eau. pp. 201. *Trévoux*, 1905. 8°. **010169**. h. **20**.

BARATIER (Édouard)

—— *See* Rambert (G.) Histoire du commerce de Marseille, *etc*. (tom. 2. De 1291 à 1423 par E. Baratier.) 1949, *etc*. 8°. W.P. 3438.

BARATIER (F.) De la coxalgie des enfants. pp 52. *Paris*, 1874. 4°. [*Collection des thèses soutenues à la Faculté de Médecine de Paris*. An 1871. tom. 1.] **7373**. m. **15**.

BARATIER (François) *See* Baratier (J. P.) An Account of the Life of John Philip Barretier . . . compiled from his father's [François Baratier's] letters, &c. 1744. 8°. **1416**. c. **37**.

BARATIER (Jean Philippe) *See* Benjamin ben Jonah, *of Tudela*. Voyages . . . Traduits de l'Hebreu . . . Par J. P. Baratier. 1734. 8°. **1936**. a. **13**.

—— —— 1855. 8°. [*Charton* (*E*.) *Voyageurs, anciens et modernes, etc*. tom. 2.] **10027**. g. **2**.

BARATIER (Jean Philippe)

—— *See* Formey (J. H. S.) La Vie de Mr. Jean Philippe Baratier, *etc.* 1755. 8°. **132.** a. **32.**

—— Anti Artemonius seu Initium evangelii Sancti Johannis Apostoli, ex antiquitate ecclesiastica adversus iniquissimam L. M. Artemonii Neo-Photiniani criticam, vindicatum atque illustratum . . . Cui in fine accedit dissertatio de dialogis tribus vulgo Theodorito tributis. pp. 526. *Norimbergæ*, 1735. 8°. **4224.** aa. **31.**

—— Disquisitio chronologica de successione antiquissimâ Episcoporum Romanorum inde a Petro usque ad Victorem . . . Accedunt quatuor dissertationes, duæ de Constitutionibus apostolicis dictis, una de scriptis Dionysii Pseud-Areopagitæ & una de annis Agrippæ junioris Judæorum regis. pp. 314. *Ultrajecti*, 1740. 4°. **859.** f. **15.**

—— *See* Whiston (William) *M.A.* Three Tracts . . . iii. An Account of Mr. Baratier's enquiries into the chronology, doctrines and discipline of the Primitive Church. 1742. 8°. **699.** g. **14.** (**15.**)

—— An Account of the Life of John Philip Barretier, who was master of five languages at the age of nine years. Compiled from his father's [François Baratier's] letters, &c. [by Samuel Johnson]. pp. 28. *J. Roberts: London*, 1744. 8°. **1416.** c. **37.**

—— [Another copy.] **641.** g. **28.** (**2.**)

BARATIER (L.) *Avocat à la Cour d'Appel.* Le Régime financier des caisses d'épargne françaises depuis la loi du 20 juillet 1895. Thèse, *etc.* pp. 170. *Paris*, 1906. 8°. **08226.** dd. **12.**

BARATIER (Léonce) Du régime en communauté et de l'administration des biens communs par le mari. Thèse, *etc.* (Jus Romanum. De emptione et venditione.) pp. 60. viii. *Alençon*, 1860. 8°. **5425.** dd. **7.**

BARATIER (Paul)

—— *See* Saint John (Henry) *Viscount Bolingbroke.* Lettres inédites de Bolingbroke à Lord Stair, 1716–1720. [Edited, with an introduction, by P. Baratier.] 1939. 8°. **10922.** d. **21.**

—— L'Autonomie syndicale et ses limites devant les cours anglaises, *etc.* pp. 315. 1928. 8°. *See* Lyons.—*Institut de Droit comparé.* **Ac.2116/10.**

—— Lord Bolingbroke, ses écrits politiques. pp. 370. *Paris*, 1939. 8°. [*Annales de l'Université de Lyon.* sér. 3 fasc. 7.] **Ac.365.(c.)**

BARATIERI (Oreste) *See* Bertacchi (C.) L'Afganistan nel conflitto eventuale fra l'Inghilterra e la Russia a proposito del recente libro dell' on. Baratieri [i.e. "L'Afganistan"], *etc.* 1880. 8°. **8023.** bb. **9.**

—— Carteggio di Oreste Baratieri, 1887–1901. Con note biografiche a cura di Bice Rizzi. [With portraits.] pp. 311. *Trento*, 1936. 8°. **010921.** g. **3.**

—— La Leggenda dei Fabi. Saggio di critica militare, *etc.* pp. 90. *Roma*, 1886. 8°. **9004.** l. **17.** (**3.**)

—— Memorie d'Africa, 1892–1896. Carta generale dell' Eritrea, *etc.* pp. viii. 487. *Torino*, 1898. 8°. **9060.** cc. **7.**

—— Mémoires d'Afrique, 1892–1896. Préface de M. Jules Claretie . . . Accompagnés d'une carte générale de l'Érythrée, *etc.* pp. xiv. 542. *Paris*, [1899.] 8°. **09061.** b. **4.**

BARATIN (Eugène) Faculté de Droit de Paris. Thèse pour la licence, *etc.* (Droit romain: De la pétition d'hérédité.—Droit français: De la preuve littérale privée.) pp. 131. *Paris*, 1855. 8°. **05402.** cc. **12.**

BARATON ( ) *Poet.* Poésies diverses, contenant des contes choisis, bon mots, traits d'histoire et de morale, madrigaux, epigrammes et sonnets. pp. 304. *Paris*, 1705. 12°. **11475.** de. **12.**

BARATONO (Adelchi) Alle fonti dell' arte. Studio di psicologia etica su Omero. pp. 117. *Torino*, 1900. 8°. **11315.** o. **2.**

—— Dante e la visione di Dio. Commento al Canto xxxiii. del "Paradiso." Conferenza, *etc.* pp. 23. *Genova*, 1909. 8°. **11420.** g. **39.** (**8.**)

BARATOTTI (Galerana) *pseud.* [i.e. Arcangela Tarabotti.]

—— La Semplicità ingannata. pp. 307. *G. Sambix: Leida*, 1654. 12°. **12330.** a. **38.**

BARATOUX (Jean) *See* Miot (C.) and Baratoux (J.) Traité théorique et pratique des maladies de l'oreille et du nez. 1884, *etc.* 8°. **7611.** b. **52.**

—— Du cancer du larynx. pp. 59. *Paris*, 1888. 8°. **07305.** e. **2.** (**6.**)

—— La Maladie de l'empereur Frédéric iii. pp. 31. *Paris*, 1888. 8°. **10604.** e. **13.** (**5.**)

BARATOV (Sulkhan) *Prince.* Исторія Грузіи. тетр. 1–5. *С.-Петербургъ*, 1865–71. 8°. **9055.** dd. **6.**

—— [Another copy of тетр. 1.] **9055.** d. **27.** (**5.**)

—— Histoire de Géorgie. Par [i.e. translated by] J. Mourier. Histoire ancienne. pp. 120. *Tiflis*, 1886. 8°. **9055.** cc. **31.**

BARATS (Germann Markovich)

—— О библейско-агадическомъ элементѣ въ повѣстяхъ и сказаніяхъ начальной русской лѣтописи . . . Отдѣльный оттискъ изъ журнала "Украіна." вып. 1. pp. 73. *Кіевъ*, 1907. 8°. **011850.** k. **57.**

—— Собраніе трудовъ по вопросу о еврейскомъ элементѣ въ памятникахъ древне-русской письменности. 2 том. *Берлинъ*, 1926, 27, 24. 8°. **011850.** dd. **60.**
Том. 1 *is in* 2 *отд.*

—— Note biographique sur Hermann Baratz. [By L. Baratz.] [*Monte Carlo*, 1947.] 4°. **011850.** dd. **60.** (**2.**)
Typewritten.

BARÁTSÁG.

—— Igaz barátságnak és szives szeretetnek tüköre . . . mellyet régi irások fragmentumából öszve-szedegetett Z. Sz. J. [By István Gyöngyösi.] 1762. 8°. *See* Z. Sz., J. [i.e. János Zólyomi Szabó.] **1472.** aa. **32.** (**4.**)

BARATSCH (W.) Kosmologische Gedanken . . . Zweite Auflage. 2 pt. *Leipzig*, 1912. 8°. **7005.** c. **34.**

BARATTA (Antonio) Epigrammi editi e inediti. pp. 99. *Torino*, 1881. 8°. **11436.** aaa. **24.**

BARATTA (Custodio Jesam) *pseud.* [i.e. João Bautista de Castro.] *See* Jesam Baratta.

BARATTA (F.)

—— *See* Cignolini (P.) Marconiterapia, *etc.* [By P. Cignolini, with the collaboration of F. Baratta.] 1936. 8°. **08756.** d. **26.**

BARATTA (Giovanni) Osservazioni pratiche sulle principali malattie degli occhi. 2 tom. *Milano*, 1818. 8°. **1186.** g. **10.**

BARATTA (Luigi) La Politica inglese nel reame di Napoli dalla Rivoluzione francese alla caduta della Repubblica partenopea, 1789–1799. pp. viii. 80. *Catania*, 1923. 8°. **09076**. b. **7**.

BARATTA (Manuel) Exemplares de diuersas sortes de letras, tirados da polygraphia de M. Baratta. *A. Aluarez, a custa de I. de Ocanha: Lisboa*, 1590. *obl.* 4°. *Imperfect; wanting the "tratado da Arismetica".* C. **31**. h. **40**. (**2**.)

BARATTA (María de)

—— Cuzcatlán típico. Ensayo sobre etnofonía de El Salvador. Folklore, folkwisa y folkway. [With a portrait.] *San Salvador*, [1951, 53.] fol. 2 pt. **10483.h.12.**

BARATTA (Mario) Bibliografia geodinamica italiana. pt. 1. 1892. pp. 35. *Roma*, 1893. 8°. **011901**. ee. **46**.

—— La Carta della Toscana di Leonardo da Vinci. [With plates.] pp. 76. *Roma*, 1911. 8°. [*Rivista Geografica Italiana. Memorie geografiche.* no. 14.] **P.P.3911.b.(3.)**

—— La Catastrofe sismica calabro messinese (28 dicembre 1908). Relazione alla Società Geografica Italiana. (Tavole.) 2 pt. 1910. *See* Florence.—*Società Geografica Italiana.* Ac. **6010/13**.

—— Curiositá Vinciane . . . Con 148 facsimili. pp. 206. *Torino*, 1905. 8°. **7858**. p. **26**.

—— La Fatalità geografica nella formazione dello Stato Sabaudo. *See* Turin. Studi su Torino e il Piemonte. 1933. 8°. [*Biblioteca della Società Storica Subalpina.* vol. 139.] Ac. **6536**.

—— Leonardo da Vinci ed i problemi della terra. pp. xiv. 318. *Torino*, 1903. 8°. **12225.f.13.**

—— Pile ed accumulatori. pp. 154. *Milano*, 1887. 8°. **8757**. cc. **7**.

—— I Terremoti d'Italia. Saggio di storia geografia e bibliografia sismica italiana. pp. 950. *Torino*, 1901. 8°. **07107**. k. **12**.

—— Il Vesuvio e le sue eruzioni, dall' anno 79 d. C. al 1896. pp. 202. *Roma*, 1897. 8°. **7109**. aa. **30**.

BARATTANI (Augusto) Della Nana di Emile Zola. Appunti e note. pp. 41. *Bergamo*, 1880. 12°. **11840**. b. **27**. (**6**.)

BARATTANI (Filippo) I Legati di Clemente vii. Dramma. [In verse.] pp. 144. *Milano*, 1877. 16°. **11715**. bbb. **14**.

—— Ugo Bassi. Ricordi e frammento della cantica "Il Viaggio dello spirito." pp. 12. *Ancona*, 1885. 8°. **11431**. e. **4**. (**3**.)

BARATTE (Gustave) Nouveau manuel complet de filetage, *etc.* pp. vii. 98. *Paris*, 1911. 12°. [*Encyclopédie-Roret. Manuels Roret.*] **12207.a.1/563.**

BARATTE (L. H. A.) Considérations sur les plaies qui guérissent par première intention ou sans suppurer. Thèse, *etc.* pp. 42. *Montpellier*, 1846. 4°. **1182**. d. **17**. (**7**.)

BARATTE (Louis Henri) Poètes normands. Portraits gravés d'après les originaux les plus authentiques par Charles Devrits. Notices bibliographiques par . . . P. F. Tissot, J. Janin [and others] . . . Publiés sous la direction de L. H. Baratte. *Paris*, [1845.] 8°. **1329**. k. **1**.

BARATTE (Louis Pierre Victor) Faculté de Droit de Paris. Thèse, *etc.* (Jus romanum. De servitudibus [*sic*].)—Droit français. 1. De l'usage et de l'habitation, *etc.* pp. 36. *Paris*, 1858. 8°. **5406**. aaa. **2**. (**21**.)

BARATTERI (Giovanni Battista) Architettura d'acque. 2 pt. *G. Bazachi: Piacenza*, 1656, 63. fol. **558***. d. **2**.

—— [Another edition.] Con le figure, *etc.* 2 pt. *L. L. Bazachi: Piacenza*, 1699. 4°. **8764**. dd. **2**. *With the autograph of G. L. Leclerc, Count de Buffon.*

BARATTI (G. Ottavio) *See* Periodical Publications.—*Milan.* La Camera oscura, rivista periodica universale dei progressi della fotografia per G. O. Baratti. 1864, *etc.* 8°. P.P. **1912**.

BARATTI (Giacomo) The Late Travels of S. Giacomo Baratti into the remote Countries of the Abissins, or of Ethiopia, Interior . . . With a confirmation of this relation drawn from the writings of Damianus de Goes, and Jos. Scaliger. Translated by G. D. pp. 238. *For Benjamin Billingsley: London*, 1670. 8°. **979**. b. **30**.

—— [Another copy.] **1051**. c. **6**.

—— [Another copy.] **280**. c. **40**.

—— [Another copy.] G. **7060**.

—— Reis-Beschreibung . . . in die entlegenen Länder der Abyssiner oder Innere Aethiopia. Hiebey ist angefüget was Damianus de Goes und Jos. Scaliger von diesen Ländern geschrieben. *See* Asiatic Memoirs. Asiatische und Africanische Denckwürdigkeiten, *etc.* 1676. 4°. **790**. f. **19**.

BARATTI (Giuseppina) *See* Mahābhārata.—*Sanatsujātīya.* Sanatsujâtîyam. L'episodio di Sanatsujâta esposto tradotto e commentato . . . dalla dott. G. Baratti. 1913. 4°. [*Memorie della Reale Accademia di Archeologia, Lettere e Belle Arti.* vol. 2.] Ac. **96/7**.

BARATTIERI (Bartolommeo) *See* Baraterius.

BARATTIERI (Carlo) *Count.* Conghiettura sulla superfluità della materia colorata, o de' colori nella luce, e del supposto intrinseco suo splendore. 1793. *See* Amoretti (C.) and Soave (F.) Opuscoli scelti sulle scienze, *etc.* tom. 16. 1778, *etc.* 4°. **981**. h. **16**.

—— Saggio sulle sensazioni dell' odorato, e del gusto. 1794. *See* Amoretti (C.) and Soave (F.) Opuscoli scelti sulle scienze, *etc.* tom. 17. 1778, *etc.* 4°. **981**. h. **17**.

—— Scoperte sul gran fenomeno della colorazione. 1796. *See* Amoretti (C.) and Soave (F.) Opuscoli scelti sulle scienze, *etc.* tom. 19. 1778, *etc.* 4°. **981**. h. **19**.

—— Seguito d'obbiezioni alla teoria del Sig. Newton intorno a' colori ed alla formazione dello spetro solare. 1791. *See* Amoretti (C.) and Soave (F.) Opuscoli scelti sulle scienze, *etc.* tom. 14. 1778, *etc.* 4°. **981**. h. **14**.

BARATTIERI (Giovanni Battista) *See* Baratteri.

BARATUINSKY (Evgeny Abramovich) *See* Andreevsky (S. A.) Литературныя чтенія : Баратынскій, *etc.* 1891. 8°. **011824**. g. **35**.

—— *See* Istomin (V. A.) Главнѣйшія особенности языка и слога произведеній Н. А. Крылова . . . и Е. А. Баратынскаго, *etc.* 1895. 8°. **011851**. ee. **10**.

—— *See* Medvedeva (I. N.) Е. А. Баратынский, *etc.* 1944. 8°. **10797**. ee. **57**.

—— *See* Pigarev (K. V.) Мураново. [With special reference to E. A. Baratuinsky. With a portrait.] 1948. 8°. **7813**. a. **53**.

—— Сочиненія Евгенія Абрамовича Баратынскаго. Съ портретомъ автора . . . и біографическими о немъ свѣдѣніями, *etc.* pp. x. 519. *Москва*, 1869. 8°. **11585**. h. **10**.

—— Изданіе четвертое. [Edited by N. Baratuinsky.] pp. viii. 574. viii. 74. *Казань*, 1884. 8°. **012264**. i. **2**.

BARATUINSKY (EVGENY ABRAMOVICH)

—— Полное собраніе сочиненій . . . Съ портретомъ автора, біографіей и его письмами. pp. viii. 404. vi. *въ Кіевѣ*, 1894. 8°. **012265**. f. 6.

—— Полное собраніе сочиненій Евгенія Абрамовича Баратынскаго. Въ двухъ томахъ . . . Съ портретомъ автора, его письмами и біографическими о немъ свѣдѣніями. Редакція изданія И. Н. Божерянова. pp. 243 [343]. *С.-Петербургъ*, 1894. 8°. *2 том.* **012265**. b. **26**.

—— Полное собраніе сочиненій . . . Подъ редакціей и съ примѣчаніями М. Л. Гофмана. 2 том. 1914, 15. 8°. *See* RUSSIA.—*Академия Наук СССР.—Разряд Изящной Словесности.* **11588**. cc. **39**.

—— Полное собрание стихотворений . . . Редакция, комментарии и биографические статьи Е. Купреяновой и И. Медведевой. Вступительная статья Д. Мирского. [With plates, including portraits.] 2 том. [*Leningrad*,] 1936. 8°. **2338**. h. **32**.

—— Эда, финляндская повѣсть, и Пиры, описательная поэма. pp. 56. *Санктпетербургъ*, 1826. 8°. **868**. i. **18**.

—— Стихотворенія. 2 част. *Москва*, 1835. 8°. **11585**. e. **7**.

—— Избранные сочинения. [With a preface by M. L. Gofman. With a portrait.] pp. 276. *Берлин*, 1922. 8°. **011586**. cc. **17**.

—— Стихотворения, поэмы, проза, письма. Вступительная статья К. Пигарева. (Подготовка текста и примечания О. Муратовой и К. Пигарева.) [With portraits and facsimiles.] pp. 645. *Москва*, 1951. 8°. **12266**. ee. **2**.

—— Сумерки. pp. 88. ii. *Москва*, 1842. 8°. **11585**. bbb. **13**.

—— Евгеній Абрамовичъ Баратынскій. [A biographical sketch.] pp. 36. *Санктпетербургъ*, 1844. 8°. Ac. **1125/35**. (**2**.)

BARATUINSKY (N.) *See* BARATUINSKY (E. A.) Сочиненія . . . съ . . . біографическими . . . свѣдѣніями, *etc.* [Edited by N. Baratuinsky.] 1884. 8°. **012264**. i. **2**.

BARATZ (GIDEON)

—— *See* BENTWICH (Norman de M.) A New Way of Life. The Collective Settlements of Israel. [By] G. Baratz [and others], *etc.* 1949. 8°. **010077**. m. **3**.

BARATZ (HERMANN MARKOVITCH) *See* BARATS (G. M.)

BARATZ (JOSEPH)

—— A Village by the Jordan. The story of Degania. [With illustrations, including portraits.] pp. vii. 176. *Harvill Press: London*, 1954. 8°. **010077**. p. **7**.

BARATZ (LÉON) *See* BARATZ (Lev)

BARATZ (LEV) *See also* GUERMANOFF (L.) *pseud.* [i.e. L. Baratz.]

—— Actualités juives. Sionisme, Congrès juif mondial, diaspora. ff. 22. *Monte-Carlo*, 1954. 4°. **4035**. d. **30**. *Reproduced from typewriting.*

—— Un Apocryphe sur le meurtre rituel chez les Juifs. (Extrait de l'Univers israélite.) [*Paris*, 1934.] *s. sh.* 4°. **1856**. g. 3. (**10**.)

—— Bolchevisme et judaïsme. Extrait de la "Juste Parole," *etc.* [1940.] 8°. **04034**. h. **40**.

—— Juifs orientaux et juifs occidentaux. Deux aspects de la question juive. ff. 18. [*Monte-Carlo*, 1948.] 4°. **4035**. d. **20**. *Reproduced from typewriting.*

BARATZ (LEV)

—— Note biographique sur Hermann Baratz. [Monte Carlo, 1947.] 4°. *See* BARATS (G. M.) **011850**. dd. **60**. (**2**.)

—— Le Problème des réfugiés juifs et l'U.R.S.S. (Article extrait de La Juste parole.) pp. 4. *Paris*, [1939.] 8°. **4034**. i. **4**.

—— La Question juive en U.R.S.S. Réponse à M. Georges Friedmann [i.e. to statements in his work "De la Sainte Russie à l'U.R.S.S."]. pp. 16. *Paris*, 1938. 8°. **04034**. k. **57**.

—— Réalités et rêveries de ghetto. Souvenirs sur Herzl et le 3me Congrès Sioniste . . . Extrait de la Revue juive de Genève. pp. 20. *Genève*, 1934. 8°. **20010**. cc. **5**.

—— La Russie soviétique et les juifs. pp. 30. *Monte-Carlo; Paris* printed, 1951. 8°. **08095**. df. **20**.

—— La Situation des juifs en U.R.S.S. [Extracted from "La Revue juive de Genève."] 1938. 8°. **04034**. i. **77**.

—— Sur les origines étrangères de la plupart des lois civiles russes, *etc.* pp. 59. 1937. 8°. *See* PARIS.—*Université de Paris.—Institut de Droit Comparé.* **5756**. s. **26**.

—— Une Version ukrainienne des "Protocoles des Sages de Sion." Souvenirs sur quelques épisodes de la "Tourmente russe." (Extrait de la Revue juive de Genève.) pp. 7. *Genève*, 1935. 8°. **4033**. h. **27**.

BARATZ (MORTON SACHS)

—— The Union and the Coal Industry. pp. xvii. 170. *Yale University Press: New Haven*, 1955. 8°. [*Yale Studies in Economics.* vol. 4.] Ac. **2692**. [illegible] **22**.

BARAUD (ALLAN) *See* FREER (Ada M. G.) afterwards SPOER (A. M.) Outer Isles . . . With illustrations by A. Baraud. 1902. 8°. **010370**. ff. **19**.

BARAUD (ARMAND) Artistes, littérateurs et savants au XIXe siècle . . . Ouvrage illustré de gravures. pp. 350. *Paris*, [1892.] 8°. **10663**. i. **28**.

—— Le Clergé vendéen victime de la Révolution française. Notices biographiques, 1790–1801. (tom. 2. Notices biographiques des prêtres qui ont survécu, 1790–1850.) 2 tom. *Luçon*, 1904, 05. 8°. **4630**. dg. **13**.

—— Nouvelles vendéennes. pp. 138. *Fontenay-le-Comte*, 1895. 8°. **010171**. i. **7**.

BARAUDE (HENRI) *pseud.* [i.e. *Baron* AUGUSTIN ANNE MARIE JOSEPH TUPINIER.]

—— L'Armée en 1900. Ce qu'elle est. Ce qu'elle devrait être. pp. 50. *Paris*, 1899. 8°. **8822**. e. **1**. (**1**.)

—— Les Arènes de Lutèce. pp. 285. *Paris*, 1931. 8°. **12517**. t. **12**.

—— Enfers d'Allemagne. Les geôles allemandes (1914–1918). pp. vi. 217. *Paris*, [1922.] 8°. **09084**. c. **37**.

—— Le Glas des monarchies. Roman. pp. iv. 295. *Paris*, 1912. 8°. **12550**. tt. **30**.

—— Orléans et Jeanne d'Arc. Ouvrage accompagné de cartes, plans et dessins de l'auteur. pp. 288. *Paris*, 1911. 8°. **4828**. eee. **10**.

—— Le Transvaal. Les origines. La guerre. Les leçons de l'histoire. pp. 24. *Paris*, 1900. 8°. **09004**. bb. 6. (**7**.)

BARAUDIN (Didier François Honorat de) *Marquis.*

—— *See* Du Chambon (P.) La "Forteresse" charentaise d'Alfred de Vigny, *etc.* [On the life of the Marquis D. F. H. de Baraudin.] 1931. 8°. **20002.** c. **17.**

BARAUDON (Alfred) Algérie et Tunisie. Récits de voyage et études. pp. xv. 327. *Paris,* 1893. 12°. **10097.** de. **25.**

—— En Écosse. Sites, légendes et récits. pp. 240. *Paris,* 1912. 8°. **010370.** eee. **47.**

—— Enracinés. pp. 350. *Paris,* 1908. 8°. **12551.** p. **11.**

—— La Maison de Savoie et la Triple Alliance, 1713–1722. pp. xi. 385. *Paris,* 1896. 8°. **09078.** b. **1.**

BARAUDON (Louis) Faculté de Droit de Paris. Thèse pour le doctorat, *etc.* (Des donations entre époux pendant le mariage.) pp. 254. *Paris,* 1857. 8°. **5406.** aa. **1.** (**14.**)

BARAULT-ROULLON (Charles Hippolyte) Dangers pour l'Europe. Origine, progrès et état actuel de la puissance russe, *etc.* [With a map.] pp. xvi. 519. *Paris,* 1854. 8°. **8093.** e. **10.**

—— Économie politique. Essai sur l'organisation de la force publique. pp. 48. *Paris,* 1850. 8°. **8827.** g. **37.** (**10.**)

—— L'Impératrice Josephine et la famille de Beauharnais. pp. 13. *Paris,* 1852. 8°. **10659.** d. **19.**

—— Le Marechal Suchet, duc d'Albufera. Éloge, *etc.* pp. 348. *Paris,* 1854. 8°. **10660.** dd. **5.**

—— Questions générales sur le recrutement de l'armée. Mémoire à consulter faisant suite aux essais sur l'organisation de la force publique, *etc.* pp. 91. *Paris,* 1853. 8°. **8827.** cc. **43.** (**1.**)

BARAUMONT (P. J.) *See* Beffroy (L. E.) Rapport sur l'emploi des matières fécales fraiches . . . Précédé d'un avant-propos, par P. J. Baraumont. [1801.] 8°. T. **486.** (**5.**)

BARAUSKAS NENDRĖ (Kazimieras)

—— *See* Beblavý (J.) Įvadas į Naująjį Testamentą. (Kalbą lygino K. Barauskas Nendrė.) 1933. 8°. [*Vytauto Didžiojo Universiteto Evang. Teologijos Fakulteto leidinys.* no. 3.] Ac. **1157.** i.

BARAUT (Cipriano)

—— *See* Joachimus, *Abbot of Fiore.* Un Tratado inédito de Joaquín de Fiore: De vita Sancti Benedicti, *etc.* [Edited by C. Baraut.] 1951. 8°. [*Analecta Sacra Tarraconensia.* vol. 24. fasc. 1.] Ac. **2006.** d **2.**

BARAVALLE (Carlo) *See* also Bonsenso (Anastasio) *pseud.* [i.e. C. Baravalle.]

—— Pagine sparse di Carlo Baravalle . . . raccolte da T. Massarani, L. Corio e G. Weiss. Con alcuni cenni critico-biografici. pp. lix. 430. *Milano,* 1903. 8°. **11429.** cc. **44.**

BARAVALLE (Hermann von)

—— *See* Ephemerides. Astronomisch-naturwissenschaftliche Beiträge für das Jahr 1939 . . . Herausgegeben von Dr. H. von Baravalle, *etc.* [1939.] 8°. **08560.** d. **4.**

BARAVALLE (Robert)

—— Deutschland braucht seine Kolonien. Ein Ruf an alle Deutschen und eine Forderung an die Welt. pp. 96. *Graz & Leipzig,* [1939.] 8°. **20003.** cc. **62.**

BARAVALUS (Christophorus)

—— Christophori Barauali . . . De tempore dandi Catapotia. pp. 24. *Ex officina Leonardi Torrentini: In Monte Regali,* 1565. 8°. C. **107.** bb. **18.**

BARAVEAU (René) Faculté de Droit de Paris. De l'influence de la chose jugée sur l'action publique. Thèse pour le doctorat, *etc.* pp. 138. *Paris,* 1898. 8°. **05402.** g. **19.**

BARAVELLI (G. C.)

—— Le Dernier rempart de l'esclavage. L'Abyssinie. pp. 79. *Roma,* 1935. 8°. **20012.** bb. **4.**

—— Integral Land-Reclamation in Italy. [With plates.] pp. 42. *Società Editrice di Novissima: Roma,* A. xiii [1935]. 8°. **8286.** f. **35.**

—— The Last Stronghold of Slavery. What Abyssinia is. pp. 70. *Società Editrice di Novissima: Roma,* 1935. 8°. **010093.** df. **47.**

—— Policy of Public Works under the Fascist Regime. [With plates.] pp. 75. *Società Editrice di Novissima: Roma,* A. xiii [1935]. 8°. **8276.** pp. **8.**

BARAYA (José María) Biografias militares o historia militar del pais [the United States of Colombia] en medio siglo. 2 pt. *Bogotá,* 1874. 8°. **9772.** f. **13.**

—— [Another copy.] **010882.** h. **1.**

BARAZA (Cyprianus) *See* Baraze (Cypriano)

BARAZABAL (Mariano) Al noble Entusiasmo que brillaba en todos los moradores de México por la noticia de la libertad de España . . . dixo D. M. Barazabal lo siguiente: Oda, *etc.* [*Mexico?* 1814?] *s. sh.* 4°. **11451.** bbb. **6.** (**9.**)

—— Aplauso poético á los ilustres Padres de la Patria, *etc.* *México,* 1820. 4°. **11451.** bbb. **45.** (**35.**)

—— Mordaza al Liberal que se dice [i.e. the author of the pamphlet entitled "El Liberal á los bajos escritores," signing himself: F. M.]. [*Mexico,* 1820.] 4°. **9770.** bb. **4.** (**54.**)

—— Poesias que adornan la pira erigida para sus hermanos difuntos, por la Real Congregacion de Cocheros y Criados del Santisimo Sacramento de la parroquia de San Pablo. Dispuestas por Don M. Barazabal. pp. 11. *México,* 1818. fol. **4425.** g. **5.** (**6.**)

—— El Sueño Verdad. Poesía publicada en el Diario de esta Capital el Sábado 30 de Mayo de 1807 núm. 608, en celebridad de los dias de nuestro . . . Soberano El Señor Don Fernando vii. entónces Principe de Asturias, *etc.* *México,* 1808. *s. sh.* 4°. **11451.** bbb. **43.** (**11.**)

BARAZE (Cypriano)

—— *See* Mata (N. U. de) *Bishop of La Paz.* Bericht von dem Leben und Tod Cypriani Baraza . . . gedruckt in Spanischen Sprach . . . jetzt aber verteutscht, *etc.* 1726. fol. [*Allerhand so lehr- als geist-reiche Brief, Schrifften, und Reis-Beschreibungen, welche von denen Missionariis der Gesellschaft Jesu . . . angelangt seynd, etc.* Bd. 1. Tl. 5.] **4767.** g. **3.**

—— *See* Mata (N. U. de) *Bishop of La Paz.* Relacion summaria de la vida y dichosa muerte del U. P. C. Baraze, *etc.* 1704. 4°. **1232.** c. **8.**

BARAZER-LANNURIEN (François Pierre Marie) Thèse pour le doctorat en médecine. (Questions sur diverses branches des sciences médicales.) pp. 62. *Paris,* 1840. 4°. [*Collection des thèses soutenues à la Faculté de Médecine de Paris.* An 1840. tom. 1.] **7371.** b. **2.**

BARAZETTI (Caesar) Das Eherecht mit Ausschluss des ehelichen Vermögensrechts nach dem Code Napoléon und dem badischen Landrecht, *etc.* pp. xv. 779. *Hannover,* 1895. 8°. **5176.** e. **12.**

BARAZETTI (Caesar)

—— Einführung in das französische Civilrecht, Code Napoléon, und das badische Landrecht . . . Mit einer Beilage: der Code de la Convention. pp. vii. 454. *Frankfurt & Lahr*, 1889. 8°. **6005.** ee. **18.**

—— Das Eltern- und Kindesrecht nach dem Code Napoléon und dem badischen Landrecht. Ein Lehr- und Handbuch. pp. xii. 580. *Hannover*, 1896. 8°. **05605.** k. **1.**

—— Das Personenrecht mit Ausschluss des Familienrechts nach dem Code Napoléon und dem badischen Landrechte, *etc.* pp. xxxii. 432. *Karlsruhe*, 1893. 8°. **5604.** aa. **1.**

—— Die Vormundschaft (la Tutelle), die Pflegschaft (la Curatelle) und die Beistandschaft (le Conseil) nach dem Code Napoléon und dem badischen Landrecht, *etc.* pp. xiii. 662. *Hannover*, 1894. 8°. **05604.** k. **7.**

—— Zur Lehre von der Prozessfähigkeit, mit Exkursen in die Lehre von der absolutio ab instantia, *etc.* pp. 48. [*Mannheim*,] 1884. 8°. **05604.** h. **44.** (**1.**)

BARAZETTI (Erich A.)

—— Die mehrstufige Kommission. Dissertation, *etc.* pp. 55. *Bern*, 1952. 8°. **6956.** aa. **44.**

BARAZIA (Henri Rubino de) *See* Rubino de Barazia.

BARAZZIO (James) *See* Barozzi (G.) called *il Vignola.*

BARB (A. A.)

—— Diva Matrix. A faked gnostic intaglio in the possession of P. P. Rubens and the iconology of a symbol. *In*: Journal of the Warburg and Courtauld Institutes. vol. 16. no. 3/4. pp. 193–238. pl. 27–33. 1953. 4°. Ac. **4569 7.**

BARB (Alfons)

—— *See* Eitler (P.) Burgenland-Führer . . . Von P. Eitler, A. Barb, *etc.* [1936.] 8°. **10215.** r. **9.**

—— *See* Eitler (P.) and Barb (A.) Burgenland-Führer, *etc.* copious ms. notes [by A. Barb]. [1932.] 8°. **10215.** l. **17.**

BARB (H. A.) Persisch-Deutsches Glossar zum Transcriptions-Lesebuch der persischen Sprache. pp. 99. *Wien*, 1886. 8°. **12906.** bbb. **21.** (**2.**)

—— Das System der Hamze-Orthographie in der arabischen Schrift. pp. 37. *Wien*, 1860. 8°. **12903.** dd. **20.** (**8.**)

—— Die Transcription des arabischen Alphabetes. pp. 87. *Wien*, 1860. 8°. **12903.** cc. **1.**

—— Transcriptions-Grammatik der persischen Sprache. pp. 201. *Wien*, 1886. 8°. **12906.** bbb. **21.** (**1.**)

—— Über das Zeichen Hamze und die drei damit verbundenen Buchstaben Elif, Waw, und Ja der arabischen Schrift, *etc.* pp. 100. *Wien*, 1858. 8°. **12903.** c. **3.**

—— Über den Organismus des persischen Verbums. pp. 96. *Wien*, 1860. 8°. **12906.** c. **36.** (**3.**)

—— Über die Conjugation des persischen Verbums. pp. 118. *Wien*, 1861. 8°. **12906.** bb. **45.**

BARB (Isak)

—— *See* Shakespeare (W.) [*Macbeth.—Hebrew.*] Macbeth . . . Nach Friedrich v. Schiller's deutscher Bearbeitung in's Hebräische übertragen von I. Barb. 1883. 8°. **01980.** a. **4.**

BARBA. Cuando veas la barba de tu vecino pelar hecha la tuya a remojar. [On the liberty of the press.] pp. 4. *Puebla*, 1823. 4°. **9770.** bb. **28.** (**43.**)

BARBA, *Saint, Virgin and Martyr. See* Barbara.

BARBA AZUL. *See* Bluebeard.

BARBA NERA. *See* Barbanera ( ) *Astronomo.*

BARBA (Alvaro Alonso) Arte de los metales, en que se enseña el verdadero beneficio de los de oro, y plata por açogue, el modo de fundirlos todos, y como se han de refinar, y apartar unos de otros. ff. 120. *Imprenta del Reyno: Madrid*, 1640. 4°. **444.** c. **3.** (**2.**)

—— [Another copy.] **987.** h. **27.**

—— [Another copy.] **234.** i. **43.**

—— [Another edition.] Con el Tratado de las Antiguas Minas de España, que escriviò don Alonso Carrillo y Laso. pp. 224. *Madrid*, 1729. 4°. **457.** c. **14.**

—— [Another edition.] pp. 271. *Lima*, 1817. 4°. **726.** f. **31.**

—— The First (second) Book of the Art of Mettals . . . Translated into English by Edward Montagu, Earl of Sandwich]. 2 vol. *For S. Mearne: London*, 1670. 8°. **987.** b. **25, 26.**

—— [Another edition.] Translated by the R.H. Edward Earl of Sandwich. 2 vol. *For S. Mearne: London*, 1674. 8°. **446.** a. **25.** (**3.**)

—— [Another copy.] **987.** b. **27.**

—— [Another edition.] *See* Collection. A Collection of scarce and interesting Treatises upon Metals, *etc.* 1738. 12°. **445.** a. **26.**

—— [Another edition.] *See* Collection. A Collection of scarce and valuable Treatises upon Metals, *etc.* 1740. 12°. **957.** e. **43.**

—— El Arte de los Metales. Metallurgy. Translated . . . by Ross E. Douglass and E. P. Mathewson. pp. ix. 288. *J. Wiley & Sons: New York*, 1923. 8°. **07105.** ee. **4.**

—— Traité de l'art métalique [translated by Charles Hautin de Villars], auquel on a joint un Memoire concernant les mines de France . . . Ouvrage enrichi de figures en taille-douce. pp. 264. *Paris*, 1730. 12°. **954.** b. **41.**

—— Métallurgie, ou l'art de tirer et de purifier les métaux, traduite de l'espagnol [by "Gosford," i.e. Nicolas Lenglet du Fresnoy]. Avec les dissertations les plus rares sur les mines & les opérations métalliques. 2 tom. *Paris*, 1751. 12°. **233.** b. **34, 35.**

—— [Another copy, with a different titlepage.] *La Haye*, 1752. 12°. **990.** b. **7, 8.**

—— Berg Büchlein . . . In Teutsch übersetzet von J. L. M. C. [i.e. Johann Lange, medicinæ candidato.] pp. 204. *Auf G. Schultzens Kosten: Hamburg*, 1676. 8°. **446.** a. **17.**

—— [Another edition.] pp. 198. *Franckfurt*, 1739. 8°. **954.** a. **19.**

—— Albaro Alonso Barba . . . Docimasie oder Probir- und Schmeltz-Kunst . . . Aus dem Frantzösischen . . . übersetzt, und . . . heraus gegeben von Matthia Godar. Mit . . . Kupfern versehen. pp. 155. *Wien*, 1749. 8°. **990.** b. **6.**

—— [Another edition.] pp. 165. *Wien*, 1767. 8°. **973.** h. **6.**

BARBA (Antonio) Osservazioni sopra la generazione de' muschi. 1782. *See* Amoretti (C.) and Soave (F.) Opuscoli scelti sulle scienze, *etc.* tom. 5. 1778, *etc.* 4°. **981.** h. **5.**

BARBA (BERNARDINO DELLA) *Bishop of Casale. See* CASTELLARI (B.)

BARBA (DAMIANUS CORYCIUS) *See* CARDULUS (F.) *Begin.* [fol. 1 *recto*:] Francisci Carduli . . . Oratio in funere . . . Ardicini .ii. dela porta Cardinalis Alerieñ, *etc.* [fol. 6 *verso*:] Paululum illud quod Benemerenti domino seruus post funera posse uidetur Damianus Coryicius Barba Novarieñ pietissimi domini sui memorię prętare Curauit. [1493?] 4°. **IA. 19336.**

BARBA (ENRIQUE M.)

—— Cómo llegó al poder don Juan Manuel de Rosas. *In*: Revista de historia de América. no. 32. pp. 83–153. 1951. 8°. **U.N.P.471/8.**

—— Don Pedro de Cevallos, Gobernador de Buenos Aires y Virrey del Río de la Plata. [With a map.] pp. 237. 1937. 8°. *See* LA PLATA.—*Universidad Nacional.—Facultad de Humanidades y Ciencias de la Educación.* Ac. 2694. g 5.

BARBA (FRANCESCO MARIA) Il Diritto pubblico ecclesiastico secondo la mente di Leone XIII. 2 vol. *Napoli*, 1900, 01. 8°. **05107. f. 31.**

—— Istituzioni di diritto ecclesiastico pubblico e privato. pp. ix. 432. *Napoli*, 1883. 8°. **5107. eee. 9.**

BARBA (FRANCISCO)

—— La Patata. Desarrollo y principales zonas de cultivo en el país. Estudio técnico-cultural y económico-social de su explotación en la zona sudeste de la provincia de Buenos Aires. pp. 24. 1933. 8°. *See* ARGENTINE REPUBLIC.—*Ministerio de Agricultura.—Dirección General de Comercio e Industria.* L.A.S. 7/12.

BARBA (FRANCISCO ESTEVE) *See* ESTEVE BARBA.

BARBA (GIOVANNI) Dell' arte e del metodo delle lingue . . . libri III. *Roma*, 1734. 4°. **825. i. 39.**
Imperfect; wanting all after p. 96.

BARBA (GREGORIO PECES) *See* PECES-BARBA DEL BRIO.

BARBA (JANUS BENEDICTUS)

—— Jani-Benedicti Barbæ Elegiarum libri quatuor. pp. 127. *Neapoli*, 1742. 8°. **1478. d. 21.**

BARBA (JEAN NICOLAS) Souvenirs de Jean Nicolas Barba. Avec le portrait de l'auteur, *etc.* pp. iii. 292. *Paris*, 1846. 8°. **10660. d. 13.**

BARBA (JOSEPH) The Use of Steel for Constructive Purposes . . . Translated from the French with a preface by A. L. Holley. pp. ix. 110. *D. Van Nostrand: New York*, 1875. 8°. **7942. b. 1.**

BARBA (JUAN) Sermon sobre la caridad discreta, que en la inauguracion de la Junta de Caridad de Villafranca del Panades dixo . . . J. Barba, *etc.* pp. 40. *Villafranca de Panades*, [1799.] 4°. **11451. c. 55. (7.)**

BARBA (LORENZO OSORIO) *See* OSORIO BARBA.

BARBA (MARIO HERNÁNDEZ Y SÁNCHEZ) *See* HERNÁNDEZ Y SÁNCHEZ BARBA (M.)

BARBA (PETRUS) *See* MOHY (E.) Erici Mohy Tertianæ crisis: qua DD. P. Barbæ . . . praxis curandæ tertianæ, & V. F. Plempii . . . animadversio discutitur, *etc.* 1642. 4°. **1166. e. 18. (5.)**

—— *See* PLEMP (V. F.) V. F. Plempii Animadversio in veram praxim curandæ tertianæ propositam à Doctore P. Barba. 1642. 4°. **1166. e. 18. (4.)**

BARBA (PETRUS)

—— *See* SOERS (M.) Martini Soers . . . Stricturæ in ceritum quemdam Eburonem inconditum blateronem controversiæ de curanda tertiana inter D. D. P. Barbam et V. F. Plempium, agitatæ judicium ἀκριτως exercentem & pronunciantem. 1642. 4°. **1166. e. 18. (3.)**

BARBA (POMPEO DELLA) *See* CICERO (M. T.) [*De Republica.—Somnium Scipionis.—Italian.*] I Discorsi filosofici di M. P. della Barba . . . sopra il platonico et diuin sogno di Scipione, di Marco Tullio. 1553. 8°. **527. d. 6.**

—— *See* CICERO (M. T.) [*Topica.—Italian.*] La Topica di Cicerone, col comento [of P. de la Barba], *etc.* 1556. 8°. **236. b. 29.**

—— *See* PICO DELLA MIRANDOLA (G.) *Count della Concordia, the Elder.* Le Sette sposizioni del S. G. Pico della Mirandola, intitolate Heptaplo, sopra i sei giorni del Genesi . . . da M. P. de la Barba raccolte in breui somme con vna pistola del medesimo al Decano di Lucca, *etc.* 1555. 8°. **3155. k. 13.**

—— Espositione d'vn sonetto platonico, fatto sopra il primo effetto d'amore . . . doue si tratta de la immortalita de l'anima secondo Aristotile, e secondo Platone. pp. 109. [*L. Torrentino*:] *Fiorenza*, 1549. 8°. **1071. f. 51.**

—— [Another copy.] **240. i. 22. (4.)**

—— [Another edition.] pp. 107. [*L. Torrentino*:] *Fiorenza*, 1554. 8°. **11421. b. 1.**

—— [Another copy.] **240. l. 35. (2.)**

BARBA (PRESTON ALBERT) *See* VOS (B. J.) and BARBA (P. A.) German Lyrics and Ballads, *etc.* [1926.] 8°. **11528. cc. 48.**

—— Balduin Möllhausen, the German Cooper. pp. 188. *University of Pennsylvania: Philadelphia*, 1914. 8°. [*Americana Germanica.* no. 17.] Ac. **2692. p/14.**

—— The Life and Works of Friedrich Armand Strubberg. pp. 149. *University of Pennsylvania: Philadelphia*, 1913. 8°. [*Americana Germanica.* no. 16.] Ac. **2692. p/14.**

BARBA (RÉNÉ ANACHARSIS) De l'influence de l'air sur l'origine, la marche, et le traitement des maladies; thèse, *etc.* pp. 24. *Paris*, 1818. 4°. **1183. d. 16. (9.)**

BARBA (SIMONE DELLA) *See* CICERO (M. T.) [*Topica.—Italian.*] La Topica di Cicerone col comento . . . tradotta da S. de la Barba, *etc.* 1556. 8°. **236. b. 29.**

—— Nuoua spositione del sonetto [of F. Petrarca] che comincia In nobil sanque uita umile, e' queta, ne la quale si dichiara qual sia stata la vera nobiltà di Madonna Laura. pp. 44. [*L. Torrentino*:] *Firenze*, 1554. 8°. **1071. g. 6. (3.)**

—— [Another copy.] **240. l. 35. (1.)**

BARBA (ZANOBI DELLA)

—— *See* BIBLE.—*Psalms.—Selections.—Italian.* [*Penitential Psalms.*] *Begin.* [fol. 1 *recto*:] E Septe Psalmi Penitentiali, *etc.* *End.* [fol. 4 *verso*:] Finiti i septe psalmi ĩ rima. (Per maestro Zanobi dalla barba.) [1510?] 4°. **11426. c. 75. (2.)**

—— Leggenda ⁊ oratione di Santo Cosimo ⁊ Damiano. [In verse.] *M. Galassi: Firenze*, 1580. 4°. **11426. c. 7.**

—— La Vita et miracoli di San Torello, *etc.* [Attributed to Z. della Barba.] [1510?] 4°. *See* TORELLO, *da Poppi, Eremita.* **11409. cc. 9.**

BARBABIANCA (Cesare) *See* Solingo, *Academico, pseud.* [i.e. C. Barbabianca.]

BARBABOSA (Mariano) *See* Gómez Bello (F. J.) and Barbabosa (M.) Aprendan los Iturbides á tener desprendimiento. 1823. *s. sh.* fol. **9770**. k. **7**. (**15**.)

—— *See* Jonama (S.) De la Prueba por Jurados, *etc.* [Edited by M. Jonama and M. Barbabosa.] 1824. 12°. **6005**. a. **31**.

—— Discurso del Señor Barbabosa en apoyo de su proposicion sobre libertad de derechos para la azucar que se extraiga por los puertos de la nacion. pp. 8. *Mexico*, 1824. 4°. **12302**. de. 8.

—— Memorias para la historia Megicana, ó los ultimos dias del Castillo de San Juan de Ulúa. pp. 18. *Jalapa*, 1826. 4°. **9771**. bb. **31**.

—— Santana solo ha pensado hacer feliz su pátria. *México*, 1823. *s. sh.* fol. **9770**. k. **8**. (**22**.)

BARBACCI (Feliciano) *Bishop of Cortona.* Epistola pastoralis ad clerum et populum civitatis et dioecesis Cortonensis. pp. 57. *Romæ*, 1854. 4°. **3902**. i. **6**. (**7**.)

BARBACCI (Guglielmo) Poesie italiane e latine di G. Barbacci. Pubblicate dal figlio di lui cav. Torquato, per cura e con prefazione di C. Trabalza. pp. xxxi. 300. *Foligno*, 1905. 8°. **11427**. bbb. **15**.

BARBACCI (Rodolfo)

—— Apuntes para un diccionario musical peruano. *In*: Fénix. no. 6. pp. 414–510. 1949. 8°. Ac. **9732** 5.

—— I Primi fasti della musica nell'Argentina. 1943. *See* Periodical Publications.—*Turin*. Rivista musicale italiana. vol. 47. 1894, *etc.* 8°. P.P. **1935**.

BARBACCI (Torquato) *See* Barbacci (G.) Poesie italiane e latine di G. Barbacci. Pubblicate dal figlio di lui cav. Torquato, *etc.* 1905. 8°. **11427**. bbb. **15**.

BARBACCIANI-FEDELI (Ranieri) Decisione dell' illustrissimo sig. avvocato R. Barbacciani Fedeli . . . nella Piscien. nullit. contract. tra il . . . cavaliere Antonio Cecchi Toldi e i signori Alienatari. pp. 22. *Pescia*, 1829. 8°. **898**. h. **2**. (**6**.)

—— Saggio storico politico agrario e commerciale dell' antica e moderna Versilia. [With "Annotazioni addizionali."] pp. 331. lxxxv. *Firenze*, 1845. 8°. **10136**. i. **21**.

—— *See* Cerù (N.) Saggio storico sulla Versilia antica e moderna dell' auditore R. Barbacciani-Fedeli, *etc.* 1844. 8°. **899**. d. **3**. (**2**.)

BARBACENA, Felisberto Caldeira Brant Pontes, *Marquis de.* *See* Caldeira Brant Pontes.

BARBACENA, Francisco Furtado de Castro do Rio de Mendonça e Faro, *Count of.* *See* Furtado de Castro do Rio de Mendonça e Faro.

BARBACHANO (Manuel) Articulos de Costumbres y Satiricos. pp. 320. *Merida*, 1850. 16°. **12352**. aaa. **27**.

BARBACHANO (Tomás Aznar) *See* Aznar Barbachano.

BARBACIAS (Andreas) *See* Barbatia.

BARBACOVI (Francesco Vigilio) *Count.* *See* Tiraboschi (G.) Compendio della Storia letteraria d'Italia [of G. Tiraboschi]. Opera postuma del conte F. V. Barbacovi. 1826. 8°. **620**. f. **17**.

—— *See* Tiraboschi (G.) Compendium of the Literary History of Italy . . . Translated from the Italian of the Count F. V. Barbacovi. 1835. 12°. **617**. e. 45.

BARBACOVI (Francesco Vigilio) *Count.*

—— Francisci Vigilii Barbacovii . . . De mensura poenarum sive de poenarum criminibus adæquandarum ratione diatriba. pp. vii. 197. *Tridenti*, 1795. 8°. **6056**. bbb. **28**.

—— Degli argomenti ed indizi nei giudizi criminali, ragionamento. pp. 61. *Milano*, 1820. 8°. **1373**. d. **19**. (**1**.)

—— Della pluralità de' suffragj nei giudizj criminali. 1821. *See* Raccolta. Raccolta di trattati e memorie di legislazione, *etc.* tom. 2. 1821, *etc.* 8°. **706**. h. **1**.

—— Discorsi intorno ad alcune parti della scienza della legislazione. 2 tom. *Milano*, 1824. 12°. **6025**. a. **4**.

—— Lettera seconda d'un professore di diritto [i.e. F. V. Barbacovi], in cui si confutano le osservazioni critiche del dottor Bosellini sopra i due libri [by F. V. Barbacovi] della pluralità de' suffragi ne' giudizi civili e criminali e della decisione delle cause dubbie. pp. 47. 1820. 8°. *See* Bosellini (C.) **1374**. h. **33**. (**1**.)

BARBACOVI (Vigilio) *Count.* *See* Barbacovi (Francesco V.)

BARBACZY (József) Rapport officiel sur l'assassinat des ministres plénipotentiaires françois [A. E. L. A. Bonnier d'Arco, C. Roberjot, and J. A. J. De Bry] à Rastadt. [Two letters signed: Barbaczy.] pp. 24. [1799.] 8°. **9226** aaa. **4**.

BARBADA. *See* Barbados.

BARBADAES. *See* Barbados.

BARBA DE CORONADO (Juan) Memorial que el capitan don Iuan Barba de Coronado dio al rey nuestro señor don Felipe quarto. Y lo que se decretò, y hizo en virtud del. [*Madrid*, 1630.] fol. **1324**. i. **2**. (**1**, **2**.)

—— [Another issue.] *Begin.* Señor. El capitan don Juan Barba de Coronado, *etc.* [*Madrid*, 1630.] fol. **1324**. i. **2**. (**45**.)

BARBADES. *See* Barbados.

BARBADICUS (Gregorius) *Cardinal.* *See* Barbarigo (Gregorio)

BARBADICUS (Joannes Franciscus) *Cardinal.* *See* Barbarigo (Giovanni F.)

BARBADICUS (Nicolaus) *See* Barbarigo (Niccolò)

BARBADIGO (Gregorio) *Cardinal.* *See* Barbarigo.

BARBADILLO (Alonso Gerónimo de Salas) *See* Salas Barbadillo.

BARBADILLO (Joaquín López) *See* López Barbadillo.

BARBADILLO DELGADO (Pedro)

—— Historia de la Ciudad de Sanlúcar de Barrameda. pp. 995. *Cádiz*, 1942. fol. **010160**. k. **15**.

BARBADILO (Alonso Gerónimo de Salas) *See* Salas Barbadillo.

BARBADO SEEDS. *See* Barbados Seeds.

BARBADO (Manuel)

—— Estudios de psicología experimental. [With a portrait. 2 tom. *Madrid*, 1946, 48. 8°. **8477.eee.23.**
Publications of the Instituto "Luis Vives" de Filosofía. Ser. C. no. 3, 8.

—— Introducción a la psicología experimental . . . Segunda edición aumentada. pp. 675. *Madrid*, 1943. 8°. **8473**. l. **36**.

BARBADOES. *See* Barbados.

BARBADORO (Aldo)

—— Leggi demografiche fasciste. Manuale teorico-pratico, *etc.* pp. 291. *Bologna*, [1940.] 8°. **5405. aa. 34.**

BARBADORO (Bernardino) *See* Dami (Luigi) and Barbadoro (B.) Firenze di Dante, *etc.* 1921. 8°. **011420. aa. 18.**

—— *See* Dante Alighieri. [*Divina Commedia.—Italian.*] Lectura Dantis. (Il canto xxxii dell'Inferno. Letto da B. Barbadoro.) 1900, *etc.* 8°. 2284.h.2.

—— *See* Florence.—*Consigli.* Consigli della Repubblica Fiorentina . . . Per cura di B. Barbadoro, *etc.* 1921, *etc.* fol. [*Atti delle assemblee costituzionali italiane.* ser. 3. sez. 4.] Ac. **102.** c.

—— La Condanna di Dante e le fazioni politiche del suo tempo. [With facsimiles.] *In:* Barbi (Michele) Studi danteschi, *etc.* vol. 2. pp. 5–74. 1920. 8°. 011421.z.1/2.

—— Le Finanze della Repubblica fiorentina. Imposta diretta e debito pubblico fino all'istituzione del Monte. pp. x. 738. *Firenze*, 1929. 8°. [*Biblioteca Storica Toscana.* no. 5.] Ac. **6508/7.**

BARBADORO (I.)

—— How to deal with Unemployment, *etc.* [Published for the Preparatory Committee of the International Conference for the Defence, Improvement and Extension of Social Insurance and Social Security.] pp. 42. *W.F.T.U. Publications: London*, [1952.] 8°. **8289.** m. **26.**

BARBADOS.

LAWS.—I. GENERAL COLLECTIONS.

—— Acts and Statutes of the Island of Barbados, made and enacted since the reducement of the same unto the authority of the Commonwealth of England . . . Together with the Charter of the said island, *etc.* [Edited by John Jennings.] pp. 176. *Will. Bentley: London*, [1654.] 8°. C. **54.** e. **13.**
Imperfect; wanting pp. 49, 50, 115 *and* 116.

—— The Laws of Barbados, collected in one volume, by William Rawlin, *etc.* pp. 239. *For William Rawlin: London*, 1699. fol. **504.** k. **14.**

—— Acts of Assembly passed in the Island of Barbadoes, from 1648 to 1718 (from 1717–18 to 1738, inclusive). 2 pt. *London*, 1732, 39. fol. **23.** d. **3.**

—— Acts, passed in the Island of Barbados. From 1643, to 1762, inclusive . . . Revised . . . in the Secretary's Office by . . . Richard Hall . . . and . . . continued by his son, Richard Hall, *etc.* (An Abridgment of the Acts . . . 1643 to 1762 . . . By R. Hall.) 2 pt. *For Richard Hall: London*, 1764. fol. C.S. f. **49/2.**

—— The Public Acts in Force; passed by the Legislature of Barbados, from May 11th 1762 to April 8th 1800, inclusive . . . A digested abridgment of the said Acts . . . By Samuel Moore. 2 pt. *For Samuel Moore: London*, 1801. 8°. C.S. f. **61.**

—— Laws of Barbados. [1646–1863.] 2 vol. *London*, 1855, 64. 8°. C.S. f. **61/2.**

—— Laws of Barbados. [1858–59, *etc.*] [*Bridgetown*, 1859– .] 8° & fol. C.S. f. **60** & f. **49.**

—— Laws of Barbados. 2 vol. *London*, 1875. 8°. C.S. f. **61/3.**

—— Laws of Barbados . . . Revised and consolidated by the Commissioners, Henry A. Bovell and W. Herbert Greaves. (Index . . . 1667-1–1894-1.) 8 vol. *Barbados*, 1893[–1912]. 8°. C.S. f. **61/4.**

BARBADOS.

—— Laws of Barbados, *etc.*
vol. 1–4. Laws of Barbados . . . Revised and consolidated by the Commissioners G. Aubrey Goodman . . . and G. P. Clarke . . . 1667–1(—1912–5). [With index and appendices.] 1912, 13.
vol. 5. pt. 1–vol. 11. pt. 2. Laws of Barbados, 1912–8 to 1913–12(–1943). [1913–44.]
Barbados. 1912–[44?] 8°. C.S. f. **61/5.**
From vol. 5. *pt.* 1 *onwards consisting of the annual volumes of legislation.*

—— Regulations and Proclamations made during the years 1914 and 1915, with index by Sir W. H. Greaves. pp. 109. 3. [*Bridgetown*, 1916.] 8°. C.S. f. **60/2.**

—— Proclamations, Orders and Regulations made during the Years 1925 & 1926 [*etc.*]. [*Bridgetown*, 1927– .] C.S. f. **60/3.**

—— Laws of Barbados, 1943 and 1944 . . . Revised and compiled by C. V. H. Archer . . . and W. K. Fergusson . . . Under the supervision of the Statute Laws Commissioners, *etc.* pp. vi. 202. iii. *Barbados*, 1944. 8°. C.S.F.61/5.(2.)

—— Laws of Barbados . . . Revised and consolidated by C. V. H. Archer . . . and W. K. Fergusson . . . Under the supervision of the Commissioners, *etc.* *Barbados*, 1944 8°. C.S. f. **61/6.**
From vol. 6 pt. 1 onwards comprising of the annual volumes of legislation for 1945 onwards.

LAWS.—V. ABRIDGEMENTS AND EXTRACTS.

—— An Abridgement of the Laws of Barbados, printed 699, *etc.* *See* Virginia, *Colony of.* [*Public Documents.*] An Abridgement of the Laws in force and use in Her Majesty's Plantations, *etc.* 1704. 8°. **883.** i. **8.**

LEGISLATURE.

—— [Legislative Debates. Session 1906–07, *etc.*] [*Bridgetown*, 1907– .] fol. C.S. f. **51.**

House of Assembly.

—— [Debates in the Barbados House of Assembly.] *See* supra: Legislature. [Legislative Debates.]

—— Minutes of Proceedings, *etc.* [With Documents laid before the Assembly.] *See* infra: *Legislative Council.* Minutes of Proceedings, *etc.*

—— The Report from a Select Committee of the House of Assembly, appointed to inquire into the origin, causes and progress of the late insurrection. pp. 63. *Barbados*, [1817?] 8°. **8154.** e. **3.** (**1.**)

—— [Another edition.] pp. 63. *T. Cadell & W. Davies: London*, 1818. 8°. **1061.** i. **27.**

—— Rules, Orders and Forms of Proceeding of the House of Assembly of Barbados, relating to public business. pp. 33. [*Bridgetown*,] 1858. 8°. C.S. f. **62.**
Interleaved.

Legislative Council.

—— [Debates in the Legislative Council of Barbados.] *See* supra: Legislature. [Legislative Debates.]

—— Minutes of Proceedings of the Honourable Board of Legislative Council and Honourable House of Assembly for session of 1904–1905 [*etc.*]. [With Documents laid before the Assembly.] *Barbados*, 1905– . fol. C.S. f. **50.**

—— A Report of a Committee of the Council of Barbadoes appointed to inquire into the actual condition of the slaves in this island, with a view to refute certain calumnies respecting their treatment, *etc.* pp. 127. *W. Scor: London*, 1824. 8°. **8156.** aaa. **1.** (**6.**)

BARBADOS.

MISCELLANEOUS OFFICIAL PUBLICATIONS.

—— Agricultural Development in Barbados, *etc.* pp. 32. [*Bridgetown*, 1941.] fol. C.S. F. **43/7.**

—— Annual Report of the Chief Medical Officer for the year 1947-48 [*etc.*]. [*Bridgetown*,] 1949- . fol. C.S. F. **55.**

—— Annual Report on Barbados, *etc.* *See* infra: Barbados. Report, *etc.*

—— Barbados. Report for 1919-20(-1930-31). (Annual Report on the Social and Economic Progress of the People of Barbados, 1931-32[-1938-39].) 20 pt. *London*, 1921-39. 8°. [*Colonial Reports—Annual.* no. 1072, 1087, 1134, 1175, 1225, 1274, 1301, 1348, 1422, 1462, 1499, 1544, 1595, 1632, 1698, 1725, 1762, 1830, 1861, 1913.] B.S. **7/51.**

Previous Reports were published as Parliamentary Papers.

—— Annual Report on Barbados for the Year 1947 [*etc.*]. *London*, 1948- . 8°. [*Colonial Annual Reports.*] B.S. **7/51.** (3.)

—— Barbados Colonial Estimates, 1949-50 [*etc.*]. [*Bridgetown*,] 1949- . fol. C.S. F. **40/2.**

—— Blue Book. 1881 [*etc.*]. *Barbados*, 1882- . fol. C.S. F. **41.**

—— Census of Barbados. 1881-'91. (C. J. Lawrance, compiler.) pp. 99. [*Bridgetown*, 1892.] fol. C.S. F. **44.**

—— Civil List. Revised to 1st January 1952 [*etc.*]. *Bridgetown*, 1952- . 8°. C.S. F. **63.**

—— Customs Tariff. pp. 21. [*Bridgetown*, c. 1945.] 8°. C.S. F. **45/3.**

—— A Declaration set forth by the Lord Lieutenant Generall, the Gentlemen of the Councell & Assembly, occasioned from the view of a printed paper, entituled. An Act prohibiting trade with the Barbados, Virginea, Bermudes and Antegoe. (An Act for defence of the Government liberties and freedomes of this Island.) pp. 7. *Samuel Brown: Hagh*, 1651. 4°. E. **644.** (4.)

—— A Fiscal Survey of Barbados. By C. G. Beasley. pp. 105. [*Bridgetown*, 1953.] 8°. C.S. F. **54/25.**
Issued as a supplement to the Official Gazette.

—— Memorandum on the Estimates 1949-50 [*etc.*]. [*Bridgetown*,] 1949- . fol. C.S. F. **40/3.**

—— Report of the Auditor General on the Audit of the Accounts of the Colony for the year 1946-47 [*etc.*]. [*Barbados*, 1947- .] fol. C.S. F. **40.**

—— Report of the Public Librarian for the year ended on the 31st March, 1946 [*etc.*]. [*Barbados*, 1947- .] 8°. C.S. F. **65.**

—— Report of the Registrar on the Vital Statistics for the year 1945 [*etc.*]. [*Barbados*, 1946- .] 8°. C.S. F. **68.**

—— Report on a Proposed Clayworking Industry in Barbados. By J. R. Brannam. pp. 17. [*Bridgetown*,] 1948. fol. C.S. F. **54/9.**

—— Report on Income Tax in Barbados. By H. R. Howie. pp. 19. [*Bridgetown*,] 1944. 8°. C.S. F. **69.**

—— Report on Local Government in Barbados. By Sir John Maude. pp. 52. [*Bridgetown*,] 1949. fol. C.S. F. **54/10.**

—— Report on Oil Development Policy in Barbados. By G. W. Lepper, *etc.* [With maps and illustrations.] pp. 32. *Bridgetown*, 1949. fol. C.S. F. **54/27.**

BARBADOS.

—— Report on Preliminary Housing Survey of Two Blocks of Chapman's Lane Tenantry, Bridgetown, June-July, 1944. By . . L. M. de Syllas . . . And comments on the report by the Town Planning Adviser and the Housing Board. pp. 8. [*Bridgetown*, 1944.] 8°. C.S. F. **69/2.**

—— Report on the Census of Barbados, 1911 . . . E. P. Boyce, compiler. pp. 97. [*Bridgetown*, 1912.] fol. C.S. F. **44/2.**

—— Report on the Census of Barbados, 1911–1921. Henry W. Lofty, compiler. pp. 115. [*Bridgetown*, 1922.] fol. C.S. F. **44/3.**

—— Report on the Treatment of Offenders for the Year 1947 [*etc.*]. [*Bridgetown*,] 1949- . fol. C.S. F. **56/2.**

—— Report on Trade and Agriculture during the quarter April to June 1953 [*etc.*] [*Bridgetown*,] 1953- . fol. C.S. F. **43/3.**
Reproduced from typewriting.

—— Report upon the Rainfall of Barbados, and upon its Influence on the Sugar Crops, 1847–71, with two Supplements, 1873-4, by Governor Rawson, *etc.* pp. 167. [*Bridgetown*,] 1874. fol. C.S. F. **54/13.**

—— Social Welfare in Barbados. pp. 26. [*Bridgetown*,] 1942. fol. C.S. F. **52/2.**

—— Trade Union Training Course, Barbados. Report, *etc.* pp. 14. *Barbados*, [1949.] 8°. C.S. F. **54/7.**

—— Tuberculosis Survey and Recommendations. By . . . W. Santon Gilmour. pp. 19. [*Bridgetown*, c. 1945.] 8°. C.S. F. **69/3.**

DEPARTMENTS OF STATE AND PUBLIC INSTITUTIONS.

Accountant General Department.

—— Abstract of Revenue and Expenditure for the year 1952–53 [*etc.*]. [*Bridgetown*,] 1954- . fol. C.S. F. **40/4.**
Issued as supplements to the Official Gazette.

Barbados Savings Bank.

—— Statement of Revenue and Expenditure for the year ended 31st December, 1951 [*etc.*]. [*Bridgetown*, 1954- .] fol. C.S. F. **57/2.**
Issued as Supplements to the Official Gazette.

British West Indies Central Sugar Cane Breeding Station.

—— Report . . . for the period ending September 30th 1934(–1947). [*Bridgetown*, 1934–47.] 8°. C.S. F. **43/6.**

—— The Yield of Sugar Cane in Barbados in 1944. pp. 13. [*Barbados*,] 1944. 8°. C.S. F. **67/2.**
Barbados. Department of Science and Agriculture. Bulletin. no. 28.

Commissioners for the Sale of Land.

—— *Begin.* Barbados, January 19, 1765. By the King's Authority. Public Notice is hereby given, *etc.* [Regulations for the sale of land in Grenada and other islands.] [*Barbados*, 1765.] *s. sh.* fol. **1865.** c. **7.** (**24.**)

Committee appointed to enquire into all Aspects of the Fancy Molasses Industry in Barbados.

—— Report of the Committee appointed to enquire into all aspects of the Fancy Molasses Industry in Barbados. pp. 40. [*Bridgetown*,] 1952. fol. C.S. F. **54/14.**

Customs Department.

—— Report of the Comptroller of Customs on the Customs Revenue, Trade and Shipping of the Island for the year (1948 [etc.].) [*Bridgetown*,] 1941– . fol. C.S. F. 45/2.
From 1948 *issued as Supplements to the Official Gazette.*

Customs Department.—Excise Branch.

—— Report on the Excise Branch of the Customs Department for the Year 1948. [*Bridgetown*,] 1949– . fol. C.S. F. 45.
Issued as a supplement to the Official Gazette. Subsequently published in the full Customs Department Report.

Department of Education.

—— [Report of the Director of Education for the year ending 31st March 1948, *etc.*] [*Bridgetown*,] 1949– . fol. C.S. F. 46/3.

—— The Evaluation of Education in Barbados. A first experiment. Memorandum by the Director of Education, *etc.* pp. 29. [*Bridgetown*, 1945.] 8°. C.S. F. 46/4.

—— The Provision for Secondary Education in Barbados. Memorandum by the Director of Education. pp. 14. [*Bridgetown*, 1945.] 8°. C.S. F. 46/6.

Department of Highways and Transport.

—— [Report of the Department of Highways and Transport for the year 1946-47, *etc.*]. [*Bridgetown*, 1947– .] fol. C.S. F. 47.

Department of Labour.

—— Department of Labour Report for the calendar year, 1946 [*etc.*]. [*Barbados*, 1947– .] 4°. C.S. F. 53.

Department of Science and Agriculture.

—— Annual Report of the Department of Science and Agriculture for the year (1946-47) [*etc.*]. *Barbados*, [1945– .] 4°. C.S. F. 67.

—— Agricultural Journal. vol. 9. no. 1, *etc.* Jan. 1940, *etc.* [*Barbados*,] 1940– . 8°. C.S. F. 67/3.

—— Bulletin no. 1 [*etc.*]. New series. [*Bridgetown*, 1944– . 8°. C.S. F. 43/4.

Education Commission.

—— Education Commission Report, 1875–76. pp. 99. *Barbados*, 1876. fol. C.S. F. 46.

Fire Brigade.

—— Report on the Administration of the Barbados Fire Brigade for the year ended on the 31st December, 1946 [*etc.*]. [*Barbados*, 1947– .] 4°. C.S. F. 64.

Government Bacteriological and Pathological Laboratory.

—— Report for the year 1945 [*etc.*]. [*Barbados*, 1947– .] 4°. C.S. F. 42.

Harbour and Shipping Department.

—— Report of the Harbour and Shipping Department for the year 1946 [*etc.*]. [*Barbados*, 1947– .] 4°. C.S. F. 48.

Income Tax and Death Duties Department.

—— Annual Report 1953–54 [*etc.*]. *Bridgetown*, 1955– . fol. C.S. F. 40/5.
Issued as supplements to the Official Gazette.

Labour Welfare (Housing Loans) Organisation.

—— Report on the Labour Welfare—Housing Loans—Organisation for the period 30th June, 1950 to 31st March, 1951 [*etc.*]. [*Georgetown*,] 1952– . fol. C.S. F. 53/3.

Peasants' Loan Bank.

—— Twelfth [*etc.*] Annual Report of the Peasants' Loan Bank, 1st June, 1948—31st May, 1949 [*etc.*]. [*Bridgetown*,] 1950– . fol. C.S. F. 43/2.

Police Force.

—— Annual Report on the Local Forces . . . For the year 1950–51 [*etc.*]. [*Bridgetown*,] 1952– . fol. C.S. F. 56/3.

—— Annual Report on the Organization and Administration of the Barbados Police Force for the year 1946 [*etc.*]. [*Barbados*, 1947– .] fol. C.S. F. 56.

Post Office Department.

—— Barbados Post Office Guide. Oct. 1932, *etc.* *Bridgetown*, 1932– . 8°. P.P. 2587. ob.

Public Works Department.

—— Annual Report of the Public Works Department for the year ended 31st December, 1949 [*etc.*]. [*Bridgetown*,] 1950– . 8°. C.S. F. 66.

Publicity Committee.

—— Annual Report from 1st April 1953—31st March 1954 [*etc.*]. [*Bridgetown*, 1954– .] fol. C.S. F. 69/4.

Social Welfare Department.

—— First [*etc.*] Annual Report, April 1st 1951—March 31st 1952 [*etc.*]. [*Bridgetown*,] 1953– . fol. C.S. F. 52.

MISCELLANEOUS INSTITUTIONS, SOCIETIES, ETC.

Barbados Museum and Historical Society.

—— The Journal of the Barbados Museum and Historical Society. *Barbados*, 1933– . 8°. Ac. 8576.

Barbados Royal and Merchant Welfare League.

—— Report of the Work of the . . . League for the year 1943-1944. [1944.] 4°. P.P. 1091. gee.

Barbados Women's Social Welfare League.

—— Report of the Work and Progress of the . . . League and affiliated societies for the year 1943-44. [1944.] 4°. P.P. 1091. gef.

Society for the Encouragement of Arts, Manufactures and Commerce.

—— Institution and first Proceedings of the Society, *etc.* [1781–84.] pp. 98. *Barbados*, [1784.] 8°. B. 676. (1.)

Society of Friends in Barbados.

—— A Short Account of the manifest hand of God that hath fallen upon several Marshals and their deputies, who have made great spoil and havock of the goods of the people of God called Quakers, in the Island of Barbadoes, for their testimony against going or sending to the militia, *etc.* pp. 23. *T. Sowle: London*, 1696. 4°. 4152. f. 23. (23.)
Pp. 3, 4 *are mutilated, and the missing portion of text is supplied in* MS.

BARBADOS.

APPENDIX.

—— Account of the fatal Hurricane by which Barbados suffered in August 1831; to which is prefixed a succinct narrative of the convulsions of the elements which at several times have visited and injured the West Indian Islands. By the Editor of the "West Indian." pp. 145. *Samuel Hyde: Bridge-Town*, 1831. 8°. **8756**. aaa. **21**.

—— An Account of the Number of Negroes delivered into the Islands of Barbadoes, Jamaica, and Antego, from the year 1698 to 1708, since the trade was opened, taken from the accounts sent from the respective Governours of those islands to the Lords Commissioners of Trade, whereby it appears the African trade is encreas'd to four times more since its being laid open, than it was under an exclusive company. [*London*, 1709?] *s. sh.* fol. **8223**. e. **4**. (**33**.)

—— Bloudy Newes from the Barbadoes, being a true relation of a great and terrible fight between the Parliament's navie commanded by Sir George Ayscue; and the King of Scots forces, under the . . . conduct and command of the Lord Willoughby, *etc.* pp. 8. *G. Horton: London*, 1652. 4°. E. **655**. (**16**.)

—— A Brief Relation of the beginning and ending of the troubles of the Barbados . . . Set forth by A. B. a diligent observer of the times. 1653. 4°. *See* B., A., *a diligent observer, etc.* E. **708**. (**5**.)

—— A Declaration of Inhabitants of Barbados, respecting the demolition of the Methodist Chapel. With an appendix. pp. 20. *Barbadian Office: Barbados*, 1826. 8°. **8155**. b. **86**. (**1**.)

—— Desultory Sketches and Tales of Barbados. pp. viii. 264. *Henry Washbourne: London*, 1840. 8°. N. **1506**.

—— A Detection of the State and Situation of the present Sugar Planters, of Barbadoes and the Leward Islands, *etc.* (A Supplement to the Detection, *etc.*) 2 pt. *J. Wilford: London*, 1732, 33. 8°. **104**. i. **40**.

—— An Early Impression of Barbados. Contributed by N. Darnell Davis. (Transcript of a broadside preserved in the Bodleian Library "Rawlinson Manuscripts." Reprinted from "The West India Committee Circular," no. 395, of Nov. 18, 1913.) [*London*, 1913.] *s. sh.* fol. **1879**. c. **8**. (**28**.)

—— For the Governour, and his Council & Assembly, and all Others in Power, both Civil and Military in this Island [Barbadoes]; from the People called Quakers. (With an Addition.) *See* Fox (George) *Founder of the Society of Friends.* To the Ministers, Teachers, and Priests, so called, and so stileing your Selves, in Barbadoes. 1672. 4°. **4152**. f. **11**.

—— Great Newes from the Barbadoes. Or, a true and faithful account of the grand conspiracy of the Negroes against the English . . . With a short description of that plantation. pp. 14. *L. Curtis: London*, 1676. 4°. **1197**. g. **5**.

—— [Another copy.] G. **19163**. (**2**.)
Imperfect; containing only the first eight or introductory pages. To conceal the imperfection the catchword on p. 8 has been erased.

—— Illustrated Souvenir of Barbados, British West Indies, *etc.* pp. xxxvi. *Barbados Publicity Committee: [Barbados;] New York* printed, 1932. 8°. **10482**. cc. **31**.

—— Land of Abiding Sunshine. Barbados. *J. Miles & Co: London*, [1924.] 8°. **10482**. e. **26**.

BARBADOS.—[Appendix.]

—— A Letter from the most considerable Proprietors of the Island of Barbadoes, to the several persons in Great Britain interested in the said Island, requesting their application to the . . . House of Commons, for establishing the African Trade by a Joint-Stock. pp. 3. [*London?* 1709.] fol. **816**. m. **5**. (**147***.)

—— An Ode Pindarick on Barbadoes. [*London?* 1710?] *s. sh.* fol. C. **38**. l. **6**. (**26**.)

—— Pages from the Early History of Barbados. 1627–1659. [Compiled by N. Darnell Davis.] [*Barbados*, 1909.] *s. sh.* fol. **1865**. c. **9**. (**68**.)

—— The Principles by which a Currency is established, a coinage formed, and the money circulations of this island may be restored and preserved. pp. 28. *Barbados*, 1791 [*W. Marchant: London*, 1806?]. 8°. B. **501**. (**1**.)

—— Relation de l'isle des Barbades. *See* Africa. Recueil de divers voyages faits en Afrique et en l'Amérique, *etc.* 1674. 4°. **214**. a. **11**.

—— Remarks on the Insurrection in Barbadoes, and the Bill for the Registration of Slaves. pp. 15. *Ellerton & Henderson: London*, 1816. 8°. **1103**. k. **51**.

—— The Seaman's Practical Guide, for Barbadoes and the Leeward Islands; with observations on the islands from Blanco to the Rocas, on the coast of Le Guayra. General instructions and observations on making the land . . . All taken from actual observation, by a Captain in the Royal Navy. pp. 76. *Smith, Elder & Co.: London*, 1832. 8°. T. **1392**. (**9**.)

—— A Short History of Barbados, from its first discovery and settlement, to the end of the year 1767. [By George Frere.] pp. viii. 121. *J. Dodsley: London*, 1768. 8°. **978**. d. **29**.

—— A new edition, corrected and enlarged. pp. xiii. 132. *J. Dodsley: London*, 1768. 8°. **278**. c. **7**.

—— Some Memoirs of the first Settlement of the Island of Barbados and other the Caribbee Islands with the succession of the Governours and Commanders in Chief . . . to the year 1741. Extracted from antient records, papers, and accounts taken from Mr. William Arnold, Mr. Samuel Bulkly, and Mr. John Summers, *etc.* [With an appendix.] pp. 84. 15. *Wm. Beeby: Barbados*, 1741. 16°. G. **14967**.

—— [Another edition.] Memoirs of the first Settlement of the Island of Barbados, *etc.* pp. 84. 15. *E. Owen: London*, 1743. 16°. **278**. a. **26**.

—— A State of the present condition of the Island Barbadoes: with some reasons, why there ought not to be any more duties or imposts laid on sugars than what already are . . . By a merchant, trading to the West-Indies. pp. 4. *For Tho. Northcott: London*, [1698?] fol. **816**. m. **13**. (**158**.)

—— To Friends in Barbadoes, Virginia, *etc.* [1666?] 4°. *See* F., G. **4151**. d. **10**.

—— *Begin.* To the Queen's most excellent Majesty, the Humble Petition (relating to the African Trade) of several Planters, and other the Inhabitants of your majesty's Island of Barbadoes. [*London*, 1710.] *s. sh.* fol. **816**. m. **18**. (**31**.)

BARBADOS, *Diocese of.* Ecclesiastical Calendar of the Diocese of Barbados and the Leeward Isles for January, 1838 (for 1839). 2 pt. *I. Bowen: Bridge-Town*, 1838, 39. 8°. P.P. **2586**. g.

BARBADOS, John, *Bishop of*. *See* Mitchinson.

——, Thomas, *Bishop of*. *See* Parry.

——, William Hart, *Bishop of*. *See* Coleridge.

BARBADOS AGRICULTURAL REPORTER. Barbadoes Agricultural Reporter and Planter's Scientific Journal. *See* Periodical Publications.—*Bridgetown, Barbados.*

BARBADOS ALMANACK. *See* Ephemerides.

—— Barbados Almanac and Diary. *See* Ephemerides.

BARBADOS AND THE LEEWARD ISLES, *Diocese of*. *See* Barbados, *Diocese of*.

BARBADOS-ANTIGUA EXPEDITION. *See* Iowa. —*State University of Iowa.*

BARBADOS GAZETTE. *See* Periodical Publications.—*Bridgetown, Barbados.*

BARBADOS GENERAL HOSPITAL. *See* Bridgetown.

BARBADOS GIRL.

—— The Barbadoes Girl. A tale . . . By the author of The Clergyman's Widow and Family [i.e. Barbara Hoole, afterwards Hofland] . . . Fifth edition. pp. 180. *A. K. Newman & Co.: London*, 1825. 12°. **12809**. a. **51**.
With an additional titlepage, engraved.

BARBADOS MERCURY. *See* Periodical Publications.—*Bridgetown, Barbados.*

BARBADOS MUSEUM AND HISTORICAL SOCIETY. *See* Barbados.

BARBADOS PACKET. The Barbadoes Packet; containing several original papers: giving an account of the most material transactions that have lately happened in a certain part of the West-Indies. pp. 68. *S. Popping: London*, 1720. 8°. **1197**. g. **6**.

BARBADOS PLANTER. The Present Case of a Barbados Planter, and reasons against laying a further duty on sugar. pp. 3. [*London*, 1695?] fol. **816**. m. **13**. (**160**.)

BARBADOS PUBLIC LIBRARY. *See* Bridgetown, *Barbados.*

BARBADOS ROYAL AND MERCHANT WELFARE LEAGUE. *See* Barbados.

BARBADOS SAVINGS BANK. *See* Barbados.

BARBADOS SEEDS.

—— Some Observations made upon the Barbado Seeds, shewing their admirable virtue in curing Dropsies. Written by a Physitian in the Countrey [i.e. J. Peachie?], to Sir George Ent at London. pp. 7. *London*, 1694. 4°. **546**. g. **18**. (**16**.)

—— [Another copy.] B. **615**. (**11**.)

BARBADOS WOMEN.

—— Barbados Women's Social Welfare League. *See* Barbados.

BARBADOS YEAR BOOK. *See* Periodical Publications.—*Bridgetown, Barbadoes.*

BARBAG (Józef)

—— Geografia gospodarcza Polski w zarysie. Wydanie drugie uzupełnione. [With maps and illustrations.] pp. 141. *Warszawa*, 1949. 8°. **10004**. pp. **38**.
Biblioteka polskiego radia. tom 8.

BARBAG (Józef)

—— Geografia gospodarcza Polski . . . Wydanie trzecie uzupełnione. pp. 175. *Warszawa, Kraków*, 1951. 8°. **010005**. c. **5**.

—— [Geografia gospodarcza Polski.] Экономическая география Польши. Сокращенный перевод . . . Ю. В. Илинича. Под редакцией П. И. Глушакова. [With maps.] pp. 141. *Москва*, 1952. 8°. **010005**. d. **38**.

BARBAG (Seweryn)

—— Studjum o pieśniach Chopina. [With musical notes.] pp. 60. 1927. 8°. *See* Leopol.—*Zakład Naukowy Imienia Ossolińskich.* Ac. **7215**/**60**.

BARBAG (Yu.) *See* Barbag (J.)

BARBAGALIN (Batistin) *pseud.* *See* Mastrogiorgeide. La Mastrogiorgeide. Poema postumo dell'autore dei Vermi. Seconda edizione . . . aumentata . . . delle' note del prof. Batistin Barbagalin. 1873. 8°. **11431**. cc. **2**.

BARBAGALLO (Corrado)

—— *See* Casini (T.) and Fiorini (V.) Biblioteca storica del risorgimento italiano, *etc.* (Nuova serie diretta da C. Barbagallo ed E. Rota.) 1932, *etc.* 8°. **9169.de.2.**

—— *See* Ferrero (G.) and Barbagallo (C.) Roma antica. 1921, *etc.* 8°. **9041**. e. **3**.

—— *See* Ferrero (G.) and Barbagallo (C.) A Short History of Rome. 1918, *etc.* 8°. **9042**. a. **3**.

—— *See* Ollivier (O. E.) Michelangelo. Introduzione e annotazioni di C. Barbagallo. [1927.] 4°. **7876**. g. **9**.

—— La Crisi economico-sociale dell'Italia della Rinascenza. *In:* Nuova rivista storica. anno 34. fasc. 5/6, anno 35. fasc. 1/2. 1950, 51. 8°. P.P. **3556**. ne.

—— Due rivoluzioni dei secoli xviii–xix. La rivoluzione americana, 1765–1783. La rivoluzione francese ed europea, 1789–1804. [With plates.] pp. vii. 324. [*Milan*,] 1945. 8°. **09010**. cc. **11**.

—— Giuseppe Fraccaroli e l'opera sua. [With a bibliography by Vincenzo Craici.] pp. 128. *Bologna*, 1919. 8°. **011853**. tt. **52**.

—— L'Italia dal 1870 ad oggi. pp. 92. *Milano*, 1918. 8°. **9168**. cc. **3**.

—— L'Opera storica di Guglielmo Ferrero e i suoi critici. pp. 222. *Milano*, 1911. 8°. **09039**. d. **16**.

—— Le Origini della grande industria contemporanea (Seconda edizione.) pp. x. 549. *Firenze*, 1951. 8°. **08231**. cc. **30**.
Storici antichi e moderni. nuova serie. no. 1.

—— Passato e presente. Saggi di storia, filosofia e politica. pp. 369. *Milano*, 1924. 8°. **012352**. g. **53**.

—— Pel materialismo storico. pp. 114. *Roma*, 1899. 8°. **8485**. ff. **2**.

—— Il Problema delle origini di Roma da Vico a noi. pp. vi. 149. *Milano*, 1926. 8°. **9042**. a. **10**.

—— Una Questione dantesca. Dante Alighieri, i Bianco-Ghibellini esuli e i Romena. pp. 111. *Roma*, 1899. 8°. **11420**. d. **35**.

—— La Questione meridionale. pp. 295. [*Milan*,] 1948. 8°. **8032**. dd. **25**.
Piani. vol. 8.

BARBAGALLO (Corrado)

—— Roma antica. [With plates and maps.] 2 vol. *Torino*, 1931, 32. 4°. [*Grande storia d'Italia.*]
9171.c.2/2.

—— Lo Stato e l'istruzione pubblica nell'Impero Romano. pp. 430. *Catania*, 1911. 8°. [*Biblioteca di filologia classica.* no. 3.]
011313.de.1/3.

—— Il Tramonto di una civiltà, o la fine della Grecia antica. 2 vol. *Firenze*, 1923. 8°. **9025.** b. **34.**

BARBAGELATA (Giacinto) *See* Solari (P. A.) and Lodi (G. T.) La Certezza e validità della volontà della Q. N. D. Selvarezza Maricona . . . difesa in jure dalle frivole opposizioni di . . . G. Barbagelata, *etc.* [1670?] fol. **501.** g. **19.** (**2.**)

BARBAGELATA (Hugo D.) *See* García Calderón (V.) and Barbagelata (H. D.) La Literatura Uruguaya, 1757–1917. 1917. 8°. [*Revue Hispanique.* tom. 40.]
P.P. **4331.** aea.

—— *See* Rodó (J. E.) Cinco Ensayos. [With an introduction by H. D. Barbagelata.] [1915.] 8°. **012352.** de. **17.**

—— *See* Rodó (J. E.) Pages choisies. Choix et préface de H. D. Barbagelata, *etc.* 1918. 8°. **12230.** k. **2.**

—— Artigas y la Revolución Americana . . . Segunda edición corregida y aumentada. [With a portrait.] pp. 319. *Paris*, 1930. fol. **10880.** tt. **16.**

—— Histoire de l'Amérique espagnole, *etc.* pp. 323. *Paris*, 1936. 8°. **9770.** p. **7.**

—— La Novela y el cuento en Hispanoamérica. pp. 316. *Montevideo*, 1947. 8°. **011853.** dd. **68.**

BARBAGELATA (Lorenzo)

—— Artigas antes de 1810. Segunda edición, *etc.* pp. 190. *Montevideo*, 1945. 8°. **10891.** aa. **29.**

—— Guayabos y otros estudios, *etc.* pp. 107. *Montevideo*, 1954. 8°. **9773.** b. **19.**

BARBAGLI (Domenica) *See* Talbot (John) 16*th Earl of Shrewsbury.* Letter . . . to A. L. Phillipps . . . descriptive of the Estatica of Caldaro . . . Second edition . . . To which is added the relation of three . . . visits to the Estatica of Monte Sansavino (D. Barbagli), *etc.* 1842. 8°. **1352.** f. **3.**

BAR BAHLŪL. *See* Ḥasan bar Bahlūl.

BARBAJA (Domenico) *See* Gigli (G.) L'Insussistente apologia del Signor D. Barbaja. [A protest against the introduction of gambling houses into Naples by Barbaja.] [1820.] *s. sh.* fol. **8032.** m. **9.** (**9.**)

—— *See* Lorenzo (L. A. di) Risposta all'apologista del Gran Giuochi di Barbaja, *etc.* [1820.] *s. sh.* fol.
8032. m. **7.** (**23.**)

—— *See* Mazzei (G.) Giustificazioni del Signor D. Barbaja. [1820.] *s. sh.* fol. **8032.** m. **7.** (**8.**)

—— Per alcuni socii nella impresa de' reali Teatri contro il Signor D. Barbaja socio impresario. pp. 43. *Napoli*, 1839. 8°. **8246.** bbb. **49.** (**15.**)

BARBA JACOB (Porfirio)

—— *See* Jaramillo (M. J.) Conversaciones de Barba-Jacob. [1946.] 8°. **010632.** a. **7.**

—— Canciones y Elegías. Edición de homenaje al Poeta. [With a portrait.] pp. 98. [*Mexico*,] 1932. 4°.
20001. aa. **43.**
The date in the colophon is 1933.

BARBAJUDAEUS. Barbaiudæi querimonia. (Disinganno del forestiere mal prattico del paese.) [A satire in verse.] [*Naples?* 1665?] 4°. **33.** d. **18.** (**5, 6.**)

BARBAKAN. Leis Desastres de Barbakan chin errant dins Avignoun. [In verse. By Michel Ange Marin?] pp. 24. *Avignon*, 1759. 12°. **11498.** b. **57.** (**8.**)

—— [Another copy.] **11475.** aa. **34.** (**1.**)

BARBALHO UCHÕA CAVALCANTI (Adolpho) Relatorio preliminar sobre a extracção da gomma elastica da mangabeira sylvestre em S. Simão e Batataes, Estado de S. Paulo. [With plates.] pp. 23. *São Paulo*, 1898. 8°. **07076.** l. **17.** (**2.**)

BARBALI.

—— Barbalı. Ein Gespräch. [By Nicolaus Manuel.] [*Zurich?*] 1526. 8°. **C.107.aa.19.(3.)**

—— [Another edition.] *C. Müllers Erben: Strassburg*, [1550?] 8°. **C.111.b.2.**

BARBAN (André) Notice sur une pastourelle de Louis Papon représentée dans la Salle de la Diana, à Montbrison, en 1588. pp. 32. *Saint-Étienne*, 1856. 8°.
11851. g. **23.** (**1.**)

—— Recueil d'hommages, aveux et dénombrements de fiefs relevant du comté de Forez du XIIIe au XVIe siècle. pp. xxv. 571. [*Montbrison*,] 1885. 8°. [*Recueil de mémoires et documents sur le Forez.* tom. 8.] Ac. **6880.**

BARBAN (Lucien) and **CALVO** (Dominique) Traité pratique de l'administration & du service des prisons. pp. 255. *Paris*, 1866. 8°. **6056.** e. **32.**

BARBANA, Almorò III. Pisani, *Count di. See* Pisani.

BARBANCEYS (E.) Étude sur la coagulation du sang dans les veines. pp. 40. *Paris*, 1870. 4°. [*Collection des thèses soutenues à la Faculté de Médecine de Paris.* An 1870. tom. 1.] **7373.** l. **9.**

BARBANÇON ( ) *See* Pasquier ( ) *Maire de Presles.* Précis au Conseil d'État, pour le sieur Pasquier . . . contre le sieur Barbançon. [1806?] 4°.
5403. c. **4.** (**89.**)

BARBANÇON (F. de) L'Odeur des oranges, à son Alteze . . . Henri Frédéric, de Nassau, *etc.* [A poem.] pp. 72. *L. S. de Vries: Utrecht*, 1641. 4°. **11474.** bbb. **26.**

BARBANÈGRE (Joseph) *See* Casteig (J. B.) La Défense d'Huningue en 1815 et le général Barbanègre, *etc.* 1897. 8°. **09078.** d. **17.**

BARBANEL' (S. R.)

—— *See* Andereg (G. F.) and Barbanel' (S. R.) Монтаж, оборудование и контроль киноустановок, *etc.* 1950. 8°.
8913. bb. **11.**

BARBANELL (Maurice)

—— [Psychic Booklets.] Edited by M. Barbanell. *Spiritualist Press: London*, [1946– .] 8°. W.P. **1260.**
Each part bears the series title "A Psychic Booklet."

—— Across the Gulf. pp. 127. *Psychic Press: London*, 1940. 8°. **8634.** ccc. **81.**

—— Banned by the Church. The secret report on spiritualism. pp. 48. *Spiritualist Press: London*, [1947.] 8°. [*Psychic Booklets.*] W.P. **1260 6.**

—— The Case of Helen Duncan. pp. 153. *Psychic Press: London*, 1945. 8°. **6059.** aa. **11.**

—— Harry Edwards and his Healing. [With a portrait.] pp. 213. *Spiritualist Press: London*, 1953. 8°.
10862. de. **64.**

BARBANELL (MAURICE)

—— Keep the Rome Fires Burning . . . A reply to Spiritualism as spiritualists have written of it, by the Rev. H. V. O'Neill. pp. 123. *Psychic Press: London,* 1946. 8°. **08631**. e. **86**.

—— Parish the Healer. [With a portrait.] pp. 100. *Psychic Press: London,* 1938. 8°. **10858**. a. 5.

—— Power of the Spirit. pp. 178. *Spiritualist Press: London,* 1949. 8°. **8634**. df. **64**.

—— Rogues and Vagabonds. [On the legal position of spiritualists.] pp. 64. *Psychic Press: London,* 1944. 8°. **8634**. ee. **34**.

—— Saga of Spirit Healing. pp. 117. *Spiritualist Press: London,* 1954. 8°. **8635**. a. **52**.

—— They shall be Comforted. [On spiritualism.] pp. 92. *Psychic Press: London,* [1936.] 8°. **8634**. aaa. **40**.

—— The Trumpet Shall Sound . . . Foreword by Hannen Swaffer. [A record of certain spiritualist séances.] pp. 160. *Rider & Co.: London,* 1933. 8°. **08632**. ee. **49**.

—— Where there is a Will. [On spiritual self-development.] pp. 153. *Rockliff: London,* 1952. 8°. **4397**. bb. **93**.

BARBANELL (SYLVIA)

—— *See* SILVER BIRCH, *pseud.* More Wisdom of Silver Birch. Edited by S. Barbanell. 1945. 8°. **8634**. f. **55**.

—— *See* SILVER BIRCH. Silver Birch speaks . . . Edited by S. Barbanell. 1949. 8°. **8634**. df. **65**.

—— Some Discern Spirits. The mediumship of Estelle Roberts. [With portraits.] pp. 199. *Psychic Press: London,* 1944. 8°. **8634**. f. **36**.

—— When a Child Dies. pp. 228. *Psychic Press: London,* 1942. 8°. **8634**. e. **42**.

—— When Your Animal Dies, *etc.* pp. 194. *Psychic Press: London,* 1940. 8°. **07294**. a. **18**.

—— Your Animal survives Death. pp. 48. *Spiritualist Press: London,* [1949.] 8°. [*Psychic Booklets.*] W.P. **1260/10**.

BARBANERA ( ) *Astronomo.* *See* CAMPITELLI (F.) La Chiave d'oro della fortuna . . . Da un . . . manoscritto del rinomato astronomo Barbanera, *etc.* 1919. 8°. **8633**. g. **9**.

—— *See* EPHEMERIDES. Le Rivoluzioni celesti . . . o sia discorso astronomico del celebre Barba-Nera, *etc.* [1838.] 16°. P.P. **2386**. c.

—— Moti celesti o siano pianeti sferici calcolati per tutta l'Italia, e sue isole, e per gran parte di Europa, ed in particolare per il polo 42. di Roma, e 41. di Napoli, per l'anno primo dopo il bisestile 1853. Dell' Astronomo degli Appennini Barba-Nera . . . F. P. del Re editore. pp. 64. *Fuligno,* [1854.] 8°. **8562**. aaa. **36**.
With the arms of Ferdinand II., King of the Two Sicilies, stamped on the covers.

BARBANSON (CONSTANTIN) *See* CONSTANTIN [Pauret], *de Barbanson.*

BARBANSON (EDMOND MARIE ARMAND) De la maladie des femmes à la suite des couches connue sous le nom de péritonite puerpérale. (Thèse.) pp. 32. *Paris,* 1844. 4°. **7372**. b. **17**. **(2.)**

BARBANSON (JOANNES PETRUS JOSEPHUS) Dissertatio inauguralis juridica de legitima et reductione, secundum jus civile hodiernum, adjunctis quibusdam de jure Romano nec-non de novissimo jure criminali, *etc.* *Praes.* D. Sauveur. pp. 62. *Leodii,* 1818. 4°. **498**. **f**. **1**. **(15.)**

BARBANTANE, HILARION PAUL FRANÇOIS BIENVENU PUGET, *Marquis de.* *See* PUGET.

BARBANTE (ANDREA) Canzona di Andrea Barbante . . . in allegrezza della felicissima vittoria riceuuta dall' armata Christiana contro l'armata Turchesca. [*Venice?* 1572?] 4°. **11426**. d. **10**.

BARBANTI (GIUSEPPE) *See* SETTI (A.) La Famiglia e l'Internazionale. Considerazioni in risposta alle difese proferite dell' avv. G. Barbanti per Costa Andrea e Matteuzzi Vincenzo, *etc.* 1877. 8°. **8275**. ee. **1**. **(25.)**

BARBANTINI (MARIA DOMENICA BRUN) *See* BRUN-BARBANTINI.

BARBANTINI (NINO)

—— *See* MINUCIUS FELIX (M.) Octavius. (Tradotto da N. Barbantini.) 1946. 8°. **3670**. df. **44**.

—— La Galleria Internazionale d'arte moderna a Venezia, *etc.* pp. xxvi. pl. 50. *Milano,* [1929.] 16°. [*Il Fiore dei musei e monumenti d'Italia.* no. 9.] W.P. **8158/9**.

—— Il R. Museo Orientale di Venezia, *etc.* [With illustrations.] pp. 98. 1939. 8°. *See* VENICE.—*Museo Orientale.* W.P. **8625/68**.

—— Scritti d'arte inediti e rari. Raccolti a cura di Gino Damerini. [With a portrait.] pp. xxix. 387. *Venezia,* 1953. 8°. **07813**. b. **31**.

BARBANTINUS (JOANNES) *See* JOANNES, *de Zantuliete, Barbantinus.*

BARBANZA (JOSÉ)

—— Lutero. Su vida, su carácter, sus controversias. pp. 136. *Buenos Aires,* 1940. 8°. **4889.a.8.**

BARBA-PANTZELIOS. *See* BARMPA-PANTZELIOS.

BARBAR (LEO) Zur wirtschaftlichen Grundlage des Feldzuges der Türken gegen Wien im Jahre 1683. pp. 45. *Wien,* 1916. 8°. [*Wiener staatswissenschaftliche Studien.* Bd. 13. Hft. 1.] **8282**. s. **1/13**.

BARBAR (LUCIUS ISRAEL)

—— A Record and Documentary History of Simsbury . . . 1643–1888. [With a portrait.] pp. 429. *Abigail Phelps Chapter, Daughters of the American Revolution: Simsbury, Conn.,* 1931. 8°. **10480**. r. **24**.

BARBAR (THOMAS)

—— *See* BIBLE.—*Revelation.* [*English.*] The Apocalyps . . . Lately set forth by Fr. Du Ion, *etc.* [The translator's address signed: T. B., i.e. T. Barbar.] 1596. 4°. **691**. b. **6**.

BARBARA.

—— Barbara—called Binkie (by Doris Canham), and other stories of school and adventure [by various authors]. 1935. 8°. *See* CANHAM (Doris). **12825**. d. **16**.

—— Barbara's Revenge. By the author of "Six China Teacups," *etc.* pp. 80. *R.T.S.: London,* [1884.] 8°. **12810**. aa. **45**.

—— Barbara's Warning. A novel. By the author of "Recommended to Mercy" [i.e. Matilda C. Houstoun], *etc.* 3 vol. *Samuel Tinsley: London,* 1874. 8°. **12631**. n. **3**.

BARBARA.

—— The Story of Barbara; her splendid misery, and her gilded cage. A novel. By the author of "Lady Audley's Secret" [i.e. Mary E. Braddon]. 3 vol. *J. & R. Maxwell: London*, [1880.] 8°. **12640**. g. **8**.

BARBARA [OF AUSTRIA], *Consort of Alphonso II., Duke of Ferrara*. See LAZZARI (A.) Le Ultime tre duchesse di Ferrara, *etc.* 1913. 8°. **10629**. df. **1**.

—— *See* PIGNA (G. B.) Io. Bap. Pignæ oratio in funere Barbaræ . . . Ducis Ferrariæ, *etc.* [1572.] 4°. **10631**. d. **29**. (**1**.)

BARBARA, *Consort of Henry, Duke of Glogau and Krossen, afterwards Queen Consort of Vladislaus IV., King of Bohemia and Hungary*. See HOEFLER (C. A. C.) Barbara, Markgräfin zu Brandenburg, *etc.* 1867. 4°. [*Abhandlungen der k. böhmischen Gesellschaft der Wissenschaften*. Folge 5. Bd. 14; Folge 6. Bd. 1.] Ac. **801**.

BARBARA [RADZIWIŁŁÓWNA], *Consort of Sigismund II. Augustus, King of Poland*. See BALIŃSKI (M.) Pamiętniki o Królowéj Barbarze żonie Zygmunta Augusta. [With a portrait.] 1837, *etc.* 12°. **10795**. aaa. **9**.

—— Barbara Radziwiłłówna, Królowa Polska, żona Zygmunta Augusta. Przez R. S. [i.e. by R. Skalska.] 1861. 8°. *See* S., R. **10795**. aaa. **39**.

—— Nieznane listy Barbary Radziwiłłówny do Mikołaja Radziwiłła Rudego, i do Zygmunta Augusta (1547–1549). [Edited by Franciszek Pułaski. With a facsimile.] pp. 9. *Warszawa*, 1906. 8°. **10921**. m. **11**.

BARBARA, *of Braganza, Queen of Spain*. See MARY BARBARA [of Portugal], *Queen Consort of Ferdinand VI., King of Spain*.

BARBARA, *pseud*. [i.e. GEORGE FREDERIC BROWN TURNER.] *See also* TURNER (George F. B.)

—— The German Colonial Claims: can she be trusted. By Barbara. pp. 19. *Blackheath*, [c. 1938.] 8°. **08074**. d. **18**.

BARBARA, *pseud*. [i.e. MABEL OSGOOD WRIGHT.] At the Sign of the Fox: a romance. By Barbara, author of "The Garden of a Commuter's Wife," *etc.* pp. ix. 372. *Macmillan Co.: New York*, 1905. 8°. **012707**. dd. **35**.

—— The Garden, You, and I. By Barbara, author of "The Garden of a Commuter's Wife," *etc.* [With illustrations.] pp. xii. 397. *Macmillan Co.: New York*, 1906. 8°. **07029**. f. **19**.

—— The Open Window. Tales of the months. Told by Barbara, author of "The Garden of a Commuter's Wife," *etc.* pp. vii. 381. *Macmillan Co.: New York*, 1908. 8°. **012705**. b. **39**.

BARBARA [OF PORTUGAL], *Queen Consort of Ferdinand VI., King of Spain*. See MARY BARBARA.

BARBARA, *Queen Consort of Vladislaus IV., King of Bohemia and Hungary*. See BARBARA, *Consort of Henry, Duke of Glogau and Krossen, etc.*

BARBARA, *Saint*. See CALYBS (P.) Diue Catharine . . . vitæ descriptio. Item vita D. Barbaræ, *etc.* [1515.] 4°. **11403**. bb. **53**.

—— *See* CHARITE (S. L.) Het Leven ende doodt van de heylige . . . Barbara, *etc.* [1762.] 8°. **4827**. aa. **19**.

—— *See* JORDAN (Laurentius) Decora nimis, virgóque pulcherrima . . . Das ist, Barbara . . . die grosse heilige Bruderschafft-Patronin in Kirchdorff, *etc.* [1704.] 4°. **478**. a. **34**.

BARBARA, *Saint*.

—— *See* MARINI (F. S.) *Bishop of Rieti*. Memorie di S. Barbara, *etc.* 1788. 4°. **4828**. g. **9**.

—— *See* OLIVER-COPÓNS (A. de) Santa Bárbara. Noticias históricas acerca de la devocion de los Artilleros Españoles á esta Santa. 1884. 16°. **4531**. aa. **20**. (**3**.)

—— *See* POTTIER (L.) La Vie et histoire de Madame Sainte-Barbe. Le mystère joué à Laval en 1493 et les peintures de Saint-Martin-de-Connée. 1901. 8°. [*Revue historique et archéologique du Maine*. tom. 50. livr. 3.] Ac. **5321/3**.

—— Aman ez dezrou buhez sãte Barba dre rym: euel maz custumer he hoary en goelet breiz. G. L. FEW MS. NOTES. *Imprimet: E: Paris euit Bernard de Leau pe hiuy* [sic] *a: chom e mouutroulles* [sic] *var pont bourret*([15]57. 8°. en Bloaz. C. **40**. b. **49**.
Imperfect; wanting ff. B1, B8, C1, G1 *and* G8. *The titlepage is mutilated.*

—— Le Mystère de Sainte Barbe. Tragédie bretonne. Texte de 1557, publié avec traduction française, introduction et dictionnaire étymologique du breton moyen par Émile Ernault. pp. xii. 404. *Nantes*, 1885 [1885–87]. 8°. [*Archives de Bretagne*. tom. 3.] Ac. **8926/10**.

—— [A reissue.] *Paris*, 1888. 4°. **11737**. h. **19**.

—— Andächtiger Ruff von dem H. Leben vnd Marterkampff, der . . . Jungfrawen Sanct Barbara, *etc.* [In verse.] *Durch A. Angermayer: Ingolstatt*, 1613. 8°. **11517**. bbb. **33**.

—— Auto de S. Babora. Obra da vida da bemauenturada S. Barbara, *etc.* [By Affonso Alvares?] *A. Aluarez: Lisboa*, 1634. 4°. C. **63**. b. **10**.

—— [Another edition.] Auto de Sta Barbara, *etc.* pp. 24. *Lisboa*, 1761. 4°. **1072**. g. **19**. (**33**.)

—— [Another edition.] Acto de Sta Barbara. pp. 24. *Lisboa*, 1853. 4°. **11728**. g. **46**. (**24**.)

—— Barbaren passie. [A poem.] *See* WEGENER (P.) Drei mittelniederdeutsche Gedichte des 15. Jahrhunderts, *etc.* 1878. 4°. **11527**. g. **6**.

—— Cantic spirituel. Histoér admirable à vuhé Santés Barbe. [A version, in the dialect of Vannes, of "Histor eus a vuez Santez Barba."] pp. 8. *Guénet*, [1840?] 8°. **11595**. aaa. **10**.

—— Curioso romance y maravillosos milagros que ha obrado Dios nuestra Señor por intercession de la gloriosa Santa Barbara, y el Santo Angel de la Guarda, y los Santos quatro Évangelios, con dos devotos suyos, *etc.* [In verse.] [*Valencia*, 1760?] 4°. T. **1956**. (**46**.)

—— La Deuotissima rapresentatione di Santa Barbara. [In verse. With woodcuts.] *Firenze*, 1554. 4°. **11426**. f. **17**.

—— [Another edition.] *Siena*, [1560?] 4°. **11426**. f. **18**.

—— [Another edition.] *G. Baleni: Firenze*, 1588. 4°. C. **34**. h. **5**. (**1**.)

—— Esta Oracion dio un Angel, en trage de peregrino, en el Convento de nuestra Señora de la Peña de Crinta, *etc.* [Headed by a woodcut representing St. Barbara, and followed by "Coplas á Santa Barbara."] [*Madrid?* 1870?] *s. sh.* 4°. **1072**. g. **27**. (**36**.)

—— [Another issue.] **1072**. g. **27**. (**37**.)

—— [Another edition.] *Barcelona*, [1855?] *s. sh.* 4°. **11450**. f. **27**. (**45**.)

BARBARA, *Saint*.

—— Cantic spirituel. Histoér admirable à vuhé Santés Barbe. [A version, in the dialect of Vannes, of "Histor eus a vuez Santez Barba."] pp. 8. [1840?] 8°. *See* supra. **11595**. aaa. **10**.

—— Histor eus a vuez Santez Barba; pehini zo mat da veza reclamet oc'h ar gurun hac oc'h ar maro subit. Var un ton ordinal. [In verse.] pp. 16. *Montroulez*, [1820?] 12°. **11595**. b. **104**. (**10**.)

—— [Another edition.] pp. 16. *Montroulez*, [1830?] 12°. **11595**. b. **13**.

—— [Another copy.] **11595**. b. **12**.

—— Incipit prolog⁹ ĩ legendā beatissime virginis Barbare. [fol. 9 *verso*:] Historia siue Legenda beatissime virginis Barbare ac martiris. necnon de passione ⁊ multis eius miraculis. [With a woodcut.] **G.L.** *apud lijskirchen* [*Ulrich Zel*]: *Colonie*, [1490?] 4°. IA. **3093, 94**.
44 leaves, 8 and 44 blank. Sig. A⁸ ; A⁸ B⁸ C⁶ D⁶ E⁸. *32 lines to the page in the Prologus, 36 lines in the Historia.*

—— [Another copy.] IA. **3095**.
Containing the Historia only.

—— Informatio ex sacra scriptura de genealogia: siue origine btĩssime v̇ginis . . . Barbare. cū prosecutione legēde ⁊ miraculorū. [fol. 2 *verso*:] Sermo septē ꝯclusionū fratris Iohānis capet, *etc.* **G.L.** [*Ulrich Zel*: *Cologne*, 1490?] 4°. IA. **3096**.
6 leaves, the last blank. Without signatures. 33 lines to a page.

—— [Another edition.] *Begin.* [H]anc informationē de genealogia beatissime virginis Xp̄i spōse Barbare cū vno sermōe theologali fecit imprimere . . . Raymūdus . . . cardinalis Burceñ . . . vt distribuat gratis diuersis psonis ⁊ ecclesiis quibus dedit reliquias, *etc.* **G.L.** [*J. Schoeffer*:] *Magūtie*, 1503. 4°. C. **53**. c. **7**.

—— Liedeken van de Heylige Maegd en Maertelaeresse Barbara, *etc.* [With other verses.] *Gent*, [1840?] *s. sh.* fol. **1871**. c. **1**. (**5**.)
No. 5 of a series of broadsides.

—— Here begynneth the Lyfe of the gloryous Vyrgyn & Marter Saynt Barbara. [With a woodcut.] **B.L.** *Julyan Notary*: *London*, 1518. 4°. **296**. h. **7**. (**1**.)

—— *Μαρτυριον της ἁγιας μεγαλομαρτυρος του Χριστου Βαρβαρας.* (Passio Sanctæ et magnæ martyris Christi Barbaræ.) *See* VITEAU (J.) Passions des saints Écaterine et Pierre d'Alexandrie, *etc.* 1897. 8°. **4829**. f. **24**.

—— Oracion y Gozos de Santa Bárbara. [In verse.] *Madrid*, 1856. 4°. **11450**. f. **24**. (**19**.)

—— Romance de la gran Importancia de la Devocion de Santa Barbara Virgen, y Martir, *etc.* [In verse.] [*Valencia*, 1760?] 4°. T. **1956**. (**32**.)

—— Sent barbaren passi. [In verse.] *Gedruckt vp Marcellen straissen* [*S. Kruffter*: *Cologne*, 1520?] 4°. **11517**. dd. **21**. (**1**.)

—— *Στιχοι ἀδηλοι περι της ἁγιας Βαρβαρας.* Carmen gr. iambographi in diuam Barbaram . . . Fed. Morellus . . . græcos trimetros è Bibliotheca Regia eruit, recensuit, & senariis latinis expressit. His accesserunt M. Ant. Mureti hymni, & Senatoris Tolosani epigr. in eandem diuam, cum græca eiusdem F. Morelli metaphrasi. pp. 24. *Apud F. Morellum*: *Parisiis*, 1614. 8°. **844**. g. **8**.

—— [Another copy.] G. **8227**. (**10**.)

BARBARA, *Saint*.

—— Die syrische Barbara-Legende. Mit einem Anhang: Die syrische Kosmas- und Damian-Legende in deutscher Uebersetzung. Von Wilhelm Weyh . . . Programm des K. Humanistischen Gymnasiums Schweinfurt für das Schuljahr 1911/12. pp. 52. *Schweinfurt*, [1912.] 8°. **11856**. c. **41**.

—— Translatio et Miracula sanctae Barbarae. (Qualiter caput beate Barbare processu temporis in Pomeraniam pervenit.) 1863. *See* HIRSCH (T.) Scriptores rerum Prussicarum, *etc.* Bd. 2. 1861, *etc.* 4°. **9385**. i. **4**.

—— La uie de Madame saincte Barbe par personnages. **G.L.** [*O. Arnoullet*: *Lyons*, 1542.] 8°. **241**. b. **42**.
Imperfect; wanting the titlepage and all after sig. I 5, *which are supplied in* MS., *and sig.* C2.

—— Жизнь и страданія святой . . . Варвары. Изданіе одинадцатое. pp. 72. *Москва*, 1884. 12°. **4823**. cc. **17**. (**2**.)

—— *Confraternity of, at Florence.* La Confrérie de Sainte-Barbe des Flamands à Florence. Documents relatifs aux tisserands et aux tapissiers. Par Mario Battistini. pp. 215. pl. III. 1931. 8°. *See* BELGIUM.—*Commission Royale d'Histoire.* Ac. **987/11**.

—— *Priory of, in Auge.* Anonymi vera narratio fundationis Prioratûs Sanctæ Barbaræ in Algia. 1806. *See* BOUQUET (M.) Recueil des historiens des Gaules, *etc.* tom. 14. 1738, *etc.* fol. **Circ.8–9.b.**

BARBARA, *Sister, a Polish Carmelite Nun.* The Horrors of Roman Catholic Convents, exposed in a true heart-rending account of the shocking imprisonment and sufferings of Sister Barbara, a Polish Carmelite nun, *etc.* pp. 16. [1872.] 8°. **4061**. f. **10**.

BÁRBARA JOSEFA [LÓPEZ RIVA DE NEYRA], *de San Francisco.* *See* TORRES (Miguel de) Vida exemplar . . . de la Madre Bárbara Josefa de San Francisco, religiosa . . . del convento de la Santissima Trinidad de la Puebla de los Angeles. 1725. 4°. **4986**. cc. **88**.

BARBARA SOPHIA, *Consort of John Frederick, Duke of Wurtemberg.* *See* OETTINGER (J.) Warhaffte historische Beschreibung der . . . Hochzeit . . . so . . . Johann Friderich Hertzog zu Würtemberg und Teck . . . mit . . . Barbara Sophia Marggrävin zu Brandenburg . . . celebriert und gehalten hat, *etc.* 1610. fol. **9930**. gg. **42**.

BARBARA (CHARLES) Ary Zang. [A novel.] pp. 324. *Paris*, 1864. 12°. **12513**. dd. **3**.

—— L'Assassinat du Pont-Rouge. pp. 364. *Paris*, 1859. 12°. **12206**. g. **6**. (**1**.)

—— Histoires émouvantes. pp. 349. *Paris*, 1856. 12°. **12513**. e. **8**.

—— Mes petites-maisons. pp. 319. *Paris*, 1860. 8°. **12206**. g. **8**. (**2**.)

—— Les Orages de la vie. sér. 1. pp. 293. ii. *Paris*, 1860. 8°. **12206**. g. **3**. (**2**.)

BARBARÁ (FEDERICO)

—— Manual o vocabulario de la lengua pampa. [With plates including a portrait.] pp. 174. *Buenos Aires*, 1944. 8°. **12912**. ee. **75**.
Colección Buen aire. Leyenda y folklore. no. 55.

—— Usos y Costumbres de los Indios Pampas y algunos apuntos históricos sobre la guerra de la frontera. pp. 98. *Buenos Ayres*, 1856. 8°. **10481**. bb. **33**.

BARBARA (GIOSAFAT) *See* BARBARO.

BARBARA (Mario) Inno a la miseria. *See* Spezia.—*Comitato dei Concorsi Poetici.* Il Risorgimento. Poesie, *etc.* 1878. 8°. **11436**. e. **16**.

BARBARAN ( ) Cronicha che comenza dell' anno 1400. (Nozze Dalle Mole-Farina.) [Edited by D. Bortolan.] pp. 26. *Vicenza*, [1889.] 8°. **09009**. c. **16**. (**2**.)

BARBARAN (Domenico) Illustrazione di quattro codici della Divina Comedia esistenti nel Seminario Vescovile di Padova.
In: Dante e Padova, *etc.*, 1865. 8°.
pp. 391-406. **11421**. g. **16**.

BARBARANI (Berto)

—— Tutte le poesie a cura di Giuseppe Silvestri, *etc.* [With plates, including a portrait.] pp. xxx. 662. [*Milan*,] 1953. 8°. **11436**. s. **12**.
Part of the series "I Classici contemporanei italiani."

BARBARANI (Emilio) Poesie . . . Seconda edizione, con aggiunte. pp. 96. *Verona*, 1903. 8°. **11427**. cc. **30**.

BARBARANO (Christoforo) *See* Horologgi (F.) Manifesto del signor . . . Horologgi nella querela, che ha col cavalliero C. Barbarano, *etc.* [1566.] 4°. **592**. b. **5**. (**2**.)

BARBARANO (Francesco) Historia ecclesiastica della città, territorio, e diocese di Vicenza. Raccolta dal M. R. P. F. Barbarano de' Mironi da Vicenza, *etc.* (Libro primo.) [With a folding plate.] pp. 295. *C. Rosio: Vicenza*, 1649. 4°. **491**. d. **21**. (**1**.)
With an additional titlepage, engraved.

BARBARANUS (Julius) Officinæ Iulii Barbarani tomi tres: promptuarium rerum electarum, in re præsertim Romana, *etc.* 3 pt. *Apud I. A. Valuassorem: Venetiis*, 1569. 4°. **590**. d. **1**.

BARBARASA (Hercole) *See* Marlianus (J. B.) Le Antichita di Roma . . . tradotte in lingua volgare da H. Barbarasa. 1622. 12°. **575**. a. **4**.

BARBARE (John) *See* Barbour.

BARBARELLI (Giorgio) called Giorgione. *See* Giorgione, *da Castelfranco.*

BARBARESI (Pasquale) *See* Bible.—*Job.* [*Italian.*] Il Libro di Giobbe. Versione poetica del sacerdote professore P. Barbaresi. 1894. 12°. **3049**. aaa. **6**.

BARBARESOS (Kuriakos Ch.)

—— *See* Kalitsounakis (D. E.) *Ἀπαντησις εἰς την εἰσηγητικην ἐκθεσιν του καθηγητου Κ. Βαρβαρεσου δια την δευτεραν τακτικην ἑδραν της πολιτικης οἰκονομιας προς την Νομικην Σχολην του ἐν Ἀθηναις Πανεπιστημιου.* 1931. 8°. **8204**. ccc. **13**.

—— Études dédiées à la mémoire d'André M. Andréadès publiées par un comité d'amis et d'élèves sous la présidence de K. Varvaressos. pp. viii. 449. *Athènes*, 1940. 8°. **8204**. dd. **18**.

BARBARESSOS (Kuriakos) *See* Barbaresos (Kuriakos Ch.)

BARBARI (Giuseppe Antonio) L'Iride, opera fisico-matematica . . . nella quale si espone la natura dell' arco celeste e si commenta il testo oscurissimo d'Aristotele de figura iridis nel terzo delle Meteore. [With plates.] pp. xxxii. 108. FEW MS. NOTES AND CORRECTIONS. *Per li Manolessi: Bologna*, 1678. 4°. **538**. e. **27**. (**10**.)

BARBARI (Jacopo de) *See* Borenius (T.) Four Early Italian Engravers. Antonio del Pollaiuolo . . . J. de' Barbari, *etc.* [With illustrations.] 1923. 4°. W.P. **6761/1**.

BARBARI (Jacopo de)

—— *See* Canditto (A. E. de) *Count.* Jacob de Barbari et A. Durer, *etc.* 1881. 8°. **10629**. bbb. **12**.

—— *See* Ephrussi (C.) Notes biographiques sur J. de Barbarj . . . Avec sept gravures, *etc.* 1876. 4°. **1763**. a. **3**.

—— *See* Hevesy (A. de) Jacopo de Barbari, *etc.* [With plates.] 1925. 4°. **7859**. s. **12**.

BARBARIAN. Hunting Vindicated from Cruelty, in a letter to the Monthly Reviewers. [Signed: A Barbarian.] pp. 30. *Printed for the benefit, if any, of the Whippers-in: Spitzbergen; sold by B. Laco: London*, 1782. 8°. **7906**. e. **31**. (**2**.)

BARBARICH (Eugenio) Albania. Monografia antropogeografica. Con 10 illustrazioni e 13 tavole fuori testo. pp. xx. 344. *Roma*, 1905. 8°. **10127**. e. **1**.

—— La Campagna del 1796 nel Veneto. Parte prima. La decadenza militare della Serenissima.—Uomini ed armi. pp. xi. 192. *Roma*, 1910. 8°. **9168**. b. **13**.
No more published.

—— Memorie storiche sull' assedio di Osoppo, 24 marzo—13 ottobre 1848, *etc.* pp. 160. *Udine*, 1902. 8°. **9165**. c. **43**.

BARBARIE. *See* Barbary.

BARBARIGO, *Family of.*

—— Insigne pinacoteca della nobile veneta famiglia Barbarigo dalla Terrazza. Descritta ed illustrata da Gian Carlo Bevilacqua. (Pinacothèque insigne, *etc.*) *Ital. & Fr.* pp. xv. 87. *Venezia*, 1845. 4°. **1266**. i. **8**.

BARBARIGO ( )

—— Per nozze Pelà-Zannini. (Un Fiore poetico [entitled: "P. Candiano iii. liberatore delle spose veneziane rapite dai Triestini"] colto nel giardino del Barbarigo dalla mano dell' illustre . . . Domenico prof. Roverini . . . nelle nozze auspicatissime del caro nipote dott. Luigi colla . . . signora C. Zannini, *etc.*) pp. 8. *Padova*, 1870. 8°. **11436**. f. **65**. (**7**.)

BARBARIGO (Andrea)

—— *See* Lane (Frederic C.) Andrea Barbarigo, Merchant of Venice, *etc.* 1944. 8°. [*Johns Hopkins University Studies in Historical and Political Science.* ser. 62. no. 1.] Ac. **2689**.

BARBARIGO (Giovanni Francesco) *Cardinal.* *See* Franzoni (S.) In funere eminentissimi & reverendissimi Joannis Francisci Cardinalis Barbadici . . . oratio, *etc.* 1730. 8°. T. **2273**. (**5**.)

—— Numismata virorum illustrium ex Barbadica gente. [Descriptions, with engravings. Numismata 1–80 edited by J. X. Valcavius, Numismata 81–85 described by A. A. Fabro.] *Patavii*, 1732 [1760]. fol. **1701**. d. **3**.
Though the work bears the date 1732, it was not published until 1760, when the last five Numismata were added.

—— [Another copy of Numismata 1–80.] **136**. g. **19**.

BARBARIGO (Giustiniano) Kurtzer vnpartheyischer, doch wolgegründter Discurs vnd Bedencken H. Justiniani Barbarique . . . von jetztschwebenden Kriegswesen vnd Feldtzug der Herrschafft Venedig gegen Herrn Ferdinanten, König in Böhmen . . . Auss dem Italianischen in die Latein, und entlich ins Teutsch vbersetzt. pp. 26. 1617. 4°. **8073**. b. **11**.

BARBARIGO (Gregorio) *Cardinal.* *See* Chilesotti (V.) Oratio de corde B. Gregorii Barbadici in ecclesia Seminarii Patavini nunc primum solemniter collocato, *etc.* 1812. 8°. **4867**. df. **13**. (**3**.)

BARBARIGO (GREGORIO) *Cardinal.*

—— *See* CHILESOTTI (V.) Il Cuore del B. Gregorio Barbarigo per la prima volta solennemente esposto nella chiesa del Seminario di Padova. Orazione, *etc.* 1812. 8°. **4867.** df. **13.** (**2.**)

—— *See* FERRARI (G. B.) *Prefect of the Seminary at Padua.* Vitae virorum illustrium Seminarii Patavini. Cum opusculo de singulari B. G. Barbadici studio et amore in idem Seminarium, *etc.* 1815. 8°. **1455.** g. **3.**

—— *See* MOTI (P. A.) Magnus sacer Apollo . . . Gregorius . . . cardinalis Barbadicus, *etc.* 1688. fol. **837.** m. **1.** (**27.**)

—— *See* PADUA.—*Accademia de' Ricovrati.* Componimenti dell' Accademia . . . per la traslazione del corpo . . . di . . . Gregorio card. Barbarigi, *etc.* 1726. 4°. **82.** g. **8.**

—— *See* RICCHINI (T. A.) De vita et rebus gestis beati G. Barbadici, *etc.* 1761. 4°. **4827.** g. **29.**

—— *See* RICCHINI (T. A.) Vita del beato G. Barbarigo, *etc.* 1761. 8°. **1223.** c. **10.**

—— *See* ROME, *Church of.—Congregatio Rituum.* Acta canonizationis sanctorum J. Cantii, J. Calasanctii . . . Quibus accedunt acta beatificationis . . . G. Barbadici, *etc.* 1769. fol. **5017.** g. **3.**

—— Scritti inediti del beato Gregorio Barbarigo . . . Si aggiunge il trattato inedito De corpore Christi di Gregorio vescovo di Bergamo primo di questo nome . . . Con prefazioni e note del sacerdote Bergamasco Pietro Antonio Uccelli. pp. xlvi. 752. *Parma,* 1877. 8°. **3676.** cc. **3.**

—— Greg. S. R. E. card. Barbadici Epistolae ad Ant. Magliabechium. 1746. *See* TARGIONI TOZZETTI (G.) Clarorum Venetorum ad Ant. Magliabechium . . . epistolae, *etc.* tom. 2. 1745, *etc.* 8°. **1082.** f. **4.**

—— Voti degli eminentissimi signori cardinali di S. R. C. B. Gregorio Barbarigo, Gieronimo Casanate, e Decio Azzolini. Nella causa della beatificazione del . . . cardinale Roberto Bellarmino. *Lat. & Ital.* pp. 64. *Ferrara,* 1761. 8°. **4827.** de. **46.**

—— Seconda edizione . . . corretta, nella quale si è aggiunto la Vita del Bellarmino scritta da lui medesimo, *etc.* (Supplemento ai voti . . . ove si esamina la relazione stampata in Roma concernente la suddetta causa, *etc.*) 4 pt. *Ferrara, Venezia,* 1762, 63. 8°. **1232.** b. **10.** (**1, 2.**)

—— Ragguaglio della vita, virtù, e miracoli del B. Gregorio Barbarigo . . . cavato da' processi esibiti alla S. Cong. de' Rite, *etc.* [With a portrait.] pp. 174. *Roma,* 1761. 4°. **1232.** e. **8.**

BARBARIGO (GREGORIO) *Venetian Ambassador to the Court of Charles Emmanuel I., Duke of Savoy.* Relazione di Savoja di Gregorio Barbarigo ambasciatore . . . a Carlo Emmanuele I dall' anno 1608 al 1611. 1862. *See* VENICE.- Senato. Relazioni degli stati Europei, *etc.* ser. 3. vol. 1. 1856, *etc.* 8°. **9073.** e.

BARBARIGO (NICCOLÒ) *See* PONA (F.) Apotheosis viventium amicorum heroum N. Barbadici, M. Trivisani. 1629. 8°. **1199.** b. **16.**

—— *See* SCAGLIA (G.) Breve racconto dell' amicitia, mostruosa nella perfettione, trà N. Barbarigo & M. Trivisano, *etc.* 1627. 4°. **525.** e. **50.**

—— Andreæ Gritti principis Venetiarum vita. [Edited by Jacopo Morelli.] pp. 15. lv. *Venetiis,* 1792. 4°. **609.** l. **15.**

BARBARIGO (NICCOLÒ)

—— [Another edition.] *Lat. & Ital. See* MOLIN (G. A.) Orazioni, elogi e vite, *etc.* tom. 1. 1795, *etc.* 4°. **1200.** cc. **5.**

—— L'Heroica, & incomparabile amicitia de gl'illustriss. Signori Nicolò Barbarigo, e Marco Triuisano . . . Celebrata con diuerse maniere di poesie, & altre compositioni volgari, e Latine da molti eccellenti ingegni del nostro secolo. Accresciuta di molte altre in questa seconda impressione. pp. 246. *M. Ginammi: Venetia,* 1628. 12°. **11427.** de. **30.**

BARBARIN ( ) A Brief Notice of the Winds on the Coast of Madagascar. *Fr. & Eng. See* LISLET GEOFFROY (J. B.) Memoir and Notice explanatory of a Chart of Madagascar, *etc.* 1819. 4°. **982.** h. **21.**

BARBARIN (ANTONIE) *Cardinal. See* BARBERINI (Antonio)

BARBARIN (C.) *See* BARBARIN (Georges)

BARBARIN (ÉMILE) Contribution à l'étude des fractures chez les enfants. pp. 59. *Paris,* 1873. 4°. [*Collection des thèses soutenues à la Faculté de Médecine de Paris.* An 1873. tom. 1.] **7373.** o.

BARBARIN (EUGENIO GARCÍA Y) *See* GARCÍA Y BARBARIN.

BARBARIN (FRANÇOIS) De l'abstinence considerée dans l'état de santé et de maladie. Dissertation, *etc.* pp. 26. *Paris,* 1815. 4°. **1183.** c. **8.** (**26.**)

BARBARIN (GABRIEL CHARLES) Dissertation sur la névralgie faciale, *etc.* pp. 30. *Paris,* 1817. 4°. **1183.** d. **7.** (**15.**)

BARBARIN (GEORGES)

—— La Danse sur le Volcan. Atlantide, Lémurie, les continents futurs. pp. 195. *Paris,* 1938. 8°. **07703.** a. **2.**

—— L'Invisible et moi. Introduction pratique à la vie secrète. pp. 191. *Paris,* 1938. 8°. **08632.** de. **105.**

—— Jesusa de Guipuzcoa. Roman. Illustrations de Delaris. pp. 56. *Paris,* 1936. fol. [*La Petite Illustration.* Roman. no. 371, 372.] P.P. **4283.** m. (**1.**)

—— Jesusa de Guipuzcoa. (Roman.) pp. iv. 228. *Paris,* 1936. 8°. **12512.** t. **38.**

—— Qu'est-ce que la radiesthésie ? *etc.* pp. 305. *Paris,* 1937. 8°. **7462.** p. **30.**

—— Le Règne de la bête. L'autorité contre l'individu. pp. 155. *Paris,* 1939. 8°. **08004.** de. **12.**

—— Saturnin Corbeau. Roman inédit. 1932. *See* PERIODICAL PUBLICATIONS.—*Paris.* Les Œuvres libres, *etc.* no. 133. 1921, *etc.* 8°. **12208.** ee. **133.**

—— Le Secret de la Grande Pyramide ou la fin du monde adamique. [With plates.] pp. vi. 121. *Paris,* 1936. 8°. **07704.** de. **81.**

—— La Sorcière. Roman, *etc.* 1939. *See* PERIODICAL PUBLICATIONS.—*Paris.* Les Œuvres libres, *etc.* no. 211. 1921, *etc.* 8°. **12208.** ee. **211.**

—— La Vie agitée des eaux dormantes. pp. 188. *Paris,* 1938. 8°. **07290.** de. **44.**

BARBARIN (J.)

—— Catalogue prix-courant de timbres rares . . . 1889-1890 (octobre 1890). 2 pt. *Paris,* [1889, 90.] 8°. Crawford **96.** (**1. 2.**)

BARBARIN (J.)

—— Nouveau catalogue complet de timbres-poste. pp. viii. 421. *Paris*, [1891.] 8°. **08247**. h. **4**.

—— [Another issue.] Nouveau catalogue complet de timbres-poste, *etc*. *Paris*, [1891.] 8°. Crawford **96**. (3.)

—— Nouveau catalogue général de timbres-poste, illustré de 3,000 gravures, *etc*. pp. 333. *Paris*, 1894. 8°. **08247**. ee. **3**.

—— [Another copy.] Nouveau catalogue général de timbres poste, *etc*. *Paris*, 1894. 8°. Crawford **97**.

—— 2me édition. pp. 351. *Paris*, 1895. 8°. **08247**. eee. **8**.

—— [Another copy.] Nouveau catalogue général de timbres-poste . . . 2me édition, *etc*. *Paris*, 1895. 8°. Crawford **98**.

—— Nouveau catalogue général de timbres-poste . . . 3me édition, complètement refondue, *etc*. pp. 367. *Paris*, 1896. 8°. Crawford **99**.

—— Prix-courant des timbres par paquets et par séries, et des albums pour timbres-poste en vente à la libraire J. Barbarin, *etc*. pp. 12. *Paris*, [1892.] 8°. Crawford **100**.

BARBARIN (Louis Léon) Des principaux aliments et des effets de l'alimentation sur l'économie. pp. 29. *Paris*, 1844. 4°. [*Collection des thèses soutenues à la Faculté de Médecine de Paris*. An 1844. tom. 1.] **7371**. e. **6**.

BARBARIN (Paul) Manuel de chirurgie de guerre à l'usage des infirmières . . . Avec 124 figures dans le texte. pp. 405. *Paris*, 1916. 8°. **07481**. f. **32**.

BARBARIN (Paul Jean Joseph) Études de géométrie analytique non euclidienne. pp. 167. *Bruxelles*, 1901. 8°. [*Mémoires couronnés par l'Académie Royale de Belgique*. Collection in-8°. tom. 60.] Ac. **985/4**.

—— Pour le centenaire de la géométrie non euclidienne. [With portraits.] pp. 40. *Buenos Aires*, 1931. fol. **8532**. dd. **32**.

BARBARIN DURIVAUD (Paul) Considérations générales sur les phénomènes physiologiques et pathologiques de la femme à la première époque de la menstruation; thèse, *etc*. pp. 19. *Paris*, 1829. 4°. **1184**. c. **16**. (**13**.)

BARBARINI (Antonio di) *Cardinal*. *See* Barberini (A.) Cardinal.

BARBARINI (Berto) Canzoniere veronese. Con ritratto . . . ed illustrazioni, *etc*. pp. 207. *Milano*, 1902. 8°. **11427**. cc. **26**.

BARBARINIE, *in Holland residirender türkischer Agent*. *See* Raphael, *Constantinopolitanischer Hof-Banquier*. Die türkische Correspondenz, oder der . . . Ducaten-Handel, zwischen dem . . . Hof-Banquier Raphael, und dem in Holland residirenden türkischen Agent Barbarinie. [1780?] 8°. **8228**. aaaa. **26**.

BARBARIQUE (Justinianus) *See* Barbarigo (Giustiniano)

BARBARITO (Saverio)

—— [For official documents issued by S. Barbarito as president of the state of Apure:] *See* Apure, *State of*.—Barbarito (S.) President.

BARBARO (Almorò) *Patriarch of Aquileia*. *See* Barbaro (Ermolao)

BARBARO (Angelo Maria) Poesie. *See* Gamba (B.) Collezione della migliore opere scritte in dialetto Veneziano. (Poeti moderni. vol. 11.) 1817. 8°. **11431**. a. **23**.

BARBARO (Antonio) Versi sciolti in dialogo bilingue . . . sopra la celebre fabbrica della nuova Chiesa della Pietà, *etc*. [By A. Barbaro.] pp. 31. 1760. 8°. *See* Venice.—*Chiesa della Pietà*. **11421**. b. **17**.

—— Vita di San Francesco di Paola . . . Poema sacro. pp. 301. *Venezia*, 1747. 4°. **4827**. dd. **11**.

BARBARO (Carlo Antonio) *Marquis*. Degli avanzi d'alcuni antichissimi edifizi scoperti in Malta l'anno 1768. Dissertazione storico-critica del Signor Marchese D. C. A. Barbaro, arricchita con copiose annotazioni del medesimo autore e preceduta dal suo elogio funebre [by Count R. Barbaro]. pp. xx. 77. *Malta*, 1794. 4°. **7707**. ee. **27**.

—— [Another copy.] **7706**. ee. **3**.

BARBARO (Cecilia) Componimento oratorio nell' occasione che celebra la sua solenne professione nel . . . monastero de' SS. Cosmo, e Damiano . . . Cecilia Barbaro, che prese il nome di Maria Giovanna. [The dedicatory epistle signed: A. B.] 1788. 8°. *See* B., A. **4867**. aaaa. **21**.

BARBARO (Daniello) *Patriarch of Aquileia*. *See* also Schio (Hypneo da) *pseud*. [i.e. D. Barbaro.]

—— *See* Aristotle. [*Ethica Nicomachea.—Summaries, etc.—Latin*.] Compendium Ethicorum librorum Hermolai Barbari. [Edited by D. Barbaro.] 1544. 8°. **520**. a. **16**. (**2**.)

—— —— 1546. 8°. **520**. a. **17**. (**2**.)

—— *See* Aristotle. [*Rhetorica.—Latin*.] Rhetoricorum Aristotelis libri tres . . . Commentaria in eosdem D. Barbari. 1544. 4°. C.77.d.18.

—— *See* Baldi (B.) Scamilli impares Vitruuiani . . . refutatis priorum interpretum G. Philandri, D. Barbari . . . sententijs. 1612. 4°. **530**. f. **3**. (**2**.)

—— —— 1739. 4°. [Poleni (G.) *Exercitationes Vitruvianae*.] **1261**. c. **20**.

—— —— 1825. 4°. [*M. Vitruvii Pollionis Architectura, etc*. vol. 1.] **560**. d. **2**.

—— *See* Barbaro (E.) *Patriarch of Aquileia*. Hermolai Barbari . . . Compendium scientiæ naturalis ex Aristotele. [Edited by D. Barbaro.] 1545. 8°. **520**. a. **16**. (**1**.)

—— —— 1547. 8°. **520**. a. **17**. (**1**.)

—— *See* Speroni degli Alvarotti (S.) I Dialogi di Messer Speron Sperone. [Edited by D. Barbaro.] 1542. 8°. **714**. a. **16**.

—— —— 1543. 8°. **721**. c. **4**.

—— *See* Vitruvius Pollio (M.) M. Vitruvii Pollionis De architectura libri decem, cum commentariis D. Barbari. 1567. fol. C.79.c.14.

—— *See* Vitruvius Pollio (M.) I dieci libri dell' Architettura di M. Vitruvio, tradutti e commentati da monsignor Barbaro, *etc*. 1556. fol. **59**. f. **23**.

—— —— 1567. 4°. **559**. e. **4**.

—— —— 1584. 4°. **1401**. k. **1**.

—— —— 1629. 4°. **559**. c. **5**.

—— *See* Vitruvius Pollio (M.) L'Architettura generale ridotta in compendio dal sig. Perrault . . . col commento di monsig. Barbaro, *etc*. 1747. 8°. **7820**. a. **42**.

—— Danielis Barbari Carmen ad Bernardum Naugerium. *See* Morelli (J.) Codices manuscripti latini Bibliothecæ Nanianæ, *etc*. 1776. 4°. **620**. i. **10**. (**1**.)

BARBARO (DANIELLO) *Patriarch of Aquileia.*

—— Della eloquenza, dialogo . . . nuouamente mandato in luce da Girolamo Ruscelli. pp. 93. MS. NOTES. *V. Valgrisio: Venetia,* 1557. 4°. **75.** a. **5.**

—— Exquisitæ in Porphirium commentationes. *Apud Aldi filios: Venetiis,* 1542. 4°. **231.** f. **25.**

—— [Another copy.] G. **17098.**

—— Opinione di Daniele Barbaro sull' introdurre i fiumi nelle lagune. [Being an extract from his commentary on Vitruvius.] *See* SELVA (G. A.) Opuscolo di Gio. Antonio Selva postumo, *etc.* 1819. 8°. T. **2275. (6.)**

—— La Pratica della perspettiva, *etc.* pp. 195. *B. & R. Borgominieri: Venetia,* 1568. fol. **536.** m. **21. (1.)**

—— [A reissue.] MS. NOTES. *Venetia,* 1569. fol. **7805.** f. **26.**

—— [Another copy.] MS. NOTES. **48.** h. **10.**

—— Relazione dell' illustrissimo Daniel Barbaro fatta nel serenissimo Senato dopo la sua legazione d'Inghilterra ove fu Ambasciatore per la Serenissima Republica, in tempo del Re Odoardo VI. nel MDLI. pp. 36. MS. NOTES. *P. Daponte & Vogel: Londra,* [1796.] 4°. **598.** i. **11.**

—— [Another edition.] *See* ALBÈRI (E.) Relazioni dello Impero Britannico nel secolo XVI., *etc.* pt. 1. 1852. 4°. C. **62.** d. **2.**

—— Sonetti . . . nella morte di Trifone Gabriele. *See* MORELLI (J.) I Codici manuscritti volgari della Libreria Naniana, *etc.* 1776. 4°. **620.** i. **10. (2.)**

—— Storia Veneziana . . . dall' anno 1512 al 1515, supplita nella parte che manca colla storia segreta di Luigi Borghi. 1843. *See* ITALIAN HISTORICAL ARCHIVES. Archivio storico italiano, *etc.* tom. 7. 1842, *etc.* 8°. P.P. **3557.** a.

BARBARO (ERMOLAO) successively *Bishop of Treviso and of Verona.*

—— Orationes contra poetas. *See* MUELICH (J. A.) Margarita facetiarum, *etc.* 1508. 4°. **12316.** c. **28.**

—— Hermolai barbari veneti . . . Orationes contra poetas. *See* MUELICH (J. A.) Margarita facetiarum, *etc.* 1509. 4°. **12315.** d. **14.**

BARBARO (ERMOLAO) *Patriarch of Aquileia. See* ARISTOTLE. [*Ethica Nicomachea.—Summaries, etc.—Latin.*] Compendium Ethicorum librorum Hermolai Barbari. 1544. 8°. **520.** a. **16. (2.)**

—— —— 1546. 8°. **520.** a. **17. (2.)**

—— *See* ARISTOTLE. [*Rhetorica.—Greek and Latin.*] Martini Borrhai . . . in tres Aristotelis de arte dicendi libros commentaria. Hermolai Barbari eorundem versio, *etc.* 1551. fol. **520.** k. **2.**

—— *See* ARISTOTLE. [*Rhetorica.—Latin.*] Rhetoricorum Aristotelis libri tres, interprete H. Barbaro, *etc.* 1544. 4°. **C.77.d.18.**

—— —— 1559. 4°. **671.** d. **3. (2.)**

—— *See* ARISTOTLE. [*Summaries and Paraphrases.—Latin.*] *Begin.* [fol. 1 *verso*:] Hermolai Barbari . . . in Paraphrasin Themistii Peripatetici praefatio, *etc. End.* [fol. 167 *recto*:] Finiunt libri Paraphraseos Themistii in posteriora Aristotelis ĩ physica: in libros de anima: in commentarios de memoria . . . de somno . . . de ĩsomniis: de diuinatione per somnum: interprete H. Barbaro, *etc.* 1481. fol. IB. **28407.**

—— —— 1499. fol. IB. **23734.**

—— —— 1500. fol. IB. **23402.**

—— —— 1502. fol. **520.** h. **6. (1.)**

BARBARO (ERMOLAO) *Patriarch of Aquileia.*

—— —— 1520. fol. **519.** i. **19. (1, 2.)**

—— —— 1528. fol. **519.** i. **6.**

—— —— 1530. 8°. **519.** b. **13. (1.)**

—— —— 1549. fol. **520.** h. **8.**

—— —— 1560. fol. **520.** l. **13. (1.)**

—— *See* BEROALDUS (P.) *the Elder.* [*Two or more Works.*] Orationes: Prelectiones Præfationes . . . Item plusculę . . . Hermolai Barbari, *etc.* [1515?] 4°. **1477.** c. **16.**

—— *See* DIOSCORIDES (P.) In hoc uolumine hæc continentur. Ioannis Baptistæ Egnatii . . . in Dioscoridem ab H. Barbaro tralatum annotamenta . . . P. Dioscoridis . . . De medicinali materia ab eodem Barbaro latinitate primum donati libri quinque, *etc.* 1516. fol. **546.** m. **3. (1, 2.)**

—— *See* FERRIGUTO (A.) Almorò Barbaro, l'alta cultura del settentrione d'Italia nel 400, *etc.* 1922. 4°. [*Miscellanea di Storia Veneta.* ser. 3. tom. 15.] **Ac.6580/2.(6.)**

—— *See* GREEK-LATIN LEXICON. Lexicon Græco-Latinum, cui . . . ingens vocabulorum numerus accessit . . . ex . . . lucubrationibus . . . G. Budæi . . . H. Barbari, *etc.* 1530. fol. **623.** m. 5.

—— *See* MELA (P.) Pomponius Mela. [fol. 1 *verso*:] Hermolai Barbari ĩ Pomponium Melam ad Alexandrum Sextum . . . Præfatio. [1495?] 4°. IA. **23536.**

—— *See* MELA (P.) Pomponius Mela De situ orbis, ab H. Barbaro et J. Camerte castigatus, *etc.* [1512.] 4°. **10004.** ccc. **17.**

—— —— [15]20. 8°. **10003.** bbb. **38.**

—— —— 1582. 4°. **569.** d. 6.

—— *See* PEROTTUS (N.) *Archbishop of Siponto.* Cornucopie nup Emendatum . . . Vna cuȝ aliquibus additionibus Magnifici dñi Hermolai Barbari, *etc.* 1508. fol. Voyn. **132.**

—— *See* PLAUTUS (T. M.) [*Works.—Latin.*] Plautus cum correctione ⁊ interpretatione Hermolai Merulae Politiani ⁊ Beroaldi, *etc.* [1500?] fol. I.B. **26760.**

—— *See* PLINIUS SECUNDUS (C.) [*Latin.*] C. Plinii Secundi Naturae Historiarum libri XXXVII. E castigationibus Hermolai Barbari quam emendatissime editi. 1497. fol. IC. **22396.**

—— —— 1499. fol. IB. **24690.**

—— —— 1511. fol. **456.** b. **1.**

—— —— 1518. fol. **443.** k. **1.**

—— —— 1525. fol. **456.** c. **13.**

—— —— 1536. 8°. **975.** b. **23.**

—— *See* PORRETANUS (G.) *Bishop of Poitiers.* Gilb. Porretani de sex principiis liber, Hermolao Barbaro interprete. 1564. 8°. **520.** a. **19.**

—— [Three prefaces, with the speech "ad Federicum imperatorem."] *See* BEROALDUS (P.) *the Elder.* Orationes, prelectiones, præfationes, *etc.* 1508. 4°. **12301.** e. **39.**

—— [Another edition.] *See* BEROALDUS (P.) *the Elder.* Spectatissime pbitatis . . . autoris P. Beroaldi . . . orationes, *etc.* 1509. 4°. **1073.** l. **4.**

BARBARO (ERMOLAO) *Patriarch of Aquileia.*

—— [Another edition.] *See* BEROALDUS (P.) *the Elder.* Orationes, prelectiones, præfationes, *etc.* 1511. 4°. **1073.** l. **1.**

—— [Another edition.] *See* BEROALDUS (P.) *the Elder.* Varia Philippi Beroaldi opuscula, *etc.* 1513. 4°. **1334.** f. **8.**

—— [Another edition.] *See* BEROALDUS (P.) *the Elder.* Varia Philippi Beroaldi opuscula, *etc.* 1515. 4°. **1073.** l. **6.**

—— Epistolae, orationes et carmina. Edizione critica a cura di Vittore Branca. 2 vol. *Firenze,* 1943. 8°. [*Nuova collezione di testi umanistici inediti o rari.* vol. 5, 6.] Ac. **47/3.**
The date in the colophon in both volumes is 1942.

—— Epistole. [Translated by L. Dolce.] *See* PLINIUS CAECILIUS SECUNDUS (C.) [*Epistolae.—Italian.*] Epistole, *etc.* 1548. 8°. **10905.** b. **24.**

—— *Begin.* [fol. 1 *verso*:] Hermolai Barbari Patricii Veneti P. Aquileiensis in Castigationes Plinianas ad Alexandrum sextū Pontificem Maximum praefatio. [fol. 3 *recto*:] Castigationes Plinianæ Hermolai Barbari Aquileiensis Pontificis. *End.* [fol. 348 *recto*:] Finiunt: Hermolai Barbari . . . Plinianæ Castigationes: Item Aeditio in Plinium secunda: Item Emendatio in Melam Pomponium: Item Obscuræ cum Expositionibus suis uoces in Pliniano Codice. *Eucharius Argenteus: Romæ,* Octauo Kalēdas Decembris [24 Nov.] 1492, Idibus Feb. [13 Feb.] 1493. fol. IB. **18955.**
348 *leaves. Sig.* a–z^8 aa^8 bb^8 cc^{10} A–I^8 K^6 L^6 a–e^8 f^6 g^8. 39 *and* 48 *lines to a page.*

—— Castigationes Plinij Hermolai Barbari. *End.* [fol. 16 *verso*:] Finiunt Hermolai Barbari Patriarchæ Aquileiensis Plinianæ Castigationes: item Aeditio in Plinium secunda: Item Emendatio in Melam Pomponium: Item Obscuræ cum Expositionibus suis uoces in Pliniano Codice. [*Venice?* 1495?] fol. IB. **25168.**
160 *leaves,* 126 *blank. Sig.* a–k^8 l–r^6 s^4 aa–cc^8 dd^6 ee^4. 60 *lines to a page.*

—— [Another copy.] **167.** c. **20.**
Without the blank leaf.

—— Castigationes Hermolai in Plinium castigatissimæ: quum Vix post Romanas: cæteris tamen adhuc impressis: uel ab opicis quidem non post habendæ, *etc.* *End.* [fol. 160 *recto*:] Habetis humanarum artium cultores cādidissimi: Plinianæ maiestatis ueluti purissimum simulacrum ab Hermolao Barbaro . . . Lucubratum opus: habetis item æditionē in Plinium secundā. Itē emendationem in Melam Pomponiū. Item obscuras cum expositiōibus suis uoces in Pliniano Codice, *etc.* ꝑ *Carolum a Darleriis: Cremonæ,* iii. nonas mēs. Apriles [3 April], 1495. fol. IB. **30843.**
160 *leaves,* 126 *blank. Sig.* a–k^8 l–r^6 s^4 aa–ee^6 ff^4. 58 *lines to a page.*

—— Hermolai Barbari . . . in C. Plinii Naturalis historiæ libros castigationes. Syllabus, siue index omniū quæ in hoc opere tractantur, accuratissimus, *etc.* [Edited by J. Oporinus.] pp. 523. MS. NOTES [by Isaac Casaubon]. *Apud I. Valderum: Basileæ,* 1534. **727.** i. **2.**

—— [Another copy.] C. **48.** f. **2.**

—— Hermolai Barbari . . . Compendium scientiæ naturalis ex Aristotele. [Edited by D. Barbaro.] ff. 75. *C. de Tridino: Venetijs,* 1545. 8°. **520.** a. **16.** (**1.**)
The date in the colophon is 1544.

BARBARO (ERMOLAO) *Patriarch of Aquileia.*

—— [Another edition.] *I. Weinreich: in Academia Regiimontis,* 1547. 8°. **520.** a. **16.** (**3.**)
Imperfect; wanting all before sig. B.

—— [Another edition.] Hermolai Barbari . . . Scientiæ naturalis compendium. Cui adjuncta est Rodolphi Goclenij . . . Physiologia de risu et lacrumis. 2 pt. *P. Egenolphus: Marpurgi,* 1597. 8°. **520.** a. **12.** (**1.**)

—— De officio legati. *See* GRABAR' (V. E.) De legatis et legationibus tractatus varii, *etc.* 1905. 8°. **5207.** f. **23.**

—— Hermolai Barbari ex. G. porretano de sex principiis. *See* ARISTOTLE. [*Works.—Latin.*] *Begin.* [fol. 1 *recto*:] Hoc in uolumine continentur infrascripta opera Aristotelis, *etc.* 1496. fol. IB. **21111.**

—— Hermolai Barbari . . . in Dioscoridem corollarium libris quinque absolutum. *See* DIOSCORIDES (P.) In hoc volumine hæc continentur, *etc.* 1516. fol. **546.** m. **3.** (**1, 2.**)

—— [Another edition.] *See* DIOSCORIDES (P.) P. Dioscoridæ pharmacorum simplicium, reiq; medicæ libri VIII., *etc.* 1529. fol. **546.** l. **7.**

—— [Another edition.] 1530. *See* DIOSCORIDES (P.) *Πεδακιου Διοσκοριδου . . . περι ὑλης ἰατρικης βιβλια Ε′ . . .* Pedacii Dioscoridae . . . De medica materia libri v, *etc.* pt. 2. 1529, *etc.* fol. **449.** i. **4.** (**1, 2.**)

—— In funere Nicolai Marcelli Venetiarum Principis, Hermolai Barbari oratio. *See* ROME, *Church of.—Popes.* Orationes funebres in morte pontificum, *etc.* 1613. 8°. **1090.** k. **5.** (**3.**)

—— [Another edition.] *Lat. & Ital.* *See* MOLIN (G. A.) Orazioni, elogi e vite, *etc.* tom. 1. 1795, *etc.* 4°. **1200.** cc. **5.**

—— *Begin.* [fol. 1 *recto*:] Oratio Hermolai Barbari Zac. F. Legati Veneti ad Federicum Imperatorem: et Maximilianum Regem Romanorum Principes Invictissimos. [*Antonius de Strata: Venice,* 1486?] 4°. IA. **21257.**
8 *leaves. Sig.* a^8. 30 *lines to a page.*

—— Oratio hermolay barbari laureati poete ad federicū et maximilianū principes cū Gratulatiōe Ludouici bruni laureati poete de regis romanoꝝ [Maximilian I.] coronatione. 𝕲.𝕷. [*Peter Wagner: Nuremberg,* 1490?] 4°. IA. **7983.**
14 *leaves. Sig.* A^8 B^6. 33 *lines to a page.*

—— Oratio Hermolai Barbari . . . Legati Veneti ad Federicum imperatorem, *etc.* [Preceded by a selection of the letters of E. Barbaro.] *See* AMBROGINI (A.) *Poliziano.* [*Works.*] Omnia opera, *etc.* 1498. fol. IB. **24472.**

—— [Another edition.] *See* AMBROGINI (A.) *Poliziano.* [*Works.*] Opera, *etc.* 1499. fol. IB. **31268.**

—— [Another edition.] *See* AMBROGINI (A.) *Poliziano.* [*Works.*] Omnium Angeli Politiani operum tomus prior, *etc.* 1512. fol. **631.** l. **14.**

—— [Another edition.] *See* AMBROGINI (A.) *Poliziano.* [*Works.*] Angeli Politiani opera, *etc.* 1553. fol. **631.** l. **15.**

—— [Another edition.] *See* LIPSIUS (J.) Iusti Lipsii Orationes octo, *etc.* 1608. 8°. **1090.** c. **7.** (**1.**)

—— [Another edition.] *See* I., A. F. G. G. Orationes gratulatoriæ, *etc.* 1613. 8°. **1090.** k. **5.** (**1.**)

BARBARO (FRANCESCO) *See* GOTHEIN (P.) Francesco Barbaro. Früh-Humanismus und Staatskunst in Venedig. 1932. 8°. **10633.** w. **13.**

BARBARO (Francesco)

—— See Manelmo (V.) Evangelistæ Manelmi . . . Commentariolum de quibusdam gestis in bello Gallico ill. v. F. Barbari præfecti præsidii Brixiæ, *etc.* 1728. 4°. **592.** e. **21.** (**1.**)

—— See Montanari (G. I.) Biografia di Francesco Barbaro. [1840?] 8°. **10630.** d. **45.** (**3.**)

—— See Plutarch. [*Vitae Parallelae.—Latin.*] *Begin.* [vol. 1. fol. 1 *recto*:] [C]Ampanus Francisco Piccolominio Cardinali Senensi meo Salutem. Collegi nuper dispersas grecorum latinorūq͂ principū uitas a Plutarcho scriptas grece, *etc.* (Cato senior per Franciscum Barbarum.) [The translation of the life of Aristides here attributed to L. Aretinus is also by F. Barbaro.] [1470?] fol. C. **1.** d. **1.**

—— —— [1472?] fol. C. **5.** d. **9.**

—— —— 1478. fol. C. **1.** d. **3.**

—— —— 1496. fol. IB. **23719.**

—— —— 1502. fol. **10607.** k. **2.**

—— —— 1552. 12°. **609.** a. **1–3.**

—— —— 1558. fol. **609.** m. **1.**

—— Diatriba præliminaris [by Cardinal A. M. Quirini] in duas partes divisa ad F. Barbari et aliorum ad ipsum epistolas ab anno Chr. mccccxxv ad an. mccccliii. nunc primum editas ex duplici ms. cod. Brixiano, & Vaticano uno. Has omnes alterum volumen complectetur. Quin ad ejus calcem aderit ampla earundem Mantissa ex Forojuliensibus Biblioth. Guarnerianæ mss. 2 vol. *Brixiæ*, 1741–43. 4°. **635.** m. **11.**

—— Centotrenta lettere inedita di Francesco Barbaro, precedute dall' ordinamento critico cronologico dell' intero suo epistolario, seguite da appendici di R. Sabbadini. pp. 146. *Salerno*, 1884. 8°. **10909.** h. **7.**

—— Francisci Barbari . . . De re vxoria libelli duo. [With two letters by Poggio Bracciolini and P. Vergerius. Edited by A. Tiraquellus.] ff. 33. few ms. notes. *Ex chalcographia Ascensiana*: [*Paris*,] 1513. 4°. **525.** f. **2.**

—— [Another copy.] G. **16539.**

—— [Another edition.] *Ex officio Seceriana*: *Haganoæ*, 1533. 8°. T. **1929.** (**5.**)

—— [Another copy.] **232.** a. **38.**

—— [Another edition.] *Apud M. Cæsarem*: *Antuerpiæ*, [1535?] 8°. **527.** f. **6.** (**1.**)

—— Francisci Barbari . . . De re uxoria libri duo ante annos septuaginta octo in imperiali Haganoa editi, nunc in lucem reproducti a Joachimo Cluten, *etc.* *Typis J. Caroli*: *Argentorati*, 1612. 12°. **1127.** a. **14.**

—— [Another edition.] pp. 178. *Typis J. Janssonii*: *Amstelodami*, 1639. 12°. **1110.** a. **12.** (**2.**)

—— Directions for Love and Marriage . . . Now translated into English by a Person of Quality. pp. 128. *John Leigh and Tho. Burrell*: *London*, 1677. 16°. **08416.** f. **47.**

—— Les deux livres de l'estat du mariage . . . Traduction nouuelle. Avec quelques traités chrestiens & moraux touchant les offices domestiques, *etc.* [The translation by C. Joly.] pp. 350. *G. de Luyne*: *Paris*, 1667. 8°. **8416.** a. **18.**

—— Prudentissimi, et gravi documenti circa la elettion della moglie . . . nouamente dal Latino tradotti per M. Alberto Lollio. ff. 62. *G. Giolito*: *Vinegia*, 1548. 8°. **231.** a. **29.**

BARBARO (Francesco)

—— See Gnesotto (A.) I Codici Marciani del De re uxoria di F. Barbaro. 1914. 8°. **011903.** cc. **31.**

—— Orazione di Francesco Barbaro . . . a Sigismondo imperatore detta in Ferrara l'anno mccccxxxiii. Ora per la prima volta dalla lingua Latina recata nell' Italiana [by Emmanuele Cigogna] col testo a fronte. pp. 21. *Venezia*, 1822. 8°. **12301.** e. **19.** (**3.**)

BARBARO (George Crispo) *Marquis.* See Crispo Barbaro.

BARBARO (Giosafat) Lettere al Senato Veneto . . . Tratte da un codice originale dell' I. R. Biblioteca di Vienna e annotate per Enrico Cornet. pp. viii. 128. *Vienna*, 1852. 8°. **10910.** i. **29.** (**1.**)

—— Viaggio del magnifico messer Iosaphat Barbaro ambasciatore della illustrissima republica di Venetia alla Tana.—Viaggio del istesso Messer Iosaphat Barbaro in Persia. See Manuzio (Antonio) Viaggi fatti da Vinetia, *etc.* 1543. 8°. **1051.** c. **1.** (**2.**)

—— [Another edition.] See Manuzio (A.) Viaggi fatti da Vinetia, *etc.* 1545. 8°. **1051.** c. **2.**

—— [Another edition.] See Ramusio (G. B.) Primo [*etc.*] volume . . . delle nauigationi et viaggi, *etc.* vol. 2. 1554, *etc.* fol. **566.** k. **2.**

—— [Another edition.] 1559. See Ramusio (G. B.) Primo [*etc.*] volume . . . delle nauigationi et viaggi, *etc.* vol. 2. 1554, *etc.* fol. **566.** k. **2.**

—— [Another edition.] 1574. See Ramusio (G. B.) Primo [*etc.*] volume . . . delle nauigationi, *etc.* vol. 2. 1563, *etc.* fol. **679.** h. **9.**

—— [Another edition.] 1583. See Ramusio (G. B.) Primo [*etc.*] volume . . . delle nauigationi, *etc.* vol. 2. 1588, *etc.* fol. C. **79.** e. **4.**

—— Travels to Tana and Persia, by Josafa Barbaro and Ambrogio Contarini. Translated from the Italian by William Thomas . . . and by S. A. Roy . . . and edited, with an introduction, by Lord Stanley of Alderley. (A Narrative of Italian Travels in Persia, in the fifteenth and sixteenth centuries. Translated and edited by Charles Gray.) 2 pt. 1873. 8°. See London.—iii. *Hakluyt Society.* Ac. **6172**/**44.**

—— Itinerarium ad Tanaim. [Translated by I. Geuderus ab Heroltzberga.] See Bizari (P.) Rerum Persicarum historia. 1601. fol. C. **75.** g. **7.**

—— Excerpta ex Itinerario J. Barbari quæ Persiam attingunt. See Laet (J. de) of Antwerp. Persia, *etc.* 1633. 16°. **166.** a. **16.**

—— [Another edition.] See Laet (J. de) of Antwerp. Persia, *etc.* 1647. 16°. **568.** a. **34.**

BARBARO (Giuseppe) Fra Girolamo Savonarola e i suoi tempi. pp. 39. *Venezia*, 1882. 8°. **4864.** bbb. **24.**

—— L'Istria considerata negl' interessi della navigazione e del commercio, premessi alcuni cenni storici sulla stessa. pp. 22. *Venezia*, 1871. 8°. **8247.** bb. **40.** (**11.**)

—— Niccolò Tommaseo, ministro per la istruzione pubblica presso il governo provvisorio della repubblica Veneta nell' anno 1848. Cenni biografici sullo stesso . . . Compilazione di G. Barbaro. pp. 48. *Venezia*, 1882. 8°. **10629.** e. **26.** (**1.**)

BARBARO (Josafa) See Barbaro (Giosafat)

BARBARO (Josaphat) See Barbaro (Giosafat)

BARBARO (MARCO ANTONIO) *of Treviso?* *See* HUNGARY, *Palatine of.* Il Palatino d'Ungheria. Novella. [Edited by M. A. Barbaro.] 1824. 4°. [*TOMITANO* (*G. B.*) *Novelle varie.*] **12470**. i. **9**.

BARBARO (MARCO ANTONIO) *Venetian Envoy at Paris.* *See* YRIARTE (C.) La Vie d'un patricien de Venise [i.e. M. A. Barbaro] au seizième siècle, *etc.* 1874. 8°. **9166**. f. **21**.

—— Despatches of Marc' Antonio Barbaro. (Dispacci di M. A. Barbaro.) *See* SURIANO (M.) Despatches of Michele Suriano and Marc' Antonio Barbaro, Venetian ambassadors at the Court of France, 1560–1563, *etc.* 1891. 8°. [*Publications of the Huguenot Society.* vol. 6.] Ac. **2073/4**.

—— Relation sur le royaume de France, par M. A. Barbaro après son ambassade de 1563. *Ital. & Fr.* 1838. *See* FRANCE. [*Appendix.—History and Politics.—Miscellaneous.*] Collection de documents inédits, *etc.* sér. 1. Histoire politique. (Rélations des ambassadeurs vénitiens.) 1835, *etc.* 4°. **1885**. c. **7**.

—— Relazione del cl. M. A. Barbaro alla Signoria Veneta delli negozj trattati co' Turchi, *etc.* 1764. *See* BALUZE (E.) Stephani Baluzii Miscellanea, *etc.* tom. 4. 1761, *etc.* fol. **13**. e. **12**.

—— Relazione dell'impero Ottomano di Marcantonio Barbaro, tornato bailo da Costantinopoli, l'anno 1573. [Edited by E. Albèri.] 1840. *See* VENICE.—*Ambassadors.* Relazioni degli ambasciatori veneti al Senato, *etc.* ser. 3. vol. 1. 1839, *etc.* 8°. **1440**. i. **13**.

—— Relatione di Costantinopoli. [Abridged from M. A. Barbaro's report to the Venetian Senate in 1573.] 1589. 4°. [*Tesoro politico.*] *See* CONSTANTINOPLE. [*Appendix.*] **521**. d. **14**.

—— [Another edition.] 1598. 8°. [*Tesoro politico.* pt. 2.] *See* CONSTANTINOPLE. [*Appendix.*] **521**. c. **19**.

—— [Another edition.] 1598. 8°. [*Tesoro politico.*] *See* CONSTANTINOPLE. [*Appendix.*] **521**. c. **20**.

—— [Another edition.] 1600. 4°. [*La prima parte del Thesoro politico.*] *See* CONSTANTINOPLE. [*Appendix.*] **29**. b. **13**.

—— [Another edition.] 1602. 12°. [*Tesoro politico.*] *See* CONSTANTINOPLE. [*Appendix.*] **521**. c. **21**.

—— Relatione di Costantinopoli.—De urbe Constantinopoli . . . relatio. [By M. A. Barbaro.] *Ital. & Lat.* 1610. 4°. [*Tesoro politico.*] *See* CONSTANTINOPLE. [*Appendix.*] **521**. d. **15**.

—— Discours de Constantinople. [A translation of the abridgment of M. A. Barbaro's report.] 1611. 4°. [*Trésor politique.*] *See* CONSTANTINOPLE. [*Appendix.*] C. **80**. a. **6**.

BARBARO (NICOLÒ) Giornale dell' assedio di Costantinopoli 1453 . . . Corredato di note e documenti per Enrico Cornet. pp. vi. 82. *Vienna,* 1856. 8°. **9135**. d. **20**. (**3**.)

BARBARO (RAMIRO)

—— Il Colera ed il governo. pp. 30. *Malta,* 1865. 8°. **7563**. d. **25**.

BARBARO (ROMUALDO) *Count.* *See* BARBARO (C. A.) *Marquis.* Degli avanzi d'alcuni antichissimi edifizj scoperti in Malta l'anno 1768. Dissertazione . . . preceduta dal suo elogio funebre [by Count R. Barbaro]. 1794. 4°. **7706**. ee. **3**.

BARBARO DI SAN GIORGIO (MARIO)

—— *See* BARBARO DI SAN GIORGIO (R. A.) *Marquis.* I Barbaro—Venezia e Malta . . . Con annotazioni [by M. Barbaro di San Giorgio]. 1912. 8°. **11431**. e. **45**. (**2**.)

BARBARO DI SAN GIORGIO (RAMIRO ALFONSO) *Marquis.*

—— *See* KAZLOV (A.) Nihilisti . . . Traduzione dal russo del marchese R. Barbaro. 1880. 8°. **12591**. aa. **41**.

—— I Barbaro—Venezia e Malta. Cent' ottave . . . Con annotazioni [by Mario Barbaro di San Giorgio]. pp. 102. *Malta,* 1912. 8°. **11431**. e. **45**. (**2**.)

BARBARO FORLEO (ALFREDO) Il Trovatello. Poema sociale. pp. 93. *Firenze,* 1888. 8°. **11429**. cc. **24**.

BARBARO FORLEO (CATERINA) *Duchess d'Este.* Farfalle, *etc.* [Tales.] pp. 232. *Bologna,* 1895. 8°. **12471**. eee. **2**.

BARBAROSSA I., *Dey of Algiers.* *See* BĀBĀ 'ARŪJ.

BARBAROSSA II., *Dey of Algiers.* *See* KHAIR AL-DĪN.

BARBAROSSA, *Emperor of Germany.* *See* FREDERICK I.

BARBAROSSA, *pseud.* [i.e. JOHN SCOTT.] The Lost Principle; or, the Sectional Equilibrium . . . By "Barbarossa." [On the Federal Constitution of the United States.] pp. 266. *J. Woodhouse & Co.: Richmond, Va.,* 1860. 8°. **8177**. e. **8**.

BARBAROSSA (FLAVIO) *See* ROME, *Church of.—* Clement XI., *Pope.* Editto. [27 Aug. 1711. Issued by F. Barbarossa as special delegate of Pope Clement XI. in the matter of the temporalities of the Abbey of St. Benignus.] [1711.] *s. sh.* fol. **1896**. d. **12**. (**115**.)

BARBAROSSA (PAOLO EMILIO) Il Serafico Eroe, *etc.* *See* POPPI (S. da) Sette canzoni in lode del Serafico P. S. Francesco, *etc.* 1606. 4°. **83**. e. **18**. (**1**.)

BARBAROTTA (GIACINTO) *See* DANTE ALIGHIERI. [*Divina Commedia.—Italian.*] Comento della Divina Commedia di I. Tediscen. Pubblicato per cura dei suoi fidi amici G. Barbarotta e F. S. Cianci. 1873. 8°. **011420**. aa. **5**.

BARBAROTTA (LUIGI) Cantata per il fausto ritorno di Ferdinando IV., re delle Sicilie, dopo l'ingresso delle vittoriose sue armi in Napoli. pp. 17. *Napoli,* 1799. 4°. Add. MS. **34990**. ff. **176–183**.

BARBAROUX (A. MAGON) *See* MAGON-BARBAROUX.

BARBAROUX (CHARLES JEAN MARIE) *See* MARSEILLES.—*Commune.* Observations de la Commune de Marseille sur l'état actuel du département des Bouches du Rhône, présentées à l'Assemblée Nationale par Barbaroux et Loys. 1792. 8°. F. **656**. (**3**.)

—— *See* MARSEILLES.—*Société Républicaine.* Les Républicains Marseillais à Charles Barbaroux. 1793. 8°. F. **655**. (**13**.)

—— Les Attentats des administrateurs de la ville d'Arles. Constatés d'après les pièces déposées au comité de surveillance. pp. 50. *Paris,* 1792. 8°. F. **653**. (**4**.)

—— Charles Barbaroux . . . aux citoyens de Marseille. [Exhorting them to march to Paris. Dated: 16 June 1793.] *Caen,* 1793. *s. sh.* fol. **Tab.443.a.3.(103.)**

—— [Another edition.] pp. 8. *Caen,* [1793.] 4°. F. **32***. (**2**.)

—— [Another edition.] pp. 7. [1793.] 8°. F. **655**. (**7**.)

—— [Another copy.] F. **981**. (**19**.)

—— Convention Nationale. Correspondance de Charles Barbaroux. [Consisting chiefly of letters addressed to him.] pp. 26. *Paris,* [1793.] 8°. F. **589**. (**3**.)

—— Convention Nationale. De l'influence de la guerre maritime sur le commerce, & de l'organisation des travaux publics. pp. 38. *Paris,* 1793. 8°. F. **1179**. (**3**.)

BARBAROUX (CHARLES JEAN MARIE)

—— Convention Nationale. Opinion . . . sur les causes de la cherté des grains et les moyens d'y remédier. pp. 26. *Paris*, [1792?] 8º. **F. 479. (8.)**

—— Convention Nationale. Opinion . . . sur les moyens de défense de Louis Capet tirés de l'inviolabilité constitutionelle. pp. 8. [*Paris*, 1793.] 8º. **F. 914. (2.)**

—— Convention Nationale. Opinion . . . sur les subsistances, *etc.* pp. 23. *Paris*, 1792. 8º. **F. 476. (12.)**

—— Les Députés du département des Bouches-du-Rhône à la Convention Nationale, à Marat. [A reply to an attack by Marat. Signed by Barbaroux and others.] pp. 11. *Paris*, [1793.] 8º. **F. 313. (122.)**

—— [Another copy.] **645. a. 38. (11.)**

—— Les Députés extraordinaires de l'administration du département des Bouches-du-Rhône, et des Communes de Marseille et d'Arles, aux citoyens de Paris. [Signed by Barbaroux and others.] pp. 8. [1792?] 8º. **F. 64**. (6.)**

—— Discours adressé à l'Assemblée électorale . . . le 5 sept. 1792. pp. 2. [*Marseilles*, 1792.] 8º. **F. 784. (24.)**

—— Discours sur les titres de Sire et de Majesté, conservés au roi par l'ajournement du décret du 5 octobre 1791 prononcé dans la Société des amis de la constitution de Marseille. pp. 12. *Marseille*, 1791. 8º. **F. 900. (3.)**

—— Lettre écrite à M. le Président de l'Assemblée Nationale, par les Députés extraordinaires de la Commune de Marseille . . . sur les commissaires civils envoyés par le Roi dans cette dernière Ville. [Signed by Barbaroux and others. 17 March, 1792.] pp. 7. [*Paris*, 1792.] 8º. **F. 64**. (27.)**

—— Lettre inédite de Barbaroux à J.-B. Salles sur la tragédie de Charlotte Corday. *See* SALLE (J. B.) *the Girondist.* Charlotte Corday; tragédie, *etc.* 1864. 4º. **11739. k. 66.**

—— Mémoire adressé à l'Assemblée Nationale, sur la procédure prévotale que l'on prend à Marseille, *etc.* pp. 28. [1789.] 4º. **R. 674. (17.)**

—— Mémoires . . . Première édition critique, conforme au manuscrit original. Avec une introduction, une biographie et des notes par Alfred-Chabaud. pp. 311. *Paris*, 1936. 8º. [*Classiques de la Révolution française.*] **W.P.12248/8.**

—— Mémoires de Charles Barbaroux . . . Avec des éclaircissemens historiques, par MM. Berville et Barrière. Troisième édition. [Edited by C. O. Barbaroux.] pp. viii. 160. *Paris*, 1827. 8º. [*Collection des mémoires relatifs à la Révolution française.*] **910. g. 29.**

—— [Another edition.] *See* PÉTION DE VILLENEUVE (J.) Mémoires inédits de Pétion, *etc.* 1866. 8º. **10661. g. 11.**

—— Quelques-uns des mensonges du commissaire Debourge dans ses observations sur l'affaire d'Arles. Dévoilés par Barbaroux . . . et par Bourget et Esmenard . . . Précédés d'une lettre de P. A. Antonelle. pp. 42. *Paris*, 1792. 8º. **F. 653. (6.)**

BARBAROUX (CHARLES OZÉ) *See* BARBAROUX (C. J. M.) Mémoires de Charles Barbaroux, *etc.* [Edited by C. O. Barbaroux.] 1827. 8º. **910. g. 29.**

—— De la transportation. Aperçus législatifs, philosophiques et politiques sur la colonisation pénitentiaire. pp. xiii. 423. *Paris*, 1857. 8º. **6055. e. 8.**

BARBAROUX (CHARLES OZÉ)

—— Essai sur l'institution et l'influence de la pairie en France. *See* LARDIER (J. A.) Histoire biographique de la Chambre des Pairs, *etc.* 1829. 8º. **10658.** bbb. **2.**

—— L'Histoire des États-Unis d'Amérique . . . Édition revue et corrigée pour l'usage des écoles. pp. 304. *Hogan & Thompson: Philadelphia*, 1838. 12º. **9602. a. 26.**

—— [Another edition.] Continuée depuis l'année 1825 jusqu'à nos jours par T. Séron . . . Nouvelle édition soigneusement revue à l'usage des écoles. pp. 360. *Moss & Brother: Philadelphia*, 1854. 12º. **9603. a. 11.**

—— Lettre de M. Barbaroux . . . sur la pétition de M. Madier de Montjau. *See* MADIER DE MONTJAU (J. P.) Lettre de M. Madier de Montjau . . . à M. Lainé, *etc.* 1820. 8º. **859. b. 3. (1.)**

BARBAROUX (CHARLES OZÉ) and **LARDIER** (JOSEPH ALEXANDRE)

—— Mémoires de Robert Guillemard, sergent en retraite, suivis de documents historiques . . . la plupart inédits, de 1805 à 1823. [By C. O. Barbaroux and J. A. Lardier.] 2 tom. 1826. 8º. *See* GUILLEMARD (R.) **932. d. 5.**

—— Adventures of a French Serjeant (Robert Guillemard) during his campaigns in Italy, Spain, *etc.* [Translated from the French of C. O. Barbaroux and J. A. Lardier.] pp. xvi. 345. 1826. 12º. *See* GUILLEMARD (R.) **612. i. 12.**

—— [Another edition.] pp. xii. 342. 1898. 8º. *See* GUILLEMARD (R.) **010663. h. 30.**

—— Memoiren Robert Guillemard's . . . Aus dem Französischen [of C. O. Barbaroux and J. A. Lardier]. Eingeführt und eingeleitet von Goethe. 2 Tl. 1827. 8º. *See* GUILLEMARD (R.) **10662. b. 20.**

BARBAROUX (J. A.) Recherches physiologiques appliquées à la médecine et à la chirurgie, ou dynamisme organique. pp. 36. *Paris*, 1847. 4º. [*Collection des thèses soutenues à la Faculté de Médecine de Paris.* An 1847. tom. 7.] **7372. a. 9.**

BARBAROUX (OZÉ) *See* BARBAROUX (Charles O.)

BARBARROSA (MERCEDES C.)

—— The Living Goya. [With reproductions.] pp. 349. *Meador Publishing Co.: Boston*, 1939. 8º. **7867. a. 2.**

BARBARROUX (ALEXANDRE) Clamart, son histoire, son bois, et ses environs, *etc.* [With a plan.] pp. 230. *Paris*, 1869. 8º. **10169. b. 36.**

BARBARROUX (J. JOSEPH A. M.) De l'utilité des bains frais pour l'entretien de la santé . . . Thèse, *etc.* pp. 20. *Montpellier*, 1833. 4º. **1181. f. 17. (18.)**

BARBARUS, *Saint and Martyr.* Les Actes de S. Barbarus. Extrait des "Analecta Bollandiana," *etc.* [From MSS. at Paris and Venice. Edited, with introduction, by H. Delehaye.] *Gr. & Lat. Bruxelles*, 1910. 8º. **4824. df. 23. (6.)**

BARBARUS (DANIEL) *Patriarch of Aquileia.* *See* BARBARO (Daniello)

BARBARUS (FRANCISCUS) *See* BARBARO (Francesco)

BARBARUS (HERMOLAUS) *Patriarch of Aquileia.* *See* BARBARO (Ermolao)

BARBARUS (JOHANNES) *pseud.* [i.e. JOHANNES VARES.] *See* VARES (J.) 010501

BARBARUS (JOSEPHUS) *See* BARBARO (Giosafat)

BARBARY. An Account of South-West Barbary: containing what is most remarkable in the territories of the King of Fez and Morocco. Written by a person who had been a slave there . . . and published from his authentick manuscript. To which are added, two letters: one from the present King of Morocco to Colonel Kirk; the other to Sir Cloudesly Shovell: with Sir Cloudesly's answer, &c. By Simon Ockley. [With a map.] pp. xxxi. 152. *J. Bowyer; H. Clements: London*, 1713. 8°. **978.** d. **35.**

—— [Another copy.] **279.** b. **5.**

—— [Another copy.] **100.** k. **48.**

—— Bibliography of the Barbary States.

1. Tripoli and the Cyrenaica. *See* Playfair (*Sir* Robert L.) *K.C.M.G.*
2. Tunisia. *See* Ashbee (Henry S.)
3. Algeria. *See* Playfair (*Sir* Robert L.) *K.C.M.G.*
4. Morocco. *See* Playfair (*Sir* Robert L.) *K.C.M.G.*, and Brown (R.)

—— A Compleat History of the Piratical States of Barbary, viz. Algiers, Tunis, Tripoli, and Morocco . . . Illustrated with a plan of Algiers, and a map of Barbary. By a Gentleman who resided there many years in a public character. [Translated by Joseph Morgan from "Histoire du Royaume d'Alger," by Langier de Tassy, with the addition of other matter.] pp. xiv. 368. *R. Griffiths: London*, 1750. 8°. **9061.** ccc. **2.**

—— Een cort ende warachtich verhael vande ghedenckweerdige gheschiedenisse in Barbaryen, ende van den grooten slagh ontrent Maroques, gheschiet den 25 Aprilis 1607. *H. Jacobsz.: s' Gravenhaghe*, 1607. 4°. T. **1729.** (**15.**)

—— A Dolorous discourse of a most terrible and bloudy battel, fought in Barbarie, the fourth day of August . . . 1578, wherein were slaine, two kings, *etc.* 𝔅.𝔏. *John Charlewood and Thomas Man: London*, [1579.] 16°. C. **33.** a. **16.**

—— Etat des royaumes de Barbarie, Tripoly, Tunis et Alger: contenant l'histoire naturelle & politique de ces pais, la maniere dont les Turcs y traitent les esclaves, *etc.* [By J. B. de La Faye.] pp. 363. *La Haye*, 1704. 8°. **793.** d. **6.**

—— Historical Memoirs of Barbary, as connected with the plunder of the Seas; including a sketch of Algiers, Tripoli, and Tunis . . . and considerations of their present means of defence; and the original treaties entered into with them by King Charles II. pp. viii. 112. *Gale & Fenner: London*, 1816. 12°. **800.** b. **13.**

—— Late Newes out of Barbary. In a letter written . . . from a Merchant there, *etc.* [Signed: R. S.] 1613. 4°. *See* S., R. **1046.** d. **26.**

—— Letters from Barbary, France, Spain, Portugal, &c. by an English Officer [i.e. Alexander Jardine]. 2 vol. *T. Cadell: London*, 1788. 8°. **980.** i. **11, 12.**

—— The second edition, corrected. 2 vol. *T. Cadell: London*, 1790. 8°. **304.** h. **6, 7.**

—— Relacion verdadero de la famosa empresa que han hecho en Berberia las galeras de Malta, desde 28. de agosto deste año de 1640. en que se declara la gran batalla que tuuieron en el Puerto Farina, *etc.* *I. Sanchez: Madrid*, 1640. fol. **1316.** h. **9.**

—— Several Voyages to Barbary . . . The second edition, corrected [of "Voyage to Algiers and Tunis," translated and edited, with additions, from the French of Philémon de La Motte by Joseph Morgan]. pp. 146. 158. *Oliver Payne: London*, 1736. 8°. **1047.** g. **3.**

—— [Another copy.] G. **15719.**

BARBARY.

—— Tratado para confirmar los pobres cativos de Berueria en la catolica y antigua fe, y religion Christiana, y para los consolar con la palabra de Dios en las afliciones que padecen por el Evangelio de Iesu Christo . . . Al fin . . . hallareys un enxambre de los falsos milagros, y ilusiones del Demonio con que Maria de la Visitacion priora de la Anunciada de Lisboa engaño à muy muchos; y de como fue descubierta y condenada . . . 1588. [By Cipriano de Valera.] pp. 145. *Pedro Shorto: [London,]* 1594. 8°. **851.** a. **8.**

—— Views in Barbary . . . Taken in 1813 by W. G. [i.e. William Gell.] 1815. *obl.* fol. *See* G., W. **3** Tab. **54.**

BARBARY, *Sultana of.* The Amours of the Sultana of Barbary [i.e. L. R. de Penancoët de Keroualle, Duchess of Portsmouth]. A novel. In two parts. pp. 176. MS. NOTES. *Sold by R. Baldwin: London*, 1689. 12°. G. **13992.**

BARBASÁN LAGUERUELA (Casto) Impresiones de Campamento. Cartas escritas desde los Alijares á M.C.C. pp. 106. *Toledo*, 1890. 8°. **8823.** aaa. **41.**

—— Memorias de un Defensor. 2 tom. *Madrid*, 1897. 8°. **6875.** de. **19.**

—— Las Primeras Campañas del Renacimiento. pp. 363. *Toledo*, 1890. 8°. **9077.** b. **1.**

BARBASÁN LAGUERUELA (Mariano)

—— *See* López Jiménez (J.) Mariano Barbasán. Ensayo biográfico y crítico. Cien ilustraciones. 1939. 8°. **7865.** ppp. **47.**

BARBASETTI (Luigi) The Art of the Foil. With a short history of fencing, *etc.* [With illustrations.] pp. xii. 276. *Hutchinson & Co.: London*, [1933.] 8°. **7916.** b. **23.**

—— [Codice cavalleresco.] Ehren-Codex. Übersetzt und den oesterreichisch-ungarischen Gebräuchen angepasst von G. Ristow. pp. xxiv. 159. *Wien*, 1898. 8°. **8425.** aaa. **48.**

BARBASH (Jack)

—— Labour Unions in Action. A study of the mainsprings of unionism. pp. x. 270. *Harper & Bros.: New York & London*, [1948.] 8°. **8288.** e. **82.**

—— Unions and Telephones. The story of the communications workers of America. By J. Barbash . . . With the assistance of Kate Barbash. pp. viii. 246. *Harper & Bros.: New York*, [1952.] 8°. **8289.** b. **62.**

—— Universities and Unions in Workers' Education. pp. xv. 206. *Harper & Bros.: New York*, [1955.] 8°. **8385.** b. **45.**

BARBASHEV (A. I.) Лѣтописные источники для исторіи Литвы въ средніе вѣка. Составилъ А. И. Барбашевъ. pp. 29. 1888. 8°. *See* Periodical Publications.—Leningrad. —*Библіографъ.* **9008.** i. **18.** (**2.**)

—— Витовтъ. Послѣднія двадцать лѣтъ княженія, 1410–1430. (Очерки Литовско-Русской исторіи XV. в.) pp. viii. 340. *С.-Петербургъ*, 1891. 8°. **9456.** f. **27.**

BARBASTE (Mathieu) De l'état des forces dans les maladies, et des indications qui s'y rapportent. Thèse, *etc.* pp. 170. *Montpellier*, 1857. 8°. **7440.** c. **2.**

—— De l'homicide et de l'anthropophagie. pp. xliv. 578. *Paris*, 1856. 8°. **1404.** g. **12.**

—— Introduction à l'étude générale des fièvres. Thèse, *etc.* pp. 71. *Montpellier*, 1850. 4°. **7379.** a. **14.** (**1.**)

BARBASTE (MATHIEU)

—— Les Miracles de la Salette et de Lourdes. Appréciation scientifique. pp. iv. 68. *Paris*, [1873.] 12°. **7660**. a. **57**. (**6**.)

—— Vues sur l'enseignement supérieur, ou plan d'étude de la science de l'homme. pp. xii. 378. *Paris*, 1876. 12°. **8306**. bb. **4**.

BARBASTE (MICHEL AUGUSTIN) De la suture des tendons, *etc*. pp. 40. *Paris*, 1873. 4°. [*Collection des thèses soutenues à la Faculté de Médecine de Paris*. An 1873. tom. 1.] **7373**. o.

BARBASTRE. *See* BARBASTRO.

BARBASTRO. Le Siège de Barbastre. Chanson de geste du XIIe siècle. Éditée par J. L. Perrier. pp. viii. 278. *Paris*, 1926. 8°. [*Classiques français du moyen âge*.] **012201**. cc. **1/54**.

—— *See* BECKER (Ph. A.) Der Siège de Barbastre. 1899. 8°. **012901**. k. **15**.

—— *See* GUNDLACH (A.) Das Handschriften-Verhältnis des Siège de Barbastre. 1883. 8°. **11498**. i. **18/4**.

—— *Cathedral Church. Begin*. Villancicos que se han de contar en la Santa Iglesia Cathedral de Barbastro, la noche del Nacimiento de Nuestro Señor . . . 1690. *J. L. de Larumbe: Huesca*, [1690.] 4°. **1073**. k. **22**. (**21**.)

BARBASTRO, PEDRO, *Bishop of*. [1951– .] *See* CANTERO CUADRADO.

BARBASZ (WILHELM)

—— Wyspiański na tle romantyzmu. pp. xxiii. 439. *Lwów*, 1932. 8°. [*Badania literackie*. tom 4.] Ac. **7215**/**18**.

BARBAT (ANTOINE) Étude sur la pathogénie de certains kystes des machoires. pp. 64. *Paris*, 1872. 4°. [*Collection des thèses soutenues à la Faculté de Médecine de Paris*. An 1872. tom. 1.] **7373**. n. **7**.

BARBAT (CHARLES) Petit dictionnaire pratique de mécanique & d'électricité. pp. viii. 994. 234. [*Paris*,] 1894. 12°. **08768**. a. **2**.

—— Dictionnaire pratique de mécanique et d'électricité . . 2e édition revue, corrigée et considérablement augmentée. 2 pt. *Paris*, 1911. 8°. **08767**. bb. **37**.

BARBAT (CLAUDE GASPARD)

—— Précis pour Claude-Gaspard Barbat, citoyen de Clermont-Ferand, ci-devant membre du Conseil général et bibliothécaire du département. pp. 12. *Paris*, [1793?] 8°. R. **171**. (**15**.)

Imperfect; wanting pp. 5–8.

BARBAT (LOUIS) *See* BIBLE.—*Liturgical Epistles and Gospels*. [*French*.] Évangiles des dimanches et fêtes. Illustrés par Barbat père et fils. 1844. 4°. C. **30**. l. **5**.

—— Histoire de la ville de Châlons-sur-Marne et de ses monuments depuis son origine jusqu'à l'époque actuelle—1854 . . . Édition ornée de cent planches et dessins lithographiés chez l'auteur. pp. 706. *Châlons-sur-Marne*, 1855. 4°. **10173**. f. **11**.

Imperfect; wanting pp. 449–456.

BARBAT (PIERRE MICHEL) *See* BIBLE.—*Liturgical Epistles and Gospels*. [*French*.] Évangiles des dimanches et fêtes. Illustrés par Barbat père et fils. 1844. 4°. C. **30**. l. **5**.

—— Tablettes historiques de Châlons-sur-Marne. [With plates.] pp. iii. 196. *Châlons-s-Marne*, 1879. 8°. **10169**. cc. **6**.

BARBAT (VIRGILE J.) Nietzsche. Tendances et problèmes. pp. 446. *Zürich & Leipzig*, 1911. 8°. **8459**. c. **17**.

BARBAT DE BIGNICOURT (ARTHUR) Les Massacres à Reims en 1792 d'après les documents authentiques. pp. 47. *Reims*, 1872. 8°. **9225**. h. **27**.

—— La Mort d'un gendarme. Comédie en un acte. pp. 29. *Reims*, 1883. 12°. **11739**. de. **10**. (**2**.)

—— Un Salon à Rheims en 1832. pp. 32. *Reims*, 1879. 8°. **010170**. ee. **11**.

BARBAT DE CLOSEL (ÉTIENNE VICTOR)

—— Adresse du second bataillon des volontaires nationaux du département du Puy-de-Dôme, à l'Assemblée nationale, *etc*. [Signed: Barbat.] [1792.] 8°. *See* PUY-DE-DÔME. *Department of the*.—*Volontaires Nationaux*. F.R. **121**. (**32**.)

—— Discours prononcé sur l'autel de la patrie, le 14 juillet, jour de la fédération, au nom de la Société des amis de la constitution de Billon. pp. 8. [*Paris*, 1792?] 8°. F. **297**. (**9**.)

BARBAT DU CLOSEL (ROGER) Faculté de Droit. Thèse pour la licence. (Jus romanum. De acquirendo rerum dominio, *etc*.—Droit français. De la translation de propriété par l'effet des contrats.) pp. 58. *Paris*, 1860. 8°. **5406**. c. **2**. (**3**.)

BARBAT DU CLOSEL D'ARNERY (CLAUDE GASPARD) Le Bon citoyen. Lettre de M. D. C. D'A * * * [i.e. C. G. Barbat du Closel d'Arnery] à M. le Comte de Pr. sur l'impôt territorial. pp. 37. 1787. 8°. *See* A * * *, M. D. C. D'. F. **408**. (**8**.)

—— Éloge funèbre d'Honnoré Riquetti Mirabeau, prononcé dans le vaisseau de l'église des ci-devant Carmes. pp. 32. *Clermont-Ferrand*, [1791.] 8°. F. **19***. (**6**.)

—— Lettre écrite par le citoyen Barbat père, à ses concitoyens le 17 juillet 1792. (Certificat des Fédérés du dix août 1792, donné au citoyen Barbat.) *Clermont-Ferrand*, 1792. 4°. F. **24***. (**39**.)

—— Moyen de constater l'état civil des Protestans. Droits et devoirs des curés à leur égard. pp. 20. *Genève*, 1787. 8°. **110**. g. **51**.

—— Précis pour Claude Gaspard Barbat, *etc*. pp. 12. *Paris*, [1794?] 8°. R. **651**. (**23**.)

—— Projet d'édit pour la restauration de la chose publique, la convocation régulière des états-généraux . . . Par l'auteur de l'Abus & des dangers de la contrainte par corps. [The introductory letter to the King signed: Duclose d'Arneri.] pp. 62. [*Paris*?] 1788. 8°. F.R. **12**. (**6**.)

BARBATES (KONSTANTINOS) *Γαλλικων συνωνυμων έγχειριδιον*. pp. 430. *'Εν Ἀθηναις*, 1882. 8°. **12954**. bb. **9**.

—— *Λεξικον ἰταλο-ἑλληνικον ἐπιτομον*. 2 tom. *'Αθηναι*, 1861. 8°. **12924**. aa. **46**.

—— *Νεον λεξικον ἑλληνογαλλικον*. pp. vii. 1175. iv. *'Αθηνησι*, 1878. 8°. **12924**. cc. **7**.

BARBATI (BARTOLOMMEO) *See* BARBATO.

BARBATI (CAJETANUS) *See* ROSINI (C. M.) *Bishop of Pozzuoli*. Caroli Mariæ Rosinii . . . Ægyptii Comœdia. Nunc primum recognita a C. Barbati. 1870. 8°. **11712**. dd. **1**.

BARBATI (GIULIO) Il Romanzo di Sara. [Tales.] pp. 222. *Milano*, 1885. 8°. **12470**. bb. **29**.

BARBATI (PETRONIO) *See* BARBATO.

BARBATIA (ANDREAS) *See* ROME, *Church of.*—Clement v., *Pope.* Clementinarum cõstitutiones . . . glossis per F. J. Thierry . . . adornate . . . Quibus multa ex commẽtariis Joan. de Imo. . . . Andr. Barb. . . . collecta adduntur. 1532. 4°. **5051**. bb. **8**. **(2.)**

—— *See* TUDESCHIS (N. de) *Cardinal.* Abbatis Panormitani in secundum Decretalium epistolarum commentaria . . . illustrata A. Barb. . . . adnotamentis. 1578, *etc.* fol. **496**. k. 12.

—— *See* UBALDIS (B. de) B. Ubaldi . . . in [primam,] secundam Digesti Veteris partem commentaria, *etc.* [With the notes of A. Barbatia and others.] 1577, *etc.* fol. **5254**. h. **5**.

—— *See* UBALDIS (B. de) Opus aureum . . . baldi de perusia super feudis cum additionibus . . . Andree barbacia necnon aliorũ clarissimorũ doctoruʒ. 1500. fol. IC. **22413**.

—— *Begin.* [fol. 1 *recto*:] Epigramma ĩ laudẽ Andreae Barbatiae Equi. ⁊ Iuris Consul. excellentissimi sumptum ex libris Antonii Urcei Codri. [fol. 2 *recto*:] Excellentissimi vtriusqꝫ iuris mõarche ⁊ hac nostra vltima tempestate in ea facultate sine contradictione facile principis domini Andree Barbatiae equitis apostolici ac Aragonũ regis consiliarii comentaria in tituluʒ de verbo. obli. vna cũ additionibus pỏstea per ipsum factis feliciter incipiunt. [fol. 177 *verso*:] Finit aurea Lectura . . . Andreæ Barbatie, *etc.* [A commentary on the Digesta of Justinian, lib. 45. cap. 1.] G.L. *Iustinianus de ruberia: bononie,* octauo ydus nouembres [6 Nov.], 1497. fol. IC. **29202**.
182 *leaves.* *Sig.* aa–zz⁶ ⁊⁊⁶ ꝯꝯ⁶ ꝶꝶ⁶ AA–CC⁶ DD⁶ [*⁴]. *Double columns,* 65 *lines to a column.* *Imperfect; wanting the last four leaves containing the table.*

—— *Begin.* [pt. 1. fol. 2 *recto*:] Accutissimi. [*sic*] vtriusqꝫ iuris interpretis . . . dñi Andree de Bartholomeo Messanensis de scicilia consilioꝝ pars prima feliciter incipit. [fol. 223 *recto*:] Cõsilia ista dụo ĩmediate sequẽtia fuerũt . . . Antonij de prato veteri ⁊ Ang. d'aretio, *etc.* [pt. 2. fol. 2 *recto*:] Acutissimi vtriusqꝫ iuris interpretis . . . d. Andree de Bartholomeo de Scicilia consiliorum pars ſa feliciter incipit. [Edited by Joannes Baptista Bossius.] G.L. 2 pt. *Philippus Lauagnia: [Milan,]* die quarto Octobris, 1490; die .xxij. Septẽbris, 1489. fol. IC. **26814, 5**.
Pt. 1. 228 *leaves, the first blank.* *Sig.* A–H⁸ I⁶ K–M⁸ ff⁸ ee⁸ dd⁸ cc⁸ bb⁸ aa⁸ aaa⁸–ccc⁸ (i–iiij)⁸ a⁸ b⁶ c⁶ d⁸ e⁸ d⁶ e⁶ k⁶. *Pt.* 2. 222 *leaves, the first and last blank.* *Sig.* A–D⁸ E⁶ F⁸ G⁸ H⁶ I–Y⁸ Z⁶ AA⁸ BB⁶ CC⁸ DD⁸ EE⁶ FF⁸. *Double columns,* 60–63 *lines to a column.*

—— *Begin.* [fol. 2 *recto*:] [I]ohaninna. Hec dicetur repetitio a nomĩe ĩfantule filie mee primogenite, *etc.* [*End.* fol. 100 *verso*:] Explicit Iohãnina cõposita ꝑ andream siculũ iuris utriusqꝫ doctorẽ famosissimũ sup. c. Raynald⁹ de testa, *etc.* [A commentary upon lib. 3. cap. 18 of the Decretals of Gregory IX.] *Bononie,* [1475 ?] fol. IC. **29272**.
100 *leaves, the first blank.* *Without signatures.* *Double columns,* 49 *lines to a column.* *Without the blank leaf.*

—— *Begin.* [fol. 1 *recto*:] Repetitio Egregia Ac Peregrina Legis Cum Accutissimi. [*sic.*] C. De. Fidei. Cõmissis Edita Per Excellentissimuʒ Virum ⁊ iurꝭ. utriusqꝫ Monarcham dominum Andream Barbaciam Siculum Messanensem. ac Militẽ nobilissimum, *etc.* [A commentary on lib. 6. cap. 42. par. 30 of the Codex of Justinian.] G.L. *per Stefanum corallum de Lugduno: Parmę,* die sexta mensis maij, 1474. fol. IC. **30220**.
44 *leaves, without signatures.* *Double columns,* 60 *lines to a column.*

BARBATIA (ANDREAS)

—— *Begin.* [fol. 1 *recto*:] Repetitio solennis rubricae: de fide instrumentorum. Edita per . . . dominũ Andream barbaciã Siculũ Messanensem. [A commentary on lib. 2. tit. 22 of the Decretals of Gregory IX.] *Bonoĩæ,* Calẽdis Februa. [1 Feb.], 1474. fol. IC. **28574**.
32 *leaves, the last blank.* *Without signatures.* *Double columns,* 54 *lines to a column.* *Without the blank leaf.*

—— [Another copy.] IC. **28573**.
Without the blank leaf.

—— *Begin.* [fol. 2 *recto*:] Repeticio solẽnis viri: et iuris vtriusqꝫ monarche: diui domini Andree Barbatia: Siculi messanẽsis sup capitl'o Raynucii de testamẽtis incipit, *etc.* [A commentary on lib. 3. tit. 26. cap. 16 of the Decretals of Gregory IX.] G.L. [Toulouse, 1475 ?] fol. & 4°. **IB. 42475.**
116 *leaves, the first and last blank.* *Without signatures.* *Double columns,* 40 *lines to a column.*

—— *Begin.* [fol. 2 *recto*:] Repetitio solemnis rubrice: de fide instrumentorum. edita per excellentissimum virũ: et iuris vtriusqꝫ monarcham: diuum dominum Andream barbaciam siculum Messanensem, *etc.* [*Martin Huss*:] *Tholose,* xii. Calendas Julii [June 20], 1476. 4°. IA. **42401**.
110 *leaves, the first and last blank, without signatures.* 27 *lines to a page.* *Wanting the first leaf.* *The first dated book printed at Toulouse.*

—— [Another edition.] *See* ROME.—*Church of.* [*Corpus Juris Canonici.*] Repetitionum in universas fere Iuris Canonici partes . . . volumen primum [*etc.*]. vol. 4. 1618. fol. **496**. i. **4**.

—— Tractat⁹ . . . de cardinalibus legatis a latere. *See* TRACTATUS. Primum [*etc.*] volumen tractatuum, *etc.* vol. 14. 1549. fol. **5305**. i.

—— [Another edition.] *See* TRACTATUS. Tractatus vniuersi iuris, *etc.* tom. 13. pt. 2. 1584. fol. **499**. g. **8**.

—— Tractatus de testibus, *etc.* *See* TRACTATUS. Primum [*etc.*] volumen tractatuum, *etc.* vol. 5. 1549. fol. **5305**. i.

—— [Another edition.] *See* TRACTATUS. Tractatus vniuersi iuris, *etc.* tom. 4. 1584. fol. **499**. f. **5**.

BARBATIAS (ANDREAS) *See* BARBATIA.

BARBATIUS (ANDREAS) *See* BARBATIA.

BARBATIUS (HIERONYMUS) *See* BARBATUS.

BARBATIUS (JOANNES) *pseud.* Barbæ maiestas, hoc est de barbis elegans, breuis et accurata descriptio . . . Omnia . . . pertractata & collecta per M. Ioannem Barbatium barbarum amatorem. pp. 20. *In officina M. Fabri: Francofurti,* 1614. 4°. **245**. g. **10**.

—— De barbis. Von Bärten. Insonderheit von Prediger Bärten. [Translated from the Latin.] *See* H., D., *M.* Curiosa theologica, *etc.* 1690. 8°. **1351**. c. **22**.

—— [Another edition.] *See* M., D.H. Collectanea curiosa theologica, *etc.* 1735. 8°. **1141**. b. **39**.

BARBATO (ANGELO) *See* BARBATUS (Angelus)

BARBATO (BARTOLOMMEO) *See* TASSO (T.) [*La Gerusalemme liberata.—Italian.*] La Gerusalemme liberata di T. Tasso, con la vita di lui, con gli argomenti à ciascun canto di B. Barbato, *etc.* 1628. 4°. **83**. f. **18**.

—— La Lettera, idillio. La Galatea, idillio. *See* BIDELLI (G. B.) Gl'Idillij di diversi ingegni illustri, *etc.* [1618.] 12°. **1062**. a. **41**.

BARBATO (BARTOLOMMEO)

—— Lettere de complimenti, *etc.* *See* ARTE. L'Arte del segretario politico e famigliare, *etc.* 1627. 4°. **1085.** l. **25.**

BARBATO (GIROLAMO) *See* BARBATUS (Hieronymus)

BARBATO (LUIGI) Chiesa libera in libero stato. Quistioni di diritto pubblico ecclesiastico. pp. 300. *Firenze,* 1866. 8°. **5107.** dd. **25.**

BARBATO (PETRONIO) Rime di P. Barbati . . . estratte da varie raccolte del secolo XVI. e da suoi manuscritti originali; con alcune lettere al medesimo scritte da diversi uomini illustri, *etc.* pp. xxiv. 296. *Foligno,* [1712.] 8°. **11429.** aaa. **7.**

—— Rime. [Selected poems.] 1553. *See* DOMENICHI (L.) Rime diuerse, *etc.* vol. 6. 1546, *etc.* 8°. **240.** d. **9.**

—— [Another edition.] *See* RUSCELLI (G.) Scelta nuoua di rime, *etc.* lib. 6. 1573. 8°. **239.** c. **42.**

BARBATUS (ANDREAS) *See* BARBATIA.

BARBATUS (ANGELUS) *See* PLUTARCH. [*De Exilio.—Latin.*] Plutarchi Chæronei De Exilio Libellus A. Barbato Inteprete [*sic*]. 1516. 4°. **525.** l. **3.**

—— —— 1517. 4°. **8461.** c. **32.**

—— —— 1517. 4°. **525.** k. **26.** (**6.**)

—— *See* PLUTARCH. [*Moralia.—Latin.*] Plutarchi Chæronei . . . Opuscula moralia, *etc.* (tom. 1. De exilio. A. Barbato interprete.) 1549, *etc.* 8°. **524.f.1.**

BARBATUS (HIERONYMUS) De arthritide libri duo . . . Accessit De sanguine, & eius sero exercitatio. pp. 88. *Typis V. Mortali: Venetiis,* 1665. 4°. **776.** f. 5. (**2.**) *With an additional titlepage, engraved.*

—— Hieronymi Barbari . . . De formatrice, conceptu, organizatione, & nutritione foetus in vtero dissertatio anatomica. pp. 144. pl. 2. *Apud Bodium: Patauii,* 1676. 4°. **778.** f. **12.** (**1.**)

—— Hieronimi Barbati . . . Dissertatio elegantissima de sanguine et eius sero, *etc.* pp. 88. *Apud R. de Ninville: Parisiis,* 1667. 12°. **783.** b. **19.** (**1.**)

—— [Another edition.] pp. 82. *Impensis J. D. Zunneri: Francofurti ad Moen.,* 1667. 12°. **783.** b. **19.** (**2.**)

BARBATUS (JOSEPHUS) *See* ABUDACNUS (J.)

BARBATUS (NICOLAUS ASCLEPIUS) *See* ASCLEPIUS BARBATUS.

BARBAUD (CLAUDE ÉTIENNE VICTOR) Dissertation sur l'inflammation aiguë et chronique de l'utérus—métrite. pp. 21. *Paris,* 1817. 4°. **1183.** d. **14.** (**15.**)

BARBAUD (GABRIEL) *See* VENDÉE, *Department of the.* Inventaire sommaire des archives départementales antérieures à 1790, rédigé par G. Barbaud . . . Vendée. 1898, *etc.* 4°. S. **148.** a. **85.**

BARBAUD (LÉONARD VICTOR) Essai sur l'endurcissement du tissu cellulaire; thèse, *etc.* pp. 20. *Paris,* 1822. 4°. **1183.** g. **3.** (**27.**)

BARBAUD (RAYMOND) Le Château de Bressuire en Poitou depuis sa fondation, au commencement du XIe siècle, jusqu'à nos jours, précédé d'une étude sur les défenses antérieures . . . Avec une préface de M. Du Seigneur. Ouvrage accompagné de douze héliogravures . . . de quatorze planches, *etc.* pp. xvi. 165. *Paris,* 1903. fol. **7816.** dd. **10.**

BARBAUD (ROGER) Manuel des candidats au surnumérariat des postes et télégraphes. pp. 311. *Paris,* 1888. 16°. **8247.** aa. **30.**

BARBAUD (ROGER)

—— Nouveau manuel de prestidigitation. Traité complet de tours de cartes à l'usage des gens du monde . . . Ouvrage orné de 72 figures dans le texte. pp. iv. 301. *Paris,* 1910. 8°. [*Encyclopédie-Roret.*] 12207.a.1/556.

—— Deuxième série: tours avec appareils, *etc.* pp. 320. *Paris,* 1910. 18°. [*Encyclopédie-Roret.*] 12207.a.1/567

BARBAULD (ANNA LAETITIA) *See* AIKIN, afterwards BARBAULD.

BARBAULD (EZECHIEL) Exercitatio theologica ad textum Marci cap. 3. vs. 28. 29. 30. de peccato in Spiritum Sanctum in æternum non remittendo, *etc.* *Praes.* H. Philiponeus de Hautecour. pp. 58. *Apud J. Gyzelaar: Franequeræ,* 1697. 4°. **1012.** d. **1.** (**1.**)

BARBAULD (THÉOPHILE) Prieres pour ceux qui voyagent sur la mer, *etc.* pp. 269. *P. Savouret: Amsterdam,* 1688. 12°. **844.** b. **14.**

BARBAULT (JEAN) Monumens antiques, ou collection choisie d'anciens bas-reliefs, et fragmens egiptiens, grecs, romains, et etrusques . . . Deux cents planches, avec leur explication en abrégé, la plûpart dessinées et gravées par M. Barbault. pp. 15. pl. 1–94. *Rome,* 1783. fol. **137.** h. **16.**

—— Recueil de divers monumens anciens répandus en plusieurs endroits de l'Italie. Dessinés par feu Monsieur Barbault . . . et gravés en 166 planches, avec leur explication historique, pour servir de suite aux monumens de Rome ancienne. pp. 52. *Rome,* 1770. fol. **146.** i. **7.**

—— Vues des plus beaux restes des antiquités romaines, telles qu'elles subsistent encore à Rome, et en divers endroits de l'Italie, dessinées par Monsieur Barbault et gravées par d'habiles maîtres en 100 planches. *Rome,* 1775. fol. **135.** g. **7.**

BARBAULT (P. F.) *See* BARBAULT-ROYER.

BARBAULT-ROYER (P. F.) De la complicité triumvirale. Discours lu à l'assemblée des citoyens de Rochefort, par le citoyen Barbault, le jour de la fête civique du 2 pluviôse an 3e, *etc.* pp. 10. *Rochefort,* [1795.] 4°. **936.** f. 7. (**18.**)

—— Resumé sur l'Angleterre. pp. 22. *Paris,* [1803?] 8°. F. **550.** (**7.**)

—— Voyage dans les départemens du Nord, de la Lys, de l'Escaut, etc. pendant les années VII. et VIII. pp. viii. 200. *Paris,* an VIII [1800]. 8°. **10170.** bb. 2.

BARBAUT (ANNA LAETITIA) *See* AIKIN, afterwards BARBAULD.

BARBAUT (ANTOINE FRANÇOIS) Cours d'accouchemens. 2 tom. *Paris,* 1775. 12°. **1176.** a. **19.**

BARBAVARA DI GRAVELLONA (FRANCESCO) Leo XIII. Pontifex Maximus et P. Virgilius Maro, *etc.* [Verses.] pp. 27. *Augustae Taurinorum,* [1888.] 8°. **11408.** g. **61.**

BARBAVARA DI GRAVELLONA (G. C.) *See* BRAVETTA (V. E.) La Canzone sabauda. Preceduta da un profilo letterario sull'autore di G. C. Barbavara di Gravellona. 1911. 8°. **11426.** h. **22.** (**7.**)

BARBAY (HERBERT URSIN ÉDOUARD) De la fistule lachrymale. pp. 38. *Paris,* 1848. 4°. [*Collection des thèses soutenues à la Faculté de Médecine de Paris.* An 1848. tom. 1.] **7372.** b. **4.**

BARBAY (PETRUS) Commentarius in Aristotelis Logicam . . . Editio tertia, emendatior multò, *etc.* pp. 600. *Apud viduam G. Josse: Parisiis,* 1680. 8°. **519.** a. **28.**

BARBAY (PETRUS)

—— Editio quinta, *etc.* pp. 600. *Apud J. B. Ville: Lugduni*, 1692. 12°. **8468. a. 10.**

—— Commentarius in Aristotelis Metaphysicam . . . Editio tertia, emendatior multò, *etc.* pp. 489. *Apud viduam G. Josse: Parisiis*, 1680. 12°. **519. a. 29.**

—— Commentarius in Aristotelis Moralem. Editio tertia, emendatior multò, *etc.* pp. 580. *Apud viduam G. Josse: Parisiis*, 1680. 12°. **519. a. 30.**

BARBAZ (ABRAHAM LOUIS) *See* JOLYOT DE CRÉBILLON (P.) Rhadamisthus en Zenobia, treurspel, gevolgd naar het Fransche . . . door A. L. Barbaz. 1812. 8°. **11755. aaa. 16.**

—— *See* RACINE (J.) [*Andromache.*] Andromaché, treurspel naar het Fransche . . . door A. L. Barbaz. 1800. 8°. **11755. bb. 48.**

—— *See* RACINE (J.) [*Iphigénie.*] Ifigenia in Aulis, treurspel gevolgd naar het Fransche door A. L. Barbaz. 1800. 8°. **11755. bb. 49.**

—— *See* VOLTAIRE (F. M. A. de) [*Les Scythes.*] De Scyten, treurspel, gevolgd naar het Fransche door A. L. Barbaz. 1796. 8°. **11755. bb. 10.**

—— Aan de bestuurders van den Stads Schouwburg, te Amsteldam, op deszelfs fraaigeschilderd Tooneel-Gordyn. [In verse.] pp. 3. *Amsteldam*, 1800. 8°. **1871. e. 1. (71.)**

—— Aan Ward Bingley, de rol van Nero spelende in het treurspel Epicharis en Nero. [In verse.] *Amsteldam*, [1799.] 8°. **11556. g. 38. (1.)**

—— Aanspraak gedaan door den akteur J. P. Kroese, by het openen van den Koningklyken Hollandschen Schouburg, te Amsteldam den eersten van Oogstmaand, 1807. [In verse.] *Amsteldam*, 1807. 8°. **11556. ccc. 73.**

—— Aanspraak gedaan door den akteur J. P. Kroese, in den stads Schouwburg, te Amsteldam; tot sluiting van het tooneel, den 7. van Bloeimaand 1803. [In verse.] pp. 7. *Amsteldam*, [1803.] 8°. **11556. dd. 6.**

—— Aanspraak van Ward Bingley, in den Schouwburg der Bataafsche Republiek, te Amsteldam, tot sluiting van het tooneel den 4den van Bloeimaand 1799. [In verse.] *Amsteldam*, 1799. 8°. **11556. dd. 5.**

—— Dankoffer van A. M. Kamphuyzen, geboren Snoek, na de vertooning van het Treurspel: Maria Stuart, en het blyspel: de Jonge driftige Vrouw voor derzelver vyf-en-twintigjarige Benefice, in den Stads Schouwburg te Amsteldam, den 11den van Louwmaand, 1821. [In verse.] *Amsteldam*, [1821.] 8°. **1871. e. 1. (72.)**

—— Elmire de Vilarez, treurspel. [In verse.] pp. 114. *Amsteldam*, 1799. 8°. **11755. bb. 11.**

—— Het Feest van Thalia, zinbeeldig divertissement . . . vertoond in den Amsteldamschen Schouwburg, ter vyf-en-twintigjarige benefice van den Heer D. Kamphuyzen, den 29sten van Louwmaand, 1818. [In verse.] pp. 8. [*Amsterdam*, 1818.] 8°. **11754. bbb. 5.**

—— Makin, of de ontdekking van Madera, tooneelspel. pp. 82. *Amsteldam*, 1800. 8°. **11755. bb. 12.**

—— Nieuwjaarswensch, by den aanvang van het jaar MDCCCII, *etc.* [In verse.] *Amsteldam*, [1802.] 8°. **11556. ccc. 18.**

—— Sigismundus, of het Leven is een droom, treurspel. [In verse.] pp. 103. *Amsteldam*, 1813. 8°. **11755. aaa. 2.**

BARBAZ (ABRAHAM LOUIS)

—— De Wysgeer of de edele Menschenhater; tooneelspel. pp. 123. *Rotterdam*, 1803. 8°. **11755. bb. 13.**

BARBAZAN (ÉTIENNE) *See* CHÂTIMENT. Le Castoiement ou instruction du père à son fils . . . Le tout précédé d'une dissertation sur la langue des Celtes [by E. Barbazan]. 1760. 8°. **C. 48. f. 14.**

—— *See* HUGUES, *de Tabarie.* L'Ordene de Chevalerie, avec une dissertation sur l'origine de la langue françoise [and other essays, by E. Barbazan]. 1759. 12°. **1065. f. 34.**

—— *See* RECUEIL. Recueil A [*etc.*]. [A collection of historical pieces. Edited successively by G. L. Calabre Pérau, E. Barbazan and others.] 1745, *etc.* 12°. **012208. ee. 1.**

—— Fâbliaux et contes des poëtes françois des XII, XIII, XIV & XVes siècles, tirés des meilleurs auteurs. [Edited by E. Barbazan.] pp. lx. 306. 1756. 12°. *See* FRENCH POETS. **683. c. 22.**

—— Nouvelle édition, augmentée et revue sur les manuscrits de la Bibliothèque impériale, par M. Méon. 4 tom. *Paris*, 1808. 8°. **2285. c. 2.**

—— *See* JUBINAL (A.) Nouveau recueil de contes des XIIIe, XIVe et XVe siècles, pour faire suite aux collections de Legrand d'Aussy, Barbazan et Méon, *etc.* 1839, *etc.* 8°. **1464. f. 2.**

BARBAZÁN (JULIÁN)

—— Bibliografía Lopista. *See* VEGA CARPIO (L. F. de) [*Separate Poems.*] Elogio en la Muerte de Juan Blas de Castro, *etc.* 1935. 4°. **20002. dd. 28.**

BARBAZANE. Cançonetta noeuva d'un imbriagon ciammou Barbazane, chi fa arraggià so moggiè Manena. [*Genoa*, 1830?] *s.sh.* 4°. **11436. c. 47. (30.)**

BARBAZANIS (MIHA MADIJER DE) *See* MADIJER (Miha)

BARBAZZA (ANDREA) *Count.* *See* also POGOMMEGA (Robusto) *pseud.* [i.e. A. Barbazza.]

—— L'Amorosa Costanza. Favola tragicomica boschereccia. [In verse.] pp. 136. *Per G. Monti: Bologna*, 1646. 4°. **11715. g. 24.**

BARBAZZA (ANDREA) *Jurisconsult.* *See* BARBATIA (Andreas)

BARBAZZA (ANTONIO GIUSEPPE) *See* BIANCHINI (F.) *the Elder.* Demonstratio historiæ ecclesiasticæ quadripartitæ comprobatæ monumentis pertinentibus ad fidem temporum et gestorum, *etc.* [With plates by A. G. Barbazza.] 1752, *etc.* 4° & fol. **703. g. 1–7** & Tab. **1226. b.**

BARBAZZI (ANDREA) *Count.* *See* BARBAZZA.

BARBE. [For Saints, Sovereigns, and Princesses of Sovereign Houses of this name:] *See* BARBARA.

BARBE, *Tante.* Les Soirées de ma tante Barbe . . . Publié par J. M. G. [1850?] 12°. *See* G., J. M. **12316. aa. 38. (3.)**

BARBE (A.) *Doctor of Medicine.* De l'hématocèle funiculaire. pp. 36. *Paris*, 1866. 4°. [*Collection des thèses soutenues à la Faculté de Médecine de Paris.* An 1866. tom. 1.] **7373. g. 4.**

BARBÉ (ANDRÉ) *See* LAIGNEL-LAVASTINE (P. M. M.) La Pratique psychiatrique . . . Par M. Laignel-Lavastine . . . A. Barbé, *etc.* 1919. 8°. **7409. aaaa. 4.**

—— Examen des aliénés. Nouvelles méthodes biologiques & cliniques, *etc.* pp. xv. 178. *Paris*, 1921. 8°. **07660. ff. 53.**

BARBÉ (Benjamin) *See* Musaeus, *the Grammarian.* [*Greek, Latin, and French.*] Héro et Léandre. Poême amoureux. Traduit librement en français et mot à mot en latin par B. Barbé. 1858. 12°. **11335. b. 31.**

—— L'Inconsolée. Avec une préface par Alexandre Dumas fils. pp. xvi. 246. *Paris,* 1879. 12°. **12356. ff. 18.**

BARBÉ (*Mme.* C. B.) *See* also Barbier (C.) *pseud.* [i.e. *Mme.* C. B. Barbé.]

—— La Bretagne. Son histoire, son peuple, ses princes, ses villes, ses légendes. pp. 382. *Rouen,* 1866. 8°. **9200. h. 10.**

A revised edition of "Les Ducs de Bretagne," entered under Barbier (*C.*) *pseud.*

—— Un Mois en Suisse. pp. 256. *Rouen,* 1864. 8°. **10195. e. 9.**

BARBE (Carolus) Disputatio philosophica de mente humana, *etc. Praes.* Joannes Regius. pp. 50. *Franequeræ,* 1713. 4°. **525.d.12.(38.)**

BARBÉ (Daniel) Lourdes hier, aujourd'hui, demain . . . Douze aquarelles de Hoffbauer. pp. 95. *Paris, Bordeaux,* 1893. 8°. **4807. eee. 13.**

—— Lourdes: yesterday, to-day, and to-morrow . . . Translated by Alice Meynell, *etc.* pp. 106. *Burns & Oates: London,* [1894.] 8°. **4808. i. 23.**

BARBÉ (Émile) Le Nabab René Madec. Histoire diplomatique des projets de la France sur le Bengale et le Pendjab, 1772–1808, *etc.* pp. 291. *Paris,* 1894. 8°. **010663. i. 9.**

BARBE (Eustache) *See* Barbe (Théodore J. E.)

BARBE (Ferdinand)

—— Essai d'une bibliographie de Bayonne et de ses environs, 1530–1920, à l'exclusion des textes basques et des ouvrages traitant spécialement de la langue et de la littérature basques. Accompagné de quelques extraits. pp. viii. 349. *Bayonne,* 1935. 8°. **11925. ff. 17.**

BARBÉ (H. J. A.) De quelques signes propres à faire reconnaitre le début de la phthisie pulmonaire, *etc.* pp. 34. *Paris,* 1856. 4°. [*Collection des dissertations soutenues à la Faculté de Médecine de Paris.* An 1856. tom. 1.] **7372. i. 1.**

BARBE (Henri) Jublains, Mayenne. Notes sur ses antiquités. Époque gallo-romaine, *etc.* pp. 200. *Le Mans,* 1865. 8°. **7707. bb. 4.**

—— Atlas. pl. xii. *Mayenne,* 1865. 4°. **7707. dd. 40.**

BARBÉ (Hortence de Céré) *See* Céré-Barbé.

BARBE, afterwards **BARBE-SCHMITZ** (Jean Baptiste Charles) Un Mot sur la broderie en présence de la levée des prohibitions. [Edited by L.-L.] pp. 36. *Nancy,* 1856. 8°. **7945. h. 35. (1.)**

BARBÉ (Jean Émile Auguste Fernand Cassou) *See* Cassou-Barbé.

BARBE (Jean François) Des climats en général, et plus particulièrement des climats chauds. Thèse, *etc.* pp. 64. *Paris,* 1837. 4°. **1184. h. 8. (22.)**

BARBÉ (Jean Julien) *See* also Jean Julien, *pseud.* [i.e. J. J. Barbé.]

—— A travers le Vieux-Metz. Les maisons historiques. [With illustrations.] pp. 476. *Metz,* 1913. 8°. **10230. ff. 18.**

BARBE (Jean Sylvain de) Considérations générales sur l'époque critique des femmes et le cancer de la matrice; thèse, *etc.* pp. 23. *Paris,* 1835. 4°. **1184. g. 1. (1.)**

—— Traité théorique et pratique de la syphilis. pp. ix. 378. *Paris,* 1847. 8°. **1175. k. 28.**

BARBÉ (Louis) Pélerinages à Notre-Dame de Lourdes. Guérison de Mademoiselle Marie Poirier, de Saint-Aubin de Terregate, *etc.* pp. 116. *Paris,* 1875. 12°. **4867. aa. 7.**

BARBÉ (Louis A.) *See* Aladdin. Histoire d'Aladdin . . . Edited by L. A. Barbé, *etc.* 1906. 8°. **12901. de. 19/1.**

—— *See* Corneille (P.) Scenes from Le Cid. Edited by L. A. Barbé. 1902. 8°. **12238. aaa. 1/13.**

—— *See* Deslys (C.) Le Zouave and La Montre de Gertrude. Edited by L. A. Barbé, *etc.* 1907. 8°. **12237. pp. 1/2.**

—— *See* Dumas (A.) *the Elder.* [*La Jeunesse de Pierrot.*] La Jeunesse de Pierrot. Edited by L. A. Barbé. 1906. 8°. **12901. de. 19/13.**

—— *See* Féval (P. H. C.) Anne des Îles and Jean et sa lettre. Edited by L. A. Barbé, *etc.* 1909. 8°. **12237. pp. 1/9.**

—— *See* Féval (P. H. C.) Le Docteur Bousseau. Edited by L. A. Barbé, *etc.* 1908. 8°. **12237. pp. 1/7.**

—— *See* Gaudichot-Masson (A. M. B.) Les Enfants célèbres . . . Edited by L. A. Barbé. 1905. 8°. **12238. aaa. 1/56.**

—— *See* Moreau (Hégesippe) Contes à ma sœur . . . Edited by L. A. Barbé, *etc.* 1907. 8°. **12237. pp. 1/3.**

—— *See* Perrault (C.) The Fairy Tales of Charles Perrault. Edited, with notes and vocabulary, by L. A. Barbé, *etc.* 1903. 8°. **12901. de. 19/40.**

—— —— 1904. 8°. **12901. de. 19/41.**

—— *See* Sand (George) *pseud.* La Petite Fadette. Edited by L. A. Barbé. 1910. 8°. **12901. de. 19/46.**

—— *See* Verne (J.) Le Tour du monde en quatre-vingts jours . . . Adapted . . . by L. A. Barbé, *etc.* 1899. 8°. **012202. ff. 5/1.**

—— Bannockburn. A poem for recitation. pp. 16. *Blackie & Son: London,* [1910.] 8°. **11601. cc. 23. (3.)**

—— The Bass Rock, and its story . . . With twelve illustrations, *etc.* [Reprinted from "The Glasgow Herald."] pp. 62. *W. Hodge & Co.: Glasgow & Edinburgh,* 1904. 8°. **010370. eee. 15.**

—— A Book of French Songs selected and edited by L. A. Barbé. pp. 51. *London,* 1905. 8°. [*Blackie's Little French Classics.*] **12238. aaa. 1/38.**

—— Phonetic edition. Selected by L. A. Barbé . . . Transcribed by Madame Giraudeau. pp. 47. *London,* 1910. 8°. [*Blackie's Little French Classics.*] **12238. aaa. 1/93.**

—— Épisodes mémorables de l'histoire de France. (General editor: L. A. Barbé.) 10 pt. *Blackie & Son: London,* 1919–20. 8°. **9210. aaa. 48.**

—— In Byways of Scottish History. pp. vii. 371. *Blackie & Son: London,* 1912. 8°. **9510. e. 10.**

—— [A reissue.] *London,* 1924. 8°. **9510. bbb. 29.**

—— John Knox, *etc.* pp. 28. *W. Wilson & Co.: Glasgow,* 1921. 16°. [*Saint Andrew Series of Famous Scots.* no. 3.] **10804.1.14/3.**

—— Kirkcaldy of Grange. pp. 157. *Oliphant & Co.: Edinburgh,* [1897.] 8°. [*Famous Scots Series.*] **10803. ccc. 23.**

BARBÉ (Louis A.)

—— Longer Poems for Recitation. Edited by L. A. Barbé. pp. 48. *London*, 1905. 8°. [*Blackie's Little French Classics.*] **12238.** aaa. **1/53.**

—— Margaret of Scotland & the Dauphin Louis: an historical study, *etc.* pp. xii. 192. *Blackie & Son: London*, 1917. 8°. **09225.** g. **29.**

—— Poems for Recitation. Edited by L. A. Barbé. *Fr.* pp. 40. *London*, 1902. 8°. [*Blackie's Little French Classics.*] **12238.** aaa. **1/15.**

—— Sidelights on the History, Industries & Social Life of Scotland. pp. xiii. 319. *Blackie & Son: London*, 1919. 8°. **9510.** dd. **8.**

—— A Third French Reader and Writer. pp. viii. 168. *S. Sonnenschein & Co.: London*, 1893. 8°. [*Parallel Grammar Series.*] **2274.** b. **18.**

—— The Tragedy of Gowrie House: an historical study. pp. 153. *A. Gardner: Paisley & London*, 1887. 4°. **2396.** e. **15.**

—— Viscount Dundee. pp. 159. *Oliphant & Co.: Edinburgh*, [1903.] 8°. [*Famous Scots Series.*] **10803.** ccc. **14.**

BARBÉ (Louis Eugène) Thèse pour le doctorat en médecine. Du diagnostic de la folie, *etc.* pp. 71. *Paris*, 1850. 4°. [*Collection des thèses soutenues à la Faculté de Médecine de Paris.* An 1850. tom. 1.] **7372.** c. **13.**

BARBÉ (Maurice) Étude historique des idées sur la souveraineté en France de 1815 à 1848. Thèse, *etc.* pp. iv. 316. *Paris*, 1904. 8°. **8051.** g. **33.**

BARBE (P.) *See* Roux (J. J.) À bas les masques! L'usine à dynamite de Paulilles; sa fondation par M. Barbe, *etc.* [1887.] 8°. **8051.** e. **34.** (**4.**)

BARBE (Paul) *Dramatist.* Les Débuts en province. Comédie en trois actes et en vers, *etc.* pp. 66. *Avignon*, 1830. 8°. **11474.** g. **6.** (**8.**)

BARBE (Paul) *Lieutenant.* Projet d'amélioration de l'abri des troupes en campagne. pp. 16. *Strasbourg*, 1860. 8°. **8828.** g. **11.**

BARBE (Paul) *of Buzet, Haut Garonne.* Picambril. Poème toulousain en quatre chants . . . Précédé d'une lettre provençale de L. Roumieux. Traduction française en regard. ff. viii. 74. *Paris*, 1875. 8°. **11498.** dd. **3.**

—— La Vérité sur la langue d'O, précédée de considérations historiques, philosophiques et philologiques. 2 vol. *Toulouse*, 1873. 12°. **12952.** b. **52.**

BARBE (Philippe) Fables et contes philosophiques. pp. 216. *Paris*, 1771. 12°. **637.** c. **30.**

—— Lettres . . . sur la Révolution française, publiées pour la première fois et précédées d'une introduction par J. Carnandet. (Le Père Barbe; épisode de 1793. [By Joséphine Amet.]) pp. xxiv. 220. *Saint-Dizier*, 1876. 8°. **9225.** bb. **13.**

BARBÉ (René Julien) Considérations générales sur l'empoisonnement par le sublimé corrosif; thèse, *etc.* pp. 29. *Paris*, 1820. 4°. **1183.** f. **10.** (**7.**)

BARBE (Simon) Le Parfumeur françois, qui enseigne toutes les manieres de tirer les odeurs des fleurs; & de faire toutes sortes de compositions de parfums, *etc.* pp. 170. *P. Marret: Amsterdam*, 1696. 12°. **1042.** a. **15.**

BARBÉ (T. M. González) *See* González Barbé.

BARBE (Théodore Jean Eustache) Cours élémentaire de philosophie, à l'usage des établissements d'éducation, mis en rapport avec les questions du programme universitaire, *etc.* pp. 745. *Paris*, 1846. 12°. **8465.** b. **27.**

—— De l'immortalité de l'âme. pp. ix. 435. *Paris*, 1864. 12°. **4378.** bbb. **4.**

—— Du lieu de naissance de Godefroi de Bouillon, à propos du projet de lui élever un monument dans la ville de Boulogne-sur-Mer. pp. 126. *Boulogne-sur-Mer*, 1855. 8°. **10659.** ee. **17.**

BARBÉ (Victor) Des taches de la cornée. pp. 36. *Paris*, 1850. 4°. [*Collection des thèses soutenues à la Faculté de Médecine de Paris.* An 1850. tom. 1.] **7372** c. **13.**

BARBEAU (Alfred) *See* Coleridge (S. T.) [*Poetical and Dramatic Works.—Lyrical Ballads.*] La Chanson du vieux marin. Traduction . . . par A. Barbeau. 1926. 8°. **11632.** b. **71.**

—— *See* Goldsmith (Oliver) *the Poet.* [*She Stoops to Conquer.*] She Stoops to Conquer . . . Édition classique par A. Barbeau. 1908. 8°. **11774.** b. **33.**

—— *See* Goldsmith (Oliver) *the Poet.* [*She Stoops to Conquer.*] Elle s'abaisse pour vaincre . . . Traduction française par A. Barbeau. 1907. 8°. **11779.** aa. **31.**

—— De usu articuli finiti Anglici, quantum differat in Scripturae Sacrae translatione A.D. MDCXI edita et in hodierno sermone. Thesim proponebat . . . A. Barbeau. pp. xi. 89. *Lutetiae Parisiorum*, 1904. 8°. **12983** h. **21.**

—— Une Université anglaise. Souvenirs de Cambridge. Conférence, *etc.* pp. 40. *Caen*, [1898.] 8°. **8304.** d. **20.** (**9.**)

—— Une Ville d'eaux anglaise au XVIIIe siècle. La société élégante et littéraire à Bath, *etc.* pp. viii. 398. *Paris*, 1904. 8°. **010360.** i. **5.**

—— Life and Letters at Bath in the XVIIIth Century . . . With a preface by Austin Dobson. pp. xxxi. 328 **F.P.** *William Heinemann: London*, 1904. 8°. K.T.C. **37.** a. **16.**

BARBEAU (Charles Marius)

—— Assomption Sash. pp. 51. [*Ottawa*, 1940.] 8°. [*National Museum of Canada. Bulletin.* no. 93.] Ac. **1883.** c.

—— Au cœur de Québec. [Historical essays.] pp. 200. *Montréal*, [1934.] 8°. **010470.** a. **25.**

—— Classification of Iroquoian Radicals with Subjective Pronominal Prefixes. pp. 30. *Ottawa*, 1915. 8°. [*Canada Geological Survey.* Memoir no. 46.] C.S. E. **16/9.**

—— Les Contes du grand-père sept-heures. sér. 2. cahier 7–12. 6 pt. *Montréal*, 1953. 8°. **12517.** t. **57.**

—— Contes populaires canadiens. [Two articles in "The Journal of American Folklore."] 2 pt. *New York*, 1916, 17. 8°. **12450.** l. **20.**

—— Cornelius Krieghoff, Pioneer Painter of North America. [With plates.] pp. 152. *Macmillan Co. of Canada: Toronto*, 1934. 4°. **7862.** r. **34.**

—— Deux cents ans d'orfèvrerie chez nous. [An offprint from "Mémoires et comptes rendus de la Société Royale du Canada." With plates.] [1939.] 8°. **07812.** v. **5.**

—— The Downfall of Temlaham . . . Illustrations, *etc.* [A novel.] pp. xii. 253. *Macmillan Co.: Toronto*, 1928. 8°. **012604.** bb. **29.**

BARBEAU (Charles Marius)

—— Folk-Songs of Old Quebec . . . Song translations by Regina Lenore Shoolman, *etc.* pp. 72. [*Ottawa*, 1935.] 8°. [*National Museum of Canada. Bulletin.* no. 75.] **Ac. 1883.** c.

—— Grand'mère raconte—, *etc.* pp. 101. *Montréal*, [1935.] 8°. **12512.** t. **28.**

—— Grand'mère Raconte, *etc.* pp. xi. 105. *Toronto*, 1947. 8°. [*Contes canadiens.*] W.P. **1817/1.**

—— Henri Julien. [With illustrations, including portraits.] pp. 44. *Ryerson Press: Toronto*, 1941. 8°. **7867.** a. **31.**

—— Huron and Wyandot Mythology. With an appendix containing earlier published records. pp. xiv. 437. *Ottawa*, 1915. 8°. [*Canada.—Department of Mines.—Geological Survey Branch.* Memoir 80.] **C.S.E.16/9.**

—— Il était une fois—, *etc.* pp. 103. *Montréal*, [1935.] 8°. **12512.** t. **29.**

—— Indian Days in the Canadian Rockies, *etc.* pp. 208. *Macmillan Co.: Toronto*, 1923. 8°. **010470.** f. **25.**

—— [Another copy.] **010470.** e. **50.**

—— The Kingdom of Saguenay . . . Illustrations by A. Y. Jackson [and others], *etc.* pp. 167. *Macmillan Co. of Canada: Toronto*, 1936. 8°. **010470.** bb. **34.**

—— Louis Jobin, statuaire, 1845–1928. [An offprint from "Mémoires de la Société Royale du Canada."] *Ottawa*, 1943. 8°. **7877.bb.10.**

—— Mountain Cloud. [A novel.] pp. 223. *Quality Press: London*, 1948. 8°. NN. **38519.**

—— Quebec. Where ancient France lingers, *etc.* pp. 173. *Macmillan Co. of Canada: Toronto*, [1936.] 8°. **010470.** hh. **2.**

—— [Another copy.] Quebec, where Ancient France lingers, *etc.* pp. 173. *Librairie Garneau: Quebec*, [1936.] 8°. **010470.** hh. **1.**

—— Romancero du Canada. [A collection of traditional songs of French Canada. With musical notes.] pp. 254. *Macmillan Co. of Canada: Toronto*, 1937. 8°. **011483.** k. **80.**

—— Saintes artisanes. 2pt. *Montréal*, [1944.] 8°. [*Cahiers d'art Arca.* no. 2, 3.] **7813.e.1/2.**

—— Totem Poles: a by-product of the fur trade. (Reprinted from The Scientific Monthly.) [1942.] 8°. **10009.** s. 32.

—— Totem Poles of the Gitksan, Upper Skeena River, British Columbia. [With plates and a map.] pp. vi. 275. *Ottawa*, 1929. 8°. [*National Museum of Canada.* Bulletin no. 61.] **Ac. 1883.** c.

—— Veillées du bon vieux temps, *etc.* [Containing examples of Canadian folk-songs, with musical notes.] pp. 102. pl. viii. 19[20]. 8°. *See* Montreal.—*Société historique.* **Ac. 8556/3.**

BARBEAU (Charles Marius) and **SAPIR** (Edward)

—— Folk Songs of French Canada. [With musical notes.] pp. xxii. 216. *Yale University Press: New Haven*, 1925. 4°. **11483.** i. **43.**

BARBEAU (Désiré) Manuel du pêcheur à la ligne. pp. 220. *Paris*, [1888.] 8°. **7907.** aa. **62.**

BARBEAU (Geoffroi de) *Cardinal.* *See* Barbo (Guifredus de)

BARBEAU (Marius) *See* Barbeau (Charles M.)

BARBEAU (Victor)

—— La Société des Écrivains canadiens. Ses règlements—son action. Bio-bibliographie de ses membres. pp. 117. 1944. 8°. *See* Montreal.—*Société des Écrivains canadiens.* **10888.** a. **31.**

BARBEAU DE LA BRUYÈRE (Jean Louis) *See* Le Long (J.) Bibliothèque historique de la France . . . augmentée par M. Févret de Fontelle. [tom. 3–5 edited by J. L. Barbeau de la Bruyère.] 1768, *etc.* fol. **L.1.h.8.**

—— *See* Lenglet du Fresnoy (N.) Tablettes chronologiques de l'histoire universelle . . . Nouvelle édition . . . augmentée par J. L. Barbeau de la Bruyère. 1778. 8°. **681.** a. **16.**

—— *See* Strahlenberg (P. J.) Description historique de l'empire russien, traduite de l'ouvrage allemand du Baron de Strahlenberg [by J. L. Barbeau de la Bruyère], *etc.* 1757. 12°. **978.** e. **3, 4.**

BARBEAU DU BARRAN (Joseph Nicolas) Convention Nationale. Rapport et projet de décret, présentés au nom des comités de salut public, de sureté générale, et des décrets. [In justification of the measures taken by Alard, employed as a republican agent in the department of Haute-Garonne.] pp. 14. [*Paris*, 1794.] 8°. **F. 1246. (5.)**

—— [Another copy.] **F. 1241. (8.)**

—— Convention Nationale. Rapport et projet de décret présentés au nom du comité de sureté générale, *etc.* [On a denunciation of Nicolau, administrateur du département de Paris, by the Section du Bonnet-Rouge.] pp. 11. [*Paris*, 1794.] 8°. **F. 1236. (4.)**

—— [Another copy.] **F. 1241. (8*.)**

—— [Another copy.] **F. 58**. (29.)**

—— Convention Nationale. Rapport fait à la Convention Nationale au nom des comités de salut public, de sureté générale et des décrets. [On the counter-revolutionary schemes of B. Dariot and the federalists of Toulouse.] pp. 18. [*Paris*, 1794.] 8°. **F. 1246. (4.)**

BARBE-BLEUE. *See* Bluebeard.

BARBECK (Fridericus Godefridus) *Praes.* *See* Brunner (E.) F. G. Barbeck et E. Brunner De corde occulto, indeque hydrope ascite consequente. Cultro anatomico . . . deprehenso. 1701. 1760. 4°. [*Haller (A. von) Baron. Disputationes ad morborum historiam . . . facientes, etc.* tom. 7.] **43.** g. **13.**

—— *See* Hennin (H. C. von) Oratio funebris quam . . . F. G. Barbeck . . . jam pie defuncto . . . dixit Dr. H. C. de Hennin. 1704. 4°. **1185.** k. **2. (19.)**

—— *Praes.* *See* Luers (A.) Disputatio . . . de spiritibus *etc.* 1676. 4°. **1185.** i. **14. (6.)**

—— *See* Lycander, *pseud.* Lessus honoribus funebribus Friderici G. Barbeck, *etc.* [1704.] 4°. **1185.** k. **2. (20*.)**

—— *Praes.* *See* Meyer (Theodorus H.) Disputatio philosophica de igne aereo et subterraneo, *etc.* 1698. 4°. **536.** f. **4. (31.)**

—— *Praes.* *See* Sudecius (J.) Disputatio . . . altera de veneno. 1689. 4°. **1185.** i. **14. (9.)**

—— Epicedia in lugubrem excessum . . . Dn. Friderici Godefridi Barbeck, *etc.* [Verses in Latin and German.] *Duisburgi ad Rhenum*, 1704. 4°. **1185.** k. **2. (20.)**

BARBECK (Hugo) *See* Meyer (Joachim) Schillers Wilhelm Tell auf seine Quellen zurückgeführt . . . Neu herausgegeben und mit Anhängen vermehrt von H. Barbeck. 1876. 4°. **11826.** i. **5.**

—— Geschichte der Juden in Nürnberg und Fürth, *etc.* pp. 114. *Nürnberg*, 1878. 8°. **4516.** bb. **12.**

—— Die soziale Frage und das Programm Bebels. Vortrag, *etc.* pp. 31. *Nürnberg*, 1890. 8°. **8277.** ee. **3. (10.)**

BARBECK (Jonas) Disputatio medica de hydropis ascitis natura et curatione, *etc. Praes.* C. F. Crocius. pp. 48. *Typis B. de Villiers: Bremæ*, 1652. 4°. **1185.** b. **8. (4.)**

—— Disputatio medica inauguralis de scorbuto. *Typis I. Ravens: Teutopoli*, 1655. 4°. **1179.** d. **7. (2.)**

BARBECKIUS (Jonas) *See* Barbeck.

BARBÉ DE MARBOIS (François de) *Marquis. See* Barbé-Marbois.

BARBEDETTE (Désiré) *See* Farges (A.) and Barbedette (D.) Cours de philosophie scolastique, *etc.* 1898. 12°. **8470.** f. **38.**

BARBEDETTE (Hippolyte)

—— Beethoven. Esquisse musicale. pp. viii. 108. *La Rochelle*, 1859. 8°. Hirsch **2299.**

—— Beethoven, sa vie et ses œuvres . . . 2e édition, revue et considérablement augmentée. (Notice publiée par le Ménestrel.) [With a portrait and manuscript facsimiles.] pp. 116. *Paris*, 1870. 8°. Hirsch **2300.**

—— [Another copy.] **10706.** k. **34. (8.)**

Imperfect; wanting the leaf of facsimiles and the transcription.

—— Chopin. Essai de critique musicale. pp. 68. *Paris*, 1861. 8°. **7891.b.25.**

—— [Another copy.] Chopin. Essai de critique musicale. *Paris*, 1861. 8°. Hirsch **2866.**

—— Félix Mendelssohn Bartholdy. Sa vie et ses œuvres. (Notice publiée par le Ménestrel.) [With a portrait and facsimiles.] pp. 167. *Paris*, 1868. 8°. Hirsch **3654.**
The date on the cover is 1869.

—— Haydn. Sa vie et ses œuvres. (Notice publiée par le Ménestrel.) [With a portrait and facsimiles.] pp. 120. *Paris*, 1874. 8°. Hirsch **3292.**

—— Stephen Heller. Sa vie et ses œuvres. (Etudes sur les artistes contemporains.) pp. 61. *Paris*, 1876. 8°. [With a plate.] **7807.** l. **10. (2.)**

—— Stephen Heller: his life and works . . . From the French . . . by R. Brown-Borthwick. (Catalogue of pianoforte works by S. Heller.) pp. iii. 89. xii. *Ashdown & Parry: London*, 1877. 8°. **10708.** de. **27.**

—— [Another copy.] Stephen Heller: his life and works, *etc.* *London*, 1877. 8°. Hirsch **3360.**

—— Weber. Essai de critique musicale, *etc.* pp. 80. *Paris*, 1862. 8°. **7895.** e. **25. (2.)**

—— [Another copy.] Weber. Essai de critique musicale, *etc.* *Paris*, 1862. 8°. Hirsch **5002.**

BARBEDETTE (L.)

—— Comprendre. Recherches sur la raison et l'expérience. pp. 105. *Limoges*, 1939. 8°. **8471.** df. **8.**

—— Le Cycle éternel. Essai de métaphysique expérimentale. pp. 92. *Limoges*, 1938. 8°. **8471.** bb. **22.**

BARBEDIENNE (Ferdinand) Bronzes d'art, fontes d'art diverses, objets en métaux repoussés. *See* Paris.—*Exposition Universelle de* 1867. Rapports du Jury International, *etc.* tom. 3. 1868. 8°. **7956.i.9.**

BARBEDOR (Louis) Les Escritures financiere et italienne bastarde dans leur naïfueté. Ouurage composé de quantité d'exemplaires . . . Auec plusierus autres escritures et alphabets de la plus-part des nations du monde. [Engraved plates, including a portrait.] *Chez l'autheur: Paris*, [1650?] *obl.* fol. **1295.i.6.**

BARBEE (Agnes) To my beloved adopted Canada I dedicate this book on my discovery of reducing flesh without drugs, starvation, diet, *etc.* pp. 27. *Agnes Barbee: Saskatoon*, 1914. 8°. **07306.** f. **33. (5.)**

BARBEE (David Rankin)

—— The Capture of Jefferson Davis. (Reprinted from Tyler's Quarterly Historical and Genealogical Magazine.) [With plates.] pp. 36. 1947. 8°. **9617.** c. **22.**

—— An Excursion in Southern History, briefly set forth in the correspondence between Senator A. J. Beveridge and David Rankin Barbee . . . Originally published in the Sunday Citizen in May 1927. pp. 64. ms. notes [by the author]. *Langbourne M. Williams: Richmond, Va.*, 1928. 8°. **9615.** tt. **24.**
Author's presentation copy.

BARBEE (Lindsey) The Making of a King. A biblical drama. *See* Gaw (Allison) and (E. T.) Pharaoh's Daughter, and other biblical plays, *etc.* 1928. 8°. **11791.** aa. **20.**

—— Ten Days before the Wedding. A play for female characters in three acts. pp. 112. *W. H. Baker Co.: Boston*, [1929.] 8°. **11791.** a. **42.**

—— [Another edition.] pp. 46. *London, New York*, [1931.] 8°. [*French's Acting Edition.*] **11791.** tt. **1/156.**

BARBEE (William J.) The Cotton Question. The production, export, manufacture, and consumption of cotton. A condensed treatise on cotton in all its aspects . . . Illustrated with engravings. pp. 251. "*Metropolitan Record*": *New York*, 1866. 12°. **7075.** aaa. **9.**

BARBEGUIÈRE (J. B.) La Maçonnerie mesmérienne, ou les leçons prononcés par Fr. Mocet, Riala, Themola, Seca & Célaphon, de l'ordre des F. de l'Harmonia, en Loge Mesmérienne de Bordeaux . . . Par Mr. J. B. B****, D.M. [i.e. J. B. Barbeguière.] pp. 83. 1784. 8°. *See* B., J. B., *Mr., D.M.* **4783.** c. **2.**

—— Pétition au Conseil des Cinq-cents, les officiers de santé de Bordeaux, soussignés. [Signed by Barbeguière and others.] pp. 6. [*Paris*, 1799.] 8°. **F. 794. (14.)**

BARBEIRAC (Jean) *See* Barbeyrac.

BARBEITO (Carlos Martínez) *See* Martínez-Barbeito.

BARBE LABARTHE (Antoine) Dissertation sur l'inflammation, *etc.* pp. 22. *Montpellier*, [1806.] 4°. **1180.** f. **3. (14.)**

BARBELENET (Daniel) De l'aspect verbal en latin ancien et particulièrement dans Térence. pp. vi. 478. *Paris*, 1913. 8°. **12933.** i. **20.**

—— De la phrase à verbe être dans l'ionien d'Hérodote. pp. 114. *Paris*, 1913. 8°. **12924.** q. **16.**

BARBELET (Louis) Essai sur les troubles vésaniques dans la fièvre typhoïde. pp. 52. *Paris*, 1874. 4°. [*Collection des thèses soutenues à la Faculté de Médecine de Paris.* An 1874. tom. 1.] **7374.** a. **6.**

BARBELI. *See* Barbali.

BARBELLION (B. D.)

—— The Letter Box. A play in three acts. ff. 111. [*Little Marlow*, 1937.] 4°. **11779**. l. **79**.
Reproduced from typewriting.

BARBELLION (W. N. P.) *pseud.* [i.e. BRUCE FREDERICK CUMMINGS.] *See* also CUMMINGS (B. F.)

—— Enjoying Life, and other literary remains of W. N. P. Barbellion. pp. xvi. 246. *Chatto & Windus: London*, 1919. 8°. **012350**. df. **75**.

—— The Journal of a Disappointed Man . . . With an introduction by H. G. Wells. pp. x. 312. *Chatto & Windus: London*, 1919. 8°. **010855**. aa. **8**.

—— [Another copy.] **010856**. aa. **20**.

—— [Another edition.] pp. x. 346. *Chatto & Windus: London*, 1923. 8°. [*St. Martin's Library*.] **12201**. b. **29/20**.

—— The Journal of a Disappointed Man. pp. 352. *Penguin Books in association with Chatto & Windus: London*, 1948. 8°. [*Penguin Books*. no. 674.] **12208**. a. **1/674**.

BARBÉ-MARBOIS (FRANÇOIS DE) *Marquis. See* WIELAND (C. M.) Socrate en délire, *etc.* [The translator's dedication signed: B. de M., i.e. F. de Barbé-Marbois.] 1772. 8°. **8407**. b. **7**.

—— —— 1797. 12°. **837**. a. **37**.

—— Barbé-Marbois, membre du Conseil des Anciens, à ses collègues. [In reply to "Réflexions des citoyens Dijon et compagnie."] pp. 4. [*Paris*, 1797.] 8°. F. **1006**. (**9**.)

—— Complot d'Arnold et de Sir Henry Clinton contre les États-Unis d'Amérique et contre le général Washington, *etc.* [By F. de Barbé-Marbois.] pp. xliv. 184. 1816. 8°. *See* ARNOLD (Benedict) **278**. f. **14**.

—— Corps Législatif. Conseil des Anciens. Motion d'ordre pour parvenir à la connaissance de la situation générale de la république ; proposée au Conseil des Anciens. pp. 35. *Paris*, an 4 [1796]. 8°. F. **1165**. (**5**.)

—— Corps Législatif. Conseil des Anciens. Opinion . . . sur la résolution du 7 nivôse an 5, concernant les salines de la république. Séance du 8 thermidor, an 5. pp. 29. *Paris*, an 5 [1797]. 8°. F. **1186**. (**2**.)

—— Corps Legislatif. Conseil des Anciens. Opinion . . . sur la résolution relative aux salines de la république. Séance du 2 messidor, an 5. pp. 23. *Paris*, an 5 [1797]. 8°. F. **1186**. (**3**.)

—— Corps Législatif. Conseil des Anciens. Rapport . . . sur la résolution qui autorise l'envoi d'agens à Saint-Domingue. pp. 7. [*Paris*,] an 5 [1797]. 8°. F. **721**. (**8**.)

—— Corps Législatif. Conseil des Anciens. Rapport sur la situation des finances de l'an IV (fait par Barbé-Marbois), présentée par le directoire exécutif au Conseil des Anciens. [With tables.] pp. 113. xvi. *Paris*, an V [1797]. 4°. F. **29***. (**3**.)

—— [Another edition.] pp. 141. *Paris*, an VI [1797]. 8°. F. **217**. (**1**.)

—— Corps Législatif. Conseil des Anciens. Rapport sur une résolution qui met des fonds à la disposition du Ministre des Finances pour les dépenses communales. Séance du 27 thermidor, an 5. pp. 12. [*Paris*, 1797.] 8°. F.R. **248**. (**13**.)

—— Dénonciation d'un membre du Conseil des Anciens, pour fait de trahison. pp. 8. [*Paris*, 1796.] 8°. F. **951**. (**17**.)

BARBÉ-MARBOIS (FRANÇOIS DE) *Marquis*.

—— Éloge du C^en Dufresne, conseiller d'état, *etc.* [By F. de Barbé-Marbois.] pp. 24. [1802.] 8°. *See* DUFRESNE (B.) **611**. f. **22**. (**7**.)

—— État des finances de Saint-Domingue, contenant le résumé des recettes & dépenses de toutes les caisses publiques, depuis le 10 novembre 1785, jusqu'au 1er janvier 1788. [With tables.] pp. 55. *Paris*, 1790. 4°. F. **28***. (**3**.)

—— État des finances de Saint-Domingue, contenant le résumé des recettes & dépenses de toutes les caisses publiques, depuis le 1er janvier 1788, jusqu'au 31 décembre de la même année. [With tables.] pp. 48. *Paris*, 1790. 4°. **936**. f. **4**. (**3**.)

—— [Another copy.] F. **30***. (**3**.)

—— Histoire de la Louisiane et de la cession de cette colonie par la France aux États-Unis de l'Amérique Septentrionale; precedée d'une discours sur la constitution et le gouvernement des États-Unis, *etc.* [With a map.] pp. 485. *Paris*, 1829. 8°. **1061**. i. **7**.

—— The History of Louisiana, particularly of the cession of that colony to the United States of America . . . Translated . . . by an American citizen [i.e. William B. Lawrence]. pp. 454. *Carey & Lea: Philadelphia*, 1830. 8°. **1061**. k. **9**.

—— Journal d'un déporté non jugé, ou déportation en violation des lois, décrétée de 18 fructidor an V. 2 tom. *Bruxelles*, 1835. 12°. **1451**. b. **13**.

—— [Another edition.] 1875. *See* BARRIÈRE (J. F.) Bibliothèque de mémoires relatifs à l'histoire de France pendant le 18me siècle. tom. 29. 1846, *etc.* 12°. **10662**. bb. **23**. (**6**.)

—— Lettres de Madame la marquise de Pompadour : depuis MDCCLIII jusqu'à MDCCLXII, inclusivement. [By F. de Barbé-Marbois.] 2 tom. 1771. 8°. *See* LENORMAND D'ÉTIOLES (J. A.) *Marchioness de Pompadour*. **1085**. h. **8**.

—— [Another edition.] 3 pt. 1772. 8°. *See* LENORMAND D'ÉTIOLES (J. A.) *Marchioness de Pompadour*. **10909**. aaa. **27**.

—— Nouvelle édition, *etc.* 2 tom. 1811. 12°. *See* LENORMAND D'ÉTIOLES (J. A.) *Marchioness de Pompadour*. **10909**. bb. **11**.

—— Letters of the Marchioness of Pompadour, *etc.* 2 vol. 1771. 8°. *See* LENORMAND D'ÉTIOLES (J. A.) *Marchioness de Pompadour*. **1085**. h. **9**.

—— Lettres et réponses écrites à madame la marquise de Pompadour, *etc.* [By F. de Barbé-Marbois.] pp. viii. 144. 1772. 8°. *See* LENORMAND D'ÉTIOLES (J. A.) *Marchioness de Pompadour*. **10909**. aaa. **27***.

—— Le Maire de Metz destitué, au Corps Législatif. pp. 10. [1796.] 8°. F. **1001**. (**8**.)

—— [Another copy.] F. **949**. (**14**.)

—— Mémoire et observations du sieur Barbé de Marbois, intendant des Isles-sous-le-vent en 1786–1789, sur une dénonciation signée par treize de MM. les députés de Saint-Domingue, et faite à l'Assemblée nationale au nom d'un des trois comités de la Colonie. pp. 58. *Paris*, 1790. 4°. **936**. c. **6**.

—— Mémoire laissé par M. Barbé de Marbois, Intendant à Saint-Domingue, *etc.* pp. 15. *Paris*, [1790.] 4°. **936**. f. **6**. (**3**.)

BARBÉ-MARBOIS (François de) *Marquis.*

—— Observations personnelles à l'Intendant de Saint-Domingue, pour être jointes aux états imprimés des finances de la colonie. pp. 24. *Paris,* 1790. 4°. **F. 76*. (6.)**

—— Observations sur les votes de quarante-un conseils généraux de département, concernant la déportation des forçats libérés; présentées à Monsieur le dauphin, par un membre de la Société royale pour l'amélioration des prisons. [Signed: Barbé Marbois.] pp. 76. *Paris,* 1828. 8°. **6059. l. 5.**

—— Rapport sur l'état actuel des prisons dans les départements du Calvados, de l'Eure, *etc.* 1825. *See* Periodical Publications.—*London.* The Pamphleteer, *etc.* vol. 25. 1813, *etc.* 8°. **P.P. 3557. w.**

—— Remontrances . . . contre l'arrêt d'enrégistrement de l'acte intitulé Ordonnance . . . concernant la liberté du commerce pour la partie du sud de Saint-Domingue. pp. 11. *M. Louis: [Port-au-Prince?* 1789?] 8°. **911. b. 19. (3.)**

BARBENIUS (Joseph Benjamin) De haemorrhoidibus vesicae in genere et in specie dissertatio inauguralis medica. pp. 45. *Typis Tyrnaviensibus,* 1777. 8°. **T. 587. (5.)**

BARBENSI (Alessandro) Sulle principali macchine presentate all' Esposizione universale di Vienna. Relazione, *etc.* pp. 242. *Roma,* 1873. 8°. **8766. de. 3.**

—— Disegni. pl. 38. fol. **14001. d. 11.**

BARBENSI (G.)

—— *See* Ciferri (R.) Primo rapporto sul caffè nell'Africa Orientale Italiana. [By R. Ciferri, with the collaboration of G. Barbensi.] 1940. 8°. **7080. bb. 17.**

—— *See* Darlington (Cyril D.) and Mather (K.) [The Elements of Genetics.] Elementi di genetica. (Traduzione di G. Barbensi.) [1952?] 8°. **7008. df. 28.**

—— *See* Hurwitz (S. M.) [Kriminologi.] Criminologia. (Traduzione di G. Barbensi.) 1954. 8°. **6058. pp. 49.**

BARBENTANE, Hilarion Paul François Bienvenu Puget, *Marquis de. See* Puget.

BARBER. An Address to the Worshipful Company of Barbers in Oxford; occasioned by a late infamous libel, intitled, The Barber and Fireworks . . . highly reflecting on one of the honourable members. By a Barber. pp. 12. *Oxford,* 1749. 4°. **11630. e. 5. (18.)**

—— The Barber turn'd Packer, a new ballad. *A. Moor: London,* [1727?] *s. sh.* fol. **1876. f. 1. (115.)**

—— The Barber's Shop. [A song.] *J. Cranwell: [London,* 1800?] *s. sh.* 4°. **11621. k. 4. (21.)**

—— The Barber's Shop. [1807, 08.] *See* Periodical Publications.—*Salem, Massachusetts.*

—— The Barking Barber: or, New Bow Wow Wow. [In verse.] [*Salisbury,* 1785?] *s. sh.* 8°. **1347. m. 8. (5.)**

—— The Dancing Barber: a farce in one act. pp. 32. *Malta,* [1845.] 8°. **011779. de. 76. (9.)**

—— Stagestruck Barber, or the Court of Apollo. Many happy returns of the day. [Songs.] *E. Hodges: [London,* 1850?] *s. sh.* 4°. **11621. k. 4. (20.)**

BARBER INSTITUTE OF FINE ARTS. *See* Birmingham.—*University of Birmingham.*

BARBER, *Family of.*

—— *See* Barberton (Ivan G. M.) The Barbers of the Peak. A history of the Barber, Atherstone and Bowker families, *etc.* 1934. 8°. **9905. dd. 23.**

BARBER ( ) *Captain.* Instructions for the formation and exercise of Volunteer Sharp-shooters. [With plates.] pp. viii. 126. *T. Egerton: London,* 1804. 12°. **8831. a. 80.**

BARBER ( ) *Captain of the Resolution Privateer.* Captain Barber's Gallant Behaviour. [A ballad.] To which is added The Sailor's Courtship. pp. 8. [*London,*] 1773. 12°. **1078. f. 16. (16.)**

BARBER ( ) *Dr.* The Humble Petition of divers Inhabitants of the County of Hertford, who have faithfully adhered to the Good Old Cause. Presented to the Parliament by Dr. Barber, with many Free-holders, and other inhabitants of the said County, May 13. 1659. Together with the Parliament's answer thereunto. *Tho. Brewster: London,* 1659. *s. sh.* fol. **669. f. 21. (32.)**

BARBER ( ) *Mrs., Author of "Scenes of Life," etc.* Moral Paralysis; or, the Gambler. [A tale.] pp. 134. *James Burn: London,* 1831. 12°. **4415. aa. 6.**

—— Scenes of Life; or, the Influence of Religion. [A tale.] pp. 300. *The Author: London,* 1827. 12°. **4413. cc. 9.**

BARBER (A. A.) *Writer on Religion.*

—— The Home at Nazareth. [Talks on the childhood of Jesus.] pp. 79. *A. H. Stockwell: London,* [1938.] 8°. **20033. aa. 58.**

BARBER (Aeleta Nichols)

—— Embryology of the Human Eye, *etc.* pp. 236. *Henry Kimpton: London; St. Louis* printed, 1955. 8°. **07612. c. 35.**

BARBER (Agnes Anne) Country Belles; or, the Gossips outwitted. 3 vol. *Longman & Co.: London,* 1824. 12°. **N. 1781.**

BARBER (Aimée Angus)

—— *See* Connecticut.—*Connecticut Council of Churches.* Thoughts of God for Boys and Girls . . . Editors, Edith Frances Welker, A. A. Barber, *etc.* [1948.] 8°. **4398. bb. 49.**

BARBER (Alex.) *Writer of Tales. See* Goodrich (Louis) Three Rags. (Old Beetle's Crime. Adapted by L. Goodrich from a short story by A. Barber.) [1931.] 8°. **11791. t. 1/247.**

—— The Room with no Escape. pp. 287. *Hutchinson & Co.: London,* [1932.] 8°. **NN. 19291.**

BARBER (Alexander) A Church of the Ejectment, Stratford-on-Avon (Rother Street Congregational Church). [With plates.] pp. vii. 88. *Rother Street Congregational Church: Stratford-on-Avon,* 1912. 8°. **04715. e. 1.**

BARBER (Alfred Thompson) Windsor in the Last Century. Six views of the town. [With descriptions.] *T. E. Luff: Windsor,* 1897. 8°. **010358. l. 43.**

BARBER (Alice A.) Ruth Irving, M.D. [A novel.] pp. 336. *Presbyterian Board of Publication: Philadelphia* 1889. 8°. **012705. g. 28.**

BARBER (Angus Caldwell)

—— Annual Flowers. A guide to the best species and garden varieties of annual flowers, including also perennial plants which can be grown as annuals, with chapters describing their cultivation and uses. [With plates.] pp. 278. *Faber & Faber: London,* 1954. 8°. **7036. bb. 28.**

BARBER (ANNE) *Mrs. See* BARBER (William) *Wesleyan Missionary.* A Brother's Portrait . . . To which is added . . . the memorials of his late wife, written by himself. 1830. 8°. **489. f. 11.**

—— *See* BARBER (William) *Wesleyan Missionary.* Memorials of the late Mrs. Barber, *etc.* 1822. 8°. **4903. gg. 5.**

BARBER (ANNE) *Murderess.* Dying Speech and Confession of Anne Barber, who was executed . . . for the wilful murder of . . . her husband, *etc.* *W. Wright: Birmingham,* [1821.] *s. sh.* fol. **1880. c. 10. (19.)**

BARBER (AQUILA) *See* BARBER (William) *Wesleyan Missionary.* A Brother's Portrait: or, Memoirs of the late Rev. William Barber . . . compiled . . . by A. Barber *etc.* 1830. 8°. **489. f. 11.**

BARBER (ARTHUR) A Useful Table for calculating the quantity of Bronze Powder required to cover a given surface, *etc.* *Phillips, Son & Entwisle: Birmingham,* 1884. *obl.* 12°. **7945. a. 30.**

BARBER (ARTHUR VAVASOUR)

—— A Century of Deposit Banking. (Reprinted from The Bankers' Magazine.) pp. 16. *Waterlow & Sons: London,* [1944.] 8°. **8233. a. 67.**

—— Engelsk krigsfinansiering under två världskrig. [An offprint from "Ekonomisk revy."] *Uppsala,* 1947. 8°. **08206. i. 76.**

BARBER (B. R.) Kali Charan Banurji, Brahmin, Christian, Saint . . . With a preface by Sir Andrew H. L. Fraser. [With a portrait.] pp. v. 73. *Christian Literature Society for India: London; Madras* [printed], 1912. 8°. **4805. aaaa. 19. (3.)**

BARBER (BENJAMIN AQUILA) *See* ENGLAND.—*Methodist Church.* [*Appendix.*] The Methodist Church . . . By A. W. Harrison . . . B. A. Barber, *etc.* 1932. 8°. **04715. de. 37.**

—— The Art of Frank O. Salisbury. [With reproductions.] pp. 87. *F. Lewis: Leigh-on-Sea,* 1936. 4°. **7861. v. 11.**

—— God and Life Series. Edited by B. A. Barber. *Epworth Press: London,* 1935– . 8°. **W.P. 11551.**

—— A Methodist Pageant. A souvenir of the Primitive Methodist Church. pp. xiv. 319. *Holborn Publishing House: London,* 1932. 8°. **04715. f. 41.**

—— What I Believe. A symposium. Edited by B. A. Barber. pp. 160. *Epworth Press: London,* 1935. 8°. [*God and Life Series.*] **W.P. 11551/6.**

BARBER (BERNARD)

—— Science and the Social Order. pp. 288. *George Allen & Unwin: London,* 1953. 8°. **8714. b. 40.**

BARBER (BERYL)

—— Floor of Heaven . . . Drawings by Helen Jacobs. pp. 80. *Livingstone Press: London,* 1952. 8°. [*Broadway Books.*] **W.P. 177/3.**

—— Gracious is the Time . . . Drawings by Helen Jacobs. [Short sketches of the work of the London Missionary Society's hospital at Jiaganj in North India.] pp. 85. *Livingstone Press: Westminster,* 1952. 8°. [*Broadway Books.* no. 2.] **W.P. 177/2.**

BARBER (C. R.)

—— *See* MANCHESTER.—*Textile Institute.* Manual of Cotton Spinning. (vol. 1. section 3. Marketing Processes. By C. R. Barber.) 1954, *etc.* 8°. **W.P. c. 561.**

BARBER (CECIL) The Dark Station. As the sun shines, *etc.* [Poems.] pp. 64. *A. H. Stockwell: London,* [1923.] 8°. **11644. dd. 84.**

—— Sandbag Ballads and Snow-water Songs. pp. 64. *Elkin Mathews: London,* 1919. 8°. **011648. ff. 53.**

BARBER (CECIL THOMAS)

—— The Natural Gas Resources of Burma . . . With plates, *etc.* *Calcutta, Delhi,* 1935. 8°. [*Memoirs of the Geological Survey of India.* vol. 66. pt. 1.] **7107. p.**

—— The Tertiary Igneous Rocks of the Pakokku District and the Salingyi Township of the Lower Chindwin District, Burma, with special reference to the determination of the felspars by the Fedoroff method. *Calcutta, Delhi,* 1936. 4°. [*Memoirs of the Geological Survey of India.* vol. 68. pt. 2.] **7107. p.**

BARBER (CHARLES ALFRED)

—— Studies in Indian Sugarcanes. 5 pt. *Thacker, Spink & Co.: Calcutta; W. Thacker & Co.: London,* 1915–19. 8°. [*Memoirs of the Department of Agriculture in India.* Botanical series. vol. 7. no. 1, vol. 8. no. 3, vol. 9. no. 4, vol. 10. no. 1, 2.] **I.S. 356. (2.)**

—— Studies in Root-Parasitism, *etc.* 4 pt. *Calcutta & London,* 1906–08. 8°. [*Memoirs of the Department of Agriculture in India.* Botanical Series. vol. 1. no. 1; vol. 2. no. 4, 5.] **I.S.356.(2.)**

—— Tropical Agricultural Research in the Empire, with special reference to cacao, sugar cane, cotton and palms. pp. 77. *London,* 1927. 4°. [*Publications of the Empire Marketing Board.* no. 2.] **B.S.12/1.**

BARBER (CHARLES BURTON) The Works of Charles Burton Barber. Illustrated with forty-one plates and a portrait. [With an appreciation by Harry Furniss.] pp. 14. *Cassell & Co.: London,* 1896. fol. **7854. k. 19.**

BARBER (CHARLES CHAPMAN) Mr. Barber's Statement on the practice and procedure of the Court of Chancery in England. *See* HAYNES (Freeman O.) Outlines of Equity, *etc.* (Appendix.) 1865. 8°. **6190. aa. 10.**

BARBER (CHARLES CLYDE)

—— An Old High German Reader. With notes, list of proper names, and vocabulary. pp. xii. 243. *Basil Blackwell: Oxford,* 1951. 8°. **12964. n. 23.**

—— Die Vorgeschichtliche Betonung der germanischen Substantiva und Adjektiva. pp. xi. 232. *Heidelberg,* 1932. 8°. [*Indogermanische Bibliothek.* Abt. 3. Bd. 12.] **2274.1.12.**

BARBER (CHARLES EDWIN) The Coal Whippers Assistant, for ascertaining the amount of wages due, *etc.* pp. 84. *H. Teape & Son: London,* 1844. 8°. **1392. c. 44. (2.)**

BARBER (CHARLES GEORGE) The Mixed-up Papers. pp. 38. *The "Garner": Walworth,* [1888.] 8°. **12316. i. 52.**

BARBER (CHARLES GILBART) [For editions of "Precedents of Bills of Costs," by W. F. Summerhays and T. Toogood, edited by C. G. Barber:] *See* SUMMERHAYS (William F.) and TOOGOOD (T.)

BARBER (CHARLES HARRISON) Besieged in Kut and after . . . With illustrations and maps. pp. viii. 344. *W. Blackwood & Sons: Edinburgh & London,* 1917. 8°. **09082. bbb. 1.**

—— Tropical and Sub-Tropical Diseases. pp. x. 189. *Oxford University Press: London,* 1942. 8°. [*Oxford War Manuals.*] **12213.aa.8/5.**

BARBER (DERRICK A.)
—— Whither Goest Thou? A play in three acts. pp. 44. *Livingstone Press: London,* [1947.] 8°. **11783. aaa. 92.**

BARBER (DONALD HERBERT)
—— *See* BUNYAN (John) [*Pilgrim's Progress.—Abridgments, Extracts and Adaptations.*] Bunyan's Pilgrim's Progress at 'Five to Ten.' Adapted for the daily broadcasts by D. H. Barber, *etc.* 1954. 8° **04414. aa. 9.**
—— Africans in Khaki . . . Drawings by Mary Gernat. pp. viii. 120. *Edinburgh House Press: London,* 1948. 8°. **9101. e. 54.**
—— The Church Army in World War II. [With plates.] pp. 95. *Society for Promoting Christian Knowledge: London,* 1946. 8°. **9100. a. 125.**
—— An English Family at Home. pp. 16. *Sheldon Press: London,* [1947.] 8°. [*African Home Library.* no. 100.] **W.P. 1606/100.**
—— Family Affairs. pp. 143. *Epworth Press: London,* 1954. 8°. **NNN. 5208.**
—— Fortune for Four. [A novel.] pp. v. 249. *Arthur Barker: London,* 1937. 8° **NN. 27653.**
—— The Good Years to be. pp. 19. *Collins: London & Glasgow.* 1944. 8°. **08286. i. 51.**
—— Letters to a Rover, *etc.* pp. 92. *C. Arthur Pearson: London,* [1955.] 8°. **8836. a. 73.**
—— The Purvis Family. A suburban cavalcade. pp. 151. *Guardian Press: London,* 1940. 8°. **12646. ee. 27.**
—— A Soldier's New Church. pp. 16. *Walthamstow Press: London,* [1941.] 8°. **4398. aa. 18.**
—— A Soldier's New World. pp. 15. *Walthamstow Press: London,* [1941.] 8°. **8140. a. 1.**
—— The Task of Youth. pp. 12. *Walthamstow Press: London,* [1942.] 8° **4398. aa. 51.**
—— Twenty Years of Free-Lancing . . . An instructional autobiography. [With a portrait.] pp. 92. *Southern Editorial Syndicate: London,* 1947. 8°. **11858. aaa. 62.**
—— Voluntary Work with Boys. A handbook for youth leaders. pp. 70. *Vawser & Wiles: London,* 1946. 8°. **8288. df. 71.**

BARBER (DONALD ROBERT)
—— *See* ALTER (George) The Fog Effect in Photographic Astro- and Spectro-Photometry. [By] G. Alter, D. R. Barber, *etc.* 1940. 8°. **8561.1.21/5.**
—— *See* EDWARDS (Donald L.) and BARBER (D. R.) Objective Prism Observations of Nova Lacertae, 1936. [1937.] 8°. **8561.1.21/1.**
—— A Sensitometric Study of some Developers and Emulsions of Astrophysical Interest. (Reprinted from the Monthly Notices of the Royal Astronomical Society.) *Edinburgh,* 1940. 8°. [*Communications from the Norman Lockyer Observatory.* no. 44.] **8561.1.21/3.**

BARBER (DONALD ROBERT) and **ALTER** (GEORGE)
—— A New Effect in Photographic Photometry. (From "The Observatory.") [1939.] 8°. **8561. b. 49.**

BARBER (E.) *of Glasgow.* English Grammar. (Compiled by E. Barber.) 14 sheets. *W. Collins & Co.: Glasgow,* [1881.] fol. **14000.k.29.**

BARBER (E. M.) *See* HENRY (J. Harold) and BARBER (E. M.) The Violin. A few facts for the use of students, *etc.* 1893. *obl.* 16°. **7899. aa. 19.**

BARBER (EDITH MICHAEL)
—— *See* COOPER (Lenna F.) Nutrition in Health and Disease for Nurses. By L. F. Cooper . . . E. M. Barber, *etc.* [1928.] 8°. **7689.k.1/26.**
—— —— 1930. 8°. **7689.k.1/42.**
—— —— [1931.] 8°. **7689.k.1/47.**
—— —— [1933.] 8°. **7689.k.1/51.**

BARBER (EDITH MICHAEL)
—— *See* COOPER (Lenna F.) Nutrition in Health and Disease for Nurses. By L. F. Cooper . . . E. M. Barber, *etc.* [1935.] 8°. **7689.k.1/57.**
—— *See* COOPER (Lenna F.) Nutrition in Health and Disease. By L. F. Cooper . . . E. M. Barber, *etc.* [1941.] 8°. **7383. tt. 63.**
—— *See* COOPER (Lenna F.) Nutrition in Health and Disease. By L. F. Cooper . . . E. M. Barber, *etc.* [1943.] 8°. **7392. b. 7.**
—— *See* COOPER (Lenna F.) Nutrition in Health and Disease. By L. F. Cooper . . . E. M. Barber, *etc.* [1947.] 8°. **7391. v. 37.**
—— *See* COOPER (Lenna F.) Nutrition in Health and Disease. [By] L. F. Cooper . . . E. M. Barber, *etc.* [1950.] 8°. **7383. tt. 78.**
—— *See* COOPER (Lenna F.) Nutrition in Health and Disease. [By] L. F. Cooper . . . E. M. Barber, *etc.* [1953.] 8°. **7385. aa. 47.**
—— Speaking of Servants. How to hire, train and manage household employees, *etc.* pp. xii. 256. *McGraw-Hill Book Co.: New York, London,* [1940.] 8°. **07941. r. 44.**
—— What Shall I Eat? . . . Illustrations by Helen E. Hokinson. pp. 106. *Macmillan Co.: New York,* 1933. 8°. **7384. ppp. 45.**

BARBER (EDMUND) *Editor of "Country Life."*
—— *See* SUSSEX.—*Sussex Rural Community Council.* Tomorrow in East Sussex, *etc.* [Edited by E. Barber.] 1946. 8°. **10359. d. 13.**

BARBER (EDMUND) *of Tring, Herts.*
—— Painters', Grainers' and Writers' Assistant: containing the colors and the quantity to be used in the imitation of fancy woods, marbles, granite, *etc.* pp. vi. 13–101. *H. Elliot: London,* 1852. 12°. **1400. b. 50. (4.)**
—— [Another edition.] pp. 104. *Brodie & Middleton: London,* [1871.] 12°. **7942. bb. 44.**
—— Der erfahrene Gehülfe für Haus- und Stubenmaler und Firmaschreiber . . . aus dem Englischen übersetzt und mit Zusätzen versehen von Emanuel Schreiber. pp. xvi. 166. *Weimar,* 1853. 8°. [*Neuer Schauplatz der Künste und Handwerke.* Bd. 204.] **896. dd. 82. (1.)**

BARBER (EDWARD) *Archdeacon of Chester,* and **DITCHFIELD** (PETER HAMPSON) Memorials of Old Cheshire. Edited by the Ven. E. Barber . . . and the Rev. P. H. Ditchfield . . . With many illustrations. pp. xii. 286. *G. Allen & Sons: London,* 1910. 8°. [*Memorials of the Counties of England.*] **010352. h. 5.**

BARBER (EDWARD) *Baptist. See* B., P. A Reply to the . . . answer of R. B. to the discourse of P. B. . . . Also a reply, in way of answer to some exceptions of E. B. [i.e E. Barber], *etc.* 1643. 4°. **E. 96. (20.)**
—— An Answer to the Essex Watchmens Watchword, being 63 of them in number. Or a discovery of their ignorance, in denying liberty to tender consciences in religious worship, to be granted alike to all. Also, shewing how persecution for conscience came in. pp. 18. [*London,* 1649.] 4°. **E. 552. (9.)**
—— [Another copy.] **E. 561. (9.)**

BARBER (Edward) *Baptist.*

—— A Declaration and Vindication of the carriage of Edward Barber, at the parish meeting house of Benetfinck London Fryday the 14. of Iuly 1648. after the morning exercise of Mr. Callamy was ended, wherein the pride of the Ministers, and Babylonish or confused carriage of the hearers is laid down . . . By E. B. freeman of England, *etc.* [*London,* 1648.] 4°. E. **458. (8.)**

—— A Small Treatise of Baptisme, or, Dipping. Wherein is cleerely shewed that the Lord Christ ordained dipping for those only that professe repentance and faith. 1. Proved by Scriptures. 2. By arguments. 3. A paralell betwixt circumcision and dipping. 4. An answere to some objections by P. B. [i.e. Praise-God Barebone.] pp. 30. [*London,*] 1641. 4°. **115.** e. **1.**

—— [Another copy.] E. **143. (17.)**

—— To the Kings most Excellent Majesty and the Honourable Court of Parliament. The humble Petition of many his Majesties loyall and faithfull subiects, some of which having beene miserably persecuted by the Prelates and their adherents . . . for their consciences, practising nothing but what was instituted by the Lord Jesus Christ, *etc.* [*London,*] 1641. *s. sh.* fol. **669.** f. **4. (31.)**

BARBER (Edward C.) The Crack Shot; or, Young Rifleman's complete guide, *etc.* pp. 342. *W. A. Townsend & Adams: New York; Sampson Low & Co.: London,* 1868. 8°. **7906.** aaa. **17.**

BARBER (Edward D.) An Address delivered before the Anti-Masonic Convention of the County of Addison, at Middlebury, *etc.* pp. 36. *Gamaliel Small: Vergennes,* 1829. 12°. **4784.** aaa. **11.**

—— An Address delivered before the Rutland County Antimasonic Convention, holden at Rutland, *etc.* pp. 14. *G. C. Smith: Castleton* [*Vermont*], 1831. 8°. **4784.** d. **27.**

—— An Oration delivered before the Addison County Anti-Slavery Society, *etc.* pp. 16. *Knapp & Jewett: Middlebury,* 1836. 8°. **8156.** aaa. **81. (2.)**

—— An Oration delivered before the Democrats of Washington County, at Montpelier, *etc.* pp. 18. *Patriot Office:* [*Montpelier, U.S.?*] 1839. 8°. **8175.** cc. **81. (6.)**

BARBER (Edward Gordon)

—— *See* Batley (Ronald L.) and Barber (E. G.) Boiler Plant Technology. 1942. 8°. **08771.** aa. **23.**

—— *See* Batley (Ronald L.) and Barber (E. G.) Boiler Plant Technology, *etc.* 1945. 8°. **8771.** a. **17.**

—— Composing the Picture. *Fountain Press: London,* [1948.] 8°. [*Photofacts.* no. 5.] W.P. **6909/5.**

—— Landscape Photography. *Fountain Press: London,* [1948.] 8°. [*Photofacts.* no. 7.] W.P. **6909/7.**

—— Pictorial Composition in Monochrome and Colour. Illustrated by the author. pp. vi. 89. *Fountain Press: London,* [1942.] 8°. **8913.** a. **10.**

—— Pictorial Composition in Monochrome and Colour. (Second edition.) pp. 104. *Fountain Press: London,* 1946. 8°. **8913.** a. **52.**

—— Seaside Photography. *Fountain Press: London,* [1948.] 8°. [*Photofacts.* no. 8.] W.P. **6909/8.**

BARBER (Edwin Atlee) *See* Periodical Publications.—*Philadelphia.* The Museum, *etc.* (Under the editorial management of E. A. Barber.) 1885. 4°. P.P. **6322.** b.

BARBER (Edwin Atlee)

—— American Glassware, Old and New. A sketch of the glass industry in the United States, *etc.* pp. 112. *Patterson & White: Philadelphia,* 1900. 8°. **07943.** i. **7.**

—— Anglo-American Pottery: old English china with American views. A manual for collectors . . . With 93 illustrations. pp. 161. xiv. *The Clay-Worker: Indianapolis,* 1899. 8°. **07807.** g. **17.**

—— Second edition . . . enlarged, *etc.* pp. 220. *Patterson & White Co.: Philadelphia,* 1901. 8°. **07807.** g. **22.**

—— Antiquity of the Tobacco-Pipe in Europe . . . Part ii.—Switzerland. pp. 6. [1882.] 8°. **7709.** bb. **49.**

—— Artificial Soft Paste Porcelain. France, Italy, Spain and England. [With illustrations.] pp. 40. 1907. *See* Philadelphia.— Philadelphia Museum of Art. **Ac.1832/15.**

—— Catalogue of Mexican Maiolica belonging to Mrs. Robert W. De Forest exhibited by the Hispanic Society of America, February 18 to March 19, 1911. [With illustrations.] pp. 151. 1911. 8°. *See* New York, *City of.—Hispanic Society of America.* **07708.** de. **24.**

—— The Ceramic Collectors' Glossary. pp. 119. 1914. 8°. *See* New York, *City of.—Walpole Society.* Ac. **4713.** c/**2.**

—— Hispano-Moresque Pottery in the collection of the Hispanic Society of America. pp. 278. pl. lxxxviii. 1915. 8°. *See* New York, *City of.—Hispanic Society of America.* **07806.** f. **43.**

—— Historical Sketch of the Green Point, N.Y., Porcelain Works of C. Cartlidge & Co. pp. 59. *"Clay-Worker": Indianapolis,* 1895. 8°. **7807.** aaaa. **18.**

—— Lead Glazed Pottery. Part First. Common Clays. Plain glazed, sgraffito and slip-decorated wares. [With plates.] pp. 31. 1907. 8°. *See* Philadelphia. Philadelphia Museum of Art. Ac. **1832/9.**

—— [Another copy, with a different titlepage.] Ac. **1832/10.**

—— The Maiolica of Mexico. pp. 115. 1908. 8°. *See* Philadelphia.— Philadelphia Museum of Art. Ac. **1832/11.**

—— Marks of American Potters . . . With facsimiles of 1000 marks, and illustrations, *etc.* pp. 174. *Patterson & White Co.: Philadelphia,* 1904. 8°. **07944.** g. **52.**

—— Mexican Maiolica in the collection of the Hispanic Society of America. pp. 60. pl. xvi. 1915. 8°. *See* New York, *City of.—Hispanic Society of America.* **07806.** f. **41.**

—— The Pennsylvania Museum and School of Industrial Art . . . Catalogue of the Collection of Tobacco Pipes deposited by E. A. Barber. [The preface signed: E. A. B., i.e E. A. Barber.] pp. 13. 1882. 8°. *See* Philadelphia. Philadelphia Museum of Art. **7706.** de. **44. (7.)**

—— [Another copy.] **7959.** e. **2. (6.)**

—— The Pottery and Porcelain of the United States. An historical review of American ceramic art. With . . . illustrations. pp. xvii. 446. *G. P. Putnam's Sons: London,* 1893. 8°. **7942.** l. **49.**

—— Second edition, revised and enlarged. With 277 illustrations. pp. xxi. 539. *G. P. Putnam's Sons: New York, London,* 1901. 8°. **7944.** cc. **43.**

BARBER (EDWIN ATLEE)

—— Third edition, revised and enlarged. With 335 illustrations. pp. xxviii. 621. *G. P. Putnam's Sons: New York, London,* 1909. 8°. **07942. k. 13.**

—— Pueblo Pottery. (From the American Naturalist.) [*Philadelphia,*] 1881. 8°. **7707. bb. 50. (1.)**

—— Salt Glazed Stoneware. Germany, Flanders, England and the United States. [With illustrations.] pp. 28. 1906. 8°. *See* PHILADELPHIA.— *Philadelphia Museum of Art.* Ac. **1832/3.**

—— [Another edition.] pp. 32. 1907. 8°. *See* PHILADELPHIA.— *Philadelphia Museum of Art.* Ac. **1832/6.**

—— Spanish Glass in the collection of the Hispanic Society of America, *etc.* pp. iii. 25. pl. x. 1917. 8°. *See* NEW YORK, *City of.—Hispanic Society of America.* **Ac.9729/22.**

—— Spanish Maiolica in the collection of the Hispanic Society of America. pp. 150. pl. xlvi. 1915. 8°. *See* NEW YORK, *City of.—Hispanic Society of America.* **07806. f. 44.**

—— Spanish Porcelains and Terra Cottas in the collection of the Hispanic Society of America. pp. 42. pl. x. 1915. 8°. *See* NEW YORK, *City of.—Hispanic Society of America.* **07806. f. 42.**

—— Tin Enameled Pottery, Maiolica, Delft and other stanniferous faience. [With illustrations.] pp. 39. 1906. 8°. *See* PHILADELPHIA.— *Philadelphia Museum of Art.* **Ac.1832/14.**

—— [Another edition.] pp. 51. 1907. 8°. *See* PHILADELPHIA.— *Philadelphia Museum of Art.* Ac. **1832/4.**

—— Tulip Ware of the Pennsylvania-German Potters. An historical sketch of the art of slip-decoration in the United States, *etc.* pp. 233. 1903. 8°. *See* PHILADELPHIA.— *Philadelphia Museum of Art.* **07806. h. 16.**

BARBER (EDWIN MASTERMAN) *See* JADASSOHN (S.) Manual of Musical Form . . . Translated from the German by E. M. Barber. 1892. 8°. **7896. v. 14.**

—— *See* JADASSOHN (S.) Manual of Simple, Double, Triple and Quadruple Counterpoint . . . Fourth edition, revised by E. M. Barber. 1904. 8°. **7898. pp. 22.**

BARBER, alias **DALEY** (ELIZABETH) *See* HOOK (Samuel) The Life and Death of J. Carpenter . . . also the particulars of E. Barber, alias Mrs. Daley, hanged for murder, *etc.* 1805. 12°. **10368. e. 3. (17.)**

BARBER (ELIZABETH) *Novelist.* Tales of Modern Days. pp. ix. 340. *Sherwood, Jones & Co.: London,* 1840. 12°. **N. 260.**

BARBER, afterwards **BARRETT** (ELIZABETH GERTRUDE) *See* BARBER (John W.) and BARBER, afterwards BARRETT (E. G.) Historical, Poetical and Pictorial American Scenes, *etc.* 1851. 12°. **11687. c. 47.**

—— —— [1852?] 12°. **11687. cc. 34.**

—— The Poems of Elizabeth G. Barber Barrett. [With an introductory memoir by S. D. Phelps, and a portrait.] pp. xiii. 453. *Hurd & Houghton: New York,* 1866. 8°. **11687. d. 45.**

BARBER (ELMER D.) Osteopathy, the new science of healing. pp. 170. *Hudson-Kimberley Publishing Co.: Kansas City,* [1896.] 8°. **7461. b. 2.**

BARBER (ELMER D.)

—— Osteopathy Complete . . . Fully illustrated. pp. 566. *Hudson-Kimberley Publishing Co.: Kansas City,* [1898.] 8°. **7461. gg. 27.**

BARBER (ELSIE MARION OAKES)

—— Jenny Angel, *etc.* pp. 255. *Putnam: London,* 1955. 8°. NNN. **6134.**

—— The Trembling Years. [A novel.] pp. 258. *John Murray: London,* 1950. 8°. **12731. bb. 38.**

BARBER (EMIL) Die Flora der Görlitzer Heide. 1893. *See* GORLITZ.—*Naturforschende Gesellschaft.* Abhandlungen, *etc.* Bd. 20. 1827, *etc.* 8°. Ac. **2938.**

—— Flora der Oberlausitz preussischen und sächsischen Anteils einschliesslich des nördlichen Böhmens, *etc.* 2 Tl. 1898, 1901. *See* GORLITZ.—*Naturforschende Gesellschaft.* Abhandlungen, *etc.* Bd. 22, 23. 1827, *etc.* 8°. Ac. **2935.**

BARBER (ERIC ARTHUR) *See* POWELL (John U.) and BARBER (E. A.) New Chapters in the History of Greek Literature, *etc.* 1921. 8°. **11311. f. 18.**

—— *See* PROPERTIUS (S.) The Elegies of Propertius. Edited with an introduction and commentary by H. E. Butler . . . and E. A. Barber. 1933. 8°. **11352. cc. 13.**

—— *See* PROPERTIUS (S.) Sexti Properti Carmina. Recognovit brevique adnotatione critica instruxit E. A. Barber. 1953. 8°. **2046. c.**

—— Alexandrian Literature. *See* HELLENISTIC AGE. The Hellenistic Age, *etc.* 1923. 8°. **11313. aa. 11.**

—— Alexandrian Literature. 1928, *etc.* *See* BURY (John B.) The Cambridge Ancient History, *etc.* vol. 7. 1923, *etc.* 8°. [Latest edition.] **2070.e-f.** [Earlier editions.] **09004. de.**

BARBER (ETHEL C.) The "Guide" Handbook of Elocution. pp. 95. *Davis & Moughton: Birmingham,* [1934.] 8°. **11805. dd. 39.**

BARBER (EVELYN) Michael. [A novel.] pp. 303. *Murray & Evenden: London,* [1912.] 8°. **012618. aa. 22.**

—— (Second edition.) pp. 303. *Murray & Evenden: London,* [1913.] 8°. **012622. de. 23.**

BARBER (FAIRLESS) The Architecture of the Church of St. John the Baptist, Halifax. Edited by H. P. Kendall. [With illustrations.] pp. 21. *Halifax,* 1917. 8°. [*Halifax Antiquarian Society. Record Series.* vol. 3.] Ac. **5653. f/3.**

—— The Church of St. John the Baptist, Chelmorton. [By F. Barber.] Reprinted from "The Buxton Advertiser." pp. 8. [1868.] 8°. *See* JOHN, *the Baptist, Saint, Church of, at Chelmorton.* **20032. f. 49.**

—— An Essay in explanation of Fountains Abbey, *etc.* pp. 13. *C. Goodall: Leeds,* 1874. 8°. **10347. d. 3. (4.)**

BARBER (FRANCIS) *Lt. Col., Commandant of the Second New Jersey Regiment.* *See* ELMER (Ebenezer) An Elogy on Francis Barber . . . 1783. 1917. 8°. **9617.k.1.**

BARBER (FRANCIS) *Negro.* *See* READE (Aleyn L.) Johnsonian Gleanings. (Part II. Francis Barber, the Doctor's negro servant.) 1909, *etc.* 8°. **10799.k.8.**

BARBER (FRANCIS M.)

—— Lecture on the Whitehead Torpedo, *etc.* pp. 39. pl. XI. 1875. 8°. *See* UNITED STATES OF AMERICA.—*Navy Department.—Bureau of Ordnance.* **8804. ff. 14.**

BARBER (Francis M.)

—— The Mechanical Triumphs of the Ancient Egyptians. pp. x. 123. *Kegan Paul & Co.: London*, 1900. 8°. **07703. k. 10.**

BARBER (Frank Louis) The Philosophy of John Wesley. pp. 18. *Ryerson Press: Toronto*, 1923. 8°. **4135. aaa. 128.**

BARBER (Frederic Delos) First Course in General Science. By F. D. Barber . . . M. L. Fuller . . . J. L. Pricer . . . and H. W. Adams. [A revision and enlargement of F. D. Barber's "The Elements of Physical Science."] pp. vii. 607. *H. Holt & Co.: New York*, [1916.] 8°. **08709. a. 52.**

BARBER (Frederick Arthur) The Horror of it. Camera records of war's gruesome glories . . . Arranged by F. A. Barber. pp. 111. *Brewer, Warren & Putnam: New York*, 1932. 8°. **08425. de. 105.**

BARBER (Geoffrey Osborn)

—— School Education in Hygiene and Sex. Lectures given at Felsted School, *etc.* [With a folding diagram.] pp. xiii. 71. *W. Heffer & Sons: Cambridge*, 1936. 8°. **7391. pp. 11.**

BARBER (George) *B.A., Scholar of Queen's Coll., Cambridge.* *See* Bos (Lambert) *of Workum, the Philologist.* A Translation of the Grecian Antiquities of L. Bos . . . By G. Barber. 1833. 12°. **585. c. 28.**

BARBER (George) *Pharmaceutical Chemist.* The British and London Pharmacopœias compared. With an abbreviated materia medica . . . Second edition, revised and . . . enlarged. pp. 112. *Simpkin, Marshall & Co.: London*, 1864. 12°. **7509. a. 17.**

—— Third edition, *etc.* pp. 126. *Simpkin, Marshall & Co.: London*, 1864. 12°. **7509. a. 16.**

—— The Pocket Companion to the British and London Pharmacopœias of 1851, 1864 & 1867 . . . Fourth edition, revised, *etc.* pp. 194. *Simpkin, Marshall & Co.: London*, 1867. 16°. **7509. a. 18.**

—— Fifth edition, revised, *etc.* [With "The Pharmaceutical or medico-botanical map of the world."] 2 pt. *Simpkin, Marshall & Co.: London; Philip, Son & Nephew: Liverpool*, 1869. 16°. **7509. a. 19.**

—— The Student's Pocket Companion to the British and London Pharmacopœias of 1851 & 1867, with the additions of 1874 . . . Eighth edition, revised, *etc.* pp. viii. 277. *G. Philip & Son: London*, 1880. 16°. **7509. de. 14.**

—— A Complete Series of Pharmaceutical Labels for bottles and drawers. pp. 224. *Simpkin, Marshall & Co.: London; Ed. Howell: Liverpool*, [1869.] 16°. **7509. a. 20.**

BARBER (George Duckett) *See* Beaumont (George D. Barber) afterwards Barber (G. D.)

BARBER (George Herbert)

—— From Workhouse to Lord Mayor. An autobiography. [With plates, including portraits.] pp. xvi. 110. *The Author: Tunstall*, 1937. 8°. **10861. e. 21.**

BARBER (George Marriott) Tables for alloying Gold & Silver. pp. 51. *Johnson & Sons: London*, 1882. 8°. **8548. d. 25.**

BARBER (George W.) *See* Caffrey (D. J.) and Barber (G. W.) The Grain Bug. 1919. 8°. [*U.S. Department of Agriculture. Bulletin.* no. 779.] A.S. **800.**

BARBER (Godfrey Louis)

—— The Historian Ephorus . . . The Prince Consort prize essay 1934. pp. xii. 189. *University Press: Cambridge*, 1935. 8°. **20020. c. 28.**

BARBER (Gordon)

—— My Diary in France. Experiences and impressions of active service, *etc.* [The editor's preface signed: H. With a portrait.] pp. 88. *H. Young & Sons: Liverpool*, 1917. 8°. **9087. bb. 30.** *Privately printed.*

BARBER (Halford Vaughan) The Tuberculin Treatment of Consumption. pp. 32. *J. Nisbet & Co.: London*, 1912. 8°. **07306. ee. 12. (7.)**

BARBER (Harold Hayden)

—— *See* Trease (George E.) A Text-Book of Pharmacognosy . . . With contributions by H. H. Barber, *etc.* 1934. 8°. **07510. ee. 43.**

—— Physiology for Pharmaceutical Students. pp. viii. 477. *Baillière & Co.: London*, 1937. 8°. **7406. ppp. 33.**

—— Physiology for Pharmaceutical Students . . . Second edition. pp. x. 526. *Baillière & Co.: London*, 1941. 8°. **7407. pp. 12.**

—— Physiology and Pharmacology for Pharmaceutical Students . . . Third edition. pp. x. 622. *Baillière, Tindall & Cox: London*, 1951. 8°. **7407. t. 8.**

BARBER (Harold Wordsworth) *See* Taylor (*Sir* Frederick) *Bart.* Taylor's Practice of Medicine. Twelfth edition, by E. P. Poulton . . . with the assistance of . . . H. W. Barber, *etc.* 1922. 8°. **07305. dd. 6.**

—— —— 1925. 8°. **7320.i.7.**

—— —— 1930. 8°. **7305. eee. 10.**

—— Skin Disease in War. *See* Hertz (Arthur F.) afterwards Hurst (*Sir* A. F.) Medical Diseases of War, *etc.* 1940. 8°. **7440. v. 13**

—— Skin Disease in War. *See* Hertz (Arthur F.) afterwards Hurst (*Sir* A. F.) Medical Diseases of War, *etc.* 1941. 8°. **7443. bb. 1**

—— Skin Disease in War. *See* Hertz (Arthur F.) afterwards Hurst (*Sir* A. F.) Medical Diseases of War. 1944. 8°. **7444. b. 6.**

BARBER (Harry Clark) Everyday Algebra for the ninth school year. pp. xii. 372. *Houghton Mifflin Co.: Boston*, [1925.] 8°. **08531. df. 72.**

—— Junior High School Mathematics. Seventh (Eighth) school year. By H. C. Barber . . . assisted by Helen M. Connelly . . . and Elsie V. Karlson. [With protractors.] 2 pt. *Houghton Mifflin Co.: Boston*, [1927.] 8°. **08532. df. 75.**

—— A Second Course in Algebra. A text and exercise book with tables. pp. xvii. 505. *Houghton Mifflin Co.: Boston*, [1930.] 8°. **08534. de. 39.**

—— Teaching Junior High School Mathematics. pp. ix. 135. *Houghton Mifflin Co.: Boston*, [1924.] 8°. **8503. ee. 44.**

BARBER (Harry Clark) and **JOHNSON** (Elsie Parker)

—— First Course in Algebra. pp. iv. 425. xiii. *Houghton Mifflin Co.: Boston*, [1935.] 8°. **08534. ff. 61.**

BARBER (Henry) British Family Names. Their origin and meaning, with lists of Scandinavian, Frisian, Anglo-Saxon, and Norman names. pp. x. 235. *Elliot Stock: London*, 1894. 8°. **9906. ee. 7.**

BARBER (Henry)

—— Second edition, enlarged. pp. xii. 286. *Elliot Stock: London*, 1903. 8°. **09917**. b. **3**.

—— A Forgotten Chapter in English Church History, A.D. 1642 to 1662, Diocese of Peterborough. pp. 152. *S. Barker & Co.: Leicester*, 1898. 8°. **04705**. aaa. **38**.

—— Furness and Cartmel Notes, or jottings of . . . antiquities, *etc.* [With plates.] pp. 391. *J. Atkinson: Ulverston*, 1894. 8°. **010358**. f. **55**.

—— Holywell Spa, Grange, Lancashire, its history, nature, and properties, with directions for drinking the water. pp. 16. *Simpkin, Marshall & Co.: London; D. Atkinson: Ulverston*, 1870. 8°. **7470**. de. **88**. **(6.)**

—— Poems, local and otherwise. pp. 239. *C. Thurnam & Sons: Carlisle*, 1904. 8°. **11650**. dd. **10**.

—— Swarthmoor Hall and its associations. pp. 56. *F. B. Kitto: London; D. Atkinson: Ulverston*, [1872.] 8°. **10360**. bbb. **54**. **(10.)**

—— A Tourist's Guide to Furness Abbey and its vicinity . . . With illustrations . . . Third edition. pp. 104. *D. Atkinson: Ulverston*, [1871.] 12°. **10347**. aa. **10**. **(7.)**

—— The Tourist's Picturesque Guide to Furness Abbey . . . Fifth edition. pp. 63. *Graphotyping Co.: London*, [1873.] 8°. **10349**. aaaa. **1**.

BARBER (Herbert Lee)

—— Making Money make Money; or, a Primer of Investing. [With a portrait.] pp. 315. *A. J. Munson & Co.: Chicago*, 1916. 8°. **8234**. e. **63**.

BARBER (Herbert Spencer)

—— North American Fireflies of the Genus Photuris, *etc.* pp. vi. 58. *Washington*, 1951. 8°. [*Smithsonian Miscellaneous Collections.* vol. 117. no. 1.] Ac. **1875/2**.

—— Raspberry Fruitworms and Related Species. pp. 32. *Washington*, 1942. 8°. [*U.S. Department of Agriculture. Miscellaneous Publication.* no. 468.] A.S. **802/5**.

BARBER (Hervey Hubbard) and **TAYLOR** (Thomas Ivan)

—— Semimicro Qualitative Analysis. The Barber pressure bulb method. pp. xvi. 446. *Harper & Bros.: New York, London*, [1942.] 8°. **8897**. f. **3**.

BARBER (Horatio) Aerobatics. pp. 64. pl. xxix. *McBride, Nast & Co.: London*, 1918. 4°. **8764**. aa. **26**.

—— The Aeroplane Speaks, *etc.* pp. vii. 144. pl. xxxvi. *McBride, Nast & Co.: London*, [1916.] 8°. **8764**. aa. **21**.

—— Seventh edition. pp. 146. *McBride, Nast & Co.: London*, [1918.] 8°. **08768**. ccc. **12**.

—— Airy Nothings. [Stories of aviation.] pp. 133. *McBride, Nast & Co.: London*, 1918. 8°. **012331**. m. **50**.

BARBER (Hugh)

—— The Occasion Fleeting. (Essays.) pp. viii. 199. *H. K. Lewis & Co.: London*, 1947. 8°. **7682**. b. **27**.

BARBER (Ivor B.)

—— The River and the Sun, and other poems. pp. 16. *Arthur H. Stockwell: Ilfracombe*, [1952.] 8°. **11657**. i. **97**.

BARBER (J.) *Writer on Tithes.* Considerations on the Law of Tithes, and particularly tithe of agistment, as due of common right, or by the common or statute laws of England. pp. 39. *The Author: London*, 1816. 8°. **5155**. b. **19**.

BARBER (James) *Captain, H.E.I.C.S.* A Letter to the Right Hon. Sir John Cam Hobhouse, Bart. M.P., President of the India Board . . . on Steam-Navigation with India, and suggesting the best mode of carrying it into effect viâ the Red Sea. pp. 51. *Pelham Richardson: London*, 1837. 8°. T. **2094**. **(5.)**

—— The Overland Guide-Book; a complete vade-mecum for the overland traveller. [With maps.] pp. viii. 134. *W. H. Allen & Co.: London*, 1845. 8°. **1298**. h. **15**.

—— Second edition. pp. viii. 114. *W. H. Allen & Co.: London*, 1850. 12°. **1298**. g. **8**.

BARBER (James) *Dramatist.* La Dame de St. Tropez! or, the Poisoner! A drama, in three acts. pp. 44. *London*, [1845?] 12°. [*Duncombe's Edition of the British Theatre.* vol. 52.] **2304**. a. **26**.

—— La Dame de St. Tropez (or, the Poisoner), *etc.* pp. 18. *London*, [1887.] 8°. [*Dicks' Standard Plays.* no. 849.] **11770**. bbb.

—— Jonathan; or, the Man of two masters. A farce, in one act. pp. 28. *London*, [1850?] 12°. [*Duncombe's Edition of the British Theatre.* vol. 62.] **2304**. b. **1**.

—— "Jonathan," and "Sister and I." Written respectively by J. Barber and Mark Lemon [or, rather, T. Mildenhall], *etc.* pp. 24. *London*, [1888.] 8°. [*Dicks' Standard Plays.* no. 983.] **11770**. bbb.

—— The Memoirs of the D***l: or, the Mystic Bell of Ronquerolles. An eccentric drama, in three acts. pp. 44. *London*, [1842?] 12°. [*Duncombe's Edition of the British Theatre.* vol. 45.] **2304**. a. **23**.

—— [Another edition.] pp. 44. *London & New York*, [1880.] 12°. [*French's Acting Edition of Plays.* vol. 116.] **2304**. h. **7**.

—— The Memoirs of the Devil, *etc.* pp. 18. *London*, [1887.] 8°. [*Dicks' Standard Plays.* no. 901.] **11770**. bbb. **4**.

—— The Weaver of Lyons! or, the Three Conscripts. A farce, in one act. pp. 19. *London*, [1845?] 12°. [*Duncombe's Edition of the British Theatre.* vol. 57.] **2304**. a. **29**.

—— [Another edition.] pp. 19. *London & New York*, [1878.] 12°. [*French's Acting Edition of Plays.* vol. 110.] **2304**. h. **1**.

—— The Weaver of Lyons, *etc.* *See* Oxberry (William H.) The Conscript, *etc.* [1888.] 8°. [*Dicks' Standard Plays.* no. 969.] **11770**. bbb.

BARBER (James) *Rev.* The Poetical Works of the Reverend Mr. J. Barber, *etc.* [With a portrait.] 3 pt. *J. Torbuck: London*, 1739 [1738, 39]. 8°. **1077**. k. **11**.

—— The Navy the sole Defence of the Nation: proved in a sermon preached at Greenwich-Hospital, *etc.* pp. 18. *The Author: London*, 1735. 8°. **225**. g. **2**. **(2.)**

BARBER (James Henry) *See* Ackworth School. A Narrative of the proceedings at the celebration of the centenary of Ackworth School . . . Edited by J. H. Barber, *etc.* 1879. 8°. **8364**. ee. **32**.

—— James Henry Barber. A memoir, mainly autobiographical. Edited by H. M. D. [With a portrait.] pp. 89. *Headley Bros.: London*, 1903. 8°. **4907**. i. **13**.

BARBER (James W.) Alternating Currents: their nature and their uses. A practical manual for the bioscope operator. pp. 32. *Ganes: London*, [1912.] 8°. **08708**. aàa. **57**. **(2.)**

—— The Bioscope Electricians' Handbook. pp. 77. *Ganes: London*, [1911.] 16°. **8758**. aa. **21**.

BARBER (Jedediah)

—— *See* Howe (Herbert B.) Jedediah Barber, *etc.* [With portraits.] 1939. 8°. [*New York State Historical Association Series.* no. 8.] Ac. **8428/2.**

BARBER (Joan)

—— Gipsy Love. pp. 128. *London,* [1937.] 8°. [*Pearson's Big Threepennies.* no. 75.] **012632.n.1/75.**

BARBER (John) *Alderman of London.* The Right Hon. John Barber, Esq; Lord Mayor of . . . London his Speech to the Court of Aldermen and Common-Council on the impending dangers of the Excise Scheme, and the Petition delivered thereupon to the Parliament by the Sheriffs of London, *etc. See* England.—*Parliament.—Parliamentary Proceedings.*—ii. The most important Transactions of the Sixth Session of the First Parliament of . . . George ii, *etc.* [1733.] 4°. **8133.** h. **12.**

—— The City Jilt; or, the Alderman [J. Barber?] turn'd Beau. A secret history. pp. 56. [1740?] 8°. *See* Alderman. **12611.** ee. **3.**

—— An Impartial History of the life, character, amours, travels, and transactions of Mr. John Barber, City-Printer, Common-Councilman, Alderman, and Lord Mayor of London. Written by several hands. [With a preface signed: Philalethes, i.e. E. Curll.] pp. xxxi. 48. 32. xvi. *E. Curll: London,* 1741. 8°. **1416.** c. **25.**

—— [Another copy.] **615.** g. **9.**
Imperfect; wanting the titlepage, and pp. i–vi *of the introductory matter. With a portrait, mutilated.*

—— [Another copy.] G. **14784.**

—— The Life & Character of John Barber, Esq; late Lord-Mayor of London, deceased. [With a portrait.] pp. 60. *T. Cooper: London,* 1741. 8°. T. **1092. (12.)**

—— The second edition. pp. 60. *T. Cooper: London,* [1741?] 8°. **1416.** c. **26.**

—— [Another copy.] **1202.** c. **22.**

—— [Another copy.] G. **13787. (1.)**

BARBER (John) *Incumbent of Bierley, Yorkshire.* A Lecture on the Importance of the Occasional Offices of the Church of England. pp. 33. *J. W. Parker: London,* 1845. 8°. **10347.** ee. **27. (5.)**

BARBER (John) *Scottish Poet. See* Barbour.

BARBER (John) *a Westminster Scholar.* The Character of . . . Dr. Robert South. Being, the oration spoken at his funeral . . . July xvi. 1716. in the College-Hall of Westminster. *Lat. & Eng.* pp. 17. *E. Curll: London,* 1716. 8°. **491.** c. **10. (13.)**

BARBER (John B.) and **ATKINSON** (George) Lakeland Passes, *etc.* [With plates.] pp. 55. *J. Atkinson: Ulverston,* [1927.] 8°. **010360.** aa. **13.**

—— Second edition. [With plates.] pp. 69. *James Atkinson: Ulverston,* 1928. 8°. **010360.** aa. **16.**

—— Third edition. pp. 69. *James Atkinson: Ulverston,* 1928. 8°. **010360.** aa. **15.**

—— Fourth edition. pp. 70. *James Atkinson: Ulverston,* 1931. 8°. **010352.** b. **24.**

—— (Fifth edition.) pp. 95. pl. xvi. *F. Warne & Co.: London & New York,* 1934. 8°. **010352.** bb. **57.**

BARBER (John Lysberg Noël) *See* Barber (Noël)

BARBER (John Robert) Christ the Rock, not Peter. A lecture, *etc.* pp. 24. *J. Nisbet & Co.: London,* 1847. 12°. **4226.** a. **20.**

—— Lectures on the Coronation Service . . . Lecture the first . . . July 27th, 1837. *See* CHURCH OF ENGLAND PREACHER. The Church of England Preacher. vol. 1. no. 8 1837. 8°. **695.** c. **16.**

—— A Letter to the Rev. H. B. Bulteel . . . containing remarks on a sermon preached by him, *etc.* pp. 12. *Rivington, Hatchard & Son: London,* 1831. 8°. T. **1376. (9.)**

—— Repentance and Faith. A farewell sermon, *etc.* pp. 20. *R. Wrightson: Birmingham,* 1824. 8°. **4475.** cc. **112. (9.)**

BARBER (John Thomas) *B.A. See* Morgan (John H.) and Barber (J. T.) An Account of the Aurora Borealis seen near Cambridge. [1848.] 8°. **1393.** k. **13.**

BARBER (John Thomas) *F.S.A.* A Tour through South Wales and Monmouthshire, *etc.* [With illustrations and a map.] pp. xiii. 359. *T. Cadell & W. Davies: London,* 1803. 8°. **287.** c. **13.**

—— [Another copy.] G. **3944.**

BARBER (John Warner) Connecticut Historical Collections, containing a general collection of interesting facts . . . relating to the history and antiquities of every town in Connecticut, with geographical descriptions . . . Second edition. [With plates.] pp. 560. *Durrie & Peck: New Haven,* [1837.] 8°. **1061.** k. **10.**

—— [Another copy.] **1061.** k. **11.**
Some of the plates in this copy are coloured.

—— Improved edition. pp. 584. *Durrie & Peck: New Haven,* [1849.] 8°. **10412.** cc. **2.**

—— Improved edition. pp. 594. *Durrie & Peck: New Haven,* [1856.] 8°. **9602.** c. **4.**

—— Historical Collections . . . relating to the history and antiquities of every town in Massachusetts, with geographical descriptions. [With illustrations.] pp. 624. *Dorr, Howland & Co.: Worcester [Mass.],* 1839. 8°. **1061.** k. **19.**

—— The History and Antiquities of New England, New York, and New Jersey, *etc.* [With illustrations.] pp. 576. *Dorr, Howland & Co.: Worcester [Mass.],* 1841. 8°. **1447.** f. **14**

—— History and Antiquities of New Haven, Conn., from its earliest settlement to the present time. Collected and compiled from the most authentic sources. [With plates.] pp. 120. *J. W. Barber: New Haven,* 1831. 8°. **10410.** c. **11.**

—— [Another edition.] With biographical sketches and statistical information . . . By J. W. Barber . . . and Lemuel S. Punderson. [With plates.] pp. 180. *L. S. Punderson & J. W. Barber: New Haven,* 1856. 8°. **10412.** bb. **14.**

—— Interesting Events in the History of the United States . . . Second improved edition, *etc.* pp. 312. *J. W. Barber: New Haven,* 1830. 8°. **9604.** a. **16.**

—— Pictorial History of the State of New York, *etc.* [Compiled from the "Historical Collections of the State of New York," by J. W. Barber and Henry Howe, published in 1841.] pp. 376. *H. & E. Phinney: Cooperstown, N.Y.,* 1846. 8°. **9603.** d. **11.**

—— [Another edition.] Historical Collections of the State of New York, *etc.* [A reprint of the "Pictorial History" brought up to date.] pp. 409. *The Author: New York,* 1851. 8°. **1446.** g. **1.**

BARBER (John Warner)

—— Thoughts on some parts of the Discipline of the Methodist Episcopal Church; with a statement of some transactions and usages in said Church. pp. 24. *Baldwin & Treadway: New-Haven*, 1829. 8°. **4183. cc. 39. (3.)**

—— Views in New-Haven and its vicinity: with a particular description to each view. Drawn and engraved by J. W. Barber. pp. 11. *J. W. Barber; A. H. Maltby & Co: New-Haven*, 1825. 12°. **10412. aa. 7.**

BARBER (John Warner) and **BARBER**, afterwards **BARRETT** (Elizabeth Gertrude)

—— Historical, Poetical and Pictorial American Scenes; principally moral and religious; being a selection of interesting incidents in American history; to which is added a historical sketch, of each of the United States. [With illustrations.] pp. 204. *J. H. Bradley: New Haven*, 1851. 12°. **11687. c. 47.**

—— [Another edition.] pp. 227. *J. H. Bradley: New Haven*, [1852?] 12°. **11687. cc. 34.**

BARBER (John Warner) and **HOWE** (Henry)

—— Historical Collections of the State of New Jersey . . . relating to its history and antiquities, with geographical descriptions of every township in the State. [With illustrations.] pp. 512. *The Authors: New York*, 1845. 8°. **1447. g. 19.**

—— [Another edition.] pp. 519. *J. H. Bradley: Newark, N.J.*, [1852.] 8°. **1447. g. 21.**

—— Historical Collections of the State of New York . . . relating to its history and antiquities, with geographical descriptions of every township in the State. pp. 616. *S. Tuttle: New-York*, 1846. 8°. **1446. g. 12.**

BARBER (Jonathan) *Frame-work Knitter.* The Apology for renouncing Infidel Opinions of J. Barber. pp. 12. *Simpkin & Marshall: London; W. Dearden: Nottingham*, [1858.] 12°. **4015. a. 1.**

—— (Second edition.) To which are added an introduction and particulars of . . . his last illness, by the Rev. J. W. Brooks. pp. 16. *Simpkin & Marshall: London; W. Dearden: Nottingham*, [1859.] 12°. **4014. b. 7.**

BARBER (Jonathan) *Surgeon.* An Address delivered before the Boston Phrenological Society on the evening of its organization . . . Dec. 31, 1832. pp. 44. *Marsh, Capen & Lyon: Boston*, 1833. 8°. **7410. cc. 23. (1.)**

—— The Elocutionist; consisting of declamations and readings in prose and poetry; for the use of colleges and schools. pp. xi. 359. *H. Howe & A. H. Maltby: New Haven*, 1829. 12°. **12296. b. 15.**

—— A Grammar of Elocution; containing the principles of the arts of reading and speaking; illustrated by appropriate exercises and examples, *etc.* pp. 344. *A. H. Maltby: New-Haven*, 1830. 12°. **011805. e. 101.**

—— [Another edition.] pp. 346. *A. H. Maltby: New-Haven*, 1832. 12°. **1421. e. 2.**

BARBER (Joseph) *Journalist.*

—— Hawaii: Restless Rampart. pp. 285. *Bobbs-Merrill Co.: Indianapolis, New York*, [1941.] 8°. **10493. ff. 41.**

—— Military Cooperation with Western Europe. A report on the views of leading citizens in twenty-two cities. Edited by J. Barber. pp. 49. Council on Foreign Relations: New York, [1949] 8°. 08026. f. 26.

BARBER (Joseph) *of London.* The Dignity and Felicity of the conquering Saint. A sermon, occasioned by the . . . death of the Reverend Thomas Reader . . . To which is added, an appendix, containing some farther account of Mr. Reader's religious character, by Samuel Rooker. pp. v. 42. *The Author: London*, 1794. 8°. **1418. f. 57.**

—— The Oration delivered at the interment of the Rev^d^ Mr. William Ford. *See* Addington (Stephen) Peace the End of the . . . upright Man. A sermon, *etc.* 1783. 8°. **1416. g. 2.**

—— The Saint's Desire to depart and to be with Christ, and the ground thereof considered and improved, in a sermon occasioned by the . . . death of the Rev. Richard Winter . . . Also the address at the interment . . . by John Humphrys. pp. iv. 42. *Bye & Law: London*, 1799. 8°. **4903. eee. 2. (3.)**

—— A Sermon, occasioned by the death of the Rev. Nathaniel Trotman . . . At the close . . . is annexed a letter, from Mr. Trotman, to his church, during his indisposition. To which is added, an address at the interment, by Thomas Towle, *etc.* pp. 43. *C. Dilly: London*, 1793. 8°. **1418. h. 36.**

—— Sermons on Regeneration: wherein its nature, necessity, and evidences are considered, and practically improved . . . Second edition, corrected, *etc.* pp. vi. 155. *T. Conder: London*, 1809. 8°. **4454. de. 4.**

BARBER (Joseph) *of New York.* Crumbs from the Round Table. A feast for epicures. pp. 106. *Leypoldt & Holt: New York*, 1866. 8°. **12352. cc. 21.**

BARBER (Kate G.) *See* Hanausek (T. F.) The Microscopy of Technical Products . . . Translated by A. L. Winton . . . with the collaboration of K. G. Barber, *etc.* 1907. 8°. **8715. dd. 37.**

BARBER (Kenneth)

—— *See* Stanford (George C.) Understudy for the Duke. A play . . . From the story by K. Barber. [1937.] 8°. **11791. t. 1/486.**

BARBER (L. H.)

—— Jack and Jill. A Christmas pantomime and dancing cabaret for children. pp. 23. *Western Mail & Echo: Cardiff*, [1942.] 8°. **11783. aa. 36.**

BARBER (L. H.) *Librarian.*

—— Clarks of Street, 1825–1950. [Compiled by L. H. Barber. With illustrations.] pp. 177. [1950.] 4°. *See* Clark (C.) and (J.) Ltd. **8230. d. 24.**

—— A Family and a Railway. (Centenary, 1854–1954. Somerset Central Railway.) [With illustrations.] pp. 48. *C. & J. Clark: Street*, 1955. 4°. **08235. aaa. 75.**

BARBER (Leslie Claud Seton)

—— Norway. Economic and commercial conditions in Norway . . . July 1949, *etc.* pp. iv. 77. *London*, 1949. 8°. [*Overseas Economic Surveys.*] **B.S.42.a/1.(36.)**

BARBER (Lois M.)

—— For Such a Time as This. Poems. pp. 15. *A. H. Stockwell: Ilfracombe*, [1943.] 8°. **11656. n. 89.**

BARBER (M.) A Bunch of Posies. An exercise for . . . children. Suitable for harvest festivals and flower services. pp. 22. *Epworth Press: London*, 1933. 8°. **3433. eee. 43.**

BARBER (M.) The Promised Hour; or, Remains of a Spanish Story. [In verse.] pp. 84. *Thomas Bosworth: London*, 1853. 8°. **11646**. ccc. **46**.

BARBER (M. E.) Mechanical Jane. A play in one act for three ladies. pp. 16. *London & New York*, [1910.] 12°. [*French's Acting Edition*.] **2304**. h. **49**.

BARBER (Margaret Fairless) *See* Fairless (Michael) *pseud*. [i.e. M. F. Barber.]

BARBER (Margaret H.) A British Nurse in Bolshevik Russia . . . April, 1916—December, 1919, *etc*. pp. 64. *A. C. Fifield: London*, 1920. 8°. **9456**. a. **9**.

BARBER (Marjorie Maud) *See* Chaucer (Geoffrey) [*Canterbury Tales.—Pardoner's Tale*.] Chaucer's Canterbury Tales. The Pardoner's Tale. Edited . . . by Alfred W. Pollard and M. M. Barber. 1929. 8°. **11630**. bb. **39**.

—— Classified Questions in English Literature. pp. viii. 102. *Sidgwick & Jackson: London*, 1928. 8°. **011824**. cc. **39**.

BARBER (Marshall Albert)

—— A Malariologist in Many Lands, *etc*. [Reminiscences. With plates.] pp. 158. *University of Kansas Press: Lawrence, Kan.*, 1946. 8°. **7689**. ee. **10**.

BARBER (Mary)

—— *See* Dible (James H.) Recent Advances in Bacteriology . . . Third edition. By J. D. MacLennan . . . with the assistance of M. Barber, *etc*. 1951. 8°. **7561**. bbb. **57**.

BARBER (Mary) *M.B.* Some Drawings of Ancient Embroidery. Thirty specimens, *etc*. [In colours, with descriptive letterpress. Edited by W. Butterfield.] pl. 30. *H. Sotheran & Co.: London & Manchester*, 1880. fol. **1809**. a. **14**.

BARBER (Mary) *M.D.*

—— *See* Russia. [*Appendix.—Miscellaneous*.] British Doctors in Russia. [By] H. Joules . . . M. Barber. 1952. 8°. **7321**. p. **1**.

BARBER (Mary) *Translator*. *See* Kelsch (G. de V.) Canon Tiburtius de composition, *etc*. [Illustrations, with an introduction and notes in French and English. The English version by M. Barber.] 1931. 4°. **7853**. v. **13**.

BARBER (Mary) *Writer of Verse*. Poems on several Occasions. [With a letter from Dean Swift to Lord Orrery, prefixed; and laudatory verses to the author, by Constantia Grierson.] pp. xlviii. 283. *C. Rivington: London*, 1734. 4°. **642**. l. **3**.

—— [Another copy.] **77**. k. **8**.

—— [Another edition.] pp. lxiv. 290. *C. Rivington: London*, 1735. 8°. **11631**. bbb. **7**.

—— [Another copy, with a different titlepage.] *London*, 1736. 8°. **11626**. e. **4**.

—— [Select poems.] *See* Poems. Poems by Eminent Ladies, *etc*. 1755. 12°. **994**. g. **1, 2**.

BARBER (Mary Ann Serrett) *See* Periodical Publications.—*London*. The Children's Missionary Magazine. (New Series. Edited by Miss M. A. S. Barber.) 1838, *etc*. 32° & 24°. P.P. **913**. a.

—— *See* Periodical Publications.—*London*. The Coral Missionary Magazine. Edited by M. A. S. Barber. [1860, *etc*.] 8°. P.P. **916**.

—— Bread-winning; or, the Ledger and the lute. An autobiography. With an introductory preface by the Rev. John Garwood. pp. xxiii. 125. *William Macintosh: London*, [1865.] 12°. **10805**. cc. **13**.

BARBER (Mary Ann Serrett)

—— Castle Rag, and its dependencies; or, the Sins and sorrows of the poor. pp. 230. *J. Nisbet & Co.: London*, 1858. 12°. **8282**. a. **69**.

—— Childhood's Duties; or, Precepts for Little Emma. pp. v. 143. *J. Nisbet & Co.: London*, 1842. 12°. **1361**. h. **19**.

—— Du Bourg; or, the Mercuriale: a sketch of the Secret Church of Paris, in the middle of the sixteenth century; being an episode in history on the points at issue between the Reformation and the Papacy. pp. vi. 186. *J. Nisbet & Co.: London*, 1851. 8°. **4632**. b. **2**.

—— The Early Days of Faith and Love; or, the Soul arising to newness of life. pp. xii. 240. *J. Nisbet & Co.: London*, 1847. 12°. **1361**. c. **15**.

—— Earning a Living; or, From hand to mouth. Scenes from the homes of working people. pp. ii. 259. *J. Nisbet & Co.: London*, 1861. 8°. **4193**. c. **43**.

—— The Hearths of the Poor: or, True English stories from real English life. pp. vi. 134. *J. Nisbet & Co.: London*, 1852. 16°. **4415**. e. **4**.

—— The Lord's Jewels; or, Sketches of unknown disciples. pp. 136. *J. Nisbet & Co.: London*, 1853. 16°. **4416**. d. **5**.

—— Missionary Tales, for little listeners. pp. 199. *J. Nisbet & Co.: London*, 1840. 12°. **694**. a. **31**.

—— Oshielle: or Village life in the Yoruba Country; from the journals and letters of a Catechist . . . describing the rise of a Christian Church in an African village. pp. xxiv. 9–222. *J. Nisbet & Co.: London*, 1857. 16°. **4765**. a. **36**.

—— The Poor Folk at Home; and what can we do for them? pp. 231. *J. Nisbet & Co.: London*, 1856. 12°. **4417**. aa. **13**.

—— Redemption in Israel; or, Narratives of conversions among the Jews. pp. xi. 356. *Seeley & Co.: London*, 1844. 8°. **1370**. b. **16**.

—— The Sorrows of the Streets. pp. ii. 9–212. *J. Nisbet & Co.: London*, 1855. 18°. **4417**. b. **7**.

—— Sunshine: or, Believing and rejoicing: a series of home and foreign missionary sketches. pp. iv. 216. *J. Nisbet & Co.: London*, 1854. 16°. **4193**. b. **5**.

—— Sweet Childhood, and its helpers in heathen lands; being a record of Church missionary work among the young, in Africa, the East, and Prince Rupert's Land. pp. x. 324. *J. Nisbet & Co.: London*, 1864. 8°. **4766**. b. **31**.

With an additional titlepage, illustrated.

BARBER (Mary I.) *See* Van Arsdale (Mary B.) Our Candy Recipes. By M. B. Van Arsdale . . . M. I. Barber. 1922. 8°. **07943**. a. **32**.

BARBER (Minnie)

—— Growing. A nature exercise . . . for children from 5 to 14, *etc*. pp. 16. *H. V. Capsey: London*, [1935.] 8°. **04400**. df. **5**.

BARBER (Muriel)

—— Building the Temple Yet to Be. pp. 67. *Order of the Great Companions: Chatham*, 1938. 8°. [*Handbooks for Pioneers*. no. 2.] W.P. **12637/2**.

—— The Cosmic Cat, and other studies. [With illustrations.] pp. 79. *Order of the Great Companions: Meopham Green*, 1948. 8°. **07295**. k. **21**.

BARBER (Muriel)

—— The Cosmic Cat, and other studies. (2nd edition.) pp. 119. *Order of the Great Companions: Meopham Green*, 1954. 8°. **07295**. k. **98**.

BARBER (Noël)

Full name: John Lysberg Noël Barber.

—— *See* Cooke (Robert C.) Cities. By R. Croft-Cooke and N. Barber, *etc.* [1951.] 8°. **010028**. m. **3**

—— Fires of Spring. [Travel memoirs. With a portrait.] pp. viii. 181. *Geoffrey Bles: London*, 1952. 8°. **10863**. bb. **16**.

—— How Strong is America? . . . With maps and diagrams by Geoffrey Dickeson. pp. 144. *G. G. Harrap & Co.: London*, 1942. 8°. **8029**. de. **2**.

—— How Strong is Japan? . . . With maps and diagrams by Dickeson. pp. 132. *G. G. Harrap & Co.: London*, 1942. 8°. **8029**. de. **7**.

—— Newspaper Reporting . . . A practical guide for young journalists. pp. ix. 130. *Sir I. Pitman & Sons: London*, 1936. 8°. **11858**. a. **48**.

—— Prisoner of War. The story of British prisoners held by the enemy. [With plates.] pp. 135. *G. G. Harrap & Co.: London*, 1944. 8°. **9100**. i. **9**.

—— Strangers in the Sun. [Reminiscences of the author's travels. With plates, including a portrait.] pp. xi. 199. *Geoffrey Bles: London*, 1955. 8°. **10028**. t. **35**.

—— Trans-Siberian. With 11 plates [including a portrait], *etc.* [An account of a journey across Siberia and Russia. With a map.] pp. 180. *G. G. Harrap & Co.: London*, 1942. 8°. **010028**. e. **35**.

BARBER (Norman Keith) *See* Marzials (F. M.) and Barber (N. K.) Primer of Arithmetic for Middle Forms. 1925. 8°. **08531**. de. **41**.

BARBER (Orion M.) *See* Vermont, *State of.—Statutes.* The Vermont Statutes, 1894, *etc.* [Edited by O. M. Barber.] 1895. 8°. A.S.**P21/9**.

BARBER (Otto)

—— H. G. Wells' Verhältnis zum Darwinismus. pp. 81. *Leipzig*, 1934. 8°. [*Beiträge zur englischen Philologie.* Hft. 27.] W.P. **7720/27**.

BARBER (Percy S.) Fresh Air. pp. 31. *R. J. James: London*, [1907.] 8°. **07306**. e. **8**. **(3.)**

BARBER (Richard) *See* Pledge (Daniel) Memorial of Mr. R. Barber, *etc.* 1842. 12°. **4920**. aaaa. **24**.

BARBER (Robert) *Dramatist.* King Khoma: or, Change for a sovereign. An original and tragi-khoma-cal extravaganza in three scenes. [In verse.] pp. 38. [*London*,] 1884. 8°. **11777**. aaa. **2**. **(3.)**

BARBER (Robert) *of Hayton Castle, Notts.* Observations on behalf of the Hosiers of Nottinghamshire and Leicestershire, upon the allegations of Mr. Barber's petition for an act of Parliament to prolong his patent term. pp. 13. *J. Nichols & Son: London*, 1811. 8°. **1102**. k. **68**.

BARBER (Robert Cecil)

—— Report on the Original Settlement of the Mamauk Tract in the Kawa Township of the Pegu District, season 1924-25. pp. ii. 3. 23. 1926. fol. *See* Burma. [*Miscellaneous Public Documents and Official Publications.*] I.S. bu. **36/52**.

BARBER (Robert Cecil)

—— Report on the Rent Settlement Operations in the Yandoon Island Colonisation Areas of the Ma-ubin District, season 1925-26. [With a map.] pp. 3. 17. 1927. fol. *See* Burma. [*Miscellaneous Public Documents and Official Publications.*] I.S. bu. **36/47**.

BARBER (Robert Heberden)

—— A Supplementary Bibliography of Hawking. Being a catalogue of books published in England between 1891 and 1943, together with criticisms, to which is added a list of the most important books published prior to that period. *Privately printed: Westminster*, 1943. 8°. **11924**. a. **27**.

BARBER (Robert William) Abbot Samson. [A poem.] From the Chronicle of Jocelin of Brackland. pp. 52. *Jarrold & Sons: London*, 1903. 8°. **11650**. ff. **37**.

—— The Children's Charter, traced upon the Cross. [The Catechism, with a paraphrase in verse.] pp. 15. 1896. 8°. *See* Liturgies.—*Church of England.—Common Prayer.—Catechism.* [*English.*] **03504**. f. **8**. **(7.)**

—— An East Anglian Village: or, Epochs in the history of Chippenham, Cambs. pp. 37. [*The Author: Bury St. Edmunds*,] 1897. 4°. **10358**. l. **11**.

—— Pentecostal Instructions for teachers and for devotional use: weekly lessons for the second half of the Christian year. pp. viii. 136. *A. R. Mowbray & Co.: Oxford, London*, 1905. 8°. **4192**. bb. **56**.

BARBER (S.) Maggie Hay; or, Talents used and misused, *etc.* pp. 76. *S.P.C.K.: London*, [1872.] 16°. **4413**. aaa. **47**. **(4.)**

—— Mattie of the Colonnade; or, a Tale of the hop-fields, *etc.* pp. 128. *S.P.C.K.: London*, [1873.] 16°. **4413**. ccc. **3**.

BARBER (S. C.)

—— *See* Mortimer (Charles G.) and Barber (S. C.) The English Bishops and the Reformation, *etc.* 1936. 8°. **20020**. cc. **71**.

BARBER (S. W.) The Arab Bride. A tale. [In verse. With "Miscellaneous Poems".] pp. 92. *Edward Bull: London*, 1842. 12°. **1466**. e. **32**.

BARBER (Samuel) *Composer.*

—— *See* Broder (Nathan) Samuel Barber. [A biography. With portraits.] [1954.] 8°. **7900**. c. **83**.

BARBER (Samuel) *Fellow of the Meteorological Society.* Beneath Helvellyn's Shade. Notes and sketches in the valley of Wythburn. pp. x. 166. *Elliot Stock: London*, 1892. 8°. **010358**. e. **18**.

—— The Cloud World, its features and significance. Being a popular account of forms and phenomena, with an extended glossary. [With illustrations.] pp. xii. 139. *Elliot Stock: London*, 1903. 8°. **8755**. g. **47**.

—— Nature's Orchestra, and other poems. pp. vi. 106. *S. Sonnenschein & Co.: London*, 1896. 8°. **011652**. k. **51**.

BARBER (Samuel) *Playwright.* Ecce Homo. A drama in three acts. [By S. Barber.] [1932.] fol. *See* Homo. **1876**. cc. **25**.

—— "The Last Decision." A play in four acts . . . Translated by W. Shand. ff. 29. [*London*, 1932.] fol. **11747**. l. **23**. *Typewritten.*

BARBER (Sydney Hilton) *See* Leeuwen (S. van) S. van Leeuwen's Censura forensis. Translated . . . by S. H. Barber, *etc.* 1896. 8°. **6006**. g. **19**.

BARBER (SYDNEY HILTON)

—— *See* ORANGE FREE STATE. The Statute Law of the Orange River Colony. Translated by C. L. Botha . . . Translation revised by S. H. Barber, *etc.* 1901. 8º. **6605**. d. **2**.

—— *See* TRANSVAAL. The Statute Law of the Transvaal. Translated by S. H. Barber, *etc.* 1901. 8º. **6605**. d. **1**.

—— *See* TRANSVAAL. Translation into English of the Transvaal Gold Law . . . By S. H. Barber. 1896. 8º. **06606**. f. **23**.

—— *See* TRANSVAAL.—*Hooggerechtshof.* Reports of Cases decided in the Supreme Court of the South African Republic—Transvaal, *etc.* (vol. III. Jan. 1889 to Dec. 1890. vol. IV. Jan. 1891 to Dec. 1892. Reported by S. H. Barber . . . and W. A. Macfadyen.) 1894, *etc.* 8º. **06606**. h. **16**.

BARBER (THOMAS) *Artist.* Barber's Picturesque Illustrations of the Isle of Wight, etc. accompanied by historical and topographical descriptions. pp. 110. *Simpkin & Marshall: London,* [1834.] 8º. **578**. g. **40**.

—— [Another edition.] pp. ii. 110. [*London,* 1845.] 8º. **10368**. f. **14**.

—— [A reissue.] [With a geological map.] [*London,* 1846.] 8º. **10368**. f. **13**.

BARBER (THOMAS) *Rector of Elmsett, Suffolk.* David: warrior, poet, prophet, king: his life related and his character described. pp. ix. 263. *Simpkin, Marshall & Co.: London,* 1876. 8º. **4807**. cc. **12**.

—— Essays & Thoughts on various subjects, theological, literary, and general. pp. vii. 396. *Simpkin, Marshall & Co.: London,* 1888. 8º. **12350**. dd. **5**.

BARBER (THOMAS) *Rector of Houghton Conquest.* The Character and Obligations of Christian Ministers: a sermon preached at the primary visitation of the . . . Archdeacon of Bedford, *etc.* pp. 39. *J. Deighton & Sons: Cambridge,* 1823. 8º. **T. 1039. (7.)**

—— The Importance and Necessity of Religion to National Education, and to the right application of all human knowledge. A sermon, *etc.* pp. 48. *J. Deighton & Sons: Cambridge,* 1825. 8º. **T. 1041. (14.)**

BARBER (THOMAS CALDWELL)

—— *See* NEWELL (Wilmon) and BARBER (T. C.) The Argentine Ant. 1913. 8º. [*U.S. Bureau of Entomology. Bulletin.* no. 122.] **A.S. 814**.

—— *See* ROSENFELD (A. H.) and BARBER (T. C.) El Gusano Chupador de la Caña de Azúcar. [1914.] 8º. **7078**. k. **13**.

BARBER (THOMAS GERRARD) *See* BRECKNOCK (Albert) The Pilgrim Poet, Lord Byron of Newstead . . . With introduction by the Rev. T. G. Barber, *etc.* 1911. 8º. **010854**. h. **14**.

—— Byron—and where he is buried. [With plates, including portraits.] pp. xxiv. 143. *H. Morley & Sons: Hucknall,* 1939. 8º. **10858**. g. **8**.

—— Hucknall Torkard Church: its history and Byron associations, *etc.* [With illustrations.] pp. 69. *Hucknall,* [1925.] 8º. **04705**. bb. **31**.

—— [Another copy.] **04705**. bb. **41**.

BARBER (THOMAS HENRY DE TREVES DESTOUET) The Treatment of Varicose Veins of the lower extremities by injections. pp. 120. *J. Wright & Sons: Bristol,* 1929. 8º. **07630**. de. **14**.

BARBER (THOMAS S.) Photo-Engraving, Electrotyping and Stereotyping. pp. vii. 274. *Sir I. Pitman & Sons: London,* 1933. 8º. [*Art and Practice of Printing.*] **7942**. t. **19/4**.

BARBER (THOMAS GERRARD)

—— Photo-Engraving. 2 pt. pp. 136. *Sir Isaac Pitman & Sons: London,* 1947. 8º. [*Printing Theory and Practice,* 16, 17.] W.P. **2467/16, 17**.

—— The Sun Compendium for Users of Photo-process Engraving . . . Compiled and edited by T. S. Barber. pp. viii. 168. *Sun Engraving Co.: London,* 1919. 8º. **07942**. c. **46**.

BARBER (THOMAS VERNON HOLLINGSWORTH)

—— Money. What it is and what it is not. pp. 16. *W. Cartmel & Sons: St. Albans,* [1938.] 8º. [" *Traveller's Friend* " *Series.*] W.P. **10833**.

—— " The Unknown God," *etc.* pp. 109. *Churchman Publishing Co.: London,* [1948.] 8º. **04376**. g. **96**.

BARBER (THOMAS WALTER) *See* LONDON.—III. *Thames Barrage Committee.* The Port of London and the Thames Barrage. A series of expert studies and reports . . . by . . . T. W. Barber [and others], *etc.* 1907. 4º. **8235**. i. **58**.

—— Civil Engineering Types and Devices . . . With 1,760 illustrations. pp. viii. 245. *C. Lockwood & Son: London,* 1915. 8º. **08768**. bb. **29**.

—— Civil Engineering Design. Types and Devices . . . Second edition, enlarged [of " Civil Engineering Types and Devices "]. pp. viii. 252. *C. Lockwood & Son: London,* 1924. 8º. **8763**. df. **14**.

—— Civil Engineering Design. Types and Devices . . . Third edition, revised and enlarged, *etc.* pp. viii. 254. *Technical Press: London,* 1937. 8º. **08770**. b. **30**.

—— Civil Engineering Design: notes and sketches . . . Fourth edition, revised and enlarged by Rolt Hammond. [With a bibliography.] pp. x. 273. *Technical Press: London,* 1955. 8º. **08774**. g. **14**.

—— The Engineer's Sketch-Book of mechanical movements, devices . . . and details . . . With . . . illustrations, *etc.* pp. 243. *E. & F. N. Spon: London,* 1889. 8º. **8768**. i. **14**.

—— Third edition, considerably enlarged, *etc.* pp. xii. 335. *E. & F. N. Spon: London,* 1897. 8º. **08766**. b. **1**.

—— Fifth edition, revised and enlarged, *etc.* pp. xii. 355. *E. & F. N. Spon: London,* 1906. 8º. **08767**. f. **25**.

—— Sixth edition, *etc.* pp. xii. 355. *E. & F. N. Spon: London,* 1918. 8º. **08768**. b. **19**.

—— The Great Thames Barrage. (Reprinted from " Public Works.") [With a view of the river as barraged, plans, etc.] pp. 15. [*London,* 1903.] 4º. **8766**. h. **18**.

—— [Another edition.] pp. 31. *St. Bride's Press: London,* [1905.] 4º. **8768**. g. **13**.

—— The Repair and Maintenance of Machinery . . . With . . . illustrations. pp. x. 466. *E. & F. N. Spon: London,* 1895 [1894]. 8º. **8767**. k. **29**.

—— Scientific Theology. Essays towards the development of religious truth on the basis of modern science. pp. x. 190. *Elliot Stock: London,* 1884. 8º. **4373**. de. **17**.

BARBER (W. E.) A Plan by which Political Parties in a Republic may be legally empowered to select Candidates for Office. *See* PHILADELPHIA.—*Union League.* Essays on Political Organization, *etc.* 1868. 8º. **8177**. c. **86**. **(10.)**

BARBER (W. T.)

—— *See* JONES (H. T.) and BARBER (W. T.) Metal Work for Senior Schools. 1934. 8º. **7943**. r. **7**.

BARBER (WILLIAM) *Barrister-at-Law.* *See* DART (Joseph H.) A Treatise on the Law and Practice relating to Vendors and Purchasers . . . By the author, and W. Barber. 1871. [1870.] 8°. **6305. cc. 2.**

—— —— 1876. [1875.] 8°. **6305. dd. 10.**

—— —— 1888. 8°. **6306. i. 9.**

BARBER (WILLIAM) *Wesleyan Missionary.* A Brother's Portrait; or, Memoirs of the late Rev. W. Barber. Compiled chiefly from his journals and . . . correspondence by Aquila Barber . . . To which is added, as an appendix, the memorials of his late wife, written by himself. pp. xvi. 438. viii. 72. [*Aquila Barber*:] *London,* 1830. 8°. **489. f. 11.**

—— Memorials of the late Mrs. Barber, *etc.* pp. 135. *J. Roberts: Gloucester,* 1822. 8°. **4903. gg. 5.**
Printed for domestic circulation only. Containing a MS. *dedication by the author.*

BARBER (WILLIAM CAMBRIDGE) The Religious Difficulty in National Education. pp. 62. *W. Stewart & Co.: London,* 1875. 8°. **8304. de. 37.**

BARBER (WILLIAM CHARLES)

—— Elmira College. The first hundred years. [With plates.] pp. xiv. 290. *McGraw-Hill Book Co.: New York,* [1955.] 8°. **08385. g. 47.**

BARBER (WILLIAM HENRY) *B.A.* *See* KINGSLEY (Charles) [*Novels.*] Hereward the Wake . . . With introduction and notes by W. H. Barber. 1914. 8°. [*Longmans' Class-Books of English Literature.*] **012273. e. 1/33.**

BARBER (WILLIAM HENRY) *Reader in French Literature, Birkbeck College.*

—— *See* JOLIVET (R.) Introduction to Kierkegaard . . . Translated by W. H. Barber. 1950. 8°. **03560. g. 11.**

—— Leibniz in France. From Arnauld to Voltaire. A study in French reactions to Leibnizianism, 1670–1760. pp. xi. 276. *Clarendon Press: Oxford,* 1955. 8°. **08486. i. 20.**

BARBER (WILLIAM HENRY) *Solicitor.* *See* STEPHEN (*Sir* George) The Royal Pardon vindicated, in a review of the case between Mr. W. H. Barber and the Incorporated Law Society, *etc.* 1851. 8°. **1132. f. 26.**

—— —— 1852. 8°. **1132. f. 26*.**

—— The Case of Mr. W. H. Barber: containing copies of all the documents recently submitted to . . . Sir George Grey . . . a Letter from Norfolk Island, showing the revolting cruelties to which Mr. Barber was there subjected; and a narrative of the steps by which his deliverance has been effected. pp. 116. *James Truscott: London,* 1849. 8°. **1414. d. 38.**
A rough proof, with a MS. *correction on the titlepage.*

—— Fourth edition. pp. 116. *Effingham Wilson: London,* 1849. 8°. **1132. f. 7. (1.)**

—— Seventh edition. pp. 144. *Effingham Wilson: London,* 1849. 8°. **1132. f. 7. (2.)**

—— [Another copy.] **1132. f. 7. (3.)**
Attached to this copy is a letter from the author, presenting two copies of the work to the Museum.

—— Eighth edition, with a declaration by the Jury, retracting verdict, observations on the refusal of his Attorney's certificate, a narrative of his . . . treatment in Norfolk Island, and petition to the House of Commons for inquiry & redress. pp. xii. 254. *Effingham Wilson: London,* 1853. 8°. **1414. d. 11.**

—— Ninth edition, *etc.* pp. xii. 254. *Effingham Wilson: London,* 1853. 8°. **1417. g. 31.**

BARBER (WILLIAM THEODORE AQUILA) Choice and Decision. *See* BUCKLAND (Augustus R.) Words of Help on Belief and Conduct, *etc.* 1905. 8°. **04429. l. 36.**

—— The Chrysanthemum and the Rising Sun. A sketch of life in Japan for boys and girls. pp. 32. *C. H. Kelly: London,* 1892. 16°. **10058. a. 36. (4.)**

—— David Hill, an Apostle to the Chinese. [With a portrait.] pp. 128. *C. H. Kelly: London,* [1906.] 8°. [*Library of Missionary Biography.*] **4907.a.16/1.**

—— David Hill, Missionary and Saint. [With a portrait.] pp. 331. *C. H. Kelly: London,* 1898. 8°. **4907. g. 13.**

—— Second edition. pp. 337. *C. H. Kelly: London,* 1898. 8°. **4907. g. 18.**

—— Fifth edition. pp. 320. *Robert Culley: London,* [1909.] 8°. **4907. e. 22.**

—— Golden Lilies and the Flowery Land. Glimpses of a Chinese city, *etc.* pp. 32. *C. H. Kelly: London,* 1894 [1893]. 16°. **10058. a. 36. (5.)**

—— The Land of the Morning Calm. A talk with English boys and girls about Corea. [With illustrations.] pp. 31. *C. H. Kelly: London,* 1895. 16°. **10058. a. 36. (7.)**

—— The Morning of Life. Addresses, *etc.* pp. 226. *C. H. Kelly: London,* 1914. 8°. **4475. ff. 22.**

—— Raymond Lull, the Illuminated Doctor: a study in mediæval missions. pp. xi. 172. *C. H. Kelly: London,* [1903.] 8°. **4864. de. 7.**

—— The Unfolding of Life, *etc.* pp. 246. *C. H. Kelly: London,* 1917. 8°. **08311. ee. 6.**

—— [Another edition.] (Revised.) pp. 128. *Epworth Press: London,* 1932. 8°. **08408. eee. 44.**

BARBER (WINIFRED)

—— The Sealyham Terrier. His origin, history and show points, *etc.* [With a portrait.] pp. 60. pl. XXVIII. *"Our Dogs" Publishing Co.: Manchester,* [1938.] 8°. **07295. f. 30.**

BARBERA, *Saint.* *See* BARBARA.

BARBERA (A. G.) Rapporto tra la eliminazione dell'urea e della bile nel digiuno e dopo differenti generi di alimentazione, *etc.* 1894. *See* BOLOGNA.—*Società Medico-Chirurgica.* Bullettino delle scienze mediche, *etc.* ser. 7. vol. 5. 1829, *etc.* 8°. **Ac. 3702/3.**

BARBÈRA (GASPERO) *See* BARBÈRA (P.) Annali bibliografici e catalogo ragionato delle edizioni di Barbèra, Bianchi e Comp. e di G. Barbèra . . . 1854–1880. 1904, *etc.* 4°. **11907. g. 4.**

—— *See* RIDOLFI (C.) *Marquis.* Toscana ed Austria. Scritto dei signori Marchese C. Ridolfi, Bar. B. Ricasoli . . . Barbera editore. 1859. 8°. **8032. d. 71. (7.)**

—— Lettere di Gaspero Barbèra, tipografo editore, 1841–1879. Pubblicate dai figli (Piero, Luigi, Gino Barbèra). Con prefazione di Alessandro d'Ancona. pp. xx. 317. *Firenze,* 1914. 8°. **010905. e. 8.**

—— Catalogo perenne delle edizioni e delle opere in deposito per ordine cronologico . . . G. Barbèra editore. Prima edizione. ff. 103. *Firenze,* 1897. 8°. **011899. g. 8.**

—— Memorie di un editore pubblicate dai figli (P. & L. Barbèra). [With a portrait.] pp. vii. 623. *Firenze,* 1883. 8°. **10629. bb. 28.**

—— [Another edition, edited by Gino Barbèra. With a portrait.] pp. viii. 424. *Firenze,* 1930. 8°. **10633. pp. 5.**

BARBÈRA (GINO) *See* BARBÈRA (Gaspero) Lettere di Gaspero Barbèra . . . Pubblicate dai figli (Piero, Luigi, Gino Barbèra), *etc.* 1914. 8°. **010905**. e. **8**.

—— *See* BARBÈRA (Gaspero) Memorie di un editore. [Edited by Gino Barbèra.] 1930. 8°. **10633**. pp. **5**.

—— *See* BARBÈRA (P.) Annali bibliografici . . . di Barbèra, Bianchi e Comp. 1854–1880. [By P., L., and G. Barbèra.] 1904, *etc.* 4°. **11907**. g. **4**.

BARBÈRA (GIUSEPPE) *Medical Officer in the Fascist Militia.*

—— L'Africa non fa paura. [Reminiscences of the Abyssinian war. With plates.] pp. 234. *Roma,* a. xv [1937]. 8°. **09061**. aaa. **37**.

BARBERA (GIUSEPPE) *Orientalist.*

—— Dizionario maltese-arabo-italiano. Con una grammatica comparata arabo-maltese. 4 vol. *Beyrouth,* 1939, 40. 8°. **012904**. k. **71**.

BARBÈRA (LUIGI) *See* BARBÈRA (Gaspero) Lettere di Gaspero Barbèra . . . Pubblicate dai figli (Piero, Luigi, Gino Barbèra), *etc.* 1914. 8°. **010905**. e. **8**.

—— *See* BARBÈRA (Gaspero) Memorie di un editore pubblicate dai figli (P. & L. Barbèra). 1883. 8°. **10629**. bb. **28**.

—— *See* BARBÈRA (P.) Annali bibliografici . . . di Barbèra, Bianchi e Comp. . . . 1854–1880. [By P., L., and G. Barbèra.] 1904, *etc.* 4°. **11907**. g. **4**.

—— *See* BARBÈRA (P.) and (L.) L'Edizione delle opere di A. Poliziano curata da G. Carducci e I. del Lungo . . . Saggio bibliografico. 1895. 8°. **11905**. d. **11**. (**3**.)

—— Della legge di universale rotazione e della unità nel sistema del mondo. pp. xi. 49. *Napoli,* 1867. 4°. **8705**. f. **33**. (**5**.)

—— *See* ANTONELLI (Giovanni) Sulla legge di universale rotazione per L. Barbera, *etc.* 1867. 8°. **8704**. e. **25**. (**4**.)

—— Lezioni di logica inventiva. vol. 1. pp. viii. 568. pl. 4. *Pisa,* 1866. 8°. **8467**. aa. **29**.

—— La Morale nella democrazia. Discorso, *etc.* pp. 34. *Bologna,* 1891. 8°. **8008**. h. **18**. (**3**.)

—— Nuovo metodo dei massimi e minimi delle funzioni primitive e integrali. pp. li. 181. *Bologna,* 1877. 8°. **8533**. h. **6**.

—— Teorica del calcolo delle funzioni. pp. vii. 130. *Bologna,* 1876. 8°. **8533**. cc. **5**.

BARBERA (MARIA TERESA)

—— Documenti inediti intorno alla vita e alle opere di Girolamo Alibrandi, pittore messinese del 500. [Edited by M. T. Barbera.] *Lat.* pp. 15. *Patti,* 1950. 8°. **10634**. i. **67**.

—— Girolamo Alibrandi detto il Raffaello messinese. pp. 37. *Patti,* 1950. 8°. **7870**. bb. **37**.

BARBÈRA (PIERO) *See* BARBÈRA (Gaspero) Lettere di Gaspero Barbèra . . . Pubblicate dai figli (Piero, Luigi, Gino Barbèra), *etc.* 1914. 8°. **010905**. e. **8**.

—— *See* BARBÈRA (Gaspero) Memorie di un editore pubblicate dai figli (P. & L. Barbèra). 1883. 8°. **10629**. bb. **28**.

—— *See* CARDUCCI (G.) Il Libro delle prefazioni. [Edited by P. Barbèra.] 1912. 32°. **11840**. a. **14**.

—— *See* LUMACHI (F.) Nella repubblica del libro. Prefazione di P. Barbèra. 1907. 8°. **011907**. g. **9**.

BARBÈRA (PIERO)

—— *See* SODINI (A.) Un Maestro del libro. P. Barbèra. [With a bibliography and a portrait.] 1922. 8°. **011851**. cc. **48**.

—— *See* STERNE (L.) [*Sentimental Journey.*] Il Viaggio sentimentale di Yorick . . . Introduzione di P. Barbèra. 1922. 16°. **944**. bb. **6**.

—— Annali bibliografici e catalogo ragionato delle edizioni di Barbèra, Bianchi e Comp. e di G. Barbèra . . . 1854–1880. [By P., L., and G. Barbèra. With " Addenda & corrigenda."] 2 pt. *Firenze,* 1904, 18. 4°. **11907**. g. **4**.

—— Editori e autori. Studi e passatempi di un libraio. pp. 337. *Firenze,* 1904. 8°. **011853**. gg. **63**.

—— Le Feste del IV. centenario cenniniano. Relazione. *See* CENNINI (B.) Le Feste, *etc.* 1871. 8°. **10631**. e. **42**. (**12**.)

—— Gino Capponi. I suoi tempi e i suoi amici. *See* TUSCANY. [*Appendix.*] La Toscana alla fine del granducato. Conferenze, *etc.* 1909. 8°. **9165**. a. **21**.

—— Nicolò Bettoni. Avventure di un editore, *etc.* pp. 136. *Firenze,* 1892. 8°. **10629**. d. **20**.

BARBÈRA (PIERO) and **BARBÈRA** (LUIGI)

—— L'Edizione delle opere di A. Poliziano curata da G. Carducci e I. del Lungo . . . Saggio bibliografico. pp. 17. **L.P.** *Firenze,* 1895. 8°. **11905**. d. **11**. (**3**.)

BARBERÁN (CECILIO)

—— Eduardo Navarro. (14 ilustraciones.) pp. 87. *Madrid,* 1932. 8°. **7857**. aa. **74**.

—— Gutiérrez Solana. [With reproductions of the artist's works, and a portrait.] pp. 89. *Madrid,* 1933. 8°. **7861**. p. **3**.

BARBERAUD (CHARLES) *See* CHER, *Department of.* Inventaire-sommaire des archives départementales antérieures à 1790, rédigé par MM. Barberaud et Boyer . . . Cher. 1883, *etc.* 4°. S. **148**. a. **19**.

BARBÈRE (BERTRAND) *See* TASSO (T.) [*Supposititious Works.*] Les Veillées du Tasse . . . Traduites par M. B. Barbère, *etc.* 1804. 12°. **1063**. f. **23**.

BARBERE (JOHN) *See* BARBOUR.

BARBEREAU (AUGUSTE MATHURIN BALTHASAR) Études sur l'origine du système musical. Premier mémoire. pp. cxxxv. *Paris, Metz,* 1852. 8°. **7895**. e. **7**.

BARBERENA (SANTIAGO I.) Monografías Departamentales. v.(—VII.) . . . Por . . . S. I. Barberena. 3 pt. 1910. 8°. *See* SALVADOR, *Republic of.* —*Dirección general de Estadística.* **8179**. e. **30**.

—— Quicheísmos. Contribución al estudio del folklore americano. ser. 1. pp. 323. *San Salvador,* [1894.] 8°. **12450**. f. **21**.

No more published.

BARBERET (CHARLES)

—— L'Histoire du moyen âge et l'histoire de France. pp. x. 383. *See* LEÇONS. Leçons d'histoire, *etc.* tom. 2. [1856.] 8°. **739**. l. **14**.

BARBERET (CHARLES) and **MAGIN-MARRENS** (ALFRED)

—— Précis de géographie historique universelle. pp. 860. *Paris,* 1841. 8°. **793**. g. **23**.

BARBERET (Denis) *See* Berryat (J.) Collection académique (partie étrangère), composée des mémoires . . . des plus célèbres académies . . . étrangères . . . traduits en françois, *etc.* [The tables to the first three volumes compiled by D. Barberet.] 1755, *etc.* 4°.
732. e. **16–19** & f. **1–8**.

—— Dissertation sur le rapport qui se trouve entre les phénoménes du tonnerre, et ceux de l'électricité, *etc.* pp. 16. *Bordeaux,* 1750. 4°. T.C.2.a.13.(6.)

—— Mémoire sur les maladies épidémiques des bestiaux, *etc.* pp. vi. 161. *Paris,* 1766. 8°. **43**. d. **3**.

BARBERET (Émile) De la méningite cérébro-spinale épidémique, et particulièrement de celle observée à Alger en 1847. pp. 42. *Paris,* 1847. 4°. [*Collection des thèses soutenues à la Faculté de Médecine de Paris.* An 1847. tom. 1.] **7372**. a. **9**.

BARBERET (Joseph) La Bohême du travail. Les faiseurs de nœuds de cravates, *etc.* pp. iii. 387. *Paris,* [1889.] 12°. **8276**. c. **84**.

—— Les Grèves et la loi sur les coalitions. pp. 189. *Paris,* 1873. 16°. **8277**. a. **5**.

—— Les Sociétés de secours mutuels. Commentaire de la loi du 1er avril, 1898. pp. x. 463. *Paris, Nancy,* 1899. 8°. **05402**. ff. **40**.

—— Le Travail en France. Monographies professionnelles, *etc.* 7 tom. *Paris,* 1886 [1885]–90. 8°. **7942**. k. **39**.

BARBERET (V.) De Columellæ vita et scriptis. Thesim . . . proponebat V. Barberet. pp. 128. *Nantiaci,* 1887. 8°. **10606**. g. **27**.

—— Le Sage et le Théâtre de la Foire. Thèse, *etc.* pp. 266. *Nancy,* 1887. 8°. **11794**. i. **23**.

BARBEREY (Hélène de) *See* Roederer (Blanche J.) *Countess.* Notice et souvenirs de famille. Par Blanche-Joséphine de Corcelle, comtesse Roederer. Annotés et complétés par sa fille Hélène, Madame de Barberey, *etc.* 1899. 8°. **10660**. v. **14**.

—— Elizabeth Seton et les commencements de l'Église Catholique aux États-Unis. [With a portrait.] pp. viii. 724. *Paris,* 1868. 8°. **4985**. cc. **40**.

—— Quatrième édition . . . augmentée. 2 tom. *Paris,* 1880. 12°. **4986**. aa. **59**.

—— Elizabeth Seton und das Entstehen der kathol. Kirche in den Vereinigten Staaten . . . Übersetzt von einer Klosterfrau aus dem Orden unserer Frau von der Liebe des guten Hirten. Mit dem Portrait E. Seton. 2 Tl. *Münster,* 1873. 8°. **4986**. de. **6**.

BARBEREY (Maurice de) *See* Neuilly (A. A. C. de) *Count.* Dix années d'émigration. Souvenirs . . . publiés par . . . M. de Barberey. 1865. 8°. **10661**. d. **5**.

BARBERI (Americo) Dizionario artistico-scientifico-storico-tecnologico-musicale (Dizionario enciclopedico universale dei termini tecnici della musica) . . . Incominciato dal defunto professore A. Barberi, e continuato . . . dal cav. professore Giovanni Beretta . . . consultando... Carlo Molossi. vol. 1. [A–D.] pp. 712. pl. civ. *Milano,* 1872 [1869–75]. 8°. **7897**. k. **16**.
Imperfect; wanting vol. 2 *and* 3.

BARBERI (Andrea) *See* Rome, *Church of.* [*Collections of Bulls.*] Bullarii Romani Continuatio, Summorum Pontificum . . . Constitutiones . . . complectens: quas collegit A. Advocatus Barberi, *etc.* 1835, *etc.* fol. **5015**. g. **1**.

—— Al vero Dio degli eserciti inno, nell' aprile dell' anno 1831. pp. 10. *Roma,* 1831. 8°. **899**. d. **12**. (**14**.)

BARBERI (Andrea)

—— In occasione della solenne adunanza tenuta dagli Arcadi per la esaltazione al pontificato di . . . Leone xii. (Endecasillabi.) pp. 5. [*Rome,* 1824.] 8°. **11426**. cc. **15**. (**4**.)

BARBERI (Ascanio de)

—— Rime diverse in lingua genovese . . . Con nuoua giunta di alcune hora date in luce, *etc.* [The dedication signed: Ascanio Barberi. In fact an augmented edition of the collection first edited by C. Zabata.] pp. 188. *Ad istanza di Bartolomeo Calzetta, & Ascanio de Barberi: Torino,* 1612. 8°. **11431**. b. **22**.
An earlier edition is entered under Orero (*A.*)

BARBERI (Domenico) *See* Devine (P.) Life of the Very Rev. Father Dominic of the Mother of God, *etc.* 1898. 8°. **4864**. cc. **36**.

—— *See* Gwynn (Denis R.) Father Dominic Barberi. [With a portrait.] 1947. 8°. **4863**. i. **30**.

—— *See* Young (Urban) Life and Letters of the Venerable Father Dominic, *etc.* [With a portrait.] 1926. 8°. **4863**. a. **16**.

—— Dominic Barberi in England. A new series of letters Translated and edited by Father Urban Young, *etc.* [With a portrait.] pp. xx. 230. *Burns, Oates & Co.: London,* 1935. 8°. **010910**. aa. **42**.

—— Venerable Fr. Dominic, C.P., an apostle of England, *etc. Dublin,* [1930.] 8°. **4903**. aaa. **31**.

BARBERI (Francesco)

—— Annali della tipografia romana di Baldassarre jr e Girolama Cartolari, 1540–1559. *In:* La Bibliofilia. anno 53. pp. 69–120. 1951. 4°. P.P. **6476**. eaa.

—— Paolo Manuzio e la stamperia del popolo romano, 1561–1570. Con documenti inediti. [With plates, including a portrait.] pp. 211. 1942. 4°. *See* Italy.—*Ministero della Pubblica Istruzione.—Direzione Generale delle Accademie e Biblioteche.* **11916**. f. **2**.

BARBERI (Giovanni) All' Illm̃o . . . Signore Monsignor Governatore di Roma e sua Congregazione Criminale . . . l'eccm̃o Sig. luogotente Monieri Relatore Romana Homicidii. Per il P. D. Giuseppe Cavalli Religioso del Terz' Ordine di S. Francesco carcerato. Contra il Fisco. Ristretto di fatto, e di raggione con sommario. [The case of G. Cavalli, accused of homicide, stated by G. Barberi as "Procurator de' Poveri."] *Roma,* [1761.] 4°. T. **81***. (**6**.)

—— Memoriale addizionale. *Roma,* [1761 ?] 4°. T. **81***. (**8**.)

BARBERI (Giovanni Battista) called *Il Guercino. See* Barbieri.

BARBERI (Giovanni Luca) I Capibrevi . . . ora per la prima volta pubblicati da G. Silvestri. [vol. 3. fasc. 5. edited by Giuseppe La Mantia.] 3 vol. *Palermo,* 1879–1904. 8°. [*Documenti per servire alla storia di Sicilia.* ser. 1. vol. 4, 8, 13.] Ac. **6537**.

BARBERI, afterwards **TISIFONTE** (Giuseppe) *See* Baccini ( ) Republica Romana. Relazione del processo, e carcerazione del cittadino Tisifonte già Barberi, edile in Roma, *etc.* [1798.] fol. **1897**. b. **5**. (**14**.)

BARBERI (Giuseppe Filippo) Grammaire des grammaires italiennes, élémentaire, raisonnée, méthodique et analytique; ou cours complet de langue italienne. 2 tom. *Paris,* 1819. 8°. **72**. a. **1**.

—— [Another copy.] **12942**. c. **21**.

BARBERI (Giuseppe Filippo)

—— Grand dictionnaire français-italien et italien-français. Continué et terminé par MM. Basti et Cerati. 2 tom. *Paris*, 1838, 39. 4°. **828.** h. **7.**

—— Petit trésor de la langue française et de la langue italienne, ou des différentes figures, appelées tropes, de la langue française et de la langue italienne, les unes correspondantes aux autres, *etc.* pp. xiv. 339. *Paris*, 1821. 8°. **12952.** c. **28.**

BARBÈRI (Guglielmo) L'Insegnamento negli istituti tecnici. Osservazioni, *etc.* pp. 51. *Ravenna*, 1879. 8°. **7945.** bbb. **13.** (**3.**)

BARBERI (J. Ph.) *See* Barberi (Giuseppe Filippo)

BARBÉRI (José) Vida de la Venerable Madre Sor Clara Andreu . . . Religiosa Geronima . . . en el monasterio de San Bartolomé de la Villa de Inca. Con un apendice historico de dicha villa. 2 pt. *Mallorca*, 1807. 4°. **4865.** b. **5.**

BARBERI (Matheo Antonio) Cartas politico-instructivas sobre las ventajas que facilita el comercio, y proporciones del reyno de Aragon, para practicarlo. Primera. pp. 74. *Zaragoza*, 1768. 8°. **8042.** a. **40.**

—— Cartas politico-instructivas sobre varios puntos de la felicidad pública: primera. pp. 54. *Madrid*, 1770. 12°. **8205.** aa. **4.**

BARBERI (Tito) Del rapporto fra la religione e la pittura e dell' ultimo lavoro del barone Vincenzo Camuccini. pp. 22. *Roma*, 1845. 8°. **898.** d. **5.** (**14.**)

BARBÈRI (Ugo)

—— L'Archivio gentilizio dei marchesi Bourbon del Monte di Sorbello a Perugia. pp. viii. 138. *Città di Castello*, 1943. 8°. **9918.** f. **24.**
Collana storica Sorbello. quad. 1.

—— I Marchesi Bourbon del Monte S. Maria, di Petrella e di Sorbello. Notizie storico-genealogiche sulla casa fino ai nostri giorni. [With genealogical tables and a bibliography.] pp. 156. *Città di Castello*, 1943. 8°. **9918.** f. **25.**
Collana storica Sorbello. quad. 2.

BARBERIE (Dominique Jacques de) *Marquis de Courteille.*

—— *See* Maier (F. G.) Marquis de Courteille. Der französische Botschafter in der schweizerischen Eidgenossenschaft von 1738 bis 1749, *etc.* 1950. 8°. **010665.** l. **45.**

BARBERIE (Jacques Michel) *Marquis de Courteille.*

—— *See* Néraud (J.) L'Administration de la généralité de Bourges sous l'intendant de Courteille, 1720–1728. 1933, *etc.* 8°. [*Mémoires de la Société historique, littéraire et scientifique du Cher.* sér. 4. vol. 40–42.] Ac. **6780.**

BARBERII (Giovanni Battista) *See* Barberio.

BARBERIIS (Philippus de) *Begin.* [fol. 1 *verso*:] Ioannis Philippi de Lignamine. equitis Siculi. ad Six. iiii. Pon. Max. prefatio, *etc.* [fol. 2 *recto*, line 21:] opuscula quæ clarissimus artiū et theologiæ interpres mgr̄ Philippus ex ordinē p̄dicatoꝝ cōterraneus et affinis meus ædidit. In q̄bus ante oīa tractatus est de discordātia īter Eusebiū Hieroninimū: et Aureliū Augustinum: approbatus Sybillaꝝ dictis: oīumq̧ gētiliū: et phōrum: et veteꝝ poetarū qui de Christo uaticinati sunt: atq̧ aliq̄ p̄dixerūt. deinde comētarii super simbolū Athanasii. oratiōem dn̄icam: et salutatiōem angelicā. Mox explanatio sup̄ Te deū laudamus. et Gloria in excelsis deo. [The com-

BARBERIIS (Philippus de)

mentaries attributed to St. Thomas Aquinas.] Demum donatus theologus: quo theologicæ q̄ōnes grāmatica arte soluūtur, *etc.* [With woodcuts.] [*J. P. de Lignamine*:] *Ro*.[*mae*], Die prima Mensis Decembris 1481. 4°. IA. **19262.**
70 leaves, without signatures. 24–26 *lines to a page. Imperfect; wanting leaves* 53–56.

—— [Another edition.] *Begin.* [fol. 1 *verso*:] Ioannis Philippi de Lignamine equitis Siculi. ad Six. iiii. Pon. Max. prefatio, *etc.* [fol. 2 *recto*, line 25:] opuscula: quæ . . . mgr̄ Philippus . . . edidit. [fol. 2 *verso*:] In quibus ante omnia tractatus est de discordātia inter Eusebium Hieronimū: & Aureliū Augustinum, *etc.* [*J. P. de Lignamine*:] *Ro*.[*mae*], Die prima Mensis Decembris, 1481 [1482?]. 4°. IA. **19263.**
82 *leaves, without signatures. Leaves* 25–28, 31–82 *are duplicates of leaves* 13–16, 19–70 *of the preceding* (IA. 19262). *Leaves* 1–6, 29, 30 *are a fresh setting-up of leaves* 1–6, 17, 18, *of the same, the words ' et prophetarum ' being added and a sentence as to previous dedications omitted from the printer's letter. Leaves* 6 *verso*–10 *contain fresh matter from Augustine's De Civitate Dei and Lactantius, leaves* 11–24 *a new series of cuts of the Sibyls and* 16 *additional cuts. The text on leaf* 25 *is continued from its prophecy of Sibylla Agrippa, which in this edition comes on leaf* 20 *recto, the word ' peccator ' being repeated.*

—— [Another copy.] IA. **19264.**
Imperfect; wanting leaves 1, 2, 8, 9, 11–14, 16, 18, 21, 23, 24, 29, 32.

—— [Another edition.] *Begin.* [fol. 1 *recto*:] Tractatus sollemnis et vtilis editus per . . . Philippū Syculū . . . in quo infrascripta perpulchre compilauit. In primis discordātias nōnullas īnter sāctos Eusebiū Hyeronymū et Aureliū Augustinū . . . Secundo duodecim sibillarum uaticinia que de christo ediderūt cum earum figuris proporcionatis. Tercio Carmina Probæ Centone . . . que ex Maronis carmībus ad corroborationē ueteris nouiq̧ testamēti . . . excerpsit. Quarto diui Athanasij Simbolū Quicūq̧ uult saluus esse Cum beati Thome aquinatis expositione. Quīto Domīcā Orationē per eundē beatū Thomā pulcherrime explanatā. Sexto Angelicā Salutationē per eundem. Septimo Hymnum Te deū laudamus cū expositiōe per eundē beatū Thomā Composita. Vltimo ponit Angelicus Hymnus in excelsis deo per eūndem beatū Thomam diuinitus explanatus. [fol. 60 *recto*:] Incipit Donatus theologus. [*Georgius Teutonicus & Sixtus Riessinger*: *Rome*, 1482?] 4°. IA. **19240.**
68 *leaves, without signatures.* 28 *lines to a page.*

—— [Another copy.] few ms. notes. IA. **19241.**

—— Quattuor hic compressa opuscula. Discordantie sanctorum doctorum. Hieronymi. Augustini. Sibyllaruꝫ de Christo vaticinia: cuꝫ appropriatis singularum figuris. Varia Judeorum ⁊ gentilium de Christo testimonia. Centones Probe Falconie de vtriusq̧ testamenti hystoriis ex carminibus uirgilii selecti: cum annotatione locorum ex quibus desumpti sunt: a diuo Hieronymo Comprobate. [Reprinted from the larger work edited by Philippus de Barberiis.] 2 pt. [1510?] 4°. *See* Jerome, *Saint.* [*Appendix.*] **1360.** i. **14.**

BARBERIN (J. Philippe Auguste) Nearoma. La paix au lieu de la guerre. Aux Italiens ses ancêtres. pp. 31. *Paris*, 1861. 8°. **8033.** d. **26.** (**2.**)

BARBERINA (Lucretia) *Duchess of Modena. See* Lucretia [de' Barberini], *Consort of Francis* i., *Duke of Modena.*

BARBERING BUSINESS. How to Master the Barbering Business. pp. 38. *Modern Barber Institute*: *Sault, Ste. Marie, Ont.*, [1909.] 4°. **7944.** h. **37.**

BARBERINI, *Family of*. *See* BEARD (Charles R.) Notes on the Barberini and some allied Armours. 1924. 8°. **07806**. k. **39**.

—— *See* BOSSI (Gaetano) La Pasquinata Quod non fecerunt barbari fecerunt Barberini. Ricerche storiche. 1898. 8°. **7705**. aa. **42**.

—— *See* LEONELLI (M.) Abbozzo delle glorie Barberine, *etc*. 1644. 4°. **11431**. ee. **17**. (**1**.)

—— *See* LINAGE DE VAUCIENNES (P.) Le Differend des Barberins avec le Pape Innocent X. 1678. 8°. **1365**. b. **13**.

—— *See* ROSICHINO ( ) Dichiaratione delle pitture della Sala de' Signori Barberini. 1570. 8°. **1044**. b. **37**.

BARBERINI (ANTONIO) *Cardinal*. *See* BENTIVOGLIO (G.) *Cardinal*. Relazione della . . . festa fatta in Roma alli XXV di Febbraio MDCXXXIV., sotto gli auspicj dell' eminentissimo Sig. Cardinale A. Barberini, *etc*. 1882. 8°. **9930**. g. **28**.

—— *See* BOVIO (C.) In funere . . . A. Barberini S. R. E. Cardinalis . . . descriptio, & oratio. 1671. fol. **702**. l. **1**. (**7**.)

—— *See* DAVIS (Edward) *Auctioneer*. Auctio Davisiana. Picturarum verè originalium: or, a Collection of valuable pictures, consisting of the collections, of Cardinal Antonio Barberini, *etc*. 1691. 4°. **1402**. g. **1**. (**105**.)

—— [For documents issued by A. Barberini as Camerlengo of the Camera Apostolica:] *See* STATES OF THE CHURCH.—*Camera Apostolica*.

—— Lettera al Cardinale Francesco Barberino. [*Rome?* 1645?] 4°. **702**. l. **1**. (**2**.)

—— Lettera al Cardinale Rapaccioli. [*Rome?* 1645?] 4°. **702**. l. **1**. (**4**.)

—— Lettera alla Santità di N. Signore [Innocent X.], *etc*. [*Rome?* 1645?] 4°. **702**. l. **1**. (**3**.)

—— Ordonnance de Monseigneur le Cardinal Antoine Barberin . . . portant defence de lire, vendre & debiter une traduction du Nouueau Testament & des Epistres de Sainct Paul [made by Le Maistre de Saci and others], imprimée à Monts, 1667. (Reims, 4 Jan. 1668.) pp. 7. *J. Multeau: Reims*, [1668.] 4°. **4999**. cc. **7**. (**4**.)

—— An Answere to His Holinesse Remonstrance . . . in the name of the rest of the Roman Clergy, *etc*. [A satire.] *See* URBAN VIII., *Pope*. The Passionate Remonstrance made by his Holinesse, *etc*. 1641. 4°. **1489.g.18.**

—— [Another edition.] *See* URBAN VIII., *Pope*. The Passionate Remonstrance made by his Holinesse, *etc*. 1884. 8°. [*Aungervyle Society. Publications*. no. 24–27.] Ac. **9942/2**.

—— At the Auction-house for Pictures in St. Alban's-Street. Will be expos'd to sale on Monday the 5th of March . . . a curious collection of pictures, being part of those which formerly belong'd to the Cardinal Antonie Barbarin, *etc*. [An advertisement.] [1680?] *s. sh*. 4°. L.R. **305**. a. **7**. (**1**.)

BARBERINI (BONAVENTURA) *Archbishop of Ferrara*. *See* BAROTTI (G. A.) Notizie intorno alla vita di Monsignor B. Barberini, arcivescovo di Ferrara, *etc*. 1753. 12°. **247**. c. **18**.

—— Epistola . . . de Canone Nicæno appellationis ad Summum Romanum Pontificem, ac de numero viginti Canonum Nicænæ Synodi. 1753. *See* CALOGIERÀ (A.) Raccolta d'opuscoli, *etc*. tom. 34. 1728, *etc*. 12°. **247**. c. **3**.

BARBERINI (CARLO) *Cardinal*. *See* AQUINO (C. d') Sacra Exequialia, in funere Jacobi II. . . . exhibita ab eminentiss. . . . principe Carolo Sanctæ Romanæ Ecclesiæ cardinali Barberino, *etc*. 1702. fol. **603**. k. **27**.

—— Elogium funebre eminentissimo principi Carolo cardinali Barberino. [*Rome*, 1704.] 4°. **838**. m. **22**. (**2**.)

—— Ultimum grati animi obsequium magno funeri . . . Caroli Barberini . . . in ecclesia S. Stanislai . . . celebratum, *etc*. *Romæ*, 1704. 4°. **838**. m. **22**. (**3**.)

BARBERINI (CARLO) *Duke of Monterotondo and Areti*. *See* CINCIUS (J.) In funere . . . Principis Caroli Barberini generalis S. R. E. Ducis oratio, *etc*. 1630. 4°. **10631**. d. **29**. (**11**.)

BARBERINI (FRANCESCO) *the Elder, Cardinal*. *See* HOLSTENIUS (L.) Collectio Romana bipartita veterum aliquot historiæ ecclesiasticae monumentorum, edi cœpta a L. Holstenio . . . absoluta post eius obitum [by Cardinal F. Barberini], *etc*. 1662. 8°. **4532**. aa. **17**.

—— *See* MUSANTIUS (J. D.) In funere . . . Francisci cardinalis Barberini . . . honorarii tumuli descriptio et oratio, *etc*. 1680. 4°. **702**. l. **1**. (**8**.)

—— *See* ZUFFUS (J.) Tractatus de criminalis processus legitimatione libri tres . . . Cum annotationibus ad Barbarinam Constitutionem (Ordini sopra i termini sustantiali da osseruarsi dalli officiali dello Stato ecclesiastico nelle cause contumaciali), *etc*. 1665. fol. **5309**. f. **19**.

—— [Letters written to Jean Morin in 1642 and 1653.] *See* MORIN (Jean) *Theologian*. Antiquitates Ecclesiæ Orientalis, clarissimorum virorum card. Barberini . . . Joh. Morini . . . dissertationibus epistolicis enucleatæ, *etc*. [Consisting chiefly of letters from and to J. Morin.] 1682. 8°. **4531**. a. **2**.

—— —— 1683. 12°. **295**. g. **45**.

—— Lettera alla Santità di N. Signore [Innocent X. Dated: 18 Jan. 1646]. [*Rome?* 1646?] 4°. **702**. l. **1**. (**5**.)

—— Lettera alla Santità di N. Signore [Innocent X. Dated 23 Jan. 1646]. [*Rome?* 1646?] 4°. **702**. l. **1**. (**6**.)

—— Recueil des instructions générales (données par . . . le cardinal François Barberini) aux nonces ordinaires de France de 1624 à 1634. Par Auguste Leman. *Ital*. pp. iv. 217. *Lille, Paris*, 1920. 8°. [*Mémoires et travaux publiés par des professeurs des facultés catholiques de Lille*. fasc. 15.] **03605**. i. **1/15**.

—— Breve sumario de las facultades que trae su señoria illustrissima del Señor Cardenal don F. Barberino, sobrino de su Santidad Urbano VIII. y su Legado a Latere, assi en materias de gracias, como de justicia. *F. de Lyra: Sevilla*, 1626. fol. **593**. h. **17**. (**48**.)

—— Index bibliothecæ, qua Franciscus Barberinus S.R.E. cardinalis . . . magnificentissimas suæ familiæ ad Quirinalem ædes magnificentiores reddidit. Tomi tres libros typis editos complectentes. tom. 1, 2. *Typis Barberinis, excudebat M. Hercules: Romæ*, 1681. fol. **619**. m. **18**, **19**.
Tom. 3 was never published. The existing volumes, however, include books from A to Z.

—— [Another copy.] **11902**. l. **3**.

—— [Another copy.] **124**. h. **5**, **6**.

—— Relacion verdadera de la entrada, y recibimiento que la ciudad de Barcelona hizo a la buena venida del Cardenal Legado [F. Barberino], en 18 de Março . . . de 1626. *B. de Guzman: Madrid*, [1626.] fol. **593**. h. **22**. (**57**.)

BARBERINI (Francesco) *the Elder, Cardinal.*

—— Verdadera relacion, en que se da cuenta como el Legado de su Santidad se vido con su Magestad en nuestra Señora de Monserrate, y consultaron cosas importantes a la corona real, y al reyno. Y la grandiosa entrada y recibimiento q̃ a su Magestad se hizo en Barcelona. *I. de Cabrera: Sevilla,* 1626. fol. **593**. h. **17**. (**64**.)

BARBERINI (Francesco) *the Elder, Cardinal,* and **BARBERINI** (Taddeo)

—— Memoriale alla Santità di N. Signore [Innocent x.] nella materia de Conti de Barberini. [*Rome?* 1645?] 4°. **702**. l. **1**. (**1**.)

BARBERINI (Francesco) *the Younger, Cardinal. See* Adda (F. d') *Cardinal,* and Barberini (F.) Relazione dello stato presente dell' acque che infestano le tre provincie di Romagna, Ferrara, e Bologna, *etc.* 1766. 4°. [*Nuova raccolta d'autori che trattano del moto dell'acque.* vol. 5.] **8775**. d. **44**.

—— —— 1768. 4°. [*Raccolta d'autori, etc.* tom. 5.] **8775**. eee. **16**

—— —— 1824. 4°. [*Raccolta d'autori, etc.* tom. 9.] **537**. l. **8**.

—— [For official documents issued by Cardinal Barberini as Legate in Romagna:] *See* Romagna.—*Legazione.*

—— [For official documents issued by Cardinal Barberini as Prefetto of the Congregazione dell'Acque, delle Chiane, etc.] *See* States of the Church.—*Congregazione dell' Acque, delle Chiane, etc.*

BARBERINI (Francesco da) *Tuscan Poet. See* Barberino.

BARBERINI (Lucrezia de') *Consort of Francis I., Duke of Modena. See* Lucretia [de' Barberini].

BARBERINI (Luigi) All'Associazione della tessitura serica. [A letter on the subject of custom duties.] *See* Bressi (G.) La Tessitura serica e i trattati di commercio, *etc.* 1877. 8°. **7942**. g. **6**. (**16**.)

BARBERINI (Maffeo) *Cardinal. See* Urban viii., *Pope.*

BARBERINI (Maffeo) *Marquis of Corezze.* Ragioni del Marchese D. M. Barberini sopra la successione della Casa Barberini, derivanti dalle dispozitioni del Pontefice Urbano viii. 1777. *See* Giannone (P.) Opere postume. tom. 2. 1770, *etc.* 4°. **663**. h. **19**.

BARBERINI (Raffaello) Relatione di Moscovia, scritta da R. Barberino [16 Oct. 1655], *etc.* 1658. *See* Russia. [*Appendix.—Descriptions and Travels.*] Viaggi di Moscovia, *etc.* 1658. 4°. **790**. i. **13**.

—— [Another edition. With "Notizie di R. Barberini, ora esistenti nella Biblioteca Barberini di Roma."] pp. 76. 1854. *See* Russia. [*Appendix.—History and Politics.*] Recueil de relations . . . concernant la géographie et l'histoire de la Russie avant 1700. 1854, *etc.* 8°. **9455**. d. 25.

BARBERINI (Taddeo) *See* Barberini (Francesco) *the Elder, Cardinal,* and Barberini (T.) Memoriale alla Santità di N. Signore nella materia de Conti de Barberini. [1645?] 4°. **702**. l. **1**. (**1**.)

BARBERINO (   ) *See* also Barberini.

BARBERINO (Andrea da) *See* Magnabotti (Andrea de') *da Barberino.*

BARBERINO (Francesco da) *Tuscan Poet. See* Thomas (Antoine) Francesco da Barberino et la littérature provençale en Italie au moyen âge. 1883. 8°. [*Bibliothèque des Écoles Françaises d'Athènes et de Rome.* Sciences religieuses. no. 35.] Ac. **5206/2**.

—— Del Reggimento e de' costumi delle donne. (Vita . . . scritta da Federico Ubaldini.—Indice di F. Ubaldini, accresciuto.) pp. xxxiv. 406. 126. *Roma,* 1815. 8°. **1063**. l. **6**.

—— [Another edition.] Per cura del Conte Carlo Baudi di Vesme. pp. xli. 443. *Bologna,* 1875. 8°. [*Collezione di opere inedite o rare.*] **12225**. h. **12**.

—— Francesco Barberino de' costumi delle donne. [The introduction only. With four other poems.] 1820. *See* Italian Parnassus. Parnaso Italiano. vol. 8. 1819, *etc.* 16°. **11421**. b. **27**.

—— Novelle dal Reggimento et costumi di donna, novellamente pubblicato a cura del Conte Carlo Vesme. pp. 67. *Bologna,* 1874. 8°. **12471**. w. **3**.

—— *See* Festa (G. B.) Un Galateo femminile italiano del Trecento. (Il Reggimento e costumi di donna di Francesco da Barberino.) 1910. 8°. **11851**. v. **6**.

—— Documenti d'amore di M. F. Barberino. (Alcune altre rime dell'istesso autore.) [With the life of the author and tables by Federigo Ubaldini, and with 15 engravings, including a portrait, by C. Bloemmaert and others.] pp. 376. few ms. corrections. *V. Mascardi: Roma,* 1640. 4°. **83**. e. **5**.

—— [Another issue.] **839**. k. **17**.
Wanting the portrait of the author. One plate is reversed in this copy.

—— [Another edition.] pp. xii. 312. 1820. *See* Italian Parnassus. Parnaso Italiano. vol. 7. 1819, *etc.* 16°. **11421**. b. **27**.

—— [Another edition.] Secondo i manuscritti originali. A cura di F. Egidi. 1902–27. 8°. *See* Rome, *the City.*—*Società Filologica Romana.* 4 vol. Ac. **9769/5**.

—— Il Trattato d'Amore di messer F. da Barberino. pp. 21. *Roma,* 1898. 8°. **11427**. h. **5**.

BARBERINO (Scipione) *See* Botero (G.) Delle cause della grandezza delle città, libri tre. [Edited by S. Barberino.] 1596. 8°. **8006**. aa. **8**.

BARBERINS, *Family of. See* Barberini, *Family of.*

BARBERINUS (Antonius) *Cardinal. See* Barberini (Antonio)

BARBERINUS (Carolus) *Cardinal. See* Barberini (Carlo)

BARBERINUS (Franciscus) *Cardinal. See* Barberini (Francesco) *the Elder, Cardinal.*

BARBERINUS (Maphaeus) *Cardinal. See* Urban viii., *Pope* [Maffeo Barberini].

BARBERIO (Fabio) *See* Barberius (Fabius)

BARBERIO (Giovanni Battista) Stupendo, e recentissimo miracolo operato . . . per mezzo del . . . beato Giovanni da Capistrano, *etc.* pp. 19. *Typis Reu. Cam. Apost.: Romæ,* 1685. 4°. **1193**. m. **1**. (**95**.)

BARBERIO (Giuseppe) *See* Barberius (Josephus)

BARBERIO (Ludovico Maria) *See* Barberius (Ludovicus M.)

BARBERIO (Sabino) Dissertazione critico-storica del Tripaldo, e suo celebre Santuario, *etc.* pp. 127. *Napoli,* 1778. 8°. **663. a. 26.**

BARBERIS (Alberto) Positivismus ac nova methodus psychologica . . . P. Siciliani. Animadversiones criticæ. pp. 389. *Placentiæ,* 1887. 8°. **8468. e. 34.**

BARBERIS (Carolus Juvenalis) Theopancratiastes, hoc est D. Pancratii M. Mirabilia, xv. elogiis comprehensa. pp. 87. *Ex typografia I. I. Rustis: Taurini,* 1657. 8°. **4824. b. 9.**

BARBERIS (Claudius Franciscus) Tentamen chirurgicum de ossium carie, *etc.* pp. 8. *Monspelii,* 1775. 4°. **T. 19. (8.)**

BARBERIS (Corrado)

—— *See* Medici (G.) Politica agraria, 1945–1952. A cura di C. Barberis. 1952. 8°. **8033. m. 13.**

BARBERIS (G. B.) *See* Turin.—*Archivio Arcivescovile.* Le Carte dello Archivio Arcivescovile di Torino fino al 1310. [Edited by F. Gabotto and G. B. Barberis.] 1906. 8°. [*Biblioteca della Società Storica Subalpina.* vol. 36.] **Ac. 6556.**

—— Interpretazione del canto xxvii dell'Inferno, *etc.* pp. 30. *Pinerolo,* 1903. 8°. **11422. i. 41.**

BARBERIS (Giulio) La Repubblica Argentina e la Patagonia. Lettere dei Missionari Salesiani. [Edited by G. Barberis. With a biographical notice of Cesare Chiala.] pp. xv. 236. *Torino,* 1877. 16°. **4767. aa. 3.**

BARBERIS (Luigi) Lo Sviluppo della rete ferroviaria degli Stati Uniti e le sue variazioni, *etc.* pp. ix. 158. *Torino,* 1898. 8°. **8235. k. 59.**

BARBERIS (Maria Verdun) *See* Verdun Barberis.

BARBERIS (Mario Ricca) *See* Ricca-Barberis.

BARBERIS (T. Giulio) Storia antica dell'Oriente. Ad uso delle scuole . . . Edizione sesta . . . accresciuta, *etc.* pp. vii. 325. *Torino,* 1890. 8°. **9055. aaa. 21.**

BARBERIS (Tarsillo) Il Buddismo esoterico. Conferenze, *etc.* pp. 68. *Milano,* 1890. 8°. **4503. dd. 2. (1.)**

—— Cinque anni in Birmania. Note. pp. 201. *Milano,* [1890.] 8°. **10056. h. 6.**

BARBERIUS (Abel) *Resp.* *See* La Place (J. de) *Praes.* Disputationes de argumentis, quibus efficitur, Christum prius fuisse, quam in utero Beatæ Virginis . . . conciperetur. (Disputatio 2 . . . Respondente Abele Barberio, *etc.*) 1649. 4°. **4226. e. 33.**

BARBERIUS (Anthonius) Computus Anthonii Barberii, clerici Domini, de expensis factis per ipsum, racione passagii Domini ultramarini, *etc.* *See* Bollati di Saint-Pierre (F. E.) Illustrazioni della spedizione in Oriente di Amedeo vi., *etc.* 1900. 8°. [*Biblioteca storica italiana.* vol. 5.] **Ac. 6550/2.**

BARBERIUS (Carolus Juvenalis) *See* Barberis.

BARBERIUS (Fabius) Fabii Barberii . . . Catalogus episcoporum Ariani sub Hispaniarum Regis nominatione vsq; ad præsens nostrum æuum anno 1635 . . . Præthereà ab eodem authore quædam alia disseruntur animaduertenda de Beneuento vrbe, *etc.* pp. 79. *Typis F. Sauij: Neapoli,* 1635. 4°. **664. b. 19. (3.)**

—— Fabii Barberii . . . De prognostico cinerum, quos Vesuvius mons, dum conflagrabatur, eructavit, *etc.* pp. 64. *Apud L. Scorigium: Neapoli,* 1632. 4°. **664. b. 19. (1.)**

BARBERIUS (Fabius)

—— Fabii Barberii . . . Manifestum eorum, quæ omninò verificata fuerunt jam antea ab ipso prædicta in Prognostico cinerum, quos mons Veseuus emisit, dum comburebatur, *etc.* pp. 14. *Typis F. Sauij: Neapoli,* 1635. 4°. **664. b. 19. (2.)**

BARBERIUS (Joannes Franciscus) *See* Barbieri (Giovanni F.) called *Il Guercino.*

BARBERIUS (Josephus) D. Josephi Barberii . . . De miseria poetarum Græcorum liber. 1701. *See* Gronovius (J.) Thesaurus Graecorum antiquitatum, *etc.* vol. 10. 1697, *etc.* fol. **1709. b. 4.**

—— [Another edition.] *See* Alcyonius (P.) Petri Alcyonii Medices legatus, sive de exilio libri duo, *etc.* 1707. 12°. **616. a. 7.**

BARBERIUS (Ludovicus) *Count.* *See* Barbieri (Ludovico)

BARBERIUS (Ludovicus Maria) Spiritus nitro-aerei operationes in microcosmo. (Dissertatio epistolica . . . de pororum biliosorum vsu.) pp. 156. *Typis J. Longi: Bononiæ,* 1680. 12°. **780. a. 19.**

BARBERO. *Begin.* Carta de Pasquas; que desde Guadalcanal escrive un Barbero à Don Pedro del Parral, vezino de Madrid, diciendole lo mal que le han parecido los Papelotes del R.mo P. Feijoò, de Torres, *etc.* pp. 8. [*Madrid?* 1726.] 4°. **3901. cc. 58. (2.)**

—— Conversacion del Barbero y su Marchante. (Conversacion segunda. [On current politics.]) 2 pt. *Méjico,* 1820. 4°. **9770. bb. 2. (46.)**

—— Un Apasionado de la partida de capa defiende su honor, y de toda corporacion de militares, y contra el Barbero [i.e. the pamphlet entitled: "Conversacion del Barbero y su Marchante"]. *Mejico,* 1820. 4°. **9770. bb. 1. (43.)**

—— Un Barbero constitucional contra el defensor de la partida de capa [i.e. against the pamphlet entitled: "Un Apasionado de la partida de capa defiende su honor . . . contra el Barbero"]. pp. 7. [*Mexico,*] 1820. 4°. **9770. bb. 1. (44.)**

—— El Nuevo Barbero y su Marchante. Vayase el uno por lo otro. pp. 4. *México,* 1822. 4°. **9770. bb. 12. (33.)**

—— Diálogo entre un Barbero y su Marchante sobre las elecciones primarias, *etc.* (Diálogo secundo . . . sobre lo que se lera. [The second dialogue signed: El amigo de la verdad, *etc.*]) 2 pt. *México,* 1826. fol. **9770. k. 9. (5.)**

—— Unos dijes al Pensador [i.e. J. J. Fernandez Lizardi. A reply to his pamphlet: Otra afeitadita. Signed: El Barbero]. pp. 4. [*Mexico,*] 1822. 4°. **9770. bb. 14. (59.)**

BARBERO (E.) *See* Dante Alighieri. [*Divina Commedia.—Italian.*] La Divina Commedia, *etc.* (Indice alfabetico . . . compilato da E. Barbero.) 1883, *etc.* 8°. **11420. dd. 1.**

BARBERO (Francisco Sánchez) *See* Sánchez Barbero.

BARBERO GARRIDO (José) El Misterio de la Atlántida y las Civilizaciones Prehistóricas, *etc.* pp. 159. *Madrid,* 1928. 8°. **7701. a. 13.**

BARBEROT (Jean Étienne Casimir) Histoire des styles d'architecture dans tous les pays depuis les temps anciens jusqu'à nos jours . . . Ouvrage orné de 928 dessins, *etc.* 2 tom. *Paris,* 1891. 8°. **7814. h. 3.**

—— Traité de constructions civiles . . . Avec . . . figures . . . dessinées par l'auteur. pp. xvi. 917. *Paris,* 1895. 8°. **8768. ccc. 3.**

—— Deuxième édition . . . augmentée, *etc.* pp. xviii. 1045. *Paris,* 1900. 8°. **08766. b. 13.**

BARBEROUSSE I., *Dey of Algiers. See* BĀBĀ 'ARŪJ, commonly called BARBAROSSA I., *Dey of Algiers.*

BARBEROUSSE II., *Dey of Algiers. See* KHAIR AL-DĪN, called BARBAROSSA II., *Dey of Algiers.*

BARBEROUSSE (FRANÇOIS)

—— Les Jours aux volets clos. Roman, *etc.* pp. 251. *Paris,* 1936. 8°. **12512**. t. **39**.

BARBEROUSSE (HARIANDAN) *pseud. See* HARIANDAN-BARBEROUSSE, *pseud.*

BARBERS. The Female Barbers. A tale. [In verse.] [*Dublin?* 1750?] *s. sh.* fol. **1890**. e. **5**. (**188**.)

BARBER-STARKEY (ROGER) *See* STARKEY (R. B.)

BARBERTON.—*Barberton and District Publicity Association.*

—— Barberton, *etc.* [Guide books, with illustrations.] *Barberton,* 1939– . 8°. W.P. **2361**.

BARBERTON AND DISTRICT PUBLICITY ASSOCIATION. *See* BARBERTON.

BARBERTON (IVAN GRAHAM MITFORD)

—— The Barbers of the Peak. A history of the Barber, Atherstone and Bowker families, *etc.* pp. xii. 258. *University Press: Oxford,* 1934. 8°. **9905**. dd. **23**.

BARBERY (BERNARD) La Banque de France et le crédit agricole. Les caisses régionales. pp. 124. *Paris,* 1899. 8°. **08228**. i. **50**.

—— En marge de la Comédie humaine. Henry de Balzac, ou une double famille. [On the relations of Honoré de Balzac with his family.] pp. 34. *Paris,* 1938. 8°. **10655**. h. **43**.

—— L'Éphémère Seigneur de Caille. [The lives of Isaac de Brun de Castellane and of his impersonator Pierre Mège. With portraits.] pp. viii. 270. *Paris,* 1932. 8°. **10655**. bbb. **21**.

—— La Merveilleuse aventure de Pierre de Provence et de la belle Maguelone. Légende provençale racontée par un berger. pp. 102. *Paris,* [1939.] 8°. **12450**. r. **16**.

BARBES (ANDRÉ) Les Traditions nationales. Autrefois et aujourd'hui dans la nation française. pp. viii. 336. *Paris,* 1873. 8°. **9220**. eee. **1**.

BARBÈS (ARMAND) *See* BARBÈS (Sigismond A. A.)

BARBÈS (RÉGINA)

—— *See* SINIBULDI (G.) called CINO DA PISTOIA. Rime d'amore . . . Traduit . . . avec une note biographique par R. Barbès. [1945.] 8°. **11427**. i. **15**.

BARBÈS (SIGISMOND AUGUSTE ARMAND) *See* BONAFOUS (H.) Lettre à Barbès [in reply to his speech before the tribunal of Bourges, and to a letter addressed to him by Louis Blanc]. [1849.] *s. sh.* fol. **1850**. c. **1**. (**50**.)

—— *See* CLARETIE (J.) Armand Barbès, *etc.* 1870. 8°. **10662**. i. **1**.

—— *See* DUQUAI (E.) Les Grands procès politiques. Les accusés du 15 mai 1848. Albert, Barbès, *etc.* 1869. 12°. **9230**. bb. **41**.

—— *See* FRANCE.—*Cour des Pairs.* Attentat des 12 et 13 mai 1839 [i.e. the conspiracy of Armand Barbès and others]. Procédure, *etc.* 1839. 4°. S. **405**. ca. (**1–4**.)

—— *See* HUNGER (V.) Barbès au Mont-Saint-Michel. 1909. 8°. **10600**. g. **32**. (**1**.)

BARBÈS (SIGISMOND AUGUSTE ARMAND)

—— *See* JEANJEAN (J. F.) Armand Barbès—1809–1870. Sa vie, son action politique, sa correspondance d'apres de nombreux documents inédits, *etc.* 1909, *etc.* 8°. **W.P.3178.**

—— *See* MIRECOURT (E. de) *pseud.* Histoire contemporaine. (No. 25. Barbès.) 1867. 16°. **10661**. aaa. **23**.

—— *See* MIRECOURT (E. de) *pseud.* Histoire contemporaine . . . Barbès, *etc.* 1869. 12°. C. T. **38**. (**5**.)

—— *See* WASSERMANN (S.) Les Clubs de Barbès et de Blanqui en 1848. 1913. 8°. [*Bibliothèque d'histoire moderne.* fasc. 12.] **09009**. d. **1/12**.

—— Lettres . . . à Georges Sand. *See* PLAUCHUT (E.) Autour de Nohant, *etc.* 1897. 12°. **010664**. i. **8**.

—— Deux jours de condamnation à mort . . . Précédé d'une lettre de Louis Blanc. pp. 31. *Paris,* 1849. 8°. **10662**. d. **43**.

—— [Another edition.] Suivie de quelques mots à ceux qui possèdent en faveur des prolétaires sans travails. Lettre de L. Blanc à Barbès. Discours de L. Blanc sur la tombe de Barbès. pp. 45. *Paris,* 1870. 12°. **10663**. aaa. **37**. (**9**.)

BARBE-SCHMITZ (JEAN BAPTISTE CHARLES) *See* BARBE, afterwards BARBE-SCHMITZ.

BARBESSA (ODOARDO) *See* BARBOSA (Duarte)

BARBET (AUGUSTE) Au peuple. État de l'economie politique et sociale de la France. pp. 32. *Paris,* 1848. 16°. **8285**. a. **6**.

—— Le Coup de sabre, ou l'empire de Satan. pp. 31. *Paris,* 1848. 16°. **8052**. b. **95**. (**2**.)

—— Le Dogme, ou la loi au dix-neuvième siècle. pp. viii. 408. *Paris,* 1849. 8°. **8008**. f. **12**.

—— Du peuple de Moïse à Louis-Philippe, ou causes et effets. 2 pt. *Paris,* 1847. 8°. **8007**. e. **9**.

—— Du sang! Pourquoi du sang? pp. 37. *Paris,* 1848. 16°. **8052**. b. **95**. (**1**.)

—— Réforme politique, ou organisation d'une nouvelle force unitaire et gouvernementale. pp. vii. 436. *Paris,* 1840. 8°. **8050**. f. **5**.

—— Système social et responsabilité de l'homme, ou de la nécessité du prêt par l'état, *etc.* pp. xiii. 364. *Paris,* 1846. 8°. **8205**. e. **13**.

BARBET (CHARLES) La Perle du Maghreb—Tlemcen. Visions et croquis d'Algérie. [With plates.] pp. v. 231. *Alger,* [1908.] 8°. **010097**. g. **65**.

—— Questions sociales et ethnographiques. France, Algérie, Maroc. pp. 172. *Alger,* 1921. 8°. **08276**. bb. **59**.

BARBET (CLÉMENT) De la version pelvienne. pp. 39. *Paris,* 1848. 4°. [*Collection des thèses soutenues à la Faculté de Médecine de Paris.* An 1848. tom. 1.] **7372**. b. **4**.

BARBET (ÉMILE) The Recovery and Rectification of Benzoles, *etc.* pp. 20. [1931.] 8°. [*Société des Ingénieurs Civils de France, British Section. Papers and addresses.*] Ac. **4305/5**. (**17**.)

—— Rectification de l'air liquide. Séparation et purification des gaz de l'atmosphère. pp. 136. *Paris,* 1918. 8°. **8710**. c. **7**.

BARBET (ÉMILE) and **ARACHEQUESNE** (G.)

—— Manuel théorique et pratique des fabricants d'alcools et d'eaux-de-vie. pp. vii. 594. *Paris*, 1894. 8°. **07944**. ee. **35**.

BARBET (G.) Essai sur les causes de la maladie scrofuleuse dans le département du Cantal . . . Thèse, *etc.* pp. 20. *Paris*, 1837. 4°. **1184**. h. **7**. (**32**.)

BARBET (J.) Liure d'architecture d'autels, et de cheminees . . . De l'inuention et dessein de I. Barbet . . . Graue . . . par I. pl. 20. *Paris*, 1641. 8°. **559***. b. **1**. (**2**.) *Engraved throughout.*

—— A Booke of Archetecture, containing seeling peeces chimny peeces and seuerall sorts vsefull for carpenters, joyners, caruers, painters. [The plates of the French edition.] *To be sould by Robert Pricke: London*, 1670. fol. C. **27**. m. **2**.

BARBET (LOUIS ALEXANDRE) Les Grandes eaux de Versailles. Installations mécaniques et étangs artificiels. Description des fontaines et de leurs origines. Avec une préface de M. Henri Roujon. [With plates.] pp. iv. 358. *Paris*, 1907. 8°. **8775**. g. **33**.

—— Catalogue de la bibliothèque de feu M. L.-A. Barbet. [A sale catalogue, with facsimiles.] *Paris*, 1932– . fol. W.P. **8453**.

BARBET (PIERRE)

—— *See* BENEDETTI (Giacopone de') *da Todi*. Quelques poésies . . . transcrites . . . par . . . P. Barbet, *etc.* [1935.] 8°. **20010**. a. **19**.

—— La Passion de N.-S. Jésus-Christ selon le chirurgien . . . Deuxième édition. pp. 221. pl. 24. *Issoudun*, [1950.] 8°. **4227**. k. **33**.

—— The Passion of Our Lord Jesus Christ . . . Translated . . . by the Earl of Wicklow. [With plates.] pp. 178. *Clonmore & Reynolds: Dublin*, 1954. 8°. **04227**. bb. **4**.

—— The Corporal Passion of Jesus Christ. By Dr. P. Barbet . . . Translated . . . by the Earl of Wicklow. [Abridged.] Holy Week. By R. H. Benson. pp. 72. *Clonmore & Reynolds: Dublin*, 1955. 8°. **04227**. a. **19**.

BARBET (STEPHEN) Barbet's Guide for the Island of Guernsey, *etc.* [With a map.] pp. viii. 208. *Stephen Barbet: Guernsey*, [1840?] 16°. **10368**. aa. **21**.

—— [A reissue.] 1844. 16°. **10351**. aaa. **8**.

BARBET (V. R.) *See* BARBET DU BERTRAND.

BARBET (VIRGINIE) Religions & libre-pensée. Conférence faite à Genève le 27 janvier 1881. pp. 36. *Genève*, 1881. 8°. **4372**. df. **12**. (**4**.)

—— Réponse d'un membre de l'Internationale à Mazzini. [On his manifesto to Italian working men.] pp. 16. *Lyon*, 1871. 8°. **8275**. ee. **1**. (**4**.)

BARBET DE JOUY (HENRY) *See* JACQUEMART (A.) Histoire du mobilier . . . Avec une notice sur l'auteur par M. H. Barbet de Jouy, *etc.* 1876. 8°. **7945**. k. **20**.

—— *See* JACQUEMART (A.) A History of Furniture, *etc.* [With a preface by H. Barbet de Jouy.] 1878. 8°. **7808**. pp. **2**.

—— Les Della Robbia, sculpteurs en terre émaillée. Étude sur leurs travaux, suivie d'un catalogue de leur œuvre fait en Italie en 1853. pp. 98. *Paris*, 1855. 12°. **7875**. aa. **40**.

BARBET DE JOUY (HENRY)

—— Étude sur les fontes du Primatice. pp. 47. *Paris*, 1860. 8°. **7877**. g. **1**. (**1**.)

—— [Another copy.] Étude sur les fontes du Primatice. *Paris*, 1860. 8°. **7877**. g. **1**. (**2**.)

—— Étude sur les fontes du Primatice. pp. 47. *Paris*, 1868. 8°. **7856**. cc. **30**. (**6**.)

—— Les Mosaïques chrétiennes des basiliques et des églises de Rome décrites et expliquées. pp. xxx. 142. *Paris*, 1857. 8°. **7707**. c. **1**.

—— Musée Impérial du Louvre. Les gemmes et joyaux de la couronne, publiés et expliqués par H. Barbet de Jouy . . . dessinés et gravés à l'eau-forte d'après les originaux par Jules Jacquemart. pl. 60. 1865[, 71]. fol. *See* PARIS.—*Louvre.* **1701**. c. **14**.

—— Musée National du Louvre. Description des sculptures du moyen âge, de la Renaissance et des temps modernes. pp. 108. 1873. 8°. *See* PARIS.—*Louvre.* **7875**. aa. **2**.

—— Notice des antiquités, objets du moyen âge, de la renaissance et des temps modernes, composant le Musée des Souverains. pp. xxviii. 262. 1866. 12°. *See* PARIS.—*Louvre.—Musée des Souverains.* **7957**. aaa. **7**.

BARBET DE VAUX (GEORGES EUGÈNE)

—— *See* PHALIPAU (M.) Georges Barbet de Vaux, citoyen français, fonctionnaire du Ministère des Finances de l'empire russe, *etc.* [With portraits.] 1934. 8°. **20002**. ff. **12**.

BARBET DU BERTRAND (V. R.) Le Canon d'alarme prêt à tirer dans toute la France, par les anarchistes. Avis pressant au nouveau tiers pour sauver la patrie. Par un impartial (Barbet). pp. 8. [*Paris*, 1791?] 8°. F. **1126**. (**16**.)

—— La Conduite du Directoire devoilée, et le détail sur l'arrivée à Paris de vingt cinq mille hommes de troupes. pp. 8. [*Paris*, 1797.] 8°. F. **1382**. (**2**.)

—— [Another edition.] pp. 8. [*Paris*, 1797.] 8°. F. **55****. (**8**.)

—— Lettres de Me de Fronsac . . . ou son histoire de quelques mois à la cour de Russie, publiée [or rather written?] par V. R. Barbet. 2 tom. 1801. 12°. *See* DU PLESSIS (A. E. S. S.) *Duke de Richelieu.* **C.108.bbb.12.**

—— Le Maximum démontré contre-révolutionnaire. pp. 24. *Arras, Paris*, [1793.] 8°. F.R. **267**. (**2**.)

—— L'Ombre de Camille Desmoulins, ou mon opinion sur le gouvernement révolutionnaire. pp. 26. *Arras*, [1794.] 8°. F.R. **89**. (**2**.)

—— Seconde édition. pp. 26. *Arras*, [1794.] 8°. F. **947**. (**8**.)

—— [Another edition.] pp. 16. *Arras*, [1794.] 8°. F. **1102**. (**4**.)

—— [Another copy.] F. **630**. (**8**.)

—— Les Trois hommes illustres, ou dissertations sur les institutions politiques de César Auguste, de Charlesmagne, et de Napoléon Bonaparte, *etc.* pp. 284. *Paris*, 1803. 12°. **714**. b. **28**.

BARBET-MASSIN ( ) Mémoire sur la rétribution universitaire adressé aux Conseils généraux des départements. [Signed by Barbet-Massin and others.] pp. 15. *Corbeil*, [1840?] 8°. **1356**. e. **52**. (**4**.)

BARBETTA ( ) La Morte del Barbetta, celebre ludimagistro bresciano del secolo passato. Compianta in Brescia in una privata letteraria adunanza, l'anno 1739. [Verses by G. M. Mazzuchelli and others.] pp. 120. *Brescia*, 1740. 8°. **11429**. c. 28.

BARBETTA (Roberto) *See* Marcucci-Poltri (G. P.) Storia della Brigata Sicilia . . . Preceduta da una breve narrazione del fatto d'armi del 22 dicembre 1911 a Tobruk [by R. Barbetta], *etc.* 1912. 8°. **08821. g. 33.**

—— La Preparazione alla guerra di montagna, *etc.* pp. 137. *Torino*, 1901. 8°. **8822. aaa. 20.**

BARBETTE (Augustin) Dissertation sur la fièvre bilieuse, ou méningo-gastrique continue, *etc.* pp. 24. *Paris*, 1820. 4°. **1183. f. 5. (29.)**

BARBETTE (J. F.) De la bouche considérée comme organe d'expression dans les passions, et comme signe dans les maladies, *etc.* pp. 79. *Paris*, 1812. 4°. **1182. i. 8. (11.)**

BARBETTE (Jay)

—— Dear Dead Days. pp. 213. *Dodd, Mead & Co.: New York*, [1953.] 8°. **12732. c. 2.**

—— Dear Dead Days, *etc.* pp. 235. *Arthur Barker: London*, 1954. 8°. **12733. de. 20.**

—— Final Copy. [A novel.] pp. 160. *Arthur Barker: London*, 1952. 8°. **12731. h. 12.**

BARBETTE (Jules André) Du périnée et des abcès urineux. pp. 46. *Paris*, 1848. 4°. [*Collection des thèses soutenues à la Faculté de Médecine de Paris.* An 1848. tom. 1.] **7372. b. 4.**

BARBETTE (Nicolas Louis) Du sublimé-corrosif, ou deuto-chlorure de mercure, et de son action sur l'économie animale; thèse, *etc.* pp. 71. *Paris*, 1826. 4°. **1183. i. 5. (24.)**

BARBETTE (Paulus) *See* Bils (L. de) Kort bericht over de waarschouwinge van de Heer Joan van Horne. Als mede een antwoord op de Aanmerkingen van de Heer P. Barbette . . . op d'anatomische schriften van Jonkheer L. de Bils. 1660. 4°. **548. f. 8. (14.)**

—— *See* Bils (L. de) Generosiss. . . . L. de Bils . . . Responsio . . . ad animadversiones P. Barbette, *etc.* 1661. 4°. **548. f. 8. (17.)**

—— *Resp. See* Sebisch (M.) *the Younger.* Disputatio de variolis et morbillis, *etc.* pt. 6. 1642. 4°. **1179. i. 6. (15.)**

—— *See* Waldschmiedt (J. J.) Joh. Jacobi Waldschmidt . . . Opera medico-practica, quibus continentur . . . notæ ad praxin chirurgicam Barbettæ, *etc.* 1695. 4°. **542. c. 10.**

—— —— 1717. 4°. **542. e. 13–16.**

—— *See* Waldschmiedt (J. J.) Joh. Jacobi Waldschmidt . . . Praxis medicinæ rationalis succincta . . . Quibus accesserunt notæ ejusdem ad praxin chirurgicam Barbettæ, *etc.* 1691. 12°. **545. d. 18.**

—— Pauli Barbette Opera omnia medica et chirurgica, notis et observationibus nec non pluribus morborum historiis et curationibus illustrata. Editio novissima . . . operâ et studio Joh. Jacob Mangeti. 2 pt. *J. A. Chouet: Genevæ*, 1688. 4°. **542. c. 8.**

—— Pauli Barbette . . . Opera chirurgico-anatomica, ad circularem sanguinis motum, aliaque recentiorum inventa, accommodata. Accedit de peste tractatus, observationibus illustratus. pp. 461. *Ex officina Hackiana: Lugd. Batav.*, 1672. 12°. **782. a. 6.**
With an additional titlepage, engraved.

BARBETTE (Paulus)

—— [Another edition.] Pauli Barbette Chirurgia, notis ac observationibus rarioribus illustrata secundum veræ philosophiæ fundamenta ac recentiorum inventa, opera Johannis Muis . . . Accedit de peste tractatus, observationibus illustratus. pp. 543. *J. Wolters: Amstelædami*, 1693. 12°. **782. a. 9.**
With an additional titlepage, engraved.

—— The Chirurgical and Anatomical Works of Paul Barbette . . . Together with a Treatise of the Plague . . . Translated out of Low-Dutch into English. pp. 342. 52. *J. Darby & Moses Pitt: London*, 1672. 8°. **783. e. 2.**

—— Thesaurus chirurgiæ: the Chirurgical and Anatomical Works of P. Barbette . . . The fourth edition . . . To which is added The Surgeon's Chest [by Gulielmus Fabritius Hildanus] . . . and . . . a Treatise of diseases that . . . attend camps and fleets. Written in High-Dutch by Raymundus Minderius. pp. 394. 119. *For Henry Rhodes: London*, 1687, 86. 8°. **782. a. 8.**
With an additional titlepage, engraved.

—— Anatomia practica, oft ontleding des menschelijken lichaems, neffens het gebruyck der selve in de chirurgie; derde deel. pp. 167. [*Amsterdam?* 1659.] 8°. **548. e. 27.**

—— Mensch-Beschryving, naer den onwederleggelijcken ommeloop des bloets. pp. 95. *J. Lescaille: Amsterdam*, 1657. 8°. **548. e. 39.**

—— Praxis Barbettiana, cum notis & observationibus Frederici Deckers, *etc.* pp. 248. MS. NOTES. *Apud Gaasbekios: Lugd. Batav.*, 1669. 12°. **545. a. 18.**
With an additional titlepage, engraved.

—— [Another edition.] pp. 248. *Apud A. Gaasbequium: Amstelodami*, 1678. 12°. **545. a. 19.**

—— The Practice of the Most Successful Physitian Paul Barbette . . . With the Notes and Observations of F. Deckers . . . Faithfully rendered into English. pp. 271. *T. R. for Henry Brome: London*, 1675. 8°. **545. c. 26.**

BARBETTI ( ) *See* Olivetti (R.) Catalogue d'une collection d'antiquités phénico-égypto-sardes . . . appartenant à . . . R. Olivetti . . . et à M. le commandant Barbetti. 1856. 8°. **7704. e. 12. (1.)**

BARBEU-DUBOURG (A.) Recherches sur les accidents produits par quelques corps étrangers des bronches. pp. 44. *Paris*, 1866. 4°. [*Collection des thèses soutenues à la Faculté de Médecine de Paris.* An 1866. tom. 1.] **7373. g. 4.**

BARBEU-DUBOURG (Jacques)

—— *See* Aldridge (Alfred O.) Jacques Barbeu-Dubourg, a French disciple of Benjamin Franklin. 1951. 4°. [*Proceedings of the American Philosophical Society.* vol. 95. no. 4.] **Ac. 1830.**

—— *See* Franklin (Benjamin) *LL.D.* Œuvres . . . Traduites . . . Par M. Barbeu Dubourg, *etc.* [In fact translated by J. B. L'Écuy and edited by Barbeu-Dubourg.] 1773. 4°. **30. d. 14, 15.**

—— *See* Saint-John (Henry) *Viscount Bolingbroke.* [Letters on the Study and Use of History.] Lettres sur l'histoire . . . Traduites de l'anglois [by Barbeu-Dubourg]. 1752. 8°. **804. a. 36. (1.)**

—— *See* Saint-John (H.) *Viscount Bolingbroke.* Le Siècle politique de Louis XIV, ou lettres du vicomte Bolingbroke sur ce sujet, *etc.* [Tom. 2 of the translation by J. Barbeu-Dubourg of "Letters on the study and use of History."] 1753. 8°. **9078. bb. 25.**

BARBEU-DUBOURG (JACQUES)

—— An variolarum morbus, absque eruptione? *Resp.* C. L. Varnier. 1782. *See* BALDINGER (E. G.) Sylloge selectiorum opusculorum, *etc.* vol. 6. 1776, *etc.* 8°. **97.** d. **10.**

—— Le Botaniste françois, comprenant toutes les plantes communes et usuelles, disposées suivant une nouvelle méthode. 2 tom. *Paris*, 1767. 12°. **448.** b. **18.**

—— [Another copy.] **236.** g. **26.**

—— Chronographie, ou description des temps, contenant toute la suite des souverains des divers peuples, des principaux événements de chaque siècle . . . depuis la création du monde jusqu'à la fin du dix-huitième siècle . . . Nouvelle édition, contenant des additions importantes, *etc.* [With tables.] pp. 77. *Paris*, 1838. fol. **798.** l. **19.**

—— Petit code de la raison humaine, ou exposition succinte de ce que la raison dicte à tous les hommes . . . Par M. B. D. [i.e. J. Barbeu-Dubourg.] pp. xxiv. 114. 1789. 12°. *See* D., ., *M. B.* **8405.** b. 5.
[The prefatory letter signed: B. D.]

—— Questio . . . an tracheotomiæ nunc scalpellum nunc trigonus mucro. *Praes.* A. Bergier. 1748. *See* HALLER (A. von) *Baron.* Disputationes chirurgicæ, *etc.* tom. 2. 1755, *etc.* 4°. **7481.** ff. **20.**

BARBEU DU ROCHER (A.)

—— Ambassade de Pétrarque auprès du roi Jean le Bon. 1854. *See* PARIS.—*Académie des Inscriptions et Belles-Lettres.* Mémoires présentés par divers savants, *etc.* sér. 2. tom. 3. 1843, *etc.* 4°. **Ac. 420/10. (2.)**

BARBEY (ALPHONSE) Un Almanach en 1718, ou description d'un tir provincial d'arquebusiers à Meaux en Brie. pp. 24. *Château-Thierry*, 1877. 8°. **7709.** g. **5.**

—— Notice historique sur la maison natale de Jean de la Fontaine à Château-Thierry. pp. 20. *Paris*, 1870. 8°. **10602.** h. **14.** (**10.**)

—— [Another copy.] **10601.** c. **29.** (**1.**)

BARBEY (ANDRÉ) *See* HAEBLER (C.) German (Italian, West-European) Incunabula . . . Translated . . . by A. Barbey. 1927, *etc.* fol. K.T.C. **113.** b. **14.**

BARBEY (AUGUSTE) Die Bostrichiden Central-Europas. Eine . . . Studie der Familie der Borkenkäfer mit Rücksicht auf den Forstschutz. [Translated by J. Carl.] . . . Mit 18 . . . Tafeln. pp. 119. *Genf, Giessen*, 1901. 4°. **7295.** k. **6.**

—— Le Peuplier. Son utilité et l'extension de sa culture en Suisse . . . Illustrée . . . Deuxième édition. pp. 56. 1947. 8°. *See* SWITZERLAND.—*Departement des Innern.—Inspektion für Forstwesen, Jagd und Fischerei.* S. P. **234.**

—— Traité d'entomologie forestière à l'usage des forestiers, des reboiseurs et des propriétaires de bois . . . Ouvrage illustré de 350 figures originales et de 8 planches hors texte en couleurs exécutées par l'auteur. [With a preface by Edmond Henry.] pp. xiv. 624. *Paris, Nancy*, 1913. 8°. **7296.** ccc. **15.**

—— 2e édition, entièrement revue et augmentée. pp. xviii. 749. pl. VIII. *Paris*, 1925. 8°. **7299.** d. **17.**

BARBEY (BERNARD) Le Camarade abandonné, *etc.* [With a portrait.] pp. 59. *Marseille*, 1927. 8°. **12515.** r. **30.**

—— Le Cœur gros. pp. 171. *Paris*, 1924. 8°. [*Les Cahiers verts.* vol. 45.] **12237.** ppp. **1/45.**

—— Le Crépuscule du matin. Roman. pp. 292. *Paris*, 1938. 8°. **12549.** aa. **41.**

BARBEY (BERNARD)

—— Les Déguisements. Nouvelle inédite. 1935. *See* PERIODICAL PUBLICATIONS.—*Paris.* Les Œuvres libres, *etc.* no. 172. 1921, *etc.* 8°. **12208.** ee. **172.**

—— P.C. du général. Journal du chef de l'état-major particulier du général Guisan, 1940–1945. pp. 280. *Neuchâtel*, 1947. 8°. **8837.** h. **53.**

BARBEY (BRIGITTE V.)

—— *See* COWARD (N. P.) [This time tomorrow.] Demain, à cette heure . . . Traduction de B. V. Barbey. 1952. 8°. [*Les Œuvres libres.* Nouvelle série. no. 74.] **12208.** ee. **299.**

BARBEY (FRÉDÉRIC) *See* BUSSY (J. M.) Notes de Jean Marc Bussy, appointé voltigeur. Campagnes d'Espagne et de Russie. [Edited by F. Barbey.] 1913. 8°. **08821.** e. **1/5.**

—— *See* DUPRÉ (R.) Correspondance de R. Dupré . . . Publiée avec une introduction et des notes par F. Barbey, *etc.* 1906. 8°. [*Mémoires et documents publiés par la Société d'histoire et d'archéologie de Genève.* sér. 2. tom. 9.] Ac. **6941.**

—— *See* LAMON (S.) Souvenirs d'un chasseur de la vieille Garde de Napoléon Ier. [With an introduction by F. Barbey.] 1916. 8°. **08821.** e. **1/7.**

—— *See* MAILLARD (J. P.) Mémoires de J. P. Maillard, de Vevey. [Edited by F. Barbey.] 1913. 8°. **08821.** e. **1/5.**

—— *See* MORSIER (J. F. de) Journal. [Edited by F. Barbey.] 1915. 8°. **08821.** e. **1/6.**

—— *See* SWISS SOLDIERS. Soldats suisses au service étranger . . . Avec notices [signed: F. B., i.e. F. Barbey], *etc.* 1908, *etc.* 8°. **08821.** e. **1/8.**

—— Une Amie de Marie Antoinette. Madame Atkyns et la prison du Temple, 1758–1836. D'après des documents inédits . . . Préface de M. Victorien Sardou. pp. xvi. 454. *Paris*, 1905. 8°. **010661.** aaa. **31.**

—— A Friend of Marie-Antoinette (Lady Atkyns). Translated from the French . . . With a preface by Victorien Sardou. pp. xix. 252. *Chapman & Hall: London*, 1906. 8°. **010662.** k. **63.**

—— La Belgique d'Albert Ier et de Léopold III 1918–1948. Le témoignage d'un diplomate. pp. 279. *Paris*, 1950. 8°. **8081.** de. **31.**

—— Félix Desportes et l'annexion de Genève à la France 1794–1799, d'après des documents inédits, avec huit gravures hors texte et deux plans. pp. xx. 448. *Paris, Genève*, 1916. 8°. **9305.** e. **19.**

—— Louis de Chalon, prince d'Orange, seigneur d'Orbe, Échallens, Grandson, 1390–1463, *etc.* [With plates, including a portrait, and a genealogical table.] pp. 396. *Lausanne*, 1926. 8°. [*Mémoires et documents publiés par la Société d'Histoire de la Suisse romande.* sér. 2. tom. 13.] Ac. **6960.**

—— La Mort de Pichegru. Biville—Paris—Le Temple. 1804. Avec cinq plans inédits du Temple et sept gravures hors texte. pp. ii. 276. *Paris*, 1909. 8°. **10660.** t. **6.**

—— Les Pierres parlent, *etc.* [Articles, mainly on Swiss history in the Napoleonic period. With plates.] pp. 307. *Lausanne*, 1941. 8°. **9305.** aaa. **30.**

—— La Route du Simplon. Illustrations de F. Boissonnas. pp. 157. *Genève*, 1906. 4°. **10108.** l. **4.**

BARBEY (Frédéric)

—— Suisses hors de Suisse. Au service des rois et de la Révolution. D'après des documents inédits . . . Stanislas Poniatowsky et Marc Reverdil. Madame de Staël et Ferdinand Christin. Jean Gaspard Schweizer. pp. 323. *Paris*, 1914 [1913]. 8°. **10601**. tt. **21**.

—— Un Vaudois à l'armée d'Espagne, d'après les souvenirs inédits du lieutenant Jean-David Maillefer, 1809–1813. [Signed: F. B., i.e. F. Barbey.] 1909. 8°. *See* B., F. **08821**. e. **1/2**.

BARBEY (Georges) *See* Coxe (H. C.) and Barbey (G.) Éléments de droit américain, *etc.* 1908. 8°. **06617**. df. **5**.

BARBEY (I. T.) ET CIE.

—— [Reports.] 2 pt. *Paris*, [1858.] 4°. **08286**. m. **57**. (**4**.)

BARBEY (J. F.) Dissertation sur l'hygiène des femmes enceintes, suivie de quelque réflexions sur l'emploi de la saignée pendant la grossesse. pp. 21. *Paris*, 1813. 4°. **1182**. i. **11**. (**23**.)

BARBEY (Jean)

—— Le Conseil des ministres sous la Restauration. pp. 284. *Paris*, 1937. 8°. **9226**. dd. **19**.

BARBEY (Léon)

—— Les Fondements éthiques et psychologiques de l'éducation de la volonté selon M. Jules Payot. Thèse, *etc.* pp. 110. *Fribourg*, 1933. 8°. **8473**. e. **42**.

BARBEY (Maurice) La Trouvaille de Valleyres. pp. 6. *Orbe*, 1893. 8°. Dept. of Coins & Medals.

—— Urba. Mosaïques et vestiges romains de Boscéaz, près Orbe. Par M. Barbey, L. Decollogny et S.-W. Poget, *etc.* (Extrait de la Revue Historique Vaudoise.) pp. 63. pl. xvii. 1929. 8°. *See* Orbe.—*Association du Vieil Orbe Pro Urba.* Dept. of Greek & Roman Antiquities.

BARBEY (Théodore Eugène) Considérations médicales et philosophiques sur la continence; thèse, *etc.* pp. 20. *Paris*, 1832. 4°. **1184**. e. **6**. (**24**.)

BARBEY (Victor Marie) Faculté de Droit de Paris. Thèse pour la Licence. (Jus romanum. De actionibus empti et venditi.—Droit français. De la vente et de l'échange.) pp. 55. *Paris*, 1860. 8°. **5406**. c. **2**. (**4**.)

BARBEY (William) *See* Belli (S.) I Hieracium di Sardegna. Rivista critica delle specie note . . . dal catalogo di W. Barbey, *etc.* 1897. 4°. [*Memorie della Reale Accademia di Scienze di Torino.* ser. 2. tom. 47.] Ac. **2816**.

—— Lydie, Lycie, Carie . . . Études botaniques [by E. Boissier and others]. Revues par W. Barbey. Avec . . . planches. pp. 82. *Lausanne*, 1890. 4°. **7028**. f. **1**.

BARBEY-BOISSIER (Caroline) La Comtesse Agénor de Gasparin et sa famille. Correspondance et souvenirs, 1813–1894 . . . Préface de M. A. Filon. 2 tom. *Paris*, 1902. 8°. **010910**. bb. **31**.

BARBEY D'AUREVILLY (Jules Amédée) *See* Audouard (O.) M. Barbey d'Aurevilly. Réponse à ses réquisitoires contre les Bas-Bleus, *etc.* 1870. 12°. **8416**. c. **1**. (**3**.)

—— *See* Balzac (H. de) [*Selections and Extracts.*] Pensées et maximes. Recueillies et classées par J. Barbey d'Aurevilly. 1909. 8°. **12350**. v. **10**.

—— *See* Beauchesne (A.) Écrivains d'autrefois. Napoléon journaliste . . . Barbey d'Aurevilly, *etc.* [With a portrait.] 1930. 8°. **11878.f.21.**

BARBEY D'AUREVILLY (Jules Amédée)

—— *See* Benigne (H.) La Côte d'Adam . . . Préface par Barbey d'Aurevilly. 1886. 12°. **12491**. o. **9**.

—— *See* Bloy (L. M.) Le Révélateur du globe . . . Préface de J. Barbey d'Aurevilly. 1884. 8°. **10629**. e. **22**.

—— *See* Bonnefon (M. F. J. J. de) Triptyche d'âmes. Chopin, Rodin, Barbey d'Aurevilly. 1926. 8°. **011840**. b. **62**.

—— *See* Bonnes (J. P.) Le Bonheur du masque. Petite introduction aux romans de "Barbey d'Aurevilly," *etc.* 1947. 8°. **11867**. bb. **37**.

—— *See* Bordeaux (H.) Barbey d'Aurevilly, *etc.* 1925. 8°. **010662**. a. **56**.

—— *See* Borély (M.) Barbey d'Aurevilly, maître d'amour. 1934. 8°. **11878.de.34.**

—— *See* Boulenger (J.) Sous Louis-Philippe: Les Dandys . . . Barbey d'Aurevilly, *etc.* 1907. 8°. **10601**. dg. **15**.

—— *See* Bourget (P. C. J.) Aux maisons de Barbey d'Aurevilly et de Balzac. 1924. 16°. **012207.p.1/61.**

—— *See* Buet (C.) J. Barbey d'Aurevilly, *etc.* 1891. 12°. **010664.i.20.**

—— *See* Buet (C.) Le Prêtre, *etc.* [With a preface by J. A. Barbey d'Aurevilly.] 1882. 8°. **11740**. i. **12**.

—— *See* Canu (J.) Barbey d'Aurevilly. 1945. 8°. **10656**. k. **29**.

—— *See* Clerget (F.) Littérateurs et artistes. Barbey d'Aurevilly (de sa naissance à 1909), *etc.* 1909. 8°. **010664**. l. **9**.

—— *See* Coppée (F. E. J.) and Artois de Bournonville (J. F. A. d') Le Petit Marquis. Pièce en quatre actes . . . Avec une préface de J. Barbey d'Aurevilly. 1909. 8°. **11736**. ccc. **18**.

—— *See* Cornilleau (R.) Barbey d'Aurevilly et la médecine, *etc.* 1933. 8°. **10655**. i. **33**.

—— *See* Creed (Elizabeth) Le Dandysme de Jules Barbey d'Aurevilly. 1938. 8°. **11859**. d. **25**.

—— *See* Crisenoy (P. de) Essai sur Jules-Amédée Barbey d'Aurevilly. 1908. 8°. **11840**. s. **3**.

—— *See* Doyon (R. L.) Barbey d'Aurevilly, amoureux et dupe, *etc.* [With portraits.] 1934. 8°. **10655**. w. **3**.

—— *See* Duchesne de la Sicotière (P. F. L.) Un Éditeur de Barbey d'Aurevilly . . . Bibliographie des ouvrages publiés par Trébutien. 1906. 8°. **11908**. r. **10**.

—— *See* Dusolier (A. E. M.) Barbey d'Aurevilly, *etc.* [Remarks on his novels.] 1862. 8°. **10663**. bb. **5**.

—— *See* Gaschon de Molènes (D. J. B. P.) Œuvres diverses. [With a preface by J. A. Barbey d'Aurevilly.] 1885, *etc.* 18°. **12234**. cc. **25**.

—— *See* Gómez de la Serna (R.) Efigies. (Barbey d'Aurevilly.) 1929. 8°. **010603**. e. **27**.

—— *See* Grelé (E.) Jules Barbey d'Aurevilly. Sa vie et son œuvre d'après sa correspondance inédite, *etc.* 1902. 8°. **010663**. l.

—— *See* Halley (Fernand) Barbey D'Aurevilly. Sa vie, ses œuvres, opinions inédites, *etc.* 1909. 8°. **10602**. ppp. **1**. (**1**.)

—— *See* HARCOURT (B. H. M. d') *Count.* Lamartine, Barbey d'Aurevilly et Paul de Saint-Victor en 1848, *etc.* 1948. 8°. **010655**. e. **46**.

—— *See* KORIGAN (Paria) *pseud.* Miséricorde, *etc.* [With a preface by J. A. Barbey d'Aurevilly.] 1901. 8°. **012550**. b. **52**.

—— *See* LAURENTIE (F.) Sur Barbey d'Aurevilly. Études et fragments. [With a bibliography.] 1912. 8°. **010664**. h. **31**.

—— *See* LA VARENDE (J. B. M. M. de) *Viscount.* Grands Normands . . . Barbey d'Aurevilly, Gustave Flaubert, *etc.* [With a portrait.] 1939. 8°. **11863**. c. **7**.

—— *See* MARIE (A.) Le Connétable des lettres. Barbey d'Aurevilly, *etc.* [With portraits.] 1939. 8°. **010655**. ee. **22**.

—— *See* MARTINEAU (R.) Aspects méconnus de Barbey d'Aurevilly. [With a portrait.] [1938.] 8°. **010655**. e. **3**.

—— *See* MARTINEAU (R.) Types et prototypes, *etc.* [Literary studies, with special reference to Barbey d'Aurevilly and Poictevin.] 1931. 8°. **10655**. d. **10**.

—— *See* MICHELET (V. E.) Figures d'évocateurs . . . Barbey d'Aurevilly, ou le croyant, *etc.* 1913. 8°. **011853**. aa. **18**.

—— *See* PÉLADAN (J. A.) La Décadence esthétique. I. L'Art ochlocratique. Salons de 1882 & de 1883. Avec une lettre de J. Barbey d'Aurevilly, *etc.* 1888. 8°. **7806**. de. **10**.

—— *See* PÉLADAN (J. A.) La Décadence latine. Éthopée. (I. Le Vice suprême. Préface de J. Barbey d'Aurevilly.) 1886, *etc.* 12°. **12517.p.1.**

—— —— [1900.] 8°. **012550**. l. **41**.

—— *See* PÉLADAN (J. A.) Études passionnelles de décadence. Le vice suprême. Préface de J. Barbey d'Aurevilly, *etc.* 1884. 12°. Tab. **603**. a. **29**.

—— *See* QUÉRU (H.) Le Dernier grand seignieur, Jules Barbey d'Aurevilly, *etc.* [With portraits.] 1946. 8°. **10656**. k. **36**.

—— *See* RIOTOR (L. E. E.) Barbey D'Aurevilly, connétable des lettres. [With a portrait.] 1933. 8°. **10655**. s. **13**.

—— *See* ROÏDES (E. D.) La Papesse Jeanne . . . Septième édition, revue et augmentée d'une étude critique par J. Barbey d'Aurevilly, *etc.* 1881. 8°. **12548**. ppp. **2**.

—— *See* SEGUIN (J. P.) Barbey D'Aurevilly. Études de bibliographie critique, *etc.* [1949?] 8°. **11926**. g. **8**.

—— *See* UZANNE (O.) Le Bric-à-brac de l'amour . . . Préface de J. Barbey d'Aurevilly. 1879. 8°. **12316**. ppp. **4**.

—— Les Œuvres complètes, *etc.* (Édition établie avec le concours de Melle Read par M. Joseph Quesnel.) 17 vol.

Les Diaboliques.
L'Ensorcelée.
Le Chevalier des Touches.
Poëmes, précédés de sa vie et d'une bibliographie par Henri Bachelin.
Une Vieille maitresse. 2 vol.
Un Prêtre marié. 2 vol.
L'Amour impossible, suivi de Pensées détachées et Du dandysme.
Ce qui ne meurt pas. La Bague d'Hannibal. 2 vol.
Une Histoire sans nom, suivi d'Une Page d'histoire et de Memoranda, 3e et 4e.
Memoranda, 1er et 2e.
Lettres à Trébutien. 4 vol.

Paris, 1926, 27. 8°. **012238**. c.

BARBEY D'AUREVILLY (JULES AMÉDÉE)

—— Œuvres, *etc.* 10 tom. *Paris*, 1873–89. 12°. **12518**. ccc. **23**.
The novels only.

—— Poussières.—Rhythmes oubliés.—Amaïdée. pp. 253. *Paris*, 1909. 12°. **011483**. e. **55**.

—— Lettres de J. Barbey d'Aurevilly à Léon Bloy. Avec . . . une lettre autographe, *etc.* pp. 240. *Paris*, 1902. 8°. **010910**. b. **54**.

—— Lettres à une amie, 1880–1887. Troisième édition. pp. 214. *Paris*, 1907. 8°. **10905**. cc. **18**.

—— Lettres de J. Barbey d'Aurevilly à Trebutien. Avec un portrait inédit de l'auteur gravé à l'eau forte par G. Noyon. 2 tom. *Paris*, 1908. 8°. **10921**. f. **25**.

—— Lettres intimes. (Recueillies et classées par Louise Read.) pp. 338. *Paris*, 1921. 8°. **010905**. df. **34**.

—— Mgr Anger-Billards et Barbey d'Aurevilly. Correspondance inédite, *etc.* [With a portrait.] 1929. 8°. *See* ANGER-BILLARDS (A.) **010905**. de. **61**.

—— Lettre . . . a Mme H. M. Carey. *See* CAREY (Harriet M.) For Ever. 1857. 16°. **11650**. c. **57**. **(2.)**

—— A côté de la grande histoire. pp. 350. *Paris*, 1904. 8°. **09009**. a. **4**.

—— Amaïdée. Poème en prose. [With a preface by Paul Bourget.] pp. vii. 74. *Paris*, 1890. 8°. **012547**. i. **31**.

—— L'Amour impossible. Chronique parisienne. pp. 274. *Paris*, 1859. 8°. **12514**. cc. **4**.

—— Le Cachet d'Onyx: Léa, 1831–1832. pp. 77. *Paris*, 1919. 8°. **12551**. s. **14**.

—— Ce qui ne meurt pas. pp. 415. *Paris*, 1884. 8°. **12510**. l. **39**.

—— What never dies. A romance. pp. 365. *Fortune Press: London*, [1933.] 8°. **12514**. r. **19**.

—— Le Chevalier des Touches. pp. 282. *Paris*, 1864. 8°. **12515**. aaa. **3**.

—— [Another edition.] Dessins de J. Le Blant gravés par Champollion. pp. 239. *Paris*, 1886. 8°. **12491**. q. **12**.

—— [Another edition.] pp. ii. 284. *Paris*, [1893.] 8°. **012548**. f. **37**.

—— [Another edition.] Edited by P. A. Lewis, *etc.* pp. 109. *London*, 1923. 8°. [*Blackie's Longer French Texts.*] **12237**. pp. **1/25**.

—— Critiques diverses. pp. 364. *Paris*, 1909. 8°. **11852**. t. **11**.

—— De l'histoire. pp. 358. *Paris*, 1905. 8°. **09009**. aaa. **6**.

—— Dernières polémiques. pp. 362. *Paris*, 1891. 12°. **012357**. e. 21.

—— Deux rhythmes oubliés. (Laocoon.—Les Yeux caméléons.) pp. 16. *Caen*, 1857. 16°. **11481**. c. **44**. **(1.)**
One of an edition of 36 copies printed for private circulation.

—— Laocoon: a forgotten rhyme, translated into English verse . . . by H. M. Carey. [Edited by F. G. S. Trebutien.] *Fr. & Eng.* pp. 15. *Caen*, 1857. 16°. **11481**. c. **44**. **(2.)**
Printed for private circulation.

—— Les Diaboliques. Introduction de Léon Gosset. pp. 328. *Paris*, 1939. 8°. **12549**. d. **7**.

—— Les Diaboliques. [Six tales.] pp. 391. *Paris*, 1891. 8°. **012548**. eee. **56**.

—— Les Diaboliques. Introduction by Peter Quennell. Drawings by Dodie Masterman. pp. 250. *Paul Elek: London*, [1947.] 8°. **012550**. bb. **45**.

—— The Diaboliques. Translated . . . with an introduction, by Ernest Boyd, *etc.* pp. xxiv. 275. *A. A. Knopf: London; printed in U.S.A.*, 1926. 8°. **12547**. h. **13**.

—— XIX siècle. Les œuvres et les hommes. 15 vol.

[*First Series.*]	*Deuxième Série.*
Les Philosophes et les écrivains religieux.	Les Philosophes et les écrivains religieux.
Les Historiens politiques et littéraires.	Les Historiens.
Les Poètes.	Les Poètes.
Les Romanciers.	Littérature étrangère.
Les Bas-bleus.	Littérature épistolaire.
Les Critiques, ou les juges jugés.	Mémoires historiques et littéraires.
Sensations d'art.	Journalistes et polémistes, chroniqueurs et pamphlétaires.
Sensations d'histoire.	

Paris, 1860–95. 12° & 8°. **10606**. cc.

—— Du dandysme et de G. Brummell. pp. 118. *Caen*, 1845. 16°. **10825**. aa. **14**.

—— [Another edition.] pp. xvi. 169. *Paris*, 1861. 16°. **10825**. aa. **24**.

—— Of Dandyism and of George Brummell. Translated . . . by Douglas Ainslie. pp. xxiii. 141. *Dent & Co.: London*, 1897. 8°. **10827**. a. **26**.

—— The Anatomy of Dandyism, with some observations on Beau Brummell; translated . . . by D. B. Wyndham Lewis: and illustrated with drypoints of Hermine David. pp. xv. 84. *Peter Davies: London*, 1928. 8°. C. **99**. h. **23**.

—— L'Ensorcelée. pp. iii. 288. *Paris*, 1859. 8°. **12548**. ppp. **31**.

—— [Another edition.] pp. 336. *Paris*, 1889. 8°. **12516**. de. **22**.

—— Bewitched . . . Translated . . . by Louise Collier Willcox, *etc.* pp. 276. *Harper & Bros.: New York & London*, 1928. 8°. **12516**. r. **5**.

—— Femmes et moralistes. pp. 340. *Paris*, 1906. 8°. **8415**. aaa. **7**.

—— Les Fleurs du mal par M. Charles Baudelaire. [A review.] *See* BAUDELAIRE (C. P.) Articles justificatifs pour Charles Baudelaire, *etc.* 1857. 4°. **11826**. g. **13**.

—— Fragment. À mettre en tête du Joseph Delorme que je dois donner à * * *. Préface de François Laurentie. pp. vii. 9. *Paris*, 1912. 16°. **12547**. aa. **25**. (**2**.)

—— Gœthe et Diderot. pp. xxiii. 290. *Paris*, 1880. 8°. **11840**. bbb. **22**.

—— Laocoon. *See* supra: Deux rhythmes oubliés.

—— Premier memorandum. 1836–1838. pp. 287. *Paris*, 1900. 8°. **010664**. f. **52**.

—— Deuxième memorandum, 1838, et quelques pages de 1864. pp. 297. *Paris*, 1906. 8°. **010664**. i. **45**.

—— Memorandum. [1856.] pp. 107. *Caen*, 1856. 16°. **10173**. a. **20**.

Printed for private circulation.

—— Memoranda. [The "Memorandum" of 1856, followed by a "Deuxième memorandum," 1858.] Préface de Paul Bourget. pp. xxvii. 152. *Paris*, 1883. 8°. **12357**. c. **20**.

—— Les Misérables de M. V. Hugo. pp. v. 95. *Paris*, 1862. 8°. **11826**. ccc. **31**. (**6**.)

—— Notice sur J.-M. Audin, auteur des Histoires de Luther, de Calvin, de Léon X. et de Henri VIII. . . . suivie de l'Introduction à l'ouvrage intitulé: La Réforme contre la réforme, traduit de l'allemand d'Hœninghaus et ornée du portrait de J.-M. Audin. pp. 96. *Paris*, 1856. 8°. **4866**. d. **4**.

—— Pensées détachées. Fragments sur les femmes. pp. 85. *Paris*, 1889. 8°. **8410**. d. **21**.

—— Philosophes et écrivains religieux et politiques. pp. 264. *Paris*, 1909. 8°. **11851**. ppp. **18**.

—— Poésie et poètes. pp. 325. *Paris*, 1906. 8°. **11853**. pp. **21**.

—— Poésies de J. Barbey d'Aurevilly. Commentées par lui-même. pp. 70. *Bruxelles*, 1870. 8°. **11483**. i. **10**.

—— Polémiques d'hier. [Political essays.] pp. 336. *Paris*, 1889. 12°. **8051**. c. **35**.

—— Poussières. [Poems.] pp. 92. *Paris*, 1897. 8°. **11483**. dd. **24**.

—— Poussières. Poésies complètes. Édition revue sur les textes originaux et les manuscrits, *etc.* [Preface signed: Ad. B.] pp. 175. *Paris*, 1918. 16°. **011483**. e. **87**.

The date in the colophon is 1917.

—— Un Prêtre marié. 2 tom. *Paris*, 1865. 8°. **12515**. dd. **3**.

—— Les Prophètes du passé. (Seconde édition.) pp. 222. *Paris*, 1860. 8°. **11826**. ccc. **18**.

—— [Another edition.] pp. 330. *Paris, Bruxelles*, 1880. 8°. **3900**. e. **8**.

—— Les Quarante médaillons de l'Académie. pp. 135. *Paris*, 1864. 8°. **11826**. bbb. **9**.

—— Rhythmes oubliés. pp. 54. *Paris*, 1897. 8°. **11483**. dd. **25**.

—— Les Ridicules du temps . . . Deuxième édition. pp. iv. 294. *Paris*, 1883. 8°. **12357**. bb. **16**.

—— Le Roman contemporain. pp. 282. *Paris*, 1902. 8°. **011853**. g. **36**.

—— Romanciers d'hier et d'avant-hier. pp. 349. *Paris*, 1904. 8°. **010664**. g. **43**.

—— Rodolphe Töpffer. pp. **28**. *Genève*, 1943. 8°. **10666**. b. **20**.

Petite collection Rodolphe Töpffer. vol. 2.

—— Théâtre contemporain, 1870–1883. 2 vol. *Paris*, 1892–96. 12°. **011795**. e. **42**.

—— Une Vieille maîtresse. 2 tom. *Paris*, 1879. 8°. **12517**. a. **8**.

—— Les Vieilles actrices. Le Musée des Antiques. pp. ii. 222. *Paris*, 1889. 18°. **010661**. g. **22**.

—— Voyageurs et romanciers. Édition du centenaire. pp. 288. *Paris*, 1908. 8°. **11840**. p. **13**.

—— L'Esprit de J. Barbey d'Aurevilly. Dictionnaire de pensées, traits, portraits et jugements tirés de son œuvre critique. Préface par Octave Uzanne. Deuxième édition. pp. 354. *Paris*, 1908. 8°. **11851**. p. **22**.

BARBEY D'AUREVILLY (LÉON) *See* DAUPHIN (Joseph) Un Poète apôtre . . . Léon Barbey d'Aurevilly. 1891. 8°. **4866**. de. **5**.

BARBEYRAC (CHARLES) Quæstiones medicæ duodecim, *etc.* pp. 20. *D. Pech: Monspelii,* 1658. 4°. **1185**. f. **3**. (**8**.)

—— Traités nouveaux de médecine, contenans les maladies de la poitrine, les maladies des femmes, *etc.* [By C. Barbeyrac.] pp. 357. 1684. 12°. *See* TRAITÉS. **776**. a. **11**.

—— [Another edition.] Par Mr. B * * *, Docteur de Montpellier [i.e. C. Barbeyrac]. pp. 358. 1712. 12°. *See* B * * *, *Mr., Docteur de Montpellier.* **776**. a. **12**.

—— [Another edition.] Dissertations nouvelles sur les maladies de la poitrine, du cœur, de l'estomac, des femmes, vénériennes, & quelques maladies particulières . . . avec deux descriptions de maladies qui n'ont jamais été écrites, *etc.* pp. 576. *Amsterdam,* 1731. 8°. **776**. b. **23**.

BARBEYRAC (JEAN) *See* BRANCHU (B.) B. Branchu . . . Observationes ad jus romanum, *etc.* (Leibnitii judicium de Puffendorfii Officiis hominis & civis a . . . J. Barbeyraccio nuper impugnatum, nunc a B. Branchu . . . vindicatum, *etc.*) pt. I. 1721, *etc.* 8°. **5254**. a. **6**.

—— *See* BYNKERSHOEK (C. van) Traité du juge compétent des ambassadeurs, tant pour le civil, que pour le criminel, traduit du latin . . . par J. Barbeyrac. 1723. 8°. **228**. b. **15**.

—— *See* BYNKERSHOEK (C. van) Traité du juge competent des ambassadeurs . . . Traduit . . . par J. Barbeyrac . . . Seconde édition revue & augmentée dans les notes du traducteur. [1730?] 4°. [WICQUEFORT (*A. van*) *L'Ambassadeur et ses fonctions.*] **1474**. c. **25**.

—— —— 1746. 4°. [WICQUEFORT (*A. van*) *L'Ambassadeur et ses fonctions, etc.* tom. 2.] **6955**. f. **33**.

—— *See* CUMBERLAND (Richard) *Bishop of Peterborough.* Traité philosophique des loix naturelles . . . Traduit . . . par . . . Barbeyrac. 1744. 4°. **8407**. g. **11**.

—— *See* CUMBERLAND (Richard) *Bishop of Peterborough.* Les Loix de la nature expliquées. Traduits du latin par Barbeyrac, *etc.* 1757. 4°. **715**. g. **1**.

—— *See* GROOT (H. de) [*De Jure Belli ac Pacis.*] Hugonis Grotii De jure belli ac pacis libri tres . . . Notulas . . . addidit J. Barbeyrac. 1720. 8°. **502**. e. **7, 8**.

—— —— 1735. 8°. **6915**. b. **15**.

—— —— 1751, *etc.* 4°. **502**. f. **1–5**.

—— —— 1853. 8°. **06955**. f. **21**.

—— *See* GROOT (H. de) [*De Jure Belli ac Pacis.*] The Rights of War and Peace. To which are added . . . the notes of Mr. J. Barbeyrac. 1738. fol. **709**. k. **17**.

—— *See* GROOT (H. de) [*De Jure Belli ac Pacis.*] Le Droit de la guerre et de la paix . . . Nouvelle traduction par J. Barbeyrac, *etc.* 1724. 4°. **6955**. g. **10**.

—— —— 1729. 4°. **502**. f. **10, 11**.

—— —— 1746. 4°. **6915**. g. **5**.

—— —— 1867. 8°. **6955**. aaa. **8**.

—— *See* NOODT (G.) The Power of the Sovereign and the Right of Liberty of Conscience . . . With a preface and notes by Monsieur Barbeyrac, *etc.* 1708. 8°. T. **1863**. (**7**.)

—— *See* NOODT (G.) Du pouvoir des souverains . . . En deux discours, traduits . . . par J. Barbeyrac . . . Seconde édition . . . augmentée . . . d'un discours du traducteur sur la nature du sort. 1714. 12°. **8409**. bbb. **2**.

BARBEYRAC (JEAN)

—— *See* PERIODICAL PUBLICATIONS.—*Amsterdam.* Bibliothèque raisonnée des ouvrages des savans, *etc.* [By J. Barbeyrac and others.] 1728, *etc.* 8°. **263**. c. **11**, *etc.*

—— *See* PERIODICAL PUBLICATIONS.—*The Hague.* Nouvelle bibliothèque, ou histoire littéraire, *etc.* [By J. Barbeyrac and others.] 1738, *etc.* 12°. **262**. a. **28**, *etc.*

—— *See* PUFENDORF (S. von) *Baron.* The Whole Duty of Man . . . With the notes of Mr. Barbeyrac. 1716. 8°. **6005**. b. **38**.

—— *See* PUFENDORF (S.) *Baron.* The Whole Duty of Man according to the Law of Nature . . . With the notes of Mr. Barbeyrac, *etc.* 1735. 8°. **1479**. aaa. **22**.

—— *See* PUFENDORF (S. von) *Baron.* Les Devoirs de l'homme et du citoien . . . Traduits . . . par J. Barbeyrac. 1715. 8°. **522**. c. **18**.

—— —— 1741. 12°. **526**. e. **36, 37**.

—— —— 1748. 8°. **526**. e. **38**.

—— —— 1756. 12°. **8404**. bb. **22**.

—— *See* PUFENDORF (S. von) *Baron.* De jure naturæ et gentium libri octo. Cum integris commentariis . . . J. Barbeyraci, *etc.* 1744, *etc.* 4°. **6915**. g. **14**.

—— *See* PUFENDORF (S. von) *Baron.* Pufendorf's Law of Nature . . . compar'd with the respective last editions of Mr. Barbeyrac's French translations and illustrated with his notes, *etc.* 1716. 8°. **1374**. e. **1**.

—— —— 1729. fol. **8406**. h. **16**.

—— —— 1749. fol. **496**. i. **17**.

—— *See* PUFENDORF (S. von) *Baron.* Le Droit de la nature et des gens . . . Traduit . . . par J. Barbeyrac. Avec des notes du traducteur, *etc.* . . . & une preface. 1706. 4° **6955**. ff. **34**.

—— —— 1712. 4°. **502**. f. **15**.

—— —— 1750. 4°. **16.b.5.6.**

—— *See* ROTHER (J. H.) Commentatio . . . in S. L. B. de Pufendorf De officio hominis et civis . . . libros II., selectissimis . . . Barbeyracii . . . notis . . . illustrata, *etc.* 1748. 4°. **6025**. cc. **24**.

—— *See* TILLOTSON (John) *Archbishop of Canterbury.* Sermons. Tome premier traduit de l'anglois par J. Barbeyrac, *etc.* 1713, *etc.* 8°. **847**. l. **22, 23**.

—— *See* WESTERVEEN (A.) Dissertation où l'on prouve le droit exclusif de la Compagnie Orientale des Provinces Unies au commerce et à la navigation des Indes Orientales. Traduite du Latin [by J. Barbeyrac]. 1724. 4°. [*Recueil de pieces en faveur des Compagnies Hollandoises.*] **523**. k. **10**. (**1**.)

—— Recueil de discours sur diverses matières importantes, traduits ou composez par J. Barbeyrac . . . qui y a joint un Éloge historique de feu Mr. Noodt. 2 tom. *Amsterdam,* 1731. 12°. **6025**. a. **1**.

—— Epistolæ aliquot ineditæ. *See* PUETTMANN (J. L. E.) Memoria Gottfridi Mascovii, *etc.* 1771. 8°. **10706**. e. **19**.

—— Defense du droit de la Compagnie Hollandoise des Indes Orientales, contre les nouvelles prétensions des habitans des Pays-Bas Autrichiens, et les raisons ou objections des avocats de la Compagnie d'Ostende. pp. 131. *La Haye,* 1725. 4°. **523**. k. **10**. (**3**.)

—— [Another copy.] **153**. e. **14**.

—— Discours sur la permission des loix, *etc.* pp. 24. *Genève*, 1715. 4°. **501**. e. **24**. (**3**.)

—— Seconde édition, revûë et corrigée. pp. 47. *Amsterdam*, 1716. 8°. **878**. f. **5**. (**14**.)

—— Discours sur l'utilité des lettres et des sciences, par rapport au bien de l'état, *etc.* pp. 58. *Amsterdam*, 1715. 8°. **1031**. f. **26**.

—— Histoire des anciens traitez . . . depuis les tems les plus reculez jusques à l'empereur Charlemagne. 2 pt. *Amsterdam, La Haye*, 1739. fol. [Du Mont (*Jean*) *Baron de Carels-Croon. Corps universel diplomatique du droit des gens, etc.* Supp. vol. 1.] 505.ee.2.

—— Joannis Barbeyraci . . . Oratio inauguralis de dignitate et utilitate iuris ac historiarum et utriusque disciplinæ amica conjunctione . . . Editio secunda, *etc.* pp. 28. *Amstelodami*, 1711. 4°. **580**. d. **26**. (**6**.)

—— Joannis Barbeyraci . . . Oratio inauguralis de studio juris recte instituendo, *etc.* pp. 47. *Groningæ*, 1717. 4°. **06005**. f. **16**.

—— [Another edition.] 1769. *See* OPUSCULA. Variorum opuscula ad cultiorem jurisprudentiam adsequendam pertinentia. tom. 2. 1769, *etc.* 8°. **1375**. c. **1**.

—— Joannis Barbeyracii . . . Oratio de magistratu, forte peccante, e pulpitis sacris non traducendo, *etc.* pp. 29. *Amstelodami*, 1721. 4°. **523**. g. **57**. (**8**.)

—— Traité de la morale des Pères de l'Église ; où en défendant un article de la preface sur Puffendorf contre l'Apologie de la morale des Pères du P. Ceillier . . . on fait diverses reflexions sur plusieurs matières importantes. pp. xlii. 334. *Amsterdam*, 1728. 4°. **6**. d. **11**.

—— [Another copy.] **1413**. h. **5**.

—— The Spirit of the Ecclesiasticks of all Sects and Ages, as to the Doctrines of Morality, and more particularly the spirit of the ancient Fathers of the Church, examin'd . . . Translated from the French by a gentleman of Gray's-Inn. With a preface by the author of the Independent Whig [i.e. Thomas Gordon]. pp. 72. *J. Peele: London*, 1722. 8°. **701**. g. **15**.

—— [Another copy.] **111**. b. **38**.

—— *See* BELIEVER. The Spirit of Infidelity detected. In answer to . . . The Spirit of Ecclesiasticks of all Sects . . . by Mons. Barbeyrac . . . By a Believer. 1723. 8°. **701**. g. **69**.

—— Traité du jeu où l'on examine les principales questions de droit naturel et de morale qui ont du rapport à cette matière. 2 tom. pp. 646. *Amsterdam*, 1709. 8°. **527**. d. **23**, **24**.

—— Seconde édition, revue & augmentée, à laquelle on a joint un discours, sur la nature du sort, et quelques autres écrits de l'auteur. 3 tom. pp. cvii. 896. *Amsterdam*, 1737. 8°. **878**. e. **9–11**.

—— Les Trois vertus chretiennes apliquées à l'usage des persecutions que l'église souffre. Ou sermon sur . . . la 1 Epît. aux Corint. chap. 13. v. 13, *etc.* pp. 80. *P. Mortier: Amsterdam*, 1686. 8°. **4427**. a. **31**.

—— Vita V. C. Gerardi Noodt. *See* NOODT (G.) Gerardi Noodt . . . Opera omnia, *etc.* 1724. fol. **496**. h. **8**.

—— [Another edition.] *See* NOODT (G.) Gerardi Noodt . . . Opera omnia, *etc.* 1735. fol. **495**. k. **18**.

—— [Another edition.] *See* NOODT (G.) Gerardi Noodt . . . Opera omnia, *etc.* 1767. fol. **5306**. i. **2**.

—— *See* HUGO (H.) De prima scribendi origine, *etc.* (Apologie pro Chr. Wæchtlero contra C. J. Barbeyraccium [in his " Vita Gerardi Noodt "].) 1738. 8°. **623**. g. **7**.

—— An Historical and Critical Account of the Science of Morality, and the Progress it has made . . . from the earliest Times down to the Publication of Pufendorf of the Law of Nature and Nations : in a prefatory discourse to the said work by Mr. Barbeyrac . . . Now done into English from the French of the author by Mr. Carew of Lincolns-Inn. pp. 88. *See* PUFENDORF (S. von) *Baron*. Of the Law of Nature and Nations, *etc.* 1729. fol. **8406**. h. **16**.

—— [Another edition.] pp. 75. *See* PUFENDORF (S. von) *Baron*. The Law of Nature and Nations, *etc.* 1749. fol. **496**. i. **17**.

BARBEYRAC DE SAINT-MAURICE (JOSEPH DE) Faculté de Droit de Paris. Thèse pour la licence. (Jus romanum. De hereditatis petitione.—Droit français. Des successions.) pp. 44. *Paris*, 1858. 8°. **5406**. aaa. **2**. (**22**.)

BARBEYRACIUS (JOANNES) *See* BARBEYRAC (Jean)

BARBEYRON (ALCIDE) Quelques considérations sur l'iritis syphilitique. pp. 58. *Paris*, 1872. 4°. [*Collection des thèses soutenues à la Faculté de Médecine de Paris.* An 1872. tom. 1.] **7373**. n. **7**.

BARBEYTO (BENITO FRANCISCO DE CASTRO Y) *See* CASTRO Y BARBEYTO.

BARBEZ ( ) *Printer*. *See* BERGUES-SAINT-WINOC.—*Redenrycke Baptisten Royaerts G'hulde, gezegd Rhetorica.* Verzameling der prys-vraegen, *etc.* [Edited by —— Barbez.] 1810. 8°. **1462**. g. **25**.

BARBEZIEUX. Barbezieux. Son prieuré au XIe–XIIe siècles ; ses origines bordelaises ; ses premiers seigneurs. (Cartulaire du prieuré de Notre-Dame de Barbezieux.—Recueil de chartes sur les premiers seigneurs de Barbezieux.) pp. cxi. 311. *Saintes*, 1911. 8°. [*Archives historiques de la Saintonge et de l'Aunis.* tom. 41.] Ac. **6892**.

BARBÉZIEUX (G.) *See* BOISSARD (Alphonse) and BARBÉZIEUX (G.) Mères et nourrissons, *etc.* 1892. 8°. **07581**. de. **29**.

BARBEZIEUX (RIGAUT DE) Les Chansons du troubadour Rigaut de Barbezieux. Texte préparé par C. Chabaneau. Introduction, traduction et notes par J. Anglade. pp. 112. *Montpellier*, 1919. 8°. [*Publications spéciales de la Société des Langues Romanes.* tom. 27.] Ac. **9809/6**.

BARBI (A. S.) *See* STROZZI (G. B.) *il Cieco*. Madrigali. [Edited by A. S. Barbi.] 1899. 8°. **11431**. ee. **31**. (**2**.)

BARBI (ANRI) *See* BARBY (Henry)

BARBI (MICHELE)

—— *See* BARBI (S. A.) Note bio-bibliografiche su Michele Barbi. 1943. 8°. [*Bullettino storico pistoiese.* vol. 45. no. 3/6.] Ac. **6561**.

—— *See* COSMO (U.) " I Problemi fondamentali della letteratura francrscana " di Michele Barbi. [On the work planned, but not completed, by M. Barbi.] 1943. 8°. [*Studi Danteschi.* vol. 27.] **011421**. z. **1**.

—— *See* DANTE ALIGHIERI. [*Works.*] Le Opere di Dante . . . A cura di M. Barbi, *etc.* 1921. 8°. 2042.c.

BARBI (MICHELE)

—— See DANTE ALIGHIERI. [*Works.*] Opere di Dante. Nuova edizione . . . Promossa e diretta da M. Barbi. 1934, *etc.* 8°. W.P. **12246.**

—— See DANTE ALIGHIERI. [*Works.*] Opere di Dante, *etc.* (vol. 2. Rime della "Vita nuova" e della giovinezza. A cura di M. Barbi e F. Maggini.) 1956, *etc.* 8°. W.P. **12246.**

—— See DANTE ALIGHIERI. [*Vita Nuova.—Italian.*] La Vita nuova. Per cura di M. Barbi. 1907. 8°. Ac. **9386/2.**

—— See DANTE ALIGHIERI. [*Vita Nuova.—Italian.*] La Vita nova . . . Sulla lezione della Società Dantesca Italiana procurata da M. Barbi. 1923. 8°. **011420.** b. **55.**

—— See DANTE ALIGHIERI. [*La Vita nuova.*] La Vita nuova. Edizione critica per cura di M. Barbi. 1932. 4°. **11421.** k. **23.**

—— See DANTE ALIGHIERI. [*Vita Nuova.—French.*] Vita nova. Suivant le texte critique préparé pour la "Società Dantesca Italiana" par M. Barbi, *etc.* 1908. 8°. **11420.** ccc. **9.**

—— See FLORENCE.—*Società Dantesca Italiana.* Bullettino. (Nuova serie . . . diretta da M. Barbi.) 1890, *etc.* 8°. Ac. **9386.**

—— See JOANNES, *Gallensis.* La Leggenda di Traiano, *etc.* [Edited by M. Barbi.] 1895. 4°. **10601.** g. **14.** (2.)

—— See MANZONI (A.) *Count.* [Works] Opere di Alessandro Manzoni. . . . A cura di M. Barbi e F. Ghisalberti. 1942, *etc.* 8°. **2042.d.**

—— Adagio col testo dei "Promessi sposi." 1941. *See* MILAN.—*Centro Nazionale di Studi Manzoniani.* Annali manzoniani. vol. 2. 1939, *etc.* 8°. Ac. **8851.**

—— Bibliografia Dantesca. 1892. *See* FLORENCE.—*Società Dantesca Italiana.* Bullettino, *etc.* no. 12. 1890, *etc.* 8°. Ac. **9386.**

—— Dante. Vita, opere e fortuna. Con due saggi su Francesca e Farinata. pp. 270. *Firenze,* 1933. 8°. **011420.** a. **45.**

—— [Dante: vita, opere e fortuna.] Life of Dante. Translated and edited by Paul G. Ruggiers. pp. x. 132. *University of California Press: Berkeley & Los Angeles,* 1954. 8°. **11421.** m. **33.**

—— Dante nel cinquecento. pp. 407. 1890. *See* PISA.—*Reale Scuola Normale Superiore.* Annali, *etc.* vol. 7. 1871, *etc.* 8°. **Ac.47.(a.)**

—— Della fortuna di Dante nel secolo XVI. pp. 407. *Pisa,* 1890. 8°. **11421.** f. **6.**

—— Due noterelle Dantesche. Lisetta. Il codice Strozzi di rime antiche citato dall'Ubaldini e dalla Crusca. pp. 18. *Firenze,* 1898. 8°. **11421.** f. **36.** (5.)

—— Notizia della vita e delle opere di Francesco Bracciolini. pp. 166. *Firenze,* 1897. 8°. **10631.** de. **48.**

—— La Nuova filologia e l'edizione dei nostri scrittori da Dante al Manzoni. [With facsimiles.] pp. xli. 259. *Firenze,* 1938. 8°. **11858.** d. **101.**

—— Per il testo della Divina Commedia. pp. 50. *Roma,* 1891. 8°. **11422.** ff. **29.** (13.)

—— Per un nuovo commento della "Divina Commedia." (Ancora per un nuovo commento della "Divina Commedia.") *See* infra: Studi danteschi, *etc.* vol. 19. pp. 5–55; vol. 21. pp. 93–156. 1935, 37. 8°. **011421.z.1/19,21.**

BARBI (MICHELE)

—— Piano per un'edizione nazionale delle opere di Alessandro Manzoni.—Note per un nuovo commento ai Promessi Sposi. 1939. *See* MILAN.—*Centro Nazionale di Studi Manzoniani.* Annali manzoniani, *etc.* vol. 1. 1939, *etc.* 8°. Ac. **8851.**

—— Poesia popolare italiana. Studi e proposte. pp. 166. *Firenze,* 1939. 8°. [*Biblioteca del Leonardo.* no. 8.] **012211.dd.1/8.**

—— Problemi di critica dantesca. Prima serie, 1893–1918. (Seconda serie. 1920–1937.) 2 vol. *Firenze,* 1934, 41. 8°. **011421.** bb. **21.**

—— I "Promessi sposi" e la critica. 1942. *See* MILAN.—*Centro Nazionale di Studi Manzoniani.* Annali manzoniani. vol. 3. 1939, *etc.* 8°. Ac. **8851.**

—— Proposta di correzioni a tre recenti commenti dei "Promessi sposi." 2 pt. 1941, 43. *See* MILAN.—*Centro Nazionale di Studi Manzoniani.* Annali manzoniani. vol. 2, 4. 1939, *etc.* 8°. Ac. **8851.**

—— La Questione di Lisetta. [On the Lisetta mentioned in sonnet XLIV of the Canzoniere of Dante Alighieri.] *See* infra: Studi danteschi, *etc.* vol. 1. pp. 17–63. 1920. 8°. **011421.z.1/1.**

—— Razionalismo e misticismo in Dante. *In:* Studi danteschi, *etc.* vol. 17. pp. 5–44; vol. 21. pp. 5–91. 1933, *etc.* 8°. **011481.z.1/17,21.**

—— Studi Danteschi diretti da M. Barbi. *Firenze,* 1920– . 8°. **011421.z.1.**
An index vol. 1–20 is contained in vol. 20. From vol. 28 published under the auspices of the Società Dantesca Italiana.

—— Studi di manoscritti e testi inediti. I. La Raccolta Bartoliniana di rime antiche e i codici da essi derivati. pp. ii. 71. *Bologna,* 1900. 8°. **11853.** g. **50.**
No more published.

—— Studi sul Canzoniere di Dante, con nuove indagini sulle raccolte manoscritte e a stampa di antiche rime italiane. pp. xvi. 542. *Firenze,* 1915. 8°. **011420.** aaa. **3.**

—— La Tenzone di Dante con Forese. *See* supra: Studi danteschi, *etc.* vol. 9. pp. 5–149. 1924. 8°. **011421.z.1/9.**

BARBI (MICHELE) and PIATTOLI (RENATO)

—— La Casa di Dante. [With plans.] *In:* BARBI (Michele) Studi danteschi, *etc.* vol. 22. pp. 5–81. 1938. 8° **011421.z.1/22.**

BARBI (PAOLO) *See* BARBUS (P.) *Soncinas.*

BARBI (SILVIO ADRASTO) *See* DANTE ALIGHIERI. [*Divina Commedia.—Italian.*] La Divina Commedia . . . Con il commento di T. Casini . . . Per cura di S. A. Barbi. 1922. 8°. **011420.** b. **32.**

—— *See* PISTOIA. Storie pistoresi . . . A cura di S. A. Barbi. 1907, *etc.* 8°. [MURATORI (*L. A.*) *Rerum Italicarum scriptores.* tom. 11. pt. 5.] **9168.** l.

—— Note bio-bibliografiche su Michele Barbi. 1943. *See* PISTOJA.—*Società Pistoiese di Storia Patria.* Bullettino storico pistoiese, *etc.* vol. 45. no. 3/4. 1931, *etc.* 8°. Ac. **6561.**

BARBIANI (MARCELLO VESTRIO) *See* MACIEJOWSKI (B.) *Cardinal.* Illustr^mi et rever. D. Bernardi episcopi Luceoriensis . . . Sigismundi iij. regis Poloniæ oratoris, oratio obedientialis coram . . . Gregorio xiiij., *etc.* (Responsio M. V. Barbiani.) 1591. 4°. **805.** d. **39.**

BARBIANI (Marcello Vestrio)

—— *See* Roscius (Julius) *Hortinus.* Ad Gregorium xiiij. . . . pro vij. pagis Helvetiorum Catholicorum oratio . . . habita, *etc.* (M. V. Barbiani . . . responsio.) 1591. 4°. **805.** d. **40.**

—— Coronatione del serenissimo signore Cosimo Medici, *etc.* *B. Sermartelli: Fiorenza,* 1569. 4°. **9930.** e. **22.**

BARBIANES (Nik.)

—— *Παυλος Καρρερης, ὁ Ζακυνθινος μουσουργος.* [With a portrait.] pp. 19. *Ἀθηναι,* 1951. 8°. **7900.** d. **58.**

BARBIANO (Alberigo da) *Count.* *See* Giorgi (F.) Alberico e Giovanni da Barbiano nel Bolognese, *etc.* 1894, *etc.* 8°. [*Atti e Memorie della R. Deputazione di Storia Patria.* ser. 3. tom. 12.] Ac. **6495.**

—— *See* Solieri (G.) Alberigo da Barbiano. 1908. 8°. **10633.** h. **33.**

BARBIANO (Giovanni da) *Count.* *See* Giorgi (F.) Alberico e Giovanni da Barbiano nel Bolognese, *etc.* 1894. *etc.* 8°. [*Atti e Memorie della R. Deputazione di Storia Patria.* ser. 3. tom. 12.] Ac. **6495.**

BARBIANO DI BELGIOJOSO (Luigi Carlo Maria di) *Count.* *See* Cauchie (A.) Le Comte L. C. M. de Barbiano di Belgiojoso et des papiers d'état conservés à Milan. 1912. 8°. [*Bulletin de la Commission Royale d'Histoire de Belgique.* tom. 81.] Ac. **986.**

—— Lettre du comte de Belgiojoso au Peuple Belgique pour justifier sa conduite et ses bonnes intentions [as Governor General of the Austrian Netherlands]. pp. 4. [*Brussels?* 1787?] 12°. **108.** a. **7.** (**11.**)

BARBIANUS (Marcellus Vestrius) *See* Barbiani (Marcello Vestrio)

BARBICAN. *See* Periodical Publications.—*London.*

BARBICAN CHAPEL. Barbican Chapel Book Society. *See* London.—iii.

BARBICAN MISSION. Barbican Mission to the Jews. *See* England.—*Church of England.*

BARBICAN (James) *pseud.* The Confessions of a Rum-Runner. pp. viii. 310. *W. Blackwood & Sons: Edinburgh & London,* 1927. 8°. **08805.** e. **65.**

BARBICHON (P. M.) Dictionnaire complet de tous les lieux de la France et de ses colonies. 2 tom. *Paris,* 1831. 8°. **1301.** i. **1, 2.**

BARBI-CINTI (Francesco) Napoleone primo e Pio settimo. Poema. [With a preface by A. Camanzi.] pp. vii. 439. *Ferrara,* 1890. 8°. **11436.** h. **1.**

BARBICINTI (Giuseppe) *See* Ovidius Naso (P.) [*Metamorphoses.—Italian.*] P. Ovidio Nasone. Le Metamorfosi tradotte in versi italiani, sul testo integro, da Barbicinti G. . . . e corredate di varie note. 1882. 8°. **11355.** bbb. **11.**

BARBICONE (Aiolpho del) *See* Aiolpho, *del Barbicone.*

BARBIÉ DU BOCAGE (Alexandre Frédéric) Dictionnaire géographique de la Bible. 1848. *See* Migne (J. P.) Encyclopédie théologique, *etc.* tom. 28. 1846, *etc.* 4°. **L.R.272.a.1.**

—— Traité de géographie générale. 2 pt. *Paris,* 1833. 12°. [*Ajasson de Grundsagne (J. B. F. E.) Viscount. Bibliothèque populaire.*] **12205.a.1/41.**

BARBIÉ DU BOCAGE (G.) *See* Barbié du Bocage (J. D.) Catalogue des cartes et plans manuscrits et gravés de la bibliothèque géographique de MM. J.-D. et G. Barbié du Bocage. 1844. 8°. Dept. of Manuscripts.

BARBIÉ DU BOCAGE (Isidore Louis) De l'éruption de sudamina; thèse, *etc.* pp. 28. *Paris,* 1828. 4°. **1184.** c. **9.** (**22.**)

BARBIÉ DU BOCAGE (Jean Denis) *See* Chandler (Richard) *D.D.* Voyages dans l'Asie Mineure et en Grèce . . . Traduits de l'anglais . . . par MM. J. P. Servois et Barbié du Bocage. 1806. 8°. **1046.** f. **5–7.**

—— *See* Fortia d'Urban (A. J. F. X. P. E. S. P. A. de) *Marquis.* Mélanges de géographie, d'histoire, et de chronologie anciennes . . . Avec deux cartes . . . de M. Barbié de Bocage, destinés à servir de supplément à l'histoire . . . de Xénophon, *etc.* [1805.] 8°. **568.** e. **22.**

—— *See* Melling (A. I.) Voyage pittoresque de Constantinople . . . d'après les dessins de M. Melling, *etc.* [The topographical portion . . . by I. D. Barbie du Bocage.] 1819. fol. Tab. **487.** d.

—— *See* Periodical Publications.—*Paris.* Revue encyclopédique, *etc.* [By J. D. Barbié du Bocage and others.] [1819, *etc.*] 8°. **257.** i. **24,** *etc.*

—— *See* Pouqueville (F. C. H. L.) Voyage dans la Grèce . . . Enrichi de cartes géographiques dressées par M. Barbié du Bocage. 1820, *etc.* 8°. **1047.** e. **9–13.**

—— *See* Pouqueville (F. C. H. L.) Voyage en Morée, à Constantinople, en Albanie, et dans plusieurs autres parties de l'Empire Othoman . . . Enrichi . . . de cartes dressées par M. Barbié du Bocage, *etc.* 1805. 8°. **1047.** e. **7, 8.**

—— *See* Walckenaer (C. A.) *Baron.* Institut Royal de France . . . Funérailles de M. Barbié du Bocage. 1825. 4°. **733.** g. **17.** (**92.**)

—— [For editions and translations of the "Analyse critique des cartes de l'ancienne Grèce dressées pour le voyage du jeune Anacharsis" of J. J. Barthélémy, together with the maps of J. D. Barbié du Bocage:] *See* Barthélemy (J. J.)

—— Institut Royal de France. Funérailles de M. Mentelle. pp. 3. [*Paris,* 1815.] 4°. **733.** g. **17.** (**45.**)

—— Notice des ouvrages de M. D'Anville . . . Précédée de son éloge. [By J. D. Barbié du Bocage.] pp. 120. 1802. 8°. *See* Bourguignon d'Anville (J. B.) T. **2352.** (**3.**)

—— Notice historique sur la construction des cartes géographiques. *See* France.—*Ministère de la Guerre.* Mémorial du Dépôt de la Guerre, *etc.* tom. 1. 1826, *etc.* 4°. *Dépôt General de la Guerre.* **818.** l. **8.**

—— Précis de géographie ancienne. *See* Pinkerton (John) *Antiquary.* Abrégé de géographie moderne, *etc.* 1811. 8°. **793.** h. **8.**

—— Rapport [on J. S. Stanhope's travels in Greece].—Histoire de la Bourgade d'Oenoe la Sacrée située dans l'Attique, *etc.* *See* Stanhope (John S.) Topography illustrative of the Battle of Platæa, *etc.* 1817. 8°. **199.** c. **4.**

—— Catalogue des cartes et plans manuscrits et gravés de la bibliothèque géographique de MM. J.-D. et G. Barbié du Bocage. pp. 80. *Paris,* 1844. 8°. Dept. of Manuscripts.

—— Catalogue des manuscrits de la bibliothèque de feu J. D. Barbié du Bocage . . . dont la vente se fera les 1er et 2 février 1850, *etc.* pp. 16. *Paris,* 1850. 8°. S.C. **673.** (**2.**)

BARBIÉ DU BOCAGE (Jean Guillaume) *See* Georges (F. E.) Traité de géographie . . . Suivant l'Atlas par J. G. Barbié du Bocage, *etc.* 1846. 12°. **1296.** a. **15.**

BARBIÉ DU BOCAGE (Victor Amédée) *See* Paris.—*Société de Géographie.* Bulletin, *etc.* (Table . . . des matières contenues dans les troisième et quatrième séries . . . Rédigée par M. V. A. Barbié du Bocage.) 1866. 8°. Ac. **6035.**

BARBIÉ DU BOCAGE (VICTOR AMÉDÉE)

—— Analyse et synthèse. Dieu, matière, âme, homme. 2 tom. *Paris*, 1888. 8°. **8463.** i. **4.**

—— Bibliographie annamite, livres, recueils périodiques, manuscrits, plans . . . Extrait de la Revue maritime et coloniale. pp. 107. *Paris*, 1867. 8° **11927.bb.12.**

—— De l'introduction des Arméniens catholiques en Algérie. pp. 48. *Paris*, 1855. 8°. **8155.** bb. **38.** (**2.**)

—— Madagascar, possession française depuis 1642 . . . Ouvrage accompagné d'une grande carte dressée par V. A. Malte-Brun. pp. xxvii. 367. *Paris*, [1859.] 8°. **10095.** f. **28.**

—— Suez et Périm. Réponse à l'article du Times du 7 avril 1858. pp. 30. *Paris*, 1858. 8°. **8235.** d. **53.** (**8.**)

BARBIÉ DU BOCCAGE (JEAN DENIS) *See* BARBIÉ DU BOCAGE.

BARBIELLINI (MICHEL ANGELO) Trattato de' giochi e de' divertimenti permessi, o proibiti ai Cristiani. pp. xxiv. 396. *Roma*, 1768. 12°. **7942.** aa. **64.**

BARBIELLINI-AMIDEI (ALESSANDRO) *Marquis.* Ad Britannos. Rapporti storici dell'Inghilterra colla Chiesa Cattolica Romana da S. Gregorio Magno ad Enrico VIII. pp. 125. *Città di Castello*, 1899. 8°. **4707.** df. **15.**

—— Una Nuova pagina della storia d'Italia, ossia la vera fine dell'ultima dinastia Longobarda e l'origine del potere temporale dei Papi . . . Da documenti inediti, secolo ottavo e nono. pp. iv. 397. *Città di Castello*, 1904. 8°. **9150.pp.9.**

BARBIELLINI AMIDEI (AMEDEO) Beatrice Cenci. Historical recollections of her life and family. pp. 45. *Rome*, 1905. 8°. **10630.** a. **53**

—— 7th edition, illustrated. pp. 55. *Rome*, 1909. 8°. **10629.** de. **9.**

BARBIER. Le Barbier de la cité, ou un Pied dans l'abîme, mélodrame en trois actes et en prose, *etc.* [By J. M. T. Baudouin.] pp. 60. *Paris*, 1816. 8°. **11738.** cc. **10.** (**6.**)

BARBIER (   ) *Chasseur. See* HESINE (P. N.) Analyse d'un mémoire adressé aux Représentans du peuple, composant le Conseil des Cinq-cents, par les chasseurs Barbier et Meunier. [1798?] 8°. **F. 1124.** (**14.**)

BARBIER (   ) *Madame.* Catalogue d'une vente de tableaux des trois écoles, bronzes anciens et modernes, figures et groupes en marbre . . . après le décès de Mme Barbier, *etc.* [With prices and notes in MS.] pp. 12. *Paris*, [1815.] 8°. **7854.** d. **30.** (**3.**)

BARBIER (   ) *Mathematical Professor. See* PAYEN (A. F.) Extrait d'une lettre de M. Payen . . . Contenant l'observation de l'éclipse de soleil, arrivée le 2 juillet 1666. Faite . . . par . . . Payen . . . Barbier, *etc.* [1666.] 4°. **531.k.38.(2.)**

BARBIER (   ) *of the "École Municipale Turgot."* Protestation contre l'avis aux familles. [Signed by Barbier and others, in behalf of 242 pupils of the Turgot Municipal School, in defence of the Director, M. Pompée.] [*Paris*, 1848.] *s. sh.* fol. **1850.** d. **5.** (**51.**)

BARBIER (   ) *Translator. See* SARCEY (F.) A Company of Actors, *etc.* (Translated by M. Barbier.) 1926. 8°. [*Publications of the Dramatic Museum of Columbia University.* ser. 5. no. 4.] Ac. **2688.** e.

BARBIER (A.) Histoire de Louis-Napoléon Bonaparte, Président de la République Française depuis sa naissance jusqu'à ce jour . . . Ornée d'un portrait de Louis-Napoléon. pp. 180. *Paris*, 1852. 8°. **10659.** b. **9.**

BARBIER (A.) *Directeur de Douanes à Chambéry. See* BARBIER (Victor) *Directeur, etc.*

BARBIER (A. J. ARMAND) Étude sur la convalescence des maladies aiguës, *etc.* pp. 38. *Paris*, 1863. 4°. [*Collection des thèses soutenues à la Faculté de Médecine de Paris.* An 1863. tom. 1.] **7373.** e. **5.**

BARBIER (ACHILLE) Des moyens de grossir les graines et les fruits, de doubler les fleurs et d'en varier à volonté les proportions et la forme, *etc.* pp. 88. *Bordeaux, Paris*, [1861.] 8°. **7075.** bb. **64.** (**6.**)

BARBIER (ALEXANDRE NICOLAS) Lettres familières sur la littérature . . . Littérature ancienne. pp. 293. *Paris*, 1862. 12°. **11825.** aaa. **23.**

—— and (VICTOIRE) Nouveau traité tout pratique de lavis et de peinture à l'aquarelle, avec des facsimile d'après les dessins originaux de MM. Charlet, A. Delacroix, Hubert, Lepoitevin, etc. pp. 33. pl. 15. *Paris*, 1860. 4°. **7855.** g. **18.**

BARBIER (ALFRED) Chroniques de Poitiers aux XVe et XVIe siècles. 2 pt. 1891, 92. *See* POITIERS.—*Société des Antiquaires de l'Ouest.* Mémoires, *etc.* sér. 2. tom. 13, 14. 1836, *etc.* 8°. Ac. **5326.**

—— Un Épisode de la ligue en Châtelleraudais. Le combat d'Isle, 6 février 1592. 1896. *See* POITIERS.—*Société des Antiquaires de l'Ouest.* Mémoires, *etc.* sér. 2. tom. 18. 1836, *etc.* 8°. Ac. **5326.**

—— Études sur le Châtelleraudais. 1894. *See* PARIS.—*Société des Antiquaires de l'Ouest.* Mémoires, *etc.* sér. 2. tom. 16. 1836, *etc.* 8°. Ac. **5326.**

—— René Descartes. Sa famille, son lieu de naissance. Documents & commentaires nouveaux. pp. 73. *Poitiers*, 1901. 8°. **10662.** ff. **30.**

—— Trois médecins poitevins au XVIe siècles [i.e. Jean I. and Jean II. Ferrand and Pierre Descartes], ou les origines châtelleraudaises de la famille Descartes. (Pièces justificatives.) 1897. *See* POITIERS.—*Société des Antiquaires de l'Ouest.* Mémoires, *etc.* sér. 2. tom. 19. 1836, *etc.* 8°. Ac. **5326.**

BARBIER (ANDRÉ)

—— *See* RONSARD (Pierre de) Poèmes. Choisis et commentés par A. Barbier. 1946. 8°. W.P. **8243/15.**

BARBIER (ANDRÉ) *of Dijon.*

—— Étude sur le genu valgum. pp. 38. *Paris*, 1874. 4°. [*Collection des thèses soutenues à la Faculté de Médecine de Paris.* An 1874. tom. I.] **7374.** a. **6.**

BARBIER (ANDRÉ THOMAS) *See* MOTIER (M. M.) *Countess de La Fayette.* Mémoires de Hollande . . . Avec des notes par A. T. Barbier. 1856. 12°. **12513.** a. **8.**

BARBIER (ANNE MARIE) *See* BARBIER (M. A.)

BARBIER (ANTOINE ALEXANDRE) *See* AUTEURS. Auteurs deguisez sous des noms étrangers, *etc.* MS. NOTES [by A. A. Barbier and others]. 1690. 12°. **11900.** b. **18.**

—— *See* BIOGRAPHIE. Biographie universelle classique, ou Dictionnaire historique portatif . . . Par une société de gens de lettres [i.e. A. A. Barbier and others]. 1829. 8°. **1329.** e. **12–14.**

—— *See* BIOGRAPHIE. [Biographie universelle classique.] Biographie universelle, ou dictionnaire historique, *etc.* 1833. 8°. **10002.** dd. **11.**

—— *See* BUTURLIN (D. P.) *Count.* Catalogue des livres de la bibliothèque de M. le comte de Boutourlin, revu par A. A. Barbier, *etc.* 1805. 8°. **270.** k. **8.**

BARBIER (ANTOINE ALEXANDRE)

—— *See* CARITAT (M. J. A. N.) *Marquis de Condorcet.* Œuvres complètes. [Edited by the Marchioness de Condorcet, with the assistance of A. A. Barbier and others.] 1804. 8°. **630. g. 31.**

—— *See* COLLÉ (C.) Journal historique, ou Mémoires critiques et littéraires . . . Imprimés sur le manuscrit de l'auteur, et précédés d'une notice sur sa vie et ses écrits [by A. A. Barbier]. 1805. 8°. **840. h. 25.**

—— *See* GRIMM (F. M. von) *Baron.* Correspondance littéraire, philosophique et critique, *etc.* [With a supplement edited by A. A. Barbier.] 1813, *etc.* 8°. **91. b. 1–16.**

—— —— 1829. 8°. **1209. i. 5–12.**

—— *See* LA HARPE (J. F. de) Nouveau supplément au Cours de littérature de M. de la Harpe, *etc.* [Edited by A. A. Barbier.] 1818. 8°. **72. d. 27.**

—— *See* LIGNE (C. J. de) *Prince.* Mémoire sur le Cte de Bonneval, *etc.* [Edited by A. A. Barbier.] 1817. 8°. **277. e. 25.**

—— Catalogue des livres de la Bibliothèque du Conseil d'État. [By A. A. Barbier.] 2 tom. [1803.] fol. *See* FRANCE.—*Conseil d'État.—Bibliothèque.* **616.n.6.**

—— Dictionnaire des ouvrages anonymes et pseudonymes, composés, traduits ou publiés en français, avec les noms des auteurs, traducteurs et éditeurs : accompagné de notes historiques et critiques. 4 tom. *Paris,* 1806–8. 8°. **11907. aa. 18.**

—— [Another copy.] **271. f. 28–31.**

—— [Another copy of tom. 1, 2.] G. **415, 16.**

—— Seconde édition, revue, corrigée et considerablement augmentée. [With a biographical notice of the author by L. N. Barbier.] 4 tom. *Paris,* 1822–27. 8°. **816. g. 37.**

—— [Another copy.] **619. d. 30.**

—— [Another copy.] **272. h. 23–26.**

—— Troisième édition, revue et augmentée par O. Barbier. 1872, *etc.* *See* QUÉRARD (J. M.) Les Supercheries littéraires dévoilées, *etc.* 1869, *etc.* 8°. **2037.d.**

—— Dissertation sur soixante traductions françaises de l'Imitation de Jésus Christ . . . Par Ant.-Alex. Barbier . . . Suivie de Considérations sur la question relative à l'auteur de l'Imitation (par J. B. M. Gence). pp. xviii. 285. *Paris,* 1812. 12°. **271. c. 16.**

—— *See* SILBERT (J. P.) Gersen, Gerson und Kempis; oder, Ist Einer von diesen Dreyen, und welcher ist der Verfasser der vier Bücher von der Nachfolge Christi? Mit einem kritischen Rückblick auf die Behauptungen der neuern französischen Kritiker A. A. Barbier und J. B. M. Gence. 1828. 8°. I.X. App. **119.**

—— Examen critique et complément des dictionnaires historiques les plus répandus depuis le Dictionnaire de Moréri, jusqu'à la Biographie Universelle inclusivement. tom. 1. A–J. pp. viii. 491. *Paris,* 1820. 8°. **10601. tt. 2.**

No more published.

—— [Another copy.] **612. f. 8.**

—— Notice du catalogue raisonné des livres de la bibliothèque de l'abbé Goujet. pp. 38. [*Paris,* 1803.] 8°. **270. d. 1.**

—— Recueil des lettres de Mme de Sévigné ; nouvelle édition, *etc.* [A notice of a reprint of S. J. B. de Vauxcelles' edition, extracted from the " Magasin encyclopédique."] pp. 16. [*Paris,* 1802.] 8°. T. **960. (2.)**

BARBIER (ANTOINE ALEXANDRE)

—— Catalogue des livres de la bibliothèque de feu M. A.-A. Barbier . . . dont la vente se fera le lundi 25 février, *etc.* pp. vi. 135. *Paris,* 1828. 8°. **011900. h. 44. (2.)**

BARBIER (ANTOINE ALEXANDRE) and **LE MOYNE DESESSARTS** (NICOLAS TOUSSAINT)

—— Nouvelle bibliothèque d'un homme de goût, entièrement refondue, corrigée et augmentée, contenant des jugemens tirés des journaux les plus connus et des critiques les plus estimés, sur les meilleurs ouvrages qui ont paru dans tous les genres, tant en France que chez l'étranger jusqu'à ce jour. 5 tom. *Paris,* 1808–10. 8°. **619. g. 39.**

—— [Another copy.] **273. k. 10–14.**

BARBIER (ARISTIDE) Éducation internationale. Documens du concours provoqué par A. Barbier . . . en décembre 1861, pour la fondation d'un collège international. pp. 123. *Paris,* 1862. 4°. **8309. h. 1.**

BARBIER (AUGUSTE) *See* BARBIER (Henri A.)

BARBIER (C.) Histoire du tabac. Ses persécutions. pp. 93. *Paris,* 1861. 16°. **8435. aa. 78. (4.)**

BARBIER (C.) *pseud.* [i.e. *Mme* C. B. BARBÉ.] L'Ange de la maison. pp. 191. *Rouen,* 1858. 8°. **12513. g. 1.**

—— [Another edition.] pp. 185. *Rouen,* 1863. 8°. **12513. f. 8.**

—— Clotilde de Bourgogne. [A tale.] pp. 118. *Limoges,* [1874.] 12°. **12516. h. 25.**

—— Deux ans dans l'Inde. pp. 188. *Rouen,* 1862. 8°. **10057. cc. 21.**

—— [Another edition.] pp. 188. *Rouen,* 1863. 8°. **10057. cc. 20.**

—— Les Deux siéges de Calais, histoire de la rivalité de la France et de l'Angleterre au moyen âge. pp. 216. *Rouen,* 1860. 12°. **9200. c. 13.**

—— [A reissue.] *Rouen,* 1861. 12°. **9200. bbb. 16.**

—— Les Ducs de Bretagne. pp. 378. *Rouen,* 1859. 8°. **9200. h. 6.**

—— L'Empire de la vertu. pp. 262. *Rouen,* [1864.] 8°. **4416. i. 35.**

—— Julia et Léontine, ou Sagesse et vanité. pp. 288. *Rouen,* 1860. 8°. **012547. l. 69.**

—— L'Orpheline de Sébastopol. pp. 142. *Rouen,* 1859. 12°. **12805. bbb. 7.**

—— Vengeance et pardon. pp. 206. *Rouen,* 1856. 8°. **012511. b. 2.**

Part of the " Bibliothèque morale de la jeunesse."

BARBIER (CHARLES) *Ingénieur Civil.* Le Cheval de la Plata comme cheval de guerre ; son importation pour la remonte de l'armée, *etc.* pp. 28. *Paris,* 1877. 8°. **7206. h. 5. (12.)**

BARBIER (CHARLES) *Instituteur municipal à Paris.* Écoles primaires, plans, mobilier et matériel des maisons d'école. —Méthodes de lecture, d'écriture, d'arithmétique et de système métrique. [Reports.] *See* PARIS.—*Exposition Universelle de* 1867. Rapports du Jury International, *etc.* tom. 13. 1868. 8°. **7956.i.9.**

BARBIER (CHARLES) *of Comines.* *See* DENYS (Pierre P.) and BARBIER (C.) Lydvina du Castellum de Comines. Roman, *etc.* [1913.] 8°. **12550. s. 8.**

BARBIER (Charles) *Professeur au Lycée de Guéret.* See Theocritus. [*French.*] Œuvres complètes . . . Avec une étude sur les Idylles de Théocrite par C. Barbier. 1899. 12°. **11340. aaa. 16.**

BARBIER (Charles Adolphe) Sténographie Aimé Paris. Manuel de lectures choisies à l'usage des écoles et des cours d'adultes précédé de l'exposé d'une nouvelle méthode d'enseignement . . . Préface de Jean P.-A. Martin. pp. xii. 68. *La Chaux-de-Fonds*, [1902.] 8°. **12991. gg. 27.**

BARBIER (Cl.) Faculté de Médecine de Montpellier. Thèse pour le doctorat en médecine . . . Questions tirées au sort, *etc.* pp. 44. *Montpellier*, 1842. 4°. **1182. c. 15. (29.)**

BARBIER (Claude Antoine) Brief . . . an R. P. J. B. du Halde . . . geschriben zu Pinnepundi in dem Königreich Carnate, Jan. 15. 1723. 1729. *See* JESUITS. [Letters from Missions.] Allerhand . . . Reis-Beschreibungen, *etc.* Bd. 2. Tl. 15. 1728, *etc.* fol. **4767. g. 3.**

BARBIER (Edme Louis) Cantique d'un libéral, ou le bon temps de l'anarchie. pp. 84. *Paris*, 1822. 12°. **11475. df. 35. (2.)**

BARBIER (Edmond) *See* Darwin (Charles R.) De la variation des animaux et des plantes à l'état domestique . . . Traduit, sur la seconde édition anglaise, par E. Barbier, *etc.* 1879. *etc.* 8°. **7006. ee. 16.**

—— *See* Darwin (Charles R.) L'Origine des espèces . . . Traduit . . . par E. Barbier. 1880. 8°. **7006. g. 39.**

—— *See* Dixon (William Hepworth) *F.S.A.* La Suisse contemporaine . . . Traduit . . . par M. E. Barbier. 1872. 12°. **10196. bb. 19.**

—— *See* Le Roy (Albert) and Barbier (E.) Dialogues in French and English, *etc.* 1867. 16°. **12954. a. 27.**

—— [A prize essay on the foundation of an international college.] *See* Barbier (Aristide) Éducation internationale. Documens du concours provoqué par M. A. Barbier en décembre 1861, *etc.* 1862. 4°. **8309. h. 1.**

—— Brief Statement of the proposed plan for the establishment of International Schools. pp. 8. *W. Trounce: London*, 1863. 8°. C.T. **269. (7.)**

BARBIER (Edmond Jean François) Journal historique et anecdotique du règne de Louis xv. Publié . . . par A. de la Villegille. 4 tom. 1847–56. 8°. *See* Paris.—*Société de l'Histoire de France.* Ac. **6884/24.**

—— [Another edition.] Chronique de la régence et du règne de Louis xv . . . Première édition complète. 8 sér. *Paris*, 1857. 12°. **9210. b. 25.**

BARBIER (Édouard) Faculté de Droit de Paris. Thèse pour le doctorat. De la publicienne.—Des actions possessoires. pp. 253. *Paris*, 1855. 8°. **5406. a. 8. (1.)**

BARBIER (Émile) *Author of "Voyage au Pays des Dollars."* Poèmes africains. Scènes de mœurs algériennes. tom. 1. pp. vii. 181. *Paris*, 1904 [1903]. 8°. **011483. eee. 106.**

—— Voyage au pays des Dollars. pp. 344. *Paris*, [1893.] 12°. **10412. aaa. 42.**

BARBIER (Émile) *Ex-Chirurgien de la Marine Impériale.* Le Diabète sucré, envisagé sur tout au point de vue de l'étiologie et du traitement. Thèse, *etc.* pp. 72. *Montpellier*, 1836. 4°. **7379. d. 3. (9.)**

BARBIER (Émile Julien Nicolas) L'Orient au point de vue médical. Ses maladies régnantes et les eaux minérales de Vichy, *etc.* pp. 224. *Paris*, 1863. 12°. **7470. aa. 14.**

BARBIER (Emmanuel) *See* Freppel (C. E.) *Bishop of Angers.* Les Origines du Christianisme. Pages choisies du cours d'éloquence sacrée, mises en ordre par l'abbé E. Barbier. 1903. 8°. **4530. df. 14.**

—— *See* Lemercher de Longpré (C.) *Baron d'Haussez.* Sur la conquête d'Alger, *etc.* [Edited by E. Barbier and L. Prévost.] 1930. 8°. **9062. a. 5.**

—— Les Erreurs du Sillon. Histoire documentaire. pp. 380. *Poitiers, Paris*, [1906.] 8°. **3900. d. 19.**

—— Histoire du catholicisme libéral et du catholicisme social en France du Concile du Vatican à l'avènement de S. S. Benoît xv, 1870–1914. 6 tom. *Bordeaux*, 1924. 4°. **4633. dd. 3.**

—— Les Infiltrations maçonniques dans l'église. Extrait de la "Critique du Libéralisme," *etc.* pp. xvi. 254. *Mont-Notre-Dame*, [1932.] 8°. **4782. k. 32.**

—— Le Progrès du libéralisme catholique en France sous le Pape Léon xiii. Histoire documentaire. 2 tom. *Paris*, 1907. 8°. **3900. d. 27.**

—— Rome et l'action libérale populaire. Histoire et documents. pp. 288. *Poitiers, Paris*, [1906.] 8°. **3900. d. 20.**

BARBIER (Eugène) *of Sauvillers-Mongival.* De l'hémorrhagie cérébrale. pp. 82. *Paris*, 1857. 4°. [*Collection des thèses soutenues à la Faculté de Médecine de Paris.* An 1857. tom. 1.] **7373. a. 1.**

BARBIER (Eugène) *of Vieux-Moulin.* Trois lettres au rédacteur de l'Écho de la Nièvre, sur Sir Robert Peel et son systême. pp. 31. *Nevers*, 1846. 8°. **1390. f. 44.**

BARBIER (Évariste Fortuné) De la menstruation. pp. 41. *Paris*, 1849. 4°. [*Collection des thèses soutenues à la Faculté de Médecine de Paris.* An 1849. tom. 1.] **7372. c. 1.**

BARBIER (F. Marguérite) *See* Barrier.

BARBIER (François) *Diplomé de l'École libre des Sciences politiques.* Les Navires-hôpitaux et la guerre de 1914–1918. pp. 166. *Paris*, 1919. 8°. **9084. cc. 18.**

BARBIER (François) *Professeur au Collège de Perpignan.* *See* Theocritus. [*French.*] Œuvres complètes . . . Traduction nouvelle, introduction . . . notes, par F. Barbier, *etc.* 1899. 12°. **11340. aaa. 16.**

BARBIER (G. J.) Dissertation sur les hémorrhagies utérines . . . Thèse, *etc.* pp. 20. *Paris*, 1836. 4°. **1184. g. 11. (29.)**

BARBIER (George) Designs on the Dances of Vaslav Nijinsky . . . Foreword by Francis de Miomandre, translated from the French by C. W. Beaumont. *C. W. Beaumont & Co.: London, Paris* [printed], 1913. 4°. L.R. **28. a. 14.**

BARBIER (Guillelmus) *See* Huguetan (J. A.) and Barbier (G.) Catalogus recens librorum, qui venales prostant in officina J. A. Huguetan & Guillelmi Barbier. 1670. 12°. S.C. **30.**

—— Libri theologici (philosophici, mathematici, *etc.*), qui Lugduni in officina Guil. Barbier, Jo. Girin, & Fr. Comba . . . reperiuntur. pp. 194. [*Lyons*, 1705 ?] 8°. S.C. **95/2.**

Imperfect; wanting the titlepage.

BARBIER (Helye) *See* Paris.—*Parlement.* Arrest de la cour de Parlement pour le règlement des dixmes [in the suit between H. Barbier and T. Buffon]. 1608. 8°. **878. f. 5. (11.)**

BARBIER (HENRI AUGUSTE) *See* DIABLE.
Le Diable à Paris . . . Texte par George Sand—P.-J. Stahl (A. Barbier), *etc.* 1845, 46. 8°.
12352. g. 30.

—— *See* SHAKESPEARE (W.) [*Julius Caesar.—French.*] Jules César . . . Traduite . . . par A. Barbier. 1848. 12°.
11762. c. 4.

—— —— 1855. 12°. **11763. c. 1.**

—— —— 1874. 12°. **11762. c. 5.**

—— *See* WAILLY (A. F. L. de) and BARBIER (H. A.) Benvenuto Cellini, opéra, *etc.* 1874. 12°. [*SHAKESPEARE (W.) Julius Caesar.—French. Études dramatiques par A Barbier, etc.*] **11762. c. 5.**

—— *See* WAILLY (A. F. L. de) and BARBIER (H. A.) Benvenuto Cellini; a lyric play, *etc.* [1853.] 8°.
11714. aa. 18. (5.)

—— *See* WAILLY (A. F. L. de) and BARBIER (H. A.) Benvenuto Cellini. Oper, *etc.* [1880?] 8°.
11747. ccc. 1/167.

—— —— [1890?] 8°. **11747. ccc. 1/187.**

—— *See* WAILLY (A. F. L. de) and BARBIER (H. A.) Benvenuto Cellini. Oper, *etc.* [1890 ?] 8°. **11747. ccc. 1/185.**

—— *See* WAILLY (A. F. L. de) and BARBIER (H. A.) Benvenuto Cellini. Oper, *etc.* [1895 ?] 8°. **11747. ccc. 1/372.**

—— Iambes et poèmes . . . Huitième édition revue et corrigée. (Iambes.—Il Pianto.—Lazare.) pp. 288. *Paris*, 1856. 8°. **11484. a. 59.**

—— Iambes et poëmes. (Iambes.—Il Pianto.—Lazare.) Onzième édition, revue et corrigée. pp. 288. *Paris*, 1860. 12°. **11481. bb. 3.**

—— [Another edition.] pp. 285. *Paris*, 1898. 12°.
11483. a. 34.

—— Douzième édition, *etc.* pp. 288. *Paris*, 1861. 12°.
11481. dd. 5.

—— Treizième édition, *etc.* pp. 291. *Paris*, 1862. 12°.
11481. bbb. 3.

—— Quinzième édition, *etc.* pp. 291. *Paris*, 1884. 12°.
011483. g. 29.

—— Trentième édition, *etc.* pp. 291. *Paris*, 1880. 8°.
011483. aa. 62.

—— [Another edition.] Edited by Ch.-M. Garnier. pp. lvi. 136. *Clarendon Press: Oxford*, 1907. 8°. [*Oxford Higher French Series.*] **12239. f. 19.**

—— Yámbicos.—Lázaro. Traduccion en versos Castellanos por A. Valdivia. [With portions of an essay on Barbier translated from the French of J. B. G. Planche.] pp. xvi. 159. *Madrid*, 1885. 16°. [*Biblioteca Universal.* tom. 101.] **739. b. 22.**

—— Silves et Rimes légères . . . [With " Rimes de voyage."] Nouvelle édition, revue et augmentée. pp. 427. *Paris*, 1872. 8°. **011483. g. 28.**

—— Histoires de voyage.—Fragments d'album. *See* FÉVAL (P. H. C.) Les Plumes d'or, romans, *etc.* 1865. 12°.
12515. g. 20.

—— Histoires de voyage, souvenirs et tableaux, 1830–1872. pp. vi. 262. *Paris*, 1880. 12°. **10168. bb. 30.**

—— Iambes. pp. xxx. 144. *Paris*, 1832. 8°. **11482. g. 23.**

—— La Lyre d'airain. [Extracted from " Lazare."] *See* PARIS.—*Salle Barthélemy.* Conférences littéraires, *etc.* sér. 2. 1864. 12°. **12237. bb. 3.**

BARBIER (HENRI AUGUSTE)

—— Nouvelles satires. pp. 287. *Paris*, 1840. 8°.
11481. g. 6.

—— [Another edition.] pp. 228. *Bruxelles*, 1840. 12°.
11736. a. 8.

—— Poésies posthumes, revues et mises en ordre par . . . A. Lacaussade et E. Grenier. pp. 216. *Paris*, 1884. 8°.
11483. cc. 9.

—— Satires. pp. 276. *Paris*, 1865. 12°. **011483. g. 30.**

—— Satires et poèmes. pp. iv. 391. *Paris*, 1837. 8°.
11481. g. 5.

A different work from the preceding.

—— [Another copy.] **11475. ccc. 23.**

—— Silves, poésies diverses. pp. 363. *Paris*, 1864. 12°.
11481. ccc. 5.

—— Souvenirs personnels et silhouettes contemporaines. pp. 378. *Paris*, 1883. 12°. **10664. c. 33.**

—— Tablettes d'Umbrano, suivies de Promenades au Louvre. pp. 298. *Paris*, 1884. 8°. **12357. c. 17.**

—— Trois passions. [In prose and verse.] pp. 263. *Paris*, 1868. 12°. **12516. b. 8.**

BARBIER (HENRY)

—— L'Âme et Dieu. A l'occasion du cinquantenaire de la mort de Victor Hugo. Discours, *etc.* pp. 27. *Paris*, 1935. 8°. **11858. bb. 24.**

BARBIER (HIPPOLYTE) *See* BARBIER (Louis S. H.)

BARBIER (J.) *Parisiensis.* *See* JANUA. Ianua linguarum quadrilinguis, *etc.* [The French translation by J. Barbier.] 1617. 4°. **12901. de. 7.**

BARBIER (J. A. L.)

—— Catalogue d'une belle collection de tableaux des écoles hollandaise et flamande, pierres gravés, mozaïques . . . rapportés des voyages d'Italie et d'Hollande, par J. A. L. B*** [i.e. J. A. L. Barbier.] (Par Ch. Paillet.) pp. 27. 1816. 8°. *See* B***, J. A. L.
7806. aaa. 19.

—— Catalogue d'une collection de jolis tableaux, bronzes, pierres gravées . . . provenants du cabinet de M. J. B. [i.e. J. A. L. Barbier.] pp. 15. 1811. 8°. *See* B., M. J.
7854. cc. 32. (6.)

—— Catalogue d'une jolie collection de tableaux de l'école hollandaise et flamande . . . la vente aura lieu le . . . 13 décembre 1819, *etc.* [The collection ascribed in a MS. note to J. A. L. Barbier.] pp. 27. MS. NOTES AND PRICES. 1819. 8°. *See* CATALOGUES. **562. e. 43. (13.)**

—— Catalogue d'une jolie collection de tableaux, la plupart des écoles flamande et hollandaise, appartenant à M. J. L. B***. [i.e. J. A. L. Barbier ?] Dont la vente aura lieu les 19 et 20 octobre 1818, *etc.* (Par Ches Paillet.) pp. 23. 1818. 8°. *See* B***, M. J. L. **562. e. 41. (21.)**

—— Catalogue de tableaux hollandais et flamands, porcelaine de Sèvres et pierres gravées, provenant des voyages de M. J.-L. B . . . [identified in a MS. note as J. A. L. Barbier.] Dont la vente aura lieu les 24 et 25 novembre 1817, *etc.* (Par Ch. Paillet.) pp. ii. 20. MS. NOTES AND PRICES. 1817. 8°. *See* B . . ., M. J. L. **562. e. 38. (7.)**

—— Notice d'un joli cabinet de tableaux, italiens, flamands et hollandais . . . dont la vente se fera . . . les 3 et 4 novembre, *etc.* [The collection ascribed in a MS. note to J. A. L. Barbier.] pp. 15. MS. PRICES. 1814. 8°. *See* CATALOGUES. **562. e. 31. (4.)**

BARBIER (J. B.) Lexique grec-français de quarante fables d'Ésope . . . Sixième édition, revue et corrigée, *etc.* pp. x. 171. *Paris*, 1829. 12°. **012305**. e. **49**.

BARBIER (J. C. Victor) La Jeune fermière. Du rôle de la femme dans une exploitation agricole. Ouvrage élémentaire, *etc.* pp. viii. 430. *Besançon*, 1868. 12°. **7077**. bb. **7**.

BARBIER (J. F.) Thèse pour le doctorat en médecine. (Questions sur diverses branches des sciences médicales.) pp. 23. *Paris*, 1838. 4°. **1184**. i. 4. (**18**.)

BARBIER (J. L. André) *See* Lamartine de Prat (M. L. A. de) Poèmes choisis. Edited by J. L. A. Barbier. 1921. 8°. **12209.tt.4/14.**

BARBIER (J. R.) De la pneumonie observée en Afrique, et de son traitement. Thèse, *etc.* pp. 33. *Montpellier*, 1851. 4°. **7379**. b. 3. (**29**.)

BARBIER (Jean) *Médecin des Hôpitaux de Lyon.*

—— Émotion. Émotivité. Constitution émotive, *etc.* pp. 166. *Lyon*, 1947. 8°. **08467**. df. **38**.

BARBIER (Jean) *of Algiers.* Abrégé des crimes de 93, poème en 17 drames ; rêve politique dédié aux amis de l'ordre, de la paix et du travail. pp. xii. 296. *Versailles*, 1858. 8°. **11481**. f. **5**.

—— Itinéraire historique et descriptif de l'Algérie, avec un vocabulaire français-arabe . . . et un résumé historique des guerres d'Afrique, *etc.* [With a map.] pp. xl. 572. *Paris*, 1855. 12°. **10096**. d. **21**.

BARBIER (Jean) *Poetical Writer.* Légendes du pays basque d'après la tradition. Illustrations, *etc.* *Fr. & Basque.* pp. 158. *Paris*, 1931. 4°. **12403**. g. **26**.

—— Nere Kantuak. Par J. B. [i.e. Jean Barbier.] pp. 32. 1910. 16°. *See* B., J. **11498**. cc. **3**.

BARBIER (Jean Baptiste Grégoire) *See* Chaumeton (F. P.) and Mérat de Vaumertois (F. V.) Dictionaire des sciences médicales, par . . . MM. Alard, Alibert, Barbier, *etc.* 1812, *etc.* 8°. **739**. d.-f.

—— Exposition de nouveaux principes de pharmacologie qui forment de la matière médicale une science nouvelle, *etc.* pp. 225 [125]. *Paris*, 1803. 8°. **1182**. b. **21**. (**5**.)

—— Précis de nosologie et de thérapeutique. 2 tom. *Paris*, 1827, 28. 8°. **776**. h. **5**.

—— Quelques réflexions sur la psychologie. pp. 118. *Paris*, 1849. 12°. **7660**. a. **55**. (**1**.)

—— Traité élémentaire de matière médicale . . . Cinquième édition, revue, *etc.* pp. xvi. 556. *Bruxelles*, 1838. 8°. **7510**. f. **20**.

BARBIER (Jean François) *See* Barbieri (Giovanni F.) called *Il Guercino.*

BARBIER (Jean Marie Gabriel) Quelques réflexions sommaires sur la pneumonie. pp. 19. *Paris*, 1813. 4°. **1182**. i. **13**. (**21**.)

BARBIER (Jean Pierre) Comment a été fondée la Maison de Balzac. *See* Royaumont (L. de) Pro Domo. La Maison de Balzac, *etc.* [1914.] 8°. **10658**. ee. **5**.

—— Juliette Drouet. Sa vie, son œuvre, par des documents inédits. pp. 168. *Paris*, 1913. 8°. **010662**. a. **30**.

BARBIER (John) *See* Saul (A.) The Famous Game of Chesse-play . . . Now augmented . . . by Io. Barbier. [1620?] 8°. **7915**. de. **1**.

—— —— 1640. 8°. **785**. a. **57**.

—— —— 1672. 8°. **785**. a. **56**.

BARBIER (Joseph) *Curé du Liernu.*

—— *See* Floreffe, *Abbey of.* Nécrologe de l'Abbaye de Floreffe . . . Publié . . . par J. Barbier. 1876. 8°. **4782**. g. **2**.

—— *See* Periodical Publications.—*Brussels.* Analectes pour servir à l'histoire ecclésiastique de la Belgique, publiés . . . par E. Reusens (J. Barbier), *etc.* 1864, *etc.* 8°. **P.P. 173**.

BARBIER (Joseph) *Curé du Liernu,* and **BARBIER** (Victor) *Ancien Professeur au Séminaire de Floreffe.*

—— Histoire de l'Abbaye de Floreffe de l'Ordre de Prémontré. pp. xvi. 519. *Namur*, 1880. 8°. **4782**. bbb. **8**.

BARBIER (Joseph Athanase) *Baron.* *See* Bayle (A. L. J.) Encyclopédie des sciences médicales. Par MM. Alibert, Barbier, *etc.* 1834, *etc.* 8°. **07305**. cc. **3**.

—— Propositions de chirurgie pratique, sur l'amputation à lambeaux. pp. 20. *Paris*, 1804. 4°. **1182**. f. **5**. (**24**.)

BARBIER (Joseph Victor) *See* Payeur-Didelot ( ) Trente mois au continent mystérieux . . . Préface de J. V. Barbier. 1899. 8°. **010095**. g. **22**.

—— *See* Winter (Georges) Un Vosgien tabou à Nouka-Hiwa. Souvenirs de voyage d'un soldat d'infanterie de marine. Résumé par J. V. Barbier. 1882, *etc.* 8°. [*Bulletin de la Société de Géographie de l'Est.* 1882. trim. 2, 4 ; 1883. trim. 1–3 ; 1884. trim. 2.] Ac. **6034**.

—— De l'orthographie du nom des pays qui s'écrivent en caractères latins, notamment au point de vue de la vulgarisation et de l'enseignement . . . Extrait du Bulletin de la Société de Géographie de l'Est. pp. 20. *Paris, Nancy*, 1891. 12°. **12901**. d. **33**. (**7**.)

—— Essai d'un lexique géographique. 1887. *See* Nancy.—*Société Royale des Sciences et Belles-Lettres, etc.* Mémoires, *etc.* sér. 5. tom. 4. 1754, *etc.* 12° & 8°. **Ac.383.**

—— Lexique géographique du monde entier. Publié sous la direction de M. E. Levasseur . . . par J.-V. Barbier . . . avec la collaboration de M. Anthoine. tom 1 ; tom. 2. pp. 1–48. *Paris, Nancy*, 1894, 98. 4°. **10005**. g. **7**. *No more published.*

—— Le Livre d'or de la géographie dans l'Est de la France. [Biographies of deceased geographers.] 1880–82. *See* Nancy.—*Société de Géographie de l'Est.* Bulletin, *etc.* 1880. trim. 4 ; 1881. trim. 1, 3, 4 ; 1882. trim. 1, 2. 1879, *etc.* 8°. Ac. **6034**.

—— Résultats d'une exploration à travers 250,000 mots de la nomenclature géographique. 3 pt. 1887–89. *See* Nancy.—*Société Royale des Sciences et Belles Lettres, etc.* Mémoires, *etc.* sér. 5. tom. 4–6. 1754, *etc.* 12° & 8°. **Ac.383.**

BARBIER (Jules) *See* Barbier (Paul J.)

BARBIER (Jules Claude) *See* Garnier (P.) La Folie à Paris . . . Préface de J. C. Barbier. 1890. 8°. **7660**. a. **11**.

—— *See* Homer. [*Iliad.—French.*] L'Iliade . . . Traduite . . . en vers français par J. C. Barbier. 1880 [1878], *etc.* 8°. **11315**. e. **20**.

—— *See* Horatius Flaccus (Q.) [*Ars Poetica.—Latin and French.*] Les Deux Arts poétiques d'Horace et de Boileau, avec traduction en vers et en prose, par J. C. Barbier. 1874. 8°. **11375**. bbb. **4**.

BARBIER (Jules Claude)

—— *See* Legrain (M.) Hygiène et prophylaxie . . . Avec une préface de J. C. Barbier, *etc.* 1895. 12°. **8436.** f. **14.**

—— Discours et réquisitoires [delivered in the Cour de Cassation]. pp. 568. *Paris,* 1888. 8°. **5403.** f. **6.**

BARBIER (Léon) La Franche-Comté. Besançon et la Vallée du Doubs. 25 eaux-fortes par . . . T. Abraham et G. Coindre. Texte par X. Marmier, F. Wey, E. Grenier, *etc.* [Edited by L. Barbier.] *Besançon,* 1874. fol. **1784.** b. **6.**

BARBIER (Léonce) En Province. Les femmes entre elles. pp. 248. *Lyon,* 1862. 12°. **12590.** ccc. **2.**

BARBIER (Louis Adolphe) Essai sur la blépharoplastie. Thèse *etc.* pp. 20. *Paris,* 1837. 4°. **1184.** h. **5.** **(6.)**

BARBIER (Louis Nicolas) *See* Periodical Publications.—*Paris.* Bulletin du bibliophile. (sér. 8, 9 avec le concours de MM. Barbier, A. Briquet, *etc.*) 1834, *etc.* 8°. P.P. **6540.**

—— Esquisse historique sur l'ivoirerie—beaux-arts et industrie. pp. 77. *Paris,* 1857. 12°. **7875.** a. **28.** **(2.)**

—— Notice biographique et littéraire sur M. Antoine A. Barbier. 1827. *See* Barbier (A. A.) Dictionnaire des ouvrages anonymes et pseudonymes, *etc.* tom. 4. 1822, *etc.* 8°. **816.** g. **37.**

BARBIER (Louis Stanislas Hippolyte) Entretiens sur la morale évangélique . . . Avec une notice biographique [by G. Bazin] et portrait. pp. xliii. 254. *Paris,* 1864. 12°. **4410.** c. **12.**

—— Les Jésuites, par un Solitaire [i.e. L. S. H. Barbier]. Réponse à MM. Michelet et Quinet, *etc.* pp. iv. 288. 1843. 12°. *See* Solitaire. **1356.** e. **18.**

—— Les Mystères du presbytère et de la vie religieuse, par le Solitaire [i.e. L. S. H. Barbier]. pp. 143. 1844. 12°. *See* Solitaire. **1356.** a. **34.**

BARBIER (M. D.)

—— Les Parallaxes dynamiques des étoiles doubles. pp. 31. *Paris,* 1936. 8°. [*Exposés d'astronomie stellaire.* no. 6.] W.P. **11177/6.**

BARBIER (Marie) *Dramatist.* Not' Claire. Comédie en un acte. pp. 48. *Paris,* 1895. 8°. **11740.** d. **16.** **(3.)**

BARBIER (Marie) *Sœur de l'Assomption.* *See* Sausseret (C. P.) Éloge historique de la sœur Marguerite Bourgeoys, *etc.* (Notice sur la sœur M. Barbier.) 1864. 8°. **4867.** cc. **35.**

BARBIER (Marie Anne)

—— *See* Pellegrin (S. J.) and Barbier (M. A.) Les Festes de l'été. Ballet, *etc.* 1734. 12°. [*Recueil général des opéra représentez par l'Académie royale de musique, etc.* tom. 12.] **242.** e. **44.**

—— *See* Pellegrin (S. J.) and Barbier (M. A.) Le Jugement de Paris. Pastorale héroïque, *etc.* 1734. 12°. [*Recueil général des opéra représentez par l'Académie royale de musique, etc.* tom. 12.] **242.** e. **44.**

—— *See* Pellegrin (S. J.) and Barbier (M. A.) Les Plaisirs de la campagne. Ballet, *etc.* 1734. 12°. [*Recueil général des opéra représentez par l'Académie royale de musique, etc.* tom. 12.] **242.** e. **44.**

BARBIER (Marie Anne)

—— Les Tragedies et autres poesies de mademoiselle Anne Barbier. Nouvelle édition, revûe, corrigée, augmentée, & enrichie de tres belles figures à la tête de chaque comédie. pp. 357. *Leide,* 1719. 12°. **640.** d. **28**

With an additional titlepage, engraved.

—— Arrie et Petus, tragédie. [In verse.] pp. 70. *Paris,* 1713. 12°. **242.** f. **24.** (4.)

—— Arria en Petus. Treurspel. Uit het Fransch. [Translated by G. van Mater.] pp. 73. *Haarlem,* 1719. 8°. **11755.** aaa. **43.** (2.)

—— De Dood van Arria en Petus, treurspel; gevolgt naar het Fransch. [The introductory verses signed: E. S.] pp. 85. *Leyden,* 1774. 8°. **11754.** bb. **36.** **(1.)**

—— Cornélie, mère des Gracques. Tragédie. [In verse.] pp. 73. *Paris,* 1703. 12°. **242.** f. **24.** **(1.)**

—— Cornelia, die Mutter der Grachen, ein Trauerspiel, *etc.* 1741. *See* Gottsched (J. C.) Die deutsche Schaubühne, *etc.* Bd. 2. 1742, *etc.* 8°. **11745.** e. **34.**

—— Le Faucon, comédie. [By M. A. Barbier.] pp. 47. 1719. 12°. *See* Faucon. **242.** f. **24.** **(5.)**

—— La Mort de Cesar, tragédie. [In verse.] pp. 68. *Paris,* 1707. 12°. **242.** f. **24.** **(3.)**

—— De Doodt van Julius Cezar. [Altered from the French of M. A. Barbier.] pp. 78. 1728. 8°. *See* Caesar (C. J.) [*Appendix.—Miscellanea.*] **11735.** a. **5.**

—— Tomyris, tragédie. [In verse.] pp. 72. *Paris,* 1707. 12°. **242.** f. **24.** (2.)

—— Tomyris, of de dood van Cyrus; treurspel. Gevolgd naar het Fransche van Mejuffrouwe Barbier [by J. Bilderdyk]. pp. 71. *Amsteldam,* 1763. 8°. **636.** c. **12.** **(5.)**

BARBIER (Michel Victor) De l'influence de la menstruation sur les maladies mentales. pp. 34. *Paris,* 1849. 4°. [*Collection des thèses soutenues à la Faculté de Médecine de Paris.* An 1849. tom. 1.] **7372.** c. **1.**

BARBIER (N. M. F.) Des perforations non traumatiques du tube digestif et de la péritonite consécutive; thèse, *etc.* pp. 35. *Paris,* 1836. 4°. **1184.** g. **18.** **(10.)**

BARBIER (Olinto) Associazione Razionalista Pisana. Conferenza tenuta dal socio O. Barbier, il 1 maggio 1887, *etc.* pp. 16. *Pisa,* 1887. 8°. **4372.** e. **25.** **(3.)**

BARBIER (Olivier Alexandre) *See* Foisy (F. M.) and Barbier (O. A.) Exposition de tableaux au Musée Royal du Louvre, *etc.* 1837. 8°. T. **2119.** **(7.)**

—— *See* Barbier (A. A.) Dictionnaire des ouvrages anonymes . . . Troisième édition, revue . . . par O. Barbier. 1872, *etc.* 8°. [*Quérard* (*J. M.*) *Les Supercheries littéraires dévoilées.*] **2037.d.**

BARBIER (Osvaldo)

—— Attuazione di un metodo per rivelare immagini ultra-acustiche. *In Civitate Vaticana,* 1942. 8°. [*Pontificia Academia Scientiarum. Acta.* vol. 6. no. 25.] Ac. **101.** b/**3.**

BARBIER (Paul) Les Idylles de Jeanne. [Poems on Saint Joan of Arc.] pp. 134. *Paris,* 1898. 16°. **011483.** e. **13.**

—— Italie. Souvenirs et impressions de voyage. Ouvrage illustrée de 82 gravures. pp. xi. 321. *Paris,* 1893. 8°. **10131.** f. **1.**

BARBIER (PAUL)

—— Notre Saint-Père le pape Léon XIII. Étude biographique et littéraire, *etc.* [With a portrait.] pp. xv. 331. *Paris*, [1892.] 4°. **4856. h. 20.**

—— [Another issue.] *Bruxelles*, [1892.] 4°. **4855. f. 2.**

—— Vie de Saint Athanase, *etc.* pp. 440. *Paris*, 1888. 18°. **4829. aa. 40.**

—— Vie de Saint Hilaire, évêque de Poitiers, *etc.* pp. viii. xviii. 461. *Paris*, 1887. 8°. **4827. df. 20.**

—— La Vierge. [Poems.] pp. 186. *Paris*, 1910. 8°. **011483. aaa. 10.**

BARBIER (PAUL ÉMILE A.) The Age of Owain Gwynedd. An attempt at a connected account of the history of Wales from December, 1135, to November, 1170. To which are added several appendices on the chronology, &c., of the period. pp. 182. *David Nutt: London; J. E. Southall: Newport, Mon.*, 1908. 4°. **9508. ccc. 2.**

BARBIER (PAUL EUGÈNE EDMOND) *See* SECONDAT (C. de) *Baron de Montesquieu.* De la grandeur des Romains et de leur décadence. Edited . . . by P. E. E. Barbier. 1888. 8°. **11736. dd. 1/32.**

—— *See* WITT (Henriette de) Les Héroïnes de Harlem. Edited . . . by P. E. E. Barbier, *etc.* 1889. 8°. **12518. c. 35.**

—— Class Book of French Poetry for the Young. pp. viii. 75. *Librairie Hachette & Cie: London*, 1877. 8°. **12954. de. 16.**

—— *See* LAZARE (Jules) and MINOGGIO (F.) A Phraseological French-English Vocabulary of the less familiar words . . . contained in Barbier's French Poetry for the Young, *etc.* [1898.] 8°. **012901. f. 2. (5.)**

—— Elementary French Course for Beginners, *etc.* pp. 160. *John Heywood: Manchester*, [1873.] 8°. **12950. aa. 42.**

—— New edition . . . revised. pp. 164. *John Heywood: Manchester*, 1883. 8°. **12952. df. 23.**

—— Key to Exercises etc. contained in Barbier's Elementary French Course for Beginners. pp. 32. *John Heywood: Manchester*, [1873.] 16°. **12950. a. 42.**

—— English Influence on the French Vocabulary. 2 pt. *Oxford*, 1921, 23. 8°. [*S.P.E. Tract.* no. 7, 13.] **Ac.9921.**

—— A Graduated French Examination Course. pp. vii. 137. *Whittaker & Co.: London*, 1891. 8°. **12954. cc. 48.**

—— A Graduated French Reader; with an introduction on the pronunciation of consonants . . . and notes. pp. vi. 154. *Rivingtons: London*, 1880. 8°. **12950. df. 14.**

—— Second edition. pp. viii. 172. *Rivingtons: London*, 1881. 8°. **12950. df. 33.**

—— Third edition. pp. viii. 172. *Rivingtons: London*, 1885. 8°. **12950. bb. 49.**

—— Fourth edition. pp. viii. 172. *Rivingtons: London*, 1887. 8°. **12950. cc. 5.**

—— A Manual of French Pronunciation . . . With lists of exceptional and difficult words, *etc.* pp. xii. 77. *Simpkin, Marshall & Co.: London*, 1876. 16°. **12953. aaa. 2.**

—— The Pictorial French Course . . . Eighth edition. pp. 146. *Modern Language Press: London*, [1906.] 8°. [*Rees' Pictorial Language Series.*] **012901. ff. 35/1.**

BARBIER (PAUL EUGÈNE EDMOND)

—— A Second French Reader and Writer. pp. 135. *S. Sonnenschein & Co.: London*, 1892. 8°. [*Parallel Grammar Series.*] **2274. b. 17.**

BARBIER (PAUL EUGÈNE EDMOND) and **DELHAVÉ** (CHARLES)

—— Cambridge Local Examination, 1876. Vocabulary and notes to Madame . . . de Staël's Dix années d'exil. Livre II., chapitres 1–8 *etc.* pp. 31. *John Heywood: Manchester*, [1876.] 8°. **12950. aa. 10.**

BARBIER (PAUL JULES) *See* BARBIER (Pierre) *Dramatist.* Struensée. Drame . . . en vers d'après le drame en prose de J. Barbier. 1899. 12°. **11740. ee. 51.**

—— *See* BARRIÈRE (T.) Laurence, drame . . . par T. Barrière, M. Carré et J. Barbier, *etc.* 1849. 8°. [*Bibliothèque dramatique.* tom. 25.] **2296. b. 25.**

—— *See* BIZET (G. A. C. L.) Georges Bizet. [An account of the erection of the Bizet monument in the Père-Lachaise cemetery. With the speech of P. J. Barbier at the unveiling.] [1877?] 8°. Hirsch **2661.**

—— *See* BOURGEOIS (A. A.) and BARBIER (P. J.) La Sorcière, *etc.* 1863. 12°. **11739. c. 19. (1.)**

—— —— [1864.] 4°. **11739. k. 49.**

—— —— 1867. fol. [*Théâtre contemporain illustré.* livr. 701, 702.] **2296. h.**

—— *See* CARRÉ (M.) L'Amour mouillé, comédie vaudeville . . . par M. Carré, Barbier et A. de Beauplan, *etc.* 1849. 8°. [*Bibliothèque dramatique.* tom. 28.] **2296. b. 28.**

—— —— 1858. fol. [*Théâtre contemporain illustré.* livr. 323, 324.] **2296. h.**

—— *See* CARRÉ (M.) Henriette Deschamps, drame . . . par M. Carré, J. Barbier et A. Dumesnil, *etc.* 1849. 8°. [*Bibliothèque dramatique.* tom. 26.] **2296. b. 26.**

—— *See* CARRÉ (M.) and BARBIER (P. J.) Les Amoureux sans le savour, comedie, *etc.* 1849. 8°. [*Bibliothèque dramatique.* tom. 31.] **2296. b. 31.**

—— *See* CARRÉ (M.) and BARBIER (P. J.) Le Cabaret des amours, *etc.* 1863. 12°. **11739. aaa. 17. (7.)**

—— *See* CARRÉ (M.) and BARBIER (P. J.) Deucalion et Pyrrha, opéra-comique, *etc.* 1854. 8°. [*Bibliothèque dramatique.* tom. 68.] **2296. d. 6.**

—— *See* CARRÉ (M.) and BARBIER (P. J.) Un Drame de famille, drame, *etc.* 1849. 8°. [*Bibliothèque dramatique.* tom. 20.] **2296. b. 20.**

—— —— 1862. fol. [*Théâtre contemporain illustré.* livr. 508, 509.] **2296. h.**

—— *See* CARRÉ (M.) and BARBIER (P. J.) Gil-Blas; opéra-comique, *etc.* 1860. 12°. **11739. aa. 41.**

—— —— 1860. 8°. [*Bibliothèque dramatique.* tom. 88.] **2296. d. 26.**

—— —— 1862. fol. [*Théâtre contemporain illustré.* livr. 536, 537.] **2296. h.**

—— *See* CARRÉ (M.) and BARBIER (P. J.) Hamlet. Opéra, *etc.* 1868. 12°. **11739. b. 15.**

—— —— 1880. 12°. **11762. df. 7. (8.)**

—— *See* CARRÉ (M.) and BARBIER (P. J.) Hamlet; an opera, *etc.* [1869.] 8°. **11764. bb. 50. (3.)**

BARBIER (PAUL JULES)

—— *See* CARRÉ (M.) and BARBIER (P. J.) Hamlet. Grosse Oper, *etc.* 1869. 8°. **11765. b. 8.**

—— *See* CARRÉ (M.) and BARBIER (P. J.) Mignon, opéra comique, *etc.* 1867. 12°. **11739. bbb. 3. (15.)**

—— *See* CARRÉ (M.) and BARBIER (P. J.) Les Noces de Jeannette, opéra-comique, *etc.* 1854. 8°. [*Bibliothèque dramatique.* tom. 49.] **2296. c. 18.**

—— *See* CARRÉ (M.) and BARBIER (P. J.) Le Pardon de Ploërmel. 1859. 8°. **11737. e. 7. (5.)**

—— —— 1859. 8°. [*Bibliothèque dramatique.* tom. 85.] **2296. d. 23.**

—— *See* CARRÉ (M.) and BARBIER (P. J.) Les Sabots de la Marquise, *etc.* 1859 [1854?]. 8°. **11737. g. 7. (14.)**

—— *See* CARRÉ (M.) and BARBIER (P. J.) La Statue, opéra-comique, *etc.* 1861. 12°. **11739. b. 32. (3.)**

—— —— [1903.] 8°. **11740. dd. 31.**

—— *See* CARRÉ (M.) and BARBIER (P. J.) Valentine d'Aubigny, opéra-comique, *etc.* 1856. 8°. [*Bibliothèque dramatique.* tom. 71.] **2296. d. 9.**

—— *See* CORDELLIER DELANOUE (A.) and BARBIER (P. J.) Une Épreuve avant la lettre, comédie-vaudeville, *etc.* 1854. 8°. [*Bibliothèque dramatique.* tom. 64.] **2296. d. 2.**

—— *See* DECOURCELLE (A.) Un Roi de la mode; comédie . . . par MM. Decourcelle, J. Barrière et Barbier. [1851.] 8°. **2296. c. 7.**

—— *See* ERCKMANN (E.) and CHATRIAN (P. A.) La Taverne des Trabans. Opéra-comique . . . de Erckmann-Chatrian et J. Barbier, *etc.* 1887. 12°. **11740. bbb. 28.**

—— *See* FIGARO. Les Noces de Figaro . . . en quatre actes. Traduit . . . par MM. J. Barbier et M. Carré, *etc.* [1855?] 8°. [*Bibliothèque dramatique.* tom. 82.] **2296. d. 20.**

—— *See* FOUSSIER (E.) and BARBIER (P. J.) Le Maître de la maison, comédie, *etc.* 1866. 12°. **11737. bb. 32.**

—— *See* RAPHANEL (J.) and LEGRAND (C.) Histoire anecdotique des théâtres de Paris . . . Avec une préface de M. Jules Barbier, *etc.* 1896. 18°. **011795. e. 81.**

—— Amour et bergerie, comédie en un acte, en vers, *etc.* pp. 36. *Paris,* 1849. 8°. [*Bibliothèque dramatique.* tom. 11.] **2296. b. 11.**

—— Les Amoureux de Cathérine. Opéra-comique en un acte, d'après la nouvelle d'Erckmann-Chatrian, *etc.* pp. 46. *Paris,* 1876. 12°. **11739. b. 17.**

—— André Chénier, ou 90, 92, 94. Drame en vers, en trois époques. pp. 62. *Paris,* 1849. 12°. **11737. e. 6. (1.)**

—— Bianca Capello. Opéra en cinq actes, *etc.* pp. 99. *Paris,* 1886. 12°. **11739. e. 60.**

—— Blandine. Drame en cinq actes. [In verse.] pp. 100. *Paris,* 1898. 12°. **11740. ee. 31.**

—— Bon gré mal gré, comédie en un acte, en prose, *etc.* pp. 36. *Paris,* 1849. 8°. [*Bibliothèque dramatique.* tom. 17.] **2296. b. 17.**

—— Cora, ou l'Esclavage, drame en cinq actes, *etc.* pp. 115. *Paris,* 1861. 12°. **11737. aaa. 7.**

—— [Another edition.] pp. 23. 1863. *See* THÉÂTRE. Théâtre contemporain illustré. livr. 571, 572. [1852, *etc.*] fol. **2296. h.**

BARBIER (PAUL JULES)

—— Cora, ou a Escravatura. Drama [from the French of P. J. Barbier] . . . Traduzido . . . por E. Biester. pp. 107. 1862. 8°. *See* CORA. **11728. bbb. 1. (3.)**

—— Une Distraction. Comédie en un acte et en prose. pp. 42. *Paris,* 1859. 12°. **11739. c. 14. (3.)**

—— La Fille d'Égypte; opéra-comique en deux actes, *etc.* pp. 59. *Paris,* 1862. 8°. [*Bibliothèque dramatique.* tom. 97.] **2296. e. 2.**

—— La Fille du maudit; drame en cinq actes, *etc.* pp. 128. *Paris,* 1864. 12°. **11739. c. 20. (1.)**

—— [Another edition.] pp. 26. [*Paris,* 1864.] fol. **11737. i. 9.**

—— La Gerbe. Poésies. 1842–1883. pp. 365. *Paris,* 1884. 8°. **11483. cc. 4.**

—— Graziella, drame lyrique en deux actes d'après le roman de Lamartine. pp. 42. *Paris,* 1877. 12°. **11739. f. 6. (3.)**

—— Jeanne d'Arc. Drame en cinq actes, en vers, avec chœurs. pp. 190. *Paris,* 1874. 12°. **11739. ee. 103. (7.)**

—— Nouvelle édition, conforme à la représentation. pp. 190 *Paris,* 1874. 12°. **11739. ee. 53**

—— Les Joyeuses commères de Windsor, opéra-comique en trois actes, *etc.* [Based on Shakespeare's "Merry Wives of Windsor."] pp. 76. *Paris,* 1862. 12°. **11765. aaa. 30. (4.)**

—— Lisbeth, ou la Cinquantaine, opéra comique en deux actes, *etc.* pp. 50. *Paris,* 1865. 12°. **11739. bb. 20. (1.)**

—— Le Magnifique. Opéra-comique en un acte, *etc.* pp. 52. *Paris,* 1876. 12°. **11740. b. 4. (5.)**

—— Le Mariage de Don Lope, opéra comique en un acte, *etc.* pp. 44. *Paris,* 1865. 12°. **11737. aaa. 39. (3.)**

—— Néron. Opéra en quatre actes, *etc.* pp. 104. *Paris,* 1885. 18°. **11739. bbb. 19.**

—— Nero. Grosse Oper in vier Acten nach der französischen Dichtung von J. Barbier für die deutsche Bühne bearbeitet, *etc.* pp. 99. *Leipzig,* [1877?] 8°. **11745. de. 10. (8.)**

—— La Nuit aux gondoles; opéra-comique en un acte, *etc.* pp. 34. *Paris,* 1862. 8°. [*Bibliothèque dramatique.* tom 95.] **2296. d. 33.**

—— Une Nuit de Cléopatre. Opéra en trois actes, *etc.* pp. 58. *Paris,* 1885. 18°. **11740. bb. 40. (1.)**

—— L'Ombre de Molière. Intermède. [In verse.] pp. 36 *Paris,* 1847. 8°. **11735. k. 65**

—— Petites fantaisies poétiques. pp. 62. *Paris,* 1904. 8°. **11483. dd. 31**

—— Les Premières coquetteries, comédie-vaudeville en un acte, *etc.* pp. 36. *Paris,* 1849. 8°. [*Bibliothèque dramatique.* tom. 13.] **2296. b. 13**

—— Princesse et Favorite, drame en cinq actes, précédés d'un prologue. pp. 126. *Paris,* 1865. 12°. **11739. c. 21. (6**

—— [Another edition.] pp. 23. [*Paris,* 1865.] 4°. **11739. k. 47**

—— Quelques mots relatifs au procès des Noces de Figaro pp. 32. *Paris,* 1861. 12°. **11795. dg. 2. (4**

—— La Reine Berthe. Opéra en deux actes, *etc.* pp. 56. *Paris,* 1879. 12°. **11740. f. 12. (5**

BARBIER (PAUL JULES)

—— Un Retour de jeunesse. Drame en cinq actes, en vers. pp. 132. *Paris*, [1877.] 8°. **11739**. f. **6**. (**1**.)

—— Sous le même toit. Comédie en un acte. pp. 43. *Paris*, 1872. 12°. **11739**. cc. **22**. (**1**.)

—— Sylvia, ou la Nymphe de Diane. Ballet en trois actes, cinq tableaux, *etc*. pp. 27. *Paris*, 1876. 8°. **11739**. aaa. **5**.

—— La Tempête. Ballet en trois actes. [Based on Shakespeare.] pp. 38. *Paris*, 1889. 8°. **11740**. aaa. **25**. (**3**.)

BARBIER (PAUL JULES) and **BARBIER** (PIERRE) *Dramatist*.

—— Daphnis et Chloe. Opéra en trois actes, *etc*. pp. 72. *Paris*, 1899. 12°. **11740**. eee. **44**.

BARBIER (PAUL JULES) and **BATTU** (LÉON)

—— L'Anneau d'argent, opéra-comique en un acte. pp. 30. *Paris*, 1854. 8°. [*Bibliothèque dramatique*. tom. 67.] **2296**. d. **5**.

BARBIER (PAUL JULES) and **CARRÉ** (MICHEL)

—— Les Antipodes, vaudeville en en acte, *etc*. pp. 26. *Paris*, 1854. 8°. [*La France dramatique au XIXe siècle*. tom. 22.] **2296**. **f**. **22**. *Imperfect; wanting all after p*. 16.

—— La Colombe. Opéra-comique en deux actes. pp. 47. *Paris*, 1861. 12°. **11739**. c. **18**. (**2**.)

—— [Another edition.] pp. 55. *Paris*, 1866. 12°. **11739**. bbb. **14**. (**1**.)

—— Les Contes d'Hoffmann, drame fantastique en cinq actes. pp. 88. *Paris*, 1854. 8°. [*Bibliothèque dramatique*. tom. 36.] **2296**. c. **5**.

—— Les Contes d'Hoffmann. Opéra en quatre actes de J. Barbier . . . d'après le drame de J. Barbier et M. Carré. pp. 95. *Paris*, 1881. 12°. **11739**. e. **49**. (**3**.)

—— Les Contes d'Hoffmann. Tales of Hoffmann. Fantastic opera in three acts, with a prologue and epilogue. By Jules Barbier [and M. Carré] . . . English version by Maurice Magnus. *Fr. & Eng.* pp. 81. *J. B. Cramer & Co.: London*, [1911.] 8°. **906**. k. **4**. (**7**.)

—— [Another edition.] Translated into English by Edward Agate. pp. 36. [*London*, 1910.] 8°. **906**. k. **4**. (**2**.)

—— Tales of Hoffmann. [By P. J. Barbier and M. Carré.] Concert version. Libretto with explanatory notes. English words by Edward Agate, *etc*. pp. viii. [1928 ?] 8°. *See* HOFFMANN (E. T. W.) **11781**. i. **61**.

—— Arien und Gesänge aus: Hoffmann's Erzählungen . . . Mit Benützung von E. T. A. Hoffmann's Novellen, *etc*. pp. 28. *Köln & Leipzig*, [1903.] 8°. **11735**. c. **41**. (**3**.)

—— *See* MUELLER (Hans von) Hoffmanns Erzählungen . . . Text von Jules Barbier nach dem gleichnamigen Schauspiel von demselben und Michel Carré . . . Kurze Einführung, *etc*. [1915.] 8°. Hirsch **4153**.

—— Les Derniers adieux, comédie en un acte et en prose. pp. 19. *Paris*, 1854. 8°. [*Bibliothèque dramatique*. tom. 39.] **2296**. c. **8**.

—— [Another edition.] pp. 5. 1856. *See* THÉÂTRE. Théâtre contemporain illustré. livr. 196, 197. [1852, *etc*.] fol. **2296**. h.

—— Don Mucarade. Opéra-comique en un acte. pp. 59. *Paris*, 1875. 12°. **11739**. b. **13**.

BARBIER (PAUL JULES) and **CARRÉ** (MICHEL)

—— Don Quichotte, opéra comique en trois actes, *etc*. pp. 88. *Paris*, 1869. 12°. **11739**. cc. **12**. (**6**.)

—— L'Éventail, opéra-comique, en un acte. pp. 42. *Paris*, 1861. 12°. **11739**. aaa. **17**. (**1**.)

—— Faust. Opéra en cinq actes, *etc*. pp. 72. *Paris*, 1859. 8°. **11737**. e. **7**. (**3**.)

—— [Another issue.] **11737**. e. **7**. (**4**.)

—— [Another edition.] pp. 60. *Paris*, 1869. 12°. **11739**. cc. **12**. (**4**.)

—— Faust. Opéra . . . Nouvelle édition. pp. 65. *Paris*, 1900. 8°. **11740**. k. **52**.

—— Faust, 1er acte. Traduction languedocienne [of the libretto by P. J. Barbier and M. Carré] par M. L. B.-S. pp. 8. 1890. 8°. *See* FAUST (Johann) *Dr*. **11747**. h. **9**. (**4**.)

—— Faust . . . As represented at the Royal Opera, Covent Garden. French-English edition. pp. 30. [1900 ?] 4°. *See* FAUST (J.) *Dr*. **906**. k. **1**. (**2**.)

—— The Opera Libretto. Gounod's grand opera of Faust. [The words of P. J. Barbier and M. Carré.] pp. 23. [1865 ?] 12°. *See* GOUNOD (C. F.) **11781**. aaa. **39**. (**7**.)

—— Book of Words of " Faust," by Ravenswood [or rather a translation of P. J. Barbier and M. Carré's libretto]. pp. 35. [1891.] 8°. *See* RAVENSWOOD, *pseud*. **11747**. c. **10**. (**6**.)

—— Faust . . . The English adaptation by Robert A. Simon. pp. 20. *C. C. Birchard & Co.: New York*, [1928.] 8°. **11746**. k. **55**.

—— Margarethe. Oper in fünf Akten. Nach Goethe . . . Deutsches Textbuch. pp. 54. *Berlin*, [1903.] 8°. **11740**. bbb. **62**. (**5**.)

—— Faust; dramma lirico, in cinque atti . . . Traduzione italiana del signor A. de Lauzières, *etc*. pp. 48. *Milano*, [1864 ?] 12°. **11714**. aa. **27**. (**10**.)

—— Faust . . . Opera bum act. Cyfieithiad a chyfaddasiad o Ffrangeg . . . gan T. H. Parry-Williams. pp. 52. *Cyhoeddir dros Gyngor yr Eisteddfod Genedlaethol gan Gwmni Cyhoeddi Gwynn: Llangollen*, [1945.] 8°. **11741**. b. **9**.

—— Fidelio, opéra en trois actes. Par Jules Barbier et M. Carré. [Based on J. Sonnleithner's translation of " Léonore " by J. N. Bouilly.] *Paris*, 1860. 8°. [*Bibliothèque dramatique*. tom. 89.] **2296**. d. **27**.

—— La Fileuse, drame en cinq actes. pp. 87. *Paris*, 1854. 8°. [*Bibliothèque dramatique*. tom. 40.] **2296**. c. **9**.

—— Court Cards. A comic drama . . . By J. P. Simpson. [Adapted from " La Fileuse " by P. J. Barbier and M. Carré.] pp. 44. *London*, [1862.] 12°. [*Lacy's Acting Edition of Plays*. vol. 53.] **2304**. e. **27**.

—— Françoise de Rimini, opéra en quatre actes, avec prologue et épilogue, *etc*. pp. iv. 64. *Paris*, 1882. 8°. **11740**. e. **12**. (**5**.)

—— Galathée, opéra comique en deux actes. pp. 47. *Paris*, 1854. 8°. [*Bibliothèque dramatique*. tom. 42.] **2296**. c. **11**.

—— Graziella, drame en un acte, tiré des Confidences de M. de Lamartine. pp. 36. *Paris*, 1849. 8°. [*Bibliothèque dramatique*. tom. 23.] **2296**. b. **23**.

—— [Another edition.] pp. 11. 1857. *See* THÉÂTRE. Théâtre contemporain illustré. livr. 26, 27. [1852, *etc.*] fol. **2296**. h.

—— Les Marionettes du docteur, drame en cinq actes. pp. 100. *Paris*, 1854. 8°. [*Bibliothèque dramatique*. tom. 40.] **2296**. c. **9**.

—— Le Mémorial de Sainte-Hélène, drame historique en 3 parties et 18 tableaux. pp. 127. *Paris*, 1854. 8°. [*Bibliothèque dramatique*. tom. 42.] **2296**. c. **11**.

—— Miss Fauvette, opéra-comique en un acte. pp. 59. *Paris*, 1854. 8°. [*Bibliothèque dramatique*. tom. 64.] **2296**. d. **2**.

—— Les Papillotes de M. Benoist, opéra comique en un acte, *etc.* pp. 58. *Paris*, 1854. 12°. **11739**. bb. **12**. (**1**.)

—— Paul et Virginie. Opéra en trois actes, six tableaux . . . [In verse. Founded on the romance of J. H. Bernardin de St. Pierre.] Nouvelle édition. pp. 64. *Paris*, 1877. 12°. **11740**. b. **8**. (**4**.)

—— Nouvelle édition. pp. 64. *Paris*, 1895. 12°. **906**. e. **16**. (**3**.)

—— Paul & Virginia. Opera in three acts, *etc.* pp. 62. *Théodore Michaelis: Paris*, 1877. 8°. **11740**. b. **8**. (**5**.)

—— Philémon et Baucis, opéra comique en trois actes. pp. 45. *Paris*, 1860. 8°. [*Bibliothèque dramatique*. tom. 8.] **2296**. d. **26**.

—— Polyeucte, opéra en cinq actes . . . d'après la tragédie de Corneille, *etc.* pp. 44. *Paris*, 1878. 8°. **11740**. b. **13**. (**3**.)

—— Polyeucte: an opera in five acts . . . from the tragedy of Corneille. The English version by J. Pittmann. (Poliuto . . . Versione ritmica di A. Zanardini.) *Eng. & Ital.* pp. 93. *H. Lemoine: Paris*, 1878. 12°. **11740**. f. **9**. (**1**.)

—— Polyeuct: Oper in fünf Akten . . . nach der Tragödie Corneille's . . . Deutsch von F. Gumbert. pp. 48. *Paris*, [1878.] 12°. **11740**. f. **9**. (**2**.)

—— Poliuto. Opera in quattro atti . . . tratta dalla tragedia di Corneille, *etc.* pp. 42. *Parigi*, 1886. 8°. **11740**. bbb. **17**. (**1**.)

—— Psyché, opéra-comique en trois actes, *etc.* pp. 87. *Paris*, 1857. 12°. **11739**. c. **12**. (**3**.)

—— [Another issue.] [*Bibliothèque dramatique*. tom. 75.] **2296**. d. **13**.

—— Nouvelle édition conforme à la représentation. pp. 68. *Paris*, 1878. 12°. **11740**. b. **14**. (**1**.)

—— La Reine de Saba, opéra en quatre actes, *etc.* [In verse.] pp. 49. *Paris*, 1862. 12°. **11739**. aaa. **17**. (**5**.)

—— Roméo et Juliette, opéra en cinq actes . . . [Based on Shakespeare.] Deuxième édition. pp. 68. *Paris*, 1867. 12°. **11765**. aaa. **30**. (**6**.)

—— Nouvelle édition, *etc.* pp. 68. *Paris*, 1888. 12°. **11740**. bbb. **37**.

—— Roméo et Juliette. Opéra en cinq actes . . . Nouvelle édition, *etc.* pp. 68. *Paris*, 1890. 8°. **11740**. k. **51**.
The date on the wrapper is 1898.

—— Romeo et Juliette. An opera in five acts. Music by Ch. Gounod. Words by J. Barbier & M. Carré. [A book of words, issued for the performance at Windsor Castle, 27 June, 1898.] / pp. 34. *Nassau Press: London*, [1898.] 8°. Eng & Fr. **11783**. g. **6**.

BARBIER (PAUL JULES) and CARRÉ (MICHEL)

—— [Another edition.] [With the music of the principal airs, and the programme of the performance given at Windsor Castle, 27 June 1898.] pp. 34. *Nassau Press: London*, 1898. 4°. **906**. k. **1**. (**1**.)

—— Romeo et Juliette. The music by Gounod. As represented at the Royal Opera, Covent Garden. French-English edition. With the music of the principal airs. [The text of the French libretto by P. J. Barbier and M. Carré, with an English translation by H. B. Farnie.] pp. 34. [1905.] 4°. *See* ROMEO. **11740**. h. **37**.

—— Romeo e Giulietta; an opera in five acts. [Translated into English and Italian from the French of P. J. Barbier and M. Carré.] The English translation by H. B. Farnie, *etc.* pp. 76. [1867.] 8°. *See* ROMEO. **11715**. aaa. **35**.

—— Arien und Gesänge aus: Romeo und Julie. Grosse Oper . . . von J. Barbier und M. Carré. Deutsch nach Shakespeare von Theodor Gassmann, *etc.* pp. 68. *Berlin*, 1869. 8°. **11765**. aa. **9**. (**2**.)

—— Les Saisons, opéra-comique en trois actes. pp. 108. *Paris*, 1856. 8°. [*Bibliothèque dramatique*. tom. 69.] **2296**. d. **7**.

—— Le Timbre d'argent. Opéra fantastique en quatre actes et huit tableaux, *etc.* pp. 77. *Paris*, 1877. 12°. **11740**. b. **10**. (**1**.)

—— Voyage autour d'une jolie femme, tableau de mœurs en un acte. pp. 32. *Paris*, 1854. 8°. [*Bibliothèque dramatique*. tom. 46.] **2296**. c. **15**.

—— [Another edition.] pp. 10. 1854. *See* THÉÂTRE. Théâtre contemporain illustré. livr. 91, 92. [1852, *etc.*] fol. **2296**. h.

BARBIER (PAUL JULES) and **CHAPELLE** (PAUL AIMÉ)

—— Le Feu de paille, comédie vaudeville en un acte, *etc.* pp. 34. *Paris*, 1849. 8°. [*Bibliothèque dramatique*. tom. 21.] **2296**. b. **21**.

BARBIER (PAUL JULES) and **CHOUDENS** (PAUL DE)

—— Clarisse Harlowe: opéra, *etc.* [Based on Richardson's novel.] pp. 93. *Paris*, 1896. 8°. **11740**. eee. **7**.

BARBIER (PAUL JULES) and **DELAHAYE** (JULES) *Dramatist.*

—— Le Roman de la Rose; opéra-comique en un acte, *etc.* pp. 54. *Paris*, 1854. 12°. **11739**. aaa. **8**. (**2**.)

BARBIER (PIERRE) *Docteur en Droit.*

—— La Coutume privée d'Andorre, envisagée dans ses sources et dans ses institutions les plus originales. pp. 157. 1938. 8°. *See* PARIS.—*Université de Paris.*—*Institut de Droit Comparé.* **5402**. c. **9**.

BARBIER (PIERRE) *Dramatist.*

—— *See* BARBIER (Paul J.) and (P.) Daphnis et Chloe, *etc.* 1899. 12°. **11740**. eee. **44**.

—— *See* MOUNET-SULLY (J.) and BARBIER (P.) La Vieillesse de Don Juan, *etc.* 1906. 8°. **11737**. ee. **39**.

—— L'Enclume. Opéra-comique en un acte, *etc.* pp. 50. *Paris*, 1884. 12°. **11740**. bb. **28**. (**4**.)

—— Indigne. Drame en quatre actes. pp. 131. *Paris*, 1884. 12°. **11739**. cc. **23**. (**1**.)

—— Le Modèle. Comédie en un acte, en vers. pp. 40. *Paris*, 1886. 12°. **11739**. d. **26**. (**1**.)

BARBIER (PIERRE) *Dramatist.*

—— Struensée. Drame . . . en vers d'après le drame en prose de Jules Barbier. pp. 142. *Paris*, 1899. 12°. **11740**. ee. **51**.

—— Vincennette. Drame en un acte en vers. pp. 45. *Paris*, 1887. 12°. **11740**. c. **14**. (**2**.)

BARBIER (PIERRE LÉO) Étude medico-légale des coups et blessures à la tête. Pour servir à l'application de la jurisprudence qui régit la matière. pp. 212. *Montpellier*, 1840. 4°. **1181**. i. **18**. (**3**.)

BARBIER (PIERRE VICTOR) *See* VOIRON (B.) Un Centenaire bibliographique . . . Avec préface par A. [or rather P. V.] Barbier. 1891. 16°. **8032**. a. **4**.

—— Aix-les-Bains and its Environs. pp. 60. *C. Smith & Son: London*, [1885.] 8°. [*Illustrated Europe*. no. 58, 59.] **10108**. de. **18**.

—— Étude sur l'industrie en Savoie. Élevage des vers à soie. pp. 54. *Chambéry*, 1872. 8°. **7294**. df. **19**.

—— Étude sur les marbres et les pierres d'ornement du royaume italien. pp. 82. *Aix-les-Bains*, 1888. 8°. **7807**. aaaa. **11**. (**5**.)

—— Monographie des directions des douanes en France, *etc.* 2 tom. *Paris, Nancy*, 1890. 8°. **08229**. g. **10**.

—— Monographie historique de la Bibliothèque de Chambéry. pp. 170. *Chambéry*, 1883. 8°. **11904**. bbb. **34**.

—— Mont Cenis, *etc.* pp. 168. *C. Smith & Son: London*, [1887.] 8°. [*Illustrated Europe*. no. 73–76.] **10108**. de. **18**.

BARBIER (PIERRE VICTOR) and **PERRIN** (ANDRÉ)

—— Bibliographie savoisienne. pp. 1–224. A—Ducis. 1892[1889–99]. 4°. *See* CHAMBÉRY.—*Société Académique de Savoie, etc.* Ac. **34**/**4**.

BARBIER (RENÉ) Sang de Camargue. Roman, *etc.* pp. 279. *Paris*, 1932. 8°. **12514**. ppp. **8**.

BARBIER (S.) *Civil Engineer.* Barème de la résistance et des moments d'inertie des métaux. pp. 220. *Paris*, 1887. 8°. **8548**. b. **16**.

BARBIER (STEPHEN) An Expedient to pay the Publick Debts. With a Letter to the King, *etc.* [The former in English and French, the latter in Latin.] pp. 24. *J. Roberts: London*, 1719. 4°. **104**. e. **36**.

—— [Another copy.] An Expedient to Pay the Publick Debts, *etc.* *London*, 1719. 4°. **1474**. dd. **21**. (**8**.)

BARBIER (VICTOIRE)

—— *See* BARBIER (Alexandre N.) and (V.) Nouveau traité tout pratique de lavis et de peinture à l'aquarelle, *etc.* 1860. 4°. **7855**. g. **18**.

—— Voyage sentimentale autour d'une vieille femme. pp. 253. *Paris*, 1878. 12°. **12517**. g. **24**.

BARBIER (VICTOR) *Ancien Professeur au Séminaire de Floreffe.* *See* BARBIER (Joseph) and (V.) Histoire de l'abbaye de Floreffe, *etc.* 1880. 8°. **4782**. bbb. **8**.

—— Le Couvent des Dominicains de Namur, 1649–1797. pp. 170. *Namur*, 1899. 8°. **04685**. d. **3**.

—— Histoire du Chapitre de Sclayn. pp. 384. *Namur*, 1889. 8°. **4685**. e. **32**.

—— Histoire du monastère de Géronsart de l'ordre des Chanoines Réguliers de Saint-Augustin. pp. 360. *Namur*, 1886. 8°. **4685**. b. **1**.

BARBIER (VICTOR) *Directeur de Douanes à Chambéry.* —— *See* BARBIER (Pierre V.)

BARBIER (VICTOR) *Missionnaire Apostolique.* Dictionnaire français-annamite (annamite-français). 2 pt. *Hong Kong, Hanoi-Haiphong*, 1919, 22. 16°. **012904**. de. **13**.

—— Voyages des Espagnols au Cambodge à la fin du XVIe siècle. 2 pt. *Hanoi-Haiphong*, 1922, 23. 8°. **010056**. i. **28**.

BARBIER (VICTOR) *Secrétaire général de l'Académie d'Arras.* —— *See* ROBESPIERRE (F. M. J. I.) Œuvres complètes . . . Publiées par V. Barbier . . . et C. Vellay. 1910. 8°. [*Revue historique de la Révolution française.* janvier-mars 1910—janvier-mars 1913. Supplément.] P.P. **3555**. afb.

BARBIER (VICTOR) *Writer of Verse.* Louise. Épisode. [A poem.] pp. 96. *Paris*, 1857. 12°. **11481**. a. **2**.

—— Les Proscrites. Chansons et prophéties, 1838–1848. pp. 71. *Paris*, 1848. 12°. **011483**. e. **6**. (**2**.)

BARBIERA (CARLO RAFFAELLO) *See* MASSARANI (T.) Illustri e cari estinti. Commemorazioni ed epigrafi, scelte, ordinate e postillate da R. Barbiera, *etc.* 1907. 8°. **10633**. de. **19**.

—— *See* MASSARANI (T.) Ricordi cittadini e patriottici, scelti, ordinati e postillati da R. Barbiera, *etc.* 1908. 8°. **9165**. aa. **14**.

—— *See* NIEVO (I.) Poesie . . . Scelte e pubblicate da R. Barbiera. 1883. 16°. **11429**. aaa. **24**.

—— Ada. Studio dal vero. pp. 95. *Milano*, 1874. 16°. **12471**. aaa. **6**.

—— Artigiani poeti. Ricordi. pp. 111. *Firenze*, 1887. 8°. **10606**. aa. **10**.

—— Carlo Porta e la sua Milano. [With a portrait.] pp. xi. 423. *Firenze*, 1921. 8°. **10634**. aaa. **16**.

—— Diademi. Donne e madonne dell' 800. Con 55 illustrazioni. pp. 363. *Milano*, 1927. 8°. **10634**. bbb. **29**.

—— Figure e figurine del secolo che muore. Con notizie inedite d'archivii segreti. pp. 437. *Milano*, 1899. 8°. **012356**. h. **50**.

—— I Fratelli Bandiera. Seconda edizione. pp. 83. *Roma*, 1923. 12°. **10634**. a. **12**.

—— Grandi e piccole memorie. (Pagine di letteratura, d'arte e di storia. 1800–1910.) pp. 505. *Firenze*, 1910. 8°. **10633**. aaa. **24**.

—— Immortali e dimenticati. pp. viii. 486. *Milano*, 1901. 8°. **10601**. dg. **8**.

—— Nella città dell'amore. Passioni illustri a Venezia, 1816–1861. Con lettere inedite di Giorgio Sand, *etc.* [With portraits.] pp. viii. 234. *Milano*, 1923. 4°. **010151**. df. **12**.

—— Nella gloria e nell'ombra. Immagini e memorie dell'ottocento. [With a portrait.] pp. 388. *Milano*, 1926. 8°. **10634**. bb. **30**.

—— Passioni del Risorgimento. Nuove pagine sulla principessa Belgiojoso e il suo tempo, con documenti inediti e illustrazioni, *etc.* [With portraits.] pp. xii. 486. *Milano*, 1903. 8°. **10632**. b. **40**.

—— Poesie moderne, 1815–1887. Raccolte e ordinate da R. Barbiera, con un proemio critico e . . . biografie di poeti e poetesse. Nova edizione arricchita coi ritratti di G. Prati e G. Carducci. pp. xxiii. 596. *Milano*, 1888. 8°. **11431**. ee. **19**.

BARBIERA (CARLO RAFFAELLO)

—— Poesie veneziane, scelte e illustrate da R. Barbiera. Con uno studio sulla poesia vernacola e sul dialetto di Venezia. pp. xlvii. 308. *Firenze*, 1886. 8°. **11429. c. 16.**

—— Poeti innamorati e poesie d'amore, dal secolo XIII al XX. pp. xxxi. 330. *Milano*, 1926. 8°. **11431. bbb. 27.**

—— I Poeti italiani del secolo XIX. Antologia compilata da R. Barbiera, con proemio, biografie, note e ritratti, *etc.* pp. lii. 1346. *Milano*, 1913. 8°. **11436. h. 30.**

—— La Principessa Belgiojoso: i suoi amici e nemici, il suo tempo, *etc.* [With a portrait.] pp. 436. *Milano*, 1902. 8°. **10632. de. 37.**

—— Ricordi delle terre dolorose [i.e. Italia irredenta]. Con 32 incisioni, *etc.* pp. 367. *Milano*, 1918. 8°. **10130. df. 20.**

—— Il Salotto della contessa Maffei e la società milanese 1834–1886, *etc.* [With a portrait.] pp. 350. *Milano*, 1895. 8°. **10633. aa. 14.**

—— Venezia nel canto de' suoi poeti, scelti e illustrati da R. Barbiera. Con pagine di musica popolare. pp. xxxi. 321. *Milano*, 1925. 8°. **11436. d. 52.**

—— Verso l'ideale. Profili di letteratura e d'arte, *etc.* pp. 436. *Milano*, 1905. 8°. **11851. aaa. 21.**

—— Vite ardenti nel teatro—1700–1900—da archivii e da memorie, *etc.* [With plates.] pp. 374. *Milano*, 1931. 8°. **11796. a. 23.**

—— Voci e volti del passato, 1800–1900. Da archivi segreti di stato e da altre fonti. pp. 372. *Milano*, 1920. 8°. **9168. cc. 8.**

—— Volo di memorie veneziane, 1797—1933. pp. 317. *Milano*, 1933. 8°. **9168. cc. 25**

BARBIERA (RAFFAELLO) *See* BARBIERA (Carlo R.)

BARBIER D'AUCOUR (JEAN) *See* RACINE (J.) [*Miscellanea.*] Abrégé de l'histoire de Port-Royal . . . augmentée de deux lettres . . . à l'auteur des Hérésies imaginaires, avec les réponses de MM. Dubois & Barbier d'Aucourt, *etc.* 1770. 16°. **4092. d. 3.**

—— Apollon charlatan, critique allégorique. [A satire in verse on Racine.] *See* RACINE (J.) [*Works.*] Œuvres de Racine, *etc.* tom. 3. 1750. 12°. **640. d. 20.**

—— Au Roy sur le commerce, ode. *See* CARNANDET (J.) Le Trésor des pièces rares . . . de la Champagne, *etc.* vol. 1. 1863, *etc.* 8°. **10173. bbb. 17.**

—— Mémoires (pour Jacques Lebrun). 1829. *See* FRANCE. —*Barreau.* Annales du Barreau français, *etc.* tom. 2. pt. 2. 1822, *etc.* 8°. **1131. h. 5.**

—— Manifeste, ou la preconisation en vers burlesques d'un nouveau livre [by Maximin of Aix] intitulé, Reflexions sur les veritez evangeliques contre la traduction, et les traducteurs de Mons, *etc.* [By J. Barbier d'Aucour.] pp. 86. 1681. 8°. *See* MAXIMIN, *Capuchin.* **11481. aaa. 35.**

—— Onguant pour la brulure, ou le secret pour empescher les Iesuites de bruler les liures. [A satire in verse, by J. Barbier d'Aucour.] pp. 47. [1665?] 4°. *See* JESUITS. [*Appendix.*] **1073. i. 6. (6.)**

—— [Another edition.] pp. 76. 1569 [1669]. 12°. *See* JESUITS. [*Appendix.*] **11474. aaa. 1. (2.)**

—— [Another edition.] pp. 60. 1582 [1682]. 12°. *See* JESUITS. [*Appendix.*] **4092. a. 25. (2.)**

BARBIER D'AUCOUR (JEAN)

—— [Another edition.] *See* JANSENISTS. Les Enluminures du fameux almanach des PP. Jesuites, *etc.* 1683. 8°. **860. d. 17.**

—— Sentimens de Cleante sur les entretiens d'Ariste et d'Eugene [of D. Bouhours. By J. Barbier d'Aucour]. Seconde édition. Reveüe et corrigée. pp. 249. 1671. 8°. *See* CLEANTE. **1089. c. 24.**

—— Quatriéme édition revue & corrigée: où l'on a joint les deux factums . . . pour Jacques le Brun. pp. xxi. 494. *Paris*, 1730. 12°. **1089. c. 25.**

—— [Another edition.] Quatriéme édition, revûe & corrigée, *etc.* pp. xxvii. 494. *Paris*, 1738. 12°. **245. g. 35.**

BARBIER DE LA SERRE (GABRIEL G. ANATOLE) *See* HAUDENT (G.) Le Variable discours de la vie humaine . . . Publié avec introduction par G. Barbier de la Serre. 1903. 8°. **Ac. 8938/65.**

BARBIER DE MEYNARD (ADRIEN CASIMIR) *See* BARBIER DE MEYNARD (Charles A. C.)

BARBIER DE MEYNARD (CHARLES ADRIEN CASIMIR) *See* 'ABD AL-RAḤMĀN IBN ISMĀ'ĪL, called ABU SHĀMAH. Le Livre des deux jardins, *etc.* [Translated by C. A. C. Barbier de Meynard.] 1898. fol. [*Recueil des historiens des Croisades. Historiens orientaux.* tom. 4.] **1899.m.31.**

—— *See* AḤMAD RĀSHID. Notice sur l'Arabie méridionale d'après un document turc. [Extracts from a historical work by Aḥmad Rāshid, translated with an introduction.] Par A. C. Barbier de Meynard. 1883. 8°. [*École Spéciale des Langues Orientales Vivantes. Mélanges orientaux, etc.*] **14003. i. 16.**

—— *See* 'ALĪ IBN ḤUSAIN, *al-Mas'ūdī.* Les Prairies d'or. Texte et traduction par C. Barbier de Meynard et Pavet de Courteille. 1861, *etc.* 8°. **14003. b. 4.**

—— *See* FATḤ 'ALĪ, *Ākhund-zādah.* L'Ours et le voleur. Comédie . . . Accompagnée d'une traduction par A. C. Barbier de Meynard. 1889. 8°. [*Recueil de textes et de traductions publié par les professeurs de l'École des Langues orientales vivantes.* tom. 1.] **14003. i. 23.**

—— *See* FIRDAUSĪ. Le Livre des rois . . . Publié, traduit et commenté par J. Mohl. [tom. 7 completed by C. A. C. Barbier de Meynard.] 1876, *etc.* fol. **14773.m.2.**

—— *See* GOLDZIHER (I.) Adrien C. Barbier de Meynard és Michael Jan de Goeje külső tagok emlékezete, *etc.* 1909. 8°. [*A Magyar Tudományos Akadémia elhúnyt tagjai fölött tartott emlékbeszédek.* köt. 14. sz. 7.] **Ac. 825/131.**

—— *See* HUBER (Charles) Journal d'un voyage en Arabie, *etc.* [Edited by C. A. C. Barbier de Meynard and others.] 1891. 8°. **10075. i. 3.**

—— *See* JA'FAR IBN SA'ĪD, *al-Ḥillī.* Droit musulman. Recueil de lois, *etc.* [Edited and revised by C. A. C. Barbier de Meynard.] 1871, *etc.* 8°. **14529. b. 1.**

—— *See* MAḤMŪD IBN AḤMAD (Badr al Dīn) *al 'Ainī.* Extraits du livre intitulé le Collier de perles, *etc.* [With a French translation by C. A. C. Barbier de Meynard.] 1887. fol. [*Recueil des historiens des Croisades. Historiens orientaux.* tom. 2. pt. 1.] **1899.m.31.**

—— *See* MAḤMŪD IBN 'UMAR, *al-Zamakhsharī.* Les Colliers d'or . . . Texte arabe suivi d'une traduction . . . par C. Barbier de Meynard. 1876. 8°. **14576. b. 12.**

—— *See* SA'DĪ. [*Būstān.—French.*] Le Boustan . . . Traduit . . . avec une introduction et des notes par A. C. Barbier de Meynard. 1880. 12°. **757. b. 31.**

BARBIER DE MEYNARD (CHARLES ADRIEN CASIMIR)

—— *See* 'UMAR IBN AHMAD, called IBN AL-'ADĪM. Extraits de la Chronique d'Alep. [With a French translation by C. A. C. Barbier de Meynard.] 1884. fol. [*Recueil des historiens des Croisades. Historiens orientaux.* tom. 3.] **1899.m.31.**

—— *See* 'UMAR IBN AHMAD, called IBN AL-'ADĪM. Extraits du dictionnaire biographique de Kemal ed-Dîn. [With a French translation by C. A. C. Barbier de Meynard.] 1884. fol. [*Recueil des historiens des Croisades. Historiens orientaux.* tom. 3.] **1899.m.31.**

—— *See* YAKŪT IBN 'ABD ALLĀH, *al-Hamawī.* Dictionnaire géographique . . . de la Perse . . . extrait du Módjem el-Bouldan de Yakout . . . par C. Barbier de Meynard. 1861. 8°. **757. h. 39.**

—— *See* YUSŪF IBN KIZ-ŪGHLĪ, called SIBT IBN AL-JAUZĪ. Extraits du Mirât ez-Zèmân. [With a French translation by C. A. C. Barbier de Meynard.] 1884. fol. [*Recueil des historiens des Croisades. Historiens orientaux.* tom. 3.] **1899.m.31.**

—— *See* YUSŪF IBN TAGHRĪ-BIRDĪ. Extraits du Nodjoûm ez-Zahireh. [With a French translation by C. A. C. Barbier de Meynard.] 1884. fol. [*Recueil des historiens des Croisades. Historiens orientaux.* tom. 3.] **1899.m.31.**

—— Considérations sur l'histoire ottomane, d'après un document turc (l'histoire de la Turquie de Djevdet-Pacha). [With extracts from the text.] *See* PARIS.—*École Spéciale des Langues Orientales Vivantes, etc.* Nouveaux mélanges orientaux, *etc.* 1886. 8°. **14003. i. 18.**

—— Dictionnaire turc-français. Supplément aux dictionnaires publiés jusqu'à ce jour, *etc.* 2 vol. *Paris,* 1881, 86. 8°. [*Publications de l'École des Langues Orientales Vivantes.* sér. 2. vol. 4, 5.] **14003. i. 21.**

—— La Poésie en Perse. Leçon d'ouverture faite au Collége de France, le 4 décembre 1876. pp. 74. *Paris,* 1877. 12°. **11840. bbb. 5.**

—— Surnoms et sobriquets dans la littérature arabe . . . Extrait du Journal asiatique, *etc.* pp. 277. *Paris,* 1907. 8°. **012904. i. 27.**

BARBIER DE MONTAULT (XAVIER) *See* DILLON (Arthur R.) successively *Bishop of Evreux* and *Archbishop of Toulouse, etc.* Vendataire au plus offrant et dernier enchérisseur, des meubles ayant appartenu au citoyen Arthur Richard Dillon, émigré, l'an 1792, *etc.* [Edited by X. Barbier de Montault.] [1891.] 8°. **7706. f. 19. (6.)**

—— *See* DROCHON (J. E. B.) Nouaillé et Ste Marie-d'Availles. [With notes by X. Barbier de Montault.] 1885, *etc.* fol. [*Paysages et monuments du Poitou.* tom. 2.] **1790. c. 1.**

—— *See* PALUSTRE (L.) and BARBIER DE MONTAULT (X.) Orfèvrerie et émaillerie limousines. [1887.] 4°. [*PALUSTRE (L.) Mélanges d'art et d'archéologie.* année 2.] **7705. h. 7.**

—— *See* PALUSTRE (L.) and BARBIER DE MONTAULT (X.) Le Trésor de Trèves. [1886.] 4°. [*PALUSTRE (L.) Mélanges d'art et d'archéologie.* année 1.] **7705. h. 7.**

—— *See* PERIODICAL PUBLICATIONS.—*Paris.* Annales archéologiques, *etc.* (tom. 28. Table analytique et méthodique par Mgr X. Barbier de Montault.) 1844, *etc.* 4°. **P.P. 1931. da.**

—— *See* PERIODICAL PUBLICATIONS.—*Poitiers.* Revue d'archéologie poitevine publiée sous la direction de Mgr. X. Barbier de Montault. 1898, *etc.* 8°. **P.P. 1931. bd.**

BARBIER DE MONTAULT (XAVIER)

—— *See* SALIGNAC DE LA MOTHE FÉNELON (F. de) *Archbishop of Cambrai.* Lettres inédites . . . Publiées par . . . X. Barbier de Montault. [1863.] 12°. **4866. aaa. 35.**

—— Œuvres complètes. 16 tom. *Poitiers,* 1889–1902. 8°. **12238. g. 3.**

—— L'Année liturgique à Rome. pp. 224. *Paris,* 1857. 16°. **3475. a. 56.**

—— L'Appareil de lumière de la cathédrale de Tours. 1883. *See* FRANCE.—*Société Française d'Archéologie.* Séances générales, *etc.* session 49. 1846, *etc.* 8°. **Ac. 5296/2.**

—— Application des règles de la graphologie. Adrien Varinard jugé d'après son écriture. *See* VARINARD (A.) Cours de graphologie en 7 leçons, *etc.* 1889. 8°. **7946. b. 34.**

—— L'Architecture et la décoration à l'abbaye cistercienne de Chatelliers du XIIe au XVIIIe siècle. 1892. *See* POITIERS.—*Société des Antiquaires de l'Ouest.* Mémoires. sér. 2. tom. 14. 1836, *etc.* 8°. **Ac. 5326.**

—— Bibliographie. Histoire de la verrerie et de l'émaillerie par E. Garnier. Extrait du Bulletin de la Société archéologique de Tarn-et-Garonne. [A review by X. Barbier de Montault.] pp. 11. *Montauban,* 1886. 8°. **7704. g. 43. (9.)**

—— La Bibliothèque Vaticane et ses annexes: le Musée chrétien, la Salle du moyen âge, les Chambres Borgia, etc. pp. 280. 1867. 8°. *See* VATICAN.—*Library.* **010136. df. 69.**

—— La Cathédrale d'Anagni. pp. 99. *Paris,* 1858. 4°. **7816. b. 6.**

—— Les Chambres Borgia au Vatican. (Extrait du journal Le Prêtre.) pp. 15. *Arras,* [1898.] 8°. **07806. i. 3. (5.)**

—— Le Château de Dissais. pp. 12. 1887. *See* POITOU. Paysages et monuments du Poitou, *etc.* tom. 3. 1890, *etc.* fol. **1790. c. 1.**

—— Collection des décrets authentiques des sacrées congrégations romaines. [Edited by X. Barbier de Montault.] 10 vol.

> Sacrée Congrégation des Indulgences. [Based on the collection compiled by L. Prinzivalli in 1862.]
> S. Congrégation des Rites. 8 tom.
> Sacrée Congrégation de l'Immunité. [The collection compiled by P. A. Riccius in 1708.]

Paris, [1868–85.] 12°. **5061. aaa. 22.**

—— Le Conclave et le pape. pp. viii. 175. *Poitiers, Paris,* 1878. 12°. **5018. a. 11.**

—— Consécration de la chapelle de Sainte-Marie-de-la-Conception à Combrée. pp. 37. *Angers,* 1858. 8°. **4632. b. 6.**

—— Le Costume et les usages ecclésiastiques selon la tradition romaine. 2 tom. *Paris,* [1898, 1901.] 8°. **2009.b.**

—— Croix-reliquaire de l'église de Saint-Florent-lès-Saumur. (Extrait de la Revue de l'Anjou et du Maine.) pp. 6. *Angers,* [1860?] 8°. **4633. i. 19. (3.)**

—— Description de la basilique de S. Paul hors-les-murs, à Rome. pp. 79. *Rome,* 1866. 8°. **7808. a. 29. (1.)**

—— Les Fers à hosties de l'arrondissement de Confolens, Charente. 1896. *See* ANGOULÊME.—*Société Archéologique et Historique de la Charente.* Bulletin. sér. 6. tom. 5. 1845, *etc.* 8°. **Ac. 5286.**

BARBIER DE MONTAULT (Xavier)

—— Les Fêtes de Noël et de l'Épiphanie à Rome, avec une description détaillée du Pontifical du Pape dans la basilique de S. Pierre. pp. 56. *Rome*, 1865. 8°. **3477**. aaa. **4**.

—— Les Fêtes de Pâques à Rome, avec une description détaillée du Pontifical du Pape dans la basilique de St. Pierre. pp. 143. *Rome*, 1866. 8°. **3475**. aa. **48**.

—— Les Inscriptions cimétériales de Senlis et de Saint-Léonard. 1895. *See* Beauvais.—*Société Académique d'Archéologie, Sciences et Arts du Département de l'Oise.* Mémoires. tom. 16. 1847, *etc.* 8°. Ac. **278/2**.

—— Menigoute et les Châtelliers. pp. 16. 1892. *See* Poitou. Paysages et monuments du Poitou, *etc.* tom. 6. 1890, *etc.* fol. **1790**. c. **1**.

—— [La Mosaïque du dôme à Aix-la-Chapelle.] Die Mosaiken im Münster zu Aachen . . . Aus dem Französischen übersetzt von And. Hub. Körner. Mit einem kurzen Vorwort von . . . F. Bock. Nebst 6 Holzschnitten. pp. iii. 78. *Köln & Neuss*, 1872. 8°. **7709**. g. **40**.

—— L'Octave des SS. Apôtres Pierre et Paul à Rome, avec une description détaillée du Pontifical du Pape dans la basilique de S. Pierre. pp. 198. *Rome*, 1866. 8°. **3475**. aa. **47**.

—— Peintures claustrales des monastères de Rome. pp. 52. *Paris*, 1860. 8°. **7707**. aaa. **44**. (**6**.)

—— Rapport sur la vraie-croix découverte à Saint-Florent le 23 avril 1858. (Extrait de la Revue de l'Anjou et du Maine.) pp. 18. *Angers*, [1858.] 8°. **4633**. i. **19**. (**2**.)

—— Le Sacré Collége. Portraits, biographies et autographes des cardinaux. *Paris*, [1870.] fol. [*Actes et histoire du Concile Œcuménique de Rome.* tom. 2.] Cup. **652**. b. **1**.

—— Le Sacré-Collége des cardinaux de la sainte Église Romaine. pp. 156. *Poitiers & Paris*, 1879. 12°. **4050**. aaa. **7**.

—— Les Souterrains et le trésor de S. Pierre, à Rome, ou description des objets d'art et d'archéologie qu'ils renferment. pp. 91. *Rome*, 1866. 8°. **4605**. a. **9**.

—— Le Spolium de l'évêque de Limoges, en 1390. 1894. *See* Limoges.—*Société Archéologique et Historique du Limousin.* Bulletin. tom. 41, 42. 1846, *etc.* 8°. Ac. **5312**.

—— Tableau raisonné des pierres et marbres antiques employés à la construction et décoration des monuments de Rome. (Extrait du Bulletin monumental publié à Caen par M. de Caumont.) pp. 42. *Caen*, 1869. 8°. **7706**. bb. **4**. (**3**.)

—— Notices archéologiques sur les tentures et les tapisseries de la cathédrale d'Angers. Par M. L. de Farcy. [A reprint of a work entitled "Les Tapisseries du Sacre d'Angers," by X. Barbier de Montault, with additions by L. de Farcy.] pp. 138 [108]. *Angers*, 1875. 8°. **7743**. bbb. **7**.

—— Traité d'iconographie chrétienne . . . Dessins par M. Henri Nodet. 2 tom. *Paris*, 1890. 8°. **2260**. d. **3**.

—— Traité de la visite pastorale selon la méthode de Benoit xiii. pp. iv. 315. *Paris*, 1877. 8°. **5063**. bbb. **4**.

—— Traité pratique de la construction, de l'ameublement et de la décoration des églises selon les règles canoniques et les traditions romaines. Avec un appendice sur le costume ecclésiastique, *etc.* 2 tom. *Paris*, 1878. 8°. **3476**. g. **5**.

—— Le Trésor liturgique de Cherves en Angoumois. [With a portfolio of 12 plates.] 1898. *See* Angoulême.—*Société Archéologique et Historique de la Charente.* Bulletin. sér. 6. tom. 7. 1845, *etc.* 8°. Ac. **5286**.

BARBIER DE MONTAULT (Xavier)

—— Le Vase antique de Saint-Savin. 1897. *See* Poitiers. —*Société des Antiquaires de l'Ouest.* Mémoires. sér. 2. tom. 19. 1836, *etc.* 8°. Ac. **5326**.

BARBIER DE TINAN ( ) *See* Toaldo (G.) [Dei conduttori per preservare gli edifizj da' fulmini.] Mémoires sur les conducteurs . . . Traduits de l'italien avec des notes & des additions par Mr. Barbier de Tinan, *etc.* 1779. 8°. **8755**. b. **48**.

BARBIER DE VÉMARS (Joseph Nicolas) *See* Barbier Vémars.

BARBIER DU BOCAGE (Jean Denis) *See* Barbié du Bocage.

BARBIER DU FAŸ (Guillaume Michel Étienne) *See* Bourgevin de Vialart ( ) *Countess de Saint-Morys.* Dénonciation contre Guillaume-Michel-Étienne Barbier, dit du Faÿ, *etc.* 1817. 8°. **1141**. h. **18**. (**17**.)

BARBIER-DUVAL ( ) L'Art du confiseur moderne, *etc.* *Paris*, 1879. 12°. **07943**. l. **46**.

BARBIERE (Simone) *Mastro, pseud.* [i.e. — Bocelli.]

—— *See* Pezza (C.) Il Ciabattino Mastro Leonardo e'l Barbiere Mastro Simone citati . . . al tribunale della lingua, *etc.* [A criticism of "Osservazioni di Mastro Simone Barbiere sopra l'Annotatore degli errori di lingua" of M. Ponza.] 1831. 8°. **11805**. d. **40**. (**1**.)

BARBIERI (Agostino) Monografia della arteria vertebrale . . . Con 14 figure, *etc.* pp. 115. *Milano*, 1867–68. fol. **7406**. i. **4**.

BARBIERI (Aloisius) *See* Barbieri (Luigi)

BARBIERI (Aloysius) Synopsis entozoorum hominis ad mentem Bremseri, Rudolphii, aliorumque, additis ipsorum ætiologia, semiotica, ac therapia speciali, *etc.* pp. 32. *Ticini Regii*, [1827.] 8°. **7383**.* b. **14**. (**10**.)

BARBIERI (Antonio)

—— La Vis comica in Terenzio, *etc.* (Tesi.) pp. 299. *Arona*, 1951. 8°. **011313**. aa. **43**.

BARBIERI (Augusto) Elementi di scienza dell' amministrazione. pp. 458. *Bologna*, 1888. 8°. **8009**. i. **22**.

—— Lo Stato ed il comune nelle quistioni della tutela amministrativa e della nomina del sindaco. Studio. pp. 270. *Bologna*, 1886. 8°. **8033**. g. **28**.

BARBIERI (Carlo) Direzione pe' viaggiatori in Italia, colla notizia di tutte le poste e loro prezzi. Terza edizione ricorretta . . . ed accresciuta, *etc.* (Direction pour les voiageurs en Italie, *etc.*) [With maps.] pp. xii. ff. 24. pl. 24. *Bologna*, 1773. 8°. **575**. f. **28**.

BARBIERI (Carlo) *Artist.*

—— Carlo Barbieri. Seconda edizione, *etc.* [Reproductions. Edited, with an introduction, by Giovanni Scheiwiller. With a portrait.] pp. 14. pl. xxxix. *Milano*, 1946. 8°. **7868**. a. **40**.
Arte moderna italiana. no. 36.

BARBIERI (Carlo) *Count.* *See* Certani (G. F.) Riti della messa solenne . . . Con note [by Count C. Barbieri], *etc.* 1750. 8°. **845**. i. **1**.

—— Canzonette ed arietti sacre e morali su quasi tutte le migliori arie e musicali e correnti, *etc.* [Compiled by Count C. Barbieri.] pp. 336. 1786. 12°. *See* Canzonette. **11429**. bb. **21**.

—— Memorie della vita e virtù del servo di Dio Ercole Maria Giuseppe Isolani . . . Raccolte da C. Barbieri. pp. 40. *Venezia*, 1761. 4°. **4865**. ff. **34**.

BARBIERI (CARLO) *Count.*

—— Orazione panegirica in lode di San Francesco di Sales, *etc.* pp. 56. *Padova,* 1742. 8°. **4823. b. 13.**

BARBIERI (CONTARDO)

—— *See* VIDA (M. H.) *Bishop of Alba.* La "Poetica" del Vida tradotta da C. Barbieri. 1943, *etc.* [*Bollettino storico cremonese.* ser. 2. anno 8. vol. 13, anni 9/10. vol. 14, anni 11/12. vol. 15, *etc.*] **P.P. 3556. ni.**

BARBIERI (DARIO) Per la grande Roma. Formazione e sviluppo delle grandi città moderne, *etc.* pp. xi. 273. pl. VIII. *Roma, Milano,* 1927. 8°. **010151. g. 12.**

BARBIERI (DOMENICO) *See* ENTIO (L.) Il Trionfo della porchetta . . . Con vna descrittione di tutto quello di fece in tal giorno l'anno passato 1627 . . . Data in luce da D. Barbieri. 1628. 8°. **1071. g. 7. (73.)**

BARBIERI (DOMENICO ANDREA) *See* SOLE. Del sole bisognevole di alimento, e dell' oceano abile a procacciarglielo. Dissertazione fisico-matematica. [By J. Belgrado? Edited by D. A. Barbieri.] [1783.] 4°. **117. c. 9.**

BARBIERI (FEDERICO) Le Rime e le commedie meneghine di Carlo Maria Maggi. pp. 129. *Milano,* 1917. 8°. **11850. aaa. 42.**

BARBIERI (FLAMINIO) Catechismo per la pratica dell' apicoltura . . . Seconda edizione . . . aumentata dall' autore. pp. 139. *Milano,* 1874. 8°. **7297. a. 29.**

BARBIERI (FORTUNATO)

—— Il Pilota aviatore. Come s'impara a pilotare. 136 figure . . . Seconda edizione riveduta. pp. viii. 232. *Milano,* 1938. 8°. **08770. aa. 45.**

BARBIERI (FRANCESCO) Un Bacio al diavolo. Melodramma in un atto. pp. 19. *Milano,* 1884. 12°. **11715. bb. 5. (6.)**

BARBIERI (FRANCISCO ASENJO) *See* ASENJO BARBIERI.

BARBIERI (GAETANO) *See* DEFOE (D.) Vita ed avventure di Robinson Crusoè. Versione dall' inglese di G. Barbieri. 1869. 16°. **12611. de. 22.**

—— *See* DELAVIGNE (C. J. F.) Il Paria. Tragedia . . . Trasportata in versi italiani dal professore G. Barbieri. 1823. 8°. [*Repertorio scelto ad uso de' teatri italiani.* tom. 1.] **11712. aaa. 16.**

—— *See* FABRE D'EGLANTINE (P. F. N.) Il Filinto di Molière . . . Traduzione del professore G. Barbieri. 1823. 8°. [*Repertorio scelto ad uso de' teatri italiani.* tom. 1.] **11712. aaa. 16.**

—— *See* GENSOUL (M. A. J.) and NAUDET (J. A. N.) Molière in famiglia. Commedia . . . Ridotta ad uso delle scene italiane . . . dal professore G. Barbieri. 1823. 8°. [*Repertorio scelto ad uso de' teatri italiani.* tom. 5.] **11712. aaa. 16.**

—— *See* MAZZONI (M.) The Biography of an Unknown. (Biografia d'uno sconosciuto. Versione di G. Barbieri.) 1839. 8°. **12355. bbb. 23. (3.)**

—— *See* PICARD (L. B.) Due case in una casa. Commedia . . . dei signori Picard, Wafflard e Fulgence. Traduzione del professore G. Barbieri. 1823. 8°. [*Repertorio scelto ad uso de' teatri italiani.* tom. 1.] **11712. aaa. 16.**

—— *See* PICARD (L. B.) Due famiglie in una casa . . . Traduzione del professore G. Barbieri. 1826. 12°. **11716. a. 6 21.**

—— *See* SCOTT (*Sir* W.) *Bart.* [*Ivanhoe.*] Ivanhoe . . . Versione del professore G. Barbieri, *etc.* 1840. 8°. **12643. s. 5.**

BARBIERI (GAETANO)

—— *See* SCOTT (*Sir* W.) *Bart.* [*Letters on Demonology and Witchcraft.*] Su la negromanzia . . . Versione con note di G. Barbieri. 1839. 12°. **012611. h. 13.**

—— *See* SHAKESPEARE (W.) [*Othello.—Italian.*] Il Moro di Venezia, Otello, *etc.* [Translated from the French version of Alfred de Vigny into Italian prose by G. Barbieri.] 1838. 8°. **11763. de. 3.**

—— *See* SIMONDE DE SISMONDI (J. C. L.) Nuovi principj di economia politica . . . Traduzione del professore G. Barbieri. 1819. 8°. **8205. aaa. 38.**

—— *See* WAFFLARD (A. J. M.) and FULGENCE, *pseud.* Il Celibe e l'ammogliato. Commedia . . . tradotta dal prof. G. Barbieri. 1823. 8°. [*Repertorio scelto ad uso de' teatri italiani.* tom. 4.] **11712. aaa. 16.**

—— Elisabetta al castello di Kenilworth. Commedia in cinque atti. [Founded on Scott's "Kenilworth."] 1824. *See* infra: Repertorio scelto ad uso de' teatri italiani, *etc.* tom. 7. 1823, *etc.* 8°. **11712. aaa. 16.**

—— Notizie biografiche di M. F. Malibran. [With a portrait.] pp. 54. *Milano,* 1836. 8°. **10630. d. 29.**

—— Il Pro e contro, ossia il Processo del matrimonio . . . Imitazione di altra commedia collo stesso titolo del signor Sewrin. 1823. *See* infra: Repertorio scelto ad uso de' teatri italiani, *etc.* tom. 6. 1823, *etc.* 8°. **11712. aaa. 16.**

—— Repertorio scelto ad uso de' teatri italiani. Compilato dal professore G. Barbieri. 8 tom. *Milano,* 1823, 24. 8°. **11712. aaa. 16.**

BARBIERI (GINO) *Artist.*

—— *See* BRUNO (G.) *Nolano.* [*Selections.*] In tristitia hilaris, in hilaritate tristis . . . Con xilografie di G. Barbieri. 1922. 8°. **08465. df. 2.**

BARBIERI (GINO) *Professor of Economic History, University of Bari.*

—— Economia e politica nel ducato di Milano, 1386–1535. pp. 255. *Milano,* 1938. 8°. **8033. l. 16.**
Pubblicazioni dell' Università Cattolica del Sacro Cuore. ser. 3. vol. 18.

—— Note e documenti di storia economica italiana per l'età medioevale e moderna. pp. viii. 135. *Milano,* 1940. 8°. **8218. d. 7.**

BARBIERI (GIOVANNI ALUIGI DE') *See* BARBIERI (Giovanni Luigi)

BARBIERI (GIOVANNI BATTISTA) Per quali cause i medici non andarono d'accordo nell' attribuire l'azione alla digitale purpurea, discorso inaugurale, *etc.* pp. 15. *Padova,* 1824. 8°. **7306. h. 2. (19.)**

BARBIERI (GIOVANNI FRANCESCO) called *Il Guercino.* *See* ATTI (G.) Intorno alla vita e alle opere di Gianfrancesco Barbieri, *etc.* [With a list of Barbieri's works.] 1861. 8°. **10631. cc. 33.**

—— *See* BOLOGNINI AMORINI (A.) *Marquis.* Vita di Francesco Barbieri, *etc.* 1839. 8°. **1402. h. 21. (4.)**

—— *See* CALVI (J. A.) Notizie della vita, e delle opere del cavaliere Gioan Francesco Barbieri, *etc.* 1808. 4°. **787. i. 2.**

—— *See* GUALANDI (M. A.) Memorie intorno alla vita di Giovan-Francesco Barbieri, *etc.* 1839. 4°. **7856. d. 27.**

—— *See* JANITSCHEK (H.) Die Malerschule von Bologna . . . Guercino. [1879.] 8°. [*Kunst und Künstler des Mittelalters.* Abt. 2. Bd. 3. no. 75–77.] **2262. f. 3.**

BARBIERI (GIOVANNI FRANCESCO) called *Il Guercino*.

—— *See* MAHON (Denis) Notes on the Young Guercino, *etc.* [With reproductions.] [1937.] 4°. **7863.** s. **25.**

—— *See* MAHON (Denis) Studies in Seicento Art and Theory. (Guercino's change of style: its nature and origins.) 1947. 8°. [*Studies of the Warburg Institute.* vol. 16.] **Ac.4569/6.(16.)**

—— *See* ORSINI (A.) La Casa del Guercino in Bologna. 1891. 8°. **10601.** ff. **6.** (**8.**)

—— *See* ORSINI (A.) Il Primo affresco del Guercino. 1890. 8°. **7807.** k. **18.** (**9.**)

—— Drawings by Guercino. By Archibald G. B. Russell. pp. 71. *E. Arnold & Co.: London,* 1923. 4°. **7808.** t. **20.**

—— Liure de portraiture de Io. François Barbier. (Second liure de portraiture.) 2 pt. pl. 44. [*Paris,*] 1642, 43. *obl.* 4°. **683.** e. **22.** (**1.**)

—— Raccolta di alcuni disegni del Barberi da Cento detto il Guercino, incisi in rame [by Bartolozzi and others] e presentati al singolar merito del Sig. Tommaso Jenkins . . . dall' architetto . . . Gio Battista Piranesi. [*Paris,* 1837?] fol. **1899.d.17.(1.)**
The plates are numbered 917–948, *and form part of the collected works of the Piranesi. The frontispiece and three of the plates are etched by G. B. Piranesi.*

—— Recueil d'estampes d'après les desseins de Fr. Barbieri dit Guercino qui n'ont pas encore été gravées . . . Par A. Bartsch. pl. XL. [*Paris,* 1837?] fol. **1899.d.17.(2.)**
The plates are numbered 949a–971, *and form part of the collected works of the Piranesi.*

BARBIERI (GIOVANNI FRANCESCO) *of Verona. See* GRAY (T.) *the Poet.* [*Elegy written in a Country Churchyard.—Translations.*] L'Elegia . . . sopra un cimitero di campagna tradotta . . . in più lingue, *etc.* [Including a translation into Latin verse by G. F. Barbieri.] 1817. 8°. **11632.** cc. **4.**

—— —— 1843. 8°. **1465.** k. **23.**

BARBIERI (GIOVANNI LUIGI) Della morte et dell' anime separate dialoghi otto . . . Con vna nuoua aggiunta dell' istesso autore di XIX. dialoghi, cioè dieci del Paradiso, & noue dell' Inferno, *etc.* pp. 368. *Gli Heredi di Gio. Rossi: Bologna,* 1600. 8°. **846.** l. **17.**

BARBIERI (GIOVANNI MARIA) *See* BERTONI (Giulio) Giovanni Maria Barbieri e gli studi romanzi nel sec. XVI. 1905. 8°. **11826.** o. **31.**

—— Dell' origine della poesia rimata . . . Con annotazioni illustrata dal cav. ab. Girolamo Tiraboschi. pp. 187. *Modena,* 1790. 4°. **839.** l. **20.**

—— La Guerra d'Atila flagello di Dio. Tratta dallo Archiuo de i Prencipi d'Esti. [By G. M. Barbieri. Stated by him in his preface to be an abridgment of Nicolo da Casola's Provençal version of a Latin chronicle by one Thomas de Aquileia, a writer otherwise unknown and probably apocryphal.] ff. 127. 1568. 4°. *See* THOMAS, *de Aquileia.* **659.** c. **1.**

—— [Another edition.] [Edited by F. Cavazzoni Pederzini, with notes by Count Giovanni Galvani and the life of G. M. Barbieri by Ludovico Barbieri.] pp. xxv. 384. 1843. 16°. *See* THOMAS, *de Aquileia.* **1440.** a. **13.**

—— Il Treperuno . . . In risposta a tre sonetti di Annibal Caro contro il Castelvetro. *See* ITALIANS. Alcune lettere d'illustri italiani, *etc.* 1827. 8°. **T. 2494.** (**2.**)

BARBIERI (GIROLAMO) Le False opinioni, opera scenica. pp. 84. *G. Monti: Bologna,* 1670. 12°. **638.** a. **38.** (**1.**)

BARBIERI (GIUSEPPE) *Professore da Bassano.*

—— *See* BASEGGIO (G. B.) Della vita e degli scritti di Giuseppe Barbieri, orazione, *etc.* 1853. 8°. **10630.** cc. **26.** (**6.**)

—— *See* BERNARDONI (G.) Per la edizione fatta in Firenze di versi e prose di Giuseppe Parini . . . epistola di G. Bernardoni al professore abbate G. Barbieri . . . e la risposta di esso. 1847. 8°. **11436.** d. **8.**

—— *See* PETRARCA (F.) [*Two or more Works.—Latin and Italian.*] Francisci Patrarchae poëmata minora quae exstant omnia, *etc.* (vol. 2. sezione 8. Al Levis detto Socrate e per Marco figlio di Bernabò Visconti epistole due volgarizzate dal prof. G. Barbieri.) 1829, *etc.* 8°. **11421.** dd. **20.**

—— *See* TOMMASEO (N.) Osservazioni sopra le lettere critiche di Giuseppe Barbieri. 1824. 8°. **11824.** de. **31.**

—— Opere. 3 vol. *Padova,* 1811. 8°. **12225.** e. **5.**

—— Orazione detta nei funerali dell' ab. Cesarotti.—Epistola ad Angelo Mazza.—Memorie intorno alla vita ed agli studj dell' abate Cesarotti.—Elogio dell' abate Cesarotti, *etc.* 1813. *See* CESAROTTI (M.) Opere, *etc.* vol. 40. 1800, *etc.* 8°. **245.** l. **42.**

—— Saggi di sacra eloquenza del professore G. Barbieri . . . che comprendono anche l'ultima benedizione da esso data ai Milanesi . . . Raccolta e pubblicata dallo stenografo Alfonso Dupuy. Vi è unito un ragionamento di Francesco Regli, un frammento di lettera, un carme di Girolamo Festari, un sermone d'Andrea Cajo, *etc.* pp. 104. *Milano,* 1833. 12°. **1367.** h. **17.** (**9.**)

—— Orazioni quaresimali. [With a portrait.] 8 vol. *Milano,* 1837, 38. 8°. **1112.** g. **18, 19.**

—— Avvento predicato in San Fedele a Milano l'anno MDCCCXLIII. Con altri discorsi. pp. 384. *Italia* [*Milan?*], 1846. 12°. **4424.** aa. **4.**

—— Per la laurea in legge del Signor Giovanni Tessier. Lettere inedite dell' ab. prof. G. Barbieri all' ab. prof. Melchior Cesarotti. [Edited by Francesco Corradini.] pp. 20. *Padova,* 1873. 8°. **10910.** g. **33.** (**7.**)

—— Considerazioni sul poema di Pronea [by Melchior Cesarotti]. pp. 73. *Bassano,* 1808. 8°. **898.** c. **19.** (**2.**)

—— Della sacra eloquenza in Italia. 1854. *See* HOUDRY (V.) Biblioteca de' predicatori, *etc.* vol. 10. 1844, *etc.* 4°. **4498.1.5/10.**

—— Delle lodi di Giovanni Belzoni orazione, *etc.* *See* ITALIAN ELOQUENCE. Florilegio di eloquenza italiana. vol. 1. 1839. 8°. **1201.** c. **34.**

—— Elogio funebre dell' abate commendator Cesarotti, *etc.* pp. 19. *Bassano,* 1809. 4°. **614.** l. **25.** (**1.**)

—— Invito ad Arquà. Epistola. [In verse. Edited by Antonio Piazza.] pp. xvi. *Padova,* 1824. fol. **1871.** d. **1.** (**3.**)

—— Ode. *See* BASSANESE ARTISTS. Catalogo degli artisti Bassanesi viventi, *etc.* 1807. 8°. **T. 2259.** (**4.**)

—— Predica della modestia. 1853. *See* HOUDRY (V.) Biblioteca de' predicatori, *etc.* vol. 9. 1844, *etc.* 4°. **4498.1.5/9.**

—— Predica della rassegnazione a' voleri divini. 1846. *See* HOUDRY (V.) Biblioteca de' predicatori, *etc.* vol. 4. 1844, *etc.* 4°. **4498.1.5/4.**

—— La Sala di fisica sperimentale. Canti tre. pp. 66. *Bassano,* 1807. 8°. **11436.** ee. **44.**

BARBIERI (Giuseppe) *Professore da Bassano.*

—— Sermoni, epistole e prose diverse . . . Seconda edizione. pp. 255. *Milano,* 1827. 12°. **11436.** m. **31.**

—— I Stagion. Cant quatter tradott da Carlo Volonteri. pp. 198. *Milano,* 1822. 12°. **11431.** aa. **4.**

BARBIERI (Guido)

—— L'Albo senatorio da Settimio Severo a Carino, 193–285. pp. xxiii. 794. *Roma,* 1952. 8°. [*Studi pubblicati dall'Istituto Italiano per la Storia Antica.* fasc. 6.] Ac. **104.** fg.

—— Conone. pp. xiv. 218. *Roma,* 1955. 8°. [*Studi pubblicati dall'Istituto Italiano per la Storia Antica.* fasc. 13.] Ac. **104.** fg.

BARBIERI (Joannes Petrus Maria) *Resp. See* Zallwein (G.) *Praes.* Collectiones juris ecclesiastici antiqui et novi, *etc.* 1760. 4°. **1127.** h. **20.**

BARBIERI (Lodovico) *Count.* Comitis Ludovici Barbieri . . . De communicatione motus & virium æstimatione. 1747. *See* Calogierà (A.) Raccolta d'opuscoli scientifici e filologici. tom. 36. 1728, *etc.* 12°. **247.** c. **5.**

—— De corporum principiis tractatus. pp. 94. *Patavii,* 1744. 8°. **232.** d. **36.**

—— De motus natura, ac legibus specimen novum. Pars prima. 1746. *See* Calogierà (A.) Raccolta d'opuscoli scientifici e filologici. tom. 34. 1728, *etc.* 12°. **247.** c. **3.**

—— Comitis Ludovici Barberii . . . De nativa maris salsedine dissertatio. 1752. *See* Calogierà (A.) Raccolta d'opuscoli scientifici e filologici. tom. 47. 1728, *etc.* 12°. **247.** c. **16.**

—— Deposito di pensieri utili alle scienze teoriche, e pratiche, dove sopra molte differenti materie si porgono lumi, e cognizioni interessanti e curiose. pp. 157. *Vicenza,* 1780. 8°. **T. 2362.** (**4.**)

—— Dissertazione academica sopra l'Eneide di Virgilio, *etc.* 1753. *See* Calogierà (A.) Raccolta d'opuscoli scientifici e filologici. tom. 48. 1728, *etc.* 12°. **247.** c. **17.**

—— Dissertazione, e parere . . . su la controversia tra li signori Clemente Baroni de Cavalcabò, e Francesco Maria Zanotti intorno la natura della felicità. pp. 93. *Venezia,* 1763. 8°. **T. 2362.** (**2.**)

—— Equitis Michaelis Angeli Georgii . . . vita. [With a portrait.] 1746. *See* Calogierà (A.) Raccolta d'opuscoli scientifici e filologici. tom. 35. 1728, *etc.* 12°. **247.** c. **4.**

—— Errores maximi circa scientiam de motu detecti. Cum appendice ad problema Regiæ Academiæ Borussicæ. pp. 79. *Vicentiæ,* 1779. 8°. **1136.** e. **19.**

—— Lettera . . . della generazione e natura de' fulmini. 1749. *See* Calogierà (A.) Raccolta d'opuscoli scientifici e filologici. tom. 41. 1728, *etc.* 12°. **247.** c. **10.**

—— Lettere due filosofiche sopra la eternità . . . all' Eminentissimo Sig. Cardinal Querini. 1756. *See* Calogierà (A.) Nuova raccolta d'opuscoli scientifici, e filologici. tom. 2. 1755, *etc.* 12°. **247.** a. **2.**

—— Nuova scoperta, e dichiarazione della vera correspondenza, ed analogia del colorito co' suoni chiamati vocali, e del chiaroscuro co' tuoni musici: con la espressione de' caratteri di varj linguaggi. pp. 37. *Vicenza,* 1780. 8°. **T. 2362.** (**3.**)

—— Nuovo saggio intorno ai vapori, e alle meteore. 1748. *See* Calogierà (A.) Raccolta d'opuscoli scientifici e filologici. tom. 39. 1728, *etc.* 12°. **247.** c. **8.**

BARBIERI (Lodovico) *Count.*

—— Nuovo sistema intorno l'anima delle bestie, con la rigezione degli altri sistemi sin' ora proposti. pp. cxxii. *Vicenza,* 1750. 8°. **232.** a. **9.**

—— Riflessioni sopra gli argomenti addotti dal Sig. Marchese Scipione Maffei a favore della sua nuova opinione intorno la formazione de' fulmini. [By Count L. Barbieri ? or Pellegrino Ferro, Bishop of Rovigo ?] pp. 52. 1748. 8°. *See* Maffei (F. S.) *Marquis.* **T. 2361.** (**10.**)

—— Storia del mare, e confutazione della favola, dove scopronsi insigni errori di varj scrittori, e specialmente del Signor de Buffon, *etc.* pp. 128. *Vinegia,* 1782. 8°. **234.** h. **34.**

—— Trattato della origine delle sorgenti, e de' fiumi. pp. 87. *Vicenza,* 1750. 8°. **233.** a. **13.**

—— Trattato di psicologia, nel quale si ragiona della natura dell' anime umane, e degli altri spiriti, della loro eccellenza sopra i corpi, della intelligenza, della volontà, della immortalità, ec. pp. xxxi. 339. *Venezia,* 1756. 8°. **232.** l. **3.**

—— Verità filosofiche fondamentali esposte con nuovo metodo in due dialoghi. pp. 256. *Bassano,* 1743. 8°. **232.** d. **37.**

BARBIERI (Lodovico) *of Bologna.*

—— *See* Lucchesi (Carlo) *Bibliotecario.* Bologna. Biblioteca comunale dell'Archiginnasio. [By C. Lucchesi, A. Sorbelli and L. Barbieri.] 1924, *etc.* 8°. [*Inventari dei manoscritti delle biblioteche d'Italia.* vol. 30, *etc.*] **011900.** dd. **20.**

—— *See* Periodical Publications.—*Florence.* Nuova Antologia di scienze, lettere ed arti, *etc.* (Indici per autori e per materie dal 1866 al 1930. A cura di L. Barbieri.) 1866, *etc.* 8°. **P.P. 4189.** c.

BARBIERI (Lodovico) *of Modena. See* Thomas, *de Aquileia.* La Guerra d'Atila, *etc.* [With the life of G. M. Barbieri by L. Barbieri.] 1843. 16°. **1440.** a. **13.**

BARBIERI (Luigi) *See* Augustine, *Saint, Bishop of Hippo.* [*Supposititious Works.—Meditationes.—Extracts, etc.*] Il Libro della vita contemplativa . . . Saggio di un volgarizzamento del sec. xiv messo per la prima volta in luce [by L. Barbieri]. 1862. 8°. **12226.** bbb. **2.** (**9.**)

—— *See* Fanfani (P.) Delle favole di Galfredo pubblicate da G. Ghivizzani. Avvertenze di P. Fanfani, e lettere di N. Tommaseo e L. Barbieri. 1867. 8°. **12226.** bbb. **18.** (**3.**)

—— *See* Hippocrates. [*Supposititious Works.—Byzantine Veterinarian.* ——*Latin and Italian.*] Trattati di mascalcia attribuiti ad Ippocrate, tradotti dall' arabo in latino da Maestro Moisè da Palermo . . . Corredati di due posteriori compilazioni in latino e in toscano e di note filologiche per cura di L. Barbieri. 1865. 8°. **12225.** g. **6.**

—— *See* Laurent, *Dominican.* Trattatello della virtù. Testo francese di Frate Lorenzo . . . e toscano di Z. Bencivenni, *etc.* [Edited by L. Barbieri.] 1863. 8°. **12226.** bbb. **3.** (**10.**)

—— *See* Petrarca (F.) [*De Viris Illustribus.—Latin and Italian.*] La Vita di Romolo composta in latino . . . Col volgarizzamento . . . di Maestro Donato da Pratovecchio. Edizione procurata da L. Barbieri. 1862. 8°. **12226.** bbb. **3.** (**1.**)

—— *See* Petrarca (F.) [*De Viris Illustribus.—Latin and Italian.*] Le Vite di Numa e T. Ostilio. Testo latino di F. Petrarca e toscano di M. Donato da Pratovecchio per cura e studio di L. Barbieri. 1863. 8°. **12226.** bbb. **4.** (**3.**)

BARBIERI (LUIGI)

—— See PEZZANA (A.) Monumenta historica ad provincias Parmensem et Placentinam pertinentia. [Edited by A. Pezzana, L. Barbieri and others.] 1855, *etc.* 4°. **9150. h. 2.**

—— See RUSIUS (L.) La Mascalcia di Lorenzo Rusio. Volgarizzamento del secolo XIV. . . . Aggiuntovi il testo latino per cura di L. Barbieri. 1867. 8°. **12225. g. 15.**

—— See VALERIUS MAXIMUS. Saggio del volgarizzamento antico di Valerio Massimo citato dagli Accademici della Crusca, *etc.* [Edited by L. Barbieri.] 1862. 8°. **12226. bbb. 3. (8.)**

—— Chronica Parmensia a sec. XI. ad exitum sec. XIV. Accedunt varia quae spectant ad historiam patriae civilem et ecclesiasticam. [Edited by L. Barbieri.] pp. xxxv. 563. *Parmae*, 1858. 4°. [*Monumenta historica ad provincias Parmensem et Placentinam spectantia.*] **9150. h. 2/3.**

—— Crema artistica. pp. 98. *Crema*, 1888. 8°. **10132. aaa. 7.**

—— Crema sacra. pp. 81. *Crema*, 1888. 8°. **10132. aaa. 6.**

—— La Donna nella famiglia e nella società. Studio sociale-educativo. pp. 81. *Crema*, 1887. 8°. **8415. ff. 11. (2.)**

—— Giordano Bruno e il suo monumento. Conferenza, *etc.* pp. 32. *Napoli*, 1889. 8°. **10630. d. 46. (5.)**

—— Illustri Cremaschi, specialmente usciti dal popolo. pp. 64. *Crema*, 1891. 8°. **10601. e. 13. (4.)**

—— Il Papato. Conferenze contro il Protestantesimo tenute in Napoli. pp. 308. *Napoli*, 1879. 8°. **4050. g. 10.**

—— Saggio di bibliografia cremasca, ovvero Crema letteraria. pp. 78. *Crema*, 1889. 8°. **011902. e. 20. (2.)**

BARBIERI (MASSIMILIANO) Nomenclatura italiana figurata . . . ad uso della gioventù . . . Terza edizione riveduta e aumentata. pp. 134. *Bologna*, 1866. 8°. **12943. aa. 34.**

—— Quinta edizione nuovamente corretta ed arricchita, *etc.* pp. 142. *Bologna*, [1870.] 8°. **12943. b. 1.**

BARBIERI (MASSIMILIANO) and **WOELFFEL** (J.)

—— Nomenclature figurée en français, italien, et allemand, suivie de 40 dialogues familiers . . . Illustrée de 495 gravures. (Nomenclatura figurata, *etc.*—Illustrirtes Woerterverzeichniss, *etc.*) pp. 159. *Bologne*, 1882. 8°. **12941. f. 20.**

BARBIERI (MATTEO) *See* BONGIOVANNI (Z.) and BARBIERI (M.) Illustrazione delle terme di Caldiero nel distretto veronese. 1795. 4°. **7462. k. 1.**

—— Notizie istoriche dei mattematici e filosofi del regno di Napoli. pp. 207. *Napoli*, 1778. 8°. **8485. bbb. 2.**

—— Storico-cliniche considerazioni sopra il corrente (anni 1795, 96) epidemico male ne' buoi. 1812. *See* VERONA.—*Accademia d'Agricoltura, Commercio ed Arti.* Memorie, *etc.* vol. 3. 1807, *etc.* 8°. **Ac. 115.**

BARBIERI (NICOLA) *Canonista, pseud.* [i.e. TOMASO MARIA SOLDATI.] Risposta di Nicola Barbieri canonista ad un quesito riguardante la proibizione delle opere de' refrattarj a varie costituzioni de' Romani Pontefici, corredata di annotazioni interessanti. pp. 56. *Palepoli*, 1789. 8°. **1356. b. 4. (6.)**

—— [Another copy.] **1374. h. 1.**

BARBIERI (NICOLÒ) called BELTRAME. L'Inauertito, ouero Scappino disturbato, e Mezzettino trauagliato: comedia. pp. 201. *A. Saluadori: Venetia*, 1630. 12°. **11715. a. 10.**

—— La Supplica, discorso famigliare . . . diretta à quelli che scriuēdo, ò parlando trattano de comici trascurando i meriti delle azzioni uirtuose, *etc.* pp. 233. *M. Ginammi: Venezia*, 1634. 8°. **11795. aa. 16.**
The titlepage is engraved.

BARBIERI (ORAZIO)

—— Cenni intorno all' origine della scrittura alfabetica. [By O. Barbieri.] pp. 64. 1884. 8°. *See* CENNI. **12902. ccc. 7. (5.)**

BARBIERI (PIETRO)

—— Il Travaglio della democrazia italiana, 1943–1947, *etc.* pp. xvi. 238. *Roma*, 1948. 8°. **9168. pp. 29.**
Documenti e testimonianze. no. 9.

BARBIERI (PIETRO PAOLO) Vita del giovinetto Alessandro Fedele Baldissera, *etc.* pp. 117. *Venezia*, 1866. 8°. **4863. ccc. 17.**

BARBIERI (S.) *See* HARTMAN (J. J.) La Poesia latina di Giovanni Pascoli. Traduzione di S. Barbieri. 1920. 8°. **11853. ss. 36.**

BARBIERI (SANTE UBERTO)

—— *See* MYERS (Alexander J. W.) A Educação Religiosa . . . Tradução de S. U. Barbieri. 1938. 8°. **04374. i. 36.**

BARBIERI (UBALDO) *See* LANCIANI (R. A.) La Villa Adriana . . . Pianta rilevata . . . sotto la direzione dei professori V. Reina e U. Barbieri. 1906. 8°. **07703. e. 34.**

BARBIERI (ULISSE) L'Assassinio di Maratona, ovvero i Briganti greci. Racconto storico. pp. 91. *Milano*, 1870. 16°. **12471. aa. 41. (4.)**

—— In Basso. Romanzo preceduto da uno schizzo di Edmondo de Amicis. pp. 254. *Roma*, 1885. 8°. **12471. d. 16.**

—— Lord Byron a Venezia, dramma in cinque atti. pp. 48. *Milano*, 1867. 8°. **11715. g. 40.**

—— Lucifero. Fantasia romantica. pp. 112. *Milano*, [1871.] 8°. **12471. aa. 41. (7.)**

—— Plauto ed il suo teatro. Scene romane. Studio storico. pp. 109. *Milano*, 1873. 16°. **11712. a. 23.**

—— La Strega di Campo dei Fiori. Romanzo originale. pt. 1. *Roma*, 1876. 8°. **12471. c. 48.**
Imperfect; wanting pt. 2.

BARBIERI (VINCENZO) *Abate.* La Madre de' Maccabei. Componimento sacro per musica, *etc.* pp. 19. *Roma*, [1790.] 8°. **11715. ee. 1. (8.)**

BARBIERI (VINCENZO) *Architetto.* La Proprietà fondiaria nell'economia sociale. Alcune idee sul suo ordinamento, *etc.* pp. 100. *Lodi*, 1891. 8°. **8225. eee. 45.**

BARBIERI-VIGNALI (GIOVANNI BATTISTA) Un Brano di storia patria, ossia diritti antichi e moderni sulle acque e sui canali del Marchesato di Vignola. pp. 103. *Bologna*, 1872. 8°. **10132. g. 34.**

BARBIERS (W. F.) *See* BIBLE.—*Old Testament.*—*Apocrypha.* [*Dutch.*] De Apokryfe Boeken . . . Met inleidingen en aantekeningen voorzien, door O. von Gerlach . . . Naar het Hoogduitsch door W. F. Barbiers. 1862. 4°. **L.13.f.4.**

BARBIERS (W. F.)

—— *See* EPHEMERIDES. Een vaste burg is onze God. Luthersche volks-almanak . . . met bijdragen van . . . Ds. W. F. Barbiers . . . en anderen, *etc.* [1854, *etc.*] 8°. **P.P. 2421**. lh.

BARBIER VÉMARS (JOSEPH NICOLAS) *See* PERIODICAL PUBLICATIONS.—*Paris*. Annales des arts et manufactures, *etc.* [By R. O'Reilly and J. N. Barbier Vémars.] 1800, *etc.* 8°. **247**. i. **11–36** & **248**. i. **1–30**.

—— Ode à Bonaparte. [*Paris*, 1801 ?] 8°. **8051**. de. **13**. (**6**.)

BARBIEUX (SENN) *See* SENN-BARBIEUX.

BARBIEUX (A. P.) *See* PERIODICAL PUBLICATIONS.—*Paris*. Le Caméléon, journal non politique; compilé par A. P. Barbieux. 1834, *etc.* 4°. **P.P. 4290**.

BARBIEUX (IGNACE JOSEPH) Dissertation sur l'opération de l'empyème, *etc.* pp. 16. *Montpellier*, [1804.] 4°. **1180**. e. **12**. (**17**.)

BARBIEUX (J. B.) Quelques considérations sur l'aménorrhée. Thèse, *etc.* pp. 12. *Paris*, 1837. 4°. **1184**. h. **6**. (**10**.)

BARBIEUX (J. PIERRE) Essais présentés à la Faculté de Médecine de Montpellier . . . sur l'affection hystérique; par J. P. Barbieux . . . Sur l'emploi thérapeutique du calorique concentré; par M. François Barbieux, *etc.* pp. 78. *Montpellier*, 1815. 4°. **1180**. h. **5**. (**22**.)

BARBIEUX (M. FRANÇOIS) Sur l'emploi thérapeutique du calorique concentré, *etc.* *See* BARBIEUX (J. P.) Essais présentés à la Faculté de Médecine de Montpellier, *etc.* 1815. 4°. **1180**. h. **5**. (**22**.)

BARBIEUX (P. J.) Quelques mots sur les hémorrhagies de l'utérus après l'accouchement. Thèse, *etc.* pp. 46. *Montpellier*, 1838. 4°. **1181**. i. **2**. (**12**.)

BARBILLION (L.) *Docteur en médecine*. Études critiques d'histoire de la médecine. pp. 237. *Paris*, 1930. 8°. **7679**. ff. **18**.

BARBILLION (LOUIS) *See* BERGEON (P.) and CASTEX (A.) *Professeur, etc.* Lignes électriques aériennes. Par P. Bergeon et A. Castex . . . avec la collaboration de L. Barbillion. 1919. 8°. **8764**. aa. **31**.

—— *See* ROBERT (L.) *Ingénieur*. Traité de télegraphie sans fil. Par L. Robert . . . Avec la collaboration et une préface de L. Barbillion. 1924. 8°. **8759**. dd. **20**.

—— Les Alternateurs industriels: constitution, fonctionnement, calcul. Par L. Barbillion . . . avec la collaboration de H. Antoine. pp. 208. *Paris*, 1919. 8°. **08768**. ccc. **17**.

—— Moteurs syncrones et convertisseurs rotatifs, *etc.* pp. 253. *Paris*, 1921. 8°. **8764**. aa. **33**.

—— La Traction électrique par courants alternatifs. L'électrification des chemins de fer. pp. 356. *Paris*, [1925.] 8°. **08755**. d. **8**.

BARBILLION (LOUIS) and **COIGNARD** (A.) *Ingénieur électricien*.

—— Lignes électriques souterraines. pp. 187. *Paris*, 1921. 8°. **08755**. d. **5**.

BARBILLION (LOUIS) and **GRIFFISCH** (G. J.)

—— Traité pratique de traction électrique. 2 tom. pp. xvi. 1530. *Paris*, 1903, 04. 8°. **8758**. f. **18**.

BARBIN ( ) *Avocat*. *See* MARAIS (J.) Reflexions sur l'écrit intitulé: Discours sur la détraction de la legitime entre les enfans. Lesquelles répondent à un autre écrit [by —— Barbin], qui a pour titre: Memoire pour montrer, que tous les enfans donataires entre-vifs, doivent contribuer à la legitime des autres. 1694. 12°. **877**. b. **7**. (**3**.)

BARBIN (CLAUDE)

—— Catalogue des livres imprimez chez Claude Barbin . . . 1687. pp. 8. [*Paris ?* 1687.] 8°. **S.C. 253**. (**7**.)

BARBIN (FRANÇOIS)

—— *See* DES JARDINS (M. C. H.) calling herself MADAME DE VILLEDIEU. Recüeil de quelques lettres ou relations galantes, *etc.* [Edited by F. Barbin.] 1668. 12°. **12518**. ccc. **4**.

—— *See* FRENCH POETS. Recueil des plus belles pieces des poëtes françois, tant anciens que modernes, avec l'histoire de leur vie, par l'auteur des Memoires & voyage d'Espagne [i.e. Marie Catherine La Mothe, Countess d'Aulnoy, or rather, by F. Barbin ?] 1692. 12°. **1065**. a. **4–8**.

—— —— 1752. 12°. **1065**. f. **1–6**.

BARBIN (GUSTAVE) *of Donges*. Thèse, *etc.* (De l'habitation dans le voisinage des marais.) pp. 29. *Paris*, 1838. 4°. **1184**. i. **3**. (**6**.)

BARBIN (GUSTAVE) *of Montoir*. De l'influence de diverses maladies et en particulier de la syphilis sur la grossesse. pp. 40. *Paris*, 1869. 4°. [*Collection des thèses soutenues à la Faculté de Médecine de Paris*. An 1870. tom. 1.] **7373**. l. **9**.

BARBIN (JEAN BAPTISTE) Quelques considérations sur la goître. Thèse, *etc.* pp. 36. *Montpellier*, 1854. 4°. **7379**. c. **10**. (**2**.)

BARBIN (OCTAVE MICHEL FRANÇOIS) Thèse pour le doctorat en médecine, *etc.* (Questions sur diverses branches des sciences médicales.) pp. 25. *Paris*, 1839. 4°. [*Collection des thèses soutenues à la Faculté de Médecine de Paris*. An 1839. tom. 1.] **7371**. a. **1**.

BARBIN (RENÉ)

—— Le Mouvement breton. Autonomisme et fédéralisme . . . Troisième édition. [With a portrait.] pp. 205. *Carhaix*, [1937.] 8°. **08052**. aa. **61**.

BARBIREAU (JACOBUS)

—— *See* DU SAAR (J.) Het Leven en de composities van Jacobus Barbireau. 1946. 8°. **7890**. d. **23**.

BARBIRINI (ANTONIO DI) *Cardinal*. *See* BARBERINO.

BARBIROLLI (JOHN)

—— *See* RIGBY (Charles) John Barbirolli, *etc.* (A biographical sketch.) [With portraits.] 1948. 8°. **10862**. e. **27**.

BARBIROLO (ALESSANDRIO) Giuochi di carte bellissimi. di regola, & memoria. Con secreti bellissimi per passar l'ozio, & il tempo, *etc.* *G. B. Bellagamba: Bologna*, 1604. 12°. **7913**. aaa. **44**.

BARBIZON HOUSE. *See* LONDON.—III.

BARBLAN (DOMENIC) Succint intraguidamaint nella religiun cristiauna per il pövel ladin evangelic del chantun Grischun. pp. vii. 142. *Cuoira*, 1855. 8°. **12941**. aaa. **12**.

BARBLAN (GAUD.) Parablas, mitos religius, mitos eroics, legendas e da tuotta sort requints populars in Engiadina Bassa. 1909. *See* COIRE.—*Societad Rhaeto-Romanscha*. Annalas, *etc.* Annada 24. 1886, *etc.* 8°. **Ac. 9817**.

BARBLAN (GUGLIELMO)

—— *See* CASELLA (A.) Strawinski . . . Con un capitolo di aggiornamento di G. Barblan. 1951. 8°. **10798. a. 9.**

—— *See* GALLINI (N.) and BARBLAN (G.) Onoranze nazionali a Giuseppe Verdi . . . Mostra degli autografi musicali di Giuseppe Verdi, *etc.* (Catalogo.) [1951.] 8°. Hirsch **375.**

—— L'Opera di Donizetti nell'età romantica. pp. 246. *Bergamo*, 1948. 8°. **7900. l. 25.**

BARBLAN (PETER)

—— *See* ZARN (A.) and BARBLAN (P.) Der Skifahrer, *etc.* 1920. 8°. **7922. b. 6.**

BARBLAN (PETER J.)

—— Der Staatshaushalt des Kantons Graubünden seit dem Beitritt zum eidgenössischen Bund bis zur Einführung der direkten Steuern im Jahre 1856. pp. 141. 1910. *See* COIRE.—*Geschichtforschende*, afterwards *Historisch-Antiquarische, Gesellschaft von Graubünden.* Achter [*etc.*] Jahresbericht, *etc.* Jahrg. 1909. [1879, *etc.*] 8°. Ac. **6930/3.**

BARBO (ALESSANDRO) Relazione di Alessandro Barbo, Capitano di Verona, 1561. [Edited by Adriano Noale.] pp. 16. *Venezia*, 1869. 8°. **10132. cc. 13.** *One of an edition of* 50 *copies.*

BARBO (EMIL) Die Theorie der Servituten des französischen Rechts—art. 637–710 des Code civil—mit den wichtigsten Streitfragen, unter stetem Hinblick auf römisches Recht bearbeitet. pp. iv. 319. *Mannheim*, 1855. 8°. **5405. c. 1.**

BARBÒ (F. RIVETTI) *See* RIVETTI BARBÒ (F.)

BARBÒ (GAETANO) *Count. See* SARTORI (L.) and RAUSCHENFELS (A. de) L'Apicoltura in Italia. Manuale teorico-pratico-industriale . . . Riveduto dal conte cav. G. Barbò, *etc.* 1878. 8°. **7297. g. 5.**

—— *See* ULIVI (G.) Lucciole per lanterne, ossia la scienza apistica del conte G. Barbò. 1882. 8°. **7297. g. 28. (6.)**

BARBO (GIOVANNI BATTISTA) L'Oracolo, ouero inuettiua contra le donne, *etc.* pp. 67. *F. Grossi: Vicenza*, [1616?] 12°. **1071. a. 17.**

—— [Another copy.] L'Oracolo, *etc. Vicenza*, [1616?] 12°. **11436. m. 10. (2.)**

BARBO (JOSÉPHINE MELZI D'ERIL) *Duchess. See* MELZI D'ERIL (Giuseppina M. T.) *Duchess di Lodi.*

BARBO (LUDOVICO)

—— *See* PITIGLIANI (R.) Il Ven. Ludovico Barbo e la diffusione dell'Imitazione di Cristo per opera della Congregazione di S. Giustina, *etc.* [With a portrait.] 1943. 8°. **4869. c. 7.**

BARBO (MARCO) *Cardinal.*

—— Il Carteggio fra il card. Marco Barbo e Giovanni Lorenzi, 1481–1490. [Edited, with an introduction, by P. Paschini.] pp. 232. *Città del Vaticano*, 1948. 8°. [*Studi e testi.* no. 137.] **012211. b. 1/137.**

BARBO (PIETRO) *Cardinal. See* PAUL II., *Pope.*

BARBO (SCIPIONE) *See* BARBUO.

BARBÒ (THEODORO) *Count.* Se vence el arte con el arte. Nueva fortificacion, *etc.* [With plans.] pp. 15. [*Naples?* 1680?] fol. **8833. h. 13.**

BARBOCCI (GIOVANNI)

—— Don Calascione. Drama giocoso, *etc.* [By G. Barbocci.] pp. 47. [1755?] 12°. *See* CALASCIONE, *Don.* **906. d. 3. (1.)**

BARBOGLIO (PIETRO) *See* APPIANI (A.) Fastes de Napoléon Ier. Peints par A. Appiani, *etc.* [With descriptive letterpress and a biographical notice of A. Appiani by P. Barboglio.] [1854?] fol. Tab. **1227. a.**

BARBOLAIN (AUGUSTE) Du système lymphatique et du poumon, thèse, *etc.* pp. 36. *Paris*, 1819. 4°. **1183. e. 10. (6.)**

BARBOLANI (FRIDERICUS) *Count. See* PRUNETTI (M. A.) *Begin.* Honori et virtuti Friderici Franc. fil. Barbolani, *etc.* 1789. 4°. **1356. k. 8. (23.)**

BARBOLANI (TORQUATO) *Marquis. See* ARIOSTO (L.) [*Orlando Furioso.—Italian and Latin.*] Orlando Furioso . . . tradotto in versi latini dall'illustrissimo Signor Marchese T. Barbolani. 1756. 4°. **638. i. 11, 12.**

BARBON (CHARLES JEAN LUBET) *See* LUBET-BARBON.

BARBON (JOHN) *Λειτουργια θειοτερα ἐργια*: or, Liturgie a most divine service: in answer to a late Pamphlet [by Vavasor Powell] stiled, Common-Prayer-Book no Divine Service. Wherein, that authors XXVII reasons against Liturgies are wholly . . . taken away, *etc.* pp. 193. *A. & L. Lichfield: Oxford*, 1662. 4°. **3475. b. 25.**

BARBON (NICOLAS) *See* BAUER (S.) Nicholas Barbon. Ein Beitrag zur Vorgeschichte der klassischen Oekonomik. [1890.] 8°. **08226. k. 5. (3.)**

—— An Apology for the Builder: or a Discourse shewing the cause and effects of the increase of building. [By N. Barbon.] pp. 37. 1685. 4°. **8245. a. 5.**

—— [Another copy.] **104. m. 42.**

—— [Another copy.] **796. h. 21. (5.)**

—— [Another copy.] T. **2029. (3.)**

—— A Discourse concerning Coining the New Money lighter. In answer to Mr. Lock's Considerations about raising the Value of Money. pp. 96. *Richard Chiswell: London*, 1696. 8°. **1139. c. 6.**

—— [Another copy.] **1139. c. 7. (1.)**

—— [Another copy.] T. **1593. (5.)**

—— [Another copy.] **104. k. 2.**

—— *See* H., E. Decus & Tutamen: or, our new money as now coined, in full weight and fineness, proved to be for the honour . . . of England. Written by way of answer to Sir R. Temple and Dr. Barbon, *etc.* 1696. 8°. **1139. c. 25.**

—— A Discourse of Trade. By N. B. M.D. [i.e. N. Barbon.] pp. 92. 1690. 8°. *See* B., N., *M.D.* **1138. b. 2.**

—— A Letter to a Gentleman in the Country, giving an account of the two Insurance-Offices; the Fire-Office & Friendly-Society. [Signed: N. B., i.e. N. Barbon.] pp. 4. 1684. fol. *See* B., N. **816. m. 10. (74.)**

—— *See* S., H. An Answer to a Letter [by N. Barbon] to a Gentleman in the Country, giving an account of the two Insurance-Offices, *etc.* 1684. fol. **816. m. 10. (75.)**

BARBON (PIERRE MADELEINE THOMAS FERNAND LUBET) *See* LUBET-BARBON.

BARBONE (DONATO)

—— *See* RUSSELL (Bertrand A. W.) *Earl Russell.* [Sceptical Essays.] Saggi scettici. Traduzione di D. Barbone. 1953. 8°. **8476. bb. 21.**

BARBONE (Praise-God) *See* Barebone.

BARBONI (Leopoldo P.) *See* Pellico (S.) Le Mie prigioni. Con la vita dell'autore scritta da L. Barboni. 1888. 8°. **10629**. a. **31**.

—— Bona di Savoia. Storia del secolo xv. pp. 262. *Firenze*, 1872. 8°. **12471**. bbb. **2**.

—— Coscienza di re. Storia del secolo xviii. pp. 238. *Napoli*, 1875. 8°. **12471**. y. **16**.

—— La Cognata di Papa Innocenzo x. [A novel.] pp. 131. *Livorno*, 1886. 12°. **12471**. aaa. **68**.

—— Fra le fiamme del Vesuvio. pp. 309. *Genova*, 1881. 8°. **10131**. bbb. **8**.

—— Geni e capi ameni dell'ottocento. Ricerche e ricordi intimi. pp. 269. *Firenze*, [1911.] 8°. **011852**. b. **10**.

—— Giosuè Carducci e la Maremma. pp. 150. *Livorno*, 1885. 16°. **11825**. de. **14**.

—— Col Carducci in Maremma. Seconda edizione. pp. 144. *Firenze*, 1906. 8°. **11853**. p. **20**.

BARBONIUS (I.) lvii. Morale Sinne-Beelden, aen sijne Hoogheydt . . . Fredrick Hendrick Prince van Orangien, Grave van Nassauw, *etc.* [With illustrations.] pp. 148. *Tot kost van den Autheur; ghedruckt by T. Iacobsz.: Amsterdam*, 1641. 12°. **12352**. a. **19**.

BARBON MAZARINI MANCINI (Louis Jules Henri) *Duke de Nivernois and d'Onziois.*

—— *See* Coquette. La Coquette fixée, comédie, *etc.* [By C. H. de Fusée de Voisenon, L. J. H. Barbon Mazarini Mancini, and C. A. Leclerc de la Bruère.] 1746. 8°. **164**. f. **41**.

—— —— 1753. 12°. [*Nouveau théâtre italien.* tom. 10.] **241**. i. **13**.

—— *See* Dupin (A. M. J. J.) Éloge de M. le duc de Nivernois, *etc.* 1840. 8°. **10660**. cc. **10**.

—— *See* Eon de Beaumont (C. G. L. A. A. T. d') Lettres mémoires et négociations particulières du Chevalier d'Eon . . . avec MM. les ducs de Praslin, de Nivernois, *etc.* 1765. 8°. **8050**. d. **15**.

—— *See* Metastasio (P. A. D. B.) Joseph reconnu par ses frères, oratorio . . . traduit de Metastasio [by the Duke de Nivernois], *etc.* [1796.] 8°. **11738**. k. **21**. (**1**.)

—— *See* Perey (L.) *pseud.* La Fin du xviiie siècle. Le duc de Nivernais, *etc.* [With a portrait.] 1891. 8°. **010661**. f. **46**.

—— *See* Perey (L.) *pseud.* Un Petit-neveu de Mazarin. Louis Mancini-Mazarini, duc de Nivernais, *etc.* [With a portrait.] 1890. 8°. **010661**. i. **20**.

—— *See* Silvestre (A. F.) *Baron.* Notice sur la vie et les ouvrages du citoyen Nivernois. [1793.] 8°. [*Rapports généraux des travaux de la Société Philomathique de Paris.* tom. 1.] **254**. l. **6**.

—— *See* Walpole (Horace) *Earl of Orford.* Essay on Modern Gardening, *etc.* (Essai sur l'art des jardins modernes . . . Traduit en françois par M. le Duc de Nivernois, *etc.*) 1785. 4°. **61**. c. **26**.

—— Oeuvres, *etc.* [With a portrait.] tom. 1–5. *Paris*, 1796. 8°. **98**. c. **17–20**.
Imperfect; wanting tom. 6–8.

—— [Another copy of tom. 1, 2.] **637**. h. **27**.

BARBON MAZARINI MANCINI (Louis Jules Henri) *Duke de Nivernois and d'Onziois.*

—— Œuvres posthumes du duc de Nivernois, publiées à la suite de son éloge par N. François, de Neufchateau. 2 tom. 4 pt. *Paris*, 1807. 8°. **98**. c. **21**, **22**.

—— [Another copy of pt. 4.] **11738**. k. **21**. (**3**.)

—— Cantate dialoguée. Tirée des manuscrits de M. de Sainte-Palaye. (L'Oracle infaillible.—Le Rendezvous.—L'Écho.) [*Paris*, 1796.] 8°. **11738**. k. **21**.(**4**.)
A fragment: pp. 189–228 *of tom.* 6 *of the works of the Duke de Nivernois.*

—— Essai sur la vie de J. J. Barthélemy. pp. 69. *Paris*, 1795. 8°. **R.178.(1.)**
—— [Another copy.] **687.g.30.(2.)**
—— [Another copy.] T. **972**. (**5**.)

—— [Another copy.] G. **14775**. (**1**.)

—— [Another edition.] *See* Barthélemy (J. J.) Voyage du jeune Anacharsis en Grèce, *etc.* 1798. 8°. **12510**. f. **5**.

—— [Another edition.] *See* Barthélemy (J. J.) Voyage du jeune Anacharsis, *etc.* 1811. 8°. **12512**. gg. **4**.

—— [Another edition.] *See* Barthélemy (J. J.) Voyage du jeune Anacharsis, *etc.* 1828. 12°. **1424**. c. **24**.

—— [Another edition.] *See* Barthélemy (J. J.) Voyage du jeune Anacharsis, *etc.* 1834. 12°. **604**. b. **26**.

—— [Another copy.] Essai sur la vie de J.-J. Barthélemy. *Paris*, 1795. 8°. **10666**. a. 52.
Imperfect: wanting the titlepage.

—— Essay on the Life of J. J. Barthélemi. *See* Barthélemy (J. J.) The Travels of Anacharsis the Younger, *etc.* 1798. 8°. **635**. h. **24**.

—— Essai sur la vie de J. J. Barthélemy. [Abridged.] *See* Barthélemy (J. J.) Carite et Polydore, *etc.* 1799. 12°. **12510**. de. **11**.

—— The Life of J. J. Barthelemy. An extract from the French. *See* Barthélemy (J. J.) Charite and Polydorus, *etc.* 1799. 12°. **838**. a. **42**.

—— Fables . . . translated into English verse. *Fr. & Eng.* pp. 259. *T. Cadell & W. Davies: London; Manners & Miller: Edinburgh*, 1799. 8°. **637**. g. **6**. (**2**.)

—— L'Hermite, ou l'Éclipse, comédie en un acte, en prose, mêlée d'ariettes. [Wholly in verse. By L. J. H. Barbon Mazarini Mancini.] pp. 18. 1778. 4°. *See* Hermite. **11736**. h. **13**. (**4**.)

—— L'Île des plaisirs tranquilles, ou le Prince Lutin, comédie . . . tirée d'un conte de fée de Mme Daulnoy, intitulé le Prince Lutin, *etc.* [*Paris*,] 1738. 8°. **11738**. k. **21**. (**2**.)
A fragment: pp. 229–280 *of tom.* 6 *of the works of the Duke de Nivernois.*

—— Imitations de différents morceaux de poésie italienne. [*Paris*, 1796.] 8°. **11738**. k. **21**. (**5**.)
A fragment: pp. 57–72 *of tom.* 6 *of the works of the Duke de Nivernois.*

—— Réponse . . . au discours de M. l'abbé Maury. *See* Maury (J. S.) *Cardinal.* Discours prononcés dans l'Académie Françoise . . . à la réception de M. l'abbé Maury. 1785. 8°. **733**. g. **12**. (**5**.)

BARBON MAZARINI MANCINI (Marie Thérèse) *Duchess de Nivernois.* Pensées diverses par la comtesse de Rochefort [afterwards Duchess de Nivernois]. *See* Loménie (L. L. de) La Comtesse de Rochefort et ses amis, *etc.* 1870. 8°. **10661**. f. **7**.

BARBON Y CASTAÑEDA (GUILLEN) Prouechosos adbitrios al consumo del vellon, conseruacion de plata, poblacion de España, y relacion de auisos importantes a las cosas que en ella necessitan de remedio. pp. 29. *A. de Parra: Madrid*, 1628. 4°. **1322**. l. **12**. (**46**.)

—— *Begin*. Señor. Haze discurso el capitan don G. Barbon y Castañeda, para sacar de España todos los años crecido numero de soldados, sin quintarlos, ni lleuarlos por fuerça, *etc*. [1640?] fol. **1324**. i. **6**. (**3**.)

BARBOR (H. R.) Aetas and Iugen, with some lyrics. pp. 29. *Cornish Bros.: Birmingham*, 1914. 8°. [*Birmingham Books*. no. 1.] **011779**. de. **37**. (**1**.)

—— Against the Red Sky. Silhouettes of revolution. pp. vii. 272. *C. W. Daniel: London*, 1922. 8°. NN. **8020**.

—— [Another edition.] pp. vii. 272. *Noel Douglas: London*, 1925. 8°. NN. **11062**.

—— The Birmingham Books. Edited by H. R. Barbor, E. S. Guise, and P. A. Wayne. 2 pt. *Cornish Bros.: Birmingham*, 1914, 15. 8°. **011779**. de. **37**.

—— Jezebel. A tragedy in three acts. pp. 151. *Arthur Brenton: London*, [1924.] 8°. **011779**. i. **36**.
No. 11 *of an edition of* 100 *copies*.

—— A Play, and other things. By H. R. Barbor and P. A. Wayne. [A play, in one act and in prose, entitled "What Women Want" by H. R. Barbor, followed by verses and prose pieces by P. A. Wayne.] pp. 40. *Cornish Bros.: Birmingham*, 1915. 8°. [*Birmingham Books*. no. 2.] **011779**. de. **37**. (**2**.)

—— The Theatre, an art and an industry . . . Introductory notes by Sybil Thorndyke and C. B. Cochran. pp. xii. 48. *Labour Publishing Co.: London*, 1924. 8°. **011795**. k. **55**.

BARBOR (WILHELMUS) Disputatio medica inauguralis de lue venerea. *J. Hulshuysen: Trajecti ad Rhenum*, 1663. 4°. **1185**. k. **11**. (**7**.)

BARBOŘÍK (JOSEF)

—— Úkoly obcí v budovatelském plánu. Poznámky osvětového prácovníka. pp. 13. *Praha*, 1946. 8°. [*Podněty*. sv. 1.] S. R. **58/4**.

BARBORKA (CLIFFORD JOSEPH)

—— Treatment by Diet, *etc*. [With a bibliography.] pp. xii. 615. *J. B. Lippincott Co.: Philadelphia*, [1934.] 8°. **7462**. r. **6**.

—— Treatment by Diet . . . Second edition, revised. pp. xii. 615. *J. B. Lippincott Co.: Philadelphia*, [1935.] 8°. **7462**. r. **17**.

—— Treatment by Diet . . . Third edition, revised. pp. xiv. 642. *J. B. Lippincott Co.: Philadelphia*, [1937.] 8°. **7462**. ppp. **7**.

—— Treatment by Diet . . . Illustrated. Fourth edition, revised. pp. xv. 691. *J. B. Lippincott Co.: Philadelphia*, [1939.] 8°. **7461**. ppp. **11**.

—— Treatment by Diet . . . Fifth edition, *etc*. pp. xvii. 784. pl. 14. *J. B. Lippincott Co.: Philadelphia*, [1948.] 8°. **7383**. v. **26**.

BARBOSA (AGOSTINHO) *Bishop of Ugento*. Augustini Barbosæ . . . Collectanea doctorum, qui suis in operibus Concilij Tridentini loca referentes, illorum materiam incidenter tractârunt, & varias quæstiones, in foro ecclesiastico versantibus maximè vtiles, & necessarias, deciderunt. Omnia ex eorum libris fideliter desumpta . . . Hac vltima editione ab ipso auctore recognita, *etc*. pp. 492. *L. Durand: Lugduni*, 1642. fol. **5005**. e. **6**.

BARBOSA (AGOSTINHO) *Bishop of Ugento*.

—— [Another edition.] pp. 492. *Lugduni*, 1704. fol. **494**. l. **11**. (**1**.

—— Collectanea doctorum tam veterum, quam recentiorum in Ius Pontificium Universum. Tomus primus(—sextus . . . ab ipsomet auctore recognitus, *etc*. 6 tom. *P. Borde, L. Arnaud & C. Rigaud: Lugduni*, 1656–67. fol. **5035**. h. **4**

—— [Another edition.] 6 tom. *Lugduni*, 1716. fol. **494**. l. **12–14**

—— Augustini Barbosæ . . . Collectanea ex doctoribus tum priscis tum neotericis in Codicem Iustiniani . . . Editio ultima. 2 tom. *P. Borde, L. Arnaud & C. Rigaud: Lugduni*, 1657, 50. fol. **5306**. i. **7**
Tom. 2 *is of an earlier edition*.

—— [Another edition.] 2 tom. *Lugduni*, 1701, 02. fol. **494**. l. **8**

—— Dictionarium Lusitanicolatinum iuxta seriem alphabeticam optimis probatisq. doctissimorum auctorum testimonijs perutili quadam expositione locupletatum cum copiosissimo latini sermonis indice, necnon libello vn aliquarum regionum, cauitatum, oppidorum . . . quibus veteres vti solebant, *etc*. 2 pt. *Typis, & expensis F. Laurentij de Basto: Bracharæ*, 1611. 4°. **627**. i. **11**

—— Duo vota consultiua, vnum de campanis, alterum de cœmeteriis. In quibus de vtriusque antiquitate, consecratione, vsu, & effectibus plenè agitur, *etc*. pp. 111. [1645?] **3478**. f. **6**
MS. correspondence relating to the book has been inserted in this copy.

—— Augustini Barbosæ . . . Iuris ecclesiastici vniversi libri tres, in quorum I. de personis, II. de locis, III. de rebus ecclesiasticis plenissimè agitur . . . Editio nouissima, ab auctore recognita, & erroribus ablatis, vtilite locupletata. vol. 1. *P. Borde, L. Arnaud & C. Rigaud: Lugduni*, 1650. fol. **5035**. i. **2**
Imperfect; wanting vol. 2, *containing lib*. 2 *and* 3.

—— [Another edition.] 2 pt. *Lugduni*, 1718. fol. **494**. l. **15**

—— Augustini Barbosæ . . . De personis ecclesiasticis. [Selected from lib. 1 of the "Jus ecclesiasticum universum."] 1697. *See* ROCABERTI (J. T. de) *Archbishop of Valencia*. Bibliotheca maxima pontificia, *etc*. tom. 4. 1698, *etc*. fol. **484**. e. **3**

—— Pastoralis solicitudinis, siue de officio, et potestate episcopi tripartita descriptio . . . Hac postrema edition ab ipsomet auctore multis in locis variis resolutionibus illustrata, *etc*. (Apostolicæ constitutiones et decret aliquot, *etc*.) 2 vol. *L. Durand: Lugduni*, 1628. fol. **1237**. i. **1**, **2**

—— [Another edition.] 2 vol. *P. Borde, L. Arnaud & C. Rigaud: Lugduni*, 1650, 49. fol. **5061**. eee. **1**

—— [Another edition.] 2 vol. *P. Borde, J. & P. Arnaud: Lugduni*, 1698. fol. **494**. l. **6**

—— [Another edition.] Hac quarta editione ab ipso auctor recognita, &c. . . . major facta. pp. 293. *Hæred. P. Prost, P. Borde & L. Arnaud: Lugduni*, 1647. fol. **5061**. eee. **2**. (**2**.

—— Quinta editio . . . emendatior. Cum . . . indicibus, *etc*. pp. 293. *P. Borde, L. Arnaud & C. Rigaud: Lugduni*, 1655. fol. **5035**. i. **10**. (**2**.

—— Ultima editio prioribus emendatior. Cum summariis & indicibus, *etc*. pp. 293. *Lugduni*, 1712. fol. **494**. l. **11**. (**2**.

BARBOSA (AGOSTINHO) *Bishop of Ugento.*

—— *See* GIRALDI (U.) *à Sancto Cajetano.* Animadversiones et additamenta ex posterioribus Summorum Pontificum constitutionibus . . . desumpta ad Augustinum Barbosa De officio et potestate parochi. 1831. fol. **494.** l. **16.**

—— Augustini Barbosæ . . . Praxis exigendi pensiones, aduersus calumniantes, et differentes illas soluere, cui accesserunt vota plurima decisiua, et consultiua canonica. Vltima editio, aucta et emendata. 2 tom. *P. Borde, L. Arnaud & C. Rigaud: Lugduni,* 1653. fol. **5035.** i. **1.**

—— Ultima editio prioribus emendatior. 2 tom. *Lugduni,* 1702. fol. **494.** l. **9.**

—— Remissiones doctorum, qui varia loca Concilii Tridentini incidenter tractarunt, *etc.* pp. 158. *P. Craesbeeck: Ulyssipone,* 1618. 8º. **5051.** aa. **15.**

—— [For editions of the "Remissiones doctorum" included in editions of the Decrees of the Council of Trent:] *See* TRENT, *Council of.*

—— D. Augustini Barbosæ . . . Repertorium juris civilis et canonici . . . Opus postumum . . . studio & industriâ D. Simonis Vaz Barbosæ . . . digestum. Editio novissima, à mendis quæ prioribus irrepserant, expurgata. pp. 250. *Lugduni,* 1712. fol. **494.** l. **10.** (**1.**)

—— Sumario de la vida, y milagros de S. Phelipe Neri. *See* HURTADO DE MENDOZA (F.) Fundacion, y chronica de la . . . Congregacion de San Phelipe Neri de . . . Granada. 1689. 4º. **4784.** d. **19.**

—— Augustini Barbosæ . . . Summa apostolicarum decisionum, extra ius commune vagantium, quæ ex variis approbatissimorum doctorum libris hucusque impressis . . . collectæ . . . alphabetico ordine disponuntur. pp. 448. *Apud P. Baleonium: Venetiis,* 1646. fol. **5309.** g. **6.**

—— Editio vltima aucta, *etc.* pp. 506. *P. Borde, L. Arnaud & C. Rigaud: Lugduni,* 1658. fol. **5035.** h. **1.**
With the arms of Nicolas Fouquet, Viscount de Malun, on the binding.

—— Editio ultima aucta et recognita. pp. 506. *L. Arnaud, P. Borde, J. & P. Arnaud: Lugduni,* 1680. fol. **5035.** i. **3.**

—— Editio ultima aucta, et recognita. pp. 506. *Lugduni,* 1703. fol. **494.** l. **7.** (**2.**)

—— Editio ultima aucta et recognita. pp. 356. *Venetiis,* 1712. fol. **495.** l. **16.**

—— Augustini Barbosæ . . . Tractatus de canonicis et dignitatibus aliisque . . . beneficiariis cathedralium . . . Hac tertia editione ab ipso auctore recognitus & . . . auctus. pp. 261. *L. Durand & L. Arnaud: Lugduni,* 1640. fol. **5061.** eee. **2.** (**1.**)

—— [Another edition.] Hac quarta editione ab ipso auctore recognitus, & . . . locupletatus. Cum summariis, & indicibus, *etc.* pp. 263. *Hæred. P. Prost, P. Borde & L. Arnaud: Lugduni,* 1648. fol. **5035.** i. **10.** (**1.**)

—— [Another edition.] Hac ultima editione ab ipso authore recognitus, *etc.* pp. 263. *P. Borde, J. & P. Arnaud: Lugduni,* 1700. fol. **494.** l. **7.** (**1.**)

—— Variæ tractationes iuris . . . videlicet: I. De axiomatibus iuris vsufrequentioribus. II. De appellatiua verborum vtriusque iuris significatione. III. De locis communibus argumentorum iuris. IV. De clausulis vsufrequentioribus. V. De dictionibus vsufrequentioribus, *etc.* 2 pt. *L. Durand: Lugduni,* 1630. fol. **5327.** g. **5.**

—— [Another edition.] pp. 818. *P. Borde, L. Arnaud & C. Rigaud: Lugduni,* 1651. fol. **5306.** i. **6.**

BARBOSA (AGOSTINHO) *Bishop of Ugento.*

—— [Another edition.] pp. 684. *Lugduni,* 1718. fol. **494.** l. **10.** (**2.**)

—— Thesaurus locorum communium jurisprudentiæ ex axiomatibus Augustini Barbosæ, et analectis Jo. Ottonis Taboris, aliorumque concinnatus. Editio post secundam Tobiæ Ottonis Taboris et per axiomata Sam. Strykii, And. Christoph. Röseneri recentiorumque JCC. auctam, quintam sexta. 2 tom. *Coloniæ Allobrogum,* 1737. fol. **5306.** h. **11.**

—— Por el Doctor Agustin Barbosa con Balthazar Diaz de Afonseca. Sobre el valor de los mandatos, sentencias, censuras, y sequestros del Auditor de la Camara Apostolica, y Sagrada Rota de Roma. [A pleading.] pp. 32. [1635?] fol. **1322.** k. **15.** (**2.**)

BARBOSA (AGUSTÍN) *Bishop of Ugento. See* BARBOSA (Agostinho)

BARBOSA (AMÁLIA GOMES) *See* GOMES BARBOSA.

BARBOSA (ANTÓNIO)

—— Novos subsídios para a história da ciência náutica portuguesa da época dos descobrimentos. pp. 332. *Porto,* 1948. 8º. **08809.** bb. **22.**

BARBOSA (ANTONIO MARIA) *See* CUNHA VIANNA (F. J. da) and BARBOSA (A. M.) Ensaio sobre a cholera epidemica. 1854. 8º. **7560.** aa. **28.**

—— *See* CUNHA VIANNA (F. J. da) and BARBOSA (A. M.) Instrucções contra a cholera morbus epidemica. 1854. 8º. **7560.** aa. **29.**

—— *See* PERIODICAL PUBLICATIONS.—*Lisbon.* Gazeta Medica de Lisboa. Redactores A. D. Guerreiro, A. M. Barbosa, *etc.* [1854, *etc.*] fol. P.P. **2711.**

—— Memoria sobre as principaes causas da mortalidade do hospital de S. José, e meios de as attenuar . . . 2ª edição. pp. 104. *Lisboa,* 1856. 8º. **7686.** c. **3.**

BARBOSA (ANTONIO SOARES) *See* SOARES BARBOSA.

BARBOSA (ARIUS) *Lusitanus. See* ARATOR, *the Subdeacon.* Aratoris Cardinalis Historia Apostolica cum Cõmentariis Arii Barbosæ lusitani, *etc.* 1516. fol. **840.** i. **37.**

BARBOSA (AUGUSTINUS) *Bishop of Ugento. See* BARBOSA (Agostinho)

BARBOSA (DUARTE) *See* MAGALHAENS (F. de) De Scheeps-Togt door de Straat na de Moluccos door Ferdinand Magellaan ontdekt; na sijn dood, onder het opper-gesag van Duarte Barboza, en Gonrado Gomez d'Espinoza . . . agtervolgt in't Jaar 1521, *etc.* 1727. fol. [*Aanmerkenswaardigste en alomberoemde Zee- en Landreizen der Portugeezen.* dl. 2.] **566.** l. **6.**

—— *See* REIS (Eduardo) Duarte Barbosa. Pioneiro revelador dos costumes das Índias. Relação biográfica, *etc.* [With a bibliography.] 1948. 8º. **10630.** l. **30.**

—— Livro de Duarte Barbosa. 1812. *See* LISBON.—*Academia das Sciencias de Lisboa.* Collecção de Noticias de Historia e Geografia das Nações Ultramarinas, *etc.* tom. 2. 1812, *etc.* 8º. **1446.** i. **3.**

—— Livro em que dá relação do que viu e ouviu no Oriente Duarte Barbosa. Introdução e notas de Augusto Reis Machado. pp. 240. 1946. 8º. *See* PORTUGAL.—*Ministério do Ultramar.—Agência Geral do Ultramar.* **10055.** d. **37.**

BARBOSA (Duarte)

—— [Livro de Duarte Barbosa.] A Description of the Coasts of East Africa and Malabar in the beginning of the sixteenth century . . . Translated [from the Spanish version made in 1524] . . . with notes and a preface, by the Hon. H. E. J. Stanley. pp. xi. 336 [236]. 1866. 8°. *See* London.—iii. *Hakluyt Society.* Ac. **6172/33.**

—— The Book of Duarte Barbosa. An account of the countries bordering on the Indian Ocean and their inhabitants . . . Translated from the Portuguese text . . . and edited and annotated by M. L. Dames. 2 vol. 1918, 21. 8°. *See* London.—iii. *Hakluyt Society.* Ac. **6172/105.**

—— Libro di Odoardo Barbessa . . . dell' Indie orientali.—Sommario [by an anonymous writer] di tutti li regni, città, & popoli dell' Indie orientali. (Discorso sopra'l libro . . . & sopra'l sommario delle Indie orientali.) [Translated, with additions, from the original Portuguese by G. B. Ramusio.] *See* Navigazioni. Primo volume delle nauigationi e viaggi, *etc.* 1550. fol. C. **46.** i. **3.**

—— [Another edition.] Libro dell' Indie, *etc.* (Nauigation d'vn Portoghese compagno d'Odoardo Barbosa che fu sopra la naue vittoria attorno al mondo.) *See* Ramusio (G. B.) Primo volume, & seconda editione delle nauigationi et viaggi, *etc.* 1554, *etc.* fol. **566.** k. **1.**

—— [Another edition.] *See* Ramusio (G. B.) Primo volume, & terza editione delle nauigationi, *etc.* 1563, *etc.* fol. **679.** h. **8.**

—— [Another edition.] *See* Ramusio (G. B.) Primo volume, & quarta editione delle nauigationi, *etc.* 1588, *etc.* fol. C. **79.** e. **4.**

—— [Another edition.] *See* Ramusio (G. B.) Delle nauigationi et viaggi . . . volume primo. 1606. fol. **566.** i. 8.

BARBOSA (Fernando Antonio da Costa de) *See* Costa de Barbosa.

BARBOSA (Francisco de la Concepción) Non plus ultra de la nobleza. Sermon fúnebre . . . en las honras que el . . . Convento . . . de Corpus Christi hizo al corazon del Excmo. Señor D. Balthassar de Zuñiga y Guzman, Marqués de Valero, Duque de Arion, *etc.* *Mexico,* 1729. 4°. **4985.** de. **5.** (**13.**)

BARBOSA (Francisco Gomes) *See* Gomes Barbosa.

BARBOSA (Francisco Vilella) *See* Vilella Barbosa.

BARBOSA (Ignacio de Vilhena) *See* Vilhena Barbosa.

BARBOSA (Jeronymo Soares) *See* Soares Barbosa.

BARBOSA (Joaquim Casimiro) *See* Periodical Publications.—*Oporto.* Jornal de Horticultura Practica, *etc.* [vol. 19 edited by J. C. Barbosa.] 1870, *etc.* 8°. P.P. **2141.** h.

BARBOSA (Joaquim Franco de Araujo Freire) *See* Franco de Araujo Freire Barbosa.

BARBOSA (José) *See* Brito (B. de) Elogios dos Reys de Portugal . . . addicionados pelo P. D. J. Barbosa. 1726. fol. **10632.** f. **24.**

—— —— 1761. 8°. **10632.** aa. **6.**

—— *See* João, *do Santissimo Sacramento, Augustinian.* Vida de S. Vicente de Paulo . . . traduzida em Portuguez por . . . J. Barbosa, *etc.* 1738. fol. **4827.** h. **12.**

—— *See* Severim de Faria (M.) Noticias de Portugal . . . acrescentadas, pelo padre D. J. Barbosa, *etc.* 1740. 8°. **10161.** f. **7.**

—— —— 1791. 8°. **10161.** aa. **31.**

BARBOSA (José)

—— Catalogo chronologico, historico, genealogico, e critico das rainhas de Portugal, e seus filhos. pp. 491. *Lisboa Occidental,* 1727. 4°. **606.** h. **8**

—— Historia da fundaçaõ do Real Convento do S. Christo da religiosas Capuchinhas Francezas, vidas das suas funda doras, e de algumas religiosas insignes em virtudes . . Offerecida a' Magestade del Rey Joaõ v. nosso Senhor pela M. Abbadessa, e mais religiosas do mesmo convento [With portraits.] pp. 477. *Lisboa,* 1748. 4°. **4625.** c. **14**

—— Illustrissimo . . . Domino Nonio Alvares Pereria d Mello . . . Archiathenæum Lusitanum, sive Regale Col legium Collimbriense d. o. et c. D. J. Barbosa, *etc.* pp. 280. *Ulyssipone,* 1733. 4°. **11405.** f. **8**

—— Memorias do Collegio Real de S. Paulo da Universidad de Coimbra, e dos seus collegiaes, e porcionistas, *etc* pp. 426. [*Lisbon,* 1727.] fol. **8305.** h. **13**

BARBOSA (José Casas) *See* Casas Barbosa.

BARBOSA (José de Freitas Amorim) *See* Freitas Amorim Barbosa.

BARBOSA (José Pereira de) *See* Pereira de Barbosa.

BARBOSA (Juan Antonio) Un Juicio sobre el aconteci miento político que tuvo lugar en Carácas el 24 de Ener de 1848 [i.e. the assassination of Miguel Riverol, an subsequent conflict between the Guard of the Chamber o Representatives and the people]. pp. 13. *Carácas* 1851. 8°. **8180.** e. **7.** (3.

BARBOSA (Manoel Maria de) *See* Barbosa du Bocage

BARBOSA (Margarida Gomes) *See* Gomes Barbosa.

BARBOSA (Mario de Lima) *See* Lima Barbosa.

BARBOSA (Odoardo) *See* Barbosa (Duarte)

BARBOSA (Petrus) Petri Barbosæ opera omnia . . Cum decisionibus S. Rotæ Romanæ recentissimis. 6 ton *Coloniæ Allobrogum,* 1737. fol. **494.** l. **3–5**

—— Petri Barbosæ . . . Commentarii ad interpretatione Tituli, ff. de Iudiciis. Operâ . . . Petri Barbosæ d Luna, *etc.* pp. 502. *E Collegio Musarum nouenaru Paltheniano: Francofurti,* 1615. fol. **504.** k. **11.** (2.

—— Dn. Petri Barbosæ . . . De matrimonio et pluribus ali materiebus, in Tit. ff. Soluto matrimonio quemadmo dos pet. . . . Accessit . . . index . . . Editio nouissim 2 tom. *I. A. Huguetan: Lugduni,* 1668. fol. **495.** l. 4

BARBOSA (Ruy)

—— *See* Delgado (L.) Rui Barbosa. Tentativa de com preensão e de síntese. 1945. 8°. W.P. **585/48**

—— *See* Jacobina Lacombe (A.) Formação literária de Ru Barbosa. 1954. 8°. Ac. **2699**/3. (**21.**

—— *See* Lemos (Miguel) Le Calendrie positiviste et M. le Ministre des Finances [i.e. R Barbosa], *etc.* 1890. 8°. **8461.** b. **28.** (4

—— *See* Lima Barbosa (M. de) Ruy Barbosa . . . Étud *etc.* 1917. 8°. **8425.** w.

—— *See* Lima Barbosa (M. de) Ruy Barbosa na politica na historia, 1849–1914. 1916. 8°. **010880.** f. **31**

—— *See* Mangabeira (J.) Rui, o estadista da república, *et* [With portraits.] 1943. 8°. [*Coleção documentos bras leiros.* vol. 40.] W.P. **585/4**

BARBOSA (RUY)

—— See PEREIRA (Baptista) Ruy Barbosa. Catalogo das suas obras. [With a facsimile.] 1929. 8°. **011900**. aaa. **4**.

—— See PIRES (H.) Anglo-American Political Influences on Rui Barbosa, etc. [With a portrait.] 1949. 8°. **8012**. d. **23**.

—— See RIO DE JANEIRO.—*Casa de Rui Barbosa*. A Simple Guide for Visitors to Casa de Rui Barbosa. [1955.] 8°. **10482**. a. **15**.

—— See SWIFT (Jonathan) *Dean of St. Patrick's*. [*Gulliver's Travels.—Translations*.] As Viagens de Gulliver . . . Prefaciadas com um artigo critico . . . pelo . . . Conselheiro R. Barbosa, etc. 1888. 8°. **12604**. i. **15**.

—— See TURNER (Charles W.) Ruy Barbosa, etc. [With portraits.] [1945.] 8°. **10889**. e. **8**.

—— See VIANA FILHO (L.) Rui & Nabuco, etc. [With a portrait.] 1949. 8°. W.P. **585/64**.

—— Antología. Selección y notas de Luís Viana Filho. Traducción de Justo Pastor Benítez. pp. 256. *Rio de Janeiro*, 1954. 8°. **12299**. g. **19**.

—— Barbosa. Prólogo y selección de Renato de Mendonça. pp. xxxii. 251. 1944. 8°. See MÉXICO.—*Secretaría de Educación Pública*. **12298**. g. **10**.

—— A Short Anthology. Translated by Gladys Petrina Medrado Stephens. [With plates, including a portrait.] pp. 102. *Casa de Rui Barbosa: [Rio de Janeiro,]* 1955. 8°. **12300**. d. **2**.

—— Acção de nullidade de arbitramento, movida pelo Espirito Santo contra Minas Geraes na questão de limites entre os dois Estados. Petição inicial. pp. 150. *Rio de Janeiro*, 1915. 8°. **6784**. bbb. **5**.

—— Americo Werneck v. Minas Geraes. Sustentação dos embargos do estado appellante. pp. 229. *Rio de Janeiro*, 1918. 8°. **6784**. h. **7**.

—— Amnistia inversa. Caso de teratologia juridica. Segunda edição. pp. xviii. 127. *Rio de Janeiro*, 1896. 8°. **8180**. dd. **13**.

—— Cartas de Inglaterra. pp. xx. 410. *Rio de Janeiro*, 1896. 8°. **012356**. ff. **46**.

—— Centenario do Marquez de Pombal. Discurso . . . Edição especial. pp. 84. *Rio de Janeiro*, 1882. 8°. **10629**. ee. **46**. (**2**.)

—— Los Conceptos Modernos del Derecho Internacional. Disertación, etc. pp. iv. 117. *J. Truscott & Son*: *Londres*, 1916. 8°. **6916**. a. **15**.

—— Conférence au profit de la Croix-Rouge des Alliés . . . 17 mars 1917. Traduction de C. Gazet. See LIMA BARBOSA (M. de) Ruy Barbosa, etc. 1917. 8°. **8425**. w. **6**.

—— Le Devoir des neutres. Avant-propos: La Sentence du juge, par M. Graça Aranha . . . Traduit . . . par Cardozo de Bethencourt . . . Avec un portrait, etc. pp. 91. *Paris*, 1917. 8°. **08027**. ee. **5**.

—— Discursos pronunciados na Conferencia de Haya. See STEAD (William T.) O Brazil em Haya . . . Notas sobre a Conferencia, etc. 1908. 8°. **8425**. de. **55**.

—— Finanças e Politica da Republica. Discursos e escriptos. pp. x. 475. [*Rio de Janeiro*,] 1892. 8°. **8179**. c. **53**.

—— A Genese da Candidatura do Sr. Wencesláo Braz. O Sr. Ruy Barbosa, no Senado, responde ás insinuações do Sr. Pinheiro Machado. [With a portrait.] pp. 83. *Rio de Janeiro*, 1915. 8°. **8179**. b. **54**.

—— Memoria apresentada pelo Sr. Senador R. Barbosa. 1911. See BRAZIL.—*Congresso Nacional*. Annaes . . . Apuração da eleição de Presidente e Vice-Presidente da Republica, etc. vol. 2. 1910, etc. 8°. **L.A.S.161/5.**

—— Oração aos moços. Edição comemorativa do centenário de nascimento do grande brasileiro. Fac-símile do texto original . . . mandada publicar pela Reitoria da Universidade de São Paulo, etc. [With portraits.] *São Paulo*, 1949. 4°. **6786**. e. **2**.

—— Orações do Apostolo. Marquês de Pombal—Lyceu de Artes e Officios—Jornal do Commercio—Ensaio sobre Swift. pp. 250. *Rio de Janeiro*, 1923. 8° **11878.aa.27.**

—— O Partido Republicano Conservador. Documentos de uma tentativa baldada. pp. 130. *Rio de Janeiro*, 1897. 8°. **8180**. dd. **12**.

—— Plataforma apresentada . . . 15 de Janeiro de 1910. 2ª edicção, etc. [With a portrait.] pp. 83. *Bahia*, 1910. 8°. **12301**. i. **15**.

—— Os Privilegios exclusivos na jurisprudencia constitucional dos Estados Unidos. pp. vi. 72. [*Rio de Janeiro*,] 1911. 8°. **6616**. ccc. **25**.

—— Problemas de Direito Internacional. Conferencia, etc. [With a portrait.] pp. 138. *J. Truscott & Son: Londres*, 1916. 8°. **6916**. a. **14**.

—— Questão Minas Werneck. Competencia do Supremo Tribunal Federal nas appellações de sentenças arbitraes. pp. 120. *Rio de Janeiro*, 1917. 8°. **6784**. bbb. **6**.

—— A Revogação da Neutralidade do Brazil. Dois discursos pronunciados pelo Senador Dr. R. Barbosa e pelo Deputado Dr. P. Moacyr. pp. 147. *R. Clay & Son: Londres*, 1918. 8°. **8180**. aa. **67**.

—— A Transacção do Acre no Tratado de Petropolis. Polemica. pp. 126. *Rio de Janeiro*, 1906. 8°. **6784**. aaa. **41**.

—— Pages choisies . . . Traduction de Clément Gazet. Préface de Paul Deschanel, etc. pp. xviii. 303. *Rio-de-Janeiro; Laval* [printed], 1917. 8°. **12230**. g. **15**.

BARBOSA (SIMON VAZ) See VAZ BARBOSA.

BARBOSA BACELLAR (ANTONIO) [Sonnets and other poems.] See PEREIRA DA SILVA (M.) A Fenix Renascida, etc. 1746, etc. 8°. **11452**. a. **23**.

BARBOSA CANAES DE FIGUEIREDO CASTELLO-BRANCO (JOSÉ) Arvores de Costados das familias nobres dos reinos de Portugal, Algarves, e dominios ultramarinos, etc. tom. 2. pp. xiii. ff. 240. x. *Lisboa*, 1831. 4°. **9905**. d. **19**.

For tom. 1 see infra: Costados das familias illustres de Portugal, etc. Four volumes were advertised by the author but only two published.

—— Collecção de Arvores de Costado. [By J. Barbosa Canaes de Figueiredo Castello-Branco.] caderno 1. pp. 32. 1855. 4°. See COLLECÇÃO. **9917.h.34.**
No more published.

—— Costados das Familias illustes [*sic*] de Portugal, Algarves, Ilhas e Indias. tom. 1. pp. viii. ff. 95. *Lisboa*, 1829. 4°. **9905**. d. **18**.

For tom. 2 see supra: Arvores de Costados das familias nobres dos reinos de Portugal, etc.

—— Estudos biographicos, ou noticia das pessoas retratadas nos quadros historicos pertencentes á Bibliotheca Nacional de Lisboa. pp. lxxvi. 317. *Lisboa*, 1854. fol. **10604**. h. **11**.

BARBOSA CARNEIRO (João Martins) *See* Martins Barbosa Carneiro.

BARBOSA CARNEIRO (Octavio) Contra a obrigatoriedade da vaccina. Rezumo dos discursos pronunciados pelos Senadores Lauro Sodré e Barata Ribeiro contra o projecto de lei tornando obrigatorias a vaccinão . . . em toda a Republica. pp. 16. [*Rio de Janeiro*, 1904.] 8°. **07561**. f. **27**.

BARBOSA DE FARIA (João)

—— *See* Silva Rondon (C. M. da) Esboço gramatical, vocabulário, lendas e cânticas dos Índios Ariti-Parici . . . com a colaboração do doutorando João Barbosa de Faria, *etc.* 1948. 8°. [*Comissão Rondon. Publicação.* no. 78.] L.A.S. **170**.

BARBOSA DE LUNA (Petrus) *See* Barbosa (P.) Petri Barbosæ . . . Commentarii ad interpretationem Tituli, ff. de Iudiciis. Operâ . . . P. Barbosæ de Luna, *etc.* 1615. fol. **504**. k. **11**. (**2**.)

BARBOSA DE REZENDE (Cassio)

—— Faculdade de Medicina do Rio de Janeiro. These apresentada . . . pelo Dr. C. Barbosa de Rezende . . . Hemothorax pleural consecutivo aos traumatismos, *etc.* pp. 98. *Rio de Janeiro*, 1903. 4°. **7379**. n. **2**. (**7**.)

BARBOSA DE SÁ (Joseph)

—— Relação das povoaçoens do Cuyabá e Mato groso de seos principios thé os prezentes tempos. 1904. *See* Rio de Janeiro.—*Bibliotheca Nacional.* Annaes, *etc.* vol. 23. 1876, *etc.* 8°. Ac. **9205**.

BARBOSA DU BOCAGE (José Vicente) Instrucções praticas sobre o modo de colligir, preparar e remetter productos zoologicos para o Museu de Lisboa. pp. 96. ii. 1862. 8°. *See* Lisbon.—*Museu Nacional de Lisboa.* **7206**. cc. **11**.

BARBOSA DU BOCAGE (Manoel Maria de) *See* Braga (T.) Bocage. Sua vida e epoca litteraria. 1876. 8°. **10632**. aa. **57**.

—— —— 1902. 8°. **011853**. gg. **18**.

—— *See* Couto (A. M. do) Memorias sobra a vida de M. M. Barbosa du Bocage. 1806. 8°. **10632**. a. **6**.

—— *See* Cardoso (J. F.) Joanni . . . Portugaliae Principi . . . de rebus a Lusit. ad Tripolim virilit. gestis carmen, *etc.* (Ao . . . Principe . . . D. João . . . canto heroico sobre as façanh. dos Portuguezes na expedição de Tripoli . . . traduzido por M. M. de Barbosa du Bocage.) 1800. 4°. **1213**. m. **41**.

—— Poesias . . . colligidas . . . dispostas e annotadas por I. F. da Silva: e precedidas de um estudo biographico e litterario sobre o poeta, escripto por L. A. Rebello da Silva. [With a portrait.] 6 tom. *Lisboa*, 1853. 8°. **11452**. cc. **14**.

—— Obras poeticas de Bocage. [With a biography by Theophilo Braga.] 7 vol. *Porto*, 1875, 76. 8°. **11422**. aaa. **7**.

—— Rimas . . . Segunda edição correcta, e augmentada. 3 tom. *Lisboa*, 1800–06. 8°. **11452**. b. **3**. *Tom. 3 is entitled: "Poesias."*

—— Collecção dos novos improvisos de Bocage na sua molestia, com as obras, que lhe forão dirigidas por varios poetas nacionaes, *etc.* pp. 100. *Lisboa*, 1805. 8°. **11452**. aaa. **14**.

—— Rimas . . . Terceira edição. 3 tom. *Lisboa*, 1806, 13, 06. 8°. **1064**. a. **26–28**. *Tom. 3 is entitled: "Poesias."*

BARBOSA DU BOCAGE (Manoel Maria de)

—— Verdadeiras ineditas, obras poeticas de M. M. de Barbosa du Bocage. Tomo iv. (v.) e 1°. (2°.) das suas obras posthumas. [tom. 5 edited by Nuño Alvares Pereira Pato Moniz.] 2 vol. *Lisboa*, 1813, 14. 8°. **1064**. a. **29**.

—— Os Amores [and other poems]. 1827. *See* Portuguese Parnassus. Parnaso Lusitano, *etc.* tom. 4. 1826, *etc.* 16°. **1161**. a. **33**.

—— Arenêo e Argira.—Tritão.—A Saudade materna. [Poems.] 1827. *See* Portuguese Parnassus. Parnasso Lusitano, *etc.* tom. 2. 1826, *etc.* 16°. **1161**. a. **32**.

—— Epistola i(–iv). [In verse.] 1827. *See* Portuguese Parnassus. Parnaso Lusitano, *etc.* tom. 5. 1826, *etc.* 16°. **1161**. a. **34**.

—— Sonetos.—Da Medicina.—Elmiro.—Improviso a morte de Socrates. 1827. *See* Portuguese Parnassus. Parnaso Lusitano, *etc.* tom. 3. 1826, *etc.* 16°. **1161**. a. **33**.

—— Obras poeticas . . . precedidas de hum discurso sobre a vida, e escriptos deste poeta . . . por José Maria da Costa e Silva. Tomo vi. pp. 308. *Lisboa*, 1842. 8°. **11451**. bb. **2**.

—— M. M. Barbosa du Bocage. (Escolha das suas obras poeticas, e noticia da sua vida e obras.) 9 pt. 1845–47. *See* Castilho (A. F. de) and Castilho Barreto e Noronha (J. F. de) Livraria Classica Portugueza, *etc.* tom. 17–25. 1845, *etc.* 16°. **12231**. aa. **2**.

—— M. M. du Bocage. Excerptos, seguidos de uma noticia sobre sua vida e obras, um juizo critico, apreciações de bellezas e defeitos e estudos de lingua por José Feliciano de Castilho Barreto e Noronha. 3 tom. *Rio de Janeiro*; *Paris* [printed], 1867. 8°. [*Livraria Classica.* tom. 6–8.] **12231.e.9/6–8.**

—— Sentença proferida na casinha da Almotaceria pelo Supremo Juizo da Inconfidencia Literaria, na sessão xi. sobre o quarto tomo das Obras poeticas de M. M. de Barbosa du Bocage, dada á luz para desengano dos patetas. [A satire on José Maria da Costa e Silva, the editor thereof, by Pedro José de Figueiredo.] pp. 15. *Lisboa*, 1813. 4°. **11900**. bbb. **17**.

BARBOSA FERREIRA TEIXEIRA GYRÃO (Antonio Lobo de) *Viscount de Villarinho de Santo Romão.* *See* Lobo de Barbosa Ferreira Teixeira Gyrão.

BARBOSA GONÇALVES PENNA (Raul)

—— Faculdade de Medicina do Rio de Janeiro. These apresentada . . . pelo Dr. R. Barbosa Gonçalves Penna . . . Das operaçoes que se praticam para a cura dos empyemas chronicos, *etc.* pp. 74. *Rio de Janeiro*, 1903. 4°. **7379**. n. **2**. (**6**.)

BARBOSA HOMEM (Pedro) Discursos de la iuridica, y verdadera razon de estado, formados sobre la vida, y acciones del Rey Don Iuan el ii. . . . Rey de Portugal, contra Machavelo, y Bodino . . . Primera parte. ff. 334. *N. Caruallo: Coimbra*, 1629. 4°. **1449**. b. **21**.

BARBOSA MACHADO (Diogo)

—— *See* Ramiz Galvão (B. F.) Diogo Barbosa Machado e seus escriptos. 1913. 8°. [*Boletim da Sociedade de Biblióphilos Barbosa Machado.* vol. 2.] Ac. **9547**. b.

—— *See* Rio de Janeiro.—*Bibliotheca Nacional.* Catalogo dos retratos colligidos por Diogo Barboza Machado. 1893, *etc.* 4°. [*Annaes da Bibliotheca Nacional do Rio de Janeiro.* vol. 16–18, 20, 21, 26.] Ac. **9205**.

BARBOSA MACHADO (Diogo)

—— Bibliotheca Lusitana historica, critica, e cronologica. Na qual se comprehende a noticia dos authores Portuguezes, e das obras, que compuseraõ desde o tempo da promulgaçaõ da ley da graça até o tempo prezente. [With a portrait.] 4 tom. *Lisboa* 1741–59. fol. **12218.ee.2.**

—— [Another copy.] G. **238–41.**

—— [Another copy of tom. 1, 2.] **124.** l. **8, 9.**

—— Summario da Bibliotheca Luzitana [of D. Barbosa Machado]. 4 tom. 1786. 12°. *See* Portuguese Library. **618.** a. **27–30.**

—— [Another copy.] **272.** a. **31–34.**

—— *See* Elisio. Elisio e Serrano. Dialogo em que se defende e illustra a Bibliotheca Lusitana [of D. Barbosa Machado] contra a prefação da Lusitania transformada, *etc.* 1782. 8°. **618.** a. **34.**

—— Elogio funebre do beneficiado Francisco Leitaõ Ferreira, *etc.* pp. 23. *Lisboa*, 1736. fol. **9181.** e. **4. (46.)**

—— Memorias para a historia de Portugal, que comprehendem o governo del Rey D. Sebastiaõ . . . do anno de 1554. até o anno de 1561. [With a portrait of the king.] 4 tom. *Lisboa*, 1736–51. 4°. **815.** l. **6–9.**

—— Diogo Barbosa Machado. (Catalogo de suas colecções, por B. F. Ramiz Galvão.) [With a portrait.] 1876–81. *See* Rio de Janeiro.—*Bibliotheca Nacional.* Annaes, *etc.* vol. 1–3, 8. 1876, *etc.* 8°. Ac. **9205.**

BARBOSA MACHADO (Ignacio) *See* also Costa Freyre (Valeriano de) *pseud.* [i.e. I. Barbosa Machado.]

—— Carta exhortatória aos padres da Companhia de Jesus da província de Portugal. [Attributed to Barbosa Machado. Edited by Mendes dos Remédios.] pp. 45. 1909. 8°. *See* Jesuits. [*Miscellaneous.*] **4091.** i. **6.**

—— Fastos politicos, e militares da antigua, e nova Lusitania, em que se descrevem as acçoens memoraveis, que na paz, e na guerra obraraõ os Portuguezes nas quatro partes do mundo . . . Com huma dissertaçaõ critica ao Anno Historico, e Diario Portuguez do Padre Francisco de Santa Maria, e hum appendix à dissertaçaõ precedente contra o Padre Doutor Lourenço Justiniano da Annunçiaçaõ. tom. 1. pp. 711. *Lisboa*, 1745. fol. **1322.** k. **4.**
No more published.

—— Historia critico-chronologica da instituiçam da festa, procissam, e officio do Corpo santissimo de Christo no Veneravel Sacramento da Eucharistia, *etc.* pp. 216. *Lisboa*, 1759. fol. **4323.** g. **9.**

—— Panegyrico historico do serenissimo Senhor Infante Dom Manoel, no qual se escrevem as gloriosas acçoens que tem obrado na paz e na guerra depois que sahio do reyno de Portugal, atè o fim da vitoriosa campanha de Hungria do anno passado de 1716, *etc.* pp. 31. *Lisboa Occidental*, 1717. 4°. **1323.** d. **22. (7.)**

—— Vindicias apologeticas e criticas contra o prologo anticritico que escreveo o P. D. Lourenço Justiniano da Annunciaçam . . . impugnando a dissertaçam e appendix dos Fastos politicos e militares da Lusitania; monstraõse os erros palmares, em que cahío o P. Francisco de Santa Maria, no seo Anno historico, *etc.* pp. 421. *Paris*, 1760. fol. **1852.** c. **8.**

BARBOSA PEREIRA CORREIA (Francisco)

—— Monsanto. A aldeia mais portuguesa de Portugal Roteiro, *etc.* pp. 21. *Castelo Branco*, 1939. 8°. **10163.** f. **21.**

BARBOSA RODRIGUES (João) *See* Ensaios. Ensaios de Sciencia, por diversos amadores. [By Guilherme Schüch de Capanema, B. C. de Almeida Nogueira and J. Barbosa Rodrigues.] 1876. 8°. **8707.** k. **4.**

—— *See* Manaos.—*Museu Botanico do Amazonas.* Vellosia. Contribuicões, *etc.* [Edited by J. Barbosa Rodrigues.] 1891, *etc.* fol. Ac. **3316.**

—— *See* Roméro (S.) Ethnographia Brazileira. Estudos criticos sobre Couto de Magalhães, Barbosa Rodrigues, *etc.* 1888. 8°. **10481.** b. **42.**

—— Contributions du Jardin botanique de Rio de Janeiro. pp. 125. pl. xxvii. *Rio de Janeiro*, 1901–07. 4°. **7033.** l. **12.**
A continuation in French of the author's "Plantas novas, etc."

—— Eclogae plantarum novarum.—Palmae Amazonensis novae.—Genera et species orchidearum novarum. *See* Manaos.—*Museu Botanico do Amazonas.* Vellosia. Contribuições, *etc.* vol. 1. 1891, *etc.* fol. Ac. **3316.**

—— Genera et species orchidearum novarum quas collegit, descripsit et iconibus illustravit J. Barbosa Rodrigues. pt. 1. pp. vii. 206. x. *Sebastianopolis* [*Rio de Janeiro*], 1877. 8°. **7031.** f. **18.**
No more published.

—— As Heveas ou Seringueiras. pp. 86. *Rio de Janeiro*, 1900. 8°. **7031.** h. **8.**

—— Hortus Fluminensis, ou breve noticia sobre as plantas cultivadas no Jardim Botanico do Rio de Janeiro, *etc.* pp. xxxviii. 307. xvi. ii. *Rio de Janeiro*, 1894. 8°. **7028.** ee. **5.**
The date on the wrapper is 1895.

—— O Jardim Botanico do Rio de Janeiro. Uma lembrança do 1° centenario. 1808–1908. [With illustrations.] pp. 43. [*Rio de Janeiro*,] 1908. *obl.* 8°. **7031.** pp. **12.**

—— Mbaé kaá tapyiyetá enoyndaua, ou a botanica e a nomenclatura indigena, *etc.* pp. vi. 87. *Rio de Janeiro*, 1905. 8°. **12910.** dd. **45.**

—— O Muyrakytã. Estudo da origem asiatica da civilização do Amazonas nos tempos prehistoricos. pt. 1. pp. xv. 162. *Manaos*, 1889. 8°. **10481.** d. **28.**

—— O Muyrakytã e os idolos symbolicos . . . Segunda edição muito augmentada. 2 vol. *Rio de Janeiro*, 1899. 8°. **4505.** h. **2.**

—— Myrtacées du Paraguay recueillies par M^r le Dr Emile Hassler et déterminées par J. Barbosa Rodrigues. pp. vi. 20. pl. xxvi. *Bruxelles*, 1903. 8°. **7033.** k. **13.**

—— Les Noces des palmiers. Remarques préliminaires sur la fécondation. pp. 90. pl. viii. *Bruxelles*, 1903. 8°. **07077.** i. **29.**

—— Palmae Hasslerianae novae, ou Relação das palmeiras encontradas no Paraguay pelo Dr. Emilio Hassler de 1898–1899, determinadas e desenhadas por J. Barbosa Rodrigues. pp. vii. 16. *Rio de Janeiro*, 1900. 4°. **7074.** m. **16.**

—— Palmae Mattogrossenses novae vel minus cognitae quas collegit descripsit et iconibus illustravit J. Barbosa Rodrigues. pp. xx. 88. *Rio de Janeiro*, 1898. fol. **7028.** h. **25.**

—— Palmae novae Paraguayenses quas descripsit et iconibus illustravit J. Barbosa Rodrigues. *Port.* pp. ix. 66. *Rio de Janeiro*, 1899. 4°. **7033.** l. **5.**

—— Plantae Mattogrossenses, ou relação de plantas novas colhidas, classificadas e desenhadas por J. Barbosa Rodrigues. pp. vii. 43. pl. iii. *Rio de Janeiro*, 1898. fol. **7028.** h. **26.**

BARBOSA RODRIGUES (João)

—— Plantas novas cultivadas no Jardim Botanico do Rio de Janeiro, descriptas, classificadas e desenhadas. 6 pt. *Rio de Janeiro*, 1891–98. 4°. **7029**. i. **14**.
Continued in French as "Contributions du Jardin botanique," etc.

—— Poranduba Amazonense ou kochiyma-uara porandub . . . 1872–1887. pp. xv. 334. 2. *Rio de Janeiro*, 1890. 8°. **12906**. t. **18**.

—— [Another copy.] **12430**. l. 9.

—— [Another issue.] Poranduba Amazonense ou Kochiyma-Uara Porandub. *Rio de Janeiro*, 1890. 8°. [*Annaes da Bibliotheca Nacional do Rio de Janeiro*. vol. 14. fasc. 2.] Ac. **9205**.

—— Relação das plantas expostas pelo Jardim Botanico do Rio de Janeiro. pp. viii. 121. 1908. 8°. *See* Rio de Janeiro.—*Exposição Nacional de* 1908. **07029**. eee. **16**. (**5**.)

—— Rio Jauapery. Pacificação dos Crichanás. pp. 274. *Rio de Janeiro*, 1885. 8°. **010480**. ee. **23**.

—— Sertum palmarum Brasiliensium, ou relation des palmiers nouveaux du Brésil découverts, décrits et dessinés d'après nature par J. Barbosa Rodrigues. 2 pt. *Bruxelles*, 1903. fol. **1827**. d. **8**.

—— O Tamakoaré: especies novas da ordem das Ternstroemiaceas. pp. 28. *Manáos*, 1887. 8°. **7073**. f. **18**. (**1**.)

—— L'Uiraêry ou Curare. Extraits et complément des notes d'un naturaliste brésilien. pp. 180. pl. vii. *Bruxelles*, 1903. 8°. **07509**. g. **17**.

—— Vocabulario indigena comparado para mostrar a adulteração da lingua. Complemento do Poranduba Amazonense, *etc.* (Vocabulario indigena com a orthographia correcta, *etc.*) 2 pt. 1892, 93. 8°. *See* Rio de Janeiro.—*Bibliotheca Nacional*. **12907**. f. **21**.

—— [Another copy of pt. 1.] **12941**. i. **15**.

—— [Another issue.] Vocabulario Indigena, *etc.* *Rio de Janeiro*, 1892, 94. 8°. [*Annaes da Bibliotheca Nacional do Rio de Janeiro*. vol. 15. fasc. 2; vol. 16. fasc. 2.] Ac. **9205**.

BARBOSA SACCHETTI (Bernardo Xavier) *See* Philocrûz (Veríssimo) *pseud.* [i.e. B. Xavier Barbosa Sacchetti.]

BARBOSA VIANNA (A. J.) O Recife, capital do estado de Pernambuco. [With illustrations and a map.] pp. 242. *Recife*, 1900. 8°. **10481**. pp. **29**.

BARBÒ SONCIN (Antonio) *See* Biaggi (L.) Trattato del cholera-morbus . . . Commentario delle febbre e dell'arterite. Opere postume . . . ordinate . . . dai dottori Ferdinando Coletti e A. Barbò-Soncin. 1855, *etc.* 8°. **7305**. c. **7**.

BARBOT (Alexandre Théobald) Quelques considérations sur la fièvre typhoïde en général, quelques mots sur sa forme ataxique observée chez les enfants. pp. 39. *Paris*, 1858. 4°. [*Collection des thèses soutenues à la Faculté de Médecine de Paris*. An 1858. tom. 1.] **7373**. a. 15.

BARBOT (Amos) Histoire de La Rochelle . . . Publiée par M. Denys d'Aussy. 3 pt. 1886–90. *See* Saintes.—*Société des Archives historiques de la Saintonge, etc.* Archives historiques, *etc.* tom. 14, 17, 18. 1874, *etc.* 8°. Ac. **6892**.

BARBOT (Charles) Traité complet des pierres précieuses . . . Ouvrage accompagné de trois planches, *etc.* pp. 567. *Paris*, 1858. 12°. **7105**. a. **7**.

—— [Another copy, with a different titlepage.] **7105**. a. **8**.

—— Guide pratique du joaillier, ou traité complet des pierres précieuses . . . Nouvelle édition revue . . . par . . . M. Charles Baye. 8 planches, *etc.* pp. 355. *Paris*, [1884.] 12°. **7106**. aa. **11**.

BARBOT (D.) Guide pratique du jeune élève en pharmacie. Contre-étiquettes pharmaceutiques renfermant . . . toutes les notions et renseignements indispensables pour instruire l'élève . . . contenant en outre le contre-poison des substances toxiques . . . 2me édition, augmentée de 400 nouvelles contre-étiquettes. *Saint-Jean-d'Angély*, 1869. 16°. **7509**. aaa. **9**.

BARBOT (Émile) Faculté de Droit de Paris. Thèse pour la licence. (Jus Romanum. De compensationibus, *etc.*—Droit français. De la novation, *etc.*) pp. 30. *Paris*, 1857. 8°. **5406**. aa. **1**. (**15**.)

BARBOT (Ernest Jacques)

—— *See* Mordacq (J. J. H.) Pourquoi Arras ne fut pas pris, 1914, *etc.* [On the part played by the 77th division under General Barbot. With portraits.] 1934. 8°. **09080**. a. **19**.

BARBOT (Fernand) Des principaux troubles fonctionnels pendant la grossesse. pp. 34. *Paris*, 1857. 4°. [*Collection des thèses soutenues à la Faculté de Médecine de Paris*. An 1857. tom. 1.] **7373**. a. **1**.

BARBOT (Gabriel) Dissertation sur la pleurésie aiguë; thèse, *etc.* pp. 27. *Paris*, 1835. 4°. **1184**. g. **5**. (**22**.)

BARBOT (Gabrielle Suzanne) *See* Gallon de Villeneuve.

BARBOT (Germain) Recherches sur les plantes du genre rhubarbe; thèse, *etc.* pp. 20. *Paris*, 1816. 4°. **1183**. c. **16**. (**15**.)

BARBOT (Jacques) An Abstract of a Voyage to Congo River, or the Zair, and to Cabinde in the year 1700, by James Barbot . . . and John Casseneuve. [With plates.] 1746. *See* Churchill (Awnsham) and (J.) A Collection of Voyages and Travels. vol. 5. 1744, *etc.* fol. **455**. f. **5**.

—— [Another edition, abridged.] 1746. *See* Collection. A New General Collection of Voyages, *etc.* vol. 3. 1745, *etc.* 4°. **212**. e. **12**.

—— An Abstract of a Voyage to New Calabar River, or Rio Real, in the year 1699, *etc.* 1746. *See* Churchill (Awnsham) and (J.) A Collection of Voyages and Travels. vol. 5. 1744, *etc.* fol. **455**. f. **5**.

—— [Another edition.] Mr. James Barbot's Voyage to New Kalabar. 1746. *See* Collection. A New General Collection of Voyages, *etc.* vol. 3. 1745, *etc.* 4°. **212**. e. **12**.

BARBOT (James) *See* Barbot (Jacques)

BARBOT (Jean) A Description of the Coasts of North and South-Guinea; and of Ethiopia Inferior, vulgarly Angola: being a new . . . account of the Western maritime countries of Africa. In six books. Containing a geographical, political and natural history of the kingdoms . . . with a full account of all the European settlements . . . and a new relation of the province of Guiana, and of the great rivers of Amazons and Oronoque in South-America. With an Appendix; being a general account of the first discoveries of America, *etc.* [With plates.] 1732. *See* Churchill (Awnsham) and (J.) A Collection of Voyages and Travels, *etc.* vol. 5. 1732. fol. **566**. k. **10**.

BARBOT (JEAN)

—— [Another edition.] 1746. *See* CHURCHILL (Awnsham) and (J.) A Collection of Voyages and Travels. vol. 5. 1744, *etc.* fol. **455. f. 5.**

—— [Another edition.] *See* CHURCHILL (Awnsham) and (J.) A Collection of Voyages and Travels, *etc.* vol. 5. 1752. fol. **215. e. 5.**

—— A Description of Sierra Leona. [With plates.] 1745. *See* COLLECTION. A New General Collection of Voyages, *etc.* vol. 2. 1745, *etc.* 4°. **212. e. 11.**

—— Eine Beschreibung von Sierra Leona. (1678.) [With plates.] 1748. *See* SCHWABE (J. J.) Allgemeine Historie der Reisen, *etc.* Bd. 3. 1747, *etc.* 4°. **10025. dd.**

BARBOT (JOHN) *Murderer.* The Tryal of John Barbot . . . for the murder of Mathew Mills . . . To which is added, the prisoner's narrative of the cause of the difference between Mr. Mills and himself, *etc.* pp. 63. *J. Whiston & B. White: London,* 1753. fol. **6605. i. 19.**

BARBOT (JOHN) *Traveller. See* BARBOT (Jean)

BARBOT (JULES) Les Chroniques de la Faculté de Médecine de Toulouse du XIIIe au XXe siècle. Thèse, *etc.* [With illustrations.] 2 tom. *Toulouse,* 1905. 8°. **08355. k. 14.**

BARBOT (P. F. ARISTIDE) Essai sur l'hépatite aiguë. Tribut académique, *etc.* pp. 21. *Montpellier,* 1827. 4°. **1181. d. 11. (6.)**

BARBOT (RAÚL) Anotaciones al Código Civil. De las Sucesiones. 2 tom. *Montevideo,* 1929. 8°. **6784. bbb. 10.**

BARBOT (THÉOPHILE DE) Éloge de M. le vicomte de Panat, *etc.* pp. 28. *Toulouse,* [1862.] 8°. **10660. bb. 37. (9.)**

BARBOT DE LA TRÉSORIÈRE (MARC ANDRÉ) Annales historiques des anciennes provinces d'Aunis, Saintonge, Poitou, Angoumois, Périgord, Marche, Limousin et Guienne. pp. 168. *Paris,* 1858. 4°. **10172. dd. 2.**

BARBOT DE MARNI (NIKOLAI PAVLOVICH) Геологическій очеркъ Херсонской губерніи . . . Съ геологическою картою, профилями и рисунками. pp. x. 165. *С.-Петербургъ,* 1869. 8°. **7109. h. 35.**

BARBOTIN (FRANÇOIS JULIEN RENÉ) Faculté de Droit de Paris. Thèse pour le doctorat. (Des rapports à succession.) *Versailles,* 1856. 8°. **5406. a. 10. (5.)** *Imperfect; wanting all after p.* 190.

BARBOTIN (LOUIS) *See* BOURGEOIS (Henri) *of Luçon.* L'Abbé Barbotin, premier aumônier de la Grande Armée (1762–1848). 1908. 8°. **4864. de. 18.**

BARBOTTE (J.)

—— *See* MONTEL (P.) Leçons sur les familles normales de fonctions analytiques et leurs applications . . . Recueillies et rédigées par J. Barbotte. 1927. 8°. 8536. c. 4.

BARBOTTI (PAOLO) Illustrazione di un gran quadro a olio di P. Barbotti, *etc.* [Signed: G. d. C.] 1858. 8°. *See* C., G. d. **7856. aaa. 28. (6.)**

BARBOU, *Family of. See* DUCOURTIEUX (P.) Les Barbou, imprimeurs, *etc.* 1894, *etc.* 8°. [*Bulletin de la Société Archéologique du Limousin.* tom. 41, 42, 43, 45.] **Ac. 5312.**

—— —— 1896. 8°. **11899. d. 28.**

BARBOU (ALFRED) Le Chien, son histoire, ses exploits, ses aventures . . . Ouvrage illustré de 87 compositions, *etc.* pp. 352. *Paris,* 1883. 8°. **7291. f. 20.**

BARBOU (ALFRED)

—— Le Chien . . . Illustré par Paul Lemagny. pp. 246. *Paris,* 1937. 4°. **7294. v. 10.**

—— Le Général Boulanger. Biographie. Illustrée, *etc.* pp. 287. *Paris,* [1887.] 8°. **10664. aa. 26.**

—— Les Généraux de la République . . . Ouvrage illustré, *etc.* pp. 236. *Paris,* 1882. 8°. **10658. bbb. 20.**

—— Les Grands citoyens de la France. Gambetta. Histoire complète de sa vie. pp. 308. *Paris,* 1879. 16°. **10658. aa. 22.**

—— Trente-septième édition. pp. 372. *Paris,* 1883. 16°. **10658. a. 20.**

—— Les Grands citoyens de la France. Jules Grévy, Président de la République. Histoire complète de sa vie. pp. 312. *Paris,* 1879. 16°. **10658. a. 11.**

—— Les Grands citoyens de la France. S. Carnot, Président de la République. Histoire complète de sa vie. pp. 310. *Paris,* 1888. 16°. **10659. aa. 36.**

—— Les Grands marins de France. Histoire populaire de la marine française depuis les temps anciens jusqu'à nos jours. pp. 377. *Paris,* 1885. 32°. **8807. a. 10.**

—— Histoire complète anecdotique et populaire du drapeau français. pp. 318. *Paris,* [1880.] 16°. **8823. f. 1.**

—— Histoire de la guerre au Dahomey. [With illustrations.] pp. 154. *Paris,* 1893. 8°. **9061. h. 11.**

—— Nos amis les Russes; histoire, mœurs et coûtumes de la Russie. L'alliance franco-russe . . . Illustré, *etc.* pp. 159. *Paris,* 1893. 4°. **10292. l. 3.**

—— Les Trois Républiques françaises. Histoire populaire de la République en France. pp. 318. *Paris,* 1879. 16°. **9230. a. 4.**

—— [Another edition.] pp. 352. *Paris,* 1892. 8°. **9226. aa. 19.**

—— Victor Hugo et son temps. Edition illustrée de 120 dessins inédits par MM. E. Bayard, Clerget, Fichel . . . etc., et d'un très grand nombre de dessins de Victor Hugo, *etc.* pp. 468. *Paris,* 1881. 4°. **10703. g. 18.**

—— [Another copy.] **11840. l. 18.**

—— Victor Hugo and his Time . . . Illustrated . . . Translated from the French by E. E. Frewer. pp. xx. 397. *Sampson Low & Co.: London,* 1882. 8°. **10703. g. 19.**

BARBOU (GABRIEL) *See* BARBOU DES COURIÈRES.

BARBOU (JACQUES) *See* DUCOURTIEUX (P.) and BOURDERY (L.) Une Imprimerie et une librairie à Limoges vers la fin du seizième siècle. Jacques Barbou, imprimeur, 1570–1605. 1899. 8°. [*Bulletin de la Société archéologique et historique du Limousin.* tom. 47.] **Ac. 5312.**

BARBOU DES COURIÈRES (GABRIEL) *See* LACROIX (D.) Le Général Barbou, 1761–1827. [1901.] 8°. **010661. d. 7.**

BARBOUR (A. M.) *Author of "He is Nigh at the Doors."* Connemara, on the Eve of the Twentieth Century. pp. 64. *S. W. Partridge & Co.: London,* 1899. 8°. **3942. a. 9.**

—— "He is Nigh at the Doors" . . . Substance of an address . . . Second edition: revised and enlarged. pp. 48. *"Christian Herald" Printing Press: London,* [1893.] 8°. **4421. e. 60. (1.)**

BARBOUR (ADAM) The Rhuvaig Smuggler. A story of the Highland crofters. pp. iv. 154. *J. Menzies & Co.: Edinburgh & Glasgow,* 1889. 8°. **12629. m. 13.**

BARBOUR (ALBERT LESLIE) *See* BLACKMORE (Richard D.) Lorna Doone . . . Edited with introduction and notes by A. L. Barbour. 1911. 8°. **12199.a.1/72.**

BARBOUR (ALEXANDER HUGH FREELAND) *See* HART (David B.) and BARBOUR (A. H. F.) Manual of Gynecology, *etc.* 1882. 8°. **7580. df. 4.**

—— —— 1883. 8°. **07581. df. 14.**

—— —— 1890. 8°. **07581. g. 4.**

—— —— 1897. 8°. **07581. ee. 44.**

—— The Anatomy of Labour, as studied in frozen sections, and its bearing on clinical work . . . With illustrations. 2 pt. *W. & A. K. Johnston: Edinburgh,* 1889. 8°. **07581. df. 16.**

—— Atlas. Second edition. *W. & A. K. Johnston: Edinburgh,* 1889. fol. **1832. e. 7.**

—— Second edition. 2 pt. *W. & A. K. Johnston: Edinburgh,* 1899. 8°. **07581. f. 47.**

—— Gynecological Treatment. pp. xi. 111. pl. IV. *W. Green & Son: Edinburgh,* 1922. 8°. **07580. g. 32.**

—— Maternity Primer. pp. 165. *W. Green & Sons: Edinburgh,* 1911. 8°. **07580. df. 3.**

—— Spinal Deformity in relation to Obstetrics, *etc.* pp. vi. 35. *W. & A. K. Johnston: Edinburgh,* [1884.] 4°. **1832. c. 17.**

BARBOUR (ALEXANDER HUGH FREELAND) and **WATSON** (BENJAMIN PHILP)

—— Gynecological Diagnosis and Pathology, *etc.* pp. xvi. 220. pl. VIII. *W. Green & Sons: Edinburgh & London,* 1913. 8°. **07581. g. 37.**

—— Third edition, *etc.* pp. xvi. 223. pl. VIII. *W. Green & Son: Edinburgh,* 1922. 8°. **07580. b. 3.**

BARBOUR (ANNA MAYNARD) At the Time appointed, *etc.* [A novel.] pp. 371. *J. B. Lippincott Co.: Philadelphia & London,* 1903. 8°. **012707. aa. 10.**

—— Breakers Ahead, *etc.* pp. 335. *J. B. Lippincott Co.: Philadelphia & London,* 1906. 8°. **012632. ccc. 35.**

—— That Mainwaring Affair, *etc.* pp. 362. *J. B. Lippincott Co.: Philadelphia,* 1901 [1900]. 8°. **012707. k. 23.**

—— [Another edition.] pp. 384. *Ward, Lock & Co.: London,* 1901. 8°. **012639. aaa. 23.**

BARBOUR (BENJAMIN M'CALL) *See* PERIODICAL PUBLICATIONS.—*Edinburgh.* Bits for our Boys. Edited by B. M'Call Barbour. 1902, *etc.* 8°. P.P. **1103. cbh.**

—— [Miscellaneous greeting cards, *etc.*] *B. M. Barbour: Edinburgh,* [1933– .] *obl.* 8°. **1878. c. 15.**

—— A Boy at Fifteen: before and after. pp. 68. *B. M. Barbour: Edinburgh,* [1903.] 8°. **04402. e. 54.**

—— Eighth edition. pp. 68. *B. M. Barbour: Edinburgh,* [1933.] 8°. **04402. g. 45.**

—— "The Common Round." (Daily meditations.) Compiled by B. M. Barbour. *B. M. Barbour: Edinburgh,* [1937.] 8°. [*Meditation Series.* no. 9.] W.P. **10428/9.**

—— "Deeper Life" Series. 6 no. *B. M. Barbour: Edinburgh,* [1933–37] 12°. **4431.bbb.6.**

—— "Evergreen" Series. [Religious tracts.] *B. M. Barbour: Edinburgh,* [1933–] 8°. **W.P.11965.**

BARBOUR (BENJAMIN M'CALL)

—— "Fear Not." (Daily meditations.) *B. M. Barbour: Edinburgh,* [1941.] 8°. ["*Meditation*" *Series.* no. 16.] W.P. **10428/16.**

—— God Who Giveth. (Daily Meditations.) Compiled by B. M. Barbour. *B. M. Barbour: Edinburgh,* [1936.] 8°. [*Meditation Series.* no. 8.] W.P. **10428/8.**

—— His Love. (Daily meditations.) Compiled by B. M. Barbour. *B. M. Barbour: Edinburgh,* [1937.] 8°. [*Meditation Series.* no. 10.] W.P. **10428/10.**

—— "Only Believe." (Daily meditations.) *B. M. Barbour: Edinburgh,* [1939.] 12°. [*Meditation Series.* no. 13.] W.P. **10428/13.**

—— The Passing Days. (Daily meditations.) *B. M. Barbour: Edinburgh,* [1933.] 8°. [*Meditation Series.* no. 2.] W.P. **10428/2.**

—— Perfect Peace. (Daily meditations.) Compiled by B. M. Barbour. *B. M. Barbour: Edinburgh,* [1937.] 8°. [*Meditation Series.* no. 11.] W.P. **10428/11.**

—— "Simply Trusting." (Compiled by B. M. Barbour.) *B. M. Barbour: Edinburgh,* [1933.] 8°. [*Meditation Series.* no. 4.] W.P. **10428/4.**

—— "Souvenir" Series. [Religious tracts. By B. M. Barbour and J. Dauson Smith.] *B. M. Barbour: Edinburgh,* [1933– .] 8°. W.P. **11966.**

—— "Uniform" Series. [Religious tracts.] 27 pt. *B. M. Barbour: Edinburgh,* [1933.] 16°. **4418. c. 88.**

—— "Wonderful." (Daily meditations. Compiled by B. M. Barbour.) *B. M. Barbour: Edinburgh,* [1935.] 8°. [*Meditation Series.* no. 6.] W.P. **10428/6.**

BARBOUR (CLIFFORD EDWARD) Sin and the New Psychology. pp. 224. *G. Allen & Unwin: London,* 1931. 8°. **08408. eee. 15.**

BARBOUR (D. N.) Psycho-analysis and Everyman. pp. 191. *G. Allen & Unwin: London,* 1923. 8°. **08463. de. 82.**

BARBOUR (*Sir* DAVID MILLER) *K.C.S.I., K.C.M.G.* The Influence of the Gold Supply on Prices and Profits. pp. xii. 104. *Macmillan & Co.: London,* 1913. 8°. **8205. dg. 12.**

—— The Standard of Value. pp. xvi. 242. *Macmillan & Co.: London,* 1912. 8°. **8207. p. 11.**

—— The Theory of Bimetallism and the effects of the partial demonetisation of silver on England and India. pp. xvi. 158. *Cassell & Co.: London,* [1886.] 8°. **8226. eee. 28.**

BARBOUR (DOROTHY DICKINSON) Making the Bible Desired. pp. xii. 146. *Doubleday, Doran & Co.: Garden City, N.Y.,* 1928. 8°. **04192. aaa. 31.**

BARBOUR (EDWIN) *See* HARKINS (James W.) and BARBOUR (E.) Northern Lights. From the . . . drama by J. W. Harkins, Jr., and E. Barbour, *etc.* [1897.] 8°. **012704. h. 6.**

BARBOUR (ELIZA BRYDEN)

—— Through the Opera Glass. Dramatised lessons [in domestic science]. pp. 79. *R. Gibson & Sons: Glasgow,* [1935.] 8°. **11780. aa. 67.**

BARBOUR (ERIC PITTY) *See* KIPPAX (Alan) Anti Body-Line. By A. Kippax . . . in collaboration with E. P. Barbour. [1933.] 8°. **7916. df. 5.**

BARBOUR (Erwin Hinckley) Notice of a new Fossil Mammal from Sioux County, Nebraska. [Extracted from the Nebraska Geological Survey.] [*Lincoln, Neb.*, 1905.] 8°. **07106**. f. **3**. **(3.)**

BARBOUR (F. W. Maxwell) *See* Slater (John H.) Engravings and their Value . . . Sixth edition, revised and enlarged by F. W. Maxwell-Barbour, *etc.* [1929.] 4°. **7852**. s. **4**.

BARBOUR (George B.)

—— The Geology of the Kalgan Area, *etc.* [A thesis. With plates and maps.] pp. xi. 148. *Peking*, 1929. 8°. **7104**. h. **11**.

No. 6 *of Ser. A of the Memoirs of the Geological Survey of China.*

BARBOUR (George Freeland) *the Elder*. China and the Missions at Amoy, with notice of the opium trade . . . Second edition, enlarged. pp. ix. 92. *W. P. Kennedy: Edinburgh*, 1855. 8°. **4765**. a. **2**.

BARBOUR (George Freeland) *the Younger*. *See* Seth (Andrew) afterwards Pattison (A. S. P.) The Balfour Lectures on Realism . . . Edited, with a memoir of the author, by G. F. Barbour. 1933. 8°. **08465**. de. **34**.

—— *See* Simpson (James Y.) *Professor in New College, Edinburgh*. The Garment of the Living God . . . With a memoir by G. F. Barbour. 1934. 8°. **2208**. cc. **9**.

—— Addresses in a Highland Chapel. pp. vii. 217. *Hodder & Stoughton: London*, 1924. 8°. **4477**. dd. **24**.

—— Church and Nation in Scotland today. pp. 44. *W. Blackwood & Sons: Edinburgh & London*, 1930. 8°. **4165**. f. **11**.

—— Essays and Addresses by George Freeland Barbour . . . Edited with a biographical introduction by A. F. Giles. [With a portrait.] pp. vi. 91. *Oliver & Boyd: Edinburgh, London*, 1949. 8°. **12360**. f. **39**.

—— The Ethical Approach to Theism. pp. vi. 115. *W. Blackwood & Sons: Edinburgh & London*, 1913. 8°. **04503**. e. **5**.

—— Katherine Scott. A memoir and other records. [With portraits.] pp. 135. *W. Blackwood & Sons: Edinburgh & London*, 1929. 8°. **010856**. aaa. **76**.

—— The Life of Alexander Whyte, D.D. pp. xv. 675. pl. xv. *Hodder & Stoughton: London*, 1923. 8°. **4956**. cc. **6**.

—— Eighth edition. pp. xvi. 675. *Hodder & Stoughton: London*, 1925. 8°. **4956**. c. **31**.

—— Lord Polwarth, 1864–1944. [With plates, including portraits.] pp. 56. *Oliver & Boyd: Edinburgh*, [1947.] 8°. **10861**. a. **48**.

—— A Philosophical Study of Christian Ethics. pp. xiv. 440. *W. Blackwood & Sons: Edinburgh & London*, 1911. 8°. **04403**. f. **5**.

—— The Unity of the Spirit. pp. xvi. 182. *Christophers: London*, 1921. 8°. **08463**. g. **60**.

BARBOUR (George M.) Florida for Tourists, Invalids and Settlers . . . With map and illustrations. pp. 310. *D. Appleton & Co.: New York*, 1882. 12°. **10413**. f. **25**.

—— Revised edition. pp. 325. *D. Appleton & Co.: New York*, 1884. 8°. **10412**. bbb. **7**.

BARBOUR (Harriot Buxton) and **FREEMAN** (Warren S.)

—— A Story of Music . . . Illustrated by Martha Powell Setchell and Arthur Lougee. pp. x. 272. *C. C. Birchard & Co.: Boston*, [1937.] 8°. **7898**. d. **29**.

BARBOUR (J. M.) Songs I taught my Mother. Lyrics from a sphagnum moss camp. pp. 31. *Bell & Bain: Glasgow*, [1918.] 8°. **011649**. f. **109**.

BARBOUR (James) *F.S.A.Scot.* *See* Macdonald (James) *F.S.A.Scot.* Birrens and its Antiquities . . . By J. Macdonald . . . and J. Barbour, *etc.* 1897. 4°. **7708**. cc. **54**.

—— The Interior Buildings at Birrens. *See* Birrens. Account of the Excavation of Birrens, *etc.* [1896.] 8°. **7709**. e. **15**.

BARBOUR (James) *of Doncaster*. *See* Harcus (William) The Origin, Progress, and Consequences of Crime: a sermon, occasioned by the execution of J. Barbour, for the murder of Alexander Robison, *etc.* 1853. 8°. **10347**. f. **14**. **(6.)**

BARBOUR (James Morrison) *See* Knopf (S. A.) Tuberculosis as a Disease of the Masses . . . Adapted for use in England by J. M. Barbour. 1902. 8°. **07306**. g. **24**. **(1.)**

BARBOUR (James Murray)

—— Tuning and Temperament. A historical survey. pp. xiii. 228. *Michigan State College Press: East Lansing*, 1951. 8°. **7900**. ee. **92**.

BARBOUR (James Samuel) A History of William Paterson and the Darien Company. With illustrations and appendices. pp. x. 284. *W. Blackwood & Sons: Edinburgh & London*, 1907. 8°. **9772**. bb. **37**.

BARBOUR (Job) Forty-Eight Days Adrift. The voyage of the "Neptune II" from Newfoundland to Scotland. [With plates, including portraits.] pp. xvi. 220. *R. Clay & Sons: London*, [1932.] 8°. **10497**. a. **11**.

—— [Another copy, with a different titlepage.] *Simpkin Marshall: London*, 1932. 8°. **10497**. a. **14**.

BARBOUR (Johannes) An Epitome of Grammar Principles. 3 pt. *Henry Hall, for the use of the Author: Oxon*, 1668. 8°. **12934**. aa. **54**.

BARBOUR (John) [For editions of "The Buik of Alexander," sometimes attributed to John Barbour:] *See* Alexander, *the Great, King of Macedon.* [*Romances on the Life of Alexander.—English.*]

—— *See* Henschel (F. H.) Darstellung der Flexionslehre in J. Barbour's Bruce, *etc.* 1886. 8°. **12902**. b. **33**. **(3.)**

—— *See* Muehleisen (F. W.) Textkritische, metrische und grammatische Untersuchungen von Barbour's Bruce, *etc.* 1913. 8°. **011852**. dd. **61**.

—— *See* Neilson (George) John Barbour: poet and translator. 1900. 8°. **011852**. g. **28**.

—— *See* Regel (E.) Nachgelieferte Arbeit zum Program der Realschule . . . zu Gera, Ostern 1877. "An Inquiry into the phonetic peculiarities of Barbour's Bruce." [1877.] 4°. **623**. k. **18**. **(10.)**

—— The Actes and Life of the most victorious conquerour, Robert Bruce, King of Scotland. Wherein also are contained the Martiall deedes of the valliant Princes, Edward Bruce, Sir Iames Dowglas, Erle Thomas Randel, Walter Stewart, and sundrie others. Newly corrected, and conferred with the best and most ancient manuscripts. [By J. Barbour.] pp. 413. 1616. 8°. *See* Robert I., *King of Scotland.* **C. 55**. b. **21**.

—— [Another edition.] pp. 413. 1620. 8°. *See* Robert I., *King of Scotland.* **C. 39**. a. **21**.

—— [Another edition.] pp. 348. 1670. 8°. *See* Robert I., *King of Scotland.* **1076**. k. **11**.

BARBOUR (JOHN)

—— The Life & Acts of . . . Robert Bruce . . . Carefully corrected from the edition printed by Andro Hart in 1620. B.L. pp. 443. *Edinburgh*, 1758. 4°. **641.** h. **27.**

—— [Another copy.] G. **1912.**

—— The Bruce; or, the History of Robert I. King of Scotland . . . The first genuine edition, published from a MS. dated 1489; with notes and a glossary, by J. Pinkerton. 3 vol. *G. Nicol: London*, 1790. 8°. **81.** k. **13.**

—— [Another copy.] G. **18902–4.**

—— The Bruce; and Wallace; published from two ancient manuscripts preserved in the library of the Faculty of Advocates. With notes, biographical sketches, and a glossary (by John Jamieson). 2 vol. *J. Ballantyne & Co.: Edinburgh*, 1820. 4°. **78.** g. **21, 22.**

—— [Another copy.] G. **18515.**

—— The Brus. From a collation of the Cambridge and Edinburgh Manuscripts. [Edited by Cosmo Innes.] pp. xliv. 524. 1856. 4°. *See* ABERDEEN, *City of.—Spalding Club.* Ac. **8244/18.**

—— The Bruce; or, the Book of . . . Robert de Broyss, King of Scots . . . Edited . . . by . . . Walter W. Skeat. 1870, 89. 8°. *See* LONDON.—III. *Early English Text Society.* Ac. **9926/10.**

—— [A reissue.] London, 1901, 1896, 1936. 8°.

—— [Another edition.] 2 vol. 1894. 8°. *See* EDINBURGH.—*Scottish Text Society.* Ac. **9943/14.**

—— [Another edition.] Edited from the best texts with literary and historical introduction, notes and appendices, and a glossary by W. M. Mackenzie. pp. xxiii. 547. *A. & C. Black: London*, 1909. 8°. **9510.** f. **28.**

—— The Bruce: being the metrical history of Robert the Bruce, King of Scots, compiled A.D. 1375 . . . Translated [into modern prose] by George Eyre-Todd. pp. xv. 368. *Gowans & Gray: London, Glasgow*, 1907. 8°. **9509.** ee. **12.**

—— The Bruce of Bannockburn. Being a translation [into modern verse] of the greater portion of Barbour's "Bruce." By Michael Macmillan. pp. 275. *Eneas Mackay: Stirling*, 1914. 8°. **9510.** d. **2.**

—— The Bruce. [Selections.] 1891. *See* TODD (George E.) Abbotsford Series of the Scottish Poets, *etc.* (Early Scottish Poetry.) 1891, *etc.* 8°. **11622.** ee. **17.**

—— The Bruce . . . Selections for use in schools. With an introduction, a section on early Scots grammar, etc., notes and a glossary, by W. M. Mackenzie. pp. xx. 130. *A. & C. Black: London*, 1909. 8°. **9509.** e. **49.**

—— Barbour's, des schottischen Nationaldichters Legendensammlung, nebst den Fragmenten seines Trojanerkrieges. Zum ersten Mal herausgegeben und kritisch bearbeitet von C. Horstmann. 2 Bd. *Heilbronn*, 1881, 82. 8°. **11595.** h. **13.**

BARBOUR (JOHN GORDON) *See* also CALEDONIUS (Cincinnatus) *pseud.* [i.e. J. G. Barbour.]

—— Unique Traditions chiefly of the West and South of Scotland. pp. 255. *Hamilton & Adams: London*, 1886. 8°. **12431.** k. **15.**

BARBOUR (JOSEPH) Kentucky Digest, embracing all the reported cases decided by the Court of Appeals, from its organization to the year 1878. 2 vol. pp. xxiii. xiii. 1845. *J. P. Morton & Co.: Louisville, Ky.*, 1878. 8°. **6686.** m. **1.**

BARBOUR (L. G.) The End of Time. A poem of the future. pp. 191. *G. P. Putnam's Sons: London*, 1892. 8°. **11688.** g. **13.**

BARBOUR (LEVI LEWIS) Peter White as man and as citizen. An address, *etc.* [With a portrait.] pp. 24. 1909. *See* ANN ARBOR.—*University of Michigan.* Ac. **2685/14.**

BARBOUR (LUCIAN) *See* HOWLAND (J. D.) and BARBOUR (L.) A Manual for Executors, *etc.* 1862. 8°. **6677.** i. **2.**

BARBOUR (MARGARET FRASER) *See* BURNS (William C.) Notes of Addresses by . . . W. C. Burns . . . Edited by M. F. Barbour. 1869. 8°. **4462.** aa. **23.**

—— *See* SIMPSON (Margaret S.) Steps through the Stream . . . With an introduction by M. F. Barbour, *etc.* 1880. 16°. **4401.** cc. **42.**

—— Baptized for Suffering: the Manuel collision. [An account of the railway accident at Manuel, 27 Jan. 1874.] pp. 15. *Morgan & Scott: London*, [1874.] 16°. **4418.** aa. **52.**

—— The Bottles broken, and how the mischief was remedied. pp. 15. *Morgan & Scott: London*, [1875.] 16°. **4422.** b. **1.** **(2.)**

—— The Child of the Kingdom. By the author of "The Way Home" [i.e. M. F. Barbour], *etc.* pp. 190. 1862. 16°. *See* CHILD. **4408.** b. **7.**

—— Golden Vials filled. A New Year's address, with notices of Sir J. Y. Simpson and other eminent men who died in 1870. pp. 32. *Peter Drummond: Stirling*, [1871.] 16°. **10602.** aa. **36.** **(2.)**

—— The Irish Orphan in a Scottish Home. By the author of "The Way Home" [i.e. M. F. Barbour], *etc.* pp. 87. 1866. 8°. *See* IRISH ORPHAN. **4986.** aa. **4.**

—— [Another edition, enlarged.] pp. 222. *J. Nisbet & Co.: London*, 1872. 8°. **4413.** aaa. **3.**

—— Memoir of Mrs. Stewart Sandeman . . . By her daughter (M. F. Barbour). [With plates, including portraits.] pp. vi. 272. *J. Nisbet & Co.: London*, 1883. 8°. **10826.** bbb. **3.**

With an additional titlepage, engraved.

—— The Soul-Gatherer. By the author of "The Way Home" [i.e. M. F. Barbour], *etc.* pp. 228. 1864. 16°. *See* SOUL-GATHERER. **4404.** aa. **52.**

—— Three Burdens laid down. pp. 15. *Morgan & Scott: London*, [1874.] 16°. **4411.** a. **54.** **(3.)**

—— The Way Home. [By M. F. Barbour.] pp. 301. 1856. 8°. *See* WAY. **4417.** c. **38.**

BARBOUR (MILDRED) A Suitor Too Many. pp. vi. 274. *Grosset & Dunlap: New York*, [1928.] 8°. **12714.** bbb. **4.**

—— Sybil, Trapper of Men. pp. vi. 313. *Grosset & Dunlap: New York*, [1928.] 8°. **12713.** c. **12.**

BARBOUR (NEVILL) *See* BAROJA (P.) Parador, King . . . Translated by N. Barbour. 1931. 8°. **12488.** s. **9.**

—— Nisi Dominus. A survey of the Palestine controversy, *etc.* pp. 248. *G. G. Harrap & Co.: London*, 1946. 8°. **08157.** ee. **30.**

BARBOUR (OLIVER LORENZO) *See* CLINTON (George W.) A Digest of the Decisions at Law and in Equity . . . contained in the . . . reports by Johnson . . . Barbour, *etc.* 1852, *etc.* 8°. **6625.** h. **7.**

BARBOUR (Oliver Lorenzo)

—— *See* Collyer (John) *of Lincoln's Inn, Barrister-at-Law.* A Practical Treatise on the Law of Partnership . . . containing the American notes of the former edition . . . To which are now added, notes of recent American and English decisions, by O. L. Barbour. 1839. 8°. **1384. i. 13.**

—— *See* New York, *State of.—Court of Chancery.* Reports of Cases argued and determined in the Court of Chancerv of the State of New-York. 1845, etc. 1847, *etc.* 8°. **6622.f.1.**

—— *See* New York, *State of.—Supreme Court.* Reports of Cases in Law and Equity in the Supreme Court of the State of New York. By O. L. Barbour. 1848, *etc.* 8°. **6622.g.3.**

—— *See* Tiffany (Joel) Condensed Digest of the Court of Appeals Reports of the State of New York, *etc.* [vol. 28 to 62 by O. L. Barbour.] 1866, *etc.* 8°. **6740. f. 1.**

—— An Analytical Digest of the Equity Cases, decided in the courts of the several States, and of the United States; in the Courts of Chancery and Exchequer in England and Ireland, and in the English Privy Council and House of Lords, since the year 1836. pp. 737. *G. & C. Merriam: Springfield, Mass.*, 1843. 8°. **1242. g. 10.**

—— A Summary of the Law of Parties to Actions at Law, and suits in equity. pp. 611. *W. C. Little: Albany*, 1864. 8°. **6617. i. 1.**

—— A Treatise on the Criminal Law of the State of New York and upon the jurisdiction, duty and authority of justices of the peace, and incidentally of the power and duty of sheriffs, constables, &c. in criminal cases . . . Second edition. pp. xvi. 870. *Gould, Banks & Co.: Albany; Banks, Gould & Co.: New York*, 1852. 4°. **6736. i. 3.**

—— A Treatise on the Law of Set Off, with an appendix of precedents. pp. 259. *W. & A. Gould & Co.: Albany; Gould, Banks & Co.: New York*, 1841. 8°. **6625. cc. 5.**

—— A Treatise on the Practice of the Court of Chancery. With an appendix of precedents. Second edition, revised, *etc.* 3 vol. *Banks & Bros.: Albany & New York*, 1874, 75. 8°. **6736. k. 1.**

—— A Treatise on the Rights of Persons and the Rights of Property, with the remedies for the protection and enforcement of those rights. 2 vol. *Williamson Law Book Co.: Rochester, N.Y.*, 1890. 8°. **06616. g. 13.**

BARBOUR (Oliver Lorenzo) and **HARRINGTON** (Ebenezer Burke)

—— An Analytical Digest of the Equity Cases decided in the courts of the several States, and of the United States, from the earliest period; and of the decisions in equity in the Courts of Chancery and Exchequer England and Ireland, and the Privy Council and House of Lords, from Hilary Term, 1822 . . . to 1836. 3 vol. *G. & C. Merriam: Springfield, Mass.*, 1837. 8°. **1242. g. 7–9.**

BARBOUR (Philip L.)

—— *See* Pushkin (A. S.) Boris Godunov. Russian text with translation and notes by P. L. Barbour. 1953. 8°. **Ac. 2688.** hc. **(11.)**

BARBOUR (Ralph Henry) *See* also Powell (Richard Stillman) *pseud.* [i.e. R. H. Barbour.]

—— Adventures of Tom Marvel, *etc.* pp. 162. *D. Appleton & Co.: New York, London*, 1928. 8°. **12801. t. 15.**

BARBOUR (Ralph Henry)

—— All Hands Stand By! *etc.* pp. vii. 261. *D. Appleton-Century Co.: New York, London*, 1942. 8°. **12723. aa. 7.**

—— Around the End. pp. 318. *D. Appleton & Co.: New York & London*, 1913. 8°. **012704. c. 30.**

—— Barclay Back, *etc.* pp. vii. 255. *D. Appleton-Century Co.: New York, London*, 1942. 8°. **12725. bbb. 6.**

—— Barry Locke, half-back, *etc.* pp. vii. 335. *Century Co.: New York & London*, [1925.] 8°. **012705. e. 77.**

—— Bases Full! pp. 276. *D. Appleton & Co.: New York, London*, 1925. 8°. **12708. c. 21.**

—— Beaton Runs the Mile, *etc.* pp. 291. *D. Appleton & Co.: New York, London*, 1933. 8°. **A.N. 1518.**

—— Behind the Line. A story of college life and football, *etc.* pp. xi. 258. *D. Appleton & Co.: New York*, 1902. 8°. **012803. a. 64.**

—— Benton's Venture. pp. 312. *D. Appleton & Co.: New York & London*, 1914. 8°. **012807. aaa. 5.**

—— The Book of School and College Sports. By R. H. Barbour . . . with the editorial assistance of R. D. Paine, Edward N. Robinson, W. A. Schick, jr., R. T. Abercrombie and others. pp. xiv. 438. *D. Appleton & Co.: New York*, 1904. 8°. **7912. d. 21.**

—— The Brother of a Hero, *etc.* pp. 301. *D. Appleton & Co.: New York, London*, 1914. 8°. **NN. 2111.**

—— Candidate for the Line, *etc.* pp. v. 272. *D. Appleton & Co.: New York, London*, 1930. 8°. **A.N. 467.**

—— Captain Chub, *etc.* pp. ix. 413. *Century Co.: New York*, 1909. 8°. **012705. b. 36.**

—— Change Signals. A story of the new football. pp. 330. *D. Appleton & Co.: New York & London*, 1912. 8°. **012704. d. 6.**

—— Comrades of the Key. pp. ix. 248. *Century Co.: New York, London*, [1928.] 8°. **12801. t. 10.**

—— Coxswain of the Eight. pp. 258. *D. Appleton & Co.: New York, London*, 1922. 8°. **12800. de. 24.**

—— The Crimson Sweater, *etc.* pp. x. 367. *Century Co.: New York*, 1906. 8°. **12813. w. 18.**

—— Crofton Chums, *etc.* pp. ix. 338. *Century Co.: New York*, 1912. 8°. **012704. dd. 41.**

—— The Cub Battery, *etc.* pp. vi. 275. *D. Appleton & Co.: New York, London*, 1932. 8°. **A.N. 1346.**

—— Danforth plays the Game. Stories for boys little and big, *etc.* pp. 333. *D. Appleton & Co.: New York & London*, 1915. 8°. **012804. d. 9.**

—— Death in the Virgins. pp. viii. 340. *D. Appleton-Century Co.: New York, London*, 1940. 8°. **12720. bb. 20.**

—— Double Play. A story of school and baseball. pp. 314. *D. Appleton & Co.: New York & London*, 1909. 8°. **012804. b. 7.**

—— Fighting Guard, *etc.* pp. viii. 304. *D. Appleton-Century Co.: New York, London*, 1938. 8°. **12718. ee. 6.**

—— The Fighting Scrub. pp. 277. *D. Appleton & Co.: New York, London*, 1924. 8°. **12708. a. 6.**

—— Finkler's Field. A story of school and baseball, *etc.* pp. vii. 226. *D. Appleton & Co.: New York & London,* 1911. 8°. **012808. b. 43.**

—— The Five-Dollar Dog . . . Illustrated, *etc.* pp. ix. 244. *D. Appleton-Century Co.: New York, London,* 1935. 8°. A.N. **2612.**

—— Five Points Service, *etc.* pp. ix. 275. *D. Appleton-Century Co.: New York, London,* 1935. 8°. A.N. **2287.**

—— Flashing Oars. pp. 272. *D. Appleton & Co.: New York, London,* 1930. 8°. **12813. d. 20.**

—— Follow the Ball. pp. vi. 251. *D. Appleton & Co.: New York, London,* 1924. 8°. **012804.** eee. **33.**

—— For Safety! *etc.* pp. 146. *D. Appleton-Century Co.: New York, London,* 1936. 8°. **012600.** cc. **65.**

—— For the Freedom of the Seas, *etc.* pp. 299. *D. Appleton & Co.: New York, London,* 1918. 8°. **12801.** bbb. **13.**

—— For the Good of the Team. pp. v. 287. *D. Appleton & Co.: New York, London,* 1923. 8°. **12802.** bb. **41.**

—— For Yardley. A story of track and field, *etc.* pp. vi. 297. *D. Appleton & Co.: New York & London,* 1911. 8°. **012704.** dd. **6.**

—— Four Afloat: being the adventures of the big four on the water. pp. ix. 275. *D. Appleton & Co.: New York,* 1907. 8°. **012626.** aa. **18.**

—— Four Afoot: being the adventures of the big four on the highway. pp. x. 285. *D. Appleton & Co.: New York,* 1906. 8°. **012706. b. 39.**

—— Four in Camp. A story of summer adventures in the New Hampshire woods, *etc.* pp. viii. 249. *D. Appleton & Co.: New York,* 1905. 8°. **012706.** a. **1.**

—— Fourth Down! pp. v. 316. *D. Appleton & Co.: New York, London,* 1920. 8°. **012802.** bbb. **4.**

—— The Fumbled Pass, *etc.* pp. v. 285. *D. Appleton & Co.: New York, London,* 1931. 8°. **12813.** cc. **7.**

—— Giles of the Mayflower, *etc.* pp. 158. *D. Appleton & Co.: New York, London,* 1929. 8°. **12812. g. 21.**

—— Goal to Go, *etc.* pp. vii. 277. *D. Appleton-Century Co.: New York, London,* 1933. 8°. **12708. f. 11.**

—— Good Manners for Boys. pp. 119. *D. Appleton-Century Co.: New York, London,* 1937. 8°. **08408.** h. **46.**

—— Grantham Gets On. pp. 249. *D. Appleton & Co.: New York, London,* 1929. 8°. **12815.** aa. **7.**

—— Guarding his Goal, *etc.* pp. 321. *D. Appleton & Co.: New York, London,* 1919. 8°. **12801.** bb. **36.**

—— Harry's Island, *etc.* pp. 306. *Century Co.: New York,* 1908. 8°. **12803.** pp. **9.**

—— Hero of the Camp, *etc.* pp. ix. 265. *D. Appleton & Co.: New York, London,* 1932. 8°. **20052.** eee. **31.**

—— Hitting the Line, *etc.* pp. 332. *D. Appleton & Co.: New York, London,* 1917. 8°. **12800.** c. **21.**

—— Hold 'em, Wyndham. pp. 269. *D. Appleton & Co.: New York, London,* 1925. 8°. **12709.** b. **5.**

—— Holly. The romance of a Southern girl, *etc.* pp. 294. *J. B. Lippincott Co.: Philadelphia & London,* 1907. 8°. **012705.** b. **11.**

—— Hunt Holds the Center. pp. 247. *D. Appleton & Co.: New York, London,* 1928. 8°. **12714. c. 15.**

—— Hurricane Sands . . . Illustrated by James Reid. pp. viii. 255. *D. Appleton-Century Co.: New York, London,* 1940. 8°. **12816.** b. **4.**

—— Infield Rivals. pp. v. 257. *D. Appleton & Co.: New York, London,* 1924. 8°. **012809. aaa. 46.**

—— The Infield Twins, *etc.* pp. viii. 273. *D. Appleton-Century Co.: New York, London,* 1941. 8°. **12826.** aa. **20.**

—— The Junior Trophy, *etc.* pp. 309. *D. Appleton & Co.: New York & London,* 1913. 8°. **012704. d. 34.**

—— Keeping his Course. pp. 285. *D. Appleton & Co.: New York, London,* 1918. 8°. **12801. bb. 7.**

—— Kick Formation. pp. 265. *D. Appleton & Co.: New York, London,* 1921. 8°. **012802. cc. 32.**

—— Kingsford, quarter, *etc.* pp. vi. 326. *Century Co.: New York,* 1910. 8°. **012705. bb. 49.**

—— Kitty of the Roses, *etc.* pp. 174. *J. B. Lippincott Co.: Philadelphia & London,* 1904. 8°. **12703. g. 56.**

—— The Land of Joy. pp. viii. 416. *Hutchinson & Co.: London; New York* printed, 1903. 8°. **012629. aa. 1.**

—— The Last Play. pp. 273. *D. Appleton & Co.: New York, London,* 1926. 8°. **12711. aaa. 3.**

—— The Last Quarter. pp. viii. 276. *D. Appleton-Century Co.: New York, London,* 1939. 8°. **12720.** cc. **10.**

—— The Long Pass. pp. 260. *D. Appleton & Co.: New York, London,* 1927. 8°. **12712. d. 7.**

—— The Lost Dirigible, *etc.* pp. v. 276. *D. Appleton & Co.: New York, London,* 1920. 8°. **12801. cc. 43.**

—— Lovell Leads Off. pp. 236. *D. Appleton & Co.: New York, London,* 1928. 8°. **12801. t. 12.**

—— The Lucky Seventh, *etc.* pp. 310. *D. Appleton & Co.: New York & London,* 1915. 8°. **12808.** c. **1.**

—— Merritt Leads the Nine . . . Illustrations by George M. Richards. pp. ix. 256. *D. Appleton-Century Co.: New York, London,* 1936. 8°. A.N. **2886.**

—— My Lady of the Fog, *etc.* pp. 220. *J. B. Lippincott & Co.: Philadelphia & London,* 1908. 8°. **012703. g. 21.**

—— Mystery Island, *etc.* pp. vii. 301. *Century Co.: New York & London,* [1931.] 8°. A.N. **763.**

—— Mystery of the Rubber Boat, *etc.* pp. ix. 260. *D. Appleton-Century Co.: New York, London,* 1943. 8°. **12827.** cc. **6.**

—— Mystery on the Bayou . . . Illustrated by Thomas McGowan. pp. 237. *D. Appleton-Century Co.: New York, London,* 1943. 8°. **012707.** l. **64.**

—— The New Boy at Hilltop, and other stories, *etc.* pp. 269. *D. Appleton & Co.: New York & London,* 1910. 8°. **012705.** bb. **46.**

—— Nid and Nod, *etc.* pp. 360. *Century Co.: New York & London,* 1923. 8°. **12800.** cc. **9.**

—— Ninth Inning Rally, *etc.* pp. 265. *D. Appleton-Century Co.: New York, London,* 1940. 8°. **12825.** cc. **6.**

BARBOUR (Ralph Henry)

—— Peggy-in-the-Rain, *etc.* pp. 244. *D. Appleton & Co.: New York & London*, 1913. 8º. **012704. c. 13.**

—— Pirates of the Shoals. pp. v. 250. *Farrar & Rinehart: New York*, [1932.] 8º. **12837.de.17.**

—— The Play that Won, *etc.* pp. vii. 240. *D. Appleton & Co.: New York, London*, 1919. 8º. **12801. bb. 39.**

—— Pud Pringle, pirate. pp. 296. *Houghton Mifflin Co.: Boston & New York*, 1926. 8º. **12710. aaa. 19.**

—— The Purple Pennant, *etc.* pp. 322. *D. Appleton & Co.: New York & London*, 1916. 8º. **012807. a. 28.**

—— The Relief Pitcher. pp. 266. *D. Appleton & Co.: New York, London*, 1927. 8º. **12712. aa. 4.**

—— Rivals for the Team, *etc.* pp. 336. *D. Appleton & Co.: New York, London*, 1916. 8º. **12800. b. 18.**

—— Rivals on the Mound . . . Illustrated by Charles Czap. pp. viii. 303. *D. Appleton-Century Co.: New York, London*, 1938. 8º. **12820. c. 16.**

—— The School that didn't care . . . Illustrated by Inglewood Smith. pp. ix. 278. *D. Appleton-Century Co.: New York, London*, 1937. 8º. **012807. f. 75.**

—— The Score Is Tied, *etc.* pp. ix. 277. *D. Appleton-Century Co.: New York, London*, 1937. 8º. **A.N. 3516.**

—— The Scoring Play, *etc.* pp. vi. 281. *D. Appleton-Century Co.: New York, London*, 1934. 8º. **A.N. 2042.**

—— The Secret Play, *etc.* pp. 334. *D. Appleton & Co.: New York & London*, 1915. 8º. **NN. 2908.**

—— Skate, Glendale! pp. 249. *Farrar & Rinehart: New York*, [1932.] 8º. **12708. ee. 15.**

—— Southworth Scores, *etc.* pp. 269. *D. Appleton-Century Co.: New York, London*, 1934. 8º. **20053. g. 27.**

—— Spaniard's Cave, *etc.* pp. 324. *Century Co.: New York & London*, [1924.] 8º. **012804. ccc. 47.**

—— The Spirit of the School. pp. ix. 272. *D. Appleton & Co.: New York*, 1907. 8º. **012706. bb. 30.**

—— Squeeze Play, *etc.* pp. 251. *D. Appleton & Co.: New York, London*, 1931. 8º. **12819. c. 25.**

—— The Story my Doggie told to me. The adventures of a turnspit, *etc.* pp. 113. *G. G. Harrap & Co.: London*, 1916. 4º. **1874. a. 55.**

—— Substitute Jimmy, *etc.* pp. vii. 321. *Century Co.: New York & London*, 1928. 8º. **12702. b. 17.**

—— The Target Pass, *etc.* pp. xi. 280. *D. Appleton-Century Co.: New York, London*, 1941. 8º. **12723. bb. 6.**

—— Team-Mates, *etc.* pp. vi. 381. *Century Co.: New York*, 1911. 8º. **012808. b. 44.**

—— Thad and the G-Man, *etc.* pp. viii. 257. *D. Appleton-Century Co.: New York, London*, 1942. 8º. **12724. c. 2.**

—— Three-Base Benson, *etc.* pp. 285. *D. Appleton & Co.: New York, London*, 1921. 8º. **012802. bb. 25.**

—— The Three-Cornered Dog . . . Illustrated by R. M. Brinkerhoff. pp. ix. 273. *D. Appleton-Century Co.: New York, London*, 1939. 8º. **12719. cc. 12.**

BARBOUR (Ralph Henry)

—— Three in a Trailer . . . Illustrated by Edward C. Caswell. pp. ix. 258. *D. Appleton-Century Co.: New York, London*, 1937. 8º. **012807. f. 71.**

—— Tom, Dick, and Harriet, *etc.* pp. 384. *Century Co.: New York*, 1907. 8º. **12804. s. 6.**

—— The Turner Twins, *etc.* pp. 280. *Century Co.: New York*, 1922. 8º. **012703. eee. 11.**

—— Under the Yankee Ensign. pp. 335. *D. Appleton & Co.: New York, London*, 1919. 8º. **NN. 5286.**

—— Watch that Pass! *etc.* pp. ix. 261. *D. Appleton Century Co.: New York, London*, 1936. 8º. **20059. aa. 21**

—— Weatherby's Inning. A story of college life and baseball, *etc.* pp. ix. 249. *D. Appleton & Co.: New York*, 1903. 8º. **012803. a. 65.**

—— Winning his Game, *etc.* pp. v. 307. *D. Appleton & Co.: New York, London*, 1917. 8º. **NN. 4098.**

—— Winning his "Y": a story of school athletics, *etc.* pp. vii. 286. *D. Appleton & Co.: New York & London*, 1910. 8º. **012705. bb. 32.**

—— The Winning Year. pp. 251. *D. Appleton & Co.: New York, London*, 1926. 8º. **12710. b. 26.**

BARBOUR (Ralph Henry) and **HOLT** (H. P.) *Novelist.*

—— Fortunes of War, *etc.* pp. 352. *Century Co.: New York*, 1919. 8º. **12801. bb. 40.**

—— [Another edition.] The Cruise of the Endeavour; or, Fortunes of war, *etc.* pp. 252. *G. G. Harrap & Co.: London; Nijmegen* printed, 1921. 8º. **12803. ppp. 13.**

—— Joan of the Island. By Henry Holt [or rather, by R. H. Barbour and H. P. Holt]. pp. 285. 1923. 8º. *See* Holt (Henry) *Author of "Joan of the Island."* **NN. 8716.**

—— [A reissue.] 1926. 8º. *See* Holt (Henry) *Author of "Joan of the Island."* **NN. 11613.**

—— Lost Island, *etc.* pp. 389. *Century Co.: New York*, 1918. 8º. **12800. cc. 25.**

—— [Another edition.] pp. 256. *G. G. Harrap & Co.: London*, 1919. 8º. **NN. 5463.**

—— The Mystery of the Sea-Lark, *etc.* pp. 321. *Century Co.: New York*, 1920. 8º. **12802. bbb. 24.**

—— Over Two Seas. pp. 262. *D. Appleton & Co.: New York & London*, 1922. 8º. **12803. ppp. 26.**

BARBOUR (Ralph Henry) and **SARRA** (La Mar)

—— Football Plays for Boys. With rules and strategies of touch football. pp. vi. 110. *D. Appleton-Century Co.: New York, London*, 1933. 8º. **7916. df. 6.**

—— Football Plays for Boys. Revised, with defensive formations. pp. vii. 126. *D. Appleton-Century Co.: New York, London*, 1940. 8º. **07907. f. 22.**

—— How to Play Better Baseball. For junior players and their coaches. pp. viii. 176. *D. Appleton-Century Co.: New York, London*, 1935. 8º. **7915. p. 17.**

—— How to play better Basketball. pp. xi. 111. *D. Appleton-Century Co.: New York, London*, 1941. 8º. **7917. aa. 6.**

BARBOUR (RALPH HENRY) and **SARRA** (LA MAR)

—— How to Play Six-Man Football. pp. x. 113. *D. Appleton-Century Co.: New York, London*, 1939. 8°. **07908**. i. **32**.

BARBOUR (ROBERT) *See* ADAMSON (Ebenezer) Judgment of the House of Lords in causa Ebenezer Adamson . . . Appellant; and R. Barbour . . . Respondent, *etc.* 1853. 8°. **6573**. b. **15**.

BARBOUR (ROBERT WILLIAM) Robert W. Barbour: Letters, Poems, and Pensées, *etc.* [With a biographical notice by James Stalker, and a portrait.] pp. xxx. 460. *Robert Maclehose: Glasgow*, 1893. 4°. **10906**. g. **7**. *Printed for private circulation.*

—— Jeroveam's Wife, and other poems. [By R. W. Barbour.] pp. vii. 138. 1879. 8°. *See* JEROVEAM. **11653**. aaa. **24**.

—— John Knox. [A biography.] 1883. *See* EVANGELICAL SUCCESSION. The Evangelical Succession, *etc.* ser. 2. 1882, *etc.* 8°. **4804**. c. **5**.

—— Letters from the Land of Luther. pp. 156. *Edinburgh Press: [Edinburgh,]* 1894. 8°. **10250**. p. **17**.

—— Thoughts from the Writings of R. W. Barbour. pp. 153. *W. Blackwood & Sons: Edinburgh*, 1900. 12°. **3751**. aa. **15**.

BARBOUR (ROSAMOND)

—— *See* BARBOUR (Thomas) Letters Written while on a Collecting Trip in the East Indies. By T. Barbour . . . and Mrs. R. Barbour. 1913. 8°. **010921**. e. **6**.

BARBOUR (SCHARLIE) On with the Dance. (Suggestions for dances.) [With illustrations.] pp. xii. 105. *G. Sully & Co.: New York*, [1928.] 8°. **7911**. e. **40**.

BARBOUR (THOMAS) *See* MONET DE LAMARCK (J. B. P. A. de) The Lamarck Manuscripts at Harvard. Edited by W. M. Wheeler and T. Barbour. 1933. 8°. **012238**. aaa. **18**.

—— *See* POPENOE (Dorothy H.) Santiago de los Caballeros de Guatemala, *etc.* [Edited, with an introduction, by T. Barbour.] 1933. 8°. **10482**. cc. **22**.

—— *See* RATHBUN (M. J.) Decapod Crustaceans collected in Dutch East India and elsewhere by Mr. T. Barbour in 1906–1907, *etc.* 1910. 8°. [*Bulletin of the Museum of Comparative Zoology at Harvard College.* vol. 52. no. 16.] Ac. **1736/2**.

—— *See* STEJNEGER (L.) and BARBOUR (T.) A Check List of North American Amphibians and Reptiles, *etc.* 1923. 8°. **07290**. g. **6**.

—— —— 1933. 8°. **07290**. ff. **14**.

—— *See* STEJNEGER (L.) and BARBOUR (T.) A Check List of North American Amphibians and Reptiles, *etc.* 1939. 8°. **07290**. h. **19**.

—— Letters Written while on a Collecting Trip in the East Indies. By Thomas Barbour . . . and Mrs. Rosamond Barbour. [Edited by C. A. Shriner.] pp. 223. *Paterson, N. J.*, 1913. 8°. **010921**. e. **6**.

—— Naturalist at large. [An autobiography. With plates.] pp. 258. *Robert Hale: London*, 1950. 8°. **10859**. d. **30**.

—— A Naturalist's Scrapbook. [With plates, including portraits.] pp. 218. *Harvard University Press: Cambridge, Mass.*, 1946. 8°. **7006**. ppp. **47**.

BARBOUR (THOMAS)

—— Notes on the Herpetology of Jamaica . . . With two plates. 1910. *See* CAMBRIDGE, *Mass.—Harvard University.—Museum of Comparative Zoology.* Bulletin. vol. 52. no. 15. [1864, *etc.*] 8°. Ac. **1736/2**.

—— Reptiles and Amphibians . . . Illustrated, *etc.* pp. xx. 125. *Houghton Mifflin Co.: Boston & New York*, 1926. 8°. **7290**. c. **23**.

—— [Another copy, with a different titlepage.] *G. G. Harrap & Co.: London*, [1926.] 8°. **7290**. c. **24**.

—— That Vanishing Eden. A naturalist's Florida . . . (Reprinted.) Illustrated. pp. x. 250. *Little, Brown & Co.: Boston*, 1945. 8°. **010410**. k. **29**.

BARBOUR (VERA) *See* FEUILLERAT (A.) French Life & Ideals . . . Translated by V. Barbour. 1925. 8°. Ac. **2692**. ml. **(6.)**

BARBOUR (VIOLET)

—— Capitalism in Amsterdam in the Seventeenth Century. pp. 171. *Johns Hopkins Press: Baltimore*, 1950. 8°. [*Johns Hopkins University Studies in Historical and Political Science.* ser. 67. no. 1.] Ac. **2689**.

BARBOUR (VIOLET) Henry Bennet, Earl of Arlington, Secretary of State to Charles II. pp. xii. 303. *Washington; Oxford University Press: London*, 1914. 8°. [*Prize Essays of the American Historical Association.* 1913.] Ac. **8504/5**.

BARBOUR (WILLARD TITUS) The History of Contract in Early English Equity. pp. 237. 1914. *See* VINOGRADOV (*Sir* P. G.) Oxford Studies in Social and Legal History. vol. 4. 1909, *etc.* 8°. **2378**. e.

BARBOUR (WILLIAM)

—— *See* MARTIN (Geoffrey) *F.I.C., M.I.Struct.Eng.* and BARBOUR (W.) Industrial Nitrogen Compounds and Explosives, *etc.* 1915. 8°. **8910**. h. **23/3**.

—— —— 1917. 8°. **8910.h.23/8.**

BARBOUTAU (PIERRE) *See* CLARIS DE FLORIAN (J. P.) Fables choisies . . . Illustrées par des artistes japonais, sous la direction de P. Barboutau. 1895. 8°. **012305**. m. **2**.

—— *See* LAFONTAINE (Jean de) [*Fables.—French.*] Choix de fables . . . Illustrées par un groupe des meilleurs artistes de Tokio. Sous la direction de P. Barboutau. 1894. 8°. **11475**. g. **49**.

—— Catalogue descriptif d'une collection d'objets d'art, rapportés de son voyage au Japon par P. Barboutau. (Table en caractères japonais des noms inscrits sur les objets, *etc.*) pp. 102. 45. *Paris*, 1893. 8°. **7808**. e. **27**.

—— Collection P. Barboutau. Peintures, estampes, et objets d'art du Japon, *etc.* (Biographies des artistes japonais dont les œuvres figurent dans la collection.) [With an introduction by A. Alexandre.] 2 vol. *Paris*, 1904. 4°. L.R. **31**. b. **13**.

BARBOUX (HENRI MARTIN) *See* CATHALA (P.) Barreau de Paris. Éloge d'H. Barboux. Discours, *etc.* 1921. 8°. **10657**. cc. **21**.

—— *See* WALDECK-ROUSSEAU (P. M. R.) Plaidoyers . . . Avec une préface de Me. H. Barboux. 1906. 8°. **8079**. bbb. **12**.

—— Discours et plaidoyers. pp. 513. *Paris*, 1889. 8°. **5408**. e. **5**.

BARBOUX (HENRI MARTIN)

—— Affaire de Panama. Cour d'Assises de la Seine. Plaidoirie de Me H. Barboux pour M. Charles de Lesseps. pp. 138. *Paris*, 1893. 8°. **5408. e. 19.**

—— Cour d'Appel de Paris, 1re Chambre. Plaidoirie de Me H. Barboux pour MM. Ferdinand et Charles de Lesseps. pp. 242. *Paris*, 1893. 8°. **5408. e. 20.**

—— [Another copy.] **5408. e. 17.**

—— Jurisprudence du Conseil des Prises pendant la guerre de 1870–1871, avec notes et commentaires. pp. 160. *Paris*, [1876.] 8°. **5424. bbb. 1.**

—— 26 juin 1907. Banquet offert à M. Barboux par le Barreau de Paris. [Speeches. With a portrait.] pp. 34. *Paris*, 1908. 8°. **12302. e. 14.**

BARBOUX (PAUL LOUIS PHILIBERT) Faculté de Droit de Paris. Thèse pour la licence, *etc.* pp. 54. *Paris*, 1857. 8°. **5406. aa. 1. (16.)**

BARBOZA (ANTONIO) *See* BARBOSA BACELLAR.

BARBOZA (DOMINGOS CALDAS) *See* CALDAS BARBOZA.

BARBOZA (DUARTE) *See* BARBOSA.

BARBOZA (FERNANDO ANTONIO DA COSTA DE) *See* COSTA DE BARBOSA.

BARBOZA (JERONYMO SOARES) *See* SOARES BARBOSA.

BARBOZA (JOSEPH JOAQUIM) Thèse pour le doctorat en médecine. (Questions sur diverses branches des sciences médicales.) pp. 41. *Paris*, 1839. 4°. [*Collection des thèses soutenues à la Faculté de Médecine de Paris.* An 1839. tom. 1.] **7371. a. 1.**

BARBOZA CARNEIRO (J. A.) Rapport sur l'unification des diverses législations relatives aux lettres de change. (Report on the unification of the laws of different countries relating to bills of exchange.) *Fr. & Eng.* pp. 31. 31. [1921.] fol. *See* LEAGUE OF NATIONS.—*Provisional Economic and Financial Committee.* **U.N.R.95.**

BARBOZA DE BARROS (JOSÉ)

—— Faculdade de Medicina e de Pharmacia do Rio de Janeiro. These apresentada . . . pelo Dr. J. Barboza de Barros . . . Da laparotomia na tuberculose do peritoneo, *etc.* pp. 79. *Rio de Janeiro*, 1901. 4°. **7380. a. 15. (5.)**

BARBOZA DE MELLO MORAES (ALEXANDRE) *See* LOSSIO E SEILBIZ (A. B. de) O Passado e o Presente. Poesias . . . colleccionadas por A. Barboza de Mello Moraes, *etc.* 1876. 8°. **11450. ee. 10. (7.)**

BARBOZA MACHADO (DIOGO) *See* BARBOSA MACHADO.

BARBOZA MACHADO (IGNACIO) *See* BARBOSA MACHADO.

BARBOZA RODRIGUES (JOÃO) *See* BARBOSA RODRIGUES.

BARBRAU (ÉLIE AUBIN FÉLIX) De la métro-péritonite puerpérale, et de son traitement par le sulphate de quinine à haute dose. pp. 66. *Paris*, 1857. 4°. [*Collection des thèses soutenues à la Faculté de Médecine de Paris.* An 1857. tom. 1.] **7373. a. 1.**

BARBRAU (P. E. HENRI) Dissertation sur l'asthme; thèse, *etc.* pp. 20. *Paris*, 1834. 4°. **1184. f. 11. (14.)**

BARBRE (MYRTLE)

—— The Boy Jesus . . . Illustrations by Mary Ellsworth. *Saalfield Publishing Co.: Akron, New York*, [1939.] 4°. **12812. b. 86.**

BARBRE (MYRTLE)

—— A Child's Book about Jesus, *etc.* *Saalfield Publishing Co.: Akron, New York*, 1940. 4°. **20092. c. 8.**

BARBRU (RAMIR) *Marquis.* *See* BARBARO (Ramiro A.)

BARBU (J. N.)

—— *See* EPHEMERIDES. Almanahul național-ilustrat al romanilor americani . . . Redactat de J. N. Barbu. [1940.] 8°. **P.P. 2459. acd.**

BARBU (LOUIS RENÉ) Faculté de Droit de Paris. Thèse pour la licence, *etc.* pp. 55. *Paris*, 1857. 8°. **5406. aa. 1. (17.)**

BARBU (NICOLAE I.)

—— *See* LIVIUS (T.) *Patavinus.* [*Roumanian.*] Istoria Romana de Titu Liviu, tradusa de N. Barbu, *etc.* 1884, *etc.* 8°. **9042.f.1.**

—— Les Procédés de la peinture des caractères et la vérité historique dans les biographies de Plutarque. pp. v. 242. *Paris*, 1934. 8°. **20002. b. 16.**

—— Les Sources et l'originalité d'Appien dans le deuxième livre des Guerres Civiles. pp. iv. 102. *Paris*, 1934. 8°. **9042. cc. 16.**

BARBUAT DE MAISON ROUGE (MARIE ANNE DE)

—— *See* GACHOT (J. E.) Le Véritable chevalier de Maison Rouge, *etc.* 1934. 8°. [*Les Œuvres libres.* no. 162.] **12208. ee. 162.**

BARBUCCHIELLI (MARIA MADDALENA) *See* AMADESI (G. L.) Prendendo l'abito religioso della Regola di S. Agostino nel . . . Monastero di S. Gio: Evangelista di Ravenna la Signora M. M. Barbucchielli. [A collection of complimentary verses.] 1719. 8°. **11431. aaa. 55. (2.)**

BARBUDA (CLAUDIO LAGRANGE MONTEIRO DE) *See* LAGRANGE MONTEIRO DE BARBUDA.

BARBUDA (LUYS COELLO DE) *See* COELLO DE BARBUDA.

BARBUDA E VASCONCELLOS (MANOEL MENDES DE) *See* MENDES DE BARBUDA E VASCONCELLOS.

BARBUDA TELLES (ROGERIO) Elogio funebre, e historico, que na sentidissima morte do Senhor Joseph Francisco da Cruz Alagoa, recitou dentro das enlutadas sombras de seu coração . . . R. Barbuda Telles. pp. 40. *Lisboa*, 1768. 4°. **10632. a. 9.**

BARBUDO (ANTONIO SÁNCHEZ) *See* SÁNCHEZ BARBUDO (A.)

BĂRBULESCU (ILIE) Cercetari istorico-filologice, *etc.* pp. 103. *Bucureşti*, 1900. 8°. **12902. h. 3.**

—— Studii privitoare la limba şi istoria Românilor. pp. 199. *Bucuresci*, 1902. 8°. **9136. de. 18.**

BARBUO (SCIPIONE) Sommario delle vite de' Duchi di Milano, cosi Visconti come Sforzeschi, *etc.* [With plates.] ff. 15. *G. Porro: Vinetia*, 1574. fol. **10631. h. 22.**

—— [Another edition.] ff. 15. *F. Ziletti: Vinetia*, 1584. fol. **660. l. 9.**

—— [Another copy.] **C. 80. d. 2.**

BARBUOTIUS (JOANNES) Fontis Sanreginalis, naturalis medicati, virtutum admirabilium in gratiam ægrotantium explicatio. pp. 84. *N. Bessin: Parisiis*, 1661. 12°. **1171.f.36.(2.)**

The date in the colophon is 1671.

BARBUS (Ludovicus) *Bishop of Treviso.* Ven. Ludovici Barbi . . . Liber de initio et progressu congregationis Benedictinæ S. Justinæ de Padua, nunc Cassinensis. Nunc primùm è ms. Cod. . . . erutus & communicatus ab Adm. . . . Josepho Maria Sandi, *etc.* 1721. *See* Pez (B.) Thesaurus anecdotorum novissimus, *etc.* tom. 2. pt. 3. 1721, *etc.* fol. **8.** c. **4.**

BARBUS (Paulus) *Soncinas. See* Thomas, *Aquinas, Saint.* [*Two or more Works.*] *Begin.* [fol. 2 *recto*:] Ad Reuerendissimū . . . Ascanium Mariaȝ: Sphortiam . . . Fratris Pauli soncinatis . . . in opuscula Diui Thome aquinatis . . . prohoemialis epistola. *End.* [fol. 313 *recto*:] Expliciūt ꝑclarissima opuscula diui thome aq̄natis . . . castigata ꝑ frēȝ Paulū sōcinatē, *etc.* 1488. fol. IB. **26365.**

—— *See* Thomas, *Aquinas, Saint.* [*Super Libros Sententiarum.—Liber II.*] Secūdꝰ sñiarū sācti thome aq̄natis, *etc.* *End.* [fol. 179 *verso*:] Explicit scriptum . . . sancti Thome aquinatis . . . in secundū sententiarum . . . emendatum: per . . . fratrem Paulum Soncinatem, *etc.* 1494. fol. IB. **29052.**

BARBUS (Petrus) *Bishop of Cervia. See* Paul II., *Pope.*

BARBUSSE (Adrien) *See* also Harley (Jean) *pseud.* [i.e. A. Barbusse.]

—— Simone. [A novel.] Illustrations de E. Béringuier. pp. 129. 1907. *See* Periodical Publications.—*Paris.* Le Monde illustré, *etc.* (Supplément. / 6 juillet—26 octobre 1907.) 1857, *etc.* fol. / Romans. P.P. **4283.** n. (**1**.)

BARBUSSE (Henri) *See* Boyer (I.) Louise Michel . . . Préface d'H. Barbusse. 1927. 8°. **10656.** e. **14.**

—— *See* Duclos (J.) and Fréville (J.) Henri Barbusse. [With a portrait.] 1946. 8°. **10661.** w. **8.**

—— *See* Gallucci (G.) Critica del terribilismo. Saggi su Papini, Barbusse, *etc.* 1924. 8°. **08465.** df. **41.**

—— *See* Gysin (A.) Die andere Hälfte der Pflicht. Gedanken zum Briefwechsel (abgedruckt in " Clarté " 1921, no. 2, 1922, no. 6, 10) zwischen Romain Rolland und H. Barbusse. 1923. 8°. **8006.** ee. **37.**

—— *See* Hertz (Henri) Henri Barbusse. Son œuvre, *etc.* [With a portrait.] 1920. 8°. **11853.** r. **21.**

—— *See* Kuechler (W.) Romain Rolland. Henri Barbusse, *etc.* 1919. 8°. **011850.** k. **46.**

—— *See* Lenin (V.I.) Lettres de Lénine à sa famille, présentées par Henri Barbusse, *etc.* 1936. 8°. **010920.** a. **57.**

—— *See* Lingner (M.) Max Lingner. Dessins et peintures. Texte par H. Barbusse, Agnès Humbert, *etc.* [1939.] 4°. **7865.** s. **40.**

—— *See* Nikolaev (V.) Анри Барбюс. Критико-биографический очерк. 1954. 8°. **10666.** d. **29.**

—— *See* Russia. [*Laws, etc.—c.—Peace and Disarmament.*] The Soviet Union and Peace . . . With an introduction by H. Barbusse. [1929.] 8°. **8095.** g. **64.**

—— *See* Wells (Warre B.) The Spanish Omnibus . . . With . . . an introduction by H. Barbusse. 1932. 8°. **12488.** t. **8.**

—— *See* Zaldumbide (G.) En Elogio de Henri Barbusse. 1909. 8°. **011852.** ee. **29.**

—— Избранные произведения. [With a portrait.] pp. 550. *Москва,* 1950. 8°. **12519.** bb. **5.**

—— Force.—L'Au-delà.—Le Crieur. (Trois films.) pp. 246. *Paris,* 1926. 8°. **12515.** ppp. **9.**

BARBUSSE (Henri)

—— Under Fire . . . and Light. Translated . . . by Fitzwater Wray [from " Le Feu " and " Clarté "]. pp. ix. 654. *J. M. Dent & Sons: London & Toronto,* 1929. 8°. **12515.** tt. **19.**

—— [Another edition.] pp. ix. 654. *J. M. Dent & Sons: London & Toronto,* 1933. 8°. **012548.** eeee. **3.**

—— Lettres de Henri Barbusse à sa femme, 1914–1917. pp. 261. *Paris,* 1937. 8°. **010921.** e. **7.**

—— Les Bourreaux, *etc.* (Sixième mille.) [On the " White Terror " in the Balkan states after the European War of 1914–1919.] pp. 282. *Paris,* 1926. 8°. **09081.** a. **3.**

—— Die Henker . . . Übersetzt von Heinrich Nelson. pp. 139. *Stuttgart,* 1927. 8°. [*Öffentliches Leben.* Neue Folge. no. 3.] W.P. **9641/3.**

—— Clarté: roman. pp. 290. *Paris,* 1919. 8°. **12547.** v. **36.**

—— Light. Translated . . . by Fitzwater Wray. pp. 308. *J. M. Dent & Sons: London & Toronto,* 1919. 8°. **12547.** ppp. **16.**

—— [Clarté.] Свет. Перевод с французского К. Жихаревой. pp. 216. *Петербург,* 1920. 8°. **12551.** s. **21.**

—— Les Enchaînements. Roman. 2 vol. *Paris,* 1925. 8°. **12514.** pp. **7.**

—— Chains . . . Translated . . . by Stephen Haden Guest. 2 vol. *Jonathan Cape: London; printed in U.S.A.,* 1925. 8°. **012548.** ccc. **66.**

—— [A reissue.] pp. 287. 302. *Martin Lawrence: London; printed in U.S.A.,* [1930.] 8°. **12516.** s. **9.**

—— L'Enfer. pp. 413. *Paris,* [1916.] 8°. **12548.** tt. **27.**

—— Inferno . . . Translated by John Rodker. pp. 263. *Joiner & Steele: London,* 1932. 8°. **12514.** r. **18.**

—— Faits divers. [Tales and sketches.] pp. 282. *Paris,* 1928. 8°. **12516.** tt. **20.**

—— [Faits divers.] Thus and Thus . . . Translated by Brian Rhys. pp. 251. *J. M. Dent & Sons: London & Toronto; printed in U.S.A.,* [1928.] 8°. **12515.** s. **32.**

—— [A reissue.] *London & Toronto,* 1932. 8°. **12514.** ppp. **13.**

—— Лицом к лицу. Ensemble. Рассказы [from Faits divers]. Перевод . . . В. Василенко. pp. 41. *Москва,* 1929. 16°. [*Библиотека "Огонек."* no. 459.] **12209.1.42/30.**

—— Le Feu. Journal d'une escouade. pp. 378. *Paris,* 1916. 8°. **12548.** tt. **32.**

—— Under Fire: the story of a squad . . . Translated by Fitzwater Wray. pp. viii. 344. *J. M. Dent & Sons: London & Toronto,* 1917. 8°. **12547.** p. **6.**

—— [Another edition.] (With an introduction by Brian Rhys.) pp. xvi. 344. *J. M. Dent & Sons: London & Toronto; E. P. Dutton & Co.: New York,* 1926. 8°. [*Everyman's Library.*] **12206.p.1/589.**

—— Under Fire. (Translated by Fitzwater Wray.) *See* War Novels. Four Dramatic War Novels, *etc.* [1938.] 8°. **12614.** h. **19.**

BARBUSSE (Henri)

—— Under Fire, *etc.* (Translated by W. Fitzwater Wray.) pp. xviii. 343. *J. M. Dent & Sons: London: E. P. Dutton & Co.: New York*, 1955. 8°. [*Everyman's Library.* no. 798.] **12206**. p. **1**/**920**.

—— [Le Feu.] Огонь, дневник одного взвода. Перевод с французского С. В. Гальперина под редакцией Е. Г. Лундберга. pp. 381. *Москва*, 1919 [1920]. 8°. **012547**. cc. **7**.

—— J'Accuse ! [Charging French politicians with complicity in plots of the 'White Army,' with special reference to the assassination of President Doumer.] pp. 32. *Paris*, 1932. 8°. **08052**. a. **71**.

—— Jésus. pp. 249. *Paris*, 1927. 8°. **4225**. h. **32**.

—— Les Judas de Jésus. [Studies of Christian origins, etc.] pp. 283. *Paris*, 1927. 8°. **04018**. ee. **51**.

—— Lettre aux intellectuels [on behalf of Communism]. Avec un portrait dessiné par Mela Muter et un fac-simile. pp. 105. *Rome*, 1921. 16°. **08282**. a. **40**.

—— La Lueur dans l'abîme. Ce que veut le groupe Clarté. pp. 153. *Paris*, 1920. 8°. **08007**. ee. **6**.

—— Manifeste aux intellectuels. pp. 45. *Paris*, 1927. 8°. **11825**. de. **48**.

—— Nous autres . . . [Tales.] pp. 363. *Paris*, 1914. 8°. **12548**. t. **28**.

—— We Others . . . Translated from the French by W. Fitzwater Wray. pp. vi. 272. *J. M. Dent & Sons: London & Toronto*, 1918. 8°. **12547**. ppp. **5**.

—— Paroles d'un combattant. Articles et discours, 1917–1920. pp. 238. *Paris*, [1920.] 8°. **08027**. e. **82**.

—— Pleureuses. Poésies. Nouvelle édition. pp. 248. *Paris*, [1920.] 8°. **011483**. c. **74**.

—— Quelques coins du cœur. Proses. Avec 24 bois dessinés et gravés par Frans Masereel. pp. 92. *Genève*, 1921. 8°. **12549.i.6.**

—— Russie. pp. 260. *Paris*, 1930. 8°. **010290**. e. **11**.

—— [Russie.] One Looks at Russia . . . Translated . . . by Warre B. Wells. pp. v. 206. *J. M. Dent & Sons: London & Toronto*, 1931. 8°. **010291**. e. **22**.

—— Staline. Un monde nouveau vu à travers un homme. pp. 320. *Paris*, 1935. 8°. **20003**. a. **24**.

—— Stalin. A new world seen through one man . . . Translated by Vyvyan Holland. With 16 illustrations [including portraits]. pp. xiii. 324. *John Lane: London*, 1935. 8°. **20019**. h. **34**.

—— Сталин. Человек через которого раскрывается новый мир. (Перевод под редакцией А. И. Стецкого.) pp. 111. *Москва*, 1936. 8°. **10797**. ee. **105**.

—— Voici ce qu'on a fait de la Géorgie. pp. 318. *Paris*, 1929. 8°. **8094**. bbb. **65**.

—— *See* Charachidzé (D.) H. Barbusse, les Soviets et la Géorgie, *etc.* [An answer to H. Barbusse's "Voici ce qu'on a fait de la Géorgie."] [1930.] 8°. **8095**. aa. **33**.

—— Zola, *etc.* [With a portrait.] pp. 296. *Paris*, 1932. 8°. **10655**. df. **31**.

—— Zola . . . Translated . . . by Mary Balairdie Green . . . and Frederick C. Green. [With portraits.] pp. 279. *J. M. Dent & Sons: London*, 1932. 8°. **10655**. f. **24**.

BARBUSSE (Henri)

—— Auf zur Wahrheit! (Autorisierte Übertragung von Lucy von Jacobi.) pp. 56. *Berlin*, 1920. 8°. [*Tribüne der Kunst und Zeit.* no. 21.] **20001**. c. **10/21**.

—— Henri Barbusse, écrivain et révolutionnaire. [Appreciations. With a portrait.] pp. 44. *Paris*, 1935. 8°. **010665**. df. **23**.

BARBUT (Jacques) The Genera Vermium exemplified by various specimens of the animals contained in the orders of the Intestina et Molusca Linnæi. (The Genera . . . Part 2[d] exemplified . . . in the orders of the Testacea, Lithophyta, and Zoophyta, *etc.*) *Eng. & Fr.* 2 pt. *The Author: London*, 1783, 88. 4°. **38**. e. **23**.
With an additional titlepage, in French, engraved.

—— [Another copy of pt. 1.] **461**. f. **20**.

—— Les Genres des insectes de Linné; constatés par divers échantillons d'insectes d'Angleterre, copiés d'après nature. *Eng. & Fr.* pp. xvii. 371. *Par Jacques Dixwell; se vend chez J. Sewell: Londres*, 1781. 4°. **458**. c. **19**.
Printed for the author. With an additional titlepage, in English, engraved, dated 1780.

—— [Another copy.] **39**. e. **16**.

BARBUT (Stephen) *See* Whitehead (Edward) *Rector of Winchelsea.* The Peace of the Upright. A sermon preached . . . the Sunday after the death of . . . S. Barbut, *etc.* [1869.] 8°. **4905**. b. **45**. (**16**.)

—— Remarks on the Rev. S. Barbut's Observations on the reply of the Chichester Diocesan Committee of the Society for Promoting Christian Knowledge. pp. 20. *F. C. & J. Rivington: London*, 1818. 8°. **702**. h. **3**. (**6**.)

—— A Reply to the Rev. S. Barbut's Attack on the members of the Chichester Diocesan Committee of the Society for Promoting Christian Knowledge in a publication entitled "Letters," &c. pp. 16. *F. C. & J. Rivington: London; Hodge: Chichester*, 1818. 8°. **701**. h. **14**. (**2**.)

BARBUTI (Francesco) Agli Onorevoli Soci del Comizio Agrario di Roma. [An address upon the cultivation of the Agro Romano.] pp. 27. *Parma*, 1877. 8°. **7078**. df. **3**. (**12**.)

—— Monografia dell'agricoltura parmense . . . e sulle condizioni della classe agricola in Italia. pp. 174. *Parma*, 1880. 8°. **7078**. g. **16**.

BARBY, *on the Elbe.* Journal einer Reise nach Barby im Jahre 178–. Aus der Handschrift. 1785. *See* Bernoulli (J.) *the Younger.* Johann Bernoulli's Sammlung kurzer Reisebeschreibungen, *etc.* Bd. 16. 1781, *etc.* 8°. **1045**. b. **16**.

BARBY, *Family of.* *See* Schwarzburg, *House of.* Derer Hoch-Gräflichen Häuser, Schwartzburg und Barby durch Oldenburg nahe-gesipte nun verneuerte Stamm-Verwandschafft. [1665?] fol. **135**. c. **5**. (**7**.)

BARBY (Henry) Au pays de l'épouvante. L'Arménie martyre, *etc.* [With illustrations.] pp. v. 260. *Paris*, [1917.] 8°. **09057**. a. **58**.

—— Avec l'armée serbe, de l'ultimatum autrichien à l'invasion de la Serbie. [With illustrations and maps.] pp. 446. *Paris*, [1918.] 8°. **09082**. d. **22**.
Part of "La Guerre mondiale."

—— L'Épopée serbe. L'agonie d'un peuple. Avec 20 illustrations, *etc.* pp. viii. 226. *Paris, Nancy*, 1916. 8°. **9081**. de. **24**.

—— Les Extravagances bolcheviques et l'épopée arménienne. (La Débacle russe.) pp. 261. *Paris*, [1919]. 8°. **09083**. aa. **25**.

BARBY (Henry)

—— La Guerre des Balkanes . . . Les victoires serbes. Préface de M. Émile Haumant. [With illustrations.] pp. v. 306. *Paris*, 1913. 8°. **9136**. b. **21**.

—— La Guerre serbo-bulgare. Brégalnitsa. [With illustrations.] pp. iii. 346. *Paris*, 1914. 8°. **9136**. bb. **39**.

—— Брегалница. Српско-Бугарски рат 1913. С француског са пишчевим одобрењем. pp. iv. 195. *Београд*, 1914. 8°. **9134**. c. **13**.

BARBY (Jean Marie) Essai sur la duodénite ; thèse, *etc.* pp. 48. *Paris*, 1836. 4°. **1184**. g. **14**. (**10**.)

BARBY (Johann Heinrich Christian) *See* Sophocles. [*Philoctetes.—Greek.*] Sophoclis Philoctetes . . . cum commentario perpetuo J. H. C. Barby. 1803. 8°. **999**. f. **7**.

—— De consilio quo C. Cornelius Tacitus librum illum de situ, moribus et populis Germaniae conscripserit, et de fide ei tribuenda. 1825. 4°. *See* Berlin.—*Friedrich-Wilhelms-Gymnasium.* [Programmes, etc.] 1797, *etc.* 8° & 4°. **8358**. cc. **36**.

BARBYER (Charles)

—— The "Favourite" French Reader . . . Edited by C. Barbyer. pp. ix. 97. *Sir I. Pitman & Sons: London*, 1934. 8°. **12951**. cc. **2**

BARBYUS (Anri) *See* Barbusse (Henri)

BARBYUSS ( ) [For the French surname in this form :] *See* Barbusse.

BARCA, Antonio Araujo de Azevedo, *Count da.* *See* Araujo de Azevedo.

BARCA (Alessandro) Lettera . . . sulla scomposizione dell' alcali flogisticato. 1783. *See* Amoretti (C.) and Soave (F.) Opuscoli scelti sulle scienze, *etc.* tom. 6. 1778, *etc.* 4°. **981**. h. **6**.

BARCA (Frances Erskine Calderón de la) *See* Calderón de la Barca.

BARCA (Fernando de Settien Calderón de la) *See* Settien Calderón de la Barca.

BARCA (Francisco) *See* Suárez Inclán (E.) and Barca (F.) Diccionario general de Política y Administracion, *etc.* 1868. 8°. **8042**. l. **8**.

—— Ensayos filosofico-politicos sobre la Revolucion francesa. pp. v. 101. *Madrid*, 1849. 8°. **8052**. g. **7**.

BARCA (José María Calderón de la) *See* Calderón de la Barca.

BARCA (Joseph Calderón de la) *See* Calderón de la Barca.

BARCA (Miguel Calderón de la) *See* Calderón de la Barca.

BARCA (Pedro Calderón de la) *See* Calderón de la Barca.

BARCA (Pietro Antonio) Auuertimenti, e regole circa l'architettura ciuile, scultura, pittura, prospettiua, et architettura militare, per offesa, e difesa di fortezze. [With plates.] ff. 46. *P. Malatesta: Milano*, 1620. *obl.* fol. **56**. b. **4**.

BARCA (Roberto de la)

—— La Barrera franqueada. [A novel.] pp. 240. *Madrid*, 1945. 8°. **12492**. bbb. **12**.

BĂRCĂCILĂ (Al.)

—— Baile Herculane—Ad Mediam—à l'époque romaine et les croyances populaires d'aujourd'hui. Avec 12 gravures. Extrait du volume : ix Congrès International d'histoire de la mèdecine [*sic*], *etc.* pp. 11. 1935. fol. *See* Turnu-Severin.—*Museŭ Regional Portile de Fier.* **1833**. a. **38**.

—— Une Ville daco-romaine : Drubeta. Extrait de "L'Archéologie en Roumanie." pp. 46. pl. xxxix. *Bucarest*, 1938. 8°. **07704**. bb. **16**.

BARCA DE ASTORGA (Petrus) *See* Heredia (P. M. de) Cl. viri D. Petri Michaelis de Heredia . . . operum medicinalium tomus primus(—quartus) . . . Editio altera . . . emendata curâ & diligentiâ D. P. Barea [*sic*] de Astorga. 1689, *etc.* fol. **541**. i. **11**, **12**.

BARCÁIZTEGUI Y MANSO (José Javier de) *Count del Llobregat, Marquis de Tabalosos.* Fuenterrabía. Noticias históricas. pp. 196. *Madrid*, 1930. 8°. **010160**. de. **57**.

—— Fuenterrabía . . . Segunda edición. pp. 194. *San Sebastián*, 1942. 8°. **10163**. e. **1**.

BARCARIOL (Piero Segala) *pseud.* *See* Segala Barcariol.

BARÇAUMA, *Bishop of Nisibis.* *See* Barsoma.

BARCA Y ABREGO (Manuel Calderón de la) *See* Calderón de la Barca y Abrego.

BARCELLENSIS (Franciscus) *See* Franciscus [de Sousa], *Barcellensis.*

BARCELLINI (Innocenzo) Industrie filologiche per dar risalto alle virtù del Santissimo Pontefice Celestino v., e liberare da alcune taccie Dante Alighieri creduto censore della celebre rinunzia fatta dal medesimo santo, *etc.* pp. 342. *Milano*, 1701. 8°. **1161**. d. **15**.

BARCELLONA (Antonino) *See* Bible.—*Obadiah.* [Polyglott.] Parafrasi della Profezia di Abdia . . . di A. Barcellona, *etc.* 1826. 8°. **4033**. dd. **22**. (**5**.)

BARCELLONA (Valentino) *pseud.* [i.e. Antonio lo Presti.] Memorie della vita letteraria, e de' viaggi di Pietro Ranzano . . . vescovo di Lucera, ricavata in maggior parte dagli otto volumi de' suoi Annali di tutti i tempi da V. Barcellona. 1761. *See* Sicilian Authors. Opuscoli di autori siciliani. tom. 6. 1758, *etc.* 4°. **663**. g. **3**.

BARCELLONA PASSALACQUA (Pietro) Le Tre Hyccari a traverso la leggenda e la storia popolare di Sicilia. Col racconto del tragico fatto della Baronessina di Carini. pp. 336. *Palermo*, 1901. 8°. **9165**. ff. **19**.

BARCELLOS, Pedro, *Count de.* *See* Pedro, *Count de Barcellos, etc.*

BARCELLOS (Franciscus de) *See* Franciscus [de Sousa], *Barcellensis.*

BARCELLOS (João Antonio de) Quelques considérations sur l'asthme. Thèse, *etc.* pp. 81. *Montpellier*, 1857. 4°. **7379**. d. **10**. (**5**.)

BARCELÓ (Antonio)

—— *See* Ferrari Billoch (F.) Barceló. Sus luchas con Ingleses y piratas berberiscos. [With a portrait.] [1941.] 8°. **10635**. a. **17**

—— *See* García de la Huerta (V. A.) Elogio del excelentisimo señor D. A. Barceló, *etc.* 1784. 4°. **12301**. e. **5**. (**11**.

—— Explicacion de la 1ª barca canoñera que se hizo por direccion del Comandante de Marina A. Barcelo. [With engravings by Ramon de Ribert.] *Madrid* [1780?] *s. sh. obl.* fol. **1881**. c. **7**. (**56**.

BARCELÓ (Antonio)

—— Nuevo y curioso romance en donde da cuenta y declara, el caso que le aconteció á Don A. Barceló saliendo con su armada del puerto de Cartagena . . . y el milagro que obró la Virgen de Guaytoca, *etc.* *Barcelona*, [1830?] 4°. **11450.** f. 26. (6.)

—— Relacion de las Disposiciones catholicas, y religiosas, executadas por el Teniente General Don A. Barcelò, para el embarco de la Imagen de Maria Santisima del Carmen, como Protectora de la Expedicion contra Argel, que se executò el Lunes 30. de Junio de este año en Cartagena. (Estado que manifiesta los buques de guerra destinados à la presente expedicion del mando del Exmo. Señor Don A. Barceló, *etc.*) 2 pt. *Puerto de Santa Maria*, 1783. fol. T. **16***. (22, 23.)

BARCELÓ (Francisco Castro y) *See* Castro y Barceló.

BARCELÓ (Gabriel)

—— *See* Bukharin (N. I.) El Materialismo Histórico. (Traducido por P. de la Torriente Brau y G. Barceló.) 1933. 8°. **09008.** b. 20.

BARCELÓ (Javier Malagón) *See* Malagón Barceló.

BARCELÓ (Joseph) Essai sur la néphrite aiguë, *etc.* pp. 17. *Montpellier*, 1821. 4°. **1180.** i. **15.** (6.)

BARCELÓ (Martín Juan) [Poems.] *See* Aguilar (J. B.) Varias hermosas flores, del Parnaso, *etc.* 1680. 4°. **11451.** e. 1.

BARCELÓ (Simón) Manual Diplomático y Consular Hispano-Americano. pp. 463. *Barcelona*, 1909. 8°. **8180.** g. 53.

—— Veteranos del Crimen. pp. vi. 35. *Puerto España, Trinidad*, 1892. 8°. **8180.** f. 45. (3.)

BARCELÓ GOSÁLVEZ (Gonzalo) *See* Canalejas y Méndez (J.) Canalejas gobernante. Discursos parlamentarios, *etc.* [Edited by G. Barceló Gosálvez and E. Berenguer Enríquez.] [1912.] 8°. **12301.** c. **47.**

BARCELONA,

OFFICIAL DOCUMENTS.

—— [For editions and translations of the " Consolat del mar " of Barcelona :] *See* Consolat.

—— Constituciones de Sanctacilia o costumbres de la ciudad de Barcelona sobre las servidumbres de los predios rústicos y urbanos [in Catalan and Spanish] . . . añadidas con el arte de edificar sin agravio del vecino ; o sea : Puntuario jurídico y elementos prácticos para ejercer este arte, escrito por . . . Poncio Cabanoch . . . 2ª edicion. pp. 111. *Lerida*, 1857. 8°. 5385.a.41.(4.)

—— Ordenanzas Municipales de Barcelona. pp. 103. *Barcelona*, 1857. 8°. 5385.a.40.(4.)

—— *Begin.* Por la ciudad de Barcelona. Aunque la mudança de las monetas, *etc.* [Complaining of the frequent changes in the value of money.] [1620?] fol. **1322.** l. 7. (6.)

MUNICIPAL INSTITUTIONS.

Ayuntamiento.

—— Anales y boletín de los museos de arte de Barcelona. vol. 4. no. 3/4, *etc.* jul./oct. 1946, *etc.* *Barcelona*, 1946– . 4°. P.P. **1931.** pkh.

—— Apuntes para la biografía de Pedro Virgili. Escritos, por encargo del excmo. Ayuntamiento de Barcelona, por Luis Comenge. pp. 221. *Barcelona*, 1893. 8°. **10631.** ee. 48.

—— Sucinta Relacion de las principales operaciones del escmo. Ayuntamiento constitucional de la ciudad de Barcelona en el año 1821. [With tables.] pp. 143. xxxix. *Barcelona*, [1822.] 4°. **1196.** f. **23.**

Cárcel.

—— Reglamento para el régimen y gobierno de la Cárcel de Barcelona. pp. 38. *Barcelona*, 1879. 8°. **6057.** g. 2. (3.)

Casa Municipal de Corrección.

—— Estadística de la situacion material y moral de los reclusos de la Casa municipal de correccion de Barcelona, precedida de un preliminar por el director del establecimiento D. J. M. Canalejas. (1859.) pp. 60. *Barcelona*, 1860. 8°. **6055.** d. 55.

Concell de Cent.

—— Manual de novells ardits vulgarment apellat Dietari del Antich Consell Barceloní, *etc.* 17 vol. *Barcelona*, 1892–1922. 8°. [*Colecció de documents histórichs inedits de Arxiu municipal.*] **10161.** eee. **6.**

—— Ordinacions fetas, y ordenades per los molt illustres Senyors Consellers y saui Consell de cent de la present Ciutat de Barcelona, celebrat a 5. de Iuliol 1626. sobre la administracio dels forments. *S. & I. Mathevat: Barcelona*, 1637. 4°. **5383.** f. **6.**
The date has been altered in ms. *to* 1640.

—— [Another edition.] *S. & I. Matevat: Barcelona*, 1640. 4°. **5383.** f. **8.**

—— Ordinacions fetas, y ordenades per los molt illustres Senyors Consellers y saui Consell de cent de la present Ciutat de Barcelona, celebrat a 9. de Agost 1635. sobre la administracio dels forments. *S. & I. Mathevat: Barcelona*, 1637. 4°. **5383.** f. **7.**

—— [Another edition.] *S. & I. Mathevat: Barcelona*, 1640. 4°. **5383.** f. **9.**

—— Proclamacion catolica a la Magestad piadosa de Felipe el Grande, Rey de las Españas . . . nuestro Señor. Los Conselleres, y Consejo de Ciento de la Ciudad de Barcelona. pp. 134. *I. Matevad: Barcelona*, 1641. 8°. [Drawn up by Gaspar Sala.] **9180.** e. 1. (5.)

—— [Another edition.] [Drawn up by Gaspar Sala.] [Edited by L. de Queiros.] pp. 169. *A. Aluarez: Lisboa*, 1641. 4°. **1445.** f. **14.** (1.)

—— *See* Aristarco. Aristarco ó censura de la Proclamacion Catolica de los Catalanes. [Generally ascribed to Francisco de Rioja.] [1640.] 4°. **9180.** cc. **10.**

—— Plainte Catholique des Catalans, addressée à Philippe le Grand, Roy des Espagnes . . . par le Conseil des Cent de la Ville de Barcelone. Contenant les motifs de la prise de leurs armes . . . Traduit de l'Espagnol en Français, *etc.* pp. 143. *Jacques Cailloue: Rouen*, 1641. 4°. [Drawn up by G. Sala.] **9180.** cc. 22.

—— Politica Christiana novament instituida en la insigne ciutat de Barcelona. En actio de gracias, de las moltas . . . victorias que goza lo Principat de Catalunya. [A proclamation announcing the establishment of a " Junta de Politica Christiana."] *S. de Cormellas: Barcelona*, 1643. 4°. **9180.** e. 2. (**37.**)

—— Transumpts y copies de les cartes escrites per los Consellers de la ciutat de Barcelona, y Procuradors de la de Tortosa, a la present ciutat de Valencia y remey contra la malaltia dels bestiars de pel, *etc.* 2 pt. *V. Cabrera: Valencia*, 1682. fol. **704.** h. **16.** (**11, 12.**)

—— [Another copy of pt. 2.] **704.** h. **16.** (**13.**)

—— Redrès, y ordinacions novaments fetas, y estatuidas per lo savi Concell de Cent . . . tingut, y celebrat als 30 de Abril del any 1703. concernents, al regimen de la Taula dels Comuns Deposits de dita ciutat, y Banch de aquella, *etc.* pp. 92. *Barcelona*, 1703. 4°. **8227**. aaa. **1**.

MISCELLANEOUS INSTITUTIONS.

ACADEMIA CIENTÍFICO-MERCANTIL DE BARCELONA.

—— Crónica Comercial . . . Eco mensual, *etc.* año 6. no. 1—año 9. no. 46. *Barcelona*, 1892–95. 8°.

—— Lista de los profesores y peritos mercantiles titulares de la Academia . . . Número extraordinario de la Crónica Comercial, *etc.* pp. 19. *Barcelona*, 1895. 8°. P.P. **1423**. ifb.

ACADEMIA DE BELLAS ARTES.

—— Album de la Exposicion Retrospectiva, de obras de pintura, escultura, arquitectura y artes suntuarias, celebrada por la Academia de Bellas Artes de Barcelona en 1867. Publicado por . . . J. Serra y Gibert. Segunda edicion. pp. 29. pl. xxxv. *Barcelona*, 1868. *obl.* 4°. **1788**. dd. **11**.

ACADEMIA DE DERECHO.

—— Proyecto de apéndice del Código Civil para Cataluña. [Edited by M. Trias y Domenech.] pp. 132. *Barcelona*, 1896. 8°. **5384**. b. **11**.

ACADEMIA DE LEGISLACIÓN Y JURISPRUDENCIA.

—— Dictámen y bases para la organizacion del personal administrativo de las cárceles y presidios de España, presentados por la Comision especial nombrada para redactar una memoria para el Congreso Internacional Penitenciario de Estocolmo. pp. 32. *Barcelona*, 1877. 8°. **5383**. e. **22**.

ACADEMIA PROVINCIAL DE BELLAS ARTES.

—— *See* supra: ACADEMIA DE BELLAS ARTES.

AMICS DELS MUSEUS DE CATALUNYA.

—— Catàleg de la Col·lecció d'Indumentària de Manuel Rocamora exposada per l'Associació d'Amics dels Museus de Catalunya. Redactat per Manuel Rocamora, *etc.* [With illustrations.] pp. 148. [1933.] 8°. *See* infra: Museu de les Arts Decoratives. **07742**. aa. **60**.

—— Doscientas piezas de cerámica persa. Catálogo de la exposición. [With plates.] pp. 34. *Barcelona*, 1950. 8°. **7813**. l. **13**.

ARCHIVO DE ETNOGRAFÍA Y FOLKLORE DE CATALUÑA.

—— *See* infra: ARXIU D'ETNOGRAFÍA I FOLKLORE DE CATALUNYA.

ARCHIVO DE LA CORONA DE ARAGÓN.

—— Archivo de la Corona de Aragón. Catálogo de la documentación relativa al antiguo reino de Valencia contenida en los registros de la Cancillería Real. Redactado por Jesús Ernesto Martínez Ferrando. MADRID. *Cuerpo Facultativo de Archiveros, Bibliotecarios y Anticuarios*; Madrid, 1934–. 8°. Ac. **2105**/5.

—— Catálogo de los Documentos y Manuscritos pertenecientes a la antigua Provincia de Aragón de la Compañía de Jesús, que se conservan en el Archivo de la Corona de Aragón. [By] Pedro Blanco Trías. pp. 48. *Barcelona*, [1944.] 8°. **11925**. aa. **42**.

—— Coleccion de Documentos Ineditos del Archivo General de la Corona de Aragon, publicada . . . por . . . D. P. de Bofarull y Mascaró (tom. 18–40, por D. Manuel de Bofarull y de Sartorio; tom. 41, por Don Francisco de Bofarull y Sans). 41 tom. 1847–1910. 8°. *See* BOFARULL Y MASCARÓ (P. de) **9181**. d.

—— Los Documentos Árabes Diplomáticos del Archivo de la Corona de Aragón. Editados y traducidos por Maximiliano A. Alarcón y Santón y Ramón García de Linares (en colaboración con Don Ángel González Palencia). [Issued by the Escuelas de Estudios Árabes de Madrid y Granada.] pp. xi. 438. 1940. fol. *See* MADRID.—*Escuela de Estudios Árabes de Madrid.* Ac. **147**. b.

—— Documentos sobre relaciones internacionales de los Reyes Católicos. [Contained in the Archivo de la Corona de Aragón.] Edición preparada por A. de la Torre. 1949– . 8°. *See* SPAIN. [*Laws, Treaties, etc.*—II. *Diplomatic Correspondence.*] Ac. **132**. p.

—— Inventario de pergaminos medievales de monasterios gerundenses. Redactado por F. Sevillano Colom, *etc.* *Madrid*, 1953– . 8°. Ac. **2105**. ba.
Part of a series published by the Dirección General de Archivos y Bibliotecas, called 'Catálogos de archivos y bibliotecas.'

Sección Cancillería Real.

—— Regesta de letras pontificias del Archivo de la Corona de Aragón . . . Por el Dr. Francisco J. Miquel Rosell. pp. 554. *Cuerpo Facultativo de Archiveros, Bibliotecarios y Anticuarios*: Madrid, 1948. 8°. **11927**. b. **17**.

ARXIU D'ETNOGRAFÍA I FOLKLORE DE CATALUNYA.

—— Estudis i materials. vol. 1, 2. *Barcelona*, 1916, 17. 4°. Ac. **6223**. d.

—— El Mito de "el Comte Arnau" en la canción popular, la tradición legendaria y la literatura. Por José Romen Figueras, *etc.* [With a bibliography, plates, maps and musical illustrations.] pp. xxiii. 272. *Barcelona*, 1948. 8°. **11868**. g. **19**.

—— Refranero internacional de la música y de la danza. Por J. Riquart Matas, *etc.* pp. xv. 377. *Barcelona*, 1950. 8°. **12361**. bb. **18**.
No. 2 of the Publications of the Institute.

ARXIU MUNICIPAL HISTÓRIC.

—— Colecció de documents históricha inédits del Arxiu municipal de la ciutat de Barcelona. vol. 1–17. *Barcelona*, 1892–1922. 8°. **10161**. eee. **6**.
No more published.

—— L'Hôtel de Ville de Barcelone. Abrégé historique. (Redactat per A. Duran i Sanpere.) [Translated into French by Paul Tachard and into English by Inés de Vaudrey. With illustrations.] *Fr. & Eng.* pp. 54. *Barcelona*, 1921. 8°. **10162**. ee. **26**.

ASOCIACIÓN ARTÍSTICO-ARQUEOLÓGICA BARCELONESA.

—— Album de la instalación artístico-arqueológica de la Real Casa en la Exposicion Universal de Barcelona, *etc.* pp. 143. *Barcelona*, [1889.] 8°. **7958**. h. **17**.

—— Album de la Sección arqueologíca de la Exposición Universal de Barcelona, *etc.* pp. 139. *Barcelona*, [1889.] 8°. **7958**. h. **18**.

—— Estudios de indumentaria española concreta y comparada . . . Cuadro histórico especial de los siglos XIII y XIV. Per D. J. Puiggarí. pp. ix. 380. pl. 46. *Barcelona*, 1890. 8°. Ac. **5245**.

ASOCIACIÓN DE ARQUITECTOS DE CATALUÑA.

—— La Catedral de Gerona. Apuntes para una monografía . . . Por D. Joaquín Bassegoda. pp. 83. *Barcelona*, 1889. 8°. **7817**. g. **19**.

—— El Claustro del Monasterio de San Pedro de las Puellas. Memoria descriptiva. Por Don Ubaldo Iranzo y Eiras. [With illustrations.] pp. 58. *Barcelona*, [1910?] 8°. **07815**. h. **39**.

—— Monasterio de Sant Llorens del Munt. Memoria descriptiva. Por D. Elías Rogent. [Edited by B. Bassegoda.] pp. 46. *Barcelona*, [1900.] 8°. **7817**. k. **26**.

ASOCIACIÓN DE BIBLIÓFILOS DE BARCELONA.

—— Estatutos y Lista de Socios de la Asociación de Bibliófilos de Barcelona. pp. 17. *Barcelona*, 1944. 4°. Ac. **9539**.

—— Asociación de Bibliófilos de Barcelona. [Addresses delivered at the first meeting of the Association, together with illustrations of an exhibition of Spanish bindings and illustrated books, 1750–1850.] pp. 21. [*Barcelona*,] 1944. 4°. Ac. **9539**/**2**.

ASOCIACIÓN INDUSTRIAL PORTUENSE EN BARCELONA.

—— Memoria de la Exposicion Peninsular en Oporto. Publicada por la Junta Corresponsal de la Asociacion Industrial Portuense en Barcelona, *etc.* pp. liv. *Barcelona*, 1863. 4°. **7957**. ee. **22**.

ASSOCIACIÓ D'EXCURSIONS CATALANA.

—— Anuari, *etc.* any 1, 2. 1881, 82. *Barcelona*, 1881, 82, 83. 8°. Ac. **8883/2**.

—— Biblioteca popular de la Associació d'Excursions Catalana. Director: Ramon Arabía y Solanas. 6 vol. *Barcelona*, 1884–91. 16°. Ac. **8883**.

—— Un Estudi de Toponomástica Catalana. Per Salvador Sanpere y Miquel. Obra llorejada, *etc.* pp. xvi. 172. *Barcelona*, 1880. 8°. **12941**. h. **17**.

ASSOCIACIÓ DE PERIODISTES DE BARCELONA.

—— Associació de Periodistes de Barcelona. [Official organ.] [*Barcelona*,] 1933– . 8°. P.P. **6477**. bb.

—— Annals del Periodisme Català. any 2. no. 8, *etc.* [*Barcelona*,] 1934– . 8°. P.P. **6477**. bc.

ASSOCIACIÓ WAGNERIANA.

—— xxv Conferencies donades a la Associació Wagneriana, 1902–1906. pp. viii. 492. *Barcelona*, 1908. 8°. **011824**. b. **30**.

ATENEO BARCELONÉS.

—— Estatutos del " Ateneo Barcelonés " reformados en 30 de Junio de 1897. (Estatuts del " Ateneo Barcelonés " reformats lo 30 de Juny de 1897.) *Span. & Cat.* pp. 47. *Barcelona*, 1897. 12°. **11825**. de. **20**.

—— Centenario del descubrimiento de América. Conferencias leídas en el Ateneo Barcelonés sobre el estado de la cultura española, y particularmente catalana, en el siglo xv. pp. 450. *Barcelona*, 1893. 8°. **9180**. g. **26**.

BIBLIOTECA BALMES.

—— Analecta sacra Tarraconensia. vol. 2–[11], 13, *etc.* 1926–35, 1937/40, *etc.* *Barcelona*, 1926– . 8°. Ac. **2006**. d/**2**.

Vol. 11 *does not bear the series numeration.*

—— Anejo al vol. xx. Indices de los tomos I–XX, 1925–1947. pp. 52*. *Barcelona*, 1948. 8°. Ac. **2006**. d 2a.

—— Biblioteca histórica de la Biblioteca Balmes. ser. 1. *Barcelona*, 1929– . 8°. Ac. **2006**. d. (**1**.)

—— ser. 2. *Barcelona*, 1934– . 8°. Ac. **2006**. d. (**2**.)

Ser. 2. *vol.* 11, 12, 14, 14a, 18, *do not bear the series title or numeration.*

Ser. 2. *vol.* 13 *was published as part of vol.* 10 *of " Analecta sacra Tarraconensia," and is placed accordingly.*

Officina Romànica de Lingüística i Literatura.

—— Anuari de l'Oficina Romànica de Lingüística i Literatura. vol. 5. 1932. *Barcelona*, 1932. 8°. Ac. **2006**. da.

BIBLIOTECA DE CATALUNYA.

—— *See* infra: INSTITUT D'ESTUDIS CATALANS.

BRITISH CHAMBER OF COMMERCE FOR SPAIN.

—— Report. (Monthly Report.) vol. 8–11. July 1915—Dec. 1918. *Barcelona*, 1915–18. 8°.
[Continued as:]
Monthly Journal. vol. 2–4. July 1919—Dec. 1921. *Barcelona*, 1919–21. 8°. (Monthly Report) P.P. **1423**. ifc.

CÁMARA DE COMERCIO Y NAVEGACIÓN.

—— *See* infra: CÁMARA OFICIAL DE COMERCIO Y NAVEGACIÓN.

CÁMARA OFICIAL DE COMERCIO Y NAVEGACIÓN DE BARCELONA.

—— Memoria de los trabajos realizados durante el año 1918(–1921). 4 vol. *Barcelona*, [1919–22.] 8°. **08229**. l. **23**.

—— Catálogo de la Biblioteca. Por orden alfabético de autores. pp. 546. *Barcelona*, 1946. 8°. **11914**. g. **35**.

—— Las Enseñanzas mercantiles. Trabajos en pro de su enaltecimiento, mejora y mayor difusión. Por Bartolomé Amengual. pp. 250. *Barcelona*, 1947. 8°. **8355**. aa. **34**.

—— Historia de la Real Junta Particular de Comercio de Barcelona, 1758 a 1847. Por D. Ángel Ruiz y Pablo. pp. xi. 447. *Barcelona*, 1919. 8°. **08245**. g. **29**.

CÁMARA OFICIAL DEL LIBRO.

—— El Libro Español. ([By] Victor Oliva.) [With plates.] pp. 24. *Barcelona*, 1930. 8°. **011899**. aa. **13**.

CAMPING CLUB DE CATALUNYA.

—— Camping Club de Catalunya. [A prospectus. With a questionnaire.] 2 pt. [*Barcelona*, c. 1920.] 4° & 8°. **1856**. g. **14**. (**91**.)

CASA DE MISERICORDIA.

—— Relacion de lo sucedido en la Casa de Misericordia de Barcelona, la noche del sábado 22 de marzo de 1845. pp. 4. *Barcelona*, 1845. 4°. **12330**. l. **10**. (**11**.)

CATHEDRAL CHURCH.

—— Antiqua statuta ecclesiæ Barcinonensis. *See* MARTÈNE (E.) and DURAND (U.) Thesaurus novus anecdotorum, *etc.* tom. 4. 1717. fol. **10**. f. **5**.

—— Relacion verdadera del origen de la Santa Imagen de la Magestad [at Lucca], cuya imitacion verdadera assiste en la Santa Iglesia desta Ciudad de Barcelona. [In verse.] *S. & I. Mathevat: Barcelona,* 1635. 4º. **11450. e. 24. (29.)**

CENTRE EXCURSIONISTA DE CATALUNYA.

—— Butlletí del Centre Excursionista de Catalunya. any 1. no. 1.—any 48. no. 518/523. jan./juny 1891—jul./des. 1938. *Barcelona,* 1891–1938. 8º. **10163. k. 1.**

Club Alpí Català.

—— Diccionari Nomenclàtor de Pobles i Poblats de Catalunya. pp. xii. 660. *Barcelona,* 1931. 8º. **010160. ee. 7.**

CLUB MUNTANYENC.

—— Discurs llegit per En R. Serra y Pagès . . . al objecte de donar a conèxer la personalitat y obres de En Rafel Patxot y Jubert ab motiu d'haver sigut nomenat Soci Honorari de l'entitat esmentada. pp. 35. *Barcelona,* 1926. 8º. **12301. p. 63.**

COLEGIO DEL ARTE MAYOR DE LA SEDA DE BARCELONA.

—— La Seda en la liturgia. Exposición, *etc.* pp. 46. pl. XXXIV. *Barcelona,* [1952.] 8º. **7960. ee. 24.**

COLLEGIUM PHARMACOPOLARUM.

—— Concordia Pharmacopolarum Barcinonensium de componendis medicamentis compositis quorum in pharmacopoliis vsus est, nuper accurate recognita . . . Consulibus Collegij Pharmacopolarum Bernardo Domenech & Ioanne Benedicto Pau. pp. 213. *Typis H. Gotard: Barcinone,* 1587. fol. **777. i. 6.**

CONSISTORI DELS JOCHS FLORALS DE BARCELONA.

—— Jochs Florals de Barcelona en 1859 (–1936). *Barcelona,* 1859–1936. 8º. **11451. i. 13.**

CONVENT DE FRA-MENORS CAPUTXINS, BARCELONA-SARRIÁ.

—— Estudis franciscans. Revista, *etc.* no. 225–240, 253–270. juny, 1926—gen./març, 1929; abril/juny, 1932—jul./set., 1936. *Barcelona,* 1926–36. 8º. **P.P. 210. sab.**

ELS XII.

—— Els XII. Primera Exposició. Catàleg, *etc.* pp. xxix. *Barcelona,* 1928. 8º. **011900. c. 26.**

ESCUELA INDUSTRIAL BARCELONESA.

—— Reglamento de la Escuela Industrial Barcelonesa. pp. 32. *Madrid,* 1853. 8º. **7943. c. 15. (3.)**

Instituto de Electridad Aplicada.

—— Escuela de Directores de Industrias Eléctricas. Curso 1917–1918. *Barcelona,* [1917.] 8º. **08755. d. 6.**

Escuela Oficial de Náutica.

—— *See* infra: UNIVERSIDAD DE BARCELONA.

ERASMO, CENTRO DE ESTUDIOS ANTROPOLÓGICOS Y HUMANÍSTICOS.

—— Humanidades. no. 1. *Barcelona,* 1952. 8º. **Ac. 6223. e.**

ESCOLA DE BIBLIOTECÀRIES DE LA GENERALITAT DE CATALUNYA.

—— Les Guies de Lectura. Conferència . . . Per Aurora Díaz-Plaja . . . Amb ampliacions i apèndixs. pp. 43. *Barcelona,* 1938. 8º. **11900. n. 48.**
No. 7 of the "Quaderns de Treball."

—— Què podria ésser una Biblioteca de referència a les Populars de Catalunya. Per Maria Cugueró. (Tesi.) pp. 27. *Barcelona,* 1938. 8º. **11900. bb. 69.**
No. 6 of the "Quaderns de Treball."

ESTUDIS UNIVERSITARIS CATALANS.

—— Estudis universitaris catalans. (Revista dels Estudis universitaris catalans.) 22 vol. *Barcelona,* 1907–36. 8º. **Ac. 2604. c.**

EXPOSICIÓN DEL LIBRO ALEMÁN, 1925.

—— Exposición del Libro Alemán. Deutsche Buchausstellung . . . Lista de las obras expuestas. Verzeichnis der ausgestellten Werke. pp. 487. *Leipzig,* [1925.] 8º. **011903. aa. 55.**

EXPOSICIÓN INTERNACIONAL, 1929.

—— El Arte en España. Guía del Museo del Palacio Nacional. Segunda edición, revisada por el Dr. D. Manuel Gómez Moreno. [With plates.] pp. 704. *Barcelona,* 1929. 8º. **7813. f. 44.**

—— Diario oficial. año 1. no. 22–29, 31, 32. 11 agosto—12 oct. 1929. *Barcelona,* 1929. fol. **1884. b. 20.**

—— Exposición Internacional de Barcelona, 1929. Guía oficial. [With illustrations and maps.] pp. 127. *Barcelona,* [1929.] 8º. **07959. ee. 53.**

EXPOSICIÓN UNIVERSAL, 1888.

—— Album de la instalación artístico-arqueológica de la Real Casa en la Exposición, *etc.* pp. 143. [1889.] 8º. *See* supra: ASOCIACIÓN ARTÍSTICO-ARQUEOLÓGICA BARCELONESA. **7958. h. 17.**

—— Album de la Sección arqueológica de la Exposición, *etc.* pp. 139. [1889.] 8º. *See* supra: ASOCIACIÓN ARTÍSTICO-ARQUEOLÓGICA BARCELONESA. **7958. h. 18.**

—— Catálogo de los objetos que la República del Paraguay exhibe en la Exposicion Universal de Barcelona. pp. 66. *Barcelona,* 1888. 8º. **7958. b. 46.**

—— Inventario de la Sección arqueológica de la Exposición Universal de Barcelona, *etc.* pp. 173. *Barcelona,* 1890. 8º. **7959. d. 36.**

FOYER ANTIFASCISTE FRANÇAIS.

—— Le Foyer Antifasciste Français, patroné par le Comissariat de Propaganda de la Generalitat de Catalunya . . . French Anti-Fascist Clubhouse, *etc.* [Seven photographs.] [*Barcelona,* 1937?] 8º. **8042. a. 74.**

FRANCISCANS.

—— Statuta generalia Barcinonensia pro familia cismontana. *See* FRANCISCANS.

FUNDACIÓ BERNAT METGE.

—— Escriptors Cristians. Text i traducció. 3 vol. *Barcelona,* 1927–31. 8º. **Ac. 137. c.**

—— Escriptors Grecs. Text i traducció. 10 pt. *Barcelona,* 1923–34. 8º. **Ac. 137. b.**

—— Escriptors Llatins. Text i traducció. 33 pt. *Barcelona,* 1923–46. 8º. **Ac. 137**

FUNDACIÓ CONCEPCIÓ RABELL I CIBILS.

—— Obra del Cançoner Popular de Catalunya. Materials. *Barcelona*, 1926– . 4°. **Ac. 8882.**

FUNDACIÓ PATXOT.

—— *See* infra : INSTITUCIÓ PATXOT.

GABINET NUMISMÀTIC DE CATALUNYA.

—— [Publications.] ser. A. no. 1, 2. *Barcelona*, 1933. 8°. **07757.** ee. **37.**

GRUPO " AMOR Y VIDA."

—— [Writings purporting to have been dictated by spirits to María Vilanova and other mediums.] 17 pt. *Barcelona*, 1930–34. 8°. **08631.** eee. **58.**

INQUISITION.

—— *See* INQUISITION, *Tribunal of.—Spain.*

INSTITUCIÓ PATXOT.

—— Memòries Patxot. *Barcelona*, 1930– . 4°. **Ac. 2006/2.**

—— Bibliografia Catalana : Premsa. Materials aplegats per Joan Givanel i Mas. / *Barcelona*, 1931–37. 4°. 3 vol. **Ac. 2006/3.**

—— The Doctrine of Personal Right. By S. Hutchinson Harris. pp. 593. *Barcelona*, 1935. 4°. **Ac. 2006/5.**

—— Estudis Universitaris Catalans. Sèrie monogràfica. no. 1. *Barcelona*, 1931. 4°. **Ac. 2006/4.**

Imperfect ; wanting all after no. 1.

—— El Repertori de manuscrits catalans de la Fundació Patxot. Per Pere Bohigas. [With plates.] *In:* Estudis universitaris catalans. vol. 15, 16. 1930, 31. 8°. **Ac. 2604.** c.

—— Quaresma de Sant Vicent Ferrer predicada a València l'any 1413. Introducció, notes i transcripció per Josep Sanchis Sivera. [With plates.] pp. lviii. 357. *Barcelona*, 1927. 4°. **Ac. 2006.**

—— Der Wandel der Ideen Staat und Volk als Äusserung des Weltgewissens. Eine völkerrechtliche und staatsrechtliche Untersuchung auf philosophischer Grundlage. Von Rudolf Laun. pp. xxx. 463. *Barcelona*, 1933. 4°. **8004.** h. **1.**

INSTITUT CATALÀ DE LES ARTS DEL LLIBRE.

—— Facsímil de la Gramàtica d'en Mates, estampada a Barcelona ab la data de l'any 1468, y noticies ilustratives de la seva celebritat, escrites per Eudald Canibell. 2 pt. *Barcelona*, 1906, 11. 8°. **12901.** e. **34.**

INSTITUT D'ESTUDIS CATALANS.

—— Anuari MCMVII(—MCMXIII/XIV, MCMXXXXI/XXVI). [any 1]–any 5. pt. 2 ; vol. 7. *Barcelona*, [1907–14, 26.] 4°. **Ac. 138.**

Wanting any 6 ; *vol.* 8.

—— [Another copy of vol. 6.] Anuari MCMXV–XX. 2 pt. *Barcelona*, 1923. 4°. **Ac. 138/9.**

—— Dictamen-Acord de Constitució. (Reglament Interior.) pp. 14. *Barcelona*, 1907. 8°. **8305.** cc. **33.** (**2.**)

—— Dictamen-Acord de l'Institut d'Estudis Catalans proposant a la excma. Diputació Provincial de Barcelona l'adquisició de la Biblioteca Aguiló. pp. 15. *Barcelona*, [1909.] 8°. **11909.** t. **37.** (**2.**)

—— L'Institut d'Estudis Catalans. Els seus primers xxv anys. [With a list of members and bibliographies. With plates.] pp. 318. *Barcelona*, 1935. 8°. **Ac. 138/8.**

—— Aribau i la Catalunya del seu temps, etc. [By M. de Montoliu. With a portrait.] pp. 366. *Barcelona*, 1936. 8°. **10635.** m. **7.**

—— Biblioteca filològica de l'Institut de la Llengua Catalana. no. 1–3, 5, 7, 8, 10–16. *Barcelona*, 1913–37. 8°. **Ac. 138.** d/**2.**

No. 11 *is of the fourth, and no.* 12 *of the seventh, edition.*

—— L'Arquitectura Romànica a Catalunya. Per J. Puig y Cadafalch, Antoni de Falguera, J. Goday y Casals, *etc.* [With illustrations.] 3 vol. *Barcelona*, 1909–1918. 4°. **07704.** f. **14.**

—— Bibliografía de las Impressions Lul·lianes. Per Elíes Rogent i Estanislau Duràn. Amb un proemi, addicions i índex de Ramón d'Alós-Moner. pp. xvi. 406. *Barcelona*, 1927. 8°. **Ac. 138.** c/**2.**

—— Butlletí de Dialectología Catalana. Publicat per les oficines del Diccionari general de la llengua catalana. vol. 1–18. *Barcelona*, 1914–30. 8°.

—— Segona època. vol. 19–24. any 1931–36. *Barcelona*, 1932–37. 8°. **Ac. 138.** c.

Vol. 21 *consists of an index to vol.* 1–20.

—— XVIIIè [XIXè, XXIè–XXVIè] cartell de premis . . . 1948 [49, 51–56]. *Barcelona*, 1948–56. 8° & fol. **Ac. 138/10.**

—— Cronica del Moviment Arqueologich, Historich, Juridich y Literari durant l'any 1907. (Extret de l'Anuari.) pp. 71. [*Barcelona*, 1908.] 4°. **7705.** g. **31.** (**6.**)

—— Cursos Monogràfics d'Alts Estudis i d'Intercanvi organisats per l'Institut d'Estudis Catalans i el Consell de Pedagogía . . . Segona (—quarta) estació . . . 1916(–1918). 3 pt. [*Barcelona*,] 1916–18. 8°. **Ac. 138/4.**

—— Diplomatari de l'Orient català, 1301–1409. Col·lecció de documents per a la història de l'expedició catalana a orient i dels Ducats d'Atenes i Neopàtria. Recollida i anotada por Antoni Rubió i Lluch. [Partly revised and edited by Jordi Rubió. With an index by Ricard Albert.] pp. lxv. 798. *Barcelona*, 1947. 8°. **09059.** d. **4.**

—— Documents per l'historia de la cultura catalana migeval. Publicats per Antoni Rubió y Lluch. 2 vol. *Barcelona*, 1908, 21. 8°. **9181.** aa. **13.**

—— Estudis romànics. Publicats a cura de R. Aramon i Serra. 1947–1948, *etc. Barcelona*, 1949– 8°. **Ac. 138.** e/**2.**

—— Forma Conventus Tarraconensis. [An archaeological survey by various authors.] *Barcelona*, 1928– . 4°. **Ac. 138/6.**

—— Gesta comitum Barcinonensium. Textos llatí i català, editats i anotats per L. Barrau Dihigo i J. Massó Torrents. pp. lxxiii. 166. pl. VIII. *Barcelona*, 1925. 4°. **Ac. 138/5.**

No. 2 *of " Cròniques Catalanes."*

—— Itinerari de Jaume I " el Conqueridor." Per Joaquim Miret i Sans. pp. 629. *Barcelona*, 1918. 4°. **Ac. 138/3.**

—— Memòria dels treballs fets per l'Institut d'Estudis Catalans des de la seva fundació fins a l'any 1914 (durant els cursos 1918-1919–1936-1937). (Extret de Discursos y Memòries de l'Institut d'Estudis Catalans.) 11 pt. *Barcelona*, 1938. 8°. Ac. **138**/**11**.
No report was published to cover the years 1915–1918.

—— Memoria presentada per l'Institut d'Estudis Catalans al excm. sr. Alcalde de Barcelona y llegida en consistori del dia 13 de novembre de 1907. pp. 11. *Barcelona*, [1907.] 8°. **11909**. t. **37**. (**1**.)

—— Memoria presentada als excelentissims senyors President de la Diputació y Alcalde de Barcelona . . . donant compte dels treballs fets desde la seva fundació fins al 31 desembre de 1908. pp. 19. *Barcelona*, [1909.] 8°. **11853**. k. **18**. (**1**.)

—— Miscel·lània Prat de la Riba. vol. 1. [With plates, including a portrait.] *Barcelona*, 1923. 8°. **012213.v.1.**
pp. 460.—*No more published.*

—— Les Monedes Catalanes. Estudi y descripció de les monedes carolingies, comtals, senyorials, reyals y locals propries de Catalunya. Per Joaquim Botet y Sisó. [With illustrations.] 3 vol. *Barcelona*, 1908–11. 4°. **7757**. cc. **22**.

—— Les Obres d'Auzias March. Edició crítica per Amadeu Pagès. 2 vol. *Barcelona*, 1912, 14. 4°. Ac. **138**/**2**.

—— Les Pintures Murals Catalanes. [With coloured plates.] fasc. 1–4. *Barcelon*, [1909–20.] fol. **7855**. s. **26**.

—— Les Relacions de Joan Lluís Vives amb els Anglesos i amb l'Angleterra. Per Foster Watson. [With plates, including portraits.] pp. 327. *Barcelona*, 1918. 8°. Ac. **138**. c/**3**.

—— Repertori de l'Antiga Literatura Catalana. Per Jaume Massó Torrents. *Barcelona*, 1932– . 4°. Ac. **138**/**7**.

Biblioteca de Catalunya.

—— Anuario de la Biblioteca Central y de las Populares y Especiales correspondiente a 1941 (1946 [*etc.*].) [With illustrations.] 1942– . 8°. *See* Barcelona, *Province of.—Diputació.* P.P. **6477**. bac.

—— Butlletí de la Biblioteca de Catalunya. vol. 1. no. 2— vol. 8. mais/agost 1914—1928/32. *Barcelona*, 1914–34. 4°. Ac. **138**. d/**4**.
Vol. 2 *is in two parts.*

—— [Lists of accessions to the Library.] no. 21–46. 15 nov. 1950—31 maig 1952. [*Barcelona*, 1950–52.] fol. Ac. **138**. d/**3**.
Reproduced from typewriting. No more published !

—— Catàleg de la Col·lecció Cervàntica formada per D. Isidro Bonsoms i Sicart i cedida par ell a la Biblioteca de Catalunya. Redactat per Joàn Givanel i Mas. 3 vol. *Barcelona*, 1916–25. 4°. Ac. **138**. d.

—— Catálogo de la Colección Cervantina. Redactado por Jan Givanel Mas. *Barcelona*, 1941– . 4°. **2782.cm.9.**

—— Catálogo de la Exposición Bibliográfica de Ajedrez, organizada con los ejemplares que formaron la collección de D. José Paluzíe y Lucena, donada a la Biblioteca Central . . . marzo de 1940. [With a portrait.] pp. 36. [*Barcelona*,] 1943. 8°. **11924**. b. **37**.

—— Catálogo de la exposición bibliográfica de Elio Antonio de Nebrija celebrada en conmemoración del v centenario de su nacimiento . . . redactado por Luis M.ª Plaza Escudero, *etc.* [With plates.] pp. xv. 39. *Barcelona*, 1950. 8°. **11927**. c. **18**.

—— Catálogo de la Exposición Bibliográfica Hispano-Italiana de los siglos xvi. a xviii celebrado en noviembre de 1940. Redactado y ordenado por Juan Givanel y Mas, con un tributo a D. Eduardo Toda y Güell por Felipe Mateu y Llopis. [With plates and a portrait of E. Toda y Güell.] pp. 64. *Barcelona*, 1942. 8°. **7960**. bb. **6**.

—— Catálogo de la exposición conmemorativa del iv centenario del nacimiento de Miguel de Cervantes—1547–1616. Ediciones del Quijote de los siglos xix y xx. pp. 161. *Barcelona*, 1947. 8°. **7960**. e. **11**.

—— Catálogo de la Exposición de Iconografía Cervantina celebrada en mayo de 1942. Precedido de un estudio acerca de los retratos de Cervantes, por Juan Givanel y Mas . . . y un apéndice sobre las medallas cervantinas, por Felipe Mateu y Llopis. pp. 127. pl. xliv. *Barcelona*, 1944. 8°. **010632**. bb. **15**.

—— Catálogo de la Exposición de Libros Cervantinos correspondientes a los siglos xvii y xviii, celebrada en Barcelona, en conmemoración del cccxxiv aniversario de la muerte de Miguel de Cervantes Saavedra . . . 23 abril—7 mayo 1940. [With plates.] pp. 47. *Barcelona*, [1940.] 8°. Ac. **138**. db **2**.

—— Homenaje dedicado al excelentísimo Señor Don Francisco Rodríguez Marín en 27 de enero de 1943 con motivo del lxxxviiio aniversario de su nacimiento. Conferencia pronunciada en la inauguración de la exposición bibliográfica, y catálogo de las obras del insigne cervantista. Por Juan Givanel Mas. [With a portrait.] pp. 38. *Barcelona*, 1943. 8°. **012301**. m. **38**.

—— La Música Española desde la edad media hasta nuestros días. Catálogo de la exposición histórica celebrada en conmemoración del primer centenario del nacimiento del maestro Felipe Pedrell, 18 mayo—25 junio, 1941. Por Higinio Anglés. [With plates.] pp. 82. *Barcelona*, 1941. 8°. **7946**. b. **62**.

—— Obres rebudes fins el dia 15 de març de 1950 [*etc.*]. [*Barcelona*, 1950– .] fol. P.P. **6477**. bd.
Reproduced from typewriting.

—— Sentencias Catholicas del divi poeta Dant Florenti compilades per . . . Jaume Ferrer de Blanes. (Meditacio o contemplatio sobre lo santissim loch de Caluari, feta per mossen J. Ferrer.—Letras reals . . . a mossen J. Ferrer: Respostes: e Regles per ell ordenades en Cosmographia y en art de Nauegar, *etc.*) [A facsimile of the edition of 1545, with a biographical and bibliographical note.] *Barcelona*, 1922. 8°. Ac. **138**. db.
One of an edition of 100 *copies not for sale.*

—— *Departament de Música.* Publicacions. *Barcelona*, 1921– . 4°. Ac. **138**. da.

Institut de Ciències: *See* infra : *Secció de Ciències.*

Laboratori de Fonètica Experimental.

—— Estudis fonètics. Publicats sota la direcció del Dr. P. Barnils. vol. 1. pp. 329. *Barcelona*, 1917. 8°. **12944**. i. **30**.
No more published.

Secció de Ciencies.

—— Arxius de l'Institut de Ciencies. any 1. no. 1. *Barcelona*, 1911. fol. Ac. **138**. b.

—— Flora catalana. Descripció de les plantes que es fan a les terres catalanes i països limítrofs. Publicada sota la direcció de Pius Font i Quer. *Barcelona*, 1950– . 4°. Ac. **138**. dd.
Arxius de la Secció de Ciències. no. 18.

Secció Històrico-Arqueològica.

—— Memòries. *Barcelona*, 1927- . 4°. Ac. **138**. dc.

Appendix.

—— Darrera paraula sóbre les Normes ortografiques del Institut d'Estudis Catalans, per un català zelós de la llénga literaria tradicional, *etc.* pp. 14. *Barcelona*, 1915. 8°. **012942**. aaa. **15**.

INSTITUT DE CIENCIES.

—— *See* supra: INSTITUT D'ESTUDIS CATALANS.

INSTITUT DE LA LLENGUA CATALANA.

—— *See* supra: INSTITUT D'ESTUDIS CATALANS.

INSTITUT-ESCOLA PI I MARGALL.

—— Institut-Escola Pi i Margall. Federació d'alumnes i ex-alumnes de l'Institut-Escola Pi i Margall. [A journal.] any 1. no. 1, 2. Oct., Nov., 1937. [*Barcelona*,] 1937. 8°. P.P. **1203**. ea.

INSTITUTO AGRICOLA CATALAN DE SAN ISIDRO.

—— Revista de agricultura práctica, economía rural, horticultura y jardineria . . . Bajo la direccion del socio D. Isidoro de Angúlo. tom. 1–17. *Barcelona*, 1852–68. 8°. [Continued as:] Revista del Instituto Agrícola Catalan de San Isidro. tom. 18–25. *Barcelona*, 1869–76. 8°. Ac. **3389**.

INSTITUTO AMATLLER DE ARTE HISPÁNICO.

—— Huguet. Por José Gudiol Ricart, Juan Ainaud de Lasarte. [Reproductions. With an introduction.] pp. 135. *Barcelona*, 1948. 8°. **7868**. c. **67**.

INSTITUTO CATÓLICO DE ESTUDIOS RELIGIOSOS.

—— Montserrat. Glosas a la carta colectiva de los obispos españoles. [By J. V. C., i.e. Joan Vilar Costa. With the text of the letter.] pp. xv. 389. *Barcelona*, 1938. 4°. Ac. **2006**. c.

Vol. 1 of the " Biblioteca Catalana de Textos y Estudios Religiosos," published by the Institute.

INSTITUTO DE ELECTRICIDAD APLICADA.

—— *See* supra: ESCUELA INDUSTRIAL BARCELONESA.

INSTITUTO DE HISTORIA DE LA CIUDAD.

—— Premio Massana. Indumentaria y iconografía de Cataluña. Convocatoria, bases y noticia de los concursos. pp. 14. 1954. 8°. *See* infra: *Patronato de las Fundaciones Massana.* **9196**. aa. **24**.

INSTITUTO ESPAÑOL DE ESTUDIOS MEDITERRÁNEOS.

—— Hispania graeca. Por Antonio García y Bellido. [With plates.] 3 tom. *Barcelona*, 1948. 8°. **07705**. bb. **7**.

One of the " Publicaciones sobre arte y arqueología " of the Institute.

—— Obras completas del trovador Cerverí de Girona. Texto, traducción y comentarios. [Edited by Martín de Riquer. With facsimiles.] pp. xv. 390. pl. VIII. *Barcelona*, 1947. 4°. **12231**. ddd. **15**.

One of the " Publicaciones sobre filología y literatura " of the Institute.

INSTITUTO NACIONAL DE EXPANSIÓN ECONÓMICA.

—— Guidebook of Teneriffe. Edited by the Excellent Insular chapter of Teneriffe. [With plates and maps.] pp. 196. *Barcelona*, 1927. 8°. **10098**. aaa. **34**.

JUNTA DE MUSEUS.

—— Butlletí dels Museus d'Art de Barcelona. *Barcelona*, 1931- . 8°. P.P. **1931**. pkf.

LA COLLA.

—— Mestre Matheu. Edició d'ofrena. [With a portrait.] pp. 128. *Barcelona*, 1931. 8°. **20002** e. **74**.

MUSEO DE ARTE DECORATIVO Y ARQUEOLÓGICO.

—— Catálogo de la Sección de tejidos, bordados y encajes. [With illustrations.] pp. xviii. 352. *Barcelona*, 1906. 8°. **7808**. aa. **57**.

MUSEO DE ARTE MODERNO.

—— Catálogo de la Exposición-Homenaje a Turner. Colección Lázaro. Noviembre–diciembre de 1947, *etc.* [With an introduction by J. Lázaro, and reproductions.] *In*: Cobalto. vol. 1. cuaderno 3. pp. 35–78. 1947. 4°. P.P. **1931**. pka.

MUSEO DE BELLAS ARTES.

—— Catálogo. pp. 224. [*Barcelona*,] 1906. 8°. **7858**. aaaa. **20**.

MUSEO DE LA CIUDADELA.

—— Museo de la Ciudadela. Catálogo de la Sección de Arte Románico por J. Folch y Torres. [With illustrations.] pp. 139. *Barcelona*, 1926. 8°. **07805**. b. **32**.

MUSEU DE LES ARTS DECORATIVES.

—— Catàleg de la Col·lecció d'Indumentària de Manuel Rocamora exposada per l'Associació d'Amics dels Museus de Catalunya. Redactat per Manuel Rocamora, *etc.* [With illustrations.] pp. 148. [*Barcelona*, 1933.] 8°. **07742**. aa. **60**.

—— Catàleg de la Col·lecció Maria Regordosa de Torres Reina. Exhibida per " Amics dels Museus de Catalunya " al Museu de les Arts Decoratives del 2 al 30 de juny del 1935. pp. 48. *Barcelona*, [1935.] 8°. **07805**. f. **63**.

—— Catàleg de les Sales que contenen la Col·lecció d'Art Xinès dipòsit del Sr. Damià Mateu al Museu de les Arts Decoratives. [With illustrations, including a portrait.] pp. 50. *Barcelona*, [1935.] 8°. **07805**. f. **64**.

—— Catàleg de les Sales que contenen la Col·lecció d'Indumentària, donatiu de Manuel Rocamora al Museu de les Arts Decoratives. [With plates, including a portrait.] pp. 41. *Barcelona*, [1935.] 8°. **07742**. d. **41**.

—— Museu de les arts decoratives. Palau de Pedralbes. Guia sumària. [With illustrations and plans.] pp. 75. *Barcelona*, 1932. 8°. **7809**. ppp. **2**

MUSEU SOCIAL.

—— Anuari d'Estatística Social de Catalunya. any 4. 1915. *Barcelona*, 1917. 8°. Ac. **2249**.

—— Boletín del Museo Social. (Butlletí del Museu Social.) no. 2–22, 32. *Barcelona*, 1910–15. 8°. Ac. **2249**.2.

NATIONAL INSTITUTE OF ECONOMIC EXPANSION.

—— *See* supra: INSTITUTO NACIONAL DE EXPANSIÓN ECONÓMICA.

PALACIO NACIONAL.

Museo.

—— El Arte en España. Guía del Museo del Palacio Nacional Segunda edición, revisada por el Dr. D. Manuel Gómez Moreno. [With plates.] pp. 704. 1929. 8°. *See* supra *Exposición Internacional*, 1929. **7813**. f. **44**

PATRONATO DE LAS FUNDACIONES MASSANA.

—— Premio Massana. Indumentaria y iconografía de Cataluña. Convocatoria, bases y noticia de los concursos. pp. 14. *Archivo Histórico de la Ciudad: Barcelona*, 1954. 8°. **9196**. aa. **24**.
The titlepage headed: Ayuntamiento de Barcelona. Instituto de Historia de la Ciudad.

REAL ACADEMIA DE BUENAS LETRAS DE BARCELONA.

—— Real Academia de Buenas Letras de la Ciudad de Barcelona; origen, progressos, y su primera junta general . . . con los papeles que en ella se acordaron. tom. 1. pp. 667. *Barcelona*, [1756.] 4°. **127**. d. **24**.

—— Memorias. *Barcelona*, 1896- . 8°. Ac. **8884**.

—— Anuario, 1947 [*etc.*]. *Barcelona*, 1947- . 8°. Ac. **8884**/5.

—— Lo Cervantisme en la "Real Academia de Buenas Letras" de Barcelona. Discurs llegit . . . per Joan Givanel y Mas. pp. 48. *Barcelona*, 1925. 8°. **11867**. p. **31**.

—— Curial y Guelfa. Novela catalana del quinzen segle publicada . . . per A. Rubió y Lluch. pp. xvi. 532. *Barcelona*, 1901. 8°. Ac. **8884**/2.

—— Discursos leídos en la Real Academia de Buenas Letras . . . en la solemne recepción pública de D. Juan Givanel y Mas, *etc.* (La Obra literaria de Cervantes. [By J. Givanel y Mas.]—Resposta de D. Ramón Miquel y Planas.) pp. 76. *Barcelona*, 1917. 8°. Ac. **8884**/3. (**1**.)

—— Discursos llegits en la "Real Academia de Buenas Letras" de Barcelona en la solemnial recepció pública de D. Ramón d'Alós-Moner y de Dou, *etc.* pp. 56. *Barcelona*, 1924. 8°. **11867**. p. **32**.

—— Discursos llegits . . . en la solemne recepció pública de D. Lluis Domenech y Montaner, *etc.* (Centcelles. Baptisteri y cellæ-memoriæ de la primitiva esglesia metropolitana de Tarragona. Per D. L. Domenech y Montaner. —Contestació de D. Joseph Maria Roca.) pp. 55. *Barcelona*, 1921. 8°. Ac. **8884**/4. (**3**.)

—— Discursos llegits . . . en la solemne recepció pública de D. Pere Bosch Gimpera, *etc.* (Assaig de reconstitució de l'etnología de Catalunya. [By P. Bosch Gimpera.]—Resposta de D. Ferran Valls y Taberner.) pp. 86. *Barcelona*, 1922. 8°. Ac. **8884**/4. (**1**.)

—— Discursos llegits . . . en la solemne recepció pública del Iltre. Sr. D. Eduart Toda el día 21 de desembre de 1930. (La Tragedia final del Princep de Viana. [By E. Toda y Güell.]—Contestació de D. Jaume Barrera.) pp. 40. *Barcelona*, 1930. 8°. Ac. **8884**/4. (**2**.)

—— Fragmentos de las traducciones catalanas de la Fiammetta y del Decamerone . . . ambas anónimas y del siglo XV. Lectura hecha ante la Real Academia de Buenas Letras de Barcelona [by Isidro Bonsoms y Sicart] . . . Seguida de algunas noticias bibliográficas (de obras . . . referentes á la literatura catalana). pp. 125. *Barcelona*, 1909. fol. **11906**. l. **7**.

—— El "Libre de les Medicines Particulars." Versión catalana trescentista del texto árabe del Tratado de los Medicamentos Simples de Ibn Wáfid, autor médico toledano del siglo XI. Transcripción, estudio proemial y glosarios por Luis Faraudo de Saint-Germain, *etc.* [With plates.] pp. xx. 198. *Barcelona*, 1943. 8°. Ac. **8884**/4. (**4**.)

—— Libro de la Orden de Caballeria del B. Raimundo Lulio traducido en lengua castellana. [Edited by J. R. de Luanco.] *Cat. & Span.* pp. vii. vi. 78. [*Barcelona*, 1901.] fol. Ac. **8884**. b.

—— **Orígenes de la filosofía de Raimundo Sibiuda—Sabunde. Discurso leído . . . por Tomás Carreras y Artau. pp. 30. *Barcelona*, 1928. 8°. 8486. h. 24.**

REAL ACADEMIA DE CIENCIAS Y ARTES.

—— Boletín de la Academia de Ciencias Naturales y Artes de Barcelona. no. 1-16. *Barcelona*, 1840-42. 8°.

—— Tercera época. vol. 1. [no. 1]—vol. 6. no. 7. *Barcelona*, 1892-1936. 4°. Ac. **2822**.
Tom. 1, 2 *of época* 3 *of the Memorias of the Real Academia de Ciencias y Artes were included in the Boletín. This set is imperfect, containing only tom.* 1. *no.* 1-18 *and tom.* 2. *no.* 1 *of the Memorias. A complete set of the Memorias, época* 3, *is entered below.*

—— **Historia de la Real Academia de Ciencias y Artes. Memoria . . . leida por . . . J. Balari y Jovany. pp. 203. *Barcelona*, 1895. 8°. Ac. 2822/4.**

REAL ACADEMIA DE MEDICINA Y CIRUGÍA.

—— **À Cervantes. [A collection of essays in honour of the tercentenary of the publication of Don Quixote.] pp. 88. L.P. *Barcelona*, 1905. 8°. Tab. 538. b. 11.**

—— **Alturas en las ciencias médicas en el reino El-Andaluz: discurso que para su acto de recepción leyó . . . Dr. Antonio González Prats. Discurso de contestación del Dr. Luis Comenge Ferrer. pp. 159. *Barcelona*, 1906. 8°. 7307. ee. 11.**

—— **Exposicion de la enseñanza de medicina clinica en el Real Estudio . . . baxo la direccion de la Real Academia medico-practica de Barcelona. Año MDCCCI. (Segundo año del Real Estudio, *etc.*—Tercer año medico clinico de la Real Escuela, *etc.*) Por . . . Francisco Salvá. 3 pt. *Barcelona*, 1802-18. 4°. 1150. g. 2.**

—— **Memoria sobre el Cólera-morbo oriental. [By Louis M. J. Robert.] Traduccion que publica la Real Academia, *etc.* pp. 47. *Barcelona*, 1831. 8°. 1168. c. 20. (7.)**

REAL ACADEMIA MÉDICO-PRÁCTICA DE BARCELONA.

—— *See* supra: REAL ACADEMIA DE MEDICINA, *etc.*

REAL COMPAÑÍA DE COMERCIO.

—— N° 1620. Accion de la Real Comp^a de Comercio establecida en Barcelona. [Dated: 25 April 1760.] ON VELLUM. [*Barcelona*, 1760.] *s. sh.* 4°. C. **18**. e. **2**. (**111**.)

REAL JUNTA Y CONSULADO DE COMERCIO.

—— Memorias históricas sobre la marina, comercio y artes de la antigua ciudad de Barcelona. Publicadas por disposicion y á expensas de la Real Junta y Consulado de Comercio de la misma ciudad. Y dispuestas por D. Antonio de Capmany y de Montpalau. 4 tom. *Madrid*, 1779, 92. **178**. c. **5**, **6**, **6***.
The half-titles of tom. 3 *and* 4 *read:* "*Suplemento à las Memorias históricas. etc.*"

REALES ESCUELAS DE LA COMPAÑIA DE JESUS.

—— Selecto de las Poesias que a vista de todo el auditorio compusieron los alumnos de las Reales Escuelas de la Compañia de Jesus, en el Theatro del Seminario de Nobles de Nuestra Señora y San-tiago [*sic*] de Cordelles, en los dias 12 y 13 de Julio de 1758, *etc.* *Barcelona*, 1758. 4°. **9930**. e. **65**. (**17**.)

SALA PARÉS.

—— [Catalogues of exhibitions of paintings from Barcelona collections held in the Sala Parés. With reproductions.] 3 vol.

Catálogo de la exposición de pintura andaluza del siglo XVII . . . Mayo MCMXLVI. pp. 145. [1946.]
Catálogo de la exposición de pintura antigua—siglos XV, XVI, XVII, XVIII . . . Diciembre MCMXLVI—enero MCMXLVII. pp. 157. [1946.]
Catálogo de la exposición de flores y bodegones—siglos XVI, XVII, XVIII, XIX . . . Mayo MCMXLVII. pp. 135. [1947.]

Barcelona, [1946, 47.] 8°. **7869.** p. **19.**

SOCIEDAD ASTRONÓMICA, DE ESPAÑA Y AMERICA.

—— Boletin. enero 1912. *Barcelona,* 1912. 8°. Ac. **4152**

SOCIEDAD FILATÉLICA CATALANA.

—— El Filatélico español. [From año 2. no. 13, oct. 1901, to año 12. no. 130, dic. 1911 issued as the official organ of the Sociedad Filatélica Catalana.] *See* PERIODICAL PUBLICATIONS.—*Barcelona.* El Filatélico español *etc.* 1900. *etc.* 8°. Crawford **2022.**

SOCIETAT CATALANA DE BIBLIOFILS.

—— Cançoner dels Comtes d'Urgell. [The text of the manuscript edited by Gabriel Llabrés.] (Estudi histórich y literari escrit per En G. Llabrés sobre'l Cançoner dels Comtes d'Urgell. [With facsimiles.]) G. L. 2 pt. *Barcelona,* 1906, 07. fol. Ac. **8881/2.**

—— Cançoner sagrat de Vides de Sants. Segle XV. Publicat per R. Foulché Delbosc y J. Massó y Torrents, *etc.* [With illustrations.] pp. 371. *Barcelona,* 1912. fol. Ac. **8881/5.**

No. 71 *of an edition of* 100 *copies.*

—— Elogi de la Follía. Autor: Desideri Erasme. Traducció precedida d'un comentari sobre la vida y obres d'Erasme per J. Pin y Soler. pp. lv. 197. *Barcelona,* 1910. 8°. **12356.** pp. **8.**

—— Istoria de Jacob Xalabin (fill d'l Amorat Senyor de la Turquía). [Edited by R. Foulché-Delbosc.] *Barcelona,* 1906. 4°. Ac. **8881.**

—— Libre de Santa Maria. Ordenat per M. Ramon Lull. G. L. pp. xiv. 157. *Barcelona,* 1905. fol. Ac. **8881/3.**

—— Llibre dels Set Savis de Roma. [With a facsimile.] pp. xxvii. 111. *Barcelona,* 1907. 8°. **011388.d.11.**

—— La Visió delectable de Alfonço de la Torra, Bachaller. Reproducció en facsimil de la única edició catalana, Barcelona, 1484. G. L. *Barcelona,* 1911. fol. Ac. **8881/4.**

No. 79 *of an edition of* 100 *copies.*

SOCIETAT DE CIRURGIA DE CATALUNYA.

—— Tres treballs premiats en el concurs d'homenatge a Gimbernat. [With illustrations, including a portrait.] pp. xi. 213. *Barcelona,* 1936. 8°. **7681.** c. **33.**

SOCIETAT FOTOGRÁFICA CATALANA.

—— Album fototípich de la Catedral de Barcelona. pp. 16. pl. 50. *Barcelona,* 1888. 4°. **7814.** ee. **18.**

TIRO NACIONAL.

—— Constitucion de la Federacion Ibérica. Es propiedad del Tiro Nacional, *etc.* pp. 15. *Barcelona,* 1869. 4°. **8042.** aaa. **45.** (3.)

UNIÓN SINDICAL DE LAS INDUSTRIAS DEL LIBRO.

—— **Las Artes del Libro. Órgano oficial de la Unión Sindical de las Industrias del Libro.** ***Barcelona,*** **1932– . 4°. P.P. 1622. afa.**

UNIVERSIDAD DE BARCELONA.

—— Anuari, 1934-1935 [*etc.*]. *Barcelona,* 1934– . 8°. Ac. **136/2.**

—— Discursos leidos ante el Claustro de la Universidad de Barcelona en el acto . . . de la recepcion del Catedratico de Historia y Elementos de Derecho Romano Dr. D. I. Samsó y Ribera. pp. 107. *Barcelona,* 1864. 8°. **5255.** bb. **16.**

—— Fontes Hispaniae antiquae. Auspiciis ac sumptibus Universitatis Litterarum Barcinonensis ediderunt A. Schulten et P. Bosch/ (L. Pericot) *Barcinone, Berolini,* 1922– . 8°. Ac. **136.**

Biblioteca Universitaria.

—— Incunables de la Biblioteca Universitaria. [With illustrations.] pp. vi. 130. *Barcelona,* 1945. 8°. **11925.** c. **19.**

Centro de Estudios Históricos Internacionales.

—— Estudios de historia moderna. [Published jointly by the Instituto Jerónimo Zurita, sección de Barcelona, and the Centro de Estudios Históricos Internacionales, Universidad de Barcelona.] 1951–54. 8°. *See* SPAIN.—*Consejo Superior de Investigaciones Científicas.—Instituto Jerónimo Zurita.—Sección de Barcelona.* tom. 1–4. Ac. **132.** te.

—— Índice histórico español. Publicación trimestral. *Barcelona,* 1953– . 8°. Ac. **136.** f.

—— [A reissue.] Índice histórico español. Bibliografía histórica de España e Hispanoamérica . . . 1953–1954 [*etc.*]. *Barcelona,* [1955– .] 8°. **11923.** b. **9.**

—— Tratado general de geopolítica. [By J. Vicens Vives. With maps.] pp. 230. *Barcelona,* 1950. 8°. **010005.** d. **6.**

Colección "Hilani." no. 2.

Escuela Oficial de Náutica.

—— Cervantes Marino. Por D. Francisco Condeminas Mascaró, *etc.* [With a portrait.] pp. 15. *Barcelona,* 1927. 8°. **10634.** c. **29.**

Facultad de Derecho.

—— El Antiguo Derecho de Obligaciones Español según sus rasgos fundamentales. Por Ernesto Mayer. [Translated by J. M. Ots de Capdequí.] pp. 305. *Barcelona,* 1926. 8°. Ac. **136.** b/**2.**

—— Costumbres de Gerona. Edición preparada por D. Eduardo de Hinojosa. *Barcelona,* 1926– . 8°. Ac. **136.** b/**4.**

—— Fuero de Jaca—última redacción. Publicado por José Mª Ramos y Loscertales. pp. xliv. 137. *Barcelona,* 1927. 8°. Ac. **136.** b/3. (3.)

—— Libro de los Fueros de Castiella. Publicado por Galo Sánchez. [From a MS. in the Bibliothèque Nationale.] pp. xvi. 166. *Barcelona,* 1924. 8°. Ac. **136.** b.

—— Sancti Raymundi de Penyafort opera omnia. 1 vol. 1. Summa Juris. Edición de J. Rius Serra. pp. 156. 1945. *Barchinonae,* 1945. 8°. Ac. 136. b. (5.)

No more published.

—— Sobre las Leyes y los Fueros de España. Por el Dr. Francisco de Espinosa. Extracto de la más antigua historia del derecho español. pp. 68. *Barcelona*, 1927. 8º. Ac. **136**. b/**3**. (**2**.)

—— Sobre los Usatges de Barcelona y sus afinidades con las Exceptiones Legum Romanorum. Por Julio Ficker. [Translated by J. Rovira Ermengol.] pp. 66. *Barcelona*, 1926. 8º. Ac. **136**. b/**3**. (**1**.)

Facultad de Filosofía y Letras.

—— L'Amor i la Percepció dels Valors. Seminari de pedagogia. [By J. Xirau] pp. 72. *Barcelona*, 1936. 8º. Ac. **136**. c. (**3**.)

—— Biblioteca Hebraico-Catalana. *See* HEBREW-CATALAN LIBRARY.

—— La Civilización Megalítica Catalana y la Cultura Pirenaica. Por . . . Luis Pericot y García. pp. 163. pl. XVII. *Barcelona*, 1925. 8º. Ac. **136**. c. (**2**.)

The second edition is entered under PERICOT Y GARCÍA (L.)

—— La Cultura del Vaso Campaniforme—su origen y extensión en Europa. Por Alberto del Castillo Yurrita. pp. 216. pl. CCVI. II. *Barcelona*, 1928. 8º. Ac. **136**. c. (**1**.)

Facultad de Filosofía y Letras.—Seminario de Estudios Hispánicos.

—— Publicaciones, *etc.* *Barcelona*, 1937– . 8º. Ac. **136**. e.

Seminari de Pedagogia.

—— El Kindergarten, Jardí d'Infants. Pel Dr. Manuel Salvat. [With plates.] pp. 73. *Barcelona*, 1932. 8º. Ac. **136**. d. (**1**.)

APPENDIX.

—— Abdruck der Relation, so an Ihro Churfürstl. Gnaden zu Mayntz, von einem Königlichen Spanischen vornehmen Ministro über die Belager- und glückliche Befreyung der Stadt Barcellona unterm 17. Maij 1706 erstattet . . . worden, *etc.* *Freyburg im Breyssgau*, [1706.] 4º. **580**. d **27**. (**6**.)

—— Barcelona Antigua. Arquitectura civil. Sesenta y cuatro ilustraciones con texto de A. D. S. [i.e. A. Duran i Sanpere.] 1942. 8º. *See* S., A. D. **7822**. a. **45**.

—— Barcelona de Julio de 1840. Sucesos de este periodo, con un apendice de los acontecimientos que siguieron, hasta el embarque de S. M. la Reyna Gobernadora en Valencia. Vindicacion razonada del pueblo de Barcelona. pp. 309. *Barcelona*, 1844. 8º. **9180**. bbb. **18**.

—— Barcelona fue la primera ciudad de España donde se introdujo la imprenta. Demuéstralo . . . D. J. R. V. [i.e. J. Ripoll Vilamayer.] 1833. 4º. *See* V., D. J. R. **4625**. cc. **1**. (**44**.)

—— Las Bullangas de Barcelona, ó sacudimientos de un pueblo oprimido por el despotismo ilustrado. pp. iv. 165. *Paris*, 1837. 12º. **9180**. aa. **5**.

—— Carta de Barcelona a esta Corte, en que se da auiso . . . q̃ vna muger esclaua . . . con fingidas apariencias de Chrstiana [*sic*] . . . descerrajô vna Iglesia, y robô el Sãtissimo . . . en la villa de Colibre. Declarasse como fue escõdido, y como fue descubierto por vna Gitana, y el fin que tuuo ella, y vn Turco amigo suyo, en 30. de Mayo de 1624. *B. de Guzman*: *Madrid*, 1625. fol. **593**. h. **22**. (**9**.)

—— Consulado del mar de Barcelona, nuevamente traducido de cathalan [i.e. from the "Consolat de mar"] en castellano por Don Cayetano de Pallejà, *etc.* pp. 199. *Barcelona*, 1732. fol. **503**. g. **31**.

—— El Consultor. Nueva guia de Barcelona . . . Por J. A. S. y M. Ll. 1863. 8º. *See* S. Y M. LL., J. A. **10160**. e. **8**.

—— Copia de vna Carta, que ha escrit vn Cavaller, a vn amich seu de Barcelona, donantli auis de la victoria que han tingut en lo lloch de Orta, *etc.* *I. Mathevat*: *Barcelona*, 1643. 4º. **9180**. e. **2**. (**15**.)

—— Costums antichs y moderns de Barcelona. [In verse.] 2 pt. *Barcelona*, 1862. *s. sh.* 4º. **1871**. e. **1**. (**158**.)

—— Diario de los sucesos de Barcelona en Setiembre, Octubre y Noviembre de 1843. Con un apéndice que contiene los documentos oficiales mas importantes. Por unos testigos presenciales. pp. 123. 117. *Barcelona*, 1843. 8º. **1444**. f. **5**.

—— Diversion de Ciudadanos, norte seguro de forasteros, y estrella luciente de Barcelona que guia à unos, y otros, para saber el numero cierto de parroquias, conventos, oratorios, cárceles, reclusiones, plazas, plazuelas, y calles de la ilustre ciudad de Barcelona . . . Su autor A.B.C.E. 1789. 12º. *See* E., A. B. C. **1478**. a. **11**.

—— Entwurff, verschiedener Sinn-Bilder, und anderer angenehmen Erfindungen, welche bey der . . . wegen glücklicher Entsetzung der von denen Frantzosen belagerten Haupt-Stadt Barcelona . . . den 6. Junii, 1706. als auf dem gehaltenen Danck-Fest, nächtlich geschehener Beleuchtung der käyserlichen Residentz-Stadt Wien zu sehen gewesen. [*Vienna?* 1706.] 4º. **580**. d. **27**. (**7**.)

—— An Exact and Faithful Journal of the Famous-Siege [*sic*] of Barcelona. pp. 15 [21]. *For R. Sare; sold by E. Whitlock*: *London*, 1698. 4º. G. **15084**.

—— An Exact and Full Account of the Siege of Barcelona by way of journal, from the 2[d] of April to the 11th of May, 1706. With previous remarks. By an officer who was in the place all the time. pp. 24. *Benj. Bragg*: *London*, 1706. 4º. **594**. c. **18**. (**6**.)

—— Kurtze Relation, dessen, so in Barcellona vom 6. biss 12. May 1706. passirt, als der Feind angefangen sich zu bewegen, um von der Belagerung abzustehen, biss solche gäntzlich verschwunden. Aus dem Spanischen in das Welsche, und nach diesem in das Teutsche übersetzt. *Augspurg*, [1706.] 4º. **580**. d. **27**. (**5**.)

—— Lamentos de Barcelona cautiva á los esforzados Catalanes. pp. 4. [*Barcelona?* 1808?] 4º. **9180**. e. **5**. (**27**.)

—— Manifestacion, en que se publican muchos, y relovantes servicios, y nobles hechos, con que ha servido à sus Señores Reyes la . . . ciudad de Barcelona; singularmente en el sitio horroroso, que acabade padecer este presente año de 1697. pp. 247. *T. Loriente*: *Barcelona*, [1697.] 4º. **1445**. f. **12**.

—— Manual del Viajero en Barcelona, redactado . . . por una reunion de amigos colaboradores. Adornado con un plano de esta Ciudad, la perspectiva de la Casa Lonja, y el croquis que representa las avenidas de esta Ciudad. pp. 227. *Barcelona*, 1840. 12º. **795**. c. **30**.

—— Mémoires et observations sur la fièvre qui a régné à Barcelonne en 1821, traduit de l'espagnol [by C. C. Pierquin de Gembloux]. pp. 126. *Montpellier*, 1822. 8º. **7561**. bbb. **29**.

BARCELONA. —[APPENDIX.]

—— Narratio de Barcinone capta à Sarracenis, tempore Lotharii Regis. 1757. *See* BOUQUET (M.) Recueil des historiens des Gaules, *etc.* tom. 9. 1738, *etc.* fol. **Circ.8-9.b.**

—— Notisia de algunas maravellas y recreos de Barcelona, ó guia y avis per aquellas personas, que ab prou diners, no saben divertirse en ella. [In verse.] *Barcelona,* [1850?] 4°. **11450.** f. **26.** (**65.**)

—— Nueva Relacion, en que se refiere el gran sentimiento, los clamores, y suspiros, que haze la Ciudad de Barcelona por la fatta de aver negado la obediencia à su legitimo dueño . . . Phelipe Quinto, *etc.* [In verse.] [*Barcelona?* 1710?] 4°. **T. 1303.** (**29.**)

—— Nueva Relacion, y curioso Romance, en que se refiere un lastimoso caso, que sucediò con una doncella, natural de Barcelona, *etc.* [*Valencia,* 1760?] 4°. **T. 1957.** (**95.**)

—— Primeras Noticias hasta el dia doze, de la Conquista de Barcelona, y su Castillo de Monjui. *Madrid,* 1714. 4°. **O.G.S.290.**
Bound up with the " Gazeta de Madrid " for 1714.

—— [Another edition.] Relacion, y primeras noticias hasta el dia 12. de la conquista de Barzelona, *etc.* *Sevilla,* 1714. 4°. **1323.** i. **13.** (**24.**)

—— Relacion de los que han sido muertos, y heridos en la expedicion de Barcelona, los dias 11. y 12. de Septiembre de 1714, *etc.* *Madrid,* [1714.] 4°. **O.G.S.290.**
Bound up with the " Gazeta de Madrid " for 1714.

—— Relacion veridica de la gran catástrofe por la inundacion . . . de Barcelona, ocurrida en la mañana del dia 15 de setiembre de 1862. [In verse.] pp. 4. *Barcelona,* 1862. 4°. **12330.** l. **8.** (**55.**)

—— Revolucion de Barcelona, proclamando la Junta central. Diario de los acontecimientos de que ha sido teatro esta Ciudad, durante los meses de Settembre, Octubre y Noviembre de 1843. Redactado par un testigo de vista. pp. xiii. 252. 8. *Barcelona,* 1844. 8°. **1445.** b. **5.**

—— Resposta a vn amich de Vich contantli los effectes que ha causada la Sancta Vnio de Barselona, folgantse dels succehits en la de Vich. [In verse.] *S. de Cormellas: Barcelona,* 1606. 4°. **11450.** e. **25.** (**24.**)

—— Resposta y copia de vna carta tramesa per vn ciutada desta Ciutat de Barcelona a vn amich seu, residint en Valencia ab la qual li dona auis de la Vnio, feta en . . . Barcelona, *etc.* [In verse.] *I. Amello: Barcelona,* 1606. 4°. **11450.** e. **25.** (**25.**)

—— La Rifa de la Olla de la Ciudad de Barcelona . . . Saynete nuevo, *etc.* [In verse.] pp. 39. *Barcelona,* 1802. 12°. **11452.** aaaa. **1.** (**3.**)

—— Romancero de Barcelona. [Printed from a MS. in the Barcelona University Library.] 1913. *See* PERIODICAL PUBLICATIONS.—*Paris.* Revue hispanique, *etc.* tom. 29. 1894, *etc.* 8°. **P.P. 4331.** aea.

—— La Semana Sangrienta. (Sucesos de Barcelona.) Historia, descripciones, documentos, retratos, vistas, etc., etc. pp. 191. *Barcelona,* [1910.] 8°. **9180.** b. **23.**

BARCELONA, *County of.*

Begin. [fol. 1 *recto*:] cOm per ordinacio deles Corts generals del principat de Cathalunya, celebrades enla Ciutat de Barçalona per lo Serenissimo Rey don Ferrando p̃mer de gloriosa memoria a .xxxi. de agost any mil quatrecents tretze, fos ordonats: que los vsatges de Barçalona e cōstitucions de Cathalūya fossen collocats en propris titols e en lenga vulgar, *etc.* 𝕲.𝕷. [1495.] fol. *See* CATALONIA.—[Laws.—I.—Collections.—i. General.] IB. 52538.

—— Antiquiores Barchinonensium Leges, quas vulgus Vsaticos appellat, cum comentariis supremorum iurisconsultorū Iacobi a mōte Iudaico, Iacobi et Guielermi a Vallesicca & Iacobi Calicii, *etc.* ff. 160. *Perk. Amorosum; impensis R. Dauder & I. Laceras: Barchinone,* 1544. fol. **C. 62.** f. **24.**

—— *See* FICKER (J.) Sobre los Usatges de Barcelona y sus afinidades con las Exceptiones Legum Romanorum. 1926. 8°. **Ac. 136.** b/**3.** (**1.**)

—— El Archivo Condal de Barcelona en los siglos IX–X. Estudio crítico de sus fondos. [Documents. Edited, with an introduction, by F. Udina Martorell.] pp. xliii. 574. *Barcelona,* 1951. 8°. **11906.** f. **19.**

—— Usatges de Barcelona i Commemoracions de Pere Albert. A cura de Josep Rovira i Ermengol. pp. 307. *Barcelona,* 1933. 8°. [*Els Nostres Clàssics.* col·lecció A. vol. 43–44.] **W.P. 4906/23.**

—— Usatici Barchinonae. Ältestes Kernstück, um 1058. *Lat. & Ger.* *See* WOHLHAUPTER (E.) Altspanisch-gotische Rechte, *etc.* 1936. 8°. **Ac. 2121.** [Germanenrechte. Bd. 12.]

—— *Counts.* *See* DIAGO (F.) Historia de los victoriosissimos antiguos Condes de Barcelona, *etc.* 1603. fol. **179.** e. **7.**

—— Gesta veterum comitum Barcinonensium, scripta circa annum MCXC. [MCCXC] a monacho quodam Rivipullensi, *etc.* *See* MARCA (P. de) successively *Bishop of Conserans, Archbishop of Toulouse, etc.* Marca Hispanica, *etc.* 1688. fol. **183.** f. **9.**

—— Gesta comitum Barcinonensium. Textos llatí i català, editats i anotats per L. Barrau Dihigo i J. Massó Torrents. pp. lxxiii. 166. pl. VIII. 1925. 4°. *See* BARCELONA.—*Institut d'Estudis Catalans.* **Ac. 138/5.**

—— Ex gestis comitum Barcinonensium, scriptis circa annum 1290 a quodam monacho Rivipullensi. 1757–1833. *See* BOUQUET (M.) Recueil des historiens des Gaules, *etc.* tom. 9, 11, 12, 19. 1738, *etc.* fol. **Circ.8-9.b.**

—— Prontuario métrico-histórico-cronológico de los Condes de Barcelona . . . Por D. J. M. V. D. G. [1800.] 8°. *See* G., D. J. M. V. D. **1464.** b. **5.**

BARCELONA, *Diocese of.*

—— La Visita pastoral a la Seu de Barcelona practicada pel Bisbe Il·lm. D. Joan Dimas Loris, en 1578. [The official account of the visitation. Edited by Josep Mas.] *Lat.* *In:* Estudis universitaris catalans. vol. 13–18. 1928–33. 8°. **Ac. 2604.** c.

BARCELONA, *Province of.*

CONSELL DE PEDAGOGIA.

—— *See* infra: DIPUTACIÓ.

DELEGACIÓN PROVINCIAL DEL FRENTE DE JUVENTUDES.

—— *See* SPAIN.—*Frente de Juventudes.—Delegación Provincial de Barcelona.*

DIPUTACIÓ.

—— Anuario de la Biblioteca Central y de las populares y especiales correspondiente a 1941 (1946) [*etc.*]. [With illustrations.] *Barcelona,* 1942– . 8°. **P.P. 6477.** bac.

BARCELONA, *Province of.*

—— Anuario de las Bibliotecas Populares, 1924–1925(–1930). 6 pt. [1926–31.] *See* CATALONIA. [*Miscellaneous Public Documents.*] Anuari de les biblioteques populars. [1923, *etc.*] 8°. P.P. **6477**. baa.

Diputació.—Biblioteca Central.

—— *See* BARCELONA.—*Institut d'Estudis Catalans.—Biblioteca de Catalunya.*

Biblioteca Musical.

—— Catàlech de la Biblioteca Musical de la Diputació de Barcelona, ab notes històriques, biogràfiques y crítiques, transcripcions en notació moderna dels principals motius musicals y facsímils dels documents més importants pera la bibliografía espanyola, per En Felip Pedrell. 2 vol. *Barcelona,* 1908, 09. 4°. **L.R.408.d.3.**

—— [Another copy.] Catàlech de la Biblioteca Musical . . . Per . . . Felip Pedrell. *Barcelona,* 1908, 09. 4°. Hirsch **218**.

Consell de Pedagogía.

—— Cursos Monogràfics d'Alts Estudis i d'Intercanvi, organisats per l'Institut d'Estudis Catalans i el Consell de Pedagogía, *etc.* 3 pt. 1916–18. 8°. *See* BARCELONA.—*Institut d'Estudis Catalans.* Ac. **138/4**.

—— Guia de les Institucions Cientifiques i d'Ensenyança. [With plates.] pp. 359. [*Barcelona,*] 1916. 8°. **8357**. ee. **10**.

Escola Elemental del Treball.

—— Ensenyament de primer grau per a obrers. [With plates.] pp. 22. *Barcelona,* [1917.] 8°. **8358**. ee. **31**.

Escola Superior d' Agricultura.

—— Curs 1917–1918. pp. 32. *Barcelona,* [1917.] 4°. **08756**. b. **5**.

ESCOLA SUPERIOR D'AGRICULTURA.

—— *See* supra : DIPUTACIÓ.

JUNTA PROVINCIAL DE AGRICULTURA, INDUSTRIA Y COMERCIO.

—— Memoria documentada acerca del concurso de ganados domésticos, celebrado . . . por la Seccion de agricultura de la Junta provincial de este ramo, industria y comercio de Barcelona. pp. 30. *Barcelona,* 1860. 8°. **7294**. ff. **11**.

BARCELONA, BENITO, *Bishop of.* *See* SALA Y DE CARAMANY (B. de) *Cardinal.*

——, BERENGARIUS, *Bishop of.* *See* BERENGARIUS.

——, BERENGARIUS, *Count of.* *See* BERENGARIUS.

——, FERDINAND II., *Count of.* *See* FERDINAND V., *King of Spain, etc.*

——, GUILLEM, *Bishop of.* *See* SERRA.

——, JOSÉ, *Bishop of.* *See* CLIMENT.

——, JOSÉ DOMINGO, *Bishop of.* *See* COSTA Y BORRÁS.

——, PABLO, *Bishop of.* *See* SICHAR (P. de)

——, PACIANUS, *Bishop of.* *See* PACIANUS, *Saint, etc.*

——, SEVERO, *Bishop of.* *See* SEVERUS, *Saint, etc.*

BARCELONA COLLECTIONS.

—— Colecciones barcelonesas. [Catalogues of a series of exhibitions.]

no. 4. Catálogo de la Segunda Exposición de Pintura Andaluza del siglo XVII . . . diciembre MCMXLVII—enero MCMXLVIII.

no. 5. Catálogo de la Exposición de Pintura Castellana de los siglos XVI, XVII, XVIII . . . enero MCMXLIX.
no. 6. Catálogo de la Exposición de siete obras maestras de arte español del siglo XVII . . . diciembre—enero MCMXLIX–MCML.

Barcelona, [1950.] 8°. **7960**. df. **38**.
Imperfect ; wanting no. 1–3.

BARCELONA CONFERENCE. *See* LEAGUE OF NATIONS. [*International Conferences convened by the League of Nations*].—*General Conference on Communications and Transit.*

BARCELONA (ANTONI MARIA DE) *See* ANTONI MARIA, *de Barcelona.*

BARCELONA (JUAN PEDRO) Doctrina republicana federal, puesta al alcance de todas las inteligencias. pp. 62. *Madrid,* 1891. 8°. **8042**. aa. **29**. (**3**.)

BARCELONE (GEORGES)

—— [Mot de passe.] Pass Word. pp. 126. *Archer Press: Hanley,* 1951. 8°. **12519**. f. **1**.

BARCELONESA. *See* BARCELONESE WOMAN.

BARCELONESE WOMAN. La Mas heroyca Barcelonesa. [A drama, in verse.] pp. 23. *Barcelona,* [1790 ?] 4°. **1342**. e. **1**. (**26**.)

BARCELOS [PEDRO AFONSO], *Count de.* *See* PEDRO AFONSO *Count de Barcelos.*

BARCELÓ Y COMBIS (FRANCISCO) Flora de las Islas Baleares, seguida de un diccionario de los nombres baleares, castellanos y botánicos de las plantas espontáneas y de las cultivadas. pp. xlviii. 645. *Palma,* 1879–81. 8°. **7030**. g. **5**.

BÁRCENA (ALONSO) Arte de la Lengua Toba . . . Con vocabularios . . . editados y comentados con un discurso preliminar por S. A. Lafone Quevedo. 1894. *See* LA PLATA.—*Museo de La Plata.* Revista, *etc.* tom. 5. 1890, *etc.* 8°. Ac. **3091**.

—— [Another edition.] pp. 153. *La Plata,* 1893. 8°. **12910**. w. **2**.
Part of the "Biblioteca lingüística del Museo de La Plata."

BÁRCENA (ANTONIO MARÍN DE LA) *See* MARÍN DE LA BÁRCENA.

BÁRCENA (GREGORIO) Peral y su barco, *etc.* pp. 83. *Madrid,* 1891. 8°. **8805**. aa. **38**.

BÁRCENA (JOSÉ CESAR BANCIELLA Y) *See* BANCIELLA Y BÁRCENA.

BÁRCENA (JOSÉ DE LA) Étude historique sur l'emploi du feu en médecine. Thèse, *etc.* pp. 33. *Montpellier,* 1848. 4°. **7379**. a. **6**. (**3**.)

BÁRCENA (JOSÉ MARIA ROA) *See* ROA BÁRCENA.

BÁRCENA (LUCAS)

—— Caracol. Versos. pp. 31. *Panamá,* 1944. 8°. **11452**. cc. **31**.

BÁRCENA (MANUEL DE LA) Manifiesto al mundo. La justicia y la necesidad de la independencia de la Nueva España. pp. 22. *Puebla, Mexico,* 1821. 4°. **8180**. bb. **39**.

—— [Another edition.] pp. 16. *Veracruz,* 1821. 4°. **8179**. f. **9**.

—— [Another edition.] [Signed: M. de B., i.e. M. de la Bárcena.] pp. 19. 1821. 4°. *See* B., M. de. **9770**. bb. **28**. (**27**.)

BÁRCENA (MANUEL DE LA)

—— Oracion funebre de su Magestad . . . Maria Luisa . . . Reina de las Españas, *etc.* pp. 32. *See* MARY LOUISA THERESA, *Queen Consort of Charles IV., King of Spain.* Breve noticia de las solemnes exequias de la Reina Madre Doña Maria Luisa, *etc.* 1820. 8°. **10632**. bbb. **17**.

—— Sermon que en la jura del Señor Don Fernando VII. . . . dixo . . . M. de la Barcena, *etc.* pp. 24. *Mexico,* 1808. 4°. **4423**. aaa. **5**.

BÁRCENA (MARIANO) Ensayo estadístico del Estado de Jalisco referente á los datos necesarios para procurar el adelanto de la agricultura y la aclimatacion de nuevas plantas industriales. pp. 729. *México,* 1888. 8°. **10481**. v. **18**.

—— Informe que el Director del Observatorio (M. Bárcena) presenta á la Secretaría de Fomento, acerca de los trabajos verificados en aquella oficina. [With a map and diagrams.] pp. 88. 1880. 8°. *See* MEXICO, *City of.—Observatorio Meteorológico Central.* **8755**. i. **21**. **(1.)**

—— Viaje á la Caverna de Cacahuamilpa. Datos para la geologia y la flora de los estados de Morelos y Guerrero. [With plates.] pp. 31. *Mexico,* 1874. 8°. **10481**. e. **41**.

BÁRCENA (RAFAEL ROA) *See* ROA BÁRCENA.

BÁRCENAS (TOMÁS DE LA CERDA Y DE LAS) *See* CERDA Y DE LAS BÁRCENAS.

BÁRCENA Y ORANGO (FERNANDO DE) Descripcion comica, La Babilonia de Europa, y Primer Rey de Romanos. [A comedy, in verse.] pp. 38. *Madrid,* 1731. 4°. **11728**. a. **35**.
Imperfect; wanting the first preliminary leaf, containing part of the dedication.

BARCENILLA (JOSÉ) Poesias epigramaticas. pp. 159. *Salamanca,* 1848. 16°. **11451**. b. **12**.

BARCHÆUS (ANDERS GUSTAF) Dissertatio academica, de historia naturali, lumine scriptorum Ciceronianorum mirabiliter collustrata, *etc. Praes.* P. Ekerman. pp. 12. *Upsaliæ,* 1759. 4°. B. **604**. **(10.)**

—— Svar . . . ingifvet af A. G. Barchæus. *See* MODÉER (A.) Svar på Kongl. Vetenskaps Academiens fråga, angående bästa sättet at uphjelpa Åkerbruket, *etc.* 1774. 8°. **965**. l. **1**. **(1.)**

—— Svar på Kongl. Vetenskaps Academiens fråga: Huru Sveriges ringa folk-hop bäst kan användas? *etc.* pp. 42. *Stockholm,* 1772. 8°. **965**. k. **14**. **(9.)**

BARCHAM (JOHN) *See* CRAKANTHORP (Richard) Defensio Ecclesiæ Anglicanæ, contra M. Antonii de Dominis . . . iniurias . . . opus posthumum a D. I. Barkham . . . in lucem editum. 1625. 4°. C. **82**. d. **3**.

—— —— 1847. 8°. **2204**. d. **5**.

—— [For editions of " A Display of Heraldrie," published under the name of John Guillim, but really compiled by him from notes supplied by John Barcham:] *See* GUILLIM (John) *Rouge Croix Pursuivant at Arms.*

BARCHAN (PAWEL)

—— *See* TOLSTOI (L. N.) *Count.* [Власть тьмы.] Macht der Finsternis . . . Übertragen von P. Barchan. [1918.] 8° **012213**. de. **1**/**233**.

BARCHAUS (HERMANNUS) Castrum doloris & honoris, oder glorwürdigestes Ehren-Gedächtnis des . . . Herrn Hn. Iohan Friedrich, Hertzogen zu Braunschweig und Lüneburg, *etc.* *See* JOHN FREDERICK, *Duke of Brunswick-Luneburg.* Iusta funebria, *etc.* pt. 2. 1685. fol. **604.1.20.**

BARCHENKO (A. V.) Волны жизни. Сборникъ разсказовъ . . . Съ . . . рисунками, *etc.* pp. 283. *С.-Петербургъ,* [1914.] 8°. **12589**. v. **1**.

BĂRCHET (WILFRED) *See* BURCHETT (Wilfred G.)

BARCHETTA (ANTONIO) Sulla costruzione delle ferrovie secondarie. Considerazioni economiche, tecniche e finanziarie. pp. xvii. 118. *Torino,* 1866. 4°. **8235**. h. **28**.

BARCHEWITZ (CHRISTIANUS GOTTHELFF GNADENREICH)
—— Dissertatio inauguralis medico-chirurgica. De puero XII. annorum anchyloblepharo laborante curato, *etc. Praes.* C. F. Kaltschmied. pp. 20. *Jenae,* 1764. 4°. T. **588**. **(27.)**

BARCHEWITZ (ERNST CHRISTOPH) Ernst Christoph Barchewitz . . . allerneueste und wahrhaffte Ost-Indianische Reise-Beschreibung, *etc.* [With a map.] pp. 657. *Chemnitz,* 1730. 8°. **10055**. a. **8**.

—— Vierte Auflage. [With plates.] pp. 687. *Erfurt,* 1762. 8°. **10055**. a. **9**.

BARCHEWITZ (MELCHIOR AUGUSTUS) Dissertatio inauguralis medica sistens spicilegia ad phosphori urinarii usum internum medicum pertinentia, *etc. Praes.* A. E. Büchner. *See* SANDIFORT (E.) Thesaurus dissertationum, *etc.* vol. 1. 1768, *etc.* 4°. **41**. g. **8**.

BARCHEWITZ (PIERRE)

—— Contributions à l'étude de la transmission infrarouge de la basse atmosphère. Par P. Barchewitz . . . Gilbert Amat . . . et Colette Rossetti, *etc.* [With plates.] pp. 67. *Paris,* 1954. 8°. [*Publications scientifiques et techniques du Ministère de l'Air. Bulletins des services techniques.* no. B.S.T. 116.] S. E. **58**.

BARCHFELD (WALDEMAR) Wilhelm Jensen als Lyriker. pp. 90. *Münster,* 1913. 8°. **011853**. b. **12**. **(3)**.

BARCHI (ALEMANO) Annotazioni alla cronologia bresciana, *etc.* pp. 40. *Brescia,* 1832. 4°. **10129**. g. **21**.

—— Sopra il nuovo libro intitolato Delle origini italiche. Lettera di risposta di un vecchio ad un giovine amico. pp. 72. *Brescia,* 1841. 8°. **1197**. k. **15**.

—— Storia dei santi martiri bresciani investigata nei primi nove secoli del Cristianesimo, *etc.* pp. lxx. 318. *Brescia,* 1842. 4°. **4824**. d. **5**.

BARCHI (GIUSEPPE MARIA) Vita, e morte della . . . Suor Anna Giuliana Gonzaga, Arciduchessa d'Austria &c. del Terz' Ordine de' Serui di Maria Verg. . . . Ristampata in Bologna dal P. Fr. Tomaso Rosa, *etc.* pp. 224. *Eredi del Cochi: Mantoua & Bologna,* 1643. 4°. **4867**. c. **9**.
With an additional titlepage, engraved.

BARCHIN (HIERONYMUS PAULUS) Practica Cancellariæ Apostolicæ cum stylo et formis in Romana Curia usitatis. Excerpta nuper ex memoralibus D. Hier. Pauli Barchin, *etc.* [1664.] *See* REBUFFI (P.) Praxis beneficiorum, *etc.* 1664, *etc.* fol. **497**. i. **9**.

BARCHINONA. *See* BARCELONA.

BARCHIUS (NICOLAUS LAURENTII) De hospitalitate Hebræorum exercitatio academica, *etc. Praes.* J. Palmroth. pp. 96. *H. Keyser: Upsaliæ,* 1698. 8°. **1090**. d. **10**. **(7.)**

BARCHMAN WUYTTERS (CORNELIUS JAN) *Archbishop of Utrecht.* *See* WUYTTERS.

BARCHOU DE PENHOËN (AUGUSTE THÉODORE HILAIRE) *Baron.* *See* FICHTE (J. G.) [Die Bestimmung des Menschen.] Destination de l'homme . . . Traduit de l'allemand par Barchou de Penhoën. 1832. 8°. **528**. h. **18**.

BARCHOU DE PENHOËN (AUGUSTE THÉODORE HILAIRE) *Baron.*

—— Essai d'une philosophie de l'histoire. 2 tom. *Paris,* 1854. 8°. **9008. e. 16.**

—— Guillaume d'Orange et Louis-Philippe. 1688–1830. pp. iv. 361. *Paris,* 1835. 8°. **9073. bbb. 5.**

—— Histoire de la conquête et de la fondation de l'Empire anglais dans l'Inde. 6 tom. *Paris,* 1840, 41. 8°. **1434. e. 9–11.**

—— Storie e viaggi nelle Indie Orientali e nel Tibet . . . Prima versione italiana [of books 1–7 of the author's "Histoire de la conquête, etc." With plates]. vol. 1; vol. 2, pp. 1–240. *Prato,* 1845, 47. 8°. [*MARMOCCHI (F. C.) Raccolta di viaggi, etc.* tom. 19, 20.] **1424. i. 9.** *No more published.*

—— Histoire de la philosophie allemande depuis Leibnitz jusqu'à Hegel. 2 tom. *Paris,* 1836. 8°. **8464. c. 21.**

—— L'Inde sous la domination anglaise. 2 tom. *Paris,* 1844. 8°. **1298. h. 19.**

—— Mémoires d'un officier d'État-Major . . . Expédition d'Afrique. pp. viii. 437. *Paris,* 1835. 8°. **1434. i. 8.**

BARCHUDARIAN (JOHANNES) Inwiefern ist Leibniz in der Psychologie ein Vorgänger Herbarts, *etc.* pp. 51. *Jena,* 1889. 8°. **8469. h. 15. (3.)**

BARCHUSEN (JOANNES CONRADUS) *See* BARCKHAUSEN.

BARCIA (ANDRES GONZALEZ) *See* GONZALEZ DE BARCIA CARBALLIDO Y ZUÑIGA.

BARCIA (ÁNGEL MARÍA DE) *See* BARCIA Y PAVÓN.

BARCIA (DOMINGO PÉREZ DE) *See* PÉREZ DE BARCIA.

BARCIA (JOSÉ RUBIA) *See* RUBIA BARCIA (J.)

BARCIA (ROQUE) *See* CARTHAGENA, *Spain.* Historia del sitio de Cartagena, ilustrada con los retratos de Lopez Dominguez, Barcia, *etc.* 1874. 8°. **9180. e. 27.**

—— *See* SPAIN. [*Constitutions.*] Constitucion de la Nacion Española . . . de 1869, y Constitucion de 1812, con . . . un prólogo por R. Barcia. 1869. 8°. **8042. b. 21. (3.)**

—— *See* ZAMORA Y CABALLERO (E.) Ecos del Alma, coleccion de poesias . . . Con un prólogo de D. R. Barcia. 1863. 8°. **11452. bb. 48.**

—— Catón político . . . [A panegyric of democracy.] Con un prólogo de E. Castelar. pp. 265. *Madrid,* 1884. 8°. **8042. bb. 17.**

—— ¡ El Dos de Mayo ! Drama original en cuatro actos . . . en verso. pp 150. *Madrid,* 1846. 16°. **11726. a. 22.**

—— Filosofia de la Lengua Española. Sinonimos castellanos. 2 tom. *Madrid,* 1863, 65. 8°. **12943. ee. 17.**

—— Segunda edicion. 2 tom. *Madrid,* 1870. 8°. **12941. g. 33.**

—— Sinónimos Castellanos . . . Edición póstuma, corregida y considerablemente aumentada por su autor. pp. 538. *Madrid,* 1910. 8°. **12941. o. 6.**

—— Filosofia del Alma Humana, ó sea teoría de los actos externos é internos del hombre, precedida de unos apuntes etimológicos . . . y seguída de otros apuntes sobre generacion de ideas. pp. 236. *Madrid,* 1857. 12°. **8407. c. 2.**

—— El Pedestal de la Estatua. Drama original, en dos actos y en verso. pp. 59. *Madrid,* 1864. 8°. **11726. bbb. 24. (1.)**

—— Primer Diccionario general etimológico de la Lengua Española. 5 tom. *Madrid,* 1880–83. 8°. **12944.k.1.**

BARCIA (ROQUE)

—— Nuevo Diccionario de la Lengua Castellana . . . Décima tercera edición . . . aumentada, *etc.* pp. xi. 1119. 37. *París, México,* 1896. 8°. **12941.** cc.

—— *See* ECHEGARAY (E. de) Diccionario general . . . Edicion . . . arreglada del Diccionario . . . de D. R Barcia, *etc.* 1887, *etc.* 8°. **12941. df. 1**

—— *See* NAVARRO VIOLA (A.) Juicio crítico del Dic cionario filológico-comparado de la Lengua Castellana [A comparison of the dictionary of M. Calandrelli wit that of R. Barcia.] 1884. 8°. **12901. b. 47. (2**

—— Prólogo del Primer Diccionario general etimológico de l Lengua Española. pp. 45. *Paris,* 1878. 4°. **12943. g. 1**

—— Teoria del Infierno, ó la ley de la vida. pp. 223. *Madrid,* [1868.] 16°. **8466. aa.**

BARCIA CABALLERO (JUAN) *See* BRAÑAS (A.) E Regionalismo . . . Precedido de un prólogo escrito p J. Barcia Caballero. 1889. 8°. **08276. g. 1**

—— Rimas. pp. xxxviii. 213. *Coruña,* 1891. 8°. [*Bibli teca Gallega.* no. 29.] **12231.**

BARCIA CARBALLIDO Y ZUÑIGA (ANDRES GON ZALEZ DE) *See* GONZALEZ DE BARCIA CARBALLIDO Y ZUÑIGA.

BARCIANU (D. P.) *See* BARCIANU (S. P.) Dicţiona român-germân şi germân-român . . . Revidat şi complecta de . . . D. P. Barcianu, *etc.* 1886, *etc.* 8°. **12941. b. 39**

BARCIANU (SAVA POPOVICI) Dicţionar român-germân ş germân-român . . . Revidat şi complectat de . . . D. P Barcianu, *etc.* (Wörterbuch, *etc.*) 2 pt. *Sibiiu* 1886, 88. 8°. **12941. b. 39**

—— [Another copy.] **12942. aa. 45**

—— Gramatica germana teoretica-practica pentru usul tinerimei romane . . . A dou'a editiune de nou prelucrata pp. v. 248. *Sabiiu,* 1864. 8°. **12963. f. 5**

—— Theoretisch-practische Grammatik der romänische Sprache. Zum Schul- und Selbstgebrauche. pp. vi. 384 *Hermannstadt,* 1858. 8°. **12941. c. 11**

—— Dritte . . . vermehrte Auflage. pp. 239. *Hermannstadt,* 1871. 8°. **12976. dd. 7**

BARCIA TRELLES (AUGUSTO)

—— Antecedentes para estudiar la personalidad y la obr de José de San Martín. (tom. 2. José de San Martí en España.—tom. 3–5. San Martín en America.) [With portrait of the author.] 5 tom. *Buenos Aires* 1941–46. 8°. **10890. f. 3**

—— El Genio Político de Inglaterra. Ensayo histórico pp. 236. *Buenos Aires,* 1942. 8°. **09504. ee. 33**

—— Las Ideas económicas de Wagemann . . . Resumen de las doctrinas del . . . Profesor E. Wagemann contenidas en el libro primero de su obra " La Estrategia económica ", *etc.* pp. 330. *Buenos Aires,* 1943. 8°. **08207. c. 64.**

—— José de San Martín en España. *See* supra : Antecedentes para estudiar la Personalidad y la Obra de José de San Martín. tom. 2.

—— San Martín en America. *See* supra : Antecedentes para estudiar la personalidad y la obra de José de San Martín. tom. 3–5.

BARCIA TRELLES (Camilo) La Doctrine de Monroë dans son développement historique particulièrement en ce qui concerne les relations interaméricaines. [With a portrait.] 1931. *See* Hague.—*Académie de Droit International.* Recueil des cours, *etc.* 1930. vol. 2. 1930, *etc.* 8°. Ac. **2099/2.**

—— Estudios de política internacional y derecho de gentes. Por Camilo Barcia Trelles. pp. 585. *Madrid,* 1948. 8°. **6956.** dd. **17.**

—— Francisco de Vitoria, fundador del derecho internacional moderno. pp. 229. [Valladolid] 1928. 8°. **Ac.173.c.**

—— El Problema de las Islas Malvinas. [With a map.] pp. 114. [*Madrid,*] 1943. 8°. **9772.** d. **39.**

—— Puntos Cardinales de la Política Internacional Española. pp. 488. [*Barcelona,*] 1939. 8°. **9180.** w. **17.**

—— Vázquez de Menchaca. Sus teorías internacionales: 1512–69, *etc.* pp. 160. *Barcelona,* [1940.] 8°. **6956.** a. **5.**

BARCIA Y PAVÓN (Ángel María de) *See* Alarcón y Meléndez (J.) Recuerdo de Recuerdos . . . 1858–1912. (Recuerdos de la vida religiosa. [With a preface by A. M. de Barcia y Pavón.]) 1912. 8°. **11452.** ee. **39.**

—— Catálogo de la Colección de Dibujos originales de la Biblioteca Nacional. pp. 962. 1906. 8°. *See* Madrid.—*Biblioteca Nacional.* **7875.** s. **25.**

—— Catálogo de la Colección de Estampas y de vasos pintados perteneciente al Ex° Sr. Duque de Berwick y de Alba. pp. viii. 167. 1890. 8°. *See* Fitzjames/y Falcó (J. M. C. M.) *Duke de Berwick y de Alba.* Stuart Dept. of Prints & Drawings.

—— Catálogo de la Colección de Pinturas del Excmo. Sr. Duque de Berwick y de Alba. pp. xvi. 278. 1911. 8°. *See* Fitzjames/y Falcó (J. M. C. M.) *Duke de Berwick y de Alba.* Stuart **7875.** eee. **34.**

—— Catalogo de los Retratos de Personajes Españoles que se conservan en la Seccion de Estampas y de Bellas Artes de la Biblioteca Nacional. pp. 895. 1901–05. 8°. *See* Madrid.—*Biblioteca Nacional.* **11907.** pp. **9.**

—— Viaje á Tierra Santa en la primavera de 1888. pp. viii. 454. *Madrid,* 1889. 8°. **010077.** e. **15.**

BARCIA Y ZAMBRANA (José de) *Bishop of Cadiz. See* Barzia y Zambrana.

BARCILON (Gustave) La Magistrature et les décrets du 29 mars 1880. 2 sér. *Avignon,* 1880, 81. 12°. **3902.** ee. **5.**

BARCINAS (Jesus C.)

—— *See* Thompson (Laura M.) Guam and its People . . . With a village journal by J. C. Barcinas. 1947. 8°. **10493.fff.19.**

BARCINO. *See* Barcelona.

BARCINO, *Coronel, pseud.*

—— La Batalla del Marne. pp. 58. [*Barcelona,*] 1938. 8°. **9083.** ff. **40.**

BARCINON. *See* Barcelona.

BARCIS (Benedictus de) *de Plumbino. See* Plumbino (B. de) called *de Barcis.*

BARCK (Dorothy C.) *See* Lloyd, *Family of, of Lloyd's Neck.* Papers of the Lloyd Family of the Manor of Queens Village, Lloyd's Neck, Long Island, New York, 1654–1826. (Edited by D. C. Barck.) 1927. 8°. [*Collections of the New York Historical Society.* vol. 59, 60.] Ac. **8425/8.**

BARCK (Dorothy C.)

—— *See* New York, *State of.—Committee for Detecting and Defeating Conspiracies.* Minutes of the Committee and of the First Commission for Detecting and Defeating Conspiracies, *etc.* (Edited by D. C. Barck.) 1924, *etc.* 8°. [*Collections of the New York Historical Society.* vol. 57, 58.] Ac. **8425/8.**

—— *See* Pintard (John) Letters from John Pintard to his daughter, Eliza Noel Pintard Davidson, 1816–1833, *etc.* [Edited, and with an analytical index, by D. C. Barck.] 1940, *etc.* 8°. [*Collections of the New York Historical Society.* vol. 70, *etc.*] Ac. **8425/8.**

—— *See* Rodney (George B.) *1st Baron Rodney.* Letter-Books and Order Book of George, Lord Rodney, *etc.* [Edited by D. C. Barck.] 1932. 8°. [*Collections of the New York Historical Society.* vol. 65, 66.] Ac. **8425/8.**

BARCK (Ghita)

—— Henry Parland. [With a portrait.] *In:* Skrifter utgivna av Svenska Litteratursällskapet i Finland. no. 335. pp. 136–218. 1952. 8°. Ac. **9082.**

BARCK (Hans Henricus) Dissertatio philosophica de nexu officiorum internorum, *etc. Praes.* A. A. Scarin. pp. 17. *Aboæ,* [1746.] 4°. **897.** d. **7.** (**37.**)

BARCK (Haraldus) Vernatio arborum, *etc. Praes.* C. Linnaeus. [With a table.] pp. 20. *Upsaliæ,* 1753. 4°. B. **149.** (**3.**)

—— [Another edition.] 1764. *See* Linnaeus (C.) Caroli Linnæi Amœnitates academicæ, *etc.* vol. 3. 1749, *etc.* 8°. **45.** c. **3.**

—— [Another edition.] 1787. *See* Linnaeus (C.) Amœnitates academicæ, *etc.* vol. 3. 1787, *etc.* 8°. **49.** b. **10.**

—— On the Foliation of Trees. *See* Linnaeus (C.) Miscellaneous Tracts relating to Natural History, *etc.* 1759. 8°. **955.** c. **22.**

—— [Another edition.] *See* Linnaeus (C.) Miscellaneous Tracts relating to Natural History, *etc.* 1762. 8°. **955.** c. **23.**

BARCK (Helmuth) Die Organisation und Zentralisation des badischen Arbeitsmarktes. pp. 107. *Tübingen,* 1914. 8°. [*Zeitschrift für die gesammte Staatswissenschaft.* Ergänzungshft. 52.] P.P. **1423.** ha.

BARCK (Oscar Theodore) New York City during the War for Independence, *etc.* [A thesis.] pp. 269. *New York,* 1931. 8°. **9616.** g. **7.**

—— [Another issue.] *Columbia University Press: New York,* 1931. 8°. [*Studies in History, Economics and Public Law.* no. 357.] Ac. **2688/2.**
Without the last leaf, containing the author's "Vita."

BARCK (Per Olov Fredrik)

—— Arvid Mörne och sekelskiftets Finland. [With a portrait.] pp. 420. *Helsingfors,* 1953. 8°. [*Skrifter utgivna av Svenska Litteratursällskapet i Finland.* no. 341.] Ac. **9082.**

BARCK (Samuel)

—— Sannfärdig berättelse angående Ryssarnes ochristelige och hårda förfahrande emot Kongl. May:tz af Swerige . . . fångne Officerare, *etc.* [By S. Barck.] 1705. 4°. *See* Russians. **9077.** dd. **6.** (**19.**)

BARCKEL (Maria van) afterwards **WITT** (Maria de) —— *See* Witt.

BARCKHAUSEN (Gottlieb) Specimen botanicum sistens fasciculum plantarum ex flora comitatus Lippiaci, *etc.* pp. 28. *Goettingæ*, 1775. 4°. **B. 39. (3.)**

BARCKHAUSEN (H.) *of Bremen.* Einige Betrachtungen über Magnetismus und Elektricität, ihre Wirkungen und Wechselwirkungen, mit einem Anhange: Betrachtungen zum Ausbruch des Krakatau. pp. 90. *Bremen*, 1892. 8°. **8755. dd. 7. (7.)**

BARCKHAUSEN (Heinrich Ludwig Wilibald) *See* Barckhausen (V.) Viktor Barckhausen's . . . Bemerkungen über die Todesstrafen . . . Herausgegeben von dessen Bruder H. L. W. Barckhausen. 1805. 12°. **6056. a. 11.**

—— *See* Periodical Publications.—*Halle.* Magdeburg-Halberstädtische Blätter. Herausgegeben von H. L. W. Barckhausen und L. H. Jakob. [1801.] 8°. **P.P. 4610.**

—— Briefe über dit Policey des Kornhandels. Herausgegeben von H. L. W. Barkhausen. pp. 176. *Lemgo*, 1773. 8°. **8244. aaa. 34.**

BARCKHAUSEN (Henri) *See* Bordeaux. Livre des coutumes; publié avec des variantes et des notes par H. Barckhausen. 1890. 4°. [*Archives municipales de Bordeaux.* tom. 5.] **5402. dd.**

—— *See* Montaigne (M. de) Essais . . . Texte original de 1580 . . . publié par . . . H. Barckhausen. 1870, *etc.* 8°. **Ac. 8918/2.**

—— *See* Secondat (C. de) *Baron de Montesquieu.* Considérations sur les causes de la grandeur des Romains et de leur décadence. Édition revue et annotée . . . par M. H. Barckhausen. 1900. fol. **1870. a. 7.**

—— *See* Secondat (C. de) *Baron de Montesquieu.* Lettres persanes. Édition revue et annotée . . . par M. H. Barckhausen. 1897. fol. **1870. c. 24.**

—— *See* Secondat (C. de) *Baron de Montesquieu.* Lettres persanes. Édition revue et annotée d'après les manuscrits du château de La Brède, avec un avant-propos et un index par H. Barckhausen. 1913. 8°. **Ac. 9812/21.**

—— Montesquieu. L'" Esprit des Lois " et les archives de La Brède. pp. 121. *Bordeaux*, 1904. 4°. **11852. gg. 44.**

—— Montesquieu, ses idées et ses œuvres, d'après les papiers de La Brède. pp. vi. 344. *Paris*, 1907. 8°. **11851. pp. 13.**

BARCKHAUSEN (Hermannus) Dissertatio de cometis eorumque generatione, figura, motu, lumine et prognosticis. *Praes.* J. Kahler. pp. 48. *Ex officina G. C. Wächters: Renthelii*, 1681. 4°. **532. e. 25. (17.)**

BARCKHAUSEN (Joachim)

—— Das gelbe Weltreich. Lebensgeschichte einer Macht. [A history of the Mongol Empire. With a map.] pp. 291. *Berlin*, [1938.] 8°. **9058. de. 19.**

—— Männer gegen Stein und Stahl. Fünftsausend Jahre Kampf um Festungen. [By] J. Barckhausen . . . Hans Springer. [With plates.] pp. 179. *Berlin*, [1942.] 8°. **8838. dd. 13.**

—— Männer und Mächte am Bosporus. Abdul Hamid und seine Zeit, *etc.* [With plates, including portraits.] pp. 313. *Berlin*, [1938.] 8°. **2402. b. 23.**

BARCKHAUSEN (Joannes Conradus) Joannis Conradi Barchusen Acroamata, in quibus complura ad iatrochemiam atque physicam spectantia, jocunda rerum varietate, explicantur. pp. 376. *Trajecti Batavorum*, 1703. 8°. **1034. k. 4.**

BARCKHAUSEN (Joannes Conradus)

—— Joh. Conr. Barchusen Collecta medicinæ practica generalis: quibus subjunctus est dialogus de optim medicorum secta. pp. 512. *Amstelodami*, 1715. 8°. **545. e. 1**

—— Johannis Conradi Barchusen Compendium ratiocin chemici more geometrarum concinnatum. pp. 70. *Lugduni Batavorum*, 1712. 8°. **1033. e. 6**

—— Joh. Conr. Barchusen De medicinæ origine et progress dissertationes; in quibus medicorum sectæ, institutione decreta, hypotheses, præceptiones, &c. ab initio medicin usque ad nostra tempora traduntur. pp. 679. *Trajecti ad Rhenum*, 1723. 4°. **550. c.**

—— Johannes Conradi Barchusen Elementa chemiæ, quibu subjuncta est confectura lapidis philosophici imaginibu repræsentata. [With plates.] pp. 532. *Lugduni Batavorum*, 1718. 4°. **1034. h. 1**

—— J. Conr. Barchusen Historia medicinæ, in qua, si no omnia, pleraque saltem, medicorum ratiocinia, dogmata hypotheses, sectæ, &c. quæ ab exordio medicinæ usque a nostre tempora inclaruerunt, pertractantur. pp. 632. *Amstelædami*, 1710. 8°. **550. c.**

—— J. Conradi Barckhausen Pharmacopoeus synopticus Plerasque medicaminum compositiones, ac formula eoremque dextram tam chemicam quam Galenicam co ficiendi & componendi methodum exhibens . . . Editi secunda, correcta, cumque plurimis curiosis aucta, *et* pp. 249. *Ex officina F. Halmæ: Trajecti ad Rhenum* 1696. 8°. **778. b. 1**

—— Joannis Conradi Barchusen Pyrosophia, succincte atqu breviter iatro-chemiam, rem metallicam et chrysopoeia pervestigans. pp. 469. *C. Boutestein Lugduni Batavorum*, 1698. 4°. **458. a. 2**

BARCKHAUSEN (Johann Ültzen) *See* Ueltzen Barckhausen.

BARCKHAUSEN (Viktor) Viktor Barckhausen's . . . Be merkungen über die Todesstrafen . . . Herausgegebe von dessen Bruder H. L. W. Barckhausen. pp. 192. *Halle & Leipzig*, 1805. 12°. **6056. a. 1**

BARCKHUSEN (Conrad Heinrich) Historica narrati de Johanne Calvino. Historische Nachricht von Johann Calvino . . . Sampt einer . . . Erzehlung von Serveto un dessen greulichen Lehren, *etc.* pp. 170. *Berlin*, 1721. 4 **4864. ccc. 3**

BARCKLAYE (Alexander) *See* Barclay.

BARCKLEY (*Sir* Richard) A Discourse of the Felicitie o Man: or his Summum bonum. pp. 618. *Printe [by R. Field] for William Ponsonby: London*, 1598. 4°. **721. k. 1**

—— [Another edition.] Newly corrected and augmente pp. 631. *Printed [by W. Jaggard] for William Ponsonby London*, 1603. 4°. **721. f. 4**

—— [Another edition.] The Felicitie of Man, *etc.* [Edite with additions, by Thomas Heywood.] pp. 717. *Printe by R. Y. [R. Young] and sold by Rich. Roystone: Londo* 1631. 4°. **721. f. 3**
The titlepage is engraved.

—— [Another copy.] **854. i. 1**
Imperfect; wanting the titlepage. This copy has a additional leaf, containing "The Illustrations to th Frontispice." The dedicatory epistle is signed: H. T.

BARCKMAN (Theodorus) Disputatio medica inaugural de apoplexia. *Ex officina Balckii: Franekeræ*, 1636. 4 **1185. i. 13. (4**

BARCKOVICH (Francesco Vincislao) *See* Barkovich.

BARCLAEUS (David) *See* Barclay (D.) *Shoemaker.*

BARCLAI (János) *See* Barclay (John) *Poet, etc.*

BARCLAI (Jean) *See* Barclay (John) *Poet, etc.*

BARCLAIO (Giovanni) *See* Barclay (John) *Poet, etc.*

BARCLAIO (Juan) *See* Barclay (John) *Poet, etc.*

BARCLAIUS (Gulielmus) *See* Barclay (William)

BARCLAIUS (Joannes) *See* Barclay (John) *Poet, etc.*

BARCLAIUS (Robertus) *See* Barclay.

BARCLAY, CURLE AND CO. Four and a Half Years' War Work, 1914–1918. pp. 37. *Glasgow,* [1919.] *obl.* 8°. **Cup.1252.a.44.**

BARCLAY, PERKINS AND CO.

—— The Anchor Magazine. vol. 1. no. 2—vol. 24. no. 9. Feb. 1921—Jan. 1957. *London.* 1921–57. 8°. P.P. **5793.** br.
Not published between September 1939 and January 1946.

—— Three Centuries. The story of our ancient brewery Barclay, Perkins & Co., *etc.* (Research & manuscript by B. W. Cockes & L. W. Cook.) [With illustrations.] pp. 28. *Harley Publishing Co.: [London,]* 1951. 8°. **7949.** f. **85.**

BARCLAY'S BANK. Monthly Review. vol. 7. no. 12, *etc.* Dec. 1925, *etc. London,* 1925– . 4°. P.P. **1423.** fam.

—— Report of the 34th [*etc.*] General Meeting . . . 1929 [*etc.*]. *London,* [1929– .] 8°. P.P. **1423.** fan.

—— Monthly Trade Cables & Reports from Branches. March, 1931 [*etc.*]. *London,* 1931– . 4°. P.P. **1423.** fao.
Reproduced from typewriting.

—— Report and Accounts 31st December, 1942 [*etc.*]. *London,* 1943– . 8°. **P.P.2501.fmm.**

—— Statement (Address) by the Chairman . . . on the Report and Accounts for the year ended 31st December, 1942 [*etc.*]. *London,* [1943– .] 8°. W.P. **15308.**

—— Barclays Bank Limited and its services. pp. 40. *London,* [1930.] 8°. **8230.** aa. **24.**

—— A Selection of Works from Barclays Bank Art Exhibition . . . held in the . . . Head Office from April 27 to May 2, 1953. [With plates.] [*London,* 1953.] 8°. **7960.** df. **64.**

—— The Spread Eagle. The staff magazine of Barclay's Bank, Limited. *London,* 1926– . 8°. P.P. **5793.** ncb.

—— The Eagle looks back. A silver jubilee anthology of twenty-five years' contributions to "The Spread Eagle," the staff magazine of Barclays Bank Limited. [With illustrations.] pp. 136. *Spread Eagle: London,* 1951. 8°. **12299.** ee. **25.**

BARCLAY'S BANK (DOMINION, COLONIAL AND OVERSEAS).

—— Report and Accounts 30th September, 1941 [*etc.*]. *London,* 1941– . 4° & 8°. **P.P.2501.fml.**

—— Report of the First [*etc.*] Ordinary General Meeting of the Shareholders . . . 1926 [*etc.*]. *London,* [1926– .] 8°. W.P. **6758.**

BARCLAY'S BANK (DOMINION, COLONIAL AND OVERSEAS).

—— A Bank in Battledress. Being the story of Barclays Bank (Dominion, Colonial and Overseas) during the second world war 1939–45. [With plates and maps.] pp. viii. 212. *For private circulation: London,* 1948. 4°. **8234.** d. **70.**

—— A Banking Centenary. Barclays Bank—Dominion, Colonial and Overseas, 1836–1936. [With plates.] pp. 269. *For private circulation: Plymouth,* [1938.] 8°. **8232.** f. **19.**

—— Overseas Markets. pp. 38. *Barclay's Bank (Dominion, Colonial & Overseas): London,* [1949.] 4°. **8219.** d. **1.**

—— Overseas Review. Covering trade and economic conditions in the overseas territories in which the Barclays Group of Banks is represented. *London,* 1946– . 8°. P.P. **1423.** faz.

—— Overseas Survey, 1951 [*etc.*]. Covering the trade and economic conditions which prevailed during the year 1951 [*etc.*] in the overseas territories in which the Barclays group of banks is represented. *London,* [1952– .] 4°. P.P. **1423.** fkt.

—— Quarterly Staff Magazine. [*London,*] 1946– . 4°. P.P. **5793.** ncd.

—— Statement by the Chairman, . . on the Report of Directors and Balance Sheet for the year ended 30th September, 1942 [etc.] [*London,* 1942–. 8°. **W.P.2037.**

BARCLAY, *Family of. See* Barclay (Charles W.) A History of the Barclay Family, *etc.* 1924, *etc.* 4°. **09915.** k. **4.**

—— *See* Barclay (Leslie G. de R.) History of the Scottish Barclays. 1915. 8°. **9902.** cc. **42.**

—— *See* Heath (James) *of Albury, Surrey.* Descendants of James Barclay, of Dalkeith. [1904.] 8°. **9903.** bb. **29.** (**1.**)

—— Brief Memoirs of the Barclay Family. pp. 20. *Tract Association of the Society of Friends: London,* 1851. 12°. [General Series. no. 93.] **4151.** b. **3.** (**32.**)

BARCLAY, *Family of, of New York. See* Moffat (R. B.) The Barclays of New York, who they are and who they are not,—and some other Barclays. 1904. 8°. **9902.** bb. **22.**

BARCLAY, *Family of, of Urie. See* Barclay (Robert) *the Younger.* A Genealogical Account of the Barclays of Urie, *etc.* 1812. 8°. **606.** c. **3.**

—— *See* Budge (Frances A.) The Barclays of Uri, *etc.* 1881. 8°. **4152.** ee. **25.**

—— A Genealogical Account of the Barclays of Urie, formerly of Mathers . . . Together with Memoirs of the life of Colonel David Barclay . . . and of . . . Robert Barclay, *etc.* [By Robert Barclay, the Younger.] pp. 61. *James Chalmers: Aberdeen,* 1740. 8°. **9914.** a. **40.**
Privately printed.

BARCLAY (A. C.) The Four Dispensations. [By A. C. Barclay.] pp. 23. [1845.] 12°. *See* Dispensations. **1361.** c. **20.**

—— The Mystery of God's Dealing with the Jews. pp. 114. *W. E. Painter: London,* 1845. 16°. **1352.** b. **22.**

—— [Another copy.] **764.** i. **13.** (**10.**)

BARCLAY (A. J. G.) *See* EUCLID. [*Elementa.*] Geometry for Schools. Comprising books I. and II. of Euclid, with some additions and numerous exercises. By A. J. G. Barclay. 1883. 8°. **8503**. df. **10**.

—— —— 1890. 8°. **8535**. b. **22**.

BARCLAY (ABRAM RAWLINSON) *See* BARCLAY (John) *of the Society of Friends.* A Select Series, biographical, narrative . . . Edited by J. Barclay. [Continued by A. R. Barclay.] 1835, *etc.* 8°. **1372**. b. **35–39**.

—— *See* BARCLAY (John) *of the Society of Friends.* A Selection from the Letters and Papers of the late J. Barclay. [Edited by A. R. Barclay.] 1841. 8°. **4152**. dd. **5**.

—— —— 1842. 8°. [*Friends' Library.* vol. 6.] **4152**. gg. **4**.

—— *See* NEALE (Samuel) *of the Society of Friends.* Some Account of the Life and Religious Labours of Samuel Neale. [Edited by A. R. Barclay.] 1847. 8°. [*Friends' Library.* vol. 11.] **4152**. gg. **4**.

—— Extracts from the Earlier Writings of Friends on the Subjects of Baptism and the Supper. [Edited by A. R. Barclay.] pp. 32. *J. & A. Arch: London,* 1838. 8°. **4325**. c. **9**.

—— Letters &c., of early Friends, illustrative of the history of the society, *etc.* [Edited by A. R. Barclay.] 1847. *See* EVANS (William) and (T.) *Publishers, of Philadelphia.* The Friends' Library, *etc.* vol. 11. 1837, *etc.* 8°. **4152**. gg. **4**.

BARCLAY (ALEXANDER) *B.D., Ph.D.* The Protestant Doctrine of the Lord's Supper. A study in the eucharistic teaching of Luther, Zwingli and Calvin. pp. xiv. 302. *Jackson, Wylie & Co.: Glasgow,* 1927. 8°. **3908**. dd. **18**.

BARCLAY (ALEXANDER) *of Jamaica.* Effects of the late Colonial Policy of Great Britain described, in a letter to the Right Hon. Sir George Murray . . . Second edition. pp. 56. *Smith, Elder & Co.: London,* 1830. 8°. T. **1282**. **(13.)**

—— *See* BARRY (John) *Wesleyan Missionary to Jamaica.* Letter . . . occasioned by certain remarks contained in a pamphlet by A. Barclay . . . entitled, " Effects of the late Colonial Policy of Great Britain," *etc.* 1830. 8°. **8155**. de. **2**. **(2.)**

—— A Practical View of the Present State of Slavery in the West Indies; or, an Examination of Mr. Stephen's " Slavery of the British West India Colonies " containing more particularly an account of the actual condition of the negroes in Jamaica; with observations on the decrease of the slaves since the abolition of the slave trade; and on the probable effects of legislative emancipation; also strictures on the Edinburgh Review, and on the pamphlets of Mr. Cooper and Mr. Bickell. pp. xxv. 462. *Smith, Elder & Co.: London,* 1826. 8°. **522**. f. **36**.

—— Third edition, with additions. pp. xxxi. 490. *Smith, Elder & Co.: London,* [1828.] 8°. **8156**. df. **3**.

—— Remarks on Emigration to Jamaica: addressed to the coloured classes of the United States. pp. 16. *Calkin & Budd: London,* 1840. 8°. **8155**. de. **2**. **(8.)**

BARCLAY (ALEXANDER) *of the Science Museum.*

—— Pure Chemistry. A brief outline of its history and development. (Handbook of the collections illustrating pure chemistry.) 2 pt. 1937. 8°. *See* LONDON.—III. *Science Museum.* B.S. **10**. b/46.

BARCLAY (ALEXANDER) *Priest. See* BRANT (S.) *Begin.* This present Boke named the Shyp of folys of the worlde was translated . . . out of Laten, Frenche, and Doche . . . by A. Barclay, *etc.* 1509. fol. G. **11593**.

—— —— 1570. fol. C. **21**. d. **1**.

—— —— 1874. 4°. **2286**. f. **7**.

BARCLAY (ALEXANDER) *Priest.*

—— *See* FRAUSTADT (F.) Über das Verhältnis von Barclay's " Ship of Fools " zur lateinischen, französischen und deutschen Quelle, *etc.* 1894. 8°. **011850**. k. **16**. **(3.)**

—— *See* GRINGORE (Pierre) called VAUDEMONT. The Castell of Labour. Translated from the French . . . by A. Barclay, *etc.* 1905. 4°. C. **101**. f. **16**.

—— *See* JAMIESON (Thomas H.) Notice of the Life and Writings of Alexander Barclay. 1874. 4°. **10855**. g. **1**.

—— *See* KOELBING (Arthur) Barclay, *etc.* 1909. 8°. [*Cambridge History of English Literature.* vol. 3.] 11870.g.1.

—— *See* MANCINUS (D.) Here begynneth a ryght frutefull treatyse, intituled the myrrour of good maners . . . translate into englysshe . . . by A. Bercley, *etc.* [1523 ?] fol. G. **11565**.

—— —— 1885. fol. Ac. **9490/22**.

—— *See* REY (A.) Skelton's Satirical Poems in their relation to . . . Barclay's Ship of Fools, *etc.* 1892. 8°. **11850**. d. **54**.

—— *See* SALLUSTIUS CRISPUS (C.) [*Jugurtha.—Latin and English.*] Here begynneth the famous cronycle of the warre . . . agaynst Jugurth . . . translated into englysshe by syr A. Barclay, *etc.* [1520 ?] fol. C. **12**. h. **15**.

—— —— 1557. 4°. [*FELICIUS (C.) Durantinus. The Conspiracie of Catiline.*] C. **13**. a. **3**.

—— Here begynneth the castell of laboure. [Translated from Pierre Gringore's " Chasteau de Labour " by A. Barclay.] B.L. [1505 ?] 4°. *See* CASTLE. Huth **29**.

—— *Begin.* ANd than whan don is this assaut, *etc.* [Translated from Pierre Gringore's " Chasteau de Labour " by A. Barclay. A fragment.] G.L. [1505 ?] 4°. *See* CASTLE. C. **59**. ff. **4**.

—— [Another edition.] The Castell of Laboure. B.L. [1510 ?] 4°. *See* CASTLE. C. **21**. c. **21**.

—— Here begynneth the Egloges of Alexander Barclay, priest, whereof the first thre conteineth the miseries of courters . . . The mattier whereof was translated . . . out of a boke named in latin, Miserie curialium, compiled by Eneas Siluius, *etc.* [Containing the three eclogues only.] B.L. *Imprinted by Humfrey Powell: London,* [1548 ?] 4°. C. **57**. b. **40**.

—— Certayne Egloges of Alexander Barclay. *See* BRANT (S.) Stultifera nauis, *etc.* 1570. fol. C. **21**. d. **1**.

—— Certain Egloges . . . Whereof the first three conteyne the Miseryes of Courtiers . . . Gathered out of a Booke named in Latin Miseriæ Cvrialivm, compiled by Eneas Siluius . . . 1570. pp. 47. 1885. fol. *See* MANCHESTER. —*Spenser Society.* Ac. **9490/23**.

—— The Eclogues . . . from the original edition by John Cawood. Edited, with an introduction and notes, by Beatrice White. pp. lxv. 272. 1928. 8°. *See* LONDON. —III. *Early English Text Society.* [Original Series. 175.] Ac. **9925/131**.

—— [Another copy.] Ac.9927/129.

—— The fyfte Eglog of Alexandre Barclay of the Cytezen and Uplondyshman. B.L. *Wynkyn de Worde: London,* [1518 ?] 4°. **239**. e. **8**.

—— The Cytezen and Uplondyshman. [The fifth eclogue.] . . . Edited, with an introductory notice of Barclay and his other eclogues, by F. W. Fairholt. pp. lxxiv. 47. *London,* 1847. 8°. [*Percy Society. Early English Poetry.* vol. 22.] Ac. **9480**.

BARCLAY (ALEXANDER) *Priest.*

—— [A fragment, consisting of one leaf, from an unknown edition of the first eclogue.] **B.L.** [1500?] 4°.
C. **40**. m. **9**. **(16.)**

—— Here begynneth the introductory to wryte and to pronounce French, *etc.* [A selection from the edition of 1521.] *See* ELLIS (Alexander J.) On Early English Pronunciation, *etc.* vol. 3. 1869, *etc.* 8°. Ac. **9930**/4.

—— The Life of St. George . . . Edited by William Nelson. pp. xxvi. 120. *London*, 1955. 8°. [*Early English Text Society. Original Series.* no. 230.] **Ac.9925/188.**

—— [Poems.] *See* SIBBALD (James) *Bookseller, of Edinburgh.* Chronicle of Scottish Poetry, *etc.* vol. 2. 1802. 8°.
991. i. **13**.

BARCLAY (ALFRED ERNEST) *See* BYTHELL (W. J. S.) and BARCLAY (A. E.) X-Ray Diagnosis and Treatment, *etc.* 1912. 8°. **20036.a.1/87.**

—— *See* FRANKLIN (Kenneth J.) The Circulation in the Foetus . . . By K. J. Franklin . . . A. E. Barclay, *etc.* 1946. 8°. **7582**. aa. **30**.

—— *See* TRUETA RASPALL (Josép) Studies of the Renal Circulation. By J. Trueta . . . A. E. Barclay [and others], *etc.* 1947. 4°. **7642**. dd. **4**.

—— The Digestive Tract. A radiological study of its anatomy, physiology and pathology. pp. xxviii. 395. pl. XXIII. *University Press: Cambridge,* 1933. 4°.
2256. g. **22**.

—— The Digestive Tract . . . Second edition. pp. xxxvi. 427. pl. XXIII. *University Press: Cambridge,* 1936. 4°.
7620. f. **26**.

—— The Foetal Circulation and Cardiovascular System, and the changes that they undergo at birth. By A. E. Barclay . . . Kenneth J. Franklin . . . and Marjorie M. L. Prichard. pp. xvi. 275. *Blackwell Scientific Publications: Oxford,* 1944. 4°. **7406**. s. **8**.

—— Micro-arteriography, and other radiological techniques employed in biological research. [With plates.] pp. xiii. 102. *Blackwell Scientific Publications: Oxford,* 1951. 4°. **7460**. ff. **42**.

—— The Stomach and Œsophagus. A radiographic study. [With a bibliography.] pp. 126. *Sherratt & Hughes: London,* 1913. 8°. **7620**. f. **28**.

BARCLAY (ALLARDICE) *See* ALLARDICE (R. B.)

BARCLAY (ALMAYER)

—— The Man with the Glaring Eyes. pp. 64. *Mellifont Press: London; Dublin* printed, [1936.] 8°.
12603. s. **12**.

BARCLAY (ANDREW) Jesus, Thou art King! [In verse.] pp. 8. *James M'Kie: Kilmarnock,* [1882.] 16°.
3437. cc. **44**. (**1**.)

—— Lines to Effie. pp. 2. [*Kilmarnock?* 1883.] 16°.
11603. aaa. **10**. (**4**.)

BARCLAY (ANDREW WHYTE) Delirium Tremens. *See* HOLMES (Timothy) A System of Surgery, *etc.* vol. 1. 1860, *etc.* 8°. **7480**. e. **30**.

—— [Another edition.] *See* HOLMES (Timothy) A System of Surgery, *etc.* vol. 1. 1870, *etc.* 8°. **7482**. bbb. **17**.

—— Diphtheria and Croup. 1864. *See* HOLMES (Timothy) A System of Surgery, *etc.* vol. 4. 1860, *etc.* 8°.
7480. e. 30.

BARCLAY (ANDREW WHYTE)

—— [Another edition.] 1870. *See* HOLMES (Timothy) A System of Surgery, *etc.* vol. 4. 1870, *etc.* 8°.
7482. bbb. **17**.

—— General Report upon the Sanitary Condition of the Parish of St. Luke, Chelsea, during the year 1856. pp. 18. 1857. 8°. *See* LONDON.—II.—Boroughs etc.—Chelsea.—Parish of Chelsea.—Vestry. **7305**. de. **10**. (**5**.)

—— Gout and Rheumatism in relation to Disease of the Heart. pp. xvi. 214. *J. Churchill & Sons: London,* 1866. 8°. **7620**. aaa. **15**.

—— The Harveian Oration. Royal College of Physicians. 1881. pp. 40. *Harrison & Sons: London,* 1881. 8°.
7679. df. **23**.

—— A Manual of Medical Diagnosis: being an analysis of the signs and symptoms of disease. pp. xx. 612. *John Churchill: London,* 1857. 12°. **7440**. a. **2**.

—— Second edition. pp. xxiv. 616. *John Churchill: London,* 1859. 12°. **7440**. a. **3**.

—— Third edition. pp. xxxi. 669. *J. Churchill & Sons: London,* 1870. 12°. **7441**. a. **24**.

—— Medical Errors. Fallacies connected with the application of the inductive method of reasoning to the science of medicine. pp. vii. 123. *J. Churchill & Sons: London,* 1864. 8°. **7320**. aa. **11**.

—— The Progress of Preventive Medicine and Sanitary Measures: being the Thruston speech on the Wendy commemoration at Caius College, *etc.* pp. 35. *Deighton, Bell & Co.: Cambridge,* 1856. 8°. **7327.b.21.(25.)**

BARCLAY (ANN) *pseud.* [i.e. MAYSIE GREIG.]

—— *See* also GREIG (M.)

—— Men as her Stepping Stones. A romance. pp. 252. *Collins: London,* 1937. 8°. NN. **28321**.

—— Other Men's Arms. A romance. pp. 250. *Collins: London,* 1936. 8°. NN. **25412**.

—— Swing High, Swing Low. A romance. pp. 252. *Collins: London,* 1936. 8°. NN. **25775**.

BARCLAY (ANNIE) Annie Barclay, or Sketches of "the Society of Friends." By one nearly connected with, but not a member of their highly respected society. pp. iii. 212. *W. N. Wright: London,* 1852. 12°.
4416. d. **6**.

BARCLAY (ANTHONY) Wilde's Summer Rose; or the Lament of the Captive. An authentic account of the origin, mystery and explanation of R. H. Wilde's alleged plagiarism. pp. 70. 1871. 8°. *See* SAVANNAH.—*Georgia Historical Society.* Ac. **8380**/4.

BARCLAY (ARMIGER)

—— *See* BARCLAY, afterwards EVANS (Marguerite F.) and BARCLAY (A.) The Activities of Lavie Jutt. [1911.] 8°.
012618. aaa. **7**.

—— —— [1919.] 8°. **12644**. a. **1/124**.

—— *See* BARCLAY, afterwards EVANS (Marguerite F.) and BARCLAY (A.) Peggy Day-by-Day. [1916.] 8°. **12601**. m. **27**.

—— *See* BARCLAY afterwards EVANS (Marguerite F.) and BARCLAY (A.) Where there are Women. 1915. 8°. NN. **2504**.

—— The Kingmakers, *etc.* pp. vi. 335. *Cassell & Co.: London,* 1907. 8°. **012634**. b. **13**.

BARCLAY (ARMIGER)

—— Playing the Game. pp. 319. *Simpkin, Marshall & Co.: London*, 1918. 8°. NN. **5151**.

—— The Worsleys: a novel. pp. 318. *Sisley's: London*, 1906. 8°. **012633**. cc. **5**.

BARCLAY (ARTHUR) *Expert on Licensed Property.* Fortune or Failure. Advice to intending licensed victuallers. pp. 8. *Arthur Barclay: London*, [1901.] 8°. **08228**. df. **24**. (5.)

BARCLAY (ARTHUR) *M.B.* On two Autoecious Cæomata in Simla. Rhododendron Uredinae. [Two papers.] 1891. *See* PERIODICAL PUBLICATIONS.—*Calcutta.* Scientific Memoirs, *etc.* pt. 6. 1885, *etc.* 4°. **7305**. h.

BARCLAY (CHARLES) Letters from the Dorking Emigrants who went to Upper Canada in the spring of 1832. Edited by C. Barclay. pp. 44. *J. & A. Arch: London*, 1833. 8°. T. **1415**. (13.)

BARCLAY (CHARLES WRIGHT) A History of the Barclay Family, with full pedigree from 1066 to 1924 (1067 to 1933). Compiled by . . . Charles W. Barclay. Illustrated. (pt. 2. The Barclays in Scotland from 1067 to 1660. Compiled by Hubert F. Barclay.—pt. 3. The Barclays in Scotland and England from 1610 to 1933. Compiled by Hubert F. Barclay and Alice Wilson-Fox.) 3 pt. *St. Catherine Press: London*, 1924–34. 4°. **09915**. k. **4**.

BARCLAY (CYRIL NELSON)

—— *See* ENGLAND.—*Army.*—*Infantry.*—*Cameronians (Scottish Rifles).* The History of the Cameronians, Scottish Rifles. (vol. 3. 1933–1946. By C. N. Nelson.) [1949, *etc.*] 8°. W.P. **13769**.

—— *See* PERIODICAL PUBLICATIONS.—London.—*Army Quarterly.* The Army Quarterly Series. [Edited by C. N. Barclay.] [1953, *etc.*] 8°. W.P. B. **438**.

—— The First Commonwealth Division. The story of British Commonwealth land forces in Korea, 1950–1953, *etc.* [With plates and maps.] pp. xviii. 236. *Gale & Polden: Aldershot*, 1954. 8°. **9103**. b. **23**.

—— The History of Duke of Wellington's Regiment, 1919–1952 . . . Edited by Brigadier C. N. Barclay. [With plates and maps.] pp. xxi. 398. 1953. 4°. *See* ENGLAND.—*Army.*—*Infantry.*—*Duke of Wellington's (West Riding Regiment).* **8838**. g. **18**.

—— The History of the Royal Northumberland Fusiliers in the Second World War, *etc.* [With plates and maps.] pp. xxii. 241. 1952. 4°. *See* ENGLAND.—*Army.*—*Infantry.*—*Royal Northumberland Fusiliers.* **8822**. g. **19**.

—— The London Scottish in the Second World War—1939 to 1945 . . . Edited by Brigadier C. N. Barclay, *etc.* [With plates and maps.] pp. xix. 459. 1952. 8°. *See* ENGLAND.—*Army.*—*Infantry.*—*Seventh Middlesex (London Scottish) Volunteer Corps.* **8839**. e. **6**.

—— The New Warfare. pp. x. 65. *William Clowes & Sons: London*, [1953.] 8°. [*Army Quarterly Series.*] W.P. B. **438 1**.

—— Part-Time Farmer. An introduction to agriculture as a part-time occupation, *etc.* pp. xii. 140. *Sifton Praed & Co.: London*, 1948 [1949]. 8°. **07078**. ff. **72**.

BARCLAY (CYRIL NELSON)

—— The Regimental History of the 3rd Queen Alexandra's Own Gurkha Rifles. Volume II, 1927 to 1947. Compiled under the direction of the Regimental History Committee, 3rd Q.A.O. Gurkha Rifles. Edited by Brigadier C. N. Barclay. [With plates and maps.] pp. xx. 316. 1953. 8°. *See* INDIA.—*Army.*—*Infantry.*—*3rd (Queen Alexandra's Own) Gurkha Rifles.* **8839**. h. **4**.

BARCLAY (D.) *Artist.* *See* BOLUS (H. M. L.) A Book of South African Flowers, *etc.* [With plates from paintings by Miss D. Barclay.] 1925. 8°. **7029**. tt. **10**.

—— *See* BOLUS (Harriet M. L.) A Second Book of South African Flowers . . . Paintings by D. Barclay, *etc.* 1936. 4°. **7032**. pp. **18**.

—— *See* SOUTH AFRICAN FLOWERS. Twelve South African Flowers and Verse, *etc.* [With plates by Miss D. Barclay.] 1925. 4°. **11607**. h. **15**.

BARCLAY (D. D. C.)

—— Spirit of Youth. Children's anthology. Compiled by D. D. C. Barclay, *etc.* [With plates.] pl. xv. *National Society; S.P.C.K.: London*, 1948. 8°. **11605**. c. **18**.

BARCLAY (DAVID) *Colonel.* *See* ARMISTEAD (Wilson) A Memoir of Robert Barclay . . . With some account of his father, Colonel D. Barclay, *etc.* 1850. 8°. **4151**. bb. **3**. (2.)

—— *See* BARCLAY (Robert) *the Younger.* A Genealogical Account of the Barclays of Urie . . . With memoirs of D. Barclay, *etc.* 1812. 8°. **606**. c. **3**.

—— Reliquiæ Barclaianæ. Correspondence of Colonel D. Barclay and Robert Barclay of Urie and his son Robert, including letters from Princess Elizabeth of the Rhine . . . William Penn, George Fox and others, *etc.* ff. x. 169. *Winter & Bailey: London*, 1870. 4°. **10921**. k. **8**.

Lithographed.

BARCLAY (DAVID) *Merchant.* Advice to Servants. [By D. Barclay.] [1800?] *s. sh.* fol. *See* ADVICE. **L.7.a.4.(12.)**

—— An Account of the Emancipation of the Slaves of Unity Valley Pen, in Jamaica. pp. 20. *William Phillips, etc.: London*, 1801. 8°. T. **362**. (5.)

—— [Another edition.] pp. 20. *J. & A. Arch: [London,]* 1825. 8°. **8156**. de. **2**. (6.)

BARCLAY (DAVID) *Shoemaker.* *Παιγνιον. Ἐπιταφια ἑπταγλωσσα*, in Davidem Barclaeum, famulum sacrorum, necnon, sutorem veteramenturium, qui . . . mortuus est Anstrutheri . . . decimo quinto Kal. Nov. 1832. [By Professor William Tennant?] *Andrew Shortrede: Edinburgh*, [1833.] 4°. **837**. i. **25**.

BARCLAY (DAVID ROBERT) *See* MISSOURI.—*Supreme Court.* Reports of Cases, *etc.* [vol. 31. Reporters: D. R. Barclay and others.] 1843, *etc.* 8°. **6622.e.1.**

BARCLAY (EDGAR) *See* BARCLAY (Hugh D.) Orpheus and Eurydice . . . and other poems . . . With illustrations by E. Barclay. 1877. 8°. **11653**. aa. **1**.

—— *See* HOMER. [*Iliad.—Greek and English.*] Homeric Similes from the Iliad. Designs by E. Barclay, *etc.* 1900. fol. **L.R.404.k.11.**

—— Mountain Life in Algeria . . . With illustrations, *etc.* pp. xviii. 119. *Kegan Paul & Co.: London*, 1882 [1881]. 4°. **10097**. h. **25**.

BARCLAY (Edgar)

—— Notes on the Scuola di San Rocco at Venice and its decorations by Tintoretto. pp. 34. *Spottiswoode & Co.: London,* 1876. 8°. **7858**. h. **21**. **(1.)**

—— The Ruined Temple. Stonehenge: its history and a short account of questions associated with it. pp. xxv. 75. *St. Catherine Press: London,* [1911.] 8°. **07709**. a. **4**.

—— Stonehenge and its Earth-works. With plans and illustrations. pp. xl. 152. *D. Nutt: London,* 1895. 4°. **7705**. ee. **36**.

BARCLAY (Edgar Norman) Big Game Shooting Records. Together with biographical notes and anecdotes on the most prominent big game hunters of ancient and modern times, *etc.* [With plates, including portraits.] pp. 288. *H. F. & G. Witherby: London,* 1932. 8°. **07912**. h. **46**.

BARCLAY (Edith Noël) A Dream of Blue Roses. pp. xi. 343. *Hodder & Stoughton: London,* 1912. 8°. NN. **167**.

—— East of the Shadows. pp. viii. 304. *Hodder & Stoughton: London,* [1913.] 8°. NN. **668**.

—— The Giant Fisher. pp. vii. 214. *Macmillan & Co.: London,* 1912. 8°. **012621**. de. **5**.

—— The Queen's Cause. Scottish Narrative, 1561–1587. [A biographical romance. With plates.] pp. 398. *Michael Joseph: London,* 1938. 8°. **12643**. ppp. **2**.

—— The Taste of Brine. pp. viii. 311. *Hodder & Stoughton: London,* [1914.] 8°. NN. **2304**.

—— Trevor Lordship. pp. viii. 389. *Macmillan & Co.: London; Norwood, Mass.* [printed], 1911. 8°. **012618**. aaa. **8**.

—— The Wilderness. A poem. pp. 13. *A. H. Stockwell: London,* 1925. 8°. **011644**. e. **126**.

BARCLAY (Edmund)

—— Khyber. [A novel.] pp. 266. *Angus & Robertson: Sydney,* 1936. 8°. NN. **26607**.

—— Shanghai. [A novel.] pp. 281. *Angus & Robertson: Sydney,* 1937. 8°. NN. **27633**.

BARCLAY (Edward) A Few Rough Sketches in Rhyme from the papers left by Major E. Barclay, *etc.* [Edited by J. H. Barclay.] pp. 179. *George Herbert: Dublin,* 1872. 8°. **11652**. b. **29**.

BARCLAY (Edward Debell) *See* also Rockaway, *pseud.* [i.e. E. D. Barclay.]

—— The History of the 45th Warwickshire—B'ham—Battalion Home Guard, *etc.* [With plates.] pp. 131. [1945.] 8°. *See* England.—*Army.—Home Guard.—Warwickshire.—45th (Birmingham) Battalion.* **8838**. d. **9**

BARCLAY (Edwyn) *See* Barlow (*Right Hon. Sir* Clement A. M.) *Bart.*, and Barclay (E.) The Licensing Act, 1904, *etc.* 1905. 8°. **6427**. cc. **13**.

BARCLAY (Evelyn)

—— Diary of Miss Evelyn Barclay . . . who was staying at the Palazzo Rezzonico at the time of Browning's illness and death. *See* Armstrong (A. J.) Baylor University Browning Interests, *etc.* 1932. 8°. [*Baylor Bulletin.* vol. 25. no. 4.] Ac. **2685**. cb.

BARCLAY (Florence Louisa Charlesworth)

—— *See* also Roy (Brandon) *pseud.* [i.e. F. L. C. Barclay.]

BARCLAY (Florence Louisa Charlesworth)

—— The Broken Halo. pp. 408. *G. P. Putnam's Sons: London & New York,* 1913. 8°. **012704**. c. **44**.

—— The Following of the Star. A romance. pp. vii. 426. *G. P. Putnam's Sons: New York & London,* 1911. 8°. **04420**. ff. **40**.

—— [Another edition.] With eight illustrations in colour by F. H. Townsend, *etc.* pp. ix. 426. *G. P. Putnam's Sons: New York & London,* [1913.] 8°. **04412**. l. **24**.

—— The Golden Censer. [A study of intercessory prayer.] pp. 70. *Hodder & Stoughton: [London,* 1914.] 8°. **3457**. ff. **38**.

—— Guy Mervyn . . . Revised by the author of "The Life of Florence L. Barclay." pp. vii. 319. *Putnam: London & New York,* 1932. 8°. NN. **22758**.

—— In hoc ✠ vince. The story of a Red Cross Flag. (First printed as a contribution to King Albert's Book.) pp. 17. *G. P. Putnam's Sons: London & New York,* 1915. 8°. **9082**. de. **19**.

—— The Mistress of Shenstone. pp. vi. 340. *G. P. Putnam's Sons: New York & London,* 1911. 8°. **012704**. aa. **11**.

—— La Châtelaine de Shenstone . . . Traduit . . . par E. de Saint-Segond. pp. 278. *Paris; Édimbourg* printed, 1940. 8°. [*Collection Nelson.*] **012199**. g. **1/366**.

—— *See* Bisson (André) *Littérateur.* La Châtelaine de Shenstone. Comédie . . . d'après le roman de F. L. Barclay. 1930. 8°. [*La Petite Illustration.* Théâtre. no. 255.] P.P. **4283**. m. **(2.)**

—— My Heart's Right There. pp. 60. *G. P. Putnam's Sons: London & New York,* 1914. 8°. **012704**. i. **54**.

—— A Notable Prisoner. *Marshall Bros.: London,* [1905.] 8°. **04420**. h. **23**.

—— [Another edition.] pp. 8. *Marshall Press: London,* [1930.] 12°. **04420**. ee. **33**.

—— Returned Empty. pp. 154. *G. P. Putnam's Sons: London & New York,* 1920. 8°. **012603**. eee. **43**.

—— The Rosary. pp. vi. 389. *G. P. Putnam's Sons: New York & London,* 1909. 8°. **012705**. b. **40**.

—— Complete edition. pp. xiv. 394. *G. P. Putnam's Sons: London & New York,* 1923. 8°. **012639**. dd. **21**.

—— *See* Bisson (André) *Littérateur.* Le Rosaire. Pièce . . . D'après le roman de F. L. Barclay. 1926. fol. [*La Petite Illustration.* Théâtre. no. 156.] P.P. **4283**. m. **(2.)**

—— Through the Postern Gate. A romance in seven days . . . With nine illustrations in colour by F. H. Townsend. pp. viii. 269. *G. P. Putnam's Sons: New York & London,* 1912. 8°. **012704**. aa. **13**.

—— The Upas Tree. pp. 246. *G. P. Putnam's Sons: London & New York,* 1912. 8°. **012704**. bb. **30**.

—— The Wall of Partition. pp. 379. *G. P. Putnam's Sons: London & New York,* 1914. 8°. NN. **2606**.

—— The Wheels of Time. (Second impression.) pp. 62. *G. P. Putnam's Sons: London,* 1910. 8°. **012705**. bbb. **48**.

—— The White Ladies of Worcester: a romance of the twelfth century. pp. 384. *G. P. Putnam's Sons: London & New York,* 1917. 8°. NN. **4537**.

BARCLAY (FLORENCE LOUISA CHARLESWORTH)

—— The Life of Florence L. Barclay . . . By one of her daughters. [With portraits.] pp. 306. *G. P. Putnam's Sons: London & New York*, 1921. 8°. **010855**. aa. **44**.

BARCLAY (FORD G.) *See* ASIA. The Big Game of Asia and North America. By D. Carruthers . . . F. G. Barclay. 1915. 4°. L.R. **259**. a. **1/4**.

BARCLAY (GEORGE) *Bishop of Cloyne. See* BERKELEY.

BARCLAY (GEORGE) *Engraver.* Barclay's Designs for Marking Silver Plate. *G. Barclay: London*, [1860.] 8°. **1269**. e. **28**.

—— Monograms by G. Barclay, assisted by I. F., W. I. R., I. B. and others. pl. 91. *G. Barclay: London*, [1860–72.] 8°. **7805**. ee. **25**.

—— Thirty Varieties of the Monogram J. B. by various hands [i.e. G. Barclay, W. H. Rogers, J. West], edited by G. Barclay. pl. 2. *Barclay: London*, [1869.] 4°. **7854**. h. **9**.

BARCLAY (GEORGE) *M.A. See* GRAY (Arthur H.) and BARCLAY (G.) Private Prayer, *etc.* [1926.] 8°. **03456**. de. **31**.

—— The Bible speaks to our Day. pp. 93. *Student Christian Movement Press: London*, 1944. 8°. **3130**. aaa. **23**.

—— Christian Convictions. pp. 90. *Student Christian Movement Press: London*, 1929. 8°. **4224**. h. **34**.

—— The Making and Meaning of the Bible. pp. 168. *Student Christian Movement: London*, 1923. 8°. **03126**. de. **2**.

BARCLAY (GEORGE) *Minister of the Gospel.*

—— *See* ROSE (Alexander) successively *Bishop of Moray* and *of Edinburgh.* A Full Vindication of the Right Reverend the Lord Bishop of Edinburgh and the other administrators of the charities there from the calumnies . . . of Mr. George Barclay, *etc.* 1712. 4°. **1477**. dd. **50**.

—— A Full Answer for Mr. George Barclay . . . to a scurrilous pamphlet published against him, in vindication of the Bishop of Edinburgh and the other administrators of the money collected; for the releif of the distressed episcopal clergy in Scotland, *etc.* pp. 28. *John Moncur: Edinburgh*, 1712. 4°. **4106**. b. **6**. (**3**.)

BARCLAY (GEORGE) *of Irvine.* An Essay on Justification by Faith: in an exposition of Romans III. 19–31, *etc.* pp. vi. 122. *Geo. Gallie: Glasgow*, 1830. 12°. **4372**. bb. **36**. (**1**.)

—— Essays: on Doctrinal, Experimental and Prophetical Subjects. pp. viii. 360. *The Author: London*, 1828. 8°. **4377**. h. **3**.

—— A Father's Letters to his Son, extracted from the papers of the latter, after his death. pp. 87. *American Sunday School Union: Philadelphia*, 1829. 12°. **864**. g. **27**.

—— Memoirs of the late Mr. James Neil, Shipmaster . . . Second edition. pp. iv. 104. *James Nisbet: London*, 1823. 12°. **4903**. aa. **12**.

—— Strictures on the "Notes and Recollections of two Sermons, by the Rev. Mr. Campbell; delivered in the Parish Church of Row" . . . Second edition. pp. 22. *Maurice Ogle: Glasgow*, 1830. 12°. **4379**. aa. **32**. (**3**.)

BARCLAY (*Sir* GEORGE) *See* ENGLAND.—*Proclamations.*—II. William III. By the King. A Proclamation. [For the apprehending of James, Duke of Berwick, Sir G. Barclay and others. 23 Feb. 1696.] 1696. *s. sh.* fol. **21**. h. **3**. (**181**.)

—— *See* ENGLAND.—*Proclamations.*—II. William III. By the Lords Justices. A proclamation. [For the apprehending of James, Duke of Berwick, Sir G. Barclay and others. 11 Nov. 1697.] 1697. *s. sh.* fol. **816**. m. **3**. (**124**.)

—— *See* JAMES II., *King of Great Britain and Ireland* [*Biography.*—II.] Discours sur la liaison & sur les rapports qui se rencontrent entre la descente resoluë par Jaques II et la conspiration [of Sir G. Barclay and others] . . contre la vie de Sa Majesté Britannique. 1696. 12°. **8122**. a. **8**.

—— *See* PLOT. The Plot. A poem. [On Sir George Barclay's plot to assassinate William III.] 1696. 4°. **11601**. ddd. **6**. (**2**.)

—— *See* SCOTLAND.—Proclamations.—William III., *King of Great Britain and Ireland.* Proclamation for apprehending Sir George Barclay. [7 May 1696.] 1696. *s. sh.* fol. K.T.C. **111**. b. **4**. (**7**.)

BARCLAY (GEORGE WATSON)

—— Colonial Development and Population in Taiwan [With maps.] pp. xviii. 274. *Princeton University Press Princeton*, 1954. 8°. **8024**. c. **33**

BARCLAY (GEORGIUS) Disputatio medica inauguralis de hæmoptoe, *etc.* pp. 8. *F. Halma: Trajecti ad Rhenum*, 1691. 4°. **1185**. k. **13**. (**69**.)

BARCLAY (GUILLAUME) *See* BARCLAY (William) *Professor of Civil Law at Angers.*

BARCLAY (GWENDOLINE R.) If I Lived in Japan, *etc.* pp. 61. *Edinburgh House Press: London*, 1928. 8°. [*Junior Background Series.* no. 2.] W.P. **8628**/**2**.

—— The Way of Partnership. With the C.M.S. in China. By G. R. Barclay and others. [With plates.] pp. 97. *C.M.S.: London*, 1937. 8°. **20031**. e. **38**

BARCLAY (H. B.) *See* BARCLAY (Robert) *Minister, of Greenock.* Robert Barclay: "Memories." Edited by his wife, *etc.* 1904. 8°. **4956**. g. **13**.

BARCLAY (HANS MARIUS EMIL)

—— *See* EPHEMERIDES. [Norsk fiskeralmanak] for 1911 . . . Redigeret af M. Barclay. [1911.] 8°. P.P. **2454**. o.

BARCLAY (HARRIET MARIA) *See* CHARLESWORTH (Maria L.) Heavenly Counsel in Daily Portions. Readings on the Gospel of St Matthew . . . Edited by H. M. Barclay. 1883. 8°. **3226**. df. **6**.

—— *See* CHARLESWORTH (Maria L.) "They two" . . . Addresses . . . Edited by H. M. Barclay. 1885. 8°. **4422**. bbb. **40**. (**3**.)

—— *See* GABHRĪ'EL BAR ALEKHSANDRŌS and BARCLAY (H. M.) Mountain Men. [1910.] 8°. **04413**. ee. **62**.

—— Light from Asia. pp. xii. 236. *Heath, Cranton & Ouseley: London*, [1914.] 8°. **04420**. k. **46**.

—— The New Jerusalem: its measures and metaphors, as explained in the temple of Ezekiel. pp. 89. *S. W. Partridge & Co.: London*, [1906.] 8°. **03187**. df. **44**

—— Noah's Ark. [In verse.] pp. xiv. *H. R. Allenson, London*, [1917.] *obl.* 16°. **011652**. de. **22**

BARCLAY (HARRIET MARIA)

—— Retold. A book for Christian workers and lovers of Bible stories. pp. 152. *S. W. Partridge & Co.: London,* [1900.] 8°. **03128.** f. **20.**

—— Seekers after Rest; or, the Children of Israel from the Exodus to Solomon. pp. xii. 291. *Seeley & Co.: London,* 1876. 8°. **4516.** aa. **1.**

—— Sunday Occupations for the Children. pp. 128. *J. Nisbet & Co.: London,* 1884. 8°. **4355.** df. **6.**

—— What Might Have Been. [A life of Christ.] pp. 143. *Marshall Bros.: London, Edinburgh,* [1926.] 8°. **04808.** de. **40.**

BARCLAY (HARTLEY WADE)

—— ¿Cómo Progresa el Comunismo en Méjico? [With plates.] pp. 63. *Caracas,* 1939. 8°. **8288.** h. **21.**

—— Ford Production Methods. [With illustrations.] pp. ix. 219. *Harper & Bros.: New York & London,* 1936. 4°. **8764.** cc. **4.**

BARCLAY (HELEN MARY DAVIDSON) and **BARCLAY** (WILLIAM DUNCAN)

—— Thoughtful Reading. pp. 95. *Robert Gibson & Sons. Glasgow,* [1952.] 8°. **012987.** bb. **22.**

—— Answer Book. pp. 54. *Robert Gibson & Sons: Glasgow,* [1952.] 8°. **012987.** bb. **22a.**

BARCLAY (HERBERT CLIFFORD) Lectures on Elementary Anatomy and Physiology . . . Second edition. pp. viii. 281. *Baillière & Co: London; [printed in Japan],* 1915. 8°. **7422.** d. **6.**

—— Elementary Anatomy and Physiology for Nurses . . . Third edition [of "Lectures on Elementary Anatomy and Physiology"]. pp. x. 411. *Baillière & Co.: London,* 1924. 8°. **7419.** f. **27.**

—— Baillière's Nurses' Complete Medical Dictionary . . . Third edition [of "The Nurses' Complete Medical Dictionary" edited by Constance M. Douthwaite]. pp. vii. 248. *Baillière & Co.: London,* 1926. 16°. **07306.** de. **26.**

—— Baillière's Nurses' Complete Medical Dictionary. Edited by C. F. Marshall . . . Fourth edition [of the work previously edited by H. C. Barclay]. pp. viii. 200. *Baillière & Co.: London,* 1932. 16°. **07306.** df. **56.**

The fifth and sixth editions are entered under HITCH *(Margaret E.)*

BARCLAY (*Mrs.* HUBERT) *See* BARCLAY (Edith N.)

BARCLAY (HUBERT FREDERICK) *See* BARCLAY (Charles W.) A History of the Barclay Family. Compiled by . . . C. W. Barclay, *etc.* (pt. 2. The Barclays in Scotland from 1067 to 1660. Compiled by H. F. Barclay.—pt. 3. The Barclays in Scotland and England from 1610 to 1933. Compiled by H. F. Barclay and A. Wilson-Fox.) 1924, *etc.* 4°. **09915.** k. **4.**

BARCLAY (HUGH) *See* also NESTOR, *pseud.* [i.e. H. Barclay.]

—— *See* MACCORRY (John S.) Two Letters addressed to Hugh Barclay . . . being a reply to "A Plea for Christian Union, by an Elder of the Church of Scotland" [i.e. H. Barclay]. 1853. 12°. **4175.** a. **56.**

—— *See* MACGLASHAN (John) *Solicitor.* Practical Notes on the Jurisdiction and Forms of Process . . . of the Sheriff Courts of Scotland . . . Third edition revised . . . by H. Barclay. 1854. 8°. **6573.** dd. **12.**

—— —— 1868. 8°. **6573.** dd. **14.**

BARCLAY (HUGH)

—— *See* MACLAURIN (John) *Writer to the Signet,* and BARCLAY (H.) The Sheriff's Small Debt Act for Scotland . . . With digest thereof and practical notes, *etc.* 1842. 8°. **6573.** d. **29.** (**1.**)

—— *See* MURDOCH (James) *Member of the Faculty of Procurators in Glasgow.* Manual of Bankrupt Law . . . Revised by H. Barclay. 1856. 8°. **6573.** cc. **16.**

—— *See* SOUTAR (Thomas) Styles of Writs in the Sheriff and Commissary Courts in Scotland . . . Revised by H. Barclay. 1859. 8°. **6553.** f. **16.**

—— The Act of Sederunt, relative to the form of process in civil causes before the Sheriff Courts of Scotland, 12th November, 1825. With the relative acts of sederunt, and decided cases. To which are added, extracts from act 9th Geo. IV. cap. 29, and 1st William IV. cap. 37 & 69. pp. 84. 10. *Thomas Clark: Edinburgh,* 1830. 12°. **1384.** c. **4.**

—— A Basket of First-Fruits. Poems in verse. pp. 63. *The Author: Edinburgh,* 1868. 12°. **11648.** aa. **65.**

—— Curiosities of the Game Laws: contributed to the "Journal of Jurisprudence." Reprinted with additions. pp. 50. *T. Murray & Son: Glasgow,* 1864. 8°. **6583.** aaa. **15.**

—— A Digest of the Law of Scotland with special reference to the office and duties of a justice of the peace. 2 vol. pp. viii. 978. *T. & T. Clark: Edinburgh,* 1852, 53. 8°. **1384.** e. **3.**

—— Second edition . . . enlarged. pp. 984. *T. & T. Clark: Edinburgh,* 1855. 8°. **6583.** b. **29.**

—— Third edition, revised and enlarged. pp. 1020. *T. & T. Clark: Edinburgh,* 1865. 8°. **6583.** f. **10.**

—— Fourth edition, revised and enlarged. pp. 884. *T. & T. Clark: Edinburgh,* 1880. 8°. **6553.** f. **7.**

—— The Justice's Digest of the Law of Scotland . . . Revised and in great part rewritten by J. Chisholm. pp. 707. *T. & T. Clark: Edinburgh,* 1894. 8°. **6583.** cc. **9.**

—— Heathen Mythology corroborative or illustrative of Holy Scripture. pp. 104. *Morison Bros.: Glasgow,* 1884. 8°. **4506.** bb. **22.**

—— Hints to Legal Students; being the substance of an address delivered . . . at the opening of the Perth Juridical Society, *etc.* pp. 26. *Oliver & Boyd: Edinburgh,* 1829. 8°. **6025.** c. **57.** (**1.**)

—— Second edition, revised. pp. 26. *James Stillie: Edinburgh,* 1853. 8°. **6005.** c. **4.**

—— Judicial Procedure in Presbyterial Church Courts. pp. 16. *W. Blackwood & Sons: Edinburgh & London,* 1876. 8°. **4175.** df. **1.** (**5.**)

—— [Another copy.] **5155.** f. **1.** (**2.**)

—— Juvenile Delinquency, its causes and cure. By a County Magistrate [i.e. H. Barclay]. 1848. 8°. *See* DELINQUENCY. **6055.** d. **32**

—— Law of Highways. The General Turnpike Act, the General Statute Labour Act for Scotland, and the whole other acts relative to highways; with practical notes and digest of decided cases in England and Scotland on questions of roads, *etc.* pp. 233. *T. & T. Clark: Edinburgh,* 1847. 8°. **6573.** d. **23.**

—— Fourth edition. pp. viii. 350. *T. & T. Clark: Edinburgh,* 1863 [1862]. 8°. **6573.** cc. **18.**

BARCLAY (Hugh)

—— The Local Courts of England and Scotland. A paper, *etc.* pp. 57. *T. & T. Clark: Edinburgh,* 1860. 8°. **6573.** b. **10.**

—— Memoir of Mr. George Baillie . . . By a Member of the Faculty of Procurators [i.e. H. Barclay. Followed by "Reminiscences in connection with the Legal Profession in Glasgow; by a Member of the Faculty of Procurators," i.e. John Buchanan]. 2 pt. 1873. 8°. *See* Baillie (G.) *Founder of the Baillie Institution, Glasgow.* **10854.** cc. **3.**

—— The New Sheriff Court Act; 15th August 1853. With practical notes. pp. 34. *T. & T. Clark: Edinburgh,* 1853. 8°. **6573.** d. **29. (6.)**

—— Notes on the Psalm Book, especially on the Scotch metrical version. pp. 51. *W. Blackwood & Sons: Edinburgh & London,* 1877. 8°. **3127.** i. **3. (8.)**

—— Notices of Decided Points in Competitions in Sequestrations. pp. vi. 66. *T. & T. Clark: Edinburgh,* 1848. 12°. **6573.** aa. **21.**

—— On the Administration of the Criminal Law in Scotland. An address, *etc.* pp. 32. *T. Murray & Son: Glasgow,* 1862. 16°. **6573.** a. **22.**

—— Public-House Statutes. "The Home Drummond Act," 9 Geo. iv. c. 58, 1828; "the Forbes Mackenzie Act," 16 & 17 Vict. c. 67, 1853; the Public-Houses Acts Amendment—Scotland—Act, 25 & 26 Vict. c. 35, 1862. With notes, decided cases, and extracts from Commissioners' Report. pp. 87. *T. & T. Clark: Edinburgh,* 1862. 8°. **6573.** c. **11.**

—— The Sinaitic Inscriptions: a brief inquiry into the evidences of their Hebrew origin. Reprinted from "The Original Secession Magazine." pp. 85. *T. Murray & Son: Glasgow,* 1866. 8°. **7705.** a. **5.**

—— A Sketch of the History of Schools in Scotland. pp. 23. *J. Tweed: Glasgow,* 1880. 8°. **8309.** bb. **54. (2.)**

—— Thoughts on Sabbath Schools, *etc.* pp. vi. 121. *Paton & Ritchie: Edinburgh,* 1855. 12°. **8307.** c. **27.**

—— Sheriff Barclay: narrative of his public life. [Reprinted from the Perthshire Advertiser.] pp. 64. *J. Menzies & Co.: Edinburgh,* 1884. 12°. **10601.** aa. **8. (2.)**

BARCLAY (Hugh Donald) Orpheus and Eurydice, Endymion, and other poems . . . With illustrations by Edgar Barclay. pp. 103. *Hardwicke & Bogue: London,* 1877. 8°. **11653.** aa. **1.**

BARCLAY (Irene Turberville)

—— Prelude to Planning. A brief examination of the Barlow, Scott and Uthwatt Reports, *etc.* pp. 11. *Peace News: [London,]* 1944. 8°. **8288.** e. **62.**

BARCLAY (Irene Turberville) and **PERRY** (Evelyn E.)

—— Report on and Survey of Housing Conditions in the Victoria Ward, Westminster. pp. 15. [1927.] 8°. *See* London.—iii. *Westminster Survey Group.* **08282.** b. **101.**

BARCLAY (Isaac) Some Friendly and Seasonable Advice to Mr. Admiral Byng. [On his approaching trial by court-martial.] [*London,* 1756.] *s. sh.* fol. **515.** l. **6. (31.)**

—— [Another copy.] **C.113.hh.3.(33.)**

BARCLAY (Isabella) The Way the World Went Then . . . With illustrations. [The story of evolution for children. Edited by Helen Blackburn and Edith Palliser.] pp. xiv. 153. *E. Stanford: London,* 1898. 8°. **7005.** b. **5.**

BARCLAY (J. H.) *See* Barclay (Edward) A few Rough Sketches in Rhyme, *etc.* [Edited by J. H. Barclay.] 1872. 8°. **11652.** b. **29.**

BARCLAY (J. M. G.)

—— *See* Dickson (William K.) and Barclay (J. M. G.) List of Fifteenth Century Books in the Library of the Faculty of Advocates. 1912, *etc.* 4°. [*Publications of the Edinburgh Bibliographical Society.* vol. 9.] **N.L.25.c.**

BARCLAY (J. T.)

—— The Use of PVC in the Manufacture of Non-Inflammable Conveyor Belts, *etc.* pp. 7. *London,* 1952. fol. B.S. **82/13.**
Reproduced from typewriting.

BARCLAY (James) *Curate of Edmonton.*

—— A Complete and Universal English Dictionary on a New Plan: including not only . . . a full explanation of difficult words and technical terms in all faculties and professions . . . but . . . a pronouncing dictionary . . . To which are prefixed, A Free Enquiry into the Origin and Antiquity of Letters (by the Abbot Anselm) . . . By . . . James Barclay . . . and others. *Richardson & Urquhart, etc.: London,* [1774?] 8°. **012987.** e. **8.**
Cropped.

—— A Complete and Universal English Dictionary: including not only . . . a full explanation of difficult words and technical terms in all faculties and professions . . . but also . . . a pronouncing dictionary . . . a free inquiry into the origin and antiquity of letters (by the Abbot Anselm) . . . A new edition corrected, *etc.* *J. F. & C. Rivington, etc.: London,* 1792. 8°. **626.** f. **28.**

—— Universal English Dictionary, including a complete modern gazetteer and atlas, with a full explanation of difficult words & technical terms in all trades, professions, arts, & sciences. *Davies & Booth: Leeds,* [1800?] 4°. **012987.ff.10.**
The titlepage is engraved.

—— The Bungay Edition of Barclay's Dictionary greatly improved & superbly embellished. pp. xxxiii. 927. *T. Kinnersley: [London,]* 1813. 4°. **12982.** f. **5.**
The titlepage is engraved.

—— [Another edition.] A Complete and Universal English Dictionary . . . Revised, compared with other dictionaries, & improved by the addition of many hundred articles. By William Shorton. pp. 964. *Nuttall & Co.: Liverpool,* [1813?] 4°. **626.** l. **1.**

—— A Complete and Universal English Dictionary: including . . . an epitome of the history of England . . . a description of the various states . . . of the known world: a statement of the sects and divisions of the Christian church . . . A new and improved edition, *etc.* [With plates, including maps.] pp. xxiv. 1016. *Thomas Kelly: London,* 1819. 4°. **012986.** dd. **21.**

—— Barclay's English Dictionary. With which is incorporated a complete modern gazetteer, a beautiful atlas of maps and also a pronouncing dictionary. (Superior edition.) pp. xi. 1209. *A. Cummings: Leeds,* [1820?] 4°. **12983.** p. **10.**
With an engraved titlepage. Imperfect; wanting the letterpress titlepage and pp. i–iii.

—— [Another edition.] pp. 972. *Henry Fisher: London,* 1822. 4°. **626.** l. **2.**
With an additional titlepage, engraved.

BARCLAY (JAMES) *Curate of Edmonton.*

—— [Another edition.] Barclay's New Universal English Dictionary . . . Now still further improved by continuations of the history of all states and people to the present time, with the most recent discoveries, geographical and nautical; the population of British towns, according to the last census; and the changes in the representation caused by the Reform Bill. By Thomas Noble. pp. 960. *H. Fisher & Co.: London*, 1835. 4°. **626**. l. **3**.
With an additional titlepage, engraved.

—— A new edition enlarged . . . and adapted to the present state of science by B. B. Woodward. pp. viii. 984. *George Virtue: London*, [1851.] 4°. **12982**. h. **10**.
With an additional titlepage, engraved.

—— What is meant by coming unto Christ, and the reasons of men's refusing to come, briefly considered in a sermon preached in the Parish Church of St. Mary, Whitechapel . . . To which is prefixed . . . an address to the inhabitants of the said parish, *etc.* pp. 43. *J. Fuller: London*, 1763. 8°. **4476**. ee. **11**. (**1**.)

BARCLAY (JAMES) *Master at Eastbank Academy, Glasgow.*

—— The Saga Reader. Book 1 [*etc.*] . . . Compiled by the authors of "A Study of Standard English" [i.e. J. Barclay, D. H. Knox and G. B. Ballantyne]. [1947– .] 8°. *See* SAGA READER. W.P. **2610**.

—— A Study of Standard English. By James Barclay . . . David H. Knox . . . George B. Ballantyne. pp. 404. *R. Gibson & Sons: Glasgow*, 1938. 8°. **12986**. a. **27**.

BARCLAY (JAMES) *Master at Eastbank Academy, Glasgow*, and **KNOX** (DAVID HEPBURN)

—— Approach to Standard English. pp. 352. *R. Gibson & Sons: Glasgow*, 1942. 8°. **12986**. h. **24**.

—— English for Practical People. pp. 263. *London*, 1946. 8°. [*Harrap's Practical English Series.*] W.P. **1600**/**1**.

—— You and your Health, *etc.* pp. 160. *Craig & Wilson: Glasgow*, 1950. 8°. **7392**. a. **41**.

BARCLAY (JAMES) *of Malmesbury.* The Incarnation of the Son of God. A sermon, *etc.* pp. iv. 21. *J. G. Goodwyn: Tetbury*, [1808.] 8°. **4473**. bb. **13**. (**6**.)

BARCLAY (JAMES) *pseud.* [i.e. WILLIAM JOHN CRABB.]

—— Why No Nurses? The nursing recruitment problem, its history, terms and solution, *etc.* pp. 176. *Faber & Faber: London*, 1946. 8°. **7689**. a. **56**.

BARCLAY (JAMES) *Rector of the Grammar School at Dalkeith.* *See* HEATH (James) *of Albury, Surrey.* Descendants of James Barclay, of Dalkeith. [1904.] 8°. **9903**. bb. **29**. (**1**.)

—— The Greek Rudiments; in which all the grammatical difficulties of that language, are adapted to the capacities of children; after the plan of Mr. Ruddiman's Latin Rudiments. pp. xii. 243. *T. & W. Ruddimans: Edinburgh*, 1754. 8°. **624**. d. **7**.

—— The Rudiments of the Latin Tongue; in which the difficulties of all the parts of our Latin grammars are made plain to the capacities of children. pp. xii. 176. *The Author: Edinburgh*, 1758. 8°. **625**. d. **24**.

—— A Treatise on Education: or, an easy method of acquiring language . . . With reflections on taste, poetry, natural history, &c. pp. vii. 240. *J. Cochran & Co.: Edinburgh*, 1743. 12°. **1030**. f. **6**.

—— [Another edition.] pp. vii. 240. *P. Vaillant: London*, 1749. 12°. **8308**. aaa. **3**.

BARCLAY (JAMES J.) An Address delivered at the Laying of the Corner Stone of the House of Refuge for Colored Juvenile Delinquents, *etc.* pp. 15. *T. K. & P. G. Collins: Philadelphia*, 1848. 8°. **6055**. e. **9**.

—— An Address delivered at the Organization of the Normal School, *etc.* pp. 23. *Philadelphia*, 1848. 8°. **8305**. ee. **28**. (**12**.)

—— An Address delivered at the Zane Street Public School House, *etc.* pp. 24. *Philadelphia*, 1841. 8°. **8365**. cc. **13**.

BARCLAY (JAMES M.) A Lesson in Love. A comedy, in two acts, *etc.* pp. 34. *London*, [1836?] 12°. [*Duncombe's Edition of the British Theatre.* vol. 20.] **2304**. a. **10**.

—— "My Friend Thompson!" A farce, in one act, *etc.* pp. 30. *London*, [1836.] 12°. [*Cumberland's Minor Theatre.* vol. 12.] **643**. a. **6**.

—— [Another edition.] [With notes in German.] pp. 45. *Hallberger's Library: Stuttgart*, 1842. 16°. **11771**. a. **6**. [British and American Theatre. no. 6.]

BARCLAY (JAMES PRINGLE) Cottage Rates. pp. 15. *J. Loder: Woodbridge*, [1836.] 16°. **8276**. a. **2**.

BARCLAY (JAMES T.) The City of the Great King; or, Jerusalem as it was, as it is, and as it is to be. [With plates, including a portrait.] pp. xxii. 627. *J. Challen & Sons: Philadelphia*, [1857.] 8°. **10076**. g. **5**.

BARCLAY (JAMES W.) A New Theory of Organic Evolution. pp. vi. 174. *W. Blackwood & Sons: Edinburgh & London*, 1903. 8°. **7006**. df. **28**.

BARCLAY (JOHN) *B.Sc.* *See* SOUTHALL (William) *F.L.S.* Southall's Organic Materia Medica . . . Fifth . . . edition by J. Barclay. 1896. 8°. **7510**. de. **6**.

—— —— 1900. 8°. **07509**. h. **15**.

—— —— 1909. 8°. **07509**. h. **35**.

BARCLAY (JOHN) *Iron-Broker.*

—— Statistics of the Scotch Iron Trade. no. 2. pp. 24. *James Hedderwick & Son: Glasgow*, 1851. 12°. **8029**. dd. **14**. (**8**.)
Printed for private circulation.

BARCLAY (JOHN) *M.D., of Edinburgh.* *See* WATERHOUSE (George R.) The Natural History of Marsupialia . . . With portrait and memoir of Barclay. 1843. 16°. [JARDINE (*Sir William*) *Bart.* *The Naturalists' Library.* vol. 8.] **1150**. a. **4**.

—— A Description of the Arteries of the Human Body . . . Second edition, corrected and improved. pp. xxiv. xxxix. 287. *Bell & Bradfute: Edinburgh*, 1820. 12°. **7420**. a. **33**. (**2**.)

—— An Inquiry into the Opinions, ancient and modern, concerning life and organization. pp. xv. 542. *Bell & Bradfute: Edinburgh*, 1822. 8°. **784**. k. **19**.

—— Introductory Lectures to a Course of Anatomy . . . With a memoir of the life of the author by George Ballingal. pp. xix. 169. *Maclachlan & Stewart: Edinburgh*, 1827. 8°. **781**. g. **12**.

—— The Muscular Motions of the Human Body. pp. xxi. 590. *W. Laing & A. Constable & Co.: Edinburgh*, 1808. 8°. **784**. k. **18**.

BARCLAY (John) *M.D., of Edinburgh.*

—— A New Anatomical Nomenclature, relating to the terms which are expressive of position and aspect in the animal system. pp. viii. 182. pl. v. *Ross & Blackwood: Edinburgh,* 1803. 8°. **776.** i. **28.**
The date has been altered in MS. *to* 1804.

—— A Series of Engravings representing the Bones of the Human Skeleton with the skeletons of some of the lower animals, by Edward Mitchell. With explanatory references by J. Barclay. 2 pt. pl. XXXII. *E. Mitchell: Edinburgh,* 1819, 20. fol. **775.** n. **5.** (**1, 2.**)

BARCLAY (John) *M.D., of Leicester.* Ale, Wine, Spirits, and Tobacco. A lecture . . . Second edition. pp. 71. *Bosworth & Harrison: London,* 1861. 8°. **8435.** c. **51.**

BARCLAY (John) *Minister at Cruden.* *See* Johnston (Arthur) *M.D.* The Epigrams of Dr. Arthur Iohnstoun, *etc.* (Englished thus, by I. B. [i.e. J. Barclay.]) 1685. 8°. [*Philopoliteius, pseud. Memorialls for the Government of the Royall-Burghs in Scotland, etc.*] **600.** b. **35.**

—— —— 1833. 12°. **797.** b. **24.**

—— A Description of the Roman Catholic Church; wherein the pretensions of it's head . . . the designs and practises of that church, are represented in a vision. [In verse.] pp. 59. [*John Forbes: Aberdeen,*] 1689. 4°. C. **53.** c. **25.**

—— [Another edition.] pp. 60. *T. Lumsden & J. Robertson: Edinburgh,* 1741. 8°. **11626.** e. **5.**

BARCLAY (John) *Novelist.* The Gilchrist Case. pp. 220. *London,* 1930. 8°. [*Methuen Clue Stories.*] **12626.** p. **1/11.**

—— The Gilchrist Case. pp. 160. *Mellifont Press: London & Dublin; Dublin* printed, [1935.] 8°. **012604.** a. **14.**

—— Lamp of Heaven. pp. 283. *Robert Hale: London,* [1939.] 8°. NN. **29958.**

—— The Unknown. pp. ix. 242. *London Book Co.: London,* [1928.] 8°. [*Novel Library.*] **12607.a.1/6.**

BARCLAY (John) *of Calcots.* A Sequel to the Diversions of Purley: containing an essay on English verbs, with remarks on Mr Tooke's work, and on some terms employed to denote soul or spirit. pp. 164. *Smith, Elder & Co.: London,* 1826. 8°. **623.** h. **22.**

BARCLAY (John) *of Glasgow.* An Essay on Baptism: proving that baptism with water is not an ordinance of Christ. pp. 84. *W. Lang: Glasgow,* 1815. 8°. **4324.** k. **5.** (**1.**)

BARCLAY (John) *of Perth Amboy.*

—— *See* Rubincam (Milton) [Pamphlets on American genealogy, *etc.*] (John Barclay of Perth Amboy.) 1938, *etc.* 8°., *etc.* **9902.** g. **34.**

BARCLAY (John) *of the Society of Friends.* *See* Jaffray (A.) Diary of Alexander Jaffray . . . To which are added particulars of his subsequent life . . . By J. Barclay. 1833. 8°. **1124.** f. **24.**

—— *See* Jaffray (Alexander) *Provost of Aberdeen.* Diary of Alexander Jaffray . . . To which are added particulars of his subsequent life . . . [Edited] by J. Barclay, *etc.* 1834. 8°. **10860.** aaa. **48.**

BARCLAY (John) *of the Society of Friends.*

—— *See* Penington (Isaac) *the Younger.* Some Deep Considerations on the State of Israel. [With an advertisement by J. Barclay.] 1837. 8°. **4377.** eee. **7.** (**1.**)

—— *See* Penn (William) *Founder of Pennsylvania.* A Summons or Call to Christendom, *etc.* [With a preface by J. Barclay.] 1835. 12°. **4372.** b. **26.** (**9.**)

—— *See* Pike (Joseph) *of Cork.* Some Account of the Life of Joseph Pike . . . With preliminary observations by J. Barclay. 1838. 8°. [*Friends' Library.* vol. 6.] **4152.** gg. **4.**

—— *See* Smith (Edward) *Member of the Society of Friends.* The Life of William Dewsbury . . . With a prefatory address by J. Barclay. 1838. 8°. [*Friends' Library.* vol. 2.] **4152.** gg. **4.**

—— An Affectionate Address to such of the People called Friends as reside in London and its vicinity, *etc.* [By J. Barclay.] pp. 24. 1818. 12°. *See* Friends, *Society of.* **4139.** aa. **22.** (**3.**)

—— Select Anecdotes and Instructive Incidents, taken from publications of several members of the Society of Friends, *etc.* pp. 261. *William Phillips: London,* 1822. 12°. **855.** h. **28.**

—— A Select Series, biographical, narrative, epistolary, and miscellaneous: chiefly the productions of early members of the Society of Friends . . . Edited by J. Barclay. [Continued by A. R. Barclay.] 8 vol. *Darton & Harvey: London,* 1835–45. 12°. **1372.** b. **3.**

—— A Selection from the Letters and Papers of the late J. Barclay. [Edited by A. R. Barclay.] pp. xviii. 309. *Harvey & Darton: London,* 1841. 8°. **4152.** dd. **5.**

—— [Another edition.] 1842. 8°. *See* Evans (William) and (T.) *Publishers, of Philadelphia.* The Friends' Library, *etc.* vol. 6. 1837, *etc.* 8°. **4152.** gg. **4.**

BARCLAY (John) *Pastor of the Berean Assembly at Edinburgh.* *See* Bible.—*Psalms.* [*English.—Miscellaneous Metrical Versions.*] The Psalms paraphrased . . . By J. Barclay. 1776. 12°. **1018.** k. **1.**

—— The Experience and Example of the Lord Jesus Christ: illustrated and improved for the consolation of the Church . . . [Translations, in verse, of select passages from the Bible.] By J. Barclay. pp. xlviii. 226. xiv. 1783. 12°. *See* Bible.—*Selections.* [*English.*] **3130.** l. **2.**

—— A New Work . . . Containing I. The Psalms, paraphrased . . . II. A select collection of spiritual songs. III. Essays on various subjects, *etc.* [With a portrait.] 3 vol. *The Author: Edinburgh,* 1776. 12°. **3752.** aaa. **10.**

—— The Works of John Barclay. [The Essays. Edited by James Thomson and David McMillan, with a memoir of the author.] pp. viii. 275. *Robert Jackson: Glasgow,* 1852. 12°. **3755.** a. **3.**

—— A General Preface to the Book of Psalms. pp. 59. *J. Parry: Dublin,* 1819. 12°. **3090.** b. **30.**

—— Hymns. *See* Evangelical Psalms. Evangelical Psalms, Hymns and Spiritual Songs; selected from various authors, *etc.* 1792. 12°. **3455.** b. **4.**

—— Without Faith, Without God; or, an Appeal to God concerning His own existence. With a preface by the Rev. David Thom. pp. xxiii. 128. *Simpkin & Marshall: London,* 1836. 12°. **1114.** b. **16.**

BARCLAY (JOHN) *Poet, Author of the "Argenis."* *See* also EUPHORMIO, *Lusininus, pseud.* [i.e. J. Barclay.]

—— *See* also POLIENUS, *Rhodiensis, pseud.* [i.e. J. Barclay.]

—— *See* BARCLAY (William) *Professor of Civil Law at Angers.* De potestate Papæ, *etc.* [Edited by J. Barclay.] 1609. 8°. **1020**. c. 9.

—— —— 1709. 8°. **227**. h. 29.

—— *See* BARCLAY (William) *Professor of Civil Law at Angers.* Gulielmi Barclaii J.C. of the Authoritie of the Pope, *etc.* [Edited by J. Barclay.] 1611. 4°. **3932**. d. **15**.

—— *See* BENSLY (Edward) Robert Burton, John Barclay, *etc.* 1909. 8°. [*Cambridge History of English Literature.* vol. 4.] **11870.g.1.**

—— *See* TH. (R.) In obitum Io. Barclaii elegia. [1621.] 4°. **1070**. l. **13**. (5.)

—— Ioannis Barclaii Argenis. pp. 1208. *N. Buon: Parisiis,* 1621. 8°. **12403**. de. **14**.

—— [Another copy.] **12403**. cc. **5**.
In this copy the titlepage of the second edition has been substituted for that of the first. An engraving of Louis XIII. and one of the author have also been inserted, and, at the end, a supplementary table of "Errata primæ editionis."

—— Joannis Barclaii Argenis. Editio repetita, & indice locupletior. pp. 480. *Impensis Eberhardi Zetzneri: Augustæ Trebocorum,* 1622. 8°. **1481**. ddd. **23**.

—— Editio secunda. [With a portrait of the author.] pp. xii. 1082. vi. *N. Buon: Parisiis,* 1622. 8°. **12410**. bb. **13**.
The titlepage is engraved.

—— Editio novissima. Cum clave, *etc.* pp. 791. *Ex officina Elzeviriana: Lugd. Bat.,* 1627. 12°. **1074**. a. **3**.
The titlepage is engraved.

—— [Another edition.] pp. 705. *Ex officina Elzeviriana: Lugd. Bat.,* 1630. 12°. **683**. a. **18**.

—— [Another edition.] pp. 690. *Ex officina Elzeviriana: Lugd. Bat.,* 1630. 12°. **1074**. a. **4**.

—— [Another copy.] **166**. c. **3**.

—— Editio novissima, prioribus . . . correctior. [Edited by Jacobus Marci.] pp. 840. *C. Schleichius: Francofurti,* 1634. 32°. **836**. a. **28**.

—— [Another edition.] Editio novissima. Cum clave, *etc.* (Discursus de autore scripti, & judicium de nominibus Argenidæis.) pp. 705. *Excudebat I. L. [John Lichfield], impensis Thomæ Huggins: Oxoniæ,* 1634. 12°. **12410**. a. **32**.

—— [Another edition.] pp. 852. *Apud I. Iansonium: Amstelodami,* 1642. 32°. **12410**. a. **26**.
The titlepage is engraved.

—— [Another edition.] pp. 569. *Apud L. Elzevirium: Amstelodami,* 1655. 12°. **1074**. a. **5**.
The titlepage is engraved.

—— [Another edition.] pp. 569. *Ex officina Elzeviriana: Amstelodami,* 1659. 12°. **1074**. a. **6**.
The titlepage is engraved.

—— [Another edition.] Nunc primum illustrata [by L. G. Bugnotius; with a life of the author]. pp. xxviii. 638. xv. *Ex officina F. Hackii: Lugd. Bat.,* 1659. 8°. G. **17763**.
The titlepage is engraved.

BARCLAY (JOHN) *Poet, Author of the "Argenis."*

—— Jo. Barclaii Argenis, nunc primum illustrata [by L. G. Bugnotius]. [With a portrait.] pp. 637. *Ex officina Hackiana: Lugd. Batav. & Roterod.,* 1664. 8°. **12431**. r. **31**.

—— [Another edition.] pp. xxviii. 638. xv. *Ex officina Hackiana: Lugd. Batav. & Roterod.,* 1664. 8°. **57**. m. **11**.

—— [Another edition.] pp. 569. *E. Weyerstraeten: Amstelodami,* 1664. 12°. **12411**. a. **4**.

—— [Another edition.] pp. 569. *Ex officina Elzeviriana: Amstelodami,* 1671. 12°. **12450**. a. **14**.
The titlepage is engraved.

—— Jo. Barclaii Argenis . . . Editio ultima correctior & emendatior. pp. 586. *Ex officina Joann. Hayes, impensis Joann. Creed: Cantabrigiæ,* 1673. 8°. **1483**. aa. **23**.
With an additional titlepage, engraved, dated 1674.

—— [Another copy.] Jo. Barclaii Argenis, *etc.* *Cantabrigiæ,* 1673. 8°. **1162**. a. **7**.
Wanting the engraved titlepage.

—— Barclay his Argenis: or, the Loves of Poliarchus and Argenis: faithfully translated out of Latine into English, by Kingsmill Long. pp. 404. *Printed by G. P. [G. Purslowe] for H. Seile: London,* 1625. fol. **12403**. g. **12**.

—— John Barclay his Argenis, translated . . . by Sir Robert Le Grys . . . and the verses by Thomas May . . . With a clauis annexed, *etc.* pp. 489. *Felix Kyngston for Richard Meighen & Henry Seile: London,* 1629. 4°. **839**. d. **40**.
An engraved portrait of the author, by Claude Mellan, has been inserted in this copy.

—— [Another copy.] MS. NOTE [by S. T. Coleridge]. C. **44**. d. **34**.
Southey's copy, with his autograph.

—— Barclay his Argenis. Or, the Loves of Polyarchus & Argenis. Faithfully translated . . . by Kingsmill Long Esquire. The second edition, beautified with pictures [including a portrait], *etc.* pp. 719. *Printed for Henry Seile: London,* 1636. 4°. **1489**. tt. **52**.
The titlepage is engraved.

—— [Another copy.] **838**. c. **1**.
Imperfect; wanting sig. A4 *containing lines to the author by Owen Felton (recto) and portrait of the author (verso).*

—— The Phoenix; or, the History of Polyarchus and Argenis. Translated from the Latin, by a Lady [i.e. Clara Reeve]. 4 vol. *John Bell: London,* 1772. 12°. **12410**. d. **8**.

—— L'Argenis, de Ian Barclay. Traduction nouuelle [by Pierre de Marcassus]. Enrichie de figures. pp. xvi. 1082. xv. *N. Buon: Paris,* 1623. 8°. **243**. k. **6**.
The titlepage is engraved, and is another state of that in the Latin edition of 1622. Several engravings from a smaller edition have been inserted in this copy.

—— L'Argenis de Iean Barclay. De la traduction nouuelle de M. G. [i.e. Pierre de Marcassus.] pp. 797. *C. Griset: Paris,* 1633. 8°. **12410**. aaa. **42**.
The titlepage is engraved. With the arms of Count d'Hoym impressed in gold on the covers.

—— L'Argénis de Barclay. Traduction nouvelle par Mr. l'Abbé Josse. 3 tom. *Chartres,* 1732. 12°. **12410**. aaa. **32**.

—— Johann Barcläyens Argenis Deutsch gemacht durch Martin Opitzen. Mit schönen Kupffer Figuren, *etc.* pp. 1047. *Inn Verlegung D. Müllers: Breslaw,* 1626. 8°. **1154.f.39.**
The titlepage is engraved.

—— [Another edition.] 2 vol. *I. Ianson: Amsterdam,* 1644. 12°. **1072**. c. **11, 12.**
The titlepage is engraved.

—— Johann Barklays Argenis . . . Mit beygefügten Erklärungen aus der Geschichte seiner Zeit, *etc.* 2 Bd. *Augsburg,* 1770. 8°. **1072**. b. **28.**
A different translation from the preceding.

—— Argenis . . . Übersetzt von Dr. Gustav Waltz. pp. xv. 684. *München,* 1891. 8°. **12410**. ee. **21.**

—— Barklájus János' Argenisse, mellyet . . . Fejér A. . . . Deák nyelvbűl Magyarra forditott, *etc.* 2 köt. *Egerben,* 1792. 8°. **1363**. g. **16.**

—— L'Argenide . . . tradotta da Francesco Pona. [With a life of the author.] pp. 749. *G. Salis, ad instantia di P. Frambotti: Venetia,* 1629. 4°. **87**. f. **18.**

—— L'Argenide . . . tradotta da C. A. Cocastello, *etc.* [Edited by Christofero Tomasini.] pp. 707. *P. M. Bertano: Venetia,* 1631. 8°. **12410**. aaa. **8.**

—— Jana Barklaiusza Argienida, ktorą W. Potocki . . . polskim wierszem z łacinskiego przetłumacył. pp. 841. *w Lipsku,* 1728. 8°. [*Bibliotheca polono-poetica.* tom. 1.] **11585**. b. **46.**

—— Argenida, ktorą . . . W. . . . Potocki . . . wierszem polskim przetłumaczył . . . roku 1743 de novo przedrukowana. 2 pt. *w Poznaniu,* [1743.] 4°. **12403**. e. **10.**

—— La Prodigiosa historia de los dos amantes Argènis y Poliarco, en prosa y verso . . . Del licenciado Don Gabriel de Corral. ff. 288. *Por Iuan Gonçalez, a costa de Alonso Perez: Madrid,* 1626. 4°. **12403**. e. **18.**

—— Histoire de Poliarque et d'Argenis. Par F. N. Coeffeteau. [An abridgment] . . . Auec le promenoir de la Reyne à Compiègne. pp. 188. *Samuel Thiboust & Iacques Villery: Paris,* 1628. 24°. **1482**. a. **29.**

—— Histoire de Poliarque et d'Argenis. Par F. N. Coeffeteau, Euesque de Marseille. [An abridgment.] Auec le promenoir de la Reyne à Compiegne. pp. 188. *I. Cailloüé: Rouen,* 1641. 12°. **12516**. aa. **27.**

—— *See* BARDINO (L.) L'Argenis di John Barclay e il romanzo greco. [1939.] 8°. W.P. **6240**/**3.**

—— *See* BOBEK (W.) "Argenida" Wacława Potockiego w stosunku do swego oryginału. 1929. 8°. **11854**. t. **43.**

—— *See* BOUCHER (Léon) *Professeur, etc.* De Joannis Barclaii Argenide, *etc.* 1874. 8°. **10854**. ee. **1.**

—— *See* BUGNOTIUS (L. G.) Archombrotus et Theopompus, sive Argenidis secunda & tertia pars, *etc.* [A sequel to the "Argenis" of J. Barclay.] 1669. 8°. **57**. m. **12.**

—— *See* COLLIGNON (A. C.) Notes sur l'Argenis de Jean Barclay. 1902. 8°. [*Mémoires de l'Académie de Stanislas.* sér. 5. tom. 19.] **Ac.383.**

—— *See* DUPOND (A.) L'Argénis de Barclai. Étude, *etc.* 1875. 8°. **11825**. ee. **10.**

—— *See* KETTELHOIT (P.) Formanalyse der Barclay-Opitzschen "Argenis," *etc.* 1934. 8°. **11856**. d. **14.**

—— *See* M., A. M. D. La Seconde partie de l'Argenis. [A sequel to the "Argenis" of J. Barclay, by A. M. de Mouchembert.] 1625. 8°. **1073**. b. **18.**

—— *See* MOUCHEMBERT (A. M. de) La Suite et continuation de l'Argenis, *etc.* 1626. 8°. **243**. k. **7.**

—— *See* SCHMID (C. F.) John Barclays Argenis. Eine literarhistorische Untersuchung. 1904, *etc.* 8°. **11852**. a. **31.**

—— *See* SEYMOUR (Henry) *Editor of "The Anarchist."* John Barclay's Argenis and Cypher Key, *etc.* [1931.] 8°. **11764**. s. **27**

—— *See* WEISE (Christian) *of Zittau.* Christian Weisens Neue Jugend-Lust . . . Von der Sicil. Argenis. [After J. Barclay's "Argenis."] 1684. 8°. **11745**. b. **59**

—— Icon animorum. *See* infra: Satyricon.

—— Ioannis Barclaii Paræenesis ad sectarios huius temporis de vera ecclesia, fide, ac religione, libri II. Editio tertia pp. 379. *Apud I. Kinckium: Coloniæ,* 1625. 12°. **1020**. b. **9**

—— Editio ultima. pp. 451. *Antverpiæ,* 1669. 12°. **3939**. aa. **24**

—— John Barclay his Defence of the most Holy Sacrament of the Eucharist, to the sectaries of the times. Book II Chap. II. [of the "Paræenesis ad sectarios"]. Englished by a Person of Quality. pp. 21. *Printed by Mary Thompson, sold by Matthew Turner & John Lane: London* 1688. 4°. **T. 1012.** (**5.**)

—— John Barclay his Vindication of the Intercession of Saints, the Veneration of Relicks and Miracles, against the sectaries of the times. Book II. chap. VII [of the "Paræenesis ad sectarios"]. Englished by a Person of Quality. pp. 20. *Printed by Mary Thompson, sold by Metthew Turner & John Lane: London,* 1688. 4°. **702**. h. **36.**

—— A' Katolika hittől elszakadott atyafiakhoz utasított oktató intés . . . Magyarra általtett Herczer Jób. pp. xvi. 341. *Miskólczon,* 1817. 8°. **3935**. bbb. **7.**

—— Ioannis Barclaii Pietas, siue publicae pro regibus ac principibus, et priuatae pro Gulielmo Barclaio parente vindiciæ, aduersus . . . Cardinalis Bellarmini Tractatum de potestate Summi Pontificis in rebus temporalibus. pp. 798. *P. Mettayer: Parisiis,* 1612. 4°. **C. 66**. c. **17.**

—— *See* EUDAEMON-JOANNES (A.) *Cydonius.* R. P. Andreæ Eudæmon-Joannis Epistola monitoria ad Ioannem Barclaium, Guillelmi filium, de libro ab eo pro patre suo contra . . . Robertum Bellarminum . . . scripto. 1613. 8°. **860**. b. **17.** (**4.**)

—— Ioannis Barclaii Poematum libri duo. pp. 109. *Impensis Ioannis Billij: Londini,* 1615. 4°. **1213**. l. **7.** (**4.**)

—— [Another issue.] *Edwardus Griffin: Londini,* 1615. 4°. **11409**. ee. **24.**

—— Editio postrema aucta. pp. 100. *G. Turner, impensis Gulielmi Webb: Oxonii,* 1636. 12°. **1213**. d. **14.**

—— [Another edition.] *See* JOHNSTON (Arthur) *M.D.* Delitiæ poetarum Scotorum, *etc.* 1637. 12°. **1213**. a. **7.**

—— Replique au sieur Coeffeteau, sur sa Responce à l'aduertissement du Roy aux princes & potentats de la chrestienté. [Attributed to J. Barclay.] pp. 120. 1610. 8°. *See* COEFFETEAU (N.) successively *Bishop of Dardania* and *of Marseilles.* **698**. b. **41.** (**1.**)

—— Euphormionis Lusinini, sive Ioannis Barclaii Satyricon, quadripartitum; nunc denuo recognitum, emendatum, & mirificè illustratum, adjecta clavi, sive obscurorum & quasi ænigmaticorum nominum, in hoc opere passim occurrentium, dilucida explicatione. pp. 488. *Ex officinâ J. Marci: Leydæ,* 1623. 12°. **836**. a. **3.**
Part 3 is entitled "Apologia pro se," part 4 "Icon animorum."

—— [Another edition.] pp. 694. *Apud I. Iansonium: Amstelodami,* 1627. 24°. **12403.** ccc. **13.**
The titlepage is engraved.

—— [Another edition.] pp. 556. *I. de La Mare: Rothomagi,* 1628. 8°. **12410.** aaa. **5.**

—— [Another edition.] 3 pt. *Ex officinâ I. Marci: Lugduni Batavorum,* 1628. 12°. **012314.** de. **8.**

—— [Another edition.] Accessit Conspiratio Anglicana. pp. 580. *Apud G. I. Cæsium: Amsterodami,* 1629. 12°. **683.** a. **17.**
The titlepage is engraved.

—— [Another edition.] pp. 782. *Excudebat I. L.* [*Iohn Lichfield*], *impensis Henrici Cripps: Oxoniæ,* 1634. 12°. **836.** a. **4.**

—— Euphormionis Lusinini sive Ioannis Barclaii Satyricon . . . Accessit Conspiratio anglicana. pp. 582. *Apud Guiljelm. Blaeuw: Amsterodami,* 1634. 16°. **1483.** b. **14.**
The titlepage is engraved.

—— [Another edition.] pp. 717. *Apud Elzevirios: Lugd. Batavorum,* 1637. 12°. **166.** c. **4.**
The titlepage is engraved.

—— [Another edition.] pp. 573. *Ex officina Elzeviriana: Amstelodami,* 1658. 12°. **836.** a. **5.**

—— [Another edition.] pp. 573. *E. Weyerstraeten: Amstelodami,* 1664. 12°. **12410.** a. **11.**
The titlepage is engraved.

—— [Another edition.] pp. 720. *Ex officina Hackiana: Lugd. Batavorum,* 1674. 8°. **57.** m. **10.**
With an additional titlepage, engraved.

—— [Another edition.] pp. 628. [*Vienna,*] 1772. 8°. **1074.** l. **33.**

—— Joannis Barclaii Icon animorum. pp. 356. *Ex officina Nortoniana, apud I. Billium: Londini,* 1614. 8°. **C. 82.** a. **9.**

—— Editio . . . auctior. pp. 182. *Sumpt. C. Hermsdorffii, literis Wustianis: Francofurti,* 1675. 12°. **8410.** a. **36.**

—— [Another edition.] Augusti Buchneri notis . . . illustrata. [Edited by J. F. Heckel.] pp. 446. *M. G. Hübneri sumtibus excud. C. Bergen: Dresdæ,* 1680. 8°. **8403.** b. **10.**

—— The Mirrour of Mindes, or, Barclay's Icon animorum, Englished by T. M. (T. May). 2 pt. *John Norton for Thomas Walkley: London,* 1631. 12°. **8403.** aa. **31.**

—— [Another copy.] **8403.** aa. **40.**

—— [Another edition.] pp. 380. *Printed by I. B.* [*John Beale*] *for Thomas Walkley: London,* 1633. 12°. **8403.** aa. **9.**

—— Euphormio's Satyricon. "Euphormionis satyricon" . . . Translated . . . for the first time, from the 1605 edition by Paul Turner . . . Ten wood engravings by Derrick Harris. pp. 158. *Golden Cockerel Press: London,* 1954. 8°. **C. 103.** g. **30.**

—— Les Avantures d'Euphormion, histoire satyrique. [An adaptation of the "Euphormionis Satyricon" of J. Barclay by Monsieur S. S. S. J. P. A. V. L. E. R. E., i.e. J. B. Drouet de Maupertuis.] 3 tom. *Amsterdam,* 1712, 13. 12°. **12510.** de. **27.**

—— Ioh. Barclai Spiegel menschlicher Gemüths Neigungen. Auss dem Latinischen ins Hoch-Teutsche versetzt [by H. J. Wynckelmann]. pp. 308. *In Verlegung E. Bergers: Bremen,* 1660. 12°. **8405.** a. **63.**
The titlepage is engraved.

—— Johann Barklai Seelengemählde. Nebst des Herrn von Saint Evremont Beobachtungen über die verschiedenen Charaktere der Römer in den verschiedenen Zeitaltern ihres Standes. pp. 16. 342. *Pest,* 1784. 8°. **8404.** ccc. **37.**

—— *See* COLLIGNON (A. C.) Le Portrait des Esprits—Icon animorum—de Jean Barclay. 1906. 8°. [*Mémoires de l'Académie de Stanislas.* sér. 6. tom. 3.] **Ac.383.**

—— *See* DUKAS (J.) Étude bibliographique et littéraire sur le Satyricon de J. Barclay. 1880. 8°. **820.** f. **40.** **(6.)**

—— *See* GUTHREUS (J.) De Britanniae magnae . . . genio . . . ad Iconem animorum J. Barclaj. [1682.] 4°. **806.** b. **28.**

—— *See* LE CERF (P. T.) De Angliæ regni genio, dotibus ac moribus, separatim, ad J. Barclaj Icon animor. . . . disseret . . . P. T. Le Cerf. [1682.] 4°. **1325.** e. **2.**

—— *See* ROLFINCK (J. E.) De Galliarum genio . . . ad Iconem animorum J. Barclaij. [1680?] 4°. **1059.** e. **30.**

—— Polonia defensa contra Joan. Barclaium [in his "Icon animorum," ch. VIII.], ubi, occasione ista de regno genteque Polona multa narrantur, hactenus litteris non tradita [by Ł. Opaliński]. pp. 138. *Sumptibus G. Försteri: Dantisci,* 1648. 4°. **10290.** f. **25.**

—— [Another copy.] **Cup.401.g.19.**

—— [Another edition.] 1747. *See* OSTROWSKI-DANEYKOWICZ (J.) *pseud.* Swada Polska y Łacińska, *etc.* tom. 2. 1745, *etc.* fol. **838.** m. **34.**

—— Series Patefacti nuper Parricidi, in ter Maximum Regem Regnúmque Britanniæ cogitati & instructi. pp. 17. *R. B.* [*Robert Barker*]: *Londini,* 1605. 4°. Mic. A. **588.** (**8.**)
MICROFILM *of the copy in the library of Emmanuel College, Cambridge. Made by University Microfilms,* 1954.

—— Ioan. Barclaii Sylvæ. [A collection of poems.] pp. 46. *Excudebat R. B.: Londini,* 1606. 4°. **1213.** l. **7.** (**2.**)

—— Sketch of the Life of John Barclay, *etc.* [By Sir D. Dalrymple.] pp. 22. [*Edinburgh,* 1786?] 4°. **G. 5399.** (**2.**)

BARCLAY (JOHN) *Rev.* The Elements of Natural and Experimental Philosophy, *etc.* [With plates.] pp. xvii. 450. *Pinnock & Maunder: London,* 1826. 12°. **1400.** a. **24.**

—— The Elements of Polite Literature and Moral Philosophy for the use of schools, *etc.* pp. xviii. 426. *Pinnock & Maunder: London,* 1826. 12°. **8403.** e. **11.**

—— The Elements of Science and Art, illustrated by one hundred and fifty engravings . . . for the use of schools, *etc.* pp. xxiv. 372. *Pinnock & Maunder: London,* 1820. 12°. **8707.** aaa. **21.**

BARCLAY (JOHN) *Shipwright. See* MORTON (Thomas) *Shipbuilder.* Infringement of a Patent. Notes of a trial . . . at Edinburgh, 15th March 1824. T. Morton pursuer, versus J. Barclay and others, *etc.* 1824. 8°. **1132.** e. **37.**

BARCLAY (John) *Vicar of Runcorn.* The Principles of Ministerial Character and Doctrine. A sermon, *etc.* pp. 20. *Holden: Liverpool,* 1863. 12°. **4462.** aa. **3. (15.)**

BARCLAY (John Bruce)

—— Edinburgh Report on Junior Cinema Clubs. pp. 32. *Glasgow,* 1951. 8°. [*Scottish Educational Film Association. Publication.* no. 6.] W.P. **323/6.**

BARCLAY (John Francis)

—— Arthur & Company, Limited, Glasgow. One hundred years of textile distribution. [With plates.] pp. 172. xiii. 1953. 8°. *See* Arthur and Co., *of Glasgow.* **8229.** aa. **55.**

BARCLAY (John M.) [For editions of Barclay's "Digest of the Rules of the House of Representatives," included in the "Constitution Manual":] *See* United States of America. [*Constitutional Documents.*]

BARCLAY (John Thomas) A Burning and a Shining Light; a sermon preached . . . on occasion of the death of the Rev. Z. H. Biddulph. pp. 31. *Hamilton & Co.: London,* 1843. 8°. **4905.** bb. **25.**

BARCLAY (Joseph) *Bishop of the Church of England in Jerusalem. See* Mishnah. [*Selections.*] The Talmud. By J. Barclay, *etc.* 1878. 8°. **2217.** bb. **20.**

—— Some Correspondence with Monsignore Capel in the Holy City of Jerusalem in . . . 1869. pp. 16. *W. H. Dalton: London,* 1874. 8°. **3940.** cc. **1. (26.)**

—— Joseph Barclay . . . A missionary biography. [By J. B. Courtenay.] pp. xii. 600. *S. W. Partridge & Co.: London,* 1883. 8°. **4956.** h. **2.**

BARCLAY (Joseph) *Brewer.* The Arts of Brewing and Distillation, *etc.* pp. 70. *William Cole: London,* [1820?] 12°. **7945.** a. **40.**

BARCLAY (Joseph Gurney) Astronomical Observations taken during the years 1862–64 (to the end of 1877) at the private observatory of J. G. Barclay. [vol. 1 by Herman Romberg; vol. 2, 3 by C. G. Talmage. The whole edited by J. G. Barclay.] 4 vol. *Williams & Norgate: London,* 1865–78. 4°. **8567.** e. **4.**

BARCLAY (Lawrance)

—— Poems, chiefly in the Scottish idiom. [With a portrait.] pp. iii. 181. *George Richardson: Glasgow,* 1832. 8°. **11654.** aaa. **34.**

BARCLAY (Leslie George de Rune) History of the Scottish Barclays. pp. 126. *Bewley: Folkestone,* 1915. 8°. **9902.** cc. **42.**

BARCLAY (Lydia Ann) A Selection from the Letters of Lydia Ann Barclay, *etc.* pp. 462. *George Harrison: Manchester,* 1862. 8°. **4985.** d. **56.**

BARCLAY (Margaret) *See* Inch (I.) Trial, Confession, and Execution of Isobel Inch . . . M. Barclay, *etc.* [1855?] 8°. **8631.** ff. **40.**

BARCLAY, afterwards **EVANS** (Marguerite Florence)

—— *See* also Barcynska (Hélène) *Countess, pseud.* [i.e. M.F. Barclay, afterwards Evans.]

—— *See* also Sandys (Oliver) *pseud.* [i.e. M.F. Barclay, afterwards Evans.]

—— Sunset is Dawn. pp. 199. *Rich & Cowan: London,* 1953. 8°. NNN. **3690.**

—— Yesterday is tomorrow. pp. 240. *Rich & Cowan: London,* 1950. 8°. NNN. **1101.**

BARCLAY, afterwards **EVANS** (Marguerite Florence) and **BARCLAY** (Armiger)

—— The Activities of Lavie Jutt. pp. 288. *Stanley Paul & Co.: London* [1911.] 8°. **012618.** aaa.

—— [Another edition.] pp. 96. *Aldine Publishing Co. London,* [1919.] 8°. [*Mascot Novels.* no. 124.] **12644.** a. **1/12.**

—— Peggy Day-by-Day. pp. 189. *Simpkin Marshall & Co.: London,* [1916.] 8°. **12601.** m. **27**

—— Where there are Women. pp. 378. *T. Fisher Unwin London,* 1915. 8°. NN. **250**

A later edition bearing the title "The Five-Hooded Cobra" is entered under Sandys (*Oliver*) *pseud.* [*i.e. Marguerite Florence Barclay, afterwards Evans.*]

BARCLAY (Maria) *See* Barclay (Harriet M.)

BARCLAY (Marie Thérèse) *Lady. See* Villiers de L'Isle Adam (J. M. M. P. A.) *Count.* The Revolt and the Escape . . . Translated by T. Barclay. 1901. 8°. **12205.** de. **8/7**

BARCLAY (Marius) *See* Barclay (Hans M. E.)

BARCLAY (Mary)

—— Shining Waters, *etc.* pp. 116. *T. Nelson & Sons, London,* 1940. 8°. [*Wide World Story Books.* no. 7.] **12834.b.24/7.**

BARCLAY (Mary Kathleen) 50 Examination Questions and Answers in General Nursing and Ward Work—Junior Course. Compiled for the use of male nurse candidates in His Majesty's Services. pp. 62. *E. O. Beck: London* [1934.] 16°. **07686.** de. **76**

—— 101 Suggestions for Ward Instructions, specially adapted for use in military hospitals. pp. 113. *E. O. Beck London,* [1933.] 16°. **07686.** de. **75**

BARCLAY (Matthew) The Evils of Drunkenness in a worldly point of view. A sermon, *etc.* pp. 24. *D. Bryce Glasgow,* 1839. 8°. **4175.** df. **26. (7.)**

BARCLAY (McKee) *See* Stevens (William O.) and Barclay (M.) The Young Privateersman, *etc.* 1910. 8°. **012705.** bb. **40**

BARCLAY (Noel)

—— The Trail of the Three Lean Men. [A novel.] pp. 318. *Lovat Dickson: London,* 1932. 8°. NN. **22483**

BARCLAY (Patrick) The Universal Traveller: or, a Complete account of the most remarkable voyages and travels . . . to the present time, *etc.* pp. 795. *J. Purser, etc.: London,* 1735. fol. **559*.** f. **33.**

BARCLAY (Peter) *A.M.* A Letter to the People of Scotland in order to remove their prejudice to the Book of Common Prayer: to which is added an appendix wherein are answer'd the objections offer'd against the Liturgy in two late pamphlets, call'd: Dialogues between a Curate and a Countryman. pp. vi. 172. *John Morphew: London,* 1713. 8°. **845.** b. **17.**

—— A Persuasive to the People of Scotland, in order to remove their prejudices to the Book of Common Prayer . . . The second edition [of "A Letter to the People of Scotland"]. pp. viii. 172. *Jonah Bowyer: London,* 1723. 8°. **1220.** f. **38.**

—— The Ruling & Ordaining Power of Congregational Bishops, or Presbyters, defended. Being remarks on . . . Mr. P. Barclay's Persuasive lately distributed in New England. By an Impartial Hand [i.e. Thomas Foxcroft], *etc.* pp. 45. *Samuel Gerrish: Boston,* 1724. 8°. **4486.** a. **55. (1.)**

BARCLAY (Peter) *M.A.* 'Unto us a Child is born' . . . A Christmas homily. pp. 32. *Elliot Stock: London,* 1900. 8°. **4475**. de. **37**.

—— Via, Veritas, Vita: discursive notes on preaching . . . By a Presbyter [i.e. P. Barclay]. pp. 94. [1881.] 8°. *See* Presbyter. **4498**. f. **10**.

BARCLAY (Peter) *Minister at Napier, N.Z.* Church Work in New Zealand. Two addresses. With an appendix and map. pp. 70. *J. Menzies & Co.: Edinburgh & Glasgow,* 1876. 8°. **4109**. e. **3**. (**5**.)

—— On the Atonement. pp. 32. *R. W. Hunter: Edinburgh,* 1902. 8°. **04420**. i. **33**. (**2**.)

—— A Survey of Foreign Missions . . . With maps. pp. xx. 272. *W. Blackwood & Sons: Edinburgh,* 1897. 8°. **4767**. bb. **31**.

—— The Word and the Work of Christ in New Zealand. Sermons preached in St. Paul's Church, Napier. With two addresses on church-work in that Colony. pp. viii. 254. *J. MacLaren: Edinburgh,* 1871. 8°. **4479**. e. **12**.

BARCLAY (Rachel) Select Pieces of Poetry intended to promote Piety and Virtue . . . Collected by R. Barclay. pp. viii. 168. *James Phillips: London,* 1795. 12°. **11602**. aaa. **3**.

—— Poems intended to promote Piety and Virtue . . . [With a memoir of the author.] The second edition. pp. xii. 170. *J. Phillips & Son: London,* 1797. 12°. **11631**. b. **7**.

BARCLAY (Rachel Elizabeth)

—— *See* Barclay (Robert L.) Rachel Barclay . . . A memoir, *etc.* [With letters and sketches by Rachel Barclay, and with portraits.] 1935. 8°. **010822**. i. **17**.

BARCLAY (Rachel Mary) *See* Kraepelin (E.) Dementia Præcox and Paraphrenia . . . Translated by R. M. Barclay, *etc.* 1919. 8°. **7660**. h. **30**.

—— *See* Kraepelin (E.) Manic-Depressive Insanity and Paranoia . . . Translated by R. M. Barclay, *etc.* 1921. 8°. **07660**. h. **54**.

—— *See* Midwifery. Midwifery. (Second [*etc.*] edition by R. M. Barclay.) [1896, *etc.*] 8°. [*Catechism Series.*]
[Latest edition:] **07306**. ee. **1/17**.
[Earlier editions:] **07306**. e. **1/17**.

BARCLAY (*Sir* Richard) *See* Barckley.

BARCLAY (Robert) *Capain, of Ury.* *See* Allardice (R. B.)

BARCLAY (Robert) *the Elder.* *See* Armistead (Wilson) A Memoir of Robert Barclay, *etc.* 1850. 8°. **4151**. bb. **3**. (**2**.)

—— *See* Barclay (Robert) *the Younger.* A Genealogical Account of the Barclays of Urie . . . With memoirs of R. Barclay . . . also Letters that passed between him, the Duke of York . . . and other distinguished characters. 1812. 8°. **606**. c. **3**.

—— *See* Bennet (Thomas) *D.D.* A Confutation of Quakerism; or, a plain proof of the falshood of what the principal Quaker writers—especially Mr. R. Barclay in his Apology and other works—do teach. 1705. 8°. **873**. k. **21**.

—— *See* Cadbury (M. C.) Robert Barclay, *etc.* 1912. 8°. **4920**. eee. **6**.

—— *See* Cadbury (M. C.) The Story of Robert Barclay. 1926. 8°. [*Friends Ancient and Modern.* no. 21.] **4804.aa.48.**

BARCLAY (Robert) *the Elder.*

—— *See* Eaton (Joseph) *Quaker, of Bristol.* Barclay and Penn self-vindicated; or, the views of those writers on certain points of Christian doctrine exhibited, *etc.* 1836. 8°. **4151**. e. **16**. (**2**.)

—— *See* Eeg-Olofsson (L.) The Conception of the Inner Light in Robert Barclay's Theology, *etc.* 1954. 8°. [*Studia theologica lundensia.* no. 5.] Ac. **1067**. d/**2**.

—— *See* Elys (Edmund) Vindiciæ quorundam R. Barclaii Noematum, contra . . . argumentationes in eo Libro, cui titulus est Antibarclaius, *etc.* 1693. 4°. **1478**. aa. **24**. (22.)

—— *See* Keith (George) *Rector, etc.* The Fundamental Truths of Christianity, *etc.* [With a preface signed: R. B., i.e. R. Barclay.] 1688. 8°. **4152**. a. **33**.

—— *See* Phipps (Joseph) Multum in Parvo contra Parvum in Multo . . . Wherein Mr. Phipps's arguments . . . against Mr. Newton . . . are shewn to be defective; and the doctrines of absolute necessity and universal redemption fairly deduced from some of the Quakers principles as laid down in Barclay's and Phipps's writings. 1773. 8°. **4151**. bb. **18**.

—— *See* Rhodes (B.) *Rev.* Three Apostles of Quakerism. Popular sketches of Fox, Penn and Barclay. [1885.] 8°. **4905**. bb. **59**.

—— *See* Wragge (J. P.) The Faith of Robert Barclay. An essay on his life and on the relevance of his thought for today, illustrated by extracts from his writing. 1948. 8°. **4175**. de. **63**.

—— Truth Triumphant through the Spiritual Warfare, Christian Labours and Writings of . . . R. Barclay. [Collected works. With a preface by William Penn.] pp. xxxviii. 908. *Thomas Northcott: London,* 1692. fol. **475**. c. **16**.

—— Universal Love considered and established upon its Right Foundation, *etc.*—A Testimony concerning the true . . . Worship of God, *etc.*—The Anarchy of the Ranters . . . the Hierarchy of the Romanists, and other pretended churches equally . . . refuted, *etc.* *See* Bancroft (Joseph) *of the Society of Friends.* A Persuasive to Unity, *etc.* 1879. 8°. **4152**. bb. **22**.

—— [Letters.] *See* Barclay (David) *Colonel.* Reliquiæ Barclaianæ. Correspondence of . . . D. Barclay and R. Barclay of Urie, *etc.* 1870. 4°. **10921**. k. **8**.

—— [A Letter to Elizabeth, Princess Palatine of the Rhine, dated: 12 July 1677.] *See* Penington (Isaac) *the Younger.* Letters, *etc.* 1796. 8°. **4920**. c. **64**.

—— The Anarchy of the Ranters and other Libertines, the Hierarchy of the Romanists, and other pretended churches, equally refused and refuted, in a two-fold apology for the Church and people of God called . . . Quakers, *etc.* pp. 87. 1676. 4°. **4152**. ee. **20**. (4.)

—— The Anarchy of the Ranters, *etc.* pp. 111. *Sam. Fuller: Dublin,* 1726. 8°. **4381**. a. **34**. (2.)

—— [Another edition.] pp. viii. 91. *Assigns of J. Sowle: London,* 1733. 8°. **4151**. d. **3**.

—— [Another edition.] (An Epistle to the National Meeting of Friends, in Dublin, concerning good order and discipline in the Church. Written by Joseph Pike.) 2 pt. *B. Franklin & D. Hall: Philadelphia,* 1757. 8°. **4106**. a. **10**.

—— [Another edition.] pp. vii. 111. *Joseph Crukshank: Philadelphia,* 1770. 8°. [*Three Treatises, in which the Fundamental Principle . . . of the people called Quakers, are plainly declared.*] **4151**. aaa. **46**.

—— [Another edition.] To which is added a brief examination and state of liberty spiritual, both with respect to persons in their private capacity, and in their church society, and communion. By William Penn. pp. viii. 113. *Mary Hinde: London,* 1771. 8°. T. **254.** (**6.**)

—— *See* Scott (Job) A Treatise on Church Discipline, taken, principally, from the writings of R. Barclay [i.e. from his "Anarchy of the Ranters"], W. Penn, *etc.* 1824. 12°. **4183.** aa. **88.** (**1.**)

—— Robert Barclay's Answers to Questions proposed by his uncle Charles Gordon, concerning the principles of the Society of Friends . . . Copied from C. Gordon's papers . . . 1678, and now for the first time printed. pp. 32. *H. T. Wake: Cockermouth,* 1864. 8°. **4372.** d. **3.** (**14.**)

—— An Apology for the True Christian Divinity, *etc. See* infra: Theses theologicæ, *etc.*

—— A Catechism and Confession of Faith, approved of and agreed unto by the general assembly of the patriarchs, prophets and apostles, Christ himself being chief speaker in and among them . . . By R. B. (R. Barclay.) pp. 190. [1675.] 8°. **873.** c. **48.**

—— The fourth edition, corrected, *etc.* pp. 167. *T. Sowle: London,* 1701. 12°. **4152.** a. **36.**

—— The fifth edition, corrected and very much amended, *etc.* pp. 156. *Assigns of J. Sowle: London,* 1716. 12°. **3505.** b. **28.**

—— The sixth edition. By R. B. [i.e. R. Barclay.] pp. 156. 1740. 12°. *See* B., R. **4412.** a. **4.**

—— The seventh edition. pp. 147. *Luke Hinde: London,* [1750?] 12°. **4152.** aa. **47.**

—— The eighth edition. pp. 147. *Luke Hinde: London,* [1755?] 12°. **4152.** b. **93.**

—— [Another edition.] pp. 111. *I. Thompson & Co.: Newcastle,* 1759. 8°. **4152.** d. **3.**

—— The ninth edition. pp. 147. *Mary Hinde: London,* [1769?] 12°. **4152.** b. **94.**

—— The tenth edition. pp. 147. *Mary Hinde: London,* [1770?] 12°. **3505.** bb. **22.**

—— The eleventh edition. pp. 147. *James Phillips: London,* [1780?] 8°. **4152.** b. **92.**

—— The twelfth edition. pp. 147. *James Phillips: London,* 1787. 12°. **4152.** b. **95.**

—— Thirteenth edition. pp. xi. 151. *William Phillips: London,* 1803. 12°. **856.** g. **26.**

—— A new edition. pp. xiii. 133. *William Phillips: London,* 1828. 12°. **4152.** aa. **40.**

—— Catechismus en belydenisse des geloofs. Die van d' algemeine vergadering der patriarchen, propheten, en apostelen . . . is goet gekeurd, *etc.* pp. 138. *J. Claus: Amsterdam,* 1675. 16°. **3505.** cc. **39.**

—— Catechismus et fidei confessio, *etc.* pp. xiv. 207. *P. van Winburge: Roterodami,* 1676. 8°. **3505.** b. **64.**

—— Editio secunda, *etc.* pp. 153. *Apud assignatos J. Sowle: London,* 1727. 12°. **856.** g. **25.**

—— An Epistle of Love and Friendly Advice, to the Ambassadors of the several Princes of Europe, met at Nimeguen . . . Wherein the true cause of the present war is discovered, *etc.* pp. 29. *Benjamin Clark: London,* 1679. 8°. **4139.** bb. **13.** (**1.**)

—— [Another edition.] *Assigns of J. Sowle: London,* 1717. 8°. **4152.** de. **12.** (**2.**)

—— The Possibility & Necessity of the inward and immediat Revelation of the Spirit of God, towards the foundatio and ground of True Faith, proved, in a letter writ i Latin to the Heer Paets and now also put into Englis pp. 28. *T. Sowle: London,* 1703. 4°. **4152.** ee. **18.** (**14**

—— Sermon preached . . . May the 16th 1688. *See* Friends *Society of.* Sermons preached by several of the peopl called Quakers, *etc.* 1775. 8°. **4151.** e.

—— [Another edition.] *See* Friends, *Society of.* Sermon or Declarations, *etc.* 1824. 8°. **4152.** c. **5**

—— Theses theologicæ . . . ad manifestandam simplice illam nudam, & claram veritatem, *etc.* (Theologis stellingen, *etc.*) [With a Dutch translation of chap. 28–3 of F. Howgill's "Invisible Things of God." Edited b Benjamin Furly.] 2 pt. *B. van Santbergen: Rotterdan* 1674. 4°. [*Collectio of versamelinge, van eenige van tractaten . . . die geschreven sijn door verscheyde vriende der waarheyt, etc.*] **855.i.1.(71,72.**

—— Theses theologicæ, or, some solid positions of soun divinity asserted, *etc.* pp. 22. *See* Lesly (John) *Aberdeen.* A True and Faithful Accompt of . . . Dispute betwixt some Students of Divinity . . . Aberdene, and the people called Quakers . . . Defendan . . . R. Barclay and G. Keith . . . To which is adde R. Barclay's offer to the preachers of Aberdene renew' *etc.* 1675. 16°. **856.** g. **6.** (**8**

—— [Another edition.] pp. 16. [*London,* 1711.] 8°. **856.** g. **7.** (**14**

—— [Another edition.] A Concise View of the Chie Principles of the Christian Religion as professed by th people called Quakers. pp. 24. [*Mary Hinde:*] *London* 1770. 12°. **4139.** b. **12**

—— Thèses théologiques, à tous clercs du Christianisme *etc. See* Crook (John) *of the Society of Friends.* Le Principes de la vérité, *etc.* 1675. 4°. **C.110.e.3.(9.**

—— Roberti Barclaii Theologiæ vere Christianæ apologia [An explanation and defence of the fifteen "Theses theo logicæ" previously published by him, and here reprinted. pp. 374. *J. Claus Amstelodami,* 1676. 4°. **1470.b.7.**

—— [Another copy.] Roberti Barclaii Theologiæ verè Chris tianæ apologia. few ms. notes. *Amstelodam* 1676. 4°. 855. i. 2
Imperfect; wanting the first leaf.

—— Editio secunda, priore emendatior. pp. xxiv. 492. *Apud assignatos J. Sowle: Londini,* 1729. 8°. **855.** i. **3**

—— An Apology for the True Christian Divinity, as the sam is held forth . . . by the people, called . . . Quakers being a full explanation of their principles and doctrines by many arguments, deduced from Scriptur and righ reason . . . Written and published in Latine . . . an now put into our own language, *etc.* [With a translatio of the "Theses theologicæ."] pp. xxiv. 412. xxvii. [*Aberdeen?*] 1678. 8°. **4152.** e. **13.** (**1.**

—— [Another edition.] pp. 392. [*London?*] 1678. 4°. G. **19629**

—— The fourth edition. pp. 574. *T. Sowle: London* 1701. 8°. **855.** i. **4**

—— The fifth edition. pp. 574. *T. Sowle: London,* 1703. 8° **4152.aaa.32.**

—— The sixth edition. pp. 574. *T. S. Raylton & Luke Hinde: London,* 1736. 8°. **855.** i. **5**

—— [Another copy.] **L.P.** **13.** a.

—— The seventh edition. pp. 574. *Mary Fuller: Dublin,* 1737. 8°. **4152**. e. **11**.

—— The seventh edition. pp. 574. *W. Richardson & S. Clark: London,* 1765. 8°. **4152**. e. **10**.

—— The eighth edition. pp. xiii. 504. *John Baskerville: Birmingham,* 1765. 4°. **475**. c. **17**.

—— The ninth edition. pp. 574. MS. NOTE. *Joseph Crukshank: Philadelphia,* 1775. 8°. **4152**. e. **12**.

—— The eighth edition. pp. 574. *J. Phillips: London,* 1780. 8°. **855**. k. **21**.

—— [Another copy.] **L.P.** **4151**. g. **13**.

—— The ninth edition. pp. 586. *John Gough: Dublin,* 1800. 8°. **4151**. e. **12**.

—— Ninth edition. pp. xvi. 558. *Thomas Tegg: London,* 1825. 8°. **4151**. f. **3**.

—— First stereotype edition, from the eighth London edition. pp. 8. ix. 587. *S. Wood & Sons: New York,* 1827. 8°. **4151**. f. **1**.

—— Tenth edition. pp. xvi. 556. *Harvey & Darton: London,* 1841. 8°. **4151**. f. **2**.

—— Eleventh edition. pp. xvi. 556. *Edward Marsh: London,* 1849. 8°. **4151**. e. **9**.

—— [Another edition.] (A Memoir of Robert Barclay . . . With some account of his father, Colonel David Barclay, &c., by Wilson Armistead.) 2 pt. *William Irwin: Manchester,* 1850. 8°. **4151**. bb. **3**.

—— Fourteenth edition. pp. viii. 435. *R. B. Murdoch: Glasgow,* 1886. 8°. **4151**. bb. **28**.

—— Forsvar for den sande christelige Theologi. Oversat . . . af C. Meidel. pp. xviii. 556. *T. S. Railton: London,* 1738. 8°. **855**. i. **7**.

—— Verantwoording van de ware christelyke Godgeleertheid, gelyk dezelve voorgedragen en gepredikt word van het volk, spotsgewyze Quakers genaamd . . . In 't Nederduitsch vertaald door J. H. Glazemaker . . . Tweede druk, *etc.* pp. 462. *Amsterdam,* 1757. 4°. **4151**. ee. **5**.

—— Apologie de la véritable théologie chrétienne, ainsi qu'elle est soutenue, & prêchée, par le peuple appellé . . . les Trembleurs, *etc.* pp. 654. *T. Sowle: Londres,* 1702. 8°. **4151**. f. **37**.

—— Apologie de la vraie théologie chrétienne . . . Traduite en françois par E. P. Bridel. pp. xxxii. 652. *J. Phillips & fils: Londres,* 1797. 8°. **855**. k. **19**.

—— Eine Apologie oder Vertheidigungs-Schrifft, der rechtchristlichen Gotts-Gelehrtheit . . . In Latein geschrieben und heraus gegeben . . . So aber hernacher . . . in das Englische, and nunmehr aus beeden ins Teutsche übergesetzet ist, *etc.* pp. 450. 1684. 4°. **4151**. ee. **8**.

—— Robert Barclay's Apologie oder Vertheidigungs-Schrifft der wahren christlichen-Gottesgelahrheit . . . Nach der zweyten lateinischen und sechsten englischen Herausgebung gantz von neuen ins Deutsche übersetzt. pp. 776. 1740. 8°. **701**. f. **31**.

—— [Another edition.] pp. 797. *Germantown,* 1776. 8°. **855**. i. **8**.

—— Apologia de la Verdadera Theologia Christiana . . . Trasladada . . . en Castellano por Antonio de Alvarado. pp. 638. *J. Sowle: Londres,* 1710. 8°. **855**. i. **6**.

—— Barclay's Apology for the True Christian Divinity . . . Abridged by George Harrison. pp. xiii. 324. *Darton, Harvey & Co.: London,* 1815. 12°. **855**. g. **22**.

—— Second edition. pp. xviii. 287. *Harvey & Darton: London,* 1822. 8°. **4151**. bb. **21**.

—— The True Christian Divinity, as set forth in eight propositions of R. Barclay's Apology. pp. 310. *Sunderland,* 1817. 8°. **4152**. dd. **4**.

—— On Baptism: being an extract from Barclay's Apology. (3rd ed.) pp. 30. *Tract Association of the Society of Friends: London,* 1831. 12°. [*General Series.* no. 39.] **1016**. e. **6**. (**8**.)

—— Selections from an Apology for the True Christian Divinity, *etc.* 1837. *See* FRIENDS, *Society of.* Friends' Library, *etc.* vol. 15. 1832, *etc.* 32°. **4152**. aaa. **3**.

—— On Justification. Extracted from Robert Barclay's Apology, *etc.* pp. 24. *Manchester & Stockport Tract Depository: Manchester,* [1835?] 12°. **1016**. e. **6**. (**9**.)

—— On Baptism. Extracted from the twelfth proposition of Barclay's Apology. pp. 16. *Tract Association of the Society of Friends: London,* 1855. 12°. [General Series no. 39.] **4151**. b. **2**. (**10**.)

—— *See* B., H. A Vindication of Robert Barclay's Apology for the Principles of the People call'd Quakers; against the attempts of William Notcutt . . . By H. B. [i.e. Henton Brown.] 1732. 8°. **4151**. d. **1**.

—— *See* B., H. An Examination of William Notcutt's Reply to H. B.'s [i.e. Henton Brown's] Vindication of R. Barclay's Apology, *etc.* 1735. 8°. **4151**. e. **4**.

—— *See* BAIER (J. W.) *the Elder.* Johannis Guilielmi Bajeri Synopseos et examinis theologiæ Enthusiastarum seu Quakerorum præcipue R. Barclaii . . . dissertationes, *etc.* 1701. 4°. **855**. f. **25**.

—— *See* BALL (Richard) *of Taunton.* Holy Scripture the Test of Truth . . . against certain passages . . . in the writings of Barclay [in his "Apology"] and Penn. 1835. 12°. **1117**. f. **16**.

—— *See* BEAVEN (Thomas) Supernatural Influence necessary to Salvation: being a vindication of the fourth proposition of R. Barclay's Apology, *etc.* 1726. 8°. **4151**. f. **12**

—— [For editions and translations of "Reasons for the Necessity of Silent Waiting, in order to the solemn worship of God. To which are added several quotations from R. Barclay's Apology":] *See* BROOK (Mary B.)

—— *See* BROWN (John) *Minister at Wamphray.* Quakerisme the Path-way to Paganisme . . . being an examination of the Theses and Apologie of R. Barclay, *etc.* 1678. 4°. **4152**. ee. **23**.

—— *See* BUGG (Francis) A Narrative of the Conference at Sleeford in Lincolnshire between F. Bugg, and H. Pickworth, wherein, not only the contradiction of the Quakers to the Holy Scriptures . . . but their great inconsistency one with another, and particularly between Fox, Whitehead . . . and R. Barclay in his Apology is . . . detected. 1702. 8°. **T. 1581**. (**1**.)

—— *See* BUGG (Francis) A Seasonable Caveat against the Prevalency of Quakerism, containing . . . a touchstone for R. Barclay's Apology. 1701. 8°. **T. 1582**. (**3**.)

—— *See* CHUBB (Thomas) An Examination of Mr. Barclay's Principles with regard to man's natural ability since the Fall, as laid down in his book, intitled, An Apology for the true Christian Divinity, *etc.* 1726. 8°. **4151**. aaa. **13**.

BARCLAY (Robert) *the Elder.*

—— *See* Chubb (Thomas) Human Nature Vindicated: or, a Reply to Mr. Beaven's book entitled, Supernatural Influences Necessary to Salvation, being a vindication of the fourth proposition of R. Barclay's Apology, *etc.* 1726. 8°. **4226**. aaa. **21**.

—— *See* Chubb (Thomas) Scripture-evidence, consider'd in a view of the controversy betwixt the author and Mr. Barclay's defenders, *etc.* 1728. 8°. **4226**. aaa. **22**.

—— *See* Combe (Charles) *Bachelier ès Lettres.* La Révélation intérieure immédiate d'après l'Apologie de R. Barclay, *etc.* 1894. 8°. **4151**. f. **10**.

—— *See* Dove (John) *Writer on Moral Philosophy.* An Essay on Inspiration . . . Wherein the fundamental principles of Barclay, in his Apology for the Quakers, are refuted, *etc.* 1756. 8°. **4376**. aa. **8**.

—— *See* Figk (B.) Doctrina fanaticorum, oder eine vollkommene Relation und Wissenschafft, von der neuen Quäcker eigentlichen Lehr und Opinion . . . wider . . . R. Barclajum [in his "Apology"], W. Caton . . . gerichtet, *etc.* 1679. 8°. **1368**. c. **4**. (**2**.)

—— *See* Fleming (Caleb) Tracts on Baptism, *etc.* (ii. A Plea for Infants, wherein Mr. R. Barclay's first principle [in his "Apology"], which denies water-baptism, is refuted.) 1745. 8°. **699**. h. **11**. (**2**.)

—— *See* Friends, *Society of.* A Second Dissertation on the Liberty of Preaching granted to Women by the people called Quakers: in answer to a late dissertation on that subject. Wherein R. Barclay's arguments [in his "Apology"] for the justification of that practice are supported, *etc.* 1739. 8°. **4152**. aaaa. **46**.

—— *See* Graham (John) *of Sunderland.* Simon Pure unmask'd: or, the Errors of Quakerism display'd. A dialogue . . . Wherein will be pointed out several . . . errors . . . of . . . R. Barclay in his Apology, *etc.* 1745. 8°. **4152**. de. **12**. (**3**.)

—— *See* Helton (John) Reasons for quitting the Methodist Society; being a defence of Barclay's Apology, *etc.* 1778. 8°. **4151**. b. **62**.

—— *See* Keith (George) *Rector of Edburton.* Ad Joh. Guilelmi Bajeri . . . dissertationem primam contra Quakeros, & præcipuè contra R. Barclajum in Thesibus suis theologicis & Apologia . . . amica responsio, *etc.* 1683. 4°. **4151**. ee. **11**. (**8**.)

—— *See* Keith (George) *Rector of Edburton.* The Arguments of the Quakers, more particularly of . . . R. Barclay . . . [in his "Apology"] against baptism . . . refuted, *etc.* 1698. 4°. **4152**. e. **4**.

—— *See* Keith (George) *Rector of Edburton.* The Standard of the Quakers examined, or an answer to the Apology of R. Barclay. 1702. 8°. **855**. e. **11**.

—— *See* Lean (William) A Letter to Robert Charleton, occasioned by his "Thoughts on Barclay's Apology." [1868.] 8°. **4152**. e. **20**.

—— *See* Lindley (Benjamin) The Necessity of Immediate Revelation, towards the foundation and ground of true faith, proved; and the gospel, its true ministers, and their Christian writings, especially R. Barclay's "Apology &c." vindicated, *etc.* 1710, *etc.* 4°. **4152**. cc. **2**.

BARCLAY (Robert) *the Elder.*

—— *See* Loeber (C. H.) Schrifftmässige Vorstellung des Quaker-Irrlichtes, darinn so wohl eines ungenannten Quakers einfältige und eilfertige Anmerckungen, über die Entdeckung des Quaker-Greuels . . . Als auch des Vornehmsten so in R. Barclaji . . . Apologia zu dero Bestärckung, enthalten . . . gründlich beantwortet . . . wird, *etc.* 1685. 8°. **1368**. c. **4**. (**4**.)

—— *See* Morgan (Thomas) *M.D., Philosophical Writer.* A Defence of Natural and Revealed Religion; occasioned by Mr. Chubb's Scripture Evidence considered, in a view of the controversy betwixt himself and Mr. Barclay's defenders, *etc.* 1728. 8°. **4151**. aaa. **29**. (**3**.)

—— *See* Morgan (Thomas) *M.D., Philosophical Writer.* A Farther Vindication of Mr. Barclay's scheme, in reply to Mr. Chubb's remarks, *etc.* 1727. 8°. **4151**. aaa. **29**. (**2**.)

—— *See* Newton (Samuel) *of Norwich.* The Leading Sentiments of the People called Quakers examined, as they are stated in Mr. R. Barclay's apology, *etc.* 1771. 8°. **855**. f. **19**.

—— *See* Notcutt (William) *the Elder.* An Impartial Review of Robert Barclay's pretended Apology for the Principles of the Quakers. 1732. 8°. **873**. k. **20**. (**1**.)

—— *See* Notcutt (William) *the Elder.* A Reply to H. B.'s [i.e. Henton Brown's] Vindication of Robert Barclay's Apology, &c. 1733. 8°. **873**. k. **20**. (**2**.)

—— *See* Perronet (V.) An Affectionate Address to the People called Quakers; with regard to water-baptism . . . Wherein the arguments of . . . R. Barclay [in his "Apology"], are considered. 1747. 8°. **4152**. aa. **59**. (**1**.)

—— *See* Philalethes, *pseud.* [i.e. Samuel Newton.] A Letter to the Author of a Letter to Dr. Formey: in which some of the prevailing sentiments of . . . Quakers, as they stand in Mr. R. Barclay's Apology are discussed, *etc.* 1767. 8°. **T. 1612**. (**2**.)

—— *See* Phipps (Joseph) Observations on a late anonymous Publication intituled a Letter to the Author of a Letter to Dr. Formey . . . in vindication of R. Barclay, *etc.* 1767. 8°. **4151**. d. **18**.

—— *See* Shirreff (A.) Quakerism canvassed: R. Barclay baffled in the defending of his Theses against young Students at Aberdene, *etc.* 1675. 4°. **4151**. aaa. **63**.

—— *See* Stebbing (Henry) *Archdeacon of Wilts.* The Charge of Heresy continu'd in a second defence of . . . water-baptism . . . Wherein also some gross errors of R. Barclay [in his "Apology"] . . . are censured and exposed. 1715. 8°. **855**. f. **12**. (**2**.)

—— Reasons for Objecting to the Republication and Circulation of Barclay's Apology, addressed to the Society of Friends by one of its members [i.e. Edward Ash]. pp. iv. 41. *S. Bagster & Sons: London,* 1849. 8°. **4139**. f. **4**.

—— Robert Barclay's Apology for the True Christian Divinity vindicated from John Brown's Examination and pretended confutation thereof, in his book, called, Quakerisme the Path-way to Paganisme. In which vindication I. B. [i.e. John Brown] his many gross perversions and abuses are discovered . . . [By R. Barclay.] Whereunto is added, a christian and friendly expostulation with Robert Macquare, touching his postscript to the said book of J. B., written to him by Lillias Skein, *etc.* pp. 205. *Benjamin Clark: London,* 1679. 4°. **4152**. e. **13**. (**2**.)

BARCLAY (ROBERT) *the Elder.*

—— Truth cleared of Calumnies; wherein a book intituled, A dialogue betwixt a Quaker and a stable Christian, printed at Aberdeen, and upon good ground judged to be writ by William Mitchell . . . is examined, and the disingenuity of the author in his representing the Quakers is discovered. pp. 72. [*London ?*] 1670. 4°. **4152**. b. **6**.

—— [Another edition.] pp. viii. 560. *Assigns of J. Sowle: London*, 1717. 8°. **4151**. bb. **30**.

—— William Michel unmasqued: or, the Staggering Instability of the pretended stable Christian discovered, his omissions observed, and weakness unvailed, in his late . . . animadversions by way of reply to a book intituled Truth cleared of Calumnies. Wherein the integrity of the Quakers' doctrine is the second time justified, *etc.* pp. 66. [*London ?*] 1672. 4°. **4151**. b. **14**.

—— Universal Love considered, and established upon its right foundation; being a serious enquiry how far charity may, and ought to, be extended towards persons of different judgments in matters of religion, *etc.* pp. 44. [*London,*] 1677. 4°. **4152**. aaa. **7**.

—— A new edition. pp. 42. *J. Phillips & Son: London*, 1799. 8°. **4151**. f. **41**. (**2**.)

—— Serious Considerations on Absolute Predestination. Extracted [by John Wesley] from a late author [Robert Barclay]. pp. 24. 1790. 12°. *See* CONSIDERATIONS. **4402**. bbb. **41**. (**8**.)

—— A Short Account of the Life and Writings of Robert Barclay. [By Joseph Gurney Bevan.] pp. 127. *W. Phillips: London*, 1802. 12°. **856**. g. **28**.

—— [Another edition.] pp. 132. *B. Johnson: Philadelphia*, 1805. 24°. **4956**. de. **4**.

—— A Short Account of the Life and Writings of Robert Barclay. (2nd ed.) pp. 36. *Tract Association of the Society of Friends: London*, 1827. 12°. [*General Series.* no. 40.] **1016**. e. **6***. (**1**.)

—— Short Account of the Life and Writings of Robert Barclay. pp. 16. *Tract Association of the Society of Friends: London*, 1854. 12°. **4151**. b. **2**. (**11**.) *A different work from the preceding.* [General Series no. 40.]

BARCLAY (ROBERT) *the Elder*, and **KEITH** (GEORGE) *Rector of Edburton.*

—— Quakerism confirmed, or a Vindication of the chief doctrines and principles of the people called Quakers from the arguments and objections of the students of Divinity . . . of Aberdeen in their book entituled Quakerism canvassed. pp. 88. [*London ?*] 1676. 4°. **4151**. aaa. **7**.

BARCLAY (ROBERT) *M.D.* Acute and Chronic Otitis Externa, including Otomycosis and cancer of the auditory canal. *See* BURNETT (Charles H.) System of Diseases of the Ear, *etc.* vol. 1. 1893. 8°. **7615**. cc. **14**.

BARCLAY (ROBERT) *Minister, of Greenock.* *See* LANG (Andrew) A Batch of Golfing Papers . . . Edited by R. Barclay. [1892.] 8°. **7907**. aa. **65**.

—— Robert Barclay: "Memories." Edited by his wife. [With "Sermons and Selections."] With preface by Andrew Lang, *etc.* pp. ix. 182. *Bryce & Murray: Glasgow*, 1904. 8°. **4956**. g. **13**.

BARCLAY (ROBERT) *of Highgate.* Lines Written in Blacklands Church Yard, by R. B. [i.e. R. Barclay] . . . 1871. [1881.] *s. sh.* 8°. *See* B., R. **1879**. c. **12**. (**168**.)

BARCLAY (ROBERT) *of the Manchester Chamber of Commerce.* The Disturbance in the Standard of Value. pp. xvi. 107. *Effingham Wilson: London*, 1893. 8°. **8228**. ccc. **50**.

—— Second edition. pp. xv. 166. *Effingham Wilson: London*, 1896. 8°. **08226**. f. **34**.

—— Essay and Letters on Bi-metallism. pp. 36. *J. Heywood: London*, [1881.] 8°. **08226**. h. **15**. (**3**.)

—— The Silver Question and the Gold Question. pp. 150. *Effingham Wilson: London*, 1885. 8°. **8228**. b. **38**.

—— Second edition. pp. 150. *Effingham Wilson: London*, 1886. 8°. **8228**. b. **41**.

—— Third edition. pp. iv. 194. *Palmer & Howe: Manchester*, [1890.] 8°. **8228**. c. **48**.

—— Fourth edition. pp. iv. 222. *E. Wilson & Co.: London*, [1894.] 8°. **08227**. de. **45**.

BARCLAY (ROBERT) *of Tottenham.* *See* EVANS (Charles) *M.D.* An Examen of Parts relating to the Society of Friends in a recent work by R. Barclay, entitled "The Inner Life of the Religious Societies of the Commonwealth." 1878. 8°. **4152**. g. **12**.

—— *See* WHATELY (Richard) *Archbishop of Dublin.* On the Truth of Christianity . . . With introduction &c. by R. Barclay, *etc.* 1865. 12°. **4014**. aa. **52**.

—— —— 1866. 8°. **4014**. aa. **53**.

—— Sermons. By R. Barclay . . . With a brief memoir. Edited by his widow [i.e. S. M. Barclay]. [With a portrait.] pp. xxii. 387. *Hodder & Stoughton: London*, 1878. 8°. **4465**. i. **11**.

—— The Crucifixion. [A sermon. Edited by S. M. Barclay.] pp. 16. *Harris & Co.: London*, 1882. 8°. **4372**. h. **16**. (**5**.)

—— The Inner Life of the Religious Societies of the Commonwealth, *etc.* pp. xxxi. 700. xxv. *Hodder & Stoughton: London*, 1876. 8°. **4715**. g. **1**.

—— On Membership in the Society of Friends . . . Being some remarks in an article lately published in the "Friends' Quarterly Examiner," on birthright membership, by J. S. Rowntree. pp. 68. *S. Harris & Co.: London*, 1873. 8°. **4139**. dd. **3**.

BARCLAY (ROBERT) *the Younger.* *See* BARCLAY (David) *Colonel.* Reliquiæ Barclaianæ. Correspondence of . . . D. Barclay and R. Barclay of Urie and his son Robert, *etc.* 1870. 4°. **10921**. k. **8**.

—— A Genealogical Account of the Barclays of Urie . . . Together with Memoirs of the Life of Colonel David Barclay and of . . . Robert Barclay, *etc.* [By R. Barclay the younger.] pp. 61. 1740. 8°. *See* BARCLAY, *Family of, of Urie.* **9914**. a. **40**.

—— [Another edition.] With . . . letters that passed between him, the Duke of York . . . and other distinguished characters, *etc.* [Edited by Henry Mill.] pp. viii. 98. *The Editor: London*, 1812. 8°. **606**. c. **3**.

—— [Another copy.] G. **1076**.

BARCLAY (ROBERT LEATHAM)

—— Rachel Barclay. High Leigh and Ceylon. A memoir, 1885–1932. [With letters and sketches of Rachel Barclay. Compiled by R. L. Barclay and others. With plates, including portraits.] pp. 119. *Privately printed: London*, 1935. 8°. **010822**. i. **17**.

—— Robert Leatham Barclay, C.B.E. A memoir. [By various authors. With plates, including portraits.] pp. 72. *University Press: Cambridge*, 1940. 8°. **10860**. bb. **14**. *Privately printed.*

BARCLAY (ROBERT S.) John A. Sutor. An appreciation and criticism. Specially written for Brochers [*sic*] abroad. (Reprinted from the Fraserburgh Herald.) pp. 16. *Herald Office: Fraserburgh*, [1910.] 8°. **4804**. e. **22**. (5.)

BARCLAY (SARAH MATILDA) *See* BARCLAY (Robert) *of Tottenham*. Sermons. By R. Barclay . . . Edited by his widow [i.e. S. M. Barclay]. 1878. 8°. **4465**. i. **11**.

—— *See* BARCLAY (Robert) *of Tottenham*. The Crucifixion. [A sermon. Edited by S. M. Barclay.] 1882. 8°. **4372**. h. **16**. (5.)

—— The Self-Revealing Jehovah of the Old Testament the Christ of the New Testament. pp. ix. 306. *J. Nisbet & Co.: London*, 1885 [1884]. 8°. **4227**. g. **21**.

BARCLAY (SHEPARD)

—— *See* RICHARD (Walter L.) Complete Backgammon . . . Edited by S. Barclay. 1938. 8°. **7911**. eee. 4.

—— The Contract Bridge Guide, *etc.* pp. 266. *Bobbs-Merrill Co.: Indianapolis*, [1931.] 8°. **7916**. aa. **12**.

—— Win at Contract with Any Partner. pp. xvii. 95. *D. Appleton & Co.: New York & London*, 1933. 8°. **7911**. f. **74**.

BARCLAY (SIDNEY) Personal Recollections of the American Revolution. A private journal . . . Edited [or rather, written] by S. Barclay. pp. 251. *Rudd & Carleton: New York*, 1859. 8°. **9604**. aa. **11**.

BARCLAY (THERESA) *Lady*. *See* BARCLAY (Marie Thérèse) *Lady*.

BARCLAY (THOMAS) *Moderator of the Presbyterian Church of England*.

—— *See* BAND (Edward) Barclay of Formosa. [With portraits.] 1936. 8°. **20031**. aaa. 46.

—— Supplement to Dictionary of the Vernacular or Spoken Language of Amoy [by Carstairs Douglas]. pp. iv. 276. *Shanghai*, 1923. 8°. **12910**. i. **41**.

BARCLAY (THOMAS) *Principal of Glasgow University*. *See* CAIRD (John) *Principal, etc.* In Memoriam. A sermon preached . . . on occasion of the death of . . . T. Barclay, *etc.* 1873. 8°. **4955**. d. **26**. (18.)

BARCLAY (THOMAS) *Writer on Political Economy*. The Rights of Labour according to John Ruskin. Arranged by T. Barclay. Third edition. [Based on passages in "Unto this Last."] pp. 16. *William Reeves: London*, [1889.] 8°. **8277**. aa. **49**. (5.)

BARCLAY (*Sir* THOMAS) *Barrister-at-Law*. Angleterre et France. Fraternité en guerre. Alliance dans la paix . . . Avant-propos de Gabriel Hanotaux. pp. 40. *Paris*, 1916. 8°. [*Pages actuelles*. no. 91.] **08052**. b. **1/91**.

—— Bearing and Importance of Commercial Treaties in the Twentieth Century. A lecture, *etc.* pp. 27. *Manchester*, 1906. 8°. [*Manchester University Lectures*. no. 3.] **Ac.2671/4.(3.)**

—— Companies in France. The law relating to British companies and securities in France and the formation of French companies. pp. x. 150. *Sweet & Maxwell: London*, 1899. 8°. **08225**. k. 12.

—— Second edition, revised and enlarged. pp. xii. 160. *Sweet & Maxwell: London*, 1899. 8°. **5425.g.35.**

BARCLAY (*Sir* THOMAS) *Barrister-at-Law*.

—— Les Effets de commerce dans le droit anglais. La lettre de change, le chèque et le billet à ordre comparés avec les principales législations étrangères. Suivi d'une traduction de la loi anglaise du 18 août 1882 et des principaux articles de la loi du 10 août 1882 sur la capacité de la femme mariée en Angleterre . . . Avec la collaboration de E. Dainville. pp. xxii. 326. *Paris*, 1884. 16°. **6376**. aa. **41**.

—— The French Law of Bills of Exchange, Promissory Notes and Cheques, compared with the "Bills of Exchange Act 1882," with a parallel table of reference and index. pp. 40. *Waterlow & Sons: London*, 1884. 8°. **5423**. bb. **17**.

—— The Hague Court and Vital Interests . . . Reprinted from the "Law Quarterly Review" of April, 1905. pp. 11. *Stevens & Sons: London*, 1905. 8°. **06955**. i. **32**.

—— International Law and Practice, with appendices containing Hague Conventions of 1907, Declaration of London, 1909, with Drafting Committee's Report, *etc.* pp. xv. 316. *Sweet & Maxwell: London; Boston Book Co.: Boston*, 1917. 4°. **6916**. eee. **9**.

—— Law and Usage of War: a practical handbook, *etc.* pp. xv. 245. *Constable & Co.: London*, 1914. 8°. **6956.a.22.**

—— The Law of France relating to Industrial Property, Patents . . . Exhibition Rewards and Medals . . . With a commentary on the Industrial Property Convention, 1883, and the provisions concerning British inventions . . . at French exhibitions. pp. xvi. 244. *Sweet & Maxwell: London*, 1889. 8°. **5424.bbb.12.**

—— Nationality, Domicile and Residence in France. Decree of October 2, 1888 concerning foreigners, with notes and instructions, *etc.* pp. 30. *W. Maxwell & Son: London; Paris* [printed], 1888. 8°. **6006**. aaa. **28**. (9.)

—— New Methods of Adjusting International Disputes and the Future. pp. xiv. 206. *Constable & Co.: London*, 1917. 8°. **06916**. f. **2**.

—— Le Président Wilson, et l'évolution de la politique étrangère des États-Unis, *etc.* pp. vii. 289. *Paris*, 1918. 8°. **08176**. d. 5.

—— Problems of International Practice and Diplomacy. With special reference to the Hague Conferences and Conventions and other general international agreements. pp. xix. 383. *Sweet & Maxwell: London; Boston Book Co.: Boston*, 1907. 4°. **6955**. g. **5**.

—— Le Roi George v d'Angleterre, *etc.* pp. 38. *Paris, Barcelone*, 1917. 8°. [*Pages actuelles*. no. 104.] **08052**. b. **1/104**.

—— The Sands of Fate. Dramatised study of an Imperial conscience. A phantasy. pp. xv. 253. *Houghton Mifflin Co.: Boston & New York*, 1917. 8°. **11791**. bb. **59**.

—— Les Tribulations d'une conscience impériale. Fantaisie dramatique. (Traduction). pp. xiii. 288. *Paris*, [1920.] 8°. **011779**. gg. **25**.

—— Thirty Years: Anglo-French reminiscences, 1876–1906. pp. viii. 389. *Constable & Co.: London*, 1914. 8°. **09077**. aaa. **27**.

—— The Turco-Italian War and its Problems. With appendices containing the chief state papers bearing on the subject . . . With an additional chapter on Moslem feeling by the Rt. Hon. Ameer Ali. pp. xiii. 259. *Constable & Co.: London*, 1912. 8°. **8027**. cc. **27**.

—— The Wisdom of Lang-Sin. A book of precepts with their reasons for the conduct of life. pp. xvii. 238. *Century Co.: New York, London*, 1927. 8°. **8403**. h. **29**.

BARCLAY (*Sir* THOMAS) *Barrister-at-Law.*

—— [Another copy.] The Wisdom of Lang-Sin, *etc.* *New York, London*, 1927. 8°. 8403. k. 24.

BARCLAY (*Sir* THOMAS) *of Birmingham.* The Class-Leader at Work . . . With an introduction by Rev. Richard Green. pp. xxi. 304. *C. H. Kelly: London*, [1905.] 8°. **4193. i. 1.**

—— The Class-Meeting in Wesleyan Methodism. [Compiled by Sir T. Barclay.] pp. 31. 1907. 8°. **4136. df. 3. (3.)**

—— "The Future Water Supply of Birmingham." A lecture, *etc.* pp. 30. *Cornish Bros.: Birmingham*, [1891.] 8°. **8708. g. 27. (7.)**

—— Second edition. pp. x. 48. *Cornish Bros.: Birmingham*, 1892. 8°. **8776. a. 68.**

—— Third edition, revised and enlarged. pp. 222. *Cornish Bros.: Birmingham*, 1898. 8°. **8777. c. 4.**

BARCLAY (THOMAS PATRICK) Memoirs and Medleys. The autobiography of a bottle-washer . . . Illustrated with portraits. [Edited by James K. Kelly.] pp. xi. 142. *Edgar Backus: Leicester*, 1934. 8°. **010825. de. 11.**

BARCLAY (THOMAS SWAIN) The Liberal Republican Movement in Missouri, 1865–1871. pp. v. 288. *Columbia*, 1926. 8°. **9615. b. 27.**

—— The Movement for Municipal Home Rule in St. Louis. [With plates.] pp. 138. *Columbia*, 1943. 8°. [*University of Missouri Studies.* vol. 18. no. 3.] Ac. **2691. m/15.**

BARCLAY (VERA CHARLESWORTH) *See also* BEECH (Margaret) *pseud.* [i.e. V. C. Barclay.]

—— *See* ALLERS (R.) [Das Werden der sittlichen Person.] Practical Psychology in Character Development. An abridged . . . version . . . made by V. Barclay. 1934. 8°. **08465. de. 45.**

—— The Book of Cub Games, *etc.* pp. xiv. 128. *J. Brown & Son: Glasgow*, 1920. 8°. **7911. de. 49.**

—— Third edition. pp. xiv. 128. *J. Brown & Son: Glasgow*, 1926. 8°. **7912. aaa. 51.**

—— The Book of Cub Games, *etc.* pp. xiv. 128. *Brown, Son & Ferguson: Glasgow*, 1930. 8°. **7922. aa. 89.**

—— Camp Fire Yarns and Stunts. A book for Rover Leaders, S.M.'s and Guiders. pp. 135. *Brown, Son & Ferguson: Glasgow*, 1932. 8°. **012305. ee. 67.**

—— Challenge to the Darwinians. pp. xvi. 296. *R. H. Johns: Newport, Mon.*, 1951 [1952]. 8°. **04018. n. 20.**

—— Character Training in the Wolf Cub Pack. pp. viii. 95. *Faith Press: London*, 1921. 8°. **08408. de. 15.**

—— Cubbing . . . A guide-book for cub masters, *etc.* pp. 60. *C. A. Pearson: London*, 1920. 8°. **08821. a. 76.**

—— Danny and the Rattlesnakes. Yarns for scouts and cubs. pp. 142. *Brown, Son & Ferguson: Glasgow*, 1930. 8°. **12819. bb. 2.**

—— Danny the Detective: a story for wolf cubs. [Reprinted from "The Wolf Cub."] pp. 88. *G. P. Putnam's Sons: London & New York*, 1918. 8°. **12801. b. 4.**

—— Danny's Pack. pp. 127. *C. A. Pearson: London*, 1928. 8°. **12808. gg. 51.**

—— Darwin is not for Children. pp. 256. *Herbert Jenkins: London*, 1950. 8°. **7008. de. 5.**

BARCLAY (VERA CHARLESWORTH)

—— The Face of a King. Group Captain Cheshire, V.C. champions the Holy Shroud, *etc.* [With plates, including portraits.] pp. 99. *Century Art Press: Bognor Regis*, 1955. 8°. **4384. bb. 14.**

—— Games for Camp and Club-Room, *etc.* pp. 86. *Brown, Son & Ferguson: Glasgow*, 1932. 8°. **7916. c. 19.**

—— Good Scouting. Notes on scouting in the Catholic parish. pp. ix. 149. *Sheed & Ward: London*, 1927. 8°. **04192. aa. 33.**

—— Gyp and the Pedlar's Ring, *etc.* pp. 127. *G. G. Harrap & Co.: London*, 1938. 8°. **12816. bb. 25.**

—— Jane and the Pale Faces . . . Illustrated by Agnès Hoffet. pp. 207. *Herbert Jenkins: London*, [1945.] 8°. **12828. bb. 16.**

—— Jane and Tommy Tomkins, *etc.* pp. 186. *Herbert Jenkins: London*, 1938. 8°. **12822. aa. 25.**

—— Jane versus Jonathan . . . Illustrated by Johanna Düby. pp. 224. *Burns, Oates & Co.: London*, 1937. 8°. **12804. h. 60.**

—— Jane versus Jonathan . . . Illustrated by A. Hoffet. pp. 186. *Hollis & Carter: London*, 1946. 8°. **12816. a. 49.**

—— [A reissue.] Jane versus Jonathan, *etc.* *London*, 1947. 8°. **12831. ee. 15.**

—— Jane Will You Behave . . . Illustrated, *etc.* pp. 244. *Burns, Oates & Co.: London*, 1936. 8°. **NN. 26495.**

—— Jane Will You Behave . . . Illustrated by A. Hoffet. pp. 194. *Hollis & Carter: London*, 1944. 8°. **12828. aa. 51.**

—— Joc and Colette at the Natural History Museum . . . Illustrated, *etc.* pp. vii. 160. *Burns, Oates & Co.: London*, 1935. 8°. **7002. pp. 22.**

—— Joc and Colette on the Seashore, *etc.* pp. vii. 179. *Burns, Oates & Co.: London*, 1935. 8°. **07290. de. 20.**

—— Joc, Colette and the Animals . . . Illustrated by A. Hoffet. (New edition.) pp. v. 136. *Hollis & Carter: London*, 1944. 8°. **12821. dd. 41.**

—— [A reissue.] Joc, Colette and the Animals, *etc.* *London*, 1947. 8°. **12831. ee. 9.**

—— Joc, Colette and the Birds, *etc.* pp. x. 183. *Burns, Oates & Co.: London*, 1934. 8°. **7286. p. 7.**

—— Joc, Colette and the Birds, *etc.* (New edition.) pp. v. 170. *Hollis & Carter: London*, 1944. 8°. **012826. ee. 33.**

—— A Jungle Scrap Book. Stories from eighteen years' scouting . . . Illustrated by C. S. Chapman. pp. 75. *Brown, Son & Ferguson: Glasgow*, 1933. 8°. **08820. a. 11.**

—— Jungle Wisdom: a book for cubmasters. pp. 84. [1925.] 8°. *See* ENGLAND.—*Boy Scouts' Association.* **04192. aaa. 24.**

—— More Potted Stories. pp. 161. *Brown, Son & Ferguson: Glasgow*, 1936. 8°. **20029. a. 64.**

—— Morning Star, and other poems. *R. H. Johns: Newport, Mon.*, [1951.] 8°. **11659. aa. 24.**

—— The Mysterious Tramp. pp. 128. *C. A. Pearson: London*, 1920. 8°. **012802. aaa. 7.**

BARCLAY (VERA CHARLESWORTH)

—— Potted Stories to tell Scouts and Cubs. pp. 176. *J. Brown & Son: Glasgow,* [1926.] 8°. **12800.** ee. **23.**

—— Saints and Adventures . . . Illustrated by Stephen Reid. pp. vi. 101. *Burns, Oates & Co.: London,* 1938. 8°. **20033.** aa. **41.**

—— Saints by Firelight. Stories for guides and rangers. pp. 206. *Sheed & Ward: London,* 1931. 8°. **4830.** ff. **35.**

—— Saints of These Islands. pp. 253. *Sheed & Ward: London,* 1931. 8°. **4830.** ff. **36.**

—— The Scout Way. pp. 144. *Sheed & Ward: London,* 1929. 8°. **08821.** aa. **58.**

—— Stories of the Saints by Candle-Light. pp. vii. 119. *London,* 1922. 8°. [*Childermote Library.*] **20041.d.20/4.**

—— Scout Discipline. Reprinted from "Good Scouting" and "The Scout Way." pp. 99. *Brown, Son & Ferguson: Glasgow,* 1934. 8°. **08820.** a. **17.**

—— Talks by Firelight. pp. 32. *Catholic Truth Society: London,* 1932. 8°. **3943.** aa. **251.**

—— They found an Elephant . . . Illustrated by Agnès Hoffet. pp. 262. *Herbert Jenkins: London,* 1950. 8°. **12831.** c. **12.**

—— They Met a Wizard . . . Illustrated by Agnes Hoffet. pp. 224. *Herbert Jenkins: London,* [1947.] 8°. **12829.** aa. **20.**

—— They Went to the Sea, *etc.* pp. 154. *Herbert Jenkins: London,* [1946.] 8°. **12828.** bb. **41.**

—— The Way into the Kingdom. A book for all who teach . . . Reprinted from "The Sower," *etc.* (Second edition.) pp. 79. *Burns Oates & Washbourne: London,* [1948.] 8°. **4401.** dd. **39.**

BARCLAY (W. A.) Alignment Characteristic for Amplifying Valves. *Glenfarg,* [1926.] *s. sh.* fol. **1820.h.8.(124.)**

—— Chronological and Genealogical Picture Chart of English History, from William the Conqueror to accession of Edward VII. Designed & drawn by W. A. Barclay. *W. & A. K. Johnston: Edinburgh & London,* [1902.] *s. sh.* fol. Cup. **649.** d. **1.** **(35.)**

—— Motor Costs Calculator. [*The Author: Murtle,* 1928.] *s. sh.* 4°. **1879.** cc. **9.** **(33.)**

—— N-Diagram. [Illustrating the formula p/q = f(r)*.] [*Bieldside,* 1930.] *s. sh.* fol. **1860.** cc. **5.** **(8.)**

—— Perpetual Calendar, 1844 to 1955. [Compiled by W. A. Barclay.] [1927.] *s. sh. obl.* 8°. See CALENDAR. **1882.** c. **1.** **(250.)**

BARCLAY (W. D.)

—— *See* SCHONELL (Fred J.) and CRACKNELL (S. H.) Right from the Start Arithmetic . . . Scottish edition, prepared by W. D. Barclay. 1943, *etc.* 8°. W.P. **1051.**

BARCLAY (WADE CRAWFORD) The Teacher's Study of the Life of Christ. *William Briggs: Toronto,* [1917.] 8°. [*New Standard Teacher Training Course.* pt. 3.] **08311.** aa. **28.**

BARCLAY (WILBUR F.) A Manual of Tennessee Corporations, *etc.* pp. vii. 355. *The Author: Nashville, Tenn.,* 1892. 8°. **6625.** aaa. **9.**

BARCLAY (WILFRID)

—— The Club of Skulls. *Modern Publishing Co.: London,* [1938.] 8°. **012643.** a. **69.**

—— The Secret Menace. [A novel.] *Modern Publishing Co.: London,* [1938.] 8°. **012614.** c. **9.**

BARCLAY (WILLIAM) *Editor of "The Banffshire Journal."*

—— Alexander Louttit, Schoolmaster. [Extracted from the transactions of the Banffshire Field Club.] [*Banff,*] 1934. 8°. **10824.** de. **20.**

—— Banffshire . . . With maps, diagrams and illustrations. pp. viii. 139. *University Press: Cambridge,* 1922. 8°. [*Cambridge County Geographies.*] **010352.** e. **1/70.**

—— In Alvah [i.e. the Parish of Alvah]. A paper read at a meeting of the Banffshire Field Club, *etc.* [By W. Barclay.] pp. 45. [1932.] 8°. *See* ALVAH. **010370.** df. **45.**

—— The Schools and Schoolmasters of Banffshire, *etc.* pp. xv. 308. *Banffshire Journal: Banff,* 1925. 8°. **8364.** dd. **30.**

BARCLAY (WILLIAM) *Lecturer in the University of Glasgow.*

—— A New Testament Wordbook. pp. 128. *SCM Press: London,* 1955. 8°. **3228.** aa. **74.**

BARCLAY (WILLIAM) *M.D.* Callirhoe, the nymph of Aberdene, resuscitat by W. Barclay . . . What diseases may be cured by drinking of the well at Aberdene, and what is the true use thereof. *Andro Hart:* [*Edinburgh*], 1615. 8°. **1171.** a. **25.** **(1.)**

—— [Another edition.] [With an "Epistle dedicatory" signed: Philopolis, i.e. Alexander Skene.] *Iohn Forbes, Younger: Aberdene,* 1670. 8°. **7462.** b. **22.**

—— [Another edition.] pp. 26. *Burnett & Rettie: Aberdeen,* 1799. 12°. **1171.** l. **30.** **(2.)**

—— Guil. Barclaii . . . Judicium de certamine G. Eglisemmii cum G. Buchanano, pro dignitate paraphraseos psalmi CIIII. . . . Adjecta sunt, Eglisemmii ipsum iudicium, ut editum fuit Londini, 1619 . . . et . . . ejusdem psalmi elegans paraphrasis Thomæ Rhædi. pp. 61. *Apud Georgium Eldum: Londini,* 1620. 8°. **847.** g. **16.** **(1.)**

—— [Another copy.] **1213.** k. **19.** **(6.)**

—— [Another edition.] *See* BIBLE.—*Psalms.*—*Selections.* [*Latin.*] Octupla; hoc est, octo paraphrases poeticæ psalmi CIV., *etc.* 1696. 8°. **1220.** c. **40.** **(1.)**

—— [Another edition.] See BIBLE.—*Hagiographa.* [*Latin.*] Poetarum Scotorum musæ sacræ, *etc.* pt. 2. 1739. 8°. **217.** h. **24, 25.**

—— Nepenthes; or, the Vertues of tobacco. *Andro Hart: Edinburgh,* 1614. 8°. **1038.** a. **43.** **(1.)**

—— Poemata. *See* JOHNSTON (Arthur) *M.D.* Delitiæ poetarum Scotorum, *etc.* 1637. 12°. **1213.** a. **7.**

—— Guil. Barclayi . . . Sylvæ tres. *Andreas Hart: Edinburgi,* 1619. 8°. **11403.** aaa. **25.**

BARCLAY (WILLIAM) *Professor of Civil Law at Angers. See* BARCLAY (John) *Poet, etc.* Ioannis Barclaii Pietas, siue publicæ pro regibus . . . et priuatæ pro G. Barclaio . . . vindiciæ aduersus . . . Cardinalis Bellarmini Tractatum de potestate Summi Pontificis, *etc.* 1612. 4°. C. **66.** c. **17.**

—— *See* BUCKERIDGE (John) successively *Bishop of Rochester* and *of Ely.* De potestate Papæ in rebus temporalibus . . . libri duo. In quibus respondetur authoribus, scripturis, rationibus . . . contra G. Barclaium allatis, *etc.* 1614. 4°. **857.** l. **8.**

BARCLAY (William) *Professor of Civil Law at Angers.*

—— *See* Eudaemon-Joannes (A.) *Cydonius.* R. P. Andreæ Eudæmon-Ioannis . . . Epistola monitoria ad Ioannem Barclaium Guillelmi filium, de libro ab eo pro patre suo contra . . . Robertum Bellarminum . . . scripto. 1613. 8°. **860.** b. **17.** **(4.)**

—— *See* Lex. Lex, Rex: the Law and the Prince. A dispute for the just prerogative of King and People . . . With a scripturall confutation of the ruinous grounds of W. Barclay, *etc.* 1644. 4°. **E. 11. (5.)**

—— *See* Paris.—*Parlement.* Remonstrance . . . sur le libure intitulé Tractatus de potestate Summi Pontificis . . . aduersus G. Barclaium, auctore . . . R. Bellarmino, *etc.* 1610. fol. **1353.** k. **9.** **(1.)**

—— *See* Robert [Bellarmino], *Saint, Cardinal, Archbishop of Capua.* [Tractatus de potestate Summi Pontificis in rebus temporalibus.] Power of the Pope in Temporal Affairs, against William Barclay, *etc.* [A reply to Barclay's "De potestate Papae."] [1950.] 4°. **4572.** dd. **7.**

—— *See* Rutherford (Samuel) Lex, Rex, or the law and the Prince . . . with a scriptural confutation of the ruinous grounds of W. Barclay, *etc.* 1843. 8°. [*The Presbyterian's Armoury.* vol. 3.] **1354.** k. **3.**

—— Gulielmi Barclaii De potestate Papæ . . . Liber posthumus. Eiusdem De regno et regali potestate aduersus . . . Monarchomachos libri vi. Editio nunc secundo in Germania adornata emendatior. pp. 825. *Hanoviæ,* 1617. 8°. **4050.** a. **32.**

—— D. Guillelmi Barclaji . . . Ad legem imperium D. de jurisdictione commentarius. 1753. *See* Meerman (G.) Novus thesaurus juris civilis, *etc.* tom. 7. 1751, *etc.* fol. **18.** h. **12.**

—— De potestate Papæ: an & quatenus in reges & principes seculares ius & imperium habeat . . . Liber posthumus. [Edited by John Barclay.] pp. 343. *F. Du Bois & I. Garnich: Mussiponti,* 1609. 8°. **1020.** c. **9.**

—— [Another issue.] **847.** h. **12.**
In this issue the preliminaries were printed in London at the Eliot's Court Press.

—— [Another edition.] Tractatus de potestate papæ . . . Cui accessit authoris vita. pp. 232. [*Amsterdam ?*] 1709. 4°. **227.** h. **29.**

—— Guil. Barclaii J.C. of the Authoritie of the Pope; whether, and how farre forth, he hath power . . . over temporall kings and princes, liber posthumus. pp. 229. [Edited by John Barclay.] *Arnold Hatfield for William Aspley: London,* 1611. 4°. **3932.** d. **15.**

—— [Another issue.] [*S., R., Priest. Certain Generall Reasons, proving the lawfulnesse of the oath of allegiance, etc.*] **1103.** f. **8.**

—— Traicté de la puissance du Pape . . . Traduit du latin. ff. 273. *Pont à Musson,* 1611. 8°. **4051.** de. **19.**

—— *See* Robert [Bellarmino], *Saint, Cardinal, Archbishop of Capua.* Tractatus de potestate Pontificis . . . aduersus G. Barclaium. 1611. 8°. **1115.** a. **3.**

—— —— 1698. fol. [*Rocaberti* (*J. T. de*) *Archbishop of Valencia. Bibliotheca maxima pontificia, etc.* tom. 18.] **484.** f. **2.**

—— Guilielmi Barclaii . . . De regno et regali potestate aduersus Buchananum, Brutum [i.e. H. Languet], Boucherium, & reliquos Monarchomachos, libri sex. pp. 542. *G. Chaudiere: Parisiis,* 1600. 4°. C. **77.** c. **17.**

—— Gulielmi Barclaji . . . In titulos pandectarum de rebus creditis, et de jurejurando, commentarii. 1727. *See* Otto (Everardus) Thesaurus juris romani, *etc.* tom. 3. 1725, *etc.* fol. **499.** d. **4.**

BARCLAY (William) *Professor of Civil Law at Angers.*

—— [Another edition.] 1733. *See* Otto (Everardus) Thesaurus juris romani, *etc.* tom. 3. 1733, *etc.* fol. **5206.** h. **1.**

—— [Another edition.] 1744. *See* Otto (Everardus) Thesaurus juris romani, *etc.* tom. 3. 1741, *etc.* fol. **5254.** f. **8.**

—— Guilielmi Barclayi Oratio pro eloquentia. pp. 30. *S. Preuosteau: Parisijs,* 1598. 8°. **1090.** k. **19.**

BARCLAY (William) *Solicitor.* Handy-book for Licensed Victuallers, Brewers . . . including the Public House Closing Act, 1864, *etc.* pp. 96. *Routledge & Co.: London,* 1865 [1864]. 12°. **7953.** aa. **28.**

BARCLAY (*Sir* William) *See* Berkeley.

BARCLAY (William Duncan)

—— *See* Barclay (Helen M. D.) and Barclay (W. D.) Thoughtful Reading. [1952.] 8°. **012987.** bb. **22.**

BARCLAY (William Robb) *See* Aitchison (Leslie) and Barclay (W. R.) Engineering Non-Ferrous Metals and Alloys, *etc.* 1923. 8°. W.P. **3417/13.**

BARCLAY (William Robb) and **HAINSWORTH** (Cecil H.)

—— Electroplating. A treatise on the electro-deposition of metals, with a chapter on metal-colouring and bronzing . . . Illustrated. pp. viii. 399. *Edward Arnold: London,* 19[illegible]. 8°. **08755.** e. **59.**

BARCLAY (William Singer)

—— *See* Spon (Charles) *Freeman of the City of London.* William Singer Barclay . . . A memoir, *etc.* [With a portrait.] [1947.] 8°. **10860.** b. **10.**

—— The Land of Magellan . . . With 28 illustrations and 3 maps. pp. viii. 240. *Methuen & Co.: London,* 1926. 8°. **10482.** c. **19.**

BARCLAY (Wilson) The Seventh Man. [A novel.] pp. 308. *Ward, Lock & Co.: London & Melbourne,* 1933. 8°. NN. **19670.**

BARCLAY-ALLARDICE (Robert) *Captain, of Ury.* *See* Allardice.

BARCLAY-ALLARDICE (Robert) *Mayor of Lostwithiel.* *See* Allardice.

BARCLAY-ALLARDICE (Robert) *the Younger.* *See* Allardice.

BARCLAY DE MOUNTENEY (Thomas J.) *See* De Mounteney.

BARCLAY-HARVEY (*Sir* Charles Malcolm) *K.C.M.G.* *See* Harvey.

BARCLAYS BANK. *See* Barclay's Bank.

BARCLAY-SMITH (Edward) *See* Smith.

BARCLAY-SMITH (Phyllis) *See* Smith.

BARCLAYUS (Gulielmus) *M.D.* *See* Barclay (William)

BARCLAYUS (Gulielmus) *Professor of Civil Law at Angers.* *See* Barclay (William)

BARCLEY (Alexander) *See* Barclay.

BARCLEY (Robert) *See* Barclay (R.) *the Elder.*

BARCO (Alexandro del) Las Colonias gemelas reintegradas en la mitad de sus respectivas poblaciones . . . Dialogos criticos. Escritos por E. M. R. P. F. A. D. B. L. J. C. D. S. O. Y. P. D. P. E. L. D. M. D. G. [i.e. A. del Barco]. pp. xxvii. 230. 1788. 4°. *See* G., E. M. R. P. F. A. D. B. L. J. C. D. S. O. Y. P. D. P. E. L. D. M. D. **9041. f. 2.**

BARCO (Bartolomeo) Madrigali . . . Con alcune annotationi, *etc.* pp. 100. *G. B. Ciotti: Venetia,* 1604. 12°. **11427. aaa. 17.**

BARCO (Giovanni Battista) *See* Aristotle. [*De Anima.—Italian.*] Esposizione critica della psicologia greca . . . Il Trattato dell' anima, lib. I. e c. 1–3 del l. II. Traduzione e note di G. Barco. 1879. 8°. **8462. d. 8.**

—— *See* Aristotle. [*Poetica.—Italian.*] L'Arte poetica . . . tradotta sul testo di G. Vahlen, da G. Barco. 1876. 8°. **11824. e. 2.**

BARCO (José Rodríguez del) *See* Rodríguez del Barco.

BARCO (Josephus de San Miguel et) *See* San Miguel y Varco.

BARCO (Juan Ortíz del) *See* Ortíz del Barco.

BARCO (Luis del) Diccionario Español de la Sagrada Escritura, acompañado del texto latino del Dr. F. P. Merz, *etc.* [With a preface by S. Catalina del Arno.] *Lat. & Span.* 2 tom. *Madrid,* 1862. 4°. **3129. g. 14.**

BARCO CENTENERA (Martín del)

—— La Argentina, poema histórico. Reimpresión facsimilar de la primera edición, Lisboa 1602. Precedida de un estudio del Doctor Juan María Gutiérrez y de unos apuntes bio-bibliográficos de Don Enrique Peña. 2 pt. *Buenos Aires,* 1912. 8°. [*Biblioteca de la Junta de Historia y Numismática Americana.* tom. 5.] Ac. **8592.**

—— Argentina y Conquista del Rio de la Plata, con otros acaecimientos de los reynos del Peru, Tucuman y estado del Brasil. [A poem.] ff. 230. *P. Crasbeeck: Lisboa,* 1602. 4°. **242. l. 6.**

—— [Another edition.] *See* Gonzalez de Barcia Carballido y Zuñiga (A.) Historiadores primitivos, *etc.* tom. 3. 1749. fol. **145.f.11.**

—— [Another edition.] pp. viii. 312. xxiii. *Buenos-Aires,* 1836. 4°. [*Angelis (P. de) Coleccion de obras y documentos relativos a la historia . . . de las provincias del Rio de la Plata, etc.* tom. 2.] **600. gg. 6. (4.)**

—— [Another edition.] *See* Diaz de Gusman (R.) Historia Argentina, *etc.* tom. 3. 1854. 4°. **9772. e. 25.**

—— [Another edition.] Facsimil de la primera edición, impresa en Lisboa, por Pedro Crasbeeck en el año 1602. Notas bibliográficas y biográficas de Cárlos Navarro y Lamarca. pp. 31. 230. iv. *Buenos Aires,* 1912. 8°. **9773. cc. 14.**

BARCOCK (C. J.)

—— Construction and Arrangement of Milk Plants. pp. 36. *Washington,* 1949. 8°. [*U.S. Department of Agriculture. Circular.* no. 800.] A.S. **804/2.**

BARCONES (Enrique Mateo) Estudios para una Nosología filipina. pp. 447. *Madrid,* 1895. 8°. **07686. e. 14.**

BARCONES (Tomas Iglesias y) successively *Bishop of Mondonedo* and *Patriarch of the West Indies.* *See* Iglesias y Barcones.

BARCÓN OLESA (J.)

—— Belgrano Educador. Desarrollo de la instrucción pública en la región Jujeña. [With illustrations.] pp. 174. *Buenos Aires,* 1933. 8°. **010885. de. 52**

BARCOS (Arthus Timoléon de) Oraison funèbre de . . Louis xiv. *See* Louis xiv., *King of France.* [*Panegyrics, Elegies, etc.*] Recueil de plusieurs oraisons funèbres de Louis xiv., *etc.* tom. 2. 1716. 12°. **236. b. 30**

BARCOS (Martin de) *See* also Auvray, *le Sieur, pseud.* [i.e. M. de Barcos.]

—— De l'authorité de S. Pierre et de S. Paul, qui reside dans le Pape, successeur de ces deux apostres . . . Pour seruir de response aux accusations atroces . . . qu'on a formée contre cette proposition du Liure de la Fréquente Communion [of Antoine Arnauld]: Que S. Pierre et S. Paul sont les deux chefs de l'Eglise, qui n'en font qu'vn. [By M. de Barcos.] pp. 71. 1645. 4°. *See* Arnauld (Antoine) *Doctor of the Sorbonne.* **1476. bb. 32**

—— Exposition de la foi de l'Église Romaine touchant la grace et la prédestination. *See* Arnauld (Antoine) *Doctor of the Sorbonne.* Instructions sur la grace, *etc.* pt. 2. 1700. 8°. **4227. a. 23**

BARCO Y GASCA (Antonio Jacobo del) Dissertacion historico-geographica sobre reducir la antigua Onuba á la villa de Huelva, *etc.* pp. 96. *Sevilla,* 1755. 8°. **10161. a. 5**

BARCROFT (Anthony)

—— *See* Montù (E.) Capolavori dell'arte moderna italiana . . . Versione inglese di A. Barcroft. 1950. 4°. **7870. bb. 25**

BARCROFT (Charles) *See* Plutarch. [*Moralia.—English.*] Plutarch's Morals, *etc.* [Translated by C. Barcroft and others.] 1870. 8°. **2236. e. 3.**

BARCROFT (David Malcolmson) *See* Garré (C.) and Quincke (H. F.) Surgery of the Lung . . . Translated . . . by D. M. Barcroft. [1913.] 8°. **7481. ccc. 1.**

BARCROFT (Henry) and **SWAN** (Harold James Charles)

—— Sympathetic Control of Human Blood Vessels. pp. vii. 165. *Edward Arnold & Co.: London,* 1953. 8°. [*Monographs of the Physiological Society.* no. 1.] Ac. **3823. c/2**

BARCROFT (John) A Brief Narrative of the Life, Convincement, Conversion, and Labours of Love in the Gospel-ministry of . . . John Barcroft, *etc.* [An autobiography. Edited by John Stoddart.] pp. xvi. 61. *Sam. Fuller: Dublin,* 1730. 8°. **4920. c. 28.**

—— [Another copy.] **1373. a. 49.**

—— A Faithful Warning to the Inhabitants of Great Britain and Ireland, to dread the Lord and turn from their evil doings, *etc.* pp. 12. *Assigns of J. Sowle: London,* 1720. 12°. **116. a. 47.**

—— [Another edition.] pp. 12. *Assigns of J. Sowle: London,* 1720. 12°. **4151. a. 11.**

BARCROFT (*Sir* Joseph)

—— *See* Franklin (Kenneth I.) Joseph Barcroft, 1872–1947. [A biography. With portraits and a list of Barcroft's publications.] 1953. 8°. **10857. g. 60.**

—— *See* Huxley (*Right Hon.* Thomas H.) Lessons in Elementary Physiology, *etc.* [Rewritten by J. Barcroft.] 1915. 8°. **2320. a. 26**

BARCROFT (*Sir* JOSEPH)

—— *See* ROUGHTON (Francis J. W.) and KENDREW (J. C.) Haemoglobin. A symposium based on a conference . . . in memory of Sir Joseph Barcroft, *etc.* [With a portrait.] 1949. 8°. **7406**. s. **25**.

—— The Brain and its Environment. pp. vii. 117. *Yale University Press: New Haven*, 1938. 8°. [*Terry Lectures.*] Ac. **2692**. mr. (**12**.)

—— Features in the Architecture of Physiological Function. pp. x. 368. *University Press: Cambridge*, 1934. 8°. [*Cambridge Comparative Physiology.*] **7211.i.1/8.**

—— Researches on Pre-Natal Life. *Blackwell Scientific Publications: Oxford*, 1946– . 8°. W.P. **1524**.

—— The Respiratory Function of the Blood. pp. x. 320. *University Press: Cambridge*, 1914. 8°. **7439**. f. **18**.

—— [Another edition.] *University Press: Cambridge*, 1925– . 8°. W.P. **8474**.

—— Die Atmungsfunktion des Blutes . . . Ins Deutsche übertragen von Dr. Wilhelm Feldberg, *etc.* *Berlin*, 1927– . 8°. [*Monographien aus dem Gesamtgebiet der Physiologie der Pflanzen und der Tiere.* Bd. 13, 18.] W.P. **5841/13**.

BARCROFT (*Sir* JOSEPH) and **SAUNDERS** (JOHN TENNANT)

—— Cambridge Comparative Physiology. General editors: J. Barcroft . . . J. T. Saunders. *University Press: Cambridge*, 1927–39. 8°. 9 pt. **7211.i.1.**

BARCROFT (RICHARD) *See* TAYLOR (Jeremy) *Bishop of Down and Connor, etc.* The Rule of Conscience; or, Bishop Taylor's Ductor Dubitantium abridg'd. By R. Barcroft, *etc.* 1725. 8°. **846**. m. **15**.

BARCROFT (W.) The Contagious Diseases Acts. Shall their repeal be permitted? An appeal, *etc.* pp. 16. *Printed for private circulation: London*, [1883.] 8°. **8282**. ee. **14**. (**4**.)

BARCS (IMRE)

—— *See* IRÓK. Írók a viharban. Barcs I., Bálint Gy. . . . [and others] irásai, *etc.* 1941. 8°. **12360**. d. **13**.

BARCSA (JÁNOS) A debreceni kollégium és pártikulái. pp. 202. *Debreczen*, 1905. 8°. **8355**. ee. **47**.

—— A tiszántuli ev. ref. egyházkerület története. köt. 1— köt. 3. füz. 1. *Debreczen*, 1906, 08. 8°. **04685**. d. **32**. *Imperfect; wanting köt.* 3, *füz.* 2, 3.

BARCSAI (ÁBRAHÁM) *See* RÉVAI (J. M.) Két nagyságos elmének [L. Orczy and A. Barcsai] költeményes szüleményei, *etc.* 1789. 8°. **11585**. c. **43**.

—— Barcsay Ábraham költeményei. [Edited by B. Szira. With a plate.] pp. 148. *Budapest*, [1933.] 8°. [*Magyar irodalmi ritkaságok.* sz. 25.] W.P.2220/25.

BARCSAI (GÉZA)

—— A magyar tudományos élet harca a német szellemi imperializmus ellen. pp. 52. *Budapest*, 1946. 8°. **11867**. g. **15**.

BARCSAY (ÁBRAHAM) *See* BARCSAI.

BARCSAY-AMANT (ZOLTÁN)

—— A komini éremlelet a Kr. u. III. századból. J. Brunšmid előmunkálatai felhasználásával feldolgozta Barcsay-Amant Zoltán. The Hoard of Komin. Antoniani of the 3rd century A.D., *etc.* [Plates with introductions in Hungarian and English.] pp. 15. pl. LXIII. *Budapest*, 1937. fol. [*Dissertationes Pannonicae.* ser. 2. no. 5.] Ac. **821**.

BARCUS (JAMES S.) The Boomerang; or, Bryan's Speech with the wind knocked out. A dialogue including the full text of Bryan's famous Madison Square Garden speech, together with complete answers to each argument, *etc.* pp. 180. See BRYAN (William J.) 1896. 8°. **8175**. de. **15**.

—— Public Service. Comprising map of political divisions, names, official titles and remuneration of officers and heads of departments in National, State, and Municipal service within the State of New York: tabulations and statements of important data concerning party organizations . . . Edited by J. S. Barcus. pp. 631. *Globe Publishing Co.: New York*, 1898. 8°. **8175**. f. **10**.

BARCUS (L. F.)

—— A Photographic Determination of the Mass Ratio of Ursae Minoris. (Reprinted from The Astronomical Journal.) pp. 3. [1938.] 4°. **08560**. dd. **17**.

BARCUS (THOMAS RANKIN)

—— Carnegie Corporation and College Libraries, 1938–1943. pp. 59. 1943. 8°. *See* NEW YORK, *City of.—Carnegie Corporation.* **11916**. a. **8**.

BARCYŃSKA (HÉLÈNE) *Countess, pseud.* [i.e. MARGUERITE FLORENCE BARCLAY, afterwards EVANS.]

—— *See also* BARCLAY, afterwards EVANS (M. F.)

—— Astrologer. pp. 176. *Rich & Cowan: London*, [1944.] 8°. NN. **34909**.

—— Astrologer . . . 42nd thousand. pp. 176. *Rich & Cowan: London*, [1948.] 8°. **12651**. dd. **15**

—— Back to the Honey-Pot. A story of the stage. pp. 287. *Hurst & Blackett: London*, [1925.] 8°. NN. **11199**.

—— Beloved Burden. pp. 207. *Rich & Cowan: London*, 1954. 8°. NNN. **5606**.

—— Black-Out Symphony. pp. 288. *Rich & Cowan: London*, [1942.] 8°. NN. **33335**.

—— Bubble over Thorn. pp. 224. *Rich & Cowan: London* 1951. 8°. NNN. **2278**

—— A Certified Bride. pp. 285. *Hurst & Blackett: London*, [1928.] 8°. NN. **13689**.

—— Conjuror. pp. 236. *Rich & Cowan: London*, [1950.] 8°. NNN. **963**.

—— Decameron Cocktails. pp. 282. *Hurst & Blackett: London*, [1926.] 8°. NN. **11767**.

—— Exit Renee. pp. 288. *Hurst & Blackett: London*, [1934.] 8°. NN. **22125**.

—— Fantoccini. pp. 280. *Chapman & Hall: London*, 1930. 8°. NN. **16153**.

—— God and Mr. Aaronson. pp. 288. *Hutchinson & Co.: London*, [1937.] 8°. NN. **28114**.

—— The Golden Snail, and other stories. pp. 287. *Hurst & Blackett: London*, [1927.] 8°. NN. **12907**.

BARCYŃSKA (Hélène) *Countess, pseud.* [i.e. Marguerite Florence Barclay, afterwards Evans.]

—— Gorgeous Brute. pp. 223. *Rich & Cowan: London,* [1949.] 8°. NN. **39669**.

—— Hearts for Gold. pp. 256. *Hutchinson & Co.: London,* [1938.] 8°. NN. **28584**.

—— The Honey Pot. A story of the stage. pp. 348. *Hurst & Blackett: London,* 1916. 8°. NN. **3277**.

—— Hand Painted. pp. 287. *Hurst & Blackett: London,* [1925.] 8°. NN. **10812**.

—— He Married his Parlourmaid, *etc.* pp. 254. *Chapman & Hall: London,* 1929. 8°. NN. **15651**.

—— I Loved a Fairy, *etc.* [With a portrait.] pp. 179. *Hurst & Blackett: London,* [1933.] 8°. NN. **15299**.

—— If Wishes were Horses. pp. viii. 328. *Hurst & Blackett: London,* 1917. 8°. NN. **4054**.

—— Jackie. pp. 288. *Hurst & Blackett: London,* [1921.] 8°. NN. **6820**.

—— Joy Comes After. pp. 196. *Rich & Cowan: London,* [1943.] 8°. NN. **34319**.

—— The Joy Shop. pp. 314. *Chapman & Hall: London,* 1931. 8°. NN. **18028**.

—— [A reissue.] *Wright & Brown: London,* [1933.] 8°. NN. **20787**.

—— [Another edition.] pp. 128. *George Newnes: London,* [1934.] 8°. **012614**. dd. **47**.

—— Keep Cheery. pp. 288. *Hutchinson & Co.: London,* [1937.] 8°. NN. **27335**.

—— Let the Storm Burst. pp. 256. *Rich & Cowan: London,* 1941. 8°. NN. **32445**.

—— The Little Mother who sits at home. [Letters from a mother to her son.] Edited by Countess Barcyńska. pp. x. 171. *T. C. & E. C. Jack: London & Edinburgh,* [1915.] 8°. **12354**. pp. **13**.

—— Love Maggy. pp. 284. *Hurst & Blackett: London,* 1918. 8°. NN. **4984**.

—— Love Never Dies. pp. 163. *Rich & Cowan: London,* [1943.] 8°. NN. **34120**.

—— Love's Last Reward. pp. 288. *Hurst & Blackett: London,* [1920.] 8°. NN. **6593**.

—— Luck is a Lady. pp. 190. *Rich & Cowan: London,* [1945.] 8°. NN. **9570**.

—— Milly Comes to Town. pp. 242. *Chapman & Hall: London,* 1928. 8°. NN. **14605**.

—— Mint Walk . . . Second edition. pp. 288. *Hurst & Blackett: London,* [1927.] 8°. NN. **12494**.

—— Pick Up and Smile. pp. 256. *Hutchinson & Co.: London,* [1936.] 8°. NN. **25833**.

—— Pretty Dear. A romance. pp. 314. *Hurst & Blackett: London,* 1920. 8°. NN. **6595**.

—— Publicity Baby. pp. 288. *Hurst & Blackett: London,* [1935.] 8°. NN. **23686**.

—— Running Free, and other stories. pp. 280. *Chapman & Hall: London,* 1929. 8°. NN. **15131**.

—— The Russet Jacket. A story of the turf. pp. 286. *Hurst & Blackett: London,* [1924.] 8°. NN. **10195**.

—— Sanity Jane. pp. 312. *Hurst & Blackett: London,* [1919.] 8°. NN. **5878**.

—— Ships Come Home. pp. 283. *Hurst & Blackett: London,* [1922.] 8°. NN. **8367**.

—— Sweetbriar Lane. pp. 256. *Hutchinson & Co.: London,* [1938.] 8°. NN. **29373**.

—— The Tears of Peace. pp. 206. *Rich & Cowan: London,* [1944.] 8°. NN. **34740**.

—— Tesha, a plaything of destiny. pp. 222. *Hurst & Blackett: London,* [1923.] 8°. NN. **8588**.

—— That Trouble Piece! pp. 293. *Rich & Cowan: London,* [1939.] 8°. NN. **30784**.

—— Those Dominant Hills. pp. 260. *Rich & Cowan: London,* 1951. 8°. NNN. **1775**.

—— Twenty-one. [Tales.] pp. 288. *Hurst & Blackett: London,* [1924.] 8°. NN. **9832**.

—— Under the Big Top. pp. 288. *Hurst & Blackett: London,* [1933.] 8°. NN. **20215**.

—— We lost our Way. pp. 219. *Rich & Cowan: London,* [1948.] 8°. NN. **38592**.

—— We Women! [A novel.] pp. 288. *Hurst & Blackett: London,* [1923.] 8°. NN. **9303**.

—— Webs. pp. 287. *Hurst & Blackett: London,* [1922.] 8°. NN. **7877**.

—— A Woman of Experience. pp. 288. *Hurst & Blackett: London,* [1931.] 8°. NN. **18041**.

—— The Wood is my Pulpit. pp. 192. *Rich & Cowan: London,* [1942.] 8°. NN. **13032**.

—— Writing Man. pp. 286. *Hutchinson & Co.: London,* [1939.] 8°. NN. **29893**.

BARCZA (Alicja) *See* Orme (Alexandra) *pseud.* [i.e. Alicja Barcza.]

BARCZA (Gedeon) and **TÓTH** (László) *Writer on Chess.*

—— Tanulj sakkozni. pp. 69. [*Budapest*?] 1951. 8°. **7921**. ee. **20**.
A magyar sakkélet könyvei. sz. 1.

BARCZA (Imre)

—— *See* Hungary.—*Magyar Könyvkiadók és Könyvkereskedők, Zeneműkiadók, és Zeneműkereskedők Országos Egyesülete.* Magyar könyvészet 1911–1920 . . . Barcza Imre címanyagának felhasználásával összeállította az Országos Széchényi-Könyvtár Bibliográfiai Osztálya, *etc.* 1939, *etc.* 8°. **2117.d.**

—— *See* Petrik (G.) Magyar könyvészet, 1901–1910, *etc.* (füz. 15–22. Szerkesztették Petrik G. és Barcza I.) 1917, *etc.* 8°. **2117.d.**

—— Az ipar és kereskedelem érdekképviseleti szervezete Csonkamagyarországon. Szerkesztette Barcza I. pp. 15. *Budapest,* 1925. 8°. **08245**. g. **46**.

—— A magyar bankkérdés és vámpolitika irodalma. Bibliographie der Bankfrage und Zollpolitik Ungarns. Előszóval ellátta Dr. Bernát I. pp. 40. *Budapest,* 1911. 8°. **11907**. aa. **4**. (**4**.)

BARCZA (Imre)

—— A magyar parlamenti választói jog legujabb irodalma. Bibliographia juris electionis Hungaricæ. pp. 51. *Budapest*, 1912. 8°. **011904.** bb. **21.** (**4.**)

—— Szent Erzsébet irodalma. Bibliographia Sanctae Elisabethae . . . Különlenyomat a "Corvina" a magyar könvkereskedők egyletének közlönyéből. pp. 14. *Budapest*, 1907. 8°. **011900.** g. **37.** (**2.**)

BARCZEWSKI (Max)

—— Kompensationsgeschäfte im Rahmen der Kontingentierungspolitik. pp. 200. *Berlin*, 1936. 8°. [*Neue Deutsche Forschungen.* Bd 72.] **012213.y.1/72.**

BÁRCZI (Géza)

—— *See* Debrecen.—*Debreceni Kossuth Lajos Tudományegyetem.—Magyar Népnyelvkutató Intézet.* Magyar népnyelv . . . Szerkeszti Csűry B. (Bárczi G.) 1939, *etc.* 8°. Ac. **829/4.**

—— Magyar nyelvjárások . . . Szerkeszti Barczi G. *Debrecen*, 1951 [1952–]. 8°. W.P. c. **563.**

BÁRCZI (Géza)

—— A Tihanyi apátság alapítólevele mint nyelvi emlék. [With the text of the charter and a facsimile.] pp. 231. *Budapest*, 1951. 8°. [*Nyelvészeti tanulmányok.* no. 1.] W.P. d. **223/1.**

BÁRCZI (Iván) A német cultura befolyása Magyarországra . . . Második bővitett . . . kiádas. pp. 112. *Sopron*, 1880. 8°. **011840.** l. **4.**

BARCZINSKY (Armiger) A Shadowy Partner; or, the Devil among the Stockbrokers. pp. 179. *Swan Sonnenschein & Co.: London*, 1888. 8°. **12627.** k. **1.**

BÁRCZY (István) *See* Ferenczi (I.) Községi lakáspolitika és lakásügyi intézmények . . . Bárczy I. . . . megbizásából végzett tanulmányok alapján irta Ferenczi I. [With a preface by I. Bárczy.] 1910. 8°. **08276.** dd. **14.**

BARCZYNSKI ( ) Die Maass- u. Gewichtsordnung für das Deutsche Reich nebst Aichordnung und Aichgebührentaxe ergänzt und erläutert. pp. ix. 192. *Magdeburg*, 1893. 8°. **8535.** ccc. **46.**

BARD.

—— *See* also Periodical Publications.—*London.*

—— The Bard. *See* London.—iii. *Human Epic Society.*

—— Am Bàrd, *etc.* *See* Periodical Publications.—*Edinburgh.*

—— "The Bard." [A poem. By Hugh Cornwall.] [*Hugh Cornwall: West Norwood*, 1945.] 8°. **11657.** ff. **30.**

—— Bard Nadwiślański. *See* Periodical Publications.—*Avignon.*

—— Bárdar saga Snæfellsáss. [Edited, and with a Danish summary, by Gudbradr Vigfússon.] *See* Vigfússon (G.) Bárdarsaga Snæfellsáss, Víglundarsaga, *etc.* 1860. 12°. **12430.** p. **9 19.**

—— The Wandering Bard: and other poems. [By John Walker Ord.] pp. 135. *John Anderson jun.: Edinburgh*, 1833. 12°. **993.** g. **45.**

BARD (Alphonse) *Docteur en Droit.* Précis de droit internationale . . . Droit pénal et privé. pp. x. 369. *Paris*, 1883. 8°. **6916.** c. **9.**

BARD (Alphonse) *Docteur en Droit*, and **ROBIQUET** (Paul)

—— Droit constitutionnel comparé. La constitution française de 1875 étudiée dans ses rapports avec les constitutions étrangères. pp. vii. 400. *Paris*, 1876. 8°. **8051.** e. **20.**

BARD (Alphonse) *Surgeon.* *See* Devergie (P. N.) Clinique de la maladie syphilitique. Enrichie d'observations communiquées par . . . Bard, *etc.* 1826, *etc.* 4°. **773.** m. **18.**

BARD (Antoine) Un Général de l'an deux en Vendée. Notes biographiques sur le Général Bard. pp. 238. *Paris*, 1897. 8°. **010662.** ff. **57.**

—— Six mois de vie judiciaire. [With special reference to the first revision of the Dreyfus case.] pp. xiv. 203. *Paris*, 1927. 8°. **5423.** df. **9.**

BARD (Antoine Marie) *See* Bard (A.) Un Général de l'an deux en Vendée. Notes biographiques sur le Général Bard. 1897. 8°. **010662.** ff. **57.**

BARD (E. S. Alphonse) Considérations générales sur la péripneumonie inflammatoire aiguë. Tribut académique, *etc.* pp. 36. *Montpellier*, 1829. 4°. **1181.** e. **7.** (**20.**)

BARD (Émile) Les Chinois chez eux. Avec 12 planches hors texte. pp. 357. *Paris*, 1899. 8°. **010057.** e. **66.**

—— The Chinese at Home. Adapted from the French . . . by H. Twitchell. [With plates.] pp. xii. 305. *George Newnes: London*, [1906.] 8°. **010058.** g. **12.**

BARD (Erwin Wilkie)

—— The Port of New York Authority. pp. x. 352. *Columbia University Press: New York*, 1942. 8°. [*Studies in History, Economics and Public Law.* no. 468.] Ac. **2688/2.**

BARD (Giuseppe) *See* Bard (Joseph)

BARD (Guillaume) Propositions et observations sur les fractures; suivies d'un aperçu sur l'extension continuelle, en proposant le mécanisme du Tour pour l'opérer graduellement. pp. 16. *Paris*, 1809. 4°. **1182.** h. **6.** (**11.**)

BARD (Harry) and **MANAKEE** (Harold S.)

—— Active Citizenship. [With illustrations.] pp. v. 506. *John C. Winston Co.: Philadelphia*, [1951.] 8°. **08286.** f. **73.**

BARD (Henri) *Association Football Player*, and **DIFFRE** (Henri)

—— Le Football Association, *etc.* pp. x. 214. *Paris*, 1927. 8°. **7904.** ee. **39.**

BARD (Henri) *de Mens.* La Lecture de la Bible, comme élément du culte. Thèse, *etc.* pp. 42. *Strasbourg*, 1868. 8°. **3678.** bb. **20.** (**4.**)

BARD (Jean Baptiste Joseph) Dissertation sur le choléra morbus, *etc.* pp. 51. *Strasbourg*, [1799.] 8°. [*Collection générale des dissertations de l'École spéciale de Médecine de Strasbourg.* tom. 1.] **7381*b.**

BARD (Josef) Shipwreck in Europe. [A novel.] pp. 314. *Harper & Bros.: New York & London*, 1928. 8°. **12713.** c. **8.**

—— The Tale of a Child, *etc.* pp. 29. *New English Weekly: London*, 1932. 8°. **012600.** l. **43.**

BARD (Joseph) L'Algérie en 1854. Itinéraire général de Tunis à Tanger, *etc.* pp. 251. *Paris*, 1854. 8°. **010096.** i. **24.**

BARD (Joseph)

—— Archéographie de l'insigne église collégiale de Notre-Dame et du beffroi de Beaune. pp. 54. pl. 2. *Beaune*, 1836. 4°. **4630. dd. 2.**

—— Chambéry, Aix-les-Bains. 1834. pp. 35. *Genève, Chambéry*, [1834?] 8°. **10169. aa. 11.**

—— De la question liturgique par rapport à la Sainte Église de Lyon. pp. 62. *Lyon*, 1860. 8°. **3475. bb. 69. (7.)**

—— Dei monumenti d'architettura bizantina in Ravenna. Relazione ai Ministri dell' Interno e dell' Istruzione Publica in Francia . . . Traduzione dal Francese. pp. 39. *Ravenna*, 1844. 8°. **7761.e.51.**

—— Le Département du Rhône. Histoire, statistique, géographie. pp. vi. 148. *Lyon*, 1857. 12°. **10169. e. 37.**

—— Derniers mélanges de littérature et d'archéologie sacrée. pp. xiii. 548. pl. 4. *Lyon*, 1847. 4°. **4632. e. 38.**

—— Dijon. Histoire et tableau, depuis les temps les plus reculés jusqu'à l'Assemblée nationale législative de 1849. pp. xii. 433. *Dijon*, 1849. 12°. **10173. b. 39.**

—— Essai d'un Plutarque militaire de la Bourgogne. 2 livr. *Dijon*, 1858, 60. 4°. **10662. i. 2.**

—— Manuel général d'archéologie sacrée burgundo-lyonnaise, *etc.* pp. xi. 424. *Lyon, Paris*, 1844. 8°. **7708. c. 5.**

—— Revue basilicale et liturgique de Rome. pp. x. 106. *Rome; Beaune* [printed], 1848. 12°. **4605. b. 23.**

—— Une Semaine à Londres pendant l'exposition de 1851. Renfermant la description du bâtiment de l'exposition . . . le guide exact et pittoresque de l'étranger dans Londres . . . Avec . . . un tableau de Londres. pp. xv. 156. *Paris*, [1851.] 12°. **10350. a. 50.**

—— Statistique générale des basiliques et du culte dans la ville de Lyon. Précédée d'instructions sur l'archéologie sacrés dans la province ecclésiastique de cette métropole, *etc.* pp. lxxvi. 340. *Lyon*, 1842. 8°. **4632. f. 8.**

—— Trains de plaisir de Paris à Lyon, avec le repas au Clos de Vougeot, *etc.* [With a map.] pp. 88. *Chalon-sur-Saône*, 1851. 12°. **10108. aa. 8. (5.)**

BARD (L. A. B.) Essai sur les bases végétales salifiables . . . Pour obtenir le grade de docteur en médecine. pp. 23. *Montpellier*, 1824. 4°. **1181. c. 14. (8.)**

BARD (Louis)

—— *See* Congrès Français de Médecine. [Lyons, 1894.] Congrès Français de Médecine. Premiere session . . . Procès verbaux . . . publiés par . . . L. Bard, *etc.* 1895, *etc.* 8°. **Ac. 3712. b.**

—— De la propagation et de la prophylaxie des épidémies de diphtérie. Relation de l'épidémie d'Oullins . . . Extrait du Lyon Médical, 1889. pp. 80. *Lyon*, 1889. 8°. **07305. g. 10. (1.)**

—— Die physikalischen Zeichen der Mitralstenose. pp. 30. *Leipzig*, 1907. 8°. [*Sammlung klinischer Vorträge.* Neue Folge. Innere Medizin. no. 137.] **7441. g.**

BARD (Mary)

—— Best Friends . . . Illustrated by Hellmuth Weissenborn. pp. 191. *Hammond, Hammond: London*, 1955. 8°. **12838. b. 48.**

—— The Doctor wears Three Faces. [An autobiography.] pp. 254. *J. B. Lippincott Co.: Philadelphia & New York*, [1949.] 8°. **10890. e. 10.**

—— The Doctor wears Three Faces. [Autobiographical reminiscences.] pp. 224. *Hammond, Hammond & Co.: London*, 1949. 8°. **10862. g. 12.**

BARD (Mary)

—— Forty Odd. [Reminiscences.] pp. 223. *Hammond, Hammond & Co.: London*, 1952. 8°. **10890. fff. 16.**

BÁRD (Miklós) *pseud.* [i.e. Ferencz Kozma.]

—— *See* Ábrahám (E.) Bárd Miklós. 1938. 8°. **11862. aaa. 3.**

—— Bárd Miklós költeményei, 1887–1913 pp. 441. 1915. 8°. *See* Pest.—*Kisfaludy-Társaság.* **Ac. 8983/57**

—— Köd. Verses regény. pp. 367. *Debrecen, Budapest*, [1929.] 8°. **011586. bbb. 50.**

—— Bárd Miklós levelei és életrajza. pp. 299. *Budapest*, [1940.] 8°. **10922. e. 17.** *Bárd Miklós művei.* köt. 6.

—— Újabb válogatott költemények. pp. 112. 1935. 8°. *See* Pest.—*Magyar Tudományos Akadémia.* **Ac. 825/223.**

BARD (P.) *Domprediger in Schwerin.*

—— Ist Jesus von Nazareth der Weltheiland oder nicht? Predigt, *etc.* pp. 16. *Schwerin*, 1872. 8°. **4427. e. 1. (12.)**

BARD (Philip)

—— *See* Macleod (John J. R.) Physiology in Modern Medicine. By J. J. R. Macleod . . . assisted . . . by P. Bard, *etc.* 1935. 8°. **2025. h.**

—— *See* Macleod (John J. R.) Macleod's Physiology in Modern Medicine. Edited by P. Bard, *etc.* 1938. 4°. **7407.tt.9.**

—— *See* Macleod (John J. R.) Macleod's Physiology in Modern Medicine. Edited by P. Bard, *etc.* 1941. 8°. **7407. s. 15.**

—— Experimental Biology Series. (Experimental Biology Monographs.) Editors: P. Bard . . . L. R. Blinks [and others], *etc.* *Macmillan Co.: New York*, 1935– . 8°. **W.P. 572.**

BARD (Samuel) *See* MacVickar (John) A Domestic Narrative of the Life of Samuel Bard. 1822. 8°. **551. d. 11.**

—— Two Discourses dealing with Medical Education in Early New York. pp. 28. 2 pt. *Columbia University Press: New York*, 1921. 8°. **7679. bb. 48.**

—— A Discourse on the Importance of Medical Education: delivered . . . at the opening of the present session of the Medical School of the College of Physicians and Surgeons. pp. 22. *C. S. van Winkle: New York*, 1812. 8°. **7679. aaa. 8.**

—— Tentamen medicum inaugurale de viribus opii, *etc.* pp. 47. *A. Donaldson & J. Reid: Edinburgi*, 1765. 8°. **T. 364. (8.)**

—— Recherches sur la nature, la cause et le traitement du croup ou angine suffocative . . . Traduit de l'anglais, *etc.* *See* Ruette (F.) Recueil d'observations sur le croup, *etc.* pt. 3. 1810. 8°. **1178. g. 11.**

BARD (Samuel A.) *pseud.* [i.e. Ephraim George Squier.] Waikna; or, Adventures on the Mosquito Shore . . . With sixty illustrations. pp. 366. *Sampson, Low & Co.: London*, 1855. 8°. **10481. bbb. 31.** *With an additional titlepage, engraved, bearing the imprint of Harper Bros.: New York.*

—— [Another edition.] pp. iv. 188. *Sampson, Low & Co.: London*, 1856. 12°. **10480. a. 12.**

—— [Another edition.] Adventures on the Mosquito Shore, *etc.* pp. viii. 310. *James Blackwood: London*, 1856. 8°. **10480. a. 13.**

BARD (W.) A Speech to the Lord General Monck at Skinners-Hall. April the fourth, 1660. [In verse.] *John Towers: London*, 1660. *s. sh.* fol. **669**. f. **24**. (**55**.)

BARD (William) A Letter to David E. Evans . . . on life insurance, *etc.* pp. 17. *William Van Norden: New York*, 1832. 12°. **8227**. aa. **8**.

—— [Another edition.] pp. 17. *J. van Norden & Co.: New York*, 1842. 12°. **8227**. aa. **9**.

BARDA (E.)

—— *See* Montel (A.) La Révision des contrats par le juge en Italie. (Traduction par E. Barda.) [1937.] 8°. **5357**. c. **10**.

BĀRDA (Fricis)

—— Dziesmas un lūgšanas Dzīvības kokam. Dzejas 1911–1919. Sestais izdevums. pp. 327. *Rīgā*, 1938. 8°. **2286**. c. **12**.

—— Zemes dēls. Dziejas. Septītais izdevums. pp. 262. *Rīgā*, 1937. 8°. **2286**. b. **17**.

BARDACH (M.)

—— *See* Steinhaus (H.) Mathematical Snapshots. (English translation by C. Irvine and M. Bardach.) [1938.] 8°. **08535**. bb. **20**.

BARDACHZI (Karl)

—— Gotische Bildschnitzer. Die Meisterwerke von Kefermarkt und St. Wolfgang im Farbbild, *etc.* pp. 46. pl. 32. *Wien*, [1944.] 8°. **7877**. d. **15**.

BARDAISAN. *See* Bardesan.

BARDAJÍ (Paulino Gil y) *See* Gil y Bardají.

BARDAKH (Yu.) *See* Geiger (A.) [Lehr- und Lesebuch zur Sprache der Mischna.] Руководство къ изученію языка Мишны . . . Перевелъ съ Нѣмецкаго . . . Ю. Бардахъ. 1871. 8°. **12906**. bb. **2**.

BARDAKOUDES (Georgios) *Ποιημα δια τον μητροπολιτην Κιτιου . . . περιεχον τας συκοφαντιας που του ἐκαμαν και τα καλα που ἐπραξεν στον τοπον.* pp. 12. *'Εν Λαρνακι*, 1900. 8°. **11586**. bb. **22**. (**2**.)

BARDALACHOS (Konstantinos) *See* Xenophon, *the Historian*. [*Anabasis.—Polyglott.*] The Anabasis of Xenophon. Book iii. With the modern Greek version of C. Bardalachos, *etc.* 1879. 8°. **9026**. b. **8**.

BARDALES B. (Rafael)

—— *See* Aguilar Paz (J.) and Bardales B. (R.) El Alfabetismo en Honduras, *etc.* 1949. 8°. L.A.S. e. **324/2**.

BARDAMIDES (Euangelos N.)

—— *'Ιστορια της νησου Μεγιστης—Καστελλοριζου—ἀπο της ἐποχης των Δωριεων και του Μινωος μεχρι των ἡμερων μας και της προσαρτησεως της νησου εἰς την 'Ελλαδα.* [With illustrations.] pp. 291. *'Αλεξανδρεια*, 1948. 8°. **9134**. l. **27**.

BARDAN (Federico) Las Cartas de Rosalia. Zarzuela en un acto, *etc.* pp. 40. *Madrid*, 1865. 8°. **11726**. bbb. **13**. (**5**.)

BARDANA (*Sir* Hypochondriasis) *pseud.* [i.e. *Sir* John Hill.] *See* Camlin, *pseud.* A Satisfactory Refutation of Sir Hypo Bardana's " Circumstances " . . . Containing some anecdotes of his motly life, previous to his commencing author. [1775?] 8°. **1080**. m. **30**.

BARDANES (Christophoros)

—— *See* Falck (J. P.) Записки путешествія Академика Фалька. [Containing matter contributed by Chr. Bardanes.] 1824, *etc.* 8°. [*Полное собраніе ученыхъ путешествій по Россіи.* том. 6, 7.] Ac. **1125/37**.

BARDANI (Alexander Angelicus) *See* Rome, Church of. [" *Index Librorum Prohibitorum*," *etc.*] Index librorum prohibitorum, *etc.* [Edited by A. A. Bardani.] 1819, *etc.* 8°. **618**. b. **40**.

BARDANNE (Jean)

—— L'Allemagne et la guerre. La ligne Siegfried. pp. 126. *Paris*, 1938. 8°. **08028**. a. **103**.

—— Documents secrets et faux passeports. pp. 220. *Paris*, [1938.] 8°. **9100**. a. **24**.

—— La Guerre et les microbes. [A novel.] pp. 253. *Paris*, [1937.] 8°. **12549**. e. **9**.

—— Perfide Albion. [An examination of British foreign policy in relation to France and Germany after the European War.] pp. 252. *Paris*, [1933.] 8°. **08028**. a. **13**.

—— Stavisky, espion allemand. pp. 239. *Paris*, [1935.] 8°. **010665**. de. **72**.

BARDARI (G. B.) *See* Musaeus, *the Grammarian*. [*Italian.*] Ero e Leandro ; antica leggenda di amore, tradotta . . . per G. B. Bardari. 1879. 8°. **11335**. cc. **3**.

BARDARI (Giuseppe) Maria Stuarda. Tragedia lirica in quattro parti, da rappresentarsi nell I. e R. Teatro dei Sigg. Accademici Immobili in Via della Pergola il Carnevale del 1839–40, *etc.* [In verse.] pp. 28. *Firenze*, 1840. 8°. **906**. c. **15**. (**2**.)

BÁRÐARSON (Guðmundur Guðmundsson)

—— *See* Periodical Publications.—*Reykjavík.* Náttúrufræðingurinn . . . Útgefendur: G. G. Bárðarson og Árni Friðriksson. 1931, *etc.* 8°. P.P. **1997**. c.

—— Islands Gletscher. Beiträge zur Kenntnis der Gletscherbewegungen und Schwankungen auf Grund alter Quellenschriften und neuester Forschung. [Edited by Finnur Guðmundsson. With a map.] pp. 60. 1934. 8°. *See* Reykjavík.—*Vísindafélag Íslendinga.* **07108**. aaa. **39**.

—— Om den marine Molluskfauna ved Vestkysten af Island. [With a map.] pp. 139. *København*, 1920. 8°. [*Det Kgl. Danske Videnskabernes Selskab. Biologiske Meddelelser.* Bd. 2. no. 3.] Ac. **1023/15**.

—— A Stratigraphical Survey of the Pliocene Deposits at Tjörnes, in Northern Iceland . . . With two maps. pp. 118. *København*, 1925. 8°. [*Kgl. Dansk Videnskabernes Selskab. Biologiske Meddelelser.* Bd. 4. no. 5.] Ac. **1023/15**.

BÁRÐARSON (Íngi) *King of Norway.* *See* Ingi [Bárðarson]. *King of Norway.*

BÁRÐARSON (Ívar) Iver Beres Historie om Grønland. *See* Jónsson (A.) Arngrimi Jonæ Grönlandia, *etc.* 1732. 8°. **572**. b. **3**.

—— Iver Beres Grønlands Beskrivelse, med et Kort og Forerindring af Arient Aschlund. pp. 12. *Kjöbenhavn*, 1832. 8°. **10460**. aaa. **14**.

—— Det gamle Grønlands Beskrivelse af Ívar Bárðarson . . . Udgiven efter Håndskrifterne af Finnur Jónsson. [With maps.] pp. 75. *København*, 1930. 8°. **010460**. e. **22**.

—— Description of Greenland in the Fourteenth Century, *etc.* *Dan., Lat. & Eng.* *See* Zeno (N.) The Voyages of the Venetian Brothers, Nicolò & Antonio Zeno, *etc.* 1873. 8°. R. Ac. **6172/45**.

BÁRÐARSON (IVAR)

—— Sailing Directions of Henry Hudson, prepared for his use in 1608, from the old Danish of Ivar Bardsen. With an introduction and notes . . . by . . . the Rev. B. F. De Costa. pp. 102. *Joel Munsell: Albany,* 1869. 8º. **10460**. dd. **8**.

—— Iver Bere's Beschreibung von Grönland. Mit einer Karte und Vorrede von A. Aschlund. Aus dem Dänischen. pp. 16. *Kopenhagen,* 1833. 8º. **10460**. a. **29**.

—— [Another copy.] T. **1477**. (**7**.)

BÁRÐARSON (THORÐR) Ein lijtel nij Bœna book, *etc.* [With a preface signed: Þ. Th. S., i.e. Thorðr Thorláksson, Bishop of Skálholt.] pp. 131. *I. Snorrasyne: Skalhollte,* 1693. 12º. **869**. a. **21**.
Imperfect; wanting pp. 41–42, 59–60 *and* 61–62.

—— Þad Andlega Bæna Reykelse . . . Þ. Baardarsonar . . . Og þad sama i Andlegt Psalma Salve sett og snwed, af Benedicht Magnus Syne Bech. pp. 183. *Hoolum i Hialltadal,* 1750. 12º. **869**. a. **30**.

—— [Another edition.] pp. 190. *Hoolum i Hialltadal,* 1769. 12º. **869**. a. **36**.

BARDAS (WALTER) *See* AUSTRIA. [*Collections of Laws, etc.*—III. *Maritime Law.*] Das öffentliche Seerecht Österreichs. Sammlung der Gesetze . . . Herausgegeben von Dr. W. Bardas. 1909. 8º. **05549**. l. **3**.

—— Verkehr und Verkehrs-Politik in Volks- und Staatswirtschaft. Bd. 1. pp. vi. 127. *Leipzig & Wien,* 1907. 8º. **8010**. g. **17**.
No more published.

BARÐASTRAND, *County of.* Reglugjörd fyrir Barðastrandarsýslu um grenjalectir, *etc.* pp. 16. *Reykjavík,* 1886. 8º. **867**. i. **42**. (**6**.)

BARDAVÍU PONZ (VICENTE) *See* ALCAÑIZ. Fouilles dans la région d'Alcañiz, *etc.* (tom. 1. Par P. Paris, V. Bardaviu Ponz.—tom. 2. Par V. Bardaviú Ponz, R. Thouvenot.) 1926, *etc.* 8º. [*Bibliothèque de l'École des Hautes Études Hispaniques.* fasc. 11.] Ac. **148**.

—— Estaciones Prehistóricos y Poblados Desiertos recientemente descubiertos y estudiados en varias localidades de la Provincia de Teruel. [With plates.] pp. 44. *Zaragoza,* 1918. 8º. **07709**. aaa. **11**.

—— Historia de la antiquísima villa de Albalate del Arzobispo. pp. viii. 668. vii. *Zaragoza,* 1914. 8º. **10162**. dd. **17**.

—— El Paleolítico inferior de los montes de Torrero: industria, arte y religión de los hombres que en él vivieron. Discurso, *etc.* pp. 32. pl. 9. *Zaragoza,* [1920.] 8º. **07708**. i. **41**.

BARDAXI (IBANDO DE) *See* BARDAXI Y ALMENARA (Juan I. de)

BARDAXÍ Y ALMENARA (JUAN DE) *See* BARDAXÍ Y ALMENARA (J. I. de) Summa de los fueros y observancias del Reyno de Aragon, *etc.* [Edited by J. de Bardaxí y Almenara.] 1587. 8º. **5385**. a. **9**.

BARDAXI Y ALMENARA (JUAN IBANDO DE)

—— Commentarii in quatuor Aragonensium fororum libros. ff. 560. *Apud L. Robles: Cæsaraugustæ,* 1592. fol. **1480**. d. **5**.

—— Summa de los fueros y observancias del Reyno de Aragon; y de las determinaciones y practicas referidas por . . . Miguel del Molino en su repertorio. [Edited by Juan de Bardaxí y Almenara, brother of the author.] ff. 252. *I. de Altaraque: Çaragoça,* 1587. 8º. **5385**. a. **9**.

BARDD CLOFF, *Bardic Name of Thomas Roberts of Amlwch. See* ROBERTS (Thomas) called BARDD CLOFF.

BARDD COCH O FÔN, *Bardic Name of Hugh Hughes. See* HUGHES (Hugh) called BARDD COCH O FÔN.

BARDD CWSG, *Bardic Name of Ellis Wynne. See* WYNNE (Ellis)

BARDD LLANGWM, *Bardic name of Hugh Jones of Llangwm. See* JONES (Hugh) called BARDD LLANGWM.

BARDDONIAETH.

—— Barddoniaeth gan hen awdwyr, or Ancient Welsh Poetry. Ex no. 2161, inter MSS. Phillipps, *etc.* pp. 4. [*Privatelty printed: Middle Hill,* 1840?] fol. Tab. **436**. b. **1**. (**11**.)

—— Barddoniaeth i'w Adrodd. Poetry for recitation . . . Safonau 1–4. pp. 16. *Wrexham* [1898.] 8º. [*Hughes's School Series.*] **12978**. bb

—— Barddoniaeth y Plant. 3 pt. *Hughes a'i Fab: Wrecsam,* 1935. 8º. **20019**. aa. **8**.

BARDDONIAETH GYMREIG.

—— Barddoniaeth Gymreig, at wasanaeth Ysgolion Elfenol a Chanolraddol. *See* THOMAS (Thomas J.)

BARDE (BENI) *See* BENI-BARDE.

BARDE (ALFRED) De l'avortement au double point de vue de l'art des accouchements et de la médecine légale. pp. 64. *Paris,* 1859. 4º. [*Collection des thèses soutenues à la Faculté de Médecine de Paris.* An 1859. tom. 1.] **7373**. b. **13**.

BARDE (ANDRÉ) *pseud.* [i.e. ANDRÉ BOURDONNEAU.] *See* DUQUESNEL (F.) and BARDE (A.) *pseud.* La Maîtresse de piano. Pièce en cinq actes, *etc.* 1907. 8º. **11736**. i. **57**.

—— *See* DUQUESNEL (F.) and BARDE (A.) *pseud.* Sa fille. Comédie en quatre actes. 1911. fol. [*L'Illustration théâtrale.* no. 193.] P.P. **4283**. m. (**2**.)

BARDE (JEAN ÉDOUARD) Commentaire sur les Actes des Apôtres. pp. 592. *Lausanne,* 1898. 8º. **03265**. g. **1**.

—— L'Histoire sainte dans l'enseignement primaire. Conférence faite . . . en réponse à M. le Prof. Buisson [i.e. to his brochure entitled: "Une Réforme urgente dans l'instruction primaire"]. pp. 44. *Genève, Bâle,* 1869. 8º. **8304**. aa. **19**. (**1**.)

—— Samuel Hebich, missionnaire bâlois aux Indes. Esquisse biographique. pp. 48. *Bâle,* 1882. 12º. **4888**. aa. **29**. (**2**.)

BARDE (JOSEPH MARIE ALFRED BENI) *See* BENI-BARDE.

BARDE (JULIUS AUGUSTUS) *Def.* De syphiliticis renum affectionibus. Dissertatio inauguralis medica, *etc. Opp.* C. Nieberding, *etc.* pp. 31. *Berolini,* [1863.] 8º. **7640**. b. **1**.

BARDE (LEROY DE) *Chevalier. See* LEROY DE BARDE (A. I.)

BARDE (LOUIS) *See* BAUDRY-LACANTINERIE (G.) Traité théorique et pratique de droit civil. [Edited by G. Baudry-Lacantinerie, assisted by L. Barde and others.] 1894, *etc.* 8º. **05402**. i.

BARDE (PAUL) Esquisse des idées théologiques de G. E. Lessing. Thèse, *etc.* pp. 78. *Genève,* 1889. 8º. **4371**. ee. **7**. (**2**.)

BARDÈCHE (MAURICE) [Single Works.]

—— *See* BALZAC (H. de) La Physiologie du marriage préoriginale . . . Présenté par M. Bardèche. 1940. 8º. **8417**. dd. **13**.

BARDÈCHE (MAURICE)

—— *See* BRASILLACH (R.) and BARDÈCHE (M.) Histoire de la guerre d'Espagne, *etc.* 1939. 8°. **9180**. r. **17**.

—— Balzac romancier. [Revised edition.] pp. 391. *Paris*, 1947. 8°. **11867**. ee. **30**.

—— Stendhal romancier, *etc.* [With portraits.] pp. 473. pl. VIII. *Paris*, 1947. 8°. **10656**. l. **13**.

BARDÈCHE (MAURICE) and **BRASILLACH** (ROBERT)

—— Histoire du cinéma. pp. 421. *Paris*, 1935. 8°. **11795**. w. **32**.

—— History of the Film . . . Translated and edited by Iris Barry. [With plates.] pp. xi. 412. *G. Allen & Unwin: London; printed in U.S.A.*, 1938. 8°. **11797**. d. **14**.

BARDEEN (CHARLES RUSSELL) Anatomy in America. pp. 121. *Madison*, 1905. 8°. [*Bulletin of the University of Wisconsin.* Science ser. vol. 3. no. 115.] Ac. **1792**.

—— Die Entwicklung des Skeletts und des Bindegewebes. *See* KEIBEL (F.) and MALL (F. P.) Handbuch der Entwicklungsgeschichte des Menschen. Bd. 1. 1910, *etc.* 8°. **7581**. h. **14**.

BARDEEN (CHARLES W.) *See* KOMENSKÝ (J. A.) The Orbis Pictus of J. A. Comenius. [Edited by C. W. Bardeen.] 1887. 8°. **7854**. f. **38**.

—— Common School Law. A digest of the provisions of statute and common law as to the relations of the teacher to the pupil, the parent, and the district . . . Fourth edition entirely re-written. pp. 95. lviii. *Davis, Bardeen & Co.: Syracuse, N.Y.*, 1878. 16°. **6616**. a. **15**.

—— [Another edition.] A Manual of Common School Law. pp. 290. *C. W. Bardeen: Syracuse, N.Y.*, 1896. 8°. **6617**. aa. **14**.

—— A Little Fifer's War Diary [of the American Civil War, 1862–4]. With 17 maps, 60 portraits, and 246 other illustrations . . . With an introduction by Nicholas Murray Butler. pp. 329. *C. W. Bardeen: Syracuse, N.Y.*, 1910. 8°. **09555**. dd. **10**.

—— Roderick Hume. The story of a New York teacher. pp. viii. 295. *Davis, Bardeen & Co.: Syracuse, N.Y.*, 1878. 16°. **12703**. aaa. **4**.

—— Some Facts about our Public School System. An address, *etc.* pp. 32. [*Utica?*] 1878. 8°. **8304**. e. **7**. (**8**.)

—— Verbal Pitfalls: a manual of . . . words commonly misused . . . arranged alphabetically, with . . . references, *etc.* pp. 223. *C. W. Bardeen: Syracuse, N.Y.*, 1883. 12°. **12981**. h. **48**.

BARDEL (F. G.) Recherches théoriques et pratiques sur le rhumatisme et la goutte, *etc.* pp. 52. *Paris*, 1803. 8°. **1183**. b. **1**. (**9**.)

BARDELEBEN (ADOLF VON) *See* BARDELEBEN (Heinrich A. von)

BARDELEBEN (ALBRECHT VON) Zweifel und Ansichten über die örtliche Lage des von Drusus im Jahre 11 vor Christus erbauten Castells an der Lippe. pp. vi. 85. *Cassel*, 1839. 8°. **10255**. bbb. **2**.

BARDELEBEN (CARL VON) Der Feldzug gegen Österreich 1809. *See* HARTTUNG (J.) afterwards PFLUGK-HARTTUNG (J. von) Revolution und Kaiserreich. Aus dem Zeitalter der Gewaltherrschaft des I. Napoleon, *etc.* [1901.] 8°. **10658**. t. **7**.

—— Die königlich preussischen genealogischen Kalender von 1724–1850. pp. 53. *Berlin*, 1909. 8°. **9904**. r. **16**. (**1**.)

BARDELEBEN (CARL HEINRICH VON) *See* JENA.—*Anatomische Gesellschaft.* Verhandlungen der Anatomischen Gesellschaft auf der neunzehnten Versammlung . . . in Genf . . . Herausgegeben von . . . K. von Bardeleben, *etc.* 1905. 8°. [*Anatomischer Anzeiger.* Bd. 27. Ergänzungshft.] P.P. **3200**. e.

—— *See* PERIODICAL PUBLICATIONS.—*Jena.* Anatomischer Anzeiger . . . Herausgegeben von Dr. K. Bardeleben. 1886, *etc.* 8°. P.P. **3200**. e.

—— Anleitung zum Präparieren der Muskeln, Fascien und Gelenke. pp. vii. 132. *Jena*, 1882. 8°. **7421**. aaa. **21**.

—— Beiträge zur Anatomie der Wirbelsäule, *etc.* pp. 39. pl. 3. *Jena*, 1874. 4°. **7420**. g. **9**.

—— Handbuch der Anatomie. Herausgegeben von . . . K. von Bardeleben. *Jena*, 1896– . 8°. **7419**. d.

—— Knochen, Bänder, Muskeln. 1892. *See* MERKEL (F.) and BONNET (R.) Anatomische Hefte, *etc.* Abt. 2. Bd. 1. 1891, *etc.* 8°. P.P.3200.ca.

BARDELEBEN (CARL HEINRICH VON) and **HAECKEL** (HEINRICH)

—— Atlas of Applied—Topographical—Human Anatomy for students and practitioners. By Dr. K. von Bardeleben and Prof. Dr. H. Haeckel in collaboration with Dr. F. Frohse and Professor Dr. T. Ziehen. Only authorised English adaptation from the third German edition, containing 204 woodcuts in several colours and descriptive text by J. Howell Evans. *Rebman: London, New York*, 1906. 4°. **7420**. g. **44**.

BARDELEBEN (CARL LUDWIG HEINRICH) Friedrich Wilhelm der Dritte und sein Volk. An Beide. pp. iv. 212. [*Frankfort on the Oder*,] 1809. 8°. **8073**. bbb. **12**.

BARDELEBEN (CURT VON) *See* BERLIN.—*Berliner Schachgesellschaft.* Schachzeitung, *etc.* (Deutsche Schachzeitung, *etc.* [Jahrg. 42–45 edited by C. von Bardeleben and H. von Gottschall.]) 1846, *etc.* 8°. Ac. **5186**.

—— *See* GERMANY.—*Deutscher Schachbund.* Der erste und zweite [*etc.*] Kongress des deutschen Schachbundes, *etc.* (Der fünfte Kongress . . . Herausgegeben von C. v. Bardeleben, H. v. Gottschall und J. Mieses.) 1883, *etc.* 8°. **7915**. ee.

—— *See* KAGAN (B.) [300 kurze Glanzpartien von erstklassigen Meistern und starken Amateuren, glossiert von C. von Bardeleben.] [1915? *etc.*] **07907**. f. **6**.

—— Das Bauernendspiel im Schach . . . Zweite verbesserte und vermehrte Auflage. pp. 24. *Berlin*, [1920.] 8°. **7911**. ee. **19**.

—— Geschichte des Schachspiels . . . Herausgegeben von Bernhard Kagan. pp. 30. *Berlin*, [1924.] 8°. **07908**. k. **3**.

—— Kritik der spanischen Partie. Die Lopez-Analyse der letzten Dezennien auf ihren wahren Werth geprüft und als nothwendige Ergänzung eines jeden Schach-Lehrbuches bearbeitet. pp. x. 102. *Leipzig*, 1885. 16°. [*Bibliothek für Schachfreunde.* Bd. 1.] **7913**. de. **35**.

—— Taschen-Lexikon der Eröffnungen. Ein Hilfsbuch für Turnierspiel, *etc.* pp. viii. 61. *Leipzig*, 1886. 16°. [*Bibliothek für Schachfreunde.* Bd. 4.] **7913**. de. **35**.

—— Die Wiener Partie. Eine schach-theoretische Abhandlung. pp. 80. *Leipzig*, 1893. 8°. 07903.h.51.

BARDELEBEN (CURT VON) and **MIESES** (JACQUES)

—— Lehrbuch des Schachspiels. Auf Grund des gegenwärtigen Standes der Theorie und Praxis . . . Zugleich sechste Auflage des von der Lasa'schen Leitfadens. pp. viii. 480. *Leipzig*, 1894. 8°. **7913**. f. **45**.

BARDELEBEN (Eveline von) Aufzeichnungen aus den Lazarethen von Gitschin während der Zeit meiner freiwilligen Krankenpflege. pp. 62. *Halle*, 1870. 8°. **9386. c. 11.**

BARDELEBEN (Eveline Ernestine von) Ein Blick auf die einstige Stellung der Oberpräsidenten Auerswald und Schön in Königsberg in Preussen mit Rücksicht auf einige dahin bezügliche Schriften. pp. 52. *Stuttgart*, 1844. 8°. **1048. c. 31. (2.)**

BARDELEBEN (Heinrich) *See* Bardeleben (Carl L. H.)

BARDELEBEN (Heinrich Adolf von)

—— *See* Frederick, *Emperor of Germany*. [1888.] [*Biography*.—1888.] Die Krankheit Kaiser Friedrich des Dritten dargestellt nach . . . den . . . Berichten der Aerzte Prof. Bardeleben . . . Prof. von Bergmann, *etc.* 1888. 8°. **10704. g. 37.**

—— *See* Frederick, *Emperor of Germany*. [1888.] [*Biography*.—1888.] The Illness of the Emperor Frederick the Third. An authentic record . . . founded upon the reports . . . made by Professor Bardeleben, *etc.* 1888. 8°. **10704. g. 38.**

—— *See* Frederick, *Emperor of Germany*. [1888.] [*Biography*.—1888.] La Maladie de l'empereur Frédéric III. exposée d'après les documents officiels et les rapports . . . par le Professeur Bardeleben, *etc.* 1888. 12°. **10704. aaa. 34.**

—— *See* Frederick, *Emperor of Germany*. [1888.] [*Biography*.—1888.] La Maladie de l'empereur Frédéric III. d'après les rapports officiels des médecins Professeur Bardeleben, *etc.* 1888. 8°. **10704. ff. 13.**

—— *See* Groeningen (G. H.) Ueber den Shock . . . Mit einem Vorwort von Dr. A. Bardeleben. 1885. 8°. **7460. ff. 11.**

—— *See* Periodical Publications.—*Leipsic*. Deutsche Zeitschrift für Chirurgie, herausgegeben von Prof. Bardeleben, *etc.* 1872, *etc.* 8°. **P.P. 3061. c.**

—— Rede zur Gedächtniss-Feier der Friedrich-Wilhelms-Universität zu Berlin gehalten am 3. August 1877. pp. 16. *Berlin*, 1877. 4°. **8356. l. 31. (8.)**

—— Lehrbuch der Chirurgie und Operationslehre . . . Achte Ausgabe. 4 Bd. *Berlin*, 1879–82. 8°. **07482. f. 2.**

—— Rückblick auf die Fortschritte der Chirurgie in der zweiten Hälfte dieses Jahrhunderts. Rede, *etc.* pp. 32. *Berlin*, 1876. 8°. **7306. bb. 10. (6.)**

—— Ueber die Bedeutung wissenschaftlicher Studien für die Ausbildung der Aerzte. Rede, *etc.* pp. 12. *Berlin*, 1877. 4°. **8356. l. 31. (6.)**

—— Ueber die Theorie der Wunden und die neueren Methoden der Wundbehandlung. Zwei Vorträge, *etc.* pp. 46. *Berlin*, 1878. 8°. **7306. c. 12. (6.)**

BARDELEBEN (Karl von) *See* Bardeleben (Carl von)

BARDELEBEN (R. von) Die Verfassungsentwickelung in Preussen und ihre neueste Phase . . . Zweite Auflage. pp. 58. *Leipzig*, 1848. 8°. **8072. a. 8.**

BARDELIN (Laget) *See* Laget-Bardelin.

BARDELL (Philip Raymond)

—— Magnetic Materials in the Electrical Industry. pp. 288. *Macdonald & Co.: London*, 1955. 8°. **8761. e. 46.**

BARDELLI (Giuseppe) *See* Bible.—*Old Testament*.—*Daniel*. [*Coptic*.] Daniel Copto-Memphitice. Edidit J. Bardelli. 1849. 8°. **754.bb.25.**

BARDELLI (Giuseppe)

—— Biografia del Professore Ippolito Rosellini. pp. 40. *Firenze*, 1843. 8°. **10630. b. 17.**

BARDELLI (Joseph) *See* Bardelli (Giuseppe)

BARDELLI (Niccolò) La Giurisdizione in Atene studiata in rapporto allo spirito e all' evoluzione della costituzione politica. pp. 432. *Torino*, 1901. 8°. **8008. i. 10.**

—— Saggio storico sulla giurisdizione studiata in rapporto allo spirito e all' evoluzione della costituzione politica. vol. 1. pp. lxvi. 538. *Pisa*, 1894. 8°. **8010. dd. 8.**

BARDELLI (Pietro) Raccolta di poetiche espressioni. pp. 20. *Pisa*, 1870. 8°. **11436. bbb. 75. (6.)**

BARDELLI (Plinio)

—— L'Infezione da B. del mal rossino nell'uomo—Erisipeloide. Un caso non comune a decorso cronico—auto-osservazione, *etc.* (Estratto dagli Atti del Reale Istituto Veneto di Scienze, Lettere ed Arti.) [With plates.] pp. 16. *Venezia*, 1937. 8°. **07560. g. 41.**

BARDEN.

—— Von den Barden, nebst etlichen Bardenliedern aus dem Englischen. [An essay, by C. F. Carmer? The translations by C. F. Weisse? or C. F. Jünger?] pp. 86. *Leipzig*, 1770. 8°. **11840. bb. 7.**

BARDEN-ALMANACH. *See* Periodical Publications.—*Neu-Strelitz*.

BARDEN (Agnes)

—— How to Work with Numbers. A first [*etc.*] number pad, *etc.* *Rand, McNally & Co.*: [*Chicago*, 1936– .] 4°. **W.P. 9119.**

BARDEN (Emil) Die reformatorische Weltanschauung in Richard Wagner's letzten Werken . . . Mit einem Vorwort von H. von Wolzogen. pp. 132. *Berlin*, 1888. 8°. **011824. g. 54.**

BARDEN (Hans Per)

—— Trekk av synsopfatningen og dens utvikling—vinkelvurdering. Et bidrag til overgangsalderens psykologi, *etc.* pp. 56. *Oslo*, 1933. 8°. [*Skrifter utgitt av Det Norske Videnskaps-Akademi*. Hist.-filos. klasse. 1933. no. 5.] **Ac. 1054/5.**

BARDEN (Jeff) By the Sounding Sea, *etc.* [Tales.] pp. 109. *A. H. Stockwell: London*, [1934.] 8°. **12602. s. 36.**

BARDEN (William)

—— What happens at the Mass. pp. 111. *Clonmore & Reynolds: Dublin*, 1950 [1951]. 8°. **3477. eeee. 55.**

BARDENAT (Jean Philippe) Dissertation sur les rapports des périodes de la vie avec les mouvemens périodiques de l'univers, *etc.* pp. 35. *Paris*, 1816. 4°. **1183. d. 6. (16.)**

BARDENET (Alfred Joseph) Aux gens du monde. Guérison des maladies des organes génito-urinaires, *etc.* pp. 123. *Paris*, 1861. 16°. **7640. a. 9.**

—— Essai sur la mort du fœtus, *etc.* pp. 59. *Paris*, 1851. 4°. [*Collection des thèses soutenues à la Faculté de Médecine de Paris*. An 1851. tom. 1.] **7372. d. 8.**

BARDENFLETH (Carl Emil) Livserindringer efterladte af . . . C. E. Bardenfleth. Udgivne . . . ved . . . I. Bardenfleth, *etc.* pp. vii. 186. *Kjøbenhavn*, 1890. 8°. **10761. ee. 28.**

BARDENFLETH (FREDERIK LØVENØRN VON) *See* MØLLER (E. H.) Tale ved Generallieutenant Bardenfleth's Bisættelse i St. Jörgens Capel i Kiel, *etc.* 1852. 8°. **4886.** bb. **46.**

—— Stormen paa Stralsund af et combineret dansk og hollandsk Troppecorps den 31te Mai 1809, med forudgaaende Fortælling af Schills Krigerliv, samt nogle Episoder fra Hertugen af Brunsvig-Oels's Streiftog igjennem Tydskland i Juli og August 1809. Met et Oversigtskaart, en Plan af Stralsund og 12 mindre Planer samt Portraiter af Generallieutenant v. Ewald, Major v. Schill og Hertugen af Brunsvig-Oels. pp. iv. 165. pl. 3. *Kjøbenhavn,* 1846. 8°. **9435.** e. **8.**

BARDENFLETH (GOTTFRIED VILHELM CHRISTIAN INGOLF) *See* BARDENFLETH (C. E.) Livserindringer efterladte af . . . C. E. Bardenfleth. Udgivne . . . ved . . . I. Bardenfleth, *etc.* 1890. 8°. **10761.** ee. **28.**

BARDENFLETH (INGOLF) *See* BARDENFLETH (Gottfried V. C. I.)

BARDENFLETH (JOHAN FREDERIK) Om Orkaner. [With a map.] pp. 76. *Kjøbenhavn,* 1831. 4°. **8755.** d. **20.**

BARDENFLETH (LØVENØRN) *See* BARDENFLETH (Frederik L. von)

BARDENHEUER (BERNARD) De partu praematuro. Dissertatio inauguralis obstetricia, *etc.* pp. 31. *Berolini,* [1864.] 8°. **7385.** b. **(6.)**

—— Leitfaden der Behandlung von Fracturen und Luxationen der Extremitäten mittelst Feder- resp. Gewichtsextension . . . Mit . . . Holzschnitten. pp. x. 211. *Stuttgart,* 1890. 8°. **7481.** i. **8.**

—— Die permanente Extensionsbehandlung. Die subcutanen und complicirten Fracturen und Luxationen der Extremitäten und ihre Folgen . . . Mit . . . Holzschnitten. pp. xxviii. 810. *Stuttgart,* 1889. 8°. **7482.** m. **15.**

—— Die Resektion des Mastdarmes. pp. 24. *Leipzig,* 1887. 8°. [*Sammlung klinischer Vorträge.* Chirurgie. no. 93.] **7441.** g.

—— Die Verletzungen der oberen Extremitäten, *etc.* 2 Tl. *Stuttgart,* 1886, 88. [*BILLROTH* (*C. A. T.*) *and LUECKE* (*A.*) *Deutsche Chirurgie, etc.* Lfg. 63.] **7482.** cc.

BARDENHEUER (RITA) Woher und Wohin. Geschichtliches und grundsätzliches aus der Frauenbewegung. pp. 122. *Leipzig,* 1918. 8°. **08415.** f. **36.**

BARDENHEWER (OTTO) *See* ARISTOTLE. [*Doubtful or Supposititious Works.—De Causis.*] Die pseudo-aristotelische Schrift . . . bekannt unter dem Namen Liber de causis . . . bearbeitet von O. Bardenhewer. 1882. 8°. **14540.** a. **25.**

—— *See* CYRIL, *Saint, Patriarch of Alexandria.* Des heiligen Kirchenlehrers Cyrillus von Alexandrien ausgewählte Schriften. Aus dem Griechischen übersetzt von O. Bardenhewer. 1935. 8°. **3606.a.1/42.**

—— *See* EPHRAIM, *Saint, the Syrian.* Des heiligen Ephräm des Syrers ausgewählte Schriften . . . Mit einer allgemeinen Einleitung von Dr. O. Bardenhewer. 1919, *etc.* 8°. **3606.a.1/11.**

—— *See* HERMES, *Trismegistus.* [*Epistola ad Animam.*] Hermetis Trismegisti qui apud Arabes fertur de castigatione animæ libellum edidit latine vertit . . . O. Bardenhewer, *etc.* 1873. 8°. **14540.** a. **27.**

—— *See* SICKENBERGER (J.) Erinnerungen an Otto Bardenhewer. Mit zwei Bildnissen, *etc.* 1937. 8°. **20013.** cc. **30.**

BARDENHEWER (OTTO)

—— Bibliothek der Kirchenväter. Eine Auswahl patristischer Werke in deutscher Übersetzung. (Völlig neu bearbeitete Auflage [of the collection edited by F. X. Reithmayr].) Herausgegeben von . . . O. Bardenhewer . . . Th. Schermann . . . K. Weyman (J. Zellinger). 61 Bd. *Kempten & München,* 1911–28. 8°. **3606.a.1.**

—— Generalregister zu Band 1–61 . . . Bearbeitet von Dr. P. Johannes E. Stöckerl. pp. vii. 366. *München,* 1931. 8°. **3606.a.1/34.**

—— Zweite Reihe. (Herausgegeben von O. Bardenhewer J. Zellinger.) 17 Bd. J Martin. München, 1932-36. 8°. **3606.a.1.**

—— Biblische Studien . . . Herausgegeben von . . . O. Bardenhewer. 23 Bd. *Freiburg i. B.,* 1895–1930. 8°. **03127.** e. **1–23.**

—— Geschichte der altkirchlichen Litteratur. Bd. 1–3. *Freiburg i. B.,* 1902. 8°. **3624.** b. **19.**

—— Zweite, umgearbeitete Auflage. 5 Bd. *Freiburg i. B.,* 1913–32. 8°. **2009.b.**

—— Des heiligen Hippolytus von Rom Commentar zum Buche Daniel. Ein literärgeschichtlicher Versuch. pp. iv. 107. *Freiburg i. B.,* 1877. 8°. **4372.** h. **6. (10.)**

—— Mariä Verkündigung. Ein Kommentar zu Lukas 1, 26–38. pp. viii. 179. *Freiburg i. B.,* 1905. 8°. [*Biblische Studien.* Bd. 10. Hft. 5.] **03127.** e. **10. (3.)**

—— Der Name Maria. Geschichte der Deutung desselben. pp. x. 160. *Freiburg i. B.,* 1895. 8°. [*Biblische Studien.* Bd. 1.] **03127.** e. **1. (1.)**

—— Patrologie. pp. x. 635. *Freiburg i. B.,* 1894. 8°. [*Theologische Bibliothek.*] **3623.** g. **1.**

—— Dritte, grossenteils neu bearbeitete Auflage. pp. xi. 587. *Freiburg i. B.,* 1910. 8°. [*Theologische Bibliothek.*] **3623.** g. **4.**

—— Patrology. The lives and works of the Fathers of the Church . . . Translated from the second edition by Thomas J. Shahan. pp. xvii. 680. *B. Herder: Freiburg i. B. & St. Louis,* 1908. 8°. **2004.** g.

—— Polychronius, Bruder Theodors von Mopsuestia, und Bischof von Apamea. Ein Beitrag zur Geschichte der Exegese. pp. iv. 99. *Freiburg i. B.,* 1879. 8°. **4867.** ee. **18.**

—— Vom Münchener Gelehrten-Kongresse. Biblische Vorträge. Herausgegeben von Prof. Dr. O. Bardenhewer. pp. 200. *Freiburg i B.,* 1901. 8°. [*Biblische Studien.* Bd. 6.] **03127.** e. **6. (1.)**

BARDENS (DENNIS)

—— Crime does pay. pp. 112. *Background Books: London,* 1948. 8°. **12643.** p. **103.**

—— A Press in Chains. (A study of the press in the USSR and the communist territories under its dominion and control.) pp. 40. *Batchworth Press: London,* 1953. 8°. [*Background Books.*] W.P. A. 303 20.

BARDES (GEORGE FRANCIS)

—— Catholic Moral Teaching on the Distribution of Profits in the Modern Corporation. A dissertation, *etc.* pp. ix. 181. *Catholic University of America Press: Washington,* 1951. 8°. [*Catholic University of America. Studies in Sacred Theology.* ser. 2. no. 61.] Ac. **2692.** y/**20.**

BARDES (Willem) Willem Bardes, tooneelspel in vijf bedrijven. [In verse. By J. P. Amersfoordt.] pp. 67. *Amsterdam*, 1858. 8°. **11755**. bb. **14**.

BARDESAN. *See* Haase (F.) Zur Bardesanischen Gnosis. Literarkritische und dogmengeschichtliche Untersuchungen. 1910. 8°. [*Texte zur Geschichte der altchristlichen Literatur.* Bd. 34. Hft. 4.] 3628.d.1/34.

—— *See* Hahn (A.) Bardesanes Gnosticus . . . Commentatio historico-theologica, *etc.* 1819. 8°. **1125**. f. **30**.

—— *See* Hilgenfeld (A.) Bardesanes, der letzte Gnostiker. 1864. 8°. **4823**. d. **20**.

—— *See* Kuehner (C.) Astronomiæ et astrologiæ in doctrina Gnosticorum vestigia . . . Bardesanis Gnostici numina astralia. Commentatio, *etc.* 1833. 8°. T. **1483**. (**2**.)

—— *See* Merx (E. O. A.) Bardesanes von Edessa, *etc.* 1863. 8°. **3627**. cc. **39**.

—— *See* Nau (François) *Docteur ès Sciences mathématiques.* Une Biographie inédite de Bardesane l'Astrologue. 1897. 8°. **10600**. g. **1**. (**1**.)

—— *'Εκ των Βαρδισανου.*—Bardesanis Syri fragmentum. Adversus Astrologos . . . Hugone Grotio interprete. *Gr. & Lat.* *See* Orelli (G. C.) Alexandri Aphrodisiensis . . . Bardesanis . . . De fato, *etc.* 1824. 8°. **714**. f. **3**.

—— The Book of the Laws of Countries. *Syr., Gr., Lat. & Eng.* *See* Cureton (W.) Spicilegium Syriacum, *etc.* 1855. 8°. 753.hh.19.

—— Le Livre des lois des pays. Texte syriaque et traduction française, avec une introduction et de nombreuses notes, par F. Nau. pp. 62. 30. *Paris*, 1899. 8°. **753**. g. **53**. (**3**.)

—— Frammento del dialogo . . . sul destino. Dal Greco in Italiano, con note, da G. B. Gallicciolli. *See* Tatian. Orazione . . . ai Greci, *etc.* 1800. 8°. **1222**. i. **9**. (**1**.)

—— The Hymn of the Soul [attributed to Bardesan] contained in the Syriac Acts of St. Thomas. Re-edited with an English translation by A. A. Bevan. *Syr. & Eng.* pp. 40. 1897. 8°. [*Texts and Studies.* vol. 5. no. 3.] *See* Thomas, *Saint and Apostle.* [*Apocryphal Works.*] 03605.h.21/5.

—— The Hymn of Bardaisan rendered into English by F. C. Burkitt. pp. 30. *E. Arnold: London*, 1899. 8°. **753**. a. **56**.

—— The Hymn of the Robe of Glory. (Hymn of the Soul.) pp. 98. *Theosophical Publishing Society: London & Benares*, 1908. 16°. [*Echoes from the Gnosis.* vol. 10.] **4504**. df.

BARDESANES. *See* Bardesan.

BARDESONO DI RIGRAS (Carlo) *Count.*

—— *See* Falqui (E.) and Prati (A.) Dizionario di marina, *etc.* [Compiled by E. Falqui and A. Prati, with the assistance of C. Bardesono di Rigras.] 1937. 8°. [*Dizionari di arti e mestieri.* no. 1.] 12944.d.23.

—— Vocabolario marinaresco, *etc.* pp. iii. 397. pl. xxiii. *Roma*, 1932. 8°. 08805. i. 57.

BARDET (A.) *Abbé.* L'Église collégiale de N. D. du Château de Loches, maintenant église paroissiale de Saint-Ours. Son histoire et son culte, *etc.* pp. 140. *Tours*, 1862. 12°. **4632**. aa. **47**.

BARDET (André)

—— Les Trophées du rêve. [Poems on the European War.] pp. 95. *Paris*, 1936. 16°. **20011**. e. 8.

BARDET (Antoine) Dissertation sur l'hémoptysie active et ses différentes espèces, *etc.* pp. 53. *Paris*, 1807. 4°. **1182**. g. **11**. (**4**.)

BARDET (Edme François)

—— Histoire de la Révolution dans une petite ville, 1789–1795 . . . Préambule et notes complémentaires de Charles P. Milandre. 2 pt. *Clamecy*, 1940, 41. 8°. [*Vieilleries clamecyçoises.*] **10175**. c. **23**/**2**.

BARDET (Eugène) Étude sur la pneumonie aiguë primitive du sommet. Thèse, *etc.* [With a table.] pp. 72. *Montpellier*, 1875. 4°. **7379**. k. **9**. (**4**.)

BARDET (Gaston)

—— Naissance et méconnaissance de l'urbanisme. Paris. [With illustrations.] pp. 436. *Paris*, 1951. 8°. **10175**. ff. **32**.

The date in the colophon is 1952.

—— Petit glossaire de l'urbaniste en six langues. pp. viii. 151. *Paris*, [1948.] 16°. **8285**. df. **20**.

—— La Rome de Mussolini. (Une nouvelle ère romaine sous le signe du faisceau.) pp. xxxviii. 322. pl. xvi. *Paris; Liège* [printed, 1937.] 8°. **010136**. ee. **17**.

—— A Study of the Underground Road Crossings of Paris. pp. 31. *London*, [1937.] 8°. [*Société des Ingénieurs civils de France. British section. Papers and addresses.*] Ac. **4305**/**5**. (**49**.)

BARDET (Godefroy) *See* Periodical Publications.—*Paris.* Formulaire des nouveaux remèdes, par G. Bardet et E. Égasse. 1886, *etc.* 8°. P.P. **3016**. m.

—— Traité élémentaire et pratique d'électricité médicale . . . Précédé d'une préface de . . . C. M. Gariel . . . Avec 234 figures dans le texte. pp. x. 645. *Paris*, 1884. 8°. **7460**. ee. **13**.

BARDET (J.) Des causes de la gangrène. pp. 46. *Paris*, 1843. 4°. [*Collection des thèses soutenues à la Faculté de Médecine de Paris.* An 1843. tom. 1.] **7375**. d. **11**.

BARDET (Jean Baptiste) Le Massacre des Carmes. [Edited by F. C. Uzureau.] pp. 32. *Paris*, 1925. 8°. **04785**. l. **54**.

BARDET (Jean Diederik Menno)

—— *See* Bolderman (M. B. N.) and Dwars (A. W. C.) Waterbouwkunde, *etc.* (dl. 2. Grondwerken, transport- en hulpmiddelen, gewone wegen, spoorwegen, door P. Barentsen . . . F. Bakker . . . ir J. D. M. Bardet.) 1946, *etc.* 8°. 08776.dd.38.

BARDET (M.) Gastrite chronique, de l'irritation ou de l'inflammation lente de l'estomac ; thèse, *etc.* pp. 26. *Paris*, 1825. 4°. **1183**. h. **11**. (**6**.)

BARDET (P. F. Adolphe) Dissertation sur la coqueluche ; thèse, *etc.* pp. 25. *Paris*, 1829. 4°. **1184**. c. **13**. (**9**.)

BARDET (Pierre) Recueil d'arrests du Parlement de Paris pris des mémoires de Me P. Bardet . . . Avec les notes et les dissertations de Me Claude Berroyer. 2 tom. *T. Girard: Paris*, 1690. fol. **21**. f. **3**, **4**.

—— Nouvelle édition, revue & augmentée . . . Par M. C. N. Lalaure. 2 tom. *Avignon*, 1773. fol. **707**. k. **12**.

BARDET (René) Le Jardin de plaisance, *etc.* [Poems.] pp. v. 247. *Paris*, 1914. 8°. **011483**. bbb. **75**.

BARDET (V.) *See* Demaillasson (L.) Journal de M. Demaillasson, avocat du roi à Montmorillon, 1664–1694. Publié par M. V. Bardet. 1907, *etc.* 8°. [*Archives historiques du Poitou.* tom. 36, *etc.*] Ac. **6887**.

BARDET DE VILLENEUVE (P. P. A.) Cours de la science militaire. 8 tom. *La Haye*, 1740, 41. 8°. **62. a. 3–10.**

BARDETTI (Stanislao) De' primi abitatori dell' Italia. Opera postuma. [Edited by Giovanni Montanari, with a life of the author and a portrait.] pp. 471. *Modena*, 1769. fol. **665. i. 3.**

—— [Another copy.] **177. f. 10.**

—— *See* Durandi (J.) Dell' antico stato d'Italia . . . in cui si esamina l'opera del P. Bardetti sui primi abitatori d'Italia, *etc.* 1772. 8°. **657. a. 1.**

—— Della lingua de' primi abitatori dell' Italia. Opera postuma. [With a life of the author.] pp. xxiv. 379. *Modena*, 1772. 4°. **665. i. 4.**

—— [Another copy.] **177. f. 11.**

BARDEVICUS (Nicolaus) *See* Bocer (J.) Ad Deum . . . In funere H. Falconis & N. Bardeuici . . . querela. 1560. 4°. **837. h. 3. (20.)**

BARDEWIC (Albertus de) *See* Albertus, *de Bardewic.*

BARDEY (Alfred) Notes sur le Harar. 1897. *See* Paris.—*Comité des Travaux historiques et scientifiques.* Bulletin de géographie historique, *etc.* année 1897. 1886, *etc.* 8°. **Ac. 437/6.**

BARDEY (C.) Neue und vollständige Kalender-Erklärung. Zum Verständniss aller Zeichen, Namen, Angaben und Ausdrücke, welche im Kalender vorkommen . . . Mit 19 . . . Abbildungen, einer Sternkarte und . . . Tafeln. pp. viii. 119. *Leipzig*, [1866.] 8°. **8561. f. 30. (2.)**

BARDEY (Ernst) Algebraische Gleichungen, nebst den Resultaten und den Methoden zu ihrer Auflösung. pp. x. 281. *Leipzig*, 1868. 8°. **8533. g. 25.**

—— Zweite . . . vermehrte und verbesserte Auflage. pp. viii. 339. *Leipzig*, 1876. 8°. **8507. f. 5.**

—— Quadratische Gleichungen mit den Lösungen für die oberen Klassen der Gymnasien, *etc.* pp. 86. *Leipzig*, 1871. 8°. **8529. ee. 1.**

—— Zur Formation quadratischer Gleichungen. pp. viii. 390. *Leipzig*, 1884. 8°. **8535. e. 11.**

BARDEY (Ernst Georg) Geschichte von Nauen und Osthavelland . . . Mit . . . Abbildungen. pp. xxiv. 653. *Rathenow*, 1892. 8°. **10240. i. 9.**

BARDEZ (M.) Quelques considérations générales sur le traitement de l'asphyxie par submersion; thèse, *etc.* pp. 29. *Paris*, 1815. 4°. **1183. c. 14. (17.)**

BARDHË (Frangu i) *See* Blanchus (Franciscus)

BARDI, Henry, *Count of.* *See* Henry Charles Louis George Abraham Paul Mary [de Bourbon], *Count of Bardi.*

BARDI, *Family of.* *See* Sapori (A.) La Crisi delle compagnie mercantili dei Bardi e dei Peruzzi, *etc.* 1926. 8°. [*Biblioteca storica toscana.* no. 3.] **Ac. 6508/7.**

BARDI (Adelmo)

—— Dall'Etiopia selvaggia all'impero d'Italia. 2. edizione. [With illustrations, including a portrait, and maps.] pp. 351. *San Remo*, 1936. 8°. **9062. b. 2.**

BARDI (Alessandra de') *See* Bisticci (V. da) Vita della Alessandra de' Bardi, donna di Lorenzo di Messer Palla Strozzi. 1843. 8°. [*Spicilegium Romanum.* tom. 9.] **832. k. 15.**

BARDI (Alessandro) *See* Strozzi (G. B.) called (Filippo) afterwards (F.) Filippo Strozzi da nuovi documenti. [Letters, edited by A. Bardi.] 1894. 8°. [*Archivio Storico Italiano.* ser. 5. tom. 14.] **P.P. 3557. a.**

—— Carlo v. e l'assedio di Firenze. pp. 85. 1893. *See* Italian Archives. Archivio Storico Italiano, *etc.* ser. 5. tom. 11. 1842, *etc.* 8°. **P.P. 3557. a.**

BARDI (Bembo) *See* Plato. [*Two or more Works.—Italian.*] Apologia di Socrate . . . Eutifrone e Critone. Versione di B. Bardi. 1884. 8°. **8462. a. 7.**

BARDI (C. F. de') Studii di questioni sociali. pp. viii. 156. *Firenze*, 1886. 8°. **8275. g. 30.**

BARDI (Christoval) *See* Berardi.

BARDI (Donato) called Donatello. *See* Alexandre (A.) Donatello . . . Biographie critique, illustrée, *etc.* [1905.] 8°. **2266. bb. 11.**

—— *See* Bertaux (E.) Donatello. [1910.] 8°. **7855. bbb. 26.**

—— *See* Bocchi (F.) Eccellenza della statua del S. Giorgio di Donatello . . . Ragionamento, *etc.* 1765. 4°. [*Baldinucci (F.) Raccolta di alcuni opuscoli, etc.*] **52. c. 33.**

—— *See* Bode (W. A. von) Donatello à Padoue. Gattamelata et les sculptures du Santo, *etc.* 1883. fol. **1762. d. 21.**

—— *See* Cavallucci (C. J.) Vita ed opere di Donatello, *etc.* 1886. fol. **7875.v.4.**

—— *See* Cruttwell (Maud) Donatello, *etc.* 1911. 8°. **07805. dd. 1/12.**

—— *See* Fechheimer (S.) *Writer on Art.* Donatello und die Reliefkunst, *etc.* 1904. 8°. **7803. t. 6. (3.)**

—— *See* Fontana (Giovanni) *of Pisa.* Un' Opera del Donatello esistente nella chiesa dei Cavalieri di S. Stefano di Pisa. 1895. 8°. **7899. ee. 6. (8.)**

—— *See* Francioni (A.) Elogio di Donatello, *etc.* 1837. 8°. **7812.de.16.**

—— *See* Hennessy (John P.) Donatello's Relief of the Ascension with Christ giving the Keys to St. Peter. 1949. 8°. **W.P. 7207.**

—— *See* Holtzhausen (F.) Donatello. 1882. 8°. [*Charakterbilder bedeutender Künstler.* Hft. 3.] **7856. df. 21.**

—— *See* Kauffmann (H.) Donatello. Eine Einführung in sein Bilden und Denken, *etc.* [With plates.] 1935. 8°. **7876. d. 6.**

—— *See* Lindsay (David A. E.) *27th Earl of Crawford and 10th Earl of Balcarres.* Donatello. 1903. 8°. **2264. b. 14.**

—— *See* Melani (A.) Donatello, *etc.* (Studio storico-critico.) 1887. 8°. **10601. c. 27. (6.)**

—— *See* Meyer (Alfred G.) Donatello, *etc.* 1908. 8°. **2263. c. 65.**

—— *See* Meyer (Alfred G.) Donatello . . . Translated by P. G. Konody. 1904. 8°. [*Monographs on Artists.*] **7873.aa.6/8.**

—— *See* Milanesi (G.) Catalogo delle opere di Donatello, e bibliografia degli autori che ne hanno scritto. 1887. 8°. **7807. l. 38. (2.)**

—— *See* Morisani (Ottavio) Studi su Donatello, *etc.* [With plates.] 1952. 8°. **7877. g. 16.**

BARDI (DONATO) called DONATELLO.

—— *See* MÜNTZ (E.) Les Artistes célèbres. Donatello. [1885.] 8°. **2264**. d. **4**.

—— *See* PASTOR (W.) Donatello. Eine evolutionistische Untersuchung auf kunsthistorischem Gebiet. 1892. 8°. **7875**. aaa. **35**.

—— *See* PRÉVOST (G.) Aperçus sur Donatello et la sculpture dite réaliste. 1878. 8°. **7807**. l. **3**. (**11**.)

—— *See* PLANISCIG (L.) Donatello. Mit 143 Abbildungen. [1939.] 8°. **7876**. d. **28**.

—— *See* REA (Hope) Donatello, *etc.* 1900. 8°. **2263**. d. **5**.

—— *See* REYMOND (Marcel) Donatello. 1917. 8°. **7875**. c. **43**.

—— *See* ROSENBERG (C. A.) Lorenzo Ghiberti. Donatello. [1878.] 8°. [*Kunst und Künstler des Mittelalters.* Abt. 2. Bd. 2. no. 45/46.] **2262**. f. **3**.

—— *See* SANPAOLESI (P.) Brunellesco e Donatello nella Sacristia Vecchia di San Lorenzo. [With plates.] [1948.] fol. **7812**. d. **18**.

—— *See* SCHMARSOW (A.) Donatello. Eine Studie über den Entwicklungsgang des Künstlers und die Reihenfolge seiner Werke, *etc.* 1886. 8°. **7806**. e. **13**. (**1**.)

—— *See* SCOTT (Leader) *pseud.* Ghiberti and Donatello, *etc.* 1882. 8°. **07807**. h. **29**.

—— *See* SEMPER (H.) Donatello, seine Zeit und Schule. Eine Reihenfolge von Abhandlungen von Dr. H. Semper . . . Im Anhange: Das Leben des Donatello von Vasari, übersetzt von obigem. Der Tractat des Francesco Bocchi über den S. Georg des Donatello übersetzt von C. Cerri, *etc.* 1875. 8°. [*Quellenschriften für Kunstgeschichte und Kunsttechnik des Mittelalters.* Bd. 9.] **2262**. b.

—— *See* SEMPER (H.) Donatellos Leben und Werke, *etc.* 1887. 8°. **10630**. ff. **28**.

—— *See* SEMRAU (M.) Donatellos Kanzeln in S. Lorenzo, *etc.* 1891. 8°. [*Italienische Forschungen zur Kunstgeschichte.* Bd. 2.] **7806**. de. **19**.

—— *See* SERAFINI (A.) Donatello and Michelozzo in an unpublished work of collaboration, *etc.* 1918. 8°. **7875**. p. **17**.

—— *See* TANFANI CENTOFANTI (L.) Donatello in Pisa. Documenti, *etc.* 1887. fol. **7806**. f. **25**.

—— *See* TROMBETTA (P.) Donatello. 1887. 8°. **10629**. h. **3**.

—— *See* VOEGE (W.) Raffael und Donatello, *etc.* 1896. 4°. **7856**. g. **17**.

—— Donatello. [Reproductions. With a preface and systematic account of Donatello's works by Ludwig Goldscheider.] *G. Allen & Unwin: London,* 1941. fol. L.R. **106**. d. **14**.

—— Donatello. Des Meisters Werke in 277 Abbildungen. Herausgegeben von Paul Schubring. pp. liv. 219. *Stuttgart & Leipzig,* 1907. 4°. [*Klassiker der Kunst.* Bd. 11.] **7854**. t. **11**.

BARDI (FERDINANDO DE') *Count.* Del benessere nella società moderna. Studii sociali. pp. xvii. 269. *Roma,* 1892. 8°. **08276**. h. **50**.

BARDI (FILIPPO DE') *See* MARMIER (X.) Storia della letteratura in Danimarca e in Svezia . . . Traduzione del cav. F. de' Bardi. 1841. 8°. **816**. k. **10**.

BARDI (FILIPPO DE')

—— Storia della letteratura araba sotto il Califato. 2 vol. *Firenze,* 1846. 8°. **11852**. i. **14**.

BARDI (FRANCESCO) Metamorfosi di P. Ovidio N. breuemente spiegate, e rappresentate con artificiose figure, accresciuta questa terza impressione di nuoue allegorie consacrate al . . . Sig. Francesco Rosa dal Sig. F. Bardi. pp. 83. *Z. Parè: Venetia,* 1676. 8°. **1001**. c. **12**. (**2**.)

—— [Another edition.] Fauole d'Ouidio istorico, politico, morale con le allegorie. Breuemente spiegato, e delineato con artificiose figure. [Edited by F. Bardi. With different illustrations.] pp. 80. 1684. 8°. *See* OVIDIUS NASO (P.) [*Metamorphoses.—Appendix.*] **11385**. aaa. **15**.

—— [Another edition.] Ouidio istorico, politico, morale. Breuemente spiegato, e delineato con artificiose figure, accresciuta questa quinta impressione di nuoue allegorie, *etc.* pp. 79. *G. Parè: Venetia,* 1688. 8°. **11388**. aa. **28**.

With the original illustrations.

BARDI (G.) *Count.* Lectures élémentaires, pour les enfans: avec une traduction interlinéaire en anglois, *etc.* [Translated from the Italian of G. Bardi by M. A. Pichet.] pp. viii. 139. *Harvey & Darton: Londres,* 1831. 12°. **1212**. e. **32**.

BARDI (GIOVANNI DE') *Count di Vernio.* *See* also ALTERATO, *Il Puro Academico, pseud.* [i.e. G. de' Bardi.]

—— *See* also INCRUSCATO, *Academico della Crusca, pseud.* [i.e. G. de' Bardi.]

—— Della Imp. Villa Adriana e di altre sontuosissime già adjacenti alla città di Tivoli descrizione. [Edited by D. Moreni.] pp. lxxviii. 78. *Firenze,* 1825. 8°. **7820**. c. **20**.

—— Discorso sopra 'l giuoco del calcio fiorentino. Del Puro Accademico Alterato (G. de' Bardi). Di nuouo ristampato. pp. 48. *Appresso i Giunti: Firenze,* 1615. 4°. **785.h.18.**

—— [Another copy.] Discorso Sopra 'l giuoco del calcio Fiorentino. Del puro accademico Alterato. Di nuovo ristampato. *Firenze,* 1615. 4°. T. **2495**. (**3**.)

—— [Another edition.] Nuouamente ristampato coll' aggiunta de' capitoli del medesimo giuoco. [Edited by O. Capponi.] pp. 36. *All' Insegna della Stella: Firenze,* 1673. 4°. **596**. e. **6**.

—— [Another copy.] **64**. d. **23**.

—— Eorum quæ vehunt[ur] in aquis experim[enta] . . . ad Archimedis tru[tinam examinata]. pp. 16. *Ex typographia B. Zanne[ri]: Roma[e],* [1614.] 4°. **8775**. c. **29**.

The first two leaves, containing the titlepage and the dedication, are mutilated.

BARDI (GIROLAMO) *Camaldolese Monk.* *See* LUCIDUS (J.) Ioan. Lucidi . . . Chronicon seu emendatio temporum . . . Cum additionibus . . . Hieronymi Bardi, *etc.* 1575. 4°. **303**. k. **6**.

—— *See* MEXIA (P.) Vite di tutti gl'Imperadori Romani . . . Alle quali da Girolamo Bardi . . . sono state . . . aggiunte le Vite di Ferdinando Primo, & di Massimiliano Secondo, & di Ridolfo Secondo, *etc.* 1589. 4°. **1481**. c. **37**.

—— Vita di Ferdinando, imperadore.—Vita di Massimiliano, secondo di questo nome, imperadore.—Vita di Ridolfo, secondo di questo nome, imperadore. *See* MEXIA (P.) Vite di tutti gl' imperadori romani, *etc.* 1583. 4°. **1199**. e. **1**.

BARDI (GIROLAMO) *Camaldolese Monk.*

—— Chronologia vniuersale, *etc.* 4 pt. *Appresso i Giunti: Venetia,* 1581. fol. **581. k. 1–3.**

—— [Another copy.] **216. e. 10–12.**

—— Delle cose notabili della città di Venetia. Libri II. [By G. Bardi.] pp. 150. 1592. 8°. *See* VENICE. [Appendix] **575. a. 16. (1.)**

—— [Another edition.] Di nuouo aggiuntavi la dichiaratione di tutte l'historie, che si contengono ne i quadri posti nuouamente nelle Sale dello Scrutinio, & del gran Consiglio del Palazzo Ducale della Serenissima Republica di Venetia, *etc.* pp. 143. *A. Salicato: Vinegia,* 1601. 8°. **575. a. 16. (2.)**
The "Dichiaratione" is, in fact, not contained in this edition.

—— [Another edition.] Di nuouo aggiuntavi la dichiaratione di tutte l'historie, che si contengono ne i quadri posti nuouamente nelle Sale dello Scrutinio, *etc.* 2 pt. *A. Salicato: Vinegia,* 1606. 8°. **10129. a. 36.**
Cropped.

—— Dichiaratione di tutte le istorie, che si contengono ne i quadri posti nuouamente nelle Sale dello Scrutinio, e del Gran Consiglio, del Palagio Ducale della Serenissima Republica di Vinegia, nella quale si ha piena intelligenza delle più segnalate vittorie; conseguite di varie nationi del mondo da i Vinitiani. ff. 64. *F. Valgrisio: Venetia,* 1587. 8°. **522. a. 9. (2.)**

—— [Another copy.] **52. b. 18.**
Imperfect; wanting the dedication and the table of contents. There is an addition on the verso of the last leaf, with the heading: "Aggiunta di nove figure fatte nel Scrutinio."

—— [Another edition.] ff. 64. *T. Bortolotto: Venetia,* 1602. 8°. **1057. b. 33.**

—— [Another edition.] ff. 46. *See* supra: Delle cose notabili della città di Venetia, *etc.* 1606. 8°. **10129. a. 36.**

—— [Another edition.] pp. 162. *N. Pezzana: Venetia,* 1660. 12°. **11436. aa. 29. (2.)**

—— Sommario, ouero età del mondo chronologiche . . . [A summary of the author's "Chronologia universale."] Quarta parte. pp. 761–2221. *Appresso i Giunti: Venetia,* 1581. 4°. **800. f. 1.**
Imperfect; wanting pt. 1–3.

—— Vittoria nauale ottenuta dalla Republica Venetiana contra Othone, figliuolo di Federigo primo Imperadore; per la restitutione di Alessandro terzo, Pontefice Massimo, venuto à Venetia. pp. 188. *F. Ziletti: Venetia,* 1584. 4°. **592. b. 4. (2.)**

—— [Another copy.] **174. b. 22.**

—— [Another edition.] pp. 155. *A. Pinelli: Venetia,* 1619. 4°. **174. b. 7.**

BARDI (GIROLAMO) *of Genoa.* Medicus politico catholicus, seu medicinæ sacræ tùm cognoscendæ tùm faciundæ idea, *etc.* pp. 387. *Typis I. M. Farroni: Genuæ,* 1644. 8°. **1038. g. 4.**

BARDI (GIROLAMO DEI) Prospetto sugli avanzamenti delle scienze fisiche in Toscana. pp. 26. [*Florence?* 1770?] 4°. **8706. f. 6.**

BARDI (GIUSEPPE) *Publisher, of Florence.*

—— *See* LASTRI (M.) L'Etruria pittrice, *etc.* [Edited by N. Pagni and G. Bardi.] 1791, *etc.* fol. **747. c. 4.**

BARDI (LEONORA DE') [For editions of the Novella di Leonora de' Bardi e Hippolito Buondelmonti:] *See* BUONDELMONTI (H.)

BARDI (LIPPO PASCI DEI) *See* PASCI DEI BARDI.

BARDI (LUIGI) *See* MISSIRINI (M.) Delle statue di Arnolfo di Lapo e di Filippo di Ser Brunellesco . . . pubblicate da L. Bardi dichiarazione. 1830. 4°. **7703. f. 20. (2.)**

—— L'Imperiale e Reale Galleria Pitti illustrata per cura di L. Bardi. 4 tom. *Firenze,* 1837–42. fol. **1265. h. 22–25.**

BARDI (PIETRO) La Poesia di Wordsworth, 1770–1808. pp. 138. *Bari,* 1922. 8°. **011850. aa. 36.**

—— Scrittori inglesi dell' ottocento. [An anthology of prose and verse.] *Eng.* pp. xii. 339. *Bari,* 1912. 8°. **012273. f. 2.**

—— Storia della letteratura inglese. pp. 218. *Bari,* 1933. 8°. **11855. aaa. 21.**

—— Traduzioni da lirici inglesi . . . Con note. *Eng. & It.* pp. 48. *Lucca,* 1901. 8°. **11602. g. 36.**

BARDI (PIETRO DE') *Count di Vernio. See* also DARPE (Beridio) *pseud.* [i.e. P. de' Bardi.]

—— *See* also PIEVERDI (Brivio) *pseud.* [i.e. P. de' Bardi.]

—— *See* also TRITO, *Il, Accademico Cruscante, pseud.* [i.e. P. de' Bardi.]

—— *See* MAXIMUS, *Tyrius.* Discorsi di Massimo Tirio . . . tradotti dal signor P. de Bardi. 1642. 4°. **231. f. 28.**

BARDI (PIETRO MARIA)

—— Lasar Segall. (Traduction française de André Rougon.) [With reproductions.] pp. 200. *São Paulo,* 1952. 4°. **7870. n. 31.**
A publication of the Museu de Arte de São Paulo.

—— Pionieri e soldati d'A. O., dall'acquisto di Assab all'Impero romano d'Etiopia. Antologia di scritti, documenti e illustrazioni, *etc.* pp. 580. pl. LXIV. *Milano,* 1936. 8°. **9062. bbb. 7.**

BARDI (SIMONE DE') *See* GABOTTO (F.) Il Marito di Beatrice. Studio. [On S. de' Bardi.] 1890. 8°. **11422. ccc. 17. (6.)**

BARDI (TOMMASO DE') Discorso politico . . . detto . . . nella sala dell' eccelentiss. Senato di Lucca . . . nell' anno 1669, *etc.* pp. 19. *Per gli HH. del Marescandoli: Lucca,* 1669. 4°. **4424. dd. 2. (7.)**

BARDI (UGO) *pseud.* [i.e. GIUSEPPE BIANCHI.]

—— Beatrice Cenci, dramma storico in versi. (Francesco Cenci e sua famiglia. Notizie e documenti storici di A. Bertolotti.) pp. xxxii. 104. *Milano,* 1879. 8°. **11714. b. 11. (4.)**

—— Trattato pratico di piscicoltura e ostricoltura. 1879. 8°. See BIANCHI (Giuseppe) Writer of Verse. **7204. bb. 9. (5.)**

BARDI DE FOURTOU (F.) *See* VIRGILIUS MARO (P.) [*Two or more Works.—French.*] Les Géorgiques et les Bucoliques (L'Énéide, Livre IVe) . . . traduites en vers français par F. Bardi de Fourtou. 1877. 8°. **11355. bbb. 30.**

BARDIDES (EMMANOUEL)

—— *See* BARMPA-PANTZELIOS. *Κρητικαι ῥιμαι. Τα τραγουδια Δασκαλογιαννη και Ἀλῃδακη. Ἐκδιδονται ὑπο Ἐ. Βαρδιδη.* 1888. 8°. **11586. bbb. 20. (2.)**

BARDIDES (Emmanouel)

—— Συλλογη κρητικων ἐπιστολων εἰς την ἐγχωριον διαλεκτον . . . Συλλεγεισα και ἐκδοθεισα ὑπο * * [i.e. E. Bardides]. pp. 58. 1878. 8°. *See* Cretan Letters. **8027.** cc. **3.** (**2.**)

BARDIER INDART (Mauro)

—— Lobos. Psicobiografía de juventud. Segunda edición, *etc.* [A novel.] pp. 173. *Montevideo,* 1946. 8°. **12492.** aaa. **3.**

BARDIES (Charles) *See* Delatheuratte (A. D.) and Bardies (C.) A propos du projet de loi Moreau. Lettres sur les armoiries, *etc.* 1891. 12°. **9905.** aaa. **22.** (**2.**)

BARDIES (Guillaume) Dissertation sur l'éducation physique des enfans, depuis la naissance jusqu'à l'époque du sevrage, *etc.* pp. 16. *Paris,* 1833. 4°. **1184.** e. **15.** (**12.**)

BARDIES (Louis de) *Baron.* L'Administration de la Gascogne, de la Navarre et du Béarn en 1740, *etc.* pp. 176. *Paris,* 1882. 8°. **8051.** a. **56.**

BARDIJA. *See* Bardiya.

BARDILAC WORK. Bardilac Work. By C. H. K. [1923.] 8°. *See* K., C. H. **07943.** a. **44.**

BARDILI, *Family of. See* Pistorius (J. F.) Burckhardtische Genealogie, oder Stamm-baum deren in sieben Haupt-Stämm bestehenden Burckhardt- und Bardilinischen Familie, *etc.* 1774. fol. **9902.** k. **8.**

BARDILI (Burckhardus) [For dissertations at which B. Bardili acted as Praeses:]

See Bengel (J. F.) — Jaeger (C. F.)
Eckestein (P. H.) — Jaeger (G. F.)
Ficker (J.) — Lutz (J.)
Frederus (C.) — Obrecht (J. J.)
Hauff (L. A.) — Rhau (B.)
Hoser (S.) — Schuetz (J. J.)

—— Die beraubte, jedoch zu Frieden gestellete Jungfrauschafft, seu Burchardi Bardili . . . tractatio juridica de satisfactione stupratæ. Editio postrema. *Lat.* pp. 76. *Quedlinburgi & Ascaniæ,* 1727. 4°. **1127.** h. **15.**

—— Disputatio juridica de contractibus in genere, *etc.* *Praes.* W. A. Lauterbach, *etc.* pp. 23. *Ex officina P. Brunnii: Tubingæ,* 1649. 4°. **897.** d. **1.** (**5.**)

—— Disputationem juridicam de auctoritate tutorum . . . publico eruditorum examini submittit B. Bardili . . . Respondente Johanne Georgio Seefrid. pp. 56. *Typis J. A. Celli: Tubingæ,* 1660. 4°. **897.** b. **5.** (**61.**)

BARDILI (Carolus) Fatum mathematicum. Hoc est, quod actiones eventusq; sublunares ad vim siderum . . . necessario nectantur, *etc.* *Praes.* C. Cellarius. pp. 38. *Typis J.-A. Celli: Tubingæ,* 1621. 8°. **8562.** a. **29.**

—— [Another copy, with a different titlepage.] Fati mathematici, hoc est; quod actiones humanæ, euentusque sublunares ad vim siderum . . . necessario nectantur; defensio, *etc.* *Typis I. A. Cellii: Tubingæ,* 1621. 8°. **719.** e. **29.** (**5.**)

BARDILI (Christoph Gottfried) Allgemeine praktische Philosophie. pp. 189. *Stuttgart,* 1795. 8°. **8463.** bbb. **5.** (**1.**)

—— Grundriss der ersten Logik, gereiniget von den Irrthümmern bisheriger Logiken überhaupt, der Kantischen insbesondere, *etc.* pp. xvi. 360. *Stuttgart,* 1800. 8°. **8468.** a. **4.**

—— Ueber die Geseze der Ideenassoziation und insbesondere ein, bisher unbemerktes, Grundgesez derselben. pp. 76. *Tübingen,* 1796. 8°. **8463.** bbb. **5.** (**2.**)

BARDILI (Christoph Gottfried)

—— Ursprung des Begriffes von der Willensfreiheit, *etc.* pp. xxx. 96. *Stuttgart,* 1796. 8°. **1249.** a. **8.**

—— Der Wirzburger Rezensent; oder Luther verderbte vollends alles! Ein Brief an Herrn Andres. [Signed: Ein Lutheraner, i.e. C. G. Bardili.] pp. 32. 1787. 8°. *See* Lutheran. **837.** d. **40.** (**2.**)

BARDILI (F.) Zu Weber's Todtenfeyer. Gesprochen in einem Kreise von Deutschen . . . den 22sten Junius, 1826. [In verse.] pp. 2. [*London,* 1826.] 8°. **011528.** l. **40.**

BARDILI (Georgius) Thesium chiriatricarum sylloge I. De phlebotomia, *etc.* *Praes.* G. B. Metzger. pp. 10. *Typis G. Kerneri: Tubingæ,* 1666. 4°. **1179.** d. **4.** (**15.**)

BARDILI (Johann Wendel) Des weyland Durchl. Printzens Maximilian Emanuels . . . Reisen und Campagnen durch Teutschland in Polen, Lithauen, *etc.* [By J. W. Bardili. With an engraved portrait.] pp. 653. 1730. 8°. *See* Maximilian Emanuel, *Prince of Wurtemberg.* **10704.** bb. **19.**

—— [Another edition.] pp. 656. 1739. 8°. *See* Maximilian Emanuel, *Prince of Wurtemberg.* **10291.** a. **22.**

—— Mémoires de Maximilien-Emanuel, duc de Wirtemberg . . . Par Mr. F. P. [or rather, for the most part translated from the German of J. W. Bardili. With a portrait.] pp. viii. 333. 1740. 12°. *See* P., F., *Mr.* **10707.** bb. **24.**

BARDILUS (Burckhardus) *See* Bardili.

BARDIN (A. G.) *See* Weise (A. J.) History of the City of Troy . . . With maps and statistical tables by A. G. Bardin. 1876. 8°. **10412.** ff. **8.**

BARDIN (Auguste Michel) Onderhandeling over den oorsprong en de geschiedenis der stad Blankenberghe, *etc.* pp. 23. *Brugge,* [1863.] 8°. **10108.** e. **9.** (**1.**)

BARDIN (Charles) On Infant Education. A charity sermon, preached in Dundalk Church, on Sunday, 11th July, 1830, *etc.* pp. 24. *A. & W. Watson: Dublin,* 1830. 8°. **4475.** cc. **114.** (**8.**)

—— On Miracles. A sermon preached in Saint Mary's Church, Dublin, on the 21st and 28th September, 1823. pp. 54. *B. Dugdale, etc.: Dublin,* 1823. 8°. **4477.** f. **71.** (**10.**)

—— Sermon . . . Hebrews iv. 10. *See* Irish Pulpit. The Irish Pulpit, *etc.* ser. 1. 1827, *etc.* 8°. **1025.** k. **14.**

—— [Another edition.] *See* Irish Pulpit. The Irish Pulpit, *etc.* ser. 1. 1839. 8°. **4462.** h. **5.**

BARDIN (Élie) Propositions de médecine et de chirurgie, *etc.* pp. 17. *Paris,* 1821. 4°. **1183.** f. **12.** (**24.**)

BARDIN (Étienne Alexandre) *Baron.* Dictionnaire de l'armée de terre, ou recherches historiques sur l'art et les usages militaires des anciens et des modernes. [Continued by N. C. V. Oudinot, Duke de Reggio. The whole edited by P. J. A. Mollière.] pt. 1–16. pp. xxiv. 1–5120. *Paris,* 1841–51. 8°. **8833.** f. **35.**
Imperfect; wanting all after p. 5120.

—— Mémorial de l'officier d'infanterie . . . Seconde édition. [By E. A. Bardin.] 2 tom. 1813. 8°. *See* Mémorial. **6875.** c. **20.**

BARDIN (G.) Cours de dessin industriel. 2 pt. *Paris,* [1861,] 1863. fol. **1802.** b. **13.**

—— Mémoire sur l'enseignement du dessin dans les écoles municipales d'enfants, d'apprentis et d'ouvriers de la ville de Paris, *etc.* pp. 47. *Orléans,* 1863. 4°. **7856.** ee. **9.**

BARDIN (Ivan Pavlovich)

—— *See* Baikov (A. A.) Собрание трудов. [Edited by I. P. Bardin and others.] 1948, *etc.* 8°. **07107.m.56.**

—— *See* Grum-Grzhimailo (V. E.) Собрание трудов. Под редакцией . . . И. П. Бардина. 1949. 8°. **7110.** c. **7.**

—— Методы выделения и анализа неметаллических включений в стали. (Ответственный редактор . . . И. П. Бардин.) pp. 53. 1954. 8°. *See* Russia.—*Академия Наук СССР.* —*Институт Металлургии.* **07107.** v. **53.**

—— Перспективы развития древесноугольной металлургии на Урале. Доклад на конференции по развитию производительных сил Моловской области, *etc.* pp. 44. 1946. 8°. *See* Russia.—*Академия Наук СССР.* —*Комиссія по Изученію Естественныхъ Производительныхъ Силъ Россіи.* **07106.** ee. **54.**

—— Проблемы северо-западной металлургии. [By I. P. Bardin, A. E. Probst and V. V. Rikman. With maps.] pp. 141. 1946. 8°. *See* Russia.—*Академия Наук СССР.* —*Комиссия по Изучению Естественных Производительных Сил России.*—*Ленинградско-Мурманская Экспедиция.* **07107.** r. **14.**

—— Советская техника за двадцать пять лет. Под редакцией . . . И. П. Бардина . . . Н. Г. Бруевича . . . А. М. Терпигорева . . . В. И. Вейца . . . А. С. Кудрявцева. (Twenty Five Years of Soviet Technique.) *Russ.* pp. 207. 1945. 8°. *See* Russia.—*Академия Наук СССР.* —*Отдѣленіе Техническихъ Наукъ.* **8768.** dd. **32.**

—— [Сталин и советская металлургия.] Stalin şi metalurgia sovietică. [A translation of an article originally published in "Иосифу Виссарионовичу Сталину Академия Наук СССР."] pp. 29. [*Bucharest,*] 1950. 8°. **07109.** h. **86.**

—— Термическая обработка рельсов. Сборник статей под редакцией . . . И. П. Бардина. [With plates.] pp. 258. 1950. 8°. *See* Russia.—*Академия Наук СССР.*—*Институт Металлургии.* **7110.** c. **13.**

—— Технические науки. Под редакцией . . . И. П. Бардина. pp. 66. *Москва, Ленинград,* 1945. 8°. [*Очерки по истории Академии Наук.*] **Ac. 1125/215. (7.)**

BARDIN (Ivan Pavlovich) and **BANNUY** (N. P.)

—— Черная металлургия в новой пятилетке. pp. 175. 1947. 8°. *See* Russia.—*Академия Наук СССР.* —*Институт Металлургии.* **07107.** r. **10.**

BARDIN (J. B.) Histoire du pays de Septème—Isère—depuis ses origines jusqu'à nos jours, avec détails sur les évènements de la Révolution. 2e édition. pp. xv. 383. *Vienne,* 1905. 8°. **010168.** h. **46.**

BARDIN (James) *See* Frías (H.) Leyendas Históricas Mexicanas . . . Edited by J. Bardin. 1918. 8°. **012213.p.12/4.**

BARDIN (John Franklin)

—— The Burning Glass. pp. 224. *Victor Gollancz: London,* 1950. 8°. **NNN. 644.**

—— Christmas comes but once a Year. pp. 223. *Peter Davies: London,* 1955. 8°. **NNN. 6159.**

—— The Deadly Percheron. pp. 192. *Victor Gollancz: London,* 1947. 8°. **012643.** tt. **53.**

—— Devil Take the Blue-Tail Fly. pp. 190. *Victor Gollancz: London,* 1948. 8°. **NN. 38937.**

BARDIN (John Franklin)

—— The Last of Philip Banter. pp. 192. *Victor Gollancz: London,* 1947. 8°. **12729.** cc. **21.**

BARDIN (Libre Irmand) Enseignement public. Géométrie descriptive. Modèles destinés à l'enseignement de la géometrie descriptive . . . La topographie enseignée par des plans-reliefs et des dessins avec tente explicatif . . . Exposition Universelle, 1855. pp. 24. *Paris,* 1855. 4°. **8532. f. 36. (7.)**

BARDIN (P.) *Citoyen.* Désespoir de Louis xvi, et du comité autrichien des Thuilleries. pp. 8. [*Paris,* 1792.] 8°. **F.R. 120. (49.)**

—— Liberté, Égalité. Législateurs, vous êtes des Jean-Foutres! ou soutenez le peuple: condamnez Capet le traître au supplice, *etc.* pp. 8. [*Paris,* 1792.] 8°. **F.R. 122. (19.)**

—— M. Bailly, maire de Paris, traité sans égard et comme il le mérite. pp. 8. [*Paris,* 1791.] 8°. **R. 657. (28.)**

—— Taisez-vous bavards, vous ne savez ce que vous dites. [In defence of Lafayette.] pp. 8. [*Paris,* 1790?] 8°. **F. 437. (7.)**

—— Vivre libre ou mourir. Pétition à tous les départemens du royaume. Les crimes du département de Paris dévoilés; ses conspirations avec la cour et Lafayette, pour consommer le malheur de la nation française, et perdre les plus grands patriotes de l'Empire, Messieurs Pétion et Manuel, *etc.* pp. 8. [*Paris,* 1792.] 8°. **F. 791. (6.)**

—— [Another copy.] **935. b. 6. (19.)**

—— [Another copy.] Vivre libre ou mourir. Pétition à tous les départemens, *etc.* [*Paris,* 1792.] 8°. **R. 78. (46.)**

—— Voilà les crimes de Lafayette. [In defence of Lafayette.] pp. 8. [*Paris,* 1790?] 8°. **F. 248. (13.)**

BARDIN (Pierre) Le Lycée du Sr Bardin, où en plusieurs promenades il est traité des connoissances, des actions, & des plaisirs d'un honneste homme. 1. partie. Des connoissances. pp. 764. *I. Camusat: Paris,* 1632. 8°. **1133. a. 25.**
Imperfect; wanting pt. 2, published in 1634.

—— Le Tombeau de Monseigneur le duc de Mayenne. Ou, le temple de la magnanimité. [In verse.] pp. 1–8. *I. Bichon: Saintes,* 1621. 8°. **1193. h. 11. (2.)**
Imperfect; wanting pp. 9–16.

—— [Another edition.] pp. 16. *Iouxte la Coppie imprimée à Xainte, par S. Crespin,* [1621.] 8°. **8050. bbb. 20. (43.)**

BARDIN (Shlomo)

—— Pioneer Youth in Palestine. pp. x. 182. *Bloch Publishing Co.: New York,* 1932. 8°. **20017.** aa. **52.**

BARDIN (Stanislas Benoît Joseph) Châteauneuf, son origine et ses développements, avec deux mémoires sur ses anciens noms. [With plates.] pp. ix. 168. 3. *Châteauneuf; Orléans,* 1864. 8°. **10171.** c. **9.**

BARDINA (Sofiya Illarionovna) Рѣчь Софіи Илларіоновны Бардиной. [In her own defence.] *See* Dragomanov (M. P.) Les Femmes du procès des socialistes de Moscou, *etc.* 1877. 8°. **8094. f. 9. (1.)**

—— Рѣчь Софіи Илларіоновны Бардиной. Издание кружка анархистовъ. (Le Discours de S. Bardine.) *Russ.* pp. 11. *Женева,* 1893. 16°. **08276. de. 14. (3.)**

—— M-lle Sophie Bardina. Софья Илларіоновна Бардина. [A biographical sketch.] *Russ.* pp. 32. *Genève,* 1883. 8°. **10601. a. 43. (1.)**

BARDINADE. La Bardinade; ou les nôces de la stupidité: poëme divisé en dix chants. [By J. B. C. Isoard Delisle.] pp. xxx. 160. 1765. 8°. **11482**. h. **7**. (**1**.)

—— Nouvelle édition, à laquelle on a joint le parallèle entre Descartes & Newton, par le même auteur. 2 pt. *La Haye; Paris*, 1768. 8°. **1065**. l. **6**.

BARDINAL (Chéri Martial) Thèse pour le doctorat en médecine, *etc.* (Questions sur diverses branches des sciences médicales.) pp. 39. *Paris*, 1848. 4°. [*Collection des thèses soutenues à la Faculté de Médecine de Paris.* An 1848. tom. 1.] **7372**. b. **4**.

BARDINARUS (Rumel F.) *Esq., Poet, pseud.* Arn at the Flail. A sequel to "John o'Arn Ha" [by James Beattie]. pp. 24. *A. Brown & Co.: Aberdeen*, 1878. 8°. **11630**. bb. **5**. (**12**.)

BARDINET (Barthélemy Alphonse) Des fractures de l'olécrane sans écartement des fragments et sans déplacement en haut du fragment supérieur. pp. 37. *Limoges*, 1868. 8°. **7481**. h. **4**.

—— Éloge de F. Mêlier . . . prononcé . . . le 15 novembre 1866. pp. 32. *Paris*, 1867. 8°. **10661**. cc. **29**. (**5**.)

—— La Luxation de l'occipital sur l'atlas peut-elle avoir lieu? *etc.* pp. 39. *Paris*, 1840. 4°. [*Collection des thèses soutenues à la Faculté de Médecine de Paris.* An 1840. tom. 1.] **7371**. b. **2**.

BARDINI (Jacobus) De staphylomate corneæ dissertatio inauguralis, *etc.* pp. 23. *Patavii*, 1826. 8°. **7306**. b. 4. (**13**.)

BARDINI (Stephano) Catalogue of a Choice Collection of Pictures, Antiquities, Works of Art of the Middle Ages and Renaissance, from the collection of Signor S. Bardini, *etc.* pp. 74. *London*, 1899. 8°. [Christie, Manson and Woods. *Auction Catalogues.*] S.C.Christie.

—— Plates. fol. [Christie, Manson and Woods. *Illustrated Sale Catalogues.*] S.C.Christie.2.

BARDINI (Vincenzo) *See* Berdini.

BARDINO (Lice)

—— L'Argenis di John Barclay e il romanzo greco. pp. 125. *Palermo*, [1939.] 8°. [*Studi palermitani di Filologia classica.* no. 3.] W.P. 6240/3.

BARDINUS (Joannes) Positiones philosophicæ, *etc.* *Praes.* G. Jachaeus. *Ex officinâ I. Patii: Lugduni Batavorum*, 1606. 4°. **7306**. f. **6**. (**49**.)

BARDIS, Léon Trippault, *Sieur de.* *See* Trippault.

BARDIUS (Joannes) *See* Bardi (Giovanni)

BARDIYA.

—— *See* Koenig (F. W.) Der falsche Bardija. Dareios der Grosse und die Lügenkönige, *etc.* 1938. 8°. 09009.f.3/4.

BARDO. O Bardo. Jornal de poesias ineditas. *See* Periodical Publications.—*Oporto.*

BARDO. The Tibetan Book of the Dead (Bardo Thödol); or, the After-death experiences on the Bardo plane, according to Lāma Kazi Dawa-Samdup's English rendering. By W. Y. Evans-Wentz . . . With foreword by Sir John Woodroffe. [With plates.] pp. xliv. 248. *Oxford University Press: London*, 1927. 8°. 15013.c.9.

—— The Tibetan Book of the Dead . . . according to Lāma Kazi Dawa-Samdup's English rendering. By W. Y. Evans-Wentz . . . Second edition. pp. l. 248. *Oxford University Press: London*, 1949. 8°. 19999. e. 79.
With foreword by Sir John Woodroffe.

BARDO.

—— Il Libro tibetano dei morti. Il libro della salvazione dall'esistenza intermedia. [Translated, with an introduction, by Giuseppe Tucci.] pp. 207. *Milano*, 1949. 8°. **19999**. f. 44
Collezione "Problemi dello spirito." no. 57.

BARDO, *Archbishop of Mainz.* *See* Schneider (Friedrich C. W.) Der heilige Bardo, Erzbischof von Mainz, *etc.* 1871. 8°. **4828**. bb. **35**

—— *See* Vulculdus. Bardonis archiepiscopi Mogunti vita duplex. Edente D. Wilhelmo Wattenbach. (I. Vita auctore Vulculdo.—II. Vita Bardonis maior.) 1854. fol. [*Monumenta Germaniae historica.* tom. 13.] Circ. **9**. b

—— Vita Sancti Bardonis archiepiscopi Moguntini prolixior 1853. *See* Boehmer (J. F.) Fontes rerum Germanicarum, *etc.* Bd. 3. 1843, *etc.* 8°. **1315**. e. **11**

BARDO, *Presbyter.* Vita Anselmi episcopi Lucensis . . Edidit Rogerus Wilmans. 1856. *See* Pertz (G. H.) Monumenta Germaniae historica, *etc.* tom. 14. 1826, *etc.* fol. Circ. **9**. b

BARDO (Alfred H.) and **ODDY** (Albert S.) Practical Psychology. Its secrets and benefits. pp. 48. *Keighley Printers: Keighley*, 1913. 8°. **07306**. f. **32**. (3.

BARDO (Lewis H.)

—— *See* Shuman (John T.) and Bardo (L. H.) How to operate a Lathe. [1944.] 8°. **7947**. a. 5

BARDOCZ (Lajos) A mechanika alapvonalai. A mivel rendek szükségeihez alkalmazva . . . 225 fametszvénynyel pp. viii. 350. *Budapest*, 1874. 8°. **8767**. bb. **1**

BARDOL (Pierre Clodomir) Essai sur le rhumatisme articulaire aigu. pp. 39. *Paris*, 1857. 4°. [*Collection des thèses soutenues à la Faculté de Médecine de Paris.* An 1857. tom. 1.] **7373**. a. **1**

BARDOLFF (Carl von) *Baron.*

—— Deutsch-österreichisches Soldatentum im Weltkrieg pp. 41. *Jena*, [1937.] 8°. **9088**. b.
Part of the series "Österreichdeutsche Schriften."

—— Soldat im alten Österreich. Erinnerungen aus meinem Leben. [With a portrait and maps.] pp. 349. *Jena* [1938.] 8°. **010709**. e. **7**

BARDOLFF (Karl von) *Baron.* *See* Bardolff (Carl von)

BARDOLPH (Richard)

—— Agricultural Literature and the Early Illinois Farmer pp. 200. *Urbana*, 1948. 8°. [*Illinois Studies in the Social Sciences.* vol. 29. no. 1, 2.] Ac. **2692**. u/1

BARDOMACHIA. Bardomachia. Poema macaronico latinum. [By Alexander Geddes.] pp. 14. *J. Johnson: Londini*, 1800. 4°. **11631**. g. **33**. (11

BARDON PAPERS. The Bardon Papers. Documents relating to the imprisonment & trial of Mary Queen of Scots. *See* Mary, *Queen of Scotland.*

BARDON ( ) *Citoyenne.* *See* Vadier (M. G. A.) Convention Nationale. Réponse . . . à la pétition de citoyenne Bardon, fille de Cazes. [1795.] 8°. F.R. **65**. (25

BARDON (Achille) *See* Nîmes.—*Bibliothèque Publique.* Catalogue de la Bibliothèque de Nîmes. Catalogue du legs Achille Bardon, *etc.* 1902. 8°. **11902**. bb. 2

—— L'Exploitation du bassin houiller d'Alais sous l'ancien régime. pp. x. 384. *Nîmes*, 1898. 8°. **07107**. l. 1

BARDON (ACHILLE)

—— Histoire de la ville d'Alais de 1250 à 1340 (1341 à 1461). 2 vol. *Nîmes*, 1894, 96. 8°. **10173**. ee. **7**.

BARDÓN (CÉSAR MORÁN) *See* MORÁN BARDÓN.

BARDON (E. ÉDOUARD) De l'accouchement dans la présentation de l'épaule. pp. 40. *Paris*, 1855. 4°. [*Collection des thèses soutenues à la Faculté de Médecine de Paris.* An 1855. tom. 1.] **7372**. h. **1**.

BARDON (FRANÇOIS) Coup-d'œil général sur le mécanisme de l'accouchement naturel; thèse. *etc.* pp. 25. *Paris*, 1818. 4°. **1183**. e. **2**. (**22**.)

BARDON (G.) Traité, contenant une nouvelle methode, pour s'assurer des longitudes, de tous les lieux de la terre, par le moyen des planettes & des étoiles. pp. 32. *C. Lucas: Londres*, 1700. 8°. **534**. b. **46**.

BARDON (H. LÉONARD) Faculté de droit de Paris. Thèse pour la licence. (Jus romanum. De solutionibus et liberationibus.—Droit français. C. Nap. 122 à 1270, *etc.*) pp. 60. *Paris*, 1857. 8°. **5406**. aa. **1**. (**18**.)

BARDON (HENRY)

—— *See* CURTIUS RUFUS (Q.) Quinte-Curce. Histoires . . . Texte établi et traduit par H. Bardon. 1947, *etc.* 8°. **2319**. d. **12**.

—— La Littérature latine inconnue.

1. L'Époque républicaine. pp. 382. 1952.
2. L'Époque impériale. pp. 338. 1956.

Paris, 1952, 56. 8°. **11313**. r. **57**.

BARDON (JEAN LÉONARD ARMAND) Quelques réflexions sur divers sujets de médecine et de chirurgie; thèse, *etc.* pp. 19. *Paris*, 1830. 4°. **1184**. d. **7**. (**5**.)

BARDON (JOSEPH) Essai sur l'antéversion de l'utérus. Thèse, *etc.* pp. 48. *Montpellier*, 1853. 4°. **7379**. c. **1**. (**20**.)

BARDON (MARCEL)

—— L'Ile d'Oleron sous la domination anglaise. Recueil de documents relevés au Public Record Office de Londres par Miss H. M. Briggs, *etc.* [Edited by M. Bardon.] pp. 36. *Rochefort*, 1935. 8°. **010167**. f. **3**.

BARDON (MAURICE)

—— *See* CERVANTES SAAVEDRA (M. de) [*Don Quixote.—French.—Miscellaneous Translations.*] L'Ingénieux hidalgo Don Quichotte de la Manche . . . Avec préface, bibliographie et notes par M. Bardon. 1941. 8°. Cerv. **706**.

—— *See* CERVANTES SAAVEDRA (M. de) [*Don Quixote.—French.—Miscellaneous Translations.*] L'Ingénieux hidalgo Don Quichotte de la Manche . . . Préface, bibliographie et notes par M. Bardon. 1954. 8°. Cerv. **729**.

—— *See* CERVANTES SAAVEDRA (M. de) [*Single Works.—Novelas ejemplares.—French.*] Les Nouvelles exemplaires . . . avec préface, bibliographie et notes par M. Bardon. [1941.] 8°. **12492**. bb. **35**.

—— *See* LESAGE (A. R.) [*Two or more Works.*] Théâtre. Turcaret. Crispin rival de son maître. La Tontine. Avec préface, notice bibliographique et notes, par Maurice Bardon. 1948. 8°. **11740**. m. **26**.

—— *See* LE SAGE (A. R.) [*Gil Blas.—French.*] Histoire de Gil Blas de Santillane. Avec préface, bibliographie et notes par M. Bardon. 1942. 8°. **12515**. v. **37**.

—— "Don Quichotte" en France au XVIIe et au XVIIIe siècle, 1605–1815. [With plates and a bibliography.] 2 tom. pp. 932. *Paris*, 1931. 8°. [*Bibliothèque de la Revue de Littérature comparée.* tom. 69.] **11870**. d. **1/69**.

BARDON (MICHEL FRANÇOIS DANDRÉ) *See* DANDRÉ BARDON.

BARDON (PHILIPPE) Essai sur l'emploi thérapeutique du vésicatoire; thèse, *etc.* pp. 22. *Paris*, 1829. 4°. **1184**. c. **13**. (**27**.)

BARDÓN (THYRSUS LOPEZ) *See* LOPEZ BARDÓN.

BARDON-DAMARZID (MARC)

—— *See* WOOG (C.) and BARDON-DAMARZID (M.) L'Indemnisation des accidentés du travail, *etc.* 1939. 8°. **5402**. cc. **19**.

BARDON DE BRUN (BERNARD) *See* PETIOT (E.) La Vie admirable . . . de Monsieur Bardon de Brun, *etc.* 1636. 8°. **4865**. aa. **38**.

BARDONE (RINALDO) L'Abissinia e i paesi limitrofi. Dizionario . . . dell' Etiopia . . . Con una carta, *etc.* pp. 160. *Firenze*, 1888. 16°. **10097**. a. **27**.

BARDONG (CURT)

—— *See* GALENUS (C.) [*De Causis Procatarcticis.*] Galeni De causis procatarcticis libellus a Nicolao Regino in sermonem latinum translatus. Ad codicum fidem recensuit, in graecum sermonem retro vertits K. Bardong. 1937. 8°. **2025.h.**

BARDONNAUT (GEORGES) *See* LEGER (L. P. M.) and BARDONNAUT (G.) Les Racines de la langue russe. 1894. 8°. **12976**. c. **45**.

BARDONNAUT (MARCELIN) Réflexions morales et politiques, ou esquisse des progrès de la civilisation en France au XIX siècle. Par M. B. Des Ol * * res [i.e. M. Bardonnaut]. Deuxième édition, refondue. pp. xxviii. 382. 1849. 8°. *See* DES OL * * RES (M. B.) **8008**. e. **9**.

BARDONNET (DE) *Viscountess. See* HYDE DE NEUVILLE (J. G.) *Baron.* Mémoires, *etc.* [Edited by the Viscountess de Bardonnet.] 1888. 8°. **010661**. ff. **10**.

BARDONNET (ABEL)

—— *See* ALPHONSO, *Count of Poitou and Toulouse. etc.* Hommages d'Alphonse, comte de Poitiers, frère de Saint Louis . . . Publié d'après un manuscrit des Archives nationales par A. Bardonnet. 1872. 8°. **9220**. ff. **17**.

—— *See* ENGLAND. [*Miscellaneous Public Documents.—Henry* V. 1413–1422.] Procès-verbal de délivrance à Jean Chandos . . . Publié . . . par A. Bardonnet, *etc.* [1867.] 8°. **9200**. h. **3**.

—— Niort et La Rochelle de 1220 à 1224. Notes et documents. pp. 75. *Niort*, 1875. 8°. **9200**. d. **3**.

—— [Another copy.] **9220**. ff. **7**.

BARDONNET (L.) Des relations sympathiques qui existent entre l'appareil génital et l'appareil digestif chez la femme en particulier. Thèse, *etc.* pp. 56. *Montpellier*, 1859. 4°. **7379**. e. **1**. (**10**.)

BARDONNET DES MARTELS (ANTOINE) Considérations générales et observations sur la phlébite . . . Thèse, *etc.* pp. 37. *Montpellier*, 1824. 4°. **1181**. c. **14**. (**6**.)

—— Zootechnie. Traité des maniements, des épreuves et des moyens de contention et de gouverne qu'on emploie sur les espèces domestiques chevaline, bovine, ovine et porcine, suivi de la coupe des animaux de boucherie en France et en Angleterre. pp. 463. *Paris*, 1854. 12°. **7294**. c. 5.

BARDON Y GÓMEZ (LÁZARO SILVERIO)

—— See OLIVES CANALS (S.) Don Lázaro Bardon, 1817–1897. Apuntes para una historia de los estudios helénicos en España. [With a portrait.] 1953. 8°. **10635. n. 13.**

—— Lectiones græcæ, sive manu-ductio Hispanæ juventutis in linguam græcam . . . Secunda editio, aucta et accuratissime emendata. pp. 510. *Matriti*, 1859. 16°. **12924. a. 44.**

—— Viaje a Egypto con motivo de la apertura del Canal de Suez, y excursion al mediodia de Italia. pp. xiv. 224. *Madrid*, 1879. 8°. **10096. aa. 43.**

BARDORF (CHARLES FREDERICK) and **BALL** (J. A. B.) The Elements of Sugar Refining. pp. x. 240. *Chemical Publishing Co.: Easton, Pa.*, 1925. 8°. **07942. c. 31.**

BÁRDOS (ARTUR)

—— Uralkodók és komédiások. [Articles on great figures of the French stage. With plates, including portraits.] pp. 243. *Budapest*, [1936.] 8°. **011794. aa. 9.**

BÁRDOS (GYÖRGY)

—— Karénekes kiskáté. 99 szabály mindenfajta énekkarok tagjai számára, *etc.* pp. 15. *Budapest*, 1944. 16°. **7900.a.8.**

BÁRDOSY (JÁNOS) Animadversiones historico-critico-diplomaticæ in opus De insurrectione nobilium, auctore J. Keresztury . . . Cum recensione apocrisium, De Banderiis Hungaricis . . . anonymo auctore 1785, editarum, *etc.* pp. 229. *Budæ*, 1792. 8°. **9315. aaa. 13.**

—— Supplementum analectorum terræ Scepusiensis, notationibus, ex veteri ac recentiore Hungarorum historia depromtis . . . illustratum, *etc.* pp. 460. *Leutschoviæ*, 1802. 4°. **10215. e. 42.**

BARDOT (GEORGES) La Question des dix villes impériales d'Alsace depuis la paix de Westphalie jusqu'aux arrêts de " réunions " du conseil souverain de Brisach, 1648–1680. pp. 295. *Paris, Lyon*, 1899. 8°. [*Annales de l'Université de Lyon.* Nouvelle sér. II. Droit, Lettres. fasc. 1.] **Ac.365.(b.)**

—— Remarques sur un passage de Richer. pp. 39. 1890. *See* LYONS.—*Faculté des Lettres.* Bibliothèque de la Faculté des Lettres, *etc.* tom. 7. 1887, *etc.* 8°. **Ac. 8922/2.**

BARDOU ( ) *Prieur de La Voux.* Poëme qui a remporté le prix de poësie donné par Monseigneur l'evesque d'Angers, *etc.* pp. 7. [1694.] 4°. **11481. h. 41. (7.)**

BARDOU (JEAN JACQUES DAVID) *Bishop of Cahors.* Mandements, instructions et lettres pastorales de Mgr. Bardou. 1856. *See* MIGNE (J. P.) Collection intégrale et universelle des orateurs sacrés, *etc.* tom. 84. 1844, *etc.* 4°. **3676. bb. 1.**

BARDOU (PAUL) Histoire des quatre fusillés de Lille pendant l'occupation allemande. Eugène Jacquet et ses amis. pp. 317. *Paris*, [1919.] 8°. **9081. aaa. 21.**

BARDOU (VALENTIN) Trois mois chèz les Kroumirs et occupation du nord de la régence. pp. 82. v. *Saint-Girons*, 1888. 8°. **010096. ee. 7. (2.)**

BARDOU BOISQUETIN (PHILIPPE RENÉ) Corps Législatif. Conseil des Cinq-Cents. Motion d'ordre de Bardou-Boisquetin, sur la résolution relative aux élections. Séance du 9 pluviôse an 6. pp. 3. *Paris*, an 6 [1798]. 8°. **F.R. 101. (22.)**

—— Corps Législatif. Conseil des Cinq-Cents. Motion d'ordre faite par Bardou-Boisquetin, sur un assassinat commis dans la commune du Mans . . . Séance du 27 brumaire an 6. pp. 3. *Paris*, an 6 [1797]. 8°. **R. 652. (6.)**

BARDOU BOISQUETIN (PHILIPPE RENÉ)

—— Corps Législatif. Conseil des Cinq-Cents . . . Rapport fait par Bardou-Boisquetin, au nom de la commission des élections. Séance du 26 pluviôse an 6. pp. 4. *Paris*, an 6 [1798]. 8°. **F.R. 101. (25.)**

—— Corps Législatif. Conseil des Cinq-Cents. Rapport fait par Bardou-Boisquetin, sur le mode d'exécution de l'article 27 de l'acte constitutionnel, relativement à l'élection des juges-de-paix & de leurs assesseurs. Séance du 6 ventôse an 6. pp. 6. *Paris*, an 6 [1798]. 8°. **F.R. 185. (22.)**

BARDOU DUHAMEL (CHARLES LOUIS) *See* FREEMASONS. [*Appendix.*] L'Étoile flamboyante, *etc.* [By Baron T. H. de Tschudy; sometimes said to be written by Baron de Tschudy in collaboration with C. L. Bardou Duhamel.] 1766. 12°. **4784. c. 19.**

—— —— [1812.] 12°. **4783. b. 14.**

—— *See* FREEMASONS. [*Appendix.*] Der flammende Stern, *etc.* [By Baron T. H. de Tschudy; sometimes said to be written by Baron T. H. de Tschudy in collaboration with C. L. Bardou Duhamel.] 1866. 16°. **4785. a. 26.**

—— Traité sur la manière de lire les auteurs avec utilité. 3 tom. *Paris*, 1747–51. 12°. **1088. i. 32.**

BARDOULAT (HENRY) Essai sur le seigle ergoté . . . Thèse, *etc.* pp. 48. *Paris*, 1830. 4°. **1184. d. 8. (28.)**

BARDOUT (CLAUDE MARTIAL) Considération générales sur la cessation du flux menstruel, et sur les précautions à prendre pour en prévenir les accidens ou les maladies; thèse, *etc.* pp. 43. *Paris*, 1816. 4°. **1183. d. 2. (7.)**

BARDOUT (JACQUES ALFRED) Idées générales sur le diagnostic des maladies. pp. 39. *Paris*, 1850. 4°. [*Collection des thèses soutenues à la Faculté de Médecine de Paris.* An 1850. tom. 1.] **7372. c. 13.**

BARDOUX ( ) Arithmétique complète, et démontrée dans tous les cas possibles . . . Nouvelle édition. pp. xv. 535. *Lyon*, 1806. 8°. **8505. cc. 27.**
With the arms of Napoleon I. stamped on the cover.

—— Appendice appartenant à l'Arithmétique complète, *etc.* pp. 65. [*Lyons?* 1807?] 8°. **716. f. 34.**

BARDOUX (AGÉNOR) *See* BARDOUX (Benjamin J. A.)

BARDOUX (BENJAMIN JOSEPH AGÉNOR)

—— *See* BARDOUX (J.) A. Bardoux. Sa jeunesse, ses amis, ses débuts. [With a portrait.] 1938. 8°. **010655. bb. 26.**

—— *See* PICOT (G. M. R.) Bardoux. Notice historique, *etc.* [With a bibliography.] 1908. 8°. **010662. e. 33.**

—— La Bourgeoisie française. 1789–1848. pp. vii. 442. *Paris*, 1886. 8°. **8276. f. 27.**

—— [Another edition.] pp. vii. 442. *Paris*, 1893. 12°. **08275. f. 7.**

—— Le Comte de Montlosier et le Gallicanisme. pp. viii. 394. *Paris*, 1881. 8°. **3902. g. 23.**

—— [A reissue.] *Paris*, [1906.] 8°. **4629. bbb. 27.**

—— La Comtesse de Beaumont—Pauline de Montmorin. pp. ix. 426. *Paris*, 1884. 8°. **10661. ff. 7.**

—— [Another copy.] **10660. gg. 13.**

—— De l'influence des légistes au moyen âge. (Extrait de la Revue historique de droit français et étranger.) pp. 39. *Paris*, 1859. 8°. **6025. c. 57. (8.)**

—— Les Dernières années de La Fayette, 1792–1834. pp. iii. 431. *Paris*, 1893. 8°. **010662. h. 26.**

BARDOUX (BENJAMIN JOSEPH AGÉNOR)

—— Dix années de vie politique. pp. ii. 383. *Paris*, 1882. 18°. **8051. b. 35.**

—— La Duchesse de Duras. pp. iv. 436. *Paris*, 1898. 8°. **010663. k. 32.**

—— Études d'un autre temps. pp. vi. 339. *Paris*, 1889. 18°. **12356. cc. 23.**

—— Guizot. [With a portrait.] pp. 222. *Paris*, 1894. 8°. [*Les Grands Écrivains français.*] **010664. e. 18/21.**

—— La Jeunesse de La Fayette, 1757–1792. pp. xii. 409. *Paris*, 1892. 8°. **010661. h. 36.**

—— Les Légistes; leur influence sur la société française. pp. xi. 319. *Paris*, 1877. 8°. **8051. dd. 26.**

—— Madame de Custine, d'après des documents inédits . . . Avec un portrait, *etc.* pp. iii. 431. *Paris*, 1888. 8°. **010661. f. 9.**

—— Note sur la correspondance de Mirabeau et de Chamfort. pp. 19. *Clermont-Ferrand*, 1867. 8°. **10601. c. 8. (4.)**

—— Notice sur la vie et les travaux de M. Ernest Havet. pp. 44. 1892. 4°. *See* PARIS.—*Institut de France.* **10604. h. 23. (2.)**

BARDOUX (F.) Les Mystères de Hombourg . . . Première partie. pp. 28. *Francfort*, 1855. 8°. **7913. f. 19.** *No more published.*

BARDOUX (F. L.) Discours civique, prononcé le 19 mars 1791, à l'occasion de l'heureuse convalescence du roi des François, *etc.* pp. 16. [*Paris*, 1791 ?] 8°. **F. 889. (6.)**

BARDOUX (JACQUES) *See* DELEMER (A.) Le Bilan de l'étatisme. Préface de M. J. Bardoux. 1922. 8°. **08282. d. 64.**

—— Angleterre et France: leurs politiques étrangères. Essai d'une définition psychologique . . . The Zaharoff Lecture for 1936. pp. 27. *Clarendon Press: Oxford*, 1937. 8°. **08028. d. 49.**

—— L'Angleterre radicale. Essai de psychologie sociale, 1906–1913. pp. vii. 559. *Paris*, 1913. 8°. **8138. g. 33.**

—— Le Chaos espagnol. Éviterons—nous la contagion? pp. 47. [*Paris*,] 1937. 8°. **08042. a. 71.**

—— [Le Chaos espagnol.] Chaos in Spain. pp. 56. *Burns Oates & Washbourne: London*, [1937.] 8°. **08042. cc. 9.**

—— Croquis d'Outre-Manche. pp. ix. 235. *Paris*, 1914. 8°. **010352. g. 58.**

—— De Paris à Spa. La bataille diplomatique pour la paix française, février 1919—octobre 1920. pp. viii. 396. *Paris*, 1921. 8°. **09084. bb. 31.**

—— De Walterio Mappio. pp. xii. 207. *Columbariis*, 1900. 8°. **10855. e. 21.**

—— Le Drame français. Refaire l'état ou subir la force. pp. 256. *Paris*, [1934.] 8°. **08052. aaa. 79.**

—— Essai d'une psychologie de l'Angleterre contemporaine. Les crises belliqueuses. pp. v. 563. *Paris*, 1906. 8°. **8469. l. 18.**

—— Essai d'une psychologie de l'Angleterre contemporaine. Les crises politiques. Protectionnisme et radicalisme. pp. xii. 291. *Paris*, 1907. 8°. **8138. g. 29.**

—— La France de demain. Son gouvernement, ses assemblées, sa justice, *etc.* pp. 291. *Paris*, 1936. 8°. **08052. aa. 35.**

BARDOUX (JACQUES)

—— L'Île et l'Europe. La politique anglaise, 1930–1932. pp. xxv. 494. *Paris*, 1933. 8°. **08027. ff. 60.**

—— J'accuse Moscou. pp. 45. *Paris*, 1936. 16°. **8028. aaaa. 37.**

—— J. Ramsay Macdonald. pp. 192. *Paris*, 1924. 8°. **08285. de. 35.**

—— Lloyd George et la France. pp. viii. 453. *Paris*, 1923. 8°. **08028. g. 46.**

—— Le Mouvement idéaliste et social dans la littérature anglaise au XIXe siècle. John Ruskin. [With a bibliography.] pp. xii. 549. [*Paris*, 1900.] 8°. **11853. a. 14.**

—— [A reissue, without the bibliography.] Le Culte du beau dans la cité nouvelle. John Ruskin, poète, artiste, apôtre, *etc.* pp. xii. 534. *Paris*, 1931. 8°. **010855. de. 51.**

—— Ni communiste, ni hitlérienne: la France de demain. Un plan, *etc.* pp. 105. [*Paris*,] 1937. 8°. **08052. aa. 52.**

—— L'Ordre nouveau. Face au communisme et au racisme. pp. 250. [*Paris*,] 1939. 8°. **08052. bb. 4.**

—— L'Ouvrier anglais d'aujourd'hui. pp. ix. 277. *Paris*, 1921. 8°. **08282. bb. 81.**

—— Silhouettes d'Outre-Manche . . . Ouvrage orné de huit portraits. pp. xi. 298. *Paris*, 1909. 8°. **10803. de. 27.**

—— Le Socialisme au pouvoir. L'expérience de 1924. Le dialogue J. Ramsay Macdonald—Édouard Herriot. pp. xviii. 307. *Paris*, 1930. 8°. **08139. a. 94.**

—— Souvenirs d'Oxford. pp. 118. *Coulommiers*, 1898. 8°. **8365. de. 27.**

—— Memories of Oxford . . . Translated from the French by W. R. Barker. With a preface by Margaret L. Woods. pp. xii. 131. *F. E. Robinson: London*, 1899. 8°. **8365. aaa. 11.**

—— Les Soviets contre la France. Quel jour éclatera la révolution communiste ? pp. 44. *Paris*, 1936. 8°. **8052. aaa. 51.**

—— Victoria I., Édouard VII., Georges V. pp. xiv. 304. *Paris*, 1911. 8°. **10806. e. 1.**

BARDOUX (JEAN)

—— A. Bardoux. Sa jeunesse, ses amis, ses débuts. [With plates, including a portrait.] pp. 307. *Toulon*, 1938. 8°. **010655.bb.26.**

BARDOU Y CRUZ ÁLVAREZ (LEOPOLDO D'OZOUVILLE DE) *See* D'OZOUVILLE DE BARDOU Y CRUZ ÁLVAREZ.

BARDOVSKY (A.) Чтеніе о "Запискахъ Охотника" И. С. Тургенева, *etc.* pp. 47. *Москва, С.-Петербургъ*, 1899. 8°. **011852. i. 45. (4.)**

BARDOWICZ (LEO) Die rationale Schriftauslegung des Maimonides und die dabei in Betracht kommenden philosophischen Anschauungen desselben . . . Sonderabdruck aus dem "Magazin für die Wissenschaft des Judenthums," *etc.* pp. 59. *Berlin*, 1893. 8°. **4034. k. 38.**

—— Studien zur Geschichte der Orthographie des Althebräischen. pp. viii. 112. *Frankfurt*, 1894. 8°. **012904. h. 23.**

BÁRÐR. Bárðar Saga Snæfellsáss. Búid hefir til prentunar V. Ásmundarson. pp. 64. *Reykjavík*, 1902. 8°. **12431. aa. 53. (7.)**

BÁRÐR.

—— Bárðarsaga Snæfellsáss, Viglundarsaga, Þórðarsaga, Draumavitranir, Völsaþáttr, ved G. Vigfússon. *Icel. & Dan.* pp. xvii. 177. *Kjøbenhavn*, 1860. 12°. [*Nordiske Oldskrifter.* no. 27.] **12430**. p. **9/19**.

BARDSEN (IVAR) *See* BÁRÐARSON.

BARDSEY BIRD AND FIELD OBSERVATORY. *See* BARDSEY ISLAND.

BARDSEY ISLAND.

—— Bardsey Island—Ynys Enlli. (The Book of Bardsey.) [With illustrations.] pp. 43. *W. G. Evans & Son: Caernarvon*, 1934. 8°. **010369**. ee. **58**.

Bardsey Bird and Field Observatory.

—— Bardsey Bird and Field Observatory Report, 1954 [*etc.*]. [*Eglwysfach*, 1955– .] 8°. P.P. **1967**. ahr.

BARDSLEY (   ) *Miss.* Snowdon Recipes. Being a collection of vegetarian recipes used at Snowdon, the Vegetarian Guest House, Cheltenham . . . Edited by Henry B. Amos. pp. 18. *R. J. James: London*, [1914.] 8°. **07943**. h. **47**.

BARDSLEY (CHARLES WAREING) *See* ULVERSTON. The Registers of Ulverston Parish Church. Edited by C. W. Bardsley . . . and L. R. Ayre. 1886. 8°. **9906**. g. **9**.

—— Brownie . . . Illustrated by E. B. Leighton. pp. 256. *M. Ward & Co.: London*, 1878. 8°. [" *Blue-Bell*" *Series.*] **12601**. bbb. **4**.

—— Chinker's Christmas Dinner. *See* HAND AND HEART CHRISTMAS BOX. " Hand and Heart " Christmas Box of Fireside Tales, *etc.* [1879.] 8°. **12809**. h. **20**

—— Chronicles of the Town and Church of Ulverston. pp. 154. *J. Atkinson: Ulverston*, 1885 [1884]. 4°. **10358**. h. **23**.

—— Curiosities of Puritan Nomenclature. pp. xii. 252. *Chatto & Windus: London*, 1880. 8°. **12983**. bbb. **9**.

—— A Dictionary of English and Welsh Surnames, with special American instances, *etc.* [With a preface by J. W. Bardsley, Bishop of Carlisle.] pp. xvi. 837. *Henry Frowde: London*, 1901. 8°. 2050.d.

—— English Surnames. *See* infra: Our English Surnames, *etc.*

—— His Grandfather's Bible. A tale of Furness Fells. pp. viii. 248. " *Home Words* ": *London*, [1886.] 8°. **4416**. k. **24**.

—— Jenny. *See* HOLT (Emily S.) Stephen Mainwaring's Wooing, *etc.* [1882.] 8°. **4421**. ff. **47**.

—— John Lexley's Troubles. 3 vol. *Chatto & Windus: London*, 1877. 8°. **12625**. k. **1**.

—— Memorials of St. Ann's Church, Manchester, in the last Century . . . To which is added a short history of church building and Sunday School work in the same town. pp. xiv. 181. *Thomas Roworth: Manchester*, 1877. 8°. **4705**. b. **2**.

—— Our English Surnames: their sources and significations. pp. ix. 543. *Chatto & Windus: London*, [1873.] 8°. **12981**. bb. **27**.

—— English Surnames . . . Second edition . . . enlarged. pp. xxi. 612. *Chatto & Windus: London*, 1875. 8°. **9903**. aaa. **12**.

BARDSLEY (CHARLES WAREING)

—— Fifth edition, with a new preface. pp. xxv. 612. *Chatto & Windus: London*, 1897. 8°. **9906**. aa.

—— The Romance of the London Directory. [A treatise surnames.] pp. 162. *' Hand and Heart ': Londo* [1879.] 8°. **12984**. ee. **1**

BARDSLEY (CLARENCE EDWARD) and **CARLTO** (ERNEST WILSON)

—— Surveyors Field-Note Forms. pp. 113. *International Textbook Co.: Scranton, Pa.*, 1936. 8°. W.P. **10837**

—— Surveyors' Field-Note Forms . . . Second edition. pp. 127. *International Textbook Co.: Scranton*, 1942. 8 [*International Texts in Civil Engineering.*] W.P. **10837/1**

—— Surveyor's Field-Note Forms . . . Third edition. pp. 120. *International Textbook Co.: Scranton*, [1952.] 8 [*International Textbooks in Civil Engineering.*] W.P. **10837/3**

BARDSLEY (CUTHBERT KILLICK NORMAN) *Bishop Croydon.*

—— Bishop's Move. [Religious discussions.] pp. 128. *A. R. Mowbray & Co.: London*, 1952. 8°. **4382**. de. **1**

—— Faith, Character and Conduct. pp. 23. *Clarke H Fellowship: [London,]* 1952 [1953]. 8°. [*Clarke H Lecture.* no. 12.] W.P. **62/1**

—— Little Words and Big Effects . . . Being the address given in the " Lift up your Hearts " series of the B.B. from July 5th to 10th. pp. 8. *The Layman (Publications Goring*, [1954.] 8°. [*Linking Christianity with Citizenshi* no. 25.] W.P. c. **536/2**

—— Recipe for Happiness, *etc.* pp. 8. *Layme Publishing Co.: Goring*, [1954.] 8°. *Linking Christiani with Citizenship.* no. 1.] W.P. c. **536/**

BARDSLEY (CYRIL CHARLES BOWMAN) successively *Bisho of Peterborough* and *of Leicester.*

—— *See* BAYLDON (Joan) Cyril Bardsley, Evangelist, *et* [With portraits.] 1942. 8°. **20040**. c. **25**

—— *See* WHEN. When G came. [Chapters on S. Francis of Assisi, etc. With preface by C. C. B. Bardsley.] 1915. 8°. **4807**. aa. **4**

—— *See* WOODS (Frank T.) successively *Bishop of Pete borough* and *of Winchester.* The Creed of a Churchma By F. T. Woods . . . C. C. B. Bardsley, *etc.* 1916. 8 **4105**. de. **3**

—— Corporate Sacrifice. pp. 16. *C.M.S.: Londo* 1911. 8°. **4767**. aa. **28**. (**1**

—— Revival: the need and the possibilities, *etc.* pp. 13 *Longmans & Co.: London*, 1916. 8°. **4107**. eee. **2**

—— " Revival: the need and the possibilities " . . . Su gestions for group study. pp. 16. *Longmans & Co London*, 1916. 8°. **4106**. ee. **2**

—— The Way of Renewal. pp. 32. *Longmans & Co. London*, 1915. 8°. **4016**. g. **2**

—— Women and Church Work. By C. C. B. Bardsley editor, Margaret G. Brooke [and others]. pp. 116. *Longmans & Co.: London*, 1917. 8°. **4107**. eee. **4**

BARDSLEY (Cyril Charles Bowman) successively *Bishop of Peterborough* and *of Leicester*, and **ROGERS** (Travers Guy)

—— Studies in Revival. Edited by C. C. B. Bardsley and T. G. Rogers. With a foreword by the Archbishop of Canterbury. pp. vii. 69. *Longmans & Co.: London*, 1915. 8°. **4106**. ee. **19**.

BARDSLEY (Harry) The Differential Motions as they are applied to Cotton Spinning. With illustrated explanations and calculations of all the different motions in practical use at the present time. pp. 105. *Cartwright & Rattray: Hyde*, 1910. 8°. **8768**. bb. **25**.

BARDSLEY (Herbert James) Cannot Churchmen and Nonconformists Co-operate? A plea for the principles embodied in the Manchester Concordat . . . Together with a prefatory note by the Rev. W. F. Adeney . . . Reprinted with additions from the "Fortnightly Review." pp. 28. *Chapman & Hall: London*, 1906. 8°. **8305**. ff. **16**. (**2**.)

—— Church and Parliament: a plea for lay rights and Church reforms. pp. 32. *Longmans & Co.: London*, 1908. 8°. [*English Church Manuals.* no. 12.] **03605**. de. **3/12**.

—— Reconstructions of Early Christian Documents. Vol. I. pp. 454. *S.P.C.K.: London*, 1935. 8°. **20040.c.27.**
No more published.

—— Reconstructions of Early Christian Documents . . . Vol. II. [Page proof, with manuscript corrections by the author.] pp. xxi. 483. *S.P.C.K.: London*, 1940. 8°. **3167.b.6.**
Not published.

—— [Galley proof of the indexes to "Reconstructions of Early Christian Documents," together with some type-written notes with manuscript corrections by the author.] [1942.] 8° & fol. L.R. 274. d. 12.

BARDSLEY (James) *See* Davenport (Francis W.) The Sin of Korah: and "The Christian Priesthood." Two sermons . . . With an introductory preface by the Rev. Canon Bardsley. 1877. 8°. **4479**. cc. **14**. (**8**.)

—— *See* Dickinson (W. L.) "The Growth of the Church in Lancashire during the present century"; an examination of the paper read by the Rev. James Bardsley . . . at the Manchester Church Congress, *etc.* 1868. 8°. **4108**. aaa. **53**. (**15**.)

—— *See* MacKerrow (William) A Lecture . . . on the Principles, History, and Aims of Protestant Nonconformity. ("The Reply" of the Rev. James Bardsley . . . reviewed by the Rev. Wm. M'Kerrow.—A Second Answer to the Rev. James Bardsley.) [1861.] 8°. [*Lectures on Voluntaryism; delivered in the Mechanics' Institution, Manchester.*] **4139**. c. **75**.

—— Christian Holiness, and its Counterfeits. *See* Truths. Truths for the Times. [1867.] 8°. **4378**. b. **50**.

—— The Christian Ministry: what it is, and what it is not. pp. 24. *Hatchards: London*, 1872. 8°. **3940**. aaa. **85**. (**3**.)

—— The Formation of English Character. *See* London.—iii. *Young Men's Christian Association.* Lectures, *etc.* 1861. 8°. **4461**. d. **25**.

—— "I will Sing of the Mercies of the Lord"; or, an Exposition of the 89th Psalm. pp. viii. 151. *Hatchards: London*, 1877 [1876]. 8°. **3089**. aaa. **1**.

—— Introduction of Christianity into Britain in Apostolic Times, with a brief history of the early English Church. pp. 64. *Longman & Co.: London*, [1849.] 12°. **4705**. b. **39**.

BARDSLEY (James)

—— Mind your Rubrics. Seasonable thoughts upon the Rubrics and other important points for the consideration of churchmen. pp. 140. *W. Hunt & Co.: London*, 1866. 8°. **3477**. bbb. **38**.

—— "The Motives of Giving." A sermon preached in St. Ann's Church, Manchester . . . March 13th, 1862. *See* Money. Money and its Responsibilities, *etc.* [1862.] 8°. **4464**. a. **42**.

—— "Original Sin, and the effects of Adam's fall on man's position and character." *See* Papers. Papers for the Times. [1866.] 8°. **4378**. bb. **24**.

—— Perils and Duties of the Present Crisis. pp. 17. *See* S., T. A. Lectures delivered in St. Ann's Church, Manchester, *etc.* 1868. 8°. **4463**. ddd. **26**.

—— Personal Visits to the Graves of Eminent Men. pp. viii. 239. *Hodder & Stoughton: London*, 1877. 8°. **4903**. aaa. **7**.

—— Scriptural Means by which the True Church of Christ is ordinarily increased and built up. *See* Churchman. The Churchman Armed. A course of lectures, *etc.* [1864.] 8°. **4464**. aaa. **7**.

—— A Sermon preached at St. Margaret's Church, Westminster, *etc.* 1871. *See* London.—iii. *London Society for promoting Christianity amongst the Jews.* Report of the Society, 1810, *etc.* (The sixty-third report.) 1810, *etc.* 8°. P.P. **1149**. a.

—— A Sermon preached . . . in St. Dunstan's Church, Fleet Street, *etc.* 1888. *See* England.—*Church of England.—Church Pastoral Aid Society.* Report of the Committee. (The fifty-third annual meeting.) 1836, *etc.* 8°. P.P. **1025**.

—— A Sermon preached . . . in the Parish Church of St. Dunstan, Fleet Street, *etc.* 1859. *See* England.—*Church of England.—Church Pastoral Aid Society.* Report of the Committee, *etc.* (Twenty-fourth annual meeting.) 1836, *etc.* 8°. P.P. **1025**.

—— Spiritual Sacrifices. Preached September 5, 1858. *See* Mackenzie (William B.) Twelve Sermons preached . . . in Exeter Hall, *etc.* 1858. 8°. **4462**. b. **35**.

—— Views of the Church of England on the Church of Rome. *See* A., B. Lent Lectures for 1859, *etc.* [1859.] 12°. **4108**. a. **70**.

BARDSLEY (James Lomax) Dissertatio medica inauguralis de rabie canina, *etc.* pp. 84. *Joannes Moir: Edinburgi*, 1823. 8°. **1184**. b. **11**. (**12**.)

—— Hospital Facts and Observations, illustrative of the efficacy of the new remedies, strychnia, brucia, acetate of morphia, veratria, iodine, *etc.* pp. ix. 223. *Burgess & Hill: London*, 1830. 8°. **1170**. l. **11**.

BARDSLEY (James Wareing) Christ the Model Teacher. An address delivered to the Greenwich Branch of the Church of England School Institute. pp. 23. *William Macintosh: London*, [1870.] 8°. **4478**. a. **124**. (**12**.)

—— Glimpses through the Veil; or, Some natural analogies and Bible types. pp. xvii. 324. *J. Nisbet & Co.: London*, 1883. 8°. **4466**. bb. **30**.

—— Illustrative Texts and Texts Illustrated. pp. xi. 132. *J. Nisbet & Co.: London*, 1873. 8°. **3128**. bbb. **14**.

—— Second edition, enlarged. pp. xv. 336. *J. Nisbet & Co.: London*, 1876. 8°. **3149**. aa. **2**.

BARDSLEY (JAMES WAREING)

—— Many Mansions, and other sermons. pp. xii. 360. *J. Nisbet & Co.: London*, 1910. 8°. **4474**. ff. **8**.

BARDSLEY (JOHN EDWIN PRINCE)

—— *See* WILLIAMSON (Sydney G.) and BARDSLEY (J.) The Gold Coast. What of the Church? 1953. 8°. **4768**. a. **93**.

—— Making a Start in Photography. [With illustrations.] pp. viii. 119. *Chapman & Hall: London*, 1950. 8°. **8911**. b. **25**.

BARDSLEY (JOHN WAREING) successively *Bishop of Sodor and Man* and *of Carlisle*. *See* BARDSLEY (Charles W.) A Dictionary of English and Welsh Surnames, *etc.* [With a preface by J. W. Bardsley.] 1901. 8°. **2050.d.**

—— Church Missionary Society. The Annual Sermon preached at St. Bride's Church, Fleet Street . . . May 4th, 1891. pp. 11. *C.M.S.: London*, [1891.] 8°. **4475**. g. **49**. (**5**.)

—— Counsels to Candidates for Confirmation. Founded upon " The Order of Confirmation " according to the use of the Church of England. pp. 78. *Elliot Stock: London*, 1882. 16°. **3457**. de. **14**.

BARDSLEY (JOHN WRIGHT) *See* MACMYN (James W.) and BARDSLEY (J. W.) Bleaching, Dyeing, Printing and Finishing, *etc.* 1928. 8°. **7941**. de. **25**.

—— —— 1932. 8°. **7941**. i. **18**.

BARDSLEY (JOSEPH) *See* PARKINSON (Henry W.) The Anti-Bicentenarian in Perplexity; or, the Charges against the Rev. Jos. Bardsley's lectures repeated and proved. 1862. 8°. **4135**. b. **57**.

—— Apostolic Succession: or, the teaching of the Church of England on the alleged necessity of episcopal ordination, in unbroken succession from the Apostles, to the valid ministration of the Word and Sacraments. pp. 23. *Hatchards: London*, 1883. 8°. **4108**. de. **23**. (**3**.)

—— Bicentenarians in Perplexity: being an examination of the contradictory reasons assigned by Dissenters for the commemoration of the ejectment of certain ministers from the Church of England in 1662. With a reply to the charges of dishonesty and perjury made against the clergy of the Church of England. pp. 32. *Wertheim & Co.: London*, 1862. 8°. **4139**. b. **14**.

—— *See* PARKINSON (H. W.) The True Reason why the Nonconformists can and will celebrate the Bicentenary of the Ejectment in 1662. In reply to the Rev. Jos. Bardsley, *etc.* [1862.] 8°. **4135**. b. **58**.

—— The Bicentenary of 1662. Report of a discussion between the Rev. Joseph Bardsley . . . and the Rev. J. S. Eastmead . . . on " The Consistency of Dissenters in commemorating the ejectment of 2000 ministers from the Church of England in 1662," *etc.* pp. 75. *Seeley & Co.: London*, 1862. 8°. **4135**. c. **5**.

—— The Church of England on Absolution. pp. 49. *See* QUESTIONS. Questions of the Day, *etc.* 1867. 8°. **4255**. aaa. **60**.

—— Church of England Principles viewed in relation to the Ministry of Non-Episcopal Communions. pp. 23. *W. Hunt & Co.: London*, [1872.] 8°. **4109**. aa. **69**. (**2**.)

—— Eucharistic Vestments and the Eastward Position: are they authorized? . . . and is the doctrine they symbolize taught by the Church of England? pp. 32. *Hatchards: London*, 1874. 8°. **3476**. d. **37**.

BARDSLEY (JOSEPH)

—— The Greek Church, her doctrines and principles con trasted with those of the Church of England. Is unio desirable, or possible? A lecture, *etc.* pp. 31. *Hatchards: London*, 1870. 8°. **3926**. g. **77**. (**11**

—— The Irish Church: should it be dis-established? A fe plain reasons why it should not, *etc.* pp. 16. *W. Hunt & Co.: London*, [1868.] 8°. **4165**. a. **1**

—— A Lecture on the Past, Present, and Prospective Cir cumstances of the Church of England, externally con sidered. Delivered . . . December 10, 1861 . . . Re printed, with corrections, from " Aris's Birminghan Gazette," *etc.* pp. 32. *J. Nisbet & Co.: London* 1862. 16°. **4108**. aa. **90**. (**2**.

—— [Another edition.] pp. 24. *See* BIRMINGHAM, *Birmingham Church Defence Association.* [Tracts.] no. 1. [1862.] 8°. **4108**. bb. **83**

—— A Plea for the Irish Church. A lecture on the " Iris Church " . . . Reprinted, with corrections, from " Th Birmingham Daily Gazette." pp. 24. *William Macintosh: London*, 1868. 12°. **4165**. a. **11**

—— Ritualism: its Origin, Tendency, and Antidotes. *Se* TRUTHS. Truths for the Times. [1867.] 8°. **4378**. b. **50**

—— Rochdale Controversies: exposure of the tactics o Liberation Society advocates. A lecture delivered . . in reply to the misrepresentations, misquotations, an false charges, contained in the lecture of the Rev. H. W Parkinson . . . With an appendix consisting of a cate chetical discussion between Mr. Bardsley on the one side and Messrs. Browne and Snashall on the other. pp. 56 *Wertheim & Co.: London*, [1862.] 8°. **4108**. aa. **51**

—— The Teaching of the Church of England on Confessio and Absolution. A paper read . . . on the 8th o November, 1858 . . . To which is added, an examinatio of the authorities cited by the Rev. William Gresley o the subject. pp. 55. *Hatchard & Co.: London T. Brakell: Liverpool*, 1859. 8°. **4108**. e. **10**

—— Weighed in the Balances. The Rev. C. H. Spurgeo self-condemned; or, his questions to the Clergy on th Prayer-Book, considered; with some additional ques tions addressed to himself. pp. 16. *William Macintosh London*, [1864.] 8°. **3475**. aaa. **25**

—— *See* BELLMAN (Robert A.) " Tekel ": " Thou ar weighed in the balances and found wanting." Ad dressed to . . . the Rev. Joseph Bardsley . . . i reply to his pamphlet, entitled, " Weighed in th Balances," *etc.* [1864.] 8°. **3477**. cc. **39**

—— What is it All About? or, an Inquiry into the statement of the Rev. C. H. Spurgeon, that the Church of Englan " teaches salvation by baptism, instead of salvation by the blood of Our Blessed Master, Jesus Christ," *etc* pp. 16. *William Macintosh: London*, [1864.] 8°. **4325**. aa. **10**

BARDSLEY (JOSEPH UDELL NORMAN) The Church o England and her Endowments. Six sermons, wit special reference to the Welsh Disendowment Bill, *etc* pp. vi. 116. *Skeffington & Son: London*, 1912. 8°. **4109**. df. **38**

BARDSLEY (REBECCA M. V.) An Acrostic in Memoriam . . . H.R.H. Prince Leopold Duke of Albany. [A card.] [*Leyton*, 1884.] *s. sh.* 12°. **1870**. d. **1**. (**124**.)

BARDSLEY (Samuel Argent) Critical Remarks on Pizarro, a tragedy taken from the German drama of Kotzebue, and adapted to the English stage by Richard Brinsley Sheridan, *etc.* pp. 48. *T. Cadell, Junior & W. Davies: London,* 1800. 8°. **641.** e. **26.** (**7.**)

—— Dissertatio physiologico-medica inauguralis quaedam continens, de somno, *etc.* pp. 44. *Lugduni Batavorum,* 1786. 4°. T. **35.** (**16.**)

—— Medical Reports of Cases and Experiments, with observations chiefly derived from hospital practice. To which are added, an enquiry into the origin of canine madness; and thoughts on a plan for its extirpation from the British Isles. pp. viii. 336. *R. Bickerstaff: London,* 1807. 8°. **774.** h. **30.**

BÁRDSSON (Ívar) *See* Bárðarson.

BARDSTOWN AND LOUISVILLE, Benoît, *Bishop of.* *See* Flaget.

BARDSWELL (Alice)

—— "Gleams." By A. B. [i.e. A. Bardswell.] [Essays.] pp. 56. [1950.] 8°. *See* B., A. **12361.** a. **3.**

BARDSWELL (Frances Anne) The Book of Town & Window Gardening. [With plates.] pp. x. 105. *John Lane: London & New York,* 1903. 8°. [*Handbooks of Practical Gardening.* vol. 19.] **7030.** ppp. **19.**

—— The Herb-Garden . . . With sixteen illustrations in colour drawn from nature by the Hon. Florence Amherst and Isabelle Forrest. pp. viii. 173. *A. & C. Black: London,* 1911. 8°. **7031.** pp. **16.**

—— Second edition. pp. xi. 173. *A. & C. Black: London,* 1930. 8°. **07031.** h. **43.**

—— Notes from Nature's Garden . . . With 34 illustrations, *etc.* pp. xi. 222. *Longmans & Co.: London,* 1906. 8°. **7001.** bb. **20.**

—— Sea-Coast Gardens & Gardening. [With illustrations.] pp. 145. *Sherratt & Hughes: London, Manchester,* 1908. 8°. **7033.** dd. **10.**

—— Twelve Moons. pp. 90. *Elkin Mathews: London,* 1912. 8°. **012354.** df. **2.**

BARDSWELL (Monica)

—— *See* Tristram (Ernest W.) English Medieval Wall Painting. (The Thirteenth Century. With a catalogue by E. W. Tristram in collaboration with M. Bardswell.) 1944, *etc.* 4°. L.R. **293.** d. **44/2.**

—— *See* Tristram (Ernest W.) English Wall Painting of the Fourteenth Century . . . with a catalogue by E. W. Tristram compiled in collaboration with M. Bardswell. 1955. 8°. **7870.** ff. **30.**

BARDSWELL (Noel Dean) Advice to Consumptives: home treatment, after-care and prevention . . . Foreword by C. Theodore Williams. pp. xv. 144. *A. & C. Black: London,* 1910. 8°. **7616.** b. **30.**

—— Second edition. pp. xvi. 153. *A. & C. Black: London,* 1920. 8°. **7616.** ee. **32.**

—— The Consumptive Working Man. What can sanatoria do for him? (Introductory chapter by Sir Wm. Broadbent.) pp. vii. 202. *Scientific Press: London,* 1906. 8°. **7616.** g. **45.**

—— The Expectation of Life of the Consumptive after Sanatorium Treatment. pp. v. 130. *Henry Frowde; Hodder & Stoughton: Edinburgh,* 1910. 8°. [*Oxford Medical Publications.*] **20036.a.1/48.**

BARDSWELL (Noel Dean)

—— Handbook for Tuberculosis Workers. pp. iv. 66. *J. Bale & Co.: London,* 1920. 12°. **7616.** e. **64.**

—— Preliminary Report on the Treatment of Pulmonary Tuberculosis with Tuberculin . . . With a prefatory note by Professor Karl Pearson. pp. xxi. 141. 1914. 8°. *See* Midhurst.—*King Edward VII. Sanatorium.* **07561.** h. **48.**

—— Tuberculosis in Cyprus. An interim report on its incidence and means of control made under the auspices of the National Association for the Prevention of Tuberculosis. [With illustrations and maps.] pp. vi. 227. 1937. 8°. *See* England.—*National Association for the Prevention of Tuberculosis.* **07616.** k. **34.**

—— The Tuberculosis Clinic. By several writers. Edited by N. D. Bardswell. pp. iv. 111. *J. Bale & Co.: London,* 1922. 8°. [*Modern Clinical Manuals.*] W.P. **5657/4.**

—— Work Centres for the Tuberculous: the experience of the Spero Firewood Factory, London. [With plates.] pp. 64. *J. Bale & Co.: London,* 1930. 8°. **8276.** ppp. **6.**

BARDSWELL (Noel Dean) and **CHAPMAN** (John Ellis)

—— Diet in Tuberculosis, with costs of foods and their preparation. pp. 62. *Henry Frowde; Hodder & Stoughton: London,* 1911. 8°. **7306.** b. **13.** (**4.**)

—— Diets in Tuberculosis: principles and economics. pp. viii. 184. *Henry Frowde; Hodder & Stoughton: London,* 1908. 8°. [*Oxford Medical Publications.*] **20036.a.1/4.**

BARDSWELL (Noel Dean) and **THOMPSON** (John Herbert R.)

—— Pulmonary Tuberculosis: Mortality after Sanatorium Treatment. (A report on the experience of the King Edward VII Sanatorium, Midhurst.) pp. 112. *London,* 1919. 8°. [*Medical Research Council. . . Special Report Series.* no. 33.] B.S. **25/8.**

BARDT (Andreas Georg Wilhelm Carl) *See* Horatius Flaccus (Q.) [*Satirae, Epistolae and Ars Poetica.—German.*] Sermonen des Q. Horatius Flaccus. Deutsch von C. Bardt. 1890, *etc.* 8°. **11385.** cc. **11.**

—— *See* Horatius Flaccus (Q.) [*Epistolae.—German.*] Die Episteln des Q. Horatius Flaccus. Deutsch von C. Bardt. 1887. 8°. **11352.** b. **12.**

—— *See* Plautus (T. M.) [*Two or more Works.—German.*] Römische Komödien. Deutsch von C. Bardt, *etc.* 1903. 8°. **11707.** de. **28.**

—— Ausgewählte Briefe aus Ciceronischer Zeit. Herausgegeben von C. Bardt. 3 pt. *Leipzig,* 1896–1901. 8°. **10905.** d. **8.**

—— Die Priester der vier grossen Collegien aus römisch-republikanischer Zeit . . . Aus dem Michaelisprogramm MDCCCLXXI des Kœnigl. Wilhelmsgymnasiums. pp. 41. *Berlin,* 1871. 4°. **9039.** h. **29.** (**7.**)

—— Quaestiones Tullianae. Dissertatio inauguralis, *etc.* pp. 44. *Berolini,* [1866.] 8°. **8363.** aa. **6.** (**2.**)

—— Römische Charakterköpfe in Briefen vornehmlich aus Caesarischer und Traianischer Zeit . . . Mit einer Karte. [Chiefly translations of letters of Cicero and Pliny.] pp. xvii. 434. *Leipzig & Berlin,* 1913. 8°. **010902.** e. **20.**

BARDT (Andreas Georg Wilhelm Carl)

—— Theodor Mommsen. pp. 38. *Berlin*, 1903. 8°. **10601**. cc. **28**. (**3**.)

BARDT (Carl) *See* Bardt (Andreas G. W. C.) **8363**. aa. **6**. (**2**.)

BARDTKE (Paul) [Darstellung der gesamten Schweisstechnik.] Technique of Modern Welding . . . Authorized translation from the second German edition, with additions and revisions by Prof. Bardtke, by Harold Kenney. pp. xi. 299. *Blackie & Son: London & Glasgow*, 1933. 8°. **07942**. cc. **50**.

BARDUA (Caroline) *See* Bardua (W.) Jugendleben der Malerin Caroline Bardua, *etc.* 1874. 8°. **10707**. bbb. **2**.

—— *See* Bardua (W.) Die Schwestern Bardua, *etc.* [With portraits.] [1937.] 8°. **10710**. b. **17**.

BARDUA (Wilhelmine) Jugendleben der Malerin Caroline Bardua. Nach einem Manuscript ihrer Schwester, Wilhelmine Bardua, herausgegeben von Walter Schwarz. Mit dem Bildniss der Caroline Bardua. pp. viii. 295. *Breslau*, 1874. 8°. **10707**. bbb. **2**.

—— Die Schwestern Bardua. Bilder aus dem Gesellschafts- Kunst- und Geistesleben der Biedermeyerzeit. Aus Wilhelmine Barduas Aufzeichnungen gestaltet von Prof. Dr. Johannes Werner. Mit 38 Bildern [including portraits]. Dritte Auflage. pp. 336. *Leipzig*, [1937.] 8°. **10710**. b. **17**.

BARDUARDINUS (Thomas) *Archbishop of Canterbury. See* Bradwardinus.

BARDUIGIN (Mikhail Nikiforovich) *See* Bible.—*New Testament.—Selections.* [*Russian.*] Созвучія Новаго Завѣта . . . Трудъ и изданіе М. Н. Бардыгина. 1925, *etc.* 8°. **3061.df.3.**

BARDUS (Marcus Antonius) De tempore vtili et continuo. *See* Tractatus. Tractatus vniuersi iuris, *etc.* tom. 5. 1584. fol. **499**. f. **6**.

BARDUZZI (Domenico) Del governo dell'Ospedale di Siena dalle origini alla caduta della repubblica. *See* Sienna.—*Reale Accademia dei Rozzi.—Commissione Senese di Storia Patria.* Conferenze tenute . . . 1895. 1895. 8°. Ac. **6521/5**.

—— Documenti per la storia della R. Università di Siena, raccolti dal Rettore Prof. D. Barduzzi. Serie prima, 1275–1479. pp. 38. *Siena*, 1900. 8° **8304**. f. **13**. (**1**.)

—— Manuale di storia della medicina. 2 vol. *Torino*, 1923, 27. 8°. **7679**. ff. **10**.

—— Ugolino da Montecatini. pp. 81. *Firenze*, 1915. 16°. **10633**. b. **10**.

BARDWELL. The Registers of Bardwell, Co. Suffolk, 1538 to 1650. Edited by Rev. F. E. Warren. pp. 40. *Mitchell & Hughes: London*, 1893. 8°. **9904**. w. **5**. *One of an edition of 20 copies.*

—— *Guild of S. Peter. See* Peter, *Saint and Apostle, Guild of, Bardwell.*

BARDWELL (Denver)

—— Beyond Midnight Chasm. pp. 250. *R. Hale & Co.: London*, 1937. 8°. A.N. 3755.

—— Calamity at Devil's Crossing. pp. 176. *World's Work: Kingswood*, 1951. 8°. **12730**. r. **19**.

BARDWELL (Denver)

—— Coyote Hunter. pp. 248. *Robert Hale: London*, [1940.] 8°. **12722**. aa. **2**

—— The Exile Returns West. pp. 252. *Robert Hale: London*, 1937. 8°. **12716**. c. **2**

—— Gunsmoke in Sunset Valley. [A novel.] pp. 288. *Wright & Brown: London; printed in U.S.A.*, [1935.] 8° A.N. 2556

—— Gunsmoke Mesa. pp. 154. *The World's Work: Kingswood*, 1954. 8°. NNN. 559 *Master Thriller Western.* no. 96.

—— Killers on the Diamond A. pp. 256. *Wright & Brown: London*, 1936. 8°. A.N. 3225

—— Killers of the Diamond A. pp. 112. *Gerald G. Swan: London*, [1949.] 8°. **12651**. dd. **2**

—— Owl-Hoot Pay-off, *etc.* pp. 172. *The World's Work: Kingswood*, 1952. 8°. **12731**. k. **3**

—— Prairie Fire. pp. 251. *Robert Hale: London*, [1942.] 8° **12725**. bb. **1**

—— Rancho Bonito. pp. 252. *R. Hale & Co.: London*, 1937. 8°. **12716**. d.

—— Rivers Westward. pp. 248. *Robert Hale: London*, [1939.] 8°. **12720**. b. **1**

—— Storm Ranch. pp. 252. *R. Hale & Co.: London*, [1937.] 8°. A.N. 367

—— Where the Sun sets. pp. 175. *The World's Work: Kingswood*, 1952. 8°. **12701**. de. **3** *Master Thriller Western.* no. 68.

BARDWELL (Earl S.) *See* Richards (Robert H.) Text Book of Ore Dressing. By R. H. Richards . . . assisted by E. S. Bardwell, *etc.* 1909. 8°. **7109**. b. **5**.

BARDWELL (Francis) The Adventure of Old Age, *etc.* pp. xii. 298. *Houghton Mifflin Co.: Boston & New York*, 1926. 8°. **012273**. aaa. **5**

BARDWELL (Horatio) The Duty and Reward of Evangelizing the Heathen. A sermon, *etc.* pp. 24. *W. B. Allen & Co.: Newburyport*, 1815. 12°. **4486**. f. **1**

—— Memoir of Rev. Gordon Hall . . . one of the first missionaries of the American Board of Commissioners for Foreign Missions, at Bombay. pp. 260. *Flagg & Co.: Andover* [*Mass.*], 1834. 12°. **1372**. b. **1**

—— [Another edition.] pp. xi. 246. *Peter Sinclair: Glasgow*, 1834. 12°. **1126**. h. **2**

—— Two Sermons on Christian Baptism. Delivered at Holden, Sept. 1825. pp. 38. *William Manning: Worcester* [*Mass.*], [1825.] 8°. **4486**. f. **1**

BARDWELL (Margery) Morning Faces. (Poems.) pp. 44. *Erskine Macdonald: London*, 1925. 8°. **011644**. e. **171**

BARDWELL (Thomas) The Practice of Painting and Perspective Made Easy: in which is contained, the art of painting in oil with the method of colouring, *etc.* [With plates.] pp. v. 64. *Printed for the Author: London*, 1756. 4°. **561***. d. **31** *The plates are cropped.*

BARDWELL (THOMAS)

—— [Another copy.] The Practice of Painting and Perspective made Easy, *etc.* *London*, 1756. 4°. 1481. e. 6. (2.)

BARDWELL (WILLIAM) Healthy Homes, and how to make them. [With plates.] pp. 71. xv. *Dean & Son: London*, [1854.] 8°. **7816**. a. **12**.

—— Temples Ancient and Modern; or, Notes on church architecture. pp. xiii. 234. pl. 15. *Printed for the Author: London*, 1837. 8°. **559***. b. **6**.

—— Westminster Improvements. A brief account of ancient and modern Westminster with observations on former plans of improvement, and on the objects and prospects of the Westminster Improvement Company, *etc.* pp. 58. *Smith & Elder, Fraser, Werle, Williams & Reid: London*, 1839. 8°. **793**. h. **25**.

—— What a House Should Be, versus Death in the House. A companion book to "Healthy Homes, and how to make them." Illustrated, *etc.* pp. viii. 95. *Dean & Son: London*, [1873.] 8°. **7816**. de. **14**.

BARDWELL (WILLIAM SCOT)

—— *See* ENGLAND.—*Admiralty.*—*Hydrographic Department.* [*Sailing Directions.*—*Australia.*] Australia Pilot. Vol. 1, *etc.* (Prepared by W. S. Bardwell.) 1949. 8°. **010498**. dd. **20**.

BARDWOOD (JAMES) *See* BURDWOOD.

BARDY (   ) *Abbé.*

—— *See* PHILANTHROPE. Grand complot entre l'abbé Bardy, accusé d'avoir assassiné son frère, et le sieur Sabarot, avocat. [c. 1790.] 8°. R. **171**. (5.)

BARDY (GUSTAVE) *Docteur en Théologie.*

—— *See* ATHENAGORAS, *Christian Apologist.* [*Legatio pro Christianis.*] Supplique au sujet des chrétiens. Introduction et traduction de G. Bardy. 1943. 8°. W.P. A. **481/3**.

—— *See* AUGUSTINE, *Saint, Bishop of Hippo.* [*Works.*—*Latin and French.*] Œuvres de Saint Augustin. (ser. 1. no. 10. Mélanges doctrinaux. Introductions, traduction et notes par G. Bardy [and others].) 1936, *etc.* 8°. W.P. **13583**.

—— *See* AUGUSTINE, *Saint, Bishop of Hippo.* [*Works.*—*Latin and French.*] Œuvres de Saint Augustin. (ser. 1. no. 12. Les Révisions. Introduction, traduction et notes par G. Bardy.) 1936, *etc.* 8°. W.P. **13583**.

—— *See* CHURCH. The Church in the Christian Roman Empire. By J. R. Palanque, G. Bardy, P. de Labriolle, *etc.* 1949, *etc.* 8°. W.P. **3817**.

—— *See* EUSEBIUS, *Pamphili, Bishop of Caesarea in Palestine.* [*Historia Ecclesiastica.*—*Greek and French.*] Histoire ecclésiastique . . . Traduction et annotation par G. Bardy. 1952, *etc.* 8°. **W.P.A.481/31,41,55.**

—— *See* FLICHE (A.) and MARTIN (V.) Histoire de l'Église, *etc.* (3. De la paix constantinienne à la mort de Théodose. Par J.-R. Palanque, G. Bardy, P. de Labriolle. 4. De la mort de Théodose à l'élection de Grégoire le Grand. Par P. de Labriolle, G. Bardy, G. de Plinval, Louis Bréhier.) 1934, *etc.* 8°. **4606.tt.1.**

—— *See* HIPPOLYTUS, *Saint, of Rome.* Commentaire sur Daniel. Introduction de G. Bardy, *etc.* 1947. 8°. W.P. A. **481/14**.

BARDY (GUSTAVE) *Docteur en Théologie.*

—— *See* JEWS. Les Trophées de Damas . . . Texte grec (*Της θειας και ανικητου Θεου ἐκκλησιας και ἀληθειας πεπραγμενα τροπαια κατα Ἰουδαιων ἐν Δαμασκῳ*) édité et traduit par G. Bardy. [*Patrologia Orientalis.* tom. 15. fasc. 2.] **2002.c-d.**

—— *See* THEOPHILUS, *Saint, Bishop of Antioch.* Trois livres à Autolycus . . . Introduction et notes de G. Bardy. 1948. 8°. W.P. A. **481/20**.

—— Didyme l'aveugle. pp. xii. 279. *Paris*, 1910. 8°. [*Études de théologie historique.* no. 1.] **2201.dd.1/1.**

—— [L'Église à la fin du premier siècle.] The Church at the End of the First Century . . . Translated by P. W. Singleton. pp. viii. 163. *Sands & Co.: London & Glasgow*, 1938. 8°. **20032**. g. **4**.

—— [L'Enfer.] L'Inferno. Di Gustave Bardy [and others], *etc.* [Translated by D. Tenderini.] pp. 247. 1953. 8°. *See* ENFER. **4257**. ppp. **16**.

—— [La Littérature grecque chrétienne.] The Greek Literature of the Early Christian Church . . . Translated by Mother Mary Reginald. pp. vii. 191. *Sands & Co.: London*, [1929.] 8°. [*Catholic Library of Religious Knowledge.* vol. 2.] **03605.g.4/2.**

—— [La Littérature latine chrétienne.] The Christian Latin Literature of the First Six Centuries . . . Translated by Mother Mary Reginald. pp. viii. 222. *Sands & Co.: London; B. Herder Book Co.: St. Louis*, [1930.] 8°. [*Catholic Library of Religious Knowledge.* no. 12.] **03605.g.4/12.**

—— Paul de Samosate. Étude historique. [With the text of the Fragments, in Greek and French, and with a bibliography.] pp. xii. 581. *Louvain, Paris*, 1923. 8°. [*Spicilegium sacrum Lovaniense.* fasc. 4.] W.P. **7396/3**.

—— La Question des langues dans l'église ancienne. *Paris*, 1948– . 8°. [*Études de théologie historique.*] **2201**. dd. **1 16**.

—— Recherches sur l'histoire du texte et des versions latines du De principiis d'Origène. pp. xii. 218. *Paris*, 1923. 8°. [*Mémoires et travaux publiés par des professeurs des Facultés catholiques de Lille.* fasc. 25.] **03605**. i. **1/25**.

—— Saint Athanase, 296–373. pp. xvi. 207. *Paris*, 1914. 12°. **4826**. ee. **47**.

—— Saint Augustin: l'homme et l'œuvre. 6e édition. pp. ix. 557. *Paris*, 1946. 8°. **4830**. h. **52**.

—— Święty Augustyn. Człowiek i dzieło. (Tłumaczyła Zofia Kobylańska.) pp. 440. *Warszawa*, 1955. 8°. **4828**. eee. **32**.

—— La Vie spirituelle d'après les Pères des trois premiers siècles. pp. 318. [*Paris*,] 1935. 8°. **3624**. bb. **12**.

BARDY (GUSTAVE) *of Poitiers.* *See* GUSTEAU (F.) Poésies patoises, *etc.* (Biographies de l'Abbé Gusteau et de M. Oressac [by G. Bardy].) 1855, *etc.* 12°. **11498**. c. **36**.

—— L'Algérie et son organisation en royaume. [By G. Bardy.] pp. 165. [1852.] 8°. *See* ALGERIA. [*Appendix.*] **8154**. bbb. **30**.

—— De l'assistance publique et de la charité privée. pp. 36. *Poitiers*, 1864. 8°. **8285**. ee. **37**. (6.)

BARDY (Gustave) *of Poitiers.*

—— Ordre souverain des Hospitaliers réformés de Saint-Jean, Jérusalem, Rhodes et Malte. Circulaire aux adhérents à sa réforme. Deuxième édition. pp. 16. *Paris*, 1860. 8°. **4784**. c. **35**. (**6**.)

—— Ordre souverain des Hospitaliers réformés de Saint-Jean, Jérusalem, Rhodes et Malte. La nouvelle question romaine. pp. 14. *Paris*, 1861. 8°. **4784**. c. **35**. (**7**.)

—— Ordre souverain des Hospitaliers réformés de Saint-Jean, Jérusalem, Rhodes et Malte. Organisation de son premier couvent en France. pp. 16. *Paris*, 1859. 8°. **4784**. c. **35**. (**4**.)

—— Société d'Agriculture de la Vienne. 3 mars 1864. Concours d'animaux reproducteurs, de bestiaux gras et de machines agricoles. Allocution de M. Gustave Bardy. (Extrait du Bulletin de mars 1864.) pp. 16. *Poitiers*, 1864. 8°. **7076**. bb. **39**. (**7**.)

BARDY (Henri) Belfort en 1815. pp. 31. *Belfort*, 1888. 8°. **09008**. c. **2**. (**2**.)

—— [Another edition.] La Dernière campagne du général Lecourbe. Belfort en 1815. pp. 77. *Saint-Dié*, [1888.] 8°. **9004**. bbb. **13**. (**2**.)

—— Enguerrand de Coucy et les Grands-Bretons. Episode de l'histoire d'Alsace, 1368–1376. pp. 38. *Paris*, *Saint-Dié*, 1860. 8°. **9210**. c. **14**.

—— Les Évènements militaires dans le pays de Saint-Dié pendant la Révolution. Discours, *etc.* pp. 32. *Saint-Dié*, [1896.] 8°. **9076**. cc. **33**. (**6**.)

—— Un Exemplaire de la Cosmographiæ Introductio, 25 avril 1507 . . . Avec 6 photogravures . . . Extrait du Bulletin de la Société Philomatique Vosgienne, *etc.* pp. 24. *Saint-Dié*, 1893. 8°. **11904**. l. **15**. (**4**.)

—— Le Général Haxo. 7 juin 1749—21 mars 1794. Discours, *etc.* pp. 49. *Saint-Dié*, [1895.] 8°. **010663**. g. **40**. (**9**.)

—— Miscellanées. pp. 67. *Saint-Dié*, 1901. 8°. **012357**. i. **69**.

—— Saint Dié pendant la guerre de 1870–71. pp. 84. *Saint-Dié*, [1895.] 8°. **9076**. cc. **33**. (**2**.)

BARDY (Joseph) An Investigation of the Written Examination as a measure of achievement with particular reference to general science. A thesis, *etc.* pp. 176. *Philadelphia*, 1923. 8°. **8310**. e. **30**.

BARDY (Josephus Fourtou) *See* Fourtou-Bardy.

BARDY (Mathieu) Observations sur la luxation du pied, *etc.* pp. 18. *Strasbourg*, 1803. 4°. [*Collection générale des dissertations de l'École spéciale de Médecine de Strasbourg.* vol. 7.] **7381*.b.**

BARDY (Pierre Martial) *See* Burque (F. X.) Le Docteur Pierre Martial Bardy, *etc.* 1907. 8°. **010883**. k. **3**.

BARDY-DELISLE (Alfred) Essai sur l'anatomie et la physiologie pathologiques du cancer. Thèse, *etc.* pp. 55. *Montpellier*, 1846. 4°. **1182**. d. **18**. (**4**.)

BARDY FOURTOU (Marie François Oscar) Faculté de Droit de Paris. Thèse pour la licence. (Jus romanum. De dote prælegata.—Droit français. Des testaments et des legs.) pp. 48. *Paris*, 1857. 8°. **5406**. aa. **1**. (**19**.)

BARDYLI (Pyrrhus) Essai sur les langues naturelles et les langues artificielles. pp. 147. *Bruxelles*, 1904. 8°. **012904**. ee. **21**.

BARDZIŃSKI (Jan Alan) *See* Lucanus (M. A.) [*Pharsalia.—Polish.*] Odrodzona w oyczystym języku Farsalia Lukana . . . Od jednego przetłumaczona Polaka [i.e. by J. A. Bardziński], ktorego imię nástępuiące wyrażóią wiersse, *etc.* [1691.] fol. **11352**. g. **5**.

—— *See* Seneca (L. A.) [*Tragedies.—Polish.*] Smutne Starożytnośći Teatrum, to iest Tragediæ Seneki . . . na Polski ięzyk . . . przetłumaczone . . . przez W. X. J. A. Bardzinskiego. 1696. 8°. **11712**. aaa. **1**.

BARE ASPECT. *See* Periodical Publications.—*Shepperton.*

BARÉ (Alphonse Théodore) Considérations générales sur la révulsion ; thèse, *etc.* pp. 25. *Paris*, 1827. 4°. **1184**. c. **2**. (**8**.)

BARE (C. O.)

—— *See* Tenhet (Joseph N.) and Bare (C. O.) Control of Insects in Stored and Manufactured Tobacco. 1951. 8°. [*U.S. Department of Agriculture. Circular.* no. 869.] A.S. **804**/**2**.

BARÉ (Émile) De l'asthme. pp. 34. *Paris*, 1862. 4°. [*Collection des thèses soutenues à la Faculté de Médecine de Paris.* An 1862. tom. 1.] **7373**. d. **12**.

BARE (Hermannus de) Tractatus formandorum libellorum, *etc.* *See* Tractatus. Primum [*etc.*] volumen tractatuum, *etc.* vol. 4. 1549. fol. **5305**. i.

—— Hermanni Barensis De formandis libellis. *See* Tractatus. Tractatus vniuersi iuris, *etc.* tom. 3. pt. 2. 1584. fol. **499**. f. **4**.

BARE (Marcel de) Les Meunières du Moulin Rouge. Anecdotes et souvenirs inédits sur le bal célèbre. 1925. *See* Periodical Publications.—*Paris.* Les Œuvres libres, *etc.* no. 48. 1921, *etc.* 8°. **12208**. ee. **48**.

BARE (Phrankiskos) *See* Goldoni (C.) [*Pamela maritata.*] *Παμελα ὑπανδρος νυν πρωτον μεταγλωττισθεισα παρα Φραγκισκου Βαρε, etc.* 1817. 8°. **11715**. ee. **20**.

BARÉ (Pierre Yon) *See* Barré.

BARÉ (Th.) La Prostitution dans la ville de Nantes. *See* Parent du Châtelet (A. J. B. B.) De la prostitution dans la ville de Paris, *etc.* tom. 2. 1857. 8°. **8276**. de. **29**.

BARE (Virginia McCarty)

—— Come Summer. [A novel.] pp. viii. 214. *Longmans & Co.: New York, Toronto*, 1936. 8°. **20059**. aa. **17**.

BAREA (Alfonso)

—— *See* Aranda (V.) Hacia la Escuela Hispánica. Por Aranda . . . Barea, *etc.* 1936. 8°. **08355**. ff. **73**.

BAREA (Arturo)

—— *See* Barea (I.) and (A.) Spain in the Post-War World. 1945. 8°. W.P. **10405**/**97**.

—— *See* Cela y Trulock (C. J.) [La Colmena.] The Hive . . . With an introduction by A. Barea. 1953. 8°. **12492**. dd. **16**.

—— [La Forja.]

The Forge . . . Translated from the Spanish with an introduction by Sir Peter Chalmers Mitchell. [An autobiography.] pp. 349. *Faber & Faber: London*, 1941. 8°. **10632**. ppp. **33**.

—— The Forge . . . Translated from the Spanish by Ilsa Barea. pp. 276. *Faber & Faber: London*, 1946. 8°. **10629**. cc. **46**.

BAREA (Arturo)

—— [La Ruta.]

The Track . . . Translated from the Spanish by Ilsa Barea. [Autobiographical reminiscences.] pp. 237. *Faber & Faber: London*, 1943. 8º. **10635**. b. **22**.

—— The Broken Root . . . Translated from the Spanish by Ilsa Barea. pp. 320. *Faber & Faber: London*, 1951. 8º. **12492**. aa. **33**.

—— The Clash . . . Translated from the Spanish by Ilsa Barea. [Autobiographical reminiscences.] pp. 332. *Faber & Faber: London*, 1946. 8º. **10629**. cc. **43**.

—— The Forging of a Rebel. [Autobiographical reminiscences.] Translated . . . by Ilsa Barea. pp. 739. *Reynal & Hitchcock: New York*, [1946.] 8º. **10634**. l. **4**.

—— Lorca: the poet and his people. Translated from the Spanish by Ilsa Barea. pp. 103. *Faber & Faber: London*, 1944. 8º. **11865**. g. **31**.

—— Struggle for the Spanish Soul. pp. 127. *Secker & Warburg: London*, 1941. 8º. [*Searchlight Books*. no. 10.] W.P. **10146**/**10**.

—— Unamuno. [A critical study. Written in collaboration with, and translated by, Ilsa Barea.] pp. 61. *Bowes & Bowes: Cambridge; Haarlem* printed, 1952. 8º. [*Studies in Modern European Literature and Thought.*] W.P. a. **280**/**4**.

BAREA (Ilsa)

—— *See* Barea (A.) [La Forja.] The Forge . . . Translated . . . by I. Barea. 1946. 8º. **10629**. cc. **46**.

—— *See* Barea (Arturo) [La Ruta.] The Track . . . Translated . . . by I. Barea. 1943. 8º. **10635**. b. **22**.

—— *See* Barea (A.) The Broken Root . . . Translated . . . by I. Barea. 1951. 8º. **12492**. aa. **33**.

—— *See* Barea (A.) The Clash . . . Translated . . . by I. Barea. 1946. 8º. **10629**. cc. **43**.

—— *See* Barea (Arturo) The Forging of a Rebel. Translated . . . by I. Barea. [1946.] 8º. **10634**. l. **4**.

—— *See* Barea (A.) Lorca: the poet and his people. Translated . . . by I. Barea. 1944. 8º. **11865**. g. **31**.

—— *See* Barea (A.) Unamuno. [Written in collaboration with, and translated by I. Barea.] 1852. 8º. W.P. a. **280**/**4**.

—— *See* González (V.) calling himself *El Campesino*. El Campesino. Life and death in Soviet Russia . . . Translated by I. Barea. [1952.] 8º. **10634**. l. **25**.

—— *See* Gonzalez (V.) calling himself *El Campesino*. Listen Comrades . . . Translated by I. Barea. 1952. 8º. **10634**. l. **29**.

—— *See* Juan Arbó (S.) Cervantes, *etc*. (Rendered from the Spanish by I. Barea.) [1955.] 8º. **10636**. d. **14**.

—— *See* Téllez (G.) [Los Tres maridos burlados.] Three Husbands Hoaxed . . . Freely translated . . . by I. Barea, *etc*. 1955. 8º. **12491**. k. **27**.

BAREA (Ilsa) and **BAREA** (Arturo)

—— Spain in the Post-War World. pp. 29. *Fabian Publications; Victor Gollancz: London*, 1945. 8º. [*Fabian Research Series* no. 97.] W.P. **10405**/**97**

BAREA (José Sanz y) *See* Sanz y Barea.

BAREA (Pedro Castro) *See* Castro Barea.

BAREA DE ASTORGA (Petrus) *See* Barca de Astorga.

BAREAU (Charles) De l'allaitement. pp. 38. *Paris*, 1854. 4º. [*Collection des thèses soutenues à la Faculté de Médecine de Paris*. An 1854. tom. 1.] **7372**. g. **1**.

BAREAU (Paul)

—— *See* Jefferys (James B.) Consumer Goods. The methods and cost of distribution. A summary [by P. Bareau] of "The Distribution of Consumer Goods," *etc*. [1950.] 8º. **8219**. i. **14**.

—— *See* United States of America.—*Bureau of Foreign and Domestic Commerce*. The Dollar Problem. An analytical summary of the U.S. Department of Commerce study "The United States in the World Economy" prepared by Mr. P. Bareau, *etc*. [1944.] 8º **W.P.755/1.**

—— The City. [On the financial business transacted in the City of London. With illustrations.] pp. 48. *News Chronicle: London*, 1951. 8º. [*Background to the News*. no. 2.] W.P. **4246**/**2**.

—— Cocoa. A crop with a future. [With illustrations and graphs.] pp. 39. *Cadbury Bros.: Bournville*, 1953. 8º. **08218**. cc. **19**.

—— Liberalism and International Trade . . . Being the Ramsay Muir Memorial Lecture delivered at Oxford on 17th July, 1955, *etc*. pp. 29. *Ramsay Muir Educational Trust: Purley*, [1955.] 8º. **8208**. a. **3**.

—— The Sterling Area. What it is and how it works. pp. 15. *Longmans Green & Co.: London*, 1948. 8º. [*British Commonwealth Affairs*. no. 3.] W.P. **5241**/**3**.

—— The Sterling Area, *etc*. (Second edition.) pp. 20. *Longmans, Green & Co.: London*, 1950. 8º. [*British Commonwealth Affairs*. no. 3.] W.P. **5241**/**3a**.

—— United States Tariff Reductions and British-American Trade, *etc*. pp. 10. *London*, 1944. 8º. [*American Chamber of Commerce in London. Economic Paper*. no. 2.] W.P. **755**/**2**.

BAREAU DE GIRAC (François) *Bishop of Rennes*.

—— Déclaration de M. l'évêque de Rennes sur la nouvelle organisation du Clergé. pp. 30. [*Paris*, 1790.] 8º. F. **104**. (**12**.)

—— Instruction addressée par M. l'évèque de Rennes aux curés, vicaires et autres ecclésiastiques de son diocèse, qui n'ont pas prêté le serment ordonné par l'Assemblée Nationale. pp. 38. *Paris*, [1791.] 8º. F. **121**. (**4**.)

—— Lettre de Mgr. l'évêque de Rennes, aux prêtres de son diocèse, exilés pour la cause de la foi. pp. 30. *Baylis: Londres*, 1796. 8º. **3901**. cc. **3**.

BAREBONE (Issachar) *pseud*. [i.e. James Ralph.] The Protester, on behalf of the people. no. 1–24. 2 June—10 Nov. 1753. 1753. fol. *See* Periodical Publications.—*London*. P.P. **3611**. e.

BAREBONE (Praise-God)

—— *See* Lane (Jane) *pseud*. [i.e. E. Dakers.] Puritan, Rake and Squire. [Short biographies of Praise-God Barebone and others. With a portrait.] 1950. 8º. **10804**. r. **16**.

——

See Preachers
New Preachers, New. Greene the Feltmaker, Spencer the Horserubber . . . with some few others . . . Whereunto is added the last tumult in Fleetstreet, raised by the disorderly preachment . . . of Mr. Barebones . . . and Mr. Greene, *etc*. [1641.] 4º. E. **180**. (**26**.)

BAREBONE (Praise-God)

—— *See* Word. A Word to Fanatics, Puritans, and Sectaries: or, New Preachers New! Green the Felt-Maker, Spencer the Horse-rubber . . . With an authentic portrait and memoir of Mr. Praise God Barebone, *etc.* 1821. 8°. **991**. l. **18**.

—— A Discourse tending to prove the Baptisme in or under the Defection of Antichrist to be the Ordinance of Jesus Christ; as also that the baptisme of infants or children is warrantable, and agreeable to the word of God . . . By P. B. [i.e. P. Barebone.] pp. 32. 1642. 4°. *See* B., P. E. **138**. (**23**.)

—— *See* Barber (Edward) *Baptist.* A Small Treatise of Baptisme . . . Wherein is cleerely shewed that the Lord Christ ordained dipping for those only that professe repentance and faith. 1. Proved by Scripture . . . 4. An answer to some objections by P. B. [i.e. P. Barebone.] 1641. 4°. E. **143**. (**17**.)

—— The Petition of Mr. Praise-God Barebone, and several others, to the Parliament. Presented on Thursday the 9th of February, 1659. *London,* 1659 [1660]. *s. sh.* fol. **190**. g. **12**. (**21**.)

—— That Wicked and Blasphemous Petition of Praise God Barbone, and his sectarian crew: presented to that so called, the Parliament of the Commonwealth of England, Feb. 9. 1659. for which they had the thanks of that House: anatomized . . . By a lover of Christ and his ordinances: ministers and their calling, *etc.* pp. 17. *Printed for Philo-Monarchæus:* [*London,* 1660.] 4°. E. **1019**. (**15**.)

—— To the Right Honorable the High Court of Parliament, sitting at Westminster: the illegal and immodest petition of Praise-God Barbone, anabaptist and leather-seller of London. [A satire.] *Hen. Mason: London,* 1660. *s. sh.* fol. **669**. f. **23**. (**62**.)

—— [Another copy.] **190**. g. **12**. (**20**.)

—— A Reply to the frivolous and impertinent Answer of R. B. to the Discourse of P. B. [i.e. P. Barebone]. In which discourse is shewed, that the Baptisme in the defection of Antichrist is the ordinance of God, notwithstanding the corruptions that attend the same, and that the baptisme of infants is lawfull, both which are vindicated from the exceptions of R. B. . . . by the same authour. There is also a reply, in way of answer to some exceptions of E. B. [i.e. Edward Barber] against the same. [The epistle to the reader signed: R. B., by error for P. B.] pp. 64. 1643. 4°. *See* B., P. E. **96**. (**20**.)

—— The Discovery of a Swarme of Seperatists, or, a Leather-sellers Sermon. Being a most true and exact relation of the tumultuous combustion in Fleet-street last Sabboth day . . . truly describing how Burboon a letherseller had a conventicle of Brownists met at his house . . . With another relation of a sermon, that prophet Hunt preached in St. Pulchers Church the same day aforesaid, *etc.* *For John Greensmith: London,* 1641. 4°. E. **180**. (**25**.)

—— The Picture of the Good Old Cause drawn to the Life in the Effigies of Master Prais-God Barebone. With several examples of Gods judgements on some eminent engagers against kingly government. *London,* 1660. *s. sh.* fol. **669**. f. **25**. (**57**.)

BARECROFT (Charles) A Letter to a Lady, furnishing her with Scripture testimonies against the principal points and doctrines of Popery. [By C. Barecroft.] pp. 83. 1688. 4°. *See* Popery. **222**. e. **19**. (**6**.)

BARECROFT (Charles)

—— The Reformed Christian's New-Year's-Gift; plainly an fully shewing how he may be able by Scripture-proo only, to answer the sophistries & artifices of Popish Pries and Jesuits . . . By a Minister of the Church of Englar [i.e. C. Barecroft]. [Another edition of "A Letter to Lady," *etc.*] pp. 83. 1690. 4°. *See* Christian. **3936**. de. **11**. (5

BARECROFT (J.) Advice to a Son in the University. I two parts . . . The third edition. To which is no added Concionatorum instructio: or, rules for preachin *etc.* 2 pt. *Jonas Browne: London,* 1713. 8°. **851**. e. **1**

The imprint of pt. 2 *of "Advice to a Son in the University reads: Edm. Powell: London,* 1710.

—— Ars concionandi: or, an Instruction to Young Student in Divinity . . . The fourth edition. Being Advice to Son in the University, with Concionatorum instructi . . . To which is now added, a short view of the live sufferings, works and failures of the Fathers in the thre first centuries, *etc.* pp. 172. *Jonas Browne: Londo* 1715. 8°. **4498**. a.

BAREFOOT (Brian) and **COTTRELL** (Tom)

—— Two Politicians in Search of a Party. pp. 192. *Quality Press: London,* 1949. 8°. 8132. aa. 4

BAREFOOTED CARMELITES. *See* Carmelites.

BARÈGES. Notice sur Barèges, Hautes-Pyrénées. pp. 1 *Toulouse,* 1878. 8°. **7462**. de. **8**. (10

BAREGGI (Giuseppe) Delle società cooperative. Stud di economia popolare. pp. 71. *Milano,* 1871. 8°. **8206**. i.

BAREILLE (Georges) Code du droit canonique. Mod fications introduites dans la précédente législation d l'Église . . . Nouvelle édition. pp. xxiv. 647. *Montréjeau,* 1922. 8°. **05107**. k. **2**

BAREILLE (J.) *See* Beschi (C. G.) Paramarta Gur Fabula . . . modo in Canaricam linguam translata, c addita est versio latina . . . Opus curante Rev. J Bareille editum. 1877. 12°. **14176**. d. **1**

—— *See* Beschi (C. G.) Paramarta Guru. A tale . . . no translated into Canarese, and accompanied by a English translation. Edited by Rev. J. Bareille. 1877. 12°. **14176**. d.

BAREILLE (Jean François) *See* Balmes (J. L.) M langes religieux, philosophiques, politiques et littérair . . . Traduits . . . avec une introduction, par J. Bareil 1854. 12°. **12230**. c. **1**

—— *See* Darras (J. E.) Histoire générale de l'Église, *et* (tom. 26 [*etc.*]. Continuée . . . par l'abbé J. Bareille 1862, *etc.* 8°. **4531**. cc.—

—— *See* John, *Chrysostom, Saint, Patriarch of Constantinopl* [*Works.—Greek and French.*] Του ἐν ἁγιοις πατρος ἡμω Ἰωαννου του Χρυσοστομου . . . τα εὑρισκομενα παντ Œuvres complètes de Saint Jean Chrysostome . . Nouvelle traduction française par l'abbé J. Bareil 1865, *etc.* 8°. **3623**. c

—— *See* Luis, *de Granada.* [Dominican [Luis Sarria].] Œuvres complètes de Louis Grenade . . . traduites . . . par M. l'abbé Bareille. 1862, *etc.* 8°. **3677**. bb.

—— École de Sorèze. 1848. pp. 16. *Toulouse,* [1848.] 4 **8355**. f. **33**. (3

—— Histoire de Saint Thomas d'Aquin . . . Troisièm édition, revue et corrigée. pp. lx. 436. *Paris,* 1859. 8°. **4807**. d.

BAREILLES (BERTRAND) *See* KARATHEODORES (A. S.) Le Rapport secret sur le Congrès de Berlin, adressé à la S. Porte. [With an introduction by B. Bareilles.] 1919. 16°. **9135**. aa. **26**.

—— *See* ORMANIAN (M.) L'Église arménienne, son histoire, sa doctrine, son régime, sa discipline, sa liturgie, sa littérature, son présent. [With a preface by B. Bareilles.] 1910. 8°. **4533**. ff. **14**.

—— Constantinople, ses cités franques et levantines, Péra—Galata—banlieue. Une planche hors texte par Edgar Chahine . . . Illustrations dans le texte par Adolphe Thiers, un plan de Constantinople. pp. 405. *Paris*, 1918. 8°. **10127**. eee. **9**.

—— Le Drame oriental. D'Athènes à Angora. pp. 272. *Paris*, 1923. 8°. **08023**. a. **91**.

—— Un Turc à Paris, 1806–1811. Relation de voyage et de mission de Mouhib Effendi, ambassadeur extraordinaire du Sultan Selim III, d'après un manuscrit autographe. pp. 106. *Paris*, 1920. 16°. **14456.a.11.**

—— Les Turcs. Ce que fut leur empire. Leurs comédies politiques. Préface de J. de Morgan. pp. 313. *Paris*, 1917. 8°. **9134**. aaa. **4**.

BAREILLIER-FOUCHÉ (LOUIS) L'Exportation et l'importation des capitaux et les avoirs à l'étranger. Ouvrage au courant de la législation la plus récente, *etc.* pp. viii. 114. *Paris*, 1926. 8°. **08229**. c. **53**.

BAREILLY.—*Reformatory School.*

—— Annual Report on the Reformatory School at Bareilly for the year 1894(–1901). 8 pt. 1895–1901. *See* CHUNAR.—*Reformatory School.* Annual Report, *etc.* 1895–1910. fol. I.S. UP. 30 4.

BAREIRA ( )

—— Catalogue d'une belle collection de tableaux, de différens maîtres des écoles flamande, française et hollandaise, provenant du cabinet de M. * * * [identified in a MS. note as — Fossard and — Bareira]. La vente . . . aura lieu le . . . 23 mars [1818], *etc.* pp. 10. MS. NOTES AND PRICES. 1818. 8°. *See* CATALOGUES. **562**. e. **39**. (**22**.)

BAREIRAT ( )

—— Vente d'une belle collection de tableaux . . . des écoles italienne, hollandaise, flamande et française, gouaches, dessins . . . formant le cabinet de M. B * * * [identified in a MS. note as — Bareirat] . . . dont la vente se fera . . . 3 et 4 février [1820], *etc.* (Par M. Laneuville.) pp. 23. MS. NOTES AND PRICES. 1820. 8°. *See* B * * *, M. 562. e. 44. (5.)

BAREIRO (S.) Scriptural Riddles in Bengali rendered into English verse, with English notes, *etc.* *Bengali & Eng.* pp. 51. *Kattra Press: Dacca*, 1849. 12°. **14123**. aa. **28**.

BAREITH. *See* BAYREUTH.

BARÉLAGA (RODRIGO P. DE) *pseud.* [i.e. GREGORIO DE BALPARDA Y DE LAS HERRERÍAS.]

—— Ardeliones. Comedia en tres actos. pp. 51. *Madrid*, 1914. 8°. **11725**. e. **11**.

—— Güelfos y Gibelinos. Drama histórico. pp. 78. *Madrid*, 1913. 8°. **11725**. df. **13**. (**1**.)

—— Tribunos de la plebe. Drama histórico en tres actos. pp. 84. *Madrid*, 1912. 8°. **11725**. df. **13**. (**2**.)

BARELETA (GABRIEL) *See* GABRIEL, *de Barletta*.

BARELL (EMIL CHRISTOPH)

—— Jubilee Volume dedicated to E. C. Barell . . . President of F. Hoffmann—La Roche & Co . . . on the occasion of the fiftieth anniversary of his association with the House of Roche, by the scientific workers of the Roche companies. [With plates.] pp. 468. *Frederick Reinhardt: Basle*, 1946. 8°. 8896. b. 19.

BARELLA (DOMENICO) *See* GABOTTO (F.) and BARELLA (D.) La Poesia macaronica e la storia in Piemonte sulla fine del secolo XV. 1888. 8°. **11850**. aaa. **29**.

BARELLA (GIULIO) La Guerra turco-balcanica vista e vissuta agli avamposti montenegrini, *etc.* pp. 164. *Venezia*, 1913. 8°. **9136**. bbb. **29**.

BARELLA (HIPPOLYTE) Les Alcools et l'alcoolisme . . . Extrait des Mémoires couronnés et autres mémoires, publiés par l'Académie Royale de Médecine de Belgique. pp. 167. *Bruxelles*, 1880. 8°. **7405**. aaa. **23**.

—— Clinique médicale des affections du cœur et de l'aorte. Observations de médecine pratique traduites de l'anglais, par le docteur H. Barella. (Extrait du Journal publié par la Société Royale des Sciences Médicales et Naturelles de Bruxelles.) tom. 1. pp. iv. 200. *Bruxelles*, 1874. 8°. **7615**. ee. **1**.
Imperfect; wanting tom. 2. *fasc.* 1.

—— De l'abus des spiritueux: maladies des buveurs. pp. 203. *Bruxelles*, 1878. 8°. **7404**. aa. **60**.

—— Une Page de l'histoire littéraire contemporaine de la Belgique. Édouard Wacken . . . Édition ornée d'un portrait. pp. 125. *Verviers*, 1888. 8°. **10759**. c. **20**.

BARELLAI (GIUSEPPE) Memorie sugli ospizi marini e scritti vari di G. Barellai. pp. 287. *Firenze*, 1870. 8°. **8285**. cc. **25**.

—— Breve discorso letto alla Società Medico-fisica Fiorentina nell'adunanza del 22 maggio 1859. pp. 7. *Firenze*, 1859. 8°. **7680**. aaa. **60**. (**5**.)

—— Degli ospizj marini e del nuovo spedale di Pietrasanta. Memorie letta nell'Accademia Medica di Firenze nell' adunanza del 30 novembre 1856. (Estratto dall' appendice delle Letture di famiglia.) pp. 16. *Firenze*, 1856. 8°. **7679**. c. **56**. (**2**.)

—— Napoli e gli ospizi marini. (Seconda edizione.) pp. 12. *Firenze*, 1882. 8°. **8275**. f. **32**. (**8**.)

—— Gli Ospizi marini d'Italia proposti e promossi da G. Barellai. pp. 172. *Firenze*, 1867. 8°. **8285**. e. **6**.

BARELLAS (ESTEVAN) Centuria, o historia de los famosos hechos del gran conde de Barcelona don Bernardo Barcino, y de don Zinofre su hijo, y otros caualleros de la Prouincia de Cathaluña, *etc.* ff. 213. *S. de Cormellas: Barcelona*, 1600. fol. **179**. c. **1**.

BARELLE, afterwards **BAYLE BARELLE** (GIUSEPPE) Analogia de' vegetabili ed animali e delle conseguenze che se ne possono dedurre a vantaggio dell' agricoltura. pp. 49. *Milano*, 1806. 8°. **7383**.*c. **16**. (**4**.)

—— Della malattia della golpe del Gran Turco. Osservazioni, ed esperienze del sig. G. Bayle-Barelle . . . Inserite nel giornale di agricoltura intitolato Biblioteca di campagna. pp. 21. *Milano*, [1808.] 8°. **7383**.*c. **16**. (**6**.)

—— Monografia agronomica dei cereali . . . Del formento, trattato diviso in tre parti, *etc.* pp. 211. pl. VI. *Milano*, 1809. 8°. **452**. d. **33**.
Pt. 1 *has a separate titlepage bearing the date* 1808.

—— [Another copy.] **7383**. c. **16**. (**5**.)
Imperfect; wanting the half-title, the separate titlepage to pt. 1. *and one, unnumbered, plate.*

BARELLE, afterwards BAYLE BARELLE (GIUSEPPE)

—— Saggio intorno agli insetti nocivi ai vegetabili economici, agli animali utili all'agricoltura, ed ai prodotti dell'economia rurale. [Followed by "Estratto di alcune memorie sugli insetti nocivi ai vegetabili economici . . . dal soc. L. Bossi. Per servire di supplemento al saggio su quest'oggetto medesimo del sig. Prof. Bayle-Barelle."] 2 pt. *Milano*, 1809. 8°. **954**. e. **12**.

BARELLER ( ) *Sugar Manufacturer*. See AUBINEAU ( ) *Sugar Manufacturer*. Mémoire présenté en 1832, à la Chambre des Députés, par trente-deux fabricans de sucre indigène, *etc*. [Signed by Aubineau, Bareller and others.] 1832. 8°. **712**. g. **30**. (**8**.)

BARELLI (BERNARDINO) *See* BIBLE.—*Job*. [*Polyglott*.] Il libro di Giobbe. Recato in versi italiani dal canonico V. Barelli, *etc*. [With a memoir of the translator by B. Barelli.] 1891. 8°. **3049**. bb. **18**.

BARELLI (FRANCESCO LUIGI) Memorie dell' origine, fondazione, avanzamenti, successi, ed uomini illustri . . . della Congregazione de' Cherici Regolari di S. Paolo, chiamati Barnabiti. 2 tom. *Bologna*, 1703, 07. fol. **205**. e. **7**, **8**.

BARELLI (GIUSEPPE)

—— *See* CARRÙ. Statuti e documenti di Carrù, *etc*. [Edited by G. Barelli.] 1952. 8°. [*Seguito alla Biblioteca della Società Storica Subalpina*. vol. 176.] Ac. **6536**.

—— *See* CEVA. Il "Liber instrumentorum" del comune di Ceva. [Edited by G. Barelli.] 1936. 8°. [*Biblioteca della Società Storica Subalpina*. vol. 147. pt. 1.] Ac. **6536**.

—— *See* GARESSIO. Il Libro della Catena del comune di Garessio. (Il Libro degli Statuti di Ormea.) [Edited by G. Barelli.] 1905. 8°. [*Biblioteca della Società Storica Subalpina*. vol. 27.] Ac. **6536**.

—— *See* GARESSIO. Statuti di Garessio, Ormea, *etc*. [Edited by G. Barelli.] 1907. 8°. [*Biblioteca della Società Storica Subalpina*. vol. 27a.] Ac. **6536**.

—— *See* MONBASILIO. Statuti e carte di franchigia di Monbasilio. [Edited by G. Barelli.] 1936. 8°. [*Biblioteca della Società Storica Subalpina*. vol. 147. pt. 2.] Ac. **6536**.

—— *See* MONDOVÌ. Il "Liber instrumentorum" del comune di Mondovi, *etc*. [Edited by G. Barelli.] 1904. 8°. [*Biblioteca della Società Storica Subalpina*. vol. 24.] Ac. **6536**.

—— *See* STEPHEN, *Saint and Martyr, Abbey of, at Ivrea*. Le Carte della Abazia di S. Stefano d'Ivrea fino al 1230, *etc*. [Edited by G. Barelli.] 1902, *etc*. 8°. [*Biblioteca della Società Storica Subalpina*. vol. 9.] Ac. **6536**.

—— Il Primo conte conosciuto della regione saluzzese. *See* SALUZZO. Studi saluzzesi, *etc*. 1901. 8°. [*Biblioteca della Società Storica Subalpina*. vol. 10.] Ac. **6536**.

BARELLI (VINCENZO) *Canon*. *See* BIBLE.—*Job*. [*Polyglott*.] Il libro di Giobbe. Recato in versi italiani dal canonico V. Barelli, *etc*. [With a memoir of the translator by B. Barelli.] 1891. 8°. **3049**. bb. **18**.

—— *See* BIBLE.—*Psalms*. [*Polyglott*.] Il Salterio recato in versi italiani dal canonico V. Barelli, *etc*. 1881. 8°. **3089**. e. **7**.

—— *See* BIBLE.—*Psalms*. [*Italian*.—*Metrical Versions*.] Il Salterio recato in versi Italiani dal canonico V. Barelli. 1871. 8°. **3089**. bb. **33**.

—— L'Allegoria della Divina Commedia di Dante Alighieri. pp. xxiv. 372. *Firenze*, 1864. 8°. **11422**. cc. **7**.

BARELLI (VINCENZO) *Canon*.

—— Notizie sulla città di Como. *See* COMO, *City of*.—*Co[ngresso] d'Agronomi*. Memorie comensi, *etc*. 1867. 8°. **7073**. e. 1

BARELLI (VINCENZO) *Mineralogist*. Cenni di statisti[ca] mineralogica degli stati di S. M. il Re di Sardegna, ovv[ero] catalogo ragionato della raccolta formatasi presso l'Azien[da] Generale dell'Interno. pp. xiii. 686. 1835. 8°. SARDINIA AND PIEDMONT.—*Azienda Generale dell' Inter[no]*. **1144**. f.

BARELLO (CASIMIRO GIOVANNI MARIA) Apuntes para historia del peregrino piamontés Casimiro Barello Mo[nli] *etc*. [With a portrait.] pp. 48. *Alcoy*, 1884. 8°. **4807**. ee. **16**. (

—— Vita del pellegrino Casimiro Barello. pp. 264. *Geno[va]* 1885. 8°. **4867**. bb.

BARELLO MONLI (CASIMIRO) *See* BARELLO (Casim[iro] G. M.)

BAREMIUS (MARTINUS) *See* HEROD, *the Great*, *King [of] Judaea*. Inscriptio vetus græca, continens dedication[em] fundi, ab Herode Magno Rege factam . . . Adiecta interpretatio latina & soluta & ligata oratione, *etc*. [O[ne] of the Latin versions by M. Baremius.] 1608. 4°. **587**. d. **15**. (

BAREN (FERDINAND ALEXANDER VON)

—— *See* MOHR (E. C. J.) and BAREN (F. A. van) Trop[ical] Soils, *etc*. 1954. 8°. **7112**. d.

BAREN (J. E. COHEN VAN) *See* COHEN VAN BAREN.

BAREN (JEAN ANTOINE VAN DER)

—— *See* BAUTIER (P.) Jean Antoine van der Baren et peintres de fleurs. [With reproductions.] [1941.] [BASTIEN (A.) *Le Paysage et la marine dans l'œuvre Rubens*.] Ac. **4613**/**2**. (

BAREN (JOHAN VAN) De Bodem van Nederland. [W[ith] maps.] 2 dl. *Amsterdam*, 1920, 27. 8°. **07109**. c.

BÄRENBACH ( ) [For the German surname of t[his] form :] *See* BAERENBACH.

BARENBOIM (L. A.)

—— *See* RUBINSTEIN (A. G.) Избранные письма. (П[од] общей редакцией, со вступительной статьей и ко[м]ментариями Л. А. Баренбойма.) 1954. 8°. **10923**. aa.

BARENBROEK (EBEL) Ter bevordering van eene goe[de] instandhouding van het kadaster is de medewerking v[an] het publiek in zijn eigen belang noodig. pp. 20. *Groningen*, 1867. 8°. **8228**. d. **63**. (

BÄRENBURG. *See* BAERENBURG.

BAREND, *pseud*. [i.e. BAREND VAN DER VEEN.]

—— De Direkt[eur]. Klucht yn ien bidriuw. pp. 44. *Berltsum*, 1920. 8°. **011755**. g.

—— Eigen wegen. Toanielstik yn trije bidriuwen. pp. *Berltsum*, [1926.] 8°. **11754**. i.

—— Oarlochs-liet. Toanielstik, *etc*. pp. 97. *Berlts[um]*, 1920. 8°. **011755**. g.

—— Takomst-Treast. Allegoarysk spil, yn tsjinst fen Drankbistriding. [With musical notes.] 2 pt. *Berltsum*, [1926.] 8°. **11754**. d.

BÄREND ( )

—— [For the German surname of this form :] *See* BAERENDT.

BÄREN-DANTZ. *See* BAERENTANZ.

BAREN DE SOTO (BASILIO) *See* VAREN DE SOTO.

BARENDREGT (TEUNIS JOHAN)

—— Onderzoekingen in vitro en in vivo over het glutaminezuur van tumorproteïnen. Proefschrift, *etc.* [With a summary in English.] pp. 90. *Utrecht*, 1949. 8°. **8900. g. 72.**

BARENDS (WILLEM) *See* BARENTSZ.

BARENDSEN (O.) De Wereldbeschouwing van het kind, over literaire kinderstudie en opvoeding. [With a bibliography.] pp. 181. *Zeist*, 1921. 8°. **08463. f. 63.**

BARENDSZ (DIRCK)

—— *See* COSTUMES. [A collection of engravings, etchings and woodcuts of various sizes mainly illustrating the costumes of different nations by or after D. Barendsz and other artists from the fifteenth to the seventeenth centuries.] **146. i. 10.**

BARENDT (FRANK HUGH) *See* BERGER (Ludwig) *M.D.* Pellagra . . . Translated and abridged by F. H. Barendt. 1893. 8°. [*Selected Monographs on Dermatology.*] **Ac. 3838/57.**

—— *See* NIELSEN (Ludvig) On the Appearance of Herpes Zoster during the Administration of Arsenic. (Clinical and Etiological Researches in Psoriasis . . . Translated by F. H. Barendt.] 1893. 8°. [*Selected Monographs on Dermatology.*] **Ac. 3838/57.**

BARENDT (JOANNES GODOFREDUS) Dissertatio inauguralis medica de febre quartana intermittente, *etc.* *Praes.* C. F. Kaltschmied. pp. 56. *Ienae*, 1757. 4°. **T. 550. (19.)**

BARENGER (ANDRÉ THOMAS) Le Guide fidele de la vraie gloire, presenté à Monseigneur le duc de Bourgogne. Instruisant ce jeune Prince des choses qu'il doit croire, demander, pratiquer . . . pour être Roy pendant tous les siecles . . . Auec des desseins en taille douce. *P. Landry: Paris*, 1688. 8°. **C.108.bbb.14.**
Engraved throughout.

BARENGO (ULDERICO) and **BLATTO** (OETE) Saggio bibliografico sulla guerra mondiale. Volumi, opuscoli, articoli . . . pubblicati a tutto il dicembre 1925. pp. lxxx. 484. *Torino*, 1926. 8°. **011899. cc. 1.**

BÄRENHOLD, *pseud.* *See* BAERENHOLD.

BÄRENHOLDT (H. C.)

—— H. C. Bärenholdt. Et Udvalg af Billeder med indledende Tekst af Kai Flor. [With plates, including a portrait.] *København*, 1938. 8°. **7865. ppp. 29.**

BARENNA (DESDA) The Emir's Wife. [A novel.] pp. 288. *Jonathan Cape: London*, 1926. 8°. **NN. 12134.**

BARENNES (JEAN) *See* BIRON (Réginald) and BARENNES (J.) Un Prince anglais, Cardinal-Légat au XVIe siècle. Réginald Pole, *etc.* [1922.] 8°. **4863. h. 5.**

—— Un Homme de loi pendant la Révolution : le Girondin Barennes, *etc.* pp. 85. *Paris*, [1937.] 8°. [*Bibliothèque d'histoire révolutionnaire.*] **W.P. 686/24.**

—— Viticulture et vinification en Bordelais au moyen âge, *etc.* pp. vii. 186. *Bordeaux*, 1912. 8°. **07076. dd. 50.**

BARENNES (RAYMOND DE)

—— *See* BARENNES (J.) Un Homme de loi pendant la Révolution : le Girondin Barennes, *etc.* [1937.] 8°. **W.P. 686/24.**

—— Corps Législatif. Conseil des Anciens. Discours prononcé . . . en présentant au Conseil des Anciens une adresse de plusieurs républicains de la commune de Bordeaux. Séance du 6 fructidor an 7. pp. 12. [*Paris*,] an 7 [1799]. 8°. **F. 65**. (17.)**

—— Corps Législatif. Conseil des Anciens. Opinion . . sur la résolution du thermidor, relative aux élections des Bouches-du-Rhône. Séance du 27 fructidor an 7. pp. 6. [*Paris*,] an 7 [1799]. 8°. **F.R. 102. (19.)**

BARENNES (YVES)

—— La Modernisation rurale au Maroc. pp. 152. *Paris*, 1948. 8°. [*Institut des Hautes-Études Marocaines. Collection des centres d'études juridiques.* tom. 26.] **Ac. 17. b/2.**

BÄRENS ( ) [For the German surname of this form :] *See* BAERENS.

BÄRENS (JOHAN HENDRICH) Johan Hendrich Bärens's Biografie. Udgivet af P. W. Heiberg. pp. viii. 61. *Kjøbenhavn*, 1813. 16°. **1451. b. 62. (1.)**

—— Kiøbenhavns Magasin for Industri-, Skole- og Fattigvæsen. Bd. 1. 1799 [1798, 99]. 8°. *See* PERIODICAL PUBLICATIONS.—*Copenhagen.* **713. b. 21.**

—— Kristian Elovius Mangor som Embedsmand. pp. 116. *Kjöbenhavn*, 1806. 16°. **1451. b. 40.**

BARENSIS (HERMANNUS) *See* BARE (H. de)

BÄRENSPRUNG ( ) [For the German surname of this form :] *See* BAERENSPRUNG.

BARENT [VAN GALEN], *Prince, Bishop of Munster.* *See* CHRISTOPHER BERNARD MATTHEW.

BARENTIN ( ) *Artist.* *See* TAXIL (L.) *pseud.* La Ménagerie républicaine . . . Illustrations par Barentin. [1889, *etc.*] 8°. **12330. m. 32.**

BARENTIN (CHARLES LOUIS FRANÇOIS DE PAULE DE) Discours de M. le Garde des Sceaux (M. de Barentin), 5 mai 1789. [On the occasion of the opening of the États Généraux.] [1792.] *See* DUGOUR (A. J.) afterwards GUROV (A. A.) École de politique, *etc.* tom. 2. [1792, *etc.*] 8°. **F. 314.**

—— [Another edition.] *See* FRANCE. [*Appendix.—History, etc.—Revolution of* 1789.] Collection de pièces intéressantes, *etc.* tom. 2. 1801. 8°. **1195. f. 12.**

—— Discours de M. le Garde des Sceaux. *See* FRANCE.—*États Généraux.* [1789.] Ouverture des États-Généraux, faite à Versailles le 5 mai 1789, *etc.* 1789. 8°. **934. c. 6. (6.)**

—— Discours de M. le Garde des Sceaux à l'Assemblée Nationale, le 7 août 1789. pp. 4. *Paris*, 1789. 4°. **28. d. 2. (17.)**

—— Mémoire autographe de M. de Barentin . . . sur les derniers conseils du roi Louis XVI publié d'après le manuscrit original de la Bibliothèque Royale . . . avec notes et pièces justificatives, et précédé d'une notice biographique sur M. de Barentin par M. Maurice Champion. pp. xxxii. 292. *Paris*, 1844. 8°. **1442. g. 10.**

—— Mémoire pour M. Barentin, ancien Garde-des-Sceaux de France . . . sur la dénonciation dans laquelle il est nommé, & qui a donné lieu à la plainte de M. le Procureur du Roi au Châtelet. pp. 68. *Paris*, 1790. 8°. **F.R. 96. (12.)**

BARENTIN (Charles Louis François de Paule de)

—— *See* Garran de Coulon (J. P.) Réponse aux observations pour le baron de Bésenval, & au mémoire de M. Barentin, *etc.* 1790. 8°. **F. 1030. (1.)**

BARENTIN (Friedrich Wilhelm) *See* Berlin.—*Physikalische Gesellschaft.* Die Fortschritte der Physik, *etc.* (Namen- und Sach-Register . . . Band I. bis XX. Bearbeitet von W. Barentin.) 1846, *etc.* 8°. Ac. **3775.**

—— *See* Handwörterbuch. Handwörterbuch der Chemie . . . Von E. F. August, F. W. Barentin, *etc.* 1842, *etc.* 8°. **1142.** k. **17, 18.**

—— *See* Periodical Publications.—*Halle.* Journal der Physik, *etc.* (Annalen der Physik und Chemie. [The index volumes for Bd. 1–150 compiled by F. W. Barentin.] 1790, *etc.* 8°. P.P. **1487.**

—— *See* Poggendorff (J. C.) Histoire de la physique . . . Traduction, *etc.* [Edited by F. W. Barentin.] 1883. 8°. **8704.** eee. **27.**

—— Lehrbuch der Technologie für Real- und Gewerbeschulen . . . Mit eingedruckten Holzschnitten. Dritte vermehrte und verbesserte Auflage. pp. iv. 223. *Giessen,* 1848. 8°. **07942.** h. **26.**

—— Die Vegetation in der Mark Brandenburg. Abhandlung, *etc.* pp. 47. *Berlin,* 1840. 4°. [*Kölnisches Gymnasium, Berlin. Programmes, etc.*] **8358.** cc. **35.**

BARENTIN (Jacques Honoré) *See* Colbert (C.) *Marquis de Croissy.* Rapport au roy concernant la province de Poitou.—Catalogue alphabétique des nobles de la généralité de Poitiers maintenus et condamnés roturiers, par Colbert, Barentin, *etc.* 1865. 8°. [*Dugast-Matifeux (C.) État de Poitou sous Louis XIV, etc.*] **9220.** g. **10.**

—— *See* Colbert (C.) *Marquis de Croissy.* La Réformation générale des forests et bois de sa Maiesté de la province de Poictou, par Messieurs Colbert et Barentin. 1667. fol. **504.** k. **10.**

BARENTIN (Wilhelm) *See* Barentin (Friedrich W.)

BARENTON (Antoine Dénis) Essai sur la chorée ou danse de Saint-Guy ; thèse, *etc.* pp. 21. *Paris,* 1819. 4°. **1183.** e. **13. (6.)**

BARENTON (Hilaire de) *See* Hilaire, *Capuchin, of Barenton.*

BARENTONIUS (Gulielmus Postellus) *See* Postel (G.)

BARENTS (Jan)

—— *See* Banning (W.) and Barents (J.) Socialistische documenten. 1952. 8°. **8012.** e. **6.**

—— Het Verschraalde denken. Een vergelijking tusschen de dialectische theologie van Karl Barth en de " reine Rechtslehre " van Hans Kelsen. pp. 112. *Den Haag,* 1946. 8°. **4380.** k. **33.**

BARENTS (Johan Willy)

—— Een Functioneel-anatomische studie der sesambeenderen bij zoogdieren. Proefschrift, *etc.* [With a summary in English.] pp. 114. *Zeist,* [1947.] 8°. **07209.** h. **30.**

BARENTS (William) *See* Barentsz.

BARENTSEN (Abraham Cornelis)

—— Bijdrage tot de kennis der techniek der groepspsychotherapie voor volwassenen. Een clinisch-psychiatrische studie. Proefschrift, *etc.* [With summaries in English and German.] pp. 132. *Leiden,* [1952.] 8°. **8475.** ff. **24.**

BARENTSEN (P.)

—— *See* Bolderman (M. B. N.) and Dwars (A. W. C.) Waterbouwkunde, *etc.* (dl. 2. Grondwerken, transport- en hulpmiddelen, gewone wegen, spoorwegen. Door P. Barentsen, F. Bakker, J. D. M. Bardet.—dl. 5. Zeewerken, rivierwerken, droogmakerijen, afwatering en ontwatering kanalen. Door C. Schagen en A. W. C. Dwars. Voltooid door P. J. Colijn en P. Barentsen.) 1946, *etc.* 8°. **08776.** dd. **38.**

BARENTSON (William) *See* Barentsz.

BARENTSZ (Jan) Klucht van Buchelioen 't Kaboutermannetge, *etc.* [In verse.] *D. C. Houthaak: Amsterdam,* 1655. 4°. **11754.** bbb. **6.**

BARENTSZ (Willem) *See* Adelung (J. C.) Jakob Heemskerks und Wilhelm Barenz nördliche Entdeckungsreise und merkwürdige Schicksale. [Abridged from J. C. Adelungs " Geschichte der Schiffahrten und Versuche, welche zur Entdeckung des nordöstlichen Weges nach Japan und China unternommen worden."] 1831. 8°. [*Campe (J. H.) Sämmtliche Kinder- und Jugendschriften, etc.* Bd. 17.] **12807.** bbb.

—— *See* Campe (J. H.) [Gemälde des Nordens.] Polar Scenes, exhibited in the Voyages of Heemskirk and Barenz, *etc.* 1822. 12°. **010460.** a. **1.**

—— *See* Campe (J. H.) Polar Scenes, exhibited in the voyages of . . . Barenz, *etc.* 1823. 12°. **12835.b.76.**

—— *See* Campe (J. H.) Polar Scenes, exhibited in the voyages of . . . Barenz, *etc.* 1825. 12°. **12835.b.75.**

—— *See* Jonge (J. K. J. de) Nova Zembla. De voorwerpen door de Nederlandsche zeevaarders [W. Barentsz and others] na hunne overwintering aldaar in 1597 achtergelaten en in 1871 . . . teruggevonden, beschreven en toegelicht, *etc.* 1873. 8°. **10460.** ee. **4.**

—— *See* Jonge (J. K. J. de) Nova Zembla. De voorwerpen door de Nederlandsche zeevaarders [W. Barentsz and others] na hunne overwintering, op Nowaja-Semlja . . in 1597 achtergelaten en in 1876 door Chs Gardiner . . aldaar teruggevonden, *etc.* 1877. 8°. **10460.** f. **3.**

—— *See* Jonge (J. K. J. de) Nova Zembla, 1596–1597 The Barents Relics : recovered in the summer of 1876 by C. L. W. Gardiner, *etc.* 1877. 8°. **10460.** ee. **7.**

—— *See* Wagenaer (L.) Le Nouveau miroir des voiages marins . . . Avec certaines notules de cartes, apparitions & descriptions adioustées . . . par G. Bernard, *etc.* 1605. fol. Maps C. **8.** b. **9.**

—— [For editions of G. de Veer's ".Waerachtighe Beschryvinghe van drie seylagien, ter werelt noyt soo vreemt ghehoort, drie jaeren achter malcanderen deur de Hollandtsche ende Zeelandtsche schepen by noorden Noorweghen, Moscovia, ende Tartaria, na de coninckrijcken van . Catthay ende China," describing the voyages of W. Barentsz and others :] *See* Veer (G. de)

BARENTZ (M. E.) Woordenboek der Engelsche spreektaal . . . Voorafgegaan door een korte geschiedenis van cant en slang, *etc.* pp. xvi. 333. *Amsterdam,* [1895.] 8°. **12981.** d. **7.**

BARENZ (Wilhelm) *See* Barentsz (Willem)

BARER (Robert)

—— Lecture Notes on the Use of the Microscope. pp. vii. 76. *Blackwell Scientific Publications : Oxford,* 1953. 8°. **8716.** i. **46.**

BARER (SHLOMO)

—— The Magic Carpet. [The story of the migration to Israel of the Jewish population of the Yemen. With plates.] pp. 267. *Secker & Warburg: London*, 1952. 8°. **04033**. g. **97**.

BARERA (ANDREA) Di alcuni danni del lusso delle donne. Dissertazione medico politica, *etc.* pp. 31. *Pavia*, [1822.] 8°. **7383**.*b. **18**. (**7**.)

BARERA (ATTILIO) L'Opera scientifico letteraria del Card. Federico Borromeo, *etc.* [With a portrait.] pp. ix. 298. *Milano*, 1931. 8°. **4863**. i. **23**.

BARERA (EUGENIO) *See* MORRIS (W.) *Poet.* La Difesa di Ginevra . . . Versione metrica italiana [by E. Barera]. 1898. fol. **11647**. g. **35**.

—— A Critical Essay on the Works of Alfred Lord Tennyson. pp. 108. *Visentini Bros.: Venice*, 1896. 8°. **011851**. i. **35**.

BARÈRE, *Family of.* La Famille Barère démasquée. [With special reference to Jacques and Jean Pierre Barère.] pp. 52. *Tarbes*, an III [1795]. 4°. F. **48***. (**3**.)

BARÈRE (BERTRAND) *See* BARÈRE DE VIEUZAC.

BARÈRE (JACQUES) *See* BARÈRE, *Family of.* La Famille Barère démasquée. [With special reference to J. Barère.] [1795.] 4°. F. **48***. (**3**.)

BARÈRE (JEAN PIERRE) *See* BARÈRE, *Family of.* La Famille de Barère démasquée. [With special reference to J. P. Barère.] [1795.] 4°. F. **48***. (**3**.)

BARÈRE DE VIEUZAC (BERTRAND) Convention Nationale. Rapport fait à la Convention Nationale, au nom du Comité de salut public, le quatre prairial, sur l'assassinat de Collot-d'Herbois . . . Réflexions des citoyens Couthon et Collot-d'Herbois sur le même objet. (Convention Nationale. Rapport . . . sur les crimes de l'Angleterre envers le peuple français, et sur ses attentats contre la liberté des nations ; par Barère.—Convention Nationale. Discours prononcé à la Convention Nationale dans la séance du 7 prairial par Maxim. Robespierre.) pp. 168. [*Paris*,] an 2 [1794]. 16°. F. **1889**. (**2**.)

—— Les Alors, ou origine des mesures révolutionnaires . . . A la Convention Nationale. no. 1, 2. pp. 32. [*Paris*, 1795.] 8°. F. **1097**. (**10, 11**.)

—— [Another copy.] F.R. **60**. (**7, 8**.)

—— B. Barère à Dubois-Crancé. Réponse à l'accusation personnelle, remise le 14 nivôse à la Commission des vingt-un ; servant de réfutation à la partie du rapport de Saladin qui concerne Dubois-Crancé, *etc.* pp. 34. *Paris*, an III [1795]. 8°. F. **1097**. (**3**.)

—— [Another issue.] *Paris*, an III [1795]. 8°. **935**. b. **19**. (**4**.)

—— Conduite des princes de la Maison de Bourbon durant la révolution, l'émigration et le consulat 1790 à 1805 . . . Ouvrage . . . enrichi de notes de M. le comte Réal. pp. 295 [342]. *Paris*, 1835. 8°. **1320**. f. **20**.

—— Convention Nationale. Discours prononcé dans la séance de la Convention Nationale du vendredi 4 janvier 1792 [*sic*] . . . sur le jugement du procès de Louis Capet. pp. 46 [44]. [*Paris*, 1793.] 8°. F. **912**. (**18**.)

BARÈRE DE VIEUZAC (BERTRAND)

—— Convention Nationale. Partie de la défense des trois membres des anciens comités [B. Barère de Vieuzac, J. M. Collot d'Herbois and J. N. Billaud-Varenne] denoncés, relativement aux prisons et maisons d'arrêt. Présenté dans la séance du 5 germinal. pp. 11. *Paris*, an III [1795]. 8°. F. **1098**. (**8**.)

—— [Another copy.] F. **847**. (**4**.)

—— Convention Nationale. Rapport, au nom du Comité de salut public, sur la commune de Marseille . . . Dans la séance du 22 frimaire. pp. 8. [*Paris*, 1792.] 8°. F. **655**. (**21**.)

—— Convention Nationale. Rapport et decret du 23 août, l'an II . . . sur la réquisition civique des jeunes citoyens pour la défense de la patrie. Présentés au nom du Comité de salut public. pp. 15. [*Paris*,] 1793. 8°. F. **945**. (**18**.)

—— Convention Nationale. Rapport et projet de décret, fait [*sic*] au nom du Comité de salut public. [6 June 1793. On the suppression of the Committees, etc.] pp. 14. [*Paris*, 1793.] 8°. F. **1300**. (**6**.)

—— [Another copy.] F. **1253**. (**17**.)

—— Convention Nationale. Rapport et projet de décret, présentés au nom des Comités de salut public et de la guerre, sur les places à décerner par la Convention Nationale aux défenseurs de la patrie qui se seront distingués par des traits de bravoure . . . Séance du premier thermidor, l'an 2, *etc.* pp. 8. *Paris*, [1794.] 8°. F. **945**. (**7**.)

—— Convention Nationale. Rapport et projet de décret, présentés au nom du Comité de salut public, sur les idiômes étrangers, & l'enseignement de la langue française . . . dans la séance du 8 pluviôse, l'an deuxième, *etc.* pp. 14. [*Paris*, 1794.] 8°. F. **496**. (**14**.)

—— Convention Nationale. Rapport et projet de décret sur l'établissement d'une commission nationale des poudres et armes de la République ; présentés au nom du Comité de salut public . . . dans la séance du 13 pluviôse. pp. 48. [*Paris*, 1794.] 8°. F. **538**. (**3**.)

—— [Another edition.] pp. 32. [*Paris*, 1794.] 8°. F. **1100**. (**5**.)

—— Convention Nationale. Rapport et projet de décret sur la division & organisation provisoire du ministère de l'intérieur, faits à la Convention Nationale, au nom du Comité de défense générale. [2 March 1793.] pp. 15. [*Paris*, 1793.] 8°. F.R. **97**. (**27**.)

—— Convention Nationale. Rapport et projet de décret sur la réorganisation des comités de la Convention Nationale, présentés au nom des Comités de salut public et de sûreté générale . . . dans la séance du 14 thermidor l'an second, *etc.* pp. 11. [*Paris*, 1794.] 8°. F.R. **60**. (**6**.)

—— Convention Nationale. Rapport fait à la Convention Nationale, au nom du Comité de salut public, dans la séance du 13 prairial, sur l'éducation révolutionnaire, républicaine & militaire ; et décret sur la formation de l'École de Mars. pp. 16. *Paris*, [1794.] 8°. F. **499**. (**6**.)

—— Convention Nationale. Rapport fait . . . au nom des Comités de salut public et de sûreté générale, et décret sur la section 11 de Marseille, et sur les patriotes qui se sont réunis à elle dans les journées du 22 au 24 août . . . Séance du 16 germinal, l'an 2, *etc.* pp. 14. *Paris*, [1794.] 8°. F. **655**. (**5**.)

—— Convention Nationale. Rapport fait au nom des Comités de salut public et de sûreté générale . . . sur la conjuration de Robespierre, Couthon, St.-Just et leurs complices. Séance du 10 thermidor, l'an deuxième, *etc.* pp. 8. *Paris*, [1794.] 8°. **F. 854. (8.)**

—— [Another edition.] Convention nationale. Rapport fait . . . sur la conspiration de Robespierre, Couthon, St.-Just et leurs complices, *etc.* pp. 8. *Paris*, [1794.] 8°. **R. 112. (15.)**

—— Convention Nationale. Rapport fait au nom du Comité de constitution . . . sur l'invitation à faire aux amis de la liberté & de l'égalité, de présenter leurs vues sur la constitution à donner à la République Française. Le 19 octobre 1792, *etc.* pp. 3. [*Paris*, 1792.] 8°. **F. 1099. (1.)**

—— Convention Nationale. Rapport fait au nom du Comité de salut public, dans la séance du 29 frimaire, an 2 . . . sur la conduite du onzième bataillon de la première réquisition de Paris . . . et le [*sic*] dixième bataillon, *etc.* pp. 32. *Paris*, [1794.] 8°. **F. 628. (22.)**

—— Convention Nationale. Rapport fait au nom du Comité de salut public, le premier août 1793, *etc.* [On the action taken by the English Government against the Republic.] pp. 35. [*Paris*, 1793.] 8°. **F. 971. (11.)**

A second pamphlet, entitled "Traduction littérale d'une lettre écrite en anglais, et déposée au Comité de salut public," containing documents referred to in the above, and subsequently published as an appendix to it, is entered under FRANCE.—*Comité de Salut Public.*

—— [Another issue.] **F. 1165. (7.)**

—— [Another issue.] **F.R. 124. (7.)**

—— Convention Nationale. Rapport fait au nom du Comité de salut public . . . Séance du 23 messidor, l'an 2, *etc.* [Concerning the Army of the North.] pp. 4. *Paris*, [1794.] 8°. **F. 946. (5.)**

—— [Another copy.] **F. 940. (20.)**

—— Convention Nationale. Rapport fait au nom du Comité de salut public, sur l'état de la fabrication révolutionnaire du salpêtre & de la poudre, & sur la nécessité de supprimer l'agence nationale, ci-devant régie des poudres et salpêtres . . . Séance du 17 messidor, l'an deuxième, *etc.* pp. 19. *Paris*, [1794.] 8°. **F. 538. (4.)**

—— Convention Nationale. Rapport fait au nom du Comité de salut public, sur l'évacuation du Fort-Vauban, dans la séance du 3 pluviôse, l'an 2, *etc.* pp. 10. [*Paris*, 1794.] 8°. **F. 940. (16.)**

—— Convention Nationale. Rapport fait au nom du Comité de salut public . . . sur l'exécution du décret du 11 brumaire, & sur la publication des tableaux du maximum des denrées & marchandises soumises à la loi du maximum, dans la séance du 4 ventôse. pp. 23. [*Paris*, 1794.] 8°. **F. 476. (20.)**

—— Convention Nationale. Rapport fait au nom du Comité de salut public, sur l'héroisme des républicains montant le vaisseau le Vengeur, dans la séance du 21 messidor, l'an 2e, *etc.* pp. 8. [*Paris*, 1794.] 8°. **F. 1259. (11.)**

—— Convention Nationale. Rapport fait au nom du Comité de salut public, sur la bataille de Fleurus donnée le 13 prairial . . . Séance du 11 messidor, l'an 2, *etc.* pp. 7. *Paris*, [1794.] 8°. **F. 940. (19.)**

—— Convention Nationale. Rapport fait au nom du Comité de salut public . . . sur la conspiration ourdie contre la représentation nationale, par Robespierre, Couthon, St.-Just, Lebas & leurs complices. Séance du 9 thermidor, l'an deuxième, *etc.* pp. 7. *Paris*, [1794.] 8°. **F. 854. (4.)**

—— Convention Nationale. Rapport fait au nom du Comité de salut public . . . sur la mission civique des envoyés des assemblées primaires du peuple français. Dans la séance du 14 août 1793. pp. 14. [*Paris*, 1793.] 8°. **F. 1213. (15.)**

—— [Another copy.] **F.R. 99. (26.)**

—— Convention Nationale. Rapport fait au nom du Comité de salut public . . . sur la prise d'Anvers. Séance du 8 thermidor, l'an deuxième, *etc.* pp. 4. *Paris*, [1794.] 8°. **F. 945. (24.)**

—— [Another copy.] **F. 946. (2.)**

—— Convention Nationale. Rapport fait au nom du Comité de salut public, sur la prise de Bruxelles, séance du 24 messidor, l'an 2, *etc.* pp. 10. *Paris*, [1794.] 8°. **F. 945. (3.)**

—— Convention Nationale. Rapport fait au nom du Comité de salut public, sur la prise de Charleroi . . . Séance du 9 messidor, l'an second, *etc.* pp. 6. [*Paris*, 1794.] 8°. **F. 945. (6.)**

—— Convention Nationale. Rapport fait au nom du Comité de salut public . . sur la prise de Namur & de Kaiserlautern. Et décret concernant les citoyens qui se sont soustraits à des mandats d'arrêts, & les fonctionnaires publics, destitués ou remplacés, qui se trouvent à Paris. Séance du 2 thermidor, l'an 2, *etc.* pp. 10. [*Paris*, 1794.] 8°. **F. 946. (4.)**

—— Convention Nationale. Rapport fait au nom du Comité de salut public . . . sur la prise de Nieuport & sur les nouveaux complots tramés par les ennemis de l'intérieur. Séance du 5 thermidor, l'an 2, *etc.* pp. 15. *Paris*, [1794.] 8°. **F. 946. (3.)**

—— Convention Nationale. Rapport fait au nom du Comité de salut public, sur la prise de Tripstat & de Landrecie . . . Séance du 29 messidor, l'an 2, *etc.* pp. 8. *Paris*, [1794.] 8°. **F. 945. (21.)**

—— Convention Nationale. Rapport fait au nom du Comité de salut public, sur la suite des évènemens du siége d'Ypres, et sur les monumens nationaux environnans Paris . . . Séance du 13 messidor, l'an 2, *etc.* pp. 4. [*Paris*, 1794.] 8°. **F. 945. (5.)**

—— [Another copy.] **F. 1237. (3.)**

—— Convention Nationale. Rapport fait au nom du Comité de salut public . . . sur la suppression des repas civiques & des fêtes sectionnaires. Séance du 28 messidor, l'an deuxième, *etc.* pp. 14. [*Paris*, 1794.] 8°. **F. 1069. (11.)**

—— Convention Nationale. Rapport fait au nom du Comité de salut public, sur le progrès des armées de la République, séance du 21 messidor, l'an 2, *etc.* pp. 8. [*Paris*, 1794.] 8°. **F. 940. (18.)**

—— [Another copy.] **F. 945. (4.)**

—— Convention Nationale. Rapport fait au nom du Comité de salut public . . . sur les armées du Midi. Du 17 floréal. pp. 15. [*Paris*, 1794.] 8°. **F. 945. (8.)**

—— Convention Nationale. Rapport fait au nom du Comité de salut public . . . sur les colonies françaises Isles-du-Vent. Dans la séance du 19 thermidor, l'an 2, *etc.* pp. 3. *Paris*, [1794.] 8°. **F. 688. (2.)**

—— [Another issue.] **F. 695. (6.)**

—— [Another copy.] **R. 638. (2.)**

—— Convention Nationale. Rapport fait au nom du Comité de salut public . . . sur les événemens de Paris, du 9 thermidor, l'an deuxième, *etc.* pp. 4. [*Paris*, 1794.] 8º. **F. 628. (20.)**

—— [Another copy.] **F. 854. (11.)**

—— Convention Nationale. Rapport fait au nom du Comité de salut public . . . sur les factions à démasquer, séance du 16 ventôse. pp. 12. [*Paris*, 1794.] 8º. **F. 971. (10.)**

—— Convention Nationale. Rapport fait au nom du Comité de salut public, sur les moyens d'exécution du décret du 17 septembre, concernant les personnes suspectes, & du décret rendu le 30 frimaire, dans la séance du 12 nivôse, an 2, *etc.* pp. 14. [*Paris*, 1794.] 8º. **F. 848. (9.)**

—— Convention Nationale. Rapport fait au nom du Comité de salut public, sur les opérations du Comité dans la campagne actuelle . . . le 6 frimaire, l'an deuxième, *etc.* pp. 19. [*Paris*, 1794.] 8º. **F. 945. (15.)**

—— Convention Nationale. Rapport fait au nom du Comité de salut public, sur les patriotes détenus, et sur les mesures à prendre pour mettre en liberté les citoyens qui ne sont pas compris dans la loi du 17 septembre . . . Séance du 22 thermidor, l'an deuxième, *etc.* pp. 4. *Paris*, [1794.] 8º. **F. 846. (3.)**

—— [Another copy.] **F.R. 227. (24.)**

—— Convention Nationale. Rapport fait au nom du Comité de salut public, sur les pétitions faites à raison des opérations de Joseph Lebon . . . dans la séance du 21 messidor, l'an 2, *etc.* pp. 4. *Paris*, [1794.] 8º. **F. 1052. (2.)**

—— Convention Nationale. Rapport fait au nom du Comité de salut public, sur les succès de l'armée du Rhin; dans la séance du 28 messidor, l'an 2e, *etc.* pp. 3. [*Paris*, 1794.] 8º. **F. 939. (3.)**

—— [Another copy.] **F. 945. (22.)**

—— Convention Nationale. Rapport fait au nom du Comité de salut public, sur les victoires remportées par les armées de la Moselle, du Rhin, de Sambre-et-Meuse et du Nord, dans la séance du 30 messidor, l'an deux, *etc.* pp. 14. [*Paris*, 1794.] 8º. **F. 945. (19.)**

—— Convention Nationale. Rapport fait au nom du Comité de salut public, sur les villes assiégées . . . Dans la séance du 16 nivôse de l'an deuxième, *etc.* pp. 7. [*Paris*, 1794.] 8º. **F. 940. (21.)**

—— Convention Nationale. Rapport général sur l'état de la République Française, fait au nom du Comité de salut public, dans la séance du mercredi 29 mai, l'an second, *etc.* pp. 63. [*Paris*, 1793.] 8º. **F. 1165. (8.)**

—— Convention Nationale. Rapport sur l'acte de navigation, fait au nom du Comité de salut public . . . Avec les deux décrets rendus dans la séance du 21 septembre de l'an II, *etc.* (Rapport sur un projet d'acte de navigation de la République Française, présenté à la Convention Nationale, le 3 juillet 1793 . . . par Pierre Marec.) pp. 39. [*Paris*, 1794.] 8º. **F. 1175. (11.)**

—— Convention Nationale. Rapport sur l'assassinat de Collot-d'Herbois . . . lu à la Convention Nationale au nom du Comité de salut public . . . Réflexions des citoyens Couthon et Collot-d'Herbois sur le même objet. Séance du 4 prairial, l'an second, *etc.* pp. 15. [*Paris*, 1794.] 8º. **F. 1263. (4.)**

—— Convention Nationale. Rapport sur la convocation des assemblées primaires, fait au nom du Comité de salut public . . . dans la séance du jeudi 27 juin 1793, l'an 2, *etc.* pp. 16. *Paris*, [1793.] 8º. **F. 1209. (17.)**

—— Convention Nationale. Rapport sur la fête du 10 août de l'an deuxième de la République, *etc.* pp. 3. *Paris*, [1792.] 8º. **F. 1059. (29.)**

—— Convention Nationale. Rapport sur la marine de la République, dans la Méditerranée . . . au nom du Comité de salut public, dans la séance du 14 nivôse, an 2. pp. 12. [*Paris*, 1794.] 8º. **F. 1175. (14.)**

—— Convention Nationale. Rapport sur la prise de l'isle de Catzan & de l'artillerie des Hollandais, fait au nom du Comité de salut public . . . dans la séance du 15 thermidor, l'an 2, *etc.* pp. 8. [*Paris*, 1794.] 8º. **F. 945. (17.)**

—— Convention Nationale. Rapport . . . sur la reprise de Toulon par l'armée de la République. Séance du 4 nivôse, l'an 2, *etc.* pp. 8. *Paris*, [1794.] 8º. **F. 945. (14.)**

—— Convention Nationale. Rapport sur la Vendée, au nom du Comité de salut public . . . dans la séance du premier octobre 1793. pp. 20. [*Paris*, 1793.] 8º. **F. 1048. (5.)**

—— Convention Nationale. Rapport sur la victoire remportée sur les Espagnols par l'armée des Pyrénées-Orientales, le 26 thermidor, fait au nom du Comité de salut public . . . dans la séance du 5 fructidor, l'an deuxième, *etc.* pp. 8. [*Paris*, 1794.] 8º. **F. 1100. (6.)**

—— Convention Nationale. Rapport sur les crimes de l'Angleterre envers le peuple français, et sur ses attentats contre la liberté des nations; fait au nom du Comité de salut public, par Barère dans la séance du 7 prairial, l'an second, *etc.* (Discours de Maximilien Robespierre, prononcé dans la séance du septidi 7 prairial, *etc.*) pp. 30. [*Paris*, 1794.] 8º. **F. 550. (5.)**

—— [Another edition.] pp. 30. *Paris*, [1794.] 8º. **F. 1099. (3.)**

—— Convention Nationale. Rapport sur les hostilités du gouvernement espagnol, et sur la nécessité de déclarer que la République Française est en guerre avec le roi d'Espagne, fait . . . au nom du Comité de défense générale dans le séance du 5 mars, de l'an IIe, *etc.* pp. 18. *Paris*, [1794.] 8º. **F. 940. (17.)**

—— Convention Nationale. Rapport sur les mesures prises par le Comité de salut public, pour la poursuite des brigands de la Vendée; fait, au nom du Comité, dans la séance du 25 frimaire de l'an 2, *etc.* pp. 59. [*Paris*, 1794.] 8º. **F. 1048. (4.)**

—— Convention Nationale. Rapport sur les nouvelles des armées, fait au nom du Comité de salut public. pp. 16. [*Paris*, 1794.] 8º. **F. 940. (22.)**

—— Convention Nationale. Rapport sur les succès des armées de la Moselle et du Rhin, fait au nom du Comité de salut public . . . dans la séance du 12 nivôse l'an 2, *etc.* pp. 22. [*Paris*, 1794.] 8º. **F. 945. (23.)**

—— Convention Nationale. Réponse de B. Barère, par pièces authentiques, au tableau des persécutions, & aux calomnies déposées contre lui par Dubois-Crancé, le 14 nivôse, à la Commission des vingt-un, relativement à sa mission près l'armée des Alpes & sous Lyon en 1793. pp. 64. *Paris*, an III [1795]. 8º. **935. b. 19. (3.)**

—— [Another copy.] **F. 1100. (3.)**

—— La Convention Nationale de France aux Bataves. (Proclamation . . . présentée . . . par Barère.) pp. 7. *See* CAMBON (P. J.) Convention Nationale. Rapport et projet de décret, sur la conduite à tenir & les pouvoirs à donner aux généraux françois, *etc.* [1793.] 8º. **F. 1237. (4.)**

—— De la pensée du gouvernement républicain . . . Séconde edition, revue et corrigée. pp. xxix [xxxix]. 178. *En France*, an 5 [1797]. 8°. **F. 1106. (2.)**

—— Défense de B. Barère. Appel à la Convention Nationale et aux républicains françois. pp. 62. *Paris*, l'an III [1795]. 8°. **935. b. 19. (2.)**

—— Discours ou opinion . . . sur la conduite des membres de la Chambre des Vacations du Parlement de Rennes. Prononcé le 11 janvier 1790. pp. 11. *Paris*, [1790.] 8°. **F.R. 175. (9.)**

—— [Another copy.] **F. 1097. (2.)**

—— Discours sur le respect dû à la loi. pp. 15. [*Paris*, 1792.] 8°. **F. 1097. (1.)**

—— Lettre d'un citoyen français [i.e. B. Barère de Vieuzac] en réponse à Lord Grenville. [A reply to a speech of Lord Grenville of 28 Jan. 1800, on the necessity of carrying on the war.] pp. 80. [1800.] 8°. *See* GRENVILLE (William W.) *Baron Grenville*. **523. e. 5. (1.)**

—— Lettre de Monsieur Barère de Vieuzac, aux communes de Bigorre ses commettans. pp. 22. [*Paris*, 1789.] 8°. **F. 1097. (14.)**

—— [Liberté des mers.] Libertad de Mares, ó el Gobierno, inglés sin máscara . . . Traducida y comentada con el epígrafe de preservativos contra el monopolio y oligarquia inglesa por el Dr. D. Manuel Maria Gutierrez. 4 tom. *Madrid*, 1841. 8°. **8026. bbb. 51.**
Imperfect; wanting the titlepage to tom. 1.

—— Mémoires de B. Barère . . . publiés par MM. Hippolyte Carnot . . . et David, d'Angers . . . précédés d'une notice historique, par H. Carnot. [With a portrait.] 4 tom. *Paris*, 1842–44. 8°. **1450. f. 7, 8.**

—— Memoirs of Bertrand Barère . . . Translated by De V. Payen-Payne. [With portraits.] 4 vol. *H. S. Nichols: London*, 1896. 8°. **010661. i. 35.**

—— Montesquieu peint d'après ses ouvrages. pp. viii. 169. *En France*, an 5 [1797]. 8°. **F. 1090. (5.)**

—— Motion . . . sur les prisons d'état. Du 15 octobre 1789, *etc.* pp. 4. *Paris*, [1789.] 8°. **F. 1098. (1.)**

—— Observations presentées à l'Assemblée Nationale, par M. Barère de Vieuzac, deputé de Bigorre sur la nécessité de faire de ce pays d'états un département, dont la ville de Tarbes soit le chef-lieu. pp. 22. [*Paris*, 1789.] 8°. **F. 1098. (3.)**

—— Observations . . . sur le rapport fait le 12 ventôse, par Saladin, à la Convention Nationale. no. 1–7. [*Paris*, 1795.] 8°. **F. 1098. (9–15.)**

—— Opinion . . . prononcée à la séance du samedi 27 août 1791, contre l'initiative du roi & des ministres concernant les contributions publiques, *etc.* pp. 11. *Paris*, [1791.] 8°. **F.R. 119. (40.)**

—— [Another issue.] *See* FRANCE.—*Assemblée Nationale Constituante.* Procès-verbal de l'Assemblée des Communes et de l'Assemblée Nationale. tom. 68. 1789, *etc.* 8°. **283. l. 4.**

—— Opinion . . . prononcée dans la séance du 19 mai 1791, sur la réélection illimitée des membres des législatures. pp. 16. *Paris*, 1791. 8°. **F.R. 53. (2.)**

—— [Another copy.] **F.R. 75. (12.)**

—— [Another issue.] *See* FRANCE.—*Assemblée Nationale Constituante.* Procès-verbal de l'Assemblée des Communes et de l'Assemblée Nationale, *etc.* tom. 56. 1789, *etc.* 8°. **284. k. 26.**

—— Opinion . . . sur la dictature ministérielle proposée par le Comité de constitution, dans le projet de décret sur l'organisation du ministère. pp. 12. *Paris*, 1791. 8°. **F.R. 98. (14.)**

—— Opinion . . . sur la motion de M. de Mirabeau, concernant les grades administratifs. Du 10 décembre, 1789. pp. 9. [*Paris*,] 1789. 8°. **F.R. 112. (15.)**

—— Opinion . . . sur la peine de mort. pp. 13 [15]. [*Paris*, 1792 ?] 8°. **F. 1159. (1.)**

—— Opinion . . . sur la réunion de la ville et territoire d'Avignon à la France. Séance du 24 mai 1791. pp. 11. *Paris*, 1791. 8°. **R. 639. (5.)**

—— Opinion sur les mesures de police à prendre contre les émigrans, prononcée dans la séance du samedi 9 juillet 1791. pp. 9. *Paris*, 1791. 8°. **F. 735. (12.)**

—— [Another issue.] *See* FRANCE.—*Assemblée Nationale Constituante.* Procès-verbal de l'Assemblée des Communes et de l'Assemblée Nationale, *etc.* tom. 62. 1789, *etc.* 8°. **284. k. 32.**

—— Projet de décret. Sur la restitution des biens des religionnaires fugitifs. Proposé . . . au nom du Comité des domaines. pp. 8. *Paris*, [1790.] 8°. **F. 156. (8.)**

—— Rapport des comités réunis des domaines, des finances, de l'aliénation des biens nationaux, de la marine, du commerce & d'agriculture. Sur les bois & forêts nationales. Fait à la séance du vendredi 6 août 1790, *etc.* pp. 29. *Paris*, [1790.] 8°. **F. 531. (4.)**

—— [Another issue.] *See* FRANCE.—*Assemblée Nationale Constituante.* Procès-verbal de l'Assemblée des Communes et de l'Assemblée Nationale, *etc.* tom. 26. 1789, *etc.* 8°. **283. k. 29.**

—— Rapport fait au nom du Comité des domaines, dans la séance du jeudi soir 9 décembre 1790 . . . sur la restitution des biens des religionnaires fugitifs & autres dont les biens ont été confisqués pour cause de religion, *etc.* pp. 27. *Paris*, 1790. 8°. **F.R. 169. (7.)**

—— [Another issue.] *See* FRANCE.—*Assemblée Nationale Constituante.* Procès-verbal de l'Assemblée des Communes et de l'Assemblée Nationale, *etc.* tom. 39. 1789, *etc.* 8°. **284. k. 9.**

—— Rapport fait au nom du Comité des domaines, sur l'échange de la ci-devant principauté d'Henrichemont & de Boisbelles. pp. 15. [1791.] *See* FRANCE.—*Assemblée Nationale Constituante.* Procès-verbal de l'Assemblée des Communes et de l'Assemblée Nationale, *etc.* tom. 73. 1789, *etc.* 8°. **283. l. 9.**

—— Rapport fait au nom du Comité des domaines, sur la régie & l'administration des biens des religionnaires fugitifs, pendant les trois années portées par l'article XX du décret du 9 décembre 1790, *etc.* pp. 12. *Paris*, 1791. 8°. **F. 218. (7.)**

—— [Another issue.] *See* FRANCE.—*Assemblée Nationale Constituante.* Procès-verbal de l'Assemblée des Communes et de l'Assemblée Nationale, *etc.* tom. 74. 1789, *etc.* 8°. **283. l. 10.**

—— Rapport sur la vente & aliénation des domaines de la couronne, fait au nom du Comité des domaines, dans la séance du samedi 10 avril 1790. pp. 63. *Paris*, [1790.] 8°. **F. 945. (11.)**

—— [Another copy.] **F. 211. (2.)**

—— [Another issue.] *See* FRANCE.—*Assemblée Nationale Constituante.* Procès-verbal de l'Assemblée des Communes et de l'Assemblée Nationale, *etc.* tom. 18. 1789, *etc.* 8°. **283. k. 21.**

—— Rapport sur les chasses du roi, fait au nom des Comités des domaines & de féodalité . . . dans la séance du 13 septembre 1790, *etc.* pp. 19. [*Paris,* 1790.] 8°. **F. 1099. (2.)**

—— [Another issue.] *See* FRANCE.—*Assemblée Nationale Constituante.* Procès-verbal de l'Assemblée des Communes et de l'Assemblée Nationale, *etc.* tom. 31. 1789, *etc.* 8°. **284. k. 1.**

—— Rapport sur les domaines nationaux à réserver au roi, fait au nom des Comités des domaines, de féodalité, des pensions & des finances, dans la séance du jeudi, 26 mai 1791. pp. 15. [*Paris,* 1791.] 8°. **F. 945. (20.)**

—— [Another edition.] pp. 18. [1791.] *See* FRANCE.—*Assemblée Nationale Constituante.* Procès-verbal de l'Assemblée des Communes et de l'Assemblée Nationale, *etc.* tom. 74. 1789, *etc.* 8°. **283. l. 10.**

—— Rapport sur les domaines nationaux de l'isle de Corse, fait au nom du Comité des domaines. pp. 25. *Paris,* 1791. 8°. **F. 945. (16.)**

—— [Another issue.] *See* FRANCE.—*Assemblée Nationale Constituante.* Procès-verbal de l'Assemblée des Communes et de l'Assemblée Nationale, *etc.* tom. 68. 1789, *etc.* 8°. **283. l. 4.**

—— Réponse d'un républicain français, au libelle de Sir Francis d'Yvernois [entitled "Des causes qui ont amené l'usurpation du général Bonaparte"] . . . contre le premier Consul de la République Française; par l'auteur de la lettre d'un citoyen français à Lord Grenville [i.e. B. Barère de Vieuzac]. pp. 118. an 9 [1800]. 8°. *See* IVERNOIS (*Sir* Francis d') **R. 120. (4.)**

—— Réponse des membres des deux anciens Comités de salut public et de sûreté générale, aux imputations renouvellées contre eux, par Laurent Lecointre . . . et declarées calomnieuses par décret du 13 fructidor dernier; à la Convention Nationale. [Signed: B. Barère, Collot, Vadier, Billaud.] pp. 112. *Paris,* an III [1795]. 8°. **935. b. 18. (3.)**

—— Second mémoire des membres de l'ancien Comité de salut public, denoncés par Laurent Lecointre. [Signed: B. Barère, J. M. Collot, J. N. Billaud.] pp. 44. *Paris,* an III [1795]. 8°. **935. b. 18. (4.)**

—— [Another copy.] **F. 1096. (20.)**

—— Le Veto de la loi, opinion de M. Barère de Vieuzac. pp. 10. [*Paris,* 1789.] 8°. **F. 1097. (15.)**

WORKS TRANSLATED, EDITED OR WITH CONTRIBUTIONS BY BARÈRE DE VIEUZAC.

—— *See* BILLAUD-VARENNE (J. N.) Convention Nationale. Réponse des membres de l'ancien Comité de salut public dénoncés, au pièces communiquées par la Commission des vingt-un. [Signed: J. N. Billaud, B. Barère, J. M. Collot.] [1795.] 8°. **F. 1100. (9.)**

—— *See* BRUCE (Thomas) *Earl of Elgin and Kincardine.* Antiquités grecques . . . Traduction de l'anglais par M. B. de V. [i.e. B. Barère de Vieuzac.] 1820. 8°. **563. a. 33.**

—— *See* CAMBON (P. J.) Convention Nationale. Rapport et projet de décret sur la conduite à tenir & les pouvoirs à donner aux généraux françois chargés de l'expédition de la Hollande . . . Suivi de la proclamation au peuple batave, presentée . . . par Barère. [1793.] 8°. **F. 1237. (4.)**

—— *See* CAMOENS (L. de) Poésies de Louis de Camoens, traduites . . . en vers anglais par Lord Strangford . . . traduites de l'anglais . . . par B. Barère. 1828. 12°. **1464. b. 22.**

—— *See* ÉTRENNES. Étrennes du peuple, ou déclaration des droits de l'homme et du citoyen, précédée d'une épître aux nations par M. Barère de Vieuzac. 1790. 18°. **F. 1879. (2.)**

—— *See* GRIFFITHS (Julius) Nouveau voyage dans la Turquie d'Europe et d'Asie et en Arabie . . . Traduit par M. B. Barère de Vieuzac. 1812. 8°. **10126. bb. 29.**

—— *See* MOYLE (Walter) Essai sur le gouvernement de Rome . . . traduit de l'anglois [by B. Barère de Vieuzac], *etc.* 1801. 8°. **589. d. 14.**

—— *See* PERIODICAL PUBLICATIONS.—*Paris.* Le Point du jour, *etc.* [Edited by B. Barère de Vieuzac.] 1790, *etc.* 8°. **F. 1586–1612.**

—— *See* PLATO. [*Appendix.*] Voyage de Platon en Italie; traduit en italien par V. Cuoco . . . et de l'italien en français par B. Barère. 1807. 8°. **12470. ff. 5.**

—— *See* TAYLOR (John) *Lieutenant-Colonel, E.I.C. Service.* Lettres politiques commerciales et littéraires sur l'Inde . . . Ouvrage traduit de l'anglais [by B. Barère de Vieuzac and others]. 1801. 8°. **583. e. 7.**

APPENDIX.

—— *See* ARRAS.—*Société Populaire.* La Société populaire d'Arras à la Convention Nationale. Déclaration sur la liberté de la presse. Dénonciation contre B. Barère. [1795?] 8°. **935. b. 5. (26.)**

—— *See* CARNOT (L. N. M.) *Count.* Convention Nationale. Opinion . . . sur l'accusation proposée contre Billaud-Varenne . . . Barère . . . par la Commission des vingt-un . . . pour l'examen de la conduite de ses représentans, *etc.* [1796.] 8°. **F. 1101. (1.)**

—— *See* COLLOT D'HERBOIS (J. M.) Convention Nationale. Discours . . . A l'ouverture des débats sur le rapport de la Commission des vingt-un, dans l'affaire des représentans Billaud, Collot, Barère, *etc.* [1795.] 8°. **F. 1097. (6.)**

—— *See* DUBOIS DE CRANCÉ (E. L. A.) Tableau des persécutions que Barère a fait éprouver à Dubois-Crancé pendant 15 mois, *etc.* [1795.] 8°. **F.R. 62. (3.)**

—— *See* LABIL (   ) Barrère, Collot et les complices de Robespierre au Tribunal Révolutionnaire, *etc.* [1795.] 8°. **F. 1098. (2.)**

—— *See* LABIL (   ) La Grande queue de Barère, ou les dangers d'aller aux Jacobins. [1795.] 8°. **F. 1097. (12.)**

—— *See* LAUNAY (R.) Barère de Vieuzac, *etc.* [With portraits.] 1929. 8°. **10658. ff. 19.**

—— *See* LE COINTRE (L.) Les Crimes de sept membres des anciens Comités de alut public et de sûreté générale, ou dénonciation formelle à la Convention Nationale contre Billaud-Varennes, Barère, *etc.* [1795.] 8°. **935. i. 14.**

—— Deuxième édition. [1795.] 8°. **F. 1099. (5.)**

BARÈRE DE VIEUZAC (BERTRAND)

—— *See* MACAULAY (T. B.) *Baron Macaulay.* [*Essays.—Barère.*] Bertrand Barère. [1924.] 16°. **012207.** g. **2/16.**

—— *See* MACAULAY (T. B.) *Baron Macaulay.* [*Essays.—Barère.*] Barère Bertrand . . . Angolból forditotta Angyal D. 1879. 16°. [*Olcsó könyvtár,* sz. 76.] **12215.a.1/76.**

—— *See* MACAULAY (T. B.) *Baron Macaulay.* [*Essays.—Barère.*] Memorias de Barrère, *etc.* 1860. 12°. **12331.** cc. **30.** (**3.**)

—— *See* MAURE (N.) Convention Nationale. Un mot à la décharge des trois membres inculpés, de l'ancien Comité de salut public [B. Barère de Vieuzac, J. N. Billaud Varenne, and J. M. Collot d'Herbois], *etc.* [1795.] 8°. F. **1100.** (**8.**)

—— *See* SALADIN (J. B. M.) Rapport au nom de la Commission des vingt-un, créée . . . pour l'examen de la conduite des représentans du peuple Billaud-Varennes, Collot-d'Herbois & Barrère, *etc.* [1795.] 8°. **935.** b. **18.** (**2.**)

—— Rapport à faire par Barère, au nom de l'opinion publique, ou Bertrand Barère, représentant du peuple, jugé de Monsieur Barère de Vieuzac, *etc.* pp. 15. *Paris,* an III [1795]. 8°. F. **1100.** (**7.**)

BARÈS (CHARLES) Le Blocus pacifique. pp. 160. *Toulouse,* 1898. 8°. **06955.** g. **18.**

BAREŠ (FRANTIŠEK) Paměti města Ml. Boleslavě. [With plates.] 2 díl. *v Mladé Boleslavi,* 1921, 20. 8°. **10205.** g. **30.**
The date on the wrapper of díl 1 *is* 1922.

—— Soupis památek historických a uměleckých v politickém okresu Mladoboleslavském. pp. 412. *v Praze,* 1905. 8°. [*Soupis památek historických a uměleckých v Království Českém.* 21.] Ac. **799.** c.

BAREŠ (GUSTAV)

—— *See* GOTTWALD (K.) *President of Czechoslovakia.* K padesátinám soudruha Gottwalda, *etc.* (Redigovali: G. Bareš, *etc.*) 1946. 8°. **10797.** e. **13.**

—— Julius Fučík. [By G. Bareš and Josef Rybák. With a portrait.] pp. 61. *v Brně,* 1950. 8°. **10797.** e. **47.**
Knihovna Socialistické akademie. sv. 13.

—— Klement Gottwald, muž proti Mnichovu. pp. 31. *Praha,* 1946. 8°. **09315.** h. **27.**

BAREŠ (JAN) Základy Slovanského rychlopisu. 1. Rychlopis český. pp. 16. xvi. *v Praze,* 1864. 8°. **12991.** g. **7.**

BARÈS (JEAN MARIE PIERRE) Thèse pour le doctorat en médecine, *etc.* (Questions sur diverses branches des sciences médicales.) pp. 17. *Paris,* 1839. 4°. [*Collection des thèses soutenues à la Faculté de Médecine de Paris.* An 1839. tom. 1.] **7371.** a. **1.**

BARÈS (JEAN RAYMOND) Considérations physiologiques sur l'appareil urinaire. Thèse, *etc.* pp. 24. *Montpellier,* 1823. 4°. **1181.** c. **11.** (**21.**)

BARÈS (JEAN S.) L'Ortografe simplifiée et les autres réformes nécessaires. pp. 426. *Paris,* 1898. 12°. **12954.** dd. **12.**

BARÉS (MANUEL A.) La Nación Española y el "Nacionalismo Vasco." [A reply to "Nacionalismo Vasco" by Tomás Otaegui.] pp. 174. *Buenos Aires,* 1922. 4°. **8042.** cc. **40.**

BARESTE (ALPHONSE) *See* GIRARD (J. B.) *of Cannes.* Cannes et ses environs. Guide . . . illustré de gravures sur bois . . . dessinés . . . par A. Bareste, *etc.* 1859. 8°. **10172.** dd. **30.**

BARESTE (EUGÈNE) Biographie des hommes du peuple. Deux cent cinquante notices sur quelques hommes qui se sont fait un nom dans l'histoire. pp. 35. *Paris,* 1852. 8°. **10604.** b. **11.**

—— Nostradamus . . . I. Vie de Nostradamus. II. Histoire des oracles et des prophètes. III. Centuries de Nostradamus. IV. Explication des quatrains prophétiques, *etc.* pp. xiii. 526. *Paris,* 1840. 12°. **8630.** bb. **40.**

BARET ( ) Requête des filles de Paris, à l'Assemblée Nationale. [A political squib.] (Par M. Baret.) pp. 7. [*Paris,* 1789.] 8°. F. **389.** (**18.**)

BARET (DE) *Chevalier. See* CHOŁODECKI (J. D.) Patrjotyzm dziadów naszych z przed stu laty w oświetleniu aktów austrjackich. Przyczynek do dziejów z lat 1809–1814. [The report of the Chevalier de Baret.] 1923. 8°. **9476.** bb. **39**

BARET (ADRIEN) Discours prononcé . . . à la distribution solennelle des prix du Lycée Henri IV le 31 juillet 1888. (Voyage au pays de Shakespeare.) pp. 14. *Paris,* [1888.] 8°. **011840.** m. **14.** (**2.**)

—— Étude sur la langue anglaise au XIVe siècle. pp. xii. 219. *Paris,* 1883. 8°. **12981.** g. **21.**

—— Lexique français-anglais rédigé conformément au décret du 19 juin 1880 . . . Troisième édition. pp. vi. 570. *Paris,* [1888.] 12°. **12954.** cc. **22.**

BARET (AUGUSTE J. A.) Le Tabac, les manufactures et les fumeurs; conclusions pratiques. pp. 34. *Paris,* 1879. 8°. **7391.** f. **1.**

BARET (CÁRLOS) Oracion funebre que pronunció el R. P. C. Baret . . . en las exequias solemnes del ilustrísimo . . . Señor Manuel José Mosquera, *etc. Fr. & Span. See* MOSQUERA (M. J. de) *Archbishop of Bogotá.* Memorial del ilustrísimo y reverendísimo Señor Manuel José Mosquera, *etc.* 1858. fol. **1896.** c. **9.**

BARET (CHARLES) Le Théâtre en province: propos d'avant guerre, *etc.* pp. xvi. 268. *Paris,* [1918.] 8°. **011795.** b. **40.**

BARET (EUGÈNE) *See* SIDONIUS APOLLINARIS, *Saint, Bishop of Clermont.* C. Soll. Apollinaris Sidonii opera. Œuvres de Sidoine Apollinaire . . . Précédées d'une introduction contenant une étude sur Sidoine Apollinaire . . . par M. E. Baret. 1878. 8°. **3678.** df. **5.**

—— *See* SIDONIUS APOLLINARIS, *Saint, Bishop of Clermont.* Œuvres complètes de Sidoine Apollinaire, traduites en français par M. E. Baret. 1887. 8°. [*NISARD (J. M. N. D.) Collection des auteurs latins, etc.* tom. 27.] **11306.** m. **22.**

—— *See* VEGA CARPIO (L. F. de) [*Plays.—Collections.—French.*] Œuvres dramatiques de Lope de Vega. Traduction de M. E. Baret, *etc.* 1869, *etc.* 8°. **11725.** ee. **18.**

—— De Themistio sophista et apud imperatores oratore, *etc.* pp. 66. *Parisiis,* 1853. 8°. **11391.** f. **18.** (**2.**)

—— Espagne et Provence. Études sur la littérature du midi de l'Europe . . . pour faire suite aux travaux de Raynouard et de Fauriel. pp. xi. 451. *Paris,* 1857. 8°. **11826.** f. **16.**

—— Les Troubadours et leur influence sur la littérature du midi de l'Europe. Avec des extraits et des pièces rares ou inédites . . . Troisième édition [of "Espagne et Provence"]. pp. x. 483. *Paris,* 1867. 12°. **011824.** de. **47.**

BARET (Eugène)

—— Études sur la rédaction espagnole de l'Amadis de Gaule, de Garcia Ordoñez de Montalvo, *etc.* pp. 203. *Paris*, 1853. 8°. **11805. dd. 14.**

—— [Another issue.] De l'Amadis de Gaule et de son influence sur les mœurs et la littérature au XVIe et au XVIIe siècle, avec une notice bibliographique. *Paris*, 1853. 8°. **11826. e. 5.**

—— Deuxième édition revue, corrigée et augmentée. pp. 234. *Paris*, 1873. 8°. **11825. i. 2.**

—— Histoire de la littérature espagnole, depuis ses origines les plus reculées jusqu'à nos jours. pp. xx. 602. *Paris*, 1863. 8°. **12230. e. 14.**

—— (Deuxième édition.) pp. xxii. 619. *Paris*, 1863. 8°. **11826. m. 1.**

—— Mémoire sur l'originalité du Gil Blas de Le Sage. pp. 15. [*Paris*,] 1864. 8°. **11853. t. 5.**

BARET (H.)

—— Histoire du travail de l'ancienne généralité de Lyon—Lyonnais, Forez, Beaujolais. pp. 166. *St. Étienne*, 1939. 8°. **08230. ee. 42.**

BARET (Jacques) *See* Joppecourt (C. de) Histoire sommaire des choses plus memorables aduenues aux derniers troubles de Moldauie . . . Composée par M. I. B. A. en P. [i.e. M. J. Baret, avocat en Parlement] sur les mémoires de Charles de Ioppecourt, *etc.* 1620. 8°. **1193. i. 4.**

BARET (Jean) Traicté sus la matiere des releuemens selon les ordonnances, droict, & coustume, contenant la maniere comment es Chancelleries de France sont les lettres de Relief chascun iour expediées . . . Reueu, corrigé & augmẽté par l'autheur d'icelluy. [By J. Baret.] ff. 48. 1548. 12°. *See* Traité. **5424. aaa. 13.**

BARET (Jean François)

—— Corps Législatif. Conseil des Anciens. Discours de Baret en présentant au Conseil les onze premiers numéros d'un Cours d'histoire naturelle, par le citoyen Vanderstegen de Putte . . . Séance du 29 fructidor an 6. pp. 4. *Paris*, an 7 [1798]. 8°. F.R. **451. (14.)**

—— Corps Législatif. Conseil des Anciens. Rapport . . . sur la résolution du 19 messidor, relative aux opérations des assemblées électorales du département des Bouches-du-Rhône. Séance du 4 fructidor an 7. pp. 24. *Paris*, an 7 [1799]. 8°. F.R. **102. (16.)**

—— Corps Législatif. Conseil des Anciens. Résumé fait . . . au nom de la Commission chargée de l'examen des opérations des assemblées électorales du département des Bouches-du-Rhône. Séance du 27 fructidor an 7. pp. 18. *Paris*, an 8 [1799]. 8°. F.R. **102. (20.)**

—— Discours prononcé par l'Accusateur public [i.e. J. F. Baret] le jour que la ville d'Anvers a planté l'Arbre de Liberté, le 10 brumaire de l'an 3me, *etc.* (Redevoering uytgesproken door den openbaeren Beschuldiger, *etc.*) *Fr. & Dutch.* [1794.] *s. sh.* fol. *See* Antwerp. [*Official Documents.*] **105. f. 7. (21.)**

—— Discours prononcé par l'Accusateur public [i.e. J. F. Baret] près le Tribunal criminel établi à Anvers, au moment où il va mettre le feu aux instrumens des anciens supplices, le 10 frimaire de l'an 3me de la République Française, *etc.* [1794.] 4°. *See* Antwerp. [*Official Documents.*] **112. e. 19.**

—— Opinion . . . sur la résolution du 2 vendémiaire qui déclare traîtres à la patrie tous négociateurs, généraux . . . qui pourroient proposer ou accepter des conditions de paix tendantes à modifier la constitution de l'an 3, *etc.* pp. 18. [*Paris?* 1795?] 8°. F. **1198. (15.)**

BARET (Jean François) and **FEIGNEAUX** (G. J.)

—— Convention Nationale. Discours des députés de la société populaire de Bruxelles, prononcé à la barre de la Convention Nationale, dans la séance du 6 février 1793, *etc.* [Signed: J. F. Baret; G. J. Feigneaux.] pp. 7. *Paris*, 1793. 8°. F. **336. (20.)**

BARET (Jean Louis) Considérations médico-chirurgicales sur l'accouchement, *etc.* [A thesis.] pp. 20. *Montpellier*, 1809. 4°. **1180. f. 13. (13.)**

BARET (John) An Aluearie or Triple Dictionarie, in Englishe, Latin, and French, *etc.* *Henry Denham: London*, [1573.] fol. **C. 75. d. 13.**

—— An Aluearie or Quadruple Dictionarie, containing foure sundrie tongues: namelie, English, Latine, Greeke, and French. Newlie enriched with varietie of wordes, phrases, prouerbs, and diuers lightsome obseruations of grammar, *etc.* [*Henry Denham: London*, 1580.] fol. **66. e. 9.**

Imperfect; wanting the last 2 leaves, containing the date and imprint.

BARET (L. J. E.)

—— Les Chansons populaires du Japon. [With the tunes of some of the songs.] pp. 13. *Paris*, 1892. 8°. Hirsch **1256.**

BARET (Marcel) Propositions sur quelques faits observés dans le midi de la France. Thèse, *etc.* pp. 18. *Paris*, 1836. 4°. **1184. g. 18. (4.)**

BARET (Michael) An Hipponomie; or, the Vineyard of Horsemanship: deuided into three bookes, *etc.* 3 pt. *George Eld: London*, 1618. 4°. **1040. c. 24.**

BARET (Nicolas) Le Triomphe d'un vrai chrétien en parallèle avec celui des sages du monde, ou éloge historique de Benoît-Joseph Labre. pp. 48. *Boulogne*, 1784. 12°. **4864. b. 3. (1.)**

BARET (Paul) *Docteur en Droit.* Histoire et critique des règles sur la preuve de la filiation naturelle en droit français et étranger. pp. 236. *Paris*, 1872. 8°. **6006. b. 1.**

BARET (Paul) *Dramatist.* Les Colifichets, ouvrage dedié à l'immortalité. [By P. Baret.] pp. xiv. 29. 1751. 12°. *See* Colifichets. **163. e. 1.**

—— Le Grelot, ou les &c. &c. &c. Ouvrage dédié à moi. [By P. Baret.] 2 pt. [1754.] 12°. *See* Grelot. **12515. de. 21.**

—— [Another copy.] **1094. b. 29.**

—— Mademoiselle Javotte. Ouvrage moral . . . Suivi de Les Amours du comte de C***. Le tout illustré de 64 dessins par Amédée Lynen. pp. vi. 146. *Bruxelles*, 1883. 8°. **12550. v. 9.**

—— Tableau de la vie, ou histoire des passions, des vertus et des événemens de tous les âges. Par M. l'abbé Prévôt [or, rather, by P. Baret] . . . Avec figures. 2 tom. 1765. 12°. *See* Prévost d'Exiles (A. F.) **12517. bb. 35.**

BARET (Pierre Gustave) Essai sur la nécessité de l'opération du trépan dans les plaies de tête par armes à feu; thèse, *etc.* pp. 24. *Paris*, 1815. 4°. **1183. c. 9. (25.)**

BARET (René) *Sieur de Rouvray.* Traicté des cheuaulx, *etc.* pp. 105. *S. Piquet: Paris*, 1651. 4°. **779. e. 10. (2.)**

The titlepage is engraved.

BARET (René) *Sieur de Rouvray.*

—— [Another edition.] La Parfaite connoissance des cheuaux, et iugement de leurs maladies . . . Nouuellement mis en lumière, *etc.* *I. B. Loyson: Paris*, 1661. 4°. **779. e. 10. (3.)**
This edition contains also the engraved titlepage of the edition of 1651, *with the imprint and date altered. Imperfect; wanting all after p.* 100.

BARETA (Zen) *pseud.* [i.e. Augusta Mosconi.] Judita e Meo: poemeto campagnol. pp. 196. *Verona*, 1906. 8°. **11431. d. 21.**

BARETARO (Bartolomio) Nozze Curti—Giaconi Bonaguro, Vicenza 1890. (Cronica ab anno 1444 usque ad annum 1532. [Relating to the history of Vicenza. Edited by Giovanni Curti.]) pp. 16. *Vicenza*, [1890.] fol. **9166. k. 26.**

BARET D'AURIOLLE (François) Essai sur l'ulcère simple de l'utérus; thèse, *etc.* pp. 17. *Paris*, 1829. 4°. **1184. c. 12. (27.)**

BARETIUS (Baretius) *See* Barezzi (Barezzo)

BARETSTSI (Baretstso) *See* Barezzi (Barezzo)

BARETT (Paul) *See* Baret (P.) *Dramatist.*

BARETTA (Alphonsus Maria) Apparatus ad Sacra Biblia. pp. viii. 579. *Neapoli*, 1883. 8°. **3109. de. 8.**

BARETTA (Annina) Le Società segrete in Toscana nel 1° decennio dopo la Restaurazione, 1814–1824. Con prefazione del senatore G. Faldella. pp. viii. 175. *Torino*, 1912. 8°. **9168. bb. 8.**

BARETTA (Liberale) Manuale sul matrimonio, ossia il diritto di matrimonio esposto e discusso secondo l'ordine . . . del codice civile generale austriaco, *etc.* pp. xxiv. 400. *Milano*, 1845. 8°. **5175. cc. 13.**

BARETTA (Pietro) Camillo Federici e il suo teatro. Saggio critico. pp. 100. *Vicenza*, 1903. 8°. **11791. d. 18.**

BARETTARIUS (Sebastianus) *See* Beretarius.

BARETTE (Jean) Histoire de la ville de Condé-sur-Noireau . . . suivie d'une notice sur Dumont-d'Urville. (Notice historique sur le bourg d'Aunay et son canton.—Notice sur la paroisse du Plessis-Grimoult.) 3 pt. *Condé-sur-Noireau*, 1844. 12°. **795. d. 28.**

—— Histoire de Balleroy, et de son canton. pp. 280. *Condé-sur-Noireau*, 1843. 12°. **10170. a. 34.**

BARETTE (Joseph) Antisepsie chirurgicale. *See* Le Gendre (L. P.) Traité pratique de l'antisepsie, *etc.* 1888. 8°. **7480. h. 2.**

BARETTI (Eraldo) *See* Piacenza (A.) Cenni biografici e bibliografici di Eraldo Baretti, *etc.* 1904. 8°. **10633. g. 23.**

BARETTI (Georges) *See* Lagorce (H. de) Les Merveilles de l'industrie à l'Exposition de Lyon par MM. H. de Lagorce . . . G. Baretti. 1872. 4°. **7956. l. 14.**

BARETTI (Giovanni Battista) Vita di Giuseppe Baretti . . . Coll'aggiunta del processo ed assoluzione dell'omicidio da lui commesso, in difesa di se medesimo, in Londra, 1769, ridotto in ottava rima. pp. 47. *Torino*, 1857. 8°. **10631. e. 42. (3.)**

BARETTI (Giuseppe Marc' Antonio) *See* also Scannabue (Aristarco) *pseud.* [i.e. G. M. A. Baretti.]

BARETTI (Giuseppe Marc' Antonio)

—— Opere di Giuseppe Baretti. [With a biographical noti[ce] extracted from vol. 3 of G. Maffei's " Storia della lette[ra]tura italiana," a bibliography, and a portrait.] 4 vol. *Milano*, 1838, 39. 8°. [*Collezione de' classici italia[ni]* vol. 371, 372.] **12201.p.1/371,37[2]**

—— Opere di Giuseppe Baretti scritte in lingua italia[na] tom. 1–3, 5. *Milano*, 1813, 14. 8°. **629. f. 15–1[8]**
Imperfect; wanting tom. 4.

—— Opere di Giuseppe Baretti. tom. 4, 6. *Mila[no]* 1818, 19. 8°. **629. f. 19, 2[0]**
Intended as a continuation of the " Opere . . . scritte [in] lingua italiana," from which tom. 4 is a reprint. Imperfe[ct;] wanting tom. 7.

—— Scritti scelti, inediti o rari di Giuseppe Baretti. C[on] nuove memorie della sua vita. [Edited by Piet[ro] Custodi.] 2 vol. *Milano*, 1822, 23. 8°. **12226. d.**

—— Prefazioni e polemiche. A cura di Luigi Piccio[ni] pp. 405. *Bari*, 1911. 8°. [*Scrittori d'Italia.* vol. 13.] **12227.eee.1/9**

—— Lettere familiari . . . a' suoi tre fratelli Filip[po] Giovanni, e Amedeo. 2 tom. [*Milan;*] *Venez[ia]* [1762,] 63. 8°. **246. k.**

—— Edizione terza. 2 tom. *Piacenza*, 1805. 8°. **1084. e.**

—— [Another edition.] Lettere familiari. Con introduzio[ne] e commento di Attilio Simioni. pp. lxiv. 299. *Mila[no]* 1911. 8°. **010902. de. 1**

—— *See* Ricciardi (G.) Giuseppe Baretti e le s[ue] Lettere famigliari ai fratelli. 1902. 8°. **10632. de. 3**

—— Lettere instruttive, descrittive e familiari di Giusep[pe] Baretti, *etc.* pp. xiv. 224. *Messina*, 1825. 12°. **10910. d.**

—— Lettere instruttive, descrittive e familiari. pp. 192. *Torino*, 1829. 12°. **10923. de.**

—— [Seven letters.] 1830. *See* Raccolta. Raccolta [di] prose e lettere scritte nel secolo xviii. vol. 3. 1829, *etc.* [*Collezione de' classici italiani.* vol. 351.] **12201.p.1/35**

—— Lettere di vario argomento. *See* Albèri (E.) Teso[ro] della prosa italiana, *etc.* 1841. 4°. **12226. g. 1**

—— La Scelta delle lettere familiari. A cura di Lu[igi] Piccioni. pp. 460. *Bari*, 1912. 8°. [*Scrittori d'Ital[ia]* vol. 26.] **12227.eee.1/25**

—— Scelta di lettere familiari, critiche e descrittive. Intr[o]duzione e note di Luigi Piccioni. Con una " Bibliogra[fia] delle opere di Giuseppe Baretti " e un " Glossario pp. xlvii. 192. *Livorno*, 1914 [1913]. 8°. **010905. e.**

—— Epistolario. A cura di Luigi Piccioni. 2 vol. *Ba[ri]* 1936. 8°. [*Scrittori d'Italia.* no. 154, 155.] **12227. eee. 1/**

—— An Account of the Manners and Customs of Italy; w[ith] observations on the mistakes of some travellers, w[ith] regard to that county. 2 vol. *W. Colles: Dubl[in]* 1769. 12°. **Cup 401.f.1**

—— An Account of the Manners and Customs of Italy; w[ith] observations on the mistakes of some travellers, w[ith] regard to that country . . . The second edition, c[or]rected, with notes and an appendix added, in answer [to] Samuel Sharp. 2 vol. *T. Davies; L. Davis: Lond[on]* 1769. 8°. **173. b. 11, 1**

BARETTI (GIUSEPPE MARC' ANTONIO)

—— A Dictionary of the English and Italian Languages . . . To which is added an Italian and English grammar. (Dizionario delle lingue italiana ed inglese.) [The dedication composed by Samuel Johnson.] 2 vol. *C. Hitch & L. Hawes, etc.: London*, 1760. 4°. **1332**. g. **2, 3**.

—— A Dictionary of the English and Italian Languages, *etc.* vol. 1. *W. Strahan: London*, 1771. 4°. **1480**. bb. **15**.
Imperfect; wanting vol. 2.

—— A new edition. 2 vol. *J. Nourse, etc.: London*, 1778. 4°. **12943**. f. **10**.

—— [Another copy.] **832**. l. **23**.

—— [Another copy.] **68**. e. **7, 8**.

—— A new edition. Corrected and improved, by Peter Ricci Rota. 2 vol. *J. F. & C. Rivington, etc.: London*, 1790. 4°. **627**. k. **7**.

—— Dizionario delle lingue italiana, ed inglese . . . Accresciuto . . . e corredato d'una grammatica delle due lingue. Seconda edizione veneta, diligentemente riveduta, ricorretta, e riordinata. (A Dictionary of the English and Italian Languages, *etc.*) 2 vol. *Venezia*, 1795. 4°. **12942**. g. **10**.

—— Dizionario delle lingue italiana ed inglese . . . Nuova edizione, corretta e migliorata, da F. Damiani. (A Dictionary of the English and Italian Languages.) 2 vol. *B. Law: Londra*, 1798. 4°. **12943**. h. **19**.

—— Dizionario italiano, ed inglese . . . Prima edizione fiorentina, diligentemente riveduta, ricorretta, riordinata, e accresciuta . . . Con una grammatica [by James Roster], *etc.* (An English and Italian Dictionary, *etc.*) 2 tom. *Firenze*, 1816. 4°. **12941**. i. **8**.

—— Dizionario delle lingue italiana ed inglese . . . Settima edizione, corretta e migliorata, *etc.* (A Dictionary of the English and Italian Languages, *etc.*) 2 vol. *C. & J. Rivington, etc: Londra*, 1824. 8°. **12941**. c. **20**.

—— Dizionario italiano, ed inglese . . . Prima edizione livornese, diligentemente ordinata, e corretta, ed accresciuta, *etc.* (English and Italian Dictionary, *etc.*) 2 tom. *Livorno*, 1828, 29. 4°. **12942**. h. **7**.

—— Dizionario delle lingue italiana ed inglese . . . Ottava edizione, corretta e migliorata, da Carlo Thomson. (A Dictionary of the English and Italian Languages, *etc.*) 2 vol. *C. J. G. & F. Rivington, etc.: Londra*, 1831. 8°. **627**. h. **7, 8**.

—— Nona edizione, corretta e migliorata, da Carlo Thomson. 2 vol. *Longman & Co., etc.: Londra*, 1839. 8°. **12942**. bbb. **6**.

—— *See* DAVENPORT (John) *Teacher of Languages*, and COMELATI (G.) A New Dictionary of the Italian and English Languages, based upon that of Baretti, *etc.* 1854. 8°. **012941**. cc. **13**.

—— A Dictionary, Spanish and English, and English and Spanish . . . The second edition, corrected and improved. 2 pt. *J. Nourse: London*, 1778. fol. **70**. h. **7**.

—— Diccionario Español e Ingles . . . Nueva edicion, revista y corregida despues de la edicion de Joseph Baretti. (A Dictionary, English and Spanish, and Spanish and English, *etc.*) 2 tom. *Piestre & Delamolliere: Londres*, 1786. 4°. **1333**. g. **32**.

—— A Dictionary, Spanish and English, and English and Spanish. A new edition, corrected and greatly enlarged. 2 pt. *F. Wingrave, etc.: London*, 1794. 4°. **627**. l. **17**.

—— A new edition, corrected and greatly enlarged. 2 pt. *F. Wingrave, etc. London*, 1800. 4°. **435**. d. **15**.

—— A Dictionary, Spanish and English, and English and Spanish . . . A new edition, corrected, and greatly enlarged. 2 pt. *F. Wingrave, etc.: London*, 1807. 8°. **12943**. e. **45**.
Subsequent editions are entered under NEUMAN *(Henry) and* BARETTI *(G. M. A.).*

—— Discours sur Shakespeare et sur Monsieur de Voltaire. pp. 185. *J. Nourse: Londres*, 1777. 8°. **82**. e. **3**.

—— [Another edition.] Per la prima volta ristampato nel testo originale, 1777, a cura di F. Biondolillo. pp. 133. *Lanciano*, 1911. 8°. **11762**. eee. **24**.

—— *See* MORANDI (Luigi) *Professor, etc.* Voltaire contro Shakespeare, Baretti contro Voltaire, con otto lettere del Baretti non mai pubblicate in Italia. 1882. 8°. **11766**. c. **10**.

—— *See* MORANDI (Luigi) *Professor, etc.* Voltaire contro Shakespeare, Baretti contro Voltaire. Con un appendice alla Frusta letteraria e 44 lettere del Baretti inedite ó sparse, *etc.* 1884. 8°. **11766**. c. **23**.

—— A Dissertation upon the Italian Poetry, in which are interspersed some remarks on Mr. Voltaire's Essay on the Epic Poets. pp. 77. *R. Dodsley: London*, 1753. 8°. **11805**. d. **5**.

—— *See* TEZA (E.) Giudizi del Baretti e del Voltaire sopra alcuni versi dei Lusiadas, *etc.* [With special reference to "A Dissertation upon the Italian Poetry."] 1899. 8°. **11853**. ee. **8**. **(5.)**

—— Easy Phraseology, for the use of young ladies, who intend to learn the colloquial part of the Italian language. [With a preface by Samuel Johnson.] pp. xv. 424. *G. Robinson; T. Cadell: London*, 1775. 8°. **72**. c. **12**.

—— La Frusta letteraria. Con una prefazione di Massimo Bontempelli. [Originally published under the pseudonym Aristarco Scannabue.] 4 vol. 1929. 4°. *See* PERIODICAL PUBLICATIONS.—*Rovereto*. P.P. **4186**. bb.

—— [Another edition.] A cura di Luigi Piccioni. 2 vol. 1932. 8°. *See* PERIODICAL PUBLICATIONS.—*Rovereto*.
12227.eee.1/74.

—— Opere drammatiche dell' abbate Pietro Metastasio. [Extracted from "La Frusta letteraria."] 1769. *See* METASTASIO (P. A. D. B.) Poesie del signor abbate Pietro Metastasio. tom. 10. 1755, *etc.* 8°. **240**. l. **13**.

—— [Another edition.] *See* METASTASIO (P. A. D. B.) Poesie del signor abbate Pietro Metastasio. tom. 1. 1773. 12°. **248**. d. **6**.

—— Giudizj intorno alle opere di Benvenuto Cellini. Baretti Frusta letteraria. No. VIII. *See* CELLINI (B.) Opere di Benvenuto Cellini. vol. 1. 1806, *etc.* 8°. [*Collezione de' classici italiani.* vol. 142.] **12201.p.1/142.**

—— *See* PICCIONI (L.) Giuseppe Baretti prima della "Frusta letteraria," 1719–1760. [With a bibliography.] 1912. 8°. [*Giornale storico della letteratura italiana.* Supplemento no. 13, 14.] P.P. **4184**. d.

—— A Grammar of the Italian Language, with a copious praxis of moral sentences. To which is added an English Grammar for the use of the Italians. 2 pt. *For C. Hitch & L. Hawes, etc.: London*, 1762. 8°. **12943**. bbb. **6**.

—— [Another edition.] pp. 448. *J. Nourse, etc.: London*, 1778. 8°. **12943**. cc. **8**.

—— A Guide through the Royal Academy. pp. 32. *T. Cadell: London*, [1781.] 4°. **679**. e. **10**. (**1**.)

—— [Another copy.] **101**. i. **58**.

—— [Another copy.] **131**. c. **22**.

—— The Introduction to the Carmen Seculare [of Horace, as set to music by Philidor in conjunction with Baretti]. pp. 14. [*London*, 1779.] 8°. B. **667**. (**2**.)

—— [Another copy.] **604**. e. **22**. (**5**.)

—— [Another copy.] **116**. i. **6**.

—— An Introduction to the Italian Language. Containing specimens both of prose and verse . . . With a literal translation and grammatical notes, *etc*. pp. xi. 467. *A. Millar: London*, 1755. 8°. **12226**. cc. **22**.

—— An Introduction to the most useful European Languages, consisting of select passages, from the most celebrated English, French, Italian, and Spanish authors. With translations . . . so disposed, in columns, as to give in one view the manner of expressing the same sentence in each language, *etc*. pp. 469. *T. Davies; T. Cadell: London*, 1772. 8°. **67**. a. **1**.

—— The Italian Library. Containing an account of the lives and works of the most valuable authors of Italy. With a preface, exhibiting the changes of the Tuscan language, from the barbarous ages to the present time. pp. xciv. 343. *A. Millar: London*, 1757. 8°. **126**. i. **5**.

—— [Another copy.] MS. NOTES. **817**. b. **49**. *Imperfect; wanting pp.* liii *to* lxii.

—— A Journey from London to Genoa, through England, Portugal, Spain, and France. 2 vol. *T. Davies; L. Davis: London*, 1770. 4°. **213**. c. **1**, **2**.

—— [Another edition.] 4 vol. *T. Davies; L. Davis: London*, 1770. 8°. **010107**. h. **11**.

—— The third edition. 4 vol. *T. Davies; L. Davis: London*, 1770. 8°. **10107**. cc. **15**.

—— *See* V., C. An Essay on the Antiquity of the Irish Language . . . To which is added . . . the mistakes committed by Mr. Baretti in his collation of the Irish with the Biscayan language, quoted in his late publications [i.e. in "A Journey from London to Genoa"], exposed and corrected. 1772. 8°. B. **688**. (**1**.)

—— Recueil nouveau des pièces choisies des plus célèbres auteurs françois. [By G. M. A. Baretti.] pp. 344. 1759. 12°. *See* FRENCH AUTHORS. **12237**. bb. **11**.

—— Remarks on the Italian Language and Writers. In a letter from Mr. Joseph Baretti to an English gentleman at Turin. Written in . . . 1751. pp. 24. *See* GREEK AND ROMAN CLASSICS. Observations on the Greek and Roman Classics, *etc*. 1753. 8°. **11824**. aaa. **35**.

—— [Another copy. Extracted from "Observations on the Greek and Roman Classics."] **12902**. aa. **32**. (**1**.)

—— Stanze di Giuseppe Baretti . . . al Padre Serafino Bianchi da Novara . . . che fa il quaresimale di quest' anno 1744, in Cuneo. *Cuneo*, [1744.] 8°. **11431**. bb. **13**.

—— Tolondron. Speeches to John Bowle about his edition of Don Quixote; together with some account of Spanish literature. pp. 338. *R. Faulder: London*, 1786. 8°. **836**. d. **31**.

—— [Another copy.] Cerv. **523**.

—— Rime di Giuseppe Baretti. *See* RACCOLTA. Raccolta di poesie satiriche scritte nel secolo XVIII. 1827. 8°. [*Collezione de' classici italiani*. vol. 348.]

—— Le più belle pagine di Giuseppe Baretti, scelte da Ferdinando Martini. pp. xi. 307. *Milano*, 1921. 12°. [*Le più belle pagine degli scrittori italiani*.] **012226**. a. **1/1**

WORKS TRANSLATED, EDITED OR WITH CONTRIBUTIONS BY BARETTI.

—— *See* HORATIUS FLACCUS (Q.) [*Carmen Saeculare.—Latin and English.*] The Carmen Seculare of Horace, *etc*. [Translated by G. M. A. Baretti.] [1779.] 4°. **11630**. c. **12**. (**8**.)

—— *See* JOHNSON (S.) *LL.D.* Letters to and from the late Samuel Johnson, *etc*. [With biographical notes on and an engraved portrait of Baretti.] MS. NOTES [by Baretti]. 1788. 8°. C. **45**. e. **5**, **6**.

—— *See* MACCHIAVELLI (N.) [*Works.*] Tutte l'opere di Niccolò Macchiavelli . . . con una prefazione di G. Baretti. 1772. 4°. **94**. h. **9**.

—— *See* MOORE (John H.) A New and Complete Collection of Voyages and Travels, *etc*. (vol. 2. Travels through several parts of Europe. By Burnet, Barretti . . . and several others.) [1785?] fol. **10003**. f. **2**.

—— *See* OVIDIUS NASO (P.) [*Works.—Latin and Italian.*] [The Works of Ovid.] (Le Epistole di P. Ovidio Nasone . . . tradotte dal P. Don M. Buzzi . . . ed i Rimedi d'amore tradotti da G. Baretti.—Degli amore di P. Ovidio Nasone, libri tre, tradotti in versi italiani da G. Baretti.) 1745. 4°. **77**. d. **5**, **6**.

—— *See* REYNOLDS (*Sir* Joshua) [Seven Discourses on Art.] Delle arti del disegno. Discorsi . . . Trasportati dall inglese nel toscano idioma [by G. M. A. Baretti]. 1778. 12°. **786**. d. **49**.

—— *See* WILLIAMS (Zachariah) An Account of an Attempt to ascertain the Longitude at Sea, by an exact theory of the variation of the needle . . . Exposizione d'un saggio, *etc*. [The translation into Italian by G. M. A. Baretti.] 1755. 4°. **533**. g. **14**.

APPENDIX.

—— *See* ARICI (C.) Un Avventuriero della critica (G. Baretti) 1926. 8°. **10634**. cc. **34**.

—— *See* BARETTI (G. B.) Vita di Giuseppe Baretti . . . Coll'aggiunta del processo ed assoluzione dell'omicidio da lui commesso, in difesa di se medesimo, in Londra, 1769, *etc*. 1857. 8°. **10631**. e. **42**. (**3**.)

—— *See* DEVALLE (A.) La Critica letteraria nel '700. Giuseppe Baretti, suoi rapporti con Voltaire, Johnson e Parini, *etc*. [With portrait.] 1932. 8°. **10633**. tt. **13**.

—— [For publications of the Società Filocritica Giuseppe Baretti:] *See* FLORENCE.—*Società Filocritica Giuseppe Baretti.*

—— *See* GALLUP (Donald C.) Giuseppe Baretti's Work in England, *etc*. [With a portrait and a bibliography.] 1939. 4°. Mic. A. **729**.

—— *See* LUBBERS-VAN DER BRUGGE (C. J. M.) Johnson and Baretti, *etc*. [With a portrait and facsimiles.] 1951. 8°. W.P. **3195/2**.

BARETTI (GIUSEPPE MARC' ANTONIO)

—— *See* MORLEY (Lacy C.) Giuseppe Baretti, with an account of his literary friendships and feuds in Italy and in England in the days of Dr. Johnson, *etc.* 1909. 8°. **10633.** dd. **6.**

—— *See* MORLEY (Lacy C.) Two Unknown Works of Joseph Baretti. (I. Observations on the Greek and Roman Classics in a series of letters to a young nobleman.—II. An Introduction to the Italian Language.) [1911.] 8°. **011851.** k. **14.** (**11.**)

—— *See* MORONCINI (E.) Il Baretti artista. 1921. 8°. **011850.** aa. **40.**

—— *See* PEDRINA (F.) La Rivolta d'Aristarco. Giuseppe Baretti. [1944, *etc.*] 8°. W.P. **13926.**

—— *See* PICCIONI (L.) Di Giuseppe Baretti la famiglia, i primi anni, *etc.* (Saggio di bibliografia Barettiana, *etc.*) 1898. 8°. **10630.** g. **41.**

—— *See* PICCIONI (L.) Studi e ricerche intorno a Giuseppe Baretti. Con lettere e documenti inediti. 1899. 8°. **10632.** de. **9.**

—— *See* RICCIARDI (G.) Giuseppe Baretti e le sue Lettere famigliari ai fratelli. 1902. 8°. **10632.** de. **35.**

—— Il Vero carattere di Giuseppe Baretti, pubblicato per amor della virtù calunniata: per disinganno degl' Inglesi: e in difesa degl' Italiani. [By Carlo Francesco Badini.] pp. 88. *Venezia* [*London* ?], [1770 ?] 8°. **11429.** b. **35.**

BARETTI (JOSEPH) *See* BARETTI (Giuseppe M. A.)

BARETTI (MARC'ANTONIO GIUSEPPE) *See* BARETTI (G. M. A.)

BARETTI (MARTINO) *See* TURIN.—*Club Alpino Italiano.* L'Alpinista, *etc.* [Edited by M. Baretti.] 1874, *etc.* 8°. Ac. **6012/2.**

—— Alcune osservazioni sulla geologia delle Alpi Graie. Memoria. pp. 20. *Bologna,* 1867. 4°. **7105.** e. **16.**

—— I Ghiacciai antichi e moderni. Dissertazione, *etc.* pp. 87. *Torino,* 1866. 4°. **7108.** ee. **16.**

BARETTI (P.) A New Book of Ornaments on 16 leaves for the year 1762, very useful for cabinet-makers, carvers, *etc.* [*London,* 1762.] 8°. **61.** b. **17.** (**5.**) *Engraved.*

BARETTO (BENJAMIN MUNIZ) *See* MUNIZ BARRETO.

BARETTO DE SOUZA (JOSEPH MICHAEL THOMAS) *Count.* Advanced Equitation, *etc.* [With plates.] pp. xxxvii. 419. *John Murray: London; printed in U.S.A.,* 1927. 8°. **7908.** g. **18.**

BARETTUS (JOANNES) *See* BARET (John)

BARETUS (JOANNES) *See* BARET (John)

BARETUS (JOHN NUNNEZ) *Patriarch of Ethiopia. See* NUNES BARRETO (João)

BARÉTY (A.) De l'adénopathie trachéo-bronchique en général et en particulier dans la scrofule et la phthisie pulmonaire, *etc.* pp. 317. pl. VI. *Paris,* 1874. 4°. [*Collection des thèses soutenues à la Faculté de Médecine de Paris.* An 1874. tom. 1.] **7374.** a. **6.**

—— Du climat de Nice, et de ses indications et contre-indications en général. pp. 128. *Paris,* 1882. 12°. **7688.** aaa. **26.**

—— Nice and its Climate . . . Translated, with additions, by Charles West . . . And an appendix on the vegetation of the Riviera, by Professor Allman. pp. xii. 162. *Edward Stanford: London,* 1882. 8°. **7687.** e. **9.**

BARÉTY (A.)

—— Le Magnétisme animal étudié sous le nom de force neurique rayonnante et circulante dans ses propriétés physiques, physiologiques et thérapeutiques, *etc.* pp. xvi. 662. *Paris,* 1887. 8°. **7410.** f. **1.**

BAREUTH. *See* BAIREUTH.

BAREUTH (JOANNES) Disputatio philologico-theologica de transitione calicis a Jesu Christo. Prima et secunda, *etc. Praes.* F. Fabricius. pp. 11. *Lugduni Batavorum,* 1731. 4°. **T. 2188.** (**19.**)

BAREUTH (JOHAN) *See* NAHOI (Htuerab) *pseud.* [i.e. J. Bareuth.]

BAREZ (STEPHAN FRIEDRICH) *See* BRAUSER (H.) Die Cholera-Epidemie des Jahres 1852 in Preussen . . . Mit einem Vorwort vom . . . Dr. Barez. 1854. 8°. **7561.** f. **52.** (**3.**)

—— *See* PERIODICAL PUBLICATIONS. — *Berlin.* Cholera-Archiv . . . Herausgegeben von J. C. Albers . . . F. D. Barez [*sic*], *etc.* 1832, *etc.* 8°. P.P. **3031.** c.

—— *See* PERIODICAL PUBLICATIONS.—*Berlin.* Journal für Kinderkrankheiten, unter Mitwirkung der Herren . . . Dr. Barez . . . und Prof. Dr. Romberg . . . herausgegeben von Dr. F. J. Behrend . . . u. Dr. A. Hildebrand. 1843, *etc.* 8°. P.P. **3031.**

—— *See* WOERTERBUCH. Medicinisch-chirurgisch-therapeutisches Wörterbuch . . . Mit einem Vorworte des . . . Professors Dr. Barez. 1839, *etc.* 8°. **783.** ee. **2.**

—— Theses inaugurales medicae, *etc. Praes.* C. F. de Hielmeyer. pp. 18. *Tubingae,* 1810. 8°. **B. 558.** (**10.**)

BAREZI (BARÈZE) *See* BAREZZI (Barezzo)

BAREZZI (BAREZZO) *See* ALEMÁN (M.) Vita del Picaro Gusmano d'Alfarace . . . Tradotta . . . da B. Barezzi, *etc.* 1606. 8°. **1074.** d. **6.**

—— *See* CERVANTES SAAVEDRA (M. de) [*Novelas Ejemplares.—Single Novels.*] La Gitanilla. Texto original, y la traducción italiana de Barezzi. 1942. 4°. **W.P.8757.a/5.**

—— *See* CESPEDES Y MENESES (G. de) Lo Spagnuolo Gerardo, felice e sfortunato. Historia tragica . . . transportata nella fauella Italiana da B. Barezzi, *etc.* 1630. 4°. **1074.** g. **5.**

—— *See* CLARUS (Julius) *of Alessandria.* Iulii Clari . . . opera omnia, *etc.* [Edited by B. Barezzi.] 1637. fol. **5309.** i. **6.**

—— *See* LAZARILLO, *de Tormes.* [*German.*] Lebens-Beschreibung des Lazarili von Tormes . . . Aus dem Italiänischen [i.e. from the version of B. Barezzi] übersetzet von Araldo. 1701. 12°. **12491.** aaaa. **34.** (**1.**)

—— *See* LAZARILLO, *de Tormes.* [*Italian.*] Il Picariglio Castigliano, cioè la vita di Lazariglio di Tormes . . . trasportata dalla Spagnuola nell' Italiana fauella da B. Barezzi, *etc.* 1622. 8°. **12490.** a. **29.**

—— —— 1635. 8°. **244.** i. **31, 32.**

—— *See* LOPEZ DE UBEDA (F.) *pseud.* Vita della Picara Giustina Diez . . . Trasportata nella fauella Italiana da B. Barezzi, *etc.* 1628, *etc.* 8°. **12490.** aa. **3.**

—— *See* MATTHIEU (Pierre) *Historian.* L'Huomo. Saggio nelle osseruationi di stato, e di historie . . . Tradotto . . . in Italiano da incerto. Et hora da B. Barezzi adornato d'annotationi ne' margini, e di sommarij ad ogni osseruatione. 1630. 8°. **8009.** bbb. **26.**

BAREZZI (Barezzo)

—— *See* Matthieu (Pierre) *Historian.* Interrotta Continuatione della Historia di Henrico Quarto . . . abbellita con gli sommari alle narrationi & con le postille nel margine da B. Barezzi. 1638. 8°. **9200**. bbb. **8**.

—— *See* Peranda (G. F.) Lettere del signor Gio: Francesco Peranda . . . Aggiuntoui nuouamente cento, e più lettere . . . dello stesso autore, che ne gli altri libri già stampati non sono, *etc.* [Edited by B. Barezzi.] 1635. 8°. **10905**. bb. **11**.

—— *See* Silva (M. da) *Bishop of Oporto.* Chronique et institution de l'ordre du Père S. François, *etc.* (La quatriesme partie . . . composée par B. Barezzi, *etc.*) 1608, *etc.* 4°. **703**. i. **30**.

—— *See* Thomas, *Aquinas, Saint.* [*Summa Theologica.—Latin.*] Gabrielis Vasquez . . . Commentariorum, ac disputationum in primam partem, ac in primam secundæ Summæ Theologiæ Sancti Thomæ Aquinatis. Tomi tres, *etc.* [Edited by B. Barezzi.] 1608, *etc.* fol. C. **81**. g. **5**.

—— Auisi, et lettere vltimamente giunte di cose memorabili, succedutte tanto in Africa nel Regno di Biguba, ch'è nella Guinea, quanto in Moscouia, doppo l'vltima relatione, che poco fà si stampò; et le cause della conuersione, di due nobilissimi baroni Oltramontani, alla santa fede cattolica. pp. 16 [18]. *B. Barezzi: Venetia,* 1606. 4°. **493**. h. **26**.

—— Il Proprinomio historico, geografico, e poetico; in cui per ordine d'alfabeto si pongono quei nomi proprij per qualche singolarità più memorabili, che nell' historie, nella geografia, & nelle fauole de' poeti registrati si ritrouano, *etc.* pp. 647. *Appresso il Barezzi: Venetia,* 1643. 4°. **608***. l. **15**.

—— Conquista di Demetrio. (Relatione della segnalatissima conquista del Paterno imperio conceguita da Demetrio Duca di Moscovia in questo anno 1605.) [By B. Barezzi. Sometimes attributed to A. Possevino.] 1737. 4°. [*D. J. W. Hoffmanns Sammlung ungedruckter . . . Nachrichten.* Tl. 2. no. 4.] *See* Demetrius, *Tsar of Russia, etc.* Pseudo Demetrius i. **9314**. bbb. **4**.

—— Повѣствованіе о Димитріи Самозванцѣ, собранное Б. Барецци. (Relazione della segnalata, et [*sic*] come miracolosa conquista del paterno imperio, conseguita dal sereniss. giouine Demetrio, gran duca di Moscouia, l'anno 1605, *etc.*—Historica narratio, *etc.*) *Russ., Ital. & Lat.* pp. vi. 22. 16. 23. *See* Obolensky (K. M.) Иностранныя сочиненія . . . относящіяся до Россіи, *etc.* no. 4. 1847. 4°. **9456**. ee. **13**.

—— Discours merueilleux et véritable de la conqueste faite par le ieune Demetrius, grand duc de Moscouie, du sceptre de son père, auenue en ceste année mdcv . . . Nouvelle édition, précédé [*sic*] d'une introduction et annotée par le prince Augustin Galitzin. [The translation by —— Moeusyenbrouck.] pp. xvi. 72. *Halle,* 1859. 8°. **10795**. a. **52**. (**1**.)

—— Historica narratio, de mirabili via, ac ratione, qua paternum imperium consecutus est serenissimus Demetrius magnus dux Moscouiæ, anno 1605. De coronatione eiusdem et rebus a coronatione gestis à mense Iulio anni 1605. [A translation of "Relazione della segnalata . . . conquista del paterno imperio, *etc.*" By B. Barezzi. Sometimes attributed to A. Possevino. With "Epistola Regis Bigubæ in Guinea Africana anno 1605. Ad Dn. Philippum Regem Hispaniæ," and "Vera relatio modi, quo conuersus est Dominus Pickering Wotton, Baro Anglus."] 1606. 4°. *See* Demetrius, *Tsar of Russia,* calling himself *Son of Ivan iv.*, Pseudo-Demetrius i. **9455**. b. **25**.

BAREZZI (Francesco) *See* Lopez d'Andrada (D. Discorsi quaresimali . . . Tradotti . . . da D. F. Barezz *etc.* 1645. 4°. **4425**. e. **17**

BARFEKNECHT (Otto Casimirus) *Praes.* *See* Vander monde (J. F.) Quæstio medica . . . An omne viven ex ovo? 1733. 4°. **1182**. e. **4**. (**35**

—— Quæstio medica . . . An melancholicis balneum? *Prae* L. H. Cosnier. pp. 4. [*Paris,*] 1731. 4°. T. **622**. (**11***

—— Quæstio medica . . . An quos morbos non sana chirurgiæ ferrum, sanat chymicus ignis? *Praes.* I Hecquet. pp. 8. [*Paris,*] 1732. 4°. **1182**. e. **4**. (**70**

—— Quæstio medico-chirurgica . . . An noxiæ vulneribu turundæ? *Praes.* J. Fourneau. pp. 4. [*Paris* 1732. 4°. T. **622**. (**11****

—— [Another copy.] T. **622**. (**11*****

—— [Another copy.] **1182**. e. **4**. (**63***

BARFETT (John) *See* Morgan (William A.) An Impartia Statement of the Scriptural Doctrine of Confirmatior occasioned by an attack of Mr. Barfett . . . on that rite [1828.] 8°. **4372**. f. **34**. (**2**.

—— Church Establishments. The Church of England as th "rallying point" of orthodoxy, considered. A lecture *etc.* pp. 21. *Simpkin & Marshall: London,* 1834. 8°. **4109**. h. **9**. (**10**

—— The Contest, Conquest, and Reward of the Christiar A sermon, preached . . . on the death of the Right Hor Baroness Barham. pp. 34. *F. Fagg: Swansea* 1823. 8°. **4905**. c. **77**. (**1**.

—— The Nature of a Christian Church, and of Apostolica Confirmation considered. A discourse, *etc.* pp. 35. *R. Baynes: London,* 1828. 8°. **4477**. aaa. **119**. (**9**.

—— The Question, "Ought the Professors of Religion t interfere with Politics?" considered, in a letter to friend. pp. 24. *Holdsworth & Ball: London,* 1832. 8°. **4377**. aa. **40**. (**1**.

BARFETT (R. F. C. C.)

—— Highways and Byways of Ontario. A complete auto mobile road guide, *etc.* pp. 96. *Motorist Guid Publishing Co.: Bronte,* [1923.] 8°. **010470**. h. **31**

BARFF (Charles) *See* Bunyan (J.) [*Pilgrim's Progress Pt.* 1.—*Tahitian.*] Te Tere o pererina . . . Triti hia e parau Tahiti. [Edited by C. Barff.] 1847. 16°. **4413**. bb. **8**

BARFF (Frederick Settle) Carbon & Certain Compound of Carbon, treated principally in reference to heating an illuminating purposes. Seven lectures . . . Reprinte from the "Journal of Society of Arts." pp. 32. *W. Trounce: London,* 1874. 8°. [*Cantor Lectures.*] R. Ac. **4470/4**. (**9**.

—— Elementary Chemistry, *etc.* pp. viii. 135. *Cassell, Petter & Galpin: London,* [1873.] 8°. **8905**. de. **24**

—— [A reissue.] *Edward Stanford: London,* 1875. 8°. **8908**. a. **2**

—— Glass and Silicates. *See* Bevan (George P.) Britis Manufacturing Industries, *etc.* vol. 7. 1876. 8°. **2270**. aa. **7**

—— [Another edition.] *See* Bevan (George P.) Britis Manufacturing Industries, *etc.* 1877,*etc.* 8°. **07943**. ee. **71/3**

—— An Introduction to Scientific Chemistry; designed fo the use of schools, *etc.* pp. xv. 315. *Groombridge & Sons London,* 1869. 8°. **8907**. a. **32**

BARFF (Frederick Settle)

—— Second edition. pp. xv. 315. *Groombridge & Sons: London*, 1869. 8°. **8907**. a. **33**.

—— Third edition. pp. xv. 320. *Groombridge & Sons: London*, 1871. 8°. **8909**. a. **24**.

—— New edition. Revised by Temple Orme. pp. xvi. 200. *O. Newman & Co.: London*, 1893. 8°. **8909**. a. **49**.

—— On Silicates, Silicides, Glass, and Glass Painting. Seven lectures . . . Reprinted from the "Journal of the Society of Arts." pp. 36. *W. Trounce: London*, 1872. 8°. [*Cantor Lectures.*] Ac. **4470/4**. **(4.)**

BARFF (Henry Ebenezer) A Short Historical Account of the University of Sydney, *etc.* pp. 162. 1902. 8°. *See* Sydney.—*University of Sydney*. **8365**. de. **44**.

BARFF (J. V.)

—— Old England. A historical causerie about peoples, places and relics, and the traditions associated with them. [With plates.] pp. 130. *C. W. Daniel Co.: London*, [1937.] 8°. **010352**. ff. **66**.

BARFF (Lionel C.) The Merchants and Shipmasters Ready Calculator of Freight on goods to all parts of the world, *etc.* pp. 134. *Kelly & Walsh: Hongkong*, 1892. *obl.* 8°. **8548**. de. **23**.

BARFIELD (Arthur) Prospectus of an Improved Copy Book, with engraved copies at the beginning of each page, *etc.* *The Author: [Great Dunmow,]* 1828. 4°. T. **32***. **(15.)**

BARFIELD (John) *See* Craven (Henry) and Barfield (J.) English-Congo and Congo-English Dictionary. 1883. 8°. **12907**. aa. **47**.

—— The Concords of the Congo Language as spoken at Palaballa. Being a contribution to the syntax of the Congo tongue. With illustrative sentences. pp. 160. *East London Missions Institute: London*, 1884. 8°. **12902**. b. **26**.

—— Congo Reading Book. [By J. Barfield?] pp. 96. [1884.] 16°. *See* K ongo Reading Book. **12902**. a. **17**.

BARFIELD (Margery) A Book of Plays for Children. By M. Barfield and others. pp. 48. *Blackie & Son: London & Glasgow*, [1929.] 4°. **11779**. l. **57**.

—— [A reissue.] *See* Children. Children's Plays for Reading and Acting. pt. 1. [1933.] 4°. **11779**. k. **74**.

BARFIELD (Margery) and **TROTTER** (Eleanor)

—— The Baron of Brandean. A historical play of the reign of King John . . . With an illustrated note on the costumes by T. C. Barfield. pp. 80. *Blackie & Son: London*, 1912. 8°. **11778**. k. **34**.

BARFIELD (Mary) *See* Summers (Samuel) Memoirs of the late Mrs. M. Barfield . . . With extracts from her correspondence. 1821. 12°. **4903**. cc. **20**.

BARFIELD (Owen) *See* Poppelbaum (H.) Man and Animal . . . Translated . . . by E. Rigby . . . O. Barfield. 1931. 8°. **07207**. i. **55**.

—— *See* Steiner (Rudolf) *Philosophical Writer.* [Translations of Unidentified Single Works.] Behind the Scenes of External Happenings . . . Translated by D. Osmond, with the help of O. Barfield. 1947. 8°. **8634**. bb. **34**.

—— History in English Words. pp. 223. *Methuen & Co.: London*, 1926. 8°. **12982**. de. **24**.

BARFIELD (Owen)

—— Second edition, revised. pp. 223. *Methuen & Co.: London*, 1933. 8°. **12984**. r. **17**.

—— History in English Words. (New edition.) pp. 239. *Faber & Faber: London*, 1954. 8°. **12987**. de. **29**.

—— Law, Association and the Trade Union Movement. pp. 32. *London*, [1938.] 12°. [*Threefold Commonwealth Research Group.* Pamphlet no. 2.] W.P. **12135/2**.

—— Poetic Diction. A study in meaning. pp. 256. *Faber & Gwyer: London*, 1928. 8°. **011840**. cc. **32**.

—— Poetic Diction, *etc.* (New edition.) pp. 216. *Faber & Faber: London*, 1952. 8°. **11868**. i. **24**.

—— Romanticism Comes of Age. pp. 161. *Anthroposophical Publishing Co.: London*, 1944. 8°. **011840**. cc. **71**.

—— The Silver Trumpet . . . Illustrated, *etc.* [A tale.] pp. v. 142. *Faber & Gwyer: London*, 1925. 8°. **012803**. h. **101**.

BARFIELD (Samuel) Thatcham, Berks, and its Manors . . . Edited and arranged for publication by James Parker. [With plates, and a preface by E. T. Child.] 2 vol. *J. Parker & Co.: Oxford & London*, 1901. 4°. **10368**. l. **10**.

BARFIELD (Thomas Charles) *See* Barfield (Margery) and Trotter (E.) The Baron of Brandean . . . With an illustrated note on the costumes by T. C. Barfield. 1912. 8°. **11778**. k. **34**.

—— Longmans' Historical Illustrations. England in the Middle Ages. Drawn and described by T. C. Barfield. 6 portfolios. *Longmans, Green & Co.: London*, 1909, 10. fol. **1855**. h. **7**.

—— Model Drawing and Shading from Casts, *etc.* pp. ix. 92. *Chapman & Hall: London*, 1896. 8°. **7858**. m. **5**.

BARFIVALA (Chunilal D.) *See* Chunī-lāl D. Barphī-vālā.

BARFLEUR, *pseud.* [i.e. *Sir* Reginald Neville Custance.] Naval Policy: a plea for the study of war. By "Barfleur." pp. xiii. 323. *W. Blackwood & Sons: Edinburgh & London*, 1907. 8°. **08806**. ff. **15**.

BARFOD, *Family of.*

—— *See* Birkedal-Barfod (N. F. S. G. G.) Stamtavle over Slægten Barfod-Barfood-Barfoed fra 1455 til 1925. 1925. 8°. L.R. **271**. e. **7**.

—— *See* Denmark.—*Slægtsforeningen Barfoed-Barfod.* Meddelelser fra Slægtsforeningen Barfoed-Barfod. 1924, *etc.* 8°. L.R. **271**. e. **7**.

BARFOD (Børge)

—— Local Economic Effects of a Large-Scale Industrial Undertaking. pp. 74. 1938. 8°. *See* Aarhus Oliefabrik.—*Economic Research Department.* **08230**. e. **2**.

BARFOD (Fr. Birkedal) *See* Birkedal-Barfod.

BARFOD (Frederik) *See* Barfod (Povl F.)

BARFOD (Hans Peter) *See* Kierkegaard (S. A.) Af Søren Kierkegaards efterladte Papirer . . . Med indledende Notiser ved H. P. Barfod. 1869, *etc.* 8°. **12264**. cc. **4**.

—— Efter en Rejse. pp. 277. *Kjøbenhavn*, 1861. 8°. **10230**. aaa. **11**.

BARFOD (Hans Peter)

—— Til Minde om Biskop Peter Christian Kierkegaard . . . og hans Jordefærd, *etc.* [With a portrait.] pp. 122. *Kjøbenhavn*, 1888. 8°. **4888.** aaa. **62.**

BARFOD (Hans Peter Gote Birkedal) Febris rheumatica acuta's Optreden og Udbredelse i Danmark i Årene 1875–1892. pp. 55. *København*, 1894. 4°. **7620.** g. **14.**

—— Hans Majestæt Kong Christian ix. Spredte Træk til et Livsbillede. [With illustrations.] 2 Bd. *København*, 1888, 1906. fol. **1763.** b. **23.**

—— Kong Frederik den Syvendes Sangkrønike. En Samling Digte til og om vor hedengangne Konge. Samlede og udgivne af H. P. G. Birkedal-Barfod, *etc.* pp. xiii. 294. *Kjøbenhavn*, 1864. 8°. **11565.** bbb. **15.**

—— Mindeblade om Dr. Med. Hans Peter Gote Birkedal Barfods Jordefærd den 5. Juli 1926. [With a portrait.] pp. 23. *København*, 1926. 8°. L.R. **271.** e. **7.** *Bound up with a copy of* " *Stamtavle over Slægten Barfod-Barfood-Barfoed* " *by N. F. S. G. G. Birkedal-Barfod.*

—— Minder fra et langt Liv. [With portraits.] pp. 188. *Kjøbenhavn*, 1921. 8°. [*Memoirer og Breve.* vol. 35.] **10759.** bb. **35.**

—— Minder fra et langt Liv. [With portraits.] pp. 167. *København*, 1928. 8°. [*Minder fra gamle Grundtvig'ske Hjem.* no. 8.] **010761.** h. **31.**

—— Minder fra gamle Grundtvig'ske Hjem. Samlede af Dr. H. P. B. Barfod. Udgivne af " Kirkeligt Samfund af 1898." (pt. 3–6. Udgivne af Dr. H. P. B. Barfod. pt. 7, 8. Udgivne af Holger Begtrup.) [With illustrations, including portraits.] 8 pt. *København*, 1921–26. 8°. **010761.** h. **31.**

BARFOD (Immanuel) Den falsterske Gejstligheds Personalhistorie. 2 Dl. *Nykjöbing*, 1851, 54. 8°. **4685.** c. **3.**

BARFOD (Jens Ivar) Da jeg var Matros. Oplevelser. pp. 185. *Kjøbenhavn*, 1895. 8°. **10761.** de. **2.**

BARFOD (Johan Christopher Georg) Märkvärdigheter rörande skånska adeln. . . . Utgifna efter författarens handskrift [by G. O. Hyltén-Cavallius]. pp. viii. 458. *Stockholm*, 1847. 8°. **1328.** c. **17.**

—— Märkvärdigheter rörande Sveriges förhållanden 1788–1794 . . . Utgifna efter författarens handskrift [by G. O. Hyltén-Cavallius]. pp. x. 230. *Stockholm*, 1846. 8°. **9435.** dd. **6.**

BARFOD (Jørgen Hammer)

—— Slaget i Køge Bugt den 1. juli 1677. pp. 78. *København*, 1952. 8°. **9435.** f. **45.** *Marinehistorisk Selskabs skrifter.* no. 1.

BARFOD (Knud) Danmark og Verdenskrigen, med særligt Henblik paa Danmarks Forhold til Tyskland og de skandinaviske Lande under og efter Krigen. Citater og Kommentarer. pp. 64. *København*, 1916. 8°. **8079.** e. **31.**

BARFOD (Kristen) Iagttagelser over Sydsællands Fugle, *etc.* pp. 45. *Aalborg*, 1892. 8°. **7204.** c. **16.** (**6.**)

BARFOD (Povl Frederik) *See* Danish Hero-Book. Den Danske Kiempebog . . . Udgivet . . . ved F. Barfod. 1860. 8°. **11565.** g. **25.**

—— *See* Fedder (J.) Den sorte Ravn . . . Udgivet af F. Barfod. 1861. 8°. **11565.** aaa. **23.**

—— *See* Nissen (J.) J. Nissens Danmarks Historie i Udtog . . . Besørget af F. Barfod, *etc.* 1857. 8°. **9425.** c. **16.**

—— —— 1862. 8°. **9425.** bb. **22.**

BARFOD (Povl Frederik)

—— *See* Periodical Publications.—*Copenhagen.* Brage og Idun . . . Udgivet . . . af F. Barfod. 1839, *etc.* 8°. P.P. **4808.**

—— *See* Periodical Publications.—*Copenhagen.* Danmarks Geistlighed. En personalhistorisk-statistik Årbog, udgivet af F. Barfod. 1848. 4°. P.P. **160.** m.

—— *See* Periodical Publications.—*Copenhagen.* Folke, et nordisk Tidsskrift, udgivet af F. Barfod. 1859. 8°. P.P. **4806.** g.

—— *See* Periodical Publications.—*Copenhagen.* Rigsdagsblad for Menigmand. Ved V. Barfod og J. A. Hansen. 1849, *etc.* 8°. **5705.** dd. **19.**

—— *See* Petersen (Richard) *Pastor at Grevinga, Holbæk.* Frederik Barfod. Et Levnedsløb. 1897. 8°. **10761.** f. **19.**

—— *See* Rasmussen Søkilde (N.) Gamle og nye Minder om Brahetrolleborg og Omegn . . . udgivne af F. Barfod. 1870. 8°. **10280.** bbb. **38.**

—— *See* Stub (A.) Ambrosius Stubs samlede Digte . . . besorget ved F. Barfod. 1852. 8°. **11565.** d. **32.**

—— *See* Welander (P. O.) Svensk-dansk-norsk Lommeordbog. Af P. O. Welander [assisted by P. F. Barfod], *etc.* 1846. 12°. **12972.** aa. **13.**

—— Billeder af Nordens Historie. pp. 294. *Kjøbenhavn*, 1874. 8°. **9425.** bb. **1.**

—— Dagbogsblade, en Samling Smådigte. pp. 177. *København*, 1841. 8°. **11557.** aaa. **35.**

—— Danmarks Historie fra 1319 til 1536. 2 Bd. *København*, 1885. 8°. **9424.** bb. **13.**

—— Danmarks Historie fra 1536 til 1670. 4 Bd. *København*, 1891–93. 8°. **9424.** cc. **7.**

—— En dansk Hverdagshistorie i lutter Aktstykker, udgivet af F. Barfod. [An account of the proceedings against P. F. Barfod for having contravened the laws relating to the press.] pp. 32. *Kjøbenhavn*, 1846. 8°. **5705.** a. **5.**

—— Dansk Rigsdagskalender. årg. 1. 1856. 8°. *See* Periodical Publications.—*Copenhagen.* P.P. **2455.** e.

—— Dronning Karoline Amalie. Nogle Pennestrøg. pp. 108. *Kjøbenhavn*, 1884. 12°. **10601.** b. **27.** (**3.**)

—— 2den Udgave. pp. 112. *Kjøbenhavn*, 1899. 8°. **10761.** a. **44**

—— Falle, en Gave i Sang til Basaren for Vesterbros Kirke [The editor's " Efterskrift " signed: Fr. B., i.e. P. F Barfod.] pp. 131. 1870. 8°. *See* B. (Fr.) **11557.** de. **69.** (**3.**

—— Fem og tresindstyve Stambogsblade fra fyrretyv nulevende danske Digtere, samlede og udgivne a F. Barfod. pp. 180. *Kjöbenhavn*, 1845. 12°. **1461.** a. **10**

—— Forelæsninger over Nordens Historie. Dl. 1. pp. x. 21 *København*, 1876. 8°. **9431.** bb. **28**

—— Fortællinger af Fædrelandets Historie. pp. x. 846. *Kjøbenhavn*, 1853. 8°. **9425.** c. **1**

—— Tredie gjennemarbejdede og meget forøgede Udgav 2 Bd. *Kjøbenhavn*, 1867, [69.] 8°. **9424.** b. **1**

—— Gjengældelsens Bog. En Del Aktstykker, samlede o udgivne af F. Barfod. pp. 189. *København*, 1846. 8°. **5725.** a. **1**

BARFOD (Povl Frederik)

—— Den grundlovgivende Rigsforsamlings historie, kortelig vortalt af L. K. D. [i.e. P. F. Barfod.] pp. 116. 1849. 8°. *See* D., L. K. **9425.** b. **24.**

—— Ingemanns Jordefærd. Taler, Digte og Bladartikler, samlede af F. Barfod. pp. 120. *Kjøbenhavn*, 1862. 8°. **11565.** aaa. **10.**

—— Knud Lyne Rahbek. Et Mindeblad ved hans Hundredaarsfest. pp. 28. *Kjøbenhavn*, 1860. 8°. **10761.** aaa. **50.**

—— Kong Frederik den Syvendes Kongegjerning. pp. 234. *Kjøbenhavn*, 1864. 8°. **10761.** aa. **28.**

—— Kong Kristian den Niendes Dagbog, samlet og udgivet af F. Barfod. Bd. 1. Hft. 1-4. *København*, 1869-74. 8°. **9425.** bbb. **16.**
No more published.

—— Ledetraad i Danmarks Historie. pp. 84. *Kjöbenhavn*, 1859. 12°. **9425.** a. **11.**

—— Ledetråd i Nordens Gudslære. pp. 60. *København*, 1870. 12°. **4506.** a. **11.**

—— Mindeblade om Grundtvigs Jubelfest, samlede og udgivne af F. Barfod. pp. 96. *Kjøbenhavn*, 1861. 8°. **3925.** c. **5.**

—— Mindre Lærebog i Danmarks Historie. pp. 160. *Kjøbenhavn*, 1861. 8°. **9425.** a. **7.**

—— Peter Andreas Fenger, en Levnedstegning. [With a portrait.] pp. 208. *København*, 1878. 8°. **4887.** e. **15.**

—— Poetisk Læsebog for Børn og barnlige Sjæle . . . Samlet, udgivet og forlagt af A.S. [i.e. P. F. Barfod.] pp. xxiv. 608. 1835-36. 8°. *See* S., A. **1462.** b. **8.**

—— Andet, omarbejdede og forøgede Oplag. Samlet og udgivet af . . . F. Barfod. pp. xxxii. 796. *Kjøbenhavn*, 1841. 8°. **11557.** aaa. **36.**

—— Tredie Udgave. Bd. 2. pp. xv. 432. *København*, 1850. 8°. **11565.** d. **8.**
No more published.

—— Politisk Visebog. Med Bistand af F. L. Liebenberg og C. Ploug redigeret af F. Barfod. pp. 160. *Kjøbenhavn*, 1842. 8°. **1461.** c. **25.**

—— Prinsen af Augustenborgs to hundrede og fire og halvtredsindstyve Aner, for saa vidt de kjendes. Samlede og udgivne af F. Barfod. *Kjöbenhavn*, 1846. *s. sh.* fol. **1881.** c. **16.** (**138.**)

—— En Rejse i Dalarne. [With a map.] pp. 205. *Kjøbenhavn*, 1863. 8°. **10281.** cc. **31.**

—— En Skærv i Sang til Basaren for Norrlændingerne. [The dedication signed: Fr. B., i.e. P. F. Barfod.] pp. 59. 1867. 12°. *See* B. (Fr.) **11565.** aa. **68.** (**3.**)

—— Skandinavisk Atlas, et historisk-statistisk-topografisk Hæfteskrift, med Staalstik. Redigeret af F. Barfod, *etc.* Bd. 1. Hft. 1. [*Copenhagen*,] 1842. 4°. **10760.** f. **4.**
Imperfect; wanting Bd. 1. *Hft.* 2.

—— Sven Hersleb Grundtvig, et Mindeskrift, samlet og udgivet af F. Barfod. pp. 78. *København*, 1883. 8°. **10601.** bb. **22.** (**2.**)

—— Thorvaldsensk Album, samlet og udgivet af F. Barfod. Hft. 1, 2. *Kjöbenhavn*, 1844. 8°. **1402.** i. **23.**
No more published.

—— Under Dannebrog. Nogle fædrelandske Digte. pp. 55. *København*, 1848. 8°. **11565.** bbb. **56.** (**2.**)

BARFOD (Thorkil) Den blaa Sommerfugl. Digte om en Drøm. pp. 64. *København*, 1921. 8°. **011755.** h. **86.**

—— Bobler. En Digt-Cyklus. pp. 97. *København*, 1920. 8°. **011557.** i. **33.**

—— En Hjærtefejl. Dysmorphistisk Foraarsfortælling fra København. pp. 160. *Kjøbenhavn*, 1924. 8°. **12582.** s. **10.**

—— Jul i Præstegaarden. Fortælling. pp. 125. *København & Kristiania*, 1920. 8°. **012582.** aaa. **38.**

—— Livets Musik. Et Tidsbillede. Dl. 1. pp. 206. *Kjøbenhavn*, 1925. 8°. **12581.** t. **21.**
No more published.

BARFOED, *Family of.*

—— *See* Birkedal-Barfod (N. F. S. G. G.) Stamtavle over Slægten Barfod-Barfood-Barfoed fra 1455 til 1925. 1925. 8°. L.R. **271.** e. **7.**

—— *See* Denmark.—*Slægtsforeningen Barfoed-Barfod.* Meddelelser fra Slægtsforeningen Barfoed-Barfod. 1924, *etc.* 8°. L.R. **271.** e. **7.**

BARFOED (Aage) Ovnen. Roman. pp. 224. *København*, 1910. 8°. **12581.** s. **21.**

—— Skyggen. Skuespil i tre Akter. pp. 128. *København & Kristiania*, 1907. 8°. **11755.** g. **46.**

—— Skytten. En Fortælling. pp. 197. *København & Kristiania*, 1907. 8°. **012582.** a. **6.**

—— Tempelherrerne. Historisk roman. pp. 342. *København, Oslo*, 1934. 8°. **20002.** f. **20.**

—— Den udvalgte Konge, Hertug Christian af Slesvig-Holsten. Historisk Roman. pp. 230. *København*, [1923.] 8°. **012582.** c. **38.**

—— Under Ørnens Vinger. Roman fra Venedig. pp. 200. *København & Oslo*, [1925.] 8°. **012582.** c. **52.**

BARFOED (Christen Thomsen) Analysen af uorganiske, i Vand opløselige Alkalisalte, *etc.* pp. 18. *Kjöbenhavn*, 1863. 8°. **8905.** aaa. **25.** (**3.**)

—— De organiske Stoffers qvalitative Analyse. pp. 517. *Kjøbenhavn*, 1878. 8°. **8908.** f. **9.**

—— Lehrbuch der organischen qualitativen Analyse, *etc.* pp. 522. *Kopenhagen*, 1880. 8°. **8907.** de. **25.**

BARFOED (Christian) *See* Barfoed (Erik C. N.)

BARFOED (Erik Christian Nissen) Oldkirkens Liturgier. pp. 174. *København*, 1902. 8°. **3476.** f. **14.**

—— Titian Vecellio. Hans Samtid, Liv og Kunst. pp. 270. *Kjøbenhavn*, 1889. 8°. **10629.** c. **22.**

BARFOED (Erikke) Kogebog for store og smaa Huusholdninger, eller Anviisning til at tillave de forskjellige Retter, *etc.* pp. 307. *Kjøbenhavn*, 1864. 8°. **7954.** aa. **5.**

BARFOED (H. P.) Lejlighedsdigte og Smaavers, *etc.* pp. 145. *Holbek*, 1858. 8°. **11557.** aa. **18.**

BARFOED (Mogens)

—— Yngste Mand mod Nord. Med Gamma-Ekspeditionen til Østgrønland. [With plates.] pp. 97. *København*, 1939. 8°. **010460.** l. **6.**

BARFOED (Niels Aage)

—— Den nye Dag. Roman om Hans Tausen. 2. Oplag. pp. 224. *København*, 1951. 8°. **12585.** bb. **12.**

BARFOED (Niels Aage)

—— Storkansleren. Roman om Griffenfeld. Andet Oplag. pp. 141. *København*, 1953. 8°. 12585. bb. 32.

BARFOED (Palle) Ok'allouzin illait Kaladlinnut attuægeksaussut, *etc.* pp. 54. *Kjøbenhavnime*, 1864. 8°. 4402. c. 10.

BARFOED (Per)

—— Samlede Digte 1923–1939. Af P. Sørensen-Fugholm. [i.e. P. Barfoed.] pp. 161. [*København*, 1949.] *obl.* 8°. Cup. 1253. de. 69.

BARFOED (Poul)

—— Conjunctivas bakterieflora. With an English summary. [A thesis.] pp. 140. *København*, 1953. 8°. 07612. cc. 17.

BARFOED (Thomas) Smaating og Leilighedsdigte fra Aarene 1799 til 1835. [Edited by A. P. Wedel.] pp. 138. *Kjøbenhavn*, 1849. 8°. 11557. aa. 19.

BARFOED (Viggo) Ærbødigst—! Nye Viser og Vers . . . Tegninger af Jensenius. (Tiende Samling.) pp. 108. *København*, 1931. 8°. 011556. m. 17.

BARFOOD, *Family of.*

—— *See* Birkedal-Barfod (N. F. S. G. G.) Stamtavle over Slægten Barfod-Barfood-Barfoed fra 1455 til 1925. 1925. 8°. L.R. 271. e. 7.

BARFOOT (Henry) *See* Holdsworth (Henry) The Doctrine of Baptismal Regeneration, as taught by the Church of England, briefly maintained and explained . . . in a letter in reply to the Rev. H. Barfoot. [An answer to "The Duty of Sponsors with Remarks on Baptismal Regeneration."] 1847. 12°. 4324. c. 48.

—— The True Baptism; or, Remission of sins by baptism, not by the sacrament of baptism. pp. 20. *J. Nisbet & Co.: London*, 1857. 12°. 4326. b. 9.

BARFOOT (J. R.) Sketches from the Animal Kingdom, arranged after the system of the Baron Cuvier, principally drawn from nature. *John Betts: London*, [1843.] fol. 1487.1.16.

BARFOOT (John) Day Schools under Government Supervision described; with reasons why Primitive Methodists should accept educational grants . . . To which are added the views of E. Baines Esq., M.P., on government education, *etc.* pp. 37. *William Lister: London*, 1867. 8°. 8304. bb. 20. (9.)

—— A Diamond in the Rough; or, Christian heroism in humble life. Being jottings concerning that remarkable peasant preacher, William Hickingbotham, *etc.* pp. xiii. 145. *J. Clarke & Co.: London*, 1874. 8°. 4905. de. 8.

—— Piety behind the Plough; or, Observations founded on the life and character of Mr. George Warren, *etc.* pp. ii. ii. 8–48. *Richard Davies: London*, [1864.] 8°. 4920. aa. 46. (10.)

BARFOOT (Peter) Two Letters addressed to the Right Hon. W. Pitt, Chancellor of the Exchequer, for obtaining an equal system of taxation, and for reducing the national debt. pp. 23. *J. Debrett: London*, 1786. 8°. E. 2152. (6.)

BARFOOT (Peter) and **WILKES** (John) *of Milland House, Sussex.*

—— The Universal British Directory of Trade and Commerce; comprehending lists of the inhabitants of London, Westminster, and Borough of Southwark; and of all the cities, towns and principal villages, in England and Wales, *etc.* [Compiled by P. Barfoot and J. Wilkes.] vol. 1. 1790. 8°. *See* Directories.—*England.* P.P.2506.vbc.(1.)

BARFOOT (Peter) and **WILKES** (John) *of Millar House, Sussex.*

—— [A reissue.] 4 vol. 1791. 8°. *See* Directories.—*England.* N.I

—— [Another copy of vol. 2, 4.] N.I

—— [Another copy of vol. 2.] N.I

—— A Supplement to the British Directory of Trad Commerce, and Manufacture, 1792. Containing th alterations, corrections, and additional names, in th list of merchants, manufacturers, brokers, ar traders; and in the law directory. To which is adde the commercial, and principal coffee-houses in th City of London, *etc.* [1792.] 8°. *See* Directorie —*England.* P.P.2506.vbc.(5.

—— The Universal British Directory of Trade, Commerc and Manufacture . . . Second edition. vol. 1, 3. [1793.] 8°. *See* Directories.—*England.* P.P.2506.vbc.(6.

—— [Another copy of vol. 3.] N.I

—— Directory to the Nobility, Gentry, and Families Distinction, in London, Westminster, &c. Being supplement to the British Directory of Trade, Co merce, and Manufacture, for 1793, *etc.* pp. 50. [1793.] 8°. *See* Directories.—*England.* P.P.2506.vbc.(8.

—— [Another edition.] vol. 5. [1798.] 8°. *See* Directori —*England.* N.

—— [Another copy of vol. 5.] N.

BARFOOT (Sidney Douglas) and **SIMON** (Werner)

—— The Meter Postage Stamp Catalogue. pp. xii. 119. *Universal Postal Frankers: London*, [1953.] 8°. 8247. h.

BARFORD. A Short Address to the Inhabitants of Barfor *etc.* [Signed: C. M.] 1841. 8°. *See* M., C. 4422. h. 6. (

BARFORD ABBEY. Barford Abbey, a novel: in a seri of letters. [By Susannah Minifie, afterwards Gunnin 2 vol. *T. Cadell & J. Payne: London*, 1768. 12°. 12614. eee.

BARFORD (Alfred Henry) and **TILLEY** (Hen Arthur) English Spelling. A series of dictation lesso for the use of schools and private students. Arranged A. H. Barford . . . and H. A. Tilley. pp. vi. 109. *Charles Bean: London*, 1867. 8°. 12984. aa. 5

—— [A reissue.] English Spelling, *etc.* *Longmans & Co London*, 1868. 8°. 12984. aa. 4

—— English Spelling as it is . . . New edition, revised a enlarged, *etc.* pp. viii. 150. *Relfe Bros.: Londo* 1878. 8°. 12981. b.

—— New edition, revised and enlarged, *etc.* pp. viii. 148. *Relfe Bros.: London*, 1884. 8°. 12981. aa.

BARFORD (Dora)

—— Evasion. pp. 344. *G. G. Harrap & Co.: Lond* 1936. 8°. NN. 258

—— The Golden Cargazon. pp. 320. *Hod & Stoughton: London*, 1932. 8°. NN. 191

—— Greek Fire. A tale of the Levant. pp. 352. *G. G. Harrap & Co.: London*, 1935. 8°. NN. 241

—— Mr. Corrington. pp. 312. *Hodder & Stoughto London*, [1931.] 8°. NN. 174

—— Tricolor. A romance of 1789. pp. 384. *Hod & Stoughton: [London,]* 1933. 8°. NN. 205

BARFORD (GULIELMUS) *See* BARFORD (William)

BARFORD (JOHN) Iohn Barford, his Petition to God for King and Parliament. [In verse.] [*London*, 1646.] *s. sh.* 4°. E. **506**. (**7**.)

—— Paraphrastical Meditations upon Isaiah 55. & Psalm 51. Likewise, short meditations; first of God and the birth of Jesus: against som sects and errors: and against sundrie sins. Also, meditations upon the sixtieth Psalm and the fourth vers. pp. 150. *Printed by W. D.* [*William Dugard*] *and are to be sold by Tho. Euster: London*, 1649. 8°. Huth **59**.

BARFORD (JOHN EDWARD QUINTUS)

—— Climbing in Britain. Edited by J. E. Q. Barford. [With plates and a portrait.] pp. 160. *Penguin Books: Harmondsworth, New York*, 1946. 8°. [*Pelican Books*. no. 160.] **012209**. d. **4/160**.

BARFORD (RICHARD) The Assembly. An heroi-comical poem. In five cantos. pp. 54. *B. Lintot: London*, 1726. 8°. **992**. h. **6**. (**6**.)

—— An Epistle to the Right Honourable Philip Dormer, Earl of Chesterfield. Occasion'd by the late and present situation of affairs in Europe, in regard to war and peace. pp. 23. *Lawton Gilliver: London*, 1730. 8°. E. **2021**. (**12**.)

—— The Virgin Queen. A tragedy, *etc.* pp. 64. *R. Gunne: Dublin*, 1728. 12°. **640**. h. **33**. (**5**.)

—— [Another edition.] pp. 65. *J. Watts: London*, 1729. 8°. **643**. g. **5**. (**6**.)

—— [Another copy.] **161**. g. **21**.

BARFORD (VALENTINE) On the Breeding of Domestic Animals; being an extract of the practical part of a communication to the Royal Agricultural Society of England. pp. 15. *J. B. Hurfurt: Towcester*, 1853. 8°. **7295**. e. **5**.

BARFORD (WILLIAM) Concio ad clerum provinciæ Cantuariensis in Æde Paulina XIV Kal. Junias MDCCLXXXIV. habita. pp. 17. *Typis Academicis: Cantabrigiæ*, 1784. 4°. **694**. k. **20**. (**5**.)

—— [Another copy.] **114**. b. **2**.

—— In Pindari primum Pythium dissertatio habita Cantabrigiæ in scholis publicis . . . A.D. MDCCL. [With the Greek text.] pp. 21. 1751. 4°. *See* PINDAR. [*Greek*.] **832**. i. **14**.

—— [Another edition.] *See* PINDAR. [*Greek and Latin*.] Pindari carmina juxta exemplar Heynianum, *etc.* 1814. 8°. **997**. g. **9**.

—— In Pindari primum Pythium dissertatio, *etc.* *See* PINDAR. [*Greek and Latin*.] Pindari Carmina, *etc.* 1821. 8°. **11315**. p. **10**.

—— Oratio habita in funere . . . Guilielmi George . . . VII^mo^ Kalendas Octobres, M.DCC.LVI. pp. 16. *Typis Academicis: Cantabrigiæ*, 1756. 4°. **695**. h. **7**.

—— [Another copy.] **113**. e. **29**.

—— A Sermon preached before the Honourable House of Commons, at St. Margaret's Westminster, on Tuesday, January XXX, 1770. pp. 22. *T. Payne: London*, 1770. 4°. **694**. i. **18**. (**26**.)

BARFORDE (WILLIAM) *See* MORE (John) *Preacher of the Gospel*. A Lively Anatomie of Death, *etc.* [With a prefatory letter by W. Barforde.] 1596. 8°. **1418**. i. **44**.

BARFOTH (EILERT HOLGER) Specimen academicum de gladiatoribus, *etc.* *Praes.* S. Bring. pp. 15. *Londini Gothorum*, 1747. 4°. T. **2216**. (**7**.)

BARFOTH (IFVAR EILERT) Dissertatio historica de Gothlandia, quondam feudo Sveciæ oblato, *etc.* *Praes.* S. Bring. pp. 23. *Londini Gothorum*, 1767. 4°. **153**. d. **20**. (**7**.)

BARFRED (ARNE)

—— Investigations into the Biological Effects of Liver Extracts with special reference to the Gastric-Stimulating Principle. (Afhandling. Translated by W. E. Calvert.) pp. 175. *Hertz: Copenhagen*, 1942. 8°. [*Acta medica Scandinavica*. suppl. 131.] P.P. **3081**. b. (**2**.)

BARFUCCI (ENRICO)

—— Lorenzo de' Medici e la società artistica del suo tempo. [With plates, including portraits.] pp. 344. *Firenze*, 1945. 8°. **7869**. dd. **7**.

BARFURTH (DIETRICH) Experimentelle Untersuchung über die Regeneration der Keimblätter bei den Amphibien. —Über organbildende Keimbezirke und künstliche Missbildungen des Amphibieneies. 1893. *See* MERKEL (F. S.) and BONNET (R.) Anatomische Hefte, *etc.* Abt. 1. Bd. 3. 1891, *etc.* 8°. **P.P.3200.ca.**

—— Regeneration. 1892. *See* MERKEL (F. S.) and BONNET (R.) Anatomische Hefte, *etc.* Abt. 2. Bd. 1. 1891, *etc.* 8°. **P.P.3200.ca.**

—— Regeneration und Involution. 1905. *See* MERKEL (F. S.) and BONNET (R.) Anatomische Hefte, *etc.* Abt. 2. Bd. 14. 1891, *etc.* 8°. **P.P.3200.ca.**

—— Ueber Nahrung und Lebensweise der Salme, Forellen und Maifische. pp. 41. *Bonn*, 1874. 8°. **7204**. aaa. 5. (**7**.)

BARFUS (EGINHARD VON) Kriegsfahrten eines alten Soldaten im fernen Osten. Nach den Aufzeichnungen eines ehemaligen Offiziers der niederländisch-ostindischen Armee erzählt. pp. 289. *Stuttgart*, 1893. 8°. **9056**. aaa. **32**.

BARFUS (HANS ALBRECHT VON) *Count*. *See* BARFUS FALKENBERG (F. W. von) H. A. Graf von Barfus, Königl. Preuss. General-Feldmarschall, *etc.* 1854. 8°. **10707**. dd. **36**. (**2**.)

BARFUS FALKENBERG (FRANZ WILHELM VON) H. A. Graf von Barfus, Königl. Preuss. General-Feldmarschall. Ein Beitrag zur Kriegsgeschichte unter den Kurfürsten Friedrich Wilhelm und Friedrich III. von Brandenburg, insbesondere der Feldzüge gegen die Türken 1683, 1686, 1691. pp. vi. 72. *Berlin*, 1854. 8°. **10707**. dd. **36**. (**2**.)

BARFUSS (FRIEDRICH WILHELM) Geschichte der Uhrmacherkunst, von den ältesten Zeiten bis auf unsere Tage, *etc.* pp. xiv. 258. pl. VIII. *Weimar*, 1837. 8°. [*Neuer Schauplatz der Künste und Handwerke*. Bd. 90.] **896**. dd. **37**. (**2**.)

—— Vierte Auflage . . . in vollständiger Neubearbeitung herausgegeben von E. Geleich. Mit einem Atlas von 11 Foliotafeln. 2 pt. *Weimar*, 1887. 8°. [*Neuer Schauplatz der Künste und Handwerke*. Bd. 90.] **896**. dd. **138**.

—— Handbuch der höheren und niederen Messkunde, oder gründliche Unterweisung in der gewöhnlichen Feldmesskunst, *etc.* pp. xxvi. 467. *Weimar*, 1842. 8°. **1146**. f. **18**.

—— Die Kunst des Böttchers oder Küfers, in der Werkstatt wie im Keller, *etc.* pp. xvi. 267. pl. XIX. *Weimar*, 1839. 8°. [*Neuer Schauplatz der Künste und Handwerke*. Bd. 102.] **896**. dd. **42**. (**1**.)

BARFUSS (Friedrich Wilhelm)

—— Lehrbuch der mathematischen Analysis besonders in Hinsicht ihrer Entwickelungsmethoden, *etc.* 2 Tl. *Weimar*, 1853, 54. 8°. **8529**. d. **6**.

—— Optik, Catoptrik und Dioptrik, oder theoretisch-praktischer Unterricht über den möglichst vollkommenen Bau aller optischen Instrumente, *etc.* pp. xxiv. 526. pl. xli. *Weimar*, 1839. 8°. [*Neuer Schauplatz der Künste und Handwerke.* Bd. 3.] **896**. dd. **2**.

—— Theorie der Spiegelmikroscope mit sphärischen Glasspiegeln, *etc.* pp. x. 80. pl. 2. *Weimar*, 1840. 8°. **8715**. a. **56**. (**2**.)

BARFUSS (Werner Paul)

—— Anfang, Mitte, Ende. Einleitung und Aufbau des Buches von Georg Schaeffner. [The collected works in prose and verse of W. P. Barfuss.] pp. 265. *Bern*, 1946. 8°. **12254**. c. **15**.

BARG (E. I.)

—— Технология синтетических пластических масс. Под редакцией . . . С. Н. Ушакова. pp. 656. *Ленинград*, 1954. 8°. **8896**. f. **46**.

BARG (M. A.)

—— Кромвель и его время. Под редакцией . . . С. Д. Сказкина. pp. 271. *Москва*, 1950. 8°. **09506**. df. **46**.
Part of a series entitled " Библиотека учителя."

BARGA (Pedro García de la) *See* García de la Barga.

BARGAEUS (Antonius Angelius) *Bishop of Massa Maritima. See* Angelius (Antonius) *Bargaeus.*

BARGAEUS (Petrus Angelius) *See* Angelio (Pietro) *da Barga.*

BARGAGLI (Celso) Insignis atque vtilissimus tractatus . . . de dolo. Huic in fine subiectæ sunt orationes viginti, ab eodem authore in celeberrimis Senensi & Maceratensi Academiis in doctorum promotionibus habitæ & recitatæ, *etc.* [Edited by Scipione Bargagli.] pp. 822. *Typis Wechelianis apud C. Marnium, & heredes I. Aubrii: Hanoviæ*, 1604. fol. **5309**. h. **6**.

BARGAGLI (Girolamo) *See* also Materiale, *Intronato, pseud.* [i.e. G. Bargagli.]

—— La Pellegrina, commedia. [Edited by Scipione Bargagli.] pp. 152. *Nella Stamperia di Luca Bonetti: Siena*, 1589. 4°. **1071**. m. **2**. (**2**.)

—— [Another copy.] **162**. g. **6**.

—— [Another edition.] pp. 155. *Matteo Florimi: Siena*, 1605. 12°. **638**. a. **20**.

—— [Another edition.] *See* Sienna.—*Accademia degl' Intronati.* Delle commedie degl'Accademici Intronati, la seconda parte. 1611. 12°. **162**. b. **40**.

BARGAGLI (Mario) Prospetti statistici relativi all'amministrazione del Monte dei Paschi di Siena, *etc.* 1863. fol. *See* Siena.—Monti Rexruti. **8225**. ff. **30**. (**2**.)

BARGAGLI (Scipione) *See* Bargagli (C.) Insignis atque vtilissimus tractatus . . . de dolo, *etc.* [Edited by S. Bargagli.] 1604. fol. **5309**. h. **6**.

—— *See* Bargagli (G.) La Pellegrina, *etc.* [Edited by S. Bargagli.] 1589. 4°. **1071**. m. **2**. (**2**.)

—— —— 1605. 12°. **638**. a. **20**.

—— —— 1611. 12°. [*Delle commedie degl' Accademici Intronati, la seconda parte.*] **162**. b. **40**.

BARGAGLI (Scipione)

—— Dell' imprese di Scipion Bargagli. Doue; doppo tutte l'opere cosi a penna, come a stampa, ch' egli ha potuto vedere di coloro, che della materia dell' imprese hanno parlato; della vera natura di quelle si ragiona. Riueduta nuouamente, e ristampata. Appresso. Orazione delle lodi dell' Accademie. (Prima parte.) pp. 142. few ms. notes. *Francesco de' Franceschi: Venetia*, 1589. 4°. **89**. k. **22**.

—— Dell' imprese di Scipion Bargagli . . . Alla prima parte, la seconda, e la terza nuouamente aggiunte, *etc.* (Due orazioni, l'vna delle lodi dell' Accademie, l'altra in morte di Monsig. Alessandro Piccolomini.) pp. 573. *Francesco de' Franceschi: Venetia*, 1594. 8°. **1473.bb.21.**
Imperfect; wanting pp. 113–116.

—— [Another copy.] Dell'imprese di Scipion Bargagli, *etc.* *Venetia*, 1594. 8°. **89**. i. **25**.
Imperfect; wanting pp. 113–116.

—— Descrizzione dell'entrata dell'illustriss. . . . Monsig. Ascanio Piccolomini, alla possession del suo Arciuescouado in Siena, il di xxj. di Nouembre. 1589. [By S. Bargagli. With " Academiae Partheniae Soc: Iesu carmina . . . De laudibus . . . Ascanii Piccolominei. *etc.*"] pp. 91. 1590. 4°. *See* Piccolomini (Ascanio) *Archbishop of Siena.* **4865**. e. **3**.

—— Oratione in lode dell' Accademia degli Intronati, dello Schietto Intronato (S. Bargagli). *See* Sienna.—*Accademia degl' Intronati.* Delle commedie degl' Accademici Intronati, la seconda parte. 1611. 12°. **162**. b. **40**.

—— I Trattenimenti di Scipion Bargagli; doue da vaghe donne, e da giouani huomini rappresentati sono honesti, e diletteuoli giuochi: narrate nouelle; e cantate alcune amorose canzonette. pp. 287. *Bernardo Giunti: Venetia*, 1587. 4°. **1080**. k. **7**. (**1**.)

—— [Another copy.] **1080**. k. **9**. (**1**.)

—— [Another copy.] G. **9918**.

—— [Another edition.] pp. 286. *Bernardo Giunti: Venetia*, 1592. 4°. **88**. i. **15**. (**1**.)

—— [Another copy.] G. **9919**.

—— Novelle. [Selected from " I Trattenimenti."] *See* Italian Novelist. Del novelliero italiano volume primo, *etc.* vol. 4. 1754. 8°. **634**. e. **23**.

—— Novelle. [Selected from " I Trattenimenti."] 1798. *See* P., G. Novelle di autori senesi. tom. 2. 1796, *etc.* 8°. **89**. b. **24**.

—— Novelle. [Selected from " I Trattenimenti."] 1834. *See* Italian Novelists. Raccolta di novellieri italiani. pt. 2. 1833, *etc.* 8°. **12470**. d. **27**.

—— Le Novelle di Scipione Bargagli, premessavi la narrazione dell'assedio di Siena. [Extracted from " I Trattenimenti."] Prima edizione senese per cura di Luciano Banchi. pp. xvi. 223. *Siena*, 1873. 8°. **12471**. bbb. **9**.
A different selection from the preceding.

—— Il Turamino, ouuero del parlare, e dello scriuer Sanese. pp. 116. *Matteo Florimi: Siena*, 1602. 4°. **72**. c. **15**.

BARGAGLI (Teresa) Vestendo l'abito domenicano nel venerabile monastero di Santa Caterina in Pistoja . . . Teresa e Angela Bargagli, *etc.* [Sonnets by " Ogireno Treteo P. A." and "il P. A. V."] 1724. 4°. *See* Treteo (O.) *P.A., pseud.* **11431**. c. **59**. (**29**.)

BARGAGLI PETRUCCI (Fabio) Le Fonti di Siena e i loro aquedotti. Note storiche dalle origini fino al MDLV. 2 vol. *Siena,* 1906. 4°. **10130**. i. **26**.

—— Montepulciano, Chiusi e la Val di Chiana Senese. Con 164 illustrazioni e 2 tavole. pp. 139. *Bergamo,* 1907. 8°. [*Collezione di monografie illustrate.* ser. 1. Italia artistica. no. 31.] **7814**. ccc. **1/30**.

—— Pienza, Montalcino e la Val d'Orcia Senese. Con 224 illustrazioni. II edizione. pp. 170. *Bergamo,* 1933. 8°. [*Collezione di monografie illustrate.* ser. 1. Italia artistica. no. 63.] **7814**. ccc. **1/61**.

—— Storia delle arti decorative e applicate. [With illustrations.] 2 vol.

1. Le età primitive. L'oriente antico. pp. vi. 220. 1924.
2. La Grecia. Parte prima. pp. 219. 1932.

Bologna, 1924, 32. 8°. **7802**. cc. **44**.
No more published.

BARGAGLI PETRUCCI PASSERINI (Onorina)

—— Nel Sudan Anglo-Egiziano. Como lo vidi dopo molti anni di dominazione inglese. Con 35 illustrazioni, *etc.* pp. 162. *Firenze,* 1941. 8°. **10098**. b. **1**.

BARGAGNA (Leto)

—— Gli Strumenti musicali raccolti nel museo del R. Istituto L. Cherubini a Firenze. Con 12 tavole. [A catalogue.] pp. 70. [1912.] 8°. *See* Florence.—*Accademia Nazionale "Luigi Cherubini" di Musica, Lettere e Arti Figurative.* Hirsch 343.

BARGAIN. A Bad Bargain: or, the Sudden death of an actor. By J. G. [1899.] 8°. *See* G., J. **4422**. cc. **71**. **(8.)**

—— The Bad Bargain; or, the World set up to sale. [A poem. By Hannah More.] pp. 7. *J. Masrhall* [sic]: *London,* [1796.] 8°. [*Cheap Repository.*] **4418**. f. **1**. **(30.)**

—— [Another edition.] pp. 7. *J. Marshall: London,* [1796.] 8°. [*Cheap Repository.*] **4418**. f. **4**. **(7.)**

BARGAINS. Bargains! An advertising circular, *etc. See* Periodical Publications.—*Barnsley.*

—— Bargains. Where to obtain them. *See* Periodical Publications.—*London.*

—— Bargains, and how they are found . . . By D. C. L. [1895.] 8°. *See* L., D. C. **08228**. df. **24**. **(2.)**

BARGALIUS (Celsus) *See* Bargagli (Celso)

BARGALIUS (Hieronymus) *See* Bargagli (Girolamo)

BARGALIUS (Scipio) *See* Bargagli (Scipione)

BARGALLÓ (Modesto) Los Pensamientos de Cajal sobre la Educación. pp. 40. *Madrid,* 1924. 8°. **8310**. b. **66**.

BARGANTIUM. *See* Braganza.

BARGANZA. *See* Braganza.

BARGAS (Abraham de) *See* Coen (Malachi) Traduccion de la Oracion del Ajuno de los Temblores de Tierra que in ydioma Hebraico compuso . . . Malahi de Jacob Coen ique en Ladino, Espanol illustrò . . . A. de Bargas. 1746. 8°. **1976**. ee. **59**.

—— Pensamientos sagrados y educciones morales divididos en dos tratados, el primero sobre el Pentateuco, i el segundo sobre Profetas. pp. 252. *Florencia,* MDDCCXLIX [1749]. 8°. **3149**. aa. **16**.

BARGAS (Francisco de) *See* Vargas.

BARGATZKY (Walter)

—— *See* Germany. [Bundesrepublik Deutschland.] [*Laws, etc.*—II. *Firearms.*] Waffenrecht der Bundesrepublik Deutschland. Textausgabe mit einer Einleitung, Verweisungen und Sachverzeichnis von W. Bargatzky. 1951. 16°. **05605**. f. **22**.

—— Der Sinn der englischen Festlandspolitik. Reden und Schriften britischer Staatsmänner aus zwei Jahrhunderten, mit einer Einführung herausgegeben von W. Bargatzky. pp. 238. *München,* 1939. 8°. **08139**. dd. **26**.

BÄRGBO (Skogekär) *pseud. See* Rosenhane (G.)

BARGE.

—— The Barge. *See* Periodical Publications.—*Oxford.*

BARGE BOYS.

—— Barge Boys' Club. *See* London.—III.

BARGE (Harry) Beschouwingen over de grondbeginselen van het strafrecht. Academiesch proefschrift, *etc.* pp. 102. *Amsterdam,* 1872. 8°. **6003.b.40.**

—— Bijdrage tot de waardeering der godsdienstloze school. Verhandeling, uitgesproken in de Vereeniging: "Regt voor Allen," den 21n Januari 1868. pp. 16. *Amsterdam,* 1868. 8°. **8305**. ee. **31**. **(9.)**

BARGE (Hermann) *See* Guenther (F.) calling himself *Bischof von der Lochau.* Verhör und Akta vor dem Bischof von Meissen gegen den Bischof zu der Lochau, und: Handlung des Bischofs von Merseburg mit den zwei Pfarrern von Schönbach und Buch . . . Herausgegeben von H. Barge. 1906. 8°. **3907**. bbb. **1**. **(2.)**

—— Aktenstücke zur Wittenberger Bewegung, Anfang 1522. Herausgegeben und erläutert von H. Barge. pp. vi. 52. *Leipzig,* 1912. 8°. **4535**. bbb. **23**. **(1.)**

—— Andreas Bodenstein von Karlstadt. 2 Tl. *Leipzig,* 1905. 8°. **4888**. k. **15**.

—— *See* Mueller (Carl F. F. von) Luther und Karlstadt, *etc.* [A reply to H. Barge's "Andreas Bodenstein von Karlstadt."] 1907. 8°. **4888**. h. **26**.

—— Florian Geyer. Eine biographische Studie. pp. iv. 39. *Leipzig & Berlin,* 1920. 8°. [*Beiträge zur Kulturgeschichte des Mittelalters und der Renaissance.* Bd. 26.] **9071**. b. **1/26**.

—— Frühprotestantisches Gemeindechristentum in Wittenberg und Orlamünde. Zugleich eine Abwehr gegen Karl Müllers "Luther und Karlstadt." pp. xxvi. 366. *Leipzig,* 1909. 8°. **4888**. k. **20**.

—— Geschichte der Buchdruckerkunst von ihren Anfängen bis zur Gegenwart, *etc.* [With plates.] pp. viii. 519. *Leipzig,* 1940. 8°. **11898**. cc. **40**.

—— Jakob Strauss. Ein Kämpfer für das Evangelium in Tirol, Thüringen und Süddeutschland. pp. 173. *Leipzig,* 1937. 8°. [*Schriften des Vereins für Reformationsgeschichte.* Jahrg. 54. Hft. 2.] Ac. **2027**.

—— Luther und der Frühkapitalismus. pp. 63. *Gütersloh,* 1951. 8°. [*Schriften des Vereins für Reformationsgeschichte.* no. 168. Jahrg. 58. Hft. 1.] Ac. **2027**.

—— Die Verhandlungen zu Linz und Passau und der Vertrag von Passau im Jahre 1552. pp. 161. *Stralsund,* 1893. 8°. **09325**. g. **6**.

BARGE (Joannes Antonius James)

—— *See* Klaauw (C. J. van der) Bibliographia biotheoretica, quam ediderunt . . . C. J. van der Klaauw . . . J. A. J. Barge, *etc.* 1938, *etc.* 8°. Ac. **940**. b/**2**.

BARGE (JOANNES ANTONIUS JAMES)

—— De Betrekking tusschen vorm en functie als biologisch probleem, *etc.* pp. 24. *Haarlem*, 1947. 12°. [*Haarlemsche voordrachten.* no. 5.] Ac.2953/9.(5.)

—— Friesche en Marker schedels. Bijdrage tot de kennis van de anthropologie der bevolking van Nederland. Academisch proefschrift, *etc.* pp. 272. *Amsterdam*, 1912. 8°. 10007. pp. 12.

—— Probleme im Kranio-Vertebralgebiet, *etc.* pp. 105. *Amsterdam*, 1918. 8°. [*Verhandelingen der Koninklijke Akademie van Wetenschappen.* sectie 2. dl. 20. no. 2.] Ac.944/2.(b.)

—— Reinier de Graaf, 1641–1941. [With a portrait.] pp. 25. *Amsterdam*, 1942. 8°. [*Mededeelingen der Nederlandsche Akademie van Wetenschappen.* Afd. Letterkunde. Nieuwe reeks. dl. 5. no. 5.] Ac. 944. (2.)

—— De Stichting van het academisch klinisch onderwijs te Leiden voor 300 jaren. Herdenkingsrede gehouden in de bijeenkomst van den Academischen Senaat der Rijksuniversiteit te Leiden op 29 October 1937, *etc.* [With plates.] pp. 32. *Leiden*, 1937. 8°. 07680. bb. 56.

BARGEBUHR (FREDERICK P.)
—— Ibn Gabirol's Poem beginning "Ahavtikha..." (Reprinted from The Review of Religion.) [*New York?* 1950.] 8°. 11869. h. 4.

BARGEDÉ (NICOLLE) Les Odes pénitentes du moins que rien. *Iehan Longis: Paris*, 1550. 8°. 240. c. 10.

BARGE FORISSIER (JEAN BAPTISTE) Dissertation médico-chirurgicale des avantages que l'on peut retirer des antispasmodiques, relâchans, révulsifs, etc. . . . pendant le travail de l'enfantement, *etc.* pp. 14. [*Montpellier*, 1804.] 4°. 1180. e. 7. (14.)

BARGELIUS (CASPAR) *Resp.* Disputatio II. De pœnitentia, *etc.* [1610.] *See* FRANTZE (W.) Augustanæ confessionis articuli fidei XXI, et articuli abusuum VII. disputationibus XXXIII. . . . explicati et ex verbo Dei confirmati. 1611, *etc.* 4°. 1353. e. 2.

BARGELLESI (GIACOMO)
—— Palazzo Schifanoia. Gli affreschi nel "Salone dei Mesi" in Ferrara. pp. 22. pl. 40. Bergamo, 1945. fol. L.R. 293. d. 30.

BARGELLINI (MARIANO) Della libertà. Lettura prima (seconda) fatta nella gran sala dell'Università di Siena, *etc.* 2 pt. *Siena*, 1868. 8°. 8005. bb. 20.

—— Storia popolare di Genova dalla sua origine fino ai nostri tempi. [With plates.] 2 vol. *Genova*, 1856, 57. 8°. 9166. h. 16.

With additional titlepages, lithographed.

—— Seconda edizione. fasc. 1–42. *Genova*, 1869. 8°. 9166. i. 13.

Imperfect; wanting fasc. 43–52.

BARGELLINI (PIERO)
—— *See* FUSERO (C.) Bargellini. 1949. 8°. 10633. s. 93.

—— L'Amorosa vicenda dei Lippi. [With reproductions.] pp. 251. *Roma*, 1951. 8°. 010632. d. 27.

—— Caffè Michelangiolo. Seconda edizione. [On the group of nineteenth century artists known as 'macchiaioli' and their meeting-place at the Caffè Michelangiolo in Florence. With reproductions.] pp. 354. *Firenze*, 1944. 8°. 7868. b. 52.

BARGELLINI (PIERO)

—— Il Convento di San Marco e le pitture del beato Angelico [With reproductions.] pp. 21. *Firenze*, [1948.] 8°. 7868. f. 41.

—— David. [A novel.] Translated by Elisabeth Abbott pp. 165. *P. J. Kenedy & Sons: New York*, [1954.] 8°. 04423. c. 8

—— La Fiaba pittorica di Benozzo Gozzoli. Seconda edizione. [With reproductions.] pp. 227. *Firenze* 1947. 8°. 7869. b. 41

—— Il Ghirlandaio del bel mondo fiorentino. Seconda edizione. [With reproductions.] pp. 249. *Firenze* 1947. 8°. 7869. b. 40

—— Giosuè Carducci. pp. 375. *Brescia*, 1934. 8°. 20002. a. 33.

—— Giosuè Carducci. Seconda edizione, con l'aggiunta di due nuovi capitoli, di una prefazione esplicativa e di un'appendice polemica. pp. 525. *Brescia*, 1935. 8°. 20003. cc. 32.

—— Il Pastore angelico, Pio XII. [With plates, including portraits.] pp. 189. *Firenze*, 1948. 8°. 4857. dd. 1

—— Pian dei Giullari. Panorama storico della letteratura italiana. 12 Vol. Firenze, 1949-52. 8°. 11869. aaa. 34

Vol. 1, 2, 5–8, 10, 11 *are of the third edition; vol.* 9 *is of the second edition.*

—— Rinascimento. 100 particolari di opere d'arte. Introduzione di Piero Bargellini. pp. xix. pl. 98. *Firenze* 1945. fol. L.R. 297. a. 21

—— Sant' Antonino da Firenze. II edizione. pp. 326. *Brescia*, [1947.] 8°. 4831. a. 31

BARGELLINI (PIERO)

—— Santa Chiara. pp. 162. pl. VIII. *Firenze*, 1953. 8°. 4832. b. 6

—— Il Sogno nostalgico di Sandro Botticelli . . . Seconda edizione. [With reproductions.] pp. 207. *Firenze* [1946.] 8°. 7869. r. 9

BARGELLINI (PIERO) and FREYRIE (ENRICO)
—— Nascita e vita dell'architettura moderna. [With illustrations.] pp. 243. *Firenze*, 1947. 8°. 07822. g. 29

BARGELLINI (SANTE) La Campana dello scandalo. Fra nemici. La Chitarra di Paganini. Novelle d'arte. pp. 193. *Roma*, [1906.] 8°. 12471. t. 31

—— Etruria meridionale. Con 168 illustrazioni. pp. 148. *Bergamo*, 1909. 8°. [*Collezione di monografie illustrate* ser. 1. Italia artistica. no. 48.] 7814. ccc. 1/46

—— I Monti del Cimino. Con 184 illustrazioni. pp. 171. *Bergamo*, 1914. 8°. [*Collezione di monografie illustrate* ser. 1. Italia artistica. no. 73.] 7814. ccc. 1/71

BARGEMAN. The Bargeman. The magazine of the Bargemen's Brotherhood. *See* SITTINGBOURNE.—*Bargemen's Brotherhood.*

BARGEMEN'S BROTHERHOOD. *See* SITTINGBOURNE.

BARGEMON (BARTHÉLEMY JOSEPH DE VILLENEUVE) *Count.* *See* VILLENEUVE-BARGEMON.

BARGEMONT (ALBAN DE VILLENEUVE) *Viscount.* *See* VILLENEUVE-BARGEMONT (Jean P. A. de)

BARGEMONT (CHRISTOPHE DE VILLENEUVE) *Count.* *See* VILLENEUVE-BARGEMONT.

BARGEMONT (JEAN PAUL ALBAN DE VILLENEUVE) *Viscount.* *See* VILLENEUVE-BARGEMONT.

BARGEMONT (LOUIS FRANÇOIS DE VILLENEUVE) *Marquis de Villeneuve-Trans.* *See* VILLENEUVE-BARGEMONT.

BÄRGEN ( ) [For the German surname of this form:] *See* BAERGEN.

BARGEN (BENDIX VON)

—— *See* TROTHA (A. L. von) Admiral von Trotha. Persönliches, Briefe, Reden und Aufzeichnungen . . . Ausgewählt und herausgegeben von Dr. B. von Bargen. 1938. 8°. **012253**. ee. **12**.

BARGEN (JACOB ARNOLD) *See* RANKIN (Fred W.) The Colon, Rectum and Anus. By F. W. Rankin . . . J. A. Bargen, *etc.* 1932. 8°. **07630**. h. **10**.

BARGEO (PIETRO ANGELIO) *See* ANGELIO (P.) *da Barga.*

BARGER (CLARENCE G.)

—— Automotive Mechanics, *etc.* 2 vol. pp. vii. viii. 336. *American Book Co.: New York,* [1943.] 8°. [*Training for Victory.*] W.P. **13056/2**.

BARGER (E.) Antwoord of het adres der Vrijzinnigen gericht aan het Kiescollegie der Ned. Herv. Gemeente te Haarlem. pp. 15. *Haarlem,* 1884. 8°. **3925**. bbb. **48**. **(2.)**

BARGER (EDGAR HUGH) and **CARD** (LESLIE ELLSWORTH)

—— Diseases and Parasites of Poultry, *etc.* pp. 354. *Henry Kimpton: London; printed in America,* 1935. 8°. **07295**. aa. **16**.

—— Diseases and Parasites of Poultry . . . Second edition, thoroughly revised, *etc.* pp. 386. *Henry Kimpton: London; printed in America,* 1938. 8°. **07295**. f. **32**.

—— Diseases and Parasites of Poultry . . . Third edition, thoroughly revised, *etc.* pp. 399. *Henry Kimpton: London; printed in America,* [1943.] 8°. **07294**. aa. **12**.

—— Diseases and Parasites of Poultry . . . Fourth edition, thoroughly revised, *etc.* pp. 400. *Henry Kimpton: London; printed in America,* [1949.] 8°. **07295**. f. **52**.
A later edition is entered under BARGER *(E. H.)*

BARGER (EDGAR LEE)

—— Tractors and their Power Units. [By] E. L. Barger . . . W. M. Carleton . . . E. G. McKibben . . . Roy Bainer. pp. viii. 496. *John Wiley & Sons: New York; Chapman & Hall: London,* 1952. 8°. [*Ferguson Foundation Agricultural Engineering Series.*] W.P. **14532** 2.

BARGER (EVERT HUGH) In the Track of the Crusaders. Overland with a rucksack to Jerusalem, *etc.* [With plates, including a portrait.] pp. 281. *Nash & Grayson: London,* 1931. 8°. **010028**. g. **29**.

BARGER (EVERT HUGH) and **WRIGHT** (PHILIP)

—— Excavations in Swat and Explorations in the Oxus Territories of Afghanistan. A detailed report of the 1938 expedition. pp. v. 67. pl. XII. *Delhi,* 1941. fol. [*Memoirs of the Archæological Survey of India.* no. 64.] W.P. **3758/64**.

BARGER (FREDA)

—— The Wanton Air. [A novel.] pp. 254. *Jarrolds: London,* 1955. 8°. NNN. **6688**.

BARGER (GEORGE) *See* FREUNDLICH (H.) The Elements of Colloidal Chemistry . . . Translated by G. Barger, *etc.* 1925. 8°. **8903**. ff. **40**.

BARGER (GEORGE)

—— [Articles on chemical subjects written independently or in collaboration, reprinted or extracted from various periodicals.] 22 pt. *Wellcome Physiological Research Laboratories: London,* [1905–11.] 8°. **8709**. m. **4**.

—— Ergot and Ergotism. A monograph based on the Dohme Lectures delivered in Johns Hopkins University. Baltimore. [With plates and a bibliography.] pp. xvi. 279. *Gurney & Jackson: London, Edinburgh,* 1931. 8°. **07687**. h. **48**.

—— Organic Chemistry for Medical Students. pp. xi. 249. *Gurney & Jackson: London, Edinburgh,* 1932. 8°. **8901**. a. **24**.

—— Organic Chemistry for Medical Students . . . Second edition. pp. xi. 251. *Gurney & Jackson: London, Edinburgh,* 1936. 8°. **8899**. h. **23**.

—— The Simpler Natural Bases. pp. viii. 215. *Longmans, Green & Co.: London,* 1914. 8°. [*Monographs on Biochemistry.*] **08909**. c. **1/15**.

—— Some Applications of Organic Chemistry to Biology and Medicine. [With a portrait.] pp. 186. *McGraw-Hill Book Co.: New York,* 1930. 8°. [*George Fisher Baker Lectureship in Chemistry.* vol. 5.] Ac. **2692**. gd.

BARGER (H. H.) J. Scharp. Een predikant uit den patriottentijd. pp. 133. *Rotterdam,* 1906. 8°. **4887**. bb. **52**.

BARGER (HAROLD)

—— Foreign Trade. pp. 39. *Victor Gollancz: London,* 1936. 8°. [*New Fabian Research Bureau. Publications.* no. 30.] W.P. **10405** 30.

—— Outlay and Income in the United States, 1921–1938. pp. xxvii. 391. *National Bureau of Economic Research: New York,* 1942. 8°. [*Conference on Research in National Income and Wealth. Studies in Income and Wealth.* vol. 4.] W.P. **13012**.

BARGER (HAROLD) and **LANDSBERG** (HANS H.)

—— American Agriculture, 1899–1939. A study of output, employment and productivity. pp. xxii. 440. *New York,* 1942. 8°. [*Publications of the National Bureau of Economic Research.* no. 42.] W.P. **651**/42.

BARGER (HAROLD) and **SCHURR** (SAM H.)

—— The Mining Industries, 1899–1939. A study of output, employment and productivity. pp. xxii. 452. *New York,* 1944. 8°. [*Publications of the National Bureau of Economic Research. no.* 43.] W.P. **651/43**.

BARGER (WILLIAM ROSS)

—— *See* ASBURY (Clyde E.) Studies on the "Raisining" of Alexandria—Muscat—Grapes in Transit. By C. E. Asbury . . . W. R. Barger. 1940. 8°. [*U.S. Department of Agriculture. Circular.* no. 574.] A.S. **804** 2.

BARGERON (ABRAHAM) Fundamenta linguæ gallicæ methodicè in succinctas tabellas redacta . . . Ex novo correcta & emendata. *T. Ritzsch: Lipsiæ,* 1648. 8°. **1033**. f. **34**. **(2.)**

BARGERY (GEORGE PERCY) *See* PARSONS (Allan C.) A Hausa Phrase Book . . . Revised by the Rev. G. P. Bargery. 1924. 8°. **12911**. a. **16**.

—— A Hausa-English Dictionary and English-Hausa Vocabulary, *etc.* pp. liv. 1226. *Oxford University Press: London,* 1934. 8°. **2272**. g. **23**.

BARGERY (George Percy) and **HONIKMAN** (Beatrice)

—— Hausa. A series of conversations and readings in Hausa. With texts, English translation and explanatory notes on the pronunciation of Hausa . . . Compiled by G. P. Bargery and B. Honikman. pp. 39. *Linguaphone Institute: London,* [1935?] 8°. [*Linguaphone Miniature Language Series.*] **012902.n.14/4.**

BARGES (Argand de) *See* Argand Debarges.

BARGÈS (Jean Joseph Léandre) *See* Aḥmad ibn Muḥammad, *al-Manūfī.* Le Livre du don abondant, ou histoire du Nil bienfaisant . . . section IIIe du chapitre Ier traduite en français par M. l'abbé Bargès. 1846. 8°. **14566.** bb. **1.**

—— *See* Bible.—*Ruth.* [*Polyglott.*] Le Livre de Ruth expliqué par deux traductions françaises . . . Avec . . . des notes . . . par . . . J. J. L. Bargès. 1854. 8°. **01903.b.24.(4.)**

—— *See* Bible.—*Psalms.* [*Polyglott.*] Libri Psalmorum . . . versio à R. Yapheth ben Heli . . . arabicè concinnata . . . Latinitate donavit J. J. L. Bargès. 1861. 4°. **14500.** d. **9.**

—— *See* Bible.—*Psalms.—Selections.* [*Polyglott.*] Rabbi Yapheth ben Heli . . . in librum Psalmorum commentarii arabici . . . Edidit specimen et in latinum convertit L. Bargès. 1846. 8°. **754.** e. **8.**

—— *See* Bible.—*Song of Solomon.* [*Polyglott.*] Rabbi Yapheth Abou Aly ibn-Aly Bassorensis . . . in Canticum Canticorum commentarium arabicum quod . . . edidit atque in linguam latinam transtulit J. J. L. Bargès. 1884. 8°. **754.** e. **3.**

—— *See* Eshmunazar, *King of Sidon.* Mémoire sur le sarcophage et l'inscription funéraire d'Eschmounazar, roi de Sidon. Par . . . J. J. L. Bargès. [With the text.] 1856. 4°. **7707.** f. **13.**

—— *See* Muḥammad ibn 'Abd al-Jalīl, *al-Tanasī.* Histoire des Beni Zeiyan, rois de Tlemcen . . . Ouvrage traduit de l'arabe par . . . J.-J.-L. Bargès. 1852. 12°. **14555.** b. **12.**

—— *See* O., M., *la Sœur.* Message de M. l'abbé Lagarde . . . auprès de M. Thiers pendant la Commune, *etc.* [Edited by J. J. L. Bargès.] 1889. 8°. **9010.** h. **6.** (**4.**)

—— *See* Severus, *Bishop of Nastaruwah.* Homélie sur St Marc . . . Texte arabe publié avec une traduction et des notes . . . par . . . J.-J.-L. Bargès. 1877. 8°. **14503.** d. **4.**

—— *See* Slaughter (Edwardus) Grammatica Hebraica . . . Curante J. J. L. Bargès . . . novissime edita. 1857. 8°. **12903.** d. **3.**

—— Aperçu historique sur l'église d'Afrique en général, et en particulier sur l'église épiscopale de Tlemcen. pp. viii. 46. *Paris,* 1848. 8°. **4765.** d. **12.**

—— Complément de l'histoire des Beni-Zeiyan, rois de Tlemcen, ouvrage du Cheikh Mohammed Abd'al-Djalil al-Tenessy. pp. xiv. 612. *Paris,* 1887. 8°. **14555.** a. **18.**

—— Excursion à Sebdou, poste français sur la frontière du Maroc. Fragment d'un ouvrage inédit intitulé Souvenirs de la province d'Oran, ou voyage à Tlemcen. pp. 27. *Paris,* 1849. 8°. **010095.** e. **10.** (**2.**)

—— Inscription phénicienne de Marseille. Nouvelle interprétation. [With the text.] pp. 37. *Paris,* 1858. 4°. **7703.** g. **7.** (**5.**)
One of an edition of 100 *copies.*

BARGÈS (Jean Joseph Léandre)

—— Inscriptions arabes qui se voyaient autrefois dans la ville de Marseille. Nouvelle interprétation et commentaire. pp. 78. *Paris,* 1889. 8°. **7704.** g. **45.**

—— Mémoire sur deux inscriptions puniques découvertes dans l'île du Port-Cothon à Carthage. pp. 16. *Paris,* 1849. fol. **7703.** d. **11.**

—— Notice sur les antiquités de Belcodène, ancien Castrum de Bolcodenis, Bouches-du-Rhône, *etc.* pp. 78. *Paris,* 1883. 4°. **7705.** g. **29.**

—— Notice sur quelques autels chrétiens du moyen âge, avec description des lieux où ils ont été découverts. Publication ornée de planches et de dessins. pp. 118. *Paris,* 1890. 8°. **3475.** g. **1.**

—— Notice sur un autel antique dédié a Jupiter, découvert à Saint-Zacharie, département du Var, et sur quelques autres monuments romains trouvés dans la même localité, ou dans les environs. pp. 48. pl. 3. *Paris* 1875. 8°. **7705.** aaaa. **2.** (**7.**)

—— Notice sur un autel chrétien antique, orné de bas-reliefs et d'inscriptions latines, découvert dans les environs de la ville d'Auriol, Bouches-du-Rhône. Avec deux planches pp. 24. *Paris,* 1861. 4°. **7707.** g. **3**

—— Notre-Dame des Victoires pendant la Commune, ou lettres justificatives et documents conservés par feu l'abbé François Amodru pour servir à l'histoire de Notre-Dame des Victoires . . . Le tout publié par M. J.-J.-L. Bargès. [With a portrait of F. Amodru.] pp. 195. 43. ix. *Paris,* 1889. 8°. **4629.** b. **25.**

—— Nouvelle interprétation de l'inscription phénicienne découverte par M. Mariette dans le Sérapéum de Memphis. Examen critique de l'interprétation donnée par M. le duc de Luynes, *etc.* (Extrait de la Revue de l'Orient, de l'Algérie et des colonies.) pp. 19. *Paris,* 1856. 8°. **7705.** aa. **1.** (**9.**)

—— Papyrus égypto-araméen appartenant au Musée Égyptien du Louvre expliqué et analysé pour la première fois. pp. 35. pl. II. *Paris,* 1862. 4°. **7702.** i. **9.**

—— Recherches archéologiques sur les colonies phéniciennes établies sur le littoral de la Celtoligurie. [With illustrations.] pp. 160. *Paris,* 1878. 8°. **7706.** aaa. **12.**

—— Les Samaritains de Naplouse. Épisode d'un pèlerinage dans les lieux saints. pp. iv. 127. *Paris,* 1855. 8°. **010077.m.1.**

—— Tlemcen, ancienne capitale du royaume de ce nom, sa topographie, son histoire, description de ses principaux monuments, anecdotes, légendes et récits divers. Souvenirs d'un voyage. [With plates.] pp. xvi. 479. *Paris,* 1859. 8°. **10096.** f. **12.**

—— Vie du célèbre marabout Cidi Abou-Médien, autrement dit Bou-Médin, *etc.* pp. xxxv. 118. *Paris,* 1884. 8°. **10606.** m. **3.**

BARGÈS (Léandre) *See* Bargès (Jean J. L.)

BARGETANUS (Petrus) *See* Angelio (Pietro) *da Barga.*

BARGETON (Daniel) *See* Balincourt (E. de) *Count.* Daniel Bargeton, *etc.* 1887. 8°. **10602.** k. **8.** (**3.**)

—— Lettre d'un imprimeur de Londres au défenseur du clergé de France, au sujet de la Réponse aux Lettres contre l'immunité des biens ecclésiastiques. [A rejoinder by D. Bargeton to Antoine Duranthon's reply to his "Lettres."] pp. 64. 1750. 12°. *See* Lettres. **857.** d. **15.** (**2.**)

—— [Another copy.] **8050.** ccc. **5.**

BARGETON (DANIEL)

—— Lettres. [On the immunities of the French clergy. By D. Bargeton.] 5 pt. 1750. 8°. *See* LETTRES. **4051**. e. **26**.

—— Dernière édition, revûë, & considérablement augmentée avec notes. 5 pt. 1750. 12°. *See* LETTRES. **857**. d. **14**.

—— *See* LETTRES. Réponse aux Lettres contre l'immunité des biens ecclésiasiques [*sic*]. [A reply to D. Bargeton's " Lettres " by Antoine Duranthon.] 1750. 12°. **857**. d. **15**. (**1**.)

BARGETON (E.) *See* CLAMOUX (E.) *pseud.* [i.e. E. Bargeton.]

BARGEVILLE ( ) La Mort et la résurrection de Louis XVI, roi des Français. [A political satire.] pp. 8. *Paris*, 1792. 8°. F. **907**. (**1**.)

BARGH (DORA)

—— The Story of the Countryside. Edited by D. Bargh. *Oxford University Press; National Federation of Young Farmers' Clubs:* [*London*,] 1943– . 8°. W.P. **708**.

BARGHEER (CARL LOUIS)

—— L. van Beethoven's fünf letzte Quartette für die Kammermusik-Abende der Philharmonischen Gesellschaft in Hamburg analysirt. pp. iv. 56. *Hamburg*, 1883. 8°. Hirsch **2301**.

BARGHON DE FORT-RION (FRANÇOIS DE) *Baron*. *See* CENALIS (R.) successively *Bishop of Vence, of Riez* and *of Avranches*. Bayeux et ses environs . . . Traduit du latin et annoté par F. de Barghon Fort-Rion. 1860. 8°. **10170**. cc. **21**.

—— *See* ELIZABETH PHILIPPINA MARIA HELEN, *Princess of France*. Mémoires de Madame Élisabeth de France . . . Annotés et mis en ordre par F. de Barghon Fort-Rion. 1860. 8°. **10659**. bb. **16**.

—— La Belle Pope née à Bayeux au IXe siècle, femme de Rollon, premier duc de Normandie. Suivi du Siége de Paris par les Normands. Études historiques. pp. viii. 116. *Paris, Caen*, 1858. 8°. **10660**. cc. **20**.

—— Le Druidisme au moyen âge. Époque tertiaire. pp. 56. *Paris*, 1874. 12°. **4506**. aa. **22**.

—— Du rétablissement de l'ordre de Malte. pp. 28. *Paris*, 1859. 8°. **4784**. e. **7**.

—— Jehanne d'Arc, chronique rimée . . . Préface du vicomte Oscar de Poli. pp. lxviii. 278. *Paris*, 1890. 8°. **11475**. bbb. **4**.

BARGHOORN (ADOLF) *See* NAKAYAMA (S.) Das Jahr im Erleben des Volkes . . . Übersetzung . . . von A. Barghoorn, *etc.* 1926. 8°. [*Mitteilungen der Deutschen Gesellschaft für Natur- und Völkerkunde Ostasiens*. Bd 20.] Ac. **1944**.

BARGHOORN (FREDERICK CHARLES)

—— The Soviet Image of the United States. A study in distortion. pp. xviii. 297. *Harcourt, Brace & Co.: New York*, [1950.] 8°. **8096**. b. **13**.
The half-title headed: Institute of International Studies, Yale University.

BARGIELA (CAMILO) *See* LANDÍN (P.) La Paternidad de " La Casa de la Troya " ante los Tribunales de Justicia, *etc.* [Defending A. Pérez Sugín's authorship of the novel against the claims of C. Bargiela.] 1925. 8°. **011824**. a. **58**.

BARGIGI (GUINIFORTO DELLI) *See* BARZIZIUS (Guinifortus)

BARGIGLI (ANGIOLO) *See* FLORENCE.—*Galleria degli Uffizi*. Reale Galleria di Firenze illustrata. [By B. Zannoni, A. Bargigli and others.] 1817, *etc.* 8°. **58**. g. **2–13**.

BARGIGLI (THEODOR) Mittheilungen über die Insel Mytilene. *See* SCHERZER (C. von) Smyrna, *etc.* 1873. 8°. **10077**. f. **3**.

—— L'Île de Mytilène. *See* SCHERZER (C. von) La Province de Smyrne, *etc.* 1873. 8°. **10077**. f. **2**.

BARGIGNAC (C. L. A.) Questions tirées au sort . . . Quels sont les principaux végétaux qui fournissent des huiles grasses employées en médecine ou dans l'économie domestique . . . Des usages du système pileux . . . Des dangers des fractures des os du bassin . . . Du catarrhe nasal non inflammatoire. Thèse, *etc.* pp. 47. *Montpellier*, 1839. 4°. **1181**. i. **14**. (**7**.)

BARGILLI (GIUSEPPE) Commemorazione di Giosuè Carducci tenuta la mattina del 24 febbraio 1907, *etc.* [The text of an address by G. Bargilli.] pp. 18. 1907. 8°. *See* ITALY.—*Ministero della Guerra.—Regia Accademia Militare*. **10601**. w. **4**. (**5**.)

—— Improbe Amor. Bozzetti villerecci, novelle e leggende. pp. 298. *Pitigliano*, 1896. 8°. **12471**. i. **39**.

—— In Sardegna. Cronache e leggende dei vecchi tempi. pp. 181. *Sassari*, 1878. 8°. **12471**. f. **13**.

—— Seconda edizione ampliata. pp. 288. *Bologna*, 1881. 8°. **12431**. bbb. **27**.

—— Manoscritti della Biblioteca della Regia Accademia Militare. Con un elenco di edizioni militari del XVI. secolo. pp. 64. *Torino*, 1905. 8°. **011907**. ee. **22**. (**3**.)

BARGILLIAT (ALAIN)

—— Offset-litho. Procédés manuels . . . Deuxième édition, revue et corrigée. pp. xi. 237. 1951. 8°. *See* PARIS.—*Institut National des Industries et Arts Graphiques*. **7949**. aaa. **40**.

—— Photo litho. Photo et copie, *etc.* pp. 521. 1951. 8°. *See* PARIS.—*Institut National des Industries et Arts Graphiques*. **8918**. d. **10**.

—— Vocabulaire pratique anglais-français et français-anglais des termes techniques concernant la cartographie, *etc.* pp. 411. *Paris*, 1944. 8°. **10003**. aaa. **77**.
Pp. 399–411 *are blank.*

—— [Another copy.] Vocabulaire pratique, *etc.* *Paris*, 1944. 8°. Maps. Ref.

BARGILLIAT (MICHEL) Prælectiones juris canonici. 2 tom. *Parisiis*, 1890, 91. 12°. **05107**. e. **4**.

BARGINET (ALEXANDRE PIERRE) *See* also ALEXANDRE, *pseud.* [i.e. A. P. Barginet.]

—— *See* CHANGEMENT. Changement de domicile . . . Par MM. *** [i.e. A. P. Roustan and A. P. Barginet], *etc.* 1819. 8°. **11738**. m. **7**. (**6**.)

—— *See* NODIER (J. E. C.) Mélanges de littérature et de critique . . . Mis en ordre et publiés par A. Barginet. **1091**. g. **16**.

—— *See* SARRAZIN DE MONTFERRIER (A. A. V.) Dictionnaire des sciences mathématiques, *etc.* [The historical articles by A. P. Barginet.] 1835, *etc.* 4°. **8531**. ee. **35**.

—— —— 1845. fol. **8531**. ee. **22**.

—— *See* SARRAZIN DE MONTFERRIER (A. A. V.) Dictionnaire universel et raisonné de marine . . . Ouvrage renfermant des recherches historiques sur l'origine, le développement et l'influence de la marine des différentes nations par A. Barginet. 1841. fol. **1263**. f. **11**.

BARGINET (Alexandre Pierre)

—— *See* Ségur (A. J. P. de) *Viscount.* Les Femmes . . . Nouvelle édition, augmentée de l'influence des femmes sous l'Empire, et de notes historiques, par M. Ch. N***. [Purporting to be edited by Charles Nodier but in fact edited by A. P. Barginet.] 1820. 12°. **08416.** df. **11.**

—— La Cotte rouge, ou l'insurrection de 1626, histoire dauphinoise du XVIIe siècle, précédée d'une notice sur le Château de Vizille. 4 tom. *Paris,* 1828. 12°. **9230.** aaa. **7.**

—— Discours sur l'histoire civile et religieuse de l'Ordre du Temple, *etc.* pp. 59. *Paris,* 1833. 8°. **4784.** c. **35.** (**2.**)

—— Le Grenadier de l'île d'Elbe. Souvenirs de 1814 et 1815. 2 tom. *Paris,* 1830. 8°. **1319.** g. **23.**

—— Martin Luther, *etc.* 2 vol. *Paris,* 1839. 8°. **12512.** gg. **14.**

—— [Another copy.] **12512.** gg. **21.**

—— Le Roi des montagnes, ou les compagnons du chêne, tradition dauphinoise du temps de Charles VIII. 5 tom. *Paris,* 1828. 12°. **634.** c. **44–48.**

—— La Trente-deuxième demi-brigade. pp. 50. *Paris,* [1862.] 8°. **12512.** k. **5.** (**6.**)

BARGINI (J. B. de) Le Comte de Saluggia; ou, le tourmenteur de la chair humaine . . . Traduit de l'original italien inédit par Numa Bonnet [or rather, written by him?]. 2 tom. *Paris, Lyon,* 1857. 8°. **12515.** i. **7.**

BARGIS (Franceschina Roggero) *See* Roggero-Bargis.

BARGISHAI (Eleazar) A Brief Compendium of the vain Hopes of the Jews Messias, the ignorant fables of their Rabbies, and the confuting of the Jewish religion. pp. 21. *London,* 1652. 4°. E. **674.** (**33.**)

BARGIUS (Joannes) De sacrosancto Eucharistiæ sacramento, theses theologicæ, *etc.* *Praes.* Gregorio de Valentia. *D. Sartorius: Ingolstadii,* 1584. 4°. **1196.** f. **43.** (**10.**)

BARGMANN (Albert Fr. J.) Der jüngste Schutt der nördlichen Kalkalpen in seinen Beziehungen zum Gebirge, zu Schnee und Wasser, zu Pflanzen und Menschen. pp. 103. *See* Ratzel (F.) Anthropogeographische Beiträge, *etc.* 1895. 8°. [*Wissenschaftliche Veröffentlichungen des Vereins für Erdkunde zu Leipzig.* Bd. 2.] Ac. **6056/2.**

BARGMANN (Helene Elizabeth) A Biology Handbook for Schools. Junior Course by H. E. Bargmann . . . Senior Course by I. F. Henderson . . . With an introduction by L. Martin-Leake, *etc.* pp. vi. 65. *Sir I. Pitman & Sons: London,* 1932. 8°. **7003.** r. 35.

—— The Development and Life-History of Adolescent and Adult Krill, Euphausia superba. 1945. *See* England.—*Colonial Office.*—" *Discovery* " *Committee.* Discovery Reports, *etc.* vol. 23. 1929, *etc.* 4°. W.P. **243/23.**

—— The Reproductive System of Euphausia superba. [With plates.] 1937. *See* England.—*Colonial Office.*—" *Discovery* " *Committee.* Discovery Reports, *etc.* vol. 14. 1929, *etc.* 4°. W.P. **243/14.**

BARGMANN (Sonja)

—— *See* Einstein (Albert) The Meaning of Relativity. (The second appendix translated by S. Bargmann.) 1950. 8°. 08710. aa. 41.

BARGOIN (Jocelyn) *See* Bargoin (Louis A. J.)

BARGOIN (Louis Albert Jocelyn) Soirs d'hiver . . Avec un portrait de l'auteur, *etc.* [The biographica notice signed: U. C.] pp. 218. *Paris,* 1880. 12°. **12356.** bbb. **29**

BARGONE (Frédéric Charles Pierre Édouard) *Se* Farrère (Claude) *pseud.* [i.e. F. C. P. E. Bargone.]

BARGONI (Angelo) *See* Bargoni (Attilio) Risorgiment italiano. Memorie di Angelo Bargoni. [With a portrait. 1911. 8°. **9165.** bbb. **43**

—— *See* Peruzzi (U.) Speeches of the Italian Ministers o the Interior and of Justice Signors Peruzzi and Pisanelli and of Signor Boncompagni . . . in answer to th questions of Signor Bargoni. [On the attitude of th government to Garibaldi.] 1864. 8°. **8033.** b. **36**

—— Commemorazione di Giuseppe Garibaldi. pp. 39. *Venezia,* 1882. 8°. **10601.** c. **7.** (**5.**

BARGONI (Attilio) Risorgimento italiano. Memorie d Angelo Bargoni, 1829–1901. [With a portrait.] pp. xi. 414. *Milano,* 1911. 8°. **9165.** bbb. **43**

BARGRAVE (Isaac)

—— A Sermon against Selfe Policy: preached at White-Ha in Lent, 1621. pp. 40. [*Printed by Nicholas Okes, fo Iohn Bartlett, and Iohn Spencer: London,* 1624.] 4°. **4473.** aaa. **35**

Imperfect; wanting the titlepage. A microfilm of a cop with the titlepage is entered below.

—— A Sermon against Selfe Policy, *etc.* *London,* 1624. 4°. Mic. A. **852.** (**2.**

Microfilm *of a copy of the preceding in Cambridge Uni versity Library. Made by University Microfilms, Inc.*

—— A Sermon preached before King Charles, March 27. 1627 Being the anniuersary of his Maiesties inauguration, *et* pp. 21. *Iohn Legatt, for Peter Paxton: London,* 1627. 4° **693.** f. **1.** (**3.**

—— [Another copy.] **114.** a. **6**

—— A Sermon preached before the Honorable Assembly of Knights, Cittizens, and Burgesses, of the lower House o Parliament: February the last. 1623, *etc.* pp. 37. *I. D. for Iohn Bartlett, and Iohn Spencer: London* 1624. 4°. **693.** f. **1.** (**2.**

—— [Another copy.] A Sermon preached before the Honorable Assembly . . . of the lower House of Parliament February the last. 1623. *London,* 1624. 4°. C. **132.** h. **31.** (**5.**

BARGRAVE (John) Pope Alexander the Seventh and th College of Cardinals. By J. Bargrave . . . With a catalogue of Dr. Bargrave's Museum. Edited by Jame Craigie Robertson. pp. xxviii. 144. *London,* 1867. 4° [*Publications of the Camden Society.* no. 92.] Ac. **8113/85**

BARGRAVE (Robert)

—— Narration of a Journey from Constantinople to Dunkirk overland. [The text of the section concerning Roumania with a Roumanian translation by I. R. Rosetti.] *Se* Babinger (F. C. H.) Robert Bargrave, un voyageu anglais dans les pays roumains du temps de Basile Lupu 1652. 1936. 8°. [*Academia Română. Memorii secţiunii istorice.* ser. 3. tom. 17. mem. 7.] Ac. **743.** (**2**

BARGUET (H.) *See* Licquet (F. I.) Rouen . . . Translated . . . by M. D. C. and M. H. Barguet. 1857. 12°. **10172.** a. **20**

—— —— 1866. 12°. **10172.** aa. **26**

ARGUM (Henning Friedrich) [For publications of, and works relating to the firm Gustmeyers Enke og Bargum :] *See* Gustmeyers Enke og Bargum.

— Pro Memoria, som i første holdne General-Forsamling blev læst d. 19 Februarii 1766, for de Høye og respective Herrer Interessentere. *Dan., Ger. & Fr.* pp. 4. ms. additions. [*Copenhagen*, 1766.] 4°. **1389**. k. **12**. (5.)

ARGUM (Ludolf Conrad) *Surveyor.* Die Landmaasse in den Herzogthümern Schleswig, Holstein and Lauenburg, *etc.* pp. 29. *Kiel*, 1863. 8°. **8530**. cc. **41**. (5.)

ARGUM (Ludolf Conrad) *Translator. See* Holberg (L. af) *Baron.* Des Freyherrn Ludwig von Holberg dänische und norwegische Staatsgeschichte . . . Übersetzt durch L. C. Bargum. 1750. 4°. **9424**. ee. **2**.

ARGUM (Ludolf Conrad Hannibal) Zur Widerlegung der Bargum'schen Vertheidigungsschrift für den Minister von Scheele. pp. 56. *Kiel*, 1856. 8°. **8092**. d. **83**. (2.)

ARGY (Henry) France d'exil. Roman. pp. 286. *Paris*, 1908. 8°. **012550**. cc. **54**.

— La Religion dans la société aux États-Unis. pp. xx. 299. *Paris*, 1902. 8°. **4182**. bbb. **53**.

ARGY (Marie Barthélemy)

— De l'akidopeirastique, *etc.* [With a plate.] pp. 32. *Strasbourg*, 1866. 4°. [*Collection générale des dissertations de la Faculté de Médecine de Strasbourg.* sér. 2. tom. 39.] **7381***e.

ARGY (Vincent) Réflexions sur l'usage des évacuans pendant la grossesse, *etc.* pp. 25. *Montpellier*, an viii [1800]. 4°. **1180**. d. **7**. (2.)

ARHĀ BĀBĀJĪ. *See* Rādhāramaṇa-charaṇa Ghosha, *Rāya.*

ARḤADHBEŠHABBA 'ARBAYA, *Bishop of Ḥalwan.*

— Cause de la fondation des écoles. Texte syriaque publié et traduit par Mgr. Addai Scher. *Paris*, [1907.] 8°. [*Patrologia Orientalis.* tom. 4.] **2002**. c.

— La Première (seconde) partie de l'Histoire de Barḥadbešabba 'Arbaïa (et controverse de Théodore de Môpsueste avec les Macédoniens). Texte syriaque édité et traduit par F. Nau. 2 pt. 1932, 13. *See* Nestorian Church. Documents pour servir à l'histoire de l'Église nestorienne. 1913, *etc.* 8°. [*Patrologia Orientalis.* tom. 9. 32.] **2002**. c.

ARHAM DOWNS. Barham Downs. A novel . . . By the author of Mount Henneth [i.e. Robert Bage]. 2 vol. *G. Wilkie: London*, 1784. 12°. **12611**. bb. **5**.

ARHAM, Charles, *Baron.* *See* Middleton.

ARHAM, Diana, *Baroness.* *See* Noel.

ARHAM, *Family of.* *See* Uniacke (Richard G. F.) The Barhams of Shoesmiths, *etc.* 1914. 8°. **9903**. cc. **36**.

ARHAM (A. M.) The Namesake of the King. A tale of the last years of Cœur-de-Lion, *etc.* pp. 159. *S.P.C.K.: London*, [1907.] 8°. **04429**. ccc. **62**.

ARHAM (Abraham) An Address to the Right Honourable Philip Henry Earl Stanhope, on the subject of a survey of Chevening Park, made for his lordship in 1817. pp. 187. *Printed by the Author: Chipsted*, 1831. 8°. **716**. d. **10**.

BARHAM (Alfred Garratt Foster) *See* Nibelungen. [*Translations.*] The Nibelungen Lied . . . Translated . . . by A. G. Foster-Barham. 1887. 8°. **11511**. bb. **24**.

—— —— 1893. 8°. **012207.1.1/51.**

—— *See* Schiller (J. C. F. von) [*Das Lied von der Glocke.—English.*] Schiller's Song of the Bell. Translated by A. G. Foster-Barham, *etc.* 1896. *obl.* 4°. **1876**. a. **20**.

BARHAM (Alist Francis) *See* Barham (Francis Foster)

BARHAM (Alkman Henryson Foster) Genealogy of the Descendants of Roger Foster of Edreston, Northumberland, *etc.* pp. xii. 181. *A. & C. Black: London*, 1897. 8°. **9906**. d. **9**.

BARHAM (Charles Foster) Report on the Sanitary State of the Labouring Classes in the Town of Truro. pp. 20. *W. Clowes & Son: London*, [1840.] 8°. **10360**. ee. **26**. (1.)

—— The Winter of 1878–9. (Reprinted from the "Royal Cornwall Gazette.") [1879.] *s. sh.* fol. **1882**. c. **2**. (82.)

BARHAM (Charles Nicolas) The Student's Text-Book of Roman Law. pp. xii. 119. *Stevens & Sons: London*, 1903 [1902]. 8°. **5207**. a. **10**.

—— Second edition. pp. xv. 152. *Stevens & Sons: London*, 1908. 8°. **5207**. aa. **11**.

BARHAM (Charles Nicolas) and **COCKLE** (Ernest)

—— Bar Examination Papers. Questions and answers, 1901(–1907), *etc.* (Kelly's Bar Examination Papers, 1908–1912.—1901, 02 by C. N. Barham and E. Cockle ; 1903–08 by C. N. Barham ; 1909, 10 by W. W. Lucas ; 1911, 12 by J. A. Shearwood.) vol. 1–11 ; vol. 12. no. 1, 2. *Kelly Law-Book Co.: London*, 1901–[12.] 8°. **6125**. aaa. 2.

BARHAM (Francis Foster) *See* Bible. [*English.*] The Bible Revised. A carefully corrected translation of the Old and New Testaments. By F. Barham. [The Book of Ecclesiastes, the Song of Solomon and the Book of Micah only.] 1848, *etc.* 16°. **3035**. a. **9**.

—— *See* Bible.—*Old Testament.* [*Polyglott.*] The Hebrew and English Holy Bible . . . Edited by F. Barham. 1841. 8°. **01903.d.2.**

—— *See* Bible.—*Minor Prophets.* [*English.*] A Revised Version of the Prophecies of Hosea and Micah. By F. Barham. 1870. 16°. **3165**. a. **9**.

—— *See* Bible.—*Hagiographa.* [*English.*] The Writings of Solomon . . . Translated by F. Barham, *etc.* 1870. 16°. **12991**. aa. **2**.

—— *See* Bible.—*Psalms.* [*English.—Prose Versions.*] The Book of Psalms ; translated . . . by F. Barham and E. Hare. 1871. 8°. **3089**. aaa. **3**.

—— *See* Bible.—*Gospels.—Harmonies.* [*English.*] Improved Monotessaron : a complete authentic gospel life of Christ ; combining the words of the four Gospels, in a revised version, and an orderly chronological arrangement. By F. Barham. 1862. 12°. **3224**. a. **11**.

—— *See* Bible. — *Gospels.* — *Harmonies.* [*English.*] A Rhymed Harmony of the Gospels. By F. Barham and I. Pitman, *etc.* 1870. 8°. **11647**. cc. **30**.

—— *See* Bible.—*John, Epistles of.* [*English.*] An Elucidated Translation of St. John's Epistles . . . With a devotional commentary. By F. Barham. 1871. 16°. **3265**. a. 25.

BARHAM (FRANCIS FOSTER)

—— *See* CICERO (M. T.) [*Two or more Works.—English.*] The Political Works of Marcus Tullius Cicero . . . Translated . . . with dissertations and notes . . . by F. Barham. 1841, *etc.* 8°. **1385**. h. **3**.

—— *See* CICERO (M. T.) [*Two or more Works.—English.*] The Treatises of M. T. Cicero on the Nature of the Gods; on Divination; on Fate; on the Republic; on the Laws; and on Standing for the Consulship. Literally translated, chiefly by . . . C. D. Yonge. [For the most part a revision of F. F. Barham's translation.] 1853. 8°. **2500**. e. **22**.

—— *See* COLLIER (Jeremy) *the Nonjuror*. The Ecclesiastical History of Great Britain. New edition, with a life of the author . . . notes, and an enlarged index, by F. Barham. 1890. 8°. **710**. g. **31**.

—— *See* GROOT (H. de) [*Adamus Exul.*] The Adamus Exul of Grotius . . . Now first translated . . . by F. Barham. 1839. 8°. **1340**. i. **12**. (**6**.)

—— *See* GUIZOT (F. P. G.) [Du catholisme, du protestantisme et de la philosophie en France.] M. Guizot's Theory of Syncretism and Coalition, *etc.* [Translated from an article in the "Revue Française" by F. F. Barham.] [1839.] 8°. **1340**. i. **12**. (**5**.)

—— *See* LUḲMĀN, called *al-Ḥakīm*. Lokman's Arabic Fables. Literally translated into English by F. Barham. 1869. 16°. **14579**. b. **2**.

—— The Spirit of Literature: a collection of remarkable tracts and pamphlets. vol. 1. [A reissue in one volume of "Alist, an autobiography," "The Alist or Divine," and "Socrates," by F. F. Barham. Together with Grotius' "Adamus Exul" and Guizot's "Essay on Syncretism and Coalition," translated by F. F. Barham.] 1844. 8°. *See* SPIRIT. **1340**. i. **11**.

—— A Key to Alism and the Highest Initiations, Sacred and Secular. With miscellaneous pieces, original and select. [A reissue in one volume "A, alphabetically interpreted"; "A. An odd medley of literary curiosities," pt. 1.; "Alist, an autobiography"; "The Alist or Divine"; "The Adamus Exul of Grotius," translated by F. F. Barham; and "Socrates."] 6 pt. *John Johnstone: London,* 1847. 8°. **8464**. bb. **5**.

—— A Memorial of Francis Barham. A selection of autobiographical and other compositions from his unpublished manuscripts, together with a few papers and reports of lectures that have already been published. Edited by Isaac Pitman. pp. lv. 493. *Fred. Pitman: London,* 1873. 8°. **10827**. e. **23**.

—— A. An odd medley of literary curiosities, original and selected. (pt. 1. A, and the doctrine thereof. pt. 2. A Memoir of the late James Pierrepont Greaves.) 2 pt. *The Author: London,* [1845.] 8°. **1340**. i. **12**. (**1**.) & **1340**. i. **13**.

—— [Another copy of pt. 1.] **1458**. g. **17**. (**3**.)

—— [Another copy of pt. 1.] A. An odd medley of literary curiosities, *etc.* *London,* [1845.] 8°. **012359**. c. **29**. (**1**.)

—— Alist, an autobiography; or, an Author's life in the nineteenth century. [By F. F. Barham.] pt. 1. pp. 20. [1840.] 8°. *See* ALIST. **1249**. c. **8**. (**2**.)

—— [Another copy.] **1340**. i. **12**. (**2**.)

—— [Another copy.] Alist, an Autobiography, *etc.* [By F. F. Barham.] [1840.] 8°. *See* ALIST. **012359**. c. **29**. (**2**.)

BARHAM (FRANCIS FOSTER)

—— The Alist or Divine, a message to our times. [By F. F. Barham.] 3 pt. pp. 48. [1840.] 8°. *See* ALIST. **1340**. i. **12**. (**3**.)

—— [Another copy.] The Alist or Divine, *etc.* [By F. F. Barham.]. [1840.] 8°. *See* ALIST. **012359**. c. **29**. (**3**.)

—— [Another copy of pt. 1, 2.] **1249**. c. **8**. (**1**.)

—— Elucidation of the Causes of the Phenomena of the Hot Waters of Bath. pp. 16. *R. E. Peach: Bath,* 1864. 8°. **07108**. f. **14**. (**1**.)

—— The Foster Barham Genealogy. pp. 28. *E. Spettigue: London,* 1844. 8°. **9905**. d. **20**. (**8**.)
Printed for private circulation.

—— A Lecture on the Advancement of Literature, Science, and the Fine Arts in Bristol and the West of England; delivered at the Bristol Institution, December 10, 1846. pp. 16. *J. Chilcott: Bristol,* 1847. 8°. **11825**. dd. **7**.

—— The Life and Times of John Reuchlin, or Capnion, the Father of the German Reformation. pp. xii. 284. *Whittaker & Co.: London,* 1843. 12°. **1371**. c. **17**.

—— A Loyal Address to the Queen's Most Gracious Majesty. [On syncretism. Signed: Δ., i.e. F. F. Barham.] pp. 8. [1840?] 8°. *See* D. **1340**. i. **12**. (**4**.)

—— The New Bristol Guide, a comic poem. [The preface signed: F. B., i.e. F. F. Barham.] pp. vi. 77. 1847. 16°. *See* B., F. **11645**. a. **75**. (**1**.)

—— The Pleasures of Piety. A poem. pp. 94. *Hamilton Adams, & Co.: London; Whereat: Weston-super-Mare* 1850. 24°. **1163**. a. **36**

—— Socrates: a tragedy in five acts. pp. vi. 74. *W. E. Painter: London,* 1842. 8°. **1344**. i. **72**

—— [Another copy.] **1340**. i. **12**. (**8**.)

—— [Another copy.] Socrates, *etc.* *London,* 1842. 8°. **012359**. c. **29**. (**5**.)

BARHAM (GEORGE) The Christian's Last Hope: or Pathetic pieces on departed friends. pp. 24. *Rhind London,* [1866.] 12°. **11649**. df. **45**. (**7**.)

—— The Emigrant. A poem. pp. 23. *Binns & Goodwin London,* [1856?] 12°. **11649**. a. **75**. (**2**.)

—— Life's Last Hours. A poem. pp. 12. *Cambridge General Steam Printing Works: London,* 1862. 12°. **11648**. aaa. **44**

—— The Merry Days of Coaching; or, Tom Tally, and other lays. By the author of Pastoral and other poems in former days. [i.e. G. Barham.] pp. 22. 1857. 12°. *See* DAYS. **11649**. a. **75**. (**3**

—— Pastoral and other poems. pp. viii. 6–162. *Printed for the Author: Brighton,* 1854. 8°. **11649**. a. **75**. (**1**

BARHAM (GEORGE BASIL) *See* also LYONESSE, *pseud.* [i.e. G. B. Barham.]

—— The Development of the Incandescent Electric Lamp, *etc.* pp. viii. 198. *Scott Greenwood & Son: London,* 1912. 8°. **8755**. bb.

—— The Line to Legend Land. G. W. R. [i.e. Great Western Railway. By G. B. Barham.] ser. 1, 2. 1922. 8°. *See* GREAT WESTERN RAILWAY COMPANY. **10359**. aa. **10**

BARHAM (GEORGE R.) Masonry. An elementary text book for students in trade schools and apprentices . . . With illustrations. pp. 184. *London,* 1914. 8°. [*Longman's Technical Handicraft Series.*] 7945.r.5/7

ARHAM (GULIELMUS) *See* BARHAM (William F.)

ARHAM (HARRY)

— Building as a Public Service. A plan of reconstruction, *etc.* pp. 33. *J. B. Mackie & Co.: Dunfermline,* [1945.] 8°. **8288.** aaa. **65.**

— The Building Industry. A criticism and a plan for the future. pp. 99. *St. Botolph Publishing Co.: London,* 1947. 8°. [*Industrial Democracy Series.* no. 1.] W.P. **2050/1.**

ARHAM (HENRY) An Essay upon the Silk-Worm, *etc.* pp. 180. *J. Bettenham & T. Bickerton: London,* 1719. 8°. **988.** f. **36.**

— The Produce of India, Italy, and France, raised in England, by the Silk Manufactures. (Being some observations collected out of . . . Mr. Barham's incomparable Essay on the Silk-Worm.) [By John Apletree. With a copy of the letters patent granted to him for raising raw silk.] pp. 20. *London,* 1720. 8°. **712.** g. **17.** (4.)

— Hortus Americanus: containing an account of the trees, shrubs, and other vegetable productions, of South-America and the West-India Islands, and particularly of the Island of Jamaica, *etc.* [Edited by Alexander Aikman.] pp. 7. 212. *Alexander Aikman: Kingston, Jamaica,* 1794. 8°. **453.** e. **22.**

ARHAM (JOANNES) De variolis. (Dissertatio medico-mechanica inauguralis.) pp. 19. *Lugduni Batavorum,* 1724. 4°. **1185.** h. **19.** (15.)

ARHAM (JOSEPH FOSTER) Considerations on the Abolition of Negro Slavery, and the means of practically effecting it. pp. vii. 85. *James Ridgway: London,* 1823. 8°. **8156.** c. **74.** (2.)

— [Another copy.] Considerations on the Abolition of Negro Slavery, *etc.* *London,* 1823. 8°. **8158.** b. **7.**

— The third edition. pp. vii. 85. *James Ridgway: London,* 1824. 8°. **8156.** d. **31.** (2.)

— Considerations on the late Act for continuing the Prohibition of Corn in the Distillery; addressed in a letter to the Right Hon. Lord Holland. pp. 72. *James Ridgway: London,* 1810. 12°. **8227.** b. **63.** (2.)

ARHAM (MARIE)

— Blossom of the Crag. [A tale.] pp. 207. *China Inland Mission: London,* 1950. 8°. **04413.** de. **94.**

— Lin of Willow Valley. pp. 222. *China Inland Mission: London,* 1952. 8°. **04413.** k. **39.**

ARHAM (RICHARD HARRIS)

This heading includes works published by R. H. Barham under his own name and under the pseudonym Thomas Ingoldsby.

INGOLDSBY LEGENDS.

Complete Editions.

— The Ingoldsby Legends; or, Mirth and marvels, by Thomas Ingoldsby, Esquire. [The third series edited, with a memoir, by Richard H. D. Barham. With illustrations by George Cruikshank, John Leech and John Tenniel.] 3 ser. *Richard Bentley: London,* 1840–47. 12°. C. **59.** d. **6.**

— The Ingoldsby Legends . . . Second edition. [First series. With illustrations by George Cruikshank and John Leech.] pp. xii. 338. *Richard Bentley: London,* 1843. 12°. **12654.** d. **4.**

— [Another edition.] pp. xi. 530. *Richard Bentley: London,* 1858. 8°. **11646.** b. **19.**

BARHAM (RICHARD HARRIS)

—— Eighteenth edition. [Edited, with a memoir, by R. H. D. Barham. With illustrations by G. Cruikshank, J. Leech and J. Tenniel, and a portrait.] 2 vol. *Richard Bentley: London,* [1860.] 12°. **11648.** e. **2.**

—— New edition. pp. xi. 530. *Richard Bentley: London,* 1862. 8°. **11646.** dd. **8.**

—— [Another edition.] With illustrations by George Cruikshank, John Leech, and John Tenniel. pp. xiv. 511. *Richard Bentley: London,* 1865 [1864]. 4°. **11651.** f. **2.**

—— Carmine edition. [With illustrations by G. Cruikshank and J. Leech.] pp. xi. 468. *Richard Bentley: London,* 1866 [1865]. 8° **11646.** cc. **1.**

—— [Another edition.] With illustrations by George Cruikshank, John Leech, and John Tenniel. pp. xiv. 513. *Richard Bentley: London,* 1866. 4°. **11651.** f. **3.**

—— [Another edition.] pp. viii. 176. *Richard Bentley: London,* 1869 [1868]. 8°. **11646.** cc. **10.**

—— [Another edition.] The Nonpareil Victoria Ingoldsby. A pocket edition. pp. xiv. 417. *Richard Bentley: London,* 1869. 8°. **11647.** aaa. **17.**

—— [Another edition.] The Ingoldsby Legends . . . Edited, with notes introductory and illustrative, by R. H. Dalton Barham. (Annotated edition.) 2 vol. *Richard Bentley: London,* 1870 [1869]. 8°. **11650.** g. **1.**

—— The Ingoldsby Legends . . . With Cruikshanks' illustrations. pp. 404. *W. J. Widdleton: New York,* 1872. 8°. **11655.** aaa. **8.**

—— [Another edition.] With illustrations by George Cruikshank, John Leech, and John Tenniel. pp. xii. 514. *R. Bentley & Son: London,* 1874. 4°. C. **70.** d. **10.**

With the autographs and photographs of G. Cruikshank and his wife.

—— [Another edition.] 3 vol. *R. Bentley & Son: London,* 1875. 8°. **11649.** de. **3.**

Known as the "Burlington Edition."

—— The Nonpareil Victoria Ingoldsby . . . A pocket edition, *etc.* pp. xiv. 417. *R. Bentley & Son: London,* 1877. 8°. **11657.** e. **18.**

A reissue of the edition of 1869.

—— Edinburgh edition. With thirty-two illustrations by Cruikshank, Leech and Tenniel. pp. xvi. 546. *R. Bentley & Son: London,* 1879. 8°. **11612.** c. **5.**

—— [A reissue.] The Victoria Ingoldsby Legends, *etc.* *London,* 1879. 8°. **11659.** a. **19.**

—— The Ingoldsby Legends, *etc.* pp. xi. 468. *Richard Bentley & Son: London,* 1880. 8°. **11657.** h. **78.**

The titlepage is engraved.

—— Edinburgh edition. With fifty illustrations by Cruikshank, Leech, Tenniel, Barham, Du Maurier, etc. pp. xvi. 546. *R. Bentley & Son: London,* 1882. 8°. **11646.** d. **62.**

—— Popular edition. With sixteen illustrations by Cruikshank, Leech, Tenniel, and Barham. pp. xi. 468. *R. Bentley & Son: London,* 1882. 8°. **11646.** e. **65.**

—— Victoria edition, *etc.* (The seventy-fourth edition.) pp. viii. 417. *R. Bentley & Son: London,* 1882. 8°. **11611.** bbb. **43.**

The date on the wrapper is 1886.

BARHAM (Richard Harris)

—— The Ingoldsby Legends . . . Popular edition, *etc.* pp. xi. 468. *Richard Bentley & Son: London,* 1887. 8°. **11657. f. 31.**

A reissue of the Popular Edition of 1882.

—— [Another edition.] 3 pt. *G. Routledge & Sons: London,* 1889 [1888]. 8°. **12316. dd. 13.**

—— [Another copy in one volume, with a collective titlepage.] **12316. dd. 12.**

—— [Another edition.] Illustrated with reproduction of the original steel engravings by Leech and Cruikshank. pp. xxii. 426. *Ward, Lock & Co.: London,* 1889. 8°. [*Minerva Library of Famous Books.*] **012207. h. 10.**

—— [Another edition.] With reproductions of the original illustrations by Cruikshank and Leech. pp. 607. *G. Routledge & Sons: London,* 1889. 8°. **012207. e. 11.**

—— Edited by his daughter, Mrs. E. A. Bond. (88th edition.) [With illustrations by G. Cruikshank, J. Leech and J. Tenniel.] 3 vol. *R. Bentley & Son: London,* 1894. 8°. **2288. e. 9.**
With additional titlepages, engraved.

—— [Another edition.] Illustrated by Arthur Rackham. pp. xxiii. 638. *J. M. Dent & Co.: London,* 1898. 8°. [*Illustrated Romances.*] **012208. i. 7.**
Imperfect; wanting the frontispiece.

—— [Another edition.] pp. xi. 604. *Grant Richards: London,* 1901. 8°. [*World's Classics.* vol. 9.] **012209. df. 9.**

—— [Another edition.] Illustrated by H. Cole. pp. xx. 640. *John Lane: London & New York,* 1903 [1902]. 8°. **11648. h. 8.**

—— [Another edition.] With notes and an introduction by J. B. Atlay. [With a portrait.] 2 vol. *Methuen & Co.: London,* 1903 [1902]. 8°. [*Little Library.*] **012208. df. 7/30.**

—— [Another edition.] pp. xiv. 656. *George Newnes: London,* 1904. 8°. **12274. df. 3.**

—— [Another edition.] With a portrait and twenty-five illustrations by Cruikshank, Leech, and others. (Oxford edition.) pp. lv. 527. *Henry Frowde: London,* 1905. 8°. **11647. dd. 25.**

—— [Another edition.] pp. viii. 599. *G. Routledge & Sons: London,* [1905.] 8°. [*New Universal Library.*] **12204. p. 2/19.**

—— [Another edition.] Illustrated by Arthur Rackham. pp. xix. 549. *J. M. Dent & Co.: London; E. P. Dutton & Co.: New York,* 1907. 4°. **11647. f. 40.**

—— [Another copy.] **L.P.** **L.R. 26. d. 4.**

—— [Another edition.] pp. 495. *Cassell & Co.: London,* 1908. 8°. [*People's Library.*] **012206.de.1/46.**

—— [Another edition.] Illustrated by Arthur Rackham. *William Heinemann: London,* 1910. 4°. **11642. g. 45.**
A reissue of the edition of 1907.

—— [Another edition.] pp. 551. *London,* [1911.] 8°. [*Nelson Classics.*] **012206. f. 45.**

—— [Another edition.] With illustrations in colour by H. G. Theaker. pp. xiii. 546. *Macmillan & Co.: London,* 1911. 8°. **011652. m. 39.**

BARHAM (Richard Harris)

Verse Legends.

—— The Ingoldsby Legends . . . With sixty illustrations by George Cruikshank, John Leech, and John Tenniel. pp. xii. 427. *Richard Bentley: London,* 1864 [1863]. 4°. **1347. k. 6.**

—— [Another copy.] The Ingoldsby Legends, *etc.* *London,* 1864 [1863]. 4°. **11660. f. 1.**

—— [Another copy.] The Ingoldsby Legends, *etc.* *London,* 1864 [1863]. 4°. **C. 129. d. 3.**

—— [Another edition.] With fifty illustrations from originals by Cruikshank, Leech, and Tenniel. pp. viii. 180. *R. Bentley & Son: London,* 1885. 8°. **12316. i. 42.**

—— [Another copy.] **F.P.** **11646. dd. 19.**
With the addition of a frontispiece.

—— [Another edition.] pp. 382. *London,* [1889.] 8°. [*Cassell's Red Library.*] **12600. ccc. 8.**

—— [A reissue.] *Cassell & Co.: London,* [1890.] 8°. **012314. i. 23.**

—— [A reissue.] *Walter Scott: London,* [1892.] 8°. **12315. e. 37.**

—— [Another edition.] [With illustrations by G. Cruikshank, J. Leech and J. Tenniel.] pp. 382. *R. E. King. London,* [1893.] 8°. **11612. e. 24**

—— [A reissue of the edition of 1889.] *Printed for the Booksellers,* [1895?] 8°. **011648. ee. 36**

—— The Ingoldsby Legends. *Walter Scott: London* [1895?] 8°. **012331. k. 9**
A reissue of the edition of 1892.

—— The Ingoldsby Legends. *R. E. King: London* [1895?] 8°. **11657. cc. 4**
A reissue of the edition of 1893 *without the illustrations*

—— [A reissue.] The Ingoldsby Legends. *London* [1897?] 8°. **11658. ee. 6**
Without the illustrations.

Select Legends.

—— The Ingoldsby Legends . . . First series. pp. 32[illegible] *D. Appleton & Co.: New York,* 1852. 8°. **11658. e. 3[illegible]**
Part of a series entitled "Appletons' Popular Library [illegible] the Best Authors."

—— The Witches' Frolic and The Bagman's Dog . . . Il[l]ustrated by Jane E. Cook. pp. 47. *R. Bentley & Son: London,* 1876. 4°. **1876. c.**

—— The Ingoldsby Legends. Illustrated by Cruikshan[k], Leech, and Tenniel. (People's edition.) [A selection] pp. 64. *R. Bentley & Son: London,* 1881. 4°. **11651. m.**

—— [A reissue.] *London,* 1882. 4°. **12205. l.**

—— The Smuggler's Leap, Bloudie Jacke of Shrewsberr[y], The Lay of St. Cuthbert, and other Ingoldsby Legend[s]. pp. vii. 118. *London, New York,* [1886.] 8°. [*Wa[rd,] Lock, and Co.'s Popular Library of Literary Treasures.*] **12205. f. 1/[illegible]**

—— The Witches' Frolic, the Black Mousquetaire, and ot[her] Ingoldsby Legends. pp. xii. 114. *London, New Yo[rk,]* 1886. 8°. [*Ward, Lock and Co.'s Popular Library [of] Literary Treasures.*] **12205. f. [illegible]**

BARHAM (Richard Harris)

—— Tales of Mirth and Marvel from the Ingoldsby Legends . . . Illustrated by Gordon Browne. pp. x. 224. *Wells Gardner & Co.: London,* 1907. 8°. **11647**. dd. **28**.

—— The Ingoldsby Legends, *etc.* [A selection.] pp. xiii. 394. *Blackie & Son: London,* 1909. 8°. [*Red Letter Library.*] **012209.fff.1/48.**

—— The Ingoldsby Legends. [A selection.] pp. 176. *Siegle, Hill & Co.: London,* [1911.] 32°. [*Langham Booklets.*] **944**. b. **96**.

—— The Jackdaw of Rheims & other Ingoldsby Legends. pp. 48. *St. Catherine Press: London,* [1912.] 16°. [*Arden Books.* no. 18.] **12209**. a. **35/18**.

—— The Ingoldsby Legends. Selection. pp. 99. *Holerth Press: London; Vienna* printed, [1924.] 16°. [*Holerth Library.* no. 19.] **012207**. g. **2/19**.

—— The Ingoldsby Legends . . . The Jackdaw of Rheims, Jack Do Rheims. Look at the Clock, Gwelwch y Cloc. *Welsh. See* Burns (Robert) *the Poet.* [*Single Poems.*] Burns ac Ingoldsby yn Gymraeg, *etc.* 1931. 8°. **11633**. df. **46**.

—— The Ingoldsby Legends . . . Selected and edited by John Tanfield . . . and Guy Boas. pp. xv. 280. *Macmillan & Co.: London,* 1951. 8°. [*Scholar's Library.*] **012209**. d. **1/87**.

Single Legends.

—— The Jackdaw of Rheims. With twelve illustrations, printed in colours. pp. 43. *Richard Bentley: London,* 1870. 4°. **11651**. i. **16**.

—— [Another edition.] Wyth ye old writing & ye new illustrations, by Ernest Maurice Jessop. *Eyre & Spottiswoode: London,* [1883.] fol. **1870**. b. **8**.
Printed on one side of the leaf only.

—— [Another edition.] Illustrated by A. R. Nicholson, *etc.* pp. 12. *S. H. Nicholson: Totteridge,* 1896. 16°. **11647**. de. **36**.

—— [Another edition.] With illustrations by Charles Folkard. *Gay & Hancock: London,* 1913. fol. **1869**. d. **29**.

—— [Another edition.] Illustrated by Martin Travers. *Society of SS. Peter & Paul: London,* 1914. 8°. **11647**. df. **55**.

—— [Another edition.] With illustrations by Charles Folkard. *Gale & Polden: London,* [1917.] 4°. **12805**. n. **59**.

—— *See* Stock (E. E.) Jim Crow. An easily staged musical play . . . Founded on 'The Jackdaw of Rheims', *etc.* [1913.] 8°. **11778**. l. **44**.

—— The Knight and the Lady . . . With the letters & illustrations of Ernest M. Jessop. pp. 19. *Eyre & Spottiswoode: London,* [1886.] fol. **1874**. e. **19**.

—— De Ridder en de dame. Eene Engelsche legende. Vrij vertaald. [A translation of "The Knight and the Lady" from "The Ingoldsby Legends."] [1852?] 16°. [Zeggelen (*W. J. van*) *Luimige verhalen.*] *See* Ridder. **11556**. b. **40**.

—— The Lay of St. Aloys . . . With the old letters & new illustrations of Ernest M. Jessop. ff. xxxiii. *Eyre & Spottiswoode: London,* [1884.] fol. **1876**. f. **9**.
Printed on one side of the leaf only.

BARHAM (Richard Harris)

—— The Lay of St. Odille . . . Illustrated by Martin Travers. *Samuel Gurney: London,* 1915. 8°. **011649**. de. **78**.

—— Look at the Clock. [An abridged version of "Patty Morgan the Milkmaid's Story" from "The Ingoldsby Legends."] [1850?] *s. sh.* 4°. *See* Clock. **11621**. b. **22**. **(30.)**

—— [Another copy.] **C.116.h.2.(47.)**

—— Vulgar Little Boy. [An abridged version of "Misadventures at Margate" from "The Ingoldsby Legends."] [1850?] *s. sh.* 4°. *See* Boy. **11621**. k. **4**. **(48.)**

—— The Smuggler's Leap . . . Illustrated by Jane E. Cook, *etc.* pp. 14. *R. Bentley & Son: London,* 1877. 4°. **1869**. a. **10**.

—— The Witches' Frolic . . . Pictured by E. M. Jessop. ff. xix. *Eyre & Spottiswoode: London,* 1888. fol. **1875**. a. **10**.
Printed on one side of the leaf only.

Appendix.

—— *See* Sealy (George W.) A Concordance to the Ingoldsby Legends. Edinburgh edition. London 1882. 1925, *etc.* fol. L.R. **257**. c. **1**.

Miscellaneous Works.

—— Baldwin; or, a Miser's heir. A serio-comic tale . . . By an Old Bachelor (George Hector Epaminondas [i.e. R. H. Barham]). 2 vol. 1820. 12°. *See* George Hector Epaminondas, *pseud.* N. **33**.

—— The Garrick Club. Notices of one hundred and thirty five of its former members . . . With facsimile of the original ms. pp. viii. 58. *Privately printed: [New York,]* 1896. 8°. **10348**. d. **26**.

—— The Ingoldsby Lyrics. By T. Ingoldsby. Edited by his son (R. H. D. Barham). [With a portrait.] pp. xii. 308. *R. Bentley & Son: London,* 1881 [1880]. 8°. **2292**. f.

—— [Personal reminiscences.] 1875. *See* Stoddard (Richard H.) Bric-à-Brac Series. (vol. 4. Personal Reminiscences by Barham, Harness, and Hodder.) 1874, *etc.* 8°. **12209**. bbb. **12**.

—— Some Account of My Cousin Nicholas. By Thomas Ingoldsby . . . To which is added, The Rubber of Life. 3 vol. *Richard Bentley: London,* 1841. 12°. N. **2172**.

—— Some Account of My Cousin Nicholas. By Thomas Ingoldsby. pp. xii. 370. *Richard Bentley: London,* 1846. 8°. [*Standard Novels.* no. 103.] **1153**. d. **21**.

APPENDIX.

—— *See* Barham (Richard H. D.) The Life and Letters of the Rev. Richard Harris Barham . . . With a selection from his miscellaneous poems. 1870. 8°. **10856**. cc. **16**.

—— —— 1880. 8°. **2408**. c. **1**.

—— *See* Harper (Charles G.) The Ingoldsby Country, *etc.* 1904. 8°. **10369**. dd. **13**.

—— —— 1906. 8°. **010347**. bb. **6**.

—— —— 1911. 8°. **2366**. c. **18**.

BARHAM (Richard Harris Dalton) *See* Barham (Richard H.) [*Ingoldsby Legends.—Complete Editions.*] The Ingoldsby Legends, *etc.* [The third series edited, with a memoir, by R. H. D. Barham.] 1840, *etc.* 12°. **C. 59.** d. **6.**

—— *See* Barham (Richard H.) [*Ingoldsby Legends.—Complete Editions.*] The Ingoldsby Legends, *etc.* [Edited, with a memoir, by R. H. D. Barham.] [1860.] 12°. **11648.** e. **2.**

—— *See* Barham (Richard H.) [*Ingoldsby Legends.—Complete Editions.*] The Ingoldsby Legends . . . Edited, with notes introductory and illustrative, by R. H. D. Barham. 1870. 8°. **11650.** g. **1.**

—— *See* Barham (Richard H.) [*Miscellaneous Works.*] The Ingoldsby Lyrics . . . Edited by his son (R. H. D. Barham). 1881. 8°. **2292.** f.

—— The Life and Letters of the Rev. Richard Harris Barham . . . With a selection from his miscellaneous poems. [With a portrait.] 2 vol. *Richard Bentley: London,* 1870. 8°. **10856.** cc. **16.**

—— A new edition. pp. viii. 421. *R. Bentley & Son: London,* 1880. 8°. **2408.** c. **1.**

—— The Life and Remains of Theodore Edward Hook. [With portraits.] 2 vol. *Richard Bentley: London,* 1849. 12°. **10855.** c. **1.**

—— New edition, revised and corrected. pp. xi. 491. *Richard Bentley: London,* 1853. 8°. **10855.** bb. **5.**

—— A new and revised edition. pp. xi. 491. *R. Bentley & Son: London,* 1877. 8°. **2408.** a. **3.**

BARHAM (Thomas Foster) *the Elder.* *See* also Elachistos, *pseud.* [i.e. T. F. Barham.]

—— Abdallah; or, the Arabian Martyr: a Christian drama, in three acts. [In verse. By T. F. Barham.] pp. 31. 1820. 8°. *See* Abdallah. **994.** l. **1.** **(7.)**

—— Abdallah . . . With a poem on the same subject, by James Montgomery . . . Second edition, revised and enlarged. pp. 45. *Hatchard: London,* 1821. 8°. **11781.** ee. **19.** **(2.)**

—— Colonel Gardiner; a Christian drama, in three parts. By a Bible Student [i.e. T. F. Barham]. pp. 59. 1823. 8°. *See* Gardiner, *Colonel.* **T. 1062.** **(12.)**

—— Elijah; a sacred poem: in four cantos. pp. 38. *Hatchard & Son: London,* 1822. 8°. **T. 1063.** **(5.)**

—— A Letter from a Trinitarian, to an Unitarian or Socinian. [By T. F. Barham.] pp. 12. 1811. 8°. *See* Trinitarian. **4107.** dd. **2.** **(7.)**

—— Scripture Millennium Nigh. By a Bible Student, *etc.* [Signed: B., i.e. T. F. Barham.] [1840?] 8°. *See* B. **9905.** d. **20.** (7.)

BARHAM (Thomas Foster) *the Younger.* *See* Bible.—*Matthew.—Selections.* [*Polyglott.*] First Lines in Greek; or, the Sermon on the Mount . . . With an interlinear translation. By T. F. Barham. 1834. 8°. **3020.** aa. **30.**

—— *See* Hephaestion, *Grammarian.* Ἡφαιστιωνος Ἐγχειριδιον περι μετρων και ποιηματων. The Enkheiridion of Hehfaistiown concerning metres and poems. Translated . . . and illustrated by notes and a rythmical notation; with prolegomena on rythm and accent. By T. F. Barham. 1843. 8°. **11805.** d. **21.**

BARHAM (Thomas Foster) *the Younger.*

—— *See* Homer. [*Iliad.—English.*] The Iliad of Homer Book i. Rendered into English hexameters by J. F Barham, *etc.* 1871. 8°. **11315.** g. **40**

—— Free Catholicism, the Principle of Unity in the Christia Church. An address, *etc.* pp. 23. *Chapple Newton Bushel; Whitfield: London,* [1862.] 12°. **702.** c. **40.** (3.

—— Greek Roots in English Rhymes; illustrated by ex amples for fixing the sense and assisting the memory pp. xvi. 161. *Baldwin & Cradock: London,* 1837. 12°. **12924.** a. **2**

—— An Introduction to Greek Grammar on a New Plar pp. xii. 151. *Rowland Hunter: London; C. Upham Exeter,* 1829. 8°. **624.** b. **2**

—— One God the Father; or, the Unitarian doctrin briefly stated . . . Third edition enlarged. pp. 120. *John Mardon: London,* 1835. 12°. **1120.** e. **2**

—— One God the Father; or, the Strict and prop monotheism of the Gospel vindicated . . . A new editio revised and enlarged. pp. vi. 175. *Whitfie Green & Son: London,* 1867. 8°. **4225.** aa.

—— Philadelphia: or, the Claims of humanity. A plea f social and religious reform. pp. viii. 448. *Chapm & Hall: London,* 1858. 8°. **8282.** d. **4**

BARHAM (William Foster) *See* Shakespeare (W [*Julius Caesar.—English and Greek.*] Versus præm Porsoniano . . . dignati . . . auctore Gulielmo Barha [1821.] 8°. **732.** c. **10.** (3

—— *See* Shakespeare (W.) [*Othello.—English and Gree* Versus præmio Porsoniano . . . dignati . . . auctore Gulie Barham. [1821.] 8°. **732.** c. **10.** (2

—— Descriptions of Niagara; selected from vari travellers; with original additions by W. Barham. [W plates.] pp. 180. *The Compiler: Gravesend,* [1847.] **1304.** i.

BARHAM (William Henry) Theory and Practice Navigation, *etc.* pp. 160. *London & Glasgo* [1893.] 8°. [*Collins' Elementary Science Series.*] **8708.** aaa.

BARHAM (William R.) Advanced Arithmetic Class Bo A collection of exercises in commercial arithmetic, pp. vii. 156. *Sir I. Pitman & Sons: London,* 1930. 8 **08534.** de.

—— Arithmetic Class Book. A collection of exercises commercial arithmetic, with answers, *etc.* pp. vi. 145. *Sir I. Pitman & Sons: London,* 1927. 8°. **08531.** c.

—— Second edition. pp. vii. 155. *Sir I. Pitman & So London,* 1931. 8°. **08534.** de.

—— Arithmetic Class Book . . . Third edition. pp. vii. *Sir I. Pitman & Sons: London,* 1934. 8°. **08534.** ee.

—— Arithmetic Class Book . . . Fourth edition. pp. vii. *Sir I. Pitman & Sons: London,* 1935. 8°. **08534.** g.

—— Arithmetic Class Book . . . Fifth edition. pp. vii. *Sir Isaac Pitman & Sons: London,* 1947. 8°. **08535.** aa.

BARHEBRÆUS. *See* Grīghōr (Abu al-Faraj) ca Bar-Hebræus.

BAR-HILLEL (Yehoshua)

—— *See* Papers. Papers on Mechanical Translation. Y. Bar-Hillel and others.] [1952.] Mic. A.

BARHYDT (David Parish) Industrial Exchanges and Social Remedies, with a consideration of taxation. pp. 238. *G. P. Putnam: New York*, 1849. 12°. 8275. b. 39.

—— Life. A poem. pp. 89. *Wm. Holdridge: New York*, 1851. 12°. 11686. b. 6.

BARI, *City of.* Chronicon ignoti civis Barensis, sive Lupi Protospatæ, cum notis Camilli Peregrinii. 1724. *See* Muratori (L. A.) Rerum italicarum scriptores. tom. 5. 1723, *etc.* fol. L.1.h.1/5.

—— Niccolò Piccinni, commemorato dal maestro Pasquale La Rotella nel II centenario della nascita. pp. 43. *Bari*, 1928. fol. Hirsch 4234.

—— Petizione de' cittadini Baresi al Parlamento Nazionale in Torino. [Praying for the revocation of a circular, issued by the Minister of War, concerning conscription.] pp. 8. [*Bari*, 1863.] 4°. 8033. dd. 13.

Church of San Nicola.

—— Le Pergamene di S. Nicola di Bari, *etc.* [Edited by Francesco Nitti.] 6 vol. *Bari*, 1900–50. 4°. [*Codice diplomatico barese.* vol. 4, 6, 13, 16, 18.] 07701.dd.23/4,6,13,16.18.

—— *Duomo.* Le Pergamene del Duomo di Bari . . . Per G. B. Nitto de Rossi e Francesco Nitti. [With facsimiles.] 3 vol. *Bari*, 1897, 1939. 4°. [*Codice Diplomatico Barese.* vol. 1, 2. Nuova Ser. vol. 15.] 07701.dd.23/1,2.

Regia Scuola Superiore di Commercio, afterwards *Regio Istituto Superiore di Scienze Economiche e Commerciali.*

—— Archivio scientifico. 3 vol. *Bari*, 1929–31. 8°. Ac. 2505. c.

—— La Terra di Bari sotto l'aspetto storico, economico e naturale. Pubblicazione della Provincia di Bari per la Esposizione Universale di Parigi. (Monografie illustrative . . . compilate dalla R. Scuola Superiore di Commercio.) [With an introduction by S. Fiorese.] 3 vol. *Trani*, 1900. fol. 10131. k. 6.

Soprintendenza bibliografica per la Puglia e la Lucania.

—— Mostra documentaria del pensiero economico-politico pugliese dei secc. XVI-XX. Catalogo. [Compiled by Beniamino d'Amato.] pp. 78. pl. XVI. *Bari*, 1951. 8°. 7960. ff. 17.

Unione Giovanile Valdese di Bari.

—— Bollettino dell'Unione Giovanile Valdese di Bari. anno 4. n. speciale. 17 feb. 1948. *Bari*, 1948. fol. 1884.b.25.(46.)

BARI, *Province of.* Anonymi Barensis monachi Chronicon de rebus in Barensi provincia gestis; additis notis . . . Nicolai Aloysia. *See* Muratori (L. A.) Antiquitates Italiæ, *etc.* tom. 1. 1738, *etc.* fol. Circ. 16. b.

—— Codice diplomatico Barese. *See* infra: *Commissione Provinciale di Archeologia e Storia Patria.*

—— *Comitato per la Mostra di Arte Pugliese alla Esposizione di Torino.* Nella terra di Bari. Ricordi di arte medioevale. Illustrati da 127 zincotipie. pp. 70. *Trani*, 1898. 4°. 7814. i. 8.

—— *Commissione Provinciale di Archeologia e Storia Patria.* *See* infra: *Società di Storia Patria per la Puglia.*

BARI, *Province of.—Società di Storia Patria per la Puglia.*

Commissione Provinciale di Archeologia e Storia Patria, 1894–1936.
Regia Deputazione di Storia Patria per le Puglie, 1936–46.
Deputazione di Storia Patria per le Puglie, 1946–48?
Società di Storia Patria per la Puglia, 1948?–.

—— Codice diplomatico Barese. *Bari*, 1897–1950. 4°. 18 Vol. 07701.dd.23.

—— Documenti e monografie per la storia di Terra di Bari. *Bari*, 1900– . 8°. 1827. g. 2.

BARI, Antonio, *Archbishop of.* *See* Puteo.

—— Ascanio, *Archbishop of.* *See* Gesualdo.

—— Giovanni Battista Ettore, *Archbishop of.* [1778–1780.] *See* Caracciolo.

——, Michele Basilio, *Archbishop of.* *See* Clary.

BARI (Aristide) Memoria storico-statistica sulla sede di Como, 1877–1887, *etc.* pp. 32. 1887. 8°. *See* Italy.—*Associazione fra gli Operai Tipografi Italiani.* 4533. ee. 13. (2.)

BĀRĪ ('Azīz) *See* 'Azīz Bārī, *Munshī.*

BARI (Francesco Antonio Cardassi da) *See* Cardassi da Bari.

BARI (N. K.)

—— *See* Luzin (N. N.) Интеграл и тригонометрический ряд. Редакция и комментарии Н. К. Бари и Д. Е. Меньшова. Вступительные статьи Н. К. Бари, В. В. Голубева, *etc.* 1951. 8°. 8536. aa. 16.

BARI (Niccolò da) called *dell'Arca.* *See* Niccolò, *da Bari* called *dell'Arca.*

BĀRIĀ (J. H.) *See* Sa'dī. [*Gulistān.—English.*] A Literal Translation of Persian Gulistan, chapter 1. By J. H. Baria. 1898. 8°. 757. b. 51. (2.)

BÁRIÁ (Sháपurji Bikháji) *See* Shāpūrjī Bikhājī Bāriā.

BARIAC (Antoine) *See* Bouillon-Landais ( ) Un Procès pour une chanson . . . Antoine Bariac contre Jean Pellenc. 1865. 8°. 5424. dd. 22.

BARIACUS LERMEUS (Gabriel) *See* Lerm (G. de)

BARIANO (Niccolo) *See* Barianus (Nicolaus)

BARIANUS (Nicolaus) Causa Vitaliana de precedentia heremitarum ꝛ minorum per . . . Niholam Barianum de Placētia . . . Decisa. G. L. *per Carolum derleriuз: Cremone*, octauo idus Aprilis [6 April], 1500. 4°. IA. 30854.

26 *leaves, the last blank. Sig.* ✠[4] a–d[4] e[6]. *Double columns*, 41 *lines to a column.*

—— De Monte Impietatis. [*Carolus de Darleriis:*] *Cremonæ*, nonis octobris [7 Oct.], 1496. 4°. IA. 30847.

34 *leaves. Sig.* a–d[4] E[4] f–h[4] i[2]. 40 *lines to a page.*

BARIAT (E.) L'Anarchie judiciaire en Algérie. pp. 104. *Oran*, 1894. 8°. 05319. k. 10.

BARIATINSKY (*Princess* Anatole Marie) *See* Baryatinskaya (Mariya Sergyeevna) *Princess.*

BARIATINSKY (Vladimir Vladimirovich) *Prince.* *See* Baryatinsky.

BARIBAL (Albertus) *pseud.* [i.e. —— Seeger.] Bierzeitungs-Poesie'n. Herausgegeben von A. Baribal. pp. vii. 118. *Breslau*, 1860. 16°. 11525. aaa. 63. (2.)

BARIC (Arnaud) Les Rares secrets, ou remedes incomparables, vniuersels, & particuliers, preseruatifs & curatifs, contre la peste des hommes, & des animaux; dans l'ordre admirable interieur & exterieur du desinfectemente des personnes & des maisons, des animaux & des estables, *etc.* *F. Boude: Tolose,* 1646. 12°. **1167**. a. **57**.

—— [Another edition.] La Conduite asseurée, du desinfectement des personnes, des maisons, des animaux, & des estables, en temps de contagion, pour en arrester le cours & conseruer la vie a plusieurs, si Dieu par sa misericorde y donne sa benediction, *etc.* pp. 137. *E. Langlois; I. Langlois: Paris,* 1668. 12°. **1168**. a. **13**.

BARIĆ (Henrik)

—— *See* Belgrade.—*Университет.—Семинар за Арбанаску Филологију.* Архив за арбанаску старину ... Уредник Х. Барић. 1923, *etc.* 8°. Ac. **1131**. g/**2**.

—— *See* Tomić (J. N.) Грађа за историју покрета на Балкану против турака крајем xvi и почетком xvii века. По италијанским архивама скупио J. H. Томић. [Edited by H. Barić.] 1933, *etc.* 8°. [*Зборник за историју, језик и књижевност српског народа.* Одељ. 2. књ. 5, 6, *etc.*] Ac. **1131**/**5**.

—— Albanorumänische Studien. *Sarajevo,* 1919– . 8°. [*Zur Kunde der Balkanhalbinsel.* vol. 7, *etc.*] **10127.ee.6/26.**

—— Ilirske jezične studije. (Poseban otisak iz 272. knjige Rada Jugoslavenske akademije znanosti i umjetnosti.) pp. 56. *Zagreb,* 1948. 8°. **12975**. l. **37**.

—— Rečnik srpskoga ili hrvatskoga i arbanaskoga jezika. (Fjalor i gjuhës sërbishte ose kroatishte dhe i shqipes.) *Zagreb,* 1950– . 8°. W.P. c. **306**.

BARIC (Jules Jean Antoine) *See* Kroknotski ( ) Histoire de Martin Landor . . . Dessinée par Baric. [1863.] 4°. **12807**. i. **53**.

BARICCO (Pietro) Gli Asili d'infanzia o le scuole infantili in Torino, *etc.* pp. 86. *Torino,* 1884. 8°. **8309**. e. **35**. (**1**.)

—— Il R. Liceo-Ginnasio Cavour. Cronaca dell' anno scolastico 1875–76. Pubblicata dal preside T. C. P. Baricco. L'Alberoni e la sua dipartita dalla Spagna. Saggio di studio storico critico. Per Vincenzo Papa. pp. 129. 1876. 8°. *See* Turin.—*Regio Liceo-Ginnasio Cavour.* **8310**. h. **2**.

BARICELLI (Giulio Caesare) *See* Baricellus (Julius Caesar)

BARICELLUS (Julius Caesar) Iulii Cæsaris Baricelli . . . De hydronosa natura, siue sudore humani corporis, libri quatuor, *etc.* pp. 428. *Apud L. Scoriggium: Neapoli,* 1614. 4°. **549**. e. **9**.
The titlepage is engraved.

—— Iulii Cæsaris Baricelli . . . De lactis, seri, & butyri facultatibus, & vsu, opuscula, *etc.* pp. 342. *Apud L. Scoriggium: Neapoli,* 1623. 4°. **1038**. i. **4**. (**1**.)
The titlepage is engraved.

—— Iulii Cæsaris Baricelli . . . Hortulus genialis: siue, arcanorum valde admirabilium tam in arte medica quàm reliqua philosophia compendium, *etc.* pp. 353. *M. Smitz: Coloniæ,* 1620. 12°. **779**. a. **11**.

—— [Another edition.] Iulii Cæsaris Baricelli . . . Hortulus genialis, siue rerum iucundarum, medicarum, & memorabilium compendium . . . Huic accessit liber de esculentorum potulentorumque facultatibus, Arnaldo Preitagio [*sic*] . . . auctore [or rather, translated by A. Freitag from the Italian of B. Pisanelli]. 2 pt. *P. Albert: Geneuæ,* 1620. 8°. **779**. a. **12**.

BARICH (Dewey F.)

—— *See* Fleming (Joseph W.) Applied Drawing and Sketching. [By] J. W. Fleming, D. F. Barich, *etc.* 1950. 4°. **7949**. g. **4**

—— *See* Fleming (Joseph W.) Applied Drawing and Sketch ing. [By] J. W. Fleming . . . D. F. Barich, *etc.* 1953. 4° **7949**. g. **33**

BARICH (Dewey F.) and **SMITH** (Leonard C.)

—— Metal Work for Industrial Arts Shops . . . Illustrated pp. 96. *American Technical Society: Chicago,* 1952. 4°. **8773**. c. **3**
A slip bearing the imprint "Technical Press: London has been pasted below the original imprint.

BARICH (Werner)

—— Lujo Brentano als Sozialpolitiker. Inaugural-Dissertation, *etc.* pp. 84. *Berlin,* 1936. 8°. **08008**. cc. **24**

BARICHELLA (Lorenzo) Maria Stuarda. Tragedia. [I verse.] pp. 53. *Vicenza,* 1829. 8°. **11715**. d. **4**

BARICHELLA (Vittorio) Alpi Vicentine. Notizie storich (Nozze auspicalissime Da Schio-Marcello.) pp. 35. *Vicenza,* 1864. 8°. **09009**. c. **16**. (**1**

—— Andrea Palladio e la sua scuola. Cenni. [With portrait and a plan.] pp. 71. *Lonigo,* 1880. 4°. **7820.s.58**

BARICO, *pseud.*

—— Cuadernos taurinos. (La Fiesta nacional. Histor sintética de la fiesta de toros en España.) [Edited "Barico."] *Madrid,* 1951– . 8°. W.P. c. **55**

BARICS (Adalbert) Die gewöhnliche Krönungsfeyer d ungarischen Könige und Königinnen beschrieben von Edlen von Baritsch. pp. 63. *Pest,* 1790. 8°. **9930**. b.

—— A' magyar királyok' és királynék' koronáztatásokn inneplése, melylynek szokott szer-tartásait Német nyelv le-írta . . . Barits A. . . . magyarra fordította Lambach pp. 71. *Pestenn,* 1790. 8°. **9930**. b.

BARIDE (Atmaram Bapuji) *See* Ātmārāma Bāp Bāride.

BAR-'IDHTĀ, *Rabban.* *See* Abraham, *the Priest.* T Praiseworthy History of our Pious and Holy Fath Rabban Bar-'Idtâ. 1902. 8°. [*Luzac's Semitic T and Translation Series.* vol. 9–11.] **753**. cc.

BARIDON (Felix E.) and **LOOMIS** (Earl H.) Person Problems. Methods of analysis and control. pp. x. 4 *McGraw-Hill Book Co.: New York & London,* 1931. 8 **8275**. tt.

BARIDON (Silvio F.)

—— *See* Tyard (P. de) *Bishop of Chalon-sur-Saône.* Œuv (Le Solitaire premier. Édition critique par S. F. Barid 1950, *etc.* 8°. W.P. **2063**

—— *See* Tyard (P. de) *Écuyer de la Grande Écurie du* Inventaire de la bibliothèque de Pontus de Tyard. Pu par S. F. Baridon. 1950. 8°. W.P. a. **3**

—— Claude de Kerquefinen, italianisant et hérétique. pp *Genève,* 1954. 4°. [*Travaux d'humanisme et renaissa* no. 12.] W.P. a. **31**

BARIÉ (Ernest) Traité pratique des maladies du c et de l'aorte, *etc.* pp. viii. 984. *Paris,* 1900. 8°. **7615**. dd.

BARIÉ (Ottavio)

—— Idee e dottrine imperialistiche nell'Inghilterra vittoriana. pp. 326. *Bari*, 1953. 8°. [*Istituto Italiano per gli Studi Storici. Publications.* no. 5.] Ac. **6534.** b.

—— Il Problema siculo-napoletana nella politica britannica dalla fine della mediazione di Lord Minto all'inizio della mediazione di Sir William Temple. Aprile–novembre 1848. *In:* Rivista storica italiana. anno 63. fasc. 3. pp. 292–339. 1951. 8°. P.P. **3899.** c.

BARIGAZZ (Jusfein) *See* Barigazzi (Giuseppe)

BARIGAZZI (Adelmo)

—— *See* Euphorion. I Frammenti euforionei del papiro fiorentino. [Edited, with a commentary, by A. Barigazzi.] 1948. 8°. [*Aegyptus.* anno 27. fasc. 1/2.] P.P. **3807.** bd.

BARIGAZZI (Giuseppe) Poesî in dialètt Bulgnèis. [With a portrait.] pp. 576. *Bulògna*, 1875. 8°. **11431.** c. **5.**

BARIGIONI (Francesco) *See* Barigioni (G.) and (F.) Notificazione per li subappalti della gabella del macinato del distretto di Roma, e di Marittima, e Campagna. 1715. *s. sh. obl.* 4°. **1896.** d. **16.** (**156.**)

BARIGIONI (Giuseppe) and (Francesco) Notificazione per li subappalti della gabella del macinato del Distretto di Roma, e di Marittima, e Campagna. *Roma*, 1715. *s. sh. obl.* 4°. **1896.** d. **16.** (**156.**)

BARIGNANA (Cosmo) *See* Cicero (M. T.) [*Letters.—Ad Familiares.—Latin and Italian.*] *Begin.* [fol. 1 *recto*:] M. T. Cicero Attilio proconsuli, *etc.* [fol. 16 *verso*:] Cosinæ [*sic*] Barignane . . . e Latino in uernaculum primo facta Interpretatio, *etc.* [1495?] 4°. IA. **26987.**

BARIGNANUS (Cosmas) *See* Barignana (Cosmo)

BARIGOZZI (Claudio)

—— Lo Studio degli spodogrammi dei cromosomi, *etc.* *Roma*, 1937. 8°. [*Pontificia Academia Scientiarum. Commentationes.* vol. 1. no. 9.] Ac. **101.** b/5.

BARIKINE (W.) *See* Baruikin (Vladimir A.)

BARIKOVA (Anna Pavlovna) *See* Baruikova.

BARIL (Jean) *See* Barilius (Joannes)

BARIL (V. L.) *Count de La Hure.* L'Empire du Brésil. Monographie complète de l'empire sud-américain, *etc.* pp. xv. 576. *Paris*, 1862. 8°. **10481.** e. **8.**

—— Le Mexique. Résumé géographique, statistique, industriel, historique et social, *etc.* pp. xviii. 271. *Douai*, 1862. 8°. **10481.** g. **17.**

—— Les Peuples du Brésil avant la découverte de l'Amérique. pp. 14. *Douai*, 1861. 4°. **9781.** e. **14.**

BARILE (Angelo)

—— Primasera. [Poems.] pp. 110. *Genova*, 1933. 8°. **20009.** f. 18.

BARILE (Giovanni Lodovico) La Grandissima allegrezza, che mostra la giouentù per li spassi del Carnevale, con la dichiaratione delle cause, che ponno succedere per tal spasso. [In verse.] *Per il Moscatelli: Bologna*, 1618. 12°. **1071.** g. **7.** (**53.**)

BARILE (Pietro)

—— Colonizzazione fascista nella Somalia meridionale. [With plates.] pp. 222. *Roma*, [1935.] 8°. **010093.** i. 49.

BARILI (Antonio)

—— Castiglione Olona e Masolino da Panicale, *etc.* [With plates.] pp. 96. *Milano*, 1938. 8°. **7865.** ppp. **16.**

—— Notizie storico-patrie di Casalmaggiore. pp. 293. *Parma*, 1812. 4°. **10132.** g. **29.**

BARILIUS (Joannes) Physiologia humana et pathologia, per tabulas synopticas, ex Hippocratis et Galeni genio. Accessit diæta sanorum generalis, cum summa de sectis medicorum. pp. 135. *I. Guesnon: Cadomi*, 1653. fol. **549.** l. **24.**

BARILLARI (Michele) La Dottrina del diritto di Goffredo Guglielmo Leibniz. pp. 186. *Napoli*, 1915. 8°. [*Atti della Reale Accademia di Scienze Morali e Politiche.* vol. 43. pt. 2.] Ac. **96/2.**

—— Studî su la satira latina. pp. xi. 145. *Messina*, 1890. 8°. **11312.** f. **51.**

BARILLAS (Francisco de Solís Cardona Gante Belvis Rodríguez de las) *Cardinal.* *See* Solís Cardona Gante Belvis Rodríguez de las Barillas.

BARILLER (Louis Marie Gabriel) Considérations pratiques sur le traitement des fractures de jambe. pp. 51. *Paris*, 1872. 4°. [*Collection des thèses soutenues à la Faculté de Médecine de Paris.* An 1872. tom. 1.] **7373.** n. **7.**

BARILLET (E. J. J.) Recherches historiques sur le Temple. Notice dans laquelle on traite de l'origine de cet enclos maison chef d'ordre du ci-devant grand prieuré de France, de son état à l'époque de la révolution, et de son état actuel. [With plans.] pp. xii. 224. *Paris*, 1809. 8°. **10169.** c. **35.**

BARILLET (Pierre) and **GRÉDY** (Jean Pierre)

—— Ami-ami. Comédie en trois actes, *etc.* pp. 31. *Paris*, 1951. 8°. [*France Illustration. Supplément théâtral et littéraire.* no. 77.] P.P. **4283.** m. (**1.**)

—— Le Bon débarras. Comédie en 3 actes, *etc.* pp. 31. *Paris*, 1952. 8°. [*France Illustration. Supplément théâtral et littéraire.* no. 111.] P.P. **4283.** m. (**1.**)

—— La Reine blanche. Comédie, *etc.* [With illustrations.] pp. 36. *Paris*, [1954.] 8°. [*France Illustration. Supplément théâtral et littéraire.* no. 148.] P.P. **4283.** m. (**1.**)

BARILLI (Arnaldo) Nuova biografia di Pomponio Torelli e critica della sua tragedia "Vittoria." pp. 82. *Parma*, 1903. 8°. **10629.** e. **5.**

—— I Piacentini nella congiura di Parma del 1611. *In:* Archivio storico per le provincie parmensi. ser. 4. vol. 1. pp. 121–173. 1949. 8°. Ac. **6539**/2.

BARILLI (Giulio)

—— Olasz beszélyek. Irták Barilli (Dodero kapitány), Ghislanzoni és Sara. Olaszból forditották Huszár I. és Mócs Zs. pp. 234. *Budapest*, 1880. 16°. [*Olcsó könyvtár.* sz. 110.] **12215.a.1/110.**

BARILLI (Giuseppe) *See* also Barilli Filopanti (Quirico) *pseud.* [i.e. G. Barilli.]

—— *See* also Filopanti (Quirico) *pseud.* [i.e. G. Barilli.]

—— Miranda! A book on wonders hitherto unheeded. [By G. Barilli.] pp. 1–240. 1858. 8°. *See* Miranda. **4373.** e. **30.**

—— [Another edition.] Miranda. A book divided into three parts, entitled Souls, Numbers, Stars, on the neo-christian religion, *etc.* [By G. Barilli.] 2 vol. 1858–60. 8°. *See* Miranda. **4373.** e. **31.**

BARILLI (GUIDO) L'Idea romana nel secondo libro della Monarchia di Dante Alighieri. pp. 68. [*Mantua*, 1921.] 8°. **011420**. d. **19**.

BARILLIÉ (CHANCHET) Li Camarad' dè l'joie. [Songs.] pp. xii. 130. *Lîge*, 1852. 12°. **11498**. bb. **74**. (**4**.)

BARILLIER (JEAN PHILIPPE) Du délire dans la pneumonie. pp. 30. *Paris*, 1856. 4°. [*Collection des thèses soutenues à la Faculté de Médecine de Paris.* An 1856. tom. 2.] **7372**. i. **2**.

BARILLI FILOPANTI (QUIRICO) *pseud.* [i.e. GIUSEPPE BARILLI.] Cesare al Rubicone. Memoria, *etc.* pp. 139. *Bologna*, 1866. 16°. **9039**. a. **13**.

BARILLON ( ) *Political Writer.* La Première au Prussiens. [On French policy towards Prussia.] pp. 14. *Paris*, 1870. 8°. **8026**. ee. **2**.

BARILLON (HENRI DE) *Bishop of Luçon.* Abregé de la vie de messire Henry de Barillon, evêque de Luçon. [By Charles François Dubos.] Avec des resolutions pour bien vivre, des pensées chrêtiennes sur les maladies, des reflexions sur la mort, la maniere de s'y préparer, & des consolations contre ses frayeurs. Par le même prelat. pp. 255. *Delft*, 1700. 12°. **846**. k. **18**. (**4**.)

BARILLON (PAUL) *Marquis de Branges.* Correspondence between Louis XIV. and M. Barillon on English Affairs, from Dec. 1684, to Dec. 1685. *Fr.* *See* FOX (*Right Hon.* Charles J.) A History of the Early Part of the Reign of James the Second, *etc.* 1808. 4°. **598**. i. **22**. (**1**.)

—— [Another edition.] *See* FOX (*Right Hon.* Charles J.) A History of the Early Part of the Reign of James the Second, *etc.* 1808. 4°. **193**. e. **2**.

—— [Correspondence between Louis XIV and Barillon, Dec. 1684—Dec. 1685.] *See* FOX (*Right Hon.* Charles T.) A Translation of the French Letters in the Appendix to Mr. Fox's History of the Early Part of the Reign of James the Second. 1808. 4°. **9525**. f. **3**.

BARILLON-BAUCHÉ (PAULA)

—— Augusta Holmès et la femme compositeur, *etc.* [With plates, including a portrait.] pp. 118. *Paris*, 1912. 8°. Hirsch **3392**.

—— [Another copy.] **7896**. tt. **17**.
Imperfect; wanting the advertisements at the end.

BARILLOT (ERNEST) *See* CHASTAING (P.) and BARILLOT (E.) Chimie organique, *etc.* 1887. 12°. **8909**. b. **14**.

—— La Distillation des bois. pp. 166. *Paris*, [1896.] 8°. [*Encyclopédie scientifique des aide-mémoire.* no. 162 A.] **08709**. de. **75**.

BARILLOT (HENRI) Deux monographies commerciales. [On book-keeping.] pp. 41. [*Paris*, 1891?] 4°. **8548**. g. **28**.
Lithographed throughout.

BARILLUS (LUDOVICUS) *See* BARILUS.

BARILUS (LUDOVICUS) *See* BIBLE.—*Liturgical Epistles and Gospels.* [*Latin.*] Ambrosianum Quadragesimale in quo, vnicuiq; Euangelio, præter ipsius expositionem, speciales tractatus apponuntur . . . à . . . L. Barillo . . . editum. 1594. 4°. **3227**. df. **1**.

BARIMORE (CHARLES) Charles Barimore . . . Troisième édition. [A novel. By Count Louis N. P. A. de Forbin.] pp. vi. 206. *Paris*, 1817. 8°. **1458**. f. **4**.

BARIN (ALOISIUS)

—— In novissimas rubricas Missalis Romani a Pio Pp. X reformati, Ss. D. N. Benedicti Pp. XV auctoritate vulgati. Commentarium. pp. 278. *Rhodigii*, 1920. 8°. **3396**. b. **11**.

BARIN (JEAN) *See* BARRIN.

BARIN (THÉODORE) Le Monde naissant, ou la création du monde, démonstrée par des principes tres simples & tres conformes à l'histoire de Moyse, Genes. chap. I. & II. [By T. Barin.] pp. 413. 1686. 12°. *See* MONDE. **3126**. a. **55**.

BARINAS, *State of.*

—— [Annual messages of Presidents reporting on the work of the government.] *Barinas*, [1939– .] fol. & 4°. L.A.S. **696/2**.

Secretaría General de Gobierno.

—— Memoria y Cuenta de la Secretaría General de Gobierno, 1938. (Memoria que presenta el ciudadano Secretario General de Gobierno del Estado Barinas, a la Asamblea Legislativa en sus sesiones ordinarias del año de 1940 [*etc.*].) *Barinas*, [1938– .] 4° & fol. L.A.S. **696**.

BARINCOU (EDMOND)

—— *See* MACCHIAVELLI (N.) [*Letters.*] Machiavel. Toutes les lettres . . . présentées et annotées par E. Barincou, *etc.* 1955. 8°. W.P. **8966/12**. 13

BARINCOU (GUSTAVE MICHEL) De l'anus accidentel et des différents procédés opératoires qui se rattachent à son traitement. pp. 43. *Strasbourg*, 1851. 4°. [*Collection générale des dissertations de la Faculté de Médecine de Bas-Rhin.* sér. 2. tom. 15.] **7381**. e

—— [Another copy, with a different titlepage.] *Strasbourg* 1852. 4°. **1167**. eee. **16**. (**4**.

BARINCOURT (LE ROY DE) *See* LE ROY DE BARINCOURT.

BARINE (ARVÈDE) *pseud.* [i.e. CÉCILE VINCENS.] *See* KING (Katharine) [The Queen of the Regiment.] La Reine du régiment. D'après le roman anglais de K. King par A. Barine. 1873. 8°. [*MONTÉPIN* (*X. A. de*) *Les Drames de l'adultère.* pt. 1.] **12516**. de. **1**

—— *See* TOLSTOI (L. N.) *Count.* [Дѣтство и отрочество.] Souvenirs. Enfance, adolescence, jeunesse. Ouvrage traduit . . . par A. Barine. 1887. 8°. **10790**. bbb. **22**

—— Alfred de Musset. [With a portrait.] pp. 182. *Paris* 1893. 8°. [*Les grands écrivains français.*] **010664**. e. **18/3**

—— Bernardin de Saint-Pierre. [With a portrait.] pp. 18 *Paris*, 1891. 8°. [*Les grands écrivains français.*] **010664**. e. **18/4**

—— Bernardin de Saint Pierre . . . Translated by J. E. Gordon . . . With portrait. pp. xviii. 209. *T. Fisher Unwin: London*, 1893. 8°. [*Great French Writers.*] **10664**. f. **20/**

—— Bourgeois et gens de peu. [Biographical essays.] pp. 297. *Paris*, 1894. 8°. **010663**. f. **3**

—— Essais et fantaisies. pp. 347. *Paris*, 1888. 8°. **12350**. cc. **2**

—— La Jeunesse de la Grande Mademoiselle (Anne Marie Louise d'Orléans), 1627–1652. Deuxième édition. pp. viii. 336. *Paris*, 1902. 8°. **010661**. a.

—— La Grande Mademoiselle, 1627–1652 . . . Authorised English version by Helen E. Meyer. [With illustrations.] pp. x. 448. *G. P. Putnam's Sons: New York & London* 1902. 8°. **010661**. b.

—— Louis XIV. et la Grande Mademoiselle, 1652–16 Ouvrage contenant deux portraits. Deuxième édition pp. viii. 392. *Paris*, 1905. 8°. **010661**. aa.

BARINE (ARVÈDE) *pseud.* [i.e. CÉCILE VINCENS.]

—— Louis XIV and la Grande Mademoiselle . . . Authorised English version. pp. xi. 394. *G. P. Putnam's Sons: New York & London*, 1905. 8°. **010661**. c. **24**.

—— Madame, mère du Régent. [A biography of Charlotte Elizabeth of Bavaria.] pp. 327. *Paris*, 1909. 8°. **010663**. ee. **40**.

—— Névrosés. Hoffmann, Quincey, Edgar Poe, Gérard de Nerval. pp. 362. *Paris*, 1898. 8°. **10600**. de. **17**.

—— Portraits de femmes. Madame Carlyle, George Eliot, une détraquée (Mary Wollstonecraft), un couvent de femmes en Italie au XVIe siècle, psychologie d'une sainte (sainte Therèse). pp. 326. *Paris*, 1887. 8°. **10602**. aaa. **12**.

—— Nouvelle édition. pp. 377. *Paris*, 1917. 8°. **08415**. ee. **80**.

—— Princesses et grandes dames. Marie Mancini—La reine Christine—Une princesse Arabe [Emily Ruete]—La duchesse du Maine—La margrave de Bayreuth. pp. 354. *Paris*, 1890. 8°. **10601**. aaa. **33**.

—— Princesses and Court Ladies . . . Authorized English version, *etc.* [With portraits.] pp. vi. 360. *G. P. Putnam's Sons: New York & London*, 1906. 8°. **10600**. v. **3**.

—— Saint François d'Assise et la légende des trois compagnons. (pt. 1. Vie de saint François d'Assise. pt. 2. La Légende des trois compagnons. [By Leo, a Franciscan of the 13th century.]) Deuxième édition. pp. x. 254. *Paris*, 1901. 8°. **4829**. cc. **39**.

BARINEAU (ÉLISABETH)

—— *See* HUGO (V. M.) *Viscount.* [*Les Orientales.*] Les Orientales. Édition critique avec une introduction, des notices, des variantes et des notes par E. Barineau. 1952, *etc.* 8°. Ac. **9812**/**66**.

BARINETTI (PIETRO) Genesi del diritto romano. pp. 214. *Milano*, 1852. 8°. **5207**. d. **2**.

BARINETTI (STEPHANUS) De natura tunicæ mediæ arteriarum dissertatio inauguralis, *etc.* pp. 24. *Ticini Regii*, [1829.] 8°. **7383**.*c. **17**. (**8**.)

BARING BROTHERS AND CO.

—— *See* HIDY (Ralph W.) The House of Baring in American Trade and Finance, *etc.* [With plates, including portraits.] 1949. 8°. Ac. **2692**/**35**.

BARING (   ) *Captain.* Words to Wayfaring Men. [A religious tract.] pp. 11. *Marshall Bros.: London*, [1893.] *obl.* 16°. **4372**. a. **31**.

BARING (ALBRECHT FRIEDRICH GEORG) Bemerkungen zu der Schrift des Herrn Advocaten Gans: "Über die Verarmung der Städte und des Landmanns &c." in Beziehung auf Steuerzahlungen. Gemeinheitstheilungen und Verkoppelungen im Königreich Hannover. pp. 58. *Hannover*, 1831. 8°. **1390**. i. **1**. (**3**.)

—— *See* GANS (S. P.) Erwiderung auf die von dem Herrn . . . Baring herausgegebenen Bemerkungen zu meiner Schrift über die Verarmung der Städte und des Landmanns u.s.w. 1831. 8°. **1390**. i. **1**. (**2**.)

BARING (ALEXANDER) *Baron Ashburton.* Correspondence between Mr. Webster and Lord Ashburton: 1. On McLeod's Case; 2. On the Creole Case; 3. On the subject of impressment. [1842.] 8°. *See* WEBSTER (Daniel) **10882**. ff. **1**. (**1**.)

BARING (ALEXANDER) *Baron Ashburton.*

—— The Financial and Commercial Crisis Considered. pp. 40. *John Murray: London*, 1847. 8°. **8229**. aaaa. **22**. (**10**.)

—— Second edition. pp. 40. *John Murray: London*, 1847. 8°. **1140**. h. **35**. (**5**.)

—— Third edition. pp. 40. *John Murray: London*, 1847. 8°. **8225**. b. **16**.

—— Fourth edition, published 1847 . . . Also, the letter of a London banker on the currency question to the editor of the Times, published December 26th, 1848. Reprinted. pp. 32. *P. S. King: London*, 1867. 8°. **08226**. h. **56**. (**17**.)

—— *See* SCHOMBERG (John D.) An Enquiry into the Currency; in which the measures of 1819 and 1844 are fully considered, the schemes of Lord Ashburton [outlined in "The Financial and Commercial Crisis Considered"] and Mr. Caley examined, *etc.* [1848.] 8°. **8225**. e. **70**.

—— An Inquiry into the Causes and Consequences of the Orders in Council; and an examination of the conduct of Great Britain towards the neutral commerce of America. pp. iv. 179. *J. M. Richardson; J. Ridgway: London*, 1808. 8°. **1103**. k. **34**.

—— [Another copy.] **6915**. aa. **37**. (**5**.)

—— [Another copy.] G. **16304**.

—— Second edition. pp. iv. 179. *J. M. Richardson; J. Ridgway: London*, 1808. 8°. **1389**. g. **35**.

—— *See* ATCHESON (Nathaniel) American Encroachments on British Rights . . . With remarks on Mr. Baring's Examination, *etc.* 1808. 8°. **982**. d. **27**.

—— —— 1815. 8°. [*Pamphleteer.* vol. 6.] P.P. **3557**. w.

—— *See* COURTENAY (*Right Hon.* Thomas P.) Additional Observations on the American Treaty. With some remarks on Mr. Baring's pamphlet ("An Inquiry into the Causes and Consequences of the Orders in Council"), *etc.* 1808. 8°. **8176**. bb. **21**.

—— Speech of Alexander Baring, Esq., M.P. in the House of Commons, on Thursday, the 3d of March, 1831, on Lord John Russell's Motion for Reform of Parliament. Extracted from the Mirror of Parliament. pp. 18. "*The Mirror of Parliament*": *London*, 1831. 8°. **8135**. e. **83**. (**7**.)

—— Speech of . . . Lord Ashburton, in the House of Lords, on the second reading of the Canada Government Bill . . . February 2, 1838. pp. 17. *A. Spottiswoode: London*, 1838. 8°. **8155**. de. **5**. (**3**.)

—— [A summary of A. Baring's speech in the House of Commons at the close of the debate upon the Reform Bill.] *See* ENGLAND.—*Parliament.*—*House of Commons.*—*Proceedings.*—II. Six Speeches delivered in the House of Commons at the Close of the Debate upon the Reform Bill, *etc.* 1831. 12°. T. **1379**. (**5**.)

BARING (CECILIA ANNE) *See* WINDHAM (*Right Hon.* William) The Diary of the Right Hon. William Windham . . . Edited by Mrs. H. Baring. 1866. 8°. **10816**. ee. **15**.

BARING (CHARLES) *See* also SMITH (J.) *Gentleman. pseud.* [i.e. C. Baring.]

BARING (CHARLES)

—— *See* DUNTZE (*Sir* John) *Bart.* State of a Reinsurance underwritten by Mr. Charles Baring . . . for Sir John Duntze, *etc.* [1783.] 8°. **08226.** h. **35.** (**2.**)

—— Peace in our Power, upon terms not unreasonable. pp. 39. *R. Trewman & Son: Exeter,* 1798. 8°. **1137.** d. **3.**

—— Sermons, selected by C. Baring. 2 vol. *J. Radford: Exmouth,* 1824. 8°. **1357.** d. **8.**

—— Thoughts on Final Universal Restoration . . . The second edition. pp. 74. *J. Radford: Exmouth,* 1823. 8°. **4373.** b. **7.**

—— The Whole State of the Case: or, Remarks on a pamphlet, entitled, " State of a Re-insurance, &c. " by which the public will be enabled to judge . . . of an insurance dispute, subsisting between Sir J. Duntze, Bt. and Mr. C. Baring. pp. 20. *R. Trewman: Exeter,* 1783. 8°. **08226.** h. **35.** (**1.**)

BARING (CHARLES THOMAS) successively *Bishop of Gloucester and Bristol,* and *of Durham.*

—— *See* BIBLE.—*Psalms.—Selections.* [*English.*] Psalms and Hymns for Public Worship. Selected [by C. T. Baring and others], *etc.* 1851. 8°. **3091.** df. **10.**

—— *See* DYKES (John B.) Eucharistic Truth and Ritual. A letter to the . . . Bishop of Durham occasioned by his lordship's reply to an address from certain laymen in the diocese, *etc.* 1874. 8°. **3478.** ccc. **43.**

—— *See* SADLER (Michael F.) Doctrinal Revision of the Liturgy Considered. An examination of the subject with special reference to the suggestions of the Bishop of Gloucester and Bristol, *etc.* 1861. 8°. **3478.** d. **16.**

—— *See* WILLIAMS (George E.) A Few Observations on a Sermon preached by . . . the Lord Bishop of Gloucester & Bristol at the opening of the Cheltenham Temporary Church . . . Nov. 3, 1859, *etc.* [1859.] 8°. **4109.** i. **11.** (**6.**)

—— A Charge delivered at the Triennial Visitation of the Diocese, September and October, 1860. By Charles, Lord Bishop of Gloucester and Bristol. pp. 33. *Seeley, Jackson & Halliday: London,* 1860. 8°. **4445.** c. **4.** (**9.**)

—— *See* BOULTBEE (Thomas P.) A Letter on Canonical and Rubrical Reform, to the Lord Bishop of Gloucester and Bristol, in reference to his recent charge. 1860. 8°. **5155.** b. **34.** (**5.**)

—— A Charge delivered to the Clergy of the Diocese of Gloucester and Bristol, at his primary visitation in October, 1857. By C. Baring. pp. 36. *Seeley, Jackson & Halliday: London,* 1857. 8°. **4445.** d. **4.** (**4.**)

—— Christ's Death a Propitiatory Sacrifice. A sermon, *etc.* pp. 28. *J. H. & J. Parker: Oxford,* 1856. 8°. **4255.** c. **6.**

—— [Another edition.] *See* ATONEMENT. The Atonement; being four discourses, *etc.* [1857.] 12°. **4226.** c. **15.**

—— A Sermon preached at St. Bride's Church . . . April 30, 1877, before the Church Missionary Society. [1877.] *See* ENGLAND.—*Church of England.—Church Missionary Society.* Proceedings, *etc.* 78th year. 1801, *etc.* 8°. P.P. **935.**

BARING (DANIEL EBERHARD) Daniel Eberhard Barings Beytrag zur Hannöverischen Kirchen- und Schul-Historia, so mit einigen Urkunden erläutert, und einer Vorrede von berühmten Denkmahlen, besonders denen, welche in und um Hannover sich befinden, begleitet worden. 2 Tl. *Hannover,* 1748. 8°. **4661.** a. **6.**

—— Clavis diplomatica, tradens specimina veterum scripturarum, nimirum alphabeta varia, compendia scribendi medii aevi, notariorum veterum signa nonnulla curiosa, una cum alphabeto instrumenti et abbreviaturis, singula tabulis aeneis exhibita . . . Subiiciuntur scriptores rei diplomaticae, *etc.* *Hanoverae,* 1737. 4°. **819.** k. **10.**

—— [Another edition.] Danielis Eberhardi Baringii Clavis diplomatica . . . Iterata hac editione sic ab auctore recognita, emendata ac locupletata, ut novum opus videri possit. [Edited by Eberhard Joannes Baring.] pp. 60. 616. *Hanoverae,* 1754. 4°. **788.** d. **20**

—— [Another copy.] **122.** f. **4**

—— Danielis Eberhardi Baringii Descriptio Salæ principatus Calenbergici locorumque adjacentium, oder, Beschreibung der Saala im Amt Lauenstein des Braunschweig-Lüneb. der Saala ... Fürstenthums Calenberg und aller in dieselbe fliessenden Quellen und Bäche, *etc.* *Ger.* 2 vol. *Lemgo,* 1744. 4° **173.** g. **17**

—— Disputatio medico-anatomica de cranii ossibus, *etc.* *Praes.* A. J. Bötticher. pp. 28. *Helmstadii,* 1718. 4°. **1179.** b. **13.** (**8**

—— [Another copy.] **T. 520.** (**41**

—— Daniel Eberhard Barings kurze historische und physicalische Nachricht von dem in Hannover zuerst erfundenen Getränk Broihan, wobey zugleich von desselben Erfinder Nachricht gegeben wird, *etc.* pp. 45. *Hannover,* 1750. 4°. **1436.** f. **1**

—— Succincta notitia scriptorum rerum Brunsvicensium a Luneburgensium . . . Accedit quoque, recensio legum atque constitutionum terrarum Brunsvico-Luneburgicarum singularium, *etc.* *Hanoveræ,* 1729. 8°. **11926.a.40**

BARING (DENZIL)

—— *See* HUBBARD (Gilbert E.) Eastern Industrializati and its Effect on the West . . . By G. E. Hubbard, assist by D. Baring, *etc.* 1935. 8°. **8286.** h. **3**

BARING (EBERHARD JOANNES) *See* BARING (D. E.) Danielis Eberhardi Baringii Clavis diplomatica, *etc.* [Edited by E. J. Baring.] 1754. 4°. **788.** d. **2**

BARING (EVELYN) *Earl of Cromer.* *See* CHÉRADAME (A.) The Pangerman Plot Unmasked . . . With an intr duction by the Earl of Cromer, *etc.* 1916. 8°. **08027.** e. **1**

—— *See* CURZON (George N.) *Marquis Curzon of Kedleston.* Subjects of the Day . . . With an introduction by t Earl of Cromer, *etc.* 1915. 8°. **012273.** b.

—— *See* DUNDAS (Lawrence J. L.) *Marquis of Zetland.* L Cromer, *etc.* [With a portrait.] 1932. 8°. **10823.** k.

—— *See* HARRIS (*Sir* John H.) Dawn in Darkest Afr . . . With an introduction by . . . the Earl of Crom *etc.* 1912. 8°. **010096.** ff.

—— *See* HARTOG (*Sir* Philippe J.) *K.B.E.* Examinati in their Bearing on National Efficiency . . . With speech by the Earl of Cromer. 1911. 8°. **8367.** e.

—— *See* HARTOG (*Sir* Philippe J.) *K.B.E.* Examinati and their Relation to Culture and Efficiency . . . Wit speech by the late Earl of Cromer. 1918. 8°. **08311.** de.

—— *See* LEAR (Edward) Queery Leary Nonsense . . . With an introduction by the Earl of Cromer. 1911. 4°. **12315**. k. **53**.

—— Second edition, revised. 1911. 4°. **12803**. w. **28**.

—— *See* LOW (*Sir* Sidney J. M.) Egypt in Transition . . . With an introduction by the Earl of Cromer. 1914. 8°. **08026**. b. **3**.

—— *See* MÉRA (E.) Une Page de politique coloniale. Lord Cromer en Égypte, 1883–1907. Avec un portrait, *etc.* 1913. 8°. **8157**. i. **9**. (**5**.)

—— *See* PAGET (Stephen) For and Against Experiments on Animals . . . With an introduction by . . . the Earl of Cromer. 1912. 8°. **8425**. e. **21**.

—— *See* PERIZONIUS (H.) The Elementary Tactics of the Prussian Infantry. Translated . . . by Lieutenant E. Baring, *etc.* 1872. 8°. **8824**. e. **24**.

—— *See* PORTAL (*Sir* Gerald H.) *K.C.M.G.* The British Mission to Uganda in 1893 . . . With . . . an introduction by Lord Cromer, *etc.* 1894. 8°. **9061**. ccc. **22**.

—— *See* PRUSSIA.—*Army.* [*Separate Regulations.*] Regulations for the Training of Troops for Service in the Field, and for the Conduct of Peace Manœuvres. Translated . . . by Lieutenant E. Baring. 1871. 8°. **8829**. cc. **22**. (**4**.)

—— *See* SANDERSON (Thomas H.) *Baron Sanderson.* Evelyn Earl of Cromer . . . Memoir, *etc.* [1917.] 8°. **10855**. f. **3**.

—— *See* TRAILL (Henry D.) Lord Cromer, a biography, *etc.* 1897. 8°. **10815**. cc. **15**.

—— *See* TSCHISCHWITZ (W. von) Rules for the Conduct of the War-Game. Compiled . . . by Captain E. Baring. (A free translation of the "Anleitung zum Kriegsspiel," by W. von Tschischwitz.) [1872.] 8°. **8829**. cc. **22**. (**7**.)

—— [The reports on the financial situation of Egypt, prepared by the Earl of Cromer in his official capacity as Agent and Consul-General, were published as Parliamentary Papers and are kept in the State Paper Room.]

—— Abbas II. pp. xxvi. 84. *Macmillan & Co.: London,* 1915. 8°. **09061**. c. **42**.

—— Ancient and Modern Imperialism. pp. vii. 143. *John Murray: London,* 1910. 8°. **8005**. ccc. **32**.

—— Disraeli. [A review of W. F. Monypenny's "Life of Benjamin Disraeli." Reprinted from the "Spectator."] pp. 40. *Macmillan & Co.: London,* 1912. 8°. **010854**. f. **30**.

—— Germania contra Mundum . . . Reprinted . . . from "The Spectator." pp. 47. *Macmillan & Co.: London,* 1915. 8°. **08027**. b. **53**.

—— Modern Egypt. 2 vol. *Macmillan & Co.: London,* 1908. 8°. **09061**. i. **32**.

—— [Another copy.] **09061**. eee. **27**.

—— Modern Egypt. (New edition.) pp. xxiv. 931. *Macmillan & Co.: London,* 1911. 8°. **9060**. cc. **34**.

—— [Another copy.] **09062**. e. **19**.
Imperfect; wanting the frontispiece.

—— *See* VERME (L. dal) *Count.* Italy in connection with Lord Cromer's "Modern Egypt." 1909. 8°. **09008**. bb. **1**. (**4**.)

—— Pan-Germanism . . . Reprinted . . . from the "Spectator," *etc.* pp. 16. *Darling & Son: London,* 1916. 8°. **08028**. de. **54**. (**1**.)

—— Paraphrases and Translations from the Greek. pp. ix. 220. *Macmillan & Co.: London; Macmillan Co.: New York,* 1903. 8°. **11340**. c. **26**.

—— Political & Literary Essays. 3 ser. *Macmillan & Co.: London,* 1913–16. 8°. **012352**. ff. **1**.

—— The Situation in Egypt. Address delivered to the Eighty Club on December 15th, 1908. pp. 32. *Macmillan & Co.: London,* 1908. 8°. **8027**. de. **19**.

—— Staff College Essays. [With maps.] pp. viii. 220. *Longmans & Co.: London,* 1870. 8°. **8824**. d. **32**.

—— Memorial to the late Earl of Cromer. Report to the contributors. (Address by Earl Curzon of Kedleston.) pp. 16. *H. R. Stokes: London,* 1920. 8°. **10856**. d. **22**.

—— Reply to Major the Hon. E. Baring's Budget Speech in the Legislative Council of his Excellency the Governor-General of India, on March 8, 1882. Reprinted from the "Friend of China," *etc.* pp. 19. *Dyer Bros.: London,* [1882.] 8°. **08226**. h. **57**. (**2**.)

BARING (*Sir* FRANCIS) *Bart.* Observations on the Establishment of the Bank of England, and on the Paper Circulation of the Country. pp. 81. *Sewell; Debrett: London,* 1797. 8°. **523**. d. **13**. (**5**.)

—— [Another copy.] **T. 1861**. (**2**.)

—— [Another copy.] **104**. d. **68**.

—— Observations on the Establishment of the Bank of England, and on the Paper Circulation of the Country . . . Second edition. pp. 81. MS. NOTES. *Sewell; Debrett: London,* 1797. 8°. **08218**. bb. **33**. (**1**.)
Jeremy Bentham's copy.

—— Further Observations on the Establishment of the Bank of England, and on the Paper Circulation of the Country. pp. 16. [*London,*] 1797. 8°. **T. 1861**. (**3**.)

—— Further Observations on the Establishment of the Bank of England, *etc.* pp. 16. vi. 1797 [1801]. 8°. **08218**. bb. **33**. (**2**.)

—— Observations on the Publication of Walter Boyd, Esq. M.P. [i.e. on his "Letter on the Influence of the Stoppage of Issues in Specie."] pp. 31. *J. Sewell; J. Debrett: London,* 1801. 8°. **8227**. c. **5**.

—— The Principle of the Commutation-Act established by Facts. pp. 62. *J. Sewell: London,* 1786. 8°. **1102**. h. **3**. (**5**.)

—— [Another copy.] **104**. c. **30**.

—— [Another copy.] The Principle of the Commutation-Act established by Facts. *London,* 1786. 8°. **08230**. b. **24**. (**10**.)
Imperfect; wanting the half-title.

—— The second edition. pp. 62. *J. Sewell: London,* 1786. 8°. **T. 105**. (**5**.)

—— A Second Twelve-Penny Answer to a New . . . Edition of a Three Shillings and Six-Penny Pamphlet [by Walter Boyd], intituled "A Letter on the Influence of the Stoppage of Issues in Specie at the Bank of England, on the Prices of Provisions and other Commodities; with additional notes and a preface." [By Sir F. Baring?] pp. 56. 1801. 8°. *See* ENGLAND.—*Bank of England.* [*Appendix.*] **08218**. bb. **33**. (**5**.)

BARING (*Sir* Francis) *Bart.*

—— A Twelve-Penny Answer to a Three Shillings and Six-Penny Pamphlet [by Walter Boyd], intituled A Letter on the Influence of the Stoppage of Issues in Specie at the Bank of England, on the Prices of Provisions, *etc.* [By Sir F. Baring?] pp. 29. 1801. 8°. *See* England.—*Bank of England.* [*Appendix.*] **08218.** bb. **33.** (4.)

BARING (Francis Guy) and **INCE** (George James)

—— The Catholic Faith in Public Schools, *etc.* pp. xiii. 144. *Williams & Norgate: London,* 1935. 8°. **4106.** cc. **43.**

BARING (*Hon.* Francis Henry) *See* Baring (Francis T.) *Baron Northbrook.* Journals and Correspondence from 1808 to 1852 . . . Edited by . . . Thomas George, Earl of Northbrook [and the Hon. F. H. Baring]. 1905,*etc.* 8°. **10816.** h. **10.**

—— *See* Domesday Book. Domesday Tables for the Counties of Surrey, Berkshire, Middlesex, Hertford, Buckingham & Bedford & for the New Forest . . . Arranged with some notes by the Hon. F. H. Baring. 1909. fol. **2061.d.**

BARING (Francis Thornhill) *Baron Northbrook. See* Clarke (Thomas G.) A Sermon preached in Michel-delver Church . . . September 16, 1866, after the funeral of . . . Francis, Baron Northbrook. 1866. 8°. **4906.** cc. **51.** (**3.**)

—— *See* Sumner (George H.) *Bishop of Guildford.* A Sermon preached at All Saints' Church, Stratton . . . on . . . September 16, 1866, after the funeral of Francis, Baron Northbrook, *etc.* 1866. 8°. **4906.** cc. **51.** (**5.**)

—— *See* Venn (Henry) *B.D., Hon. Secretary of the Church Missionary Society.* A Sermon preached in All Saints' Church, Stratton . . . on . . . September 16, 1866, after the funeral of . . . Francis, Baron Northbrook. 1866. 8°. **4906.** cc. **51.** (**6.**)

—— Journals and Correspondence from 1808 to 1852 . . . Edited by . . . Thomas George, Earl of Northbrook [and the Hon. Francis H. Baring]. 2 Vol. *Printed for private circulation: Winchester,* 1905, 02. 8°. **10816.** h. **10.**

—— Speech of the Rt. Hon. Francis Baring, Chancellor of the Exchequer, on . . . May 17th, 1841, in the House of Commons. Ways and Means, Corn Laws, Sugar Duties, &c. pp. 23. *James Ridgway: London,* 1841. 12°. **8247.** a. **46.** (**1.**)

—— To the Electors of the Borough of Portsmouth. [An election address.] *Charpentier: Portsmouth,* [1859.] *s. sh.* fol. **1899.r.44.**

BARING (Franciscus) *See* Baringius.

BARING (*Hon.* Frederick) *See* Fair Play, *pseud.* Letter to the Honble & Reverend F. Baring, with reference to the statements reported to have been made by him . . . at St. James' Hall . . . 11th of June, 1858. 1858. 8°. **4106.** cc. **16.** (**1.**)

—— Astounding Revelations of Puseyism in Belgravia, containing the most frightful disclosures of diabolical plots against female chastity by the Rev. Mr. Poole and Miss Joy at the fashionable Church of St. Barnabas, Pimlico . . . As detailed by the Hon. and Rev. F. Baring, at the great public meeting held in St. James's Hall, Piccadilly on Friday, June 11, 1858, *etc.* pp. 16. *William Roche: London,* [1858.] 8°. **6495.** bb. **3.** (**31.**)

—— [Another copy, with a different titlepage.] *J. Hatswell: London,* [1858.] 8°. **6496.** aa. **22.**

BARING (Georg)

—— Die "Wormser Propheten." Eine vor-Luthersche evangelische Prophetenübersetzung von 1527 [i.e. the translation by Ludwig Hätzer and Hans Denck]. *In:* Deutsches Bibel-Archiv. Dritter Bericht. pp. 1–9. 1933. 8°. Ac. **2027.** d.

BARING (George) *See* Carne (Robert H.) The Proper Deity, and Distinct Personality, Agency, and Worship of the Holy Spirit Vindicated, against the recent cavils of Messieurs Baring, Bevan, Cowan, *etc.* 1818. 12°. **853.** e. **23.**

BARING (*Mrs.* Henry) *See* Baring (Cecilia A.)

BARING (Johann Niclaus) *See* Hanover. Chur-Braunschweig-Lüneburgische Landes-Ordnungen und Gesetze, *etc.* [Edited by J. N. Baring and others.] 1739, *etc.* 4°. **28.** b. **8–11.**

—— —— 1741, *etc.* 4°. **5511.** d. **5.**

BARING (John) *Baron Revelstoke.* British Staying Power . . . Interview, *etc.* pp. 8. *Sir J. Causton & Sons: London,* 1916. 8°. **08028.** h. **14.** (**2.**)

BARING (John L.)

—— *See* Heering (W.) [Das Rolleiflex-Buch.] The Rolleiflex-Book. Translated . . . by J. L. Baring. 1934. 8°. **8910.** e. **4.**

—— *See* Helwich (O.) [Die Infrarot-Fotografie und ihre Anwendungsgebiete.] Practical Infra-Red Photography. A translation by J. L. Baring, *etc.* [1935.] 4°. **8910.** e. **5.**

BARING (*Hon.* Maurice) *See* Benkendorf (P. K.) *Count.* Last Days at Tsarskoe Selo . . . Translated by M. Baring. 1927. 8°. **010795.** aa. **37.**

—— *See* Chaigne (L.) Maurice Baring, *etc.* [With a portrait.] [1935.] 8°. **010822.** de. **37.**

—— *See* Chaundy (Leslie) A Bibliography of the First Editions of the Works of Maurice Baring . . . With poems by M. Baring, *etc.* 1925. 8°. **11902.** aa. **72.**

—— *See* Fraser (Laura) *Baroness Lovat.* Maurice Baring. A postscript . . . With some letters and verse. [With portraits.] 1947. 8°. **10858.** g. **30.**

—— *See* Las Vergnas (R.) Portraits anglais. G. K. Chesterton . . . M. Baring. 1937. 8°. **11859.** e. **8.**

—— *See* Las Vergnas (R.) Chesterton, Belloc, Baring, *etc.* 1938. 8°. **11860.** bb. 5

—— *See* Liverpool.—*University of Liverpool.—School of Russian Studies.* The Russian Review . . . Editors B. Pares, M. Baring, *etc.* 1912, *etc.* 8°. Ac. **2662.** h

—— *See* Musset (L. C. A. de) Fantasio . . . Translated by M. Baring. 1927. 8°. C. **100.** k. **21**

—— *See* Pushkin (A. S.) Poems Translated from Pushkin by M. Baring. 1931. 4°. **20019.** i. **7**

—— *See* Smyth (*Dame* Ethel M.) *D.B.E.* Maurice Baring. [With portraits.] 1938. 8°. **10857.** b.

—— The Collected Poems of Maurice Baring. pp. vii. 236 *John Lane: London,* 1911. 8°. **011650.** i. **44**

—— Collected Poems. pp. viii. 359. *William Heinemann: London,* 1925. 8°. **11645.** d. **4**

—— Passing By, and Overlooked. pp. 279. *William Heinemann: London,* 1929. 8°. NN. **1494**

—— Unreliable History. (Diminutive Dramas. Dead Letters. Lost Diaries.) pp. vii. 521. *William Heinemann: London, Toronto*, 1934. 8°. **012273**. bbb.**25**.

—— Algæ. An anthology of phrases, collected by M. Baring. pp. xiv. 115. *William Heinemann: London*, 1928. 8°. **012305**. m. **44**.
No. 16 *of an edition of* 100 *copies printed on handmade paper.*

—— [Another edition.] (First ordinary edition.) pp. xii. 115. *William Heinemann: London*, 1928. 8°. **011644**. eee. **94**.

—— The Black Prince, and other poems. pp. 144. *John Lane: London & New York*, 1903 [1902]. 8°. **011651**. i. **92**.

—— The Brass Ring. (Reprinted from "The Saturday Review.") pp. 6. [*Privately printed*:] *London*, 1917. 8°. Ashley **2332**. (**7**.)
No. 3 *of ten copies printed on hand-made paper.*

—— C. [A novel.] pp. xxxi. 741. *William Heinemann: London*, 1924. 8°. NN. **9778**.

—— C. Traduzido . . . por Cabral do Nascimento. pp. 610. *Lisboa*, [1945 ?] 8°. **12649**. dd. **8**.

—— Cat's Cradle . . . Illustrated by Daphne Baring. pp. xiii. 720. *William Heinemann: London*, 1925. 8°. NN. **11096**.

—— Cecil Spencer. [A commemorative poem.] *Privately printed: London*, 1928. 4°. Ashley **4687**. (**3**.)

—— Cecil Spencer. [A commemorative poem.] pp. 4. *William Heinemann: London*, 1929. 4°. **11642**. i. **22**.

—— The Coat without Seam. pp. 321. *William Heinemann: London*, 1929. 8°. NN. **15127**.

—— Comfortless Memory. pp. 192. *William Heinemann: London*, 1928. 8°. NN. **14242**.

—— Daphne Adeane. pp. viii. 327. *William Heinemann: London*, 1926. 8°. NN. **12413**.

—— Darby and Joan. pp. vii. 247. *William Heinemann: London, Toronto*, 1935. 8°. NN. **24494**.

—— Dead Letters. (Re-printed from the 'Morning Post.') pp. xiii. 243. *Constable & Co.: London*, 1910. 8°. **12350**. y. **24**.

—— [Another edition.] pp. xi. 198. *Martin Secker: London*, 1920. 8°. **012350**. de. **79**.

—— [Another edition.] pp. x. 208. *William Heinemann: London*, [1925.] 8°. **012352**. f. **60**.

—— Dead Letters. pp. xvi. 208. *William Heinemann: London*, [1938.] 8°. **12359**. b. **4**.

—— Desiderio: a drama in three acts. [In verse.] pp. 128. *B. H. Blackwell: Oxford; Simpkin, Marshall & Co.: London*, 1906. 8°. **11778**. i. **17**.

—— [Another edition.] pp. 104. *B. H. Blackwell: Oxford*, 1911. 8°. **11775**. f. **83**.

—— Diminutive Dramas. pp. viii. 224. *Constable & Co.: London*, 1911. 8°. **11775**. f. **74**.

—— [Another edition.] pp. 200. *Martin Secker: London*, 1919. 8°. **011779**. gg. **6**.

—— [Another edition.] pp. vii. 183. *William Heinemann: London*, 1925. 8°. **011779**. ee. **53**.

—— Diminutive Dramas. (Fourth edition.) pp. xii. 198. *William Heinemann: London, Toronto*, 1938. 8°. **011781**. k. **46**.

—— Ten Diminutive Dramas, *etc.* [Selected from "Diminutive Dramas."] pp. xii. 85. *William Heinemann: London*, 1951. 8°. [*Drama Library.*] W.P. **13760/10**.

—— English Landscape. An anthology. Compiled by M. Baring. pp. 122. *Humphrey Milford: London*, 1916. 16°. **11609**. ee. **10**.

—— Fifty Sonnets. pp. 57. *For private circulation: [London?]* 1915. 8°. Ashley **2332**. (**6**.)
One of three copies printed on hand-made paper.

—— Flying Corps Headquarters, 1914–1918. *See* infra: R.F.C., H.Q., 1914–1918.

—— Forget-Me-Not and Lily of the Valley. *See* infra: The Story of Forget-Me-Not and Lily of the Valley.

—— French Literature. pp. 79. *London*, 1927. 16°. [*Benn's Sixpenny Library.* no. 52.] **12199**. c. **1/52**.

—— Friday's Business. pp. 267. *William Heinemann: London*, 1932. 8°. NN. **22591**.

—— Gaston de Foix, and other plays. [In verse.] pp. 263. *Grant Richards: London*, 1903. 8°. **11779**. ddd. **20**.

—— Gaston de Foix. A play in three acts. [In verse.] (Second edition, revised.) pp. 72. *B. H. Blackwell: Oxford; Simpkin, Marshall & Co.: London*, 1913. 8°. **11773**. e. **49**. (**4**.)

—— The Glass Mender, and other stories. [With illustrations.] pp. xii. 260. *J. Nisbet & Co.: London*, 1910. 8°. **12804**. v. **34**.

—— [Another edition.] pp. ix. 210. *William Heinemann: London*, 1926. 8°. **012643**. h. **51**.

—— [Another edition.] Illustrated by S. B. pp. xii. 188. *William Heinemann: London*, 1926. 8°. NN. **12096**.

—— The Grey Stocking, and other plays. pp. 366. *Constable & Co.: London*, 1912. 8°. **11773**. e. **44**.

—— Half a Minute's Silence, and other stories. pp. x. 204. *William Heinemann: London*, 1925. 8°. NN. **10539**.

—— [A reissue.] *London*, 1930. 8°. [*Travellers' Library.*] **012208.m.1/60**

—— Have You Anything to Declare? A note-book with commentaries. pp. viii. 323. *William Heinemann: London*, [1936.] 8°. **2350**. h. **2**.

—— Hildesheim. Quatre pastiches. pp. viii. 19. **F.P.** *William Heinemann: London*, 1924. 8°. **12356**. i. **34**.

—— His Majesty's Embassy, & other plays. pp. 222. *William Heinemann: London*, 1923. 8°. **011779**. g. **135**.

—— I.M.H. By C. [i.e. M. Baring.] pp. 7. 1924. 4°. *See* C. Ashley **4687**. (**2**.)

—— In Memoriam Auberon Herbert, Captain Lord Lucas, Royal Flying Corps, killed November 3, 1916. [A poem.] pp. 14. *B. H. Blackwell: Oxford*, 1917. 8°. **011649**. ff. **12**.

—— In My End is My Beginning. pp. xv. 331. *William Heinemann: London*, 1931. 8°. **12602**. k. **20**.

—— Landmarks in Russian Literature. pp. xvii. 299. *Methuen & Co.: London,* 1910. 8°. **11840.** pp. **23.**

—— Second edition. pp. xvii. 299. *Methuen & Co.: London,* 1910. 8°. **11825.** pp. **4.**

—— Letters from the Near East, 1909 and 1912. pp. 187. *Smith, Elder & Co.: London,* 1913. 8°. **9136.** de. **29.**

—— Litany for those in the Train. By M. B. [i.e. M. Baring.] pp. 6. [c. 1895.] 8°. *See* B., M. Ashley **4687.** **(1.)**

—— The Lonely Lady of Dulwich. pp. 146. *William Heinemann: London,* 1934. 8°. NN. **22699.**

—— Lost Diaries. pp. viii. 214. *Duckworth & Co.: London,* 1913. 8°. NN. **1417.**

—— Lost Lectures; or, the Fruits of Experience. pp. ix. 317. *William Heinemann: London,* 1932. 8°. **10823.** aa. **20.**

—— [Another copy, with a different titlepage.] *Peter Davies: London,* 1932. 8°. **10823.** aa. **19.**

—— Mahasena: a play in three acts. pp. 49. *B. H. Blackwell: Oxford; Simpkin, Marshall & Co.: London,* 1905. 8°. **11779.** c. **98.**

—— The Mainsprings of Russia. pp. 328. *T. Nelson & Sons: London,* 1914. 8°. **10292.** bb. **21.**

—— Orpheus in Mayfair, and other stories and sketches. pp. x. 306. *Mills & Boon: London,* 1909. 8°. **012624.** d. **13.**

—— *See* SHANKS (Edward B.) Fête Galante. A dance-dream in one act, after M. Baring's story of that name [in "Orpheus in Mayfair, and other stories"], *etc.* [1923.] 8°. **11777.bb.2.**

—— An Outline of Russian Literature. pp. 256. *Williams & Norgate: London; H. Holt & Co.: New York,* 1915. 8°. [*Home University Library.*] **12199.** p. **1/104.**

—— [Another edition.] pp. 256. *Thornton Butterworth: London,* 1929. 8°. [*Home University Library.*] **12199.** p. **1/153.**

—— Overlooked. pp. 200. *William Heinemann: London,* 1922. 8°. NN. **8106.**

—— The Oxford Book of Russian Verse. Chosen by the Hon. M. Baring. pp. xxxix. 211. *Clarendon Press: Oxford,* 1924. 8°. **011586.** f. **70.**

—— The Oxford Book of Russian Verse . . . Second edition supplemented by D. P. Costello. pp. xliv. 311. *Clarendon Press: Oxford,* 1948. 8°. **011586.** ff. **90.**

—— [A reissue.] The Oxford Book of Russian Verse . . . Second edition, *etc. Oxford,* 1953. 8°. **2044.** g.

—— Palamon and Arcite. A play for puppets. [In verse.] pp. 48. *B. H. Blackwell: Oxford,* 1913. 8°. **11773.** e. **49.** **(3.)**

—— Passing By. pp. 342. *Martin Secker: London,* 1921. 8°. **012602.** h. **9.**

—— Poems. By M. B. [i.e. M. Baring.] pp. 15. [1897.] 16°. *See* B., M. Ashley **2332.** **(1.)**

—— Poems. By M. B. [i.e. M. Baring.] pp. 24. [1899.] 8°. *See* B., M. Ashley **2332.** **(2.)**

—— Poems. ["Blossom" and six sonnets.] By M. B. [i.e. M. Baring.] pp. 10. [1905.] 8°. *See* B., M. Ashley **2332.** (3.)

—— Poems. ["The Wounded" and five other sonnets.] By M. B. [i.e. M. Baring.] pp. 8. [1905.] 8°. *See* B., M. Ashley **2332.** (4.)

—— Poems: 1914–1917. pp. 39. *Martin Secker: London,* 1918. 8°. **011649.** ee. **10**

—— Poems: 1914–1919. pp. 57. *Martin Secker: London,* 1920. 8°. **011648.** h. **40**

—— Proserpine. A masque. [In verse.] pp. 67. *B. H. Blackwell: Oxford,* 1908. 8°. **11778.** dd. **9**

—— Punch and Judy, & other essays. pp. x. 370. *William Heinemann: London,* 1924. 8°. **012352.** b. **16**

—— The Puppet Show of Memory. pp. ix. 457. *William Heinemann: London,* 1922. 8°. **010855.** bb. **31**

—— Une Enfance anglaise. Souvenirs . . . Traduction d Taneette Prigent. [A translation of parts of "Puppe Show of Memory."] [1948.] *See* PERIODICAL PUBLICA TIONS.—*Paris.* Les Œuvres libres, *etc.* no. 251. 1921, *etc.* 8°. **12208.** ee. **251**

—— The R.F.C. Alphabet. By M. B. [i.e. M. Baring Illustrated by R. C. 1915. *obl.* 8°. *See* B., M. **12316.** f. **5**

—— R.F.C., H.Q., 1914–1918. pp. 315. *G. Bell & Sons London,* 1920. 8°. **09083.** cc. **6**

—— Flying Corps Headquarters, 1914–1918. [A new editio of "R.F.C., H.Q., 1914–1918."] pp. 313. *William Heinemann: London,* 1930. 8°. **09081.** bbb. **1**

—— Robert Peckham. [A novel.] pp. 279. *William Heinemann: London,* 1930. 8°. NN. **1670**

—— Robert Peckham. [Second edition.] pp. 225. *Private printed for the Author: London,* 1934. 8°. **12602.** r. **3**
No. 1 *of an edition of* 100 *copies.*

—— Round the World in any Number of Days. pp. vii. 182. *Chatto & Windus: London,* 1919. 8°. **010025.** e. **6**

—— [Another edition.] Illustrated by B. T. B. pp. xv. 140. *William Heinemann: London,* 1926. 8°. **010025.** h. **7**

—— Russian Essays and Stories. pp. xvii. 295. *Methuen & Co.: London,* 1908. 8°. **12352.** tt. **20**

—— Russian Lyrics. Translated by Maurice Baring. pp. 26. *William Heinemann: London,* 1943. 8°. **11643.** m. **61**

—— The Russian People . . . With four maps. pp. xix. 36 *Methuen & Co.: London,* 1911. 8°. **2364.** e. **1**

—— Sarah Bernhardt, *etc.* [With a portrait.] pp. 162. *Peter Davies: London,* 1933. 8°. **10632.** ppp. **2**

—— Sarah Bernhardt. pp. 162. *T. Nelson & Son London,* 1938. 8°. [*Short Biographies.* no. 20.] **010604.aa.3/20**

—— Sonnets. pp. 55. *Chiswick Press: London,* 1914. 8°. Ashley **2332.** (5
Privately printed. One of twelve copies.

—— Sonnets and Short Poems. pp. 67. *B. H. Blackwel Oxford,* 1906. 8°. **11649.** g. **2**

—— The Story of Forget-Me-Not and Lily of the Valley . . Illustrated by S. B. pp. 119. *J. Nisbet & Co London,* [1909.] 8°. **012804.** c.

—— [Another edition.] Forget-Me-Not and Lily of t Valley. pp. xi. 83. *William Heinemann: Londo* 1928. *obl.* 8°. **12810.** a. **4**

BARING (*Hon.* MAURICE)

—— Ten Diminutive Dramas, *etc.* *See* supra: Diminutive Dramas.

—— Tinker's Leave. pp. ix. 348. *William Heinemann: London*, 1927. 8°. **012603**. i. **45**.

—— Translations, found in a commonplace book. Edited by S. C. [A collection of original pieces by M. Baring.] 1916. 8°. *See* C., S. **012305**. k. **22**.

—— [Another edition.] Translations: ancient and modern. pp. 43. *Martin Secker: London*, 1918. 8°. **12274**. bb. **14**.

—— [Another edition.] With originals [by various authors]. pp. xiii. 77. *William Heinemann: London*, 1925. 8°. **012273**. bbb. **9**.

—— A Triangle. Passages from three notebooks. pp. 193. *William Heinemann: London*, 1923. 8°. **012601**. bb. **31**.

—— With the Russians in Manchuria. pp. xv. 205. *Methuen & Co.: London*, 1905. 8°. **09055**. c. **22**.

—— A Year in Russia. pp. xix. 319. *Methuen & Co.: London*, 1907. 8°. **10291**. bbb. **15**.

—— Revised and cheaper edition. pp. xxxi. 296. *Methuen & Co.: London*, 1917. 8°. **2364**. c. **10**.

—— What I Saw in Russia. [Selected from "With the Russians in Manchuria," "A Year in Russia," and "Russian Essays and Stories."] pp. 381. *London*, [1913.] 8°. [*Nelson's Shilling Library.*] **12204**. d. **17/87**.

—— What I Saw in Russia. pp. x. 386. *William Heinemann: London*, [1927.] 8°. **010290**. eee. **20**.
With some differences from the preceding selection.

—— Maurice Baring. [Twenty-two Poems.] pp. 31. *Ernest Benn: London*, [1926.] 8°. [*Augustan Books of Modern Poetry.*] **11605**. cc. **12/35**.

—— Selected Poems. pp. 100. *William Heinemann: London*, 1930. 8°. **011644**. h. **147**.

BARING (MAX) *pseud.* [i.e. CHARLES MESSENT.] The Canon's Butterfly. pp. 299. *Greening & Co.: London*, 1903. 8°. **012628**. d. **10**.

—— A Doctor in Corduroy. pp. 320. *Greening & Co.: London*, 1905. 8°. **012631**. bb. **43**.

—— Joanna and His Reverence. A story. pp. iv. 312. *Simpkin, Marshall & Co.: London*, 1910. 8°. **012623**. aa. **36**.

—— A Prophet of Wales. A story. pp. 311. *Greening & Co.: London*, 1905. 8°. **012632**. a. **42**.

—— The Shattered Idol, *etc.* pp. 309. *Simpkin, Marshall & Co.: London*, 1907. 8°. **012627**. a. **13**.

—— The Troubles of a Shovel Hat, and other stories. pp. 128. *Simpkin, Marshall & Co.: London*, [1901.] 8°. **012627**. e. **103**.

—— Whiffs from a Short Briar. [Short stories.] pp. 124. *Simpkin, Marshall & Co.: London*, [1896.] 16°. **012330**. e. **63**.

BARING (MELCHIOR LAURENTIUS) *See* BARINGIUS.

BARING (NATALIE) Hannoversche Dorf-Geschichten. pp. 364. *Hamburg*, 1876. 8°. **12554**. bb. **7**.

BARING (NINA)

—— Wilhelm Diltheys Philosophie der Geschichte. Inaugural-Dissertation, *etc.* pp. 148. *Bückeburg*, 1936. 8°. **9011**. cc. **20**.
Reproduced from typewriting.

BARING (NORAH)

—— A Friendly Hearth, *etc.* [An account of the author's experiences with evacuated children during the war of 1939–45.] pp. 128. *Jonathan Cape: London*, 1946. 8°. **08311**. e. **85**.

BARING (RUBY FLORENCE MARY) *Countess of Cromer.* Lamuriac, and other sketches. pp. vi. 150. *Methuen & Co.: London*, 1927. 8°. **012352**. bb. **10**.

—— Such Were These Years. [Reminiscences. With plates, including portraits.] pp. 275. *Hodder & Stoughton: London*, 1939. 8°. **10859**. d. **2**.

—— Unfettered Ways . . . Illustrations by Violet Baring. pp. 148. *Hodder & Stoughton: London*, 1935. 8°. **12356**. s. **29**.

BARING (T.) *Traveller.* A Tour through Italy, Sicily, Istria, Carniola, the Tyrol, and Austria . . . The second edition. pp. iv. 268. *Gale & Fenner: London*, 1817. 8°. **10106**. f. **7**.

BARING (THOMAS) *See* CONYBEARE (John C.) Mr. Baring and the Grand Trunk Railway. [1863.] 8°. **8235**. bb. **25**.

BARING (*Sir* THOMAS) *Bart.*

—— Elegy on the Lamented Death of Sir Thomas Baring, Bart. . . . By Rabbi A. B. [i.e. Abraham Belaïs.] 1848. 8°. *See* B., A., *Rabbi.* **1963**. d. **29**.

BARING (THOMAS CHARLES) *See* HORATIUS FLACCUS (Q.) [*Carmina, Epodi and Carmen Saeculare.—English.*] The Lyrics of Horace. Done into English rhyme by T. C. Baring. 1870. 8°. **11375**. bbb. **41**.

—— *See* LUCRETIUS CARUS (T.) [*English.*] The Scheme of Epicurus: a rendering into English verse of . . . "De Rerum Natura" . . . by T. C. Baring. 1884. 8°. **11386**. f. **13**.

—— *See* PINDAR. [*English.*] Pindar in English Rhyme; being an attempt to render the Epinikian Odes, with the principal remaining fragments, of Pindar, into English rhymed verse, by T. C. Baring. 1875. 8°. **11335**. bb. **2**.

BARING (THOMAS GEORGE) *Earl of Northbrook. See* BARING (Francis T.) *Baron Northbrook.* Journals and Correspondence from 1808 to 1852 . . . Edited by Thomas George, Earl of Northbrook [and the Hon. F. H. Baring]. 1905, etc. 8°. **10816**. h. **10**.

—— *See* BIBLE.—Gospels.—Selections. [*English.*] The Teaching of Jesus Christ in His Own Words . . . Compiled . . . by the Earl of Northbrook. 1900. 8°. **03225**. de. **9**.

—— —— 1901. 8°. **4224**. de. **40**.

—— —— [1902.] 8°. **03225**. de. **16**.

—— *See* BIBLE.—Gospels.—*Selections.* [*Hindi.*] The Teaching of Jesus Christ in His Own Words. Compiled . . . by the Earl of Northbrook, *etc.* 1901. 12°. **14154**. a. **27**. **(3.)**

—— *See* GOSHṬHAVIHĀRI MALLIKA. Lord Northbrook and his Mission in India . . . With an appendix containing all the important speeches of Lord Northbrook, as well as the addresses of welcome presented to His Excellency by the public bodies in India with His Excellency's replies. 1873. 8°. **8023**. f. **10**.

—— *See* MALLET (*Sir* Bernard) *K.C.B.* Thomas George, Earl of Northbrook, G.C.S.I. A memoir, *etc.* 1908. 8°. **010827**. g. **19**.

—— The Afghan Question. Speech . . . in the Guildhall, Winchester . . . November 1878. pp. 16. *National Press Agency: London*, [1878.] 8°. **8023**. ee. **17**. **(2.)**

BARING (Thomas George) *Earl of Northbrook.*

—— A Brief Account of Recent Transactions in Afghanistan. pp. 105. *Privately printed: London,* [1880.] 8°. **8023**. f. **13**. (**7**.)

—— Indian Criminal Procedure Bill. Speech . . . in the Colston Hall, Bristol, on the 13th of November, 1883. pp. 15. *National Press Agency: London,* [1883.] 8°. **8022**. bbb. **4**. (**1**.)

—— Memorandum by the Earl of Northbrook, on Viscount Cranbrook's Despatch to Lord Lytton of November 18th, 1878. pp. 12. *National Press Agency: London,* [1882.] 8°. **8023**. ee. **17**. (**9**.)

—— The Natives of India, *etc.* pp. 38. *Birmingham,* [1880.] 8°. [*Birmingham and Midland Institute. Presidential Addresses.* 1880.] Ac. **1193**. c.

—— North-Western Frontier of India. Speech . . . in the House of Lords . . . March 7, 1898 . . . With preface, notes, appendices, and a map. pp. 45. *E. Stanford: London,* 1898. 8°. **8022**. bbb. **20**. (**5**.)

—— Speech of the Earl of Northbrook, in the House of Lords, July 14, 1885, on the Vote of Credit and the Naval Administration of the late Government. pp. 16. *National Press Agency: London,* [1885.] 8°. **8139**. bb. **40**. (**1**.)

—— Speech of the Earl of Northbrook, in the House of Lords, on the 5th of August, 1878, on presenting a petition from the inhabitants of Calcutta. pp. 23. *National Press Agency: London,* 1878. 8°. **8022**. c. **102**. (**13**.)

—— A Descriptive Catalogue of the Collection of Pictures belonging to the Earl of Northbrook. The Dutch, Flemish and French Schools by Mr. W. H. James Weale; the Italian and Spanish Schools by Dr. Jean Paul Richter. With twenty-five illustrations. pp. 222. *Griffith & Co.: London,* 1889. 4°. Tab. **438**. c. **13**.

—— Lord Northbrook's Government of India, 1872–76. Reprinted from the "Times of India." pp. 37. *Times of India Steam Press: Bombay,* 1876. 8°. **9006**. dd. **19**. (**1**.)

BARING (*Hon.* Venetia Marjorie Mabel) Deafness & Happiness. pp. vii. 35. *A. R. Mowbray & Co.: London & Oxford,* 1930. 8°. **4403**. c. **54**.

BARING (*Lady* Violet Mary) *See* Herbert (Sir Alan P.) Tantivy Towers . . . Derby Day . . . With decorations by Lady V. Baring. 1932. 8°. **011781**. i. **80**.

BARING (Walter) Mr. Baring's and Mr. Schuyler's Reports on the Atrocities committed upon the Christians in Bulgaria. pp. 16. *Goubaud & Son: London,* 1876. 4°. **8028**. g. **4**.

BARING (William) Wie Arbeiterwohnungen gut und gesund einzurichten und zu erhalten seien. Preisschrift, *etc.* pp. 106. *Basel,* 1860. 8°. **8282**. e. 2. (**5**.)

BARING (William Bingham) *Baron Ashburton. See* Macaulay (Thomas B.) *Baron Macaulay.* [*Minutes on Indian Affairs.*] The Indian Civil Service. Report to the Rt. Hon. Sir C. Wood . . . by the Right Hon. T. B. Macaulay, Lord Ashburton, *etc.* 1855. 8°. **8308**. e. **36**.

—— Ashburton Prizes for the Teaching of "Common Things." An account of the proceedings at a meeting between Lord Ashburton and the elementary schoolmasters, assembled at Winchester, on . . . December 16, 1853, *etc.* pp. 32. *Groombridge & Sons: London,* 1854. 8°. **8308**. aa. **34**. (**2**.)

BARING (William Bingham) *Baron Ashburton.*

—— A Letter to the Electors of Winchester by Bingham Baring, M.P., in vindication of his conduct in Parliament. Second edition. pp. 23. *J. Ridgway & Sons: London,* 1835. 8°. **1027**. b. **28**. (**1**.)

BARINGER (William)

—— Lincoln's Rise to Power . . . With illustrations [including a portrait]. pp. xi. 373. *Little, Brown & Co.: Boston,* 1937. 8°. **10887**. f. **14**.

BARING-GOULD (Alexander) *See* Gould.

BARING-GOULD (Sabine) *See* Gould.

BARINGIUS (Daniel Eberhardus) *See* Baring.

BARINGIUS (Franciscus) Francisci Baringii De παραδειγματισμῳ sponsæ adulteræ ad Matth. i. 19. disputatio. —De ceto Jonæ et Matth. xii. 40.—De tribus diebus et tribus noctibus commorationis Christi in corde terræ.— De corde terræ e Matth. xii. comm. 40. *See* Hase (T.) and Iken (C.) Thesaurus novus theologico-philologicus, *etc.* tom. 2. 1732. fol. **L.16.f.2.**

—— Franc. Baringii Dissertatio de πινακιδιῳ Zachariæ, ad Luc. 1: 63. 1702. *See* Menthen (G.) Thesaurus theologico-philologicus, *etc.* tom. 2. 1701, *etc.* fol. **5**. g. **6**.

BARINGIUS (Melchior Laurentius) Ex historia ecclesiastica de ascetis dissertatio academica, *etc. Praes.* G. T. Meier. *Typis H. Mulleri: Helmestadii,* 1672. 4°. **1179**. b. **9**. (**13**.)

—— Editio secunda. *Typis H. D. Mulleri: Helmestadii,* 1680. 4°. **700**. h. **8**. (**1**.)

—— [Another copy.] T. **2237**. (**2**.)

BARINGOU (Antoine) Dissertation sur le rhumatisme articulaire, *etc.* pp. 32. *Paris,* 1833. 4°. **1184**. f. **1**. (**18**.)

BARINGOU (Jean) Essai sur la topographie physique et médicale de la vallée d'Aspe, suivi d'un coup d'œil sur les principales maladies qu'on y observe, *etc.* pp. 32. *Paris,* 1832. 4°. **1184**. e. **7**. (**1**.)

BARINGTON (Cedric) The Gospel of Expediency. [A novel.] pp. vii. 436. *G. Routledge & Sons: London,* [1910.] 8°. **012618**. aaa. **9**.

BARINI (Concetta)

—— *See* Augustus (C. J. C. O.) *Emperor of Rome.* Monumentum Ancyranum. Res Gestae Divi Augusti. Testo e commento storico di C. Barini, *etc.* 1930. 4°. [*Biblioteca della rivista Historia del "Popolo d'Italia."* no. 1.] P.P. **4186**. bc.

—— *See* Augustus (C. J. C. O.) *Emperor of Rome.* Res gestae divi Augusti. Ex monumentis Ancyrano, Antiocheno, Apolloniensi C. Barini recensuit. 1937. 8°. Ac. **102**. b/2. (**6**.)

—— Triumphalia. Imprese ed onori militari durante l'Impero Romano. [With illustrations.] pp. 221. *Torino,* 1952. 8°. **07705**. pp. **5**

BARINI (Giorgio) Cantàri cavallereschi dei secoli xv e xvi. Raccolti e pubblicati da G. Barini. pp. xxii. 276. *Bologna,* 1905. 8°. [*Collezione di opere inedite o rare pubblicata per cura della R. Commissione pe' testi di lingua nelle provincie dell' Emilia.*] **12225**. k. **12**.

BARINKAY (Sandor) *pseud.* [i.e. Anne Kraus.] Buch der Rosen. Gedichte. pp. viii. 81. *Dresden & Leipzig,* 1892. 8°. **011528**. f. **19**. (**4**.)

—— Lava. Ein Jahr aus meinem Leben. [Poems.] pp. viii. 137. *Leipzig,* 1894. 8°. **011528**. g. **31**.

BARINKAY (Sandor) *pseud.* [i.e. Anne Kraus.]

—— Liebestraum. Lieder-Cyklus, *etc.* pp. 96. *München*, [1889.] 8°. **11528. f. 16.**

BARINS (de) *pseud.* [i.e. Louis François Raban.] Vie, voyages et aventures de l'amiral Dumont-d'Urville, *etc.* pp. 108. *Paris*, 1845. 12°. **1450. a. 15.**

—— [A reissue.] *Paris*, [1863.] 12°. **10026. a. 16.**

BARINUS, *Phaborinus, Bishop of Nocera Camelana. See* Varinus, *Phavorinus.*

BARIOD (J. A.) Études critiques sur les monomanies instinctives, *etc.* pp. 50. *Paris*, 1852. 4°. [*Collection des thèses soutenues à la Faculté de Médecine de Paris.* An 1852. tom. 1.] **7372. e. 5.**

BARIOLA (Aloysius) Flores directorii inquisitorum, collecti à fratre A. Bariola . . . Accesserunt tractatus de sollicitatione penitentium. De propositionum gradibus, & qualitate . . . Noua hac impressione omnia ab eodem recognita, & aucta. pp. 490. *Apud hær. P. Pontij, & I. B. Piccaleam: Mediolani*, 1625. 8°. **4071. de. 25.**

BARIOLA (Felice) *of Florence. See* Niggóra. Una Novellina popolare. (Malthru Niggóra mannu e malthru Niggoreddu.) [Edited by F. Bariola.] 1887. 8°. **12431. i. 31. (1.)**

BARIOLA (Felice) *of Pavia.* De china ejusque corticis proprietatibus medicis dissertatio inauguralis, *etc.* pp. 33. *Ticini Regii*, [1827.] 8°. **7383.*c. 8. (32.)**

—— Del vajuolo e delle sue differenze. Osservazioni. pp. 39. *Pavia*, 1830. 8°. **7383.*b. 8. (3.)**

BARIOLA (Henri) Chemins de fer de Thessalie. Rapports de M. H. Bariola et de M. Paul de Hees. pp. 41. *Constantinople*, 1883. 4°. **8235. l. 43. (4.)**

—— [Another copy.] **8235. l. 70.**

BARIOLA (Joanne) Epitoma delli successi del Regno di Sicilia. *See* Pelliccia (A. A.) Raccolta di varie croniche . . . appartenenti alla storia del Regno di Napoli. tom. 1. 1780, *etc.* 4°. **1318. h. 1.**

BARIOLA (Plinio) Storia della ragioneria italiana, *etc.* pp. xiii. 701. *Milano*, 1897. 8°. **08228. i. 26.**

BARIOLI (Gino)

—— Catalogo della I mostra di ceramiche antiche di Bassano, delle Nove e di Vicenza, *etc.* [With plates.] pp. 80. 1954. 8°. *See* Bassano.—*Museo Civico.* **07813. ee. 61.**

BARION (Jacob) Die intellektuelle Anschauung bei J. G. Fichte und Schelling und ihre religionsphilosophische Bedeutung. pp. viii. 115. *Würzburg*, 1929. 8°. [*Abhandlungen zur Philosophie und Psychologie der Religion.* Hft. 22.] **4383.f.1/22.**

—— Macht und Recht und das Wesen des Staates. pp. 50. *Braunschweig*, 1951. 8°. [*Beiträge zum Geschichtsunterricht.* no. 21.] **9526.de.22/21.**

—— Plotin und Augustinus. Untersuchungen zum Gottesproblem. pp. 175. *Berlin*, 1935. 8°. [*Neue Deutsche Forschungen.* Bd. 2.] **012213. y. 1/2.**

—— Recht, Staat und Gesellschaft. pp. 202. *Krefeld*, 1949. 8°. **5695. b. 18.**

BARIONA (Joannes) *See* Blomevenna (P.) Enchiridion sacerdotum, *etc.* [Edited by J. Bariona.] 1532. 8°. **846. b. 18.**

BARIONA (Laurentius) *pseud.* [i.e. Laurence Johnson.] Cometographia quædam Lampadis aeriæ quę 10. die Nouemb. apparuit anno a virgineo partu, 1577. *Robertus Walley: Londini*, 1578. 4°. **532. e. 54.**

BARIOT-DELILE (N. V.) Essai sur les hémorrhoïdes. pp. 30. *Montpellier*, an XII [1803]. 4°. **1180. e. 4. (18.)**

BARIS. *See* Paris.

BARIS. (Alber.) *See* Barisoni (Albertino)

BARISANI (Joseph) Dissertatio inauguralis chemico-medica de thermis Gasteinensibus, *etc.* pp. 52. *Vindobonae*, [1780.] 8°. **1171. g. 6.**

—— Physikalisch-chemische Untersuchung des berühmten Gasteiner Wildbades. pp. 62. *Salzburg*, 1785. 8°. **1171. i. 25.**

BARISANI (Sigismundus) Dissertatio inauguralis medico-practica de insitione variolarum. pp. 45. *Vindobonae*, 1780. 8°. **1174. f. 1. (5.)**

BARISANI (Sylvester) Didymi monstrosi foetus admiranda historia, *etc.* [With plates.] *Salisburgi*, [1757.] 4°. **778. f. 23. (5.)**

BARISH (Norman Norton)

—— *See* Juran (Joseph M.) and Barish (N. N.) Case Studies in Industrial Management. 1955. 4°. **8228. l. 50.**

—— Systems Analysis for Effective Administration. pp. x. 316. *Funk & Wagnalls Co.; Modern Industry Magazine: New York*, [1951.] 8°. **8229. k. 55.**
One of the "Modern Industry Books."

BARISIEN (Josephus Ernestus)

—— Augusta Austriæ virtus coronata . . . triumphans . . . Maria Theresia, Hungariæ Bohemiæq; Regina . . . quam in septem meditatis arcubus triumphalibus . . . varijs conceptibus poëticis, ad vivum adumbratam, palam proposuit, & exposuit . . . Josephus Ernestus Barisien, *etc.* *Vetero-Pragæ*, 1743. fol. **1482. f. 7. (2.)**

—— Fragmenta poëtarum veterum recentiorúmque, ponderosioribus metris, cùm laudi, cùm vituperio inservituris . . . per alphabeticos titulos in ordinem disposita . . . à I. E. Barisien. 2 pt. pp. 466. *Vetero-Pragæ*, 1747. 8°. **1213. k. 24.**

BARISON (Eugenio) Falische. Rime in dialetto triestino. pp. 127. *Trieste*, 1903. 8°. **11429. f. 37.**

BARISONI (Albertino) *Bishop of Ceneda. See* Tassoni (A.) *Count.* La Secchia . . . con gli argomenti del Can. Alber. Baris. [i.e. A. Barisoni], *etc.* 1622. 12°. **239. a. 29.**

—— Albertini Barisoni . . . De archivis commentarius. *See* Poleni (G.) *Marquis.* Utriusque thesauri antiquitatum Romanorum Græcorumque nova supplementa. vol. 1. 1737. fol. **1489.1.7.**

—— [Another edition.] [Edited by the Marquis Giovanni Poleni.] coll. 48. *Venetiis*, 1737. fol. **823. k. 18.**

BARISONIUS (Albertinus) *See* Barisoni (Albertino)

BARISSE (Rita)

—— *See* Vercors, *pseud.* [Les Animaux dénaturés.] Borderline . . . Translated by R. Barisse. 1954. 8°. **12519. ee. 16.**

BARISTER. *See* Barrister.

BARITERIPOSUNDS PFEIFFENTHAL, *pseud. See* Pfeiffenthal (Bariteriposunds)

BARIŢIU (Georgiu) *See* Calvinistic Catechism. Catechismulu Calvinescu . . . insocitu de una escursiune istorica . . . de G. Bariţiu, *etc.* 1879. 8°. **3506**. f. **22**.

—— *See* Lupaş (I.) Un Capitol din istoria ziaristicei românești-ardelene.—Gheorghe Bariţiu. [With a portrait.] 1906. 8°. **11853**. t. **11**. (5.)

—— *See* Polizŭ (G. A.) Romänisch-deutsches Wörterbuch . . . Bereichert und revidirt von G. Baritz, *etc.* 1857. 8°. **12942**. e. **19**.

—— *See* Tacitus (P. C.) [*Works.—Roumanian.*] Opurile lui C. Corneliu Tacitu traduse de G. J. Munteanu . . . Biografi'a traductoriului [by G. Bariţiu] annessata. 1871. 8°. **9041**. c. **26**.

—— Parti alese dîn istoria Transilvaniei pre doue sute de ani dîn urma. 3 vol. *Sibiiu*, 1889, 91. 8°. **09315.ee.1.**

—— Raportŭ asupra călĕtorieĭ la ruinele Sarmisagetuseĭ . . . Extrasŭ din Analele Academieĭ Române, *etc.* pp. 12. *Bucuresci*, 1883. 4°. **7704**. g. **41**. (3.)

BARIŢIU (Georgiu) and **MUNTEANU** (Gavrülu J.)

—— Dikционарiŭ Цер-mano-Pomънŭ, *etc.* (Deutsch-romänisches Wörterbuch, bearbeitet . . . von G. Baritz und G. Munteanu.) 2 том. pp. vi. 880. *Брашовŭ*, 1853, 54. 8°. **12976**. g. **30**.

BARIŢIU (Octaviu) Dicţionariu portativ magiar-român . . . Ediţiunea ii. emendată şi amplificată. (Magyar-román zsebszótár, *etc.*) pp. 210. *Cluj*, 1893. 8°. **12942**. bb. **39**.

BARITONE. A "Dozen Don'ts" for all who play the Pianoforte, accompaniments in particular. By "Baritone." pp. 12. *Kibble & Co.: London*, [1916.] 8°. **7898**. bbb. **49**.

BARITS (Albert) *See* Barics (Adalbert)

BARITSCH (Adalbert von) *See* Barics (Adalbert)

BARITSCH (Carl) Deutsche Industrien und der Krieg . . . Mit 71 Abbildungen und 7 Zahlentafeln. pp. 48. *Hamburg*, 1916. 8°. **08227**. i. **68**.

BARITSCH (Karl) *See* Baritsch (Carl)

BARITZ (Georg) *See* Bariţiu (Georgiu)

BARIUS (Gabriel) *See* Barrius.

BARIUS (Nicolaus) *Bánfalvai.*

—— *See* Juhász (L.) Nicolaus Barius. Georgius Polycarpus de Kostolan . . . Reliquiae, *etc.* 1932. 8°. **012208.1.2/4.**

BARI-WOOLLSS (J.) *See* Woollss.

BARIZIEN (Élizabeth Wilhelmine du Collin de) *Countess de Civry.* *See* Du Collin de Barisien.

BARIZIEN (Marie Auguste Jean Joseph du Collin de) *Viscount de Civry.* *See* Du Collin de Barizien.

BARIZIEN (Pierre du Collin de) *Count de Civry.* *See* Du Collin de Barizien.

BARIZIEN (Ulric Guelfe Eugène Honoré du Collin de) *Count de Civry.* *See* Du Collin de Barizien.

BARJA (César) En torno al lirismo gallego del siglo xix. pp. viii. 149. *Northampton, Mass., Paris*, 1926. 8°. [*Smith College Studies in Modern Languages.* vol. 7. no. 2, 3.] Ac. **1877/2**.

—— Libros y autores contemporáneos, *etc.* (Literatura española.) pp. vii. 493. *Madrid*, [1935.] 8°. **11857**. aa. **5**.

BARJA (César)

—— Literatura Española. Libros y autores modernos pp. xxvi. 644. *Madrid*, 1925. 8° **2043.c.**

BARJAC, *Vicomte de.* Le Vicomte de Barjac, ou, mémoire pour servir à l'histoire de ce siècle. [A novel. By Jea P. L. de La Roche du Maine, Marquis de Luchet.] 2 tom *Wilson: Dublin*, 1784. 12°. **12510**. de. **26**

BARJAKTAROVIĆ (Mirko R.)

—— О земљишним међама у Срба. pp. 105. *Београд* 1952. 8°. [*Српска Академија Наука. Посебна из дања.* књ. 203.] Ac. **113**

BARJAKTAROVIĆ (Svetislav Sp.)

—— Акушерство за лекаре и медицинаре. 2 књ. *Београд* 1950. 8°. **7582**. d. **23**
The titlepage headed: Медицинска Велика Школа Београду.

BARJALÉ (Étienne) Réflexions sur les plaies d'armes feu, *etc.* [A dissertation.] pp. 20. *Montpellier* 1812. 4°. **1180**. g. **7**. (3.

BARJANSKY (Catherine)

—— Portraits with Backgrounds . . . In collaboration wit Elinore Denniston. [Autobiographical reminiscences.] pp. 223. *Geoffrey Bles: London*, 1948. 8°. **10797**. g. **4**

BARJAUD (Jean Baptiste) De la mort par submersio pp. 26. *Paris*, 1858. 4°. [*Collection des thèses soutenue à la Faculté de Médecine de Paris.* An 1858. tom. 1.] **7373**. a. **15**

BARJAUD (Jean Baptiste Benoît) *See* Cornillon (Jean Un Poète-soldat au commencement du xixe siècle, Jean Baptiste Barjaud de Montluçon, *etc.* 1915. 8°. **010662**. bb. **29**

—— *See* D., F. v. Napoleon in Dresden. Zwei Unter redungen des Kaisers mit dem Dichter Barjaud und den Minister Daru, *etc.* 1813. 8°. **9080**. aa. **18**

—— Le Dix-neuvième siècle. Satyre première. [In verse By J. B. B. Barjaud.] pp. 16. [1805?] 8°. *See* Siècle **899**. e. **23**. (10.

BARJAUD (Jean Baptiste Benoît) and **D*****.

—— Le Bavard et l'entêté, comédie en un ac et en vers. Par MM. Barjaud et D * * * [i.e. L. D chemin]. pp. 39. *Paris*, 1809. 8°. **11738**. a. **34**. (

BARJAUD (Jean Baptiste Benoît) and **LANDO** (Charles Paul)

—— Description Londres et de ses édifices, avec un précis historique et d observations sur le caractère de leur architecture, et sur l principaux objets d'art et de curiosité qu'ils renferme . . . Ouvrage faisant suite à la Description de Pari [With plates and a plan.] pp. viii. 239. 4. *Pari* 1810. 8°. **577**. d. **1**

BARJAUD DE LAFOND (J. F.) Étiologie de l'hype trophie du cœur. pp. 28. *Paris*, 1855. 4°. [*Collectic des thèses soutenues à la Faculté de Médecine de Pari* An 1855. tom. 1.] **7372**. h.

BARJAVEL (Casimir) Essai sur l'unité du corps vivan Tribut académique, *etc.* pp. 70. *Montpellier*, 1826. 4 **1181**. d. **10**. (15

BARJAVEL (Casimir François Henri) *See* Fabre d Saint-Véran (J. D.) Mémoire historique sur la vie e les écrits de Dom M. d'Inguimbert . . . Publié avec de réflexions et des details préliminaires par C. F. H Barjavel. 1860. 12°. **4804**. aa. **23**. (7

BARJAVEL (Casimir François Henri)

—— *See* Remerville (J. F. de) *Sieur de Saint-Quentin.* Fragments de l'Autel despoüillé et restably . . . Suivis de cinq pièces de vers . . . Le tout publié . . . avec un avant-propos, des commentaires, des rapprochements et des notes historiques et littéraires par C.-F.-H. Barjavel. 1859. 8°. **11475**. d. **38**.

—— Dictionnaire historique, biographique et bibliographique du département de Vaucluse, ou recherches pour servir à l'histoire religieuse, civile et militaire des villes et arrondissements d'Avignon, de Carpentras, d'Apt et d'Orange. 2 tom. *Carpentras,* 1841. 8°. **10658**. k. **14**.

—— [Another copy.] **1330**. f. **2**.

—— Dictons et sobriquets patois de villes, bourgs et villages du département de Vaucluse; traduits, éclaircis et annotés, *etc.* pp. 306. *Carpentras,* 1849–53. 8°. **12305**. f. **20**.
One of an edition of 100 *copies. Published in parts.*

BARJAVEL (François) Liberté, Egalité, ou la Mort. Mémoire justificatif pour François Barjavel . . . aux représentans du peuple composans le Comité de Sûrété [*sic*] Générale. pp. 14. *Paris,* [1794.] 8°. **F. 1010**. (**14**.)

BARJAVEL (René)

—— [Tarendol.] The Tragic Innocents . . . Translated . . . by Eithne Wilkins. [A novel.] pp. 336. *Hamish Hamilton: London,* 1948. 8°. **012550**. ee. **75**.

BARJEAU (Jean Paul Charles Philip de) *See* Philip de Barjeau.

BARJOLEAU, *Vicomte de.* Le Vicomte de Barjoleau, ou le souper des noirs. Comédie, en deux actes et en vers. [A satire upon A. B. L. de Riquetti, Vicomte de Mirabeau.] pp. 51. [*Paris,* 1790?] 8°. **F. 434**. (**1**.)

—— [Another copy.] **11738**. aaa. **2**. (**4**.)

—— [Another copy.] **164**. f. **29**.

BARJOLLE (Théophile) Dissertation sur la péricardite aiguë, *etc. Paris,* 1835. 4°. **1184**. g. **5**. (**10**.)

BARJOLS (Elias de) *See* Elias, *de Barjols.*

BARJON (François) *See* Regaud (C.) and Barjon (F.) Anatomie pathologique du système lymphatique . . . dans la sphère des néoplasmes malins, *etc.* 1897. 8°. [*Annales de l'Université de Lyon. fasc.* 33.] **Ac. 365**.

—— [Radiodiagnostic des affections pleuropulmonaires.] Radio-diagnosis of Pleuro-pulmonary Affections . . . Translated by James A. Honeij. pp. xix. 183. *Yale University Press: New Haven,* 1918. 8°. **7616**. d. **16**.

BARJON (Louis)

—— Gide et Saint-Exupéry. Dialogue des deux ferveurs. pp. 31. *Paris,* [1953.] 8°. **11869**. aaa. **1**.
Part of a series entitled "Routes et jalons."

BARJONA (Antonio Joaquim) Breve Memoria das Febres Intermittentes em Portugal. pp. 47. *Coimbra,* 1862. 8°. **7306**. aa. **6**. (**6**.)

BARJONA (Emmanuel Josephus) *See* Barjona (Manuel J.)

BARJONA (Manuel José) Taboas Mineralogicas . . . Segunda edição. pp. 256. *Coimbra,* 1835. 4°. **7107**. aaa. **9**.

BARJONA (Manuel José)

—— Metallurgiae elementa, quae amplissimi Philosophici Ordinis jussu ad usum academicum elucubravit Emmanuel Josephus Barjona. pp. xii. 302. pl. 4. *Conimbricae,* 1798. 8°. **7943**. aa. **3**.

BARJONA DE FREITAS (Augusto Cesar) A Questão Ingleza. Discurso proferido na Camara dos Pares do Reino em sessão de 10 de junho de 1891. pp. 24. *Lisboa,* 1891. 8°. **8042**. dd. **9**. (**5**.)

BARJORJĪ KHURSHEDJĪ SANJĀNĀ. *See* Bombay, *City of.—University of Bombay.* The Bombay University Matriculation Examination Papers in English, with their answers, from 1871 to 1888. With a copious appendix by B. C. Sanjana and F. K. Mulla. [1889.] 12°. **8366**. dd. **31**.

BARJORJĪ NAVAROZJĪ. *See* Periodical Publications.—Bombay.—*Hindi Punch.* Cartoons from the Hindi Punch . . . Edited by Barjorjee Nowrosjee. 1905, *etc.* 4°. **P.P. 3800**. ed.

—— *See* Periodical Publications.—Bombay.—*Hindi Punch.* The Indian National Congress Cartoons from the Hindi Punch . . . Edited by Barjorjee Nowrosjee. [1901, *etc.*] *obl.* fol. & 4°. **1876**. b. **61**.

BARJORJĪ SOHRABJĪ KĀṄGĀ. Handbook on Tuberculosis. pp. viii. 150. *J. Bale & Co.: London,* 1930. 8°. **07616**. de. **29**.

BARJOT (Henri Marie René) Contribution à l'étude de l'ozone comme agent d'assainissement de l'air des agglomérations. Thèse, *etc.* pp. 55. *Bordeaux,* 1925. 8°. **8903**. i. **12**.

BARJOT (Pierre)

—— L'Aviation militaire française, *etc.* [With illustrations.] pp. viii. 245. *Paris; Liège* [printed, 1936.] 8°. **8769**. e. **18**.

—— Une Réussite stratégique: le débarquement du 8 novembre 1942 en Afrique du Nord. pp. 222. *Paris,* [1948.] 8°. **09100**. a. **59**.
Part of a series entitled "Collection 'L'Étrave.'"

BARK. My Bark, which o'er the tide.—It is all serene. [Songs.] *Ryle & Co.: London, Portsea,* [1860?] *s. sh.* 4°. **11621**. k. **4**. (**22**.)

—— My Bounding Bark. [A song.] *Watts: Birmingham,* [1820?] *s. sh.* 8°. **1872**. a. **1**. (**168*****.)

BARK (Conrad Lyddon Voss)

—— Sealed Entrance. A novel. pp. 223. *Chapman & Hall: London,* 1947. 8°. **NN. 36798**.

BARK (D. L. Voss) Pen Pictures. pp. 32. *A. H. Stockwell: London,* [1930.] 8°. **011644**. h. **106**.

BARK (Ernst) Deutschlands Weltstellung und Stellung und Aufgabe der Deutschen im Auslande. pp. iv. 94. *Zürich,* 1890. 8°. **8154**. aa. **13**.

—— Estadística Social . . . El problema de la miseria . . . La España Social . . . Los Reyes del oro. pp. 313. *Barcelona,* [1903.] 8°. **08275**. ee. **78**.

—— La Prensa Española. Estudio comparativo de un cosmopolita. pp. 32. *Madrid,* 1889. 8°. **11850**. aaaa. **38**. (**2**.)

—— El Programa Comun del Republicanismo Iberico, *etc.* pp. 32. *Madrid,* 1892. 8°. **8042**. aa. **29**. (**4**.)

—— Russlands Culturbedeutung. Betrachtungen eines Deutsch-Livländers. pp. 194. *Berlin,* 1882. 8°. **8094**. aaa. **22**.

BARK (Ernst)

—— Socialismo Positivo, *etc.* pp. 253. *Madrid*, [1901.] 8°. **08275**. e. **60**.

—— Los Vencidos. Novela política contemporánea. pp. 203. *Alicante*, 1891. 8°. **12489**. aaa. **7**.

—— Wanderungen in Spanien und Portugal, 1881–82. pp. 352. *Berlin*, 1883. 8°. **10161**. de. **9**.

BARK (Georg R.) Boden als Geld. Ein Beitrag zur Geschichte des Papiergeldes. pp. 99. *Berlin*, 1930. 8°. [*Volkswirtschaftliche Studien.* Hft. 25 **W.P.14651/25.**

BARK (Nils) *Count.*

—— Svenske envoyén i Wien grefve Nils Barks bref, dels till kongl. maj:t, dels till kanslipresidenten, *etc.* 1862. *See* Gustavus III., *King of Sweden.* Bidrag till konung Gustaf III:s historia. 1861, *etc.* 8°. [*Historiska handlingar.* dl. 2.] **9425**. g. **12**.

BARK (Samuel) Bref från Samuel Bark till Olof Hermelin, 1702–1708. Utgifna af Carl von Rosen. 2 dl. *Stockholm*, 1914, 15. 8°. **010902**. i. **23**.

BARK (Violet)

—— *See* Hantzakos (H.) The Visitation of God. By H. Hantzakos in collaboration with the medium Mrs. Bark. [1936.] 8°. **4223**. c. **41**.

BARK (Willy)

—— Chronik von Alt-Westend mit Schloss Ruhwald, Spandauer Bock und Fürstenbrunn. [With plates.] pp. 87. *Berlin*, 1937. 8°. [*Schriften des Vereins für die Geschichte Berlins.* Hft. 56.] Ac. **7328**.

BARKA (Vasil')

—— Апостоли. [Poems.] pp. 47. *Авґсбурґ*, 1946. 8°. **11588**. a. **54**.

—— Білий світ. Поезії. pp. 179 *Мюнхен*, 1947. 8°. **11588**. cc. **45**.

BARKAN (D. D.)

—— Сейсмовзрывные волны и действие их на сооружения. pp. 47. 1945. 8°. *See* Russia.—*Всесоюзная Научно-исследовательская Лаборатория по Изучению Оснований Сооружений.* **07822**. p. **78**.

BARKAN (Manuel)

—— A Foundation for Art Education. pp. xi. 235. *Ronald Press Co.: New York*, [1955.] 8° **8313**. de. **9**.

BARKANOV (M.)

—— Повесть о том как помирился Иван Иванович с Иваном Никифоровичем. pp. 123. *Москва, Ленинград*, 1927. 8°. **12590**. v. **1**.

BARKAR (John) *See* Barker (John) *Ballad-writer.*

BARKAR (William) *See* Barker (William) *of Magdalen College, Oxford.*

BARKAS (Albert Atkin) A Chapter in the History of our Local Institutions—Richmond, Surrey. The Mechanics' Institution. The Old Baths. The Royal Assembly Rooms. pp. 19. *F. W. Dimbleby & Sons: Richmond*, 1907. *obl.* 8°. **10352**. e. **67**.

—— An Interesting Corner of Richmond Green, Surrey . . . Reprinted from the "Richmond and Twickenham Times." pp. 7. 1914. 8°. **10368**. g. **56**.

—— Soldiers and Soldiering in Richmond, Surrey . . . 1515–1915 . . . Reprinted from the "Richmond and Twickenham Times." pp. 24. 1915. 8°. **8827**. g. **17**.

BARKAS (Geoffrey)

—— The Camouflage Story. From Aintree to Alamein [By] G. Barkas in collaboration with Natalie Barkas With illustrations by Brian Robb. [With a map. pp. viii. 216. *Cassell & Co.: London*, 1952. 8°. **9102**. ee. **35**

—— Filming the Flight. *See* Fellowes (Peregrine F. M.) First Over Everest, *etc.* [1938.] 8° **12634.p.1/24**

BARKAS (Henry Dawson) Art Student's Pocket Manual. Part I. Technical instruction in shading from the cast. pp. 34. *Beecroft & Son: Reading; Simpkin, Marshall & Co.: London*, 1892. 12°. **7854**. b. **24**.

BARKAS (Natalie)

—— *See* Barkas (Geoffrey) The Camouflage Story . . [By] G. Barkas in collaboration with N. Barkas, *etc.* 1952. 8°. **9102**. ee. **35**

—— Behind the Camera. [Reminiscences of film-making in West Africa. With plates.] pp. vii. 237. *Geoffrey Bles. London*, 1934. 8°. **2358**. f. **19**

—— The Quest of the Bellamy Jewels . . . From an origina play by Michael Barrenger. Illustrated by A. Barclay pp. 208. *Blackie & Son: London & Glasgow*, [1949.] 8°. **12651**. e. **35**

—— [A reissue.] The Quest of the Bellamy Jewels, *etc.* *London & Glasgow*, [1954.] 8°. **12837**. b. **5**

—— Thirty Thousand Miles for the Films. The story of th filming of "Soldiers Three" and "Rhodes of Africa." [With plates, including a portrait.] pp. viii. 197. *Blackie & Son: London & Glasgow*, 1937. 8°. **11796**. bb. **13**

BARKAS (Pallister)

—— A Critique of Modern English Prosody, 1880–1930. pp. 100. *Halle*, 1934. 8°. [*Studien zur Englischen Philologie.* Bd. 82.] **12981**. f. **82**.

—— Storm Song, and other poem. pp. 71. *Elkin Mathews: London*, 1912. 8°. **011650**. h. **7**

BARKAS (Thomas Pallister) Outlines of Ten Years' Investigations into the Phenomena of Modern Spiritualism, embracing letters, lectures, &c. pp. viii. 160. *Frederick Pitman: London; T. P. Barkas: Newcastle*, 1862. 8°. **8631**. d. **15**.

BARKAS (Wilfred Watson)

—— The Mechanical Properties of Wood and their Relatio to Moisture . . . With a chapter by R. F. S. Hearmon *In:* Meredith (Reginald) Mechanical Properties o Wood and Paper. pp. 1–98. 1953. 8°. W.P. b. **683** 4

—— The Principles of Woodworking. A survey of present knowledge on this subject. By W. W. Barkas . . . E. D. Van Rest . . . and W. E. Wilson. [With plates.] pp. vi. 35. *London*, 1932. 8°. [*Department of Scientific and Industrial Research. Forest Products Research. Bulletin.* no. 13.] B.S. **38**

—— Recent Work on the Moisture in Wood in relation to Strength and Shrinkage. pp. ii. 35. *London*, 1938. 8°. [*Department of Scientific and Industrial Research. Forest Products Research Board. Special Report.* no. 4.] B.S. **38**. e **6**.

—— The Swelling of Wood under Stress, *etc.* pp. iv. 103. 1949. 8°. *See* England.—*Department of Scientific and Industrial Research.—Forest Products Research Board.* B.S. **38**. e/**20**.

BARKAS (Wilfred Watson)

—— Swelling Stresses in Gels and the calculation of the elastic constants of gels from their hygroscopic properties. pp. ii. 62. *London*, 1945. 8°. [*Department of Scientific and Industrial Research. Forest Products Research. Special Report.* no. 6.] B.S. **38.** e/**6.**

BARKAUSKAS (Pranas) and **VABALAS** (Aleksandras)

—— Vadovas po Lietuvą. Redagavo P. Barkauskas ir A. Vabalas. [With maps.] pp. 380. 1938. 8°. *See* Lithuania.—*Lietuvos Turizmo Draugija.* **10291.** aa. **48.**

BARKAWAY (Charles)

—— He Found Adventure. A play in three acts. pp. 64. *Play Rights & Publications: London*, [1937.] 8°. [*Amateur Theatre Series of Plays.*] **11784.f.1/58.**

—— Peter Lends a Hand. A play in three acts. pp. 75. *London*, [1938.] 8°. [*French's Acting Edition.*] **11791.** t. **1/573.**

BARKE (Herbert)

—— Bales "Kynge Johan" und sein Verhältnis zur zeitgenössischen Geschichtsschreibung. pp. x. 145. *Würzburg*, 1937. 8°. **11860.** b. **4.**

BARKE (Hugon) and **JAROSZYK** (Kazimierz)

—— Walka o Mazowsze Pruskie. pp. 103. *Poznań*, 1931. 8°. **08073.** bb. **47.**

BARKE (James)

—— *See* Burns (Robert) *the Poet.* [*Smaller Collections.*] Poems and Songs of Robert Burns . . . Edited and introduced by J. Barke. 1955. 8°. **11606.** b. **49.**

—— The Crest of the Broken Wave, *etc.* *See* infra: Immortal Memory.

—— The End of the High Bridge. pp. 255. *Collins: London*, 1935. 8°. NN. **23468.**

—— The Green Hills Far Away. A chapter in autobiography. pp. 288. *Collins: London*, [1940.] 8°. **10859.** h. **15.**

—— Immortal Memory. [Novels based on the life of Robert Burns.] 5 pt.

The Wind that Shakes the Barley, *etc.* pp. 384. 1946. **12650.** de. **84**/**1.**
The Song in the Green Thorn Tree, *etc.* pp. 512. 1947. **12650.** de. **84**/**2.**
The Wonder of all the Gay World, *etc.* pp. 671. 1949. **12650.** de. **84**/**3.**
The Crest of the Broken Wave, *etc.* pp. 320. 1953. **12650.** de. **84**/**4.**
The Well of the Silent Harp, *etc.* pp. 351. 1954. **12650.** de. **84**/**5.**

Collins: London, 1946–54. 8°. **12650.** de. **84.**

—— The Land of the Leal. pp. 640. *Collins: London*, [1939.] 8°. **12632.** tt. **9.**

—— [A re-issue.] The Land of the Leal. *London*, 1950. 8°. **12646.** h. **27.**

—— Major Operation. A novel. pp. 495. *Collins: London*, 1936. 8°. **012600.** d. **29.**

—— Major Operation. The play of the novel. pp. 89. *William Maclellan: Glasgow*, 1943. 8°. **11782.** cc. **39.**

—— Major Operation. pp. 495. *Collins: London*, 1955. 8°. NNN. **6847.**

—— The Song in the Green Thorn Tree. *See* supra: Immortal Memory.

—— The Well of the Silent Harp, *etc.* *See* supra: Immortal Memory.

BARKE (James)

—— The Wild Macraes. pp. 252. *Collins. London*, 1934. 8°. NN. **21920**

—— The Wind that Shakes the Barley. *See* supra: Immortal Memory.

—— The Wonder of all the Gay World, *etc.* *See* supra: Immortal Memory.

—— The World his Pillow. pp. 424. *Collins: London*, 1933. 8°. NN. **19938.**

BARKE (Lizzie) Life Scenes from a Children's Hospital. pp. 125. *R.T.S.: London*, [1881.] 8°. **4421.** f. **27.**

BARKEER (John) *See* Barker (John) *Colonel.*

BARKEIJ (Johan Willem) De Nederlandsche wetgeving op het notaris-ambt. Academisch proefschrift, *etc.* pp. 126. *Leiden*, 1882. 8°. **5686.** cc. **19.**

BARKEL (Kathleen)

—— *See* I-Em-Hotep. The Dawn of Truth . . . Being the teachings of I-Em-Hotep through Mrs. K. Barkel. [1940, *etc.*] 8°. **8634.aaa.73.**

—— *See* I-Em-Hotep. The Hermetic Philosophy . . . Being the teachings of I-Em-Hotep through Mrs. K. Barkel. [1941, *etc.*] 8°. W.P. **9013.**

BARKELEY (Alexander) *See* Barclay (Alexander) *Priest.*

BARKELEY (*Sir* Richard) *See* Barckley.

BARKELY (*Sir* Robert) *See* Berkeley.

BARKÉN (Mauritius) De clade Folkungorum ad Her-revads-bro disquisitio. Quam . . . p.p. mag. Ericus Aug. Hallander . . . et M. Barkén, *etc.* pp. 16. *Upsaliæ*, [1837.] 8°. **9435.** d. **32.** (**1.**)

BARKER, *Ship.* De Schipbreuk van het Eng. Oost-Ind. Compagnieschip, The Barker. Of de gelukkige redding. Toneelspel in vier bedryven, *etc.* pp. 63. *Amsterdam*, 1781. 8°. **11755.** g. **27.** (**1.**)

BARKER AND CO. Barkers' Review of Politics, Literature, Religion, and Morals. *See* Periodical Publications.—*London.*

BARKER AND SON.

—— A Catalogue of Books . . . including . . . Old Plays . . . now selling . . . by Barker and Son. pp. 136. *London*, 1804. 8°. S.C. **735.** (**1.**)

BARKER'S CANADIAN MONTHLY MAGAZINE. *See* Periodical Publications.—*Kingston, Ont.*

BARKER'S FACTS AND FIGURES. *See* Periodical Publications.—*London.*

BARKER'S PANORAMA, *Leicester Square.* *See* London.—iii. *Panorama, Leicester Square.*

BARKER'S PANORAMA, *Strand.* *See* London.—iii. *Panorama, Strand.*

BARKER'S TRADE AND FINANCE ANNUAL. *See* Periodical Publications.—*London.*

BARKER, *Family of.* The Pedigree of the Barker Family. pp. 41. *Mitre Press: London*, [1931.] 8°. **9917.** bb. **28.**

BARKER, *Family of, of Aston.* *See* Barker (Arthur L.) The Barkers of Aston. [1932.] 4°. **09915.** ff. **19.**

BARKER, *Family of, of Horton.*

—— *See* Barker (John B.) The Pedigree of Barker, formerly of Horton, Co. Chester. Re-arranged by Major J. B. Barker. 1903. 4°. **09917.** df. **24.**

BARKER (   ) *Drawing Master.* Barker's Plantform Copies from the Blackberry & Wild Rose. Second grade. [12 cards.] *Liverpool,* [1879.] 4°. [*Gill's School Series.*] **12202.** df. **8/12.**

BARKER (   ) *Minister of God's Word at Pytchley. See* C., J. The Araignment of Hypocrisie . . . Being a fearfull example of Gods judgements on Mr. Barker . . . who for living in adultery with his neer kinswoman, and concealing the murder of her infant, was . . . executed at Northampton, *etc.* 1652. 8°. E. **1290. (3.)**

BARKER (   ) *Miss.* Lines addressed to a Noble Lord [i.e. Lord Byron] . . . By one of the small fry of the Lakes [i.e. Miss —— Barker]. pp. 23. 1815. 8°. *See* LINES. **11645.** bbb. **46.**

BARKER (   ) *Miss, Translator of "La Morale chrétienne." See* BOURDALOUE (L.) Some Instructions on Lent and its Duties. [Translated and compiled from "La Morale chrétienne" of L. Bourdaloue by Miss Barker.] 1885. 32°. **4401.** a. **42.**

BARKER (A.) *Clockmaker.* How to Examine and Clean Anglo-American, French, and English Clocks. pp. 8. *A. Barker: Stockton-on-Tees,* 1903. 8°. **08708.** aaa. **20. (2.)**

BARKER (A.) *Medical Herbalist.*

—— Medical Jurisprudence and the Unregistered Practitioner. Notes on the laws affecting the practice. [The foreword signed: A. Barker.] pp. 19. *National Association of Medical Herbalists of Great Britain: London,* [1938.] 12°. **6095.** a. **41.**

BARKER (A. A.) The Sunday School Teacher's Prize Essay on the Sabbath. pp. 63. *Sunday School Union: London,* [1886.] 8°. **4372.** df. **27. (9.)**

BARKER (A. C.)

—— "Spunyarn." [Short stories.] pp. 118. *Rankin Bros.: Bristol,* [1954.] 8°. **12654.** f. **1.**

BARKER (A. CLAYTON) Notes upon the Organisation of Election Meetings. pp. viii. 123. *Midland Unionist Association: Birmingham,* 1923. 8°. **08139.** aa. **30.**

BARKER (A. E.) *Miss.* Lady Barbara's Birthday. A comedietta. *See* BLANCHARD (E. L. L.) Lazinella, *etc.* [1883.] 8°. **11781.** df. **14.**

—— [Another edition.] *J. Williams: London,* [1899.] 8°. **11779.** aaa. **68. (2.)**

BARKER (A. MABEL) Our Dead Selves. A novel. pp. 288. *A. H. Stockwell: London,* [1930.] 8°. NN. **16784.**

BARKER (A. R.) *Architect. See* ENGLAND.—*Church of England.—Church Societies.—Church Penitentiary Association.* Penitentiary Work in the Church of England, *etc.* (Practical Suggestions as to the Selection of a Site, Description of Houses, etc. [By A. R. Barker.]) 1873. 8°. **4192.** cc. **26.**

BARKER (ABIGAIL) Calumny Refuted; or a Glance at John Wilbur's book [i.e. "A Narrative and Exposition of the late Proceedings of New-England Yearly Meeting"]. (Comments on Mutilated Extracts from the Writings of Joseph John Gurney [contained in Wilbur's book], contrasted with selections from the writings of Fox, Barclay, Penn, and others; by the late A. Barker, and other Friends in America.—Letters to Friends of the Monthly Meeting of Adrian, Michigan. By J. J. Gurney.) pp. 108. *John Hasler: London,* 1845. 8°. **4152.** cc. **34.**

—— Second edition . . . With new prefatory remarks. pp. xvii. 92. *Charles Gilpin: London,* 1846. 8°. **4152.** cc. **33.**

BARKER (ABIGAIL)

—— *See* WILBUR (John) Is it Calumny? or is it truth? An examination of a pamphlet entitled "Calumny Refuted," *etc.* 1846. 8°. **1355.** g. **34.**

BARKER (ALBERT) *Playwright. See* BARKER (Edwin L.) and (A.) Dirty Hands, *etc.* [1932.] 8°. **11791.** pp. **27.**

—— *See* BARKER (Edwin L.) and (A.) The Man on Stilts, *etc.* [1934.] 8°. **011781.** g. **1/370**

—— Ladies in Linen. A comedy in one act. pp. 24. *Samuel French: New York,* [1935.] 8°. **20018.** f. **88**

BARKER (ALBERT) *Sapper.* Memories of Macedonia pp. 34. *A. H. Stockwell: London,* [1921.] 8°. **09083.** a. **84**

BARKER (*Mrs.* ALBERT) *See* BARKER (M. A.) *Mrs.*

BARKER (ALBERT GORDON)

—— Poems. pp. xxvii. *Phoenix Press: [London,]* 1935. fol **011653.** o. **60**

BARKER (ALBERT SMITH) Everyday Life in the Navy. Autobiography of Rear Admiral A. S. Barker. [With plates, including portraits.] pp. viii. 422. *R. G. Badger: Boston,* [1928.] 8°. **8804.** bbb. **3**

BARKER (ALDRED FARRER) *See* PERIODICAL PUBLICATIONS.—*Manchester.* The Wool Year Book and Diary *etc.* [1908/09–1911 compiled by A. F. Barker; 1912, 191[illegible] compiled by the editor of the "Textile Mercury" with the assistance of A. F. Barker and others.] [1908, *etc.*] 8°. P.P. **2491.** t

—— The Analysis & Reproduction of Textile Fabrics, *etc* pp. ix. 230. *Marsden & Co.: Manchester; The Author Bradford,* 1894. 8°. **7743.** bb. **62**

—— Camping with Motor-Car & Camera . . . Illustrated with photographs, maps and diagrams. pp. xiii. 306. *J. M. Dent & Sons: London,* 1913. 8°. **010347.** f. **39**

—— Embroideries and Embroidery Machines . . . Reprinted from the "Textile Recorder," *etc.* pp. 71. *J. Heywood Manchester,* [1898.] 8°. **07945.** i. **5**

—— First Experiences with Motor Car & Camera. By A. F. B. [i.e. A. F. Barker.] Edited by B. M. B. [With illustrations.] pp. 229. [1911.] 8°. *See* B., A. F. **010352.** g. **22**

—— An Introduction to the Study of Textile Design . . With numerous illustrations and diagrams. pp. xvii. 21[illegible] *Methuen & Co.: London,* 1903. 8°. [*Text-Books of Technology.*] **07944.** [illegible]

—— Justice to Japan. pp. xvi. 184. *Jowett & Sowry Leeds,* 1937. 8°. **8231.** de. **35**

—— Ornamentation and Textile Design, *etc.* pp. xvii. 30[illegible] pl. XCIV. *Methuen & Co.: London,* 1930. 4°. **07742.** cc. **24**

—— The Prospective Development of Peru as a sheep-breeding and wool-growing country, *etc.* [With plates.] pp. xii. 174. *Jowett & Sowry: Leeds,* 1927. 8°. **07294.** i. **25**

—— A Report on the Cottage Textile Industries of Kashmi[r] and their Prospective Development. [With illustrations.] pp. 120. [*Leeds,* 1933.] 8°. **7742.** pp. **7**

—— The Sheep and Wool of South Africa, Rhodesia, and Kenya Colony. [With illustrations.] pp. 57. [*Leeds* 1930.] 8°. **7291.** d. **18**

BARKER (ALDRED FARRER)

—— Textiles . . . With chapters on the mercerized and artificial fibres, and the dyeing of textile materials by W. M. Gardner . . . silk throwing and spinning by R. Snow, the cotton industry by W. H. Cook, the linen industry by F. Bradbury. pp. xii. 375. *Constable & Co.: London*, 1910. 8°. [*Westminster Series*.] **12208. v. 20.**

—— Revised edition. pp. xii. 386. *Constable & Co.: London*, 1922. 8°. [*Westminster Series*.] **12208. v. 30.**

—— University Ideals. The Presidential Address to the Yorkshire Natural Science Association . . . Genetics and Wool Production. An address to the Pan-Pacific Science Congress, *etc.* pp. 59. *Leeds*, [1925.] 8°. **07294. l. 19.**

—— Wool and the Textile Industries . . . With a technical glossary. A series of articles . . . written to introduce the technical words and phrases . . . Translated by C. A. Lièvre. *Eng., Fr., Ital. & Span.* 2 pt. [1920.] 4°. **7943. g. 27.**

—— Woollen and Worsted Spinning . . . With 100 illustrations. pp. xvi. 343. *Cassell & Co.: London*, 1922. 8°. **07943. a. 7.**

BARKER (ALDRED FARRER) and **MIDGLEY** (EBER)

—— Analysis of Woven Fabrics . . . With . . . eighty-two illustrations. pp. xii. 307. *Scott, Greenwood & Son: London*, 1914. 8°. **07945. k. 45.**

—— Second, revised and enlarged, edition, *etc.* pp. xv. 322. *Scott, Greenwood & Son: London*, 1922. 8°. **07942. d. 82.**

BARKER (ALDRED FARRER) and **PRIESTLEY** (E.) *Lecturer at Bradford Technical College.*

—— Wool Carding and Combing, with notes on sheep breeding and wool growing . . . With 100 illustrations. pp. xii. 264. *Cassell & Co.: London*, 1912. 8°. **07942. de. 36.**

BARKER (ALFRED) *Head Master of the Grammar School, Keighley.* Introduction to Chemical Analysis—inorganic qualitative—for the use of schools, *etc.* pp. 43. *J. W. Bean & Son: Leeds; Simpkin, Marshall & Co.: London*, [1884.] 12°. **8906. df. 14.**

BARKER (ALFRED) *M.D., M.R.C.S.* Deafness and Diseases of the Ear. With cases, illustrating the mode of cure discovered and practised only by A. Barker. pp. 64. *The Author: London*, [1855.] 32°. **1189. a. 35.**

BARKER (ALFRED) *of Wigan.* Diocesan Examination Questions in Religious Knowledge. One thousand questions classified and arranged by A. Barker. pp. 84. *R. Platt: Wigan*, [1897.] 8°. **4375. aaa. 3.**

BARKER (ALFRED) *Rector of Hailsham.* Practical Sermons, on various subjects. pp. 231. *E. Brown: Hailsham*, 1815. 8°. **4461. c. 2.**

BARKER (ALFRED) *Rev., of Taunton.* The Character of a Good King; a sermon, occasioned by the death of . . . King George III. Preached at Taunton, *etc.* pp. 41. *J. W. Marriott: Taunton*, 1820. 8°. **10805. c. 8.**

BARKER (ALFRED TREVOR) *See* BLAVATSKY (Helen P.) The Complete Works of H. P. Blavatsky. Edited by A. T. Barker. 1933, *etc.* 8°. **8635.1.14.**

—— *See* BLAVATSKY (Helen P.) The Letters of H. P. Blavatsky to A. P. Sinnett . . . Transcribed, compiled, and with an introduction by A. T. Barker. 1925. 8°. **10906. f. 21.**

BARKER (ALFRED TREVOR)

—— *See* DE PURUCKER (G.) Fundamentals of the Esoteric Philosophy . . . Edited by A. T. Barker. 1932. 8°. **8633. g. 34.**

—— *See* MORYA. The Mahatma Letters to A. P. Sinnett . . . Transcribed, compiled, and with an introduction by A. T. Barker. 1923. 8°. **8633. b. 26.**

—— —— 1926. 8°. **8633. e. 26.**

—— *See* MORYA. The Mahatma Letters to A. P. Sinnett . . . Transcribed, compiled, and with an introduction by A. T. Barker, *etc.* 1930. 8°. **08632. h. 14.**

—— *See* MORYA. The Mahatma Letters to A. P. Sinnett . . . Transcribed, compiled, and with an introduction by A. T. Barker, *etc.* 1948. 8°. **8634. ff. 58.**

BARKER (ALFRED WILLIAM KENT) and **CHAPMAN** (ARTHUR HENRY) Workshop Practice for the School and Laboratory. pp. vii. 181. *Sidgwick & Jackson: London*, 1928. 8°. **7941. de. 18.**

BARKER (ALICE) Mrs. Colonel Barker, friend of the poor. pp. 36. *London*, 1930. 16°. [*Salvation Army Miniature Biographies.* no. 8.] **W.P. 9922/8.**

BARKER (AMBROSE GEORGE) *See* HUNT (H. E.) *of Walthamstow.* 1862–1912. Fifty Years a Club, *etc.* [By H. E. Hunt and A. G. Barker.] 1913. 8°. **08248. aa. 14.**

—— 1862–1932. Seventy Years a Club . . . By Ambrose G. Barker. [A reissue of "1862–1912. Fifty Years a Club," by H. E. Hunt and A. G. Barker, with additional matter by A. G. Barker.] pp. 147. 1933. 8°. *See* WALTHAMSTOW.—*Walthamstow Working Men's Club and Institute.* **20017. ee. 13.**

—— Henry Hetherington, 1792–1849, *etc.* pp. 62. *G. W. Foote & Co.: London*, [1938.] 8°. **10856. l. 10.**

BARKER (AMELIA M.) *See* THACKERAY (W. M.) [*The Rose and the Ring.*] The Rose and the Ring . . . Adapted and rearranged in verse by A. M. Barker. [1899.] 8°. **11781. dd. 44. (12.)**

—— Forty Fancies and Seven Songs. pp. 88. *H. J. Drane: London*, [1902.] 8°. **011651. h. 33.**

—— Tom-All-Alone. pp. 331. *J. Macqueen: London*, 1899. 8°. **012642. dd. 36.**

BARKER (ANDREW) A True and Certaine Report of the Beginning, Proceedings, Ouerthrowes and now present Estate of Captaine Ward and Danseker, the two late famous pirates . . . As also the firing of 25. saile of the Tunis, *etc.* [With a woodcut.] B.L. pp. 27. *Printed by William Hall; sold by Iohn Holme: London*, 1609. 4°. **C. 27. c. 6.**

BARKER (ANNE) The Complete Servant Maid: or young woman's best companion. Containing full . . . directions for qualifying them for service in general . . . Including a variety of useful receipts, *etc.* pp. 48. *J. Cooke: London*, [1770?] 8°. **787. f. 22.**

BARKER (ANTHONY)

—— South Seas Martyr: Blessed Peter Chanel, S.M., 1803–1841. pp. 26. *Catholic Truth Society of Ireland: Dublin*, 1953. 8°. **3939. k.**

BARKER (ANTHONY RAINE) The Fairyland Express. A book of woodcuts for children, *etc.* pp. 63. *John Lane: London*, 1925. 8°. **011645. f. 122.**

BARKER (Anthony Raine)

—— Hidden Gold. A book of woodcuts . . . A story of exciting adventure told in verse. pp. 125. *John Lane: London,* [1926.] 8°. **11643. cc. 40.**
Printed on one side of the leaf only.

BARKER (Arthur) The British Corn Trade from the earliest times to the present day. pp. viii. 132. *London,* [1920.] 8°. [*Pitman's Common Commodities and Industries.*] **07077. f. 1/41.**

BARKER (Arthur) *Medical Herbalist.*

—— The Herbal Pocket Prescriber. pp. xii. 180. *E. H. Eardley: Tunstall,* 1938. 16°. **07510. de. 37.**

—— The Herbal Pocket Prescriber. (Second edition.) pp. xiv. 129. *Warwick Savage: Burslem,* 1948. 16°. **07510. de. 61.**

BARKER (Arthur) *Spiritualist.*

—— Experiences in Spiritual Healing. By an East Anglian Farmer (Arthur Barker). pp. 147. *W. E. Harrison & Sons: Ipswich,* [1937.] 8°. **4182. b. 56.**

—— Songs of Suffolk. pp. 57. *W. E. Harrison & Sons: Ipswich,* [1937.] 8°. **11655. f. 25.**

BARKER (Arthur) *Writer on Squash Rackets.*

—— Squash Rackets. pp. 141. *Eyre & Spottiswoode: London,* 1936. 8°. [*Aldin Series.*] **7921.f.28/6.**

BARKER (Arthur Charles)

—— Nautical Nonsense . . . Drawings by "H. P." (2nd impression.) [Verses.] pp. 79. *Rankin Bros.: Bristol,* 1948. 8°. **12316. s. 68.**

—— Nobby and Pincher in Civvy Street. pp. 122. *Rankin Bros.: Bristol,* [1950.] 8°. **12332. ee. 33.**

BARKER (Arthur Edward) Collections of Works.]

—— *See* Milton (John) [Smaller / Samson Agonistes and Shorter Poems. Edited by A. E. Barker. [1950.] 8°. **11630. b. 44.**

—— Milton and the Puritan Dilemma, 1641–1660. pp. xxiv. 440. [*Toronto,*] 1942. 8°. [*University of Toronto. Department of English. Studies and Texts. no.* 1.] **Ac. 2702. al.**

—— [Another copy.] Milton and the Puritan Dilemma, 1641–1660. 1942. 8°. **04715. i. 4.**

BARKER (Arthur Edward James)

—— *See* Coote (Holmes) Diseases of the Tongue . . . Re-written by A. E. Barker. 1883. 8°. [*Holmes* (*Timothy*) *A System of Surgery, etc.* vol. 2.] **07482. k. 1.**

—— *See* Frey (H.) The Histology and Histochemistry of Man . . . Translated . . . by A. E. J. Barker, *etc.* 1874. 8°. **7421. ee. 23.**

—— *See* Lennander (K. G.) Observations on the Sensibility of the Abdominal Cavity . . . Translated . . . by A. E. Barker. 1903. 8°. **7620. aaa. 60.**

—— Hunterian Lectures on Intra-cranial Inflammations starting in the Temporal Bone. Their complications and treatment, *etc.* pp. 72. *H. K. Lewis: London,* 1890. 8°. **07305. e. 21. (8.)**

—— Operations for Hernia. *See* Burghard (F. F.) A System of Operative Surgery, *etc.* vol. 2. 1914. 8°. **20036.a.1/529.**

BARKER (Arthur Edward James)

—— A Short Manual of Surgical Operations, *etc.* pp. vi. 423. *Longmans & Co.: London,* 1887. 8°. **7482. ee. 6.**

—— The Surgical Affections of the Stomach and their Treatment, *etc.* pp. 153. *Medical Publishing Co.: London,* [1898.] 8°. **7630. de. 22.**

BARKER (Arthur Gladstone) *See* Sewell (Archibald H.) and Barker (A. G.) The Drink Trade and the Nation. 1926. 8°. **8436. f. 58.**

BARKER (Arthur Henry) Barker on Heating. The theory and practice of heating and ventilation. pp. xvi. 640. lxxvi. *Carton Press: London,* 1912. 8°. **8776. ee. 47.**

—— Domestic Fuel Consumption. pp. x. 159. *Constable & Co.: London,* 1920. 8°. [*Chadwick Library.*] **12211.r.3/7.**

—— Fuel Economy in Cooking Apparatus: a course of lectures . . . Reprinted from "The Builder." pp. 27. *London,* [1918.] 4°. **8715. g. 40.**

—— Graphic Methods of Engine Design. Including a graphical treatment of the balancing of engines. pp. iv. 210. *Technical Publishing Co.: Manchester,* 1897. 8°. **08766. aa. 2.**

—— Second edition. pp. iv. 210. *Technical Publishing Co.: Manchester,* [1905.] 8°. **08767. de. 23.**

—— Graphical Calculus . . . With an introduction by J. Goodman. pp. vii. 188. *Longmans & Co.: London,* 1896. 8°. **8535. de. 21.**

—— The Management of Small Engineering Workshops. pp. v. 256. *Technical Publishing Co.: Manchester,* 1899. 8°. **08766. aa. 35.**

—— The Relative Advantages of Heating by Coke, Gas and Electricity. [A lecture.] *See* London.—iii. *Chadwick Trust.* The Modern House and its Equipment, *etc.* 1937. 8°. **07815. bb. 20.**

—— Tests on Ranges and Cooking Appliances . . . An extract from the report of the Building Materials Research Committee. [With plans.] pp. vi. 55. *London,* 1922. 8°. [*Fuel Research Board. Special Report. no.* 4.] **B.S. 38. f/4.**

BARKER (Arthur J.)

—— Principles of Small Arms. pp. xi. 82. *Gale & Polden: Aldershot,* 1952. 8°. **8839. a. 109.**

BARKER (Arthur Leigh)

—— The Barkers of Aston. *Mayflower Press: Plymouth,* [1932.] 4°. **09915. ff. 19.**

—— The Hymnal Appendix. A supplement to "Hymns, Ancient and Modern" . . . "Church Hymns" . . . "The Hymnal Companion." Compiled by A. L. Barker. pp. ix. 121. *Skeffington & Son: London,* 1907. 16°. **3436. aaaa. 44.**

BARKER (Audrey Lilian)

—— Apology for a Hero. A novel. pp. 263. *Hogarth Press: London,* 1950. 8°. **NNN. 453.**

—— Innocents. Variations on a theme. [Tales.] pp. 204. *Hogarth Press: London,* 1947. 8°. **NN. 37240.**

—— Novelette, with other stories. pp. v. 231. *Hogarth Press: London,* 1951. 8°. **NNN. 2749.**

BARKER (Austin Stansfield)

—— The Use of Fertilizers. A guide to the manuring of crops in Great Britain, *etc.* pp. x. 204. *Oxford University Press: London,* 1935. 8°. **07076.** cc. **13.**

BARKER (Austin Stansfield) and **HADDEN** (M. A.)

—— Self-Sufficiency in Milk Production . . . A case study of Mr. John O'Neill's farm . . . Lurgan, Co. Armagh, *etc.* [With plates.] pp. 27. *London,* 1953. 8°. [*Imperial Chemical Industries. Agricultural Development Department. Bulletin.* no. 4.] P.P. **2304.** bbc.

BARKER (B.) *Esq.* The Commodore's Daughter. pp. 68. *E. Lloyd: London,* [1847.] 8°. **12621.** g. **11.**

—— The Suicide Restored, or, Mystery unravelled. pp. 4 [46]. *Gleason's Publishing Hall: Boston,* 1846. 8°. **12703.** g. **51.**

BARKER (Bathshua) *See* Harris (William) *D.D., Minister at Crutched-Friars.* The Scripture Consolations in the Death of Good Men. A Sermon . . . occasion'd by the death of Mrs. Bathshua Barker, *etc.* 1719. 8°. **1416.** c. **28.**

BARKER (Benjamin) *Highwayman.* The Life of Benjamin Barker, a notorious highwayman . . . who was executed at Chelmsford . . . the 18th of May, 1750, *etc.* pp. 16. *J. Underwood: London,* 1750. 12°. **1416.** c. **27.**

BARKER (Benjamin) *of Burley, Leeds.* Infidelity: its cause and cure, *etc.* pp. 39. *Walker & Laycock: Leeds,* 1885. 8°. **4399.** ccc. **40. (10.)**

BARKER (Benjamin Fordyce) Lectures on Uterine Displacements . . . Reported by B. T. Roath. Lecture first. From the New York Medical Gazette. pp. 23. *Baker, Godwin & Co.: New York,* 1853. 8°. **7581.** c. **32. (2.)**

—— On Sea-sickness. pp. 36. *D. Appleton & Co.: New York,* 1870. 8°. **7620.** a. **25.**

BARKER (Benjamin George)

—— The New National Anthem of Great Britain and Ireland. God Save Our Emperor King. Suggested for use on the occasion of the Coronation in May, and thenceforth. [*Indianapolis,* 1937.] 4°. **1879.** cc. **10. (22.)**

BARKER (Bernard) Eliot the Younger. A fiction in freehand. 3 vol. *S. Tinsley & Co.: London,* 1878. 8°. **12640.** cc. **1.**

BARKER (Bertie Thomas Percival)

—— Agricultural and Horticultural Research in War Time. pp. 58. *Bath,* 1943. 8°. [*Bath and West and Southern Counties Society. Pamphlet.* no. 10.] **7080.de.42/10.**

—— Cider Apple Production. (Second edition.) pp. iv. 64. pl. viii. *London,* 1954. 8°. [*Ministry of Agriculture and Fisheries. Bulletin.* no. 104.] B.S. **3/75.**

BARKER (Bertram) North of '53. The adventures of a trapper and prospector in the Canadian Far North . . . With 20 illustrations [including a portrait], *etc.* pp. ix. 242. *Methuen & Co.: London,* 1934. 8°. **010460.** ff. **7.**

BARKER (Brian)

—— Labour in London. A study in municipal achievement, *etc.* pp. x. 232. *G. Routledge & Sons: London,* 1946. 8°. **8287.** i. **70.**

BARKER (Burt Brown)

—— *See* Ogden (Peter S.) Peter Skene Ogden's Snake Country Journals . . . With an introduction by . . . B. B. Barker. 1950. 8°. [*Publications of the Hudson's Bay Record Society.* vol. 13.] Ac. **8565/6.**

BARKER (C. Edward)

—— "Whom Shall I Send?" An introduction to membership of the Methodist Church. pp. 63. *Epworth Press: London,* 1942. 8°. **20041.** cc. **22.**

BARKER (C. H.) *Writer on Banking.* Banks as Trustees. How banks can help in the administration of wills and trusts. pp. x. 138. *Sir I. Pitman & Sons: London,* 1933 [1932]. 8°. **6425.** cc. **7.**

BARKER (C. J.) *Astrologer.* The Astrologer's Ready Reckoner for ascertaining from the Ephemerides the approximate zodiacal position of the sun, moon and planets . . . With tables, *etc.* pp. vii. 33. *Occult Book Co.: Halifax,* [1895.] 8°. **8610.** f. **19.**

BARKER (Carnaby Johnson)

—— Office for a Devotional Meeting of Sunday School Teachers. pp. 12. *S.P.C.K.: London,* [1895?] 8°. **03456.** ee. **102.**

BARKER (Catherine)

—— Yesterday Today. Life in the Ozarks . . . Illustrated with photographs. pp. 263. *Caxton Printers: Caldwell, Ida.,* 1941. 8°. **10413.** s. **5.**

BARKER (Catherine Sweazey) *See* Barker (Catherine)

BARKER (Charles) *M.A., of Trinity College, Cambridge.* Character and Anecdotes of Charles the Second. pp. iv. 111. *Chapman & Hall: London,* 1853. 8°. **1155.** g. **4.**

—— Testimonials in favour of Charles Barker, as a candidate for the situation of English Master in the Edinburgh Academy. (Additional Testimonials in favour of Charles Barker.) 2 pt. *J. & C. Muirhead: Edinburgh,* 1824. 8°. **8364.** b. **31. (5.)**

BARKER (Charles) *Vicar of Hollym.* A Charity Sermon, preached at Hollym, in Holderness, Yorkshire, July 21, 1822. pp. 27. *Isaac Wilson: Hull,* 1825. 8°. **4476.** bb. **99. (8.)**

BARKER (Charles Albro)

—— *See* Crosby (Elisha O.) Memoirs . . . Edited by C. A. Barker. 1945. 8°. W.P. **9803/29.**

—— The Background of the Revolution in Maryland. pp. x. 419. *New Haven,* 1940. 8°. [*Yale Historical Publications.* Miscellany. no. 38.] Ac. **2692.** md/**3.**

—— Henry George. [A biography. With a portrait.] pp. xvii. 696. *Oxford University Press: New York,* 1955. 8°. **010885.** g. **70.**

BARKER (Charles Alfred)

—— *See* Vance (B. B.) Biology Activities. [By] B. B. Vance . . . C. A. Barker, *etc.* [1946.] 4°. **7008.** bb. **12.**

—— *See* Vance (Bruce B.) Biology Activities. [By] B. B. Vance . . . C. A. Barker, *etc.* 1948. 4°. **7008.** bb. **20.**

BARKER (Charles F.) *of Richmond, Surrey.* Two Years in the Canaries: an account of travel . . . in the Canary Islands, with the object of circulating the Scriptures in the Spanish tongue. pp. ix. 205. *Eyre & Spottiswoode: London,* 1917. 8°. **010094.** de. **6.**

BARKER (Charles Fiott) Memoir on Syria: designed to illustrate the condition of that country before and subsequent to the evacuation of the Egyptian army, and its position under the Ottoman yoke. To which are added, Remarks on its produce and resources, *etc.* pp. 53. *Madden & Malcolm: London,* [1845.] 8°. **1434.** f. **2. (4.)**

BARKER (Charles Francis) *See* Barker (William Robert) *Draughts Player,* and (C. F.) The World's Checker Book, *etc.* 1879. 8°. **7915.** bb. **9.**

BARKER (Charles Francis)

—— The American Checker-player: comprising twenty-two openings, *etc.* (The Game of Checkers. Barker vs. Martins. International match games, *etc.*) 2 pt. *H. A. Young & Co.: Boston*, 1888. 8°. **7912. aa. 43.**

—— The American Checker-Player: comprising twenty-two openings, *etc.* pp. 179. *Henry A. Young & Co.: Boston*, [1880.] 8°. **7920. aa. 11.**

BARKER (Charles John) *See* Boehme (J.) [*Smaller Collections.*] The Forty Questions of the Soul and The Clavis . . . Reissued by C. J. B. [i.e. C. J. Barker], *etc.* 1911. 8°. **03558. g. 25.**

—— *See* Boehme (J.) [*Beschreibung der drei Principien göttlichen Wesens.*] Concerning the Three Principles of the Divine Essence . . . Reissued by C. J. B. (C. J. Barker), *etc.* 1910. 8°. **3558. g. 15.**

—— *See* Boehme (J.) [*Morgenröte im Aufgange.*] The Aurora . . . Edited by C. J. B. (C. J. Barker) and D. S. H. 1914. 8°. **3559. dd. 10.**

—— *See* Boehme (J.) [*Mysterium Magnum.*] Mysterium Magnum . . . Edited by C. J. B. (C. J. Barker.) [With a portrait of the editor.] 1924. 8°. **03166. k. 20.**

—— *See* Boehme (J.) [*Vom dreifachen Leben des Menschen.*] The High and Deep Searching Out of the Threefold Life of Man . . . Reissued by C. J. B. (C. J. Barker), *etc.* 1909. 8°. **3558. e. 19.**

—— *See* Boehme (J.) [*Weg zu Christo.*] The Way to Christ, *etc.* [Edited by C. J. Barker.] 1911. 8°. **765. b. 21.**

—— *See* Penny (Anne J.) Studies in Jacob Böhme. [With a preface by C. J. Barker.] 1912. 8°. **3716. f. 16.**

—— Pre-requisites for the Study of Jacob Böhme . . . Reprinted from " The Seeker," *etc.* pp. 32. *J. M. Watkins: London*, 1920. 8°. **03558. f. 27.**

BARKER (Charles Joseph)

—— The Johannine Epistles, *etc.* [With the text.] pp. 115. 1948. 8°. *See* Bible.—*John, Epistles of.* [*English.*] **3054. aa. 29.**

—— The Way of Life. A study in Christian ethics. pp. 280. *Lutterworth Press: London & Redhill*, 1946. 8°. **4381. bb. 47.**

BARKER (Charles Spackman) Barker, Charles Spackman, facteur d'orgues, *etc.* [1860?] 8°. **07807. l. 23. (3.)** *Pp. 421–425 of a larger work.*

BARKER (Charles Thomas) Sermons. pp. xviii. 288. *University Press: Oxford*, 1813. 8°. **1021. c. 21.**

—— On the Use of History. *See* Oxford.—*University of Oxford.* [*Prize Poems and Essays.*] The Oxford English Prize Essays, *etc.* vol. 1. 1836. 12°. **8364. b. 39.**

—— A Sermon preached at the Anniversary Meeting of the Sons of the Clergy . . . May 5, 1805, *etc.* pp. xx. 31. *F. & C. Rivington, etc.: London*, 1806. 4°. **694. h. 7. (1.)**

—— A Sermon, preached in the Chapel at Lambeth . . . at the consecration of . . . Charles Moss, D.D. Lord Bishop of Oxford. pp. 22. *T. Cadell & W. Davies: London*, 1807. 4°. **1200. cc. 23. (8.)**

BARKER (Charles W.) *See* Romeike (H.) The Wife-Beaters' Manual . . . Edited by C. W. Barker. 1884. 8°. **6146. h. 18. (18.)**

BARKER (Christopher) *Arithmetician.* Product Calculator and Day Reckoner. For use in banks in connection with what is known as the decimal system, *etc.* *Bemrose & Sons: London*, 1901. 8°. **08548. ff. 1.**

BARKER (Christopher) *of Huddersfield.* The Development of the Associative Principle during the Middle Ages. Three lectures, *etc.* pp. viii. 100. ii. *Longman & Co.: London*, 1859. 8°. **8282. a. 63.**

BARKER (Cicely Mary) *See* Hymnals. [*English.*] The Little Picture Hymn Book. Illustrated and decorated by C. M. Barker. [1933.] 16°. **3433. ee. 45.**

—— Beautiful Bible Pictures. Painted by C. M. Barker. [6 cards.] *Blackie & Son: London & Glasgow*, [1932.] 8°. **3129. g. 30.**

—— The Book of the Flower Fairies, *etc.* pp. 92. *Blackie & Son: London & Glasgow*, [1927.] 8°. **011645. i. 59.**

—— Fairies of the Flowers and Trees, *etc.* (Flower fairies of the wayside. Flower fairies of the garden. Fairies of the trees.) [With plates.] pp. 92. *Blackie & Son: London & Glasgow*, [1950.] 8°. **12833. ee. 32.**

—— Fairies of the Trees. Poems and pictures by C. M. Barker. *Blackie & Son: London & Glasgow*, 1940. 16°. **12822. a. 22.**

—— Flower Fairies of the Autumn . . . Poems and pictures by C. M. Barker. *Blackie & Son: London*, [1926.] 16°. **12810. a. 35.**

—— Flower Fairies of the Garden. Poems and pictures by C. M. Barker. *Blackie & Son: London & Glasgow*, [1944.] 16°. **11657. e. 38.**

—— Flower Fairies of the Spring. Poems and pictures by C. M. Barker. *Blackie & Son: London*, [1923.] 16°. **11646. de. 82.**

—— Flower Fairies of the Summer. Poems and pictures by C. M. Barker. *Blackie & Son: London*, [1925.] 16°. **12801. a. 76.**

—— Flower Fairies of the Wayside. Poems and pictures by C. M. Barker. *Blackie & Son: London & Glasgow*, [1948.] 16°. **11658. de. 31.**

—— A Flower Fairy Alphabet. Poems and pictures by C. M. Barker. *Blackie & Son: London & Glasgow*, [1934.] 16°. **011641. de. 98.**

—— Cicely Barker's Flower Fairy Picture Book, *etc.* *Blackie & Son: London & Glasgow*, [1955.] 4°. **12837. l. 2.**

—— Groundsel and Necklaces. Story and pictures by C. M. Barker. pp. 48. *Blackie & Son: London & Glasgow*, [1946.] 16°. **12816. aa. 3.**

—— A Little Book of Old Rhymes. Collected and illustrated by C. M. Barker. pp. 48. *Blackie & Son: London & Glasgow*, [1936.] 16°. **11655. e. 28.**

—— Lively Stories. *Macmillan & Co.: London*, 1954– . 4°. **W.P. d. 825.**

—— The Lord of the Rushie River. Story and pictures by C. M. Barker. pp. 48. *Blackie & Son: London & Glasgow*, [1938.] 8°. **12821. a. 2.**

—— Old Rhymes for all Times. Collected and illustrated by C. M. Barker. pp. 64. *Blackie & Son: London & Glasgow*, [1928.] 4°. **11603. h. 32.**

—— Rhymes New and Old. Collected and illustrated by C. M. Barker. [With plates.] pp. 96. *Blackie & Son: London & Glasgow*, [1933.] 8°. **11601. l. 27.**

—— A Little Book of Rhymes New and Old. [A new edition of " Rhymes New and Old ".] Collected and illustrated by C. M. Barker. pp. 96. *Blackie & Son: London & Glasgow*, 1937. 16°. **20030. e. 79.**

BARKER (Cicely Mary)

—— When Spring came in at the Window. A one-act play. With songs from "Flower Fairies of the Spring" . . . Music by Olive Linnell. pp. 48. *Blackie & Son: London & Glasgow*, 1942. 8º. **11783.** aaa. **4.**

BARKER (Cicely Mary) and **WALDRAM** (Beatrice A.)

—— The "Guardian Angel" Series of Birthday Cards. Illustrated by C. M. Barker and B. A. Waldram. 6 pt. *S.P.C.K.: London*, [1923.] *obl.* 8º. **1879.** c. **13.** (**75.**)

BARKER (Clare Wright) and **ANDERSON** (Ira Dennis)

—— Principles of Retailing. pp. xi. 46. 4. *McGraw-Hill Book Co.: New York & London*, 1935. 8º. **8230.** cc. **47.**

—— Principles of Retailing . . . Second edition. pp. xii. 494. *McGraw-Hill Book Co.: New York & London*, 1941. 8º. **8232.** g. **48.**

A later edition is entered under Barker (*C. W.*)

BARKER (Clare Wright) and **ANSHEN** (Melvin)

—— Modern Marketing. pp. viii. 326. *McGraw-Hill Book Co.: New York & London*, 1939. 8º. **8232.** f. **41.**

BARKER (Clarence Hedley)

—— *See* also Hedley (Frank) *pseud.* [i.e. C. H. Barker.]

—— *See* also Seafarer, *pseud.* [i.e. C. H. Barker.]

—— Blue Water. pp. 279. *Cassell & Co.: London*, 1933. 8º. NN. **19914.**

—— The Case of the Secret Plans. pp. 82. *London*, [1921.] 8º. [*Lloyd's Detective Series.* no. 6.] **12645.** a. **2/6.**

—— Dark Road of Danger. pp. 96. *Withy Grove Press: London & Manchester*, [1943.] 8º. [*Cherry Tree Book.* no. 187.] **12634.** p. **1/187.**

—— Devil's Brood. pp. 275. *Cassell & Co.: London*, 1941. 8º. NN. **32577.**

—— Eight Went Cruising. pp. 222. *Robert Hale: London*, 1946. 8º. NN. **36488.**

—— The Hallam Moor Mystery. pp. 96. *Withy Grove Press: London & Manchester*, [1944.] 8º. [*Cherry Tree Book.* no. 199.] **12634.** p. **1/199.**

—— Hangman's Honeymoon. pp. 11–220. *Robert Hale: London*, 1943. 8º. NN. **34030.**

—— They Stole a Ship. pp. 192. *Robert Hale: London*, 1945. 8º. **12639.** pp. **4.**

—— The Wayward Nymph. pp. 306. *Cassell & Co.: London*, 1933. 8º. NN. **21652.**

BARKER (Colin) The Golden Belt; or, the Carib's pledge. pp. 125. *London*, [1862.] 8º. **12706.** a. **29.** (**2.**)
No. 11 *of "Beadle's American Library."*

BARKER (Conrad Robert) *See* Smith (*Sir* William) *LL.D.* Key to Dr. W. Smith's Initia Græca. (Key to the additional exercises in the appendix to Initia Græca, part I., by Rev. C. R. Barker.) 1891, *etc.* 8º. **12923.** cc. **13.**

—— *See* Smith (*Sir* William) *LL.D.* Key to Dr. W. Smith's Principia Latina. (Key to the exercises in the appendix to the Principia Latina, part I., by Rev. C. R. Barker.) 1892, *etc.* 8º. **12935.** cc. **24.**

BARKER (Conrad Robert)

—— Rhyme of the English Sovereigns. Embracing the dates of their accession, length of reign, *etc.* pp. 12. *Thomas Murby: London*, [1882.] 12º. **11646.** a. **61.**

BARKER (Culver Maynard)

—— Some Positive Values of Neurosis. pp. 20. *London*, [1948.] 8º. [*Guild of Pastoral Psychology. Guild Lecture.* no. 50.] W.P. **13328/50.**

BARKER (Cyril Moffatt) Incense and other kinds of Sense. [Papers on Church subjects.] pp. 116. *Vacher & Sons: London*, 1929. 8º. **04376.** i. **59.**

BARKER (Dalgairns Arundel) *See* Halévy (E.) A History of the English People . . . Translated . . . by E. I. Watkin and D. A. Barker. 1924, *etc.* 8º. **09525.1.1.**

—— *See* Halévy (E.) A History of the English People in the Nineteenth Century . . . Translated . . . by E. I. Watkin and D. A. Barker, *etc.* 1949, *etc.* 8º. **9512.cc.14.**

—— Cash and Credit. pp. vi. 143. *University Press: Cambridge*, 1910. 8º. [*Cambridge Manuals of Science and Literature.*] **12199.** b. **1/6.**

—— The Great Leviathan. [A novel.] pp. 283. *John Lane: London, New York*, 1920. 8º. NN. **6464.**

—— The Rani's Dominion. pp. 286. *Hutchinson & Co.: London*, [1926.] 8º. NN. **12059.**

—— The Theory of Money. pp. vii. 141. *University Press: Cambridge*, 1913. 8º. [*Cambridge Manuals of Science and Literature.*] **12199.** b. **1/67.**

BARKER (David) *Minister of the Gospel.*

—— The Parent's Monitor; or, Narratives, anecdotes, and observations on religious education and personal piety, *etc.* pp. viii. 368. *Richard Baynes: London*, 1827. 8º. **1030.** k. **14.**

—— Second edition enlarged. pp. viii. 380. *Richard Baynes: London*, 1827. 12º. **4902.** b. **43.**

BARKER (David Bateson)

—— *See* Brueys (D. A. de) and Palaprat (J.) [L'Avocat Patelin.] Let's get back to the Sheep . . . Adapted for stage production for Africans at Chalimbana by D. B. Barker, *etc.* 1952. 8º. **11740.** n. **48.**

BARKER (*Sir* David Wilson) *See* Carpenter (Alfred F. B.) and Barker (*Sir* D. W.) Nature Notes for Ocean Voyagers, *etc.* 1915. 8º. **7004.** c. **3.**

—— —— 1926. 8º. **07001.** h. **31.**

—— Clouds and Weather Signs . . . Illustrated with original photographs. pp. 31. "*Knowledge*": *London*, [1902.] 8º. **8758.** df. **8.**

—— The Compass: historical—theoretical—practical. pp. 39. *London*, 1892. 8º. [*Shipmasters' Society. Papers.* no. 19.] **08805.** bb. **1/19.**

—— The Development of Instrumental Nautical Astronomy, and Sounding in Shallow Water. [With plates.] pp. 19. *London*, 1891. 8º. [*Shipmasters' Society. Papers.* no. 10.] **08805.** bb. **1/10.**

—— A Manual of Elementary Seamanship . . . With frontispiece, twelve plates, *etc.* pp. xii. 120. *London*, 1896. 8º. [*Charles Griffin & Company's Nautical Series.*] **8804.** b. **1/1.**

BARKER (*Sir* DAVID WILSON)

—— Third edition, revised, and considerably enlarged. pp. xvi. 192. *London*, 1902. 8°. [*Charles Griffin & Company's Nautical Series.*] **8804**. b. **1/2**.

—— Fourth edition, revised. pp. xvi. 192. *London*, 1905. 8°. [*Charles Griffin & Company's Nautical Series.*] **8804**. b. **1/3**.

—— Fifth edition, revised. pp. xvi. 243. *London*, 1909. 8°. [*Charles Griffin & Company's Nautical Series.*] **8804**. b. **1/4**.

—— Sixth edition, revised. pp. xvi. 260. *London*, 1913. 8°. [*Charles Griffin & Company's Nautical Series.*] **8804**. b. **1/5**.

—— Seventh edition, revised. pp. xvi. 271. *London*, 1917. 8°. [*Charles Griffin & Company's Nautical Series.*] **8804**. b. **1/21**.

—— Eighth edition, revised. pp. xvi. 271. pl. XXIX. *London*, 1919. 8°. [*Charles Griffin & Company's Nautical Series.*] **8804**. b. **1/27**.

—— Ninth edition, revised. pp. xvi. 280. pl. XXX. *London*, 1922. 8°. [*Charles Griffin & Company's Nautical Series.*] **8804**. b. **1/25**.

—— Tenth edition, revised. pp. xx. 296. *London*, 1929. 8°. [*Charles Griffin & Company's Nautical Series.*] **2248**. d. **5**.

—— A Note on the Relative Value of Sail and Steamship Training, *etc. London*, 1900. 8°. [*Shipmasters' Society. Papers.* no. 66.] **08805**. bb. **1/66**.

—— Notes on Handling Ships. pp. 30. *London*, 1895. 8°. [*Shipmasters' Society. Papers.* no. 39.] **08805**. bb. **1/39**.

—— Things a Sailor Needs to Know, *etc.* pp. xvi. 335. pl. XX. *C. Griffin & Co.: London*, 1918. 8°. **8804**. cc. **25**.

—— Second edition, revised, *etc.* [With plates.] 2 vol. *C. Griffin & Co.: London*, 1930, 31. 8°. **8804**. g. **17**.

BARKER (*Sir* DAVID WILSON) and **ALLINGHAM** (WILLIAM) *Prizeman, Society of Arts.*

—— Navigation: practical and theoretical, *etc.* pp. xii. 154. *London*, 1896. 8°. [*Charles Griffin & Company's Nautical Series.*] **8804**. b. **1/6**.

—— Second edition, revised, *etc.* pp. xii. 156. *London*, 1904. 8°. [*Charles Griffin & Company's Nautical Series.*] **8804**. b. **1/7**.

—— Third edition, revised, *etc.* pp. xii. 156. *London*, 1913. 8°. [*Charles Griffin & Company's Nautical Series.*] **8804**. b. **1/22**.

—— Fourth edition. Revised by Sir D. Wilson-Barker . . . and Lieut. Gordon C. Steele, *etc.* pp. xii. 158. *London*, 1923. 8°. [*Charles Griffin & Company's Nautical Series.*] **2248**. d. **9**.

BARKER (DENIS WILFRED)

—— Beginnings. An anthology of apprenticeship and successful ventures. Selected and edited by D. W. Barker . . . With illustrations by Norman Howard. pp. 115. *Macmillan & Co.: London*, 1953 [1954]. 8°. **12299**. eee. **30**.

—— Exercises in Good English. 5 bk. *Macmillan & Co.: London*, 1951–54. 8°. **012987**. a. **30**.

—— Key, etc. 2 pt. *Macmillan & Co.: London*, 1953. . 8°. **012987**. a. **30a**.

BARKER (DOROTHY O.)

—— He Leadeth Me. A book of Bible stories . . . Pictures by Cicely M. Barker. pp. 256. *Blackie & Son: London & Glasgow*, [1936.] 8°. **03127**. g. **47**.

BARKER (DUDLEY RAYMOND)

—— Berlin Air Lift. An account of the British contribution. (Prepared by the Air Ministry and the Central Office of Information. Text by D. Barker.) [With illustrations.] pp. 61. 1949. 4°. *See* ENGLAND.—*Air Ministry.* [*Miscellaneous Publications.*] B.S. **81/13**.

—— A Few of the People. pp. 184. *Jarrolds: London*, 1946. 8°. NN. **36929**.

—— Grandfather's House. pp. 223. *William Heinemann: London*, 1951. 8°. NNN. **2179**.

—— Green and Pleasant Land. pp. 283. *William Heinemann: London*, 1955. 8°. NNN. **5965**.

—— Laughter in Court. [Sketches of London police courts.] pp. vii. 174. *Methuen & Co.: London*, 1935. 8°. **06055**. eee. **43**.

—— Lord Darling's Famous Cases, *etc.* [With plates, including a portrait.] pp. 256. *Hutchinson & Co.: London*, 1936. 8°. **6496**. g. **3**.

—— The Official Story of the Great Floods of 1947 and their Sequel. Harvest Home. Prepared for the Ministry of Agriculture and Fisheries by the Central Office of Information. (Text written by D. Barker.) [With illustrations.] pp. 95. 1948. 8°. *See* ENGLAND.—*Board of Agriculture and Fisheries.* B.S. **81/7**.

—— Palmer, the Rugeley Poisoner. pp. 192. *Duckworth: London*, 1935. 8°. [*Rogues Gallery.*] W.P. **11661/3**.

—— People for the Commonwealth. The case for mass migration. pp. x. 140. *T. Werner Laurie: London*, 1948. 8°. **8287**. a. **82**.

—— The Voice. pp. 263. *William Heinemann: London*, 1953. 8°. NNN. **3950**.

BARKER (E. G.) The Eureka. The key signiture [*sic*] finder, *etc. W. Milne: Falkirk*, [1922.] **1879**. cc. **13**. **(26.)**

A circular card, with a revolving disc.

BARKER (E. V.)

—— *See* MUSCHLER (R. C.) [Die Unbekannte.] One Unknown . . . Translated by M. A. & E. V. Barker. 1935. 8°. **12557**. ppp. **27**.

BARKER (EDITH JOHNSON) In Safe Keeping. A story of true incidents. pp. 160. *R.T.S.: London*, [1889.] 8°. **4420**. o. **35**.

—— [A reissue.] *London*, [1904.] 8°. **04429**. h. **38**.

—— In Safe Keeping. pp. 48. *R.T.S.: London*, [1909.] 8°. [*Sandringham Series of Penny Stories.* no. 9.] **4430**. ee. **23/9**.

—— Worth Waiting For. pp. 126. *S.P.C.K.: London*, [1907.] 8°. **04429**. ccc. **65**.

BARKER (EDMOND) *See* EDWARDS (George) *F.R.S., F.S.A.* Gleanings of Natural History, *etc.* (Glanures d'histoire naturelle . . . IIIme partie . . . traduite par Mr. E. Barker.) 1758, *etc.* 4°. **683**. h. **7–9**.

BARKER (EDMUND) *of Ipswich.* A Voyage with three Tall Ships . . . to the East Indies . . . begunne by M. George Raymond, in the yeere 1591, and performed by M. Iames Lancaster, and written from the mouth of Edmund Barker . . . his lieutenant in the sayd voyage, by M. Richard Hakluyt. 1599. *See* HAKLUYT (R.) The Principal Nauigations . . . of the English Nation, *etc.* vol. 2. pt. 2. 1598, *etc.* 4°. **683**. h. **5**.

BARKER (Edmund) *of Ipswich.*

—— [Another edition.] 1810. *See* Hakluyt (R.) Hakluyt's Collection of the Early Voyages . . . of the English Nation, *etc.* vol. 2. 1809, *etc.* 4°. **208.** h. **11.**

—— [Another edition.] 1889. *See* Hakluyt (R.) The Principal Navigations . . . of the English Nation, *etc.* vol. 11. 1884, *etc.* 8°. **10027.** dd. **4.**

—— [Another edition.] 1904. *See* Hakluyt (R.) The Principal Navigations . . . of the English Nation, *etc.* vol. 6. 1903, *etc.* 8°. **2060.aa.**

—— [Another copy.] **10024.** k. **3.**

—— [Another edition.] [1908.] *See* Hakluyt (R.) The Principal Navigations . . . of the English Nation, *etc.* vol. 4. [1907, *etc.*] 8°. **12206.p.1/217**

—— [Another edition.] 1927. *See* Hakluyt (R.) The Principal Navigations . . . of the English Nation, *etc.* vol. 4. 1927, *etc.* 8°. **010025.** ee. **28.**

—— A Voyage to the East Indies in the year 1591, *etc.* (Taken from the description of Mr. E. Barker.) *See* Moore (John H.) A New and Complete Collection of Voyages, *etc.* vol. 1. [1785?] fol. **10003.** f. **2.**

—— Eine Reise nach Ostindien im Jahre 1591 . . . Nach der Erzählung E. Barkers . . . aufgesetzt. *See* Schwabe (J. J.) Allgemeine Historie der Reisen, *etc.* Bd. 1. 1747, *etc.* 4°. **10025.** dd.

BARKER (Edmund) *Rector of Buriton, Hampshire.* A Sermon preached at the funerall of . . . the Lady Elizabeth Capell, Dowager. Together with some brief memorialls of her most holy life and death. [With an elegy and an epitaph.] pp. 47. *I. R. for Iohn Williams: London,* 1661. 4°. **1359.** b. **11.**

—— [Another copy.] E. **1046.** (**14.**)

—— [Another edition.] [1665?] fol. **1418.** k. **3.**
Pp. 19–39 of an edition of " Θρηνοικος. *The house of mourning."*

—— Votum pro Cæsare; or, a Plea for Cæsar; discovering briefly the great sinfulness of opposing the authority of the higher powers. Delivered in a sermon, *etc.* *For John Williams: London,* 1660. 4°. **693.** f. **1.** (**4.**)
Imperfect; wanting all after p. 32.

BARKER (Edmund Henry) *See* also Vindex, *pseud.* [i.e. E. H. Barker?]

—— *See* Aesop. [*Latin.—Selections.*] Æsopi fabulae selectae. With English notes, for the use of schools, *etc.* [Edited by E. H. Barker.] 1815. 12°. **1211.** g. **16.**

—— *See* Arcadius, *Grammaticus.* Ἀρκαδιου περι τονων. E codicibus Parisinis primum edidit E. H. Barkerus. Addita est editoris epistola critica ad Jo. Fr. Boissonade. 1820. 8°. **623.** f. **8.**

—— *See* Buttmann (P. C.) Dr. Philip Buttmann's Intermediate or Larger Greek Grammar. Translated . . . by D. Boileau . . . Edited by E. H. Barker. 1833. 8°. **624.** d. **27.** (**1.**)

—— *See* Caesar (C. J.) [*De Bello Gallico.—Latin.*] C. Julius Cæsar's Commentaries on the Gallic War . . . With a selection of notes . . . By E. H. Barker, *etc.* 1831. 12°. **1211.** h. **17.**

—— *See* Cicero (M. T.) [*Two or more Works.—Latin.*] Cicero De senectute et De amicitia, from the text of Ernesti, with all his notes . . . and a new collation . . . By E. H. Barker. 1811. 12°. **1211.** g. **11.**

—— —— 1813. 12°. **1211.** g. **12.**

—— —— 1839. 12°. **8407.** aaa. **27.**

BARKER (Edmund Henry)

—— *See* Cicero (M. T.) [*Orations.—In L. Sergium Catilinam.—Latin.*] i. Cicero's Catilinarian Orations . . . With some notes by the editor E. H. Barker, *etc.* 1829. 12°. **1211.** g. **13.**

—— *See* Cudworth (Ralph) *the Younger.* i. Dr. Cudworth's Sermon, 1 John, 2, 3–4. Preached before the House of Commons, March 31, 1647. ii. Bishop Hoadly's Sermon on the Nature of Christ's Kingdom, March 31, 1717. iii. Bishop Lowth's Visitation-Sermon, 1758. Reprinted by E. H. Barker, *etc.* 1832. 8°. **908.** d. **2.** (**4.**)

—— *See* Demosthenes. [*Two or more Works.—Greek.*] Select Orations of Demosthenes . . . With notes . . . by E. H. Barker, *etc.* 1830. 12°. **1211.** h. **3.**

—— *See* Dunbar (George) and Barker (E. H.) A Greek and English Lexicon, *etc.* 1831. 8°. **826.** f. **37.**

—— See Etymologicum Gudianum.
Etymologicum graecae linguae Gudianum . . . Accedunt notae ad Etymologicon Magnum ineditae E. H. Barkeri, *etc.* 1818. 4°. **12923.** f. **13.**

—— *See* Faber (M. A. M.) The Will of Mary Ann Magdalena Faber . . . With facts and observations, proving its authenticity . . . By E. H. Barker. 1821. 8°. **1245.** b. **43.** (**1.**)

—— *See* Hale (*Sir* Matthew) The Judgment of . . . Sir Matthew Hale, of the Nature of True Religion . . . Reprinted by E. H. Barker. 1832. 8°. **908.** d. **14.** (**4.**)

—— *See* Lempriere (J.) Bibliotheca Classica: or, a Classical dictionary . . . Re-edited by E. H. Barker, *etc.* 1828. 8°. **609*.** b. **6.**

—— —— 1832. 8°. **609*.** b. **4.**

—— —— 1838. 8°. **609*.** i. **19.**

—— *See* Lempriere (John) *D.D.* Lempriere's Classical Dictionary . . . Corrected and enlarged by Professor Anthon & E. H. Barker, *etc.* [1843.] 8°. **11312.** t. **61.**

—— *See* Lempriere (J.) Barker's Lempriere Abridged. Lempriere's Classical Dictionary, abridged . . . By E. H. Barker. [1833.] 8°. **609*.** b. **5.**

—— —— 1843. 8°. **609*.** b. **20.**

—— *See* Palairet (E.) Thesaurus ellipsium latinarum . . . Recensuit et cum additamentis suis edidit E. H. Barker. 1829. 8°. **625.** d. **26.**

—— *See* Pierpont (John) *the Elder.* The National Reader: a selection of exercises in reading and speaking . . . Re-edited by E. H. Barker . . . With an appendix by the present editor. 1829. 12°. **992.** e. **18.**

—— *See* Rambles. Juvenile Rambles through the Paths of Nature . . . Revised by E. H. Barker, *etc.* 1830. 12°. 012808. e. 104.

—— *See* Sillig (C. J.) Dictionary of the Artists of Antiquity . . . With four indexes and a preface by E. H. Barker. 1836. 8°. **1401.** d. **19.**

—— *See* Tacitus (P. C.) [*Two or more Works.—Latin.*] The Germany and Agricola of C. Cornelius Tacitus, from Brotier's text . . . With critical and philological remarks, by E. H. Barker. 1813. 12°. **588.** c. **13.**

—— —— 1824. 12°. **9040.** c. **24.**

—— —— 1836. 12°. **9039.** bbb. **25.**

—— *See* Valpy (A. J.) and Barker (E. H.) Materials for the Improvement of the New Edition of Stephens' Greek Thesaurus. [1814.] 8°. **1203.** k. **12.** (**19.**)

BARKER (EDMUND HENRY)

—— *See* WEBSTER (Noah) *LL.D.* A Dictionary of the English Language . . . Reprinted by E. H. Barker, *etc.* 1832. 4°. **12982.** i. **11.**

—— *See* XENOPHON, *the Historian.* [*Cyropaedia.—Greek.*] The Cyropædia of Xenophon . . . With notes, critical and explanatory, from Dindorf . . . accompanied by the editor's comments . . . By E. H. Barker. 1831. 12°. **1211.** h. **14.**

—— [Articles on various subjects, extracted from the Classical Journal.] [*London,* 1811.] 8°. **1203.** k. **12.** (**14.**)

—— Articles written by E. H. Barker . . . printed in the seventh number of the Classical, Biblical, and Oriental Journal, for September, 1811. pp. 30. [*A. J. Valpy: London,* 1811.] 8°. **1203.** k. **12.** (**15.**)

—— The Articles of E. H. Barker . . . extracted from the eighth number of the Classical, Biblical and Oriental Journal for December, 1811. pp. 27. *A. J. Valpy: London,* [1811.] 8°. **1203.** k. **12.** (**16.**)

—— The Articles of E. H. Barker . . . extracted from the ninth number [or rather, the ninth and tenth numbers] of the Classical, Biblical, and Oriental Journal, for March [or rather, March and June], 1812. pp. 47. [*A. J. Valpy: London,* 1812.] 8°. **1203.** k. **12.** (**17.**)

—— The Articles of E. H. Barker . . . extracted from the eleventh number of the Classical, Biblical, and Oriental Journal, for September, 1812. pp. 28. [*A. J. Valpy: London,* 1812.] 8°. **1203.** k. **12.** (**18.**)

—— I. The Claims of Sir Philip Francis to the Authorship of Junius's Letters, disproved: II. Some Enquiry into the Claims of the late Charles Lloyd, Esq. to the composition of them: III. Observations on the Conduct, Character, and Style of the writings, of the late Right Hon. Edmund Burke: IV. Extracts from the writings of several eminent philologists on the Laconic and Asiatic, the Attic and Rhodian styles of eloquence. pp. lxxii. 504. *John Bohn: London,* 1828. 12°. **713.** d. **8.**

—— [Another copy.] MS. NOTES. **8005.** df. **6.**

—— Aristarchus Anti-Blomfieldianus: or, a reply to the notice [by C. J. Blomfield] of the new Greek Thesaurus [i.e. the revision by A. J. Valpy and E. H. Barker of Henri Estienne's Thesaurus], inserted in the 44th number of the Quarterly Review. By E. H. Barker . . . To which are added the Jena-reviews of Mr. Blomfield's edition of Callimachus, and Æschyli Persæ. Translated from the German. pt. 1. pp. xx. 109. *J. H. Bohte: London,* 1820. 8°. **12923.** dd. **16.** (**2.**)
No more published.

—— The Claims of Sir Philip Francis to the Authorship of Junius disproved by impartial inquiry. In a letter addressed to Charles Butler, *etc.* pp. 4. [*Thetford?* 1826.] fol. **8005.** dd. **1.** (**1.**)

—— The Claims of Sir Philip Francis to the Authorship of Junius disproved: in a letter addressed to Godfrey Higgins Esq. pp. 16. *A. J. Valpy:* [*London,* 1827.] 8°. **8005.** dd. **1.** (**3.**)

—— [Another edition.] 1827. *See* PERIODICAL PUBLICATIONS.—*London.* The Pamphleteer, *etc.* vol. 27. 1813, *etc.* 8°. P.P. **3557.** w.

—— The Claims of Sir Philip Francis to the Authorship of Junius disproved: in a letter addressed to Sir James Mackintosh. pp. 16. *Mills: Thetford,* [1827.] 8°. **8005.** dd. **1.** (**8.**)

BARKER (EDMUND HENRY)

—— The Claims of Sir Philip Francis to the Authorship of Junius disproved. In a letter addressed to the Rev. Dr. Martin Davy, *etc.* pp. 16. *Mills: Thetford,* [1827.] 8°. **8005.** dd. **1.** (**2.**)

—— The Claims of Sir Philip Francis to the Authorship of Junius disproved: in a letter addressed to Uvedale Price Esq. pp. 18. [*Thetford,* 1827.] 8°. **8005.** dd. **1.** (**4.**)

—— [Another edition.] pp. 20. *Mills: Thetford,* [1827.] 8°. **8006.** d. **6.**

—— [Another copy.] **8005.** dd. **1.** (**4*.**)

—— Classical Recreations interspersed with Biblical Criticisms. vol. 1. pp. xxxvi. 492. *A. J. Valpy: London,* 1812. 8°. **246.** l. **1.**
No more published.

—— Epigrammata numismate annuo dignata . . . A.D. 1809 (Ἀρχη ἥμισυ παντος.—Strenua inertia.) [*Cambridge* 1809.] 8°. **732.** c. **9.** (**27.**)

—— The Legitimacy of the late Robert Barker vindicated by his eldest son, E. H. Barker . . . in a letter to the Rev. Wm. Dealtry. pp. 16. *Edward Baines: Leeds,* 1822. 8°. **1245.** b. **43.** (**3.**)
One of an edition of 50 *copies.*

—— A Letter addressed to the Rev. T. S. Hughes . . . Occasioned by the perusal of the Address to the People of England in the Cause of the Greeks. pp. 26. *Thomas Baker: Southampton,* 1822. 8°. **8028.** b. **9.**

—— Second edition with additions. 1822. *See* PERIODICAL PUBLICATIONS.—*London.* The Pamphleteer, *etc.* vol. 21. 1813, *etc.* 8°. P.P. **3557.** w.

—— Fourth edition, with considerable additions and corrections. pp. xvi. 228. *G. & W. B. Whittaker: London,* 1823. 8°. **1102.** g. **23.** (**13.**)

—— Literary Anecdotes and Contemporary Reminiscences of Professor Porson and others; from the manuscript papers of the late E. H. Barker. 2 vol. *J. R. Smith: London,* 1852. 8°. **12315.** g. **11.**

—— Parriana: or Notices of the Rev. Samuel Parr . . . Collected from various sources, printed and manuscript, and in part written by E. H. Barker. 2 vol. *Henry Colburn: London,* 1828, 29. 8°. **614.** f. **16, 17.**

—— *Begin.* Yorkshire Lent Assizes. Nisi-Prius. Before Mr. Justice Bayley . . . Barker v. Ray and others. [Cuttings from a newspaper report of the proceedings in an issue sent down from Chancery to try the legitimacy of E. H. Barker, and of those in another issue, to inquire into the existence of an alleged will of Edmund Barker.] [1822.] fol. **1245.** b. **43.** (**4.**)

BARKER (EDWARD) A New and Easy Grammar of the English Tongue for the Italians . . . Second edition corrected, and increased by the author. (Nuova e facile grammatica della lingua inglese, *etc.*) pp. xvi. 338. *J.-B. Stecchi & A.-J. Pagani: Florence,* 1771. 4°. **12985.** cc. **5.**

—— Grammar of the English Tongue for the Italians . . . Third of [*sic*] Venitian edition after the third of Florence. Corrected, increased and illustrated by the author. pp. 358. *J. Rosa: Venice,* 1799. 12°. **12985.** bb. **17.**

BARKER (EDWARD BRUCE BOUGHTON) *See* BARKER (John) *Consul-General at Aleppo.* Syria and Egypt under the last five Sultans of Turkey . . . Edited by . . . E. B. B. Barker. 1876. 8°. **10815.** ee. **1.**

BARKER (EDWARD BRUCE BOUGHTON)

—— The Mendal, a mode of oriental divination, *etc.* pp. xxxiii. 276. *J. Burns: London*, 1874. 8°. **8632. f. 12.**

BARKER (EDWARD HARRISON) A British Dog in France. His adventures in divers places and conversations with French dogs . . . With 43 illustrations by L. R. Brightwell. pp. ix. 283. *Chatto & Windus: London*, 1913. 8°. **012809. dd. 54.**

—— The Dreamer's Soliloquy, or, the Votary of Fame: a rhapsody. pp. 38. *Simpkin & Marshall: London*, 1869. 8°. **11648. cc. 42. (6.)**

—— France of the French. pp. x. 271. *Sir I. Pitman & Sons: London*, 1908. 8°. **010169. ff. 25.**

—— The Opera Guide. A concise description of plot and incidents of the principal operas, with brief biographical notices of eminent singers. pp. viii. 198. *Griffith, Farran & Co.: London*, 1887. 8°. **7897. bb. 58.**

—— Through Auvergne on Foot. pp. 142. *Griffith & Farran: London*, 1884. 12°. **10171. aa. 15.**

—— Two Summers in Guyenne. A chronicle of the wayside and waterside . . . With map and illustrations. pp. xii. 411. *R. Bentley & Son: London*, 1894. 8°. **010171. f. 45.**

—— Wanderings by Southern Waters. Eastern Aquitaine . . . With illustrations. pp. 403. *R. Bentley & Son: London*, 1893. 8°. **010171. f. 39.**

—— Wayfaring in France . . . With fifty illustrations. pp. viii. 431. *R. Bentley & Son: London*, 1890. 8°. **010171. h. 32.**

—— Wayfaring in France. From Auvergne to the Bay of Biscay. [With illustrations.] pp. xv. 540. *Macmillan & Co.: London*, 1913. 8°. **010171. f. 58.**
A different work from the preceding.

BARKER (EDWARD JOHN) Barker's Canadian Monthly Magazine. *See* PERIODICAL PUBLICATIONS.—*Kingston, Ont.*

BARKER (EDWARD PHILLIPS) *See* AUGUSTINE, *Saint, Bishop of Hippo.* [*De Catechizandis Rudibus.*] A Treatise of Saint Aurelius Augustine . . . on the Catechizing of the Uninstructed. Translated by E. P. Barker. 1912. 8°. **3805. df. 19.**

—— *See* OVIDIUS NASO (P.) [*Ars Amatoria.—English.*] The Lover's Manual of Ovid. Translated into English verse by E. P. Barker, *etc.* 1931. 8°. **11352. cc. 10.**

—— *See* SENECA (L. A.) [*Letters.*] Seneca's Letters to Lucilius. Translated by E. P. Barker. 1932. 8°. **10906. de. 16.**

BARKER (EDWARD RAYMOND) Cable-Fault Localisation Graphs in Practice . . . Reprints of articles published in the Electrical Review, 1909. pp. 68. *H. Alabaster, Gatehouse & Co.: London*, [1910.] 8°. **08755. ff. 18.**

—— Graphs in a Cable-Ship Drum-Room: notes for junior assistants . . . Reprints of articles published in the Electrical Review, *etc.* pp. 46. *H. Alabaster, Gatehouse & Co.: London*, [1913.] 8°. **8754. cc. 50.**

—— Hand-Book in Cable-Break Localisation. Graphic methods. The calculator board in practice . . . Reprints of articles published in the Electrical Review, *etc.* pp. 68. [1904.] 8°. **08755. f. 2.**

BARKER (EDWARD WALLER) Vigilemus et oremus. Practical hints on reading and some prayings. In usum Scholarum Cancellarii Lincoln: [Signed: E. W. B., i.e. E. W. Barker?] pp. 34. 1876. 16°. *See* B., E. W. **3127. aa. 27.**

BARKER (EDWIN) and **PRESTON** (RONALD)

—— Christians in Society. pp. 190. *Student Christian Movement Press: London*, 1939. 8°. **04373. df. 17.**

BARKER (EDWIN L.) and **BARKER** (ALBERT) *Playwright.*

—— Dirty Hands. A clean comedy in three acts. pp. 93. *Samuel French: New York*, [1932.] 8°. **11791. pp. 27.**

—— The Man on Stilts. A comedy of the great American gah-gah, in three acts. [With musical notes.] pp. 95. *New York*, [1934.] 8°. [*French's Standard Library Edition.*] **011781. g. 1/370.**

BARKER (EILEEN ALICE ARTHURTON) *See* ARTHURTON (Eileen A.)

BARKER (ELISABETH MARY) *See* ELISABETH, *pseud.* [i.e. E. M. Barker.]

BARKER (ELIZABETH)

—— Macedonia. Its place in Balkan power politics. pp. 129. *Royal Institute of International Affairs: London & New York*, 1950. 8°. **08028. cc. 86.**

—— The Religious Instruction of Children at Home. pp. 76. *Wells, Gardner & Co.: London*, 1903. 8°. **8310. bbb. 23.**

—— Truce in the Balkans. [1945-46.] pp. 256. *Percival Marshall: London*, 1948. 8°. **8029. eee. 18.**

BARKER (ELIZABETH RAYMOND) *See* also ARIEL, *pseud.* [i.e. E. Raymond-Barker.]

—— *See* ESPINEY (C. d') Some Account of Don Bosco and his work; gathered chiefly from the narrative of Dr. d'Espiney by Mrs. F. Raymond-Barker. 1885. 16°. **4867. de. 6.**

—— *See* GAUTIER (L.) Regina sæculorum; or, Mary venerated in all ages . . . Partly translated from the French of M. L. Gautier, by E. A. M. [i.e. E. Raymond-Barker.] 1875. 8°. **3456. b. 58.**

—— *See* LASSERRE (Henri) *Editor of "Le Monde catholique."* Bernadette . . . Translated . . . by Mrs. F. Raymond-Barker. [1882.] 8°. **4864. bb. 12.**

—— *See* MARQUIGNY (E.) Sketch of the Life and Letters of the Countess Adelstan. An abridged translation . . . by E. A. M. [i.e. E. Raymond-Barker.] 1874. 8°. **4867. de. 56.**

—— *See* PRUSSIA.—William I., *King.* [1861–1888.] A Victim of the Falk Laws, *etc.* [The appendix by the translator signed: E. R. B., i.e. E. Raymond-Barker.] 1879. 8°. **12601. cc. 13.**

—— *See* RICHE (A.) Agreement of Science and Faith upon the Sacred Heart of Jesus . . . Translated by E. Raymond-Barker. 1883. 8°. **4225. df. 2.**

—— *See* SEIGNERET (P. M. J. C.) The Life of Paul Seigneret . . . Translated and abridged by E. A. M. [i.e. E. Raymond-Barker.] 1873. 8°. **4867. aa. 67.**

—— *See* SYLVAIN (C.) Life of the Reverend Father Hermann . . . Translated . . . by Mrs. F. Raymond-Barker. 1882. 8°. **4886. h. 6.**

BARKER (ELLEN) Graäb. [A novel.] pp. ii. 288. *Remington & Co.: London*, 1885. 8°. **12621. dd. 15.**

BARKER (Elsa) The Book of Love. [Poems.] pp. xii. 231. *Duffield & Co.: New York*, 1912. 8º. **011686**. ee. **13**.

—— The C. I. D. of Dexter Drake. pp. 323. *John Hamilton: London*, [1931.] 8º. **012614.a.38.**

—— The Cobra Candlestick. pp. viii. 293. *J. H. Sears & Co.: New York*, [1928.] 8º. **012706**. i. **11**.

—— [Another edition.] pp. 278. *John Hamilton: London*, [1930.] 8º. **012614.a.33.**

—— Fielding Sargent. A novel. pp. 319. *E. P. Dutton & Co.: New York*, [1922.] 8º. **012703**. eee. **8**.

—— The Frozen Grail, and other poems. pp. 126. *Duffield & Co.: New York*, 1910. 8º. **11688**. f. **40**.

—— Last Letters from the Living Dead Man, *etc.* pp. 240. *W. Rider & Son: London*, 1919. 8º. **8633**. aaa. **37**.

—— Letters from a Living Dead Man. Written down by E. Barker, *etc.* pp. vii. 309. *W. Rider & Son: London*, 1914. 8º. **08631**. e. **71**.

—— Tenth edition. pp. vii. 309. *Rider & Co.: London*, 1932. 8º. **08632**. de. **95**.

—— The Son of Mary Bethel. [A novel.] pp. 549. *Duffield & Co.: New York*, 1909. 8º. **012705**. cc. **2**.

—— [Another edition.] pp. vii. 551. *Chatto & Windus: London*, 1909. 8º. **012705**. bbb. **10**.

—— Songs of a Vagrom Angel. Written down by E. Barker. pp. 55. *Mitchell Kennerley: New York*, 1916. 8º. **011686**. de. **50**.

—— Stories from the New Testament for Children. [With illustrations.] pp. ix. 410. *Duffield & Co.: New York*, 1911. 8º. **4806**. ff. **13**.

—— Stories from the New Testament for Children, *etc.* [With illustrations.] pp. viii. 410. *Rich & Cowan: London; U.S.A.* printed, 1936. 8º. **2200**. cc. **17**.

—— War Letters from the Living Dead Man, *etc.* pp. 318. *Mitchell Kennerley: New York*, 1915. 8º. **08631**. e. **72**.

—— [Another copy, with a different titlepage.] *W. Rider & Son: London*, [1915.] 8º. **08631**. e. **73**.

BARKER (Emily) Extracts from the Writings of Eminent Authors: moral, historical and poetical . . . Third edition, greatly enlarged. 2 vol. *Whittaker & Co.: London*, 1847. 8º. **12270**. e. **34**.

BARKER (Eric) Day Gone By. The tragedy of a fool. pp. 284. *Stanley Paul & Co.: London*, [1933.] 8º. NN. **20255**.

—— The Watch Hunt. [A tale.] pp. 254. *Ward, Lock & Co.: London & Melbourne*, 1933. 8º. **20053**. aa. 24.

BARKER (Eric Ernest)

—— *See* Talbot, *Family of.* Talbot Deeds, 1200–1682. Edited by E. E. Barker. 1953. 8º. [*Record Society for the Publication of Original Documents relating to Lancashire and Cheshire.* vol. 103.] Ac. **8121**.

BARKER (Ernest) *of Streatham.* The Glorious Appearing and . . . reasons why the Church will not pass through the Great Tribulation. pp. 48. *Hulbert Publishing Co.: London*, [1928.] 12º. **03187**. e. **65**.

—— Joseph. A type of Christ. pp. 38. *G. F. Vallance: Goodmayes*, [1928.] 8º. [*Scripture Studies.* no. 1.] W.P. **9291/1**.

—— Keep Smiling. [With a portrait.] pp. 127. *Pickering & Inglis: London*, [1932.] 8º. **4406**. de. **48**.

BARKER (Ernest) *of Streatham.*

—— The " Parklands " Series. [Religious tracts.] *John Ritchie: Kilmarnock*, [1938– .] 12º. W.P. **1338**

—— The Path of Life. Primarily for young Christians, e pp. 56. *Victory Press: London*, 1954. 8º. **4409**. p.

—— Twenty-one Difficult Texts in the Bible. Suggest explanations. pp. 78. *Pickering & Inglis: Londo Glasgow*, [1930.] 8º. **03126**. de. **7**

—— Wheels within Wheels, and other messages, *etc.* pp. 26 *Hulbert Publishing Co.: London*, [1928.] 8º. **04403**. i. **8**

—— Winning the Crowd, *etc.* pp. 159. *Oliphants: Londo Edinburgh*, [1933.] 8º. **04192**. aaa. **8**

BARKER (*Sir* Ernest)

—— *See* Aristotle. [*Single Works.—Politica.—English.*] T Politics of Aristotle. Translated with an introductic notes and appendixes by E. Barker. 1946. 8º. **8006**. f. **4**

—— *See* Aristotle. [*Single Works.—Politica.—Englis* The Politics of Aristotle. Translated with notes by Barker, *etc.* (A shortened form of the translation pu lished in 1946.) 1948. 8º. **8012**. a.

—— *See* Augustine, *Saint, Bish of Hippo.* [*De Civitate Dei.*] The City of God . With an introduction by E. Barker. 1931. 8º. **3805**. bbb.

—— *See* Augustine, *Saint, Bishop of Hippo.* [*De Civit Dei.—English.*] The City of God, *etc.* (Introduction Sir E. Barker.) 1945. 8º. **12206**. p. **1/76**

—— *See* Beazley (Charles R.) Russia from the Varangia to the Bolsheviks . . . With an introduction by E. Barke 1918. 8º. **9454**. aaa.

—— *See* Beneš (E.) *President of Czechoslovakia.* Edwa Beneš . . . [By] Sir E. Barker . . . and others, *etc.* 1945. 8º. **10797**. ee. **4**

—— *See* Gierke (O. von) Natural Law and the Theory Society, 1500–1800 . . . Translated with an introductic by E. Barker. 1934. 8º. **8004**. f.

—— *See* Jarrett (Bede) The Emperor Charles iv. . With a short biographical introduction by E. Barker, e 1935. 8º. **10709**. c.

—— *See* Mill (James) *Economist.* An Essay on Governme With an introduction by E. Barker. 1937. 8º. **08007**. de. **9**

—— *See* Periodical Publications.—*Paris.*—*La Revue Phi sophique.* La Révolution de 1789 et la pensée moderr Par E. Barker [and others], *etc.* 1940. 8º. **8465**. i. 3

—— *See* Plato. [*Respublica.—English.*] The Republic Plato. [With an introduction by E. Barker.] 1906. 8 **012203**. f. **33/1**

—— *See* Social Contract. Social Contract. Essays b Locke, Hume and Rousseau. With an introduction b Sir E. Barker. [1947.] 8º. **012209**. df. **38**

—— Age and Youth. Memories of three universities, an Father of the Man. [With a portrait.] pp. vii. 347. *Oxford University Press: London*, 1953. 8º. **10864**. aa.

—— Britain and the British People. [With illustrations pp. 141. *Oxford University Press: London*, 1942. 8 [*The World To-Day.*] **010028.p.1/9**

—— Britain and the British People . . . Second edition. pp. 186. *Oxford University Press: London*, 1955. 8°. **010368.** w. **139.**

—— Nagybritannia és a brit nép. Forditotta Körmendi Ferenc. [With plates.] pp. 186. *Longmans, Green & Co.: London*, 1945. 8°. **10359.** aa. **17.**

—— British Constitutional Monarchy. pp. 27. *Oxford University Press: London, New York*, [1945.] 8°. **8135.** aaa. **28.**

—— British Constitutional Monarchy. (Completely revised.) pp. 28. 1950. 8°. *See* ENGLAND.—*Central Office of Information.* **8139.** eee. **35.**

—— [A reissue.] British Constitutional Monarchy. 1951. 8°. *See* ENGLAND.—*Central Office of Information.* **8140.** df. **27.**

—— La Monarquía Constitucional de la Gran Bretaña. pp. 23. *Oxford University Press: Londres, Nueva York*, [1945.] 8°. **8135.** aaa. **27.**

—— British Statesmen . . . With 12 plates, *etc.* pp. 46. *William Collins: London*, 1941. 8°. [*Britain in Pictures.*] **W.P. 10933/1. (7.)**

—— British Universities . . . Illustrated. pp. 36. *Published for the British Council by Longmans & Co.: London*, 1946. 8°. [*British Life and Thought.* no. 24.] **10353.** k. **3/24.**

—— British Universities, *etc.* (Revised edition.) pp. 40. *Published for the British Council by Longmans, Green & Co.: London*, 1949. 8°. [*British Life and Thought.*] **10353.** k. **3/24a.**

—— Uniwersytety brytyjskie, *etc.* pp. 44. 1948. 8°. *See* ENGLAND.—*British Council.* **08368.** cc. **7.**

—— Burke and Bristol. A study of the relations between Burke and his constituency during the years 1774–1780. (The Lewis Fry Memorial Lectures, 1930.) pp. 131. *J. W. Arrowsmith: Bristol*, 1931. 8°. **10823.** a. **7.**

—— Change and Continuity . . . Being the Ramsay Muir Memorial Lecture . . . 1949, *etc.* pp. 16. *Victor Gollancz: London*, 1949. 8°. **08466.** gg. **43.**

—— The Character of England. Edited by Ernest Barker. [With plates.] pp. xii. 595. *Clarendon Press: Oxford*, 1947. 8°. **10359.** d. **18.**

—— Christianity & Nationality, *etc.* pp. 32. *Clarendon Press: Oxford*, 1927. 8°. [*Burge Memorial Lecture.* 1927.] **W.P. 4556/1.**

—— Church, State and Study. Essays. pp. vii. 280. *Methuen & Co.: London*, 1930. 8°. **4380.** d. **8.**

—— The Citizen's Choice. [Essays on political subjects.] pp. ix. 185. *University Press: Cambridge*, 1937. 8°. **08008.** aa. **61.**

—— A Confederation of the Nations: its powers and constitution. pp. 54. *Clarendon Press: Oxford*, 1918. 8°. **8425.** t. **35.**

—— The Crusades. [With maps. A reprint of the article in the "Encyclopaedia Britannica."] pp. 112. *Humphrey Milford: London*, 1923. 8°. **09055.** a. **32.**

—— Current Problems. General editor: Ernest Barker. *University Press: Cambridge*, 1940– . 8°. **W.P. 147.**

—— The Development of Administration, Conscription, Taxation, Social Services, and Education. 1937. *See* EYRE (Edward) European Civilization, *etc.* vol. 5. 1934, *etc.* 8°. **09075.bb.13/5.**

—— The Development of Public Services in Western Europe, 1660–1930. pp. viii. 93. *Oxford University Press: London*, 1944. 8°. **8287.** k. **28.**

—— A Direct Reply to each of Mr. Chiozza Money's Free Trade Points. pp. 100. *Hanbury, Tomsett & Co.: [London*, 1909.] 8°. **8229.** a. **28.** (**6.**)

—— The Dominican Order and Convocation. A study of the growth of representation in the Church during the thirteenth century. pp. 83. *Clarendon Press: Oxford*, 1913. 8°. **4782.** h. **2.**

—— Education for Citizenship . . . A lecture, *etc.* pp. 17. *London*, 1936. 8°. [*University of London Institute of Education. Studies and Reports.* no. 10.] **Ac. 2666.** e.

—— Essays on Government. pp. vii. 269. *Clarendon Press: Oxford*, 1945. 8°. **8011.** df. **17.**

—— Essays on Government . . . Second edition. pp. vii. 304. *Clarendon Press: Oxford*, 1951. 8°. **8010.** dd. **26.**

—— The European Inheritance. [By various authors.] Edited by Sir E. Barker, Sir George Clark, Professor P. Vaucher. [With plates and maps.] 3 vol. *Clarendon Press: Oxford*, 1954. 8°. **10107.** dd. **26.**

—— Father of the Man. Memories of Cheshire, Lancashire and Oxford, 1874–1898. [With plates, including a portrait.] pp. 116. *National Council of Social Service: London*, [1948.] 8°. **10862.** ee. **13.**

—— The Future Government of India and the Indian Civil Service. Papers edited by E. Barker. pp. vi. 91. *Methuen & Co.: London*, 1919. 8°. **08023.** a. **13.**

—— Great Britain's Reasons for going to War. pp. 10. *Darling & Son: London*, 1915. 8°. **08028.** i. **14.** (**3.**)

—— Greek Political Theory: Plato and his predecessors. pp. xiii. 403. *Methuen & Co.: London*, 1918. 8°. **8007.** ff. **1.**

—— Greek Political Thought and Theory in the Fourth Century. 1927, *etc.* *See* BURY (John B.) The Cambridge Ancient History, *etc.* vol. 6. 1923, *etc.* 8°.
[Latest edition.] **2070.e f.**
[Earlier editions.] **09004.** de.

—— The Ideas and Ideals of the British Empire. pp. viii. 167. *University Press: Cambridge*, 1941. 8°. [*Current Problems.*] **W.P. 147/7.**

—— The Ideas and Ideals of the British Empire . . . Second edition. pp. viii. 171. *University Press: Cambridge*, 1951. 8°. [*Current Problems.* no. 7.] **W.P. 147/7.** a.

—— Ireland in the last Fifty Years, 1866–1916. pp. 108. *Clarendon Press: Oxford*, 1917. 8°. **8146.** f. **8.**

—— Second and enlarged edition. pp. 148. *Clarendon Press: Oxford*, 1919. 8°. **8146.** f. **15.**

—— Italy and the West, 410–476. *See* BURY (John B.) The Cambridge Medieval History, *etc.* vol. 1. 1911, *etc.* 8°.
[Latest edition] **2070.f.**
[Earliest editions] **09004.g.**

—— Leonard Trelawny Hobhouse, 1864–1929. From the Proceedings of the British Academy, *etc.* pp. 21. *Humphrey Milford: London*, [1931.] 8°. **10823.** k. **6.**

—— The Library of Greek Thought. Edited by E. Barker. *J. M. Dent & Sons: London & Toronto; E. P. Dutton & Co.: New York*, 1923– . 8°. **W.P. 7677.**

BARKER (*Sir* ERNEST)

—— Linguistic Oppression in the German Empire. pp. 48. *Longmans & Co.: London*, 1918. 8°. **12901**. bb. **37**.

—— Mothers & Sons in War Time, and other pieces. Reprinted from The Times. (Second edition.) pp. ix. 56. *A. L. Humphreys: London*, 1915. 16°. **012357**. g. **16**.

—— [Another edition.] pp. xi. 91. *A. L. Humphreys: London*, 1917. 8°. **012352**. e. **18**.

—— New and enlarged edition. pp. xi. 99. *A. L. Humphreys: London*, 1918. 8°. **012352**. e. **49**.

—— National Character and the Factors in its Formation. pp. vii. 288. *Methuen & Co.: London*, 1927. 8°. **08007**. f. **61**.

—— National Character and the factors in its formation. (Fourth and revised edition.) pp. xix. 268. *Methuen & Co.: London*, 1948. 8°. **8011**. eee. **37**.

—— Nietzsche and Treitschke. The worship of power in modern Germany . . . Fifth impression. pp. 28. *Oxford University Press: London*, 1914. 8°. [*Oxford Pamphlets*, 1914. no. 20.] **08028**. de. **93/20**.

—— Oliver Cromwell and the English People. pp. 105. *University Press: Cambridge*, 1937. 8°. [*Cambridge Miscellany*. no. 18.] W.P. **10116/18**.

—— "Philosophy and Politics," *etc.* pp. 18. [*London*,] 1934. 8°. [*Haldane Memorial Lecture*. no. 6.] Ac. **2669**. f.

—— Political Thought in England 1848 to 1914. (Second edition.) pp. 256. *Thornton Butterworth: London*, 1928. 8°. [*Home University Library*.] **12199**. p. **1/152**.

—— Political Thought in England from Herbert Spencer to the present day. pp. 256. *Williams & Norgate: London; H. Holt & Co.: New York*, [1915.] 8°. [*Home University Library*.] **12199**. p. **1/107**.

—— The Political Thought of Plato and Aristotle. pp. xxii. 559. *Methuen & Co.: London*, 1906. 8°. **8006**. h. **10**.

—— Principles of Social & Political Theory. pp. viii. 284. *Clarendon Press: Oxford*, 1951. 8°. **8008**. dd. **54**.

—— Reflections on Family Life. (An address.) pp. 24. *National Council of Social Service: London*, 1947. 8°. **8417**. b. **50**.

—— Reflections on Government. pp. 424. *Oxford University Press: London*, 1942. 8°. **8011**. c. **26**.

—— Reflections on Leisure. Adapted from broadcast talks originally composed for Persia. pp. 20. *National Council of Social Service: London*, [1947.] 8°. **8288**. h. **68**.

—— The Relations of England and Holland. pp. 27. *T. Nelson & Sons: London*, [1915?] 8°. **09077**. bb. **17**.

—— The Study of Political Science and its Relation to Cognate Studies. [A lecture.] pp. 50. *University Press: Cambridge*, 1928. 8°. **8007**. bb. **27**.

—— The Submerged Nationalities of the German Empire. pp. 64. *Clarendon Press: Oxford*, 1915. 8°. **08072**. bb. **34**.

—— Traditions of Civility. Eight essays. pp. viii. 370. *University Press: Cambridge*, 1948. 8°. **12360**. f. **11**.

—— Universities in Great Britain: their position and their problems. pp. 98. *Student Christian Movement Press: London*, 1931. 8°. **08364**. e. **63**.

BARKER (*Sir* ERNEST)

—— The Uses of Leisure. pp. 13. [1936.] 8°. *See* LONDON.—III. *World Institute of Adult Education*. **8287**. cc. **47**.

—— The Values of Life. Essays on the circles and centres of duty. pp. 134. *Blackie & Son: London & Glasgow*, 1939. 8°. **8412**. aa. **5**.

—— W. P. Ker, a Scholar. By E. B. (Ernest Barker.) [Reprinted from "The Times."] *St. Nicolas Press: Cambridge*, 1953. 8°. **10864**. k. **5**.

—— [For editions and translations of "Why we are at War. Great Britain's case. By members of the Oxford Faculty of Modern History," i.e. E. Barker and others:] *See* ENGLAND.—*Appendix*. [*History and Politics*.—II. 1914.]

—— World History Series. Edited by Ernest Barker. vol. 1, 2, 4. *Cassell & Co.: London*, 1926, 27, 25. 8°. **9012**. a. **5**.

Imperfect; wanting vol. 3.

—— Biographical Notes on Sir Ernest Barker and Thomas Greenwood. Issued in connection with the unveiling of plaques in their honour at the Bredbury and Romiley Branch of the Cheshire County Library . . . 12th October 1950. [The notes on Sir E. Barker signed: M. L. C., i.e. M. L. Cousins; those on T. Greenwood signed: G. C. With portraits.] [1950.] 8°. *See* C., M. L. **10863**. de. **5**.

BARKER (ERNEST FRANKLIN)

—— *See* GALLAWAY (William S.) and BARKER (E. F.) The Infra-Red Absorption Spectra of Ethylene and Tetra-Deutero-Ethylene under High Resolution. [1942.] 8°. **8716**. l. **2**.

—— *See* SHENG (Hsi-yin) Further Resolution of Two Parallel Bands of Ammonia and the Interaction between Vibration and Rotation. [By] Hsi-yin Sheng, E. F. Barker, *etc.* [1941.] 4°. **08712**. dd. **29**.

—— Selective Radiation from Osmium Filaments . . . A dissertation . . . Reprinted from the Physical Review, *etc.* [1916.] 8°. **8909**. ccc. **10**

BARKER (ETHEL ROSS) Buried Herculaneum . . . With nine plans and sixty-four illustrations [and a bibliography]. pp. xvi. 253. *A. & C. Black: London*, 1908. 8°. **07702**. bbb. **1**.

—— Rome of the Pilgrims and Martyrs. A study in the martyrologies, itineraries, syllogæ, & other contemporary documents . . . With four maps. pp. xv. 379. *Methuen & Co.: London*, 1913. 8°. **4830**. ee. **10**.

BARKER (EUGENE CAMPBELL) *See* AUSTIN (Moses) The Austin Papers. Edited by E. C. Barker. [1789—Sept. 1834.] 1924, *etc.* 8°. [*Annual Report of the American Historical Association*. 1919. vol. 2; 1922. vol. 2.] A.S. **931**.

—— *See* AUSTIN (Moses) The Austin Papers, October, 1834—January, 1837. Edited by E. C. Barker. [1926.] 8°. **10906**. g. **9**.

—— *See* HOUSTON (Samuel) The Writings of Sam Houston, 1813–1863. Edited by Amelia W. Williams and E. C. Barker. 1938, *etc.* 8°. **09196.b.17.**

—— The Life of Stephen F. Austin, founder of Texas, 1793–1836, *etc.* [With portraits and maps.] pp. xv. 551. *Cokesbury Press: Nashville, Dallas*, 1925. 8°. **010884**. i. **13**.

BARKER (EUGENE HENRY) Computing Tables and Mathematical Formulas. Arranged for the use of high schools and colleges. pp. v. 88. *Ginn & Co.: Boston*, [1913.] 8°. 08548. ff. 28.

BARKER (Eugene Henry) and **MORGAN** (Frank Millett)

—— Mathematics in Daily Life. pp. vi. 432. iv. *Houghton Mifflin Co.: Boston,* [1939.] 8°. **08535**. a. **41**.

BARKER (F. R. Peter)

—— History of the Argyll & Sutherland Highlanders, 9th Battalion, 54th Light A.A. Regiment, 1939–45, *etc.* [By F. R. P. Barker, W. S. Hutton and R. C. Ross.] pp. ix. 131. pl. 11. 1950. 8°. *See* England.—*Army.—Infantry.—Princess Louise's (Argyll & Sutherland Highlanders).—9th Battalion.* **9101**. f. **93**.

BARKER (Felix) *See* Barker (Richard F. R.)

BARKER (Fordyce) *See* Barker (Benjamin F.)

BARKER (Frances Shirley)

—— The Dark Hills Under, *etc.* pp. 59. *Yale University Press: New Haven,* 1933. 8°. [*Yale Series of Younger Poets.* no. 32.] W.P. **6198/32**.

—— Peace my Daughters. pp. 263. *W. H. Allen: London,* [1952.] 8°. **12730**. t. **18**.

—— Rivers Parting, *etc.* pp. 360. *W. H. Allen: London,* [1951.] 8°. **12730.f.32.**

BARKER (Francis) *Professor of Chemistry in Trinity College, Dublin. See* Dublin.—*House of Recovery.* The First Report on the Object and Effects of the House of Recovery in Dublin, by the Physicians to that Institution (F. Barker, W. Stoker, G. Hagan). 1806. 8°. **7686**. aaa. **7**.

BARKER (Francis) *Professor of Chemistry in Trinity College, Dublin,* and **CHEYNE** (John)

—— An Account of the Rise, Progress, and Decline of the Fever lately epidemical in Ireland, together with communications from physicians in the provinces, and various official documents. 2 vol. *Baldwin, Cradock & Joy: London; Hodges & M'Arthur: Dublin,* 1821. 8°. **1168**. h. **22**.

BARKER (Francis) *Professor of Chemistry in Trinity College, Dublin,* and **MONTGOMERY** (William Fetherston H.)

—— Observations, Chemical and Practical, on the Dublin Pharmacopœia: with a translation annexed. pp. xiv. 721. *Hodges & Smith: Dublin,* 1830. 8°. **777**. g. **25**.

BARKER (Francis) *Wesleyan Minister.* Manna: or, Scripture texts for every day in the year; with appropriate verses of sacred poetry. pp. 173. *John Mason; Simpkin, Marshall & Co.: London; T. Gill: Easingwold,* [1853.] 18°. **3107**. a. **56**.

—— A Methodical Guide to the Daily Reading of the Scriptures . . . Second edition. *J. Mason; Simpkin & Co.: London,* 1844. 32°. **1112**. a. **38**. *The date on the wrapper is* 1845.

BARKER (Francis) *Writer of Verse.* Boadicea. pp. vi. 210. *Jarrold & Sons: London,* [1859.] 8°. **11651**. d. **19**.

BARKER (Francis Edwin)

—— The Church of the Apostles and the Fathers, *etc.* pp. x. 234. *S.P.C.K.: London,* 1938. 8°. **20032**. ff. **39**.

—— Our Christian Profession . . . Twelve lessons for seniors, *etc.* pp. 78. *National Society; S.P.C.K.: [London,* 1944.] 8°. [*Church Education Publications.*] W.P. **6246/34**.

BARKER (Francis Edwin)

—— Through the Ages. The story of the Christian Church, *etc.* [With plates.] 2 vol. pp. xix. xxiii. 340. *Published for the Church Assembly Children's Council by the Church Information Board: Westminster,* 1955. 8°. **4535**. g. **25**.

BARKER (Frank) *of Sheffield.*

—— Weights of Steel Bars, *etc.* pp. 33. *F. Barker: Sheffield,* 1898. 8°. **8548**. cc. **17**.

BARKER (Frank Granville)

—— Stars of the Opera, *etc.* [With portraits.] pp. 51. *Lotus Press: [York,]* 1949. 8°. [*British Poetry-Drama Guild Series.*] **012213.p.11/1.**

—— Voices of the Opera. [With plates.] pp. 61. *Arthur Unwin: London,* 1951. 8°. **10604**. l. **32**.

BARKER (Fred)

—— With Christ on Australian Tracks. pp. 136. *Marshall, Morgan & Scott: London, Edinburgh,* [1939.] 8°. **20033**. e. **9**.

BARKER (Fred C.) and **DANFORTH** (John S.) Hunting and Trapping on the Upper Magalloway River and Parmachenee Lake. First winter in the wilderness. pp. 238. *D. Lothrop & Co.: Boston,* 1882. 8°. **7905**. bb. **42**.

BARKER (Fred Drummond) An Angler's Paradise. Recollections of twenty years with rod and line in Ireland. pp. 296. *Faber & Gwyer: London,* 1929. 8°. **07906**. e. **48**.

BARKER (Fred G.) *See* Shakespeare (W.) [*Selections and Extracts.*] Forty-Minute Plays from Shakespeare. By F. G. Barker. 1927. 8°. **012201**. bb. **1/18**.

BARKER (Frederic) *Bishop of Sydney. See* Bible.—*Psalms.—Selections.* [*English.*] Thirty-six Psalms; with commentary and prayer . . . By the Rev. F. Barker. 1854. 8°. **3090**. b. **38**.

—— *See* Cowper (William M.) Episcopate of the Right Reverend Frederic Barker . . . With portrait, *etc.* 1888. 8°. **4903**. gg. **22**.

—— A Charge delivered to the Clergy of the Diocese of Sydney, November 23rd 1858, *etc.* pp. 28. *Reading & Wellbank: Sydney,* 1859. 8°. **4445**. c. **8**.

—— On the Rise of the Errors of the Church of Rome. *See* Roman Catholicism. A Course of Sermons on Romanism, *etc.* [1840.] 12°. **1113**. e. **11**.

—— Pharisaism. *See* Grange, *in Cartmel.* Twenty-two Sermons, *etc.* 1854. 12°. **4455**. h. **8**.

—— The Supposed Sacrament of Penance. *See* Rome, *Church of.* [*Appendix.*] A Course of Sermons on the Principal Errors of the Church of Rome, *etc.* 1838. 12°. **1119**. f. **28**.

BARKER (Frederic Allan)

—— Imprisonment, *etc.* pp. xi. 191. *Christian Literature Society for India: Madras,* 1930. 8°. **6055**. ppp. **3**.

—— The Modern Prison System of India . . . The progress of prison reform in India during the twenty years following the publication of the Report of the 1919–1920 Indian Jails Committee, *etc.* pp. xvi. 139. *Macmillan & Co.: London,* 1944. 8°. [*English Studies in Criminal Science.* vol. 3.] **W.P.10/3.**

—— The Principles of Borstal Treatment as applied to Indian Prisoners. pp. 37. xviii. 1915. fol. *See* Punjab. Miscellaneous Public Documents, etc. I.S.P.U. 16/2.

BARKER (Frederick F.) *See* United States of America. [*Laws and Statutes.—II. Special Collections.—Alaska.*] Compilation of the Acts of Congress and Treaties realting to Alaska from March 30, 1867, to March 3, 1905 . . . By F. F. Barker. 1906. 8°. A.S. **639/6.**

BARKER (*Mrs.* Frederick Raymond) *See* Barker (Elizabeth R.)

BARKER (G.) **AND CO.** Barker's Facts and Figures. *See* Periodical Publications.—*London.*

—— Barker's Trade and Finance Annual. *See* Periodical Publications.—*London.*

BARKER (G.) *of Manchester.* Agony's Anguish. (Experiences in the Great War with the 23rd Manchesters.) pp. 96. *Alf Eva: Manchester,* 1931. 8°. **09080.** aa. **38.**

BARKER (G.) *Rev., of Leighton Buzzard.* Lost and Found. [A religious tract.] pp. 16. *Judd & Glass: London,* 1857. 8°. **4407.** c. **71.** (**6.**)

—— Prize Essay on Article xxxvii of the Church of England. The expediency of principle. An attempt to show what is erroneous or defective in the thirty-seventh article of the Church of England, in its teaching on the lawfulness of war, and what is the Christian's duty under such circumstances. pp. v. 71. *A. W. Bennett; N. H. Cotes: London,* 1862. 16°. **8425.** a. **17.**

BARKER (G. Bell)

—— An Introduction to Planning. With illustrations.] pp. 84. *Percival Marshall & Co.: London,* [1949.] 8°. **8289.** de. **52.**

—— Science of Planning Series. (G. B. Barker, editor.) *Percival Marshall & Co.: London,* [1949– .] 8°. W.P. **2850.**

BARKER (G. H.) *M. Coll. H.*

—— Modern Woodwork and Furniture Making, *etc.* pp. xi. 146. pl. viii. *Technical Press: London,* 1937. 8°. **7944.** ppp. **11.**

—— Woodcraft Design & Construction. A manual for teachers, students and craftsmen. [With plates.] pp. x. 146. *C. Lockwood & Son: London,* 1930. 8°. **07943.** d. **32.**

BARKER (Geoffrey Russell)

—— Some Problems of Incentives and Labour Productivity in Soviet Industry. A contribution to the study of the planning of labour in the U.S.S.R. pp. 129. xii. *Basil Blackwell: Oxford,* [1955.] 8°. [*Monograph on the Soviet Economic System.* no. 1.] Ac. **2661.** d **2.**

BARKER (George) *B.D.* Sermons upon Several Texts of Scripture. pp. 6. 278. *John White for Francis Hildyard, etc.: York,* 1697. 8°. **4452.** bbb. **9.**

—— [Seven sermons.] *See* Sermons. Fourteen Sermons on Various Subjects, *etc.* 1831. 12°. **4461.** bb. **33.**

BARKER (George) *of Birmingham. See* Whateley (William) *of Birmingham.* A Reply to a Letter of Mr. G. Barker, Attorney, contained in Documents relative to an investigation of the manner in which the funeral of the late M. Boulton, Esq., was furnished. 1811. 8°. **1414.** g. **46.** (**1.**)

—— An Answer to the Letter of Mr. W. Whateley. (Copy of a letter from Mr. W. Whateley to Mr. G. Barker, in reply to his letter of September, 1811. Copy of a letter from Mr. Whateley to Mr. G. Barker [dated: 23 Dec. 1811, with appendix].) pp. 22. 3. *R. Jabet: Birmingham,* 1811. 8°. **1414.** g. **46.** (**2.**)

BARKER (George) *of the Theatre Royal, Drury Lane.* Impunity of Military Insolence and Licentiousness, exhibite in a correspondence between George Barker . . . Captai Sutton . . . and . . . the Duke of Wellington. pp. 23. *James Ridgway: London,* 1845. 8°. **1202.** c. **13.** (**3.**

BARKER (George) *of York.* The Country Gentleman; or the Force of gratitude. A play, in five acts. pp. 72. *The Author: York,* 1828. 12°. T. **1209.** (**5.**

BARKER (George Carpenter)

—— *See* Prodigal Son. The Shepherds' Play of the Prodig Son . . . Edited and translated by G. C. Barker. 1953. 8 [*University of California Publications. Folklore Studie* no. 2.] Ac. **2689.** g **6**

BARKER (*Sir* George Digby) *G.C.B. See* Porte (Edward G.) Remarks concerning the Recent Visit o Lieutenant General George Digby Barker, C.B., and th Diary of Lieutenant John Barker . . . during the siege o Boston, *etc.* 1898. 8°. **10600.** g. **7.** (**2**

—— Letters from Persia and India, 1857–1859: a subaltern' experiences in war . . . Edited by Lady Barker. [With portrait.] pp. xxiv. 183. *G. Bell & Sons: London* 1915. 8°. **9057.** aaa. **4**

BARKER (George Fisher Russell) *See* Walpol (Horace) *Earl of Orford.* Memoirs of the Reign of Kin George the Third. Re-edited by G. F. R. Barker, *et* 1894. 8°. **2394.** h.

—— Memoir of Richard Busby . . . With some account o Westminster School in the seventeenth century. [With portrait.] pp. xii. 164. *Lawrence & Bullen: London* 1895. 4°. **4905.** f. **2**

BARKER (George Fisher Russell) and **DAUGLISH** (Milverton Godfrey)

—— Historic and Political Handbook. pp. xviii. 374. *Chapma & Hall: London,* 1886. 8°. **08229.** de. **1**

—— New edition, revised, *etc.* pp. xviii. 374. *Chapma & Hall: London,* 1888. 8°. **8139.** de. **2**

BARKER (George Fisher Russell) and **STENNING** (Alan Herbert)

—— The Record of Old Westminsters. A biographical li of all those who are known to have been educated a Westminster School from the earliest times to 1927, *et* [With plates.] 2 vol. pp. xv. 1148. 1928. 8°.

—— A Supplementary Volume . . . Comprising . . addenda and corrigenda to the original work . . . biographical list of all those who have been admitte to the school from Play Term 1919 to Election Ter 1937 . . . Compiled by J. B. Whitmore . . . an G. R. Y. Radcliffe. [With plates.] pp. ix. 246. 1938. 8°.
See Westminster School. **08366.r.38**

—— The Westminst School Register from 1764 to 1883. Compiled and edite with biographical notes . . . by G. F. R. Barker ar A. H. Stenning, *etc.* pp. x. 276. 1892. 8°. *See* Westminster School. **8365.** f. **3**

BARKER (George Frederick) *See* Philadelphia.—*Franklin Institute, etc.* The Franklin Journal, *etc.* (ser. 3 vol. 67. no. 5—vol. 69 edited by G. F. Barker.) 1826, *etc.* 8°. P.P. **1612**

—— Biographical Memoir of Matthew Carey Lea, 1823 1897, *etc.* [With a portrait.] 1905. *See* Washington D.C.—*National Academy of Sciences.* Biographical Memoirs. vol. 5. 1902, *etc.* 8°. A.S. **939/2**

BARKER (George Frederick)

—— The Correlation of Vital and Physical Forces. pp. 36. *C. C. Chatfield: New Haven*, 1870. 8°. **7405. aa. 10.**
No. 2 of the "University Series."

—— [A reissue.] *See* Half Hours. Half Hours with Modern Scientists, *etc.* ser. 1. 1872, *etc.* 8°. **8708. h. 19.**

—— The Forces of Nature. An address, *etc.* pp. 45. *J. Munsell: Albany, N.Y.*, 1863. 8°. **8906. c. 20. (10.)**

—— Memoir of John William Draper. 1811–1882 . . . Read before the National Academy, *etc.* [With a bibliography and a portrait.] [*Washington*, 1886.] 8°. **10883. dd. 6.**

—— Physics. Advanced course. pp. x. 902. *Macmillan & Co.: London; New York* printed, 1892. 8°. **8705. cc. 31.**

BARKER (George Granville)

—— Alanna Autumnal. pp. 87 *Wishart: London*, 1933. 8°. **12601. s. 6.**

—— Calamiterror. [A poem.] pp. 53. *Faber & Faber: London*, 1937. 8°. **11662.c.7.**

—— The Dead Seagull. [A novel.] pp. 142. *John Lehmann: London*, 1950. 8°. **NNN. 887.**

—— Eros in Dogma. [Poems.] pp. 61. *Faber & Faber: London*, 1944. 8°. **11656. f. 30.**

—— Janus. (The Documents of a Death.—The Bacchant.) [Two tales.] pp. 301. *Faber & Faber: London*, 1935. 8°. **NN. 24464.**

—— Lament and Triumph. [Poems.] pp. 78. *Faber & Faber: London*, 1940. 8°. **11656. e. 25.**

—— News of the World. [Poems.] pp. 64. *Faber & Faber: London*, 1950. 8°. **11657. g. 39.**

—— Poems. pp. 64. *Faber & Faber: London*, 1935. 8°. **11654. b. 63.**

—— Thirty Preliminary Poems. pp. 37. *David Archer: London*, 1933. 8°. **011641. e. 55.**

—— The True Confession of George Barker. [A poem.] pp. 36. *Fore Publications: London*, 1950. 8°. [*Key Poet.* no. 2.] **W.P. 8498 2.**

—— A Vision of Beasts and Gods. [Poems.] pp. 62. *Faber & Faber: London*, 1954. 8°. **11659. cc. 12.**

BARKER (George Hollington) A Catalogue of the Numismatic Books, and beautifully illuminated Missals of the late G. H. Barker Esq.; also his . . . collection of ancient and modern prints, *etc.* pp. 21. [*London*, 1803.] 8°. **821. g. 18. (5.)**

BARKER (George M.) A Tea Planter's Life in Assam . . . With . . . illustrations by the author. pp. viii. 247. *Thacker, Spink & Co.: Calcutta; London* [printed], 1884 [1883]. 8°. **10058. bbb. 26.**

BARKER (George T.) Instructions in the Preparation, Administration, and Properties of Nitrous Oxide, Protoxide of Nitrogen, or Laughing Gas. pp. 61. *Rubencame & Stockton: Philadelphia*, 1866. 8°. **8905. e. 4.**

BARKER (George Thomas Mathias) Essays. [Edited, with a preface, by Julia Wickham.] pp. 52. *Parker & Son: Oxford*, 1905. 8°. **12355. de. 28.**

BARKER (Gilbert David)

—— Aided Schools if Possible. pp. 11. *National Society; S.P.C.K.: London*, 1947. 8°. **8367. aa. 55.**

BARKER (Gilbert David)

—— The Diocesan Education Committee's Measure, 1943. Very wide scope of the Committee's duties. *National Society & S.P.C.K.:* [*London*, 1945.] 8°. **08366. o 33.**

—— The Education Act 1944. A general summary. pp. 15. *National Society; S.P.C.K.: London*, [1945.] 8°. **8367. aa. 45.**

—— Managers and Governors of Voluntary Schools. Their duties and opportunities under the Education Act 1944. pp. 30. *National Society; S.P.C.K.: London*, [1945.] 8°. **8367. aa. 50.**

—— A New Guide for Church School Managers, Governors and Others interested in Church Day Schools, *etc.* pp. 191. *National Society: S.P.C.K.: London*, 1948. 8°. **08367. de. 12.**

—— Religious Education and the Education Act. pp. 19. *National Society; S.P.C.K.: London*, [1945.] 8°. **08366. p. 42.**

BARKER (Gilbert Welch)

—— Antoine Watteau . . . With eight plates. pp. 218. *Duckworth: London*, 1939. 8°. **7863. ppp. 62.**

—— Sextet. [Short stories.] pp. 184. *George Ronald: Oxford*, [1951.] 8°. **12634. pp. 8.**

BARKER (Granville) *See* Barker (Harley G.)

BARKER (H.) *of Matlock?* The Panorama of Matlock and its environs: with the tour of the Peak . . . Second edition. pp. 50. *Longman & Co.: London*, 1828. 12°. **10360. b. 25.**

—— Tenth edition. pp. 48. *Longman & Co.: London*, 1829. 12°. **10358. aa. 35. (2.)**
The titlepage is engraved. The author's name appears on the wrapper.

BARKER (H. A. F.) The Principles and Practice of Banking for South African Students, *etc.* pp. 411. *Juta & Co.: Cape Town & Johannesburg*, [1930.] 8°. **8224. w. 36.**

—— The Principles and Practice of Banking in South Africa . . . Second edition. pp. 512. *Juta & Co.: Cape Town & Johannesburg*, 1934. 8°. **8230. eee. 2.**

—— The Principles and Practice of Banking in South Africa . . . Third edition. pp. 549. *Juta & Co.: Cape Town & Johannesburg*, 1952. 8°. **08231. cc. 42.**

BARKER (H. Anne) Crown Jewels, scattered for Youth, *etc.* pp. vii. 120. *Charles Bean: London*, 1854. 12°. **11647. b. 87.**

BARKER (H. D.) and **BERKLEY** (Elmer Eugene)

—— Fiber and Spinning Properties of Cotton, with special reference to varietal and environmental effects. pp. 36. *Washington*, 1946. 8°. [*U.S. Department of Agriculture. Technical Bulletin.* no. 931.] **A.S. 800/2.**

BARKER (Harley Granville)

—— *See* Adams (William B.) *Director of the Stratford-upon-Avon Festival Theatre.* The Lost Leader. W. Bridges-Adams on H. Granville-Barker. With a portrait, *etc.* 1954. 8°. **10864. cc. 4.**

—— *See* Álvarez Quintero (S.) and (J.) Four Plays . . . In English versions by Helen and Harley Granville-Barker, *etc.* 1927. 8°. **11726. d. 67.**

—— *See* Álvarez Quintero (S.) and (J.) Four Comedies . . . in English versions by Helen and Harley Granville-Barker, *etc.* 1932. 8°. **11728. aaa. 27.**

BARKER (Harley Granville)

—— *See* Archer (William) *Critic*, and Barker (H. G.) A National Theatre, *etc.* 1907. 4°. **2306. h. 9.**

—— *See* Archer (William) *Critic.* The Vedrenne-Barker Season. 1904-1905, *etc.* [With a portrait.] [1905.] 4°. **11795. t. 78.**

—— *See* Calthrop (Dion C.) and Barker (H. G.) The Harlequinade, *etc.* 1918. 8°. **11779. h. 67.**

—— *See* Guitry (Sacha) Deburau . . . In an English version by H. Granville-Barker. 1921. 8°. **11735. d. 40.**

—— *See* Henderson (Archibald) *of the University of North Carolina.* European Dramatists. (Granville Barker.) 1914. 8°. **11826. dd. 30.**

—— *See* Housman (Laurence) Little Plays of St. Francis . . . With a preface by H. Granville-Barker. 1922. 8°. **011781. i. 25.**

—— *See* Housman (Laurence) and Barker (H. G.) Prunella, *etc.* 1906. 8°. **11779. d. 42.**

—— —— 1930. 8°. **011779. ee. 97.**

—— *See* Maeterlinck (M.) [P.M.B.] Three Plays . . . With introduction by H. G. Barker. 1911. 8°. **012199. e. 1/2.**

—— *See* Martínez Sierra (G.) The Plays of G. Martínez Sierra, *etc.* (vol. 1. In English versions by J. G. Underhill. With a critical appreciation of the plays by H. Granville-Barker. vol. 2. In English versions by Helen & Harley Granville-Barker.) 1923. 8°. **20018. ff. 4.**

—— *See* Martínez Sierra (G.) [El Reino de Dios.] The Kingdom of God . . . In an English version by Helen and Harley Granville-Barker. 1927. 8°. **11726. d. 66.**

—— *See* Martínez Sierra (G.) [El Sueño de una noche de Agosto.] The Romantic Young Lady . . . In an English version by Helen and Harley Granville-Barker. 1929. 8°. **11725. de. 44.**

—— *See* Martínez Sierra (G.) [Triángulo.] Take Two from One . . . In an English version by Helen and Harley Granville-Barker. 1931. 8°. **11728. aa. 25.**

—— *See* Martínez Sierra (G.) The Two Shepherds: a play in two acts, in an English version by Helen and H. G. Barker. 1935. 8°. **20019. aaa. 29.**

—— *See* Merrick (Leonard) The Works of Leonard Merrick. (One Man's View . . . With an introduction by G. Barker.) [1918, *etc.*] 8°. **012272.aa.13/10.**

—— *See* Purdom (Charles B.) Harley Granville Barker, *etc.* [With portraits and a list of Barker's writings.] [1955.] 8°. **10864. k. 14.**

—— *See* Romains (Jules) [Amédée et les messieurs en rang.] Six Gentlemen in a Row . . . In an English version by H. Granville-Barker. 1927. 8°. **11736. dd. 20.**

—— *See* Romains (Jules) Doctor Knock . . . In an English version by H. Granville-Barker. 1925. 8°. **11735. dd. 60.**

—— *See* Romains (Jules) Doctor Knock . . . In an English version by H. G. Barker. 1935. 8°. **20019. aaa. 36.**

—— *See* Schnitzler (A.) Anatol . . . Paraphrased for the English stage by G. Barker. 1911. 8°. **11748. f. 16.**

—— *See* Shakespeare (W.) [*Works.*] The Players' Shakespeare. [With introductions by H. G. Barker.] 1923, *etc.* fol. **L.R.408.f.7.**

BARKER (Harley Granville)

—— *See* Sharp (Cecil J.) The Songs & Incidental Music arranged & composed . . . for G. Barker's production of A Midsummer Night's Dream at the Savoy Theatre in January, 1914. 1914. 4°. **F. 1268. o. (6.)**

—— *See* Thomas (Berte) and Barker (H. G.) "The Family of the Oldroyds," *etc.* [c. 1895.] 4°. **C. 116. h. 10.**

—— *See* Thomas (Berte) and Barker (H. G.) "Our Visitor to 'Work-a-day'." [1899.] 4°. **C. 108. f. 4.**

—— *See* Vedrenne (John E.) Complimentary Dinner to Mr. J. E. Vedrenne and Mr. H. G. Barker . . . 7th July, 1907, *etc.* [With a portrait.] [1907.] 8°. **010825. ff. 50.**

—— [Offprints of contributions by Granville-Barker to various publications. Including a tale, "Georgiana."] 9 pt. [1910.] 8°. **C. 116. g. 13.**

—— Agnes Colander. Play in three acts. 3 pt. [1901.] 4°. **C. 116. g. 9.**

Author's typescript, with MS. *corrections.*

—— Associating with Shakespeare . . . An address, *etc.* pp. 31. 1932. 8°. *See* London.—III. *Shakespeare Association.* **Ac. 9489. b/3. (5.)**

—— The Eighteen-Seventies. Essays by Fellows of the Royal Society of Literature. Edited by H. Granville-Barker. pp. xiv. 284. University Press: Cambridge Press: Cambridge, 1929. 8°. **011824. d. 33.**

—— The Exemplary Theatre. pp. xv. 287. *Chatto & Windus: London,* 1922. 8°. **011795. b. 57.**

—— Exit Planché—Enter Gilbert. [Extracted from "The London Mercury."] *London,* 1932. 8° **C.132.g.73.**

—— From Henry v to Hamlet. pp. 29. *London,* [1925.] 8°. [*British Academy. Annual Shakespeare Lecture.* 1925.] **Ac. 1186/4.**

—— His Majesty. A play in four acts. pp. viii. 131. *Sidgwick & Jackson: London,* 1928. 8°. **011781. ee. 102.**

—— [Another edition.] pp. 127. *Little, Brown & Co.: Boston,* 1929. 8°. **011781. ee. 101.**

—— The Madras House. A comedy, in four acts. pp. 144. *Sidgwick & Jackson: London,* 1911. 8°. **11775. ff. 30.**

—— [Another edition.] pp. 140. *Sidgwick & Jackson: London,* 1925. 8°. **11781. ee. 56.**

—— The Marrying of Ann Leete. A comedy in four acts. 4 pt. [1901.] 4°. **C. 116. g. 8.**
Author's typescript, with MS. *corrections.*

—— A National Theatre. [With a folding plan.] pp. xvi. 134. *Sidgwick & Jackson: London,* 1930. 8°. **11795. p. 22.**

—— On Dramatic Method. Being the Clark Lectures for 1930. pp. 192. *Sidgwick & Jackson: London,* 1931. 8°. **11822. s. 3.**

—— On Poetry in Drama . . . The Romanes Lecture delivered in the Taylor Institution, 4 June 1937. pp. 42. *Sidgwick & Jackson: London,* 1937. 12°. **11840. a. 20.**

—— The Perennial Shakespeare, *etc.* pp. 27. *London,* 1937. 8°. [*Broadcast National Lectures.* no. 20.] **W.P. 9691/20.**

—— Prefaces to Shakespeare. (First written for The Players' Shakespeare.) 5 ser. *Sidgwick & Jackson: London,* 1927–48. 8°. **011768.de.2.**

BARKER (HARLEY GRANVILLE)

—— [A reissue.] Prefaces to Shakespeare. ser. 3. Hamlet. MS. ALTERATIONS [by the author]. *London*, 1937. 8°. C. **116**. g. **14**.

—— Quality. pp. 17. *London*, 1938. 8°. [*English Association. Presidential Address.* 1938.] Ac. **2664/13**.

—— The Red Cross in France . . . With a preface by Sir Frederick Treves. pp. xii. 168. *Hodder & Stoughton: London*, 1916. 8°. **09082**. b. **4**.

—— Rococo: Vote by Ballot: Farewell to the Theatre. [Three plays.] pp. 117. *Sidgwick & Jackson: London*, 1917. 8°. **011779**. e. **14**.

—— The Secret Life. A play in three acts. pp. vii. 160. *Chatto & Windus: London*, 1923. 8°. **011779**. e. **113**.

—— Souls on Fifth . . . [A tale.] With frontispiece by Norman Wilkinson. pp. 61. *Little, Brown & Co.: Boston*, 1917. 8°. C. **116**. g. **15**.

—— The Study of Drama . . . A lecture . . . with notes subsequently added. pp. 92. *University Press: Cambridge*, 1934. 8°. [*Cambridge Miscellany.* no. 16.] W.P. **10116/16**.

—— Three Plays . . . The Marrying of Ann Leete—The Voysey Inheritance—Waste. pp. 347. *Sidgwick & Jackson: London*, 1909. 8°. **2303**. b. **2**.

—— Transcription of a Speech made by Granville Barker at the St. James's Theatre on . . . December 17th [1913], *etc.* [*London*, 1913.] *s. sh.* 8°. **1865**. c. 3. (**162**.)

—— The Use of the Drama. pp. vi. 91. *Princeton University Press: Princeton*, 1945. 8°. **11865**. i. **14**.

—— The Use of the Drama. The substance of three lectures delivered at Princeton University, U.S.A., upon the Spencer Trask Foundation in 1944. pp. 78. *Sidgwick & Jackson: London*, 1946. 8°. **11867**. bb. **2**.

—— The Voysey Inheritance. A play, *etc.* 5 pt. [1905?] 4°. C. **116**. g. **10**. *Author's typescript, with MS. corrections.*

—— The Voysey Inheritance, *etc.* pp. 83–210. MS. CORRECTIONS [by the author]. *Sidgwick & Jackson: London*, 1910. 8°. C. **116**. g. **16**. *A reissue of pp.* 83–210 *of* " *Three Plays.*"

—— Waste. A play in four acts. 4 pt. 1907. 4°. C. **116**. g. **11**. *Author's typescript, with MS. corrections.*

—— Waste: A tragedy in four acts. (Revised edition.) pp. 115. *Sidgwick & Jackson: London*, 1927. 8°. **011781**. e. **95**.

BARKER (HARLEY GRANVILLE) and **HARRISON** (GEORGE BAGSHAWE)

—— A Companion to Shakespeare Studies. Edited by H. Granville-Barker and G. B. Harrison. pp. x. 408. *University Press: Cambridge*, 1934. 8°. **11766**. i. **47**.

BARKER (HARLOW JAMES)

—— *See* DUNN (Colon H.) and BARKER (H. J.) Electrical Measurements Manual. 1952. 8°. **8762**. bb. **51**.

BARKER (HAROLD PRIMROSE)

—— *See* PERIODICAL PUBLICATIONS.—*London.* Gospel Tidings . . . Edited by A. J. Pollock & H. P. Barker. [1911, *etc.*] 16°. P.P. **353**. cmk.

BARKER (HAROLD PRIMROSE)

—— The Baptism of the Spirit: is it a thing for Christians to seek? pp. 12. *Central Bible Truth Depot: London*, [1925.] 8°. **4324**. bb. **41**.

—— Be it Known. By H. P. B. [i.e. H. P. Barker.] pp. 24. [1898.] 32°. *See* B., H. P. **04420**. de. **3**. (**2**.)

—— Christ in the Minor Prophets. pp. 111. *G. F. Vallance: Goodmayes; New York* printed, [1927.] 8°. [*Treasury Series.* no. 1.] W.P. **7626/1**.

—— [A reissue.] *Pickering & Inglis: London; New York* printed, [1934.] 8°. **03187**. g. **96**.

—— Christ's Vicar. pp. 234. *G. F. Vallance: Barkingside*, [1938.] 8°. [*Treasury Library.* no. 30.] W.P. **7626/30**.

—— Coming Twice. (On the Second Coming of Christ.) pp. 159. *G. F. Vallance: Barkingside*, [1938.] 8°. [*Treasury Library.* no. 25.] W.P. **7626/25**.

—— Disappointed Christians. pp. 15. *John Ritchie: Kilmarnock*, [1937.] 12°. **04402**. fff. **82**.

—— " Divine Healing " scripturally examined, *etc.* pp. 48. *Pickering & Inglis: London, Glasgow*, [1925.] 8°. **03126**. de. **18**.

—— The Doctrine of " Doing." By H. P. B. [i.e. H. P. Barker.] pp. 24. [1898.] 32°. *See* B., H. P. **04420**. de. 3. (3.)

—— Four Negative Facts. [A religious tract.] pp. 23. *Bible Truth Depôt: Hull*, [1898.] 32°. **04420**. de. **3**. (**4**.)

—— From Start to Finish. A guide to the journey heavenward. pp. vii. 110. *Pickering & Inglis: London & Glasgow*, [1921.] 8°. **04402**. fff. **43**.

—— Incidents of Australian Life in city and bush. Collected by H. P. Barker. [A religious tract.] pp. 80. *Central Bible Truth Depot: London; Bible, Book & Tract Depot: Sydney*, [1922.] 16°. **04420**. e. **25**.

—— A Knock at the Door. A Gospel volume compiled by H. P. Barker. pp. 32. *Bible Truth Depôt: Hull*, [1898.] 8°. **4418**. h. **42**.

—— Review and Reward. Will the lives of all Christians be reviewed; their fidelity rewarded? pp. 95. *Pickering & Inglis: London; printed in U.S.A.*, [1933.] 8°. **4257**. bbb. **46**.

—— Royal Service. A study in Christian leadership. pp. 99. *G. F. Vallance: Barkingside*, [1938.] 8°. [*Treasury Library.* no. 28.] W.P. **7626/28**.

—— Why I abandoned Exclusivism, *etc.* pp. 16. *Pickering & Inglis: London, Glasgow*, [1930.] 8°. **03089**. e. **45**.

—— Windows in Words. Illustrations and pen-pictures used by H. P. Barker. pp. 164. *Pickering & Inglis: London*, 1954. 8°. **4383**. de. **28**.

BARKER (HAROLD WOOD) *See* BRADFORD, *Yorkshire.*—*Bradford Engineering Society.* Minutes of Proceedings of the Bradford Engineering Society. Edited by H. W. Barker. 1905, *etc.* 8°. Ac. **4389**.

BARKER (HARRY) Public Utility Rates. A discussion of the principles and practice underlying charges for water, gas, electricity, *etc.* pp. xiv. 387. *McGraw-Hill Book Co.: New York*, 1917. 8°. **08226**. l. **61**.

BARKER (HEDLEY)

—— The Man they could not Kill. pp. 96. *Withy Grove Press: London & Manchester*, [1942.] 8°. [*Cherry Tree Book.*] **12634**. p. **1/173**.

BARKER (Helen Manchester Granville) *See* Álvarez Quintero (S.) and (J.) Four Plays . . . In English versions by Helen and Harley Granville-Barker, *etc.* 1927. 8°. **11726.** d. **67.**

—— *See* Álvarez Quintero (S.) and (J.) Four Comedies . . . in English versions by Helen and Harley Granville-Barker, *etc.* 1932. 8°. **11728.** aaa. **27.**

—— *See* Gómez de la Serna (R.) Some Greguerías . . . Translated by H. Granville-Barker. 1944. 8°. **012305.** l. **46.**

—— *See* Martínez Sierra (G.) The Plays of G. Martínez Sierra, *etc.* (vol. 2. In English versions by Helen & Harley Granville-Barker.) 1923. 8°. **20018.** ff. **4.**

—— *See* Martínez Sierra (G.) [El Reino de Dios.] The Kingdom of God . . . In an English version by Helen and Harley Granville-Barker. 1927. 8°. **11726.** d. **66.**

—— *See* Martínez Sierra (G.) [El Sueño de u a noche de Agosto.] The Romantic Young Lady . . . In an English version by Helen and Harley Granville-Barker. 1929. 8°. **11725.** de. **44.**

—— *See* Martínez Sierra (G.) [Triángulo.] Take Two from One . . . In an English version by Helen and Harley Granville-Barker. 1931. 8°. **11728.** aa. **25.**

—— *See* Martínez Sierra (G.) The Two Shepherds: a play in two acts, in an English version by H. and Harley G. Barker. 1935. 8°. **20019.** aaa. **29.**

—— Ada. [A novel.] pp. 394. *Chatto & Windus: London,* 1923. 8°. **NN. 9234.**

—— Come, Julia. pp. 321. *Sidgwick & Jackson: London,* 1931. 8°. **NN. 17512.**

—— Living Mirrors. pp. 280. *Sidgwick & Jackson: London,* 1928. 8°. **NN. 14241.**

—— The Locked Book. An anthology [of allusions to angels in prose and verse] made by Helen Granville-Barker. pp. xiv. 138. *Sidgwick & Jackson: London,* 1936. 8°. **12298.** de. **37.**

—— Moon in Scorpio. pp. 283. *Sidgwick & Jackson: London,* 1932. 8°. **NN. 21738.**

—— Nineteen Poems. pp. 37. *Sidgwick & Jackson: London,* 1944. 8°. **11657.** cc. **86.**

—— Poems. pp. vii. 127. *Sidgwick & Jackson: London,* 1939. 8°. **11656.** aa. **43.**

—— Songs in Cities and Gardens. pp. 92. *Chatto & Windus: London,* 1919. 8°. **011649.** g. **92.**

—— Traitor Angel. pp. 299. *Sidgwick & Jackson: London,* 1935. 8°. **NN. 25158.**

—— Wives and Celebrities. [Tales.] pp. 261. *W. Collins, Sons & Co.: London,* [1927.] 8°. **NN. 12492.**

BARKER (Henry) *See* Brown (Thomas) *of Shifnal, Shropshire.* Letters from the Dead to the Living. By . . . T. Brown . . . H. Barker, *etc.* 1702. 8°. **1079.** m. **11.**

—— *See* Gentleman. The Polite Gentleman . . . Done out of French. [The translator's dedication signed: Hen. Barker.] 1700. 12°. **8403.** b. **14.**

BARKER (Henry Aston) [For descriptions of views painted by H. A. Barker and exhibited at the Panorama, Leicester Square:] *See* London.—iii. *Panorama, Leicester Square.*

BARKER (Henry Aston)

—— [For descriptions of views painted by H. A. Barker and exhibited at the Panorama, Strand:] *See* London.—iii. *Panorama, Strand.*

—— Description of the Panorama of Venice, taken, and painted by Messrs. Barker & Burford, from the Piazza di S. Marco . . . now exhibiting in the Panorama, Lower Abbey Street, Dublin, *etc.* pp. 12. *William Heriot: Leith,* 1823. 8°. **7856.** aaa. **40. (8.)**

—— Description of the View of Naples, and surrounding scenery, painted by Henry A. Barker & J. Burford; now exhibiting in the Pavilion, Lower Abbey-Street, Dublin. pp. 12. *William Folds: Dublin,* 1824. 8°. **7856.** aaa. **40. (7.)**

BARKER (Henry Colin) Progressive Lino Cuts, *etc.* pp. 64. *Sir I. Pitman & Sons: London,* 1932. 4°. **7941.** i. **4.**

BARKER (Henry James) Comic School Tales. pp. 203. *Jarrold & Sons: London,* [1904.] 8°. **12314.** aaaa. **42.**

—— The Comic Side of School Life. Very original English . . . Sixth edition, *etc.* pp. 161. *Jarrold & Sons: London,* [1900.] 8°. **012314.** ee. **92.**

—— King Edmund the Martyr, and other poems. pp. 163. *Jarrold & Sons: London,* [1909.] 8°. **011650.** e. **32.**

—— Lays and Ballads of Heroism. pp. 136. *J. Nisbet & Co.: London,* [1884.] 8°. **11653.** cc. **43.**

—— 'Lisha Ridley, the Pitman, and other poems, *etc.* pp. 242. *Jarrold & Sons: London,* [1892.] 8°. **011653.** m. **33.**

—— Little Humorists at School, as illustrated by children's oral answers and written exercises. pp. 110. *Jarrold & Sons: London,* [1913.] 8°. **12331.** e. **40.**

—— Merry Moments with Scholars. pp. viii. 119. *Harper & Bros.: London & New York,* 1909. 8°. **12316.** s. **8.**

—— A Nice Pair, and others. pp. vii. 244. *Harper & Bros.: London & New York,* 1909. 8°. **012625.** a. **19.**

—— Our Boys and Girls at School: their naiveté, humour, and wit. pp. 187. *Bristol,* [1891.] 8°. [*Arrowsmith's Bristol Library.* vol. 45.] **12207.** g.

—— Scarlet Feather. A story of adventure among the Indians of Arizona. pp. 188. *Griffith & Co.: London,* [1897.] 8°. **012806.** g. **3.**

—— The Wonder Seekers, *etc.* pp. 166. *S. W. Partridge & Co.: London,* [1901.] 8°. **012809.** ff. **52.**

BARKER (Henry John)

—— The Bible Ahead of Date. pp. 16. *London,* [1946.] 8°. [*Bible Testimony Booklet.* no. 2.] **W.P. 1146** 2.

—— The Book of the Crown. A memento and meditation. pp. xvi. 166. *Thynne & Co.: London,* 1937. 8°. **9930.** bb. **38.**

—— The Book of the King. A Royal Jubilee souvenir, *etc.* [Notes on the Bible.] pp. 56. *Marshall, Morgan & Scott: London & Edinburgh,* [1935.] 8°. **03128.** g. **111.**

BARKER (Henry Matthew) *See* Barker (Matthew H.)

BARKER (*Sir* Herbert Atkinson) Leaves from my Life, *etc.* [With portraits.] *Hutchinson & Co.: London,* [1927.] 8°. **010855.** h. **14.**

BARKER (HORACE ROSS) East Suffolk, illustrated . . . 566 illustrations . . . Compiled by H. R. Barker (assisted by V. B. Redstone) . . . The account of Ipswich written by Mr. F. Woolnough. pp. 564. *F. G. Pawsey & Co.: Bury St. Edmunds*, 1908, 09. 4°. **10368**. r. 3.
Published in parts.

—— History of, and Guide to, Bury St. Edmund's, *etc.* pp. 104. *Barker: Bury St. Edmund's*, 1885. 8°. **10351**. dd. 12.

—— Looking Back. [Poems.] pp. 47. *Catling: Bury St. Edmund's*, 1891. 8°. **11601**. dd. 14. (1.)

—— Onward and Upward. [Poems.] pp. 30. *Bury & Norwich Post Co.: Bury St. Edmund's*, 1919. 8°. **011648**. df. 154.

—— Shadow and Sunshine. [Poems.] pp. 47. *Barker: Bury St. Edmunds*, [1885.] 8°. **11601**. dd. 9. (5.)

—— A Short Account of Moyses Hall, Bury St. Edmund's, and its contents. [With an illustration.] *Bury Post Co.: Bury*, [1948.] 16°. **7812**. a. 1.

—— West Suffolk, illustrated . . . 566 illustrations, *etc.* pp. 411. *F. G. Pawsey & Co.: Bury St. Edmund's*, 1907. 4°. **10351**. h. 36.

BARKER (HOSEA) *See* BARKER (Jacob) Mr. Jacob Barker's Speech, in the case of Barker vs. Barker . . . against a claim preferred by Hosea Barker, for ten thousand dollars damages, for an alleged malicious prosecution of said Hosea for felony. [1843.] 8°. **8177**. d. 4.

BARKER (HOWARD)

—— Fourteen Poems. pp. 15. *Arthur H. Stockwell: Ilfracombe*, 1950. 8°. **11658**. g. 56.

BARKER (HOWARD WILSON) First-Aid Manual for Field Parties . . . Illustrated, *etc.* pp. 98. 1917. 8°. *See* UNITED STATES OF AMERICA.—*Department of Agriculture.—Forest Service.* A.S. **893/19**.

BARKER (ISAAC) An English Grammar, shewing the nature and grounds of the English language in its present state, *etc.* pp. 51. *John Hildyard: York*, [1733.] 12°. **828**. c. 41. (1.)

BARKER (ISABEL FANNIN) Lays of Love and Trust. pp. 192. *Elliot Stock: London*, 1911. 8°. **011650**. i. 29.

BARKER (J. ELLIS) *See* ELTZBACHER (O. J.) afterwards BARKER (J. E.)

BARKER (J. F.)

—— And—the Ghost came. A thriller for boys. pp. 11. *W. Paxton & Co.: London*, 1949. 8°. **11784**. aa. 13.
Paxton Playlets. no. 15765.

—— Cough Mixture. A play for boys. pp. 9. *W. Paxton & Co.: London*, 1949. 8°. **11784**. aa. 12.
Paxton Playlets. no. 15763.

—— Work for the Ghosts. A musical comedy for young actors. (Words by J. F. Barker. Music by J. K. Payen.) pp. 25. *Paxton: London*, [1951.] 8°. **11783**. g. 19.

BARKER (JACOB) Mr. Jacob Barker's Speech, in the case of Barker vs. Barker . . . before the Parish Court, in his own defence, against a claim preferred by Hosea Barker for ten thousand dollars damages, for an alleged malicious prosecution of said Hosea for felony. pp. 9. *"Crescent City": [New Orleans*, 1843.] 8°. **8177**. d. 4.

—— Incidents in the Life of Jacob Barker, of New Orleans, Louisiana, *etc.* [With a portrait.] pp. v. 285. *Washington*, 1855. 8°. **10880**. ee. 3.

BARKER (JACOB)

—— Trial of Jacob Barker, Thomas Vermilya, and Matthew L. Davis, for alleged conspiracy. Testimony as reported by Hugh Maxwell . . . and certified . . . by Ogden Edwards, *etc.* pp. 328. iv. *Coke Law Press: New-York*, 1827. 8°. **6738**. c. 4.

BARKER (JAMES) *Dramatic Publisher.* Barker's Continuation of Egerton's Theatrical Remembrancer, Baker's Biographia Dramatica, &c. . . . To which is added, a complete list of plays . . . to 1801. The whole arranged, &c., by W. C. Oulton. MS. NOTES. [1801.] 12°. *See* OULTON (Walley C.) **840**. b. 29.

—— [Another edition.] Barker's Complete List of Plays . . . to 1803, *etc.* pp. iv. 350. [1803.] 12°. *See* OULTON (Walley C.) **641**. f. 32.

—— [Another edition.] The Drama recorded; or, Barker's List of Plays . . . from the earliest period, to 1814; to which are added, Notitia Dramatica; or, a chronological account of events relative to the English stage. [By W. C. Oulton.] pp. iv. 212. MS. NOTES [by T. H. Lacy]. *J. Barker: London*, 1814. 12°. **11795**. bb. 42.
Interleaved. Earlier editions are entered under OULTON *(W. C.)*

—— [Another copy.] **82**. e. 38.

—— [Another copy.] FEW MS. CORRECTIONS. **82**. e. 39.

—— A Catalogue of Books, in various languages . . . with the greatest assemblage of old plays, ever collected . . . Now on sale . . . by J. Barker, *etc.* pp. 158. *J. Barker: London*, 1800. 8°. **129**. k. 21. (2.)

BARKER (JAMES) *Minister of Redbourn, Herts.* The Royal Robe: or, a Treatise of Meeknesse upon Col. 3. 12, *etc.* pp. 252. *E. M. for Robert Gibbs: London*, 1661. 12°. E. **1857**. (1.)

BARKER (JAMES) *of the Salvation Army.* *See* CARPENTER (Minnie L.) Three Great Hearts . . . Colonel J. Barker, *etc.* [With a portrait.] 1921. 8°. **4908**. e. 30.

—— James Barker, the prisoners' friend. pp. 43. *London*, 1930. 16°. [*Salvation Army Miniature Biographies.* no. 1.] W.P. **9922/1**.

BARKER (JAMES) *Phrenologist.* Barker's New Chart, or, Index of Character, considered phrenologically, physiologically, and physiognomically, *etc.* pp. 80. *J. Barker: Brighton*, [1889.] 8°. **07305**. g. 1. (5.)

—— The Chart, with the phrenological and physiological development and character of General Booth, of the Salvation Army. pp. 16. *J. Barker: Brighton*, [1887.] 8°. **4907**. aaa. 36. (3.)

—— A Secret Book for Men, *etc.* pp. 48. *J. Barker: Brighton*, [1888.] 8°. Tab. **603**. a. 32.

BARKER (JAMES MADISON)

—— *See* LYON (Leverett S.) Your Business and Postwar Readjustment . . . Edited by L. S. Lyon, J. M. Barker. *etc.* 1944. 8°. **8234**. cc. 47.

BARKER (JAMES NELSON) *See* MUSSER (Paul H.) James Nelson Barker . . . With a reprint of his comedy Tears and Smiles. [With a bibliography.] 1929. 8°. **10885**. b. 17.

—— Sketches of the Primitive Settlements on the River Delaware. A discourse delivered before the Society for the Commemoration of the Landing of William Penn, *etc.* pp. 62. *Carey, Lea & Carey: Philadelphia*, 1827. 8°. **9604**. b. 15.

BARKER (JAMES NELSON)

—— *See* MEASE (James) *M.D.* A Reply to the Criticisms by J. N. Barker [in his "Sketches of the Primitive Settlements on the River Delaware"] on the historical facts of the Picture of Philadelphia. 1828. 8°. **T. 1406. (4.)**

—— Tears and Smiles. *See* MUSSER (Paul H.) James Nelson Barker, *etc.* 1929. 8°. **10885. b. 17.**

—— L'Enfant du Montagne Vert. [A tale.] *See* LE RAT DE MAGNITOT (A.) Les Américaines, traduites de l'anglais. vol. 1. 1829. 12°. 12808.u.31.

BARKER (JAMES P.)

—— *See* BARKER (Roland) The Log of a Limejuicer. The experiences under sail of J. P. Barker, *etc.* [With a portrait.] 1934. 8°. **10498. bb. 42.**

BARKER (JANE) *of Stockwell.* *See* PRITCHARD (Charles) The Rest which remains to the People of God . . . A sermon preached . . . on the occasion of the death of Mrs. Jane Barker. 1833. 8°. **4903. eee. 6. (14.)**

BARKER (JANE) *of Wilsthorpe.* *See* SALIGNAC DE LA MOTHE FÉNELON (F. de) *Archbishop of Cambray.* The Christian Pilgrimage . . . Made English by Mrs. J. Barker, *etc.* 1718. 12°. **4410. g. 48.**

—— *See* STANGLMAIER (C.) Mrs. Jane Barker, *etc.* 1906. 8°. **011850. e. 33.**

—— The Entertaining Novels of Mrs. Jane Barker . . . The second edition. 2 vol. pp. 310. 64. *A. Bettesworth & E. Curll: London,* 1719. 12°. **1076. e. 5.**

—— The third edition. 2 vol. *Bettesworth & Hitch; E. Curll: London,* 1736. 12°. **635. c. 4.**

—— Exilius; or, the Banish'd Roman. A new romance . . . written after the manner of Telemachus, *etc.* 2 pt. *E. Curll: London,* 1715. 12°. **012611. h. 25.**
The plate, representing Somerset House, inserted as a frontispiece, was first issued with "The Adventures of Rivella . . . by Sir Charles Lovemore" in 1714.

—— The Lining of the Patch-Work Screen; design'd for the farther entertainment of the ladies. pp. 201. *A. Bettesworth: London,* 1726. 12°. **12611. e. 4.**

—— Love Intrigues: or, the History of the amours of Bosvil and Galesia, as related to Lucasia . . . A novel. Written by a young lady. [The dedication signed: J. B., i.e. J. Barker.] pp. 71. 1713. 8°. *See* B., J. **11646. ccc. 17.**

—— A Patch-Work Screen for the Ladies; or, Love and Virtue recommended: in a collection of instructive novels, *etc.* pp. viii. 143. *E. Curll . . . and T. Payne: London,* 1723. 12°. **1079. d. 13.**

—— Poetical Recreations: consisting of original poems, songs, odes &c. with several new translations. In two parts. Part I. Occasionally written by Mrs. Jane Barker. Part II. By several Gentlemen of the Universities, and others. pp. 287. *For Benjamin Crayle: London,* 1688. 8°. **994. g. 3.**

BARKER (JEMIMA) Poems, on miscellaneous subjects. pp. 145. x. *Lupton Relfe: London,* 1822. 8°. **994. f. 2.**

BARKER (JESSIE M.) Mary Elwood. A novel. 2 vol. *Remington & Co.: London,* 1884. 8°. **12619. p. 2.**

—— Our Boy. A story. pp. 249. *Roper & Drowley: London,* 1888. 8°. **12807. m. 19.**

BARKER (JOHN) *Ballad-writer.* A Balade declaryng how neybourhed love, and trew dealyng is gone. B.L. *Richard Lant: London,* [1561.] *s. sh.* fol. Huth **50. (5.)**

—— The Plagues of Northomberland. To the tune of Appelles. [A ballad. With woodcuts.] B.L. *Thomas Colwell: London,* [1570.] *s. sh.* fol. Huth **50. (20.)**

—— The true description of a monsterous Chylde, Borne in the Ile of wight, in this present yeare of oure Lord God, M.D.LXIIII. the month of October, after this forme with a cluster of longe heare about the Nauell, the Fathers name is Iames Iohnsun, in the parys of Freswater. [A ballad. With a woodcut.] B.L. *William Gryffith: London,* [1564.] *s. sh.* fol. Huth **50. (40.)**

BARKER (JOHN) *Baptist Minister, of Lockwood.* "A Good Minister of Jesus Christ." An address delivered to the students of the Northern Baptist Education Society, Rawdon College, Leeds, *etc.* pp. 16. *J. E. Wheatley & Co.: Huddersfield,* 1870. 8°. **4477. bb. 76. (19.)**

BARKER (JOHN) *Colonel.* Extraordinary Newes from Colonell Iohn Barkeer Governour of Coventry, to a merchant of London. Shewing how Sir William Brereton hath raised the siege from Namptwich in Cheshire. *E. G. for John Rothwell: London,* 1643. *s. sh.* fol. **669. f. 8. (45.)**

BARKER (JOHN) *Consul-General at Aleppo.* Syria and Egypt under the last five Sultans of Turkey: being experiences, during fifty years, of Mr. Consul-General Barker. Chiefly from his letters and journals, edited by his son, Edward B. B. Barker. [With a portrait.] 2 vol. *Samuel Tinsley: London,* 1876. 8°. **10815. ee. 1.**

BARKER (JOHN) *Lieutenant, of the King's Own Regiment.* The British in Boston, being the diary of Lieutenant John Barker of the King's Own Regiment from November 15, 1774 to May 31, 1776; with notes by Elizabeth Ellery Dana. [With plates.] pp. x. 73. *Harvard University Press: Cambridge* [*Mass.*], 1924. 8°. **010409. eee. 27.**

—— *See* PORTER (Edward G.) Remarks concerning the Recent Visit of Lieutenant General George Digby Barker, C.B. and the Diary of Lieutenant John Barker . . . during the siege of Boston, *etc.* 1898. 8°. **10600. g. 7. (2.)**

BARKER (JOHN) *M.A., Ph.D.*

—— *See* BLACKMAN (Frederick F.) Analytic Studies in Plant Respiration. [Edited by J. Barker.] 1954. 8°. **7036. d. 5.**

—— *See* MORRIS (Thomas N.) The Preservation of Fruit and Vegetables by Freezing. By T. N. Morris . . . J. Barker, *etc.* 1948. 8°. [*Department of Scientific and Industrial Research. Food Investigation Board. Leaflet.* no. 2.] B.S. **38.** d/4. **(2.)**

BARKER (JOHN) *M.A., Ph.D.*, and **FURLONG** (CECIL ROY)

—— The Conditioning of Imported Plums and Pears. pp. 9. *London,* 1937. 8°. [*Department of Scientific and Industrial Research. Food Investigation Leaflet.* no. 7.] B.S. **38.** d/4.

BARKER (JOHN) *M.A., Ph.D.*, and **MORRIS** (THOMAS NORMAN)

—— The Preservation of Fruit and Vegetables by Freezing. pp. 9. *London,* 1932. 8°. [*Department of Scientific and Industrial Research. Food Investigation Board. Leaflet.* no. 2.] B.S. **38.** d/4.
A revision of this pamphlet is entered under Morris (Thomas Norman).

BARKER (JOHN) *M.D.* A Defence of a Late Treatise intitled, An Inquiry into the nature, cause and cure, of the present epidemick fever. In answer to the objections of Dr. Henry Hele. In which the rise and progress of the controversy on this subject, is explain'd. Together with an appendix. Containing all the papers, relating to it, which have hitherto been printed. pp. xii. 53. 12. *B. Collins; E. Easton: Sarum*, 1743. 8°. T. **246**. (**2**.)

—— An Essay on the Agreement betwixt ancient and modern Physicians: or a Comparison between the practice of Hippocrates, Galen, Sydenham, and Boerhaave, in acute diseases, *etc.* pp. xii. 290. *G. Hawkins: London*, 1747. 8°. **550**. c. **17**.

—— Essai sur la conformité de la médecine ancienne et moderne dans le traitement des maladies aiguës. Traduit . . . par M. Schomberg . . . Nouvelle édition, revue, corrigée & augmentée par M. Lorry. pp. lxvi. 426. *Paris*, 1768. 8°. **774**. e. **28**.

—— An Inquiry into the Nature, Cause and Cure of the present Epidemick Fever . . . In a letter to a physician. [By J. Barker.] pp. 128. 1742. 8°. *See* ENQUIRY. T. **246**. (**1**.)

BARKER (JOHN) *of Coleshill.* Epidemicks, or, General Observations on the air and diseases, from the year 1740, to 1777 inclusive; and particular ones from that time to the beginning of 1795, *etc.* pp. 232. *E. Piercy: Birmingham; T. Longman: London*, [1796.] 8°. **7561**. bbb. **47**. (**4**.)

—— A Final Answer to the Editor of Benj. Ben Mordecai's Letters, and in particular to his eighth letter, called "An Inquiry into the opinions of the learned Christians" &c. . . . By the author of "The Harmony of the Truth" [i.e. J. Barker]. pp. 112. [1778?] 4°. *See* BENJAMIN BEN MORDECAI. **108**. c. **61**.

—— The Harmony of the Truth; an absolute confutation of all infidelity, addressed to Mr. L——y [i.e. Theophilus Lindsey], on the publication of the Sequel to the Apology: being chiefly a comment on . . . the Author's Reply to the Author of the Remarks [i.e. Anthony Temple] in a Scriptural Confutation [by William Burgh] of the Apology; with some strictures on the Critical and London Reviewers, *etc.* [By J. Barker.] pp. 55. 1786. 8°. *See* L——Y, *Mr.* **1016.f.21.**

—— The Nature of Inoculation explained, and its merits stated, *etc.* [By J. Barker.] pp. xi. 38. 1769. 8°. *See* NATURE. **7561**. bbb. **47**. (**1**.)

—— Observations on a late Publication on Cheltenham Water: and on some remarks of the Cr——l R——rs upon a treatise on that subject. pp. 20. *Pearson & Rollaston: Birmingham*, 1787. 8°. **7561**. bbb. **47**. (**3**.)

—— A Treatise on Cheltenham Water, and its great use in the present pestilential constitution, *etc.* pp. 83. *Pearson & Rollaston: Birmingham*, 1786. 8°. **7470**. ee. **3**.

—— A Treatise on the Putrid Constitution of 1777 and the preceding years, and the pestilential one of 1778 . . . Also, of the causes of disease in general, *etc.* pp. 96. *Pearson & Rollaston: Birmingham*, 1779. 8°. **7561**. bbb. **47**. (**2**.)

BARKER (JOHN) *Rev. See* TOMS (Isaac) The Christian Instructor . . . With a recommendatory preface by . . . J. Barker and . . . S. Chandler. 1748. 12°. **873**. e. **16**.

—— Sermons on the following subjects; viz. Of the Worth of the Soul, and the Folly of losing it, *etc.* pp. 313. *R. Hett; J. Buckland: London*, 1748. 8°. **1021**. c. 22.

—— The second edition. pp. 339. *James Buckland: London*, 1764. 8°. **4453**. bb. 7.

BARKER (JOHN) *Rev.*

—— Sermons on the following subjects: viz. The Resurrection of Christ illustrated, and improved . . . Vol. II. pp. 340. *James Buckland: London*, 1763. 8°. **4453**. bb. **31**.

—— Charity recommended upon the Motives and Incouragements of Christianity: a sermon, *etc.* pp. 35. *R. Hett: London*, 1740. 8°. **4474**. cc. **117**. (**2**.)

—— Conversion, the Act of Christ, an obligation to service, and an encouragement to prayer. A sermon, *etc.* pp. 34. *J. & B. Clark: London*, 1723. 12°. **4473**. e. **12**. (**2**.)

—— Death a True Christian's Gain. A sermon occasion'd by the death of . . . Mr. John Gledhill, *etc.* pp. 40. *J. Clark & R. Hett: London*, 1728. 8°. **4476**. ee. **8**. (**6**.)

—— The End of Created Perfection. A funeral sermon for the late Reverend Mr. Samuel Newman . . . By John Barker. To which is added, the Speech at the Grave. By Obadiah Hughes. pp. viii. 32. *Richard Hett: London*, 1735. 8°. **1418**. e. **31**.

—— [Another copy.] **1418**. e. **32**.

—— A Funeral Sermon for John Jacob, Esq., *etc.* pp. 32. *London*, 1738. 8°. **1415**. k. **26**.

—— [Another copy.] **1415**. k. **27**.

—— Of the Prevailing Love of Pleasure. *See* PROTESTANT SYSTEM. The Protestant System, *etc.* vol. 2. 1758. 8°. **3751**. c. **13**.

—— Popery the Great Corruption of Christianity. A sermon, *etc.* pp. 34. *Richard Hett: London*, 1735. 8°. **4475**. de. **5**. (**7**.)

—— The third edition. pp. 34. *Richard Hett: London*, 1735. 8°. **3936**. c. **6**.

—— The fourth edition. pp. 32. *Richard Hett: London*, 1735. 8°. **4474**. c. **25**.

—— *See* CHANDLER (Samuel) *D.D.* A Letter from a Friend to S. Chandler . . . With some remarks on Mr. Barker's sermon [against Popery], *etc.* 1735. 12°. **3940**. h. **5**. (**1**.)

—— *See* PHILALETHES, *pseud.* [i.e. Richard Challoner.] A Specimen of the Spirit of the Dissenting Teachers . . . or some remarks upon Mr. John Barker's sermon against Popery, *etc.* 1736. 12°. **3935**. a. **33**.

—— Preparation to meet God in the Way of his Judgments, the present duty of Christians. A sermon, *etc.* pp. 28. *John Clark: London*, 1720. 8°. **4474**. cc. **117**. (**1**.)

—— Resignation to the Will of God, consider'd, in a funeral sermon for the late Reverend Mr. John Newman . . . By John Barker . . . To which is added, the substance of what was delivered at his interment, with the addition of some particulars . . . By P. Dodderidge. pp. 41. *R. Hett: London*, 1741. 8°. **1418**. e. **30**.

—— A Sermon, occasioned by the death of the Reverend Benjamin Grosvenor, *etc.* pp. 40. *J. Buckland: London*, 1758. 8°. **1416**. h. **24**.

—— [Another copy.] **1416**. h. **25**.

—— [Another copy.] T. **1691**. (**3**.)

—— A Sermon, preach'd to the Societies for Reformation of Manners, at Salters-Hall, *etc.* pp. 24. *Eman. Matthews: London*, 1721. 8°. **695**. f. **1**. (**3**.)

BARKER (John) *Rev.*

—— To Walk in Newness of Life, the great duty of Christians. A sermon, *etc.* pp. 30. *R. Hett: London,* 1735. 8°. **1112**. e. **20**. (**2**.)

—— [Another copy.] **225**. h. **20**. (**6**.)

BARKER (John) *Vicar of St. Mary's, Hull. See* Walker (Samuel) *Curate of Truro.* Ten Sermons . . . With a recommendatory preface by the Rev. Mr. Barker. 1790. 12°. **4461**. aa. **29**.

BARKER (John Albert) Present-Day Commercial French Correspondence. pp. 96. *G. Routledge & Sons: London,* [1920.] 8°. **12951**. aaa. **28**.

BARKER (John Barnett)

—— The Pedigree of Barker, formerly of Horton, Co. Chester. Re-arranged by Major J. B. Barker. pp. 9. *Mitchell & Hughes: London,* 1903. 4°. **09917**. df. **24**.

BARKER (John Crawford) The Education of the Poor . . . A sermon, *etc.* pp. 15. *Free Press: Grenada,* 1828. 8°. [*Fourth Annual Report of the Society for the Education of the Poor.*] **8306**. e. **3**.

BARKER (John E.)

—— *See* Charley (Fr.) The New Opera Glass, *etc.* [Extracts from the fourth edition of the work originally by J. E. Barker, and revised by Fr. Charley, *etc.*] 1951. 8°. **7900**. m. **11**.

—— The New Opera Glass, containing the plots of the popular operas and a short biography of the composers. pp. vii. 91. *K. F. Pfau: Leipzig,* 1887. 8°. **7898**. bbb. **5**.

BARKER (John E.) *Methodist Minister.*

—— 'Yea, Lord.' Evangelism within the Church. pp. 71. *Epworth Press: London,* 1949. 8°. **4480**. ee. **70**.

BARKER (John G.) Early History and Transactions of the Grand Lodge of Free and Accepted Masons of the State of New York, 1781–1815. [Compiled by J. G. Barker.] pp. xl. 587. 1876. 8°. *See* Freemasons.—*Grand Lodge of the State of New York.* **04785**. l. **21**.

BARKER (John Henry) The Story of the Marsh Gibbon Group of Congregational Churches, *etc.* pp. 80. *Marshall, Morgan & Scott: London & Edinburgh,* [1933.] 8°. **04715**. de. **41**.

BARKER (John Henry James)

—— Chastening. A word to Christian people who are perplexed by suffering. pp. 18. *Epworth Press: London,* [1939.] 12°. **04402**. fff. **110**.

—— The Five Crucifixions in the Epistle to the Galatians. pp. 16. *The Author: Buckie,* [1940.] 16°. **3265**. de. **18**.

—— This is the Will of God. A study in the doctrine of entire sanctification as a definite experience. pp. 110. *Epworth Press: London,* 1954. 8°. **4409**. p. **25**.

BARKER (John J. S.) Barker's Assessment Tables, *etc.* pp. 15. *Hadden, Best & Co.; Shaw & Sons: London,* [1929.] *obl.* 8°. **8548**. aaa. **83**.

—— Barker's Assistant Overseers' and Rate Collectors' Calculator, *etc.* pp. 101. *Shaw & Sons: London,* [1919.] fol. **8534**. h. **13**.

—— Barker's "PN" Calculator. Showing the number of persons "permitted to use a house for sleeping," as provided by the First Schedule, Table II of the Housing Act, 1935. [A folding card.] *Hadden, Best & Co.: London,* [1935.] 8°. **6425**. t. **9**.

BARKER (John J. S.)

—— Barker's Rent-Rate Tables, *etc.* pp. 26. *Hadden, Best & Co.: London,* [1933.] *obl.* 8°. **8548**. ccc. **36**.

—— Rates Apportionment Tables, *etc.* pp. 27. *Hadden, Best & Co.: London,* [1929.] *obl.* 8°. **8548**. ccc. **35**.

—— Sq. Yards as Decimal of One Acre. [A table.] *A. M. Brown: So. Shields,* [1930.] 8°. **08548**. a. **24**.

BARKER (John Marshall) Colleges in America . . . With an introduction by Rev. S. F. Scovel. pp. 265. *Cleveland Publishing Co.: Cleveland, O.,* 1894. 8°. **8385**. aa. **5**.

—— Semi-centennial Sketch of the Ohio Wesleyan University. pp. 36. *Oak Hill Publishing Co.: Delaware, O.,* 1894. 8°. **8365**. aa. **24**.

—— The Social Gospel and the New Era. pp. ix. 232. *Macmillan Co.: New York,* 1919. 8°. **04375**. e. **8**.

BARKER (John Richard) Rust, Roses and Rue. [Poems.] pp. 211. *Andrew Melrose: London,* [1918.] 8°. **011648**. f. **40**.

BARKER (John Robert Kean) British Kaffrarian Bank. (Reprinted from the "Queenstown Free Press.") pp. 19. *"Free Press": Queenstown, South Africa,* 1901. 8°. **08226**. h. **57**. (**15**.)

—— Inconvertible Paper Money. A review of some of the currency and financial episodes in the history of South Africa . . . Reprinted from the "Journal of the Institute of Bankers in South Africa," *etc.* pp. 27. *Capetown,* [1920.] 8°. **08228**. aaa. **38**.

—— London & South African Bank. (Reprinted from the "Queenstown Free Press.") pt. 1. pp. 32. *"Free Press": Queenstown, South Africa,* 1901. 8°. **8248**. ee. **26**.

—— Mr. Sidney Mendelssohn. The "South African Bibliography." (Reprint from "The Star.") [Signed: J. R. K. B., i.e. J. R. K. Barker.] [1918.] *s. sh.* 8°. *See* B., J. R. K. **1865**. c. **3**. (**128**.)

—— Queenstown Mutual Building Society. Its origin and development. (Reprinted from the "Queenstown Free Press.") pp. 11. *"Free Press": Queenstown* [*South Africa*], 1900. 8°. **08226**. h. **51**. (**8**.)

—— Standard Bank of South Africa, Limited. (Reprinted from the "Queenstown Free Press.") pt. 1. pp. 32. *"Free Press": Queenstown, South Africa,* 1901. 8°. **8248**. ee. **25**.

BARKER (John Stevenson) Games for the Playground . . . With preface by Dr. Alfred A. Mumford . . . With twenty-five illustrations. pp. xxii. 65. *Longmans & Co.: London,* 1910. 8°. **7911**. bbb. **12**.

BARKER (John Stewart Scott) The Shooting of Field Artillery, *etc.* pp. 18. [1892.] 8°. *See* Ireland.—*Military Society of Ireland.* **8828**. bb. **48**.

BARKER (John Theodore) *First of the Name, Congregational Minister at Deptford.* "Jehovah-Shammah," the true glory of a Christian Church. A discourse, *etc.* pp. 33. *Josiah Conder: London,* 1812. 8°. **4473**. cc. **15**. (**7**.)

—— Prayer for the Life of the King. The outlines of a discourse, *etc.* pp. 32. *Samuel McDowall: London,* [1809.] 8°. **4475**. cc. **6**.

BARKER (John Theodore) *First of the Name, Congregational Minister at Deptford.*

—— The Ship Launch. The substance of a sermon, preached at Deptford on occasion of the launching of the Queen Charlotte, July 17. 1810. pp. 47. *T. Conder: London,* [1810.] 8°. **4473**. e. **6**. **(6.)**

BARKER (John Theodore) *Second of the Name, Schoolmaster. See* Ephemerides. Time's Telescope, *etc.* [1830–34 by J. T. Barker.] 1814, *etc.* 8°. P.P. **2479**. a.

—— The Beauty of Flowers in Field and Wood: containing the natural orders or families of British wild plants, *etc.* [With plates.] pp. xii. 228. *Binns & Goodwin: Bath,* [1852.] 8°. **7030**. c. **5**.

BARKER (John Theodore) *Third of the Name, Congregational Minister at Louth.* A Brief Memoir of Mr. John Gray, of Louth . . . To which is added, an obituary of his brother Mr. Edward Gray. pp. 31. *D. Marples: Liverpool,* 1849. 8°. **4903**. de. **26**. (2.)

—— Congregationalism in Lincolnshire. A paper, *etc.* pp. 60. *Judd & Glass: London,* 1860. 8°. **4715**. b. **14**.

BARKER (John Thomas) *See* Barker (Joseph) *Preacher.* The Life of Joseph Barker . . . Edited by . . . J. T. Barker, *etc.* 1880. 8°. **4920**. ee. **8**.

—— The Pilgrimage of Memory: a romance of the Yorkshire moors; and other poems. pp. viii. 203. *Simpkin, Marshall & Co.: London; Walker & Laycock: Leeds,* [1886.] 16°. **11652**. a. **84**.

BARKER (John William) *M.A., Ph.D.*

—— *See* Edwards (Percival) **and** Barker (J. W.) Ejercicios de Gramática Española para principiantes. 1923. 8°. **012942**. **c**. **10**.

—— *See* Góngora y Argote (L. de) Poesías: Polifemo. Soledades and other poems. Edited with an introduction by J. W. Barker. 1942. 8°. **11453**. aa. **13**.

—— *See* Rojas Zorrilla (F. de) García del Castañar. Edited, with introduction, by J. W. Barker. 1935. 8°. **2322**. bb. **48**.

—— *See* Vega Carpio (L. F. de) [*Plays.—Separate Plays.*] El Remedio en la Desdicha. Edited . . . by J. W. Barker. 1931. 8°. **12204**. d. **5/77**.

—— Notas sobre la Influencia de Quevedo en la Literatura Inglesa. [An offprint from "Boletín de la Biblioteca de Menéndez Pelayo."] *Santander,* 1945. 8°. **11866**. cc. **19**.

—— Sidgwick & Jackson's New Term Portuguese Texts. General editor: J. W. Barker. *Sidgwick & Jackson: London,* 1935– . 8°. **12943.e.34.**

—— Sidgwick & Jackson's New Term Spanish Texts. General editor: J. W. Barker. Ipt. *Sidgwick & Jackson: London,* 1933–35. 8°. **12944.aa.41.**

—— Teach Yourself Portuguese. [With plates.] pp. 196. *Hodder & Stoughton: [London,]* 1945. 8°. [*E.U.P. Teach Yourself Books.*] W.P. **706/57**.

BARKER (John William) *Professor of Chemistry, Wittenberg College,* and **GLASOE** (Paul Kirkwold)

—— First Year College Chemistry. pp. x. 501. *McGraw-Hill Book Co.: New York,* 1951. 8°. **08909**. ppp. **15**.

BARKER (Johnson) *Congregational Minister. See* Barker (Thomas W. J.)

BARKER (Johnson) *Curate of All Saints', Wandsworth.* A Digest of Deductive Logic, *etc.* pp. viii. 161. *Methuen & Co.: London,* 1897. 8°. **8470**. ccc. **22**.

—— Holy Scripture the Classic of Religion. I. Its authenticity and authority. II. Its study and interpretation. Two sermons, *etc.* pp. 15. *Elliot Stock: London,* 1886. 8°. **4473**. d. **9**. **(12.)**

—— [Another copy.] **4478**. d. **82**. (5.)

BARKER (Joseph) *A.M., Pastor of the First Church in Middleborough.* A Discourse delivered in Middleborough, Mass. . . . the day of the National Fast. pp. 24. *S. T. Armstrong: Boston,* 1812. 8°. **4486**. f. **14**.

—— On the Unity of Christ's Church. A sermon, *etc.* *Lincoln & Edmands: Boston,* 1807. 8°. **4486**. dd. **2**.

—— A Sermon, preached before the Massachusetts Missionary Society, at their annual meeting, *etc.* pp. 21. *Haven Pool: Salem,* 1806. 8°. **4486**. f. **13**.

—— The Stability of Christ's Church. A century sermon, preached at Middleboro', January 6, 1795, *etc.* pp. 31. *J. Bumstead: Boston,* 1796. 8°. **4487**. dd. **7**. (7.)

BARKER (Joseph) *Farmer, of Brandon, Vermont.* An Interesting Narrative . . . of the Sufferings of Mr. Joseph Barker and his wife Martha, who were taken by a scouting party of British and Indians . . . in the year 1777. pp. 16. *W. E. Hutchins: Rochester, N.Y.,* 1836. 8°. **9602**. c. **12**.

BARKER (Joseph) *of the Community of the Resurrection.*

—— Grace. pp. 68. *Dacre Press: Westminster,* 1945. 8°. [*Mirfield Books.*] W.P. **729/1**.

—— Intercommunion. Is there any objection? pp. 7. *Pax House: London,* [1941.] 8°. **20046**. aa. **33**.

—— The Sacrifice of the People. pp. 74. *Dacre Press: Westminster,* 1948. 8°. [*Mirfield Books.*] W.P. **729/6**.

—— Sacrificial Priesthood. Historical origins and developments. pp. 40. *Dacre Press: London,* 1941. 8°. **4431.b.50.**

—— Yet Trouble Came. pp. 63. *Dennis Dobson: London,* 1946. 8°. **4398**. aa. **128**.

BARKER (Joseph) *Preacher.* The Abominations of Socialism exposed, in reply to the Gateshead Observer. pp. 12. *J. Blackwell & Co.: Newcastle,* [1840.] 12°. **8276**. a. **3**.

—— *See* Buchanan (Robert) *Social Missionary.* An Exposure of the Falshoods . . . of a pamphlet entitled "The Abominations of Socialism exposed" being a refutation of the charges . . . of . . . J. Barker. [1841?] 12°. **1350**. b. **16**. **(2.)**

—— An Account of J. Barker's Visit to Ireland, with outlines of his lectures, &c. pp. 24. [*Newcastle,* 1845.] 12°. **4224**. b. **82**. (2.)

—— All War Anti-Christian. pp. 12. [*J. Barker: Newcastle,* 1840?] 12°. **1355**. c. **62**. (2.)

—— [Another copy.] **4139**. bbb. **25**. (4*.)

—— The American Question. A lecture delivered . . . in answer to the speeches delivered by the Hon. and Rev. B. Noel, Dr. Massey, and others, in the Free-Trade Hall, Manchester, *etc.* [By J. Barker.] pp. 8. [1863.] 8°. *See* American Question. **8177**. aa. **36**.

—— The American Question. A speech delivered . . . at Burnley, in reply to Messrs. Dennison and Sinclair. [By J. Barker.] pp. 8. [1863.] 8°. See American Question. **8156**. a. **24**.

—— The American Question. Mediation, intervention, recognition. A lecture, *etc.* pp. 8. *Barker & Co.: London,* [1863.] 8°. **8177.** aa. **10.**

—— An Answer to the Question, How did you become an infidel? With some account of my religious experience. pp. 28. *Holyoake & Co.: London,* [1859.] 8°. **4427.** d. **7.** (**4.**)

—— Answers to Questions with regard to large families, &c. pp. 15. *Barker & Co.: London,* [1863.] 8°. **7640.** b. **2.**

—— Aristocracy and Democracy. The speech of Mr. Barker at the Bolton Tea Party . . . September 28, 1848. pp. 8. *J. Barker: Wortley,* [1848.] 4°. P.P. **3612.** am. (**4.**)

—— The Atonement. [A series of tracts, by J. Barker.] 5 pt. [1845?] 12°. *See* Atonement. **4226.** b. **9.**

—— The Atonement; on God's way of speaking, and man's way of speaking. [By J. Barker.] From the Christian Investigator. Second edition. [Edited by Francis Bishop.] pp. 11. 1843. 12°. *See* Atonement. **4224.** aaa. **26.**

—— The Blessings of Free Trade, and how they may be increased and made lasting, a speech delivered at the Wortley Free Trade rejoicing dinner . . . July 27, 1846. pp. 24. [*Wortley,* 1846.] 12°. **8246.** a. **39.** (**3.**)

—— Both Sides of the Question: or, Three letters, two to Joseph Meir . . . and another to John Ridgway . . . containing answers to various charges preferred against the author, in the Hanley Quarterly Meeting, together with observations on the present policy of the leading officials in the New Connexion. pp. 24. *J. Blackwell & Co.: Newcastle,* [1841.] 12°. **1355.** c. **63.** (**5.**)

—— [Another copy.] **4139.** bbb. **24.** (**8*.**)

—— The Cause of the Distress at present prevailing in Great Britain and Ireland, and the means by which that distress may be cured, *etc.* [By J. Barker.] pp. 48. [1845?] 12°. *See* England. [*Appendix.—Miscellaneous.*] **8276.** a. **16.**

—— The Character and Tendency of the Christian Religion, a discourse. pt. 1. pp. 24. *T. Scott: Sheffield,* 1833. 12°. **4476.** aa. **3.**

—— [Another edition.] The Character and Tendency of Christianity. 4 pt. pp. 90. *Chapman & Bros.: London,* [1846?] 12°. **4016.** a. **5.**

—— Christian Liberty, and Evangelical Reform. pp. 12. *J. Barker: Newcastle,* 1847. 12°. **4377.** aa. **40.** (**2.**)

—— Christian Perfection. A discourse. pp. 72. *R. Groombridge: London,* 1840. 12°. **1355.** f. **27.** (**1.**)

—— [Another copy.] **4139.** bbb. **24.** (**1*.**)
Without the wrapper.

—— The Church and the Press: or the Duty of Christians to make a more liberal use of the unbounded powers which God, by means of the printing press, has put into their hands: exhibited in a correspondence between Joseph Barker and the Annual Committee of the Methodist New Connexion. pp. 42. *Blackwell & Co.: Newcastle,* [1841.] 12°. **4136.** de. **1.** (**10.**)

—— [Another copy.] **4139.** bbb. **24.** (**7*.**)

—— Confessions of Joseph Barker, a convert from Christianity. Reprinted from the "Reasoner," *etc.* pp. 16. *Holyoake & Co.: London,* 1858. 8°. **4014.** c. **6.**

—— The Deceitfulness of Sin, or, the madness of procrastination. A sermon. pp. 24. *J. Livesey: Preston,* [1840?] 12°. **1358.** c. **88.**

—— A Discourse on Christian Perfection. *See* supra: Christian Perfection, *etc.*

—— The Drink Trade and the Temperance Movement. pp. 8. *Barker & Co.: London,* [1863.] 8°. **8435.** aa. **25.**

—— The Duty of Christian Churches to provide for their Poor Members, and the impropriety of professing Christians connecting themselves with benefit societies, *etc.* pp. 24. *J. Blackwell & Co.: Newcastle,* [1840?] 12°. **1355.** c. **63.** (**1.**)

—— [Another copy.] **4139.** bbb. **24.** (**2*.**)

—— The Duty of Parents with respect to the Religious Education of their Children. pp. 84. *C. Gilpin & Co.: London,* [1845?] 12°. **4409.** d. **9.**

—— Education. pp. 24. *Barker & Co.: London,* [1863.] 8°. **8309.** c. **27.**

—— An Essay on the "Essays and Reviews," *etc.* pp. 104. *Barker & Co.: London,* [1863.] 8°. **4373.** aaa. **44.** (**5.**)

—— A Few Discoveries which people will make if they set fairly to work to investigate the question as to the divine authority of the Bible. pp. 16. *Barker & Co.: London,* [1863.] 8°. **4016.** b. **4.**

—— A Full Account of the Arrest, Imprisonment, and Liberation on bail, of Joseph Barker: together with an account of his triumphant election for the borough of Bolton. pp. 8. *J. Barker: Wortley,* [1848.] 4°. P.P. **3612.** am. (**2.**)

—— The Happy Tendency and Final Triumph of the Christian Religion. [By J. Barker?] pp. 20. [1845?] 12°. *See* Christian Religion. **4015.** a. **12.**

—— Health, and the Laws of Health. [By J. Barker.] pp. 40. [1863.] 8°. *See* Health. **7390.** aa. **18.**

—— Hell. [By J. Barker.] pp. 27. [1863.] 8°. *See* Hell. **4418.** ee. **37.**

—— The History and Confessions of a Man, as put forth by himself, *etc.* [By J. Barker.] vol. 1. pp. 422. 1846. 12°. *See* History. **4920.** bb. **39.**

—— The Life of Joseph Barker. Written by himself. Edited by . . . John Thomas Barker. With steel portrait. [Being "The History and Confessions of a Man," with a continuation.] pp. xiv. 385. *Hodder & Stoughton: London,* 1880. 8°. **4920.** ee. **8.**

—— Human Progress. pp. 30. [*Barker & Co.: London,* 1863.] 8°. **8464.** a. **18.**

—— The Imperfections of the Bible. pp. 16. *Holyoake & Co.: London,* 1858. 8°. **4372.** df. **7.** (**2.**)

—— The Influence of Christianity. Report of a public discussion which took place at Oldham February 19th and 20th, 1839. between the Rev. J. Barker . . . and Mr. Lloyd Jones . . . Social Missionary, on the influence of Christianity. Revised by the disputants. pp. 216. *Cave & Sever: Manchester,* 1839. 12°. **4016.** a. **6.**

—— The Influence of the Bible on Sciences, Art, and Literature. pp. 16. [*Barker & Co.: London,* 1863.] 8°. **4014.** cc. **2.**

—— Inspiration,—Infallibility, &c. [By J. Barker.] pp. 23 [1845?] 12°. *See* Inspiration. **4139.** bbb. **25.** (**12.**)

—— J. Barker's Address to his Belfast Friends. pp. 24. [*Newcastle,* 1845.] 12°. **4224.** b. **82.** (**1.**)

—— [Another issue.] **4139.** bbb. **25.** (**10.**)

—— Lectures on the Church of England Prayer Book. pp. xii. 392. *Joseph Barker: Wortley*, 1847. 12°. **3478.** c. **35.**

—— Letter to J. Carveth, Wesleyan Association travelling preacher. pp. 44. [*Newcastle*, 1845?] 12°. **4224.** b. **82.** (**3.**)

—— Letters to J. J. Gurney, containing remarks on his views of the Atonement, imputed righteousness, *etc.* pp. 24. *J. Barker: Newcastle*, [1840?] 12°. **4226.** b. **11.**

—— The Life of Joseph Barker, *etc.* *See* supra: The History and Confessions of a Man.

—— Life of William Penn, the celebrated Quaker and Founder of Pennsylvania. pp. 320. *J. Chapman: London; Joseph Barker: Wortley*, 1847. 8°. **4903.** bb. **7.**

—— Love and Marriage; or, the Way to Domestic Happiness. pp. 40. *Barker & Co.: London*, [1863.] 8°. **8415.** b. **36.**

—— Love and Marriage, *etc.* pp. 32. *James Beveridge: London*, [1868?] 8°. **8418.** b. **14.**

—— Memoirs of Several Eminent Christians, lately members of the Methodist New Connexion, Mossley Circuit. pp. 82. *R. Groombridge: London*, 1839. 12°. **1373.** b. **7.** (**1.**)

—— [Another copy.] **4139.** bbb. **24.** (**1.**)

—— Mercy Triumphant; or, Teaching the children of the poor to write on the Sabbath Day, proved to be in perfect agreement with the Oracles of God, *etc.* pp. 36. *R. Groombridge: London*, [1840.] 18°. **1353.** b. **54.** (**2.**)

—— I. Might and Right. II. A Few Words to a Young Student. pp. 16. *Barker & Co.: London*, [1863.] 8°. **8464.** a. **19.**

—— Noah's Flood. pp. 16. *Barker & Co.: London*, [1863.] 8°. **3155.** bb. **46.**

—— The Oath Question; or, the New Inquisition. pp. 8. *Barker & Co.: London*, [1863.] 8°. **6281.** aa. **4.**

—— Objections to Peace-Principles answered. pp. 12. [*Newcastle*, 1840?] 12°. **1355.** c. **62.** (**1.**)

—— The Obligations of Christians to seek the Salvation of their Fellow-men. A sermon. pp. 24. *Cave & Sever: Manchester*, [1840?] 12°. **1355.** c. **62.** (**3.**)

—— Origin and Authority of the Bible. Report of a public discussion between J. Barker, Esq., and the Rev. Brewin Grant, held at Halifax, *etc.* pp. 439. *Robert Stark: Glasgow*, [1855]. 12°. **4014.** f. **5.**

—— Orthodoxy and Heterodoxy, or a Correspondence between J. Barker and one of his old Methodistical friends [i.e. Samuel Phillips]. pp. 63. [*Newcastle*, 1845?] 12°. **4224.** b. **82.** (**4.**)

—— [Another copy.] **4139.** bbb. **25.** (**1*.**)

—— The Overthrow of Infidel Socialism; or the Gospel & infidel socialism contrasted. pp. 72. *R. Groombridge: London*, [1840?] 12°. **4016.** a. **7.**

—— Fourth thousand. pp. 72. *R. Groombridge: London*, [1840?] 12°. **1350.** b. **23.** (**3.**)

—— The Popular Imperfections of the Bible. A speech, *etc.* pp. 24. *James Watson: London*, 1853. 12°. **4014.** e. **4.**

—— Principles of Evangelical Reform. [By J. Barker.] pp. 8. [1845?] 12°. *See* PRINCIPLES. **4139.** bbb. **25.** (**2.**)

—— Proposal for a new Library, of three hundred volumes, *etc.* pp. 8. [*Wortley*, 1846.] 8°. **11826.** bbb. **12.**

—— A Review of the Bible. [By J. Barker.] pp. 93. 1848. 8°. *See* BIBLE.—*Appendix.* [*Miscellaneous.*] **4016.** a. **8.**

—— A Review of the Bible, *etc.* [By J. Barker.] pp. 96. 1848. 12°. *See* BIBLE.—*Appendix.* [*Miscellaneous.*] **3130.** a. **71.** (**2.**)

—— A Review of the 'Elements of Social Science' [by George Drysdale]. pp. 38. *Barker & Co.: London*, [1863.] 8°. **7640.** b. **3.**

—— Saving Faith, or the way of salvation made plain. [By J. Barker.] 2 pt. [1845?] 12°. *See* FAITH. **4139.** bbb. **25.** (**5.**)

—— The Scripture Doctrine of Justification. A sermon. pp. 24. *Cave & Sever: Manchester*, [1841?] 12°. **1358.** c. **64.**

—— Self-Abasement and Self-Exaltation, *etc.* [Signed: J. B., i.e. J. Barker.] 2 pt. [1845?] 12°. *See* B., J. **4404.** cc. **2.**

—— Self-Culture. pp. 24. *Barker & Co.: London*, [1863.] 8°. **8408.** b. **23.**

—— Seven Lectures on the Supernatural Origin & Divine Authority of the Bible. By J. Barker. Containing his reply to the Rev. Mr. Sergeant, *etc.* pp. 120. *George Turner: Stoke-upon-Trent*, 1854. 12°. **3130.** a. **71.** (**1.**)

—— Slanders Refuted. [On his conduct of his printing business.] pp. 4. [*Wortley*, 1845.] 12°. **4406.** g. **1.** (**121.**)

—— The Socinianism, Infidelity and Blasphemy of Barkerism; letter to P. Budd, Methodist travelling preacher. pp. 12. [*Wortley*, 1845?] 12°. **4224.** b. **82.** (**5.**)

—— Teachings of Experience; or, Lessons I have learned on my way through life. pp. viii. 280. *James Beveridge: London*, 1869. 8°. **4906.** bbb. **27.**

—— Author's edition. pp. xii. 300. *E. W. Allen: London*, 1885. 8°. **4906.** d. **70.**

—— The Theistic Controversy. pp. 16. [*J. Barker & Co.: London*, 1860?] 8°. **4014.** cc. **3.**

—— Toleration, Human Creeds, &c. A letter to Thomas Allin, in reply to his letter to J. Barker. pp. 16. [*Newcastle*, 1841?] 8°. **1355.** c. **63.** (**3.**)

—— [Another copy.] **4139.** bbb. **24.** (**7**.**)

—— A Tract for the Times. First: the way to national wealth and greatness. Second: the English Constitution and speculative and practical reforms. Third: Economy. The great impending danger, and how to prepare for it. pp. 16. *Barker & Co.: London*, [1863.] 8°. **8408.** bb. **10.**

—— The Triumph of Right over Might; or, a full account of the attempt made by the Manchester magistrates . . . to rob J. Barker of his liberty, *etc.* pp. 8. *J. Barker: Wortley*, [1848.] 4°. P.P. **3612.** am. (**3.**)

—— True Religion. [By J. Barker.] 3 pt. [1845?] 12°. *See* RELIGION. **4139.** bbb. **25.** (**6.**)

—— A True Statement of Facts, in reply to T. Allin's brief & erroneous statements. pp. 11. *Nicholson & Wilson: Halifax*, [1840?] 12°. **1355.** c. **63.** (**2.**)

—— [Another copy.] **4139.** bbb. **24.** (**9*.**)

BARKER (JOSEPH) *Preacher.*

—— Truth against Misrepresentation: being a reply to the lectures of T. Allin and S. Hulme, in Wesley Chapel, Dudley. pp. 24. "*Courant*": *Newcastle*, [1841.] 12°. **1355**. c. **63**. (**4**.)

—— [Another copy.] **4139**. bbb. **24**. (**12***.)

—— Two Letters to the Church at Newcastle. pp. 24. *J. Barker: Newcastle upon Tyne*, [1843.] 12°. **4136**. de. **6**. (**7**.)

—— Water Baptism. A letter to Thomas Allin, *etc.* pp. 20. *J. Blackwell & Co.: Newcastle*, [1841.] 12°. **1355**. c. **61**. (**1**.)

—— The Way to be Happy. pp. 16. *Barker & Co.: London*, [1860?] 8°. **8408**. e. **24**.

—— Who are the Cowards and Deceivers? or, Extracts from correspondence between J. Barker, A. Dyson, and the Huddersfield Committee, and between J. Barker and W. Cooke, respecting a public discussion. [Edited by J. Barker.] pp. 24. *J. Barker: [Newcastle upon Tyne*, 1845.] 12°. **4136**. de. **6**. (**9**.)

—— Winter Fashions. pp. 12. *J. Barker: Newcastle-upon-Tyne*, [1845?] 12°. **4139**. bbb. **25**. (**14**.)

WORKS EDITED OR WITH CONTRIBUTIONS BY JOSEPH BARKER.

—— *See* BERG (Joseph F.) Great Discussion on the Origin, Authority, & Tendency of the Bible, between . . . J. F. Berg . . . and J. Barker, *etc.* 1854. 8°. **3103**. cc. **7**.

—— *See* BERG (Joseph F.) The Bible vindicated against the Aspersions of J. Barker. [A report of a debate between J. F. Berg and J. Barker.] 1854. 12°. **4016**. c. **6**.

—— *See* BOWES (John) *of Cheltenham*. The Report of the Public Discussion at Stockport between Mr. J. Bowes and Mr. J. Barker. 1855. 8°. **4014**. c. **9**.

—— *See* BOWRING (*Sir* John) *LL.D.* The Press and the People, or a report of the proceedings connected with the opening of the Barker Steam Press . . . Speeches . . . by Dr. Bowring, Mr. Barker, *etc.* [1846.] 12°. **11826**. bbb. **13**.

—— *See* COOKE (William) *Rev., of the Methodist New Connexion.* The Authentic Report of the Theological Discussion between W. Cooke and J. Barker. 1845. 12°. **1350**. b. **39**.

—— *See* COOPER (Thomas) *the Chartist.* The Belief in a Personal God and a Future Life. Six nights' discussion between T. Cooper and J. Barker, *etc.* [1860.] 8°. **4014**. a. **18**.

—— *See* EPHEMERIDES. The Reformer's Almanac and Companion to the Almanacs . . . By J. Barker. 1848, *etc.* 8°. P.P. **2470**. ec.

—— *See* FOX (Joseph) *Shoemaker.* The Methodist Travelling Preacher and the Shoemaker. [A correspondence between J. Fox and P. Budd, with two letters by J. Barker.] [1847.] 12°. **4139**. b. **50**.

—— *See* PENN (William) *Founder of Pennsylvania.* The Sandy Foundation Shaken, *etc.* [Edited by J. Barker.] [1845?] 12°. **4139**. bbb. **25**. (**13**.)

—— *See* PERIODICAL PUBLICATIONS.—*London.* Barkers' Review of Politics, Literature, *etc.* [1861, *etc.*] 8°. P.P. **636**. h.

—— *See* PERIODICAL PUBLICATIONS.—*London.* The Christian Investigator and Evangelical Reformer. By J. Barker and others. 1842, *etc.* 8°. P.P. **541**. a.

BARKER (JOSEPH) *Preacher.*

—— *See* PERIODICAL PUBLICATIONS.—*Newcastle-upon-Tyne.* The Christian. By J. Barker. 1844, *etc.* 8°. P.P. **597**. dd

—— *See* PERIODICAL PUBLICATIONS.—*Wortley.* The People *etc.* [Edited by J. Barker.] [1848, *etc.*] 4°. P.P. **3612**. am. (**1**.)

—— *See* WRIGHT (Henry Clarke) Non-resistance. In two letters, the first from H. C. Wright . . . and the second from J. Barker, *etc.* [1843?] 12°. **1355**. c. **62**. (**5**.)

APPENDIX.

—— *See* ALLIN (Thomas) *Rev., etc.* A Brief Statement of Facts relating to the Rev. J. Barker, *etc.* [1841.] 12°. **4139**. bbb. **24**. (**9**.)

—— *See* ALLIN (Thomas) *Rev., etc.* Vindication of the Methodist New Connexion. Remarks on the report of the trial of the Revs. J. Barker and W. Trotter; in a letter to the Rev. J. Barker. 1841. 12°. **4139**. bbb. **24**. (**10**.)

—— *See* ENGLAND.—*Methodist New Connexion.* Address of the Methodist New Connexion Conference, held at Halifax 1841 [concerning J. Barker]; together with the correspondence between J. Ridgway . . . and the Rev. J. Barker. 1841. 12°. **4139**. bbb. **24**. (**11**.)

—— *See* FEMALE. A Letter to Mr. J. Barker, on the Miraculous Conception of Christ, *etc.* 1845. 8°. **4372**. de. **21**. (**7**.)

—— *See* GRANT (Brewin) The Life of Joseph Barker the Infidel, done from his own works, *etc.* [1860.] 8°. **4014**. f. **17**

—— *See* MINTON, afterwards MINTON-SENHOUSE (Samuel) Lectures on Unitarianism, more especially as taught by Mr. J. Barker, *etc.* 1847. 12°. **4225**. c. **45**

—— *See* QUASIMODO, *pseud.* Joseph Barker, and his expulsion from the secular body, *etc.* [1861.] 8°. **4015**. aa. **35**

—— *See* TROTTER (William) *of York.* The Justice and Forbearance of the Methodist New Connexion Conference . . . With an appendix, containing a full answer to sundry tracts . . . published by J. H. Robinson and T. Allin . . . in opposition to the brief Report of the Conference proceedings published by J. Barker and W. Trotter, *etc.* 1841. 12°. **4139**. bbb. **24**. (**12**.)

—— *See* WATSON (Joseph) *of Whitby.* An Answer to the Question, "Who is Mr. J. Barker?" *etc.* 1848. 8°. **10347**. e. **29**. (**10**.)

BARKER (JOSEPH) *Preacher*, and **TROTTER** (WILLIAM) *of York.*

—— A Brief Report of the Proceedings of the Conference of the Methodist New Connexion in the case of J. Barker and W. Trotter together with advice to their friends and a reply to the Conference Address. By J. Barker and W. Trotter. pp. 40. *W. Blackwell & Co.: Newcastle*, [1841.] 12°. **1355**. c. **63**. (**8**.)

BARKER (JOSEPH HENRY)

—— *See* BIBLE.—*Acts.* [*English.*] Apostolic Missions; or the Sacred History amplified and combined with the Apostolical Epistles and contemporary secular history. By the Rev. J. H. Barker. [A paraphrase of the Acts, supplemented by extracts from the Epistles.] 1858. 8°. **3126**. b. **14**

BARKER (Joseph Henry)

—— The Ages to Come, or the Future Destiny of our globe considered, *etc.* pp. 28. vi. *W. Phillips: Hereford*, 1853. 8°. **4376. b. 5.**

—— Diderot's Treatment of the Christian Religion in the Encyclopédie, *etc.* [A thesis.] pp. 143. *King's Crown Press: New York*, 1941. 8°. **4018. i. 33.**

—— The Ruling Mind. By a Student of Nature [i.e. J. H. Barker] . . . Second edition. 3 pt. 1875. 8°. *See* Mind. **4017. b. 33.**

—— [Another edition.] 3 pt. 1876. 8°. *See* Mind. **7002. aa. 27.**

—— True Materialism; a suggestion for the harmonising of modern materialism with Christian theism. pp. 20. *Hamilton, Adams & Co.; W. Brown & Co.: London*, 1876. 8°. **8704. de. 2. (5.)**

—— Second edition. pp. 28. *Hamilton, Adams & Co.; W. Brown & Co.: London*, 1877. 8°. **4016. e. 4. (10.)**

BARKER (Joseph M.)

—— The Unipolar Electrocardiogram. A clinical interpretation, *etc.* [With illustrations and a bibliography.] pp. xii. 655. *Appleton-Century-Crofts: New York*, [1952.] 8°. **7471. d. 21.**

BARKER (Josiah) *See* Edes (Harry H.) A Memorial of Josiah Barker, of Charlestown, Mass. 1871. 8°. **10882. dd. 23. (11.)**

BARKER (Joyce)

—— Praps Farm . . . Illustrated by Catherine Cummins. pp. 116. *Faber & Faber: London*, 1946. 8°. **12828. bbb. 15.**

BARKER (Katherine Weston) *Lady. See* Barker (*Sir* George D.) *G.C.B.* Letters from Persia and India, 1857–1859 . . . Edited by Lady Barker. 1915. 8°. **9057. aaa. 42.**

BARKER (Kathleen Frances) *See* Buckingham (M. E.) Phari . . . Illustrated by K. F. Barker. 1933. 8°. **12812. h. 29.**

—— *See* Sewell (Anna) Black Beauty . . . With illustrations by K. F. Barker. 1936. 8°. **20055. i. 13.**

—— Bellman. The story of a beagle . . . Illustrated by the author. pp. vii. 206. *A. & C. Black: London*, 1933. 8°. **20052. ff. 14.**

—— Bellman Carries on . . . With many illustrations from drawings by the author. pp. viii. 199. *A. & C. Black: London*, [1933.] 8°. **20053. c. 25.**

—— Bellman, *etc. London*, 1936. 8°. **20053. cc. 29.**
An enlarged photographic reproduction of the 1933 *edition.*

—— Champion. The story of a bull-terrier. Written and illustrated by K. F. Barker. pp. 158. *Country Life: London*, 1936. 4°. **20053. d. 44.**

—— Dog Days. With drawings, *etc.* pp. 146. *William Heinemann: London, Toronto*, 1938. 4°. **7294. v. 13.**

—— Himself . . . With pen and pencil sketches by the author. [A tale.] pp. 96. *Country Life: London*, 1935. 4°. **7294. t. 1.**

—— The January Tortoise. Written and illustrated by K. F. Barker. pp. 103. *George G. Harrap & Co.: London*, 1955 [1954]. 8°. **12838. c. 1.**

—— Just Dogs. Sketches in pen & pencil. [With plates.] pp. xiv. 73. *Country Life: London*, 1933. 4°. **7291. i. 21.**

BARKER (Kathleen Frances)

—— Just Pups. Sketches in pen & pencil by K. F. Barker. pp. xiv. 64. *Country Life: London*, 1937. 4°. **7294. v. 8.**

—— The Mole who was Different. Written and illustrated by K. F. Barker. pp. 120. *George G. Harrap & Co.: London*, 1955. 8°. **12837. f. 29.**

—— Nothing but Dogs . . . With one hundred drawings by the author. pp. 142. *A. & C. Black: London*, 1938. 4°. **7291. i. 22.**

—— Nothing but Horses . . . With one hundred drawings by the author. pp. ix. 150. *A. & C. Black: London*, 1937. 4°. **7294. v. 9.**

—— Rogues' Gallery. With drawings, *etc.* pp. xiii. 135. *William Heinemann: London, Toronto*, 1939. 4°. **12643. t. 1.**

—— Traveller's Joy. Gentleman and puller. [A tale.] Written and illustrated by K. F. Barker. pp. viii. 163. *Country Life: London*, 1934. 4°. **20053. i. 15.**

—— The Young Entry. Fox-hunting, beagling and otter-hunting for beginners . . . With forty illustrations from drawings by the author. pp. vii. 138. *A. & C. Black: London*, 1939. 4°. **7915. s. 37.**

BARKER (L.) Needlework Patterns by Paper Folding . . . Arranged to meet the requirements of Schedule 3 of the Code Scholarship and Certificate Examinations, *etc.* pp. 21. *J. W. Bean & Son: Leeds*, [1896.] 8°. **7742. b. 53.**

BARKER (Landen Hall) Elementary Physics, *etc.* pp. 254. *G. Gill & Sons: London*, 1893. 8°. **8705. aaa. 47.**

BARKER, afterwards TAYLOR (Laura Wilson) *See* Home Thoughts. Home Thoughts and Home Scenes. In original poems by Jean Ingelow . . . Mrs. Tom Taylor, *etc.* 1865. 4°. **1347. k. 15.**

BARKER (Laurence) Christs Checke to S. Peter for his curious question, out of those words in Saint Iohn: Quid ad te? . . . In sixe seueral sermons. *P. S.* [*Peter Short*] *for Cuthbert Burbie and Thomas Gosson: London*, 1599. 8°. **4452. a. 10.**

BARKER (Leo Vaughn)

—— Lay Leadership in Protestant Churches, *etc.* [A thesis.] pp. xii. 240. *Association Press: New York*, 1934. 8°. **4182. g. 12.**

BARKER (Leonard Noel) *See* Noel (L.) *pseud.* [i.e. L. N. Barker.]

BARKER (Lewellys Franklin) *See* Siemens (H. W.) Race Hygiene and Heredity . . . Translated and edited by L. F. Barker. 1924. 8°. **08285. de. 13.**

—— *See* Spalteholz (W.) Hand-Atlas of the Human Anatomy . . . Edited and translated . . . by L. F. Barker, *etc.* [1907.] 8°. **7419. g. 14.**

—— *See* Spalteholz (W.) Hand Atlas of Human Anatomy . . . Translated by L. F. Barker, *etc.* [1943.] 8°. **7422. cc. 7.**

—— Anatomical Terminology, with special reference to the BNA . . . With vocabularies in Latin and English and illustrations. pp. ix. 103. *J. & A. Churchill: London; Philadelphia* [printed], 1907. 8°. **7419. g. 15.**

—— The Clinical Diagnosis of Internal Diseases . . . With . . . plates, *etc.* 3 vol. *D. Appleton & Co.: New York & London*, 1916. 8°. [*Monographic Medicine.* vol. 2–4.] **07305. dd. 1.**

BARKER (Lewellys Franklin)

—— [Another edition.] 3 vol. *D. Appleton & Co.: New York & London,* 1923. 8°. **7440.** f. **13.**

—— Endocrinology and Metabolism . . . By ninety-eight contributors. Edited by L. F. Barker . . . Associate editors . . . R. G. Hoskins . . . Herman O. Mosenthal. [With a bibliography.] 5 vol. *D. Appleton & Co.: New York, London,* 1922. 8°. **7422.** c. **8.**

—— Live Long and Be Happy. How to prolong your life and enjoy it. pp. viii. 224. *D. Appleton-Century Co.: New York, London,* 1936. 8°. **7391.** pp. **40.**

—— The Nervous System and its Constituent Neurones. Designed for the use of practitioners of medicine and of students of medicine and psychology, *etc.* pp. xxxii. 1122. *D. Appleton & Co.: New York,* 1899. 8°. **7630.** ddd. **11.**

—— [Another copy, with a different titlepage.] *H. Kimpton: London,* 1900 [1899]. 8°. **7630.** ddd. **12.**

—— Psychotherapy, *etc.* pp. ix. 218. *D. Appleton-Century Co.: New York, London,* 1940. 8°. **07660.** aa. **50.**

—— Treatment of the Common Diseases met with by the General Practitioner. pp. vii. 319. *J. B. Lippincott Co.: Philadelphia,* [1934.] 8°. **20017.** b. **29.**

—— The Young Man and Medicine. pp. xiv. 202. *Macmillan Co.: New York,* 1928. 8°. [*Vocational Series.* no. 4.] W.P. **6349/4.**

BARKER (Lewellys Franklin) and **COLE** (Norman Brown)

—— Blood Pressure: cause, effect, and remedy. pp. 153. *D. Appleton & Co.: New York, London,* 1924. 8°. **7439.** aa. **18.**

—— Rheumatism: its meaning and its menace. pp. vi. 165. *D. Appleton & Co.: New York, London,* 1926. 8°. **07616.** de. **15.**

BARKER (Lewellys Franklin) and **SPRUNT** (Thomas Peck)

—— The Degenerative Diseases: their causes and prevention. pp. 254. *New York & London,* [1925.] 8°. [*Harper's Public Health Series.*] **7385.aa.44/3.**

BARKER (Lewellys Franklin) and **TRESCHER** (John Henry)

—— Backache, *etc.* pp. xiii. 235. *J. B. Lippincott Co.: Philadelphia & London,* [1931.] 8°. **7384.** ppp. **26.**

BARKER (Lillian) Cabaret Love. [A novel.] pp. vi. 278. *Grosset & Dunlap: New York,* [1933.] 8°. A.N. **1316.**

—— The Truth about the Dionne Quins. [With plates, including portraits.] pp. 192. *Hutchinson & Co.: London,* 1951. 8°. **10889.** b. **20.**

BARKER (Lucy D. Sale) *See* Coward. Coward or Hero? Translated from the French by Mrs. Sale Barker, *etc.* 1884. 8°. **12805.** r. **32.**

—— *See* Memoirs. Memoirs of a Poodle. Translated by Mrs. Sale Barker, *etc.* 1877. 8°. **12803.** gg. **6.**

—— *See* Periodical Publications.—*London.* Little Wide-Awake . . . By Mrs. Sale Barker, *etc.* 1875, *etc.* 8° & 4°. P.P. **5992.** gb.

BARKER (Lucy D. Sale)

—— Lily's Drawing-Room Book. Containing Lily's Home in the Country, Lily's Screen, and Lily's Visit to Grandmamma, *etc.* pp. 128. *G. Routledge & Sons: London* [1877.] 8°. **12809.** c. **18**

—— Birds, Beasts and Fishes, drawn by Harrison Weir, with prose and poetry by Mrs. Sale Barker. pp. 63. *G. Routledge & Sons: London,* 1886 [1885]. 4°. **12810.** dd. **38**

—— The Child's Letter-Writer. A help to young correspondents. pp. 64. *G. Routledge & Sons: London* 1883. 8°. **10910.** bbb. **37**

—— Ethel's Florin [and other tales]. *See* Child. Every Child's Stories, *etc.* 1896. 8°. **012808.** eee. **4**

—— Eva's Locket, and other tales, *etc.* pp. 93. *G. Routledge & Sons: London,* [1879.] 8°. **12809.** aaa. **53**

—— For Very Little People. [Tales and verses.] pp. 175. *G. Routledge & Sons: London,* [1883.] 4°. **12805.** s. **4**

—— [A reissue of pp. 1–88.] *London,* [1885.] 4°. **12810.** dd. **56**

—— [A reissue of pp. 89–175.] Flowers in May, *etc.* *London* [1885.] 4°. **12810.** dd. **52**

—— Found in the Snow, and other tales, *etc.* pp. 97–187 *G. Routledge & Sons: London,* [1879.] 8°. **12809.** aaa. **50**

—— Golden Hours . . . With illustrations from designs b M. E. Edwards. pp. 64. *G. Routledge & Sons: London* 1885 [1884]. 8°. **12805.** w. **23**

—— Good Girls' Gift, *etc.* *G. Routledge & Sons: London* 1880 [1879]. 8°. **12809.** e. **29**

—— Illustrated Poems and Songs for Young People. Edited by Mrs. Sale Barker. pp. viii. 342. *G. Routledge & Sons London,* 1885 [1884]. 8°. **11602.** g. **13**

—— Inmates of Our Home. (Verses . . . Illustrations b A. M. Cooper.) *G. Routledge & Sons: London; Lah* printed, 1888 [1887]. 4°. **11653.** l. **38**

—— Kate Greenaway's Birthday Book for Children, wit 382 illustrations, drawn by K. Greenaway . . . Verse by Mrs. Sale Barker. pp. 127. *G. Routledge & Sons London,* [1880.] 16°. **12809.** de.

—— [A reissue.] Kate Greenaway's Birthday Book, *etc.* *F. Warne & Co.: London & New York,* [1937.] 16°. **012305.** de. **8**

—— Lily's Home in the Country, *etc.* pp. 128. *G. Routledge & Sons: London & New York,* [1876.] 8° **12809.** aaa. **3**

—— Lily's Magic Lantern, *etc.* pp. 128. *G. Routledge & Sons: London,* 1880 [1879]. 8°. **12809.** f. **2**

—— Lily's Scrap-Book, *etc.* pp. 128. *G. Routledge & Sons London & New York,* 1877 [1876]. 8°. **12803.** df. **1**

—— Lily's Screen, *etc.* pp. 128. *G. Routledge & Sons London & New York,* 1877 [1876]. 16°. **12809.** aaa. **3**

—— [A reissue.] 2 ser. pp. 128. *London & New York* 1878. 8° **12809.** aaa. **5**

—— Lily's Visit to Grandmamma. pp. 128. *G. Routledge & Sons: London & New York,* 1877. 8°. **12809.** dd. **3**

BARKER (LUCY D. SALE)

—— Little Bright Eyes' Picture Book for Little Children, *etc.* pp. 191. *G. Routledge & Sons: London & New York,* 1877 [1876]. 8°. **12803**. gg. **4**.

—— Little Curly Pate's Picture Book . . . Reprinted from "Little Wide Awake," *etc.* pp. 192. *G. Routledge & Sons: London & New York,* 1878 [1877]. 8°. **12803**. dd. **6**.

—— The Little Dowager, *etc.* pp. 234. *G. Routledge & Sons: London,* 1894. 8°. **012807**. ff. **43**.

—— Little Golden Locks' Picture Book for Little Children, *etc.* pp. 192. *G. Routledge & Sons: London & New York,* 1877 [1876]. 8°. **12803**. gg. **5**.

—— Little Laughter Lover, *etc.* *G. Routledge & Sons: London,* 1880 [1879]. 8°. **12809**. d. **20**.

—— Little Rosy Cheek's Story Book . . . Reprinted from "Little Wide Awake," *etc.* pp. 192. *G. Routledge & Sons: London & New York,* 1878 [1877]. 8°. **12803**. dd. **5**.

—— Little Ruby Lips' Story Book, *etc.* pp. 159. *G. Routledge & Sons: London,* 1880 [1879]. 8°. **12805**. k. **24**.

—— Little Silverlock's Story Book, *etc.* pp. 160. *G. Routledge & Sons: London,* 1880 [1879]. 8°. **12805**. k. **23**.

—— Little Wide-Awake Pictures, described by Mrs. Sale Barker, *etc.* pp. 167. *G. Routledge & Sons: London,* [1878.] 8°. **12805**. l. **10**.

—— Little Wide-Awake Poetry Book for Children. pp. 158. *G. Routledge & Sons: London,* 1881 [1880]. 8°. **12809**. dd. **9**.

—— Only a Little Child, *etc.* pp. 183. *G. Routledge & Sons: London,* 1883 [1882]. 8°. **12810**. b. **3**.

—— Our Friends. A book of original verse . . . With illustrations by F. A. Fraser. pp. 32. *G. Routledge & Sons: London,* [1887.] 8°. **12806**. n. **11**.

—— Our Home. *See* supra: Inmates of Our Home.

—— Our Pets. Original verses . . . Illustrated by Paul Hardy. pp. 31. *G. Routledge & Sons: London,* [1887.] 8°. **12806**. n. **12**.

—— Pet's Picture Posies, *etc.* *G. Routledge & Sons: London,* 1880 [1879]. 8°. **12809**. e. **30**.

—— Puff, the Pomeranian, and other tales . . . With illustrations . . . by A. W. Cooper, *etc.* pp. 103. *G. Routledge & Sons: London,* [1885.] 8°. **12810**. dd. **37**.

—— Routledge's Holiday Album for Girls, *etc.* pp. 189. *G. Routledge & Sons: London & New York,* [1877.] 8°. **12809**. bb. **15**.

—— [Another issue.] *See* FRITH (Henry) The Holiday Album for Children, *etc.* [1877.] 8°. **12809**. bb. **16**.

—— Some of my Feathered and Four-footed Friends . . . With . . . plates, *etc.* pp. 96. *G. Routledge & Sons: London,* 1883 [1882]. 4°. **12810**. cc. **7**.

—— Some of my Little Friends . . . With . . . plates, *etc.* pp. 96. *G. Routledge & Sons: London,* 1882 [1881]. 8°. **12805**. l. **22**.

—— Sunday Talks with Mamma, *etc.* pp. 160. *G. Routledge & Sons: London,* 1884 [1883]. 8°. **4422**. n. **5**.

BARKER (LUCY D. SALE)

—— Sunny Childhood . . . With coloured illustrations by S. Mc. Cloy. *G. Routledge & Sons: London,* [1887.] 8°. **12811**. f. **49**.

—— Those Boys, *etc.* pp. 80. *G. Routledge & Sons: London,* [1882.] 8°. **12810**. cc. **9**.

—— Those Girls, *etc.* pp. 80. *G. Routledge & Sons: London,* [1882.] 8°. **12810**. cc. **8**.

—— Tiny Tot's Treasure, *etc.* *G. Routledge & Sons: London,* 1880 [1879]. 8°. **12809**. d. **19**.

—— With a Stout Heart. pp. 367. *G. Routledge & Son: London,* [1874.] 8°. **12804**. g. **22**.

BARKER (M.) *of Hongkong.* *See* PEPLOW (Samuel H.) Hongkong . . . 2nd edition, revised and enlarged. [By S. H. Peplow and M. Barker.] 1931. 8°. **010055**. aa. **45**.

BARKER (M. A.) *Mrs.* Poems to Recite. Selected and edited by Mrs. A. Barker. First series. pp. 24. *Simpkin, Marshall & Co.: London,* [1892.] 8°. **11601**. e. **44**.

BARKER (M. A.) *Translator.*

—— *See* MUSCHLER (R. C.) [Die Unbekannte.] One Unknown . . . Translated by M. A. & E. V. Barker. 1935. 8°. **12557**. ppp. **27**.

BARKER (MABEL MARY) L'Utilisation du milieu géographique pour l'éducation. Avec un appendice sur le "civic survey" par Alasdair Geddes. [With plates.] pp. 196. *Montpellier,* 1926. 8°. **010004**. h. **12**.

BARKER (MARGARET) *See* also WINGATE (Margaret Hill)

—— The Dream-Child. [Verses.] pp. 24. *Jarrold & Sons: Great Yarmouth,* 1916. 8°. **011648**. df. **46**.

BARKER (MARGARET) *M.A.*

—— A Technique for Studying the social-material Activities of Young Children, *etc.* [A thesis.] pp. 69. *Teachers College, Columbia University: New York,* 1930. 8°. **8311**. f. **34**.

BARKER (MARIE LOUISE)

—— *See* DURIAN (W.) [Kai aus der Kiste.] Bill of the Black Hand . . . Translated . . . by M. L. Barker. 1935. 8°. **12316**. tt. **32**.

—— *See* KLINGHARDT (H.) and FOURMESTRAUX (M. de) French Intonation Exercises . . . Translated and adapted . . . by M. L. Barker. 1923. 8°. **12951**. d. **2**.

—— —— 1933. 8°. **12951**. bb. **32**.

—— *See* KLINGHARDT (H.) and FOURMESTRAUX (M. de) Selections from French Intonation Exercises . . . Translated and adapted for English readers by M. L. Barker, *etc.* [1935?] 8°. **12956**. a. **22**.

—— Basic German for Science Students, *etc.* pp. xi. 164. *W. Heffer & Sons: Cambridge,* 1933. 8°. **12964**. bbb. **8**.

—— Second edition. pp. xiii. 181. *W. Heffer & Sons: Cambridge,* 1934. 8°. **12964**. d. **33**.

—— Basic German for Science Students . . . Third edition. pp. xiii. 186. *W. Heffer & Sons: Cambridge.* 1937. 8°. **12964**. dd. **22**.

—— Basic German for Science Students . . . Fourth edition. pp. x. 176. *W. Heffer & Sons: Cambridge,* 1945. 8°. **12964**. m. **17**.

BARKER (MARIE LOUISE)

—— Basic German Reader for Beginners, *etc.* [With musical notes.] pp. viii. 121. *W. Heffer & Sons: Cambridge,* 1934. 8°. **12964**. bb. **27**.

—— Basic German Reader for Beginners, *etc.* (Second impression.) pp. viii. 120. *W. Heffer & Sons: Cambridge,* 1937. 8°. **12964**. bbb. **17**.

—— German for Middle Forms. A new-method reader and work-book . . . With illustrations by Katerina Wilczynski. pp. ix. 137. *W. Heffer & Sons: Cambridge,* 1949. 8°. **12965**. b. **8**.

—— German for Sixth-Form and Adult Beginners. An introduction to German language, literature and landscape, *etc.* pp. xx. 290. *W. Heffer & Sons: Cambridge,* 1939. 8°. **12963**. n. **22**.

—— German Intonation and Verse-Speaking Exercises . . . Based on "German for Sixth Form and Adult Beginners." pp. 19. *Linguaphone Institute: [London,* 1939?] 8°. **12965**. df. **5**.

—— A Handbook of German Intonation for University Students. pp. x. 102. *W. Heffer & Sons: Cambridge,* 1925. 8°. **12963**. b. **45**.

BARKER (MARIE LOUISE) and **HOMEYER** (HELENE)

—— The Pocket Oxford German Dictionary. (Oxford German-English Dictionary.) pp. xvi. 432 *Clarendon Press: Oxford,* 1946. 16°. **12962**. a. **52**.

—— The Pocket Oxford German Dictionary. German-English, compiled by M. L. Barker and H. Homeyer. English-German, compiled by C. T. Carr. 2 pt. *Clarendon Press: Oxford,* 1951. 16°. **12965**. aa. **14**.

BARKER (MARIE LOUISE) and **WOELCKEN** (FRITZ)

—— Modern German Texts for Rapid-Reading. [Edited by M. L. Barker and F. Wölcken.] *W. Heffer & Sons: Cambridge,* [1934- .] 8°. W.P. **10678**.

BARKER (MARION)

—— The Story of a Water Sprite, *etc.* pp. 46. *Westminster Press: London,* 1942. 8°. **12824**. g. **28**.

—— The Story of a Water Sprite . . . Illustrated by P. R. Kelleher and Roy Williams. pp. 77. *Westminster Press: London,* 1944. 4°. **012826**. g. **45**.

BARKER (MARY) The Way to make Home Comfortable: or, the History of Mary Barker. pp. 40. *Darton & Clark: London,* [1850?] 12°. **4422**. bb. **7**.

BARKER (MARY) *Authoress of "A Welsh Story."* A Welsh Story. 3 vol. *Hookham & Carpenter: London,* 1798. 8°. **12613**. f. **6**.

BARKER, afterwards **BROOME** (MARY ANNE) *Lady.* See BRASSEY (Annie) *Baroness Brassey.* The Last Voyage, 1887. [Edited by Lady Barker.] 1889. 8°. **010026**. h. **21**.

—— *See* PERIODICAL PUBLICATIONS.—*London.* Evening Hours . . . Edited by Lady Barker. [1875, *etc.*] 8°. P.P. **268**. ce.

—— The Bedroom and Boudoir. pp. 116. *Macmillan & Co.: London,* 1878. 8°. [*Art at Home Series.*] **07943**. k. **32/2**.

—— Boys . . . With illustrations. pp. 345. *G. Routledge & Sons: London,* [1874.] 8°. **12803**. ccc. **15**.

—— A Christmas Cake in Four Quarters . . . With illustrations. pp. 304. *Macmillan & Co.: London & New York,* 1871. 8°. **12808**. bbb. **13**

BARKER, afterwards **BROOME** (MARY ANNE) *Lady.*

—— Colonial Memories. pp. xxii. 301. *Smith, Elder & Co.: London,* 1904. 8°. **10491**. cc. **31**.

—— First Lessons in the Principles of Cooking. pp. vi. 101. *Macmillan & Co.: London,* 1874. 16°. **7944**. aa. **43**.

—— First Lessons in the Principles of Cooking, *etc.* pp. vi. 101. *Macmillan & Co.: London,* 1886. 8°. **7948**. a. **119**.

—— Harry Treverton, his tramps and troubles told by himself. Edited [or rather, written] by Lady Broome. pp. 311. *G. Routledge & Sons: London,* 1889 [1888]. 8°. **12806**. p. **40**.

—— Holiday Stories for Boys and Girls . . . With illustrations. pp. 288. *G. Routledge & Sons: London,* 1873. 8°. **12803**. bbb. **7**.

—— Houses and Housekeeping. A fireside gossip upon home and its comforts. pp. 170. *W. Hunt & Co.: London,* 1876. 8°. **7944**. aa. **3**.

—— Letters to Guy. [Describing life in Australia.] pp. 227. *Macmillan & Co.: London,* 1885. 8°. **10492**. bbb. **19**.

—— Ribbon Stories . . . Illustrated, *etc.* pp. viii. 242. *Macmillan & Co.: London,* 1872. 8°. **12803**. bbb. **8**.

—— Spring Comedies, *etc.* pp. viii. 340. *Macmillan & Co.: London & New York,* 1871. 8°. **12637**. b. **7**.

—— Station Amusements in New Zealand. pp. 278. *W. Hunt & Co.: London,* 1873. 8°. **10492**. bb. **27**.

—— Station Amusements in New Zealand. (New Zealand edition.) [With a portrait.] pp. 235. *Whitcombe & Tombs: Christchurch,* 1953. 8°. **10492**. eee. **39**.

—— Station Life in New Zealand. [With a preface signed: F. N. B., i.e. Sir Frederick N. Broome.] pp. xi. 238. *Macmillan & Co.: London,* 1870. 8°. **10491**. pp. **3**.

—— New edition. pp. xi. 238. *Macmillan & Co.: London,* 1871. 8°. **10491**. bb. **20**.

—— Station Life in New Zealand. [With a map.] pp. 237. *Whitcombe & Tombs: Christchurch,* 1950. 8°. **10492**. bb. **85**.

—— Une Femme du monde à la Nouvelle-Zélande. Traduction de Mme E. B. pp. vii. 292. *Paris,* 1882. 18°. **10492**. bb. **11**.

—— Stories about: —— . . . With illustrations. pp. 285. *Macmillan & Co.: London,* 1871 [1870]. 8°. **12807**. ccc. **14**.

—— Sybil's Book. pp. vi. 275. *Macmillan & Co.: London,* 1874. 8°. **12809**. bbb. **13**.

—— This Troublesome World; or, 'Bet of Stow' . . . Second edition. pp. vi. 269. *Hatchards: London,* 1875. 8°. **12803**. g. **13**.

—— Travelling About over New and Old Ground, *etc.* pp. xii. 353. *G. Routledge & Sons: London,* 1872. 8°. **10026**. ccc. **30**.

—— [A reissue.] *London,* [1883.] 8°. **10024**. b. **23**.

—— The White Rat, and some other stories . . . With illustrations, *etc.* pp. vii. 236. *Macmillan & Co.: London,* [1880.] 8°. **12809**. m. **33**.

—— A Year's Housekeeping in South Africa . . . With illustrations. pp. viii. 335. *Macmillan & Co.: London,* 1877. 8°. **10096**. c. **33**.

BARKER (MATTHEW) *See* EVERARD (John) *D.D.* The Gospel Treasury opened, *etc.* [Edited by T. Brookes and M. Barker.] 1659, *etc.* 8°. **4452. b. 5.**

—— *See* HAMOND (George) *M.A., etc.* A Discourse of Family Worship . . . With an appendix [by M. Barker], *etc.* 1694. 12°. **694. c. 32. (3.)**

—— A Christian Standing & Moving upon the True Foundation. Or, a word in season . . . expressed in a sermon, preached before the Honourable House of Commons upon the day of their monthly fast, Octob. 25. 1648. pp. 62. *M. S. for R. Harford: London,* 1648. 4°. **E. 468. (40.)**

—— A Discourse of the Right Way of Obtaining, and Maintaining Communion with God. *See* ANNESLEY (Samuel) *LL.D., etc.* A Continuation of Morning-Exercise Questions, *etc.* 1683. 4°. **855. k. 15.**

—— [Another edition.] 1844. *See* ANNESLEY (Samuel) *LL.D., etc.* The Morning Exercises at Cripplegate, *etc.* vol. 4. 1844, *etc.* 8°. **1356. h. 4.**

—— Flores intellectuales: or, Select notions, sentences and observations, collected out of several authors, *etc.* pp. 145. *J. Astwood for John Dunton: London,* 1691. 8°. **4410. h. 12.**

—— Flores intellectuales: the second part, containing three centuries more, *etc.* pp. 102. *Tho. Snowden for John Dunton: London,* 1692. 12°. **4407. de. 19.**

—— Natural Theology, or, the knowledge of God from the works of creation; accommodated, and improved, to the service of Christianity. pp. 218. *For Nathaniel Ranew: London,* 1674. 8°. **853. e. 4.**
Imperfect; wanting pp. 129-160.

—— A Religious Fast. The duty whereof is asserted, described, perswaded, *etc.* *See* ANNESLEY (Samuel) *LL.D., etc.* A Supplement to the Morning-Exercise, *etc.* 1676. 4°. **855. k. 14.**

—— [Another edition.] 1844. *See* ANNESLEY (Samuel) *LL.D., etc.* The Morning Exercises at Cripplegate, *etc.* vol. 2. 1844, *etc.* 8°. **1356. h. 2.**

—— Wherein and wherefore, the Damnation of those that perish under the Gospel will be more intolerable than the Damnation of Sodom, *etc.* *See* ANNESLEY (Samuel) *LL.D., etc.* Casuistical Morning-Exercises, *etc.* 1690. 4°. **858. k. 12.**

—— [Another edition.] 1844. *See* ANNESLEY (Samuel) *LL.D., etc.* The Morning Exercises at Cripplegate, *etc.* vol. 4. 1844, *etc.* 8°. **1356. h. 4.**

BARKER (MATTHEW HENRY) Floating Remembrances and Sketches of a Sea Life. By the Old Sailor [i.e. M. H. Barker]. pp. 372. 1854. 8°. *See* REMEMBRANCES. **10825. a. 43.**

—— The Fortunes of Frank Fairfield. (A tale of the sea. Illustrated by E. Duncan.) pp. vi. 149. *W. S. Orr & Co.: London,* 1845. 8°. **12614. a. 32.**
With an additional titlepage, engraved.

—— The Four P's, or the Fortunes of Frank on his road to wealth. A tale of the sea for boys. pp. 178. *Dean & Son: London,* [1859.] 8°. **12807. bb. 23.**

—— Greenwich Hospital, a series of naval sketches, descriptive of the life of a man-of-war's man. By an Old Sailor [i.e. M. H. Barker]. With illustrations by George Cruikshank. pp. 184. 1826. 4°. *See* LONDON.—III. *Greenwich Hospital.* **C. 59. f. 17.**

—— Hamilton King, or, the Smuggler and the Dwarf. By the Old Sailor [i.e. M. H. Barker], *etc.* 3 vol. 1839. 12°. *See* KING (Hamilton) **N. 1637.**

BARKER (MATTHEW HENRY)

—— Jem Bunt. By the Old Sailor [i.e. M. H. Barker]. pp. iv. 388. [1841.] 8°. *See* BUNT (Jem) **12600. o. 1.**

—— Jem Bunt . . . By "The Old Sailor" [i.e. M. H. Barker] . . . With twenty-three illustrations on steel by R. Cruikshank. pp. vii. 312. [1850?] 8°. *See* BUNT (Jem) **12835. d. 2.**

—— [Another edition.] pp. 312. [1855.] 8°. *See* BUNT (Jem) **12631. e. 2.**

—— Land and Sea Tales. By the Old Sailor [i.e. M. H. Barker], *etc.* 2 vol. 1836. 8°. *See* LAND TALES. **N. 1321.**

—— [Another edition of vol. 1.] pp. 286. 1860. 8°. *See* LAND TALES. **12632. aaa. 13.**

—— [A reissue.] [1890.] 8°. *See* LAND TALES. **012611. i. 14.**

—— The Life of Nelson, revised and illustrated . . . By the Old Sailor [i.e. M. H. Barker]. pp. 486. 1836. 8°. *See* NELSON (Horatio) *Viscount Nelson.* **615. c. 26.**

—— [A reissue.] 1867. 8°. *See* NELSON (Horatio) *Viscount Nelson.* **10816. aaa. 12.**

—— The Mariner's Compass; for the use of young officers of the navy, *etc.* (New edition.) [With compass-card.] *Droosten, Allan & Co.: London,* [1860.] 4°. **8804. dd. 3.**

—— The Naval Club; or, Reminiscences of service. 3 vol. *Henry Colburn: London,* 1843. 8°. **N. 2250.**

—— Nights at Sea; or, Naval life during the war. By the Old Sailor [i.e. M. H. Barker]. pp. 148. 1852. 16°. *See* NIGHTS. **1155. h. 10.**

—— The Old Sailor's Jolly-Boat, laden with tales, yarns, scraps, fragments, etc. etc., to please all hands . . . Steered by M. H. Barker. [Edited and largely written by him.] pp. 456. 1844. 8°. *See* PERIODICAL PUBLICATIONS.—*London.* **P.P. 4046.**
With plates by George Cruikshank and Isaac R. Cruikshank.

—— The Old Sailor's Jolly Boat, laden with tales and yarns to please all hands, *etc.* [Selections.] pp. vi. 280. *Henry Lea: London,* 1855. 8°. **12631. b. 3.**

—— The Quarter-Deck; or, Home and abroad. By an Old Sailor [i.e. M. H. Barker]. pp. 307. 1847. 8°. *See* QUARTER-DECK. **012614. dd. 12.**

—— Topsail-sheet Blocks; or, the Naval Foundling. By "the Old Sailor" [i.e. M. H. Barker], *etc.* 3 vol. 1838. 8°. *See* TOPSAIL-SHEET BLOCKS. **N. 1415.**

—— [Another edition.] pp. iv. 444. 1859. 8°. *See* TOPSAIL-SHEET BLOCKS. **12601. ff. 17.**

—— [Another edition.] pp. 192. *F. Warne & Co.: London,* [1881.] 8°. **12602. bbb. 39.**

—— [A reissue.] *G. Routledge & Sons: London,* [1889.] 8°. **12611. h. 14.**

—— Tough Yarns; a series of naval tales and sketches . . . By the Old Sailor [i.e. M. H. Barker]. Illustrated by George Cruikshank. pp. 351. 1835. 8°. *See* YARNS. **N. 1192.**

—— The Victory; or, the Ward-room Mess. 3 vol. *Henry Colburn: London,* 1844. 8°. **N. 2437.**

—— Walks round Nottingham. By a Wanderer [i.e. M. H. Barker]. [With an appendix.] pp. vii. 296. xc. 1835. 4°. *See* WANDERER. **10360. ee. 25.**

—— The Warlock. By the Old Sailor [i.e. M. H. Barker] . . . A new edition. pp. 272. 1860. 8°. *See* WARLOCK. **12632. aaa. 24.**

BARKER (MELVERN J.)

—— How Little Boats grow. pp. 32. *J. B. Lippincott Co.: Philadelphia, New York*, [1955.] 4°. **12837**. m. **13**.

—— Little Island Star. [A tale for children. With illustrations.] *Oxford University Press: New York*, 1954. 4°. **12836**. e. **35**.

—— Little Sea Legs. [A tale for children. With illustrations.] *Oxford University Press: New York*, 1951. 4°. **12830**. h. **3**.

—— 6 O'Clock Rooster. *Oxford University Press: New York*, 1953. 4°. **12833**. d. **55**.

BARKER (NELSON W.)

—— *See* ALLEN (Edgar V.) Peripheral Vascular Diseases. By E. V. Allen . . . N. W. Barker, *etc.* 1946. 8°. **7621**. c. **9**.

—— *See* ALLEN (Edgar V. N.) Peripheral Vascular Diseases . . . [By] E. V. Allen . . . N. W. Barker, *etc.* 1955. 8°. **7615**. t. **29**.

BARKER (NUGENT)

—— Written with my Left Hand. Twenty-one tales, *etc.* pp. ix. 233. *Percival Marshall & Co.: London*, [1951.] 8°. NNN. **1589**.

BARKER (P. W.)

—— Rubber: history, production and manufacture . . . Prepared under the direction of E. G. Holt. pp. vi. 47. *Washington*, 1940. 8°. [*U.S. Bureau of Foreign and Domestic Commerce. Trade Promotion Series.* no. 209.] A.S. **126/2**.

—— Rubber Industry of the United States, 1839–1939, *etc.* pp. vi. 42. *Washington*, 1939. 8°. [*U.S. Department of Commerce. Trade Promotion Series.* no. 197.] A.S. **126/2**.

—— Rubber Statistics, 1900–1937. Production, absorption, stocks and prices, *etc.* pp. iv. 55. *Washington*, 1938. 8°. [*U.S. Bureau of Foreign and Domestic Commerce. Trade Promotion Series.* no. 181.] A.S. **126/2**.

BARKER (PATRICK G.)

—— Inglewood. A tale of the Border and Merrie Carlisle. pp. 122. *A. H. Stockwell: London*, [1937.] 8°. **012601**. aa. **67**.

BARKER (PAUL SHIRMER) *See* WILSON (Frank N.) The Distribution of the Currents of Action and of Injury displayed by heart muscle and other excitable tissues. By F. N. Wilson . . . and P. S. Barker. 1933. 4°. [*University of Michigan Studies. Scientific Series.* vol. 10.] Ac. **2685/21**.

BARKER (PERCY BONDFIELD) and **YOUNG** (HORACE JAMES) A Manual of Soil Physics. pp. vi. 101. *Ginn & Co.: Boston*, [1915.] 8°. **7074**. cc. **59**.

BARKER (PERRY) *See* PARR (Samuel W.) and BARKER (P.) The Occluded Gases in Coal. 1909. 8°. [*University of Illinois Engineering Experiment Station. Bulletin.* no. 32.] Ac. **2692**. u/4.

—— *See* WHITE (Alfred H.) and BARKER (P.) Coals available for the Manufacture of Illuminating Gas, *etc.* 1911. 8°. [*U.S. Bureau of Mines. Bulletin.* 6.] A.S. **229.**

BARKER (PETER) A Learned and Familiar Exposition upon the Ten Commandements . . . The second edition, *etc.* pp. 423. *J. Harison: London*, 1633. 4°. **3506**. ee. **12**.

BARKER (PHILIP) Philip Barker, Founder of Willaston School, Nantwich. [The compiler's preface signed: G. E. E., i.e. George E. Evans. With a portrait.] [1915.] 8°. *See* E., G. E. **10855**. dh. **17**.

BARKER (PHILIP CHAPMAN) *See* BATH AND WELLS, *Diocese of.* The Bath & Wells Diocesan Kalendar, *etc.* [Edited by P. C. Barker.] [1888, *etc.*] 8°. P.P. **2506**. es.

—— *See* SPENCE, afterwards SPENCE-JONES (Henry D. M.) *Dean of Gloucester*, and EXELL (J. G.) The Pulpit Commentary, *etc.* (I. Chronicles. Exposition and homiletics by Rev. Professor P. C. Barker.) 1880, *etc.* 8°. **3131.d.1/11.**

—— *See* SPENCE, afterwards SPENCE-JONES (H. D. M.) *Dean of Gloucester*, and EXELL (J. S.) The Pulpit Commentary, *etc.* (II. Chronicles. Exposition and homiletics by Rev. P. C. Barker.) 1880, *etc.* 8°. **3131.d.1/12.**

—— *See* SPENCE, afterwards SPENCE-JONES (H. D. M.) *Dean of Gloucester*, and EXELL (J. G.) The Pulpit Commentary *etc.* (The Acts of the Apostles . . . Homilies by . . P. C. Barker [and others], *etc.*) 1880, *etc.* 8°. **3131.d.1/42.**

—— The Christian's Present Service and Coming Sleep. The sermon preached . . . on occasion of the death of Mr Richard W. Taylor, *etc.* pp. 27. *Jackson & Co.: London* [1866.] 8°. **4906**. cc. **51**. **(1.**

—— The Conversion of Sinners—the grand object of the Christian Ministry. Prize essay, *etc.* pp. 64. *Hodder & Stoughton: London*, 1871. 8°. **4372**. de. **11**. **(3.**

—— The Knowledge of the Living Redeemer—the refuge of failing heart and flesh. The sermon preached . . . on occasion of the death of Mr. Alderman Trevor, *etc.* pp. 48. *Jackson & Co.: London*, 1866. 8°. **4906**. cc. **51**. **(2.**

BARKER (PRISCILLA) The Secret Book, containing private information and instruction for women and young girls, by a Woman (Priscilla Barker). pp. 32. *P. Barker: Brighton*, [1888.] 8°. **8416**. d. 9. **(17.)**

BARKER (R. S.) *See* DIRECTORIES.—*Manufacturers.* The Illustrated Guide to the Manufacturers . . . of England, *etc.* (The Illustrated Guide and Directory of Manufacturers of Great Britain and Ireland for . . . 1871 . . . Edited by R. S. Barker.) [1869, *etc.*] 4°. **P.P.2506.tsc.**

BARKER (RALPH) *D.D.* *See* TILLOTSON (J.) *Archbishop of Canterbury.* [Sermons, edited by R. Barker.] 1695, *etc.* 8°. **1357**. b. **1–14**

—— *See* TILLOTSON (J.) *Archbishop of Canterbury.* Several Discourses upon the Attributes of God . . . Being the sixth volume; published from the originals, by R. Barker. 1699. 8°. **693**. e. **14**. **(6.**

—— *See* TILLOTSON (J.) *Archbishop of Canterbury.* Sixteen Sermons, preached on several subjects and occasions . . Being the second volume; published from the originals by R. Barker. 1700. 8°. **1025**. f. **16**

—— *See* TILLOTSON (J.) *Archbishop of Canterbury.* The Works of the Most Rev. J. Tillotson . . . Published from the originals by R. Barker. 1717. 8°. **479**. f. **6, 7**.

—— *See* TILLOTSON (John) *Archbishop of Canterbury.* The Works of the Most Reverend Dr. John Tillotson . . Published . . . by R. Barker, *etc.* 1735. fol. **4467**. d. **2**

—— A Sermon preached at St. Mary Le Bow . . . at the consecration of John Lord Archbishop of Canterbury *etc.* pp. 26. *For James Adamson: London*, 1691. 4°. **694**. k. **10**. **(1.**

—— [Another copy.] **225**. i. **11**. **(1.**

BARKER (RALPH) *Flight Lieutenant.*

—— Down in the Drink. True stories of the Goldfish Club. [With plates.] pp. 253. *Chatto & Windus: London,* 1955. 8°. **09100**. c. **40**.

BARKER (RALPH) *Vicar of Pagham.* The Church's Safety in the Hour of Temptation. A sermon preached in the Cathedral Church of Chichester . . . at the Primary Visitation of the Ven. J. Garbett . . . Archdeacon of Chichester. pp. 34. *Thomas Hatchard: London,* 1851. 8°. **4445**. d. **13**.

BARKER (RALPH E.)

—— Small Fruits . . . Edited and adapted . . . by C. E. Lucas Phillips. [With illustrations.] pp. 62. *William Heinemann: London,* 1955. 8°. [*Small Garden Library.*] W.P. D. **424**/**3**.

BARKER (*Mrs.* RAYMOND)

—— A Chaplet of Stories. pp. 32. *Catholic Truth Society: London,* [1893.] 8°. **3943**. aa. **246**.

—— A Chaplet of Stories. pp. 32. *Catholic Truth Society: London,* [1915.] 8°. **3943**. aa. **247**.

—— The Child's Pathway through Bible and Gospel History. pp. 70. *Jarrold & Sons: London,* [1861.] 12°. **3129**. a. **22**. (**3**.)

—— Don Bosco. pp. 24. *Catholic Truth Society: London,* 1890. 8°. **3943**. aa. **232**.

—— A Guiltless Thief. (The Lace Legend of Bruges. Reprinted from the Catholic World.) pp. 32. *Catholic Truth Society: London,* [1893.] 8°. **3943**. aa. **340**.

—— The Land of Promise; an account of the Holy Land and the Chosen People, for the young. pp. x. 228. *Seeley & Co.: London,* 1859. 8°. **3129**. c. **9**.

—— Our Lady of the Lilacs. (Georgie Penroz.) [Two tales, the first based on "Histoires du bon vieux temps," by Oscar de Poli.] pp. 28. *Catholic Truth Society: London,* [1895.] 8°. **3943**. aa. **326**.

—— The White Cornette. *See* DALY (*Mrs.* Dominic) The Fate of a Rosary, *etc.* [1894.] 8°. **3943**. aa. **327**.

BARKER (REGINALD CHARLES)

—— Gentleman Grizzly, *etc.* pp. 318. *L. C. Page & Co.: Boston,* 1928. 8°. **12811**. aaa. **8**.

—— Gentleman Grizzly . . . Illustrated by Griswold Tyng. pp. 255. *G. G. Harrap & Co.: London,* 1939. 8°. **12719**. ccc. **1**.

—— The Hair-Trigger Brand, *etc.* pp. 311. *L. C. Page & Co.: Boston,* 1929. 8°. **12715**. cc. **5**.

—— The Hair-Trigger Brand. pp. 251. *London,* 1937. 8°. [*Harrap's Wild West Novels.* no. 38.] **012604.p.2/38.**

—— Wild-Horse Ranch, *etc.* pp. 314. *L. C. Page & Co.: Boston,* 1927. 8°. **12713**. a. **9**.

—— Wild-Horse Ranch, *etc.* pp. 288. *G. G. Harrap & Co.: London,* 1935. 8°. A.N. **2594**.

BARKER (REGINALD J.)

—— Christ in the Valley of Unemployment. pp. 126. *Hodder & Stoughton: London,* 1936. 8°. **04400**. e. **63**.

—— Day-Dreams. Stories for children, *etc.* pp. 95. *Epworth Press: London,* 1921. 8°. **04419**. g. **78**.

BARKER (REGINALD J.)

—— It Began in Galilee. A study in revolutionary Christianity. [On the life and doctrine of Jesus Christ.] pp. 366. *Hodder & Stoughton: London,* 1938. 8°. **20032**. aa. **32**.

—— Off to Philadelphia. [A religious tract.] pp. 11. *Wesleyan Methodist Sunday School Department: London,* [1927.] 12°. **4194**. a. **8**.

—— Who made me a Divider? pp. 223. *Meridian Books: London,* 1949. 8°. **4381**. eee. **23**.

BARKER (RICHARD)

—— The Fatal Caress... and other accounts of English murders from 1551 to 1888. Edited by R. Barker, *etc.* pp. xiii. 210. *Duell, Sloan & Pearce: New York,* [1947.] 8°. **6058**. b. **21**.

BARKER (RICHARD) *Flying Control Officer.*

—— Still Binding with Cheque-Mate, *etc.* pp. 96. *Punch Bowl Press: Preston, London,* [1949.] 8°. **12332**. ee. **20**.

—— Stop Binding . . . Illustrated, *etc.* pp. 32. *Punch Bowl Press: Preston,* [1946.] 8°. **12332**. e. **25**.

BARKER (RICHARD) *of Thetford.* Tales of the Blest. A poem. First series. Infancy and Childhood. pp. 59. *T. Priest: Thetford,* 1840. 12°. T. **2471**. (**2**.)

BARKER (RICHARD) *Rector of Saint Maurice, Winchester.* The Danger of Pleasing Men: a sermon preached in the Cathedral-Church of Winchester, *etc.* pp. 26. *John Morphew: London,* 1707. 4°. **226**. g. **4**. (**8**.)

BARKER (*Sir* RICHARD) Consilium Anti-Pestilentiale: or, Seasonable Advice, concerning sure, safe, specifick, and experimented medicines, both for the preservation from, and cure of this present plague, *etc.* pp. 7. *For the Author: London,* 1665. 4°. **1167**. a. **39**.

—— The Excellency and Usefulnesse of the true Spirit of Salt, more fully discovered then formerly, *etc.* [By Sir R. Barker.] pp. 6. 1663. 4°. *See* EXCELLENCY. **778**. e. **41**. (**5**.)

—— The Great Preservative of Mankinde: or the transcendent vertue of the true Spirit of Salt, *etc.* (Directions for the use of the Spirit of Salt.) pp. 5. 4. *Printed by R. D.: London,* 1662. 4°. **778**. e. **41**. (**4**.)

—— Sudorificum regale; or, the Royal Sudorifick, *etc.* [By Sir R. Barker.] pp. 32. 1676. 8°. *See* SUDORIFICUM. **117**. k. **4**.

BARKER (RICHARD FELIX RAINE)

—— Gordon Highlanders in North Africa and Sicily, August 1942 to October 1943. A short account of a battalion during the two campaigns, *etc.* (Revised edition.) pp. 32. *Bydand Press: Sidcup,* 1944. 8°. **9102**. fff. **1**.

—— The Oliviers. A biography. [With plates, including portraits.] pp. xiv. 313. *Hamish Hamilton: London,* 1953. 8°. **10863**. f. **35**.

BARKER (RICHARD HINDRY)

—— Mr Cibber of Drury Lane. [With a bibliography.] pp. 278. *New York,* 1939. 8°. [*Columbia University Studies in English and Comparative Literature.* no. 143.] Ac. **2688**/**12**. (**29**.)

BARKER (RICHMOND) *See* HAGMANN (J. G.) Reform in Primary Education . . . Translated from the second German edition by . . . R. Barker, *etc.* 1906. 8°. **8304**. bbb. **23**.

BARKER (Robert) *Carpenter on board the Thetis.* The Genuine Life of Robert Barker, dictated by himself while in a state of total darkness . . . containing a clear account of his remarkable travels, *etc.* pp. 391. *For the Author: London,* 1809 [1809–11]. 8°. **615.** c. **16.**

—— Barker's Genuine Life . . . Fourth edition. pp. 391. *For the Author: London,* 1810 [1810, 11]. 8°. **10826.** aaa. **38.**

—— The Unfortunate Shipwright: or, Cruel Captain. Being a faithful narrative of the unparallel'd sufferings of Robert Barker, late carpenter on board the Thetis Snow, of Bristol, in a voyage to the coast of Guinea and Antigua. pp. 40. *Printed for, and sold by the Sufferer: London,* [1760 ?] 8°. **T. 1090. (4.)**

—— The Unfortunate Shipwright [i.e. R. Barker] & Cruel Captain. [In verse.] [1756.] *s. sh.* fol. **1876.** f. **1.** **(154.)**

BARKER (Robert) *Esq.* Bibliotheca Barkeriana; or, a Catalogue of the library, of Robert Barker, Esq.; and also of a Gentleman of Lincoln's Inn . . . which will begin to be sold . . . by F. Clay . . . the 11th of February. pp. 59. [*London,* 1725.] 8°. **128.** i. **4.** **(7.)**

BARKER (Robert) *Rector of Cherry Burton. See* Barker (Edmund H.) The Legitimacy of the late Robert Barker vindicated, *etc.* 1822. 8°. **1245.** b. **43.** **(3.)**

BARKER (Robert S.)

—— Work Injuries in the United States during 1948. pp. iii. 19. *Washington,* 1950. 8°. [*U.S. Bureau of Labor Statistics. Bulletin.* no. 975.] A.S. **111.**

BARKER (Roger Garlock)

—— Child Behavior and Development. A course of representative studies. Edited by R. G. Barker . . . Jacob S. Kounin . . . Herbert F. Wright, *etc.* pp. viii. 652. *New York & London,* 1943. 8°. [*McGraw-Hill Publications in Psychology.*] W.P. **10156/21.**

BARKER (Roger Garlock) and **WRIGHT** (Herbert Fletcher)

—— One Boy's Day. A specimen record of behavior, *etc.* (Under the editorship of Gardner Murphy.) [With plates.] pp. x. 435. *Harper & Bros.: New York,* [1951.] 8°. **8473.** i. **17.**

BARKER (Roland)

—— Jonah's Ark. pp. 286. *Carlyle House: New York,* 1940. 8°. **12721.** d. **10.**

—— The Log of a Limejuicer. The experiences under sail of James P. Barker . . . as told to R. Barker. [With plates, including a portrait.] pp. 264. *Putnam: London,* 1934. 8°. **10498.** bb. **42.**

BARKER (Roland) and **DOERFLINGER** (William)

—— The Middle Passage. [A novel.] pp. 410. *Macmillan & Co.: London,* 1939. 8°. NN. **30808.**

BARKER (Ronald Ernest) *See* [also] Ronald (E. B.) *pseud.* [i.e. R. E. Barker.]

BARKER (*Sir* Ross) *K.C.I.E. See* Barker (*Sir* Wilberforce R.)

BARKER (Ruth Laughlin) Caballeros . . . Illustrations by Norma van Sweringen. [An account of Santa Fe and New Mexico.] pp. 379. *D. Appleton & Co.: New York, London,* 1931. 8°. **010410.** i. **42.**

BARKER (S. Darling) Mars. [A tale.] pp. vi. 340. *Hutchinson & Co.: London,* 1898. 8°. **012623.** h. **14.**

BARKER (S. Darling)

—— A Tortured Soul. pp. 94. *Roxburghe Press: London,* [1897.] 8°. **012625.** ee. **29.**

—— The Trials of Mercy. pp. 366. *Hutchinson & Co.: London,* 1899. 8°. **012642.** b. **6.**

BARKER (*Mrs.* Sale) *See* Barker (Lucy D. S.)

BARKER (Samuel) *Chaplain to the Duke of Cambridge.* Britain in Tears. Consolation under affliction to be found only in religion . . . A sermon, preached . . . on the twenty-third day of November, 1817, being the Sunday after the interment of . . the Princess Charlotte Augusta of Wales. pp. 14. *C. Sloman: Yarmouth,* [1817.] 4°. **10805.** ee. **14.**
Printed for private circulation.

—— [Another copy.] **4476.** i. **29.** **(2.)**

—— The Conduct of King Hezekiah, and the Reign of the Departed Sovereign, briefly examined and compared. A sermon preached . . . on the eighth day of July, 1830, being the Sunday after the interment of . . . King George the Fourth. pp. 14. *J. Loder: Woodbridge,* 1830. 4°. **10805.** f. **8.**

—— [Another copy.] **T. 1342. (9.)**

—— Offerings of Parental Love and Conjugal Affection. [In verse.] pp. iv. 51. *C. Sloman: Yarmouth,* 1820. 4°. **1466.** i. **27.** **(4.)**

—— Short Refutation; or, a few Scriptural texts, with observations, intended as an antidote to the positions contained in a syllabus, entitled "A Course of Lectures, to be delivered in the Old Meeting-House, Framlingham, by Mr. J. Esdaile." pp. 36. *J. Loder: Woodbridge,* 1829. 8°. **4225.** e. **4.**

—— Two Sermons &c. [One on the National Jubilee, 1809; the other on the General Thanksgiving, 1814. With a poem "On the Majesty and Worship of the Godhead, and coming to judgment".] pp. 63. *Keymer: Yarmouth,* 1815. 4°. **4475.** e. **3.**
Printed for private circulation.

—— Three Sermons, &c. &c. 2 pt. *Keymer: Yarmouth,* 1816. 4°. **4476.** i. **29.** **(1.)**
A reissue of the preceding, with an additional sermon. Printed for private circulation.

—— [Another copy of pt. 2.] **4475.** c. **114.** **(14.)**

—— The Union of Righteousness and Greatness considered and illustrated. A sermon, preached . . . on the twentieth day of February, 1820, being the Sunday after the interment of . . . King George the Third. pp. 11. *C. Sloman: Yarmouth,* [1820.] 4°. **10805.** ee. **15.**
Printed for private circulation.

BARKER (Samuel) *M.D.* The Diet of Infancy and Childhood. pp. ii. 70. *Robert Hardwicke: London,* 1864. 8°. **7580.** aa. **6.**

—— The Domestic Management of Infants and Children in health and sickness. pp. xii. 192. *Robert Hardwicke: London,* 1865. 8°. **7390.** bb. **3.**

—— [Another edition.] Children, and how to manage them in health and sickness, *etc.* pp. 351. *Robert Hardwicke: London,* [1875.] 8°. **7581.** df. **1.**

BARKER (Samuel) *M.D.*, and **HENDERSON** (Joseph)

—— The Prevention and Cure of Skin Diseases by heat & fumigation. With a chapter on syphilitic eruptions and ulcers. pp. vii. 125 *Henry Renshaw: London,* [1862.] 8°. **7630.** a. **16**

BARKER (Samuel) *M.D.*, and **HENDERSON** (Joseph)

—— Thermo-Therapeutics; or, the Turkish Bath in the treatment of diseases. pp. vii. 109. *Henry Renshaw: London*, [1861.] 16°. **7461**. a. **19**.

BARKER (Samuel) *of Lyndon*. Poesis vetus hebraica restituta. Accedunt quædam de carminibus Anacreonticis, de accentibus græcis, de scriptura veteri ionica, de literis consonantibus et vocalibus, et de pronunciatione linguæ hebraicæ. pp. 34. *J. Whitson & B. White: Londini*, 1761. 4°. **827**. eee. **13**. (**1**.)

—— [Another copy.] **74**. f. **21**.

BARKER (Samuel) *Vicar of Chippenham, Cambridgeshire*. A Sermon preach'd at the Funeral of the . . . Countess of Orford, *etc*. pp. 24. *S. Smith & B. Walford: London*, 1702. 4°. **4473**. e. **17**. (**3**.)

—— [Another copy.] **1419**. e. **17**. *Imperfect; wanting the half-title. Pp. 23, 24 are mutilated.*

BARKER (Sara)

—— How the Labour Party works. pp. 15. *Victoria House Printing Co.: London*, [1946.] 8°. **08139**. d. **63**.

BARKER (Sarah) The Norfolk Wonder, or, the Maiden's trance: being a strange and true relation, of one Sarah Barker of Elsom . . . who . . . fell into a trance, *etc*. pp. 8. *T. Wells: London*, 1708. 8°. **1076**. l. **22**. (**24**.)

BARKER (Sergeant Ben. G.) "All the World" Revival Hymns. Compiled by Rev. S. Barker. *S. Barker: Cardiff*, [1925.] 8°. **3436**. k. **49**.

BARKER (Sydney George) Coir. Report on the attributes and preparation of coconut fibre. pp. 66. *London*, 1933. 4°. [*E.M.B.* 71.] **B.S.12/1.**

—— Sisal. A note on the attributes of the fibre and their industrial significance. [With plates.] pp. 74. *London*, 1933. 4°. [*E.M.B.* 64.] **B.S.12/1.**

—— Wool. A study of the fibre. pp. 166. *London*, 1929. 8°. [*E.M.B.* 21.] **B.S.12/1.**

—— Wool Quality. A study of the influence of various contributory factors, their significance and the technique of their measurement. [With plates and a bibliography.] pp. 328. 1931. 4°. *See* England.—*Dominions Office.—Empire Marketing Board.* **B.S.12/4.**

BARKER (T. B.) *Principal of the Pestalozzian School, London*. The Great Want of the Age: or, Education as it ought to be . . . A discourse, *etc*. pp. 24. *B. L. Green: London*, 1852. 12°. **8306**. ccc. **8**. (**7**.)

BARKER (T. W.) *of Carmarthen*.

—— Handbook to the Natural History of Carmarthenshire. pp. vi. 110. *W. Spurrell & Son: Carmarthen*, [1905?] 8°. **7003**. r. **28**.

BARKER (T. W.) *of Sydenham*.

—— Secrets of Successful Salesmanship. *T. W. Barker: London*, 1936. 8°. **8231**. c. **25**.

—— Selling. [On salesmanship. By T. W. Barker.] ff. 17. [1935.] 4°. *See* Selling. **08229**. l. **38**.

BARKER (Theodore Cardwell) and **HARRIS** (John Raymond)

—— A Merseyside Town in the Industrial Revolution: St. Helens, 1750–1900. [With plates and maps.] pp. xviii. 508. *University Press: Liverpool*, 1954. 8°. **10361**. bb. **53**.

BARKER (Thomas) *A.M. Cantab.* Nassau: a poem, occasion'd by the Peace. pp. 10. *For Will. Rogers: London*, 1698. fol. **193**. d. **14**. (**17**.)

BARKER (Thomas) *A.M.*

—— A Poem, dedicated to the memory of Dr. Joseph Beaumont, Regius Professor of Divinity, in Cambridge. pp. 20. *J. Hayes, for E. Hall: Cambridge*, 1700. 4°. **11632**. df. **40**.

BARKER (Thomas) *Artist*. *See* Harington (*Sir* Edward) A Schizzo on the Genius of Man; in which . . . the merit of . . . T. Barker . . . is particularly considered, *etc*. 1793. 8°. **7814**. bb. **13**.

—— A Descriptive Account of the Historical Picture, the Trial of the Queen, in the House of Lords, by Thomas Barker, *etc*. pp. 12. *Richard Cruttwell: Bath*, 1821. 8°. **7856**. aaa. **40**. (**6**.)

BARKER (Thomas) *Curate at Leeds*. An Inquiry into the Scripture meaning of the word Satan, and its synonimous terms . . . Wherein also, the notions concerning devils, or demons, are brought down to the standard of Scripture. [By T. Barker.] pp. iii. 40. 77. 1772. 8°. *See* Satan. **679**. d. **9**. (**3**.)

BARKER (Thomas) *Dramatic Writer*. [For editions of "The Bloodie Banquet. By T. D.," sometimes attributed to T. Barker:] *See* D., T.

BARKER (Thomas) *Gent*. Analecta: or, a Collection of some of the choicest notions, and what seemed most remarkable in more than forty authors . . . By T. B. Gent. [i.e. T. Barker]. pp. 120. 1693. 8°. *See* B., T., *Gent*. **1135**. b. **14**.

—— [Another copy.] **123**. k. **19**.

BARKER (Thomas) *M.D.* *See* Barker (Thomas Herbert)

BARKER (Thomas) *of Bracemeale, Salop*. The Art of Angling. Wherein are discovered many rare secrets, *etc*. [By T. Barker.] pp. 18. 1653. 4°. *See* Art. **988**. f. **31**.

—— [Another issue.] 1654. 4°. [*The Countrymans Recreation, etc.*] *See* Art. E. **806**. (**16**.)

—— Barker's Delight: or, the Art of angling . . . The second edition, much enlarged. pp. 52. *J. G. for Richard Marriot: London*, 1657. 8°. E. **1661**. (**3**.)

—— [A reissue.] *Humphrey Moseley: London*, 1659. 8°. E. **1908**. (**1**.)

—— [Another edition.] The Art of Angling, *etc*. [By T. Barker.] pp. 16. 1817. 8°. *See* Art. **7907**. ee. **20**.

—— The Art of Angling, *etc*. [A reprint of the edition of 1651.] pp. 22. *J. H. Burn: [London,]* 1820. 12°. G. **19318**. (**1**.) *One of an edition of 100 copies.*

—— Barker's Delight: or, the Art of angling, *etc*. [A reprint of the edition of 1657.] pp. iv. 40. *J. H. Burn: [London,]* 1820. 12°. G. **19318**. (**2**.) *One of an edition of 100 copies.*

BARKER (Thomas) *of Lyndon*. *See* Bible.—*Selections. [English.]* The Messiah. Being the prophecies concerning him, methodized, with their accomplishments. By T. Barker. 1780. 8°. **3165**. c. **35**.

—— An Account of the Discoveries concerning Comets, with the way to find their orbits, *etc*. [With a folding plate.] pp. 52. *J. Whiston & B. White: London*, 1757. 4°. **8560**. e. **15**. (**3**.)

—— The Duty, Circumstances, and Benefits of Baptism, determined by evidence . . . With an appendix shewing the meaning of several Greek words in the New Testament, *etc*. pp. x. 208. *B. White: London*, 1771. 8°. **4324**. ccc. **12**.

BARKER (THOMAS) *of Lyndon.*

—— The Nature and Circumstances of the Demoniacks in the Gospels, stated and methodized, and considered in the several particulars. pp. vi. 56. *B. White: London,* 1783. 8°. **679**. d. **9**. (**7**.)

BARKER (THOMAS) *of Queen's College, Oxford. See* LITURGIES.—*Church of England.—Morning and Evening Prayer.—Canticles.* The Canticles, pointed for Anglican Chants . . . By an English Presbyter (T. B. [i.e. T. Barker]). [1863.] 16°. **3408**. aaa. **32**.

—— Ad populum. The Enthusiasm of Christ, the Love of the Father. A sermon . . . With reference to 'Ecce Homo' [by J. R. Seeley]. pp. vi. 41. *J. Parker & Co.: Oxford & London,* 1868. 8°. **4823**. d. **6**.

—— Chanting the Psalms with the Understanding. A letter to . . . the Archbishop of York, on the true fundamental principle of Anglican chanting. pp. 23. *Pawson & Brailsford: Sheffield; Rivingtons: London,* 1864. 12°. **3477**. cc. **38**.

—— Lessons of Bereavement. A sermon, preached in the Cathedral Church, Bridgetown, Barbados. January, 1853. pp. 16. *J. H. & J. Parker: Oxford,* 1856. 8°. **4476**. c. **8**.

—— Plain Sermons preached in Parish Churches. pp. viii. 295. *J. H. & J. Parker: Oxford,* 1858. 8°. **4463**. dd. **8**.

—— Strictures on "The Doctrine of Sacrifice deduced from the Scriptures," a series of sermons by the Rev. F. D. Maurice. pp. viii. 147. *J. H. & J. Parker: Oxford,* 1858. 8°. **4377**. d. **3**.

BARKER (THOMAS) *V.D.M. See* WELLS (Edward) *D.D.* Some Animadversions on Mr. Barker's Answer to Dr. Wells's Letter to a dissenting parishioner. 1707. 8°. **700**. c. **22**. (**9**.)

BARKER (THOMAS BURGESS) Abney Park Cemetery: a complete descriptive guide to every part of this beautiful depository of the dead. With . . . a ground plan, *etc.* pp. 94. *Houlston & Wright: London,* [1869.] 8°. **10349**. bbb. **6**.

BARKER (THOMAS CHILDE) *See* FUSTEL DE COULANGES (N. D.) Aryan Civilization . . . Based on the work of De Coulanges. By . . . T. C. Barker. 1871. 8°. **10006**. aaa. **27**.

—— Why not Baptize an Infant? or, the Earnest question answered. pp. 10. *J. Parker & Co.: Oxford & London,* 1873. 8°. **4324**. bb. **30**. (**5**.)

BARKER (THOMAS EDWARD) [For descriptions of views painted by T. E. Barker and exhibited at the Panorama, Strand:] *See* LONDON.—III. *Panorama, Strand.*

BARKER (THOMAS FRANCIS) Some Account of the Parish of Thornton. pp. 22. *Phillipson & Golder: Chester,* 1874. 8°. **10360**. bbb. **10**.

BARKER (THOMAS H.) *Estate Agent.* On Water Meadows as suitable for Wales and other mountain districts. Bickford's system of irrigation, as adopted by the late Mr. Pusey, described by T. Barker, in a letter to T. D. Acland, Esq. With plans. Reprinted . . . from the Bath and West of England Agricultural Journal, *etc.* pp. 24. *J. Ridgway: London,* 1859. 8°. **7075**. e. **43**. (**8**.)

—— [Another edition.] The Bickford System of Irrigation. A method specially devised for saving labour, expense and water by the use of small gutters . . . Reprinted . . . from the Journal of the Bath and West of England Society . . . With . . . preface by C. T. D. Acland. pp. viii. 20. *Edward Stanford: London,* 1893. 8°. **8777**. bbb. **29**. (**5**.)

BARKER (THOMAS HERBERT) Foul Air and Fever, as Cause and Effect, exemplified in the sanitary condition of Bedford. pp. 16. *Hamilton, Adams & Co.: London,* 1854. 8°. **7560**. c. **8**.

—— Illustrations of the Origin and Propagation of certain Epidemic Diseases . . . Reprinted from the Transactions of the Epidemiological Society. pp. 24. *T. Richards: London,* 1859. 8°. **7306**. bb. **11**. (**3**.)

—— On Cystic Entozoa in the Human Kidney, with an illustrative case. pp. 18. *Hamilton, Adams & Co.: London,* 1856. 8°. **1188**. f. **22**. (**8**.)

—— On Malaria and Miasmata and their influence in the production of typhus and typhoid fevers, cholera, and the exanthemata: founded on the Fothergillian Prize Essay for 1859. pp. xv. 251. *J. W. Davies: London,* 1863. 8°. **7686**. aaa. **8**.

—— On the Hygienic Management of Infants and Children. pp. xii. 7–120. *John Churchill: London,* 1859. 8°. **7580**. e. **10**.

—— Photographs of Eminent Medical Men of all countries, with brief analytical notices of their works. Edited by T. H. Barker . . . The photographic portraits from life, by Ernest Edwards, *etc.* 2 vol. *J. Churchill & Sons: London,* [1865, 68.] 8°. **10804**. cc. **1**.

—— Practical Observations on the Diet of Infancy and Childhood. pp. 54. *Simpkin, Marshall & Co.: London,* 1850. 8°. **1178**. d. **19**. (**2**.)

—— Right Foods for Infants and Children. pp. 48. *S. O. Beeton: London,* [1866.] 8°. **7581**. a. **62**. (**2**.)

—— The Treatment of Fevers, with special reference to ventilation, *etc.* pp. 50. *T. Richards: London; Grey & Co.: Bedford,* 1857 [1856]. 8°. **7560**. b. **8**.

BARKER (THOMAS HOLLIDAY) Thoughts and Facts on Human Dietetics . . . Fourth edition: revised. pp. 15. *W. Tweedie & Co.: London; Vegetarian Depot: Manchester,* 1879. 8°. **7383**. aaaa. **39**.

BARKER (THOMAS JONES) *See* EMPSON (C.) Memoranda relative to the Bride of Death, a picture painted by T. J. Barker. 1845. 8°. **1402**. k. **20**.

BARKER (THOMAS VIPOND) *See* FEDOROV (Evgrafy S.) Das Krystallreich . . . Von E. von Fedorow. Unter Mitwirkung von . . . Th. Barker, *etc.* 1920. 4°. [*Записки Россійской Академіи Наукъ.* sér. 8. Classe physico-mathématique. vol. 36.] Ac. **1125/3**.

—— *See* PORTER (Mary W.) and SPILLER (R. C.) The Barker Index of Crystals, *etc.* [With a portrait.] 1951, *etc.* 4°. **8906.s.39.**

—— Graphical and Tabular Methods in Crystallography as the foundation of a new system of practice, *etc.* pp. xiv. 152. *T. Murby & Co.: London,* 1922. 8°. **07105**. k. **5**.

—— Practical Suggestions towards the Study of Crystals in Schools. pp. 14. *Holywell Press: Oxford,* [1921.] 8°. **07106**. de. **20**.

Interleaved.

—— The Study of Crystals. A general introduction, *etc.* pp. xvi. 137. *T. Murby & Co.: London,* 1930. 8°. **07109**. b. **5**.

—— The Study of Crystals in Schools. pp. 15. *Holywell Press: Oxford,* [1920.] 8°. **07106**. de. **19**.

—— Systematic Crystallography: an essay on crystal description, classification and identification, *etc.* pp. xi. 115. *T. Murby & Co.: London,* 1930. 8°. **07109**. b. **6**.

BARKER (THOMAS WILLIAM JOHNSON) Forbidden Fruit: a series of sermons on temptation, *etc.* pp. vi. 120. *W. Kent & Co.: London,* 1879. 8°. **4466.** b. **22.**

—— Poems. pp. vi. 120. *John Nicholson: Hull; Houlston & Stoneman: London,* 1849. 12°. **11646.** c. **12.**

BARKER (TOMMIE DORA)

—— Libraries of the South. A report on developments, 1930–1935. [With maps.] pp. xvi. 215. 1936. 8°. *See* UNITED STATES OF AMERICA.—*American Library Association.—Library Extension Board.* **11914.** b. **32.**

BARKER (VERNON DUCKWORTH)

—— *See* BONN (E.) [Das Kind im Spiegel.] The Silver Key. (Translated by V. D. Barker.) 1936. 8°. **012553.** l. **65.**

—— *See* KARINTHY (F.) A Journey round my Skull . . . Translated . . . by V. D. Barker. 1939. 8°. **12593.** d. **1.**

—— Mai angol dekameron. A bevezető tanulmányt és az életrajzokat írta: V. D. Barker, *etc.* [With portraits.] pp. 303. [*Budapest,* 1935.] 8°. **12625.** r. **58.**

BARKER (VIOLET)

—— Little People's Recitations. pp. 16. *A. H. Stockwell: London,* [1940.] 8°. **11657.** aa. **59.**

BARKER (VIRGIL)

—— *See* MACFEE (Henry L.) Henry Lee McFee. By V. Barker. [Reproductions, with an introduction.] [1931.] 8°. Ac. **4713.** g/2. **(7.)**

—— American Painting. History and interpretation. [With reproductions.] pp. xxvii. 717. *Macmillan Co.: New York,* 1950. 8°. **7869.** ppp. **12.**

—— Pieter Bruegel the Elder. A study of his paintings. [With illustrations.] pp. 63. *G. Allen & Unwin: London; Arts Publishing Corporation: New York,* 1927. 4°. **7855.** i. **42.**

BARKER (VIRGINIA)

—— *See* WILSON (Pixie J.) The Campaign against Veneral [*sic*] Diseases. By P. J. Wilson assisted by V. Barker, *etc.* [1944.] fol. B.S. **81**/**15. (15.)**

BARKER (W.) *Lecturer in Weaving at the Oldham Technical College.*

—— Winding, Warping and Weaving. Mill practice & management, *etc.* pp. 31. *Emmott & Co.: Manchester,* 1938. 8°. [" *Textile Manufacturer* " *Monographs.* no. 1.] W.P. **7911**/**1.**

BARKER (W.) *of Leeds.* Poverty; its cause and cure. A worker's appeal for direct united action. pp. 16. *J. Scholefield: Leeds,* 1906. 8°. **08275.** a. **58. (3.)**

BARKER (W. E.) Pigeon Racing. A practical guide to the sport. [With illustrations.] pp. 187. *Racing Pigeon Publishing Co.: London,* [1913.] 8°. **7285.** cc. **35.**

BARKER (W. H.) *M.I.F.E.*

—— Drill-Book and Manual of Instructions. For use with the Auxiliary Fire Service. pp. 62. *Sydenham & Co.: Bournemouth,* [1938.] 16°. **8715.** aa. **65.**

BARKER (WALTER GOODYER) On Diseases of the Respiratory Passages and Lungs, sporadic and epidemic, *etc.* pp. xvi. 282. *J. Churchill & Sons: London,* 1866. 8°. **7615.** aa. **9.**

—— On the Climate of Worthing: its remedial influence in disease, especially of the lungs. pp. viii. 72. xiv. *John Churchill: London,* 1860. 8°. **7686.** b. **9.**

BARKER (WALTER GOODYER)

—— Second edition. pp. xii. 95. xxiii *J. Churchill & Sons: London,* 1867. 8°. **7687.** aa. **14.**

BARKER (WHARTON) Bimetallism: or the evils of gold monometallism and the benefits of bimetallism. pp. xv. 330. *Barker Publishing Co.: Philadelphia,* 1896. 8°. **08228.** i. **5.**

BARKER (*Sir* WILBERFORCE ROSS) *K.C.I.E.* *See* BARDOUX (J.) Memories of Oxford . . . Translated by W. R. Barker, *etc.* 1899. 8°. **8365.** aaa. **11.**

—— *See* DANIEL (Charles H. O.) and BARKER (*Sir* W. R.) *K.C.I.E.* Worcester College. 1900. 8°. **2234.** e. **20.**

—— *See* OWEN (*Sir* Hugh) *G.C.B.* Owen's Education Acts Manual . . . 23rd edition. By Sir R. Barker. 1936. 8°. **6425.** w. **9.**

—— Dr. Johnson as Representative of the Character of the Eighteenth Century. (The Chancellor's English Essay Prize, 1899.) pp. 64. *F. E. Robinson & Co.: London,* 1899. 8°. **10854.** a. **28.**

—— The Superannuation of Teachers in England and Wales, *etc.* pp. viii. 245. *Longmans & Co.: London,* 1926. 8°. **08364.** e. **35.**

BARKER (WILFRED EDGAR) and **MORGAN** (ROBERT T.)

—— The British & Colonial Philatelic Directory for Dealers & Collectors. Edited by W. E. Barker & R. T. Morgan. pp. 72. 1900. 8°. *See* DIRECTORIES.—*Stamp Dealers and Collectors.* Crawford **830.** (3.)

BARKER (WILL)

—— *See* RHODE (Clarence J.) and BARKER (W.) Alaska's Fish and Wildlife, *etc.* 1953. 8°. [*U.S. Fish and Wildlife Service. Circular.* no. 17.] A.S. **199**/**2.**

BARKER (WILLIAM) *Baptist Minister.* *See* BEBBINGTON (J. B.) Why I was an Atheist . . . With an introduction by W. Barker, *etc.* [1864.] 8°. **4014.** cc. **4.**

—— *See* WARD (William Gibson) Everlasting Torments Unscriptural. Two lectures . . . in reply to two . . . by W. Barker, *etc.* [1871.] 12°. **4379.** aa. **56.**

—— Civil and Ecclesiastical Government. Two lectures, *etc.* pp. 54. *Elliot Stock & Co.: London; Murphy: Hastings,* 1876. 8°. **4109.** aa. **12. (12.)**

—— " Digging a little deeper." How they got there! An answer to a pamphlet entitled " How did they get there? " [by G. Venables]. pp. 32. *William Freeman: London,* 1862. 16°. **4135.** b. **9.**

—— The " False Christs," their history, and its lessons. A lecture, *etc.* *E. Stock: London; Randle & Jenner; J. Chevens: Hastings,* 1879. 8°. **4808.** bbb. **5.**

—— Nonconformity; or, the Right of private judgment. A lecture in defence of Nonconformity, with special reference to the late controversy between the Rev. W. Barker and the Rev. C. Robinson, *etc.* pp. 43. *R. Wharton: Blackburn,* [1854.] 12°. **4139.** c. **15.**

—— Scriptural Features of Antichrist, a sermon . . . From the shorthand notes of Mr. Joseph Tendall. pp. 16. *Elliot Stock: London,* [1871.] 8°. **4478.** ee. **2.**

—— Shall I live for ever? or, Arguments from reason and Scripture, proving the natural immortality of man, and the endless duration of future punishments, *etc.* pp. 80. *Elliot Stock: London,* 1870. 8°. **4372.** df. **10. (2.)**

BARKER (WILLIAM) *Dean of Carlisle. See* EDWARDS (Walter N.) Platform, Pulpit, and Desk . . . With an introduction by the Rev. W. Barker. [1901.] 8°.
8436. c. **31.**

BARKER (WILLIAM) *M.D. See* PARKES (Samuel) *F.L.S., etc.* A Catechism of Chemistry . . . A new edition . . . enlarged by W. Barker. 1837. 12°. **1037.** i. **10.**

—— —— 1854. 8°. **1142.** a. **32.**

BARKER (WILLIAM) *of Magdalen College, Oxford. See* GELLI (G. B.) The Fearfull Fansies of the Florentine Couper . . . Translated into English by W. Barker. 1568. 8°. **243.** e. **37.**

—— —— 1599. 8°. **1081.** d. **1.**

—— *See* XENOPHON, *the Historian.* [*Cyropaedia.—English.*] The Bookes of Xenophon contayning the Discipline . . . of Cyrus . . . Translated . . . by W. Barker. [1552?] 8°.
C.114.a.2.

—— —— 1567. 8°. **294.** a. **31.**

—— Epitaphia et inscriptiones lugubres. A Gulielmo Berchero, cum in Italia, animi causa, peregrinaretur, collecta. *In ædibus Iohannis Cawodi: Londini,* 1566. 4°.
C.122.bb.3.

—— The Nobility of Women. By William Bercher, 1559. Now for the first time edited, with introduction and notes by R. W. Bond [and a preface by C. B. Marlay]. (Addenda, Glossary and Index . . . By R. W. Bond.) 2 vol. 1904, 05. 4°. *See* LONDON.—III. *Roxburghe Club.*
C. **101.** h. **1.**

BARKER (WILLIAM) *Rector of Silverton.* A Sermon . . . preached on the anniversary meeting of the Exeter Diocesan Association of the Society for Promoting Christian Knowledge. pp. 35. *J. L. Penny: Exeter,* 1831. 8°.
T. **1375.** (**18.**)

BARKER (WILLIAM) *Stockbroker.* Sound Advice to Investors. pp. 30. *London,* 1885. 8°. **8229.** k. **10.** (**6.**)

BARKER (*Sir* WILLIAM) *Bart. See* SUFFOLK. A Copy of the Poll for the Knights of the Shire for the County of Suffolk . . . Aug. 30 . . . 1727 . . . Candidates Sir W. Barker, Sir J. Danvers, *etc.* 1727. 8°. **807.** b. **27.**

—— Sir William Barker, Bart. Appellant. John Damer and Jos. Damer, executors of Jos. Damer, Esq; deceas'd, and Nath. Evans, Gent. Respondents. The appellant's case. pp. 4. [1731.] fol. **6496.** k. **3.** (**3.**)

—— Sir William Barker, Baronet, Appellant. John Damer and Joseph Damer, Esqrs; executors of the last will and testament of Joseph Damer, Esquire, deceased, and Nathaniel Evans, Gent. Respondents. The respondents case. pp. 3. MS. NOTE. [1731.] fol. **6496.** k. **3.** (**3*.**)

—— Sir William Barker, Bart. Appellant. Thomas Ivers, Esq; Letitia Barker, and Darby Egan, Esq; Respondents. The appellant's case. pp. 4. [1724.] fol.
19. h. **2.** (**89.**)

—— Sir William Barker of Ireland, Bart., Appell^t. Tho. Jevers Esq; Letitia Barker . . . and Darby Egan Esq; Respd^ts. The respondent Jevers's case. pp. 4. [1724.] fol.
19. h. **2.** (**90.**)

BARKER (WILLIAM ALAN)

—— Documents of English History, 1688–1832. Edited by W. A. Barker . . . G. R. St. Aubyn . . . and R. L. Ollard. pp. vii. 85. *A. & C. Black: London,* 1952. 8°.
9507. aa. **22.**

BARKER (WILLIAM ALAN)

—— Documents of English History, 1832–1950. Edited by W. A. Barker . . . G. R. St. Aubyn . . . and R. L. Ollard. pp. viii. 86. *A. & C. Black: London,* 1954. 8°.
09525. l. **22.**

—— A General History of England, 1688–1832. By W. A. Barker . . . G. R. St. Aubyn . . . and R. L. Ollard. pp. vii. 329. *A. & C. Black: London,* 1952. 8°.
09525. k. **18.**

—— A General History of England, 1832–1950. By W. A. Barker . . . G. R. St. Aubyn . . . and R. L. Ollard. pp. 320. *A. & C. Black: London,* 1953. 8°.
09525. k. **28.**

BARKER (WILLIAM ALLEYNE) Mathematical Tables containing the Logarithms of all numbers from 1 to 10000, *etc.* pp. xv. 226. *W. & P. Reynolds; Black, Parry & Co.: London,* 1814. 12°. **8548.** aa. **63.**

BARKER (WILLIAM BASIL)

—— *See* COOKE (Herbert J.) Biology. By H. J. Cooke . . . and W. B. Barker, *etc.* 1949. 8°. **7007.** aa. **31.**

—— Biology for General Science. pp. x. 329. *Longmans, Green & Co.: London,* 1955. 8°. [*General Science Course.*]
W.P. **13868/3.**

BARKER (WILLIAM BOULTON) *See* HAAB (O.) An Atlas of Ophthalmoscopy . . . . Translated and edited by W. B. Barker. [1928.] 8°. Ac. **3832.** b/**7.**

—— Early Treatment of Air Raid Casualties. Edited by: W. B. Barker . . . from material largely supplied by W. R. Challis . . . Published under the joint auspices of the British Optical Association and the Joint Council of Qualified Opticians. pp. 44. *British Optical Association, Joint Council of Qualified Opticians: London,* [1940.] 16°.
07481. de. **47.**

BARKER (WILLIAM BULLOCK) Lame Dogs. An impressionist study. pp. 160. *Bliss & Co.: London,* 1894. 8°. **012630.** f. **32.**

BARKER (WILLIAM BURCKHARDT) *See* ALBERT, *Prince Consort of Victoria, Queen of Great Britain and Ireland.* [*Works.*] Exhibition of the Works of Industry of all Nations. The Speech of . . . Prince Albert . . . translated into the principal European and Oriental languages (by W. B. Barker). [1851.] fol. **1265.** h. **30.**

—— *See* BAITĀL-PACHĪSĪ. The Baitál Pachísí; or Twenty-five Tales of a Demon . . . With a . . . literal English interlinear translation . . . and explanatory notes by W. B. Barker, *etc.* 1855. 8°. **14156.** i. **33.**

—— Lares and Penates: or, Cilicia and its governors; being a short historical account of that province from the earliest times to the present day . . . Edited by William Francis Ainsworth. [With plates and a map.] pp. 394. *Ingram, Cooke & Co.: London,* 1853. 8°. **741.** d. **6.**

—— Odessa and its Inhabitants. By an English Prisoner in Russia [i.e. W. B. Barker]. pp. xi. 174. 1855. 8°. *See* ODESSA. **9077.** b. **46.**

—— A Practical Grammar of the Turkish Language. With dialogues and vocabulary. By W. B. Barker [and A. H. Bleeck]. pp. 157. *Bernard Quaritch: London,* 1854. 8°.
12911. a. **5.**

—— A Reading Book of the Turkish Language, with a grammar and vocabulary, *etc.* 3 pt. *James Madden: London,* 1854 8°. **12907.** c. **20.**

BARKER (WILLIAM BURCKHARDT)

—— A Short Historical Account of the Crimea, from the earliest ages and during the Russian occupation, *etc.* pp. xvi. 240. *Stephen Austin: Hertford; Trübner & Co.: London,* 1855. 8°. **9455. a. 20.**

BARKER (WILLIAM GIBBS) The Doctrine and Practice of the Church of Rome, in the dispensation of Indulgences; a sermon . . . Being the eleventh of a course of sermons "on the errors of the Church of Rome" . . . Fifth thousand. pp. 34. *T. Simpson: Wolverhampton,* 1840. 12°. **3939. aaa. 7. (8.)**

—— Friendly Strictures upon certain portions of the Rev. E. B. Elliott's Horae Apocalypticae. pp. 112. *J. Nisbet & Co.: London,* 1847. 8°. **1218. g. 17.**

—— Lecture on Job xxxvi. 18, 19. *See* D., W. A Course of Sermons on the Creed of Pope Pius IV., *etc.* 1841. 8°. **1352. e. 10.**

—— The Perpetual Abode of the Church with Christ. *See* BIRKS (Thomas R.) The Hope of the Apostolic Church, *etc.* 1845. 12°. **1356. g. 9.**

BARKER (WILLIAM GIDEON MICHAEL JONES) The Desolate One, a poem. pp. 34. *W. E. Painter: London,* 1842. 12°. **11648. a. 29.**

—— The Three Days of Wensleydale; the Valley of the Yore. [With plates.] pp. xxiii. 296. *Charles Dolman: London,* 1854. 8°. **1303. b. 20.**

—— Historical and Topographical Account of Wensleydale . . . Illustrated . . . Second edition [of "The Three Days of Wensleydale"]. pp. xxiii. 296. *J. R. Smith: London,* 1856. 8°. **10360. f. 32.**

BARKER (WILLIAM HENRY) *B.Sc., F.R.G.S.* *See* BOULTON (William H.) and BARKER (W. H.) The Apocalypse and History, *etc.* [1928.] 8°. **03187. e. 64.**

—— The British Isles, *etc.* pp. 140. *"Geographia": London,* [1922.] 8°. **10003. bbb. 37.**

—— Geography in Education & Citizenship. pp. xiii. 203. *University of London Press: London,* 1927. 8°. **10005. bbb. 31.**

BARKER (WILLIAM HENRY) *B.Sc., F.R.G.S.*, and **BROOKS** (LEONARD)

—— Junior Regional Geographies. 3 bk. *University of London Press: London,* 1922, 23. 8°. **010005. e. 14.**

BARKER (WILLIAM HENRY) *B.Sc., F.R.G.S.*, and **REES** (WILLIAM) *M.A., D.Sc.*

—— The Making of Europe. A geographic treatment of the historical development of Europe. pp. viii. 298. *A. & C. Black: London,* 1920. 8°. **09076. aa. 9.**

BARKER (WILLIAM HENRY) *B.Sc., Principal of the Government Institution, Accra,* and **SINCLAIR** (CECILIA) West African Folk-Tales. Collected and arranged by W. H. Barker . . . and C. Sinclair. With frontispiece & twenty-three drawings by C. Sinclair. pp. 183. *G. G. Harrap & Co.: London,* 1917. 8°. **12410. r. 3.**

—— West African Folk-Tales. [Abridged edition.] pp. 128. *Sheldon Press: London,* 1928. 8°. **012403. de. 85.**

—— [A reissue.] *C.M.S. Bookshop: Lagos; printed in England,* [1929.] 8°. **012403. df. 44.**
With the plates of the original unabridged edition.

BARKER (WILLIAM HENRY) *Engineer.* The Sermons and Addresses of a Young Engineer. pp. 50. *Houghton Publishing Co.: London,* 1932. 8°. **04478. k. 8.**

BARKER (WILLIAM HENRY) *J.P., Queensland.* The Croydon Gold Field, North Queensland. A full . . . account . . . with survey plans. pp. 87. *Howard & Jones: London,* 1892. 8°. **7108. b. 14.**

—— The Gold Fields of Western Australia. With . . . geological map, *etc.* pp. 86. *Simpkin & Marshall: London,* 1894. 8°. **07108. g. 10.**

BARKER (WILLIAM HENRY) *Principal of the East Ham Technical College.* The "Akribos" Pocket Card of Four Figure Logarithmic and other Tables. *Philip & Tacey: London,* [1923.] 8°. **8505. k. 1. (12.)**

BARKER (WILLIAM HIGGS) The Hebrew and English Lexicon improved . . . to which is added, a compendious grammar of the Hebrew language. pp. viii. ix. 241. *The Author: Carmarthen,* 1776. 8°. **12903. cc. 14.**

—— [Another edition.] pp. viii. 241. ix. *Lackington, Allen & Co.: London,* 1811. 8°. **825. e. 34.**

BARKER (WILLIAM ROBERT) *Draughts Player,* and **BARKER** (CHARLES FRANCIS) The World's Checker Book: comprising three hundred and fifty-five . . . games, *etc.* pp. 105. *H. A. Young & Co.: Boston,* 1879. 8°. **7915. bb. 9.**

BARKER (WILLIAM ROBERT) *of Bristol.* An Account of the Remains of a Roman Villa discovered at Brislington, Bristol, December, 1899, with a classified list of the objects found, *etc.* pp. 39. pl. IX. 1901. 8°. *See* BRISTOL.—*Bristol Museum and Library, etc.* **07707. h. 9.**

—— Ancient Standard Weights and Measures of the City of Bristol, now in the Bristol Museum of Antiquities. pp. 27. *J. W. Arrowsmith: Bristol,* 1908. 8°. **07708. e. 28. (5.)**

—— The Bristol Museum and Art Gallery. The development of the institution during a hundred and thirty-four years, 1772–1906. [With plates.] pp. 75. 1906. 8°. *See* BRISTOL.—*Bristol Museum and Library, etc.* **7958. f. 29.**

—— A Catalogue of the Autograph Manuscripts and other remains of Thomas Chatterton now in the Bristol Museum of Antiquities. With notes and illustrations. Edited by W. R. Barker. pp. 54. 1907. 8°. *See* BRISTOL.—*Bristol Museum and Library, etc.* **011907. e. 17. (6.)**

—— St. Mark's, or the Mayor's Chapel, Bristol. Part I. The Restoration. By W. R. Barker. Part II. Historical Memoranda. From the works of local historians and the Corporation records. pp. 36. 1889. 8°. *See* BRISTOL.—*Clifton Antiquarian Club.* **Ac. 5628/2.**

—— St. Mark's; or, the Mayor's Chapel, Bristol, formerly called the Church of the Gaunts . . . Illustrated. pp. 219. *W. C. Hemmons: Bristol,* 1892. 8°. **4707. g. 16.**

BARKER-MILL (PETER) *See* MILL.

BARKER-WEBB (PHILIP) *See* WEBB.

BARKESHIRE. *See* BERKSHIRE.

BARKESTEAD (JOHN) *See* BARKSTEAD.

BARKEY (ANTONIUS CORNELIUS) Antonii Cornelii Barkey . . . Observatio ad Dissertatiunculam anonymi in Gen. IV, 7, quae legitur in Symbolarum harum fasciculo I. n. 3. 1778. *See* BARKEY (N.) Symbolae litterariae Haganae, *etc.* classis 1. fasc. 3. 1777, *etc.* 8°. **689. a. 25.**

BARKEY (Nicolaus) *See* Paris (J. G.) Jo. Wilh. Paris . . . Dissertatio ad locum Jerem. xxxi: 22. . . . qua hypotheses . . . N. Barkey . . . examinantur, *etc.* 1768. 8°. [*Bibliotheca Hagana.* classis 1. fasc. 1.] **1013**. a. **2**.

—— *See* Periodical Publications.—*Bremen.* Bibliotheca Bremensis nova historico-philologico-theologica. [Edited by N. Barkey.] 1760, *etc.* 8°. **1014**. a. **17–20** & **1014**. aa. **1, 2**.

—— *See* Schulze (B. W. D.) Epistola ad virum maxime reverendum, Nicolaum Barkey . . . qua pauca ad locum vexatissimum Actor. iii: 19, 20. modeste disputantur . . . Cum animadversionibus N. Barkey, in notis subjectis. 1773. 8°. [*Bibliotheca Hagana.* classis 5. fasc. 2.] **1013**. a. **4**.

—— Nicol. Barkey . . . Ad locum Act. i: 10. conjectura.—Ejusdem observatio ad Luc. ii: 15.—Nicol. Barkey . . . Disquisitio quare Ezechiel in quamplurimis Vaticinii sui locis nomine בן־אדם Filii hominis compellatur. 1739. *See* Gerdes (D.) Miscellanea Duisburgensia, *etc.* (Miscellanea Groningana. tom. 2.) [1732, *etc.*] 8°. **851**. g. **4**.

—— Bibliotheca Hagana historico-philologico-theologica, ad continuationem Bibliothecæ Bremensis novæ constructa a N. Barkey. 6 classes. *Amstelodami & Lugduni Batav.*, 1768–77. 8°. **1013**. a. **2–4**.

—— [Another copy of classes 1, 2.] **219**. d. **10**.

—— Nicolai Barkey, Commentatio de scopo evangelii, quod est secundum Joannem, *etc.* 1771. *See* supra: Bibliotheca Hagana, *etc.* classis 3. fasc. 3. 1768, *etc.* 8°. **1013**. a. **3**.

—— Nicolai Barkey . . . De Sabiis, vel Christianis Sancti Joannis diatribe. 1772. *See* supra: Bibliotheca Hagana, *etc.* classis 4. fasc. 2. 1768, *etc.* 8°. **1013**. a. **3**.

—— Dissertatio theologica inauguralis, in Psalmum decimum octavum, *etc.* pp. 45. *Groningæ*, 1754. 4°. **3091**. aa. **25**.

—— Museum Haganum historico-philologico-theologicum: exstructum a N. Barkey. 4 tom. *Hagae Comitum*, 1774–80. 8°. **1013**. a. **5, 6**.

—— Nicolai Barkey, Observatio exegetica ad Act. i: 6, 7. 1768. *See* supra: Bibliotheca Hagana, *etc.* classis 1. fasc. 3. 1768, *etc.* 8°. **1013**. a. **2**.

—— Nicolai Barkey, Observationes exegeticæ ad Act. ii, iii, iv. 1769. *See* supra: Bibliotheca Hagana, *etc.* classis 2. fasc. 2. 1768, *etc.* 8°. **1013**. a. **2**.

—— Nicolai Barkey . . . Observationum exegeticarum, in Actorum caput tertium, trias, *etc.* 1770. *See* supra: Bibliotheca Hagana, *etc.* classis 3. fasc. 1. 1768, *etc.* 8°. **1013**. a. **3**.

—— Symbolae litterariae Haganae, ad incrementum scientiarum omne genus, a variis . . . collatae: editore N. Barkey. [In continuation of the Bibliotheca Hagana historico-philologico-theologica.] 2 classes. *Hagae Comitum*, 1777–80. 8°. **689**. a. **25**.
Imperfect; wanting fasc. 3 *of classis* 2.

BARKHAM (*Sir* Edward) *See* Middleton (Thomas) *Dramatist.* The Sunne in Aries. A noble solemnity performed through the Citie . . . at the confirmation and establishment of . . . E. Barkham, in the high office of . . . Lord Maior of the famous Citie of London, *etc.* 1621. 4°. C. **33**. e. **7**. (**18**.)

BARKHAM (John) *See* Barcham.

BARKHASH (I. M.)

—— *See* Germany.—Allgemeiner Kongress der *Arbeiter und Soldatenräte Deutschlands.* 1-й (2-й) Всегерманский с'езд рабочих и солдатских советов, *etc.* (Перевод с немецкого: Бархаш И. М.) 1934, *etc.* 8°. Ac. **2352**. d/8.

BARKHASHOV (Boris)

—— В бакинском подполье. Второе, исправленное издание. pp. 108. *Москва*, 1933. 8°. **9454**. aa. **14**.

BARKHATNAYA KNIGA. *See* Russia.—*Princes.* Родословная книга князей и дворянъ россійскихъ . . . Содержащая въ себѣ родословную книгу . . . которая извѣстна подъ названіемъ Бархатной Книги, *etc.* 1787. 8°. **1328**. c. **11, 12**.

BARKHATOV (M. E.) and **FUNKE** (V. V.) "Исторія Русско-Японской войны" . . . Редакторы-издатели: М. Е. Бархатовъ и В. В. Функе. (Иллюстрированная.) 5 том. pp. 1281. *С.-Петербургъ*, 1907–09. 4°. **9055**. f. **32**.

BARKHAUSEN (Carl Georg)

—— *See* Barkhausen (Georg H.) Tagebuch eines Rheinbund-Offiziers . . . 1808 bis 1814. Herausgegeben von seinem Enkel (G. Barkhausen). 1900. 8°. **09078**. dd. **19**.

—— *See* Blum (Alfred) Die Eisenbahn-Technik der Gegenwart . . . Herausgegeben von Blum . . . Barkhausen. 1903, *etc.* 8°. **8764**. f. **1**.

—— —— 1912, *etc.* 8°. **8768**. g. **20**.

—— Betrachtungen über das Verhältnis der höheren Einheitsschule zur Technischen Hochschule. 1888. *See* Germany.—*Deutscher Einheitsschulverein.* Schriften, *etc.* Hft. 4. 1887, *etc.* 8°. **8357**. cc. **56**.

—— Zwanglose Beiträge zur Kenntniss der forstlichen Verhältnisse im Königlich Preussischen Regierungs-Bezirke Lüneburg mit besonderer Berücksichtigung der Aufforstungs-Bestrebungen daselbst. pp. vii. 80. *Hannover*, 1888. 8°. **07028**. i. **12**. (**4**.)

BARKHAUSEN (Carl Georg) and **LAUTER** (W. H.)

—— Ueber die praktische Ausbildung der Studirenden des Baufaches während der Studienzeit, *etc.* pp. 27. *Darmstadt*, 1894. 8°. [Durm (*J.*) *Handbuch der Architektur.* Ergänzungshft. 3.] **7816**. p. **5/1**.

BARKHAUSEN (Ernst)

—— Die Tuchindustrie in Montjoie: ihr Aufstieg und Niedergang. pp. 181. *Aachen*, 1925. 8°. **08223**. f. **55**.

BARKHAUSEN (Georg) *M.D.* *See* Albers (J. A.) Icones ad illustrandam anatomen comparatam. [fasc. 2 edited by G. Barkhausen.] 1818, *etc.* fol. **578.m.17.(1.)**

—— Beobachtungen über den Säuferwahnsinn oder das Delirium tremens. pp. 243. *Bremen*, 1828. 8°. **1174**. i. **30**.

—— Rückblick auf Dr. Heinr. Wilh. Matth. Olbers' Gesundheitszustand in den beiden letzten Decennien seines Lebens. pp. 25. *Bremen*, 1842. 8°. **10708**. d. **37**.

BARKHAUSEN (Georg) *Professor in the Technische Hochschule at Hanover.* *See* Barkhausen (Carl G.)

BARKHAUSEN (Georg Heinrich) Tagebuch eines Rheinbund-Offiziers aus dem Feldzuge gegen Spanien und während spanischer und englischer Kriegsgefangenschaft. 1808 bis 1814. Herausgegeben von seinem Enkel (G. Barkhausen). pp. viii. 209. *Wiesbaden*, 1900. 8°. **09078**. dd. **19**.

BARKHAUSEN (HEINRICH LUDWIG WILIBALD) *See* BARCKHAUSEN.

BARKHAUSEN (MAX) Francesco Guicciardinis politische Theorien in seinen " Opere inedite." pp. vii. 117. *Heidelberg*, 1908. 8°. [*Heidelberger Abhandlungen zur mittleren und neueren Geschichte.* Hft. 22.] **09009.ff.2/22.**

BARKHAUSEN (WERNER MEYER) *See* MEYER-BARKHAUSEN (W.)

BARKHAUS-WIESENHUETTEN (VON) *Baroness.* Ueber olographe und mystische Testamente. Eine Deductionsschrift in der Rechtssache des Testamentserben der verstorbenen Freyfrau von Barkhaus-Wiesenhütten, gebornen von Veltheim, gegen die Intestaterben derselben. [By C. L. W. von Grolmann.] pp. 275. *Giessen & Darmstadt*, 1814. 8°. **6025.** aaa. **9.**

BARKHIN (G. B.)

—— Архитектура театра. pp. 245. 1947. fol. *See* MOSCOW.—*Академия Архитектуры СССР.* L.R. **261.** b. **20.**

BARKHIN (M. G.)

—— *See* SUISOEV (E. V.) Военно-инженерное дело, *etc.* [By M. G. Barkhin and others.] 1946. 8°. **8838.dd.33.**

BARKHOLT (ERICH) Die Ontologie Hugos von St. Victor. Inaugural-Dissertation, *etc.* pp. 52. *Bonn*, 1930. 8°. **3851.** df. **11.**

BARKHUDAROV (S. G.)

—— *See* OBNORSKY (S. P.) and BARKHUDAROV (S. G.) Хрестоматия по истории русского языка, *etc.* 1952, *etc.* 8°. W.P. c. **12.**

—— *See* SHCHERBA (L. V.) Грамматика русского языка, *etc.* [A new edition of the work originally written by S. G. Barkhudarov.] 1950. 8°. **012977.** e. **7.**

—— *See* VINOGRADOV (V. V.) Грамматика русского языка. (Редакционная коллегия: В. В. Виноградов, Е. С. Истрина, С. Г. Бархударов.) 1952, *etc.* 8°. **012977.** ee. **10.**

BARKHVURDĀR IBN MAHMUD, called MUMTĀZ, *Farāhī.* History of Nassar.—History of Farrukhruz.—Persian stories. [Selected from the Mahbūb ul-Kulūb, translated by E. Rehatsek.] *See* CLOUSTON (William A.) A Group of Eastern Romances, *etc.* 1889. 8°. **14003.** h. **21.**

BARKIN (S. R.)

—— *See* DIPMAN (Carl W.) How to sell Fruits and Vegetables . . . By C. W. Dipman . . . S. R. Barkin. [1936.] 8°. **8233.** cc. **21.**

BARKING, *Essex.*

—— Barking. Official Guide. pp. 72. *New Centurion Publishing & Publicity Co.: Derby*, [1931.] 4°. **010352.** d. **6.**

—— The Book of Barking. Being a souvenir of the Charter celebrations, historical pageant and industrial exhibition, October, 1931. [With plates.] pp. 108. *Fleetway Press: London*, [1931.] 4°. **010352.** d. **5.**

Abbey of SS. Mary and Ethelburga.

—— Barking Abbey Rental. [1937, 38.] *See* BARKING.—*Barking and District Archæological Society.* Transactions. 1936, 1937. [1936, *etc.*] 8°. Ac. **5646.** c.

—— The Early Charters of Barking Abbey. By Cyril Hart. [The texts of the Charters, with English translations and commentary. With facsimiles and a map.] pp. 44. *Benham & Co.: Colchester*, 1953. 8°. **04785.** n. **25.**

BARKING, *Essex.*

—— *Barking and District Archaeological Society.* *See* infra: *Barking Historical Society.*

Barking Baptist Tabernacle.

—— A Century of Christian Witness . . . Barking Baptist Tabernacle, 1850–1950. Centenary souvenir brochure. [Edited by Harold Cowling. With illustrations.] pp. 19. [*Barking*, 1950.] 8°. **4716.** a. **56.**

Barking Historical Society.

Founded as Barking and District Archaeological Society.
Name subsequently changed to Barking Historical Society.

—— Transactions, 1935 [*etc.*]. [*Barking*, 1935– .] 8°. Ac. **5646.** c.

Barking Social Services Committee.

—— Souvenir of the Opening Ceremony of Lodge Farm Centre . . . June 21st, 1934. pp. 7. *Barking*, [1934.] 8°. **8286.** f. **42.**

Borough Council.

—— The Annual Report of the School Medical Officer for the year 1931 [*etc.*]. [*Ilford*, 1932– .] 4°. A.R. **40.**
Previous reports are entered under BARKING.—*Urban District Council.*

—— Barking Vestry Minutes, and other parish documents. By J. E. Oxley. [With facsimiles.] pp. xiv. 344. pl. 14. *Benham & Co.: Colchester*, 1955. 8°. **9506.** e. **18.**

—— A Century of Progress in Local Government in Barking, 1835–1935. [With illustrations.] pp. 119. *Drayton Press: Ilford*, [1935.] 4°. **8286.** d. **23.**

—— Report of the Medical Officer of Health for the year 1931 [*etc.*] *Ilford*, [1932– .] 4°. A.R. **43.**
Previous reports are entered under BARKING.—*Local Board, and* BARKING.—*Urban District Council.*

Borough Council.—Education Committee.

—— Dorothy Barley and Bifrons Schools, Barking. A brief description, with photographs and plans, issued on the occasion of the formal opening by H. Ramsbotham . . . on 28th June, 1934. pp. 20. [*Barking*, 1934.] 4°. **08367.** dd. **1.**

—— The Schools of Barking. A brief survey, with photographs and plans, issued on the occasion of the formal opening of the Eastbury, Cambell, Erkenwald, Roding, Dawson and Monteagle Schools by Sir Henry Hadow . . . on 6th October, 1932. pp. 40. [*Barking*, 1932.] 4°. **08367.** dd. **2.**

Borough Council.—Public Library Committee.

—— 43rd (-49th) Annual Report, 1st April 1931—31st March, 1932(-1938). [1932-38.] 8°. *See* supra: *Urban District Council.—Public Library Committee.* Annual Report of the Librarian, *etc.* 1924, *etc.* 8°. A.R. **168.**

Central Minor Ailments Clinic.

—— Souvenir of the Official Opening of the Central Minor Ailments Clinic . . . 18th October, 1934. pp. 8. *Barking*, [1934.] 8°. **7686.** b. **21.**

Infectious Diseases Hospital.

—— Souvenir of the Official Opening of the First Portion of the New Infectious Diseases Hospital . . . 29th September, 1932. [With plates.] pp. 11. *Barking*, [1932.] 8°. **7686.** dd. **11.**

BARKING, *Essex.*

Local Board.

—— Annual Report of Medical Officer [for 1892]. (The Inspector of Nuisances Report.) pp. 5. [*Barking*, 1893.] fol. **A.R. 41.**

Public Library.

—— [For reports of the Public Library Committee of the Urban District Council of Barking, and of the Borough Council of Barking:] *See* supra: *Urban District Council.—Public Library Committee.*

Urban District Council.

—— The Annual Report of the Medical Officer of Health and Sanitary Inspector (Report of the Medical Officer of Health.—Report of the Medical Officer of Health and School Medical Officer) for the year 1921(–1930). *Barking*, [1922–31.] 8°. **A.R. 42.**

An earlier report is entered under BARKING.—*Local Board. Subsequent reports are entered under* BARKING.—*Borough Council.*

—— The Annual Report of the School Medical Officer for the year 1923 (29, 30). 3 pt. *Barking*, [1924–31.] 8°. **A.R. 39.**

Wanting the report for 1927. *The reports for the years* 1924–26 *and* 1928 form part of *the Annual Report of the Medical Officer of Health. Later reports are entered under* BARKING.—*Borough Council.*

—— *Urban District Council.—Public Health Department.* A Guide to Health. pp. 71. *Barking*, [1927.] 8°. **7384. r. 46.**

Urban District Council.—Public Library Committee.

—— Annual Report of the Librarian 1923–1924 (1924–1925). (Thirty seventh—forty second Annual Report of the Public Library, April 1925 to March 1926—1st April, 1929 to 31st March 1931.—Borough of Barking Public Library 43rd (-49th) Annual Report 1st April 1931—31st March, 1932–1938.) *London*, 1924–38. 8°. **A.R. 168.**

BARKING, *Suffolk.—Church of St. Mary the Virgin.*

—— Notes on St. Mary's Church, Barking, Suffolk. [Signed: H. R. L.] [1954.] 8°. *See* L., H. R. **010368. k. 229.**

BARKING, JAMES THEODORE, *Bishop of.* *See* INSKIP.

BARKING, WILLIAM FRANK PERCIVAL, *Bishop of.* *See* CHADWICK (William F. P.) *Bishop of Barking.*

BARKING ABBEY.

—— *See* BARKING, *Essex.—Abbey of SS. Mary and Ethelburga.*

BARKING AND DISTRICT ARCHÆOLOGICAL SOCIETY.

—— *See* BARKING, *Essex.—Barking Historical Society.*

BARKING BAPTIST TABERNACLE. *See* BARKING, Essex.

BARKING HISTORICAL SOCIETY. *See* BARKING, *Essex.*

BARKING—SAINT ALBANS'—OLD GUIDES' ASSOCIATION. *See* ENGLAND.—*Girl Guides Association.*

BARKLA (CHARLES GLOVER) and **CARSE** (GEORGE A.) Notes on Practical Physics for junior students. pp. xii. 113. *Gurney & Jackson: London*, 1915. 8°. **8706. e. 5.**

—— Second edition. pp. xii. 114. *Gurney & Jackson: London, Edinburgh*, 1926. 8°. **8710. aa. 19.**

BARKLAI DE TOLLI (MIKHAIL BOGDANOVICH) *Prince.* *See* KHARKEVICH (V. I.) Барклай-Де-Толли въ отечественную войну . . . Съ приложеніемъ переписки съ Императоромъ Александромъ I. 1904. 8°. **09077. eee. 8.**

BARKLAIUSZ (JAN) *Poet and Author of the "Argenis.* *See* BARCLAY (John)

BARKLÁJUS (JÁNOS) *Poet and Author of the " Argenis."* *See* BARCLAY (John)

BARKLAY (JOHN) *Poet and Author of the "Argenis."* *See* BARCLAY.

BARKLEY (ALBEN WILLIAM)

—— *See* UNITED STATES OF AMERICA. [*Miscellaneous Public Documents.*] Surrender of Italy, Germany and Japan World War II. Instruments of surrender, public papers and addresses of the President and of the Supreme Commanders. Presented by Senator Barkley, *etc.* 1946. 8° [*U.S. Senate Documents.* 79th Congress. 1st Session no. 93.] **A.S. 10/4**

BARKLEY (BONITA)

—— Suddenly it was May! A refreshing comedy of college life in three acts. pp. 108. *Samuel French: New York*, [1947.] 8°. **011791. bb. 2**

BARKLEY (CHRISTINA A.) The Shack on Cedar Creek. pp. viii. 339. *J. McKelvie & Sons: Greenock*, 1917. 8°. **NN. 4710**

BARKLEY (GEORGE) A Briefe Memoriall of the great Trauells by Sea and Land of Master G. Barkley . . . in Europe, Asia, Africa, and America. *See* PURCHAS (Samuel) *the Elder.* Purchas his Pilgrimes, *etc.* pt. 3. 1625. fol. **679. h. 13**

—— [Another edition.] 1906. *See* PURCHAS (S.) *the Elder.* Hakluytus Posthumus, *etc.* vol. 13. 1905, *etc.* 8°. **2060.a.**

—— [Another copy.] **010026. k**

BARKLEY (HENRY)

—— Thunderstorms in Australia. [With a map.] pp. 6. *Melbourne*, 1934. 8°. [*Commonwealth of Australia Bureau of Meteorology.* Bulletin no. 19.] **C.S. G. 502**

—— Zones of Relative Physical Comfort in Australia [With a map.] pp. 7. *Melbourne*, 1934. 8°. [*Commonwealth of Australia. Bureau of Meteorology.* Bulletin no. 20.] **C.S. G. 502**

BARKLEY (*Sir* HENRY) *See* BARKLY.

BARKLEY (HENRY C.) Between the Danube and Black Sea; or, Five years in Bulgaria. pp. xviii. 313. *John Murray: London*, 1876. 8°. **10125. aaa. 32**

—— Second edition. pp. xx. 313. *John Murray: London*, 1877. 8°. **10126. cc. 25**

—— Bulgaria before the War, during seven years' experience of European Turkey and its inhabitants. pp. xxiv. 344 *John Murray: London*, 1877. 8°. **10126. cc. 26**

—— My Boyhood; a story book for boys . . . With illustrations. pp. xii. 237. *John Murray: London*, 1877. 8°. **12809. bbb. 17**

—— A Ride Through Asia Minor and Armenia: giving a sketch of the characters, manners and customs of both the Mussulman and Christian inhabitants. pp. x. 350. *John Murray: London*, 1891. 8°. **10076. eee. 18**

—— Studies in the Art of Rat-Catching, *etc.* pp. vii. 185. *John Murray: London*, 1891. 8°. **7908. ee. 23**

—— Popular edition. pp. vii. 185. *John Murray: London*, 1911. 8°. **07906. f. 18.**

BARKLEY (JOHN) Report of the Trial of John Barkley, one of the shop-men of Richard Carlile, prosecuted by the Constitutional Association for publishing a seditious and blasphemous libel. pp. iv. 20. *Effingham Wilson: London*, 1822. 8°. **8135**. ccc. **5**. **(11.)**

—— Second edition, with an appendix containing an account of the proceedings in the House of Commons on the petition of the defendant. *See* CARLILE (J.) The Trials with the Defences at Large of Mrs. Jane Carlile, Mary Ann Carlile, *etc.* 1825. 8°. **6495**. bb. **13**.

BARKLEY (JOHN FERDINAND) *See* KREISINGER (H.) and BARKLEY (J. F.) Measuring the Temperature of Gases in Boiler Settings. 1918. 8°. [*U.S. Bureau of Mines. Bulletin.* no. 145.] A.S. **229**.

—— Fundamentals of Smoke Abatement. pp. 34. pl. 2. *Pittsburgh*, 1950. 4°. [*U.S. Bureau of Mines. Information Circular.* no. 7588.] A.S. **229/6**

—— A Guide for Reducing Fuel Consumption in Commercial Plants. By J. F. Barkley, Thos. C. Cheasley and K. M. Waddell. pp. vi. 168. *Washington*, 1947. 8°. [*U.S. Bureau of Mines. Bulletin.* no. 466.] A.S. **229**.

—— The National Fuel Efficiency Program during the War Years 1943–45. By J. F. Barkley, Thos. C. Cheasley, and K. M. Waddell. pp. iii. 100. *Washington*, 1949. 8°. [*U.S. Bureau of Mines. Bulletin.* no. 469.] A.S. **229**.

—— Questions and Answers for the Coal Fireman. pp. 17. 1930. 16°. *See* UNITED STATES OF AMERICA.—*Bureau of Mines.* A.S. **231/10**.

—— Questions and Answers for the Coal Fireman. pp. 17. 1938. 8°. *See* UNITED STATES OF AMERICA.—*Bureau of Mines.* A.S. **231/15**.

—— Questions and Answers for the Home Fireman. pp. ii. 34. 1933. 16°. *See* UNITED STATES OF AMERICA.—*Bureau of Mines.* A.S. **231/6**.

—— Questions and Answers for the Home Fireman. (Revised, Jan. 17, 1940.) pp. 34. 1940. 8°. *See* UNITED STATES OF AMERICA.—*Bureau of Mines.* A.S. **231/14**.

BARKLEY (JOHN FERDINAND) and **MORGAN** (RAY EARLAND)

—— Burning Wood Waste for Commercial Heat and Power. [With plates and diagrams.] pp. 12. [*Washington*,] 1950. 4°. [*U.S. Bureau of Mines. Information Circular.* no. 7580.] A.S. **229/6**.

—— Fuel-Burning Equipment Dimensions required by Smoke-Abatement Ordinances. pp. 19. [*Washington*], 1950. 4°. [*U.S. Bureau of Mines. Information Circular.* no. 7557.] A.S. **229/6**.

BARKLEY (JOHN TREVOR) Report on the Purchase and Occupation of Landed Property in Connaught; with estimates of present value. pp. 28. *Trelawny Saunders: London*, 1850. 8°. **8276**. d. **3**.

BARKLEY (*Sir* ROBERT) *See* BERKELEY.

BARKLEY (WILLIAM) *M.A.*

—— Bad Language . . . A discussion and illustration of a simpler form of written English. pp. 48. *War Facts Press: London*, 1945. 8°. **12986**. b. **45**.

—— Bad Language . . . A discussion and illustration of a simpler form of written English. pp. 48. *War Facts Press: London*, 1946. 8°. **12982**. p. **51**.
With a label bearing the imprint of Sir I. Pitman & Sons, London, pasted over the original imprint.

BARKLEY (WILLIAM) *M.A.*

—— The Two Englishes. Being some account of the differences between the spoken and the written English languages, *etc.* pp. 52. *Sir I. Pitman & Sons: London*, 1941. 8°. **012986**. bb. **1**.

—— William Barkley's Notebook, *etc.* pp. 199. *Daily Express: [London,]* 1948. 8°. **12360**. d. **19**.

BARKLEY (WILLIAM) *M.B., B.Ch.*

—— *See* TWEDDELL (Francis) About Baby . . . British edition, revised and edited by W. Barkley. 1913. 8°. **07580**. e. **37**.

BARKLY (FANNY ALEXANDRA) Among Boers and Basutos. The story of our life on the frontier . . . Second edition. pp. viii. 270. *Remington & Co.: London & Sydney*, 1894. 8°. **10095**. de. **21**.

—— Among Boers and Basutos and with Barkly's Horse . . . Extended and thoroughly revised to date. pp. 257. *Roxburghe Press: London*, [1896.] 8°. **010096**. g. **23**.

—— From the Tropics to the North Sea, *etc.* pp. 252. *Roxburghe Press: London*, [1897.] 8°. **010025**. df. **26**.

BARKLY (*Sir* HENRY) *G.C.M.G.*

—— [For Proclamations, etc. by Sir Henry Barkly as Governor of Basutoland :] *See* BASUTOLAND.

—— *See* MELBOURNE.—*Public Library, Museum and National Gallery of Victoria.* Address of the Trustees of the Melbourne Public Library . . . to Sir H. B. . . . With his Excellency's Reply. [1861.] *s. sh.* 4°. L.R. **110**. d. **6**. **(92.)**

—— *See* STOW (Fred) A Review of the Barkley Administration in relation to the South African Diamond Fields, setting forth the unconstitutional way in which the early diggers were deprived of their bona fide rights, *etc.* 1893. 8°. **8154**. dd. **20**. **(8.)**

—— *See* TRANSVAAL. Official Correspondence. Reply of President Burgers to despatches of Sir H. Barkly [upon the Keate Award], *etc.* 1874. 8°. **8154**. e. **6**. **(3.)**

—— Testa de Nevill. Returns for County of Gloucester. [1888–90.] *See* GLOUCESTER, *County of.*—*Bristol and Gloucestershire Archæological Society.* Transactions. vol. 12–14. [1876, *etc.*] 8°. Ac. **5650/4**.

BARKMAN (ÅKE)

—— Études cliniques sur les syndromes moteurs et réflexes de la paroi abdominale et d'origine cérébrale . . . Thèse pour le doctorat, *etc.* [With a bibliography.] pp. 303. *Uppsala*, 1929. 8°. **07620**. h. **33**.

BARKMAN (CHARLES PRUDEN) Peking, and other poems. pp. x. 118. *Commercial Press: Shanghai*, 1923. 8°. **011645**. e. **144**.

BARKMAN (GUSTAF BERTIL CARLSON) Gustaf II Adolfs regementsorganisation vid det inhemska infanteriet. En studie över organisationens tillkomst och huvuddragen av dess utveckling mot bakgrunden av kontinental organisation. pp. xii. 221. *Stockholm*, 1931. 8°. [*Meddelanden från Generalstabens krigshistoriska avdelning.* 1.] **8838.d.38/1.**

BARKMAN (HILDING) Bidrag till den transscendentala kategoriläran, I. Akademisk afhandling, *etc.* pp. 52. *Uppsala*, 1901. 8°. **8462**. e. **46**.
No more published.

BARKMANN (JOANNES CAROLUS) Dissertatio inauguralis medica descriptionem febris castrensis sistens, quae inter exercitum Borussicum moenia Gedani obridentem anno proximo epidemice grassabatur, *etc.* pp. 14. *Berolini*, 1814. 8°. **7385.*a**. **(2.)**

BARKMEIER (Joseph H.)

—— Trading under the Laws of Canada. pp. viii. 143. *Washington*, 1938. 8°. [*U.S. Bureau of Foreign and Domestic Commerce. Trade Promotion Series.* no. 176.] A.S. **126/2.**

BAR KOBA, *pseud. See* Arabian Nights. [*Abridgments, etc.*] The History of the Fisherman and the Genius . . . With notes by . . . Bar-Koba, *etc.* 1859. fol. **1751.** b. **8.**

BARKÓCZI (László)

—— *See* Párducz (M.) Intercisa, *etc.* [By L. Barkóczi and others.] (Szerkesztő: Párducz M.) 1954, *etc.* fol. [*Archaeologia hungarica.* új folyam. no. 33, *etc.*] Ac. **7301.** b/**6.**

—— Brigetio. [An archaeological description.] *Hung.* 2 pt. pp. 79. pl. lxv. *Budapest*, 1951, 44. fol. [*Dissertationes Pannonicae.* ser. 2. no. 22.] Ac. **821.**

BARKÓCZY (Krisztina) *Károlyi Sándor Grófné. See* Takáts (S.) Szalai Barkóczy Krisztina, 1671–1724. 1910. 8°. **010795.** ee. **34.**

BARKÓCZY-KLOPSCH (Béla) Der Heimzug der Armee des Generalfeldmarschalls von Mackensen durch Ungarn, nach dem Zusammenbruch, *etc.* pp. vi. 80. *Budapest*, 1928. 8°. **09081.** c. **36.**

BARKOSES (Nikolaos) *See* Baumeister (F. C.) *Φρεδερικου Χριστιανου Βαϋμαϊστερου λογικη . . . μεταφρασθεισα . . . απο της λατινιδος . . . παρα του . . . διδασκαλου . . . Ν. Βαρκοση, etc.* 1795. 4°. **871.** e. **16.**

BARKOV (Aleksandr Sergeevich)

—— *See* Kruber (A. A.) Азія. Иллюстрированный географическій сборникъ, составленный . . . А. Круберомъ, С. Григорьевымъ, А. Барковымъ, *etc.* 1908. 8°. **10076.** g. **25.**

—— *See* Russia. [*Appendix.—Descriptions and Travels.*] Азіатская Россія. Иллюстрированный географическій сборникъ, составленный . . . А. Круберомъ . . . А. Барковымъ, *etc.* 1910. 8°. **010055.** f. **24.**

—— *See* Russia. [*Appendix.—Descriptions and Travels.*] Европейская Россія. Иллюстрированный географическій сборникъ, составленный . . . А. Круберомъ . . . А. Барковымъ, *etc.* 1913. 8°. **10292.** k. **35.**

—— Словарь справочник по физической географии. Пособие для учителей географии. Издание 3-е, переработанное и дополненное. pp. 307. *Москва*, 1954. 8°. **010005.** c. 16.

BARKOV (Ivan Semenovich)

—— *See* Kantemir (A. D.) *Prince.* Сатиры и другія стихотворческія сочиненія . . . съ краткимъ описаніемъ его жизни [by I. S. Barkov]. [Published by the Academy, under the editorship of Barkov.] 1762. 4°. **11585.** h. **32.** (**1.**)

—— *See* Kantemir (A. D.) *Prince.* Satyres du Prince Cantemir, traduites du Russe en François [by L. A***, i.e. L'Abbe Count O. de Guasco]; avec l'histoire de sa vie [by the same from the life by I. S. Barkov]. 1750. 12°. **1160.** b. **10.**

—— Сочиненія и переводы И. С. Баркова. 1762–1764 г. Съ біографическимъ очеркомъ автора. pp. v. 308. *С.-Петербургъ*, 1872. 8°. **12264.** c. **1.**

BARKOV (N. V.) Мотивы Русскаго орнамента xi, xii, xiii, xiv, xv и xvi вѣковъ, собранные Н. В. Барковымъ. [Fifty-one plates with explanatory text.] pp. 107. *въ Москвѣ*, [1912.] 8°. **07806.** f. **29.**

BARKOVA (Ol'ha)

—— Кожний день. Повість. [With illustrations.] pp. 340. *Львів*, 1951. 8°. **12594.** f. **29.**

—— Трудное счастье. Роман. pp. 519. *Москва*, 1954. 8°. **12595.** c. **20.**

BARKOVIĆ (Josip)

—— Iza prve linije. pp. 116. *Zagreb*, 1945. 8°. **012593.** ff. **21.**
Partizanska književnost. knj. 6.

—— [Another copy.] Iza prve linije. *Zagreb*, 1945. 8°. **012593.** ff. **5.**

—— Tri smrti. pp. 139. *Zagreb*, 1951. 8°. [*Mala biblioteka.* no. 96.] W.P. d. **294/14.**

BARKOVICH (Francesco Vincislao) Saggio della origine e natura delle passioni. *See* Chiaramonti (G. B.) Dissertazioni istoriche, scientifiche, erudite, *etc.* tom. 1. 1765. 4°. **128.** a. **4.**

—— [Another edition.] 1832. *See* Italian Classics. Collezione de' classici italiani. vol. 352. 1804, *etc.* 8°. **12201.p.1/352.**

BARKOVIUS (A. F.) *See* Barkow.

BARKOVSKY (I. Valerianovich Dunin)

—— *See* Dunin-Barkovsky.

BARKOW (August Friedrich) *See* Rome. [*Collections of Laws.*] Corpus iuris Romani anteiustiniani. Consilio . . . E. Böckingii A. Bethmann-Holwegii et . . . E. Puggaei institutum. Curaverunt iidem assumptis sociis L. Arndtsio A. F. Barkovio, *etc.* 1841, *etc.* 4°. **705.** h. **16.**

—— De Davide Maevio narratio. *See* Greifswald.—*Alberts-Universität.* Viros . . . quibus summos in utroque jure honores . . . conferendos decrevit jurisconsultorum Gryphiswaldensium ordo . . . renuntiandos indicit D. G. Beseler, *etc.* [1857.] 4°. **10707.** h. **42.** (**7.**)

BARKOW (Erich) *See* Philipp (H.) Ergebnisse der W. Filchnerschen Vorexpedition nach Spitzbergen 1910, mit . . . Beiträgen der Herren Dr. Barkow, Dr. Potpeschnigg, *etc.* 1914. 8°. [*Petermanns Mitteilungen.* Ergänzungshft. 179.] P.P. **3946.**

BARKOW (Gustavus Adolphus Theodorus) De diphtheritide. Dissertatio inauguralis medica, *etc.* pp. 31. *Berolini*, [1863?] 8°. **7615.** aa. **10.**

BARKOW (Hans Carl Leopold) Anatomische Untersuchungen über die Harnblase des Menschen nebst Bemerkungen über die männliche und weibliche Harnröhre, *etc.* pp. 60. pl. xiii. *Breslau*, 1858. fol. **1831.** b. **8.**

—— Die angiologische Sammlung im anatomischen Museum der Königlichen Universität zu Breslau . . . Mit 58 . . . Holzschnitten und 11 Tafeln, *etc.* pp. cxlvii. 447. *Breslau*, 1869. 4°. **7421.** g. **17.**

—— Beiträge zur pathologischen Entwickelungsgeschichte. 3 Abt. *Breslau*, [1858,]1859. 4° & fol. **1830.** b. **4.**

—— Bemerkungen zur pathologischen Osteologie. Mit . . . lithographirten Tafeln. 2 Abt. *Breslau*, 1864. fol. **1831.** b. **21.**

—— Comparative Morphologie des Menschen und der menschenähnlichen Thiere. Mit . . . Tafeln. [Tl. 1 edited by W. Reinhardt.] 6 Tl. *Greifswald, Breslau*, 1875, 62–68. fol. **1831.** c. **7.**
Tl. 1, *which was published in* 1875, *after the death of the author, is incomplete.*

BARKOW (Hans Carl Leopold)

—— Disquisitiones circa originem et decursum arteriarum mammalium, *etc.* pp. viii. 114. pl. v. *Lipsiæ*, 1829. 4°. **7406. g. 28.**

—— Erläuterungen zur Lehre von den Erweiterungen und Verkrümmungen der Gefässe, *etc.* pp. xxiv. 38. pl. xix. *Breslau*, 1871. fol. **1831. c. 1.**

—— Das Leben der Walle in seiner Beziehung zum Athmen und zum Blutlauf, *etc.* pp. 40. *Breslau*, 1862. fol. **7407. i. 5.**

—— Monstra animalium duplicia, per anatomen indagata; habito respectu ad physiologiam, medicinam forensem, et artem obstetriciam. Accedunt tabulæ. 2 tom. *Lipsiae*, 1828, 36. 4°. **728. i. 18, 19.**

—— Syndesmologie oder die Lehre von den Bändern, durch welche die Knochen des menschlichen Körpers zum Gerippe vereint werden. pp. vi. 121. *Breslau*, 1841. 8°. **7421. g. 16.**

—— Ueber Pseudacormus, oder den scheinbar rumpflosen Kopf, *etc.* [With a plate.] pp. 35. *Breslau*, 1854. fol. **1833. a. 28**

—— Die Venen der obern Extremität des Menschen, *etc.* pp. lxviii. pl. vi. *Breslau*, 1868. fol. **1832. e. 9.**

—— Der Winterschlaf nach seinen Erscheinungen im Thierreich dargestellt, *etc.* pp. x. 525. pl. iv. *Berlin*, 1846. 8°. **1257. h. 14.**

—— Zootomische Bemerkungen, *etc.* pp. 28. *Breslau*, 1851. fol. **505.h.18.(1.)**

BARKOWIUS (Augustus) *See* Barkow (August F.)

BARKOWIUS (Joannes Carolus Leopoldus) *See* Barkow (Hans C. L.)

BARKS (Dora) *See* Barks (Ethel J.) and (D.) The Meet of the Gay Gissyquacks. [1922.] 16°. **12801. a. 60.**

—— *See* Barks (Ethel J.) and (D.) The Tale of a Tail. [1922.] 16°. **12801. a. 59.**

BARKS (Ethel J.) King Barbine, *etc.* pp. 94. *W. Clowes & Sons: London & Beccles*, [1932.] 8°. [*Youngsters' Library.*] W.P. **10482/2.**

—— The Old Woman of Cheese Hill, *etc.* pp. 94. *W. Clowes & Sons: London & Beccles*, [1932.] 8°. [*Youngsters' Library.*] W.P. **10482/1.**

BARKS (Ethel J.) and **BARKS** (Dora)

—— The Meet of the Gay Gissyquacks. [Verses.] *Art & Humour Publishing Co.: London*, [1922.] 16°. **12801. a. 60.**

—— The Tale of a Tail. [Verses.] *Art & Humour Publishing Co.: London*, [1922.] 16°. **12801. a. 59.**

BARKSDALE (Clement) *See* Bible.—*New Testament.—Selections.* [*Latin.*] Adagialia Sacra Novi Testamenti, selecta & exposita ab Andr. Schotto. Compendifacta in gratiam studiosæ juventatis, operâ C. B. [i.e. C. Barksdale.] 1651. 12°. E. **1412. (2.)**

—— *See* Charles i., *King of Great Britain and Ireland.* [*Extracts.*] A Collection of Many Declarations for the Protestant Religion from the writings, speeches &c. of King Charles the First, of blessed Memory, and King Charles the Second, *etc.* [Compiled by C. Barksdale.] 1683. 4°. **3935. b. 12.**

BARKSDALE (Clement)

—— *See* Charles ii., *King of Great Britain and Ireland.* [*Extracts.*] Aurea Dicta. The King's gracious words for the Protestant Religion of the Church of England, *etc.* [Compiled by C. Barksdale.] 1681. 4°. **8122. d. 17.**

—— *See* Cunaeus (P.) [Petri Cunæi De republica Hebræorum libri iii.] Of the Commonwealth of the Hebrews. Translated by C. B. [i.e. C. Barksdale.] 1653. 12°. E. **1311. (2.)**

—— *See* Cyprian, *Saint, Bishop of Carthage.* St. Cyprian . . . Of Discipline, Prayer, Patience . . . Translated by C. B. [i.e. C. Barksdale.] 1675. 12°. **4376. a. 66. (3.)**

—— *See* Groot (H. de) [*Letters.*] The Mourner Comforted . . . Translated . . . by C. B. [i.e. C. Barksdale.] 1652. 12°. **873. b. 28. (2.)**

—— *See* Groot (H. de) [*De Imperio Summarum Potestatum circa Sacra.*] Hugo Grotius of the Authority of the Highest Powers About Sacred things . . . Put into English by C. B. M.A. (Barksdale). 1651. 8°. E. **1244. (1.)**

—— *See* Groot (H. de) [*De Jure Belli ac Pacis.*] The Illustrious Hugo Grotius Of the Law of Warre and Peace, *etc.* [The translator's preface signed: C. B., i.e. C. Barksdale.] 1654. 8°. **E. 1445.**

—— *See* Groot (H. de) [*De Veritate Religionis Christianae.*] Two Discourses . . . out of the Illustrious Hugo Grotius. With annotations, and the authours life . . . By the translator of the same author, De Imperio (Cl. Barksdale), *etc.* 1653. 12°. **873. b. 28.**

—— *See* Groot (H. de) [*De Veritate Religionis Christianae.*] Hugo Grotius, his most choice Discourses, out of that excellent Treatise, De veritate Religionis Christianæ . . . Translated . . . by Cl. Barksdale, *etc.* 1658. 12°. **4372. aa. 3.**

—— —— 1669. 12°. **874. c. 33.**

—— *See* Groot (H. de) [*De Veritate Religionis Christianae.*] Hugo Grotius, Against Paganism, Iudaism, Mahumetism. Translated by C. B. (Cl. Barksdale.) 1676. 8°. **4376. a. 66. (1.)**

—— *See* Groot (H. de) [*De Veritate Religionis Christianae.*] Hugo Grotius's Defence of Christian Religion . . . Together with some account of the three former discourses. For God, Christ, Scripture. Newly collected and translated by C. B. (Cl. Barksdale.) 1678. 8°. **4372. aa. 18.**

—— *See* Groot (H. de) [*Miscellanea.*] Hugo Grotius, Of the Government and Rites of the Antient Church, *etc.* [The translator's dedicatory epistle signed: Cl. Barksdale.] 1675. 12°. **698. c. 33.**

—— *See* Groot (H. de) [*Works translated, annotated or edited by H. de Groot.*] Annotationum selectarum, ex Hugone Grotio ad Novum Testamentum, specimen .h e. ad vii. capita S. Matthæi. [The editor's address to the reader signed: Barksdallus tuus.] 1675. 12°. **1017. e. 19. (1.)**

—— *See* Higford (William) The Institution of a Gentleman, *etc.* [The editor's address to the reader signed: C. B., i.e. C. Barksdale.] 1660. 8°. **1388. a. 27.**

—— *See* Hooker (Richard) Judicious Hooker's Illustrations of Holy Scripture in his Ecclesiastical Polity. [Compiled by C. Barksdale.] 1675. 8°. **4376. a. 66. (4.)**

—— *See* Schurman (A. M. von) The Learned Maid; or, Whether a maid may be a scholar? *etc.* [The translator's preface signed: C. B., i.e. C. Barksdale.] 1659. 8°. E. **1910. (3.)**

BARKSDALE (Clement)

—— *See* Thou (J. A. de) *the Elder*. [*The Histories.—Abridgments, etc.*] Monumenta litteraria, sive obitus et elogia doctorum virorum . . . opera C. B. [i.e. C. Barksdale.] 1640. 4°. **276. g. 16.**

—— *See* Thou (J. A. de) *the Elder*. [*The Histories.—Abridgments, etc.*] Doctorum virorum elogia Thuanea. Opera C. B. [i.e. C. Barksdale.] 1671. 8°. G. **947.**

—— The Disputation at Winchcombe, Nov. 9. mdcliii. pp. 39. *Printed by L. L.* [*Leonard Lichfield*] *and are to be sold by Edmund Thorne: Oxford,* [1653.] 8°. **4326. aa. 8.**

—— [Another edition.] The Disputation at Winchcomb, November 9. 1653. Together with the letters and testimonies pertinent thereto, *etc.* [The editor's preface signed: N. N.] *For William Lee: London,* 1654. 8°. **1368. a. 16.**

—— [A reissue, with additional preliminary matter.] The Winchcomb-Papers Revived, *etc.* *For John Barksdale: London,* 1675. 8°. **1368. a. 13.**

—— *See* Collinges (John) Responsoria Bipartita, sive, Vindiciæ suspensionis Ecclesiasticæ ut et Presbyterii Evangelici . . . To which is prefixed an epistle . . . fully answering whatsoever, Mr. T. Marshall, in his three Sermons . . . Mr. Barksdale in a letter of his dated May 26. 1652. and printed with a disputation at Winchcomb Nov. 9. 1653. and Mr. Timson in his late book . . . have said in these for promiscuous communion. [1655.] 4°. E. **832. (2.)**

—— The Kings Return. A sermon preached at Winchcomb in Gloucestershire upon the Kings-Day, Thursday, May 24. 1660. pp. 21. *For R. Royston: London,* 1660. 4°. E. **1033. (5.)**

—— Memorials of Alderman Whitmore, Bishop Wilkins, Bishop Reynolds, Alderman Adams. [The compiler's preface signed: C. B., i.e. C. Barksdale.] pp. 42. 1681. 8°. *See* B., C. **701. b. 39.**

—— Memorials of Worthy Persons: Two Decads. pp. 204. *Printed by J. R.: London,* 1661. 12°. G. **2227.**

—— [Another copy.] **609. a. 13.**
Imperfect; wanting sig. *3 *and* *4.

—— [A reissue, without the leaf containing "The Names of the Persons."] Characters, and Historical Memorials, on the Lives and Actions of England's late Worthies, in Church and State. *For J. W.: London,* 1662. 12°. **609. a. 14.**

—— Memorials of Worthy Persons. The third decad. pp. 104. *Printed by A. & L. Liechfield: Oxford,* 1662. 8°. G. **2228. (1.)**

—— Memorials of Worthy Persons. Lights and ornaments of the Church of England. The fourth decad. pp. 135. *Printed by A. and L. Lichfield: Oxford,* 1663. 8°. G. **2228. (2.)**

—— Nympha Libethris: or the Cotswold Muse, presenting some extempore verses to the imitation of young scholars . . . In four parts. [The dedication signed: C. B., i.e. C. Barksdale.] pp. 96. 1651. 8°. *See* B., C. C.117.a.23.

—— [Another edition.] A new edition. [The editor's advertisement signed: S. E. B., i.e. Sir Samuel Egerton Brydges.] pp. xiv. ix. 105. *Longman & Co.: London,* 1816. 12°. **992. f. 36. (1.)**
One of an edition of 41 *copies.*

—— [Another copy.] **238. f. 49.**

—— [Another copy.] G. **11420.**

BARKSDALE (Clement)

—— A Remembrancer of excellent Men. [The compiler's preface signed: C. B., i.e. C. Barksdale.] pp. 164. 1670. 8°. *See* B., C. **857. h. 16.**

BARKSDALE (Jelks)

—— General Chemistry for Colleges. pp. viii. 504. *Longmans, Green & Co.: New York,* 1950. 8°. **8898. ff. 32.**

—— General Chemistry for Laboratories. pp. xiii. 152. *Longmans, Green & Co.: New York,* 1951. 4°. **8904. l. 47.**

—— Thermodynamic Properties of Dilute Thallous Chloride Solutions. Dissertation, *etc.* pp. 28. *New York,* 1933. 8°. **8899. ff. 107.**

BARKSDALE (John) *See* Hilton (Thomas) A Funeral Sermon, occasion'd by the death of John Barksdale, *etc.* 1700. 8°. **4903. ee. 28.**

BARKSDALE (Lena)

—— The First Thanksgiving, *etc.* [A tale.] pp. 64. *Frederick Muller: London,* 1948 [1949]. 8°. **12832. ee. 41.**

BARKSDALLUS (Clemens) *See* Barksdale (Clement)

BARKSHIRE. *See* Berkshire.

BARKSTEAD'S REGIMENT. *Begin.* May 27. 1651. For as much as the Inhabitants of Pauls Churchyard are much disturbed by the Souldiers and others, *etc.* [An order with respect to the behaviour of the soldiery. Signed: John Barkested. Benjamin Blundell.] [*London,*] 1651. *s. sh.* fol. **669. f. 16. (5.)**

—— A True Narrative of the Ground and Manner of the Late Skirmish, between the Souldiers of Colonell Barksteads Regiment, and the Petitioners of Surrey in the Pallace-yard at Westminster, May the 16. 1648. Published by the Officers of the said Regiment, by way of vindication from the false reports of injurious men, *etc.* pp. 8. *Printed by John Clowes: London,* 1648. 4°. E. **443. (29.)**

BARKSTEAD (John) [For declarations and resolutions emanating from, and for anonymous works relating to, the regiment of the Parliamentary army commanded by J. Barkstead:] *See* Barkstead's Regiment.

—— *See* Hacker (Francis) The Two Grand Traytors Lamentation . . . Being the several speeches of Col. Hacker . . . and Col. J. Barkstead, *etc.* 1660. 4°. E. **1040. (15.)**

—— *See* Marten (Henry) A Declaration concerning Colonel Henry Martin, Colonel Robert Lilburn [and others] . . . As also, a discovery of their treasonable designs with those two perfidious Hannibals, Collonel J. Barkstead, and Collonel J. Hewson. 1660. 4°. **8122. b. 112.**

—— *See* Netherlands.—*United Provinces.—Staten Generaal.* [*Appendix.*] A Memorial intended to be delivered . . . Monday 10 March . . . to the . . . Lords the States of Holland. by the Forraign Anabaptist Churches, upon the apprehending and giving up Colonel Barkestead, Colonel Okey, and Mr. Miles Corbet. To the English Resident, *etc.* 1662. 4°. **100. g. 53.**

—— A Letter from Colonel Barkestead, Colonel Okey, and Miles Corbet, to their friends in the Congregated Churches in London. With the manner of their apprehension. pp. 7. *London,* 1662. 4°. **100. g. 52.**

BARKSTEAD (JOHN)

—— The Speeches and Prayers of John Barkstead, John Okey, and Miles Corbet. Together with several passages at the time of their execution at Tyburn, the nineteenth of April, 1662. With some due and sober animadversions on the said speeches. pp. 22. 8. *For Nathaniel Brook & Edward Thomas: London*, 1662. 4°. **1416**. c. **29**.
The pagination is irregular.

—— [Another edition.] pp. 22. 8. *For Nathaniel Brook & Edward Thomas: London*, 1662. 4°. **100**. g. **51**.
The pagination is irregular.

—— The Speeches, Discourses, and Prayers, of Col. John Barkstead, Col. John Okey, and Mr. Miles Corbet; upon the 19th of April, being the day of their suffering at Tyburn. Together with an account of the occasion and manner of their taking in Holland: as also of their several occasional speeches, discourses, and letters, both before, and in the time of their imprisonment. Faithfully and impartially collected, for a general satisfaction. pp. 1–48. 25–71. [*London*,] 1662. 4°. **1416**. c. **30**.

—— [Another edition.] [*London*,] 1662. 4°. **1132**. b. **59**.
The pagination is irregular.

—— [Another edition.] pp. 95. [*London*,] 1662. 4°. **100**. g. **54**.

—— The First and Second Parts of Invisible John made Visible: or, a Grand Pimp of Tyranny portrayed, in Barksteads arraignment at the barre, where he stands impeached of high treason, and other gross misdemeanours . . . Whereunto is added, his barbarous cruelty to . . . Dr John Hewyt and others, *etc*. pp. 6. *London*, 1659. 4°. E. **985**. **(11.)**

—— The Full and Exact Relation of the Apprehension, Arraignment, Tryal Condemnation and Execution of those three grand Regicides, Iohn Berkstead, Iohn Okey, and Miles Corbet. *N. Brooke & E. Thomas: London*, 1662. *s. sh*. fol. Cup. **645**. e. **1**. **(20.)**

—— The New Lord's Winding-Sheet; or, an Arrow shot at randome, to the Tower of London . . . With the articles, charge, speeches, and sentences; and the voting of Col. Barkstead from his command in the Tower, *etc*. pp. 7. [*London*,] 1659. 4°. E. **986**. **(7.)**

—— [Another copy.] **100**. f. **79**.

—— White-Hall Fayre: or, Who buyes good Penniworths of Barkstead? [A satire, in verse.] pp. 8. *For A. P.*: [*London*,] 1648. 4°. E. **434**. **(16.)**

—— [Another copy.] **164**. k. **12**.

BARKSTEAD (WILLIAM) *See* BARKSTED.

BARKSTED (WILLIAM) *See* JUVENALIS (D. J.) [*Imitations and Parodies*.] That which seemes best is worst. Exprest in a paraphrastical transcript of Iuuenals tenth Satyre . . . By W. B. [i.e. W. Barksted?] 1617. 8°. C. **39**. a. **4**.

—— The Poems of William Barksted . . . Edited, with introduction and notes, by the Rev. Alexander B. Grosart. *Printed for the subscribers: Manchester*, 1876. 4°. [*Occasional Issues of Unique or Very Rare Books*. vol. 3.] **2326**. g. **3**. **(1.)**
No. 4 of an edition of fifty copies.

BARKULABOVSKAYA LYETOPIS. *See* KORSAK (Barkulab Ivanovich)

BARKWAY (JAMES LUMSDEN) successively *Bishop of Bedford* and *of St. Andrews, Dunkeld and Dunblane*.

—— *See* UNDERHILL (Evelyn) An Anthology of the Love of God . . . Edited by . . . L. Barkway . . . and L. Menzies. 1953. 8°. **4383**. b. **5**.

BARKWAY (JAMES LUMSDEN) successively *Bishop of Bedford* and *of St. Andrews, Dunkeld and Dunblane*.

—— *See* UNDERHILL (Evelyn) Collected Papers . . . With an introduction by L. Barkway, Bishop of St. Andrews. 1946. 8°. **12269**. aa. **15**.

—— *See* UNDERHILL (Evelyn) Collected Papers of Evelyn Underhill . . . With an introduction by L. Barkway. 1946. 8°. **4381**. aaa. **61**.

—— The Christian Belief about Christ. pp. 58. *A. R. Mowbray & Co.: London & Oxford*, 1942. 8°. **04227.aa.18.**

—— The Creed and its Credentials. pp. 132. *S.P.C.K.: London*, 1935. 8°. **03504**. ff. **81**.

—— The Creed and its Credentials. (Revised edition.) pp. 132. *S.P.C.K.: London*, 1953. 8°. [*Handbooks for Teachers*.] **4383.a.13/5.**

—— An Introduction to the Inner Life. pp. 85. *A. R. Mowbray & Co.: London*, 1954. 8°. **3457**. k. **65**.

BARKWAY (LUMSDEN) successively *Bishop of Bedford* and *of St. Andrews, Dunkeld and Dunblane*. *See* BARKWAY (James L.)

BARKWORTH (ARTHUR BROMBY WILSON) *See* DOMESDAY BOOK. Domesday Book for the East Riding of Yorkshire . . . Arranged under places . . . by A. B. Wilson-Barkworth. 1925. 8°. **10368**. r. **16**.

—— *See* KIRK ELLA. The Register of Kirk Ella, co. York . . . Transcribed and edited by . . . the Rev. J. Foord . . . assisted by A. B. Wilson-Barkworth. 1897. 8°. Ac. **8107/11**.

—— The City and County of Kingston-upon-Hull. *W. H. Smith & Son: Scarborough*, 1926. 4°. **10368**. r. **21**.

—— The Composition of the Saxon Hundred in which Hull and neighbourhood were situate, as it was in its original condition. [With plates.] pp. x. 97. *A. Brown & Sons: Hull & London*, [1920.] 4°. **10368**. k. **57**.

BARKWORTH (JOHN) *See* KING (John) *Incumbent of Christ's Church, Hull*. A Sermon, preached in the Parish Church of Hessle, on Sunday, the 5th April, 1846, on occasion of the death of John Barkworth, *etc*. 1846. 12°. **10347**. de. **15**. **(10.)**

BARKWORTH (SHADWELL MORLEY) "The Accepted Substitute." A sermon, *etc*. pp. 11. *T. Barcham: Reading*, 1866. 8°. **4477**. bb. **73**. **(5.)**

—— Grace, and the Knowledge of Jesus Christ: its source, character, and obligation. A sermon, *etc*. pp. 20. *T. Barcham: Reading*, 1867. 8°. **4477**. dd. **77**. **(1.)**

—— "Self Righteousness its own Condemnation." A sermon, *etc*. pp. 12. *T. Barcham: Reading*, 1865. 8°. **4477**. bb. **73**. **(2.)**

BARLA (JEAN BAPTISTE) Les Champignons de la province de Nice, et principalement les espèces comestibles, suspectes ou vénéneuses, dessinés d'après nature et décrits par J. B. Barla, *etc*. pp. lv. 138. pl. 48. *Nice*, 1859. *obl*. fol. **1823**. a. **5**.

—— Flore illustrée de Nice et des Alpes-Maritimes. Iconographie des orchidées . . . Ouvrage orné de 63 planches, *etc*. pp. 83. *Nice*, 1868. 4°. **7028**. h. **13**.

BARLA (Jean Baptiste)

—— Flore mycologique illustrée. Les champignons des Alpes-Maritimes, *etc.* [With plates.] pp. 80. *Nice*, 1888–92. fol. **7028.** h. **11.**
Published in parts.

BARLAAM, *Bishop of Gerace. See* Barlaamus.

BARLAAM, *Metropolitan of Moldavia and Suczawa. See* Varlaam.

BARLAAM, *Saint, of Asia Minor. See* Delehaye (H.) S. Barlaam, martyr à Antioche. 1903. 8°. **4824.** de. **22.** **(10.)**

—— Житіе св. Варлаама Сирокавказскаго. Къ вопросу о "Варлаамѣ и Іоасафѣ." *Armen. & Russ.* 1901. *See* Marr (N. Ya.) Агіографическіе матеріалы по грузинскимъ рукописямъ Ивера. част. 2. 1900, *etc.* 8°. **17026.** g. **8.** **(1.)**

BARLAAM, *Saint, of India.*

The Legend of Barlaam and Josaphat.

Polyglott.

—— Baralâm and Yĕwâsĕf: being the Ethiopic version of a Christianized recension of the Buddhist legend of the Buddha and the Bodhisattva. The Ethiopic text edited . . . with an English translation and introduction, etc., by Sir E. A. Wallis Budge. [With plates.] 2 vol. *University Press: Cambridge*, 1923. 8°. **754.** eee. **6.**

—— St. John Damascene. Barlaam and Ioasaph. With an English translation by the Rev. G. R. Woodward . . . and H. Mattingly. *Gr. & Eng.* pp. xx. 640. *William Heinemann: London; Macmillan Co.: New York*, 1914. 8°. [*Loeb Classical Library.*] **2282.** d. **18.**

—— Балһваръ и Іодасафъ. Грузинскій текстъ, по рукописямъ XI–XII вв. Съ приложеніемъ двухъ палеографическихъ таблицъ. Съ переводомъ и предисловіемъ издалъ А. Хахановъ. *Georg. & Russ.* pp. xv. 32. *Москва*, 1902. 4°. [*Труды по востоковѣдѣнію.* вып. 9.] **17068.g.1.**

—— Die Grieksche christelijke roman Barlaam en Joasaf en zijne parabels. Door Dr S. J. Warren. *Gr. & Dutch.* pp. 56. *Rotterdam*, 1899. 4°. **11851.** f. **39.**

—— Die Legende von Barlaam und Josaphat auf der iberischen Halbinsel. Untersuchungen und Texte. Von Gerhard Moldenhauer. *Span. & Cat.* 2 pt. *Halle*, 1929. 8°. [*Romanistische Arbeiten.* no. 13.] W.P. **2259/13.**

English.

—— The History of the Five Wise Philosophers; or, the wonderful Relation of the Life of Jehosaphat the Hermit . . . By H. P. Gent. [i.e. H. Parsons. A version of the legend of Barlaam and Josaphat. Edited by Nicholas Herrick.] pp. 133. *For D. Page, T. Passenger, & B. Hurlock: London*, 1672. 12°. **693.** c. **3.**

—— [Another edition.] By N. H. Gent. [i.e. Nicholas Herrick; or rather, written by H. Parsons, and edited by N. Herrick.] pp. 128. *Eben. Tracy: London*, 1711. 12°. **4805.** a. **19.**

—— [Another edition.] By H. P. Gent. [i.e. H. Parsons. Edited by Nicholas Herrick.] *J. Tracy: London*, [1725?] 12°. **12403.** a. **22.**

—— [A reissue.] To which is added, Meditations on the seven stations of life, with the three great stepts [*sic*] to eternal salvation . . . By H. P. Gent. [i.e. H. Parsons. Edited by Nicholas Herrick.] 2 pt. *Edw. Midwinter: London*, 1732. 12°. **4805.** a. **27.**
With different preliminary matter and with the addition of "A Guide from the Cradel to the Grave."

BARLAAM, *Saint, of India.*—[The Legend of Barlaam and Josaphat.]

—— [Another copy of "A Guide from the Cradel to the Grave."] **11631.** a. **25**

—— The Heathen's Conversion; or, the Life of Jehoshaphat the son of King Avernio, of Barma in India. [A version of the legend of Barlaam and Josaphat. In verse.] pp. 8. [*London*, 1770?] 8°. **11603.** b. **41.** **(1.)**

—— Barlam und Josaphat, aus ms. Bodl. 779. *See* Horstmann (C.) Altenglische Legenden, *etc.* 1875. 8°. **11601.** ddd. **1.**

—— The Story of Barlaam and Joasaph: Buddhism & Christianity. Edited by K. S. Macdonald . . . With philological introduction and notes to the Vernon, Harleian and Bodleian versions, by the Rev. John Morrison. [Containing "The History of the Five Wise Philosophers," "The Hystorye of the Hermyte Balaam" from William Caxton's "Golden Legend," and the versions of the Vernon, Harleian and Bodleian mss.] 2 pt. *Thacker, Spink & Co.: Calcutta*, 1895. 8°. **4503.** b. **24.**

—— Barlaam and Josaphat. English lives of Buddha. Edited and induced by Joseph Jacobs. [With plates.] pp. cxxxii. 56. *David Nutt: London*, 1896. 8°. [*Bibliothèque de Carabas.* vol. 10.] **12202.** ff. **1**
No. 8 *of an edition of* 60 *copies.*

—— Barlaam a Josafat. Přeložil Tomáš ze Štítného. (Z rukopisu k vydání připravil a poznámkami doprovodil František Šimek.) pp. 206. *Praha*, 1946. 8°. [*Památky staré literatury české.* řada A. čís. 2.] Ac. **800.** ba. **(2.**

Danish.

—— Barlaam og Josaphat. En religiøs roman. Oversat fra oldnorsk af H. E. Kinck. pp. iiii. 299. *Christiania*, 1852. 8°. **12430.** aaa. **37**

Dutch.

—— Het Leven en bedrijf van Barlaäm den heremijt, en Josaphat koning van Indien, beschreven door . . Joannes Damascenus, en nu in Nederduits vertaelt door F. v. H. [i.e. Frans van Hoogstraten. With plates.] pp. 431. *C. Woons: Antwerpen*, 1672. 12°. **12431.** b. **11**
With an additional titlepage, engraved.

French.

—— Barlaam und Josaphat, französisches Gedicht des dreizehnten Jahrhunderts von Gui de Cambrai; nebst Auszügen aus mehreren andern romanischen Versionen herausgegeben von Hermann Zotenberg und Paul Meyer. pp. 419. *Stuttgart*, 1864. 8°. [*Bibliothek des Literarischen Vereins in Stuttgart.* Bd. 75.] Ac. **8963**

—— Josaphat, le prince indien, traduit de l'anglais par Mme Sophie G . . ., *etc.* [A version of the legend of Barlaam and Josaphat.] pp. 105. *Paris*, 1877. 12°. **4412.** d. **1**

—— Gui von Cambrai. Balaham und Josaphas. Nach den Handschriften von Paris und Monte Cassino herausgegeben von Carl Appel. pp. lxxxii. 467. *Halle*, 1907. 8°. **11498.** k. **24**

German.

—— *Begin.* [fol. 2 *recto*:] HIe vahet an eyn gar loblich vn[nd] heylsam allen christglaubigen cr[o]nica. Sagend von eynem heylige[n] kúnig mit namen Josaphat. wie der ward bekeret von eynem heyligen vatter vnnd aynsidel genant Barlaam, *etc.* *End.* [fol. 97 *verso*:] Eyn end hatt das bůch der christenlichen lere die hystori Josaphat vnd Barlaam genannt, *etc.* [With woodcuts.] [*Günther Zainer: Augsburg*, 1476?] fol. G. **11766**
98 *leaves, the first and last blank, without signatures.* 36 *lines to a page. Wanting the first leaf.*

—— *Begin.* [fol. 2 *recto*:] HIe vahet an eÿn gar lôblich vnd heÿlsam allen christgelaubigen cronica. Sagēd vō einē heÿligen künig mit namen Josaphat, wie d' ward bekeret von eÿnem heÿligen vatter vnd ainsideln genant Barlaam, *etc.* *End.* [fol. 97 *recto*:] Eÿn ende hatt das bůch der Christenlichen lere die hÿstori Josaphat vnd Barlaam genannt, *etc.* [With woodcuts.] [*Anton Sorg: Augsburg,* 1480?] fol. IB. **5918.**
97 *leaves, the first probably blank, without signatures.* 35 *lines to a page. Wanting the first leaf.*

—— [Another copy.] IB. **5919.**
96 *leaves. With no blank leaf. This copy differs from the preceding in having the first page printed in red.*

—— Historia: von dem Leben vnnd Thaten, beyder heyligen Beichtiger vnnd Eremiten, Barlaam vnnd Josaphats . . . Durch den H. Joannem Damascenum . . . inn Griechischer Sprach beschriben: hernach durch Georgium Trapezuntium in das Latein, vnd jetzt in vnsere Teutsche Sprach durch Vlrichen Satler gebracht, *etc.* ff. 256. *A. Meltzer: Dilingen,* 1603. 8°. **1362.** g. **37.**

—— Historia von dem Leben der zweyen H. Beichtiger Barlaam Eremiten, vnd Josaphat . . . Durch den Heil. Joannem Damascenum . . . Griechisch beschrieben, in das Teutsche aber ausz dem Lateinischen übersetzt, durch die zwen . . . Grafen . . . Herren Schweickharden, Grafen zu Helffenstein . . . dann Johann Georgen Grafen von Hohenzollern, *etc.* pp. 602. *S. Rauch: München,* 1684. 8°' **12410.** aaa. **6.**

—— Fragmenta aus dem Josaphat. [Edited by Johann Jacob Bodmer.] *See* NIBELUNGEN. [Modern German Versions] Chriemhilden Rache, *etc.* 1757. 4°. **88.** a. **7.**

—— Barlaam und Josaphat. Von Rudolf von Montfort. Herausgegeben und mit einem Wörterbuch versehen von Fr. Karl Kopke. pp. xii. 527. *Königsberg,* 1818. 8°. **11511.** b. **29.**

—— Mittheilungen über eine noch ungedruckte mittelhochdeutsche Bearbeitung des Barlaam und Josaphat aus einer Handschrift auf der gräflichen Bibliothek zu Solms-Laubach von Dr. L. Diefenbach. [Extracts from the text, with a brief introduction.] pp. 16. *Giessen,* 1836. 8°. 11511. c. 38. (4.)

—— [Another edition.] Barlaam und Josaphat. Von Rudolf von Ems. Herausgegeben von Franz Pfeiffer. *Leipzig,* 1843. 8°. [*Dichtungen des deutschen Mittelalters.* Bd. 3.] **2286.** d. **1.**

—— Der Laubacher Barlaam. Eine Dichtung des Bischofs Otto II. von Freising, 1184–1220. Herausgegeben von Adolf Perdisch. pp. xxxii. 574 *Tübingen,* 1913. 8°. [*Bibliothek des Litterarischen Vereins in Stuttgart.* Bd. 260.] Ac. **8963.**

Greek.

—— [For editions of the Greek text included in collected editions of the works of St. John of Damascus:] *See* JOHN, *of Damascus, Saint.*

—— Ἱστορια ψυχωφελης . . . ἐν ᾗ ὁ βιος Βαρλααμ και Ἰωασαφ, *etc.* pp. x. 365. 1832. *See* BOISSONADE (J. F.) Ἀνεκδοτα. Anecdota græca, *etc.* tom. 4. 1829, *etc.* 8°. 011306.e.1.

—— Ἱστορια συγγραφεισα παρα του ἐν ἁγιοις Ἰωαννου του Δαμασκηνου διαλαμβανουσα τον βιον των ὁσιων πατερων ἡμων Βαρλααμ και Ἰωασαφ. Ἀνεκδοτος οὖσα ἐκδιδοται ἤδη ἑλληνιστι ὑπο Σωφρονιου Μοναχου Ἁγιορειτου, *etc.* pp. 256. Ἐν Ἀθηναις, 1884. 8°. 4824. de. 8.

Italian.

—— *Begin.* [fol. 1 *recto*:] Lezese antichamēte che in india era un re, *etc.* *End.* [fol. 24 *verso*:] Qui si finisse la istoria de san iosafat. [A version of the legend of Barlaam and Josaphat.] [*Venice?* 1480?] 4°. IA. **24855.**
24 *leaves. Sig.* a[8] b[8] c[4] d[4]. 36 *lines to a page.*

—— Rappresentatione di Barlaam et Josafat. (Composta per Bernardo Pulci.) [In verse.] *Fece stampare F. di G. Benuenuto: [Florence,]* 1516. 4°. **11426.** dd. **24.**

—— La Vita del Beato Josaphat Convertito per Barlaam. G.L. *Benedetto & Augustino de Bendoni: Venetia,* 1524. 8°. **1471.** a. **14.**

—— Vita di San Giosafat convertito da Barlaam, nuovamente corretto, ristampato, e di belle figure adornato. pp. 78. *G. A. Remondini: Venezia & Bassano,* [1650?] 16°. **4827.** a. **31.**

—— Storia de' SS. Barlaam e Giosaffatte. Ridotta alla sua antica purità di favella, coll' ajuto degli antichi testi a penna, *etc.* [Edited with an introduction by G. G. Bottari.] pp. xxxvi. 127. *Roma,* 1734. 4°. **12410.** g. **3.**

—— [Another copy.] **7.** b. **20.**

—— Vita di S. Giosafat convertito da Barlaam. Nuovamente ristampata, e di bellissime figure adornata. pp. 88. *Modena,* 1768. 16°. **4867.** a. **33.**

—— [Another edition.] Nuovamente ristampata, e da errori corretta, e di molte figure adornata. pp. 64. *Treviso,* [1775?] 16°. **4823.** b. **8.**

—— Vita del glorioso S. Giosafat convertito da S. Barlaam . . . Diligentemente corretta, ed adornata di varie figure. pp. 70. *Pesaro,* 1810. 8°. **4824.** bb. **3.**

—— Storia de' SS. Barlaam e Giosaffatte ridotta alla sua antica purità di favella coll' ajuto degli antichi testi a penna. Edizione seconda, eseguita sopra quella del 1734. [With an introduction by G. G. Bottari.] pp. xxii. 146. *Roma,* 1816. 8°. **1371.** d. **19.**

—— Vita di San Giosafat convertito da Barlaam. pp. 96. *Milano,* [1820?] 12°. **11715.** c. **1.** (4.)

—— Al nome sia di Dio e della sua dolce Madre Vergine Maria e di tutti i Santi. Qui incomincia la santissima vita di Santo Iosafat figliuolo del Re Avenero, re dell'India . . . Da un Cod. Rossiano. [A version of the legend of Barlaam and Josaphat.] *See* BINI (T.) Rime e prose del buon secolo della lingua, *etc.* 1852. 8°. **12225.** d. **4.**

Latin.

—— [For editions of the Latin text included in collected editions of the works of St. John of Damascus:] *See* JOHN, *of Damascus, Saint.*

—— *Begin.* [fol. 2 *recto*:] [C]Vm cepissent monasteria construi, *etc.* *End.* [fol. 78 *verso*:] Explicit Liber Barlaam et Iosaphat. [*Spire?* 1475?] fol. IB. **8428.**
78 *leaves, the first blank. Sig.* a–f[8] G[8] h[8] I[8] k[6]. 36 *lines to a page.*

—— *Begin.* [fol. 1 *recto*:] Incipit liber gestorū barlaam et iosophat seruorū dei greco sermone editus a iohāne damasceno, *etc.* [*H. Eggesteyn: Strasburg,* 1475?] 4°. G. **11741.**
148 *leaves, the last blank, without signatures.* 29 *lines to a page.*

—— [Another copy.] G. **11767.**
Without the blank.

—— Vitæ et res gestæ SS. Barlaam eremitæ, et Iosaphat Indiæ Regis, S. Io. Damasceno auctore, Iac. Billio Prunæo interprete. pp. 435. *Sumptibus viduæ & hæredum I. Belleri: Antuerpiæ*, 1602. 12°. **859. a. 7.**

—— [Another edition.] [S. Joannis Damasceni] Historia, de vitis et rebus gestis SS. Barlaam Eremitæ, et Josaphat Indiæ Regis, Jacobo Billio Prunæo . . . interprete. Nunc denuò accuratissimè . . . reuisa & correcta. pp. 462. *Sumptibus B. Gualtheri: Coloniæ*, 1624. 12°. **4827. a. 29.**

The titlepage is mutilated.

Norwegian.

—— Barlaams ok Josaphats Saga. En religiös romantisk Fortælling om Barlaam og Josaphat, oprindelig forfattet paa Græsk i det 8de Aarhundrede, senere oversat paa Latin, og herfra igjen i fri Bearbeidelse ved Aar 1200 overfört paa Norsk af Kong Haakon Sverressön. Udgivet af R. Keyser og C. R. Unger, *etc.* pp. xxiv. 262. *Christiania*, 1851. 8°. **12430. g. 23.**

Polish.

—— Żywot Barlaama i Jozafata. (Od S. Iana Damascena pisany. Od Iakoba Billiusa Prunego tłumáczony.) [Translated by Sebastyan Piskorski.] Wydał i wstępem poprzedził Jan Janów. pp. ccviii. 322. *Lwów*, 1935. 8°. [*Zabytki piśmiennictwa polskiego.* tom 6.] Ac. **764/6.**

Provençal.

—— Die provenzalische Prosa-Redaktion des geistlichen Romans von Barlaam und Josaphat. Nebst einem Anhang über einige deutsche Drucke des XVII. Jahrhunderts. Herausgegeben von Ferdinand Heuckenkamp. pp. civ. 154. *Halle*, 1912. 8°. **12403. ff. 24.**

Russian.

—— Житіе святаго Іоасафа, царевича индійскаго. Изданіе третье. [A version of the legend of Barlaam and Josaphat.] pp. 34. *Москва*, 1887. 12°. **4823. cc. 14. (6.)**

—— Повесть о Варлааме пустыннике и Иосафе царевиче индийском. Перевод . . . В. Р. Розена под редакцией и с введением . . . И. Ю. Крачковского. pp. 187. 1947. 8°. *See* RUSSIA.—*Академия Наук СССР.* **4830. h. 63.**

Slavonic.

—— Житіе и жизнь преподобныхъ отецъ нашихъ Варлаама пустинника и Іоасафа царевича индійскаго. Творенiе . . . Іоанна Дамаскина. [A lithographic facsimile of the manuscript.] pp. 538. 1887. 8°. *See* LENINGRAD.—*Общество Любителей Древней Письменности.* Ac. **9086/55.**

Spanish.

—— Historia de los dos Soldados de Christo, Barlaan, y Iosafat. Escrita por san Iuan Damasceno, *etc.* [Translated by Juan de Arce Solorzeno.] ff. 215. *Iuan Flamenco: Madrid*, 1608. 8°. **4823. a. 13.**

—— Verdad nada amarga: hermosa bondad: honesta, vtil, y deleitable, grata, y moral historia. De la rara vida de los famosos, y singulares Sanctos Barlaan, y Iosaphat. Segun la escriuio en su idioma Griego . . . S. Iuan Damasceno: y la passo al Latino . . . Iacobo Biblio: de donde la expone en lengua Castellana . . . Baltasar de Sancta Cruz . . . Con vn corollario deuoto de meditacion y contemplacion de la Via mas Sacra, *etc.* 2 pt. *Gaspar de los Reyes: Manila*, 1692. 4°. **12410. f. 21.**

Swedish.

—— Barlaam och Josaphat. 1887. *See* KLEMMING (G. E.) Prosadikter från Sveriges medeltid, *etc.* 1887, *etc.* 8°. Ac. **9068/27.**

Appendix.

—— *See* ARMSTRONG (Edward C.) The French Metrical Versions of Barlaam and Josaphat, *etc.* 1922. 8°. W.P. **4150/10.**

—— *See* FRANKO (I.) Варлаам і Йоасаф. Старохристиянський духовний роман і его літературна істория. 1895, *etc.* 8°. [*Записки Наукового Товариства імени Шевченка.* том. 8, 10, 18, 20.] Ac. **762/11.**

—— *See* HARRIS (James R.) The Sources of Barlaam and Joasaph, *etc.* 1925. 8°. **4825. f. 38.**

—— *See* HAYES (Will) How the Buddha became a Christian Saint. [A summary of the legend of Barlaam and Josaphat, with notes on its relation to the story of Buddha's life.] 1931. 8°. **04505. e. 9.**

—— *See* KIRPICHNIKOV (Alexander I) Греческіе романы въ новой литературѣ. II. Повѣсть о Варламѣ и Іоасафѣ. 1896. 8°. **011824. i. 51.**

—— *See* KUHN (E.W. A.) Barlaam und Joasaph. Eine bibliographisch-literargeschichtliche Studie. 1894. 4°. [*Abhandlungen der Königlich Bayerischen Akademie der Wissenschaften.* Philos.-philol. Classe. Bd. 20.] Ac. **713/6.**

—— *See* MACDONALD (Kenneth S.) Introduction to the Story of Barlaam and Joasaph. [1895?] 8°. **011851. h. 14. (4.)**

—— *See* MARR (N. Ya.) Агіографическія матеріалы по грузинскимъ рукописямъ Ивера. част. 2. (Житіе св. Варлаама Сирокавказскаго. Къ вопросу о „Варлаамѣ и Іоасафѣ.") 1900, *etc.* 8°. **17026. g. 8. (1.)**

—— *See* NOVAKOVIĆ (S.) Варлаам и Јоасаф. Прилог к познавању упоредне литерарне и хришћанске белетристике у Срба, Бугара и Руса, *etc.* 1881. 8°. **12410. ff. 19.**

—— *See* PERDISCH (A.) Der Laubacher Barlaam, *etc.* 1904. 8°. **011853. f. 61.**

—— *See* SOEHNS (F.) Das Handschriftenverhältnis in Rudolfs von Ems Barlaam. 1878. 8°. **11840. f. 8. (6.)**

—— *See* SONET (J.) Le Roman de Barlaam et Josaphat. Recherches sur la tradition manuscrite latine et française. 1949. 8°. [*Université de Louvain. Recueil de travaux d'histoire et de philologie.* sér. 3. fasc. 33.] Ac. **2646/4.**

—— *See* TĒR NERSESĒAN (S.) L'Illustration du Roman de Barlaam et Joasaph d'après les clichés de la Frick Art Reference Library et la Mission Gabriel Millet au Mont-Athos, *etc.* 1937. fol. L.R. **106. c. 1.**

—— *See* WEISSLOVITS (N.) Prinz und Derwisch. Ein indischer Roman enhaltend die Jugendgeschichte Buddha's, in hebräischer Darstellung nebst einer Vergleichung der arabischen und griechischen Paralleltexte. 1890. 8°. **14579. d. 20.**

—— *See* ZOTENBERG (H.) Notice sur le livre de Barlaam et Joasaph, accompagné d'extraits du texte grec et des versions arabe et éthiopienne. 1886. 8°. **11850. l. 12.**

BARLAAM (HIERONYMOS M.) *See* BOLESLAOS. *'Ο Βολεσλαος . . . Μεταφρασις ἐκ του ἰταλικου. 'Υπο 'Ι. Βαρλααμ, etc.* 1892. 8°. **12470. aa. 40.**

BARLAAM (HIERONYMOS M.)

—— *See* MARONITE. *'Η μνηστη του Μαρωνιτου . . . Μεταφρασθεισα ἐκ του ἰταλικου ὑπο 'Ι. Βαρλααμ, etc.* 1893. 8°. **012590. de. 5.**

—— *'Αλληλογραφια εἰς ἀττικην γλωσσην, διαμειφθεισα μεταξυ 'Ι. Μ. Βαρλααμ και ἑνος καθηγητου. 'Επιγραμματα. 'Ασμα Κυπριακον, Χρηστοφη και 'Εμινες.* pp. 74. *'Εν Λεμησσῳ,* 1895. 8°. **012331. g. 4.**

—— *'Επιταφιοι δυο, εἰς τον ἀοιδιμον Πατριαρχην 'Ιεροσολυμων, Βικεντιον Βρακχον, και εἰς την πολυκλαυστον 'Αλεξανδραν, Μεγαλην Δουκισσαν της 'Ρωσσιας. 'Ων ὁ τελευταιος και ἐν τῃ καθωμιλημενῃ γλωσσῃ.* pp. 88. *'Εν Λεμησσῳ Κυπρου,* 1895. 8°. **11586. bbb. 22. (13.)**

BARLAAM (I.) *See* BARLAAM (Hieronymos M.)

BARLAAMO, *Calabrese, Fra.* *See* BARLAAMUS, *Bishop of Gerace.*

BARLAAMUS, *Bishop of Gerace.* *See* JOHN V. [Cantacuzenus], *Emperor of the East.* *Τομος ἐκτεθεις παρα της θειας και ἱερας Συνοδου της συγκροτηθεισης κατα των φρονουντων τα Βαρλααμ τε και 'Ακινδυνου, etc.* 1672. fol. [COMBEFIS (F.) *Bibliothecæ Græcorum patrum auctarium novissimum.* pt. 2.] **477. g. 1.**

—— *See* JOHN V. [Cantacuzenus], *Emperor of the East.* *Τομος γεγονως παρα του πατριαρχου 'Ιωαννου και της συνοδου κατα της του Βαρλααμ κακοδοξιας.* 1763. 8°. [BANDINI (A. M.) *Graecae Ecclesiae vetera monumenta ex Bibliotheca Medicea.* tom. 2.] **1123. k. 5.**

—— *See* LO PARCO (F.) Petrarca e Barlaam, *etc.* 1905. 8°. **10634. g. 19.**

—— *See* LO PARCO (F.) Gli ultimi oscuri anni di Barlaam, *etc.* 1910. 8°. **10634. g. 18.**

—— *See* MANDALARI (G.) Fra Barlaamo Calabrese, *etc.* 1888. 8°. **4864. d. 17.**

—— B. Barlaami . . . Epistolæ ad Græcos, de vnione cum Romana Ecclesia & Processione Sancti Spiritus. Nunc primum in lucem editæ . . . per Henricum Canisium. 1618. *See* LA BIGNE (M. de) Magna bibliotheca veterum patrum, *etc.* tom. 14. 1618, *etc.* fol. **469.e.14.**

—— [Another edition.] *See* LA BIGNE (M. de) Magna bibliotheca veterum patrum, *etc.* tom. 3. 1654. fol. **3624. e. 1.**

—— [Another edition.] 1677. *See* LA BIGNE (M. de) Maxima bibliotheca veterum patrum, *etc.* tom. 26. 1677, *etc.* fol. **465. f. 11.**

—— [Another edition.] 1697. *See* ROCABERTI (J. T. de) *Archbishop of Valencia.* Bibliotheca maxima pontificia, *etc.* tom. 5. 1698, *etc.* fol. **484. e. 4.**

—— [Another edition.] *See* CANISIUS (H.) Thesaurus monumentorum ecclesiasticorum et historicorum, *etc.* tom. 4. 1725. fol. **12. e. 4.**

—— Ethica secundum Stoicos, *etc.* 1618. *See* LA BIGNE (M. de) Magna bibliotheca veterum patrum, *etc.* tom. 14. 1618, *etc.* fol. **469.e.14.**

—— [Another edition.] *See* LA BIGNE (M. de) Magna bibliotheca veterum patrum, *etc.* tom. 3. 1654. fol. **3624. e. 1.**

—— [Another edition.] 1677. *See* LA BIGNE (M. de) Maxima bibliotheca veterum patrum, *etc.* tom. 26. 1677, *etc.* fol. **465. f. 11.**

—— [Another edition.] 1725. *See* CANISIUS (H.) Thesaurus monumentorum ecclesiasticorum et historicorum, *etc.* tom. 4. 1725. fol. **12. e. 4.**

BARLAAMUS, *Bishop of Gerace.*

—— Barlaami monachi Logistica nunc primum latinè reddita, & scholijs illustrata à Ioanne Chambero. (*Βαρλααμου του μοναχου λογιστικη, etc.*) *Lat. & Gr.* 2 pt. *G. Auuray: Parisiis,* 1600. 4°. **519. e. 29.**
The date in the colophon is 1599.

—— [Another copy.] **48. c. 17.**

—— [For editions of the text "*περι του καθαρτηριου πυρος,*" sometimes attributed to Barlaamus:] *See* PUR.

—— *Του σοφωτατου Βαρλααμ λογος περι της του Παπα ἀρχης.* Barlaami de Papae principatu libellus. Nunc primùm græcè & latinè editus opera Ioannis Luidi, *etc.* 2 pt. *Excudebat Iosephus Barnesius: Oxoniæ,* 1592. 4°. **C.108.c.11.**

—— [Another copy.] **484. b. 17. (3.)**

—— [Another edition.] Barlaami monachi lib. I. de principatu Papæ. Iohanne Luydo interprete. *Gr. & Lat.* *See* NEILOS, successively *Archbishop of Thessalonica* and *Patriarch of Constantinople.* Nili . . . De primatu Papæ Romani lib. duo, *etc.* 1608. 8°. **1020. d. 10.**

—— [Another edition.] Barlaami monachi liber de principatu Papæ, Johanne Luydo interprete. *Gr. & Lat.* *See* SAUMAISE (C. de) Cl. Salmasii librorum de primatu Papæ pars prima, *etc.* 1645. 4°. **849. i. 13.**

—— *Του σοφωτατου Βαρλααμ λογος περι της του παπα ἀρχης.* *See* NEILOS, successively *Archbishop of Thessalonica* and *Patriarch of Constantinople.* *Νειλου . . . βιβλια δυο, etc.* [1650?] 4°. **475. a. 11. (3.)**

BARLAAN, *Saint.* *See* BARLAAM.

BARLACCHI (DOMENICO) *See* BARLACCHIA.

BARLACCHIA (DOMENICO) Motti, facetie et burle del Barlacchia. *See* MAINARDI (A.) *Piovano.* Facezie, motti, buffonerie, et burle, *etc.* 1565. 8°. **245. e. 26.**

—— [Another edition.] *See* MAINARDI (A.) *Piovano.* Facezie, motti, buffonerie, et burle, *etc.* 1568. 8°. **1080. f. 29. (6.)**

—— Facetie del Barlacchia. *See* MAINARDI (A.) *Piovano.* Scelta di facetie, motti, burle, et buffonerie, del Piouano Arlotto, & altri auttori, *etc.* 1599. 8°. **1080. f. 2.**

—— Facetie del Barlacchia. *See* MAINARDI (A.) *Piovano.* Scelta di facetie, motti, burle & buffonerie di diuersi, *etc.* 1606. 12°. **1080. e. 22.**

BARLACE (ALEX.)

—— A Catalogue of . . . Books . . . to be sold . . . by A. Barlace. pp. 55. *London,* 1809. 12°. **S.C. 749. (1.)**

BARLACE (JAMES GEORGE) An Historical Sketch of the Progress of Knowledge in England, from the conversion of the Anglo-Saxons, to the end of the reign of Queen Elisabeth. [With a portrait.] pp. vi. 358. xxi. *J. & J. Arch: London,* 1819. 4°. **806. g. 5.**
With an additional titlepage, engraved.

BARLACH (CARL RICHARD) Beobachtungen aus der letzten Diphtheritisepidemie in Kiel. Inauguraldissertation, *etc.* pp. 13. *Kiel,* 1871. 4°. [*Schriften der Universität zu Kiel.* Bd. 18.] **Ac. 1030.**

BARLACH (ERNST)

—— *See* NEITZKE (H. J.) Barlach, deutscher Geist zwischen Westen und Osten. 1934. 8°. **10709. c. 9.**

—— *See* SCHUREK (P.) Begegnungen mit Ernst Barlach. [With reproductions and a portrait.] [1946.] 8°. **7877. aa. 17.**

BARLACH (Ernst)

—— Aus seinen Briefen. pp. 94. *München*, [1947.] 8°. **10923. aaa. 31.**

—— Ernst Barlach. Leben und Werk in seinen Briefen. Mit 25 Bildern. Herausgegeben von Friedrich Dross. [With portraits.] pp. 268. *München*, [1952.] 8°. **10922. g. 33.**

—— Der arme Vetter. (Drama.) Dritte Auflage. pp. 127. *Berlin*, 1919. 8°. **11746. k. 52.**

—— Die echten Sedemunds. Drama. pp. 111. *Berlin*, 1920. 8°. **11746. k. 51.**

—— Der Findling. Ein Spiel in 3 Stücken mit Holzschnitten. pp. 77. *Berlin*, 1922. fol. **11747. l. 22.**

—— Fragmente aus sehr früher Zeit. pp. 175. *Berlin*, 1939. 8°. **12359. f. 45.**

—— Die gute Zeit. Zehn Akte. pp. 100. *Berlin*, [1929.] 8°. **11748. dd. 28.**

—— Ein selbsterzähltes Leben. pp. 73. pl. lxxxiii. *Berlin*, 1928. 4°. **7860. ppp. 4.**

—— Ein selbsterzähltes Leben. Mit 91 Abbildungen. [With a portrait.] pp. 49. pl. 90. *München*, [1948.] 8°. **7869. g. 6.**

—— Der tote Tag. Drama in fünf Akten . . . Zweite Auflage. pp. 137. *Berlin*, 1918. 4°. **11746. k. 50.**

BARLACH (Georgius) De amplificationibus vasorum lymphaticorum penis. Dissertatio inauguralis medica, *etc.* pp. 10. *Kiliae*, 1864. 4°. [*Schriften der Universität zu Kiel.* Bd. 11.] **Ac. 1030.**

BARLAEUS (Caspar) *See* Baerle (Kasper van)

BARLAEUS (Daniel) Carmen de Filio Prodigo. *A. de Ruyter: Amstelodami*, 1660. 4°. **837. h. 65. (10.)**

BARLAEUS (Lambertus) *See* Lucian, *of Samosata*, [*Works.—Greek and Latin.*] Λουκιανου Σαμοσατεως ἁπαντα . . . Cum notis integris I. Bourdelotii . . . L. Barlæi, *etc.* 1687. 8°. **166. m. 12, 13.**

—— *See* Thysius (Antonius) *the Younger.* Antonii Thysii Oratio funebris in obitum . . . D. Lamberti Barlæi, *etc.* 1655. 4°. **835. g. 13. (18.)**

—— Lamberti Barlæi . . . In Hesiodi Theogoniam commentarius luculentus. pp. 259. *Typis L. & D. Elzeviriorum: Amstelodami*, 1658. 8°. **160. c. 11. (2.)**

—— [Another edition.] *See* Hesiod. [*Works.—Greek and Latin.*] Ἡσιοδου Ἀσκραιου τα εὑρισκομενα, *etc.* 1658. 8°. **997. b. 14.**

—— Lamberti Barlæi Oratio inauguralis de græcarum litterarum præstantia ac utilitate, habita . . . die xxii Octobris, anni cIↃ IↃcxli. pp. 29. *Ex officina B. & A. Elsevir.: Lugduni Batavorum*, 1642. 4°. **624. f. 2. (12.)**

—— Lamberti Barlæi Oratio funebris in excessum clarissimi viri Marci Zuerii Boxhornii, *etc.* pp. 19. *Ex officina P. Leffen: Lugduni Batavorum*, 1653. 4°. **835.g.13.(10.)**

BARLAEUS (Melchior) Melchioris Barlæi De vetustissima Brabanticæ gentis origine, siue Brabantiados libri .v. Eiusdem Vrbis Antuerpiæ encomium. [In verse.] *Typis A. Diestemij: Antuerpiæ*, 1562. 8°. **1213. i. 5.**

—— Melchioris Barlæi . . . Brabantiados liber. *See* Barlandus (H.C.) Ducum Brabantiæ chronica, *etc.* 1600. 4°. **155. a. 16.**

BARLAEUS (Melchior)

—— De raptu Ganymedis.—Galatea. Ecloga. *See* Gherus (R.) *pseud.* Delitiæ C. poetarum belgicorum, *etc.* pt. 1. 1614. 12°. **238. i. 7.**

—— Melchioris Barlæi Myrmacostrategia. [A poem.] *See* Argumenta. Argumentorum ludicrorum et amœnitatum scriptores varij, *etc.* 1623. 8°. **245. d. 7.**

BARLAGE (Heinrich) Die Lebensmittelpolitik der Stadt Duisburg bis zum Verlust der städtischen Selbstverwaltung, 1713. Tl. 1. pp. xii. 178. *Münster*, 1916. 8°. [*Münstersche Beiträge zur Geschichtsforschung.* Neue Folge. Hft. 35.] **W.P.11911/47.**
No more published.

BARLAGEN BUSSEMAKER (Jan) *See* Bussemaker.

BARLAMONT (Noel van) *See* Barlement.

BARLAND (Hadrianus) *See* Barlandus.

BARLAND (Hubert) *See* Barlandus.

BARLAND (Katharine) Poems. pp. vii. 208. *David Bogue: London*, 1845. 8°. **11645. aa. 5.**

—— Songs of Consolation. pp. ii. 59. *James Hogg: Edinburgh*, 1851. 8°. **11645. aa. 10.**

—— [Another copy.] Songs of Consolation. *Edinburgh*, 1851. 8°. 03440. h. 26. (2.)

BARLANDE (Adrian de) *See* Barlandus (Hadrianus C.)

BARLANDUS (Adrianus) *See* Barlandus (Hadrianus C.)

BARLANDUS (Adrianus Aelius) *See* Barlandus (H.) Huberti Barlandi . . . epistola medica, de aquarum destillatarum facultatibus, de Adriani Ælij Barlandi mortis genere, *etc.* 1536. 8°. **1190. f. 1. (1.)**

BARLANDUS (Adrien) *See* Barlandus (Hadrianus C.)

BARLANDUS (Hadrianus Cornelius)

—— **[For editions of Aesop translated by, or with the addition of fables by, H. Barlandus:] *See* Aesop.**

—— *See* Daxhelet (E.) Adrien Barlandus, humaniste belge, *etc.* 1938. 8°. [*Université de Louvain. Recueil de travaux publiés par les membres des Conférences d'Histoire et de Philologie.* sér. 2. fasc. 45.] Ac. **2646**/4.

—— *See* Erasmus (D.) [*Letters.—Selections.*] Epistolae aliquot selectae ex Erasmicis per H. Barlandum. 1520. 4°. **C. 66. c. 10. (1.)**

—— *See* Scribonius (C.) *Grapheus.* Cornelii Graphei Alosteñ Androtheogonia .i. hominis dei natiuitas [and other poems. Edited by H. Barlandus]. 1514. 8°. **1481. a. 11.**

—— *See* Terentius (P.) *Afer.* [*Works.—Latin.*] P. Terentii Sex comœdiæ, ex diuersis antiquis exemplaribus emendatæ, cum non vulgaribus Commentarijs . . . A. Barlãdi, *etc.* 1530. 4°. **C. 46. e. 18.**

—— *See* Terentius (P.) *Afer.* [*Works.—Latin.*] P. Terentii Afri . . . Comœdiæ, *etc.* [With a commentary by H. Barlandus and others.] 1552. fol. **11707. i. 8.**

—— *See* Terentius (P.) *Afer.* [*Works.—Latin.*] Terentius, a M. Antonio Mureto . . . emendatus . . . Accesserunt . . . argumenta A. Barlãdi in singulas scenas. 1572. 8°. **11707. aaa. 5.**

—— —— 1574. 8°. **1000. c. 6.**

—— See VIRGILIUS MARO (P.) [*Works.—Latin.*] Pub. Vergilii Maronis opera, quæ quidem extant, omnia . . . Accesserunt . . . P. Sabini . . . A. Barlandi, & aliorum annotationes utilissimæ, *etc.* 1586. fol. **840.m.42.**

—— See VIRGILIUS MARO (P.) [*Aeneis.—Latin.*] Enarrationes in primos quatuor libros Aeneidos Vergilij, quibus miro compendio tota fere carminis cuiusq; sententia, & Poetę consiliū exponitur, nuper e vetusto quodā codice per H. Barlandū publicatæ & in lucē æditę, *etc.* 1535, *etc.* 4°. **11386. bb. 25.**

—— See VIRGILIUS MARO (P.) [*Selections.*] Proverbialium versuum ex principe poëtarum Vergilio collectanea, A. Barlando auctore. 1535. 8°. **11355. a. 22.**

—— La Correspondance de Barlandus. *See* DAXHELET (E.) Adrien Barlandus, humaniste belge, *etc.* 1938. 8°. [*Université de Louvain. Recueil de travaux publiés par les membres des Conférences d'Histoire et de Philologie.* sér. 2. fasc. 45.] Ac. **2646/4.**

—— Hoc in libello continentur Hadriani Barlandi de literatis vrbis Romæ Principibus opusculum. Elisii Calentii oppido q̃ elegantes Epistolæ a Barlando & recognitæ & argumentis auctæ. Menandri dicta eximia ab eodem Barlando adnotationibus illustrata, *etc. In bibliotheca T. Martini: Louanii,* 1515. 4°. **11824. aaa. 4.**

—— Hadriani Barlandi . . . libelli tres . . . Vno, Principum Hollandiæ, altero, Episcoporum insignis ecclesiæ Traiectensis, tertio, res gestæ cōtinentur inuictissimi Principis Caroli, Burgūdiæ ducis, Principum Hollandiæ opusculo, adiecta sunt scholia eiusdem Barlandi, *etc. In edibus M. Hillenij: apud Antuerpiam,* 1520. 4°. **1054. d. 1. (6.)**

—— Historica Hadriani Barlandi . . . nunc primum collecta, simulq́ edita. [Edited, with a biographical sketch, by Bernardus Gualtherus.] pp. 434. *Sumptibus B. Gualtheri: Coloniæ,* 1603. 8°. **1193. k. 5.**

—— Hadriani Barlandi ad . . . Guilielmum Zagarum de prælegendis autoribus in scholis Epistola. *See* FILELFO (F.) Francisci Philelphi elegantes & familiares Epistolæ, *etc.* [1520 ?] 4°. **10905. ccc. 27.**

—— Compendiosæ institutiones artis oratoriæ. *See* VIVES (J. L.) De conscribendis epistolis . . . libellus uerè aureus, *etc.* 1537. 8°. **1084. g. 2.**

—— Hadrianus Barlandus . . . De Hollandię principibus. *Apud I. Theobaldū: Anuerpiæ,* 1519. 4°. **804. b. 38.**

—— [Another edition.] Hadriani Barlandi Hollandiæ Comitum historia et icones: cum selectis scholiis ad lectoris lucem. Eiusdem Barlandi Caroli Burgundiæ Ducis vita. Item Vltraiectensium Episcoporum catalogus et res gestæ. Eiusdem argumenti libellus, Gerardo Nouiomago auctore. 2 pt. *Ex officina C. Plantini: Lugduni Batauorum,* 1584. *fol.* **153. g. 19.**

—— [Extracts from "De Hollandiae principibus."] *See* MEYER (Jacobus) *Historian.* Hollandiæ Zelandiæque historia. Ex Meiero & Barlando aliisque, suis locis addenda. 1609. 4°. [SCHRIJVER (P.) *Batavia illustrata, etc.*] **10271. c. 12.**

—— Hadriani Barlandi . . . libri tres, de rebus gestis Ducum Brabantię. Eiusdem de Ducibus Venetis, liber unus. *Ex officina R. Rescij; vænundantur a B. Grauio: Louanij,* 1532. 8°. **9405. aa. 25.**

—— [Another copy.] **G. 15381. (1.)**

—— Dialogi XLII. per Hadrianum Barlandū . . . Ad priorem editionem accesserunt tredecim dialogi. Eiusdē dialogi duo, post tredecim illos iam recens excusi, *etc.* FEW MS. NOTES. *Apud E. Ceruicornum: Coloniae,* 1527. 8°. **12355. b. 2.**

—— [Another edition.] Dialogi LVII. . . . quibus jam recens accesserunt sex ante hac non excusi. Item Augustini Reymarij . . . Dialogus unus, de ludo chartarum. Barlandi opusculum de insignibus oppidis inferioris Germaniæ. *Apud M. Hillenium: Antuerpiæ,* 1527. 8°. **12331. aaa. 21.**

—— [Another edition.] Dialogi LXIII, *etc. Apud M. Hillenium: Antuerpiæ,* 1539. 8°. **12331. aa. 51. (1.)**

—— [Another edition.] Dialogi LXV, *etc. Excudebat I. Crinitus: Antuerpiæ,* 1542. 8°. **714. a. 18. (1.)**

—— [Another edition.] Dialogi omnes Hadriani Barlandi, sanequàm elegantes ac lepidi, admodùm pueris utiles. Vnà cum dialogo Augustini Reymarij . . . de chartarū ludo: ac Barlandi opusculo, de insignibus oppidis Germaniæ inferioris. *Apud C. Wechelum: Parisiis,* 1542. 8°. **12330. c. 19.**

—— [Another copy.] **12316. e. 26. (7.)**

—— Institutio Christiani hominis, per Hadrianum Barlandum aphorismis digesta. *See* SCHOTTENNIUS (H.) Vita honesta, *etc.* 1532. 8°. **4411. df. 38.**

—— Howe a man may attaine to the chiefe pointes of Christianitie, or deduction of a Christian life. [Translated by N. Boorman.] *See* HERMAN IV., *Archbishop and Elector of Cologne, Landgrave of Hesse.* The Gouernement of all estates, *etc.* [1565 ?] 8°. **8409. a. 28.**

—— Iocorum ueterum ac recentiū duæ centuriæ, cum scholijs per H. Barlandum. Iouiani Pontani . . . de Grammaticorum contentione dialogus, cum eiusdem Hadriani scholijs. *Apud P. Martinum: Louanij,* 1524. 8°. **G. 15381. (3.)**

—— Iocorum veterum ac recentium libri tres . . . Primæ æditioni nunc adiecti sunt libri duo. *Apud M. Hilleniū; veneunt à G. Bontio: Antuerpiæ,* 1529. 8°. **1080. e. 3. (2.)**

—— [Another copy.] **12315. a. 20.**

—— [Another copy.] **245. e. 30.**

—— Memorabilis obsidio Ticini siue Papiæ, quæ anno . . . M.D. xxiiij . . . a Francisco . . . Galliarum rege aduersus Carolū Cæsarē inchoata, exijt in Calen. fere Martias anni insequentis . . . Tumultus Germanorum. Tumultus popularis apud Buscunducis [*sic*]. *Apud H. Tilianū, & I. Hoochstratanum: Antuerpiæ,* 1526. 8°. **1057. a. 37.**

—— [Another edition.] Papiensis obsidionis, et eorum quæ in ea accidêre, historica narratio, *etc. See* SCHARDIUS (S.) Schardius redivivus, *etc.* tom. 2. 1673. fol. **9366. l. 6.**

—— Rerum gestarum à Brabantiæ Ducibus Historia, nunc primum Latine conscripta . . . usq; in annum Vigesimū Sextū supra M.D. . . . Catalogus insignium oppidorum Germaniæ inferioris, *etc. H. Tilianus, & I. Hoochstratanus: Antuerpiæ,* 1526. 8°. **9414. aa. 14.**

—— [Another edition.] Chronica Brabantiæ ducum. *See* FEYERABEND (S.) Annales, siue historiæ rerum Belgicarum, *etc.* tom. 2. 1580. fol. **591. k. 12.**

—— [Another edition.] Ducum Brabantiæ chronica . . . Item Brabantiados poema Melchioris Barlæi: iconibus nunc primùm illustrata, ære ac studio Ioan. Bapt. Vrientii: operâ quoque . . . Antonii de Succa. pp. 191. *Apud I. Moretum: Antuerpiæ,* 1600. 4°. **155. a. 16.**

—— [Another edition.] Historia rerum gestarum a Brabantiæ ducibus . . . Editio nova. pp. 237. *Typis F. Foppens: Bruxellæ,* 1665. 12°. **1193. b. 24.**

BARLANDUS (HADRIANUS CORNELIUS)

—— Chroniques des Ducs de Brabant . . . Nouuellement enrichies de leurs figures & pourtraicts. [Edited by Jean Baptiste Vrints.] pp. 192. *Chez la vefue & le fils de I. Moretus: Anvers*, 1612. fol. **591. f. 18.**

—— Had. Barlandi Traiectensium Episcoporum catalogus et eorum res gestæ. pp. 109. *Apud I. Wechelum: Francofurti*, 1585. 8°. **867. a. 4. (2.)**
Previously published as part of the 1584 *edition of "De Hollandiae principibus."*

—— [Another edition.] Vetustissimorum Vltraiectensium pontificum indigitamenta, et res gestæ, maxime memoratu dignæ. Auctoribus H. Barlando et Gerardo Noviomago. *See* SCHRIJVER (P.) Batavia illustrata, *etc.* 1609. 4°. **10271. c. 12.**

BARLANDUS (HUBERTUS) [For editions of the complete works of Galen translated into Latin by H. Barlandus and others:] *See* GALEN [*Works.—Latin.*]

—— *See* GALEN [*De Remediis facile Parabilibus.—Latin.*] Claudii Galeni De paratu facilibus libellus, H. Barlando . . . interprete. 1533. 8°. **540. d. 1. (1.)**

—— *See* OROSCIUS (C.) Annotationes in interpretes Ætii, *etc.* COPIOUS MS. NOTES [by H. Barlandus]. 1540. 4°. **541. e. 16.**

—— Huberti Barlandi . . . epistola medica, de aquarum destillatarum facultatibus, de Adriani Ælij Barlandi mortis genere, hacque occasione, multa obiter de fluxuum ventris et hæmorrhoidum generibus, inter quæ enucleatur Pauli Æginetæ caput de hęmorrhoidibus, eruditissimis etiam viris non satis intellectum, *etc.* *Apud I. Steelsium: Antuerpiæ*, 1536. 8°. **1190. f. 1. (1.)**

—— [Huberti Barlandi . . . Velitatio cum Arnoldo Nootz . . . qua docetur non paucis abuti nos uulgo medicaminibus simplicibus, *etc.*] *Ex ædibus H. Petri: Antuerpiæ*, 1532. 8°. **546. b. 21. (1.)**
Imperfect; wanting the titlepage.

BARLARO (GAETANO) L'Azione d'intervento in dritto internazionale. pt. 1. pp. 17. *Napoli*, 1884. 8°. **6955. df. 2.**
No more published.

BARLAS (JOHN EVELYN) *See* also DOUGLAS (Evelyn) *pseud.* [i.e. J. E. Barlas.]

—— *See* LOWE (David) John Barlas, Sweet Singer and Socialist. 1915. 8°. **10855. aa. 52.**

—— Holy of Holies. Confessions of an Anarchist. [Poems. By J. E. Barlas.] pp. 47. 1887. 8°. *See* ANARCHIST. **11602. e. 38. (4.)**

—— Selections from the Poems of John E. Barlas. [Edited with preface by H. S. Salt.] pp. 64. *Elkin Mathews: London*, 1925. 8°. **011644. e. 52.**

BARLAS (WILLIAM) *See* MACKENZIE (George J.) Remains of a Year's Ministry . . . With a brief memoir, by . . . W. Barlas, *etc.* 1848. 16°. **4460. a. 21.**

BARLASINA (MATTHAEUS) *Begin.* [fol. 1 *recto*:] Matthæi barlasine legum doctoris Mediolanensis. Oratio. Rogatus . . . ut sup Ludouici Romani: & Matthæi bononiēsis . . . accurate singularibus exqsitis nouū uellem opus conficere, *etc.* [An index to the edition of the Singularia juris of L. Pontanus and M. Mattaselanus printed by P. de Lavagna at Milan in 1477.] [*J. and B. de Honate: Milan*, 1477.] fol. **IC. 26323.**
36 leaves, in three quires of ten and one of six leaves, the last three quires signed by numbers. Double columns, 51 lines to a column.

—— [Another edition.] *See* PONTANUS (L.) *Begin.* [fol. 2 *recto*:] Singularia Domini Ludo. pontani, *etc.* 1485. fol. **IC. 22088.**

BARLASINA (MATTHAEUS)

—— [Another edition.] *See* PONTANUS (L.) Singularia, *etc.* 1489. fol. **IC. 22695.**

BARLASS (MARY ELLEN) *See* BARLASS (Thomas) and BARLASS (M. E.) The Spider, *etc.* [1926.] 8°. **11795. cc. 57.**

BARLASS (THOMAS) Spiritual Regeneration as the Basis of World Reconstruction. pp. 94. *John Heywood: Manchester*, [1924.] 8°. **08285. de. 24.**

—— Self; or, Spiritual Regeneration as the basis of world reconstruction. (Second edition.) pp. 94. *John Heywood: Manchester*, [1924.] 8°. **08282. ff. 80.**

BARLASS (THOMAS) and **BARLASS** (MARY ELLEN)

—— The Spider, *etc.* [A film scenario.] pp. 30. *Mark Buckley: Manchester*, [1926.] 8°. **11795. cc. 57.**

BARLASTON. Barlaston Parish Register. [Edited by F. J. Wrottesley.] pp. 135. 1905. 8°. *See* STAFFORD, *County of.—Staffordshire Parish Register Society.* **Ac. 8131. f.**

BARLA-SZABÓ (TITUS) Legrégibb nyelvemlékünk. A halotti beszéd kora, keletkezési helye és szerzője. Teljesen új adatok alapján. pp. 14. *Lőcse*, 1913. 8°. **12975. ccc. 9.**

BARLATIER (PIERRE)

—— L'Aventure tragi-comique du grand général Boulanger. Récit historique, *etc.* pp. 219. [*Paris*,] 1949. 8°. **9231. a. 22.**

BARLATIER DE MAS (FRANÇOIS ÉDOUARD EUGÈNE)

—— Instructions nautiques sur les côtes d'Islande rédigées . . . par M. Barlatier de Mas, *etc.* 1862. 8°. **S.323/335.**

BARLAY (KATE)

—— The Story of a Carrot . . . Drawings by Biro. pp. 49. *Sylvan Press: London*, 1944. 8°. **12827. g. 23.**

—— The Story of Frisky . . . With drawings by Walter Trier. pp. 61. *Sylvan Press: London*, 1945. 8°. **12830. aa. 39.**

BARLAZ (JOSHUA)

—— *See* SZÁSZ (Otto) Introduction to the Theory of Divergent Series . . . Written by J. Barlaz. 1946. 4°. **08535. l. 7.**

BARLÈ (JANKO)

—— Prinosi slovenskim nazivima bilja. pp. 172. 1936, 37. *See* ZEGREB.-*Jugoslavenska Akademija Znanosti i Umjetnosti.* Zbornik za narodni život i običaje, *etc.* knj. 30. sv. 2. knj. 31. sv. 1. 1896, *etc.* 8°. **Ac. 741/15.**

BÂRLEA (ION) *See* BÎRLEA.

BARLECTANUS (FRANCISCUS) *See* BARLETTANI (Francesco)

BARLEE (ANNETTE)

—— The Bunnies of Bunkham Hall. pp. 32. *London & Dublin; Dublin* printed, [1944.] 8°. [*Mellifont Press Children's Series.*] **W.P. 9916/68.**

—— Fairy Flittings. pp. 32. *London; Dublin* printed, [1944.] 8°. [*Mellifont Press Children's Series.*] **W.P. 9916/62.**

—— The Magic Window. pp. 32. *London & Dublin; Dublin* printed, [1944.] 8°. [*Mellifont Press Children's Series.*] **W.P. 9916/73.**

—— Mr. Owl, House-agent. pp. 32. *London & Dublin; Dublin* printed, [1947.] 8°. [*Mellifont Press Children's Series.*] **W.P. 9916/120.**

BARLEE (Annette)

—— Mr. String Sees the World. pp. 32. *London & Dublin; Dublin* printed, [1947.] 8°. [*Mellifont Press Children's Series.*] W.P. **9916/119.**

—— On Our Hill. pp. 100. *W. Tempest: Dundalk*, 1941. 8°. **12360.** a. **13.**

—— The Runaway Engine. pp. 32. *London; Dublin* printed, [1945.] 8°. [*Mellifont Press Children's Series.*] W.P. **9916/86.**

—— The Silver Dot. pp. 32. *London & Dublin; Dublin* printed, [1946.] 8°. [*Mellifont Press Children's Series.*] W.P. **9916/107.**

—— Sloopy the Sea Serpent. pp. 32. *London; Dublin* printed, [1944.] 8°. [*Mellifont Press Children's Series.*] W.P. **9916/61.**

—— Tales of other Lands. pp. 32. *Mellifont Press: London; Dublin* printed, [1949.] 8°. [*Mellifont Press Children's Series.*] W.P. **9916/180.**

—— Toy Town. pp. 32. *London & Dublin; Dublin* printed, [1944.] 8°. [*Mellifont Press Children's Series.*] W.P. **9916/75.**

—— Woodland Revels. pp. 32. *London; Dublin* printed, [1944.] 8°. [*Mellifont Press Children's Series.*] W.P. **9916/51.**

BARLEE (C. H.) *See* Periodical Publications.—*Sydney.* The Sydney Once a Week Magazine. Edited by C. H. Barlee. 1878. 8°. P.P. **6228.** dab.

BARLEE (Charles) *See* Buckle, afterwards Barlee.

BARLEE (Edward) *See* Bible.—*Minor Prophets.* [*English.*] An Explanatory Version of the Minor Prophets . . . By E. Barlee. 1839. 8°. **1110.** c. **8.**

—— *See* Bible.—*Epistles.* [*English.*] A Free and Explanatory Version of the Epistles. By E. Barlee. 1837. 8°. **843.** k. **9.**

—— *See* Childers (Charles) Life and Death in Christ . . . A sermon . . . on . . . the death of the Rev. E. Barlee. 1853. 16°. **4903.** c. **37.**

BARLEE (Ellen) *See* Baker (William T.) Emigration Papers for the Working Classes. Emigration to Iowa . . . Edited by E. Barlee. [1869.] 8°. **10412.** aaa. **32. (4.)**

—— The Bible in Rome, with a record of Protestant missions established since 1873. pp. vii. 280. *Hatchards: London*, 1876. 8°. **4605.** aa. **14.**

—— Effie's Prayer; or, "Thy will be done." A tale explanatory of the Lord's Prayer . . . Second edition. pp. iv. 245. *Seeley & Co.: London*, 1871. 8°. **4413.** l. **8.**

—— Family Prayers and Exhortations for Cottage Hearths . . . With preface by Rev. B. Philpot. pp. 54. *Hunt & Co.: London*, [1874.] 8°. **3457.** c. **10.**

—— Friendless and Helpless. [On the condition of the poor in London.] pp. viii. 292. *Emily Faithfull: London*, 1863. 8°. **8282.** b. **47.**

—— Good and Bad Managers . . . Three stories. pp. 257. *Seeley & Co.: London*, 1874. 8°. **4414.** ff. **6.**

—— Helen Lindsay; or, the Trial of faith . . . Second edition. pp. vi. 417. *Emily Faithfull: London*, 1863. 12°. **4414.** cc. **14.**

—— Homeward: or, the Rest that remaineth. A memoir [of "H——"]. pp. viii. 237. *Seeley & Co.: London*, 1867. 8°. **4905.** aa. **56.**

—— Individual Exertion: a Christmas call to action. pp. 23. *E. Faithfull & Co.: London*, 1861. 8°. **4193.** e. **82. (8.)**

BARLEE (Ellen)

—— Life of the Prince Imperial of France. With portrait. pp. viii. 389. *Griffith & Farran: London*, 1880. 8°. **10664.** bbb. **14.**

—— Locked out. A tale of the strike. pp. 121. *H. S. King & Co.: London*, 1874. 16°. **12638.** a. **53.**

—— Our Homeless Poor . . . By the author of "Helen Lindsay" [i.e. E. Barlee], *etc.* pp. viii. 239. 1860. 8°. *See* Poor. **8276.** a. **63.**

—— Pantomime Waifs; or, a Plea for our city children . . . With introduction by the Earl of Shaftesbury. pp. xviii. 276. *S. W. Partridge & Co.: London*, 1884. 8°. **8277.** c. **34.**

—— Sketches of Working Women. pp. iv. 234. *Seeley & Co.: London*, 1871. 8°. **10602.** c. **18.**

—— Three Paths in Life. A tale for girls. pp. 196. *J. Nisbet & Co.: London*, 1872. 8°. **4413.** l. **9.**

—— A Visit to Lancashire in December, 1862. pp. 156. *Seeley & Co.: London*, 1863. 16°. **8282.** a. **70.**

BARLEE (John)

—— *See* Rowe (Daniel F.) Soccer . . . With photographs by J. Barlee, *etc.* 1949. 8°. **7917.** bbb. **23.**

—— *See* Sugden (Mark) and Hollis (G.) Rugger . . . With photographs by J. Barlee. [With a portrait.] 1946. 8°. **7916.** f. **48.**

—— Birds on the Wing. [With illustrations.] pp. 128. *Collins: London*, 1947. 4°. **7286.** r. **44.**

BARLEE (Thomas Dalling) Miscellaneous Poetry. pp. xii. 192. *E. Collings: Bath*, 1837. 8°. **994.** d. **3.**

BARLEE (William) *of Clavering, Essex.* "A Concordance of all written Lawes concerning Lords of Mannors, theire Free Tenantes, and Copieholders" . . . addressed . . . to the High Sheriff of Essex, in 1578 . . . With a biographical preface by the Deputy Registrar of the Society [i.e. A. L. Hardy]. pp. iv. 72. *London*, 1911. 8°. [*Monographs and Publications of the Manorial Society.* no. 6.] Ac. **8115.** e.

BARLEE (William) *Rector of Brockhole.* Prædestination as before privately, so now at last openly defended against Post-destination in a Correptorie Correction given in by way of answer to a so-called correct copy of some notes concerning God's decrees, especially of reprobation . . . by Mr. T. P. [i.e. Thomas Pierce, Dean of Salisbury] . . . To which are prefixed the epistles of Dr. Edward Reynolds, and Mr. Daniel Cawdrey [and of Thomas Whitfield]. pp. 232. *W. H. for George Sawbridge: London*, 1656. 4°. E. **904. (1.)**

—— *See* Pierce (Thomas) *Dean of Salisbury.* Αὐτοκατακρισις, or, Self-condemnation, exemplified in Mr. Whitfield, Mr. Barlee, *etc.* 1658. 4°. E. **950. (2.)**

—— *See* Pierce (Thomas) *Dean of Salisbury.* The Divine Philanthropie defended against . . . certain late-printed papers intitl'd "A correptory correction" [by W. Barlee], *etc.* 1657. 4°. E. **909. (9.)**

—— —— 1658. 4°. E. **949. (2.)**

—— *See* Pierce (Thomas) *Dean of Salisbury.* The Divine Purity defended: or, a vindication of some "Notes concerning God's decrees" . . . from the censure of D. Reynolds in his epistolary præface to Mr. Barlee's Correptory Correction. 1657. 4°. E. **923. (9.)**

—— *See* Pierce (Thomas) *Dean of Salisbury.* Ἑαυτοντιμωρουμενος, or, the Self-Revenger exemplified in Mr. W. Barlee: by way of rejoynder to the first part of his reply, *etc.* 1658. 4°. E. **950. (1.)**

BARLEMENT (Noel van)

—— Noel van Berlaimont, walsche Schoelmeester Thantwerpen. Die cōiugaciē in Franchoys eñ in Duytsch oft in Vlaems, om alderhande verba eñ redenen te leerē veranderē in diuersche manierē . . . ghestelt bi exempelē. Nu opt nyeuwe ghebetert eñ vermeerdert. Les cōiugatiōs, *etc.* FEW MS. NOTES. *H. de Laet: Thantwerpen,* 1545. 8º. **12962.** c. 4.

—— Dictionario. Coloquios, o dialogos en quatro lenguas, Flamengo, Frances, Español y Italiano: con las Conjugaciones, Instructiones en que se contiene la manera de bien pronunciar y leer las dichas lenguas . . . Dictionaire. Colloques, ou dialogues, *etc.* [By N. van Barlement.] 1569. *obl.* 16º. *See* Diccionario. **12901.** a. **17.**

—— Colloques ou Dialogues auec vn dictionnaire en six langues: Flamen, Anglois, Alleman, François, Espaignol & Italien. [By N. Barlement.] 1576. *obl.* 8º. *See* Colloques. **12901. a. 13.**

—— Familiaria Colloquia cum dictionariolo sex linguarum: Latinæ, Teutonicæ, Gallicæ, Hispanicæ, Italicæ & Anglicæ. [By N. Barlement.] Cornelio Valerio interprete Latino, *etc.* 1584. *obl.* 8º. *See* Colloquia. **12901. a. 14.**

—— Colloquia et Dictionariolum septem linguarum, *etc.* [By N. Barlement.] 1589. *obl.* 8º. *See* Colloquia. **12901. a. 11.**

—— [Another edition.] 1593. *obl.* 8º. *See* Colloquia. **629. a. 1.**

—— Dictionario. Coloquios, o dialogos en quatro lenguas, Flamenco, Frances, Español y Italiano . . . Dictionaire. Colloques, ou dialogues, *etc.* [By N. van Barlement.] 1596. *obl.* 16º. *See* Diccionario. **12901.** a. **18.**

—— Ghemeyne spraken oft Tsamencoutinghen, met eenen Vocabulaer . . . Nv op een niew ouersien ende verbetert. Propos communs, *etc.* *Dutch & Fr.* *By M. Huyssens: t'Hantwerpen,* 1599. 4º. **12972.** ee. **1.**

—— [Another edition.] 1600. *obl.* 8º. *See* Colloquia. **12901. a. 12.**

—— Colloquia et dictionariolum sex linguarum, Latinæ, Gallicæ, Teutonicæ, Hispanicæ, Italicæ, et Anglicæ . . . Colloques ou Dialogues, *etc.* [By N. van Barlement.] pp. 507. 1602 [1608]. *obl.* 8º. *See* Colloquia. **1482. a. 42.**

—— Colloquia et Dictionariolum octo linguarum, *etc.* [By N. Barlement.] 1630. *obl.* 8º. *See* Colloquia. **629. a. 2.**

—— [Another edition.] 1631. *obl.* 8º. *See* Colloquia. **828. a. 71.**

—— Dictionariolum cum colloquiis aliquot quatuor linguarum, Latinè, Germanicè, Gallicè & Italicè . . . Dictionarium . . . jetzund gebessert unnd gemehret, *etc.* [By N. van Barlement.] ff. 1–174. 1634. 16º. *See* Dictionariolum. **623.** a. **33.**

—— Dictionario. Coloquios, o dialogos en quatro lenguas, flamenco, frances, español y italiano . . . Dictionaire. Colloques, ou dialogues, *etc.* [By N. van Barlement.] [c. 1635.] *obl.* 16º. Diccionario. **12901.** a. **16.**

—— The English, Latine, French, Dutch, Schole-master. Or, an Introduction to teach young gentlemen and merchants to travell or trade. Being the onely helpe to attaine to those languages, *etc.* [An edition of the work by N. van Barlement, published originally with the title "Vocabulare" and subsequently with the title "Colloquia."] 1637. 8º. *See* English Schoolmaster. **12901.** b. **16.**

—— [Another edition.] 1639. *obl.* 8º. *See* Colloquia. **629. a. 3.**

—— [Another edition.] 1646. *obl.* 8º. *See* Colloquia. **12901. a. 6.**

BARLEMENT (Noel van)

—— Dictionaire, et colloques en quatre langues, a sçavoir flamen, françois, español, italien: reveus & augmentez par I. M. [i.e. Jean Mommart?] Woorden-boeck, ende t'samen-spraken, *etc.* [By N. van Barlement.] 1647. *obl.* 16º. *See* Dictionnaire. **12901.** a. **1**[illegible]

—— [Another edition.] 1656. *obl.* 8º. *See* Colloquia. **629. a. 4.**

—— Dictionariolum et colloquia octo linguarum, Latinæ, Gallicæ, Belgicæ, Teutonicæ, Hispanicæ, Italicæ, Anglicæ & Portugallicæ . . . Dictionaire et colloques en huict langues, *etc.* [By N. van Barlement.] pp. 358. 1662. *obl.* 8º. *See* Dictionariolum. **12901. aa. 6**

—— [Another copy.] **12901. aa. 14**

—— Colloquia et dictionariolum septem linguarum. Gedrukt door Fickaert te Antwerpen in 1616. Opnieuw uitgegeven door Prof. Dr. R. Verdeyen. [With plates and a list of editions.] 3 pt. *Antwerpen; 's Gravenhage* 1926, 25, 35. 8º. [*Uitgave van de Vereeniging der Antwerpsche Bibliophilen.* no. 39, 40, 42.] Ac. **9629/2**

BARLEMONT (E.) Essai sur certaines modifications de la nutrition pendant la grossesse. pp. 48. *Paris,* 1869. 4º. [*Collection des thèses soutenues à la Faculté de Médecine de Paris.* An 1869. tom. 1.] **7373.** k. **7.**

BARLEMONT (Jean Baptiste de) *See* Bene (S. del) Le Coronement de Messire F. Petrarque . . . faict a Rome . . . Traduit de toscan en françois. [Edited by J. B. de Barlemont.] 1565. 4º. **11850.** e. **6.**

BARLEN (D.)

—— Ачи и другіе разсказы. pp. 79. *Парижъ,* [1927.] 8º. **12590.** pp. **2**[illegible]

—— Русскія былины въ свѣтѣ тайнъ вѣдѣнія. pp. 79. *Парижъ,* 1932. 8º. **20001.** c. **4.**

BARLEN (David)

—— First Steps in Mental Training. [Pictorial mental tests.] [*The Author: Duffus,* 1948.] 8º. **8471.** bb. **92**

—— Sound Spelling. *The Author: Elgin,* 1952– . 8º. W.P. b. **277**

BARLÈS (Louis) Les Nouvelles découvertes sur toutes les parties principales de l'homme, et de la femme. Ensemble leur composition, connexion, action, & usages, *etc.* [With plates.] 4 tom. *E. Vitalis: Lyon,* 1675, 76. 12º. **1172.** b. **4–7.**

With an additional titlepage, engraved.

BARLES DE MANVILLE (A.)

—— *See* Ancora (G. d') [Guida ragionata per le antichità e per le curiosità naturali di Pozzuoli.] Guide du voyageur pour les antiquités et curiosités naturelles de Pouzol et des environs . . . Traduit . . . par M. A. Barles de Manville. 1792. 8º. **1480.** b. **2.**

BARLESIO (Marino) *See* Barletius (Marinus)

BARLÉS Y LLOPIS (Venanci) Esclats del Cor. Apléch de poesías, *etc.* pp. 216. *Barcelona,* 1885. 8º. **11450.** de. **22.**

BARLET ( ) *Ingénieur.* Rapport sur les procédés et les appareils de chauffage et d'éclairage. pp. 81. *Paris,* 1881. 8º. [*Exposition Universelle Internationale de* 1878. *Rapports du Jury International.* groupe 3. classe 27.] **07959. g. 1/17.**

BARLET (ANNIBAL) Le Vray et methodique cours de la physique resolutiue, vulgairement dite chymie . . . Pour connoistre la theotechnie ergocosmique, c'est à dire, l'art de Dieu, en l'ouurage de l'vniuers. [With plates.] pp. 626. *N. Charles: Paris*, 1653. 4°. **1034. h. 2.**
With an additional titlepage, engraved.

—— Seconde edition, avec l'indice . . . & quelques additions. pp. 626. *N. Charles: Paris*, 1657. 4°. **1034. h. 3.**
With an additional titlepage, engraved.

—— Abregé des choses plus necessaires du vray et methodique cours de la physique resolutiue vulgairement dicte chymie, *etc.* pp. 241 [124]. [*Paris?* 1653?] 12°. **1032. b. 13.**

BARLET (CHARLES HENRI) Géographie industrielle et commerciale de la Belgique, indiquant les productions minérales, agricoles et industrielles de chaque localité, *etc.* pp. viii. 224. *Malines*, 1858. 8°. **10270. bbb. 9.**

—— Manuel d'économie domestique, ou l'art de diriger un ménage selon ses revenus . . . Deuxième édition. pp. 66. *Malines*, 1868. 12°. **7957. aa. 13.**

—— Manuel d'économie domestique, à l'usage des écoles de filles, *etc.* pp. 82. *Liége*, 1876. 12°. **7955. de. 2. (1.)**

BARLET (ÉDOUARD) Essai sur l'histoire du commerce et de l'industrie de la Belgique, *etc.* pp. 278. *Liége*, 1858. 12°. **8246. aaa. 29.**

—— 3e édition, revue, *etc.* pp. vi. 334. *Malines*, 1885. 8°. **8229. c. 29.**

BARLET (F. CH.) *See* SCIENCE. La Science secrète. [By F. C. Barlet, V. I. P. Ferran and others.] 1890. 12°. **4785. cc. 13.**

—— Essai sur l'évolution de l'idée. pp. 174. *Paris*, 1891. 12°. **8465. aaa. 41.**

BARLET (F. CH.) and **LEJAY** (JULIEN)

—— L'Art de demain. La peinture autrefois et aujourd'hui, *etc.* pp. 176. *Paris*, 1897. 12°. **7858. aaa. 14.**

BARLET (MARIN) *See* BARLETIUS (Marinus)

BARLET (ROBERT) *See* AFFOUX (J.) Histoires tunisiennes. Précédées d'une lettre-préface par R. Barlet. 1887. 8°. **12430. g. 37.**

BARLET (STÉPHANE) *See* AHN (F.) Dr. Ahn's First French Course; thoroughly revised . . . by S. Barlet. 1876. 12°. **12950. aaa. 6.**

—— *See* AYMON. [*Les Quatre fils Aymon.—Prose Versions. —French.*] Histoire des quatre fils Aymon . . . racontée aux enfants par S. Barlet . . . et A. Canivet. 1906. 8°. **12238. aaa. 1/66.**

—— *See* BORNIER (E. C. H. de) *Viscount.* Un Cousin de passage . . . Edited by S. Barlet, *etc.* 1894. 8°. **11740. aa. 52/9.**

—— *See* HUON, *of Bordeaux, Duke de Guienne.* Huon de Bordeaux. Raconté par S. Barlet . . . et J. Cornuel. 1907. 8°. **12238. aaa. 1/79.**

—— *See* LAMARTINE DE PRAT (M. L. A. de) Le Tailleur de pierres de Saint-Point . . . Edited with biographical notice . . . by S. Barlet. 1890. 8°. **012547. i. 50.**

—— *See* LONDON.—III. *University of London.* [*Examinations.*] London University Matriculation Papers, with translations . . . and solutions, January, 1882. By S. Barlet, *etc.* 1882. 8°. **8365. aa. 6.**

—— *See* MACÉ (Jean) Contes du petit château . . . Edited . . . by S. Barlet. 1895, *etc.* 8°. **012550. l. 6.**

BARLET (STÉPHANE)

—— *See* MAISTRE (F. X de) *Count.* La Jeune Sibérienne et Le lépreux de la cité d'Aoste. Edited . . . by S. Barlet. 1885. 8°. **12200. eee. 1/10.**

—— *See* MASSON (Jules) Aventures de l'ânon Baudinet . . . Edited by S. Barlet. [1885.] 16°. **12202. aa. 51.**

—— *See* OGIER, *the Dane.* Ogier le Danois. Raconté par S. Barlet . . . et J. Cornuel. 1907. 8°. **12238. aaa. 1/81.**

—— *See* POUVILLON (E.) Petites âmes . . . Edited by S. Barlet. 1898, *etc.* 8°. **012202. ff. 7/9.**

—— *See* ROLAND. La Chanson de Roland racontée pour les enfants par S. Barlet . . . et L. Duchemin. 1906. 8°. **12238. aaa. 1/65.**

—— *See* SAND (George) *pseud.* Les Maîtres sonneurs . . . Edited by S. Barlet. 1910. 8°. **12239. f. 32.**

—— *See* ZELLER (B.) Henri IV. . . . Edited . . . by S. Barlet. 1885. 8°. **10664. a. 21.**

—— The "Grand Orient de France": a plea. pp. 8. [1918.] 8°. **4784. ff. 42.**

—— The Preceptors' Junior French Course. pp. xiv. 176. *Relfe Bros.: London*, [1895.] 8°. **12950. df. 53.**

BARLET (STÉPHANE) and **MASOM** (WILLIAM FREDERICK)

—— An Advanced French Reader. Arranged by S. Barlet . . . and W. F. Masom. pp. 153. *W. B. Clive & Co.: London*, [1890.] 8°. [*Tutorial Series.*] **12205. c. 140.**

—— Second edition. pp. 153. *W. B. Clive: London*, [1896.] 8°. [*Tutorial Series.*] **12205. c. 265.**

—— A French Prose Reader. Arranged by S. Barlet . . . and W. F. Masom. pp. 144. *W. B. Clive & Co.: London*, [1890.] 8°. [*Tutorial Series.*] **12205. c. 141.**

—— [Another edition, with a vocabulary.] pp. 211. *W. B. Clive & Co.: London*, [1892.] 8°. [*Tutorial Series.*] **12205. c. 73.**

—— Second edition. pp. viii. 211. *W. B. Clive: London*, [1894.] 8°. [*Tutorial Series.*] **12205. c. 214.**

—— Third edition. pp. viii. 191. *W. B. Clive: London*, [1896.] 8°. [*Tutorial Series.*] **12205. c. 316.**

—— *See* JUST (H. E.) and TARRANT (H. C. A.) Notes and Key to Barlet and Masom's French Prose Reader. [1893.] 8°. **12205. c. 103.**

BARLETA (GABRIEL DE) *See* GABRIEL, *de Barletta.*

BARLETANO (FRANCESCO) *See* BARLETTANI.

BARLETIO (MARINO) *See* BARLETIUS (Marinus)

BARLETIUS (MARINUS)

—— *See* PALL (F.) Marino Barlezio, *etc.* 1938. 8°. **10633. v. 32.**

—— Chronicorum Turcicorum, in quibus vita, indoles, et aduersus Turcas res gestæ Georgii Castrioti, Epirotarum principis, qui . . . Scanderbegus, hoc est, Alexander Magnus, cognominatus fuit, libris XIII. describuntur à M. Barletio . . . tomus tertius. Accesserunt autoris eiusdem libri III. de Scodra . . . à Turcis expugnata. Omnia figuris et viuis imaginibus illustrata, *etc.* ff. 271. *Apud I. Feyerabendt, impensis S. Feyerabendt: Francofurti ad Mœnum*, 1578. fol. [LONICERUS (P.) *Chronicorum Turcicorum . . . tomus primus, etc.* tom. 3.] **434. i. 17.**

BARLETIUS (Marinus)

—— Historia de vita et gestis Scanderbegi, Epirotarum principis, *etc.* ff. 159. *Per B. V.* [*B. de Vitalibus*]: *Rome*, [1520?] fol. **148. h. 3.**

—— [Another copy.] **G. 1452.**

—— De uita moribus ac rebus præcipue aduersus Turcas gestis, Georgii Castrioti, clarissimi Epirotarum principis . . . libri tredecim . . . nunc primum in Germania castigatissime æditi. [Edited by C. Hedio.] pp. 371. *Apud C. Mylium: Argentorati*, 1537. fol. **10605. i. 20.**

—— The Historie of George Castriot, surnamed Scanderbeg, King of Albanie . . . Newly translated . . . into English by Z. I. Gentleman [i.e. Zachary Jones]. [Translated from J. de La Vardin's expansion of Barletius.] pp. 498. 1596. fol. *See* La Vardin (J. de) **10605. g. 13.**

—— [Another copy.] C. **64.** e. **8.**

—— Histoire de Georges Castriot surnommé Scanderbeg, roy d'Albanie . . . Par Iacques Delavardin. [Mainly a translation of "Historia de vita et gestis Scanderbegi" by M. Barletius.] ff. 485. 1576. 4°. *See* La Vardin (J. de) **10605.** e. **2.**

—— [Another edition.] ff. 462. 1593. 8°. *See* La Vardin (J. de) G. **15178.**

—— Dernière édition, augmentée d'une Chronologie Turquesque, *etc.* pp. 601. 1621. 4°. *See* La Vardin (J. de) **10605.** e. **4.**

—— Des aller streytparsten vñ theüresten Fürsten vnd Herrn Georgen Castrioten, genañt Scanderbeg, Hertzogen zu Epiro vnd Albanien etc. Ritterliche thaten, so er zu erhalten seiner Erbland, mit den Türckischen Kaysern in seinem leben, glücklich begangen. In Latein beschriben, vñ yetz durch J. Pinicianũ newlich verteütscht. [With a portrait.] ff. ccxci. *Durch H. Steiner: Augspurg*, 1533. fol. **10630.** h. **19.**

—— Des aller Streÿttbarsten vnd Theüresten Fürsten vnd Herrn, Herrn Georgen Castrioten, genannt Scanderbeg . . . Ritterliche Thaten . . . Vorhin in Latein beschriben, vñ jetzt durch Joannem Pinicianum verteüscht. ff. 319. *W. Han & G. Raben: Franckfurt*, 1561. 4°. **10805. c. 1.**

—— [Another edition.] Scanderbeg. Warhaffte eigentliche und kurtze Beschreibung aller . . . Schlachten vnd Thaten, so . . . Georg Castriot, genannt Scanderbeg . . . gethan . . . Jetzt von neuwem . . . gebessert, *etc.* ff. 156. *G. Raben, in Verlegung S. Feyrabends: Franckfurt*, 1577. fol. **805. h. 12. (1.)**

—— Des streitbaren Castrioti ruhmwürdigste Geschichte . . . Teutsch vorgestellet durch Gabriel Tzschimmern. pp. 647. *In Verlegung A. Löfflers: Dresden*, 1664. 8°. **1434. b. 9.**

—— Historia del magnanimo, et valoroso Signor Georgio Castrioto, detto Scanderbego . . . Dal latino in lingua Italiana, per Pietro Rocha nouamente tradotta. ff. 403. *F. & A. Zopini: Venetia*, 1580. 8°. **1201. b. 2.**

—— Chronica do valeroso Principe & inuenciuel Capitão Iorge Castrioto . . . chamado Scanderbego . . . escrita em Latim . . . & tresladada em Portuguez por Francisco Dandrade, *etc.* ff. 245. *M. Borges: Lisboa*, 1567. fol. **G. 6424.**

—— Chronica del esforçado principe y capitan Iorge Castrioto rey de Epiro . . . [By M. Barletius.] Traduzida del lenguaje Portugues enel Castellano, por I. Ochoa de la Salde, *etc.* ff. 191. 1588. fol. *See* George [Castriota], *Prince of Epirus, etc.* **10605.** i. **3.**

—— Coronica del Esforçado Principe . . . Jorge Castrioto [by M. Barletius] . . . Traduzida de lengua Portuguesa en Castellano por Iuan Ochoa de Lazalde. ff. 207. 1597. fol. *See* Castriot (G.) called Scander Beg, *Prince of Epirus.* **814. l. 16.**

BARLETIUS (Marinus)

—— Marini Barletii De obsidione Scodrensi ad serenissimũ Leonardũ Lauretanũ aristocratię Venetæ principem. Conciones uarię a Meumethe turcaꝝ principe, & ab aliis militiæ præfectis artificiose compositæ. *Per B. Venetũ de Vitalibus: Venetiis*, 1504. 4°. **592. c. 18.**

—— [Another copy.] **175. a. 9.**

—— [Another edition.] De Scodrensi expugnatione libri III. *See* Chalcocondylas (L.) De origine et rebus gestis Turcorum, *etc.* 1556. fol. **C. 80. f. 8.**

BARLETIUS (Marinus)

—— *See* Duponcet (J. N.) Histoire de Scanderbeg roy d'Albanie. [Based on "Historia de vita et gestis Scanderbegi" by M. Barletius.] 1709. 12°. **1201.** b. **5.**

—— Dell'assedio di Scutari. [1561.] *See* Sansovino (F.) Dell' historia universale dell'origine et imperio de' Turchi, *etc.* pt. 3. lib. 4. 1560, *etc.* 4°. **280.** g. **18.**

—— Dell' asedio di Scutari. *See* Sansovino (F.) Historia vniuersale . . . de Turchi, *etc.* 1568. 4°. **1053. h. 2. (2.)**

—— [Another edition.] *See* Sansovino (F.) Historia vniuersale . . . de' Turchi, *etc.* 1582. 4°. **1053. h. 3.**

—— [Another edition.] *See* Sansovino (F.) Historia vniuersale . . . de' Turchi, *etc.* 1600. 4°. **1053. h. 4.**

BARLETTA.—*Archivio Capitolare.*

—— Le Pergamene di Barletta, Archivio Capitolare, 897–1285. Per Francesco Nitti di Vito [i.e. edited by him, with an introduction] . . . Con 7 facsimili, *etc.* pp. lxxxvii. 508. *Bari*, 1914. 4°. [*Codice Diplomatico Barese.* vol. 8.] **07701.dd.23/8.**

Biblioteca Comunale.

—— Le Pergamene della Biblioteca Comunale di Barletta, 1186–1507. [Edited, with an introduction, by Giovanni Italo Cassandro.] pp. xl. 135. *Trani*, 1938. 4°. [*Codice diplomatico barese.* vol. 14.] **07701.** dd

BARLETTA (Andrea di) *See* Barulo (Andreas de)

BARLETTA (Cristina Arcamone) *See* Arcamone (C.)

BARLETTA (Gabriel) *See* Gabriel, *de Barletta.*

BARLETTA (Leonidas)

—— La Ciudad de un Hombre. Novela, *etc.* pp. 324. *Buenos Aires*, 1943. 8°. **12491.** y. **24.**

—— Como naufragó el capitán Olssen. pp. 127. [*Buenos Aires*, 1945?] 8°. **12492.** a. **36.**

—— Pájaros negros, *etc.* [Short stories.] pp. 188. *Buenos Aires*, 1946. 8°. **12492.** bbb. **9.**

—— La Señorita Enriqueta y su Ramito. [A novel.] Con doce ilustraciones cinegráficas de Augusto Ignacio Vallmitjana. pp. 129. *Buenos Aires*, 1943. 8°. **12490.** s. **13.**

BARLETTANI (Francesco) [An eclogue.] 1719. *See* Italian Poets. Carmina illustrium poetarum italorum. tom. 2. 1719, *etc.* 8°. **237. g. 28.**

BARLETTE (Marinus) *See* Barletius.

BARLETTI (Carlo) Analisi d'un nuovo fenomeno del fulmine. 1780. *See* Amoretti (C.) and Soave (F.) Opuscoli scelti sulle scienze, *etc.* tom. 3. 1778, *etc.* 4°. **981.** h. **3.**

—— Physica specimina, *etc.* pp. 184. pl. II. *Mediolani*, 1772. 8°. **232.** e. **28.**

BARLETTI DE SAINT PAUL (François Paul) Barletti-Saint-Paul . . . aux citoyens . . . formant le Comité d'instruction publique. [On his plans of education. With the reply of the Committee.] [*Chartres?* 1793.] *s. sh.* 4°. **935. b. 7. (10.)**

—— Description du cabinet litteraire que Madame de * * * . . . & Don Francisco Barletti de Saint Paul . . . ont exécuté en 1773, à Madrid, pour faciliter les études de feu Don Carlos-Clemente-Antonio, Infant d'Espagne. Précédée d'un extrait du manuscrit dans lequel elle se trouve, *etc.* [With tables.] pp. 32. [*Paris,*] 1777. 4°. **124. f. 16. (1.)**

—— Nouveau système typographique, ou moyen de diminuer de moitié . . . le travail & les frais de composition, de correction & de distribution, découvert en 1774, par Mme de * * *. [With tables.] pp. viii. 66. *Paris,* 1776. 4°. **124. f. 16. (2.)**

—— Vues relatives au but et aux moyens de l'instruction du peuple français, considérée sous le seul rapport de l'enseignement. pp. 22. [*Paris,*] 1793. 4°. **936. f. 12. (25.)**

BARLEUF (Vincent) Recit veritable de la venue d'une canne sauuage en la Ville de Montfort. Réimpression de l'ouvrage composé en 1652 par le P. Vincent Barleuf, précédée d'une notice sur la Cane de Montfort. *See* Joüon des Longrais (F.) Jacques Doremet, *etc.* 1894. 8°. **010663. f. 28.**

BARLEUS (Caspar) *See* Baerle (Kasper van)

BARLEX (William George)

—— The Taxation of Women. pp. 24. *Hallmark Books: London,* 1949. 8°. **8218. c. 46.**

BARLEY-BREAK. Barley-Breake; or, a Warning for Wantons, of W. N., Gentleman . . . Edited . . . by . . . A. B. Grosart. 1877. 4°. *See* N., W., *Gentleman.* **2326. g. 5. (5.)**

BARLEY-LOAF. The Barley-Loaf. *See* Periodical Publications.—*London.*

BARLEY LOAVES. Barley Loaves. By A. J. J., *etc.* 1877. 16°. *See* J., A. J. **11652. df. 45.**

BARLEY (Alfred H.) The Drayson Problem. An astronomical survey . . . in . . . reply to a recent article (by E. O. Fountain) in the Journal of the British Astronomical Association entitled "The Draysonian Fallacy," *etc.* pp. xxiv. 48. *W. Pollard & Co.: Exeter,* 1922. 8°. **08560. ee. 29.**

—— The Rationale of Astrology . . . With an additional chapter by Alan Leo on the Education of Children in the light of Astrology. pp. 112. *L. N. Fowler & Co.: London,* [1905.] 8°. [*Astrological Manuals.* Introductory.] **8610. dg. 13/1.**

—— A Thousand and One Notable Nativities. "The Astrologer's 'Who's Who.'" Compiled by the sub-editor of "Modern Astrology" [i.e. A. H. Barley]. pp. viii. 116. 1911. 8°. *See* Nativities. **8610. dg. 13/11.**

BARLEY (Ann)

—— Patrick Calls Me Mother, *etc.* pp. 227. *Harper & Bros.: New York,* [1948.] 8°. **12729. ff. 16.**

BARLEY (Frederick C.) The Twins: their visit to the Queen. A story for parents to read to their children, *etc.* pp. 27. *Robert Scott: London,* 1912. 8°. **012808. d. 32.**

BARLEY (John) *Captain. See* Burley.

BARLEY (Leslie John) The Riddle of Rationalisation. A review of the potentialities of the scientific reorganisation of industry under a national plan, *etc.* pp. 128. *G. Allen & Unwin: London,* 1932. 8°. **8277. p. 49.**

BARLEY (Maurice Willmore)

—— *See* Scott (Judith D. G.) and Barley (M. W.) Preserving Churchyard Monuments, *etc.* [1952.] 8°. **7877. i. 8.**

—— *See* York, *Diocese of.—Parochial Documents Commission of the Archdeaconry of the East Riding.* Parochial Documents of the Archdeaconry of the East Riding. An inventory. Edited by M. W. Barley. 1939. 8°. [*Yorkshire Archæological Society. Record Series.* vol. 99.] **Ac. 5652/8.**

—— Lincolnshire and the Fens . . . Illustrated, *etc.* pp. viii. 191. *B. T. Batsford: London,* 1952. 8°. [*Face of Britain Series.*] **W.P. 11741/29.**

BARLEY (R. Ewart) Romance around Stony Stratford . . . With a sketch of its history and charities by C. P. Woollard. [With plates.] pp. 80. *O. C. Barley: Eastbourne,* 1928. 8°. **010368. f. 62.**

BARLEY (William) A new Booke of Tabliture, containing sundrie . . . Instructions, shewing howe to attaine to the knowledge, to guide and dispose thy hand to play on sundry Instruments, as the Lute, Orpharion, and Bandora: together with diuers new Lessons to each of these Instruments. Whereunto is added an introduction to Pricke song, and certaine familliar rules of descant, *etc.* 3 pt. *For W. Barley: London,* 1596. *obl.* 8°. **M.K. 1. c. 18.**

BARLEYCORN.

The little Barly-corne,
Whose properties and vertues here,
Shall plainly to the world appeare,
To make you merry all the yeere.

[A ballad.] B.L. 2 pt. *For E. B.: London,* [1645?] *s. sh.* fol. **Rox. i. 214.**

BARLEYCORN (*Sir* John) The Dying Groans of Sir John Barleycorn . . . To which is added Donal Drouth's reply, with a large description of his drunken wife, *etc.* pp. 8. [*London,* 1790?] 8°. **11621.e.2.(31.)**

—— The Monopolist; or the Installation of Sir John Barleycorn, Knight: a poetical tale. Addressed to servant maids. pp. 16. *S. Hazard: Bath,* 1795. 4°. **644. k. 35. (2.)**

—— A pleasant new Ballad to sing both even and morne, Of the bloody murther of Sir John Barley-corne. B.L. *For Iohn Wright: London,* [1650?] *s. sh.* fol. **Rox. i. 343.**

—— [Another edition.] *Printed by W. D., sold by A. Bettesworth: London,* [1710?] *s. sh.* fol. **Rox. iii. 364.**

—— [Another edition.] [*London?* 1730?] *s. sh.* fol. **Rox. iii. 360.**

Described as "Part 1."

—— The Whole Tryal and Indictment of Sir John Barley-Corn, Knight . . . Taken in short-hand by Timothy Toss-pot, foreman of the Jury. [By Thomas Robins.] pp. 8. *J. Dutton: London,* 1709. 8°. **1076. l. 22. (34.)**

—— [Another edition.] pp. 8. [*Newcastle?* 1760?] 8°. **C.116.bb.11.(32.)**

—— [Another edition.] pp. 8. [*Newcastle,* 1780?] 12°. **1078. k. 21. (7.)**

—— The Arraigning and Indicting of Sir John Barleycorn, Knt. newly composed by a well-wisher to Sir John, and all that love him. [A slightly different version from the preceding.] pp. 24. *London,* [1750?] 12°. **T. 1855. (5.)**

—— [Another copy.] **1079. i. 13. (4.)**

—— [Another edition.] pp. 24. *London,* [1785?] 12°. **1076. l. 7. (1.)**

BARLEYCORN (*Sir* John)

—— *See* Featherstone (Thomas) *Temperance Writer.* Trial of Dr. Abstinence . . . or, " The Trial of John Barleycorn " reversed, *etc.* 1854. 12°. **8436.** aa. **24.** **(8.)**

BARLEZIO (Marino) *See* Barletius (Marinus)

BARLIARIO (Pietro) *See* Cataloni (F.) Vita, conversione, e morte di P. Barliario nobile Salernitano e famosissimo mago, *etc.* [1800?] 12°. **11426.** b. **74.** **(17.)**

—— Bellissima istoria della vita, conversione e morte di Pietro Barliario nobile Salernitano e famoso mago. [By Filippo Cataloni. In verse.] [*Naples,* 1800?] 12°. **1071.** c. **24.** **(7.)**

BARLICKI (Norbert)

—— Proletariat. pp. 47. *Warszawa,* 1947. 8°. **8289.** ee. **3.**

BARLIETI (Gabriel de) *pseud.* [i.e. Bartholomaeus Gericke.] *See* Gabriel, *de Barlieti.*

BARLING (A. A.) and **MARTIN** (Ronald Russell)

—— Careers in the Civil Service. pp. 180. *Gregg Publishing Co.: London,* [1927.] 8°. **08364.** e. **46.**

BARLING (Edith M.)

—— Back to G. B. S. [i.e. George Bernard Shaw], or a Midsummer Nightmare. (Shaw Tercentenary Celebration, Malvern A.D. 2156.) [A play in one act.] pp. 23. *Ad-Visers: London, Worcester,* [1933.] 8°. **011781.** i. **86.**

—— The Governor. A play in one act. pp. 19. *Play Rights & Publications: London,* [1936.] 8°. [*Amateur Theatre Series of Plays.*] **11784.f.1/29.**

—— His Majesty Masquerades. A one-act play. pp. 21. *Oxford University Press: London,* 1938. 8°. **011781.** k. **45.**

—— A Sword for the King. pp. 12. *Oxford University Press: London,* 1940. 8°. [*Oxford School Plays.*] W.P. **2969/8.**

BARLING (Frederick Harvey) Leonidas; or, the Bridal of Thanatos. A dramatic poem. pp. 90. *Wyman & Sons: London,* 1885. 8°. **11641.** bbb. **46.**

BARLING (*Sir* Gilbert) *Bart.* *See* Barling (*Sir* Harry G.)

BARLING (*Sir* Harry Gilbert) *Bart.* On Appendicitis and on Perforation of Gastric and Duodenal Ulcer. (The Ingleby Lectures, 1895.) pp. 92. *Cornish Bros.: Birmingham,* 1895. 8°. **7482.** g. **19.**

BARLING (John) Leaves from my Writing Desk: being tracts 6, 7 and 8, on the question What do we know? By an Old Student [i.e. J. Barling]. pp. vi. 81. 1872. 8°. *See* Leaves. **8468.** bb. **5.**

—— A Lecture in behalf of the Sunday League, *etc.* pp. 16. *E. T. Whitfield: London,* 1856. 8°. **4355.** d. **1.**

—— A Review of Trinitarianism; chiefly as it appears in the writings of Pearson, Bull, Waterland, Sherlock, Howe, Newman, Coleridge, Wallis and Wardlaw. With a brief notice of sundry passages of the New Testament, bearing on the controversy. pp. xvi. 240. *John Chapman: London,* 1847. 8°. **4225.** c. **7.**

BÄRLING (Olof) Iordabalken. *See* Stiernhöök (J.) Förarbeten till Sveriges rikes lag 1666–1686. 1933. 8°. [*Uppsala Universitets Årsskrift.* 1933. bd. 2.] Ac. **1075/6.**

BARLING (Seymour Gilbert) *See* Parsons (*Sir* Leonard G.) and Barling (S. G.) Diseases of Infancy and Childhood. 1933. 8°. **20036.a.1/511.**

—— *See* Parsons (*Sir* Leonard G.) and Barling (S. G.) Diseases of Infancy and Childhood, *etc.* 1954. 8°. **20036.** a. **1/805.**

BARLING (Seymour Gilbert) and **MORRISON** (John Tertius)

—— A Manual of War Surgery, *etc.* pp. xvi. 479. *Henry Frowde; Hodder & Stoughton: London,* [1919.] 8°. [*Oxford Medical Publications.*] **20036.a.1/127.**

BARLING (W. E.) British Shipping: its basis and its services. *See* England. [*Appendix.—Trade and Commerce.*] Lectures on British Commerce, *etc.* [1912.] 8°. **8226.** r. **14**

BARLING (William Frederick)

—— Law and Grace. A devotional study of the Law of Moses, *etc.* pp. 208. *The Christadelphian: Birmingham,* [1952.] 8°. **5061.** b. **36.**

BARLING (William Tyler) Memoir of William Tyler Barling, *etc.* pp. 16. *J. L. Linney: York,* 1844. 32°. **4920.** a. **38.**

—— [Another edition.] pp. 32. *William Simpson: York,* 1856. 16°. **4986.** a. **63.** **(11.)**

BARLIUS (Casparus) *See* Baerle (Kasper van)

BARLOCCI (Gianguelberto) L'Oreste. Drama per musica da recitarsi nella sala dell' illmo sig. Federico Capranica l'anno 1723, *etc.* [In verse.] pp. 65. *Roma,* 1723. 12°. **906.** b. **6.** **(4.)**

BARLOCCI (Giovanni) Don Calascione. Drama giocoso per musica per il teatro di S. M. B. [By G. Barlocci.] *Ital. & Eng.* pp. 103. 1749. 8°. *See* Calascione, *Don.* **907.** i. **6.** **(9.)**

—— [Another edition.] La Finta cameriera, intermezzo per musica in due atti . . . La Fausse suivante, *etc.* [By G. Barlocci.] *Ital. & Fr.* pp. 53. 1752. 12°. *See* Cameriera. **905.** i. **1.** **(3.)**

BARLOCCI (Saverio) Congetture sulla origine della elettricità atmosferica. Memoria, *etc.* pp. 21. *Roma,* 1830. 8°. **7680.** aa. **66.** **(3.)**

—— Ricerche fisico-chimiche sul lago Sabatino, sulle sorgenti di acque minerali che scaturiscono nei suoi contorni e principalmente sulle acque termali di Vicarello. Memoria . . . Seconda edizione, *etc.* pp. 30. *Roma,* 1830. 8°. **899.** d. **6.** **(6.)**

BARLONE (Daniel)

—— Une Fiancée de Charlemagne, Irène Impératrice de Byzance, *etc.* pp. 238. *Paris; Oran* printed, 1945. 8°. **10607.** ee. **73.**

—— A French Officer's Diary, 23 August 1939—1 October 1940 . . . Translated . . . by L. V. Cass, *etc.* [With maps.] pp. vii. 155. *University Press: Cambridge,* 1942. 8°. **9100.** f. **29.**

BARLOT (Leon du Chastelier) *See* Du Chastelier Barlot.

BARLOUW (Francis) *See* Barlow.

BARLO-VENTO, *Dr., Natural de Cargagente, pseud.* L'Apología de los Ciegos ó la Homeopato-Mania. Historia critico-medica por el Dr. Barlo-vento. pp. 56. *Madrid,* 1851. 8°. **7391.** c. **3.**

BARLOVIUS (Franciscus) *See* Barlow (Francis)

BARLOVIUS (Thomas) *Bishop of Lincoln. See* Barlow.

BARLOW, *Family of. See* Barlow (*Right Hon. Sir* Clement A. M.) *Bart.* Barlow Family Records, *etc.* [With pedigrees.] [1932.] 8°. **9907. b. 29.**

—— *See* Barlow (George D.) Published Matter and Records relating to the Families of the name of Barlow. 1911. 8°. **9914. s. 12.**

BARLOW ( ) *of the Blackfriars Road.* Mr. Barlow's Proposals for establishing, with or without an act of Parliament, a Gas-light Company in the County of Surrey, *etc.* [*London,* 1815 ?] *s. sh.* fol. **8223. e. 10. (8.)**

BARLOW ( ) *Shopkeeper in Shoreditch.* The Duke of Shoreditch; or, Barlow's Ghost. [An address on the threatened invasion.] *J. Asperne: London,* [1803.] *s. sh.* fol. **806. k. 1. (66.)**

—— [Another copy.] **1851. c. 3. (31.)**

—— [Another copy.] **1851. c. 3. (63.)**

BARLOW (A. C.) The Railway Invoice and Shipping Clerks' Ready Reckoner, *etc.* pp. 100. *Brown Thomson & Co.: Wellington* [*N.Z.*], 1895. *obl.* 8°. **8548. aa. 40.**

BARLOW (A. Ruffell)

—— *See* Bible.—*Psalms.* [*Kikuyu.*] Thaburi. [Translated by A. R. Barlow.] 1936. 8°. **03068. e. 129.**

—— *See* Bible.—*Psalms.* [*Kikuyu.*] Thaburi. [Translated by A. R. Barlow.] 1948. 8°. **3091. aaa. 2.**

—— *See* Bible.—*Mark.* [*Kikuyu.*] Ũhoro Mwega wa Mũathani Witu Yesu Kristo ta ũrĩa watemiruo marũa nĩ Marko. [Translated by A. R. Barlow.] 1909. 8°. **03068. ff. 35.**

—— —— 1912. 8°. **03068. h. 4.**

—— —— 1917. 8°. **03068. h. 41.**

—— —— 1924. 8°. **03068. h. 145.**

—— *See* Bible.—*John, Gospel of.* [*Kikuyu.*] Ũyũ nĩ Ũhoro mwega ũrĩa waandikirũo nĩ Johana. [Translated by A. R. Barlow.] 1919. 8°. **03068.h.66.**

—— Tentative Studies in Kikuyu Grammar and Idiom. pp. xii. 236. *Foreign Mission Committee of the Church of Scotland: Edinburgh,* 1914. 8°. **12910. t. 47.**

BARLOW (Adela F.)

—— Convent Experiences. By Miss A. F. B. [i.e. A. F. Barlow.] pp. 44. 1875. 8°. *See* B., A. F., *Miss.* **4017. e. 9.**

BARLOW (*Sir* Alan) *Bart. See* Barlow (*Sir* James A. N.) *Bart.*

BARLOW (Alfred) The History and Principles of Weaving by hand and by power. Reprinted, with considerable additions from " Engineering," with a chapter on lace-making machinery, reprinted from the " Journal of the Society of Arts " . . . With . . . illustrations. pp. xii. 443. *Sampson Low & Co.: London,* 1878. 8°. **07944. k. 20.**

BARLOW (Alfred Ernest) *See* Adams (Frank D.) and Barlow (A. E.) Geology of the Haliburton and Bancroft Areas, Province of Ontario. 1910. 8° **C.S.E.16/9.**

—— *See* Adams (Frank D.) and Barlow (A. E.) The Nepheline and Associated Alkali Syenites of Eastern Ontario. 1909. 8°. **07109. b. 25.**

BARLOW (Alfred Ernest)

—— Corundum, its occurrence, distribution, exploitation, and uses. pp. vii. 377. pl. xxviii. *Ottawa,* 1915. 8°. [*Geological Survey of Canada. Memoir.* no. 57.] **C.S.E.16/9.**

—— Report on the Geology and Natural Resources of the area included in the Nipissing and Temiscaming Map-sheets, *etc.* pp. 302. *Ottawa,* 1899. 8°. [*Geological Survey of Canada. Annual Report.* New ser. vol. 10.] **C.S.E.16.**

BARLOW (Alice) Alice Barlow; or, Principle in everything. A country village history. pp. 226. *R.T.S.: London,* [1861.] 12°. **4419. c. 20.**

—— [Another edition.] pp. 280. *Presbyterian Board of Publication: Philadelphia,* [1863 ?] 12°. **4416. aaa. 6.**

BARLOW (Ambrose)

—— *See* Camm (Bede) The Martyr-Monk of Manchester (Ven. Ambrose Barlow). [1910.] 8°. **3943.aa.65.**

—— *See* Camm (Bede) The Martyr-Monk of Manchester, *etc.* 1930. 8°. **3943.aa.66.**

—— The Apostolical Life of Ambrose Barlow, O.S.B. Edited, from the original ms. in the Manchester University Library, by W. E. Rhodes. pp. vii. 15. *Manchester,* 1908. 8°. [*Chetham Society. Remains.* New ser. vol. 64.] **Ac. 8120.**

BARLOW (Annie Katherine)

—— *See* Schauwecker (F.) [Der Panzerkreuzer.] The Armoured Cruiser . . . Translated by A. K. Barlow. [1938.] 8°. **12557. w. 13.**

BARLOW (Arthur G.)

—— Almost in Confidence. [A biography. With plates, including portraits.] pp. 345. *Juta & Co.: Cape Town, Johannesburg,* 1952. 8°. **010854. b. 5.**

BARLOW (Billy) Billy Barlow.—The Wounded Hussar. [Songs.] [*London,* 1840 ?] *s. sh.* 4°. **C.116.i.1.(210.)**

BARLOW (Charles) *See* Periodical Publications.—*London.* The Patent Journal and Inventors' Magazine. Edited by C. Barlow, *etc.* 1846, *etc.* 8°. **P.P. 1716.**

—— How to make Money by Patents; or, Hints and suggestions to inventors and patentees. pp. 55. *Barlow & Clare: London,* [1869.] 8°. **6375. b. 47. (10.)**

—— Third edition. pp. 142. *E. Marlborough & Co.: London,* [1873.] 8°. **08246. eee. 1.**

—— Sixth edition. pp. xii. 78. *E. Marlborough & Co.: London,* [1880.] 8°. **8244. de. 8.**

BARLOW (Claude W.)

—— *See* Martin, *Saint, successively Bishop of Dumio and Archbishop of Braga.* Martini Episcopi Bracarensis opera omnia. Edidit C. W. Barlow. 1950. 8°. [*Papers and Monographs of the American Academy in Rome.* vol. 12.] **Ac. 5790. f/2.**

BARLOW (*Right Hon. Sir* Clement Anderson Montague) *Bart. See* England.—*Army.—Infantry.—Lancashire Fusiliers.* The Lancashire Fusiliers. The Roll of Honour of the Salford Brigade . . . Edited by Sir C. A. M. Barlow. 1919. 4°. **8833. cc. 6.**

—— Barlow Family Records. By Rt. Hon. Sir Montague Barlow . . . assisted by G. Dudley Barlow . . . and Vernon Barlow. [With plates, including portraits, and pedigrees. With a supplement by Sir C. A. M. Barlow assisted by Mary B. Rundle.] 2 vol. *Bemrose & Sons: London & Derby,* [1932, 35.] 8°. **9907. b. 29.**

BARLOW (*Right Hon. Sir* CLEMENT ANDERSON MONTAGUE) *Bart.*

—— Church and Reform: being essays relating to reform in the government of the Church of England . . . [By various authors. Edited by Sir C. A. M. Barlow.] With . . . an introduction by the Bishop of Liverpool [F. J. Chavasse]. pp. xiii. 181. *Bemrose & Sons: London,* 1902. 8°. **4109**. df. **1**.

—— The Companies Act, 1900. *See* LONDON.—III. *King's Weigh House.* The King's Weigh House Lectures to Business Men, *etc.* 1901. 8°. **08228**. ff. **28**.

BARLOW (*Right Hon. Sir* CLEMENT ANDERSON MONTAGUE) *Bart.*, and **BARCLAY** (EDWYN)

—— The Licensing Act, 1904. With an introduction giving a summary of the law as to grants and transfers of licences, *etc.* pp. xi. 204. *Jordan & Sons: London,* 1905. 8°. **6427**. cc. **13**.

BARLOW (*Right Hon. Sir* CLEMENT ANDERSON MONTAGUE) *Bart.*, and **GOMME** (*Sir* GEORGE LAURENCE)

—— The Old Age Pensions Act, 1908, together with the regulations made thereunder, official circulars, and financial instructions by the Treasury. With notes by C. A. M. Barlow . . . and G. L. Gomme. pp. 180. *Eyre & Spottiswoode: London,* 1908. 8°. **6427**. aa. **25**.

BARLOW (*Right Hon. Sir* CLEMENT ANDERSON MONTAGUE) *Bart.*, and **HICKS** (WILLIAM JOYNSON) *Viscount Brentford.*

—— *Viscount Brentford.* The Law of Heavy and Light Mechanical Traction on Highways in the United Kingdom, *etc.* pp. xv. 302. *Sir I. Pitman & Sons: London,* 1906. 8°. **6427**. cc. **16**.

BARLOW (*Right Hon. Sir* CLEMENT ANDERSON MONTAGUE) *Bart.*, and **HOLLAND** (RICHARD) *of Brixton.* The Education Act, 1918, with notes and introductory chapters, *etc.* pp. 143. *National Society's Depository: London,* [1918.] 8°. **6426**. p. **15**.

BARLOW (*Right Hon. Sir* CLEMENT ANDERSON MONTAGUE) *Bart.*, and **LEESE** (WILLIAM HARGREAVES)

—— The Port of London Act, 1908, 8 Ed. VII. c. 68, together with the Watermen's and Lightermen's Amendment Act, 1859, the Thames Watermen's and Lightermen's Act, 1893, the Thames Conservancy Act, 1894, and the Thames Conservancy Act, 1905, as amended by the Port of London Act, 1908. Also a summary of the principal acts affecting the chief dock companies, together with the Thames Conservancy bye-laws, the watermen's bye-laws, the bye-laws of the dock companies, regulations of the Board of Trade, *etc.* pp. x. 433. *Effingham Wilson; Sweet & Maxwell: London,* 1910. 8°. **6375**. r. **9**.

BARLOW (*Right Hon. Sir* CLEMENT ANDERSON MONTAGUE) *Bart.*, and **MACAN** (HUGH O'DONOGHUE)

—— The Education Act, 1902, with notes, together with a summary of the existing law and of the provisions of the Education Act, 1902; hints to education committees and voluntary school managers, *etc.* pp. viii. 188. 11. *Butterworth & Co.: London,* 1903. 8°. **6425**. de. **3**.

—— Second edition. pp. xii. 236. 26. *Butterworth & Co.: London,* 1903. 8°. **6425**. de. **13**.

—— The Education Act, 1902 . . . and Education—London—Act, 1903 . . . Second revised edition. pp. xii. 250. 25. *Butterworth & Co.; Shaw & Sons: London,* 1903. 8°. **6427**. bb. 5.

BARLOW (*Right Hon. Sir* CLEMENT ANDERSON MONTAGUE) *Bart.*, and **WILLIAMS** (W. GORDON)

—— War Pensions, Gratuities, Allowances, Treatment and Training for officers, N.C.O.'s and men. A handbook, *etc.* pp. 44. *J. Davy & Sons: London,* [1918.] 8°. **6875**. bb. **32**.

BARLOW (CRAWFORD) The New Tay Bridge. A course of lectures, *etc.* pp. 46. *E. & F. N. Spon: London,* 1889. 4°. **8765**. h. **22**.

BARLOW (CROSSLEY WILLIAM CROSBY) *See* LONDON.—III. *University of London.* [*Examinations.*] Matriculation Model Answers: Chemistry and Mechanics. Being the London University Matriculation Papers . . . from June 1888 to January 1891. With answers by C. W. C. Barlow . . . and R. W. Stewart. [1891.] 8°. **12205**. g.

—— *See* LONDON.—III. *University of London.* [*Examinations.*] Matriculation Model Answers: Mathematics. Being the London University Papers . . . from June 1888 to January 1891. With answers by C. W. C. Barlow . . . and G. H. Bryan. [1891.] 8°. **12205**. **g**.

—— Mathematical Physics. Volume 1. Electricity and Magnetism. pp. vii. 312. *W. B. Clive: London,* 1913. 8°. **08534**. g. **2**.

BARLOW (CROSSLEY WILLIAM CROSBY) and **BAUSOR** (HAROLD WILLIAM)

—— Key to Briggs' General Elementary Science. pp. iv. 102. *W. B. Clive: London,* [1901.] 8°. [*Tutorial Series.*] **12205**. c. **490**.

BARLOW (CROSSLEY WILLIAM CROSBY) and **BRYAN** (GEORGE HARTLEY)

—— Elementary Mathematical Astronomy, with examples and examination papers. pp. vi. 434. *W. B. Clive & Co.: London,* [1892.] 8°. [*Tutorial Series.*] **12205**. c. **76**.

—— [Another edition.] pp. vi. 442. *W. B. Clive & Co.: London,* 1893. 8°. [*Tutorial Series.*] **12205**. c. **100**.

—— Third edition. pp. xvi. 445. *W. B. Clive: London,* 1923. 8°. **08560**. e. **46**.

—— Fourth edition. Revised by A. C. D. Crommelin. pp. xvii. 445. *W. B. Clive: London,* 1930. 8°. **8565**. e. **14**.

—— Elementary Mathematical Astronomy . . . Revised by Sir Harold Spencer Jones. (Fifth edition, revised.) pp. viii. 387. *University Tutorial Press: London,* 1944. 8°. **8565**. c. 25.

—— Geometry of the Similar Figures and the Plane. pp. viii. 123. *W. B. Clive: London,* [1895.] 8°. [*Tutorial Series.*] **12205**. c. **245**.

BARLOW (DONALD SPIERS MONTEAGLE)

—— Report on the Thoracic Services of Ceylon with special reference to Pulmonary Tuberculosis by D. Barlow . . . And the decisions of the Government on the recommendations made in the report. pp. 35. 1952. 8°. *See* CEYLON.—*Ministry of Health and Local Government.* C.S. B. 29/9.

BARLOW (E. D.) Barlow's Profiles of the Natives. [Lithographs.] *E. D. Barlow: Sydney,* [1840?] 8°. **788**. b. **40**.

BARLOW (EDWARD) *Meteorologist.* An Exact Survey of the Tide. Explicating its production and propagation, variety & anomaly in all parts of the world especially near the coasts of Great Britain & Ireland. With a preliminary treatise concerning the origin of springs, generation of rain, and production of wind. With twelve curious maps. 2 vol. *Benj. Tooke & J. Hooke: London,* 1717. 8°. **537**. g. **24**.

BARLOW (Edward) *Meteorologist.*

—— Second edition, *etc.* 2 pt. *John Hooke: London,* 1722. 8°. **8776. a. 21.**

—— Meteorological Essays, concerning the origin of springs, generation of rain, and production of wind . . . [By E. Barlow.] Illustrated with divers copper plates. 2 pt. 1715. 8°. *See* Essays. **958. k. 6.**

BARLOW (Edward) *O.S.B.* *See* Barlow (Ambrose)

BARLOW (Edward) *Seaman.* Barlow's Journal of his Life at Sea in King's Ships, East & West Indiamen & other Merchantmen from 1659 to 1703. Transcribed from the original manuscript by Basil Lubbock. With 13 coloured illustrations and 43 coastline drawings. 2 vol. pp. 575. *Hurst & Blackett: London,* 1934. 8°. **10498. cc. 34.**
One of an edition of 100 *copies.*

BARLOW (Edward Robert)

—— Management of Foreign Manufacturing Subsidies. pp. xi. 223. *Division of Research, Graduate School of Business Administration, Harvard University: Boston,* 1953. 8°. **08227. e. 124.**

—— Operating Results of Limited Price Variety Chains in 1951. pp. vi. 33. *Harvard University Graduate School of Business Administration: Boston,* [1952.] 4°. [*Bureau of Business Research Bulletin.* no. 138.] Ac. **2692. as/7.**

BARLOW (Edward William) *See* Berget (A.) The Earth . . . Translated by E. W. Barlow, *etc.* 1915. 8°. **8565.aaa.15.**

—— The Meteorology of Solar Eclipses. [With a bibliography.] pp. 24. *Edward Stanford: London,* 1927. 8°. [*Quarterly Journal of the Royal Meteorological Society.* vol. 53. Suppl.] Ac. **4093.**

BARLOW, afterwards **DAVIE** (Elizabeth) *See* Davie.

BARLOW (Emma Nora) *Lady.*

—— *See* Darwin (Charles R.) Charles Darwin's Diary of the Voyage of H.M.S. "Beagle." Edited from the ms. by N. Barlow. 1933. 8°. **2252. e. 16.**

—— *See* Darwin (Charles R.) Charles Darwin and the Voyage of the Beagle. Edited with an introduction by N. Barlow. 1945. 8°. **7006. cc. 40.**

BARLOW (Enrico Clark) *See* Barlow (Henry C.)

BARLOW (Esther Sophia)

—— *See* Sophocles. [*Trachiniæ.—English.*] The Trachiniae of Sophocles. Translated . . . by E. S. Barlow, *etc.* 1938. 8°. **11705. df. 54.**

—— Poems and Translations. pp. 68. *Basil Blackwell: Oxford,* 1936. 8°. **11655. bb. 49.**

—— Return, and other poems. pp. 45. *Grant Richards: London,* 1924. 8°. **011645. ee. 140.**

BARLOW (Ethel M.) *See* Ellis (*Mrs.* John D.) Herbs used in Medicine . . . With . . . sixteen coloured plates by Miss E. M. Barlow. 1917. 8°. **7029. b. 56.**

—— Nature Study Drawing Copies . . . An exact reproduction in outline of the natural form. Set 1. pl. 12. *Relfe Bros.: London,* 1907. *obl.* 4°. **7875. t. 29.**

BARLOW (F.) *Jun., pseud.* A Sequel to Cœlebs; or, the Stanley Letters: containing observations on religion and morals, *etc.* pp. 372. *M. Jones: London,* 1812. 12°. **4371. aaa. 20.**

BARLOW (Francis) [For editions of Aesop's fables illustrated by F. Barlow:] *See* Aesop.

—— Multæ et diversæ avium species multifarijs formis & pernaturalębus figuris. [*London,* 1671?] 4°. **Dept.of Prints & Drawings.**
Nineteen plates, including the title. Two, viz. Partridges and Pigeons, occur in duplicate.

—— *Begin.* Illustrissimo heroi Richardo domino Maitland . . . has avium tabulas . . . Francisci Barlow manu . . . delineatas . . . d. d. d. . . . P. Tempest. [Twelve plates.] [*London,* 1700?] *obl.* 4°. **1899.cc.27.**

—— Various Birds and Beasts drawn from the life by F. Barlow. pl. 67. *T. Bowles, J. Bowles & Son, & R. Sayer: London,* [1710?] *obl.* 4°. **433. b. 13.**

—— A Collection of Birds and Beasts; on thirty-six quarto plates; finely drawn and engraved after life . . . New edition. *Robert Laurie & James Whittle: London,* 1799. *obl.* 4°. **7205. de. 6.**

BARLOW (Frank)

—— *See* Arnulphus, *Bishop of Lisieux.* The Letters of Arnulf of Lisieux. Edited . . . by F. Barlow. 1939. 8°. [*Camden Third Series.* vol. 61.] **Ac.8118/7.**

—— Durham Annals and Documents of the Thirteenth Century. Edited by F. Barlow. pp. xxxix. 260. *Durham, London,* 1945. 8°. [*Publications of the Surtees Society.* vol. 155.] Ac. **8045/107.**

—— Durham Jurisdictional Peculiars. pp. xviii. 164. *Oxford University Press: London,* 1950. 8°. [*Oxford Historical Series.*] W.P. **6660/20.**

—— The Feudal Kingdom of England, 1042–1216. [With maps and genealogical tables.] pp. xi. 465. *Longmans, Green & Co.: London,* 1955. 8°. [*History of England.*] W.P. b. **595/2.**

BARLOW (Fred) *Librarian, of Croydon.*

—— Public Library Finance. pp. 111. *A. J. Philip: Gravesend,* 1938. 8°. [*The Librarian Series of Practical Manuals.* vol. 11.] W.P. **11216/11.**

BARLOW (Fred) *Magician.*

—— Mental Prodigies. An enquiry into the faculties of arithmetical, chess and musical prodigies, famous memorizers, precocious children and the like, *etc.* pp. 256. *Hutchinson's Scientific & Technical Publications: London,* 1951. 8°. **7661. de. 7.**

BARLOW (Frederick) A Complete English Dictionary: or, General repository of the English language. Containing a copious explanation of all the words in the English language . . . To which is prefixed, a complete English grammar. 2 vol. *The Author: London,* [1772.] 8°. **12983. f. 21.**

—— [Another copy.] **12983. ff. 9.**

—— The Complete English Peerage: or, a Genealogical and historical account of the peers and peeresses of this realm, to the year 1775, inclusive . . . The second edition, with additions. [With 25 plates.] 2 vol. *The Author: London,* 1775. 8°. **607. i. 12.**
Imperfect; wanting pl. 8.

—— The Complete English Peerage: or, a Genealogical and historical account of the peers and peeresses of this realm, to the year 1775, inclusive . . . The second edition, with additions. 2 vol. pl. 25. *Printed for the Author: London,* 1775. 8°. **9919. f. 13.**
Published in parts. The titleleaf to each volume is a cancel. Without the list of subscribers.

BARLOW (Frederick)

—— [Another copy.] The Complete English Peerage, *etc.* *London*, 1775. 8°. **607**. c. **12**.
With the list of subscribers. Imperfect; wanting pl. 8. *In this copy the plates have been coloured.*

BARLOW (Frederick Watkins) *See* England.—*Army.—Infantry.—Regiments.—Lancashire Fusiliers.* Orders, Memoirs, Anecdotes, etc. connected with the xx Regiment. [Edited by F. W. Barlow.] 1868. 8°. **8826**. dd. **16**.

BARLOW (G.) *of the Scottish Mountaineering Club. See* Steeple (E. W.) Island of Skye. Edited by E. W. Steeple, G. Barlow, *etc.* 1923. 8°. [*Scottish Mountaineering Club Guide.* vol. 3. Section A.] **Ac.6183.(3.)**

BARLOW (George) *Poet. See also* Hinton (James) *pseud.* [i.e. G. Barlow.]

—— *See* Bennett (Edward T.) The Poetical Work of George Barlow. A study. 1903. 8°. **011853**. ee. **25**.

—— The Poetical Works of George Barlow. 11 vol. *H. J. Glaisher: London*, [1902–14.] 8°. **011652**. m. **37**.

—— An Actor's Reminiscences, and other poems. pp. xiv. 332. *Remington & Co.: London*, 1883. 8°. **11653**. h. **14**.

—— A Coronation Poem. pp. 11. *H. J. Glaisher: London*, 1902. 8°. **11651**. d. **41**.

—— The Crucifixion of Man: a narrative poem. pp. xix. 231. *Swan Sonnenschein & Co.: London*, 1893. 8°. **011653**. n. **69**.

—— The Daughters of Minerva. A novel of social life. pp. 216. *Roxburghe Press: London*, [1898.] 8°. **012643**. g. **38**.

—— From Dawn to Sunset, *etc.* [Poems.] pp. xii. 498. *Swan Sonnenschein & Co.: London*, 1890. 8°. **011653**. k. **22**.

—— The Genius of Dickens. (Reprinted from "The Contemporary Review.") pp. 60. *H. J. Glaisher: London*, [1909.] 8°. **11826**. p. **23**.

—— The Gospel of Humanity; or, the Connection between spiritualism and modern thought. pp. 27. *James Burns: London*, 1876. 8°. **8708**. i. **2**. **(35.)**

—— The Higher Love. A plea for a nobler conception of Human Love. (Reprinted from "The Contemporary Review.") pp. 61. *Simple Life Press: London*, 1905. 8°. [*Simple Life Series.* no. 17.] **012203**. e. **7/17**.

—— A History of the Dreyfus Case from the arrest of Captain Dreyfus in October, 1894, up to the flight of Esterhazy in September, 1898. pp. xi. 480. *Simpkin, Marshall & Co.: London*, 1899. 8°. **05402**. ff. **13**.

—— Jesus of Nazareth. A tragedy. pp. 188. *Roxburghe Press: London*, [1896.] 8°. **11781**. d. **33**.

—— A Life's Love. [Sonnets.] pp. viii. 99. *J. C. Hotten: London*, [1873.] 8°. **11687**. e. **26**.

—— New edition. pp. xiii. 342. *Remington & Co.: London*, 1882. 8°. **11653**. m. **56**.

—— Love-Songs. pp. 179. *Remington & Co.: London*, 1880. 8°. **11650**. df. **44**.

—— A Lost Mother. [A poem.] pp. 153. *Swan Sonnenschein & Co.: London*, 1892. 4°. **011653**. f. **124**.

—— Loved beyond Words. [Poems.] pp. 227. *Remington & Co.: London*, 1885. 8°. **11645**. ff. **34**.

BARLOW (George) *Poet.*

—— A Man's Vengeance, and other poems. pp. 100. *H. J. Glaisher: London*, 1908. 8°. **11647**. eee. **21**.

—— The Marriage before Death, and other poems. pp. 230. *Remington & Co.: London*, 1878. 8°. **11653**. b. **3**.

—— The Pageant of Life. An epic poem in five books. pp. xxxi. 443. *Swan Sonnenschein & Co.: London*, 1888. 8°. **011653**. f. **22**.

—— New edition. pp. 295. *H. J. Glaisher: London*, 1910. 8°. **011650**. e. **54**.

—— New edition. pp. xiii. 561. *H. J. Glaisher: London*, [1913.] 8°. **11646**. i. **11**.

—— Poems, real and ideal. pp. x. 403. *Remington & Co.: London*, 1884. 8°. **11653**. i. **54**.

—— Song-Bloom. pp. xii. 290. *Remington & Co.: London*, 1881. 8°. **11653**. c. **35**.

—— Songs of England Awaking. pp. 57. *H. J. Glaisher: London*, 1909. 8°. **011650**. e. **18**.

—— Second edition. pp. 68. *H. J. Glaisher: London*, 1910. 8°. **11647**. df. **48**. **(1.)**

—— Song-spray. pp. xiv. 335. *Remington & Co.: London*, 1882. 8°. **11653**. ee. **15**.

—— Through Death to Life. [Poems.] *S. Tinsley & Co.: London*, 1878. 8°. **11653**. aaa. **15**.

—— Time's Whisperings: sonnets and songs. pp. 105. *Remington & Co.: London*, 1880. 12°. **11653**. aaa. **44**.

—— To the Women of England, and other poems. pp. xv. 223. *H. J. Glaisher: London*, 1901. 8°. **11650**. g. **68**.

—— The Triumph of Woman. Prose essays. pp. 100. *Ambrose Co.: London*, 1907. 8°. **12352**. p. **5**.

—— The Two Marriages: a drama, in three acts. pp. 87. *Remington & Co.: London*, 1878. 8°. **11781**. bbb. **26**.

—— Under the Dawn. [Poems.] pp. xxii. 211. *Chatto & Windus: London*, 1875 [1874]. 8°. **11649**. eee. **11**.

—— Vox Clamantis: sonnets and poems. pp. 59. *H. J. Glaisher: London*, 1904. 8°. **11653**. aaa. **56**.

—— Woman Regained. A novel of artistic life. pp. 360. *Roxburghe Press: London*, [1896.] 8°. **012626**. ee. **46**.

—— [Selections, edited by A. H. Miles.] [1893.] *See* Miles (Alfred H.) The Poets and the Poetry of the Century. vol. 8. [1891, *etc.*] 8°. **11603.cc.20/8.**

—— [Selections.] *See* Sextet. A Sextet of Singers, *etc.* [1896.] *obl.* 8°. **11652**. de. **80**.

—— Selected Poems . . . with portrait [and an introductory note signed, C. W.]. pp. 167. *H. J. Glaisher: London*, [1921.] 8°. **011649**. ff. **105**.

BARLOW (George) *Wesleyan Minister. See* Bible. *Appendix.—Old Testament.* [*Miscellaneous.*] The Preacher's Complete Homiletical Commentary on the Old Testament, *etc.* (A Homiletic Commentary on the Book of Psalms. vol. 2 . . . On Psalms 121–130. By G. Barlow.) 1879, *etc.* 8°. **3165**. ee. **5**.

—— *See* Bible.—*Appendix.—Old Testament.* [*Miscellaneous.*] The Preacher's Complete Homiletical Commentary, *etc.* (A Homiletic Commentary on . . . Ezekiel . . . Chapters xxx.—xlviii. by . . . G. Barlow.) 1879, *etc.* 8°. **3165**. ee. **5**.

—— *See* Bible.—*Appendix.—New Testament.* [*Miscellaneous.*] The Preacher's Complete Homiletical Commentary on the New Testament, *etc.* (A Homiletical Commentary on the Epistles of St. Paul the Apostle to Timothy, Titus, Philemon. By Rev. G. Barlow.) 1896. 8°. **03126**. g. **9**.

BARLOW (George) *Wesleyan Minister.*

—— *See* Watt (David G.) A Homiletic Commentary on the Book of Lamentations . . . Homiletics by . . . G. Barlow. 1891. 8°. **3165. ee. 5.**

—— A Homiletical Commentary on the Books of Kings. pp. 654. x. *R. D. Dickinson: London,* 1885. 8°. [*The Preacher's Complete Homiletical Commentary on the Old Testament.*] **3165. ee. 5.**

—— A Homiletical Commentary on the Epistles of St. Paul the Apostle to the Galatians, Ephesians, Philippians, Colossians and i. and ii. Thessalonians. pp. 603. *Funk & Wagnalls: New York,* 1896. 8°. [*The Preacher's Complete Homiletical Commentary on the New Testament.*] **03126. g. 9.**

BARLOW (George) *Writer on Motor-Cycling.* Gardening without Worry, *etc.* pp. 190. *Seeley, Service & Co.: London,* 1928. 8°. [*New Library.*] W.P. **4542/4.**

—— Motor-Cycling without Tears . . . With . . . illustrations. pp. 188. *Seeley, Service & Co.: London,* 1927. 8°. [*New Library.* vol. 3.] W.P. **4542/3.**

BARLOW (George Dudley) *See* Barlow (*Right Hon. Sir* Clement A. M.) *Bart.* Barlow Family Records. By Rt. Hon. Sir M. Barlow . . . assisted by G. D. Barlow, *etc.* [1932.] 8°. **9907. b. 29.**

—— Published Matter and Records relating to the Families of the name of Barlow. Extracted . . . by G. D. Barlow. pp. xxiii. 215. *Simson & Co.: Hertford,* 1911. 8°. **9914. s. 12.**

BARLOW (George Hilaro) *M.D.*

—— *See* Bright (Richard) *M.D., Physician to Guy's Hospital.* Clinical Memoirs on Abdominal Tumours and Intumescence . . . Edited by G. H. Barlow. 1860. 8°. Ac. **3838/6*.**

—— *See* London.—iii. *Guy's Hospital.* Guy's Hospital Reports. Edited by G. H. Barlow, *etc.* 1836, *etc.* 8°. **1151. i.**

—— A Manual of the Practice of Medicine. pp. x. 706. *John Churchill: London,* 1856 [1855]. 12°. **7320. a. 4.**

—— Second edition. pp. xii. 738. *John Churchill: London,* 1861. 12°. **7321. c. 20.**

BARLOW (*Sir* George Hilaro) *Bart.* *See* Indus, *pseud.* A View of the Policy of Sir George Barlow, *etc.* 1810. 8°. **1103. k. 42.**

—— *See* Marsh (Charles) *M.P.* Review of some important Passages in the late Administration of Sir G. H. Barlow, *etc.* 1813. 8°. **8023. e. 26.**

—— *See* Marsh (Charles) *M.P.* An Exposure of the Misrepresentations . . . in Mr. Marsh's review of Sir George Barlow's administration at Madras, *etc.* 1813. 8°. C. **58. e. 21. (3.)**

—— *See* Sherson (Robert) A Reply to the examined Case and Trial of Mr. Sherson . . . also to Marsh's review of the administration of Sir G. H. Barlow. 1816. 8°. **583. f. 14. (2.)**

—— *See* Waddington (Samuel J.) A Letter to the Directors of the Hon. East-India Company, in consequence . . . of the recall of Sir G. H. Barlow. [1806.] 8°. **1102. g. 9. (2.)**

—— A Brief Sketch of the Services of Sir G. H. Barlow . . . Governor of Madras, founded on a series of authentic papers and correspondence. pp. viii. 77. *E. Blackader: London,* 1811. 8°. **1202. k. 18.**

—— [Another copy.] G. **15109.**

BARLOW (*Sir* George Hilaro) *Bart.*

—— A Letter from a Gentleman high in office at Madras, upon the late discontents in that presidency: containing comments on the principal transactions of Sir George Barlow's government. pp. vii. 47. *Black & Co.: London,* 1810. 8°. **8022. c. 3.**

—— [Another copy.] A Letter from a Gentleman High in Office at Madras . . . containing comments on the Principal Transactions of Sir George Barlow's Government. *London,* 1810. 8°. **8023. e. 27. (4.)**

—— A Letter signed by C. Grant . . . W. Astell [and others] . . . Directors of the East-India Company; containing a minute examination and full vindication of the measures adopted by Sir George Barlow, during the dissentions at the Presidency of Madras, *etc.* pp. xii. 131. *Black, Parry & Co.: London,* 1812. 8°. **8023. e. 28. (1.)**

BARLOW (Glyn) Indian Melodies. pp. 144. *Thacker & Spink: Calcutta,* 1891. 8°. **011652. ee. 16.**

—— Industrial India. pp. iii. 178. *G. A. Natesan & Co.: Madras,* [1905.] 8°. **08275. h. 41.**

—— Memoirs of Gurrumpore. pp. 80. *W. Newman & Co.: Calcutta,* 1893. 8°. **012628. g. 53.**

—— Miracles of the Master. pp. 217. *John Heritage: London,* 1937. 8°. **20031. aaa. 36.**

—— Naganathan at School. pp. 187. *K. & J. Cooper: Bombay,* [1916.] 8°. **12800. bb. 19.**

—— Fifth edition. pp. 187. *K. & J. Cooper: Bombay,* [1918.] 8°. **12802. b. 38.**

—— The Story of Madras . . . With maps and illustrations by the author. pp. x. 117. *Humphrey Milford: London; Madras* printed, 1921. 8°. **010056. de. 45.**

BARLOW (Harold) and **MORGENSTERN** (Sam)

—— A Dictionary of Musical Themes, *etc.* pp. 656. *Crown Publishers: New York,* [1948.] 8°. **7900. c. 34.**

BARLOW (Harold Everard Monteagle) *See* Sprague (Ernest H.) and Barlow (H. E. M.) Solutions to the Questions set in Section A . . . in the October 1930 and April 1931 examination papers of the Institution of Civil Engineers. 1932. 8°. **08531. g. 44.**

—— Currents and Fields in Electrical Engineering . . . An inaugural lecture delivered at University College London, 21 November 1950. pp. 18. *H. K. Lewis & Co.: London,* 1952. 8°. **8761. cc. 10.**

—— Micro-Waves and Wave Guides. pp. x. 122. *Constable & Co.: London,* 1947. 8°. **08756. b. 56.**

BARLOW (Harold Everard Monteagle) and **CULLEN** (Alexander Lamb)

—— Micro-Wave Measurements. pp. xvi. 399. *Constable & Co.: London,* 1950. 8°. **8713. e. 14.**

BARLOW (Harry J.)

—— The Law relating to Local Elections . . . Third edition. pp. xxxvii. 358. 1936. 8°. *See* England.—*Laws and Statutes.*—iv. *Elections.* **6426. t. 27.**

—— The Ratepayers' Guide to the Rating of Houses and Shops, outside the metropolis. pp. 80. *H. J. Drane: London,* 1912. 8°. **6427. b. 18.**

BARLOW (Harry J.)

—— The Statutes and Local Government Board Orders relating to Elections of Guardians; Rural District Councillors; Parish Councillors & Urban District Councillors in England and Wales. Together with cross-references and index. pp. xxi. 343. 1912. 8°. *See* England.—*Laws and Statutes.*—iv. *Elections.* **6425.** ee. **21.**

—— The Statutes and Orders relating to Local Elections . . . Second edition. pp. xxi. 338. 1925. 8°. *See* England. —*Laws and Statutes.*—iv. *Elections, and Franchise.* **6426.** r. **20.**

BARLOW (Henry) *of Congleton. See* Cartlidge (J. E. G.) Newbold Astbury and its History . . . By Rev. J. E. G. Cartlidge . . . assisted by H. Barlow, *etc.* 1915. 8°. **010358.** l. **46.**

BARLOW (Henry) *of Newington Butts.* Henry Barlow . . . A memoir in memoriam. [By H. C. Barlow.] pp. 32. *Privately printed: London,* 1859. 8°. **10825.** bbb. **31. (3.)**

—— Reason and Faith. In memoriam. [Verses, with a brief memoir of Henry Barlow. By H. C. Barlow.] pp. 4. [*London,* 1858.] 8°. **11647.** e. **1. (35.)**

BARLOW (Henry Bernoulli) A Comparative Account and Delineation of Railway Engine & Carriage Wheels. [With a plate.] pp. 51. *John Weale: London,* 1848. 8°. **8765.** c. **17.**

—— Description of Messrs. Sharpe Brothers and Co.'s Outside Cylinder Tank-Engine. *See* Tredgold (Thomas) The Principles and Practice and Explanation of the Machinery of Locomotive Engines, *etc.* vol. 1. 1850, *etc.* 4°. **8766.** g. **12.**

BARLOW (Henry Clark) *See* Aleardi (A.) A Few Words of Commemoration on P. Emiliani-Giudici, *etc.* [Translated by H. C. Barlow.] [1872.] 8°. **10631.** bb. **3.**

—— *See* Dante Alighieri. [*Divina Commedia.—Italian.—Selections.*] Testi di tre canti della Divina Commedia, tratti da codici conservati nella Biblioteca del Museo Britannico per opera . . . del . . . dottore E. C. Barlow, *etc.* 1870. 4°. **11422.** g. **21. (5.)**

—— *See* Dante Alighieri. [*Divina Commedia.—Appendix.*] Sei cento lezioni della Divina Commedia tratte dall' edizione di Napoli del mccccLxxxvii. Confrontate colle corrispondenti lezioni delle prime quattro edizioni per opera e cura del dottore E. C. Barlow. 1875. 4°. **11421.** h. **25.**

—— *See* London.—iii. *University of London.—University College.—Library.* Catalogue of the Dante Collection in the Library of University College. With a note on the correspondence [relating to Dante] of H. C. Barlow, *etc.* 1910. 8°. **11908.** bb. **8.**

—— Beatrice. Discorso . . . Pubblicato ora la prima volta dal march. F. Raffaelli. pp. xi. 23. *Fermo,* 1890. 8°. **11422.** ccc. **17. (5.)**

—— Il Conte Ugolino e l'arcivescovo Ruggieri; a sketch from the Pisan chronicles. pp. 23. *Trübner & Co.: London,* 1862. 8°. **10601.** d. **2. (1.)**

—— Critical, Historical, and Philosophical Contributions to the study of the Divina Commedia. [With a supplement.] pp. xiv. 607. 24. *Williams & Norgate: London; Leipzig* [printed], 1864, 65. 8°. **11422.** g. **5.**

—— A Dissertation on the Causes and Effects of Disease, considered in reference to the moral constitution of man. pp. viii. 79. *A. & C. Black: Edinburgh,* 1837. 8°. **7406.** b. **4.**

BARLOW (Henry Clark)

—— La Divina Commedia. Remarks on the reading of the fifty-ninth verse of the fifth canto of the Inferno. pp. 3. [*London,* 1850.] 4°. **11421.** f. **11.**

—— Essays on Symbolism. pp. x. 144. *Williams & Norgate: London,* 1866. 8°. **4505.** aaa. **13.**

—— Francesca da Rimini, her lament and vindication; with a brief notice of the Malatesti, *etc.* pp. 52. *David Nutt: London,* 1859. 8°. **10631.** d. **31. (10.)**

—— [Another copy.] **10631.** d. **32.**

—— Second edition. pp. 52. *Frederic Norgate: London,* 1875. 8°. **11422.** d. **28. (13.)**

—— Francesca da Rimini suo lamento e difesa con brevi cenni sui Malatesti . . . Traduzione dall' inglese del Cav. G. Ferrari. *See* Scolari (Filippo) *Dottore in Legge.* Proposta e saggio per una edizione del testo della Divina Commedia di Dante Allighieri, *etc.* 1865. 8°. **11421.** g. **31.**

—— God's Temple-Throne. [A hymn, signed: H. C. B., i.e. H. C. Barlow.] [1855?] 4°. *See* B., H. C. **11647.** e. **1. (39.)**

—— Il Gran rifiuto, what it was, who made it, and how fatal to Dante Alighieri. A dissertation on verses fifty-eight to sixty-three of the third canto of the Inferno. pp. 22. *Trübner & Co.: London; Berlin* [printed], 1862. 8°. **11422.** d. **28. (7.)**

—— Il Gran rifiuto, che fu, chi lo fece, e come fu fatale a Dante Alighieri. Dissertazione su i versi 58 a 63 del terzo canto dell' Inferno . . . Dall' inglese voltata in italiano da G. G. [i.e. Guglielmo Guiscardi.] pp. 18. *Napoli,* 1864. 8°. **11422.** ff. **29. (2.)**

—— Henry Barlow . . . A memoir in memoriam. [By H. C. Barlow.] pp. 32. 1859. 8°. *See* Barlow (Henry) *of Newington Butts.* **10825.** bbb. **31. (3.)**

—— Industry on Christian Principles. pp. 36. *Seeleys: London,* 1851. 8°. **8245.** a. **68. (7.)**

—— Letteratura Dantesca. Remarks on the reading of the 114th verse of the viith canto of the Paradise of the Divina Commedia. pp. 23. *London,* 1857 [1856]. 8°. **11422.** d. **28. (3.)**

Printed for private circulation.

—— On the Vernon Dante, with other dissertations. pp. 87. *Williams & Norgate: London; Leipzig* [printed], 1870. 8°. **11421.** g. **35. (11.)**

—— Opere dantesche del cavaliere dottore E. C. Barlow. [A catalogue, by H. C. Barlow.] pp. 8. [*London,* 1872.] 8°. **11421.** dd. **1.**

—— Reason and Faith. In memoriam. [Verses, with a brief memoir of H. Barlow. By H. C. Barlow.] pp. 4. [1858.] 8°. *See* Barlow (Henry) of *Newington Butts.* **11647.** e. **1. (35.)**

—— Rome from Monte Mario, with other way-side sketches. [In verse. By H. C. Barlow.] pp. 32. 1860. 8°. *See* Rome, *the City.* [*Appendix.—Miscellaneous.*] **11646.** g. **51. (18.)**

—— Sacred Trees. Reprinted from "The Journal of Sacred Literature," *etc.* pp. 22. *For private circulation: London,* [1862.] 8°. **4377.** cc. **6.**

BARLOW (HENRY CLARK)

—— The Sixth Centenary Festivals of Dante Allighieri in Florence and at Ravenna. By a Representative [i.e. H. C. Barlow]. pp. viii. 80. 1866. 8º. *See* REPRESENTATIVE. **11422**. ff. **29**. **(10.)**

—— Symbolism in reference to Art. [An extract from the Transactions of the Royal Institute of British Architects.] [*London*, 1860.] 4º. **7806**. d. **4**.

—— The Young King [Henry, son of Henry II., King of England], and Bertrand de Born. [With reference to Dante, Inf. xxviii. 135.] pp. 36. *Trübner & Co.: London*, 1862. 8º. **10804**. bbb. **7**. **(5.)**

—— A Brief Memoir of Henry Clark Barlow. pp. 32. *Privately printed: London; Leipzig* [printed], 1868. 8º. **10826**. h. **20**. **(4.)**

BARLOW (HERBERT EDWARD)

—— Wiehe Family Records, Mauritius branch, *etc.* [With plates, including portraits and genealogical tables.] pp. 45. *General Printing & Stationery Co.: Port Louis, Mauritius*, 1949. 4º. **09915**. g. **22**.

—— Supplement to Wiehe Family Records. *General Printing & Stationery Co.: Port Louis, Mauritius*, 1949. 4º. **09915**. g. **22**.

—— [Another copy.] Wiehe Family Records, Mauritius branch, *etc.* *Port Louis*, 1949. 4º. **9919**. d. **6**.

BARLOW (HILARÉ EDITH) The Mystery of Jeanne Marie. pp. 315. *Lynwood & Co.: London*, 1913. 8º. NN. **903**.

—— The Sentence of the Judge. pp. viii. 286. *Lynwood & Co.: London*, 1912. 8º. NN. **168**.

—— "Waldmann," the autobiography of a dachshund. pp. 62. *Everett & Co.: London*, 1910. 8º. **07293**. h. **77**.

BARLOW (HORACE MALLINSON) *See* LONDON.—III. *Royal College of Physicians.* Catalogue of the Library. [Compiled in part by H. M. Barlow.] 1912. 8º. **011904**. d. **16**.

—— A Descriptive Catalogue of the legal and other documents in the archives of the Royal College of Physicians. [Compiled by H. M. Barlow.] ff. iv. 313. 1924. fol. *See* LONDON.—III. *Royal College of Physicians.* **11902**. v. **10**.

—— The Medical Library Association: a few observations . . . Reprinted from the Library Association Record, April, 1910. pp. 21. *University Press: Aberdeen*, 1910. 8º. **11909**. t. **36**. **(2.)**

—— Old English Herbals, 1525–1640 . . . Reprinted from the "Proceedings of the Royal Society of Medicine," *etc.* pp. 42. *J. Bale & Co.: London*, 1913. 8º. **11907**. bb. **7**. **(4.)**

BARLOW (IMA CHRISTINA)

—— The Agadir Crisis. pp. vi. 422. *University of North Carolina Press: Chapel Hill*, 1940. 8º. **09077**. i. **39**.

BARLOW (J. SWINDELLS) The Great Afrikander Conspiracy. [A tale.] pp. 188. *Ward, Lock & Co.: London*, 1900. 8º. **012627**. e. **98**.

—— A Mighty Empire, *etc.* [A novel.] pp. 311. *Ward, Lock & Co.: London*, 1902. 8º. **012637**. c. **44**.

BARLOW (JAMES) A New Theory accounting for the Dip of the Magnetic Needle, being an analysis of terrestrial magnetism, with a solution of the lines of variation and no variation, and an explanation of the nature of a magnet. [With a map.] pp. xxvii. 183. *Wiley & Long: New York*, 1835. 8º. **538**. g. **22**.

BARLOW (*Sir* JAMES ALAN NOEL) *Bart.*

—— *See* ENGLAND.—*Committee on Scientific Man-Power.* Scientific Man-Power. Report of a committee appointed by the Lord President of the Council, *etc.* [Chairman, Sir J. A. N. Barlow.] 1946. 8º. B.S. **68/25**. (8.)

—— *See* ENGLAND.—*Treasury.—Civil Service National Whitley Council Committee on the Marriage Bar.* Marriage Bar in the Civil Service. Report of the Civil Service, National Whitley Council Committee, *etc.* [Chairman, Sir J. A. N. Barlow.] 1946. 8º. B.S. **44/84**. (25.)

—— An Exhibition of Chinese Ceramics from Sir Alan Barlow's Collection. pp. 15. pl. 8. *Arts Council: [London,]* 1953. 8º. **W.P.12368/189.**

BARLOW (JAMES WILLIAM) Doctors at War: studies of the French medical profession circa the 17th century. pp. 144. *David Nutt: London*, 1914. 8º. **7680**. eee. **11**.

—— Eternal Punishment and Eternal Death; an essay. pp. vi. 171. *Longman & Co.: London*, 1865. 8º. **4376**. g. **9**.

—— The History of Ireland during the period of Parliamentary Independence. A lecture. pp. 48. *Hodges, Foster & Co.: Dublin*, 1873. 8º. **09008**. df. **10**. **(3.)**

—— The Immortals' Great Quest: translated from an unpublished manuscript in the library of a continental university [or rather, written] by J. W. Barlow. pp. xii. 177. *Smith, Elder & Co.: London*, 1909. 8º. **012625**. k. **59**.

—— A Short History of the Normans in South Europe. pp. xi. 208. *Kegan Paul & Co.: London*, 1886. 8º. **09073** d. **18**.

—— The Ultimatum of Pessimism. An ethical study. pp. 109. *Kegan Paul & Co.: London*, 1882. 8º. **4380**. cc. **16**.

BARLOW (JANE) *See* HOMER. [*Batrachomyomachia.—English.*] The Battle of the Frogs and Mice. Rendered into English by J. Barlow, *etc.* 1894. 4º. K.T.C. **11**. a. **12**.

—— Between Doubting and Daring. Verses. pp. 35. *B. H. Blackwell: Oxford*, 1916. 8º. **011649**. ee. **76**.

—— Bog-Land Studies. [In verse.] pp. 104. *T. Fisher Unwin: London*, 1892 [1891.] 8º. **011653**. m. **22**.

—— Second edition . . . enlarged. pp. 187. *Hodder & Stoughton: London*, 1893. 8º. **011652**. l. **7**.

—— By Beach and Bog-Land. Some Irish stories, *etc.* pp. 301. *T. Fisher Unwin: London*, 1905. 8º. **012630**. dd. **2**.

—— A Creel of Irish Stories. pp. 320. *Methuen & Co.: London*, 1897. 8º. **012623**. e. **13**.

—— Doings and Dealings. pp. 309. *Hutchinson & Co.: London*, 1913. 8º. NN. **1217**.

—— The End of Elfintown . . . [In verse.] Illustrated by Laurence Housman. pp. 77. **L.P.** *Macmillan & Co.: London*, 1894. 8º. K.T.C. **35**. a. **4**.

—— The Founding of Fortunes. pp. 335. *Methuen & Co.: London*, 1902. 8º. **012637**. c. **39**.

—— Flaws. A novel. pp. vii. 344. *Hutchinson & Co.: London*, 1911. 8º. **012618**. aaa. **11**.

—— From the East unto the West. [Tales.] pp. ix. 342. *Methuen & Co.: London*, 1898. 8º. **012643**. cc. **6**.

BARLOW (JANE)

—— From the Land of the Shamrock. [A novel.] pp. 318. *Methuen & Co.: London,* 1901. 8°. **012639.** aa. **10.**

—— Ghost-Bereft. With other stories and studies in verse. pp. viii. 167. *Smith, Elder & Co.: [London,]* 1901. 8°. **011651.** ee. **83.**

—— In Mio's Youth. A novel. pp. 340. *Hutchinson & Co.: London,* 1917. 8°. NN. **4291.**

—— Irish Idylls. pp. viii. 284. *Hodder & Stoughton: London,* 1892. 8°. **012641.** i. **50.**

—— [Another copy.] Irish Idylls. *London,* 1892. 8°. **C.117.c.16.**
A presentation copy from the author.

—— Illustrated edition, being the eighth. pp. 284. *Hodder & Stoughton: London,* 1898. 8°. **012623.** i. **45.**

—— Irish Neighbours. [Tales.] pp. 342. *Hutchinson & Co.: London,* 1907. 8°. **012627.** aaa. **17.**

—— Irish Ways . . . With illustrations in colour and black and white by Warwick Goble. pp. ix. 262. *G. Allen & Sons: London,* 1909. 8°. **12352.** v. **16.**

—— Kerrigan's Quality, *etc.* pp. viii. 254. *Hodder & Stoughton: London,* 1894. 8°. **012629.** g. **23.**

—— Mac's Adventures. pp. 319. *Hutchinson & Co.: London,* 1911. 8°. **012618.** aaa. **10.**

—— Maureen's Fairing, and other stories . . . With illustrations by B. Newcombe. pp. 191. *J. M. Dent & Co.: London,* 1895. 8°. [*Iris Series.*] **012601.** ee. **52/1.**

—— The Mockers, and other verses. pp. viii. 115. *G. Allen & Sons: London,* 1908. 8°. **11647.** eee. **14.**

—— Mrs. Martin's Company, and other stories . . . With illustrations by B. Newcombe. pp. 218. *J. M. Dent & Co.: London,* 1896. 8°. [*Iris Series.*] **012601.** ee. **52/2.**

—— Strangers at Lisconnel. A second series of Irish Idylls. pp. viii. 341. *Hodder & Stoughton: London,* 1895. 8°. **012628.** k. **32.**

BARLOW (JEROME) *See* BARLOWE.

BARLOW (JOCELYN ARTHUR) The Elements of Rifle Shooting, *etc.* pp. 118. pl. 7. *Gale & Polden: Aldershot,* [1932.] 8°. **08821.** i. **42.**

—— Second edition. pp. 118. *Gale & Polden: Aldershot,* [1933.] 8°. **8820.** b. **25.**

—— The Elements of Rifle Shooting . . . Third edition. pp. 122. *Gale & Polden: Aldershot,* [1938.] 8°. **08820.** d. **31.**

—— The Elements of Rifle Shooting . . . Fourth edition. pp. xii. 126. *Gale & Polden: Aldershot,* 1951. 8°. **8838.** e. **15.**

—— Rifle and Rifle Shooting.—Facts about Home Guard Automatic Weapons and Hints on Training. *See* DAVIES (John L.) The Home Guard Training Manual, *etc.* 1940. 16°. **8836.** a. **23.**

—— Small Arms Manual, *etc.* pp. 216. *John Murray: London,* 1942. 16°. **8835.** de. **55.**

BARLOW (JOEL) *See* BIBLE.—*Psalms.* [*English.—Metrical Versions.—Dr. Watts.*] Doctor Watts's Imitation of the Psalms of David, corrected and enlarged, by J. Barlow, *etc.* [1785?] 12°. **3435.** c. **14.**

—— —— 1799. 12°. **3437.** aaa. **6.**

BARLOW (JOEL)

—— *See* BRISSOT (J. P.) *de Warville.* New Travels in the United States of America . . . Translated from the French [by J. Barlow]. 1792. 8°. **10412.** d. **2.**

—— —— 1794. 8°. **10411.** f. **1.**

—— *See* MARBLE (Annie R.) The Hartford Wits [i.e. J. Trumbull, J. Barlow and others]. 1936. 8°. **9605.** p. **1/59.**

—— *See* MILLER (Victor C.) Joel Barlow: Revolutionist, London, 1791–92. [With the text of "The Conspiracy of Kings."] 1932. 8°. **11872.w.19/2.**

—— *See* TODD (Charles B.) Life and Letters of Joel Barlow, *etc.* 1886. 8°. **010882.** m. **16.**

—— *See* TRUMBULL (John) *LL.D., etc.* M'Fingal: a modern epic poem . . . The fifth edition, with explanatory notes [by J. Barlow]. 1792. 8°. **11686.** c. **24.**

—— *See* TYLER (Moses C.) Three Men of Letters. (G. Berkeley . . . J. Barlow.) 1895. 8°. **10883.** d. **4.**

—— *See* ZUNDER (Theodore A.) The Early Days of Joel Barlow, a Connecticut Wit . . . His life and works from 1754 to 1787. [With a portrait.] 1934. 8°. **010885.** df. **37.**

—— The Political Writings of Joel Barlow . . . A new edition corrected. pp. 258. *Mott & Lyon: New York,* 1796. 12°. **1061.** a. **32.**

—— Advice to the Privileged Orders in the several States of Europe, resulting from the necessity and propriety of a general revolution in the principle of government. Part I. [By J. Barlow.] pp. 156. 1792. 8°. *See* EUROPE. **T. 135.** (5.)

—— Second edition. pp. 156. *J. Johnson: London,* 1792. 8°. **8135.** ccc. **2.** (4.)

—— The third edition. pp. 167. *J. Johnson: London,* 1793. 8°. **8135.** b. **14.** (1.)

—— Advice to the Privileged Orders in the several States of Europe . . . Part II. pp. 101. *English Press: Paris,* 1793. 8°. **1104.** c. **20.** (7.)

—— [Another edition. Edited by L. Goldsmith.] pp. 64. *D. I. Eaton: London,* 1795. 8°. E. **2092.** (1*.)

—— Avis aux ordres privilégiés . . . Troisieme édition. 2 pt. *J. Johnson: Londres,* 1794. 8°. **1250.** l. **14.**
Pt. 1 *only is of the third edition. Pt.* 2 *was published in Paris.*

—— The Columbiad. A poem. [With plates, including a portrait.] pp. xvi. 454. *Fry & Kammerer: Philadelphia,* 1807. 4°. **1346.** m. **9.**

—— The Columbiad. A poem. pp. xxxiii. 428. *Richard Phillips: London,* 1809. 8°. **11654.** d. **33.**

—— [Another edition.] With the last corrections of the author. pp. xl. 448. *F. Schoell: Paris,* 1813. 8°. **642.** k. **27.**

—— The Conspiracy of Kings; a poem: addressed to the inhabitants of Europe from another quarter of the world. pp. 20. *J. Johnson: London,* 1792. 4°. **11630.** d. **17.** (14.)

—— [Another copy.] **T. 4.** (4.)

—— The Conspiracy of Kings . . . The second edition. pp. 20. *J. Johnson: London,* 1792. 4°. **11611.** k. **8.** (12.)

BARLOW (JOEL)

—— The third edition. pp. 12. *The Booksellers: London,* 1796. 12°. **8135. a. 86. (5.)**

—— The Hasty-Pudding: a poem . . . [By J. Barlow.] Together with The Ruling Passion by R. T. Paine. pp. 32. 1815. 12°. *See* HASTY-PUDDING. **11686. c. 10.**

—— The Hasty-Pudding . . . With a memoir on maize or Indian corn; compiled by D. J. Browne. pp. 56. *W. H. Graham: New York,* 1847. 12°. **11686. c. 11.**

—— [Another edition.] pp. 48. *C. M. Saxton: New York,* [1850?] 12°. **7075. c. 57. (2.)**

—— The History of England, from . . . 1765, to . . . 1795, *etc.* 5 vol. *London,* 1795. 12°. [*Parsons's Genuine Pocket Edition of Hume's History.*] **9504. a. 18–22.**

—— Letter to Henry Gregoire . . . in reply to his letter on the Columbiad. pp. 14. *R. C. Weightman: Washington,* 1809. 8°. **8176. bbb. 4. (4.)**

—— A Letter to the National Convention of France, on the defects of the constitution of 1791, and the extent of the amendments which ought to be applied. pp. 70. *J. Johnson: London,* 1792. 8°. **E. 2071. (7.)**

—— [Another copy.] **T. 200. (4.)**

—— [Another copy.] **8135. ccc. 4. (9.)**
Imperfect; wanting the half-title.

—— Lettre à la Convention Nationale de France sur les vices de la constitution de 1791 et sur l'étendue des amendemens à y porter . . . Traduite de l'anglais [by C. Ludger]. pp. 68. *Paris,* 1792. 8°. **F.R. 82. (18.)**

—— A Letter . . . to the People of Piedmont, on the advantages of the French Revolution, and the necessity of adopting its principles in Italy . . . Translated from the French by the author. pp. 48. *D. I. Eaton: London,* 1795. 8°. **8032. bb. 16. (1.)**

—— Letters from Paris, to the citizens of the United States of America, on the system of policy hitherto pursued by their government relative to their commercial intercourse with England and France, &c. pp. 116. *James Ridgway: London,* 1800. 8°. **8176. aa. 20. (1.)**

—— [Another edition.] Two Letters to the Citizens of the United States, and one to General Washington, written from Paris in the year 1799, on our political and commercial relations. pp. 119. *Sidney's Press: New-Haven,* 1806. 12°. **1389. a. 40.**

—— An Oration, delivered at the North Church in Hartford . . . July 4th, *etc.* pp. 20. *Hudson & Goodwin: Hartford,* 1787. 4°. **12301. c. 44. (4.)**

—— Joel Barlow to his fellow citizens of the United States. Letter II. On certain political measures proposed to their consideration. [With an appendix entitled, "Memoir on Certain Principles of Public Maritime Law: written for the French Government," and signed: Fulwar Skipwith, Joel Barlow.] pp. 70. *William Duane: Philadelphia,* 1801. 8°. **1104. c. 20. (8.)**

—— The Vision of Columbus; a poem. pp. 258. *Hudson & Goodwin: Hartford,* 1787. 8°. **11686. c. 40.**

—— [Another edition.] pp. xx. 244. *C. Dilly & J. Stockdale: London,* 1787. 12°. **994. c. 2.**

—— [Another edition.] With explanatory notes . . . From a revised edition of the author. pp. 288. *W. D. Bell & J. D. Toye: Baltimore,* 1814. 12°. **11686. a. 44.**

BARLOW (JOHN) John Barlow's Ward. [A novel.] 2 vol. *Smith, Elder & Co.: London,* 1881. 8°. **12643. f. 5.**

BARLOW (JOHN) *F.R.S.* The Connection between Physiology and Intellectual Philosophy, *etc.* pp. vi. 64. *William Pickering: London,* 1842. 12°. [*Small Books on Great Subjects.* no. 2.] **1154. f. 7.**

—— Second edition, enlarged. pp. ix. 112. *William Pickering: London,* 1846. 12°. [*Small Books on Great Subjects.* no. 2.] **1154. f. 8.**

—— On Man's Power over himself to prevent or control insanity, *etc.* pp. iv. 68. *William Pickering: London,* 1843. 12°. [*Small Books on Great Subjects.* no. 3.] **1154. f. 9.**

—— Second edition, enlarged. pp. viii. 123. *William Pickering: London,* 1849. 12°. [*Small Books on Great Subjects.* no. 3.] **1154. f. 10.**

—— Het Vermogen van zelfbeheersching, een middel, om krankzinnigheid te voorkomen of in bedwang te houden. Naar het Engelsch bewerkt en met toelichtende en wijzigende aanmerkingen voorzien door Dr. Th. Kroon. pp. iv. 154. *Zutphen,* 1861. 8°. **7461. bb. 18.**

—— The Probable Effects of Clothing Societies in improving the habits and principles of the poor. A sermon. To which are added a system of rules, and other facts and suggestions which appear best calculated to facilitate the introduction of these societies into such parishes as may be disposed to receive them. pp. 30. *C. J. G. & F. Rivington: London,* 1828. 8°. **T. 1257. (2.)**

BARLOW (JOHN) *Lecturer on Physiology.* Reserve Force in relation to Disease. 1889. *See* GLASGOW.—*Insurance and Actuarial Society.* Transactions, *etc.* ser. 2. no. 12. 1881, *etc.* 8°. **08227. e.**

BARLOW (JOHN) *Minister of the Word.* An Exposition of the first and second chapters of the latter Episte [*sic*] of the Apostle Paul to Timothie, *etc.* (A seasonable Discourse of Spirituall Stedfastnes, *etc.*—The True Guide to Glory, *etc.*—The Good Mans Refuge in affliction, *etc.* —The Ioy of the Vpright Man, *etc.*—Hieron's last Fare-well, *etc.*—A Christians last Day, is his best Day.) 4 pt. *Printed by R. Y.* [*Robert Young*], *sold by Iames Boler & George Lathum,* 1632. fol. **3266. gg. 1.**
The five tracts composing pt. 4 bear the imprint: "Iohn Haviland, for Nathanael Newberie: London."

—— A Christians Last Day is his Best Day. A sermon upon the first Epistle to the Thessalonians, chap. 4. vers. 18. *William Stansby for William Butler: London,* 1618. 4°. **4474. c. 26.**
Pp. 39–79 of a larger work.

—— An Exposition of the second Epistle of the Apostle Paul to Timothy, the first chapter, *etc.* pp. 446. *I. D.* [*John Dawson*] *for Iohn Bellamie: London,* 1625. 4°. **3266. b. 8.**

—— The Good Man's Priuiledge. A sermon lately preached at Plimmouth in Deuon, by I. B. [i.e. J. Barlow], *etc.* pp. 25. 1618. 4°. *See* B., I. **4474. aaa. 119.**

—— Hierons last Fare-well. A sermon preached at Modbury in Deuon, at the funerall of that reuerend . . . seruant of Iesus Christ Samuel Hieron . . . By I. B. [The dedication signed: Io. B., i.e. J. Barlow.] pp. 33. 1618. 4°. *See* B. (Io.) **1419. b. 3.**

—— The Ioy of the Vpright Man. In a sermon preached at Grayes Inne: by I. B. [i.e. J. Barlow], *etc.* pp. 36. 1619. 4°. *See* B., I. **4473. aa. 7.**

—— The True Guide to Glory. A sermon preached . . . at the funeral of . . . the Lady Strode of Newingham. pp. 51. *Thomas Snodham, for Nathaniel Newberrie: London,* 1619. 4°. **1417. h. 1.**

BARLOW (JOHN) *Professor of Anatomy and Physiology in the Veterinary College, Edinburgh.* A Memoir of John Barlow. pp. 8. *Tract Association of the Society of Friends: London,* [1860.] 8°. **4920.** bb. **4.**

BARLOW (JOHN) *Writer of Verse.* Poems of Peace and Progress, *etc.* pp. 16. *The Author: Manchester,* 1930. 8°. **11609.** h. **25.**

BARLOW (JOHN H.)

—— George Whitehead, the last of the early Friends. *London,* 1908. 8°. [*Friends Ancient and Modern.* no. 10.] **4804.** aa. **48.**

Various editions.

BARLOW (JOHN JAMES) Our Real Danger and how to meet it. The substance of a speech. [On the Church of Rome.] pp. 72. *Edward Power: Gloucester,* 1850. 8°. **3939.** e. **13.**

BARLOW (JOHN MOUNT) *See* CORNET, *pseud.* [i.e. J. M. Barlow.]

BARLOW (JOHN S.)

—— Dene of the Secret Service. pp. 128. *Mellifont Press: London; Dublin* printed, [1939.] 8°. **12632.** p. **40.**

BARLOW (JOSEPH) A New Method of finding the Longitude, by an altitude of the moon, when two three or more hours distant from the meridian; independent of the longitude by account. pp. 12. *W. C. Drake: London,* 1818. 4°. **B. 471. (22.)**

—— [Another copy.] **717. l. 11.**

BARLOW (JOSEPH W.) *See* PALACIO VALDÉS (A.) Sinfonía Pastoral. Edited by J. W. Barlow, *etc.* 1933. 8°. **012942.** bbb. **22.**

—— Basic Spanish. pp. xiii. 208. *F. S. Crofts & Co.: New York,* 1946. 8°. **12944.** aa. **29.**

—— Basic Spanish. pp. xii. 194. *G. Bell & Sons: London,* 1951. 8°. **12944.** aa. **51.**

—— Exercises and Review Tests for Basic Oral Spanish. pp. 69. *Appleton-Century-Crofts: New York,* [1949.] 4°. **12944.** d. **10.**

BARLOW (KATHLEEN) Standard African Readers. 5 bk. *Christian Literature Society for India & Africa: London; C.M.S. Bookshop: Lagos,* [1928–30.] 8°. **12980.** h. **27.**

BARLOW (KENNETH ELLIOTT)

—— The Discipline of Peace. pp. 214. *Faber & Faber: London,* 1942. 8°. **08425.** g. **51.**

—— A Home of Their Own, *etc.* [On family life and its social significance.] pp. 96. *Faber & Faber: London,* 1946. 8°. **8286.** aa. **83.**

—— The State of Public Knowledge. pp. 111. *Faber & Faber: London,* 1946. 8°. **8312.** b. **57.**

BARLOW (L.) The Substance of a Sermon preached . . . at Longside, on that part of the highway between Disley and Whaley, where William Wood was barbarously murdered, *etc.* pp. 8. *J. Pratt: Manchester,* [1823.] 8°. **4452.** cc. **7. (7.)**

BARLOW (MADGE) The Cairn of the Badger. pp. 343. *Cassell & Co.: London,* 1908. 8°. **012627.** aaa. **22.**

BARLOW (MARGARET) The Life of William Hagger Barlow, D.D., late Dean of Peterborough. Edited by M. Barlow. With an introduction by the Bishop of Liverpool and chapters by the Bishop of Durham, the Dean of Canterbury, and others . . . Fifteen full-page illustrations. pp. xvii. 216. *G. Allen & Sons: London,* 1910. 8°. **4902.** df. **16.**

BARLOW (*Right Hon. Sir* MONTAGUE) *Bart. See* BARLOW (*Right Hon. Sir* Clement A. M.)

BARLOW (NATHAN) and **THOMPSON** (JAMES C.) Small Pneumothorax in Tuberculosis. [With plates.] pp. 260. *Washington,* 1922. 8°. [*U.S. Public Health Service. Hygienic Laboratory.* Bulletin no. 132.] **A.S. 522.**

BARLOW (NED) Dare to be Singular: or, the Story of Ned Barlow, the miner, *etc.* [1877.] 8°. *See* H., S. M. **4418.** bb. **16.**

BARLOW (NORA) *See* BARLOW (Emma N.)

BARLOW (P. CRAWFORD) A Description of a Tonal Method of Notation applicable for all Musicians, *etc.* pp. 12. [*London,* 1907.] 8°. **7898.** s. **15. (6.)**

—— Transposing Card. Revolving circle has the degrees of the scale. [By C. Barlow.] 1910. *s. sh.* 16°. *See* TRANSPOSING CARD. **1879.** c. **11. (28.)**

BARLOW (P. W.) *Jun.* Broadstairs: past and present . . . Accompanied by a map. pp. 55. *Parsons Sisters: Broadstairs,* 1882. 8°. **10347.** aa. **13. (4.)**

BARLOW (P. W.) *Settler in New Zealand.* Kaipara, or experiences of a settler in North New Zealand. Written and illustrated by P. W. Barlow. pp. xii. 219. *Sampson Low & Co.: London,* 1888. 8°. **10491.** bb. **36.**

BARLOW (PERCIVAL) The General History of Europe; and Entertaining Traveller. Comprising an historical and geographical account of all the empires, kingdoms, &c. in Europe . . . With maps . . . copper-plates, *etc.* pp. 825. *W. & J. Stratford: London,* [1791?] fol. **1853.** c. **5.**

—— [Another copy.] **Cup.1247.aa.11.**
Imperfect; wanting fifteen of the engravings.

BARLOW (PETER) *See* LECOUNT (P.) An Examination of Professor Barlow's Reports on Iron Rails, *etc.* [1836.] 8°. **1136.** h. **23.**

—— *See* LECOUNT (P.) A Letter from "Jonah" to Professor Barlow on Iron Rails. [1836.] 8°. **8767.** bb. **37.**

—— *See* MAHAN (D. H.) An Elementary Course of Civil Engineering . . . Edited by Professor Barlow. 1838. 4°. **717.** k. **25.**

—— —— 1846. 4°. **1263.** f. **21.**

—— *See* SMITH (*Sir* JOHN MARK F.) *K.H.*, and BARLOW (P.) Report of Lieut. Colonel Sir Frederic Smith . . . and Professor Barlow . . . on the Atmospheric Railway, *etc.* 1842. fol. [*Parliamentary Papers.* 1842. vol. 41.] B.S.

—— *See* TREDGOLD (T.) Elementary Principles of Carpentry . . . Fourth edition . . . With an appendix . . . by P. Barlow. 1853. 4°. **1269.** f. **10.**

—— —— 1870. 4°. **7816.** e. **32.**

—— An Elementary Investigation of the Theory of Numbers, with its application to the indeterminate and diophantine analysis, the analytical and geometrical division of the circle, and several other curious algebraical and arithmetical problems. pp. xiv. 507. *J. Johnson & Co.: London,* 1811. 8°. **716.** e. **20.**

—— An Essay on Magnetic Attractions, and on the laws of terrestial and electro magnetism; comprising a popular course of curious and interesting experiments on the latter subject, and an easy experimental method of correcting the local attraction of vessels on the compass in all parts of the world . . . Second edition, *etc.* pp. xii. 303. pl. 5. *J. Mawman; J. Taylor: London,* 1823. 8°. **538.** g. **20.**

BARLOW (PETER)

—— [Another issue, with an appendix.] pp. xii. 368. pl. 5. *London*, 1824. 8°. **538. f. 38.**

—— An Essay on the Strength and Stress of Timber, founded upon experiments performed at the Royal Military Academy . . . preceded by an historical review of former theories and experiments . . . Also an appendix on the strength of iron, and other materials . . . Third edition, corrected. pp. xviii. 306. pl. vi. *J. Taylor: London*, 1826. 8°. **538. b. 28.**

—— [Another edition.] A Treatise on the Strength of Timber, Cast Iron, Malleable Iron, and other materials, *etc.* pp. xii. 492. pl. vii. *John Weale: London*, 1837. 8°. **538. b. 33.**

—— A new edition, revised and corrected by I. F. Heather . . . To which is added an essay on the effects produced by causing weights to travel over elastic bars. By the Rev. Robert Willis, *etc.* pp. xii. 516. pl. ix. *John Weale: London*, 1851. 8°. **8765. e. 13.**

—— New edition. Revised by . . . P. W. Barlow . . . and W. H. Barlow . . . To which are added a summary of experiments by Eaton Hodgkinson . . . William Fairbairn . . . and David Kirkaldy; an essay, with illustrations, on the effect produced by passing weights over elastic bars. By the Rev. Robert Willis . . . and formulæ for calculating girders, etc. The whole arranged and edited by William Humber, *etc.* pp. xii. 396. pl. x. ix. *Lockwood & Co.: London*, 1867. 8°. **8765. dd. 28.**

—— Experiments on the Transverse Strength and other Properties of Malleable Iron, with reference to its uses for railway bars; and a report founded on the same, *etc.* pp. 97. *B. Fellowes: London*, 1835. 8°. **T. 1936. (5.)**

—— Recherches sur les rails et leurs supports. Extrait des ouvrages anglais de P. Barlow (" Expériences sur la force transversale et les autres propriétés du fer malléable ") et N. Wood (" Description des différentes espèces de rails employés jusqu'à present," &c.), suivi de la description des rails . . . employés sur les principaux chemins de fer d'Europe et d'Amérique. Et de notes . . . par E. Locard. pp. viii. 616. *Paris*, 1853. 8°. **8766. d. 3.**

—— Atlas. *Paris*, 1853. 4°. **8766. e. 5.**

—— A New Mathematical and Philosophical Dictionary; comprising an explanation of the terms and principles of pure and mixed mathematics, and such branches of natural philosophy as are susceptible of mathematical investigation, *etc.* [With thirteen plates.] *G. & S. Robinson: London*, 1814. 8°. **60. e. 2.**

—— New Mathematical Tables, containing the factors, squares, cubes, square roots, cube roots, reciprocals, and hyperbolic logarithms of all numbers from 1 to 10000, *etc.* pp. lxi. 336. *G. & S. Robinson: London*, 1814. 8°. **530. f. 19.**

—— Barlow's Tables of Squares, Cubes, Square Roots, Cube Roots, Reciprocals, of all integer numbers up to 10,000. Stereotype edition, examined and corrected [by A. de Morgan]. pp. vii. 200. *Walton & Maberly: London*, 1856. 8°. **8505. e. 29.**

—— Third edition. Edited by L. J. Comrie. pp. xii. 208. *E. & F. N. Spon: London*, 1930. 8°. **08548. aaa. 7.**

—— Barlow's Tables of Squares, Cubes, Square Roots, Cube Roots and Reciprocals of all integer numbers up to 12,500. Edited by L. J. Comrie . . . Fourth edition. pp. xii. 258. *E. & F. N. Spon: London*, 1941. 8°. **08548. aaa. 36.**

BARLOW (PETER)

—— Tables des carrés, cubes, racines carrées, racines cubiques et inverses de tous les nombres entiers de 1 jusqu'à 10.000. pp. 199. *Paris & Liége*, 1913. 8°. **08548. aa. 23.**

—— Second Report addressed to the Directors and Proprietors of the London and Birmingham Railway, founded on an inspection of, and experiments made on, the Liverpool and Manchester Railway. pp. 116. *B. Fellowes: London*, 1835. 8°. **T. 2016. (1.)**

BARLOW (PETER) and **LUNN** (FRANCIS)

—— Greek Physics. 1853. *See* SMEDLEY (Edward) *Fellow of Sidney Sussex College, Cambridge.* Encyclopædia Metropolitana. (Third division. History and biography.) 1848, *etc.* 8°. **12220. b. 15.**

BARLOW (PETER WILLIAM) *See* BARLOW (Peter) A Treatise on the Strength of Materials . . . A new edition. Revised by P. W. Barlow, *etc.* 1867. 8°. **8765. dd. 28.**

—— Experiments and Observations, which prove that by lighting fires at or near the top . . . great economy of coal will arise. pp. 8. *Vacher & Sons: London*, 1882. 8°. **8768. bbb. 19. (8.)**

—— Investigation of the Power consumed in overcoming the Inertia of Railway Trains, and of the resistance of the air in the motion of Railway trains at high velocities. pp. 34. *John Weale: London*, 1848. 8°. **1396. f. 27. (4.)**

—— Observations on the Niagara Railway Suspension Bridge, made during a recent tour in America. On the practicability of connecting Liverpool and Birkenhead, and New York and Brooklyn, by wire suspension bridges of one span, *etc.* pp. 40. *John Weale: London*, 1860. 8°. **8776. b. 55. (9.)**

—— On the Relief of London Street Traffic, with a description of the Tower subway now shortly to be executed. pp. 23. *E. & F. N. Spon: London*, 1867. 8°. **8776. bb. 58. (8.)**

—— The Proposed Tower Bridge. Observations to prove that a new bridge east of London Bridge is unnecessary . . . Second edition, *etc.* pp. 8. *E. & F. N. Spon: London*, 1878. 16°. **8767. bb. 16. (10.)**

—— The Relief of Street Traffic. Advantages of the City and Southwark subway, with reasons why the proposed connection of street tramways from the Elephant and Castle through the City is unnecessary . . . Second pamphlet. pp. 6. *E. & F. N. Spon: London*, 1871. 8°. **8235. bbb. 48. (11.)**

—— Report to the Directors of the South-Eastern Railway Company on Permanent Way. pp. 16. pl. 2. *James Truscott: London*, [1850.] 4°. **8765. f. 36. (3.)**

—— Smoke Abatement. Experiments and observations to prove that feeding fires directly under the chimney is not consistent with scientific laws, *etc.* pp. 11. *Vacher & Sons: London*, 1882. 8°. **C.T. 291. (1.)**

BARLOW (R. F.) Inspection of Aero-Engines before Flight. *See* AERO-ENGINES. Aero-Engines, *etc.* 1934. 8°. **08773.e.21/4.**

—— Aero-Engines. Inspection of, before flight. " C " licence. [By R. F. Barlow and A. McIsaac.] (Second and revised edition [of parts 1 and 3 of " Aero-Engines," by R. F. Barlow, A. N. Barrett and A. McIsaac].) pp. vi. 36. *Sir I. Pitman & Sons: London*, 1935 [1934]. 8°. [*Aeronautical Engineering Series. Ground Engineers.*] **08773.e.21/7.**

BARLOW (R. Fred.) *of the Hakluyt Society. See* Hedges (*Sir* W.) The Diary of William Hedges . . . With notes . . . by R. Barlow, *etc.* 1887, *etc.* 8°. Ac. **6172/62.**

BARLOW (Randle)

—— *See* Jones (Francis S. T.) Hit or miss: being the adventures of Driver Randle Barlow, *etc.* 1954. 8°. **09101.** de. **30.**

BARLOW (Richard) *Captain, of Mansfield.* Jamaica of One Hundred Years Ago and Reminiscences of the Napoleonic Wars. Letters and documents of Capt. Richard Barlow of Mansfield. By [or rather, edited by] L. Graham H. Horton-Smith. (Reprinted from the "Mansfield, Sutton and Kirkby Chronicle.") pp. 43. *Mansfield, Sutton & Kirkby Chronicle: Mansfield,* 1932. 12°. **10482.** aa. **33.**

BARLOW (Richard) *Dr. Med.* Mittheilungen über Reduktion der Überosmiumsäure durch das Pigment der menschlichen Haut, *etc.* pp. 10. *Cassel,* 1895. 4°. [*Born* (*G.*) *Bibliotheca Medica, etc.* D^{II}. Hft. 5.] **7391.w.1.**

BARLOW (Richard Bawden)

—— Introduction to Chemical Pharmacology, *etc.* pp. xiv. 343. *Methuen & Co.: London; John Wiley & Sons: New York,* 1955. 8°. **8896.** a. **6.**

BARLOW (Richard Gorton) Forty Seasons of First-Class Cricket: being the autobiography and reminiscences of R. G. Barlow . . . With . . . illustrations and over 300 autographs of county cricketers. pp. xi. 255. *John Heywood: Manchester, London,* [1908.] 8°. **7904.** cc. **5.**

BARLOW (*Sir* Robert) *G.C.B.*

—— The Dissents, or Protests, of Edward Parry, Esq., William Astell, Esq., George Smith, Esq., John Bebb, Esq., and Charles Grant, Esq., directors of the East India Company, against the resolutions of the court by which . . . Earl Minto was recalled from the government-general of India; Lieut.-General Sir George Nugent, Bart., from the command-in-chief of the land forces; and Sir George Barlow, Bart. . . . from the government of Madras. Published by Sir R. Barlow. pp. 38. *John Murray: London,* 1813. 8°. **08139.** ccc. **34.** (**8.**)

BARLOW (Robert Hayward)

—— *See* Paris.—*Bibliothèque Nationale.* [*Manuscrits.*] Anales de Tlatelolco. Unos annales históricos de la nación mexicana, y códice de Tlatelolco . . . con un resumen de los anales y una interpretación del códice por R. H. Barlow. 1948. 8°. **9770.** ppp. **20.**

—— The Extent of the Empire of the Culhua Mexica. [With a map.] pp. viii. 144. *University of California Press: Berkeley & Los Angeles,* 1949. 8°. [*Ibero-Americana.* no. 28.] W.P. **1387/28.**

BARLOW (Robert Hayward) and **MAC AFEE** (Byron)

—— Diccionario de elementos fonéticos en escritura jeroglífica—Códice Mendocino. Por Roberto Barlow y Byron MacAfee. pp. 46. *México,* 1949. 4°. **7708.** t. **49.** *Publicaciones del Instituto de Historia. Primera serie.* no. 9.

BARLOW (Robert Joseph) The Queen the Head of the Church. pp. 31. *Seeley & Co.: London,* 1856. 8°. **4108.** c. **6.**

—— Third edition. pp. 31. *Seeley & Co.: London,* 1857. 8°. **4106.** h. **32.** (**2.**)

—— A Sermon preached at the Visitation of the Archdeaconry of Cleveland, *etc.* pp. 32. *J. S. Pratt: Stokesley,* 1833. 8°. T. **1453.** (**10.**)

BARLOW (Roger) *See* Fernández de Enciso (M.) A Brief Summe of Geographie, *etc.* [Translated by R. Barlow, with additional matter.] 1932. 8°. Ac. **6172/123.**

BARLOW (Samuel) Relief for Sufferers: or, Directions for the cure of tic-doloreux [*sic*], neuralgia, sciatica, toothache, *etc.* pp. 28. xx. *Harrison Penney: Darlington,* [1859.] 12°. **7460.** a. **13.**

BARLOW (Samuel Latham Mitchill) *See* Colombo (C.) Letter of Christopher Columbus describing his first voyage to the Western Hemisphere. [With a note signed: S. L. M. B., i.e. S. L. M. Barlow.] 1875. 8°. C. **32.** g. **31.**

—— *See* Harrisse (H.) The Late Samuel L. M. Barlow, *etc.* 1889. 8°. **10601.** g. **9.** (**5.**)

—— A Brief Disquisition concerning the early History of Printing in America. [By S. L. M. Barlow.] pp. 18. 1866. 4°. *See* America. **11903.** i. **15.**

—— Catalogue of the American Library of the late S. L. M. Barlow. Prepared by J. O. Wright. [With a preface by Henry Harrisse.] pp. xv. 450. *New York,* 1889. 8°. **011902.** k. **43.**

BARLOW (Sarah) The Golden Net. [A novel.] pp. 264. *Jonathan Cape: London,* 1933. 8°. NN. **20914.**

BARLOW (Stephen) The History of Ireland, from the earliest period to the present time; embracing also a statistical and geographical account of that kingdom, *etc.* 2 vol. *Sherwood & Co.: London,* 1814. 8°. **286.** b. **17, 18.**
With an additional titlepage, engraved.

BARLOW (T.) *Rev., of Leicester.* Astronomy simplified: for the use of schools and families. pp. 63. *Jarrold & Sons: London,* [1855.] 12°. **8560.** a. **7.**

BARLOW (T.) *Rev., of Madely, Staffordshire. See* Hampson (John) *A.B.* A Scriptural and Rational Defence of the Doctrine of Regeneration. In a letter to . . . T. Barlow. Occasioned by his letter on that subject to Mr. Stubbs, *etc.* 1765. 8°. **4257.** c. **35.**

BARLOW (T. M.) A History of Manchester Wheelers' Club . . . Compiled by T. M. Barlow. pp. 42. 1933. 8°. *See* Manchester.—*Manchester Wheelers' Club.* **7916.** cc. **37.**

—— Record Breaking on Bicycles. A history of the Northern Road Records Association from 1890 to 1940. pp. 44. [1948.] 8°. *See* Manchester.—*Northern Road Records Association.* **7919.** cc. **47.**

BARLOW (Theodore) *See* Jenkins (David) *One of the Judges for South Wales.* Eight Centuries of Reports . . . published originally in French and Latin . . . Translated by T. Barlow, *etc.* 1777. fol. **20.** d. **3.**

—— —— 1885. 8°. **6121.** g. **2.**

—— The Justice of Peace: a treatise containing the power and duty of that magistrate . . . To which is added an appendix, being a summary of all the Acts of Parliament, whereby one or more Justices are authorized to act either in or out of Sessions. pp. xxii. 592. *J. & P. Knapton; John Nourse: [London,]* 1745. fol. **516.** m. **3.**

BARLOW (Thomas) and **BROTHER.** A Chinese Trade Circular. *J. Heywood: Manchester,* [1888.] *s. sh.* fol. **1882.** d. **2.** (**262.**)

BARLOW (Thomas) *Bishop of Lincoln.*

—— *See* Bellasis (Edward) *Serjeant-at-Law.* Was Barlow a Bishop? *etc.* [1890.] 8°. **3943.aa.72.(4.)**

BARLOW (Thomas) *Bishop of Lincoln.*

—— See Gunpowder Treason. The Gunpowder-Treason . . . A preface touching that horrid conspiracy, by . . . Thomas Lord Bishop of Lincoln, *etc.* 1679. 8°. **808.** c. **9.**

—— —— 1850. 12°. **1326. a. 4.**

—— *See* Rome, *Church of.—Popes.* Pius v. [1566–1572.] Brutum fulmen: or the bull of Pope Pius v. [dated: 27 April 1570] concerning the damnation . . . of Q. Elizabeth . . . with some observations upon it . . . by Thomas, Lord Bishop of Lincoln, *etc.* 1681. 4°. **851.** d. **23.**

—— *See* Usher (James) successively *Bishop of Meath* and *Archbishop of Armagh.* J. Usserii Armachani Annales veteris et novi Testamenti . . . Accedunt . . . tractatus duo. i. Chronologia sacra Veteris Testamenti, *etc.* [Edited by Thomas Barlow.] 1673. fol. **L.16.e.3.**

—— —— 1722. fol. **206.** h. **6.**

—— *See* Usher (James) successively *Bishop of Meath,* and *Archbishop of Armagh.* Jacobi Usserii . . . Chronologia sacra . . . Opus posthumum . . . accurante T. Barlow. 1660. 4°. E. **1024. (1.)**

—— The Genuine Remains of . . . Dr. T. Barlow, late Lord Bishop of Lincoln. Containing divers discourses theological, philosophical, historical, &c. In letters to several persons . . . To which is added the resolution of many abstruse points. As also directions to a young divine for his study of divinity, and choice of books, &c. With great variety of other subjects. pp. 643. *John Dunton: London,* 1693. 8°. **1019.** i. **3.**

—— *See* Brougham (Henry) *of Queen's College, Oxford.* Reflections to a late book, entituled, The Genuine Remains of Dr. T. Barlow, *etc.* 1694. 4°. **700.** d. **43.**

—— An Answere [to] Mr. Hunt's letter concerning two questions proposed by him. 1°. Whether Syriaque be the originall of the New Testament? 2°. What is the true meaneinge of that place, 1 Joh. 5. 7, 8? [From a ms. in the library of Queen's College, Oxford.] *See* Burgess (Thomas) successively *Bishop of Saint David's,* and *of Salisbury.* A Selection of Tracts and Observations on 1 John v. 7, *etc.* 1824. 8°. **4224.** f. **5.**

—— *Αὐτοσχεδιασματα,* de studio theologiæ: or, Directions for the choice of books in the study of divinity: publish'd from the original manuscript, by William Offley. pp. 79. *Leon. Lichfield: Oxford,* 1699. 8°. **480. a. 19. (1.)**

—— [Another copy.] ms. notes [by Robert Jenkin]. **125.** k. **17.**

—— Bishop Barlow's stating of this case, Whether any books may be lent out of Sir T. Bodley's Library . . . Publish'd from the original paper found in the said Library. pp. 11. *See* Chandler (Henry W.) On Lending Bodleian Books, *etc.* 1886. 8°. **11900.** b. **40. (1.)**

—— The Bishop of Lincoln's Arguments, that Bishops ought not to vote in Parliament, with the answers thereunto. [*London,* 1683.] fol. **514.** l. **1. (2.)**
Pp. 13–16 *of a larger work.*

—— The Case concerning setting up images or painting of them in Churches, writ by . . . Dr. T. Barlow . . . upon his suffering such images to be defaced in his diocess . . . Published upon occasion of a painting set up in White-Chappel Church. pp. 22. *James Roberts: London,* 1714. 8°. **1418.** k. **34. (5.)**

BARLOW (Thomas) *Bishop of Lincoln.*

—— De historicis Anglicanis commentatio. [Signed: T. B., i.e. T. Barlow.] 1742. 4°. [*Taylor* (*John*) *LL.D., etc. Commentarius ad L. Decemviralem, etc.*] *See* B., T. **11630.** e. **3.**

—— Directions for the study of the English History and Antiquities. [Signed: T. B., i.e. T. Barlow.] 1742. 4°. [*Taylor* (*John*) *LL.D., etc. Commentarius ad L. Decemviralem, etc.*] **11630.** e. **3. (9.)**

—— A Discourse of the Peerage & Jurisdiction of the Lords Spiritual in Parliament. Proving from the fundamental laws of the land, the testimony of . . . authors, and the practice of all ages, that they have no right in claiming any jurisdiction in capital matters. [By T. Barlow.] pp. 28. 1679. fol. *See* England.—*Church of England.—Archbishops & Bishops.* [*Appendix.*] **515.** k. **24. (11.)**

—— The Rights of the Bishops to judge in capital cases in Parliament, cleared [by Thomas Hunt?], being a full answer to two books . . . the first [by Denzil Holles] entituled, A Letter from a Gentleman to his Friend, &c. The other [by Thomas Barlow], A Discourse of the Peerage and Jurisdiction of the Lords Spiritual in Parliament, *etc.* 1680. 8°. **883.** e. **23.**

—— Excercitationes aliquot metaphysicæ, de Deo: quòd sit objectum metaphysicæ, quòd sit naturaliter cognoscibilis, quousque, & quibus mediis. Quòd sit æternus, & immensus —contra Vorstium—& quomodo, &c. . . . Editio secunda. pp. 329. *A. Lichfield, impensis Jos. Godwin & Tho. Robinson: Oxoniæ,* 1658. 4°. E. **952. (1.)**

—— A Few Plain Reasons why a Protestant of the Church of England, should not turn Roman Catholick. By a real Catholic of the Church of England [i.e. Thomas Barlow. The author's postscript signed: N. N.]. pp. 53. 1688. 4°. *See* N., N. **108.** e. **52.**

—— [Another copy.] few ms. notes. T. **1872. (4.)**

—— [Another copy.] T. **1030. (11.)**

—— [Another copy.] **222.** e. **1. (11.)**

—— A Letter concerning invocation of Saints and adoration of the Cross, writ . . . to John Evelyn, *etc.* pp. 39. *John Martin: London,* 1679. 4°. T. **1946. (3.)**

—— [Another copy.] **3936.** g. **4.**

—— [Another copy.] C. **64.** h. **12. (7.)**

—— *Begin.* My Reverend Brother, Whereas his Sacred Majesty, in his Brief graciously granted for the relief of the French Protestants, *etc.* [A letter recommending the "Brief" to the notice of the clergy of the Diocese of Lincoln.] [1686.] *s. sh.* fol. **816.** m. **22. (5.)**

—— Pegasus, or the Flying Horse from Oxford, *etc.* [Two letters, the first by T. Barlow.] [1648.] 4°. *See* Oxford, *City of.—University of Oxford.* [*Appendix.*] E. **437. (20.)**

—— [Another copy.] G. **4116.**

—— Pietas in Patrem, or a few teares upon the lamented death of his father Richard Barlow . . . who dyed December 29. Ann. 1636. By T. Barlow [and others. In verse]. pp. 16. *William Turner: Oxford,* 1637. 8°. C. **59.** a. **22.**

—— Popery: or, the Principles and positions approved by the Church of Rome, when really believ'd and practis'd, are very dangerous to all; and to Protestant kings and supreme powers, more especially pernicious: and inconsistant with that loyalty which, by the law of nature and Scripture, is indispensably due to supreme powers. pp. 116. *James Collins: London,* 1679. 4°. **108.** d. **60.**
With a presentation inscription by the author.

BARLOW (THOMAS) *Bishop of Lincoln.*

—— [Another copy.] T. **1946**. (**1.**)
Without the License and Errata leaves.

—— [Another copy, with a different titlepage.] T. **1981**. (**6.**)
Without the Errata leaf.

—— [Another copy.] **11**. a. **16**.
Without the Errata leaf.

—— [Another edition.] pp. 116. *Tho. Newcomb for James Collins: London,* 1679. 4°. **701**. e. **10**. (**2.**)
The Errata mentioned in the first edition are here corrected.

—— [Another copy.] C. **64**. h. **12**. (**9.**)

—— [Another copy.] T. **1980**. (**1.**)
Without the License leaf.

—— [Another edition.] pp. 224. *J. C. & Fr. Collins for James Collins: London,* 1679. 8°. **702**. e. **18**.

—— [Another edition.] 1712. *See* PAPAL USURPATION. Papal Usurpation and Tyranny. pt. 1. 1712, *etc.* fol. **489**. l. **21**.

—— [Another edition.] Popery dangerous to Protestant Princes. 1851. *See* BROGDEN (James) Catholic Safeguards, *etc.* vol. 3. 1846, *etc.* 8°. **1354**. i. **7**.

—— Papismus regiæ potestatis eversor . . . Robertus Grovius S.T.B. de Anglicano Latinum fecit: Justitiam Britannicam [by William Cecil, Lord Burleigh], & alia quædam, adjici curavit. Quibus ab alio adjunguntur Monarchia Solipsorum [by Lucius Cornelius Europaeus] et Conclave Ignatii [by John Donne]. 4 pt. *Apud Jacobum Collins & Samuelem Lowndes: Londini,* 1682. **1025**. a. **28**.
The 'Papismus' has a separate titlepage dated 1681. *The "Monarchia Solipsorum" and the "Conclave Ignatii" have separate titlepages dated* 1680.

—— *See* ENGLISH PROTESTANTS. A Præfatory Discourse to a late pamphlet, entituled A Memento for English Protestants, &c. being an Answer to that part of the Compendium, which reflects upon the Bishop of Lincoln's book [entitled "Popery," *etc.*], *etc.* 1681. 4°. **8122**. d. **16**.

—— *See* WALSH (Peter) Four letters . . . the fourth being an answer to the Bishop of Lincoln's Book, entituled, Popery, *etc.* 1686. 8°. **224**. b. **14**.

—— Several Miscellaneous and Weighty Cases of Conscience, learnedly and judiciously resolved by . . . Dr. T. Barlow . . . I. Of toleration of Protestant dissenters. II. The King's power to pardon murder. III. Objections from Gen. 9. 6. answered. IV. Mr. Cottington's case of divorce: With the judgments of Dr. Allestrey, Dr. Hall, Sir Richard Lloyd, Sir Richard Raines, Dr. Oldys, and the doctors of Sorbonne, upon the same. V. For toleration of the Jews. VI. About setting up images in churches. VII. An dominium fundatur in gratiâ? With two pages omitted in the English Machiavel, & his Lordship's censure thereupon. [With a portrait.] 6 pt. *Mrs. Davis: London,* 1692. 8°. **852**. c. **13**.

—— [Another copy.] T. **494**.
Without the portrait.

—— Two Letters written by . . . Dr. T. Barlow . . . concerning justification by faith only. To a minister in his Diocess. Published from his Lordship's original copy: together with the ministers Letters [signed: J. W.] that occasion'd them. [The editor's preface signed: Ri. Mayo.] pp. 214. *Thomas Parkhurst: London,* 1701. 8°. **4255**. b. **7**.

BARLOW (THOMAS) *of Leeds.* A Trip to Rome, at railway speed; being the journal of a rapid tour in the summer of 1835, *etc.* pp. iv. 427. *Hamilton, Adams & Co.: London; I. Y. Knight: Leeds,* 1836. 12°. **1050**. d. **28**.

BARLOW (THOMAS) *Poet.* Poems. pp. vi. 56. *Horace Cox: London,* 1894. 8°. **011652**. k. **24**.

BARLOW (THOMAS) *Writer on Sewage Disposal.* Hydraulics, Gauging of Sewage Flows, *etc.* pp. 75. *C. Lockwood & Son: London,* 1926. 8°. **08776**. aaa. **17**.

BARLOW (*Sir* THOMAS) *Bart.* *See* BUNTING (Evelyn M.) A School for Mothers . . . With an introduction by Sir T. Barlow, *etc.* [1907.] 8°. **7580**. ff. **26**.

—— *See* RAYNAUD (A. G. M.) On Local Asphyxia and Symmetrical Gangrene of the Extremities (New Researches on the Nature and Treatment of Local Asphyxia of the Extremities) . . . Translated by T. Barlow. 1888. 8°. [*New Sydenham Society. Selected Monographs, etc.*] Ac. **3838/50**.

—— The Annual Address delivered to the Royal College of Physicians on April 1st, 1912, by the President, Sir T. Barlow. pp. 48. *J. Bale & Co.: London,* 1912. 8°. **07306**. h. **10**. (**5.**)

—— The Annual Address delivered to the Royal College of Physicians, on April 6, 1914, by the President, Sir T. Barlow. pp. 28. *J. Bale & Co.: London,* [1914.] 8°. **7680**. cc. **47**.

—— The Incidence of Venereal Diseases and its Relation to School Life and School Teaching. An address, *etc.* pp. 15. *London,* 1917. 8°. [*National Council for Combating Venereal Diseases.* N.C. 28.] **7642.de.1/28.**

—— The Prevailing Intemperance among Women: its cause and its remedy. A paper, *etc.* pp. 12. *Church of England Temperance Society: London,* [1902.] 8°. **8436**. e. **10**.

—— The Problem of Venereal Diseases. How ministers of religion can help. By Sir T. Barlow . . . and Sir Malcolm Morris, *etc.* pp. 23. *London,* 1917. 8°. [*National Council for Combating Venereal Diseases.* N.C. 23.] **7642.de.1/23.**

BARLOW (*Sir* THOMAS DALMAHOY) *G.B.E.*

—— *See* DUERER (A.) Woodcuts of Albrecht Dürer. [Selected and with an introduction by] T. D. Barlow. 1948. 8°. **12208**. a. **4** 39.

—— *See* HUXLEY (Sir Julian S.) Scientific Research and Social Needs. With . . . discussions with Professor H. Levy, Sir T. D. Barlow, *etc.* 1934. 8°. W.P. **10652/1**.

—— Albert Dürer: his life and work, *etc.* [With plates.] pp. 39. *London,* [1924.] 4°. [*Print Collectors' Club. Publication no. 3.*] Tab. **443**. b. **13/3**.

—— Engravings by Albert Dürer, 1471–1528. From the collection of Sir Thomas D. Barlow, G.B.E. 1st February —19th March, 1950. [The catalogue compiled by Sir T. D. Barlow. With plates.] pp. 15. [1950.] 8°. *See* BIRMINGHAM.—*Museum and Art Gallery.* **7869**. p. **14**.

—— Woodcuts & Engravings by Albert Dürer. Collected & described by T. D. Barlow. pp. ix. 48. *University Press: Cambridge,* 1926. 8°. **Dept. of Prints & Drawings.**

BARLOW (THOMAS DISNEY) Rays from the Sun of Righteousness. Sermons. pp. viii. 256. *J. Nisbet & Co.: London,* 1863. 8°. **4463**. a. **3**.

BARLOW (Thomas Greaves) *See* Periodical Publications.—*London.* The Journal of Gas Lighting . . . Edited by T. G. Barlow. 1849, *etc.* fol. Hendon.

—— A Letter to the Right Honourable Sir G. C. Lewis, on the supply of gas in the metropolis. pp. 32. *W. B. King: London,* 1859. 8°. C.T. **326.** (10.)

BARLOW (Thomas Herbert)

—— Our Lord's Disciples. pp. 16. *Epworth Press: London,* 1937. 8°. [*Little Books of the Kindly Light.* no. 38.] **3628.aa.7/38.**

BARLOW (Thomas Lambert) *See* MacNair (John F. A.) and Barlow (T. L.) Oral Tradition from the Indus, *etc.* 1908. 4°. **12410.** h. **19.**

BARLOW (Thomas Oldham) A Catalogue of the Works of John Phillip, R.A., exhibited at the London International Exhibition, 1873. pp. xvi. 120. **L.P.** *Chiswick Press: London,* 1873. 8°. **7857.** f. 26.

—— A Catalogue of the works of Thomas Creswick, R.A., exhibited at the London International Exhibition, 1873. pp. xi. 59. **L.P.** *Chiswick Press: London,* 1873. 8°. **7857.** f. 25.

BARLOW (Thomas Worthington) *See* Periodical Publications.—*London.* The Cheshire and Lancashire Historical Collector; edited by T. W. Barlow. 1853, *etc.* 8°. **10352.** h. 20.

—— A Chart of British Ornithology, designed for popular use. *W. W. Robinson: London,* [1847?] 4°. **1257.** e. 18.
A folding sheet.

—— Cheshire: its historical and literary associations, illustrated in a series of biographical sketches. pp. viii. 88. *Burge & Perrin: Manchester; W. Kent & Co.: London,* 1852. 8°. **10804.** c. 15.

—— [Another edition.] With a reprint of the Diary of Edward Burghall, the Puritan Vicar of Acton, 1628 to 1663. [With illustrations.] pp. viii. 196. *J. G. Bell: Manchester; J. R. Smith: London,* 1855. 8°. **10804.** c. 16.

—— Memoir of William Broome . . . With selections from his works. pp. 40. *J. G. Bell: Manchester; J. R. Smith: London,* 1855. 8°. **10854.** aa. 25. (2.)

—— The Mystic Number: a glance at the system of nature. pp. ii. 55. *Burge & Perrin: Manchester; W. S. Orr & Co.: London,* 1852. 8°. **8703.** d. 3.

—— A Sketch of the History of the Church at Holmes Chapel, Cheshire. pp. 34. *Burge & Perrin: Manchester,* 1853. 8°. **10352.** h. **19.**
One of an edition of 70 *copies.*

BARLOW (Thomas Wotton) *See* Wotton (Richard) Sanctified by the Holy Ghost. A sermon . . . Edited by T. W. Barlow. 1852. 8°. **4225.** e. 39.

BARLOW (Trafford Brereton)

—— *See* Emmett (Eric) and Barlow (T. B.) Principles of South African Company Law. 1940. 8°. **06605.** b. 61.

—— *See* Emmett (Eric) and Barlow (T. B.) Principles of South African Company Law, *etc.* 1948. 8°. **6608.** ff. 20.

—— Digest of the Law of Murder and Culpable Homicide, *etc.* [Reprinted from the "South African Law Journal."] pp. xii. 43. *Juta & Co.: Cape Town & Johannesburg,* 1951. 8°. **6608.** bbb. 29.

BARLOW (Trafford Brereton)

—— The South African Law of Vicarious Liability in Delict, and a Comparison of the Principles of other Legal Systems, *etc.* pp. xxiii. 195. *Juta & Co.: Cape Town & Johannesburg,* 1939. 8°. **06605.** c. 4.

BARLOW (Vernon) *See* Barlow (*Right Hon. Sir* Clement A. M.) *Bart.* Barlow Family Records. By Rt. Hon. Sir M. Barlow . . . assisted by G. D. . . . and V. Barlow. [1932.] 8°. **9907.** b. **29.**

—— *See* Etherton (Percy T.) The Last Strongholds. By . . . P. T. Etherton [with the collaboration of V. Barlow]. 1934. 8°. **010055.** bbb. 24.

—— *See* Etherton (Percy T.) and Barlow (V.) Tempestuous Isle, *etc.* 1950. 8°. **010368.** s. **21.**

—— *See* Etherton (Percy T.) and Barlow (V.) Lundy—the Tempestuous Isle. 1954. 8°. **10362.** aa. **28.**

—— *See* Etherton (Percy T.) and Barlow (V.) The Trail of the Conquerors, *etc.* 1936. 8°. **10481.** t. **23.**

—— Cloudy Ladder. pp. 315. *Heath Cranton: London,* 1932. 8°. NN. **19207.**

—— The Green Murder. pp. 282. *Heath Cranton: London,* 1931. 8°. NN. **17511.**

—— Quest for Sheba. [An account of a journey in Arabia made by Norman Stone Pearn. With plates, including a portrait.] pp. 258. *I. Nicholson & Watson: London,* 1937. 8°. **010076.** ee. **55.**

—— Up the Chimney . . . [Tales for children.] Illustrations by Dora Pettigrew. pp. ix. 142. *Claude Stacey: London,* [1930.] 8°. **12813.** bb. **6.**

BARLOW (W. H.) *of the University of Virginia.* Harmonic Cards. [7 cards.] *W. H. Barlow: Charlottesville, Va.,* [1909.] *obl.* 8°. **7898.** e. **48.**

BARLOW (Walter Sydney Lazarus) *See* Thompson (Edmund S.) and Barlow (W. S. L.) The Climate of Devonshire, *etc.* 1895. 8°. *The Climates and Baths of Great Britain.* vol. 1.] **7462.** g. **11.**

—— The Elements of Pathological Anatomy and Histology for students. pp. xiii. 705. *J. & A. Churchill: London,* 1903. 8°. **7421.** dd. **23.**

—— A Manual of General Pathology, *etc.* pp. xi. 795. *J. & A. Churchill: London,* 1898. 8°. **7442.** ee. **9.**

—— Second edition. pp. xii. 736. *J. & A. Churchill: London,* 1904. 8°. **7442.** dd. **16.**

BARLOW (Warren Sumner) Immortality Inherent in Nature. [A poem. With a portrait.] pp. 40. *Fowler & Wells Co.: New York,* 1885. 8°. **11686.** ee. **19.**

—— The Voices . . . [A poem.] Second edition. pp. 184. *W. White & Co.: Boston; American News Co.: New York,* 1870. 8°. **11688.** c. **43.**

BARLOW (William) *Archdeacon of Salisbury.* Magneticall Aduertisements: or, diuers pertinent obseruations, and approued experiments concerning the nature and properties of the Load-Stone, *etc.* [Partly compiled from William Gilbert's work "De Magnete." With a letter from Gilbert to the author.] pp. 86. *E. Griffin for Timothy Barlow: London,* 1616. 4°. **C.112.b.9.**

—— [Another edition.] Whereunto is annexed a breife Discouerie of the idle animaduersions of Mark Ridley, Dr in Physicke, vpon this treatise . . . The second edition. 2 pt. *E. Griffin for Timothy Barlow: London,* 1618. 4°. **1395.** d. **1.**

BARLOW (WILLIAM) *Archdeacon of Salisbury.*

—— New edition, with notes by W. Sturgeon. pp. xv. 78. *Sherwood & Co.: London*, 1843. 18°. **8757**. aaa. **49**.

—— *See* RIDLEY (Mark) Magneticall Animaduersions . . . vpon certaine Magneticall Aduertisements . . . from Maister W. Barlow. 1617. 4°. **538**. f. **42**.

—— A Breife Discovery of the idle Animadversions of Marke Ridley, Doctor in Phisicke vpon a Treatise entituled, Magneticall Aduertisements. pp. 13. *G. Griffin, for Timothy Barlow: London*, 1618. 4°. **538**. f. **43**.

—— The Nauigators Supply. Conteining many things of principall importance belonging to Nauigation, with the description & vse of diuerse Instruments framed chiefly for that purpose; but seruing also for sundry other of cosmography in generall, *etc.* [With plates.] *G. Bishop, R. Newbery and R. Barker: London*, 1597. 4°. **C.112.b.5.**

BARLOW (WILLIAM) *Barrister-at-Law.* *See* GAMBLE (Richard W.) and BARLOW (W.) An Index to all the Reported Cases in the several Courts of Equity in Ireland, from Trinity Term 1838 to Hilary Term 1867, *etc.* 1868. 4°. **6503**. f. **7**.

BARLOW (WILLIAM) successively *Bishop of Rochester* and *of Lincoln.* [For the "Authorised Version" of 1611, of which Rom.—Jude was translated by William Barlow and others:] *See* BIBLE. [*English.*]

—— *See* LAVATER (L.) Three Christian Sermons . . . of Famine and Dearth of Victuals . . . Translated . . . by W. Barlow, *etc.* 1596. 8°. **3433**. aa. **39**.

—— *See* LEGG (John W.) The Form of the Consecration of the Church and Churchyard of Fulmer in 1610, as used by William Barlow, Bishop of Lincoln, *etc.* 1907. 4°. **3407**. f. **13**.

—— An Answer to a Catholike English-man [Robert Parsons, the Jesuit], so by him-selfe entituled, who, without a name, passed his censure vpon the Apology, made by the Right High and mightie Prince Iames . . . King of Great Brittaine . . . for the Oath of Allegeance; which censure is heere examined and refuted, *etc.* pp. 370. MS. NOTES. *T. Haveland, for Mathew Law: London*, 1609. 4°. **1019**. m. **3**.

—— *See* PARSONS (Robert) *Jesuit.* A Discussion of the Answere of M. W. Barlow to the Booke entituled: The Judgment of a Catholicke Englishman, *etc.* 1612. 4°. **860**. i. **8**.

—— *See* T., F. A Supplement to the discussion of M. D. Barlowes Answere to the Judgment of a Catholike Englishman, &c. 1613. 4°. **3939**. cc. **3**.

—— *See* T., F. An Adioynder to the Supplement of Father Robert Parsons his Discussion of M. Doctor Barlowes Answere, *etc.* 1613. 4°. **3939**. cc. **6**.

—— A Brand, Titio erepta. On the fift day of Nouember last, before the Honourable Lordes of his Maiesties Priuie Councell . . . this sermon preached, *etc.* *Iohn Windet for Mathew Law: London*, 1607. 4°. **694**. g. **28**.

—— A Defence of the Articles of the Protestants Religion, in aunsweare to a libell [by Thomas Wright?] lately cast abroad, intituled Certaine Articles, or forcible reasons, discouering the palpable absurdities, and most intricate errours, of the Protestantes Religion. pp. 227. *Imprinted by Iohn Wolfe; sold by Mathew Law: London*, 1601. 4°. **1019**. g. **5**. **(1.)**

—— The Eagle and the Body; described in one sermon preached before Queene Elizabeth . . . Anno 1601 . . . Newly called for, and set foorth. *For Matthew Law: London*, 1609. 4°. **4474**. c. **27**.

BARLOW (WILLIAM) successively *Bishop of Rochester* and *of Lincoln.*

—— One of the foure Sermons preached before the King[s] Majestie at Hampton Court . . . This concerning th[e] Antiquitie and Superioritie of Bishops. *I. W[indet] fo[r] Matthew Law: London*, 1606. 4°. **693**. f. **1**. **(5.)**

—— [Another edition.] The first of the foure sermons preached before the Kings Maiestie, *etc.* *I. W[indet] fo[r] Matthew Law: London*, 1607. 4°. **693**. f. **1**. **(6.)**

—— A Sermon preached at Paules Crosse, on the first Sunday in Lent; Martij 1. 1600. With a short discourse of the late Earle of Essex his confession, and penitence, before and at the time of his death . . . Whereunto is annexed a true copie, in substance, of the behauiour, speache, and prayer of the said Earle at the time of his execution. *For Mathew Law: London*, 1601. 8°. **693**. a. **3**
The "Copie of the behauiour," etc. is signed by Thoma[s] Montford and William Barlow.

—— [Another copy.] G. **19925**

—— The Sermon preached at Paules Crosse, the tenth day o[f] Nouember, being the next Sunday after the discouerie o[f] this late Horrible treason [the Gunpowder Plot], *etc.* *I. W[indet] for Mathew Law: London*, 1606. 4°. **694**. g. **27**

—— The Summe and Substance of the Conference, which i[t] pleased his Excellent Majestie to haue with the Lords Bishops, and other of his Clergie . . . in his Majestie[s] Priuy-Chamber, at Hampton Court Ianuary 14. 1603 Contracted by William Barlow . . . Whereunto ar[e] added, some copies, scattered abroad, vnsauory, an[d] vntrue. pp. 103. *Iohn Windet for Mathew Law London*, 1604. 4°. **4705**. a. **5**

—— [Another copy.] **105**. c. **66**. **(2.**
Imperfect; wanting the titlepage and three leaves at th[e] end.

—— [Another edition.] pp. 103. *Iohn Windet fo[r] Mathew Law: London*, 1604. 4°. **698**. g. **4**. **(2.**
The errata are corrected in this edition, and the spelling changed occasionally.

—— [Another copy.] **700**. f. **15**. **(2.**

—— [Another copy.] Burney **1**

—— [Another copy.] **108**. b. **7**

—— [Another edition.] pp. 99. *V. S[immes] fo[r] Mathew Law: London*, 1605. 4°. **4106**. b. **16**

—— [Another edition.] pp. 106. *J. Bill: London*, 1625. 4° **4103**. aaa. **27**
Cropped.

—— [Another edition.] pp. 106. *Printed by John Norton sold by Ioshua Kirton and Thomas Warren: London* 1638. 4°. **698**. g. **4**. **(3**

—— [Another copy.] **858**. g. **(**

—— [Another edition.] 1707. *See* PHOENIX. The Phenix *etc.* vol. 1. no. 6. 1707, *etc.* 8°. **1103**. e. **1**

—— [Another edition.] pp. xxii. 87. [*London*, 1804.] 8°. **4105**. d. **:**

—— [A reissue.] *See* CHURCHMAN. The Churchman's Re membrancer, *etc.* vol. 1. 1807. 8°. **1120**. f. **7**

—— De Summe ende Substantie vande Conferentie de welck syne Konincklicke Majesteyt van Groot Britannien belief heeft te houden met de Heeren, Bischoppen ende ander van sijn Clergie . . . opt' Hoff tot Hampton den 14 Jan 1603 . . . Overgheset uyt de Engelsche Copie, *etc.* pp. 56 *G. Basson: Leyden*, 1612. 4°. T. **2242**. **(10.**

BARLOW (William) successively *Bishop of Rochester* and *of Lincoln.*

—— Vita et obitus . . . Richardi Cosin . . . per Guilielmum Barlowum . . . amoris sui & officij ergô edita. (Carmina funebria, in eiusdem . . . triste fatum, à quibusdam Cantabrigensibus, illius amicis, *etc.*) 2 pt. pp. 80. *Deputati Christopheri Barker: Londini,* 1598. 4°. **613**. k. **7**. (**1**.)

—— [Another copy.] **133**. a. **11**.

—— [Another copy.] **1416**. b. **35**. *Imperfect; wanting all after p.* 56.

BARLOW (William) successively *Bishop of Saint Asaph, of Saint David's, of Bath and Wells,* and *of Chichester. See* Barnes (Arthur S.) Bishop Barlow and Anglican Orders, *etc.* 1922. 8°. **3940**. i. **24**.

—— *See* Jenkins (Claude) Bishop Barlow's Consecration and Archbishop Parker's Register: with some new documents, *etc.* [A review of "Bishop Barlow and Anglican Orders: a study of the original documents," by A. S. Barnes.] 1935. 8°. **04429**. dd. **18/17**.

—— A dialoge describing the originall ground of these Lutheran faccions, and many of their abuses. B.L. *John Cawood: London,* 1553. 8°. **3932**. a. **36**.

—— [Another copy.] **1412**. a. **27**. *Imperfect; wanting the titlepage, which is supplied in MS.*

—— [Another edition.] Bishop Barlowe's Dialogue on the Lutheran Factions . . . With an introduction bearing on the question of Anglican Orders and notes by John Robert Lunn. pp. 124. *Ellis & Keene: London,* 1897. 8°. **3932**. d. **57**.

BARLOW (William) *of Amsterdam. See* Bohemia.—*Landtag.* Two Letters or Embassies. The one sent by the States of Bohemia, to the Elector of Saxony: the other from the Popes Holines to the Emperour, *etc.* [Translated by W. Barlow.] 1620. 4°. G. **15499**. (**1**.)

BARLOW (William) *of Muswell Hill.* New Theories of Matter and of Force. pp. xii. 395. *Sampson Low & Co.: London,* 1885. 8°. **8704**. de. **15**.

BARLOW (William) *Rector of Chalgrove, Oxford.* A Treatise of Fornication . . . upon 1 Cor. vi. xviii. Also, a penitentiary sermon upon John viii. ii. By W. B., M.A. [i.e. W. Barlow.] 2 pt. pp. 110. 1690, 91. 8°. *See* B., W., *M.A.* **4373**. a. **6**.

BARLOW (William) *Rector of Claremont.* Considerations on the employment of the Press as a means of diffusing the principles of the Church; with the plan of a Society, and the draft of a proposed Constitution, adapted to that object. pp. 24. *T. & J. Swords: New York,* 1826. 12°. **4183**. aaa. **24**.

BARLOW (William) *Rev., of New York.* The Smithsonian Institution . . . An address on the duties of government, in reference chiefly to public instruction; with the outlines of a plan for the application of the Smithsonian fund to that object. Delivered, in substance, before the American Institute, *etc.* pp. 40. *B. R. Barlow: New-York,* 1847. 8°. **8305**. ee. **32**. (**9**.)

BARLOW (William Crosby) *See* Lord's Supper. The Lord's Supper . . . a clerical symposium. (Contributors. C. E. Luthardt . . . W. C. Barlow, *etc.*) 1881. 8°. **4326**. f. **3**.

—— The World and the Word; or, Teaching by parables. pp. 16. *Speirs: London,* 1882. 8°. **3716**. aa. **16**. (**26**.)

—— [Another edition.] *See* New-Church Doctrine. A Circle of New-Church Doctrine. 1882. 8°. **3716**. df. **6**.

BARLOW (William Frederick) Case of Softening—ramollissement—of the Brain; with general observations . . . From the London Medical Gazette. pp. 21. *Wilson & Ogilvy: London,* 1851. 8°. **7306**. bb. **15**. (**6**.)

—— On Fatty Degeneration. pp. 92. *John Churchill: London,* 1853. 12°. **7406**. b. **5**.

—— Remarks on Animal Magnetism. pp. 16. [*London,* 1838.] 8°. **7410**. c. **36**. (**2**.)

BARLOW (William Hagger) *Dean of Peterborough. See* Barlow (Margaret) The Life of William Hagger Barlow, *etc.* [With portraits.] 1910. 8°. **4902**. df. **16**.

—— *See* Greenup (A. W.) William Hagger Barlow, D.D. [1908.] 8°. **4902**. f. **43**.

—— [A funeral sermon.] *See* Anderson (David) *Bishop of Rupert's Land.* Faithful and Fruitful. Two sermons . . . preached . . . after the funeral of the Rev. William Bruce, *etc.* 1872. 8°. **4478**. cc. **3**. (**9**.)

BARLOW (William Henry) *Barrister-at-Law.* The Celestial Writing; or, the Normal Script Phonetic Writing . . . Founded on a modified form of Gabelsberger, *etc.* pp. 15. *Eyre & Spottiswoode: London,* 1894. fol. **12991**. k. **5**. *The text is lithographed.*

—— Normal Phonography. Adapted to all styles of reporting, *etc.* pp. 115. *J. B. Lippincott Co.: Philadelphia,* 1886. 8°. **12991**. c. **19**.

BARLOW (William Henry) *Civil Engineer. See* Barlow (Peter) A Treatise on the Strength of Materials . . . A new edition. Revised by . . . W. H. Barlow, *etc.* 1867. 8°. **8765**. dd. **28**.

—— An Analytical Investigation of the Board of Trade Returns of the Capital and Revenue of Railways in the United Kingdom. pp. 48. *Effingham Wilson: London,* 1868. 8°. **8235**. f. **43**. (**6**.)

—— [Another copy.] An Analytical Investigation, *etc. London,* 1868. 8°. **8236**. m. **4**. (**9**.)

—— Description to Diagrams for facilitating the construction of Oblique Bridges. pp. 6. [*London,* 1855?] 4°. **8766**. e. **25**. (**1**.)

—— [Another edition.] *See* Buck (George W.) A Practical and Theoretical . . . Essay on Oblique Bridges, *etc.* 1857. 8°. **786**. l. **42**.

—— [Another edition.] *See* Buck (George W.) A Practical and Theoretical Essay on Oblique Bridges, *etc.* 1880. 8°. **8768**. e. **7**.

BARLOW (William Henry) *M.D.* On Regressive Paralysis, infantile paralysis, spinal paralysis of adults. pp. 88. *J. E. Cornish: Manchester,* 1878. 8°. **7306**. bb. **11**. (**4**.)

BARLOW (William Ruxton) Notes on Ammunition. [By W. R. Barlow.] pp. 108. 1872. 8°. *See* England.—*Army.—Regulations and Orders.*—ii. *Ammunition.* **8829**. h. **17**.

—— Fourth edition, *etc.* pp. 135. 1877. 8°. *See* England.—*Army.—Regulations and Orders.*—ii. *Ammunition.* **8831**. i. **2**.

—— Treatise on Ammunition. [By W. R. Barlow. A revised edition of "Ammunition" by V. D. Majendie & C. O. Browne.] (Errata and Addenda . . . Corrected up to and including September 1878.) 2 pt. 1874, 75. 8°. *See* England.—*Army.—Regulations and Orders.*—ii. *Ammunition.* **8830**. i. **27**.

BARLOW (WILLIAM RUXTON)

—— [Another edition.] Corrected up to December, 1877 [by J. P. Cundill]. pp. xxxvi. 363. 1878. 8°. *See* ENGLAND.—*Army.—Regulations and Orders.*—II. *Ammunition.* **8821**. d. **28**.

BARLOW (WILLIAM SMYTH) The Good old Bury Simnel: being an attempt to trace the origin and history of an ancient custom celebrated in Bury annually on Mid-Lent Sunday. pp. x. 80. *W. S. Barlow: Bury,* 1892. 4°. **12431**. a. **35**.

BARLOWE (ARTHUR)

—— Captain Arthur Barlowe's Narrative of the first Voyage made to the coasts of America by two ships . . . commanded by Philip Amadas and A. Barlowe . . . in the year 1584, *etc.* *See* BRY (T. de) [America.—Part I, II.—*English.*] The New World, *etc.* 1946. 4°. Dept. of Prints & Drawings.

BARLOWE (FRANCIS) *See* BARLOW.

BARLOWE (JEROME) [For editions of "Rede me and be nott wrothe," a satire against Cardinal Wolsey, by William Roy, with the collaboration of J. Barlowe:] *See* ROY (William) *Franciscan Friar.*

BARLOWE (MARIA) The History of Miss Maria Barlowe. In a series of letters. 2 vol. *Fielding & Walker: London,* 1777. 12°. **12612**. ccc. **12**.

BARLOWE (RALEIGH)

—— *See* JOHNSON (Vernon W.) and BARLOWE (R.) Land Problems and Policies. 1954. 8°. **7082**. b. **9**.

BARLOWE (SY)

—— A Child's Book of Stars. *Publicity Products: London,* [1954.] 8°. [*Florin Colour Books.* no. 6.] W.P. A. **531** 6.

BARLOWE (THOMAS) successively *Bishop of Rochester* and *of Lincoln.* *See* BARLOW.

BARLOWE (WILLIAM) *Archdeacon of Salisbury.* *See* BARLOW.

BARLOWE (WILLIAM) successively *Bishop of Saint Asaph, of Saint David's, of Bath and Wells,* and *of Chichester.* *See* BARLOW.

BARLOWUS (GULIELMUS) *See* BARLOW (William) successively *Bishop of Rochester* and *of Lincoln.*

BARLOW VON WENTZEL (GRACE) *See* WENTZEL (Grace Barlow von)

BARLTROP (*Mrs.* ARTHUR HENRY) *See* BARLTROP (Mabel)

BARLTROP (MABEL) *See* also BESMA, *pseud.* [i.e. M. Barltrop.]

—— *See* also OCTAVIA, *pseud.* [i.e. M. Barltrop].

—— How to Speak and what to say . . . Together with twelve addresses to working women. pp. v. 86. *Wells Gardner & Co.: London,* 1903. 16°. **4499**. de. **13**.

—— Third and revised edition. pp. v. 86. *Wells Gardner & Co.: London,* [1911.] 8°. **4499**. de. **36**.

BÄRLUND (HUGO)

—— *See* COLLANDER (R.) and BÄRLUND (H.) Über die Protoplasmapermeabilität von Rhoeo discolor, *etc.* 1927. 8°. [*Societas Scientiarum Fennica. Commentationes biologicae.* tom. 2. no. 9.] Ac. **1094**. (2.)

BARLUZZI (ANTONIO)

—— *See* JERUSALEM.—*Church of the Holy Sepulchre.* Santo Sepolcro di Gerusalemme, *etc.* [By L. H. Vincen A. Barluzzi and others.] 1949. fol. **7823**. dd. 1

BARLUZZI (GIULIO) De Pontificia Pompa ad Vaticanur in festo Sacrosancti Corporis D. N. Iesu commentarius Editio altera. pp. 52. *Romae,* 1847. 8°. **3478**. h. **27**. (1

—— Elogio storico del cavaliere L. Armellini. (Estratt dall' Album.) pp. 26. *Roma,* 1842. 8°. **10602**. h. **13**. (5.

—— Relazione storica del viaggio di Sua Santità Papa Pio I da Portici a Roma nell' aprile dell' anno 1850. pp. 95. *Roma,* 1850. 8°. **8033**. bb. **41**. (9.

BARLYAEV (K. M.) and **ALEKSEEV** (S. N.)

—— Бетононасосы. pp. 110. *Москва,* 1953. 8°. **08774**. ff.

BARMA (HUGINUS À) Saturnia Regna S. M. T. F. P. i aurea sæcula conversa: id est, Magisterium seu Aqu Sapientum hactenus occultatum, nunc . . . per posi tiones hermeticas jurispublici factum, adjuncto suo lapid Lydio & praxi facillima impensis D. H. à Barma. [Wit plates.] pp. 168. MS. NOTES. [*The Author:*] *Parisiis* 1657. 12°. **1036**. a. **16**. (2.

—— [Another edition.] Nunc secundò prælo commissum cum figuris. [With a preface signed: Pe. Th. An . . . . . pp. 167. *Parisiis,* 1779. 12°. **8630**. b. **5**. (1.

—— Le Règne de Saturne, changé en siècle d'or, S. M. I. S. P. ou le magistère des sages . . . Le tout traduit du lati d'H. à Barmâ, par Mr. Pi. Th. An . . . . . Avec figures pp. 192. *Paris,* 1780. 12°. **8630**. b. **5**. (2.

—— Tractatus III. Saturnia Regna, *etc.* (Saturnisches Reich Magisterium oder Wasser der Weisen.) *Ger.* *See* TAEDA Tæda trifida chimica, das ist: Dreyfache chimisch Fackel, *etc.* 1674. 8°. **1033**. c. 5

BARMA (ISAN CHUNDRA KUNAR) *See* ĪṢĀNACHANDR. KUNĀR VARMĀ.

BARMA (MATHURA NATH) *See* MATHURĀNĀTHA VARMĀ.

BARMACK (JOSEPH EPHRAIM)

—— Boredom and other Factors in the Physiology of Ment Effort: an exploratory study. pp. 83. *New York* 1937. 8°. [*Archives of Psychology.* no. 218.] P.P. **1247**. g

BARMAID PROBLEM. The Barmaid Problem. pp. 7 *Joint Committee on the Employment of Barmaids: London* [1904.] 8°. **8415**. e. **56**

BARMAN ALPHABET. *See* BURMESE ALPHABET.

BARMAN (CHRISTIAN) *See* GIBBS (James) *Architect.* Th Rules for Drawing the Several Parts of Architecture . . With an introduction by C. Barman. [1924.] 8°. **07816**. c. **40**

—— Architecture. pp. 80. *London,* 1928. 8°. [*Benn' Sixpenny Library.* no. 67.] **12199**. c. **1/67**

—— Balbus, or the future of architecture. pp. 80. *Kegan Paul & Co.: London,* [1926.] 8°. [*To-day an To-morrow.*] **012201**. a. **1/38**

—— The Bridge. A chapter in the history of building Illustrated . . . by Frank Brangwyn, *etc.* pp. xvii. 249 *John Lane: London; Dodd, Mead & Co.: New York* 1926. 4°. **07815**. i. **26**
One of 125 *copies printed on hand-made paper, with two additional illustrations.*

BARMAN (Christian)

—— The Danger to Saint Paul's. pp. 159. *Jonathan Cape: London*, 1925. 8°. **07815.** g. **15.**

—— Early British Railways, *etc.* pp. 39. pl. 16. *Penguin Books: Harmondsworth*, 1950. 8°. [*King Penguin Books.* no. 56.] **12208.a.4/56.**

—— An Introduction to Railway Architecture. [With illustrations.] pp. 104. *Art & Technics: London*, 1950. 8°. [*Introductions to Architecture.*] W.P. **2251**/6.

—— Next Station. A railway plans for the future. [With illustrations.] pp. vi. 113. *George Allen & Unwin: London*, 1947. 4°. **8218.** c. **17.**

—— Public Transport. pp. 64. *Penguin Books: Harmondsworth*, [1949.] 4°. [*The Things We See.* no. 5.] W.P. **2117**/5.

—— Sir John Vanbrugh, *etc.* [With plates.] pp. 27. *Ernest Benn: London*, 1924. 8°. [*Masters of Architecture.*] **07815.aaa.15/3.**

BARMAN (Mani Charan) *See* Maṇicharaṇa Varman.

BARMAN (Maurice) La Contre-Révolution en Valais au mois de mai 1844. pp. 51. *Vevey*, 1844. 8°. **9305.** d. **6.**

BARMAN (Ole)

—— Ein Mann gjekk heim, *etc.* pp. 163. *Oslo*, 1933. 8°. **012584.aaa.11.**

BARMAN (Satyabhushan) *See* Satyabhūshaṇa Varman.

BARMAN (T. G.)

—— *See* Cook (Thomas) and Son. [*Guide Books.—Belgium.*] Guide to Belgium & Luxembourg . . . Edited by T. G. Barman and J. de Geynst, *etc.* 1938. 8°. **10271.** aa. **46.**

—— *See* Cook (Thomas) and Son. [*Guide Books.—Scandinavia.*] Cook's Traveller's Handbook to Norway, Sweden, Denmark, Finland, Iceland. Sixteenth edition. Completely revised by T. G. Barman, *etc.* 1936. 8°. **010281.** de. **32.**

—— —— 1939. 8°. **10281.** a. **65.**

BARMANI. *See* Burmese.

BÄRMANN ( ) [For the German surname of this form:] *See* Baermann.

BARMARCIN (A.) Kacerska sekta mankietników, jej początek i odstępstwo od kościoła. pp. 71. *Warszawa*, 1906. 8°. **4535.** f. 2. (2.)

BARMAT (Louis Isaak)

—— De Regel "Locus regit actum" in het internationaal privaatrecht. Proefschrift, *etc.* pp. xvi. 396. *Amsterdam*, 1936. 8°. **06916.** l. **51.**
With a review extracted from the "Rechtsgeleerd Magazijn."

BARMBY (Beatrice)

—— Betty Marchand. [A novel.] pp. 318. *G. H. Doran Co.: New York*, [1918.] 8°. N.N. **6367.**

—— Sunrise from the Hill-Top. pp. 308. *G. H. Doran Co.: New York*, [1919.] 8°. N.N. **6351.**

BARMBY (Beatrice Helen)

—— Gísli Súrsson: a drama; ballads and poems of the old Norse days, and some translations . . . With a preface by F. York Powell, *etc.* pp. xxiv. 206. *A. Constable & Co.: London*, 1900. 8°. **011651.** ee. **58.**

BARMBY (Beatrice Helen)

—— The Gods are Just. [A novel.] pp. 374. *Duckworth & Co.: London*, 1904. 8°. **012628.** d. **26.**

—— Poems. pp. 240. *A. Constable & Co.: Westminster*, 1903. 8°. **011651.** ee. **113.**

—— Rosslyn's Raid, and other tales. pp. 232. *Duckworth & Co.: London*, 1903. 8°. [*Greenback Library.* no. 6.] **12201.** d. **52**/6.

BARMBY (Cuthbert) James Cope . . . [A novel.] Illustrated, *etc.* pp. 329. *Ward, Lock & Co.: London*, [1899.] 8°. **012643.** g. **44.**

BARMBY (Goodwyn) *See* Periodical Publications.—*London.* The Promethean; or Communitarian Apostle . . . By G. Barmby. 1842. 4°. P.P. **3391.** b.

—— Aids to Devotion; or, Religious readings in the order of the natural and the Christian year. pp. vii. 239. *Whitfield, Green & Son: London*, 1865. 8°. **4410.** ccc. **5.**

—— New Tracts for the Times; or, Warmth, light, and food for the masses. Bible proofs from Isaiah against Jesus Christ's being the Messiah. [By G. Barmby.] no. 1. vol. 1. [1842?] 8°. *See* Tracts. **4016.** bb. **37.** (1.)

—— The Poetry of Childhood: a poem. pp. 29. *William Tweedie: London*, 1852. 8°. **11647.** b. **62.**

—— The Poetry of Home: a poem, *etc.* pp. 52. *William Tweedie: London*, 1853. 8°. **11647.** b. **40.**

—— The Poetry of Spring. A poem. pp. 47. *William Tweedie: London*, 1860. 8°. **11651.** b. **56.** (5.)

—— The Return of the Swallow, and other poems. pp. x. 73. *Simpkin, Marshall & Co.: London*, 1864. 8°. **11651.** aa. **16.**

BARMBY (Henry) Short Hand unmask'd, or an easy elegant character illustrated and explain'd, *etc.* [With plates.] pp. 19. *The Author: London*, [1772.] 8°. **7942.** g. **16.**

BARMBY (James) *See* Gregory i., *Saint, surnamed the Great, Pope.* The Book of Pastoral Rule and Selected Epistles of Gregory the Great . . . Translated . . . by . . . J. Barmby. 1895. 8°. [*Nicene & Post-Nicene Fathers.* vol. 12.] **3606.f.1/12.**

—— *See* Pittington. Churchwardens' Accounts of Pittington and other parishes in the diocese of Durham, from A.D. 1580 to 1700. [Edited by J. Barmby.] 1888. 8°. R. Ac. **3045/64.**

—— *See* Saint Giles, *Durham, Parish of.* Memorials of St. Giles's, Durham, *etc.* [Edited by J. Barmby.] 1896. 8°. R. Ac. **8045/73.**

—— *See* Spence, *afterwards* Spence-Jones (Henry D. M.) and Exell (J. S.) The Pulpit Commentary, *etc.* (Hebrews. Exposition by . . . J. Barmby.) 1880, *etc.* 8°. **3130.d.1/54.**

—— *See* Spence, *afterwards* Spence-Jones (Henry D. M.) and Exell (J. S.) The Pulpit Commentary, *etc.* (Romans. Exposition by . . . J. Barmby.) 1880, *etc.* 8°. **3131.d.1/43.**

—— *See* Williams (Thomas I.) The Visions of S. Paul . . . Gregory's Letter to John of Constantinople, *etc.* (Trans. by Rev. J. Barmby.) [1921.] 8°. **03265.** ee. **29.**

BARMBY (James)

—— Gregory the Great. pp. 207. *S.P.C.K.: London; Pott, Young & Co.: New York*, 1879. 8°. [*The Fathers for English Readers.*] **4421. a. 42.**

—— [Another edition.] pp. 207. *S.P.C.K.: London & Brighton*, 1892. 8°. [*The Fathers for English Readers.*] **4421. a. 51.**

—— Plays for Young People, with songs and choruses, suitable for private theatricals, *etc.* [With musical notes.] pp. vi. 208. *S. Tinsley & Co.: London; Andrews & Co.: Durham*, 1879. 8°. **11781. g. 12.**

—— A Sermon preached in the Parish Church of Houghton-le-Spring . . . March 24, 1867. pp. 32. *William Skeffington: London*, 1867. 12°. **4477. aa. 135. (14.)**

BARMEN.—*Evangelische Gesellschaft für die protestantischen Deutschen in Amerika*, afterwards *Evangelische Gesellschaft für die protestantischen Deutschen in Süd-Amerika.*

—— Der deutsche Ansiedler. Organ der evangelischen Gesellschaft, *etc.* *See* Berlin.—*Berliner Verein für die ausgewanderten Deutschen der evangelischen Kirche im Westen Nordamerika's, etc.* Der Ansiedler im Westen, *etc.*

—— *Missions - Gesellschaft.* Das Missions - Blatt. Herausgegeben von der Missions-Gesellschaft zu Barmen. Jahrg. 1–76. *Barmen*, 1826–1901. 4°. **P.P. 953. b.**

—— *Progymnasium.* Jahresbericht über die Realschule . . . und das Progymnasium, *etc.* 1863. 4°. *See* infra: *Realschule.* **12901. k. 36. (1.)**

—— *Realschule.* Jahresbericht über die Realschule . . . und das Progymnasium zu Barmen . . . Inhalt: 1. Ueber den Einflusz der Metapher auf die Entwicklung der Sprache. Von Dr. A. Burmester. 2. Schulnachrichten. 3. Ordnung der öffentlichen Prüfung. pp. 45. *Barmen*, 1863. 4°. **12901. k. 36. (1.)**

—— *Staedtische Bibliothek.* Catalog der Städtischen Bibliothek zu Barmen. pp. 98. *Barmen*, 1873. 8°. **11903. b. 2.**

—— *Wohlfahrtzentrale.* Wohlfahrtzentrale der Stadt Barmen. Ihr Wesen und bisheriges Wirken. Bericht, erstattet von . . . Paul Heumann. [With plates and illustrations.] pp. 179. *Barmen*, 1917. 4°. **8285. f. 58.**

BARMER BEKENNTNISSYNODE. *See* Germany.—*Evangelical Church.*

BARMIN (Aleksandr)

—— Memoirs of a Soviet Diplomat. Twenty years in the service of the U.S.S.R. . . . Translated by Gerard Hopkins. [With plates, including portraits.] pp. xvi. 360. *Lovat Dickson: London*, 1938. 8°. **10796. dd. 3.**

—— Vingt ans au service de l'U.R.S.S. Souvenirs d'un diplomate soviétique. Traduction française de Victor Serge. [With portraits.] pp. 382. *Paris*, 1939. 8°. **10797. b. 2.**

BARMINE (Alexander) *See* Barmin (Aleksandr)

BARMM (Rudolph) Deutsche und englische Industrie auf dem Weltmarkte. Eine handelsstatistische Untersuchung über das Jahr 1913, *etc.* pp. vi. 45. *Jena*, 1916. 8°. [*Kriegswirtschaftliche Untersuchungen aus dem Institut für Seeverkehr und Weltwirtschaft an der Universität Kiel.* Hft. 9.] **Ac. 1030/10.**

BARMOND (C. F. Perrotin de) *Abbé.* *See* Perrotin de Barmond.

BARMONDIÈRE (François Bottu de La) *Seigneur de Saint Fonds* and *de Limas.* *See* Bottu de La Barmondière.

BARMONT (Perrotin de) *See* Perrotin de Barmond.

BARMPA-PANTZELIOS.

—— *Κρητικαι ῥιμαι. Τα τραγουδια Δασκαλογιαννη* [by Barmpa-Pantzelios] *και Ἀλῃδακῃ* [transcribed by G. Pateros]. *Ἐκδιδονται ὑπο Ἐ. Βαρδιδη.* pp. 62. *ἐν Ἀθηναις*, 1888. 8°. **11586. bbb. 20. (2.)**

—— *Το Τραγουδι του Δασκαλογιαννη. Εἰσαγωγη, σχολια Βας. Λαουρδα. Χαρτογραφια: Κωνστ. Λαστθιωτακη.* [With a map.] pp. 64. *Ἡρακλειον*, 1947. 8°. **11410. b. 64**

BARMSTEDT, *Family of.* *See* Haupt (Richard) *Ph.D.* Haus Barmstedt, *etc.* 1918. 8°. [*Quellen und Forschungen zur Geschichte Schleswig-Holsteins.* Bd. 6.] **Ac. 7638/7.**

BARMUDAS. *See* Bermuda.

BARMWATER (Ferdinand)

—— Lærebog i mekanisk Fysik, Varme og Elektricitet, *etc.* pp. 245. *København*, 1894. 8°. **8707. g. 26**

BARN. The Barn and the Steeple. [A satirical dialogue on the Established Church and Dissent. By Jefferys Taylor.] pp. vi. 197. *B. J. Holdsworth: London*, 1828. 12°. **4106. cc. 1**

BARN-OWL, *Mr.* Four Feet by Two. Animal Talks and Tales. By Mr. Barn Owl . . . and other animal writers [Written by Edric Vredenburg and others. With Illustrations.] pp. 72. *E. Nister: London; Nuremberg* [printed, 1892.] 4°. **012803. h. 23**

BARN THEATRE STUDIO. *See* Sonning.

BARNA, *da Siena.*

—— *See* Hodges (Margaret A.) Die Fresken von Barna da Siena in San Gimignano, *etc.* 1938. 8°. **7863. ppp. 57.**

BARNA, *Mesté.*

—— Mesté Barna, marchand de vin ei grands carmés . . . Comédie en un acte et en vers provençaux, par Mr. C*****, de Marseille [i.e. — Carvin]. 1809. 8°. *See* C*****, *Mr., de Marseille.* **1343. g. 16. (1.)**

BARNA (Endre) Románia nemzetiségi politikája és a oláhajkú magyar polgárok . . . Dákó-Románia hivatalos térképével. pp. xi. 186. *Kolozsvár*, 1908. 8°. **08072. bb. 13**

BARNA (Ferdinánd) *See* Kalevala. Kalevala . . . A eredetiből fordította Barna F. 1871. 8°. **11585. i. 10**

—— *See* Martius (G.) Jellemvonások Mátyás Király életé ből . . . Fordítá: Barna N. 1862. 8°. **10706. cc. 48. (4.)**

—— Egy szavazat a nyelvujitás ügyében. pp. 88. *Budapest* 1877. 8°. [*Magyar Tudományos Akadémia. Értekezések a nyelv- és széptudományi osztály köréből.* köt. 7. sz. 1.] **Ac. 825/20**

—— A finn költészetről tekintettel a magyar ősköltészetre pp. 153 [135]. *Pesten*, 1872. 8°. [*Magyar Tudományos Akadémia. Értekezések a nyelv- és széptudományi osztály köréből.* köt. 3. sz. 6.] **Ac. 825/20**

—— A hangsúlyról a magyar nyelvben. pp. 48. *Budapest* 1875. 8°. [*Magyar Tudományos Akadémia. Értekezések a nyelv- és széptudományi osztály köréből.* köt. 5. sz. 3.] **Ac. 825/20**

BARNA (FERDINÁND)

—— A határozott és határozatlan mondatról. pp. 31. *Budapest*, 1874. 8°. [*Magyar Tudományos Akadémia. Értekezések a nyelv- és széptudományi osztály köréből.* köt. 4. sz. 4.] Ac. **825/20.**

—— Az ik- és igékről. pp. 33. *Budapest*, 1875. 8°. [*Magyar Tudományos Akadémia. Értekezések a nyelv- és széptudományi osztály köréből.* köt. 4. sz. 9.] Ac. **825/20.**

—— Kapcsolat a magyar és szuomi irodalom között. pp. 17. *Budapest*, 1878. 8°. [*Magyar Tudományos Akadémia. Értekezések a nyelv- és széptudományi osztály köréből.* köt. 7. sz. 4.] Ac. **825/20.**

—— A mordva nép házassági szokásai. pp. 56. *Budapest*, 1887. 8°. [*Magyar Tudományos Akadémia. Értekezések a nyelv- és széptudományi osztály köréből.* köt. 14. sz. 3.] Ac. **825/20.**

—— A mordvaiak pogány istenei és ünnepi szertartásai. pp. 84. *Budapest*, 1879. 8°. [*Magyar Tudományos Akadémia. Értekezések a nyelv- és széptudományi osztály köréből.* köt. 8. sz. 2.] Ac. **825/20.**

—— A mordvaiak történelmi viszontagságai. pp. 40. *Budapest*, 1877. 8°. [*Magyar Tudományos Akadémia. Értekezések a nyelv- és széptudományi osztály köréből.* köt. 6. sz. 8.] Ac. **825/20.**

—— A mutató névmás hibás használata. pp. 15. *Budapest*, 1876. 8°. [*Magyar Tudományos Akadémia. Értekezések a nyelv- és széptudományi osztály köréből.* köt. 5. sz. 8.] Ac. **825/20.**

—— Néhány ősműveltségi tárgy neve a magyarban. pp. 54. *Budapest*, 1878. 8°. [*Magyar Tudományos Akadémia. Értekezések a nyelv- és széptudományi osztály köréből.* köt. 7. sz. 5.] Ac. **825/20.**

—— Nyelvészkedő hajlamok a magyar népnél, *etc.* pp. 40. *Budapest*, 1875. 8°. [*Magyar Tudományos Akadémia. Értekezések a nyelv- és széptudományi osztály köréből.* köt. 5. sz. 1.] Ac. **825/20.**

—— Ősvallásunk főistenei. pp. 71. *Budapest*, 1881. 8°. [*Magyar Tudományos Akadémia. Értekezések a nyelv- és széptudományi osztály köréből.* köt. 9. sz. 7.] Ac. **825/20.**

—— Ősvallásunk kisebb isteni lényei, és áldozati szertartásai. pp. 48. *Budapest*, 1881. 8°. [*Magyar Tudományos Akadémia. Értekezések a nyelv- és széptudományi osztály köréből.* köt. 9. sz. 9.] Ac. **825/20.**

—— Vámbéry Ármin " A Magyarok eredete " czímü műve néhány főbb állitásának birálata. pp. 98. *Budapest*, 1884. 8°. [*Magyar Tudományos Akadémia. Értekezések a nyelv- és széptudományi osztály köréből.* köt. 11. sz. 10.] Ac. **825/20.**

—— A votják nép multja és jelene. pp. 43. *Budapest*, 1885. 8°. [*Magyar Tudományos Akademia. Értekezések a nyelv- és széptudományi osztály köréből.* köt. 13. sz. 2.] Ac. **825/20.**

—— A votjákok pogány vallásáról. pp. 37. *Budapest*, 1885. 8°. [*Magyar Tudományos Akademia. Értekezések a nyelv- és széptudományi osztály köréből.* köt. 13. sz. 5.] Ac. **825/20.**

BARNA (G. V.)

—— Table Tennis. A book of instructional hints on the game. [With illustrations, including portraits.] pp. 18. *Walford & Son : Buckingham*, [1935.] 8°. **7915.** p. **49.**

BARNA (IGNÁCZ) *See* JUVENALIS (D. J.) [*Satirae.—Latin and Hungarian.*] D. Junii Juvenalis Satirae. In Hungaricum convertit et notis illustravit I. Barna. 1876. 8°. **11386.** h. **8.**

—— *See* VERGILIUS MARO (P.) [*Aeneis.—Hungarian.*] P. Vergilius Maro Æneise. Forditotta . . . Dr. Barna I., *etc.* 1890. 8°. Ac. **825/123.**

—— A rómaiak satirájáról és satira iróikról. Székfoglaló. pp. 36. *Budapest*, 1876 [1877]. 8°. [*Magyar Tudományos Akadémia. Értekezések a nyelv- és széptudományi osztály köréből.* köt. 6. sz. 3.] Ac. **825/20.**

BARNA (LEANDER) VII. Gergely egyházpolitikai viszonyai és reformtörekvései. pp. 174. *Budapest*, 1903. 8°. **4570.** dd. **7.**

BARNA (NÁNDOR) *See* BARNA (Ferdinánd)

BARNA (TIBOR)

—— Profits during and after the War. pp. 25. *Fabian Publications; Victor Gollancz: London*, [1945.] 8°. [*Fabian Society. Research Series.* no. 105.] W.P. **10405/105.**

—— Redistribution of Incomes through Public Finance in 1937. pp. xi. 289. *Clarendon Press: Oxford*, 1945. 8°. **8288.** cc. **88.**

BARNA (VICTOR) *See* BARNA (G. V.)

BARNABA, *da Caprile, Capuchin.* Predica del peccato veniale.—Predica della necessità della penitenza. Predica I. della predestinazione.—Predica II. della riprovazione. 1855. *See* HOUDRY (V.) Biblioteca de' predicatori, *etc.* vol. 11. 1844, *etc.* 4°. **4498.1.5/11.**

—— Predica della santificazione delle feste. 1847. *See* HOUDRY (V.) Biblioteca de' predicatori, *etc.* vol. 5. 1844, *etc.* 4°. **4498.1.5/5.**

—— Predica delle tribolazioni. 1844. *See* HOUDRY (V.) Biblioteca de' predicatori, *etc.* vol. 1. 1844, *etc.* 4°. **4498.1.5/1.**

BARNABA, *da Genova, Capuchin.* La Libertà incatenata. Discorso fatto nella sala dell' Eccellentiss. Senato di Lucca, *etc.* pp. 16. *I. Paci: Lucca*, 1675. 4°. **4424.** dd. **2.** (**15.**)

BARNABA, *da S. Niccola, Augustinian* [GIOVANNI VITTA]. Copia dell' elogio posto dentro la cassa di Fr. Barnaba da S. Niccola, *etc.* [With a portrait.] *Lat. & Ital. Roma*, 1790. 4°. **1897.** b. **7.** (**12.**)

BARNABÀ, *Saint. See* BARNABAS.

BARNABÀ (DOMENICO) Da 17 marzo a 14 ottobre, 1848. Ricordi . . . Seconda edizione riveduta e corretta dall'autore. pp. 205. *S. Vito al Tagliamento*, 1891. 8°. **9166.** f. **10.**

BARNABA (FRANCISCUS) Eenige oude reliquien die de Catholijcken by dese nieuwe Herstellinge, in den Dom van Uytrecht wederom opgezocht en te voorschijn gebracht hebben . . . Tot troost aller gehoorsame Catholijcken . . . opgeteeckent door d'Eerw. Pater F. Barnaba. [A satire.] *H. Sweerts: Amsterdam*, 1673. *s. sh.* fol. **8079.** l. **3.** (**24.**)

BARNABAS [VISCONTI], *Duke of Milan. See* DATI (G.) Novelle . . . intorno a Messer Bernabò Visconti, Duca di Milano. 1877. 8°. **12471.** g. **9.**

—— *See* ROFFIA (G.) Ghiribizzi di Mess. Bernabò Visconti, *etc.* 1868. 8°. **12330.** bbb. **43.** (**6.**)

BARNABAS, *pseud.*

—— Christian Witness in Communist China. pp. 79. *SCM Press: London*, 1951. 8°. **4767.** ff. **32.**

BARNABAS, *pseud.*

—— Christian Witness in Communist China. (Second edition.) pp. 79. *SCM Press: London*, 1952. 8°.
4768. bb. **51**.

—— False Charges refuted; or, the Atonement viewed in relation to its objects. [Signed: Barnabas.] pp. 7. *J. F. Shaw & Co.: London*, 1872. 8°.
4227. a. **36**.

BARNABAS, *Saint.* [For editions of, and works on, the "Epistle of Barnabas," formerly attributed to Saint Barnabas:] *See* BARNABAS, *Writer of the "Epistle of Barnabas."*

—— [For editions of the Epistle to the Hebrews, sometimes attributed to Saint Barnabas:] *See* BIBLE.—*Hebrews.*

ACTS OF BARNABAS.

—— [For editions of the Acts of Barnabas contained in editions of the collection known as the Apocryphal Acts of the Apostles, or in editions of two or more books thereof:] *See* APOSTLES. [*Apocrypha.—Acts.*]

—— *Περιοδοι και μαρτυριον του άγιου Βαρναβα του ἀποστολου.* (Acta Barnabae auctore Marco [i.e. falsely attributed to St. Mark].) *Gr. See* TISCHENDORF (L. F. C.) Acta Apostolorum apocrypha, *etc.* 1851. 8°.
3020. d. **11**.

—— The Acts of Barnabas. The journeyings and martyrdom of St. Barnabas the Apostle. 1870. *See* ROBERTS (Alexander) *D.D.*, and DONALDSON (*Sir* James) *Principal, etc.* Ante-Nicene Christian Library, *etc.* vol. 16. 1867, *etc.* 8°.
3628.bb.1/16.

GOSPEL OF BARNABAS.

—— De Evangelio Mohammedanis probato, & illo quod fertur sub nomine S. Barnabæ Apostoli. (De Evangelio Barnabæ quod MS. exstat Italice in Bibliotheca . . . Sabaudiæ Ducis Eugenii . . . ex illo loca quædam . . . cum Latina versione.) *See* FABRICIUS (J. A.) Codex apocryphus Novi Testamenti, *etc.* tom. 3. 1719. 8°.
3226. de. **10**.

—— The Gospel of Barnabas. Edited and translated from the Italian MS. in the Imperial Library at Vienna by Lonsdale and Laura Ragg. With a facsimile. pp. lxxvi. 500. *Clarendon Press: Oxford*, 1907. 8°.
3623. f. **6**.

APPENDIX.

—— *See* BRAUNSBERGER (O.) Der Apostel Barnabas. Sein Leben und der ihm beigelegte Brief wissenschaftlich gewürdigt. 1876. 8°. **4808**. i. **3**.

—— *See* MURIANTHEUS (K.) *Ἀποστολος Βαρναβας ὁ ἱδρυτης της ἐκκλησιας της Κυπρου.* [1942.] 16°. **04808**. e. **15**.

—— *See* PAUL, *Saint and Apostle.* Paul and Barnabas. A tract for the times. 1854. 8°. **4108**. a. **28**.

—— *See* PUCCINELLI (P.) Vita di S. Barnaba Apostolo, primo pastore di Milano, *etc.* [1649.] 4°. **4827**. e. **22**.

—— *See* QUICK (Muriel) The Story of Barnabas. 1950. 8°.
4804. ee. **20**.

—— *See* RYLEY (George B.) Barnabas; or, the Great Renunciation. 1893. 8°. **4808**. aaa. **27**.

—— *See* SALĪM 'ABD AL-AḤAD, and GAIRDNER (W. H. T.) The Gospel of Barnabas: an essay and inquiry. 1908. 8°.
03128. g. **83**. (**3**.)

BARNABAS, *Saint.*

—— *See* SOTERIOU (G. A.) *Ὁ ναος και ὁ ταφος του Ἀποστολου Βαρναβα παρα την Σαλαμινα της Κυπρου, etc.* 1937. 8°. **20014**. bb. **19**.

—— *See* TOLAND (John) Nazarenus, or, Jewish, Gentile, and Mahometan Christianity. Containing the history of the ancient Gospel of Barnabas, and the modern Gospel of the Mahometans, attributed to the same Apostle, *etc.* 1718. 8°. **699**. d. **10**. (**2**.)

—— *See* WIESELER (C.G.) Eine Untersuchung über den Hebräerbrief, namentlich seinen Verfasser [here identified with Saint Barnabas], *etc.* 1861. 8°. **3266**. dd. **34**.

—— Baptismal Vows; or, the Feast of S. Barnabas. pp. 90. *Joseph Masters: London*, 1866. 16°. **4415**. aa. **7**.

—— Life of S. Barnabas. A sketch for nurses. By S. E. A. pp. vii. 88. [1896.] 16°. *See* A., S. E. **4824**. a. **8**.

—— S. Barnabas' Day. June 11. [A tale.] pp. 16. *Joseph Masters: London; Mozleys: Derby*, 1852. 24°.
4415. a. **71**. (**10**.)

CHURCHES AND INSTITUTIONS.

—— The Building of St. Barnabas. A novel. 2 vol. *Chapman & Hall: London*, 1883. 8°. **12635**. t. **3**.

—— *London.—Church of St. Barnabas, Dulwich.* Parish Magazine . . . S. Barnabas, Dulwich. May, 1910. *Dulwich*, 1910. 8°. P.P. **343**. ie. (**6**.)

—— *London.—Church of St. Barnabas, South Kennington.* Report of the Subscriptions for the New Church and Schools of St. Barnabas, South Kennington, *etc.* pp. 44. *E. Billing & Son: Southwark*, 1851. 8°. **4135**. d. **3**.

—— *London.—Guild of St. Barnabas for Nurses.* Misericordia. (Monthly Paper of the Guild of St. Barnabas for Nurses.) *W. Knott: London*, [1883– .] 8°. **04192**. a.

—— *London.—St. Barnabas Hostels.* Gallipoli. Salonika. St. Barnabas, 1926. [Accounts of the pilgrimages. By various authors. With illustrations.] pp. 39. [*London*, 1927.] *obl.* 4°. **10077**. pp. **4**.

—— St. Barnabas Pilgrimages (Ypres—The Somme) 1923. [With illustrations.] pp. 39. *London*, [1924.] *obl.* 8°.
9081. c. **10**.

SWINDON.—*Church of St. Barnabas.*

—— A History of St. Barnabas' Church, Swindon. Diamond Jubilee Year 1886–1946. [With illustrations.] pp. 20. *British Publishing Co.: Gloucester*, [1946.] 8°.
07822. aaa. **11**.

BARNABAS, *Serbian Patriarch.* *See* VARNAVA, *Patriarch of Serbia.* [Petar Rosić.]

BARNABAS, *Writer of the "Epistle of Barnabas."*

Greek.

—— S. Barnabae epistola catholica. [The Latin text from chap. I. to chap. v. 7; the Greek text from chap. v. 7 to the end.] *See* HEFELE (C. J. von) *Bishop of Rottenburg.* Patrum Apostolicorum opera, *etc.* 1839. 8°.
1125. e. **2**.

—— [Another edition.] *See* HEFELE (C. J. von) *Bishop of Rottenburg.* Patrum Apostolicorum opera, *etc.* 1842. 8°.
3627. cc. **28**.

—— *Του Βαρναβα· Κλημεντος· Ἰγνατιου· Πολυκαρπου· και προς Διογνητον ἐπιστολαι.* The Epistles of Barnabas, Clement, Ignatius, Polycarp, and the Epistle to Diognetus: edited from the text of Hefele, with an introduction and notes, by Algernon Grenfell. [Chap. I—chap. v. 7 of the Epistle of Barnabas supplied from the Latin version.] *Gr.* pp. xiii. 161. *J. S. Crossley: Rugby; G. B. Whittaker & Co.: London,* 1844. 8°. **1109. a. 14.**

—— *Ἡ καθολικη του Βαρναβα ἐπιστολη.* [Chap I.—Chap. v. 7 in the Latin version.] *See* MURALT (E. von) Codex Novi Testamenti deutero-canonicus . . . Particula I. Barnabae et Clementis Romani epistolae. 1847. 16°. **3020. a. 12.**

—— *Βαρναβα ἐπιστολη.* [A facsimile.] *See* BIBLE. [*Greek.*] Bibliorum Codex Sinaiticus, *etc.* tom. 4. 1862. fol. **1702. d. 1.**

—— *Βαρναβα ἐπιστολη.* *See* BIBLE.—*New Testament.* [*Greek.*] Novum Testamentum Sinaiticum, *etc.* 1863. fol. **L.9.h.7.**

—— *Βαρναβα ἐπιστολη.* *See* GEBHARDT (O. von) Patrum Apostolicorum opera . . . Editio minor. 1877. 8°. **3622. bb. 3.**

—— Der Barnabasbrief kritisch untersucht von J. Weiss. [With the Greek text.] pp. 143. *Berlin,* 1888. 8°. **3805. bb. 7.**

—— *Βαρναβα ἐπιστολη.* *See* FUNK (F. X. von) Die apostolischen Väter, *etc.* 1901. 8°. [*Sammlung ausgewählter kirchen- und dogmengeschichtlicher Quellenschriften.* Reihe 2. Hft. 1.] **3622. c. 4/1a.**

—— *Βαρναβα ἐπιστολη.* 1911. *See* BIBLE. [*Greek.*] Codex Sinaiticus Petropolitanus. The New Testament, the Epistle of Barnabas . . . preserved in the Imperial Library of St. Petersburg, now reproduced in facsimile . . . With a description by K. Lake. vol. 1. 1911, *etc.* fol. **MS. Facs. 165.**

—— The Epistle of Barnabas. Edited by T. W. Crafer. pp. 32. *S.P.C.K.: London; Macmillan Co.: New York,* 1920. 8°. [*Texts for Students.* no. 14.] **W.P. 4683/14.**

—— [Epistle of Barnabas. The Greek text of Chap I.—Chap. v. 14. Edited by Gustav Volkmer.] pp. 21. *See* ZURICH.—*Universität Zurich.* Index lectionum in literarum Universitite Turicensi . . . habendarum. Praemissum est monumentum vetustatis Christianae ineditum, *etc.* 1864. 4°. **3627. dd. 9.**

—— Barnabae expositio duarum viarum. [Chap. 18–20 of the Epistle.] *Gr.* *See* FUNK (F. X. von) Doctrina duodecim Apostolorum, *etc.* 1887. 8°. **3623. aa. 18.**

Polyglott.

—— A Dissertation on the Epistle of S. Barnabas, including a discussion of its date and authorship. By the Rev. William Cunningham. Together with the Greek text, the Latin version, and a new English translation and commentary [by G. H. Rendall]. pp. cxvii. 130. *Macmillan & Co.: London,* 1877. 8°. **3267. c. 4.**

Greek and Latin.

—— *Ἡ φερομενη του ἁγιου Βαρναβα ἀποστολου ἐπιστολη καθολικη.* Sancti Barnabæ apostoli, vt fertur, epistola catholica . . . Hanc primum e tenebris eruit notisque & obseruationibus illustrauit . . . Hugo Menardus . . . Opus posthumum. [Edited by Luc D'Achery.] pp. 245. *S. Piget: Parisiis,* 1645. 4°. **849. i. 1.**

—— *Ἡ καθολικη του Βαρναβα ἐπιστολη.* Catholica Barnabæ epistola. [Edited, with notes, by Isaac Vossius.] *In:* IGNATIUS, *Saint, Bishop of Antioch.* Epistolæ genuinæ, *etc.* pp. 207–254. 1646. 4°. **1476. bb. 40.**

—— Sancti Barnabæ Apostoli epistola catholica. [The Greek version from chap. v. 7; the Latin version by J. B. Cotelerius. Followed by the old Latin version.] *See* COTELERIUS (J. B.) SS. Patrum qui temporibus Apostolicis floruerunt . . . opera, *etc.* pt. 1. 1672. fol. **3625. b. 4.**

—— *Ἡ καθολικη του Βαρναβα ἐπιστολη.* Catholica Barnabæ epistola. Edidit & notas addidit Isaacus Vossius. Editio secunda. *Gr. & Lat.* *See* IGNATIUS, *Saint, Bishop of Antioch.* [*Greek and Latin.*] S. Ignatii Martyris Epistolæ genuinæ, *etc.* 1680. 4°. **849. k. 1.**

—— Barnabae epistola. *See* LE MOYNE (S.) Varia sacra, *etc.* tom. 1. 1685. 4°. **854. e. 7.**

—— *Του ἁγιου Βαρναβα . . . ἐπιστολη καθολικη.* Sancti Barnabæ . . . epistola catholica. Accessit S. Hermæ . . . Pastor. 2 pt. *E Theatro Sheldoniano: Oxoniæ,* 1685. 12°. **3628. a. 8.**

—— *Του ἁγιου Βαρναβα του ἀποστολου ἐπιστολη καθολικη.* Sancti Barnabæ apostoli epistola catholica. *See* COTELERIUS (J. B.) SS. Patrum qui temporibus Apostolicis floruerunt . . . opera, *etc.* 1698. fol. **3625. b. 5.**

—— Sancti Barnabae apostoli epistola catholica. *See* COTELERIUS (J. B.) SS. Patrum . . . opera. tom. 1. 1724. fol. **676. i. 10.**

—— S. Barnabæ epistola catholica, una cum versione Latina, tum vetere, tum recentiore [⁄ J. B. Cotelerius] selectisque . . . notis, *etc.* 1746. *See* RUSSELL (Richard) *M.A.* SS. Patrum Apostolicorum . . . opera, *etc.* vol. 1. 1746. 8°. **855. c. 1.**
⁄ the letter by

—— [Another issue.] *See* RUSSELL (Richard) *M.A.* SS. Patrum Apostolicorum . . . opera, *etc.* vol. 1. 1746. 8°. **G. 19864.**

—— Sancti Barnabae Apostoli epistola catholica. [With the old Latin version and that of J. B. Cotelerius.] 1765. *See* GALLANDIUS (A.) Bibliotheca veterum Patrum, *etc.* tom. 1. 1765, *etc.* fol. **469. h. 1.**

—— S. Barnabae epistola catholica. *See* CLEMENT I., *Saint, Pope.* Patrum Apostolicorum S. Clementis Rom., S. Barnabae . . . epistolae . . . Textum recensuit Fr. X. Reithmayr. 1844. 16°. **1222. b. 21.**

—— S. Barnabae epistola catholica. *See* HEFELE (C. J. von) *Bishop of Rottenburg.* Patrum Apostolicorum opera, *etc.* 1847. 8°. **3622. e. 22.**

—— *Βαρναβα του ἀποστολου ἐπιστολη.* Barnabae Apostoli epistola. [The Latin version from chap. v. based on Cotelerius.] *See* DRESSEL (A. R. M.) Patrum Apostolicorum opera, *etc.* 1857. 8°. **3627. d. 31.**

—— *Του ἁγιου Βαρναβα του ἀποστολου ἐπιστολη καθολικη.* Sancti Barnabae Apostoli epistola catholica. 1857. *See* MIGNE (J. P.) Patrologiæ cursus completus . . . Series Græca. tom. 2. 1857, *etc.* 4°. **2001. b.**

—— Barnabae epistula. Integram graece primum edidit, veterem interpretationem latinam, commentarium criticum ed adnotationes addidit Adolphus Hilgenfeld. pp. xiv. 80. 1866. *See* HILGENFELD (A.) Novum Testamentum extra canonem receptum, *etc.* fasc. 2. 1866. 8°. **03225. h. 16.**

—— [Another edition.] 1877. *See* HILGENFELD (A.) Novum Testamentum extra canonem receptum, *etc.* fasc. 2. 1876, *etc.* 8°. **2200. dd. 9.**

BARNABAS, *Writer of the "Epistle of Barnabas."*

—— *Βαρναβα ἐπιστολη.* Epistula Barnabae. *See* FUNK (F. X. von) Opera Patrum Apostolicorum, *etc.* 1878. 8°. **3622. bb. 2.**

—— Barnabae epistula graece et latine. Recensuerunt et illustraverunt, Papiae quae supersunt, presbyterorum reliquias ab Irenaeo servatas vetus ecclesiae Romanae symbolum epistulam ad Diognetum adiecerunt Oscar de Gebhardt, Adolphus Harnack, *etc.* pp. lxxiv. 172. *Lipsiae,* 1878. 8°. [*Patrum Apostolicorum Opera.* fasc. 1. pt. 2. Ed. 2.] **3623. aa. 23.**

—— The Editio princeps of the Epistle of Barnabas by Archbishop Ussher, as printed . . . 1642, and preserved in an imperfect form in the Bodleian Library, with a dissertation on the literary history of that edition, by . . . J. H. Backhouse. pp. xxv. 241–270. *Clarendon Press: Oxford,* 1883. 4°. **3623. c. 1.**
This edition contains chap. v. i–ix. i *of the Greek, and chap.* i–ix. i *of the Latin text.*

—— Die Versio latina des Barnabasbriefes und ihr Verhältnis zur altlateinischen Bibel. Erstmals untersucht, nebst Ausgabe und Glossar des griechischen und lateinischen Textes, von Joseph Michael Heer . . . Mit einer Tafel. pp. lxxxiv. 132. *Freiburg i. B.,* 1908. 8°. **03166. k. 14.**

—— *Βαρναβα 'Επιστολη, etc.* (Recensuit vertit adnotavit T. Klauser.) *See* APOSTLES. [*Apocrypha.—Didache.—Greek and Latin.*] Doctrina duodecim apostolorum, *etc.* 1940. 8°. **3623.** df. **20/1** a.

Greek and English.

—— *Βαρναβα ἐπιστολη.* The Epistle of Barnabas from the Sinaitic manuscript of the Bible, with a translation, by Samuel Sharpe. [Ascribed here to Saint Barnabas.] pp. xxvii. 63. *Williams & Norgate: London & Edinburgh,* 1880. 8°. **3805. aaa. 8.**

—— The Epistle of Barnabas. *See* LIGHTFOOT (Joseph B.) *Bishop of Durham.* The Apostolic Fathers, *etc.* 1891. 8°. **2003.h.**

—— The Epistole of Barnabas. 1912. *See* LAKE (Kirsopp) The Apostolic Fathers, *etc.* vol. 1. 1912, *etc.* 8°. [*Loeb Classical Library.*] **2282. d. 1.**

Latin.

—— Sancti Barnabæ Apostoli, vt fertur, epistola catholica, ab antiquis olim Ecclesiæ Patribus, sub eiusdem nomine . . . vsurpata. Hanc primum . . . eruit P. R. Dominus Hugo Menardus, *etc.* 1677. *See* LA BIGNE (M. de) Maxima Bibliotheca veterum Patrum, *etc.* tom. 2. pt. 1. 1677, *etc.* fol. **464. f. 2.**

—— Sancti Barnabæ Apostoli epistola catholica. *See* BIBLE. [*Latin.*] Biblia sacra vulgatæ editionis, *etc.* 1731. fol. **L.91.f.7.**

English.

—— The Catholique Epistle of Saint Barnabas the Apostle. *See* POLYCARP, *Saint, Bishop of Smyrna.* [*English.*] The Famous Epistles of Saint Polycarp and Saint Ignatius, *etc.* 1668. 12°. **3627. a. 23.**

—— The Catholick Epistle of St. Barnabas. *See* WAKE (William) successively *Bishop of Lincoln* and *Archbishop of Canterbury.* The Genuine Epistles of the Apostolical Fathers, *etc.* pt. 2. 1693. 8°. **857. c. 1.**

—— [Another edition.] *See* WAKE (William) successively *Bishop of Lincoln* and *Archbishop of Canterbury.* The Genuine Epistles, *etc.* pt. 2. 1710. 8°. **862. i. 4.**

—— [Another edition.] *See* WAKE (William) successively *Bishop of Lincoln* and *Archbishop of Canterbury.* The Genuine Epistles, *etc.* pt. 2. 1719. 8°. **3627. c. 7.**

—— [Another edition.] *See* WAKE (William) successively *Bishop of Lincoln* and *Archbishop of Canterbury.* The Genuine Epistles, *etc.* pt. 2. 1817. 8°. **3627. bb. 12.**

—— The General Epistle of Barnabas. *See* HONE (William) *Bookseller.* The Apocryphal New Testament, *etc.* 1820. 8°. **3205. bbb. 22.**

—— The Epistle of Barnabas. 1867. *See* ROBERTS (Alexander) *D.D.*, and DONALDSON (*Sir* James) Ante-Nicene Christian Library, *etc.* vol. 1. 1867, *etc.* 8°. **3628.bb.1/1.**

—— The Epistle of S. Barnabas. *See* HOOLE (Charles H.) The Apostolic Fathers, *etc.* 1872. 8°. **3627. aa. 17.**

—— (Second edition.) *See* HOOLE (Charles H.) The Apostolic Fathers, *etc.* 1885. 8°. **3627. aaa. 4.**

—— The Epistle of St. Barnabas. [1888.] See FATHERS. The Apostolic Fathers. pt. 1. [1887, *etc.*] 8°. [*Ancient & Modern Library of Theological Literature.*] **3605. g. 3/7.**

—— The Catholic Epistle of St. Barnabas. *See* WAKE (William) successively *Bishop of Lincoln* and *Archbishop of Canterbury.* The Genuine Epistles of the Apostolical Fathers, *etc.* pt. 2. 1893. 8°. [*Sir J. Lubbock's Hundred Books.* no. 44.] **012207.1.1/44.**

—— An English Translation of the Epistle of Barnabas. [By William K. L. Clarke.] pp. 32. *S.P.C.K.: London; Macmillan Co.: New York & Toronto,* 1923. 8°. [*Texts for Students.* no. 14A.] W.P. **4683/14.**

—— The Epistle of Barnabas. *In:* KLEIST (JAMES A.) The Didache, *etc.* pp. 27–65. [1948.] 8°. W.P. A. **373/6.**

—— The Letter of Barnabas. *In:* GOODSPEED (Edgar J.) The Apostolic Fathers, *etc.* pp. 19–45. [1950.] 8°. **3628.** aaa. **11.**

Dutch.

—— De Brief van Barnabas. 1869. *See* DUKER (A. C.) and MANEN (W. C. van) Oud Christelijke Letterkunde, *etc.* dl. 1. 1869, *etc.* 8°. **3627. aaa. 16.**

French.

—— Epistre catholique de S. Barnabé. *See* BIBLE.—*Apocrypha.* [*French.*] Livres apocryphes de l'Ancien (du Nouveau) Testament en françois, *etc.* tom. 2. 1742. 12°. **1410. e. 5.**

German.

—— Das Sendschreiben des Apostels Barnabas aufs Neue untersucht, übersetzt und erklärt von Dr. Carl Joseph Hefele. pp. x. 267. *Tübingen,* 1840. 8°. **3670. bb. 5.**

—— Die Epistel des Apostels St. Barnabä. *See* SCHOLZ (H.) Die Schriften der apostolischen Väter, *etc.* 1865. 8°. **3670. aa. 35.**

—— Das Sendschreiben des Apostels Barnabas. 1869. *See* REITHMAYR (F. X.) Bibliothek der Kirchenväter, *etc.* 1869, *etc.* 16°. **3677.** de. **6.**

—— Zur Feier der fünfzigjährigen Lehrerwirksamkeit wünscht den Herren . . . Karl Rudolf Hagenbach und Johann Jakob Stæhelin . . . Glück . . . die theologische Facultät. Inhalt: Der sogenannte Brief des Barnabas. I. Uebersetzung. II. Bemerkungen. Ein Beitrag zum Verständniss des Briefes, von C. J. Riggenbach. pp. 47. *Breslau,* 1873. 4°. **836. i. 23.** (4.)

BARNABAS, *Writer of the "Epistle of Barnabas."*

—— Der Barnabasbrief. Erklärt von D. Dr. Hans Windisch. *Tübingen*, 1920. 8°. [*Handbuch zum Neuen Testament.* Ergänzungsband: *Die apostolischen Väter.* pt. 3.] **03025.** i. **6/16.**

Polish.

—— List Barnaby. *See* LISIECKI (A.) Pisma Ojców apostolskich, *etc.* 1924. 8°. [*Pisma Ojców Kościoła w polskiem tlumaczeniu.* tom 1.] 3623.c.37/1.(2.)

Welsh.

—— Epistol Sant Barnabas. *See* DAVIES, afterwards DE HIRSCH-DAVIES (John Edwin) Y Tadau Apostolig. 1898. 8°. **3623.** df. **5.**

Summaries.

—— Doctrina sancto Barnabæ adscripta. [A summary of the Epistle of Barnabas.] *See* MARECHAL (B.) R. P. D. Bernardi Marechal . . . Concordantia Sanctorum Patrum, *etc.* tom. 1. 1769. fol. **477.** g. **2.**

—— S. Barnabae Apostoli epistola catholica. [An analysis.] 1780. *See* SCHRAM (D.) P. Dominici Schram . . . Analysis operum S.S. Patrum, *etc.* tom. 1. 1780, *etc.* 8°. **474.** a. **1.**

—— Sancti Barnabæ Apostoli . . . opera. [An analysis of the Epistle.] 1842. *See* CAILLAU (A. B.) Patres Apostolici, *etc.* tom. 1. 1842, *etc.* 8°. **3622.** h.

—— Épitre catholique. [A summary.] 1837. *See* GENOUD (A. E.) Les Pères de l'Église, traduits en français, *etc.* tom. 1. 1837, *etc.* 8°. **1125.** d. **10.**

—— Der Brief des Barnabas. [A summary.] *See* ROESSLER (C. F.) Christian Friederich Rössler . . . Bibliothek der Kirchen-Väter, *etc.* Tl. 1. 1776. 8°. **1222.** d. **13.**

Appendix.

—— *See* BARTLET (James V.) The Epistle of Barnabas, *etc.* 1905. 8°. [*The New Testament in the Apostolic Fathers.*] Ac. **2072.**

—— *See* BRAUNSBERGER (O.) Der Apostel Barnabas. Sein Leben und der ihm beigelegte Brief, wissenschaftlich gewürdigt. 1876. 8°. **4808.** i. **3.**

—— *See* HAEUSER (P.) Der Barnabasbrief neu untersucht und neu erklärt. 1912. 8°. 3071.aa.1/11.

—— *See* HEINISCH (Paul) Der Einfluss Philos auf die älteste christliche Exegese—Barnabas, *etc.* 1908. 8°. [*Alttestamentliche Abhandlungen.* Hft. 1/2.] 3091.ff.2/1.

—— *See* HENKE (E. L. T.) De Epistolae, quae Barnabae tribuitur, authentia. 1827. 8°. T. **1254.** (**2.**)

—— *See* HEYDECKE (C.) Dissertatio qua Barnabae epistola interpolata demonstretur. 1874. 8°. **4372.** h. **13.** (**2.**)

—— *See* MUELLER (Johann Georg) *of Basle, etc.* Erklärung des Barnabasbriefes, *etc.* 1869. 8°. **3627.** cc. **9.**

—— *See* ROBINSON (Joseph A.) successively *Dean of Westminster* and *of Wells.* Barnabas, Hermas and the Didache, *etc.* 1920. 8°. **3623.** de. **8.**

—— *See* TSONEVSKI (I. K.) Посланието на ап. Варнава, *etc.* 1945. 8°. [*Годишник на Софийския Университет. Богословски Факултет.* том. 22.] Ac. **1137.** (**6.**)

—— *See* WEIZSAECKER (C. H.) Zur Kritik des Barnabasbriefes aus dem Codex Sinaiticus. 1863. 4°. [*Tübinger Universitätsschriften.* 1863.] Ac. **730.**

—— *See* WREDE (W.) Das literarische Rätsel des Hebräerbriefs. Mit einem Anhang über den literarischen Charakter des Barnabasbriefes. 1906. 8°. **03129.** h. **6/8.**

BARNABAS (JEAN) Les Entretiens de la truche, ou les Amours de J. Barnabas et de la Mère Roquignard. Réimpression avec une notice. pp. viii. 24. *Genève*, 1868. 12°. **12234.** cccc. **2.** (**2.**)
Part of a series entitled "Gazetés Françoises." No. 41 *of an edition of* 100 *copies.*

BARNABAUD (JEAN CLAUDE) *See* PINGAUD (L.) Voyages des curés de Plombières et de Vielverge (F. Bernardy, J. C. Barnabaud) dans l'Allemagne du Nord et en Suède . . . 1794–1795, *etc.* [1892.] 8°. **10107.** ff. **28.** (**7.**)

BARNABÉ, *Minorite.* Le Mont Thabor. Notices historiques et descriptives . . . Ouvrage orné d'une carte . . . et d'autres illustrations, *etc.* pp. ix. 176. *Paris*, 1900. 8°. **10075.** e. **27.**

—— Le Prétoire de Pilate et la forteresse Antonia . . . Avec 32 illustrations, *etc.* pp. xxiii. 251. *Paris*, 1902. 8°. **010077.** h. **14.**

—— Questions de topographie palestinienne. Le lieu de la rencontre d'Abraham et de Melchisédech. Avec un appendice sur le tombeau de sainte Anne à Jérusalem . . . Avec une carte, *etc.* pp. 154. *Jérusalem*, 1903. 8°. **07702.** bb. **78.**

BARNABÈ (STEPHANUS) Grammatica, seu Instructio linguæ Germanicæ. pp. 68. *Typis M. Rictij: Viennæ Austriæ*, 1658. 8°. **628.** a. **9.**

BARNABEE (HENRY CLAY) Reminiscences of Henry Clay Barnabee. Being an attempt to account for his life, with some excuses for his professional career. Edited by George Leon Varney. [With portraits.] pp. 461. *Chapple Publishing Co.: Boston*, 1913. 8°. **010881.** f. **44.**

BARNABEI (FELICE) Degli scritti di A. S. Mazzocchi su la storia di Capua e su le tavole di Eraclea. Studii, *etc.* pp. 66. *Napoli*, 1874. 4°. **7701.** aaa. **1.** (**1.**)

—— Dei fittili scoperti nella necropoli di Narce. 1894. *See* ROME, *the City.—Accademia de' Lincei.* Monumenti antichi, *etc.* vol. 4. 1890, *etc.* 4°. Ac. **102/15.**

—— La Villa Pompeiana di P. Fannio Sinistore scoperta presso Boscoreale, *etc.* pp. 86. pl. XI. *Roma*, 1901. fol. Dept. of Greek & Roman Antiquities.

BARNABEUS (HIERONYMUS) Vita Caesaris Baronii . . . S. R. E. Presbyteri Cardinalis et Apostolicæ Sedis Bibliothecarij. pp. 199. *Apud V. Mascardum: Romæ*, 1651. 4°. **486.** c. **9.**

—— [Another edition.] Purpura Sancta, seu vita . . . Cæsaris Baronii Cardinalis . . . Cui accedunt . . . elogia Baronio ab illustribus . . . viris attributa, operâ Gregorii Fritz, *etc.* [With a portrait.] pp. 274. *Viennæ Austriæ*, 1718. 8°. **4863.** ccc. **18.**

BARNABIDES (P. L.)

—— *Ἐμπορικα μαθηματικα, για τις ἀνωτερες ταξεις των ἐμπορικων σχολων, etc.* Λευκωσια, 1940– . 8°. W.P. **13100.**

—— *Π. Λ. Βαρναβιδου . . . Στοιχειωδης ἀριθμητικη προς χρησιν των μαθητων της Α', Β' και Γ' ταξεως των γυμνασιων, λυκειων και ἐμπορικων σχολων. Ἐκδοσις δευτερα.* pp. 216. Λευκωσια, 1942. 8°. **8508.** b. **7.**

BARNABITES. *See* PAUL, *Saint and Apostle.—Congregation of Regular Clerks of St. Paul.*

BARNABIUS (RICHARDUS) *See* BARNABY (Richard)

BARNABY. [For editions of "Barnabae Itinerarium," or "Drunken Barnaby's Four Journeys," by Richard Brathwait, published under the pseudonym of Corymbaeus:] *See* CORYMBAEUS, *pseud.*

—— [For editions of the above under Brathwait's own name:] *See* BRATHWAIT (R.)

BARNABY.

—— Drunken Barnaby's Four Journeys, to the North of England, *etc.* [By Richard Brathwait. The English version only.] pp. 36. *George Wilson: Leeds*, 1805. 8º. **11642**. a. **37**.

—— Barnabies Summons: or, Paie your groat in the morning. [*London*, 1652.] *s. sh.* fol. **669**. f. **16**. **(66.)**

BARNABY, *Junior, pseud.* [i.e. *Rev.* THOMAS JAMES.] Journey to Little Gidding. By Barnaby, Junior. [In verse.] *Lat. & Eng.* pp. 9. *Langley: Stamford*, [1856?] 4º. **11651**. bbb. **41**.

BARNABY, *Uncle.* Uncle Barnaby; or, Recollections of his character and opinions. pp. iv. 356. *R.T.S.: London*, [1843.] 18º. **4420**. d. **28**.

—— [Another edition, abridged.] Uncle Barnaby's Budget. pp. 96. *R.T.S.: London*, [1875.] 16º. **12804**. df. **12**.

BARNABY, *Widow.* La Veuve Barnaby [by Frances Trollope]. Roman traduit de l'anglais par Mme Ambroise Tardieu. 2 tom. *Paris*, 1877. 8º. **12604**. df. **7**.

BARNABY BRIGHT'S NEW JOURNAL. *See* EPHEMERIDES.

BARNABY (HENRY) Historic Notes of Chatham and Rochester in bygone days. pp. 15. *Miss Baker: Brighton*, 1899. 8º. **10352**. g. **40**. **(5.)**

BARNABY (JOSEPH T.)

—— Fluctuations in Abundance of Red Salmon, Oncorhynchus nerka—Walbaum—of the Karluk River, Alaska, *etc.* *Washington*, 1944. 4º. [*U.S. Fish and Wildlife Service. Fishery Bulletin.* no. 39.] A.S. **96**.

BARNABY (KENNETH CLOUES)

—— Basic Naval Architecture. pp. 340. *Hutchinson's Scientific and Technical Publications: London*, [1949.] 8º. **8809**. cc. **17**.

—— Basic Naval Architecture. (Second edition, revised and enlarged.) pp. 460. *Hutchinson's Scientific & Technical Publications: London*, 1954. 8º. **08809**. ee. 4.

BARNABY (*Sir* NATHANIEL) *K.C.B.* *See* BARNABY (Sydney W.) Marine Propellers, *etc.* [With an introduction by N. Barnaby.] 1885. 8º. **8807**. c. **7**.

—— —— 1887. 8º. **8807**. aaa. **39**.

—— *See* HENWOOD (Charles F.) Sir R. S. Robinson . . . and N. Barnaby . . . arraigned at the bar of public opinion. 1874. 8º. **8829**. d. **2**. **(14.)**

—— Christmas 1892 in Connaught. A study of the Irish Question. (With resumé of the Home Rule Bill, 1893.) pp. 35. *E. Marlborough & Co.: London*, [1893.] 8º. **8146**. cc. **5**. **(15.)**

—— The Declaration of Paris. A memorandum prepared for the First Lord of the Admiralty. *See* PARIS.—*Congress of* 1856. The Declaration of Paris, *etc.* 1876. 8º. **8026**. dd. **8**. **(7.)**

—— *See* ROSS-OF-BLADENSBURG (*Sir* John F. G.) *K.C.B.* Copy of a Letter from Mr. Ross-of-Bladensberg to Mr. Barnaby . . . in reply to his memorandum on "The British Navy and the Mercantile Marine." [1876.] 8º. **08805**. f. **8**. **(5.)**

—— Naval Development in the Century. [With a portrait.] pp. xv. 468. *Linscott Publishing Co.: London*, 1902. 8º. [*Nineteenth Century Series.* vol. 19.] **09008**. df. **1/19**.

BARNABY (*Sir* NATHANIEL) *K.C.B.*

—— [Another edition.] pp. 468. *Linscott Publishing Co.: Toronto & Philadelphia; W. & R. Chambers: London & Edinburgh*, 1904. 8º. [*Nineteenth Century Series.*] **09008**. e. **4/19**.

—— The Naval Review of British, French, Italian, German, and Russian large Ships of War, being an inspection of two hundred and fifty-three sea-going fighting ships. [With two diagrams.] pp. 17. *E. Marlborough & Co.: London*, [1886.] 8º. **8807**. c. **13**.

—— Songs by the Way: being a collection of the hymns by Sir N. Barnaby, K.C.B., composed in connection with, and for the love of, the Lee Chapel Sunday School. pp. 34. *For private circulation: London*, 1905. 4º. **11650**. h. **35**.

BARNABY (RICHARD) *See* BRIMELLUS (I.) Viri generosissimi . . . R. Barnabii . . . vita atque obitus. [1610?] fol. **1871**. e. **1**. **(1.)**

BARNABY (SYDNEY WALKER) Marine Propellers, *etc.* [With an introduction by N. Barnaby.] pp. xi. 165. *E. & F. N. Spon: London*, 1885. 8º. **8807**. c. **7**.

—— Second edition. pp. xiii. 78. *E. & F. N. Spon: London*, 1887. 8º. **8807**. aaa. **39**.

—— Third edition. pp. viii. 115. *E. & F. N. Spon: London*, 1891. 8º. **8806**. dd. **15**.

—— Fourth edition. pp. vi. 187. *E. & F. N. Spon: London*, 1900. 8º. **08805**. f. **30**.

—— Fifth edition, revised. pp. viii. 185. *E. & F. N. Spon: London*, 1908. 8º. **08806**. ff. **26**.

—— Sixth edition, revised. pp. vii. 222. *E. & F. N. Spon: London*, 1921 [1920]. 8º. **08806**. c. **43**.

BARNACLE. Barnacle; or, the Hut on the Devil's Peak [and other tales]. pp. 192. *James Henderson: London*, 1873. 16º. [*People's Pocket Story Books.*] **12600**. a. **3**.

BARNACLE, *Captain, pseud.* [i.e. CHARLES M. NEWELL.] Leaves from an Old Log. Péhe Nú-e, the tiger whale of the Pacific. By Captain Barnacle. pp. 112. *D. Lothrop & Co.: Boston*, 1877. 8º. **12705**. eee. **7**.

BARNACLE, *pseud.* The First Class Badge, and how to get it. By "Barnacle." pp. 62. *"The Scout": London*, 1931. 8º. **8820**. a. **19**.
The fourth edition, which is signed: H.E.S. is entered under S., H.

—— Steps to the Second Class Badge. pp. 48. *The Scout: London*, 1935. 8º. **08820**. aa. **35**.

—— Steps to the Second Class Badge. By "Barnacle." (New and revised edition.) pp. 47. *C. A. Pearson: London*, 1938. 8º. **08820**. a. **80**.

BARNACLE (HENRY GLANVILLE) The Lancashire and Cheshire Weather Forecast for 1893 (94, 95, 97). *J. Heywood: Manchester*, [1892–96.] *s. sh.* fol. **1820.h.8.(40.)**

BARNACLES ( ) *Mr.* Mr. Barnacles and his Boat. By the author of the "Adventures of a Salmon" [i.e. William Ayrton]. pl. 24. *Whittaker & Co.: London; Prichard & Roberts: Chester*, [1856.] 8º. **555**. a. **41**.

BARNADES (MIGUEL) Principios de Botanica, sacados de los mejores escritores, y puestos en lengua castellana . . . Parte primera. Con las estampas necesarias. pp. 220. *Madrid*, 1767. 4º. **450**. g. **19**.

BARNADISTON. Barnadiston. A tale of the seventeenth century. 3 vol. *Saunders & Otley: London*, 1834. 12º. N. **1030–32**.

BARNAGAUD-PRUNIER (SIMONE GENEVIÈVE)

— *See* BOUZY (M.) Madame Prunier's Fish Cookery Book, *etc.* 1938. 8°. **7944.** pp. **13.**

— — 1955. 8°. **7949.** aa. **64.**

BARNALES (KOSTAS)

— *Κωστα Βαρναλη Το 'Ημερολογιο της Πηνελοπης. Σατιρικη μυθιστορια.* pp. 145. *'Αθηνα,* 1947. 8°. **012593.** c. 3.

— The True Apology of Socrates. Translated from the Greek by Stephen Yaloussis. A satire. pp. 79. *Zeno Publishers: [London,]* 1955. 8°. **011313.** aaa. **21.**

BARNARD. Barnard. A modern romance. [By John Stores Smith. In verse.] pp. 39. *Simpkin, Marshall & Co.: London,* 1846. 8°. **1466. f. 38.**

BARNARD, CHRISTOPHER, *Baron. See* VANE.

BARNARD, *Saint, Abbot of Clairvaux. See* BERNARD.

BARNARD, *Saint, Archbishop of Vienne. See* BERNARD.

BARNARD AND WESTWOOD.

— Éditions Barnard. *See* LABARTHE (A.)

BARNARD CASTLE. Barnard Castle; or, the Monk: a poem, founded on a legend of the twelfth century; with notes, and an introduction . . . Canto the first. pp. 79. *W. Benning: London,* 1828. 8°. **11641.** cc. **8.** *No more published.*

— Barnard Castle, County Durham . . . Official guide. [With illustrations.] pp. 51. *Barnard Castle and District Publicity Society: [Barnard Castle,* 1931.] 8°. **010360.** a. **69.**

— Handbook to Barnard Castle and the neighbourhood, with a map of Teesdale. pp. 48. *R. W. Atkinson: Barnard Castle,* [1872.] 12°. **10360.** bb. **49. (8.)**

— Fifth edition. pp. 72. *R. W. Atkinson: Barnard Castle,* 1882. 8°. **10358.** bbb. **69.**

— The "Borough" Pocket Guide to Barnard Castle (Barnard Castle, Durham, as a Health and Holiday Resort. Official guide), *etc.*, 4 pt. *E. J. Burrow: Cheltenham,* [1919–29.] 8°. **10354.** a. **55.** *Various editions.*

— The Bowes Museum. An illustrated survey, *etc.* 1954. *obl.* 8°. *See* WAKE (Thomas) **07813.** p. **6.**

— Handbook to the Bowes Museum, Barnard Castle. Compiled by the Curator (Sydney L. Harrison). pp. 118. pl. VIII. *Middlesbrough,* 1934. 8°. **7801.** aa. **25.**

— *1st Group of Boy Scouts.* The Good Deed. Souvenir magazine, *etc. Barnard Castle,* 1933– . 8°. P.P. **1102.** adp.

— *Local Board of Health.* Report upon Public Works. pp. 11. *Eyre & Spottiswoode: London,* 1852. 8°. C.T. **360. (15.)**

Rural District of.

— Official Guide to the Barnard Castle Rural District, Co. Durham. *Home Publishing Co.: Croydon,* [1949-] 8°. *Various editions.* **010368.** k. **109.**

BARNARD COLLEGE.

— *See* NEW YORK.—*Columbia University.*

BARNARD, *Family of. See* BARNARD (Finch) More Light on Shakespeare and the Barnard and Lucy Families. 1914. 8°. **11761. df. 9.**

— *See* BARNARD (Finch) Shakespeare and the Barnard Family. 1914. 8°. **11761. df. 10.**

— Barnard Letters, 1778–1884. Edited by Anthony Powell. [With plates, including portraits.] pp. 319. *Duckworth; London,* 1928. 8°. **010920. d. 6.**

BARNARD ( ) *Author of " Chess Shorthand for the Blind."* Barnard's Chess Shorthand for the Blind. *London Society for Teaching the Blind: London,* [1900.] fol. **13008. a. 42.**

BARNARD ( ) *Captain.* Captain Barnard's Grenadier. [A song.] *See* LOVE SONG. A Favourite Love Song. [1780?] fol. Rox. III. **596.**

BARNARD ( ) *Doctor, Minister at Tredagh. See* BERNARD (Nicholas) *Dean of Ardagh.*

BARNARD (A.) *Gymnast. See* GRAF (Ferdinand) *Gymnast.* Hints to Gymnasts . . . Compiled and arranged by F. Graf . . . with the kind assistance of Messrs. A. Barnard . . . and T. Gowland. [1898.] 8°. **7913. dd. 14.**

BARNARD (A. R. K.)

— *See* REDMAN (Alvin) Somewhat "Shaggy" . . . Edited by A. R. K. Barnard. [1952.] 8°. **012332.** aa. **52.**

BARNARD (A. SEDGWICK) Ragged-Staff Rhymes. pp. 20. *Cornish Bros.: Birmingham,* [1914.] 8°. **011604.** ee. **3. (2.)**

BARNARD (ALFRED) Every Way of Earning a Living . . . With an introduction by Hamilton Edwards. pp. 144. *Amalgamated Press: London,* 1908. 8°. **08226.** f. **70.**

— The Moral Debt of a Proud Nation. British issues of the war loans of France. pp. 154. *Barnard's Press: London,* 1929. 8°. **08225.** ccc. **73.**

BARNARD (ALFRED) *Writer on Brewing.* The Noted Breweries of Great Britain and Ireland. [Illustrated.] 4 vol. *Sir J. Causton & Sons: London,* [1889–91.] 4°. **07945.** n. **8.**

— Orchards and Gardens Ancient and Modern. With a description of the orchards, gardens, model farms and factories owned by W. Whiteley, *etc.* pp. iv. 260. *Sir J. Causton & Sons: London,* 1895. *obl.* 8°. **7078.** de. **28.**

— The Whiskey Distilleries of the United Kingdom. With illustrations and maps. pp. xi. 457. *"Harper's Weekly Gazette": London,* 1887. 8°. **7953.** dd. **19.**

BARNARD (*Mrs.* ALFRED) *See* BARNARD (Frances C.)

BARNARD (ALICE MARGARET) "Death and Beyond." [In verse.] *W. Ball: London,* [1917.] 8°. **1879.** c. **12. (176.)**

BARNARD (AMY BEATRICE)

— The Girl's Book about Herself, *etc.* pp. viii. 224. *Cassell & Co.: London,* 1912. 8°. **08415.** ee. **3.**

— The Girl's Encyclopædia. pp. xii. 207. *Pilgrim Press: London,* [1909.] 8°. **08415. df. 5.**

— The God-Man. A phrenological study of Jesus Christ. pp. 173. *J. Clarke & Co.: London,* 1933. 8°. **4223. d. 14.**

— The Golden Book of Youth. Noble deeds of boys and girls, *etc.* pp. xiv. 272. *Pilgrim Press: London,* [1910.] 8°. **10601.** tt. **8.**

BARNARD (Amy Beatrice)

—— The Home Training of Children. A practical manual for parents. pp. xi. 205. *Pilgrim Press: London*, [1910.] 8°. **8305**. cc. **32**.

—— Memory. How it works and ways of helping it. pp. 20. *London*, [1922.] 8°. **08464**. e. **93**.

—— Mind and Brain: phrenology for beginners, *etc.* [With plates.] pp. 288. *L. N. Fowler & Co.: London*, 1929. 8°. **7409**. d. **42**.

—— Talks with Children about Themselves. pp. vii. 228. *Cassell & Co.: London*, 1911. 8°. **8410**. i. **25**.

BARNARD (*Lady* Anne) *See* Lindsay, afterwards Barnard.

BARNARD (Arthur Seaton Cary) A First Latin Course. *G. Bell & Sons: London*, 1934,35. 8°.**012933.c.30.**

—— Imperitis. [A Latin reader.] pp. viii. 107. *G. Bell & Sons: London*, 1941. 8°. **012935**. aa. **12**.

—— Res Gestae Populi Romani. pp. x. 84. *G. Bell & Sons: London*, 1931. 8°. **012933**. a. **68**.

BARNARD (B. F.) *See* Hall (Henry S.) Skool Algebra ... In Afrikaans vertaal deur B. F. Barnard. 1929, *etc.* 8°. W.P. **9675**.

—— *See* Torstenson (M. B.) Laboratorium-Handboek ... In Afrikaans vertaal deur B. F. Barnard. [1930.] 4°. **8710**. e. **14**.

—— *See* Ward (Frederick G. S.) and Dick (R. H.) Juta se Suid-Afrikaanse skool-meetkunde ... Vertaal deur B. F. Barnard. [1932, *etc.*] 8°. **08534.ff.50.**

—— Alledaagse rekenkunde vir Suid-Afrikaanse skole. Deur B. F. Barnard ... N. E. Lambrechts ... B. Taute ... Standerd I(–VI). 6 pt. *Kaapstad*, [1950?] 8°. **8508**. c. **18**.

—— Tweede voorloper en werkboek ... Deur B. F. Barnard ... N. E. Lambrechts ... B. Taute ... In medewerking met Mej. E. M. Olivier, *etc.* dl. 2, *etc.* *Kaapstad*, [1951– .] 4°. **8508**. c. **18a**.

—— Everyday Arithmetic for South African Schools. By B. F. Barnard ... N. E. Lambrechts ... B. Taute ... Standard I (–VI). 6 pt. *Maskew Miller: Cape Town*, [1950.] 8°. **8508**. c. **15**.

—— Everyday Arithmetic for South African Schools ... By B. F. Barnard ... N. E. Lambrechts ... B. Taute ... in collaboration with E. M. Olivier ... Drawings by Plik. *Maskew Miller: Cape Town*, [1951– .] 8°. W.P. **2354**.

BARNARD (Benjamin) *See* Palmer (Eleanor) Trial for Breach of Promise of Marriage, Miss Eleanor Palmer against Benjamin Barnard, Esq., *etc.* 1792. 8°. **1419**. e. **39**.

BARNARD (Caroline) The Parent's Offering; or, Tales for Children. 2 vol. *M. J. Godwin: London*, 1813. 12°. **.804**. eee. **15**.

—— Improved edition. pp. 214. *M. J. Godwin & Co.: London*, 1823. 12°. **12806**. r. **3**.

—— The Prize; or, the Lace-Makers of Missenden. pp. 167. *M. J. Godwin & Co.: London*, 1817. 12°. **12807**. ccc. **6**.

BARNARD (Charles) *See* also Kingsford (Jane) *pseud.* [i.e. C. Barnard.]

BARNARD (Charles)

—— *See* De Mille (William C.) The Forest King, by W. C. de Mille. Founded on the play by W. C. de Mille & C. Barnard. [1915.] 4°. **1873**. e. **17**.

—— *See* Mayer (Alfred M.) and Barnard (C.) Light: a series of simple ... experiments in the phenomena of light, *etc.* 1877. 8°. **8716**. bbb. **27**.

—— —— 1878. 12°. **2244**. b. **9**.

—— Camilla: a tale of a violin. Being the artist life of Camilla Urso. pp. v. 141. *Loring: Boston*, [1874.] 12°. **10882**. aa. **1**.

—— The Door in the Book through which the children of to-day pass, to walk and to talk with the children of Bible times, *etc.* pp. 197. *F. H. Revell Co.: New York*, 1903. 8°. **04412**. k. **1**.

—— Farming by Inches; or, "With brains, Sir," *etc.* [By C. Barnard.] pp. 123. [1869.] 12°. *See* Farming. **1145**. d. **26**.

—— Money and Music. An art story. Being the sequel to "The Soprano." pp. 208. *H. L. Shepard & Co.: Boston*, 1874. 8°. **12705**. b. **12**.

—— The Strawberry Garden. How it was planted—what it cost ... A very practical story. pp. 102. *Loring: Boston*, [1871.] 8°. **7074**. cc. **56**. **(9.)**

—— Talks about our Useful Plants, *etc.* pp. xvi. 133. *Funk & Wagnalls Co.: New York*, 1894. 8°. **7006**. aaa. **21**.

—— Talks About the Soil in its relation to Plants and Business, *etc.* pp. xiv. 127. *Funk & Wagnalls Co.: New York*, 1894. 8°. **7006**. aaa. **20**.

—— Talks about the Weather in its relation to Plants and Animals. A book of observations for farmers, students and schools. pp. xv. 121. *Chautauqua Press: Boston*, 1885. 8°. **07077**. e. **17**.

—— [Another edition.] pp. xv. 121. *Funk & Wagnalls Co.: New York*, 1894. 8°. **7006**. aaa. **22**.

—— The Tone Masters. A musical series for young people. vol. 2, 3.

2. Handel and Haydn.
3. Beethoven and Bach.

Lee & Shepard: Boston, 1870, 71. 8°. **7898**. ee. **42**. *Imperfect; wanting vol.* 1, *entitled:* "*Mozart and Mendelssohn.*"

BARNARD (Charles) and **BURGESS** (Neil)

—— The County Fair. A comedy in four acts. pp. 100. *New York, London*, [1922.] 8°. [*French's Standard Library Edition.*] **011781**. g. **1/24**.

BARNARD (Charles Douglas) Barnard on Learning to Fly, *etc.* [With plates, including a portrait.] pp. xi. 172. *Sampson Low & Co.: London*, [1931.] 8°. **08768**. b. **49**.

BARNARD (Charles Francis) *See* Boston, *Mass.—Warren Street Chapel.* Proceedings of the Annual Meeting of the Association for the Support of the Warren Street Chapel, with Mr. Barnard's Report [for each year, from 1838 to 1862]. 1838, *etc.* 8°. P.P. **1164**. p.

—— Mr. Barnard's First Report (to the Executive Committee of the American Unitarian Association) of his service as a minister at large in Boston. pp. 16. 1833. 8°. *See* United States of America.—*American Unitarian Association.* **4183**. aa. **29**.

BARNARD (Charles Francis)

—— Mr. Barnard's Second Report of his Service as a minister at large in Boston. [Signed: C. F. Barnard, F. T. Gray.] pp. 16. 1834. 8°. *See* United States of America.—*American Unitarian Association.* **4183**. aa. **28**.

BARNARD (Charles H.) A Narrative of the Sufferings and Adventures of Capt. Charles H. Barnard, in a Voyage round the World, during the years 1812, 1813, 1814, 1815, & 1816 . . . With six copperplate engravings, also a chart, *etc.* pp. 296. *Printed for the Author: New York,* 1829. 8°. **10880**. e. **41**.

BARNARD (Charles Inman) Paris War Days: Diary of an American. [With illustrations.] pp. x. 226. *Little, Brown & Co.: Boston,* 1914. 8°. **09082**. aaa. **2**.

—— [Another copy, with a different titlepage.] *T. Werner Laurie: London; [Boston, Mass.* printed], [1914.] 8°. **09231**. h. **14**.

BARNARD (Charles W.) Barnard's Herringbone Perforation Gage. [A card.] [*Technical Records: London,* 1934.] 8°. **1879**. cc. **12**. **(29.)**

BARNARD (Charlotte Alington) *See* also Claribel, *pseud.* [i.e. C. A. Barnard.]

—— Verses and Songs. pp. 55. *J. Nisbet & Co.: London,* [1870?] 8°. **11649**. cc. **50**.
Printed for private circulation.

BARNARD (Chester Irving)

—— *See* United States of America.—*Department of State.—Committee on Atomic Energy.* A Report on the International Control of Atomic Energy. Prepared . . . by . . . C. I. Barnard [and others], *etc.* 1946. 8°. **8425**. d. **79**.

—— The Functions of the Executive. pp. xvi. 334. *Harvard University Press: Cambridge, Mass.,* 1938. 8°. **08286**. h. **24**.

—— Organization and Management. Selected papers. pp. xi. 244. *Harvard University Press: Cambridge, Mass.,* 1948. 8°. **8288**. h. **86**.

BARNARD (Cyril Cuthbert)

—— A Classification for Medical Libraries. With introduction, local list, index of parasites and general index. Being a thesis, *etc.* pp. 142. *P. Lund, Humphries & Co.: London,* 1936. 8°. **11913**. b. **10**.
Reproduced from typewriting.

—— [A Classification for Medical Libraries.] A Classification for Medical and Veterinary Libraries . . . Second edition. pp. viii. 278. *H. K. Lewis & Co.: London,* 1955. 8°. **11918**. l. **1**.

—— History of the Library, *etc.* [By C. C. Barnard.] pp. 24. 1947. 8°. *See* London.—iii. *University of London.—London School of Hygiene and Tropical Medicine.* **11914**. a. **4**.

BARNARD (Daniel Dewey) *See* Hunt (Washington) Letters to the People, from Washington Hunt, Daniel D. Barnard, and Sam. Houston. [1856.] 8°. **8177**. h. **6**.

—— An Address delivered at Amherst, before the Literary Societies of Amherst College, August 27, 1839. pp. 63. *Hoffman & White: Albany,* 1839. 8°. **8407**. ff. **24**. **(2.)**

—— An Address delivered before the Philoclean and Peithessophian Societies of Rutgers College . . . July 18th, 1837, *etc.* pp. 46. *Hoffmann & White: Albany,* 1837. 8°. **8175**. bb. **61**. **(2.)**

BARNARD (Daniel Dewey)

—— An Address to the Class of Graduates of the Albany Medical College, delivered . . . January 27, 1846. pp. 26. *C. Van Benthuysen & Co.: Albany,* 1846. 8°. **7680**. d. **27**. **(3.)**

—— Anniversary Address, delivered before the American Institute, at the Tabernacle in New York, on the 20th October, 1843. pp. 28. *J. Van Norden & Co.: New York,* 1843. 8°. **7955**. d. **33**. **(3.)**

—— Daniel Webster. Speech of Mr. Barnard . . . delivered at a meeting of Americans in Paris; on the 16th of November, 1852. pp. 21. *C. & F. Unger: Berlin,* 1853. 8°. **10880**. c. **37**. **(4.)**

—— A Discourse delivered before the Senate of Union College, on the 24th day of July, 1843. pp. 55. *Weed & Parsons: Albany,* 1843. 8°. **8175**. bb. **62**. **(1.)**

—— A Discourse on the Life, Services and Character of Stephen Van Rensselaer . . . With an historical sketch of the colony and manor of Rensselaerwyck in an appendix. pp. 144. *Hoffman & White: Albany,* 1839. 8°. **1453**. e. **6**.

—— A Discourse pronounced at Burlington before the Literary Societies of the University of Vermont, August 1st, 1838, *etc.* pp. 56. *Hoffman & White: Albany,* 1838. 8°. **8305**. ee. **29**. **(8.)**

—— An Introductory Address delivered before the Young Men's Association for Mutual Improvement, of the City of Albany, on the 7th January, 1834. pp. 31. *Packard & Van Benthuysen: Albany,* 1834. 8°. **8305**. ee. **28**. **(6.)**

—— Lecture on the Character and Services of James Madison, delivered before the "Young Men's Association for Mutual Improvement in the City of Albany." February 28, 1837. pp. 47. *Hoffman & White: Albany,* 1837. 8°. **10880**. c. **37**. **(1.)**

—— Letter from the Hon. Daniel D. Barnard, addressed to James A. Hamilton, Esq., on the political condition of the country and the state of parties, and in favour of Millard Fillmore for President. pp. 16. *J. Munsell: Albany,* 1856. 8°. **8177**. g. **20**.

—— Man and the State, social and political. An address delivered before the Connecticut Alpha of the Phi Beta Kappa at Yale College . . . August 19, 1846. pp. 51. *B. L. Hamlen: New Haven [Conn.],* 1846. 8°. **8007**. d. **37**. **(1.)**

—— An Oration delivered before the Honourable the Corporation and the Military and Civic Societies of the City of Albany on the fourth of July, 1835. pp. 51. *E. W. & C. Skinner: Albany,* 1835. 8°. **12301**. dd. **24**. **(3.)**

—— A Plea for Social and Popular Repose; being an address delivered before the Philomathean and Eucleian Societies of the University of the City of New York, July 1, 1845. pp. 22. *Tribune Job Printing Establishment: New York,* 1845. 8°. **4183**. cc. **39**. **(9.)**

—— Political Aspects and Prospects in Europe. A lecture delivered before the Young Men's Association in the City of Albany, January 31, 1854. pp. 51. *Weed, Parsons & Co.: Albany,* 1854. 8°. **8010**. cc. **49**. **(2.)**

—— The Sovereignty of the States over their Navigable Waters. Argument of Daniel D. Barnard, in the Albany Bridge Case, submitted to the Supreme Court of the United States at the term held in the City of Washington, in February, 1860. pp. 96. *Atlas & Argus Print: Albany,* 1860. 8°. **6625**. ee. **10**.

BARNARD (Daniel Dewey)

—— Speech of Mr. Barnard . . . in favor of a uniform system of electing representatives by districts throughout the United States. Delivered in the House of Representatives . . . April 28, 1842. pp. 15. *National Intelligence Office : Washington*, 1842. 8°. **8177**. cc. **50**. **(6.)**

—— Speech of Mr. Barnard in the House of Representatives . . . December 29, 1843, and January 2, 1844, on the bill to refund the fine imposed upon General Jackson. pp. 20. *Gales & Seaton : Washington*, 1844. 8°. **8175**. c. **94**. **(3.)**

—— Speech of Mr. Barnard . . . on his provisional bill for supplying a national currency : in the House of Representatives, February 20, 1843. [1843.] *See* United States of America.—*Congress*. Speeches. 27th Congress, Third Session. [1842, *etc.*] 8°. **8177**. cc. **46**.

—— Speech of Mr. Barnard . . . on the policy of a protective tariff. Delivered in the House of Representatives . . . July 6, 1842. pp. 14. *National Intelligence Office: Washington*, 1842. 8°. **8246**. e. **6**.

—— [Another copy.] **8177**. cc. **50**. **(8.)**

—— Speech of Mr. Barnard . . . on the Report and Resolutions of the Committee on Elections, relative to the elections by general ticket in the four recusant States of New Hampshire, Georgia, Mississippi, and Missouri. pp. 16. *J. & G. S. Gideon : [Washington*, 1844.] 8°. **12301**. g. **58**. **(3.)**

—— Speech of Mr. Barnard . . . on the Tariff Bill . . . Delivered in the House of Representatives . . . May 14, 1844. pp. 32. *J. & G. S. Gideon : Washington*, 1844. 8°. **12301**. g. **58**. **(2.)**

—— Speech of Mr. Barnard . . . on the Veto of the Provisional Tariff Bill. Delivered in the House of Representatives, July 1, 1842. pp. 12. *National Intelligence Office : Washington*, 1842. 8°. **8177**. cc. **50**. **(7.)**

—— Speeches and Reports in the Assembly of New York at the annual session of 1838. [The editor's preface signed : J. B. V. S.] pp. xi. 228. *Oliver Steele : Albany*, 1838. 12°. **1061**. g. **87**.

BARNARD (Edna A.) A Frontier Romance. Maple Range. pp. viii. 444. *H. A. Sumner & Co. : Chicago*, 1882. 8°. **12703**. h. **6**.

BARNARD (Edward) *Agent General of the Colony of Sierra Leone, in London. See* Sierra Leone. The Ordinances of the Colony of Sierra Leone . . . Published . . . under the revision of E. Barnard. 1857, *etc.* fol. C.S.C.525/2.

BARNARD (Edward) *Headmaster of Eton. See* Eton College. Eton under Barnard, 1754–1765, *etc.* 1904. 8°. **8304**. ff. **10**. **(4.)**

BARNARD (Edward) *Historian.*

—— The New, Comprehensive and Complete History of England from the earliest period of authentic information, to the middle of the year, MDCCLXXXIII, *etc.* [With plates.] pp. 710. *Printed for the Author: London*, [1783.] fol. Cup. **1247**. cc. **17**.

—— The New Impartial and Complete History of England; from the very earliest period of authentic information . . . to the end of the present year . . . With . . . engravings, *etc.* pp. iv. 712. *Alex. Hogg : London*, [1790?] fol. **9502**. i. **6**.

BARNARD (Edward) *Historian.*

—— The New, Comprehensive, Impartial and Complete History of England: from the very earliest period of authentic information to the end of the present year, *etc.* [With plates.] pp. 714. 709–12. *Alexander Hogg London*, [1791?] fol. L.R. **295**. d. **5**.

BARNARD (Edward) *Lieutenant, R.N.* Christ Walking on the Sea. The emigrant's companion. A discourse *etc.* pp. 32. *G. Simms : Plymouth*, 1852. 8°. **4473**. f. **18**. **(10.)**

BARNARD (Edward) *of London?* Experimental Christianity of Eternal Advantage. Exemplified in the life of Miss Lydia Allen of London, who died November 17 1740. Second edition, greatly enlarged. pp. xii. 155. *J. Buckland : London*, 1741. 8°. **1415**. c. **27**.

—— Virtue the Source of Pleasure. [Poems, and plays in verse. By E. Barnard.] pp. vii. 319. 1757. 8°. *See* Virtue. **1465**. e. **2**.

BARNARD (Edward) *of the Houghton Fishing Club.* Angling Memories and Maxims . . . Illustrated by the author and others. *See* Houghton Fishing Club. Chronicles of the Houghton Fishing Club, 1822–1908, *etc.* 1908. 4°. **7915**. k. **13**.

BARNARD (Edward) *of Tunbridge Wells. See* Whitaker (Daniel) Funeral Sermon preached . . . on the death of Mr. Edward Barnard. 1869. 8°. **4920**. aaa. **52**. **(10.)**

BARNARD (Edward) *Pastor of the First Church in Haverhill. See* Barnard (Thomas) *D.D., of Salem, Mass* Tyranny and Slavery in Matters of Religion caution'd against . . . A sermon preached at the ordination of Mr Edward Barnard, *etc.* 1743. 8°. **4486**. b. **60**. **(3.)**

—— Goodness consider'd as an Eminent Qualification of a Christian Minister. In a sermon preached at the ordination of the Reverend Mr. Henry True, *etc.* pp. 31 *J. Winter: Boston*, 1752. 8°. **4486**. bb. **57**. **(2.)**

—— A Sermon preached at the Ordination of the Rev Mr. Gyles Merrill, *etc.* pp. 26. *T. & J. Fleet Boston*, 1765. 8°. **4486**. b. **60**. **(9.)**

—— A Sermon preached before his Excellency Francis Bernard, Esq., Governor . . . and the Honourable House of Representatives, of the Province of the Massachusetts Bay . . . May 28th, 1766. pp. 39. *R. & S. Draper Boston*, 1766. 8°. **4486**. bb. **8**.

—— A Sermon preached before the Annual Convention of Ministers of the Massacchusetts-Bay, in Boston, May 27th 1773. pp. 32. *Thomas Leverett : Boston*, 1773. 8°. **4486**. bb. 58. **(3.)**

BARNARD (Edward) *Surgeon.*

—— A Catalogue of the curious Musæum of . . . Mr. E Barnard, surgeon, deceas'd . . . which will be sold by auction, *etc.* pp. 10. [*London*, 1737.] 8°. S.C. **244**.

BARNARD (Edward A.) Manuel d'agriculture . . . Ouvrage enrichi de 260 gravures, *etc.* pp. 534. *Senécal & Fils : Montréal*, 1895. 8°. **07077**. g. **6**.

BARNARD (Edward Emerson)

—— *See* Frost (Edwin B.) Biographical Memoir Edward Emerson Barnard, *etc.* [With a portrait and a bibliography.] 1926. 4°. [*Memoirs of the National Academy of Sciences.* vol. 21.] A.S. **940**.

—— *See* Frost (Edwin B.) Edward Emerson Barnard, *etc.* [With a portrait.] [1923.] 4°. **10883**. ff. **2**.

BARNARD (EDWARD EMERSON)

—— Micrometric Measures of Star Clusters . . . Edited by Edwin B. Frost, George Van Biesbroeck and Mary R. Calvert. pp. 106. *University of Chicago Press : Chicago*, 1931. 4°. [*Publications of the Yerkes Observatory*. vol. 6.] Ac. **4186**. e.

—— A Photographic Atlas of Selected Regions of the Milky Way . . . Edited by Edwin B. Frost . . . and Mary R. Calvert. 2 pt. *Washington*, 1927. *obl.* 4°. [*Carnegie Institution of Washington*. Publication no. 247.] Ac. **1866**.

—— Catalogue of 349 Dark Objects in the Sky. Reprinted . . . from . . . " A Photographic Atlas of Selected Regions of the Milky Way." *University Press : Chicago*, 1927. *obl.* 4°. **8563**. f. **34**.

BARNARD (EDWARD WILLIAM) *See* FLAMINIO (M. A.) Fifty Select Poems of Marc-Antonio Flaminio imitated by the late Rev. E. W. Barnard . . . With a short memoir of the author, *etc.* 1829. 8°. T. **2035**. (2.)

—— *See* WRANGHAM (Francis) M. S. Rev. Edv. Gul. Barnard, A.M. Carmen, *etc.* 1828. 8°. **11408**. g. **27**.

—— The Protestant Beadsman ; or, a Series of biographical notices and hymns, commemorating the Saints and Martyrs, whose holidays are kept by the Church of England, *etc.* [By E. W. Barnard.] pp. xxiii. 176. 1822. 12°. *See* PROTESTANT BEADSMAN. **843**. g. **19**.

—— Trifles imitative of the chaster style of Meleager. [By E. W. Barnard.] pp. 48. 1818. 8°. *See* MELEAGER, *the Poet*. **11335**. aa. **34**.

BARNARD (ELLSWORTH)

—— Edwin Arlington Robinson. A critical study. pp. xiii. 318. *Macmillan Co.: New York*, 1952. 8°. **11871**. r. **10**.

—— Shelley's Religion. pp. xii. 320. *University of Minnesota Press: Minneapolis*, [1937.] 8°. **11859**. bb. **23**.

BARNARD (ELSIE)

—— *See* STOREY (Barbara) and BARNARD (E.) A Key to Speech and Song. 1940. 8°. **11806**. a. **12**.

BARNARD (ESTHER GERTRUIDA)

—— Old-Time Recipes. Edited by E. Barnard, *etc.* (Outydse reseppies.) *Eng. & Afrikaans.* pp. 64. 64. *Maskew Miller: Cape Town*, 1952. 8°. **7949**. p. **46**.

BARNARD (ETTWELL AUGUSTINE BRACHER) *See* BADSEY. Churchwardens' Accounts of the Parish of Badsey, with Aldington, in Worcestershire, from 1525 to 1571 . . . Edited by E. A. B. Barnard. 1913. 8°. **4535**. de. **16**. (2.)

—— *See* BIRMINGHAM.—*King Edward's School.* The Records of King Edward's School, Birmingham, *etc.* (vol. 3. Edited by W. F. Carter and E. A. B. Barnard.) 1924, *etc.* 8°. [*Publications of the Dugdale Society.* vol. 12.] Ac. **8024**.

—— *See* BOMFORD (G. F.) Other Days : Other Ways, *etc.* [Edited by E. A. B. Barnard.] 1930. 8°. **10824**. aaa. **7**.

—— *See* HUMPHREYS (John) *M.D.S.* Studies in Worcestershire History . . . Edited, with introduction, appendices and annotations, by E. A. B. Barnard. 1938. 8°. **10353**. b. **39**.

—— *See* NORTON (T. E. G.) A Memoir of Tom Edgar Grantley Norton, *etc.* [Edited by E. A. B. Barnard.] [1915.] 8°. **012273**. bb. **19**.

BARNARD (ETTWELL AUGUSTINE BRACHER)

—— *See* SHAWCROSS (John P.) Bengeworth . . . By J. P. Shawcross . . . assisted by E. A. Barnard. 1927. 8°. **010368**. g. **60**.

—— [For editions of W. Smith's " Evesham," revised by E. A. B. Barnard :] *See* SMITH (William) *of Evesham.*

—— *See* SOUTH LITTLETON, *Worcestershire.* Churchwardens' Accounts of the Parish of South Littleton . . . Transcribed . . . and annotated by E. A. B. Barnard, *etc.* [1926.] 8°. **04705**. b. **32**.

—— The Bigges of Lenchwick and their Tombs in Norton Church, Evesham. [With illustrations.] pp. 17. " *Lincolnshire Chronicle* " : *Lincoln*, 1917. 8°. **9914**. tt. **18**.

—— The Edens of Honeybourne, Gloucestershire. An old-time correspondence : 1785–1839. (Reprinted from " The Evesham Journal.") pp. 25. *Evesham*, 1929. 8°. **9902**. bb. **3**.

—— Evesham Churchyard Inscriptions, A.D. 1899. pp. 11. [1912.] 8°. **9904**. cc. **19**. (2.)

—— The Hemmings of Alcester and Oxford. An old-time family correspondence, 1791–1819. (Reprinted from " The Evesham Journal.") [Consisting for the most part of abstracts of letters written by Mary and Richard Hemming. With portraits.] pp. 23. *W. & H. Smith: Evesham*, 1931. 8°. **09915**. h. **5**.

—— The Last Days of Hailes Abbey and of Gretton Chapel . . . Reprinted from " The Evesham Journal & Four Shires Advertiser." (With three illustrations.) pp. 23. *Evesham*, 1928. 8°. **04784**. de. **49**.

—— List of the Printed Papers and Miscellanea, with index ; and of the Pedigrees and Portraits, in the Prattinton Collections of Worcestershire History, in the possession of the Society of Antiquaries. ff. ii. 162. 1932. 4°. *See* LONDON.—III. *Society of Antiquaries.* **10358**. l. **42**.

—— New Links with Shakespeare. [Based on the Hanley Court collection of documents. With a map.] pp. xiv. 135. pl. XVI. *University Press : Cambridge*, 1930. 8°. **011761**. f. **15**.

—— Notes & Queries concerning Evesham and the Four Shires. Being a selected collection of original contributions to the antiquarian column of the " Evesham Journal " during the period July, 1906—July, 1908 (—July 1912). Edited by E. A. Barnard. 3 vol. *W. & H. Smith : Evesham*, 1911–14. 8°. **010352**. f. **49**.

—— Old Barcheston, Warwickshire. 1626–1725. pp. 21. *Journal Press : Evesham*, 1927. 8°. **010352**. de. **103**.

—— Old Bromsgrove. The strange adventures of John Lynold, 1611–1619. (Reprinted from the Bromsgrove " Messenger.") pp. 31. " *Messenger* " : *Bromsgrove*, 1927. 8°. **010855**. a. **35**.

—— Old Bromsgrove from 1649 to 1721. pp. 31. "*Messenger:* " *Bromsgrove*, 1926. 8°. **010352**. de. **95**.

—— Old Evesham and District. A handlist of original articles and notes contributed to the antiquarian column of the Evesham Journal during the period July 27th, 1912 —July 25th, 1936 . . . Being an addendum to Evesham and Four Shires Notes and Queries, vols. I.–III., *etc.* pp. 23. *W. & H. Smith: Evesham*, 1937. 8°. **010351**. k. **50**.

—— Old Evesham Pamphlets. 3 pt.

1. The Story of Dresden House, Evesham. pp. 16. 1914.
2. The Story of the Round House, commonly known as the Booth Hall, Evesham. pp. 16. 1915.
3. Evesham and a Reputed Son of Queen Elizabeth [i.e. Robert Dudley]. pp. 12. 1926.

1914–26. 8°. **10358**. e. **35**.

BARNARD (Ettwell Augustine Bracher)

—— The Prattinton Collections of Worcestershire History. [With portraits and a map.] pp. 128. pl. vi. *Journal Press: Evesham,* 1931. 8°. **010360. aaa. 67.**

—— The Rouses of Rous Lench, Worcestershire. pp. 20. *W. & H. Smith: Evesham,* 1921. 8°. **9907. e. 25.**

—— The Ruined Norman Chapel of Netherton, near Elmley Castle, Worcestershire. [With plates.] pp. 31. 1921. *obl.* 8°. **7815. a. 44.**

—— [Another edition.] *Journal Press: Evesham,* [1931.] 8°. **7817. aaa. 47.**

—— A Seventeenth Century Country Gentleman—Sir Francis Throckmorton, 1640–80. [With plates, including a portrait.] pp. viii. 99. *W. Heffer & Sons: Cambridge,* 1944. 8°. **10861. bb. 11.**

—— A Seventeenth Century Country Gentleman, Sir Francis Throckmorton, 1640–80. (Second edition.) [With plates, including a portrait.] pp. viii. 99. *W. Heffer & Sons: Cambridge,* 1948. 8°. **10862. ee. 15.**

—— The Sheldons. Being some account of the Sheldon family of Worcestershire and Warwickshire. pp. xi. 138. pl. ix. *University Press: Cambridge,* 1936. 8°. **9907. p. 10.**

—— Some Notes on the Evesham Branch of the Washbourne Family. [With illustrations.] pp. 60. *W. & H. Smith: Evesham,* 1914. 8°. **9904. ccc. 19.**

—— Some Notes on the Old Evesham "Mercy & Truth" Lodge, No. 703, *etc.* [Signed: E. A. B. B., i.e. E. A. B. Barnard.] pp. 8. [1914.] 8°. *See* B., E. A. B. **4763. c. 22.**

—— Further Notes on the Old Evesham "Mercy & Truth" Lodge, No. 703, *etc.* pp. 7. [*Evesham,* 1917.] 8°. **4763. c. 21.**

—— Souvenir of Abbey Manor, Evesham, Red Cross Hospital, 1914–1919. [With illustrations.] pp. 12. [1919.] *obl.* 16°. **07687. de. 38.**

—— Stanton and Snowhill, Gloucestershire. pp. 122. pl. xvii. *University Press: Cambridge,* 1927. 8°. **010360. aa. 3.**

—— The Tower and Bells of Evesham. pp. 40. *W. & H. Smith: Evesham,* 1910. 8°. **07816. ee. 57.**

—— The True Story of John Washbourne, of Wichenford, co. Worcester, born 1620; died 1652. [With maps.] pp. 19. *Journal Press: Evesham,* [1923.] 8°. **10827. bb. 38.**

—— A Vanished Palace: being some account of Tickenhill House, Bewdley. pp. 13. *J. Palmer: Cambridge,* 1925. 8°. **010360. bb. 6.**

—— Second impression. pp. 13. *J. Palmer: Cambridge,* 1927. 8°. **010352. ff. 38.**

BARNARD (Ettwell Augustine Brachen) and **WACE** (Alan John Bayard)

—— The Sheldon Tapestry Weavers and their Work, *etc.* (From "Archaeologia.") [With plates.] *Oxford,* 1928. 4°. **7742. eee. 34.**

BARNARD (Eunice Fuller) *See* Fuller, afterwards Barnard (E.)

BARNARD (Everett L.)

—— It's in the Bag. A farcical comedy in one act. pp. 28. *Abel Heywood & Son: Manchester,* [1947.] 8°. [*White House Plays.* no. 476.] **11778.p.1/476.**

BARNARD (F. A.) *Anarchist.*

—— La Pluralité en amour . . . [By F. A. Barnard.] La Valeur de la chasteté. [By John R. Coryell.] Traduction de E. Armand. pp. 24. *Paris & Orléans,* [1925?] 8°. **08416. bb. 65.**

BARNARD (F. A.) *of Cincinnati.*

—— American Biographical History of Eminent and Self-Made Men, with portrait illustrations . . . Michigan volume. 9 pt. *Western Biographical Publishing Co.: Cincinnati,* 1878. 4°. **10880. k. 7.**

BARNARD (Finch) The Charlemagne Pedigrees. pp. 112. *Drane's: London,* [1915.] 8°. **9905. aaa. 47.**

—— The Imperial Pedigrees. pp. 27. *H. J. Drane: London,* 1914. 8°. **9904. c. 46.**

—— More Light on Shakespeare and the Barnard and Lucy Families. pp. 16. *Finch Barnard: London,* 1914. 8°. **11761. df. 9.**

—— [A reissue, with additional matter inserted.] ms. notes. 1914 [1916]. 8°. **011765. f. 49.**

—— Science and the Soul. The Psychology of Shakespeare as revealed in the Sonnets. Christianity and the Barnards. Buddhism and Christianity. pp. 96. *Selwyn & Blount: London,* 1918. 8°. **11764. pp. 23.**

—— Shakespeare and the Barnard Family. pp. 15. *Finch Barnard: London,* 1914. 8°. **11761. df. 10.**

—— [A reissue, with additional matter inserted.] 1914 [1916]. 8°. **011765. f. 48.**

BARNARD (Florence)

—— How to Manage Money Successfully by Money Management Method. pp. 32. *American Association for Economic Education: Boston,* 1939. 8°. **08230. c. 20.**

—— Money Management Method . . . Achievement Test, *etc.* 2 bk. *American Association for Economic Education: Boston,* [1937.] 8°. **08230. a. 9.**

BARNARD (Frances Catherine) *See* Ball (Charles) *Negro Slave.* The Life of a Negro Slave. Re-edited by Mrs. Alfred Barnard. 1846. 8°. **1453. b. 9.**

—— The Doleful Death and Flowery Funeral of Fancy. [A poem.] pp. 42. *Harvey & Darton: London,* 1837. 8°. **11645. aa. 11.**

—— Embroidered Facts. pp. 153. *Orr & Smith: London,* 1836. 8°. **1210. b. 39.**

BARNARD (Frances Kinderley) *See* Edgeworth (Maria) Heinrich und Luzie. Translated . . . by F. K. Barnard. 1846. 24°. **12805. b. 11.**

—— *See* Paalzow (H. von) Godway Castle . . . Translated from the German by F. K. Barnard. 1846. 8°. **12410. e. 34.**

BARNARD (Francis) A Sermon preach'd in the Parish Church of St. Bartholomew . . . at the funeral of Mrs. Elizabeth Fullerton. Novemb. 26, 1734. pp. 26. *G. Strahan: London,* 1735. 8°. **1416. g. 46.**

BARNARD (Francis Pierrepont) *See* England.—*Miscellaneous Public Documents.*—iii. Edward iv. [1461–1483.] Edward iv's French Expedition of 1475. The leaders and their badges: being MS. 2. M.16 College of Arms. Edited . . . by F. P. Barnard. 1925. 4°. **9505. d. 13.**

—— *See* Shakespeare (W.) [*Smaller Collections of Plays.—English.*] Arnold's School Shakespeare, *etc.* (The Life and Death of King John. Edited by F. P. Barnard. [1894, *etc.*] 8°. **011765. ee. 15.**

BARNARD (FRANCIS PIERREPONT)

—— *See* SHAKESPEARE (W.) [*Smaller Collections of Plays.—English.*] Arnold's School Shakespeare. (The Tragedy of King Richard the Third. Edited by F. P. Barnard.) [1894, *etc.*] 8°. **011765**. ee. **15**.

—— *See* UPTON (Nicolaus) The Essential Portions of Nicholas Upton's De Studio Militari before 1446. Translated by J. Blount . . . Edited by F. P. Barnard. 1931. 4°. **11630**. ee. **31**.

—— The Casting-Counter and the Counting-Board : a chapter in the history of numismatics and early arithmetic. pp. 357. pl. LXIII. *Clarendon Press : Oxford,* 1916. 4°. **7756**. e. **22**.

—— A Century of Epigrams. Englished by F. P. Barnard. *Privately printed : Stratford-upon-Avon,* 1916. 4°. **011604**. ee. **16**.

—— Companion to English History, Middle Ages. Edited by F. P. Barnard . . . With ninety seven plates. pp. xv. 372. *Clarendon Press : Oxford,* 1902. 8°. **9510**. cc. **26**.

—— Mediaeval England. A new edition of Barnard's Companion to English History. Edited by H. W. C. Davis. pp. xxi. 632. *Clarendon Press : Oxford,* 1924. 8°. **9510**. ccc. **21**.

—— A Fardel of Epigrams. Done into English by F. P. Barnard. pp. 114. *Humphrey Milford : London,* 1922. 16°. **011648**. de. **148**.

—— The Historical Monograph Series. General editor : F. P. Barnard.

1. William Cecil, Lord Burghley. [By Augustus Jessop and others.]

T. C. & E. C. Jack : London, 1904. fol. L.R. **31**. b. **9**.
No more published.

—— Portuguese Jettons . . . Reprinted from the " Numismatic Chronicle," *etc.* pp. 40. [*London,*] 1923. 8°. Dept. of Coins & Medals.

—— Satirical and Controversial Medals of the Reformation. The biceps or double-headed series. pp. 45. pl. VI. *Clarendon Press : Oxford,* 1927. 4°. **07757**. cc. **12**.

—— Strongbow's Conquest of Ireland. Translations from the Works of Gerald of Barri, Roger of Howden [and others], *etc.* pp. 214. *David Nutt : London,* 1888. 8°. [*English History by Contemporary Writers.*] **2394**. a. **10**.

BARNARD (FRANCIS PIERREPONT) and **SHEPARD** (THOMAS) *F.S.A.*

—— Arms & Blazons of the Colleges of Oxford. [With illustrations in colour.] pp. 61. *Oxford University Press : London,* 1929. 8°. **9914**. e. **58**.

BARNARD (FRANK) Picturesque Life in Shetland, from drawings by F. Barnard. With descriptive notes. *G. Waterston & Sons : Edinburgh & London,* 1890. *obl.* 4°. **1782**. a. **2**.

BARNARD (FREDERICK) *See* APAQUE (L. H.) A Baker's Dozen . . . With illustrations by F. Barnard. [1882.] 8°. **4419**. l. **10**.

—— *See* ARCHER (Thomas) *Author of " Wayfe Summers."* Charles Dickens . . . With . . . character sketches . . . by F. Barnard. [1894 ?] fol. **L.R.404.1.10.**

—— —— [1902.] fol. **1899.r.7.**

—— *See* BESANT (*Sir* Walter) All Sorts and Conditions of Men . . . With illustrations by F. Barnard. 1882. 8°. **12642**. d. **10**.

BARNARD (FREDERICK)

—— *See* BUNYAN (John) [*Pilgrim's Progress.—Pt.* I., II.] The Pilgrim's Progress . . . With . . . illustrations by F. Barnard, *etc.* 1880. 8°. **560***. d. **1**.

—— —— [1888.] 8°. **4415**. l. **19**.

—— *See* DICKENS (Charles) [*Works.*] The Works of Charles Dickens. Household edition. With illustrations [by F. Barnard and others]. [1873, *etc.*] 8°. **12603**. h. **13–33**.

—— *See* DICKENS (Charles) [*Works.*] The Waverley Edition of the Works of Charles Dickens. (Illustrated by . . . coloured reproductions from the original drawings by F. Barnard.) [1913, *etc.*] 8°. **12272**. s. **1**.

—— *See* DICKENS (Charles) [*Sketches by Boz.*] Schetsen van Boz . . . Houtgravuren naar teekeningen van F. Barnard. [1876.] 8°. **12620**. k. **28**.

—— *See* DICKENS (Charles) [*Single Tales and Plays.*] A Christmas Carol . . . With . . . illustrations by John Leech and F. Barnard, *etc.* 1907. 8°. **012618**. fff. **2**.

—— *See* DICKENS (Charles) [*Selections.*] Pictures from Dickens with readings. With illustrations by H. M. Paget, F. Barnard, *etc.* [1895.] 4°. **12604**. h. **29**.

—— *See* DICKENS (Charles) [*Appendix.*] Scenes and Characters from the Works of Charles Dickens : being eight hundred and sixty-six drawings by F. Barnard [and others], *etc.* 1908. 4°. **12271**. i. **15**.

—— *See* HOOD (Thomas) *the Younger.* Life in Lodgings . . . With . . . drawings by F. Barnard. [1880.] 8°. **12316**. h. **26**.

—— *See* HOOD (Thomas) *the Younger.* Petsetilla's Posy . . . With . . . illustrations by F. Barnard, *etc.* [1871.] 8°. **12807**. ff. **22**.

—— *See* JENKINS (John E.) Ginx's Baby . . . Illustrated by F. Barnard. 1876. 8°. **12638**. d. **4**.

—— *See* JENKINS (John E.) Jobson's Enemies. (Illustrated by F. Barnard.) 1879, *etc.* 8°. **12641**. dd. **2**.

—— *See* MITFORD (Mary R.) Children of the Village. With illustrations by F. Barnard . . . and other artists. 1880. 4°. **12356**. h. **9**.

—— *See* MURRAY (David C.) Joseph's Coat . . . With . . . illustrations by F. Barnard. 1881. 8°. **12642**. bb. **2**.

—— *See* MURRAY (Eustace C. G.) People I have Met . . . Illustrated with . . . engravings, from designs by F. Barnard. 1883. 8°. **12330**. k. **31**.

—— *See* SHERIDAN (*Right Hon.* R. B. B.) [*Dramatic Works.*] Sheridan's Comedies . . . With illustrations by E. A. Abbey, F. Barnard [and others], *etc.* 1885. 8°. **11779**. h. **17**.

—— *See* SIMS (George R.) How the Poor Live . . . With . . . illustrations by F. Barnard. 1883. 4°. **8276**. i. **12**.

—— *See* SUNLIGHT. Sunlight and Shade . . . Illustrations by F. Barnard [and others], *etc.* 1883. 8°. **11602**. gg. **14**.

—— A Series of Character Sketches from Dickens, from original drawings by F. Barnard. Reproduced in photogravure. 3 vol. *Cassell & Co. : London,* 1884–87. fol. **1872**. c. **13**.

BARNARD (Frederick)

—— A Series of Character Sketches from Dickens in colour. From original drawings by F. Barnard. *Waverley Book Co.: London*, [1913.] fol. K.T.C. **123**. b. **5**.
A different work from the preceding.

—— A Series of Character Sketches from Thackeray, from original drawings by F. Barnard, reproduced in photogravure. [Six plates.] *Cassell & Co.: London*, [1887.] fol. **1872**. c. **16**.

BARNARD (Frederick) and **ROSS** (Charles Henry)

—— Behind a Brass Knocker. Some grim realities in picture and prose. pp. 146. *Chatto & Windus: London*, 1883. 8°. **12315**. h. **38**.

—— [Another edition.] pp. 121. *"Judy" Office: London*, [1884.] 8°. **12315**. h. **46**.

BARNARD (*Sir* Frederick Augusta) [A ms. Classed Catalogue of the Library of George III., acquired by the British Museum in 1823.] 12 vol. [1812–20?] fol. *See* George III., *King of Great Britain and Ireland.* [*Appendix.*] **102**. gg. & **103**. gg.

—— [A manuscript in the handwriting of Nicholas Carlisle, dated 19 June 1828, containing a list, compiled by Sir F. A. Barnard, of books withdrawn in 1828 by order of King George IV. from the Library of King George III. acquired by the British Museum; together with "A List of Books given to the King by Mr Bryant, October 1st, 1782 . . . written by Mr Bryant," with notes by Sir F. A. Barnard.] [1828.] 4°. *See* London.—III. *British Museum.—Department of Printed Books.* **11912**. b. **55**.

—— Bibliothecæ Regiæ catalogus. [A catalogue of the library of George III., acquired by the British Museum in 1823.] 5 tom. 1820–29. fol. *See* George III., *King of Great Britain and Ireland.* [*Appendix.*] **L.2.b.2.**

BARNARD (Frederick Augustus Porter) *See* Bridge (Bewick) A Treatise on the Construction . . . of the Three Conic Sections . . . With additions and alterations by the American editor (F. A. P. Barnard). 1836. 8°. **1393**. f. **24**.

—— *See* Fulton (John) *D.D.* Memoirs of Frederick A. P. Barnard. 1896. 8°. **4985**. d. **65**.

—— *See* Encyclopaedias. Johnson's New Universal Cyclopædia . . . Editors-in-chief: F. A. P. Barnard . . . Arnold Guyot, *etc.* 1875, *etc.* 8°. **741**. dd. **3**.

—— *See* New York, *Columbia University*. Proceedings at the Inauguration of Frederick A. P. Barnard . . . as President of Columbia College, *etc.* 1865. 8°. **8366**. cc. **25**.

—— *See* Woolsey (Theodore D.) The First Century of the Republic. A review of American progress. By the Rev. T. D. Woolsey . . . F. A. P. Barnard [and others], *etc.* 1876. 8°. **9605**. f. **2**.

—— Analytic Grammar; with symbolic illustration. pp. 264. *E. French: New-York*, 1836. 12°. **12982**. b. **51**.

—— Art Culture: its relation to national refinement and national morality. An oration pronounced before the Alabama Alpha of the Society of the Phi Beta Kappa . . . July 11th, 1854. pp. 43. *D. Van Nostrand: New York*, 1864. 8°. **7805**. bb. **34**. **(6.)**

—— The Imaginary Metrological System of the Great Pyramid of Gizeh . . . From the Proceedings of the American Metrological Society. . . . Reprinted from School of Mines Quarterly, *etc.* pp. iv. 106. *J. Wiley & Sons: New York*, 1884. 8°. **7704**. bb. **30**.

BARNARD (Frederick Augustus Porter)

—— The Later Days of Old Columbia College. From the annual reports of F. A. P. Barnard, President of Columbia College, 1864–1889. Edited by William F. Russell, *etc.* [With a portrait.] pp. xi. 415. *See* New York, *Columbia University.* The Rise of a University. vol. 1. 1937. 8°. **08385**. ee. **14**.

—— Letter to the President of the United States, by a Refugee [i.e. F. A. P. Barnard]. pp. 32. 1863. 8°. *See* Refugee. **8177**. bb. **104**. **(5.)**

—— Letters on College Government, and the evils inseparable from the American college system in its present form, *etc.* pp. 104. *D. Appleton & Co.: New York*, 1855. 8°. **8365**. d. **3**.

—— Machinery and Processes of the Industrial Arts, and Apparatus of the Exact Sciences. pp. ix. 669. pl. VIII. *Washington*, 1870. 8°. [*Reports of the United States Commissioners to the Paris Universal Exposition*, 1867. vol. 3.] A.S. **408/11**.

—— The Metric System of Weights and Measures . . . Third edition, with additions and index, *etc.* pp. vi. 456. *American Metric Bureau: Boston*, 1879. 8°. **8507**. g. **17**.

—— Theory of Magic Squares and Magic Cubes. 1888. *See* Washington, *Columbia.—National Academy of Sciences.* Memoirs, *etc.* vol. 4. pt. 1. 1884, *etc.* 4°. A.S. **940**.

—— A Treatise on Arithmetic, designed particularly as a text book for classes, *etc.* pp. x. 288. *Packard & Butler: Hartford* [Conn.], 1830. 12°. **1393**. b. **5**.

BARNARD (Frederick Augustus Porter) and **PRATT** (John W.)

—— Report on a Proposition to modify the plan of instruction in the University of Alabama, made to the Faculty of the University. pp. 104. *D. Appleton & Co.: New York*, 1855. 8°. **8365**. d. **4**.

BARNARD (Frederick J.) *See* Sprague (William B.) A Sermon preached . . . on occasion of the death of Frederick J. Barnard, Jr. 1856. 8°. **4985**. ee. **12**. **(13.)**

BARNARD (Frederick Lamport) A Three Years' Cruize in the Mozambique Channel, for the suppression of the Slave Trade. pp. xiii. 319. *Richard Bentley: London*, 1848. 12°. **10095**. b. **22**.

BARNARD (Geoffrey L.)

—— Grunter Pig . . . (English for Beginners Series.) Illustrated by H. Douglas Williams. [A reader for young children.] 4 bk. *Hugh Evans & Sons: Liverpool*, 1954–57. 8°. **012987**. ppp. **13**.

—— Hints for Teachers. 3 pt. *Hugh Evans & Sons: Liverpool*, 1955–57. 8°. **012987**. ppp. **13**a.

BARNARD (George) *Artist.* *See* Hoole, afterwards Hofland (Barbara) Richmond and the Surrounding Scenery [drawn by J. D. Harding, G. Barnard, and others], *etc.* 1832. 4°. **10352**. k. **19**.

—— Barnard's Trees. A new work consisting of studies of trees from nature . . . Drawn on stone by the author, with . . . short descriptive letter press. pl. 30. *Winsor & Newton: London*, 1868. fol. **1758**. c. **14**.

—— The Brunnens of Nassau and the River Lahn. [A series of views drawn from nature and engraved on stone.] *Thos. McLean: London*, [1840?] fol. **1784**. c. **9**.

BARNARD (George) *Artist.*

—— Drawing from Nature: a series of progressive instructions in sketching, from elementary studies to finished views, with examples from Switzerland and the Pyrenees; to which are appended lectures on art delivered at Rugby School. Illustrated by eighteen coloured and lithographic plates, *etc.* pp. vi. 348. *Longmans & Co.: London,* 1865. 8°. **7856.** ee. **29.**

—— New edition. pp. vi. 348. *G. Routledge & Sons: London,* 1877. 8°. **7856.** eee. **8.**

—— Handbook of Foliage and Foreground Drawing. Illustrated by numerous examples of trees, shrubs, *etc.* pp. viii. 125. pl. 60. *Ingram, Cooke & Co.: London,* 1853. 8°. **7075.** d. **11.**

—— New and enlarged edition. pp. xii. 128. pl. 60. *Griffith & Farran: London,* 1870. 8°. **7854.** r. **8.**

—— Switzerland. Scenes and incidents of travel in the Bernese Oberland, &c., drawn from nature and on stone. *Thomas McLean: London,* 1843. fol. **1264.** h. **22.**

—— The Theory and Practice of Landscape Painting in Water-Colours. Illustrated by a series of twenty four designs, coloured diagrams and numerous woodcuts, *etc.* 7 pt. pp. 176. *W. S. Orr & Co.: London,* 1855. 8°. **7855.** g. **25.**

—— New and enlarged edition. pp. 286. *Hamilton, Adams & Co.: London,* 1858. 4°. **7855.** g. **26.**

—— Seventh thousand. pp. ii. 286. *Routledge & Co.: London,* 1861. 8°. **2262.** e. **7.**

BARNARD (George) *M.R.C.S.* Cholera Maligna is a specific acute inflammation of the mucous tissue of the small intestines. pp. 26. xxx. MS. NOTES. *Thacker, Spink & Co.: Calcutta,* 1869. 8°. **7306.** ccc. **3.** (**17.**)

BARNARD (George) *Novelist.* Dugdale's Success. pp. 252. *Methuen & Co.: London,* 1927. 8°. NN. **12798.**

BARNARD (George) *Religious Writer.* The Mexican Reformation. pp. xiii. 73. *Sheed & Ward: London,* [1927.] 8°. **4745.** de. **20.**

BARNARD (George G.) Proceedings in the Court of Impeachment in the matter of the impeachment of George Barnard, a Justice of the Supreme Court of the State of New York. 3 vol. 1874. 8°. *See* New York, *State of.—Court of Impeachment.* A.S. **41**/**4.**

BARNARD (George Philip)

—— Modern Mass Spectrometry, *etc.* pp. 326. *Institute of Physics: London,* 1953. 8°. [*Physics in Industry.*] W.P. **4549**/**25.**

—— The Selenium Cell: its properties and applications, *etc.* pp. xxix. 331. *Constable & Co.: London,* 1930. 8°. **8901.** dd. **7.**

BARNARD (George Robert) Simple Lessons on Elementary Science, *etc.* pp. viii. 121. *London,* [1902.] 8°. [*Brown's School Series.*] **012210.a.1/23.**

BARNARD (Gladys Violet)

—— Guide to the Regalia & Plate of the Corporation of the City of Norwich. [Compiled by G. V. Barnard. With plates.] pp. 28. 1939. 8°. *See* Norwich.—*Corporation.* **07805.** f. **90.**

—— Paintings of the Norwich School. [With reproductions.] *Jarrold & Sons: Norwich,* [1950.] 8°. [*Magna-Crome Books.* no. 8.] W.P. **3517**/**8.**

BARNARD (Guy Christian) An Elementary Puzzle Arithmetic. pp. xii. 68. *G. Allen & Unwin: London,* 1925. 8°. **08531.** de. **38.**

—— The Supernormal. A critical introduction to psychic science. pp. 256. *Rider & Co.: London,* 1933. 8°. **08632.** h. **29.**

BARNARD (Hannah) *See* Christicola, *pseud.* Some Tracts relating to the Controversy between Hannah Barnard and the Society of Friends, *etc.* 1802. 8°. **4152.** e. **16.** (**2.**)

—— *See* Friends, *Society of.* An Appeal to the Society of Friends, on the primitive simplicity of their Christian principles, *etc.* [A defence of Hannah Barnard in her controversy with the Society of Friends.] 1801. 8°. **4152.** e. **17.**

—— A Narrative of the Proceedings in America, of the Society called Quakers, in the case of Hannah Barnard. With a brief review of the previous transactions in Great Britain and Ireland: intended as a sequel to an Appeal to the Society of Friends. [By Thomas Foster.] pp. xvi. 145. *J. Johnson: London,* 1804. 8°. **4152.** g. **3.**

BARNARD (Harold Leslie) Contributions to Abdominal Surgery . . . Edited by James Sherren. (Memoir of H. L. Barnard. By H. H. Bashford.) pp. xix. 391. *Edward Arnold: London,* 1910. 8°. **07481.** h. **52.**

BARNARD (Harry) *Biographer.*

—— "Eagle Forgotten." The life of John Peter Altgeld . . . Illustrated. [With portraits.] pp. 496. *Bobbs-Merrill Co.: Indianapolis, New York,* [1938.] 8°. **10885.** dd. **37.**

BARNARD (Harry) *of Stoke-on-Trent.*

—— The Art of the Potter, *etc.* [With plates.] pp. vi. 88. *A. & C. Black: London,* 1932. 8°. [“*Peeps*” *Series.*] W.P. **8673**/**5.**

—— Artes Etruriae renascuntur. A record of the . . . works (of Josiah Wedgwood & Sons) at Etruria as they exist to-day . . . Told by H. Barnard. Drawn by James Hodgkiss. pp. 39. *Bemrose & Sons: [London,]* 1920. 4°. **7816.** v. **16.**

—— Chats on Wedgwood Ware . . . With . . . illustrations. pp. 260. *T. Fisher Unwin: London,* 1924. 8°. **07805.** b. **23.**

BARNARD (Henry)

—— *See* Blair (Annal.) Henry Barnard, School Administrator. [With a portrait.] [1938.] 8°. **10888.** h. **4.**

—— *See* Connecticut.—State Board of Education. First (—Fourth) Annual Report of the Board . . . Together with the first (—fourth) annual report of the Secretary (H. Barnard). 1839, *etc.* 8°. **A.S.C.97.**

—— *See* Connecticut.—State Board of Education. *Schools.* The Connecticut Common School Journal . . . Edited by H. Barnard. 1838, *etc.* 4°. **A.S.C.97/9.**

—— *See* Goodwin (Nathaniel) Genealogical Notes, or Contributions to the family history of some of the first settlers of Connecticut and Massachusetts. [Edited in part by H. Barnard.] 1856. 8°. **9914.** a. **17.**

—— *See* Monroe (W. S.) Bibliography of Henry Barnard. 1897. 4°. **11901.** bb. **36.** (**6.**)

—— *See* Periodical Publications.—*New York.* The American Journal of Education and College Review. Editors: A. Peters . . . H. Barnard. 1856, *etc.* 8°. P.P. **1225.** b.

—— *See* PROVIDENCE, *Rhode Island.—Rhode Island Institute of Instruction.* Journal of the Rhode Island Institute of Instruction . . . Edited by H. Barnard. 1846, *etc.* 8°. P.P. **1219**. f.

—— *See* STEINER (B. C.) Life of Henry Barnard, *etc.* 1919. 8°. [*U.S. Bureau of Education. Bulletin.* 1919. no. 8.] A.S. **202**.

—— *See* THURSFIELD (Richard E.) Henry Barnard's American Journal of Education. 1945. 8°. [*Johns Hopkins University Studies in Historical and Political Science.* ser. 43. no. 1.] Ac. **2689**.

—— Armsmear: the Home, the Arm, and the Armory of Samuel Colt. A memorial. [With plates, including a portrait.] pp. 399. *New York*, 1866. 4°. **10882**. k. **11**.

—— A Discourse in Commemoration of the Life, Character and Services of the Rev. Thomas H. Gallaudet, LL.D., *etc.* pp. 62. *Brockett & Hutchinson: Hartford*, 1852. 8°. **4985**. e. **1**.

—— [Another edition.] Tribute to Gallaudet. A discourse . . . With an appendix, containing a history of deaf-mute instruction and institutions, *etc.* pp. 267. *Brockett & Hutchinson: Hartford*, 1852. 8°. **4985**. e. **49**.

—— Second edition. [With a portrait.] pp. 228. *F. C. Brownell: New York; Hutchinson & Bullard: Hartford*, 1859. 8°. **4986**. bbb. **40**.

—— Education and Educational Institutions [in the United States]. *See* UNITED STATES OF AMERICA. [*Appendix.—Miscellaneous.*] Eighty Years' Progress of the United States, *etc.* vol. 2. 1868. 8°. **10412**. ff. **27**.

—— Educational Biography. Memoirs of teachers, educators and benefactors of education, literature, and science. Reprinted from the American Journal of Education. Edited by H. Barnard . . . (Second edition.) Part I. Teachers and Educators. Volume 1. United States. (vol. 2. German Educational Reformers. Memoirs of eminent teachers and educators in Germany. [An abridged translation, by L. W. Fitch and F. B. Perkins, of vol. 1, 2 of Karl von Raumer's "Geschichte der Pädagogik."]) 2 vol. *F. C. Brownell: New York*, 1859, [63.] 8°. **10881**. ee. **26**.
No more published.

—— English Pedagogy. Education, the school, and the teacher, in English literature. Republished from Barnard's American Journal of Education. Second edition. pp. 480. *J. B. Lippincott & Co.: Philadelphia*, 1862. 8°. **8307**. h. **12**.

—— German Schools and Pedagogy. Organization and instruction of common schools in Germany, with the views of German teachers and educators on elementary instruction. Republished from Barnard's American Journal of Education. 2 pt. *F. C. Brownell: New York*, 1861. 8°. **8305**. ee. **23**.
Pt. 2 *consists largely of a translation of vol.* 3 *of Karl von Raumer's "Geschichte der Pädagogik."*

—— Legal Provision respecting the Education and Employment of Children in Factories . . . Education and Labor; or the influence of education on the quality and value of labor, and its connection with insanity and crime. pp. 4. 52. 32. 1842. 8°. *See* CONNECTICUT.—*Board of Commissioners of Common Schools.* **8305**. d. **48**. (3.)

—— Military Schools and Courses of Instruction in the Science and Art of War, in France, Prussia, Austria, Russia, Sweden, Switzerland, Sardinia, England, and the United States . . . Part 1. France and Prussia. [Originally issued in the American Journal of Education under the title: "Miltary Schools in France and Prussia."] pp. 399. *J. B. Lippincott & Co.: Philadelphia*, 1862. 8°. **8824**. d. **49**.
No more published.

—— Revised edition. pp. 960. *E. Steiger: New York*, 1872. 8°. **8824**. f. **1**.

—— National Education. 3 pt.

Systems, Institutions and Statistics of Public Instruction in different countries. 2 pt.
Systems, Institutions and Statistics of Scientific Instruction, applied to national industries in different countries. vol. 1. pp. 807.

E. Steiger: New York, 1872. 8°. **08355**. g. **69**.

—— Normal Schools, and other institutions, agencies, and means designed for the professional education of teachers. 2 pt. *Case & Co.: Hartford*, 1851. 8°. **8307**. g. **18**.

—— National Education in Europe; being an account of the organization . . . of public schools . . . in the principal states . . . Second edition [of "Normal Schools," much enlarged]. *Case, Tiffany & Co.: Hartford*, 1854. 8°. **8307**. g. **19**.

—— Object Teaching and Oral Lessons on Social Science and Common Things . . . Republished from Barnard's American Journal of Education. pp. 434. *F. C. Brownell: New York*, 1860. 8°. **8306**. f. **15**.

—— [Another copy.] **8305**. ee. **25**.

—— Papers on Froebel's Kindergarten, with suggestions on principles and methods of child-culture in different countries. Republished from the "American Journal of Education" . . . American Froebel Union edition. pp. 16*. 799. *American Journal of Education: Hartford*, 1881. 8°. **8306**. g. **6**.

—— Pestalozzi and Pestalozzianism. Life, educational principles, and methods, of John Henry Pestalozzi; with biographical sketches of several of his assistants and disciples. (Second edition.) Reprinted from the American Journal of Education, *etc.* (pt. 2. Selections from the publications of Pestalozzi.) [With a portrait.] 2 pt. *F. C. Brownell: New York*, 1859. 8°. **8309**. d. **50**.

—— Practical Illustrations of the Principle of School Architecture. *See* infra: School Architecture, *etc.*

—— Report on the Condition and Improvement of the Public Schools of Rhode Island . . . Nov. 1, 1845. pp. 255. 1846. 8°. *See* RHODE ISLAND.—*School Commissioners.* **8365**. d. **5**.

—— School Architecture; or Contributions to the improvement of school houses in the United States . . . Fourth edition. [In part based on the author's "School-House Architecture," published in 1842.] pp. 425. *A. S. Barnes & Co.: New York*, 1850. 8°. **8307**. g. **17**.

—— Fifth edition. pp. 464. *Case, Tiffany & Co.: Hartford*, 1854. 8°. **7820**. e. **7**.

—— Practical Illustrations of the Principles of School Architecture. [Extracted, with modifications, from the author's "School Architecture."] pp. 175. *Case, Tiffany & Co.: Hartford*, 1851. 8°. **8307**. g. 5. (3.)

BARNARD (HENRY)

—— School-House Architecture. [A report.] pp. xii. 48. 1842. 8°. *See* CONNECTICUT.—*Board of Commissioners of Common Schools.* 07816. k. 13. (1.)

—— Systems, Institutions and Statistics of Public Instruction in different countries. *See* supra : National Education.

—— Tribute to Gallaudet. *See* supra : A Discourse in Commemoration of the Life . . . of the Rev. Thomas H. Gallaudet, *etc.*

—— Henry Barnard on Education. Edited by John S. Brubacher. [Selections from the Works of H. Barnard. With portraits.] pp. x. 298. *New York & London,* 1931. 8°. [*McGraw-Hill Education Classics.*] W.P. 7657/8.

BARNARD (*Mrs.* HENRY) Dick's First School-Days. A story for little boys. pp. 282. *J. Nisbet & Co.: London,* 1875. 16°. 12804. df. 5.

BARNARD (HOWARD CLIVE) *See* BAGOT (Richard) *Novelist.* The Italian Lakes, *etc.* (Edited by H. C. Barnard.) 1925. 8°. 010028. de. 1/24.

—— *See* CURR (Alexander L.) Commercial Geography . . . Edited by H. C. Barnard. 1930. 8°. 010004. eee. 21.

—— *See* PORT ROYAL, *Abbey of.* The Port-Royalists on Education : extracts . . . selected, translated and furnished with an introduction and notes by H. C. Barnard. 1918. 8°. 8355. b. 31.

—— *See* STEEL (Flora A.) India, *etc.* (Revised by H. C. Barnard.) 1923. 8°. 010028. de. 1/10.

—— *See* STOW (V. A. S.) and BARNARD (H. C.) The Motherland in Pictures, *etc.* 1920. 8°. 10347. g. 15.

—— Africa in Pictures. pp. 64. *A. & C. Black : London,* 1923. 4°. 010094. l. 19.

—— America in Pictures . . . Containing fifty-eight illustrations . . . and also a full-page map in colour. pp. 64. *A. & C. Black : London,* 1916. 4°. 10408. m. 25.

—— Asia in Pictures . . . Containing sixty-five illustrations, *etc.* pp. 64. *A. & C. Black : London,* 1915. 8°. 10055. e. 32.

—— Australia, New Zealand and Oceania in Pictures . . . Containing fifty-nine illustrations . . . including maps and diagrams. pp. 64. *A. & C. Black : London,* 1923. 4°. 10493. ff. 8.

—— Black's Graded Geographies. General editor: H. C. Barnard. / *A. & C. Black: London,* 1935-4 . 8°. 4pt. 10005.pp.11.

—— The British Empire in Pictures . . . Containing fifty-eight illustrations . . . and also a full-page map. pp. 64. *A. & C. Black : London,* 1910. 4°. 10026. k. 28.

—— (New edition.) pp. 64. *A. & C. Black : London,* 1924. 4°. 010004. ff. 10.

—— The British Isles in Pictures. A geographical reading book . . . Containing fifty-eight illustrations . . . and also a full-page map. pp. 64. *A. & C. Black : London,* 1910. 4°. 10369. r. 12.

—— [Another edition.] pp. 64. *A. & C. Black : London,* 1923. 4°. 10369. r. 13.

—— [Another edition.] pp. 64. *A. & C. Black : London,* 1930. 4°. 010360. dd. 7.

BARNARD (HOWARD CLIVE)

—— Europe in Pictures . . . Containing fifty seven illustrations . . . and also four maps. pp. 64. *A. & C. Black: London,* 1911. 4°. 10107. gg. 9.

—— Second edition. pp. 64. *A. & C. Black : London,* 1920. 4°. 10107. gg. 21.

—— The Expansion of the Anglo-Saxon Nations. A short history of the British Empire and the United States. By several contributors. Edited by H. C. Barnard. pp. viii. 404. *A. & C. Black : London,* 1920. 8°. 09007. a. 19.

—— The French Tradition in Education, Ramus to Mme Necker de Saussure. [With plates, maps and bibliography.] pp. vi. 319. *University Press : Cambridge,* 1922. 8°. 8357. c. 28.

—— A Geography of Common Things, *etc.* pp. iv. 123. *A. & C. Black : London,* 1925. 8°. 10003. eeee. 6.

—— Girls at School under the Ancien Régime. Three lectures, *etc.* pp. xii. 82. *Burns & Oates: London,* 1954. 8°. 8356. a. 46.

—— How Other People Live . . . Containing sixty illustrations, *etc.* pp. 64. *A. & C. Black : London,* 1911. 8°. 10024. g. 19.

—— India in Pictures . . . Containing fifty-three illustrations . . . and also thirteen maps, *etc.* pp. 64. *A. & C. Black : London,* 1922. 4°. 10056. i. 33.

—— An Introduction to Teaching. pp. 256. *University of London Press: London,* [1952.] 8°. 8369. de. 26.

—— Introductory Geography, *etc.* pp. iv. 154. *A. & C. Black : London,* 1917. 8°. 10004. c. 51.

—— Second edition. pp. iv. 154. *A. & C. Black : London,* 1921. 8°. 10003. eee. 21.

—— The Little Schools of Port-Royal. pp. x. 263. *University Press : Cambridge,* 1913. 8°. 08355. g. 22.

—— Madame de Maintenon and Saint-Cyr. [With a portrait.] pp. xi. 240. *A. & C. Black : London,* 1934. 8°. 10655. r. 14.

—— The Making of the British Empire. General editor : H. C. Barnard. 2 vol. *A. & C. Black : London,* 1922, 25. 8°. 09008. b. 19.

—— Observational Geography and Regional Survey, *etc.* pp. 45. 1935. 8°. *See* LONDON.—III. *Le Play Society.* 010004. g. 55.

—— Outlines of Physical Geography . . . Containing 93 illustrations, maps, and diagrams. pp. viii. 156. *A. & C. Black : London,* 1914. 8°. 10001. df. 34.

—— Second edition, *etc.* pp. viii. 156. *A. & C. Black: London,* 1917. 8°. 10003. eee. 2.

—— Third edition, *etc.* pp. viii. 156. *A. & C. Black: London,* 1925. 8°. 10004. cc. 37.

—— Outlines of Scripture History . . . Containing twenty-two full-page illustrations . . . and three maps. pp. viii. 120. *A. & C. Black : London,* 1915. 8°. 03127. ee. 44.

—— Pictures of Famous Travel . . . Containing fifty-nine illustrations, *etc.* pp. 64. *A. & C. Black : London,* 1913. 4°. 10024. g. 20.

—— Principles and Practice of Geography Teaching. pp. xi. 233. *University Tutorial Press : London,* 1933. 8°. 010005. e. 3.

BARNARD (Howard Clive)

—— Principles and Practice of Geography Teaching. (Second edition.) pp. viii. 235. *University Tutorial Press: London*, 1948. 8°. **010005**. e. **55**.

—— Principles and Practice of Geography Teaching. (Third edition.) pp. viii. 235. *University Tutorial Press: London*, 1949. 8°. **10004**. ccc. **29**.

—— A Short History of English Education. From 1760 to 1944. pp. xvii. 400. *University of London Press: London*, [1947.] 8°. **8367**. b. **47**.

BARNARD (Howard Clive) and **TAYLOR** (F. N.) *Old Ruymian.*

—— Records, 1909–1922, of the Ramsgate County School, *etc.* [With plates, including portraits.] pp. 204. 1933. 8°. *See* Ramsgate.—*Ramsgate County School for Boys, etc.* **08364**. de. **17**.

BARNARD (I. W.) *See* Barnardt.

BARNARD (Inman)

—— Cities and Men . . . Edited and with an introduction by Sisley Huddleston. [With plates.] pp. x. 264. *Geoffrey Bles: London*, 1940. 8°. **10888**. ee. **13**.

BARNARD (J.) *Artist.* *See* Barnard (Frederick)

BARNARD (J.) *of the Parliamentary Army.* A Full and Exact Relation of the Horrid Murder committed upon the body of Col. Rainsborough . . . Also the killing of Capt. Layton . . . Certified by letters [the first signed: J. Barnard, the second: S. T.] to both Houses of Parliament, *etc.* pp. 6. *Printed for R. A.: London*, 1648. 8°. **E. 470. (4.)**

BARNARD (J.) *Sunday School Teacher.* Catechism on the Rules of the Church . . . Revised by the Rev. T. T. Carter. pp. 53. *Skeffington & Son: London*, 1897. 12°. **3506**. aaaa. **9**.

BARNARD (J. F. W.) The Hythe New Class Targets. Indoor aiming drill. *Simpkins, Marshall & Co.: London; W. T. F. Ellis: Southampton*, [1865.] *s. sh. obl.* 8°. **1811**. a. **1**. **(21.)**

BARNARD (J. Laurens)

—— Marine Amphipoda of Oregon. [With illustrations.] pp. iv. 103. *Corvallis*, 1954. 4°. [*Oregon State Monographs. Studies in Zoology.* no. 8.] Ac. **2686**. e/3.

BARNARD (Jack) *Playwright.*

—— Mumbo-Jumbo. A mystery farce in three acts. pp. 102. *Samuel French: New York*, [1940.] 8°. **011791**. a. **79**.

BARNARD (James) *See* Parishioner. A Dialogue between a Parishioner and the Rector of his Parish, concerning the oath required by the National Assembly, to be taken by the established clergy. Translated from the second edition printed at Paris, by the Rev. J. Barnard. 1793. 8°. **8135**. b. **18**. **(3.)**

—— A Catechism: or collection of some points of christian faith and morality, composed in verse . . . To which is added an invitation to and method of making a spiritual retreat. pp. 84. *J. P. Coghlan: London*, 1786. 12°. **1018**. i. **31**. **(3.)**

—— The Divinity of our Lord Jesus Christ demonstrated from the Holy Scriptures and from the doctrine of the Primitive Church, in a series of letters addressed to the Rev. Dr. Joseph Priestley, in answer to his letters to the Rev. Dr. Geddes. pp. xxii. 371. *Robinsons: London*, 1789. 12°. **852**. h. **17**.

BARNARD (James)

—— A General View of the Arguments for the Divinity of Christ, and plurality of persons in God, from the Holy Scriptures and from the doctrine of the Primitive Church. pp. 30. *Printed for the Author: London*, 1793. 12°. **479**. a. **21**. **(4.)**

A different work from the preceding.

—— The Life of the Venerable and Right Reverend Richard Challoner . . . collected from his writings . . . and from near twenty years personal acquaintance with him. [With a portrait.] pp. xii. 284. *J. P. Coghlan: London*, 1784. 8°. **201**. c. **17**.

—— [Another copy.] G. **14451**.

—— [Another copy.] **1415**. e. **29**.
Imperfect; wanting the portrait.

BARNARD (James Lynn) Factory Legislation in Pennsylvania: its history and administration. pp. xi. 178. *Philadelphia*, 1907. 8°. [*Publications of the University of Pennsylvania. Series in Political Economy and Public Law.* no. 19.] Ac. **2692**. p.

—— The Teaching of Community Civics. Prepared by . . . J. L. Barnard, F. W. Carrier, A. W. Dunn and C. D. Kingsley. pp. 55. iv. *Washington*, 1915. 8°. [*U.S. Bureau of Education. Bulletin.* 1915. no. 23.] A.S. **202**.

BARNARD (James Munson) A Sketch of Anne Robert Jaques Turgot. With a translation of his Letter to Doctor Price. [The dedication signed: J. M. B., i.e. J. M. Barnard.] pp. 63. 1899. 8°. *See* B., J. M. **010664**. e. **11**.

BARNARD (John) *D.D., Rector of Waddington.* Censura Cleri; or, a Plea against Scandalous Ministers, not fit to be restored to the Churches livings in point of prudence, piety, and fame. By a True Lover of the Church of England in Doctrine, Ceremony and Discipline [i.e. J. Barnard]. pp. 21. 1660. 4°. *See* England.—*Church of England.—Clergy.* [*Appendix.*] **111**. b. **13**.

—— Theologo-Historicus, or the True Life of the Most Reverend Divine . . . Peter Heylyn . . . Written . . . to correct the errors . . . and confute the calumnies of a late writer [i.e. George Vernon, in his Life of Heylyn]. Also an Answer to Mr. Baxter's false accusations of Dr. Heylyn. pp. 301. *Printed for J. S.; sold by Ed. Eckelston: London*, 1683. 8°. **275**. g. **39**.

—— [Another copy.] G. **14468**.

—— [Another edition.] The Life of the Most Reverend and Learned Divine, Dr. Peter Heylyn. *See* Heylyn (Peter) Ecclesia restaurata, *etc.* vol. 1. 1849. 8°. Ac. **2065/4**.

BARNARD (John) *Fellow of Queen's College, Cambridge.* *See* Bernard.

BARNARD (John) *Minister, of Andover, Mass.* Christian Churches form'd and furnish'd by Christ. A sermon preach'd at the gathering of a Church and the ordination of the Reverend Mr. Timothy Walker . . . Nov. 18. 1730, *etc.* pp. 42. *John Phillips: Boston*, 1731. 8°. **4486**. aa. **19**.

—— The Presence of the Great God in the Assembly of Political Rulers. A sermon preached . . . May 28th, 1746, being the day for the election of His Majesty's Council, *etc.* pp. 30. *Daniel Gookin: Boston*, 1746. 8°. **4486**. bb. **69**.

BARNARD (John) *Minister of Batcomb.* *See* Bernard (Richard) *Rector of Batcomb, Somersetshire.*

BARNARD (John) *of Johannesburg.*

—— South African Marketing, Advertising and Sales Research. Edited and compiled by J. Barnard. (Second edition.) pp. 50. *J. Barnard & Co.: Johannesburg,* [1939.] 8°. **8222.** b. **23.**

BARNARD (John) *Pastor, of Marblehead. See* Ashton (Philip) Ashton's Memorial: or, an Authentic Account of the strange adventures . . . of Mr. Philip Ashton . . . To which is added, a sermon on Dan. iii. 17. By J. Barnard. [The whole edited by J. Barnard.] 1726. 12°. **G. 14347.**

—— *See* Bible.—*Old Testament.—Psalms.* A New Version of the Psalms of David . . . By J. Barnard. 1752. 8°. **3435.** e. **22.**

—— *See* Green (S. A.) Rev. John Barnard of Marblehead. [Biographical notes.] [1896.] 8°. **4804.** i. **11.** (**10.**)

—— Autobiography of the Rev. John Barnard. 1836. *See* Boston, *Mass.—Massachusetts Historical Society.* Collections, *etc.* ser. 3. vol. 5. 1825, *etc.* 8°. **Ac. 8400.**

—— The Certainty, Time, and End, of the Birth of our Lord and Saviour Jesus Christ, with the accomplishment of several of the prophecys relating thereto. A Sermon . . . to which is added, An Appendix attempting more clearly to state the true year of our Lord's nativity. pp. 66. *S. Gerrish: Boston,* 1731. 8°. **4486.** aa. **18.**

—— Elijah's Mantle. A sermon preached at the funeral of . . . the Reverend Mr. Samuel Cheever, *etc.* pp. 41. *S. Gerrish: Boston,* 1724. 8°. **4985.** aa. **4.**

—— The Imperfection of the Creature, and the excellency of the Divine Commandment; illustrated in nine sermons on Psal. cxix. 96. pp. 248. *Rogers & Fowle: Boston,* 1747. 8°. **4478.** d. **85.**

—— Janua coelestis; or, the Mystery of the Gospel in the salvation of a sinner, opened and explained . . . in several discourses on Acts xvi. 30. pp. 442. *Rogers & Fowle; D. Gookin: Boston,* 1750. 8°. **4485.** bb. **61.**

—— The Lord Jesus Christ the only, and Supreme Head of the Church. A sermon, *etc.* pp. 34. *H. Foster: Boston,* 1738. 8°. **4486.** aaa. **90.** (**1.**)

—— The Nature and Manner of Man's Blessing God; with our obligations thereto. A sermon preached . . . the Thursday after the death of the Rev. Mr. George Curwin, *etc.* pp. ii. 42. *Samuel Gerrish: Boston,* 1717. 8°. **4986.** de. **37.**

—— A Proof of Jesus Christ his being the ancient promised Messiah: a sermon, *etc.* pp. 55. *J. Draper: Boston,* 1756. 8°. **4486.** aa. **64.** (**3.**)

—— Sermons on Several Subjects, *etc.* pp. 190. *London; printed for S. Gerrish, & D. Henchman: Boston,* 1727. 8°. **4485.** aaa. **1.**

—— The Throne established by Righteousness. A sermon preach'd before his Excellency Jonathan Belcher and the representative, of the Province of the Massachusetts-Bay, May 29, 1734. Being the day for the electing his majesty's Council there. pp. 60. *Boston,* 1734. 8°. **4486.** b. **2.**

—— The True Divinity of Jesus Christ; evidenced in a discourse at the Public Lecture in Boston . . . July 16, 1761. pp. 38. *Edes & Gill: Boston,* 1761. 8°. **4486.** aaa. **91.** (**6.**)

BARNARD (John) *Pastor, of Marblehead.*

—— Two Discourses addressed to Young Persons: to which is added, a Sermon occasioned by the Earthquake, which was October 29. 1727. pp. iv. 99. *S. Gerrish: Boston,* 1727. 8°. **4486.** aa. **17.**

—— A Zeal for Good Works excited and directed; in a sermon, *etc.* pp. 43. *S. Eliot: Boston,* 1742. 8°. **4486.** aa. **67.** (**1.**)

BARNARD (John) *Son of Sir John Barnard.* A Catalogue of that superb and well known Cabinet of Drawings of John Barnard . . . Which will be sold by auction . . . Feb. 16, 1787, *etc.* pp. 43. *Logographic Press: London,* 1787. 4°. **59.** b. **13.**

—— [Another copy, with the prices and purchasers' names in ms.] **679.** e. **27.** (**2.**)

—— [Another copy.] **7805.** e. **5.** (**26.**)
The imprint has been cut away in binding.

—— Catalogue of the superb and entire Collection of Prints and Books of Prints of John Barnard . . . which will be sold by auction . . . the 16th of April, 1798, *etc.* [With a list of prices in ms. inserted.] *G. Hayden: London,* 1798. 8°. **679.** c. **29.**
Interleaved.

—— [Another copy, with the prices in ms.] **58.** f. **8.**

BARNARD (John) *Writer on Mechanics.* Every Man his own Mechanic . . . New edition [of the work by F. C. Young] entirely re-written and revised . . . Fully illustrated. pp. 504. *Ward, Lock & Co.: London,* 1914. 8°. **7817.** a. **1.**

—— Every Man his own Mechanic . . . New edition re-written and revised, *etc.* pp. 542. pl. xxxii. *Ward, Lock & Co.: London & Melbourne,* [1951.] 8°. **7949.** f. **32.**

—— Home Carpentry . . . Illustrated. (Compiled and edited from Every Man his own Mechanic.) pp. 190. *Ward, Lock & Co.: London,* [1916.] 8°. **07816.** g. **52.**

—— The Handy Boy's Book . . . Entirely new edition by J. Barnard, assisted by many experts. With thirty plates, *etc.* pp. 384. *Ward, Lock & Co.: London & Melbourne,* 1921. 8°. **07942.** ccc. **25.**

—— The Handy Boy's Book . . . Third edition. By J. Barnard, assisted by many experts. With thirty plates, *etc.* pp. 384. *Ward, Lock & Co.: London & Melbourne,* [1925?] 8°. **7946.** aa. **33.**

—— Seventh edition, *etc.* pp. 384. *Ward, Lock & Co.: London & Melbourne,* [1933.] 8°. **07942.** cc. **44.**

—— The Handy Boy's Book . . . Entirely new edition, *etc.* pp. 352. *Ward, Lock & Co.: London & Melbourne,* [1948.] 8°. **7947.** aa. **41.**

—— The Handy Boy's Book. An entirely new edition, *etc.* pp. 352. *Ward, Lock & Co.: London & Melbourne,* 1951. 8°. **7949.** f. **26.**

—— The Handy Boy's Book, *etc.* (Revised edition.) pp. 352. *Ward, Lock & Co.: London & Melbourne,* 1954. 8°. **7947.** b. **88.**

BARNARD (*Sir* John) *Lord Mayor of London. See* Bellamy (*Sir* Edward) Reasons for electing Sir Edward Bellamy . . . Sir John Barnard . . . Members in the ensuing Parliament for this Metropolis. [*London,* 1741.] *s. sh.* fol. **10350.g.13.(14.)**

BARNARD (*Sir* JOHN) *Lord Mayor of London.*

—— *See* BYSTANDER. A True State of the Case concerning the good or evil which the Bill for the Naturalization of the Jews may bring upon Great Britain. With some remarks on the speeches of Sir J—— B——d [i.e. Sir J. Barnard], and H——s Fra——y, Esq ; upon the said Bill. 1753. 8°. **1093**. e. **40**.

—— *See* GRESHAM (*Sir* Thomas) The Court Broker : a Description of an Anti-Patriot [i.e. Sir J. Barnard] : in a conference between Sir Thomas Gresham's statue, in the Royal Exchange and its near neighbour. 1747. 4°. **840**. k. **4**. (**2**.)

—— *See* VENN (Henry) *Vicar of Huddersfield.* Memoir of the late Sir John Barnard, *etc.* [1810 ?] 8°. [*Cottage Library of Christian Knowledge.* vol. 1. no. 9.] **4418**. f. **20**.

—— Considerations on the Proposal for Reducing the Interest on the National Debt. [By Sir J. Barnard.] pp. 34. 1750. 8°. *See* CONSIDERATIONS. T. **1627**. (2.)

—— [Another copy.] E. **2043**. (4.)

—— [Another copy.] **104**. e. 3.

—— *See* CONSIDERATIONS. Annotations on a late Pamphlet [by Sir J. Barnard] intituled, Considerations on the Proposal for Reducing the Interest on the National Debt. 1750. 8°. T. **1627**. (2*.)

—— A Defence of Several Proposals for raising of Three Millions for the service of the Government, for the year 1746, *etc.* pp. 77. *J. Osborn : London*, 1746. 8°. **1102**. h. **9**. (**3**.)

—— [Another copy.] A Defence of several Proposals for Raising of Three Millions for the Service of the Government, *etc.* *London*, 1746. 8°. **1476**. aaa. **12**. (4.)

—— [Another copy.] **08218.b.4.(5.)**

—— [Another copy.] T. **1627**. (**5**.)

—— [Another copy.] E. **2040**. (**4**.)

—— [Another copy.] **104**. c. **68**.

—— [Another copy.] **104**. e. **30**.

—— [Another copy.] **288**. c. **10**.

—— A Letter to Sir John Barnard, upon his Proposals for raising three Millions of Money for the service of the year 1746. From a Member of the House of Commons. pp. 24. *John Hinton : London*, [1746.] 8°. E. **2040**. (**3**.)

—— [Another copy.] **104**. e. **29**.

—— The second edition. pp. 24. *John Hinton : London*, [1746.] 8°. **104**. c. **69**.

—— Third edition. pp. 24. *John Hinton : London*, [1746.] 8°. T. **1623**. (**10**.)

—— A Letter to a Member of Parliament, occasioned by the rejecting Sir John Barnard's scheme. [In answer to : " A Letter to Sir John Barnard, upon his Proposals, *etc.*"] pp. 29. *J. Hinton : London*, 1746. 8°. T. **1623**. (**9**.)

—— [Another copy.] **104**. e. **41**.

—— Remarks on a Letter to Sir John Barnard : in which the Proposals of that worthy patriot are vindicated . . . By an Enemy to Jobbs. pp. 28. *J. Hinton : London*, 1746. 8°. **08218.b.4.(6.)**

—— [Another copy.] **104.e.28.**

BARNARD (*Sir* JOHN) *Lord Mayor of London.*

—— (The second edition.) pp. 28. *J. Hinton : London*, 1746. 8°. T. **1623**. (**12**.)

—— A Present for an Apprentice : or, a Sure Guide to gain both esteem and an estate . . . By a late Lord Mayor of London [i.e. Sir J. Barnard]. pp. 80. 1740. 8°. *See* PRESENT. **8404**. d. **15**.

—— A Present for an Apprentice . . . By a late Lord Mayor of London [i.e. Sir J. Barnard]. pp. iv. 87. 1742. 12°. *See* PRESENT. **8411**. de. **37**.

—— [Another edition.] pp. 76. [1745 ?] 8°. *See* PRESENT. **12274**. i. **16**.

—— The fifth edition. pp. 76. 1747. 8°. *See* PRESENT. **8408**. bb. **7**.

—— [Another edition.] pp. 124. 1750. 12°. *See* PRESENT. **8403**. e. **16**.

—— The tenth edition. pp. 84. [1750 ?] 12°. *See* PRESENT. **8407**. bb. **19**.

—— [Another edition.] pp. iv. 68. 1769. 8°. *See* PRESENT. **8408**. aa. **45**.

—— [Another edition.] pp. iii. 68. 1787. 12°. *See* PRESENT. **8407**. de. **24**.

—— [Another edition.] pp. 80. 1788. 12°. *See* PRESENT. **8406**. aa. **30**.

—— [Another edition.] pp. 130. [1790 ?] 12°. *See* PRESENT. **8408**. a. **24**.

—— [Another edition.] pp. 107. 1822. 12°. *See* PRESENT. **8408**. a. **25**.

—— Reasons for the Representatives of the People of Great Britain to take advantage of the present Rate of Interest for the more speedy lessening the national debt, *etc.* [By Sir J. Barnard.] pp. 3. [1737.] fol. *See* ENGLAND. [*Appendix.—Finance.*] **8223**. e. **3**. (**1**.)

—— *See* CONSIDERATIONS. Considerations upon a Proposal [by Sir J. Barnard] for Lowering the Interest of all the redeemable National Debts to three per cent. per ann., *etc.* 1737. 8°. **8226**. a. **58**. (**1**.)

—— *See* CONSIDERATIONS. Considerations occasioned by a Proposal [by Sir John Barnard] for Reducing Interest to Three per Cent., *etc.* 1737. 8°. T. **1744**. (**11**.)

—— Some Thoughts on the Scarcity of Silver Coin : with a proposal for remedy thereof. pp. 3. [*London*,] 1759. fol. **105**. e. **61**. (**5**.)

—— A Letter to the Right Honourable the Lord Mayor [i.e. Sir J. Barnard], occasioned by his Lordship's nomination of five persons, disqualified by Act of Parliament, as fit and proper persons to serve the office of Sheriffs. In which the nature and design of the Corporation Act is impartially considered and stated. [By Samuel Chandler.] pp. 44. *J. Robert, etc : London*, 1738. 8°. T. **1770**. (**3**.)

—— [Another copy.] A Letter to the Right Honourable the Lord Mayor [i.e. Sir J. Barnard], occasioned by his Lordship's nomination of five persons, disqualified by Act of Parliament, as fit and proper persons to serve the office of sheriffs, *etc.* *London*, 1738. 8°. **1137**. i. **27**. (**1**.)

—— [Another copy.] **101**. h. **12**.

—— [Another copy.] **116**. e. **29**.

—— The second edition. pp. 44. *J. Roberts, etc.: London*, 1738. 8°. **1137**. i. **27**. (2.)

BARNARD (*Sir* John) *Lord Mayor of London.*

—— *See* Sabourn (Reay) An Answer to Tentandum Est: being Remarks on a Scurrilous Letter [i.e. "A Letter to the Right Honourable the Lord Mayor, occasioned by his Lordship's nomination of five persons, *etc*," bearing on the titlepage the motto: "Tentandum est"] lately published, *etc.* 1738. 8°. **T. 1770. (4.)**

—— A Letter to the Worshipful Sir John Barnard, Kn[t] . . . on the Act of Parliament for Naturalizing the Jews. pp. 19. *J. Bouquet: London,* 1753. 8°. **T. 2231. (17.)**

—— Memoirs of the late Sir John Barnard, *etc.* [By Henry Venn.] pp. 22. *W. Oliver, etc.: London,* 1776. 4°. **614. k. 20. (3.)**

—— [Another copy.] MS. NOTES in short hand. **1418. k. 2.**

—— [Another copy.] **115. i. 28.**

—— [Another copy.] **G. 1444. (1.)**

—— [Another edition.] Together with notes furnished by Mr. Overall . . . With a preface by T. Hankey. pp. iv. 37. *Printed for private circulation: London,* 1885. 8°. **10815. aaa. 38.**

—— National Prejudice, opposed to the National Interest, candidly considered in the detention or yielding up Gibraltar and Cape-Briton by the ensuing Treaty of Peace . . . In a Letter to Sir John Barnard, Knight. pp. 50. *W. Owen; J. Swan: London,* 1748. 8°. **T. 1600. (5.)**

BARNARD (*Sir* John) *of Stratford-upon-Avon.* A Facsimile of an Indenture executed by Sir John and Lady Barnard, in October, 1652, in which they covenant to levy a fine settling a portion of the Estates of Shakespeare to themselves for their lives, *etc.* [Edited with a prefatory note by J. O. Halliwell-Phillips.] *J. G. Bishop: Brighton,* 1883. fol. **1861. c. 6.**
One of an edition of 26 copies.

BARNARD (John Burra Clothier) *See* Leach (Percy L. W.) and Barnard (J. B. C.) English for Present-Day Examinations. 1934. 8°. **12984. cc. 27.**

BARNARD (John Burra Clothier) and **LEACH** (Percy Lionel William)

—— English for Present-Day Examinations . . . Fifth edition. pp. viii. 241. *MacDonald & Evans: London,* 1949. 8°. **012986. f. 7.**
The sixth edition is entered under Barnard (J. B. C.)

BARNARD (John Douglas)

—— Bygone Cavendish. pp. 33. [*The Author: Sudbury,*] 1951. 8°. **010368. pp. 55.**

BARNARD (John Edwin) Practical Photo-Micrography . . . Illustrated. pp. xii. 322. *Edward Arnold: London,* 1911. 8°. **08909. b. 20.**
Subsequently published under the joint-authorship of J. E. Barnard and F. V. Welch.

BARNARD (John Edwin) and **WELCH** (Frank V.)

—— Practical Photo-Micrography . . Second edition [of the work by J. E. Barnard]. pp. xii. 316. *E. Arnold & Co.: London,* 1925. 8°. **8906. eee. 12.**

—— Practical Photo-Micrography. (Third edition.) pp. xii. 352. pl. xxiii. *E. Arnold & Co.: London,* 1936. 8°. **8910. e. 6.**

BARNARD (John Gross) *See* Williams (J. J.) *Civil Engineer.* The Isthmus of Tehuantepec: being the results of a survey . . . made by the scientific commission under the direction of Major J. G. Barnard, *etc.* 1852. 8°. **10480. e. 19.**

—— *See* Williams (J. J.) *Civil Engineer.* El Istmo de Tehuantepec. Resultado del reconocimiento que para la construccion de un ferro-carril de comunicacion entre los océanos Atlántico y Pacífico ejecutó la comision . . . bajo la direccion del Sr. J. G. Barnard, *etc.* 1852. 4°. **10481. bbb. 8.**

—— The C.S.A. and the Battle of Bull Run. A Letter to an English friend . . . With five maps. pp. 136. *D. Van Nostrand: New York,* 1862. 8°. **9604. bb. 20.**

—— Letter to the Editors of the National Intelligence, in answer to the charges against the United States Military Academy, in the Report of the Secretary of War, of July, 1861. pp. 18. *D. Van Nostrand: New York,* 1862. 8°. **8828. cc. 43. (1.)**

—— Notes on Sea-Coast Defence, *etc.* pp. 110. *D. Van Nostrand: New York,* 1861. 8°. **8824. e. 37.**

—— On the Internal Structure of the Earth considered as affecting the phenomena of precession and nutation . . . being the third of the problems of rotary motion. pp. 16. 1881. *See* Washington.—*Smithsonian Institution.* Smithsonian Contributions to Knowledge. vol. 23. 1848, *etc.* 4°. **Ac. 1875.**

—— The Peninsular Campaign and its Antecedents, as developed by the report of Maj.-Gen. Geo. B. McClellan, *etc.* [With a map.] pp. 96. *D. Van Nostrand: New York,* 1864. 8°. **9602. dd. 12.**

—— Problems of Rotary Motion presented by the gyroscope, the precession of the equinoxes, and the pendulum. 1874. *See* Washington.—*Smithsonian Institution.* Smithsonian Contributions to Knowledge. vol. 19. 1848, *etc.* 4°. **Ac. 1875.**

—— A Report on the Defenses of Washington, to the Chief of Engineers, U.S. Army. pp. 152. pl. 30. *Washington,* 1871. 4°. [*Professional Papers of the Corps of Engineers, U.S. Army.* no. 20.] **A.S. 635.**

—— Report on the Fabrication of Iron for defensive purposes, and its uses in modern fortifications. Especially in works of coast defence. [By J. G. Barnard, H. G. Wright, and P. S. Michie.] (Supplement.) 2 pt. *Washington,* 1870. 4°. [*Professional Papers of the Corps of Engineers, U.S. Army.* no. 21.] **A.S. 635.**

—— Report on the North Sea Canal of Holland; and on the improvement of navigation from Rotterdam to the sea, *etc.* pp. 77. pl. xi. *Washington,* 1872. 4°. [*Professional Papers of the Corps of Engineers, U.S. Army.* no. 22.] **A.S. 635.**

BARNARD (John Gross) and **BARRY** (William F.)

—— Report of the Engineer and Artillery Operations of the Army of the Potomac, from its organization to the close of the Peninsular Campaign, *etc.* pp. 230. pl. 18. *D. Van Nostrand: New York,* 1863. 8°. **9604. cc. 2.**

BARNARD (John H. H.) *See* Barnard (Jonathan) Jonathan Barnard. His autobiography, fragments and verse. [Edited by J. H. H. Barnard.] [1913.] 8°. **4804. ee. 2. (5.)**

BARNARD (John Terence Owen)

—— A Handbook of the Răwang Dialect of the Nung Language. Containing a grammar of the language, colloquial exercises and a vocabulary, with an appendix of Nung manners and customs. pp. xi. 118. *Supdt., Govt. Printing & Stationery: Rangoon,* 1934. 8°. **12911. ff. 17.**

BARNARD (JOHN TOLSON)

—— The Endless Years. A personal record of the experiences of a British officer as a prisoner of war in Japanese hands from the fall of Singapore to his liberation. Written during his captivity. [With plates, including a portrait.] pp. xii. 160. *Chantry Publications: London*, 1950. 8°. **09059**. f. **19**.

BARNARD (JONATHAN) Jonathan Barnard. His autobiography, fragments and verse. [Edited by John H. H. Barnard.] pp. 78. *London Sunday School Choir: London*, [1913.] 8°. **4804**. ee. **2**. **(5.)**

BARNARD (JOSEPH) Among the Gods; and other poems. pp. viii. 125. *Bemrose & Sons: London*, 1874. 8°. **11652**. f. **25**.

BARNARD (JOSEPHINE DESNOYERS) *See* ANDREWS (William W.) Josephine Desnoyers Barnard. [An obituary notice.] [1891.] 8°. **764**. i. **5**. **(27.)**

BARNARD (KATE)

—— Birds. In a Wynberg garden. pp. 26. *Juta & Co.: Cape Town*, [1930.] 8°. **7286**. p. **4**.

BARNARD (KEPPEL HARCOURT) *See* ENGLAND.—*Colonial Office.—" Discovery " Committee.* Discovery Reports. (vol. 5. Amphipoda, by K. H. Barnard.) 1929, *etc.* 4°. W.P. **243/5**.

—— *See* LONDON.—III. *British Museum.* British Antarctic —" Terra Nova "—Expedition, 1910. Natural History Report. (Crustacea. pt. 11. Amphipoda. By K. H. Barnard.) 1914, *etc.* 4°. **7006.w.1/8.**

—— Amphipoda, *etc.* *London*, 1937. 4°. [*John Murray Expedition*, 1933–34. *Scientific Reports.* vol. 4. no. 6.] W.P. **3216/4**.

—— A Beginner's Guide to South African Shells . . . Illustrated by the author. pp. ii. 215. *Maskew Miller: Cape Town*, [1951.] 8°. **07299**. b. **43**.

—— [Another copy.] A Beginner's Guide to South African Shells, *etc.* *Cape Town*, [1951.] 8°. **7211**. aa. **25**.

—— A Monograph of the Marine Fishes of South Africa. *Cape Town*, 1925– . 4°. [*Annals of the South African Museum.* vol. 21.] Ac. **1994**.

—— A Pictorial Guide to South African Fishes, marine and freshwater . . . Illustrated by the author. pp. xvii. 226. *Maskew Miller: Cape Town*, [1947.] 8°. **07290**. f. **33**.

—— South African Shore-Life . . . Illustrated by the author. pp. 135. *Maskew Miller: Capetown; printed in Holland*, 1954. 8°. 7009. aa. 15.

BARNARD (L.) *of the " A.S.W. Journal."* Roofing with the Steel Square. pp. 31. *L. Barnard: London*, [1928.] 8°. **07942**. ccc. **57**.

BARNARD (L.) *of the " A.S.W. Journal,"* and **HOWE** (H. G.)

—— Construction of Staircases and Handrails. pp. 174. *L. Barnard: London*, 1928. 8°. **07942**. ccc. **58**.

BARNARD (L. E.) *See* CONFUCIUS. Moral Sayings of Confucius . . . To which is added a sketch of his Life; with emendations by L. E. Barnard. 1855. 12°. **11099**. b. **23**.

BARNARD (L. W.) Ten Years in the C.L.B. pp. 32. *C. Baker & Son: London*, [1901.] 8°. **4193**. k. **5**.

BARNARD (LESLIE GORDON)

—— Jancis. [A novel.] pp. 245. *L. Dickson & Thompson: London; Montreal* printed, 1936. 8°. **12601**. v. **26**.

BARNARD (LESLIE T.)

—— The Adventures of Rollo and Reckel . . . Illustrations by R. S. Sherwood. pp. 64. *E. J. Arnold & Son: Leeds*, [1948.] 8°. [*Broadcast Echoes.* no. 12.] W.P. **13307/12**.

—— The Boy from B'Gomi . . . Illustrated by S. Drigin. pp. 128. *E. J. Arnold & Son: Leeds*, [1950.] 8°. [*Adventure Stories.* no. 11.] W.P. **7951/11**.

—— The Interrupted Wedding. pp. 192. *T. V. Boardman & Co.: London*, 1951. 8°. NNN. **2317**.

—— The Mystery of the Marshes . . . Illustrated by J. R. Henderson. pp. 128. *E. J. Arnold & Son: Leeds*, [1950.] 8°. [*Adventure Stories.* no. 4.] W.P. **7951/4**.

—— Rollo and Reckel go adventuring again . . . Illustrations by R. S. Sherwood. pp. 64. *E. J. Arnold & Son: Leeds*, [1949.] 8°. [*Broadcast Echoes.* no. 13.] W.P. **13307/13**.

—— Stories of Marsh Farm. pp. 64. *Frederick Warne & Co.: London & New York*, 1948. 8°. [*Sunshine Stories.*] W.P. **13281/2**.

—— Tales from Field and Hedgerow . . . Illustrations by Brunton Richards. pp. 72. *Churchman Publishing Co.: London*, [1948.] 8°. **12831**. b. **19**.

BARNARD (LUDWIG) Die Debatten über die Judenfrage auf dem ersten Preussischen und letzten Weimarschen Landtage. pp. 500. *Grimma*, 1847. 8°. **4033**. a. **33**.

BARNARD (MANISTER) *See* BIBLE.—*Epistles.* [*English.*] A Paraphrase, with Critical Annotations, on the Epistles of St. Paul to the Romans and Galatians . . . Published by M. Barnard. 1752. 4°. **1124**. cc. **1**.

BARNARD (MARJORIE C.) " Angel Pig." A school story for girls. pp. 324. *T. Nelson & Sons: London*, [1925.] 8°. **012808**. l. **66**.

—— Donald Marston, *etc.* pp. 159. *Sheldon Press: London*, [1923.] 8°. **12801**. ccc. **36**.

—— The Misfortunes of Tony, *etc.* pp. 96. *Sheldon Press: London*, [1929.] 8°. **12813**. d. **2**.

—— Mrs. Noah. A school story for girls. pp. 240. *T. Nelson & Sons: London & Edinburgh*, [1926.] 8°. **12801**. ff. **2**.

—— The Secret Brotherhood, *etc.* pp. 192. *T. Nelson & Sons: London*, [1925.] 8°. **12810**. bbb. **25**.

—— The Twins at Thorncliff, *etc.* pp. 192. *T. Nelson & Sons: London*, [1928.] 8°. **12800**. f. **16**.

—— Westcote Towers, *etc.* pp. 151. *Sheldon Press: London*, [1922.] 8°. **12800**. bb. **48**.

BARNARD (MARJORIE FAITH)

—— *See* also ELDERSHAW (M. Barnard) *pseud.* [i.e. F. S. Eldershaw and M. Barnard.]

—— Australian Outline. A brief history of Australia . . . New and revised edition, *etc.* pp. 40. pl. 16. *Ure Smith Pty.: Sydney*, 1949. 8°. [*Ure Smith Miniature Series.* no. 1.] **012213.r.3/1.**

—— The Sydney Book . . . Drawings by Sydney Ure Smith. pp. 48. *Ure Smith Pty.: Sydney*, [1948.] *obl.* 4°. Cup. **1253**. de. **12**.

BARNARD (MICHAEL)

—— The History of Civilizations. pp. 15. *African Bookman: Cape Town,* 1944. 8°. [*Sixpenny Library.* no. 2.] W.P. 957/2.

BARNARD (MORDAUNT) *See* HOMER. [*Odyssey.—English.*] The Odyssey of Homer, rendered into English blank verse, by M. Barnard. 1876. 8°. **11315.** e. **4.**

—— The Education of the Christian Minister. A sermon preached in the Parish Church of Skipton-in-Craven, June 4, 1821, *etc.* pp. 24. *J. Hatchard & Son: London,* 1821. 8°. **695.** g. **14. (4.)**

—— Reasons of a Clergyman for acting as a Guardian of the Poor. pp. 49. *Simpkin & Co.: London,* 1837. 8°. **C.T.207.(6.)**

—— Registration of Births and Deaths. A hand-bill, as originally published . . . together with remarks thereon by George Graham, Esq. . . . and a rejoinder by the Rev. M. Barnard. pp. 20. *H. T. Cooke & Son: Warwick,* [1872.] 8°. **6426.** aaa. **20. (12.)**

BARNARD (MORDAUNT ROGER) *See* BLANCHE (August T.) Master of his fate . . . Translated by Rev. M. R. Barnard, *etc.* 1886. 8°. **12581.** aaaa. **31.**

—— *See* BULL (Jacob B.) Fridtjof Nansen . . . Translated . . . by the Rev. M. R. Barnard. 1898. 8°. **10761.** f. **24.**

—— *See* KEYSER (J. R.) The Private Life of the Old Northmen. Translated . . . by M. R. Barnard. 1868. 8°. **9435.** c. **33.**

—— *See* PAIJKULL (C. W.) A Summer in Iceland . . . Translated by M. R. Barnard. 1868. 8°. **10281.** dd. **8.**

—— *See* SCHÜBELER (F. C.) Synopsis of the Vegetable Products of Norway . . . Translated . . . by M. R. Barnard. 1862. 4°. **7030.** i. **37. (7.)**

—— *See* THIELE (J. M.) The Life of Thorvaldsen, collated from the Danish . . . by Rev. M. R. Barnard. 1865. 12°. **2264.** bb. **12.**

—— *See* THORESEN (A. M.) Signe's History: a Norwegian tale . . . Translated by the Rev. M. R. Barnard. 1865. 12°. **12581.** dd. **30.**

—— Sketches of Life, Scenery, and Sport in Norway. pp. viii. 312. *Horace Cox: London,* 1871. 8°. **10281.** c. **27.**

—— Sport in Norway, and where to find it. Together with a short account of the vegetable productions of the country, *etc.* pp. xvi. 334. *Chapman & Hall: London,* 1864 8°. **7906.** cc. **5.**

BARNARD (NICHOLAS) *Dean of Ardagh.* *See* BERNARD.

BARNARD (OWEN) Mind and Matter. Two lectures. pp. 76. *J. Heywood: Manchester,* [1890.] 8°. **8461.** b. **29. (1.)**

BARNARD (PATRICIA)

—— The Contemporary Mouse. A fable for art lovers . . . Drawings by Constance Jean Dowling, *etc.* pp. 47. *Coward-McCann: New York,* [1954.] 8°. **7877.** ff. 8.

BARNARD (PERCY MORDAUNT) *See* BIBLE.—*Gospels.—Selections.* [*Greek.*] The Biblical Text of Clement of Alexandria in the four Gospels and the Acts of the Apostles. Collected and edited by P. M. Barnard, *etc.* 1899. 8°. [*Texts and Studies.* vol. 5. no. 5.] **03605.h.21/5.**

—— *See* CLEMENS (T. F.) *Alexandrinus.* Quis dives salvetur. Re-edited together with an introduction on the MSS. of Clement's works by P. M. Barnard. 1897. 8°. [*Texts and Studies.* vol. 5. no. 2.] **03605.h.21/5.**

BARNARD (PERCY MORDAUNT)

—— *See* CLEMENS (T. F.) *Alexandrinus.* A Homily of Clement of Alexandria, entitled "Who is the rich man that is being saved?" By P. M. Barnard. 1901. 8°. **04430.aaa.1/51.**

—— [Catalogues of books offered for sale by P. M. Barnard.] *Tunbridge Wells, Manchester,* [1905?– .] 8°. **S.C.1094.**

BARNARD (R. W.) *Novelist.*

—— A Century of Service. The story of the Prudential, 1848–1948. Compiled by R. W. Barnard. [With plates.] pp. viii. 139. [1948.] 8°. *See* PRUDENTIAL ASSURANCE COMPANY. **8233.** bb. **57.**

—— Random Journey. pp. 287. *Hutchinson & Co.: London,* [1937.] 8°. [*First Novel Library.* no. 57.] **12627.p.1/57.**

—— Sam and the Popski Dog . . . Illustrated by R. A. Hobbs. pp. 80. *Hutchinson's Books for Young People: London,* [1948.] 8°. **12831.** cc. **22.**

BARNARD (RAYMOND WALTER)

—— *See* MOORE (Eliakim H.) General Analysis . . . By E. H. Moore, with the cooperation of R. W. Barnard. 1935, *etc.* 8°. [*Memoirs of the American Philosophical Society.* vol. 1, *etc.*] Ac. **1830/8.**

BARNARD (RICHARD) *Rector of Batcombe, Somersetshire.* *See* BERNARD.

BARNARD (ROBERT) The Leisure Hour Improved; or, Moral Miscellanies, in prose and verse, original and selected. [By R. Barnard.] pp. 192. 1809. 8°. *See* LEISURE HOUR. **4410.** bb. **25.**

—— A Wreath from the Wilderness: being a selection from the metrical arrangements of Robert Barnard. pp. xv. 150. *William Smith: Ironbridge,* 1817. 8°. **11643.** m. **3.**

BARNARD (ROBERT JAMES ALLMAN) Elementary Dynamics of the Particle and Rigid Body. pp. vi. 374. *Macmillan & Co.: London,* 1916. 8°. **8763.** a. **1.**

—— Second edition. pp. vi. 386. *Macmillan & Co.: London,* 1932. 8°. **08769.** a. **14.**

—— Elementary Dynamics of the Particle & Rigid Body . . . Third edition. pp. vi. 406. *Macmillan & Co.: London,* 1940. 8°. **08709.** aaa. **7.**

—— Elementary Statics of two and three dimensions. pp. 254. *Macmillan & Co.: London,* 1921. 8°. **08531.** df. **11.**

—— Elementary Statics of two and three dimensions. (Second edition.) pp. 263. *Macmillan & Co.: London,* 1939. 8°. **08535.** df. **74.**

BARNARD (ROY MAYNE) Radio Receiver Measurements. pp. xii. 116. *Iliffe & Sons: London,* [1934.] 8°. **08756.** aa. **34.**

BARNARD (SAMUEL) *Dissenting Minister.* An Address to Backsliders; being the substance of a sermon, preached at Howard-Street Chapel, Sheffield. pp. 31. *Slater, Bacon & Co.: Sheffield,* 1804. 8°. **4475.** c. **28.**

—— An Address to the Congregation at the New Chapel, Dagger Lane, Kingston-upon-Hull. In which is vindicated the doctrine of Justification. pp. 34. *J. Ferraby: Hull,* 1790. 8°. **4256.** c. **3.**

—— An Essay on the Pre-existence and Divinity of Christ. [By S. Barnard?] pp. 48. [1790?] 12°. *See* JESUS CHRIST. **4226.** a. **44.**

BARNARD (Samuel) *Dissenting Minister.*

—— An Exhortation, to Consideration, being a charge delivered at the ordination of the Rev. Peter Feast, at York, December 29th, 1789. pp. 32. *J. Ferraby: Hull*, 1790. 8°. **4446. c. 1. (5.)**

—— The Faith of God's Elect no Duty . . . Containing a reply, to the Rev. A. McLean's Sermon, intitled The Belief of the Gospel saving Faith. pp. 36. FEW MS. NOTES. *J. Ferraby: Hull*, 1791. 8°. **695. f. 34. (1.)**

—— The Fruits and Effects of God's Love. Being the substance of a sermon preached . . . October 21, 1787. pp. 31. *W. & A. Lee: Lewes*, 1787. 8°. **4475. cc. 112. (2.)**

—— Second edition. pp. 31. *J. Ferraby: Hull*, 1790. 8°. **4473. c. 9. (1.)**

—— A Glance at Ordination; or, an Enquiry into the rights . . . of a Church of Jesus-Christ . . . and a comparison of the conduct of particular Baptist Churches in regard to ordination, *etc.* pp. 35. *Printed for the Author: Hull*, 1818. 12°. **4139. aaa. 1. (14.)**

—— The Hearer's Remembrancer; containing a view, of the leading ideas, of a number of sermons, preached at New Chapel, Dagger-Lane, Hull. pp. 557. *J. Ferraby:* [*Hull*], 1795. 12°. **4461. aaa. 2.**

—— Third edition. pp. viii. 322. *Ann Day: London*, 1837. 8°. **4461. cc. 3.**

—— The Infant's Cause Pleaded; or, the Rite of Infant Baptism defended, being the substance of a discourse delivered . . . on January 22, 1786 . . . Together with some remarks on the Rev. Joseph Middleton's Letters. pp. 24. *Sammells & Ritchie: London*, [1786.] 8°. **4372. d. 8. (5.)**

—— On Baptism. Being the substance of a discourse delivered . . . at the baptism of the Rev. P. Feist's child, on Wednesday, April 11th, 1792. pp. 32. *J. Ferraby: Hull*, [1792.] 8°. **4325. b. 3.**

—— On Reconciliation and Communion with God. Being the substance of a sermon preached at the New Chapel, Dagger-Lane, at Kingston-upon-Hull. pp. 32. *J. Ferraby: Hull*, 1789. 8°. **4475. cc. 112. (3.)**

—— On the Faith of the Operation of God, being the substance of a sermon preached at the New Chapel, Dagger-Lane, at Kingston-upon-Hull. pp. 32. *J. Ferraby: Hull*, 1790. 8°. **4475. cc. 112. (4.)**

—— *See* MacLean (Archibald) The Belief of the Gospel Saving Faith . . . With an Appendix containing some strictures upon a sermon [by S. Barnard] entitled: "The Faith of the Operation of God." 1791. 12°. **10347. de. 5. (1.)**

—— The Remembrancer. *See* supra: The Hearer's Remembrancer, *etc.*

—— Spiritual Songs for Zion's Travellers, being a collection of hymns from different authors; together with many original pieces . . . Second edition corrected. *Slater, Bacon & Co.: Sheffield*, 1803. 12°. **3435. ccc. 54.**

—— Spiritual Songs for Zion's Travellers . . . Third edition, corrected. pp. iv. 428. xiv. *John Slater: Sheffield*, 1817. 12°. **3440. e. 2.**

BARNARD (Samuel) *M.A.*, and **CHILD** (James Mark)

—— Advanced Algebra. pp. x. 280. *Macmillan & Co.: London*, 1939. 8°. **08535. b. 38.**

BARNARD (Samuel) *M.A.*, and **CHILD** (James Mark)

—— Elements of Geometry. [With answers.] Parts I–VI. pp. ix. 415. *Macmillan & Co.: London*, 1914. 8°. **8503. gg. 36.**

No more published.

—— [A reissue of pt. 4, 5.] Elements of Geometry . . . Parts IV.–V. pp. vi. 254–385. xvii. *Macmillan & Co.: London*, 1934. 8°. **08534. ff. 48.**

—— Higher Algebra. pp. xiv. 585. *Macmillan & Co.: London*, 1936. 8°. **08535. ee. 36.**

—— A New Algebra . . . Parts I. II. and III. (Part IV.) 2 vol. *Macmillan & Co.: London*, 1908, 09. 8°. **8507.k.32.**

—— A New Algebra . . . Parts I.–IV. (Parts IV.–VI.—Key to A New Algebra.) 4 vol. *Macmillan & Co.: London*, 1909–13. 8°. **08534. g. 10.**

—— Exercises from A New Algebra. Parts I.–IV. pp. 274. *Macmillan & Co.: London*, 1913. 8°. **8505. i. 14.**

—— A New Geometry for Schools. pp. xxvi. 514. *Macmillan & Co.: London*, 1903. 8°. **8529. de. 27.**

—— [Another edition.] A New Geometry for Junior (Senior) Forms. 2 pt. *Macmillan & Co.: Macmillan Co.: New York*, 1904. 8°. **08534. g. 9.**

—— A New Geometry. Part I, equivalent to Euclid, Book I. pp. xii. 224. *Macmillan & Co.: London*, 1912. 8°. **8503. gg. 13.**

—— A New Geometry. Parts I. and II. Being a new edition of "A New Geometry for Junior Forms." pp. xviii. 315. *Macmillan & Co.: London*, 1912. 8°. **8503. gg. 19.**

—— A New Geometry for Middle Forms. Being parts I., II., and III. of "A New Geometry" . . . With additional matter. pp. xviii. 420. *Macmillan & Co.: London*, 1907. 8°. **8530. ff. 12.**

—— A New Geometry. Part III, *etc.* pp. ix. 307–408. *Macmillan & Co.: London*, 1907. 8°. **8530. ff. 11.**

—— A New Geometry. Parts III & IV, *etc.* pp. xii. 307–562. *Macmillan & Co.: London*, 1907. 8°. **8534. df. 2.**

BARNARD (Samuel) *of Philadelphia.* A Polyglot Grammar of the Hebrew, Chaldee, Syriac, Greek, Latin, English, French, Italian, Spanish, and German languages, reduced to one common rule of syntax, *etc.* pp. 312. *Abraham Small: Philadelphia*, 1825. 8°. **12901. g. 18.**

BARNARD (Seymour) *See* Fuller (Eunice) The Book of Friendly Giants . . . With . . . verses by S. Barnard, *etc.* 1914. 4°. **12410. ee. 32.**

BARNARD (Sidney) *See* Ross (J. H.) and Barnard (S.) 'Mid Tropic Isles. 1922. 8°. **NN. 7938.**

BARNARD (Sophia) Travels in Algeirs, Spain, &c., &c. With a faithful and interesting account of the Algerines, *etc.* [By S. Barnard.] pp. viii. 140. [1820?] 8°. *See* Algiers. **10095. g. 35.**

BARNARD (Stephanus Cecil Rutgert)

—— *See* Bulpin (Thomas V.) The Ivory Trail, *etc.* [A biography of S. C. Barnard. With a portrait.] 1955. 8°. **10864. i. 10.**

BARNARD (Stephanus Philippus)

—— Algemene en vaderlandse geskiedenis vir die eerste jaar van die Vrystaatse skool-eindeksamen. pp. 164. *Bloemfontein*, 1923. 8°. **9042. aa. 19.**

BARNARD (Theodore Robert)

—— Mechanical Engineering. pp. xv. 440. pl. 10. *Virtue & Co.: London*, 1954. 4°. [*Coal Mining Series.*] **W.P. A. 560/3.**

BARNARD (Theodore Robert)

—— Miners' Safety Lamps. Their construction and care. [With illustrations.] pp. xi. 88. *Sir I. Pitman & Sons: London*, 1936. 8°. **8716**. i. **1**.

BARNARD (Thomas) *Barrister-at-law*. Observations on the Proceeding of the Friends of the Liberty of the Press, &c. December 22, 1792. And an Answer to Mr. Erskine's Speech, of January 19, 1793. pp. 39. *J. Evans: London*, 1793. 8°. **8135**. b. **24**. **(5.)**

BARNARD (Thomas) *D.D. of Salem, Mass.* See Prince (John) *LL.D.* A Sermon, preached before the North Church and Society in Salem . . . on the death of their pastor, the Rev. Thomas Barnard, *etc.* 1814. 8°. **4905**. dd. **1**.

—— A Discourse before the Society for Propagating the Gospel among the Indians and others in North America, delivered November 6, 1806. pp. 39. *Samuel Etheridge: Charlestown* [*N.H.*], 1806. 8°. **4485**. f. **17**.

—— A Discourse, delivered before the Humane Society of the Commonwealth of Massachusetts, at the semiannual meeting, June 10, 1794. pp. 25. 1794. 8°. *See* Massachusetts.—*Humane Society of the Commonwealth of Massachusetts*. T. **175**. **(1.)**

—— A Discourse on Natural Religion, delivered in the Chapel of the University in Cambridge, September 3, 1795, at the Lecture founded by the Honorable Paul Dudley, Esq. pp. 24. *Samuel Hall: Boston*, 1795. 8°. **4486**. b. **60**. **(15.)**

—— The Power of God, the Proof of Christianity. A discourse delivered at the Dudleian Lecture in the Chapel of Harvard College . . . May 11th, 1768. pp. 28. *Samuel Hall: Salem*, 1768. 8°. **4015**. b. **4**.

—— A Sermon delivered at Salem on March 31, 1796, the day of general fasting, *etc.* pp. 20. *John Dabney: Salem*, [1796.] 8°. **4485**. i. **23**.

—— A Sermon delivered before the Congregational Ministers of the Commonwealth of Massachusetts . . . May 30, 1793. pp. 23. *Samuel Hall: Boston*, 1793. 8°. **4486**. b. **60**. **(14.)**

—— A Sermon, delivered in the North Meeting House in Salem, before the Bible Society of Salem and Vicinity . . . April 20, 1814. (Third Report of the Trustees of the Bible Society of Salem and Vicinity.) 2 pt. *T. C. Cushing: Salem*, 1814. 8°. **4485**. f. **19**.

—— A Sermon, delivered June 7th, 1809, at the ordination of the Rev. Ichabod Nichols, *etc.* pp. 23. *J. M'Kown: Portland* [*Me.*], 1809. 8°. **4485**. f. **18**.

—— A Sermon, delivered on the Day of Annual Thanksgiving, December 15, 1796. pp. 22. *T. C. Cushing: Salem*, [1796.] 8°. **4485**. i. **22**.

—— A Sermon, delivered on the Day of National Thanksgiving, February 19, 1795. pp. 25. *T. C. Cushing: Salem*, 1795. 8°. T. **154**. **(5.)**

—— A Sermon, preached at the ordination of the Rev. Aaron Bancroft . . . February 1, mdcclxxxvi. pp. 50. *Isaiah Thomas: Worcester* [*Mass.*], 1786. 8°. **4487**. e. **5**. **(6.)**

Pp. 5, 6 *are mutilated.*

—— A Sermon preached at the ordination of the Rev. William Whitwell . . . August 25. 1762, *etc.* pp. 51. *J. Draper: Boston*, 1762. 8°. **4486**. b. **60**. **(7.)**

BARNARD (Thomas) *D.D. of Salem, Mass.*

—— A Sermon, preached at the request of the Antient and Honourable Artillery Company, in Boston, June 1, 1789; being the anniversary of their election of officers. pp. 29. *Benjamin Russell: Boston*, 1789. 12°. **4486**. aaa. **91**. **(11.)**

—— A Sermon preached before his Excellency Francis Bernard . . . May 25th 1763. Being the anniversary for the election of His Majesty's Council, *etc.* pp. 45. *Richard Draper: Boston*, 1763. 8°. **4486**. b. **60**. **(8.)**

—— A Sermon, preached December 29, 1799 . . . the Lord's Day after the melancholy tidings were received of the death of General George Washington, *etc.* pp. 27. *Salem*, [1800.] 8°. **1358**. d. **2**. **(1.)**

—— A Sermon preached in Boston, New-England, before the Society for Encouraging Industry and Employing the Poor, September 20. 1758. pp. 25. *S. Kneeland: Boston*, 1758. 8°. **4486**. aa. **65**. **(1.)**

—— A Sermon, preached January 15th, 1801 . . . before the interment of the Rev. Phillips Payson, *etc.* pp. 16. *Charlestown* [*N.H.*], 1801. 8°. **4985**. cc. **1**.

—— A Sermon preached to the Ancient and Honourable Artillery Company in Boston . . . June 5, 1758. Being the anniversary of their election of officers. pp. 32. *Edes & Gill: Boston*, 1758. 8°. **4486**. b. **60**. **(4.)**

—— Tyranny and Slavery in Matters of Religion, caution'd against; and true humility recommended to ministers and people. A sermon preach'd at the ordination of Mr. Edward Barnard, *etc.* pp. 35. *Samuel Eliot: Boston*, 1743. 8°. **4486**. b. **60**. **(3.)**

BARNARD (Thomas) *M.A., Master of the Free-School in Leeds.* An Historical Character relating to the holy and exemplary Life of the Right Honourable the Lady Elisabeth Hastings, *etc.* pp. xxviii. 191. *John Swale: Leedes*, 1742. 12°. **1417**. a. **41**.

—— [Another copy.] **275**. d. **20**.

—— [Another copy.] **F.P.** G. **2224**.

—— [Another edition.] The Life of the Right Honourable Lady Elizabeth Hastings. 1839. *See* Jackson (Thomas) *Wesleyan Minister.* A Library of Christian Biography, *etc.* vol. 11. 1837, *etc.* 12°. **1124**. a. **4**.

—— A Sorrowful Respect paid to the Dead Vindicated . . . In a sermon preach'd . . . on the occasion of the death of the Reverend Mr. Henry Lodge, *etc.* pp. 26. *Francis Hilyard: York*, 1718. 8°. **1417**. d. **48**.

—— [Another copy.] **1417**. d. **49**.

—— [Another copy.] **225**. g. **14**.

BARNARD (W. T.) *Assistant to the President of the Baltimore and Ohio Railway Company.*

—— Baltimore & Ohio Railroad Company . . . Service report on technical education, with special reference to the Baltimore & Ohio Railroad Service, *etc.* pp. 168. 67. *Isaac Friedenwald: Baltimore*, 1887. 8°. **8310**. e. **20**.

The last leaf is mutilated.

BARNARD (Walter Green) Regulation. pp. 124. *B. F. Stevens & Brown: London; Binghamton, N.Y.* [printed, 1913.] 8°. **08248**. aaa. **28**.

BARNARD (Walter Henry) Comparative Prices of Metals. (July 1st, 1904.) *London*, 1904. *s. sh.* fol. **1882**. d. **2**. **(126*.)**

BARNARD (Walter Henry)

—— Tin and Tin Ore. Comparative list of outside supplies to Europe in fine tin contents. 1912. *s. sh.* fol. **1882**. d. **2**. **(4**.)**

BARNARD (Wilhelmus)

—— *See* Graft (G. van der) *pseud.* [i.e. W. Barnard.]

BARNARD (William) *Barrister*, and **STOCKER** (G. Bertram) Medical Partnerships, Transfers and Assistantships. pp. xi. 249. *Stevens & Sons: London*, 1895. 8°. **6376**. e. **35**.

BARNARD (William) successively *Bishop of Raphoe* and *of Derry*. A Sermon preached . . . on the 10th Day of May, 1752, before the Incorporated Society, for promoting English Protestant Schools in Ireland . . . With a continuation of the Society's proceedings to the Twenty-fifth of March, 1752. pp. 53. *S. Powell: Dublin*, 1752. 4°. **694**. f. **12**. **(5.)**

—— [Another copy.] **225**. i. **22**. **(16.)** *Imperfect; wanting all after pp.* 12.

BARNARD (William) *of Abingdon Street, Westminster*. Serious Thoughts on the Trial of Mr. Barnard. With a state of the conduct of the D * * * * of M * * * *, and the magistrate . . . Addressed to a Person of Honour. [Signed: A British Subject.] pp. 16. *J. Coot: London*, [1758?] 8°. **518**. e. **21**. **(6.)**

BARNARD (William E.) Post-Meridian. pp. 48. *Erskine Macdonald: London*, [1917.] 8°. [*Little Books of Georgian Verse.*] **11655.aaa.27/16.**

BARNARD (William George)

—— *See* Kettle (Edgar H.) Kettle's Pathology of Tumours. By W. G. Barnard . . . and A. H. T. R. Smith, *etc.* 1945. 8°. **7443**. bb. **7**.

—— The Cattle of the Swazi. [*Bremersdorp*,] 1951– . fol [*Mpisi Series*. no. 2, 3, *etc.*] C.S. d. **469/2**.

—— Elementary Pathological Histology . . . With . . . plates. pp. x. 70. *H. K. Lewis & Co.: London*, 1928. 8°. **7442**. i. **20**.

—— Elementary Pathological Histology . . . Second edition, *etc.* pp. x. 75. *H. K. Lewis: London*, 1940. 4°. **7441**. r. **10**.

—— Elementary Pathological Histology . . . Second edition, *etc.* (Reprinted, with additions.) pp. x. 75. *H. K. Lewis & Co.: London*, 1947. 4°. **7444**. d. **4**.

—— Elementary Pathological Histology . . . Third edition, *etc.* pp. x. 77. *H. K. Lewis & Co.: London*, 1953. 8°. **7423**. dd. **32**.

BARNARD (William Nichols) *See* Hirschfeld (Clarence F.) and Barnard (W. N.) Elements of Heat-Power Engineering. 1913. 8°. **08767**. cc. **28**.

—— —— 1915. 8°. **08768**. d. **51**.

—— —— 1926, *etc.* 8°. **8772.g.27.**

—— *See* Thurston (Robert H.) A History of the Growth of the Steam-Engine . . . With a supplementary chapter by W. N. Barnard. 1939. 8°. **8772**. ee. **25**.

BARNARD (William Steven)

—— "Phantom Heartbeats?" *etc.* ff. 4. *University, Ala.*, [1942.] 8°. [*Blackfriar Series of Original Plays*. no. 53.] W.P. **12459/53**.

Reproduced from typewriting.

BARNARD (Winifred Eva)

—— *See* Baker (Betty) The Friend of Little Children . . . Notes by B. Baker, W. E. Barnard, *etc.* [1939.] 8°. W.P. **12722/1a**.

—— The Beginners' Department [of the Sunday School]. pp. 72. *National Sunday School Union: London*, [1923.] 8°. **4193**. i. **23**.

—— Beginner's Work and Worship. A manual for leaders and teachers in beginners' departments. [With musical notes.] pp. 159. *Ludgate Circus House: London*, [1933.] 8°. [*Concise Guide Series*. no. 3.] **12828.a.90/3.**

—— Kembo, a little girl of Africa, *etc.* pp. 60. *Edinburgh House Press: London*, 1924. 16°. **012803**. de. **108**.

—— Mitsu: a little girl of Japan, *etc.* pp. 56. *Edinburgh House Press: London*, 1928. 16°. **012804**. df. **34**.

—— More Stories for Beginners. pp. 63. *National Sunday School Union: London*, [1935.] 8°. **04419**. i. **33**.

—— Round-the-Week Stories. Nursery stories for day and Sunday school and home . . . Illustrations by Kendall. pp. 127. *Religious Education Press: Wallington*, 1950. 8°. [*Tales to tell Series*. no. 4.] W.P. **3733/4**.

BARNARD (Winifred Eva) and **SPRIGGS** (Elsie Helena)

—— Tales to Tell to Little Children, *etc.* pp. 126. "*Teachers and Taught*": *London*, 1925. 8°. [*Concise Guide Story-Series*. no. 1.] **12828.a.90/1.**

—— [Another edition.] pp. 127. *Livingstone Press: London*, [1934.] 8°. **20054**. aa. **14**.

—— More Tales to Tell to Little Children . . . With illustrations, *etc.* pp. 127. *Livingstone Press: London*, 1931. 8°. [*Concise Guide Story-Series*, no. 2.] **12828.a.90/2.**

BARNARDE (John) *See* Bernard (J.) *Fellow of Queen's College, Cambridge.*

BARNARDISTON (Anne) *See* Shower (John) A Sermon preacht upon the Death of Mrs. Anne Barnardiston, *etc.* 1682. 4°. **1416**. c. **32**.

BARNARDISTON (Giles) The Life of Christ Magnified in his Minister. Or, Certain testimonies thereof, relating to . . . Giles Barnardiston . . . which were given forth severally by Samuel Cater [and others], *etc.* pp. 67. *For John Bringhurst: London*, 1681. 8°. **1415**. a. **33**.

—— A Testimony against Jeffery Bullock his antichristian and foolish pamphlet, stiled, Antichrist's Transformations within Discovered by the light within, *etc.* pp. 15. 1676. 4°. **4152**. ee. **21**. **(2.)**

BARNARDISTON (John) A Sermon preached, before the Honourable the House of Commons . . . on Thursday, January the 30th, 1766. Being the day appointed to be observed in memory of the martyrdom of Charles I. pp. 24. *R. Matthews: Cambridge; Edw. Johnson: London*, 1766. 4°. **694**. i. **18**. **(22.)**

BARNARDISTON (*Sir* Nathaniel) *See* Fairclough (Samuel) Ἅγιοι ἄξιοι, or the Saints worthinesse . . . declared in a sermon preached at the funerall of . . . Sir N. Barnardiston, *etc.* 1653. 4°. **1416**. c. **33**.

BARNARDISTON (*Sir* NATHANIEL)

—— Suffolks Tears: or Elegies on that renowned Knight Sir N. Barnardiston. [With a dedication in verse by Samuel Fairclough, and with an engraved frontispiece.] pp. 66. *R.I. for Tho. Newberry: London*, 1653. 4°. **1416. c. 36.**

—— [Another copy.] G. **11498.**
In this copy are inserted a portrait and a duplicate of the plate of the arms of Sir N. Barnardiston with verses by Fairclough added at the foot.

BARNARDISTON (NATHANIEL WALTER) *See* ENGLAND.—*War Office.—Intelligence Division.* Handbook of the French Army . . . Revised by Major N. W. Barnardiston. 1901. 8°. **8831. ee. 49.**

—— Handbook of the Belgian Army, *etc.* pp. 137. 1899. 8°. *See* ENGLAND.—*War Office.—Intelligence Division.* **8832. de. 52.**

BARNARDISTON (*Sir* ROBERT) *Bart.* Sir Robert Barnardiston, Bart., Samuel Barnardiston, Esq; and John Coppin Esq; Appellants. William Carter, Esquire, Respondant. The Appellants Case. pp. 4. [1717.] fol. **19. h. 1. (20.)**

—— Sir Robert Barnardiston Bart., Samuel Barnardiston Esq; and John Coppin Esq; Appellts. William Carter Esq; Respondt. The Respondent's Case. pp. 3. [1717.] fol. **19. h. 1. (21.)**

—— Sir Robert Barnardiston Bart., and others, Appellts. William Carter Respondt. The Respondent's Answer to the case of Lodington and Kime, in 3 Levins, 431. [1717.] *s. sh.* fol. **19. h. 1. (22.)**
Cropped.

BARNARDISTON (SAMUEL) *See* BARNARDISTON (*Sir* R.) *Bart.* Sir Robert Barnardiston, Bart., Samuel Barnardiston, Esq; and John Coppin, Esq; Appellants. William Carter, Esquire, Respondent. The Appellants Case. [1717.] fol. **19. h. 1. (20.)**

—— *See* BARNARDISTON (*Sir* R.) *Bart.* Sir Robert Barnardiston Bart., Samuel Barnardiston, Esq; and John Coppin, Esq; Appellts William Carter, Esq; Respondt. The Respondent's Case. [1717.] fol. **19. h. 1. (21.)**

BARNARDISTON (*Sir* SAMUEL) *Bart.* *See* ATKYNS (*Sir* Robert) *Chief Baron of the Exchequer.* A Defence of the late Lord Russel's Innocency . . . Together with an Argument in the great case concerning elections of members to Parliament, between Sr Samuel Barnardiston Bar. Plaintiff, and Sr Will. Soames Sheriff of Suffolk, Defend', *etc.* 1689. fol. **1486.g.11.(27.)**

—— *See* BARNARD . . . ON (*Sir* Samuel) The Whig Intelligencer: or, Sir Samuel (Barnard . . . on [i.e. Barnardiston]) in the Pound, *etc.* 1684. *s. sh.* fol. **C.121.g.9.(76.)**

—— *See* NORTH (Francis) *1st Baron Guilford.* The Late Lord Chief Justice North's Argument. In the case between Sir William Soames . . . and Sir Sam. Barnardiston, *etc.* 1689. fol. **515. k. 24. (2.)**

—— An Argument of a learned Judge [i.e. Lord Chief Justice North] in the Exchequer Chamber upon a writ of error out of the King's-Bench, in a cause, wherein Sir Samuel Barnardiston was plaintiff against Sir William Soame . . . Defendant, wherein the privilege of the House of Commons, in determining matters relating to the right of elections of their own members, is justified, *etc.* pp. 24. *For Geo. Sawbridge; sold by J. Nutt: London*, 1704. 4°. **1243. b. 3.**

—— [Another copy.] **115. h. 31.**

BARNARDISTON (*Sir* SAMUEL) *Bart.*

—— The Tryal and Conviction of Sr Sam. Bernardiston, Bart for High-Misdemeanor . . . before the Right Honorable Sir George Jeffreys . . . on Thursday, Feb. 14. 1683. pp. 34. *For Benjamin Tooke: London*, 1684. fol. **515. l. 4. (2.)**

—— [Another copy.] **1890. b. 2. (7.)**
Imperfect; wanting pp. 33, 34.

BARNARDISTON (THOMAS) Reports of Cases determined in the Court of King's Bench . . . From Trin. 12 Geo. I. to Trin. 7 Geo. II., *etc.* B.L. 2 vol. 1744. fol. *See* ENGLAND.—*Court of King's Bench.—Reports.* **1242. i. 10, 11.**

—— Reports of Cases determined in the High Court of Chancery, from April 25. 1740 to May 9. 1741, *etc.* pp. 502. FEW MS. NOTES. 1742. fol. *See* ENGLAND.—*Court of Chancery.—Reports.* **510. i. 13.**

BARNARDISTON (THOMASIN) *See* ROBINSON (Ralph) *Puritan Divine.* Safe Conduct, or the Saints Guidance to Glory. Opened in a sermon preached . . . November the second, MDCLIV. At the funerall of . . . Mtis Thomasin Barnardiston, *etc.* 1654. 4°. **E. 823. (7.)**

BARNARDO (FREDERICK ADOLPHUS FLEMING) Report on Experiments with Nastin B in Leprosy. By Captain F. A. F. Barnardo . . . and Major J. W. D. Megaw . . . With notes by Colonel G. F. A. Harris. [With plates.] pp. iii. 33. 1912. fol. *See* BENGAL.—*Civil Medical Service.* **I.S. 91/9.**

BARNARDO (SYRIE LOUISE) and **MARCHANT** (*Sir* JAMES) *K.B.E.* Memoirs of the late Dr. Barnardo . . . With an introduction by W. Robertson Nicoll. [With illustrations]. pp. xxiii. 404. *Hodder & Stoughton: London*, 1907. 8°. **010827. g. 6.**

BARNARDO (THOMAS JOHN) *See* BARNARDO (S. L.) and MARCHANT (*Sir* J.) *K.B.E.* Memoirs of the late Dr. Barnardo, *etc.* 1907. 8°. **010827. g. 6.**

—— *See* BATT (John H.) Dr. Barnardo, *etc.* 1904. 8°. **08275. aa. 14.**

—— *See* BREADY (John W.) Doctor Barnardo, *etc.* [With a portrait.] 1930. 8°. **10823. aaa. 4.**

—— *See* BREADY (John W.) Doctor Barnardo, *etc.* 1935. 8°. **010825. f. 20.**

—— *See* GRIFFITH (W. M.) *of Dyffryn.* Tri o Gedyrn Gras: George Müller, J. Hudson Taylor, Dr. Barnardo, *etc.* [1910.] 8°. **4804. e. 24.**

—— *See* HOPKINS (Ellice) "God's Little Girl" . . . Facts concerning a poor "waif" admitted into "Dr. Barnardo's Village Home," *etc.* [1885.] 24°. **8277. a. 42. (3.)**

—— [For publications issued officially by Dr. Barnardo's Homes:] *See* LONDON.—III. *Dr. Barnardo's Homes.*

—— *See* LONDON.—III. Family Welfare Association. The Charity Organisation Society and the Reynolds-Barnardo Arbitration. 1878. 8°. **8282. e. 37. (2.)**

—— *See* MARCHANT (*Sir* James) *K.B.E.* Tales for the Homes, *etc.* [A collection of original contributions by leading authors published on behalf of the National Barnardo Memorial Fund.] 1907. 8°. **4408. ff. 18.**

—— *See* NEUMAN (A. R.) Dr. Barnardo as I knew him, *etc.* 1914. 8°. **010603. a. 15/8.**

BARNARDO (THOMAS JOHN)

—— *See* PERIODICAL PUBLICATIONS.—*London*. Father William's Stories. (Edited by Dr. Barnardo.) [1866, *etc.*] 4°. P.P. **1163**. ed.

—— *See* PERIODICAL PUBLICATIONS.—*London*. Night and Day. A monthly record of Christian missions . . . Edited by Dr. Barnardo. 1877, *etc.* 4°. P.P. **1103**. cc.

—— *See* PERIODICAL PUBLICATIONS.—*London*. Our Bubble . . . Edited by Dr. Barnardo, *etc.* [1894, *etc.*] 4°. P.P. **1103**. ccc.

—— *See* POWELL (Jessie) The Man Who Didn't Go to China. The story of T. J. Barnardo. 1947. 8°. **10860**. aa. **24**.

—— *See* POWELL (Jessie) Thomas John Barnardo. 1947. 16°. W.P. **1404/8**

—— *See* REYNOLDS (George) *Baptist Minister*. Dr. Barnardo's Homes. Containing startling revelations, *etc.* [1877?] 8°. **8277**. d. **15**. **(1.)**

—— *See* ROGERS (Evan J. G.) Thomas Barnardo, 1845-1905, *etc.* [1948.] 8°. W.P. **1551/2C**

—— *See* S., M. E. My Cottage: a story of Dr. Barnardo's Village Home, *etc.* [1885.] 24°. **8277**. a. **42**. **(4.)**

—— *See* WILLIAMS (Arthur E.) The Adventures of Dr. Barnardo, *etc.* 1949. 8°. **10862**. de. **15**.

—— *See* WILLIAMS (Arthur E.) Barnardo of Stepney, *etc.* [With portraits.] 1943. 8°. **10860**. b. **21**.

—— *See* WILLIAMS (Arthur E.) Barnardo of Stepney, *etc.* 1953. 8°. **10863**. ff. **19**.

—— *See* WYMER (Norman G.) Father of Nobody's Children. A portrait of Dr. Barnardo, *etc.* [With portraits.] 1954. 8°. **10864**. cc. **8**.

—— A Brief Account of the Institutions known as Dr. Barnardo's Homes. pp. 24. [*London*, 1879.] 24°. **8277**. a. **18**.

—— A City Waif: how I fished for and caught her. pp. 32. *J. F. Shaw & Co.: London*, [1883.] 24°. **8277**. a. **42**. **(1.)**

—— [Another copy.] **4422**. aaa. **48**. **(6.)**

—— Kidnapped! A narrative of fact. pp. 24. *J. F. Shaw & Co.: London*, [1885.] 12°. **8277**. a. **42**. **(6.)**

—— "The King's Business requireth Haste." pp. 10. *J. F. Shaw & Co.: London*, [1885.] 16°. **8277**. a. **41**. **(2.)**

—— My First Arab; or, How I began my life work. pp. 32. *J. F. Shaw & Co.: London*, [1888.] 16°. **8277**. a. **48**. **(2.)**

—— "Never had a Home!" A very commonplace history. pp. 24. *Shaw & Co.: London*, [1890.] 16°. **8277**. a. **76**. **(1.)**

—— Preventive Homes, and the work done in them, *etc.* pp. 47. *Haughton & Co.: London*, [1878.] 12°. **8275**. aaa. **7**. **(8.)**

—— Rescued for Life: the true story of a young thief. pp. 48. *J. F. Shaw & Co.: London*, [1885.] 24°. **8277**. a. **42**. **(2.)**

—— Saved from a Crime: incidents in the life of a waif and stray. pp. 40. *J. F. Shaw & Co.: London*, [1888.] 16°. **8277**. a. **48**. **(3.)**

BARNARDO (THOMAS JOHN)

—— "The Seed of the Righteous," among the children of the poorest. pp. 32. *J. F. Shaw & Co.: London*, [1886.] 16°. **8277**. a. **48**. **(1.)**

—— "Taken out of the Gutter." A true incident of child life on the streets of London, *etc.* pp. 40. *Haughton & Co.: London*, [1881]. 24°. **8282**. aa. **15**.

—— Worse than Orphans: how I stole two girls and fought for a boy. pp. 32. *J. F. Shaw & Co.: London*, [1885.] 16°. **8277**. a. **42**. **(5.)**

—— A Year's Work in the Institutions known as "Dr. Barnardo's Homes." pp. 143. *J. F. Shaw & Co.: London*, [1884.] 16°. **8277**. a. **41**. **(1.)**

—— Children Reclaimed for Life. The story of Dr. Barnardo's work in London. By the author of 'The Romance of the Streets' [i.e. J. H. Pike] . . . With illustrations. pp. xvii. 169. *Hodder & Stoughton: London*, 1875. 8°. **4192**. bbb. **39**.

BARNARDO (*Mrs.* THOMAS JOHN) *See* BARNARDO (Syrie L.)

BARNARD . . . ON (*Sir* SAMUEL) The Whig Intelligencer: or, Sir Samuel (Barnard . . . on [i.e. Barnardiston]) in the Pound, for publishing scandalous and seditious letters, *etc.* [A ballad, with the notes of the music.] [*London*,] 1684. *s. sh.* fol. C.121.g.9.(76.)

BARNARDT (IGNATIUS WILLEN)

—— Rooikrans se dogters. pp. 94. *Port Elizabeth & Kaapstad*, 1945. 8°. **012580**. e. **30**.

—— Rooikrans se seuns. [A tale.] pp. 116. *Kaapstad & Port Elizabeth*, 1944. 8°. **012580**. a. **8**

BARNARDUS (RICHARDUS) *See* BERNARD (Richard)

BARNATO (BARNETT ISAACS) *See* ISAACS (B.)

BARNAUD (GERMAINE)

—— Le Nain. Peintures, dessins, *etc.* [A catalogue of an exhibition of works by Antoine, Louis and Mathieu Le Nain. With reproductions.] pp. 61. 1934. 8°. *See* PARIS.—*Petit Palais*. **7856**. df. **55**.

BARNAUD (J.) *Ingenieur*.

—— Nouveau traité de fortification, contenant vne nouvelle methode pour fortifiér tant sur le papier que sur le terrain quelque polygone . . . pour la conservation des places avec la methode de Mr Ozanam . . . & celle de Mr de Vauban. pp. 28. pl. II. MS. NOTES. *Berlin* 1705. 4°. M.L. bbb. **30**

BARNAUD (JEAN)

—— Le Christianisme: religion historique. *See* CHRISTIANITY. Le Problème du Christianisme. 1945. 8°. **W.P.c.570/1.**

BARNAUD (LOUIS) Notre-Dame de Romay et les souvenirs qui s'y rattachent. pp. xiv. 309. *Blois*, 1904. 8°. **4629**. bb. **19**.

BARNAUD (LOUIS GABRIEL DE VILLENEUVE-LAROCHE) *See* VILLENEUVE LAROCHE BARNAUD.

BARNAUD (NICOLAS) *See* also EUSEBIUS PHILADELPHUS COSMOPOLITA, *pseud.* [i.e. N. Barnaud.]

—— *See* also FROUMENTEAU (Nicolas) *pseud.* [i.e. N. Barnaud?]

—— *See* also MONTAND (Nicolas de) *pseud.* [i.e. N. Barnaud.]

BARNAUD (Nicolas)

—— *See* Lambsprinck (von) Lambsprinck . . . Libellus de lapide philosophico, e germanico versu latine redditus, per N. Barnaudum. 1749. 4°. [*Musaeum Hermeticum reformatum.*] **1032**. c. **6**.

—— *See* Triplanus (G.) Chimica scripta . . . Georgij Triplani . . . Latinè iampridem edita à N. Barnaudo. 1646. 8°. [Basilius Valentinus *Currus triumphalis antimonii.*] **1033**. a. **8**.

—— Le Cabinet du roy de France, dans lequel il y a trois perles precieuses d'inestimable valeur, *etc.* [The dedicatory epistle headed: " Au Roy de France . . . N. D. C. [i.e. N. Barnaud du Crest], paix & salut."] pp. 647. 1581. 8°. *See* C., N. D. **C.125.aa.1.**

—— [A reissue.] 1582. 8°. *See* C., N. D. **1059**. b. **20**. **(1.)**

—— De occulta philosophia, epistola cujusdam patris ad filium . . . Nunc primum in lucem edita. *Ex officinâ T. Basson: Lugduni Batavorum,* 1601. 8°. **1033**. e. **30**. **(1.)**

—— [Another copy.] **234**. a. **24**. **(1.)**

—— Dialogus, quo multa exponuntur quæ Lutheranis et Hugonotis Gallis acciderunt, *etc.* [By N. Barnaud.] pp. 170. 1573. 8°. *See* Lutherans. **285**. b. **13**.

—— Dialogue, auquel sont traitees plusieurs choses auenues aux Lutheriens & Huguenots de la France, *etc.* [By N. Barnaud.] pp. 164. 1573. 8°. *See* Lutherans. **701**. a. **29**.

—— [Another edition.] [The author's preface to the reader signed: P. D. L. V. By N. Barnaud.] pp. 154. 1612. 12°. *See* V., P. D. L. **701**. a. **9**. **(1.)**

—— Nicolai Barnaudi . . . In aenigmaticum quoddam epitaphium Bononiæ studiorum. 1659. *See* Zetzner (L.) Theatrum chemicum, *etc.* vol. 3. 1613, *etc.* 8°. **1034**. d. **3**.

—— [Another edition.] *See* Manget (J. J.) Jo. Jacobi Mangeti . . . Bibliotheca chemica, *etc.* tom. 2. 1702. fol. **44**. i. **12**.

—— The Massacre of St. Bartholomew's Day, from the Réveille-Matin des François [by N. Barnaud, originally published under the pseudonym Eusebius Philadelphus Cosmopolita]. *See* Coligny (Gaspar II. de) *Admiral of France.* Memoirs of Gaspar de Coligny, *etc.* 1844. 8°. **1451**. b. **12**.

—— Tractatulus chemicus, theosophiæ palmarium dictus, anonymi cuiusdam philosophi antiqui a N. Barnaudo . . . nunc primùm editus, *etc.* *Ex officinâ T. Basson: Lugduni Batavorum,* 1601. 8°. **1033**. e. **30**. **(2.)**

—— [Another copy.] **234**. a. **24**. **(2.)**

BARNAUDUS (Nicolaus) *See* Barnaud (Nicolas)

BARNAVAL DE KERLEREC (Louis) The Love-Poems of Louis Barnaval. Edited, with an introduction [or rather, written] by Charles De Kay. pp. xix. 215. *D. Appleton & Co.: New York,* 1883. 12°. **11688**. f. **14**.

BARNAVE (Antoine Pierre Joseph Marie)

—— *See* Barnavophile, *pseud.* Lettre à Monsieur Barnave, par un habitant des montagnes du Dauphiné. [Signed: Barnavophile. An attack on A. P. J. M. Barnave.] [1791.] 8°. R. **207**. (2.)

—— *See* Bradby (E. D.) The Life of Barnave. 1915. 8°. **010661**. dd. **41**.

BARNAVE (Antoine Pierre Joseph Marie)

—— *See* Cazalès (J. A. M. de) Détail du combat qui a eu lieu au bois de Boulogne entre M. de Cazalès et M. Barnave. [1790.] 8°. F.R. **53**. **(4.)**

—— *See* Cazalès (J. A. M. de) Grand duel . . . entre Messieurs Cazalès et Barnave. [1790.] 8°. **F**. **381**. **(15.)**

—— *See* Chevallier (J. J.) Barnave, ou les deux faces de la Révolution, *etc.* [With portraits.] 1936. 8°. 010665. i. **48**.

—— *See* Clermont-Tonnerre (S. M. A. de) *Count.* Rèponses sommaires à quelques objections de M. Barnave. [Concerning the decree proposed to the Assembly by Clermont-Tonnerre respecting the right of declaring war.] 1790. 8°. **F**. **1520**. **(4.)**

—— *See* Duchesne, *Père, pseud.* Je suis le véritable père Duchêne, foutre. Déjeuner du père Duchene avec M. Barnave et M. de Mirabeau, et leur conversation sur les grands dangers de la patrie. [A political satire.] [1790 ?] 8°. **F**. **1035**. **(26.)**

—— *See* France.—*Assemblée Nationale Constituente.* [1789–91.] Suite de la discussion sur l'affaire de la Chambre des Vacations du Parlement de Rennes. Discours de M. Barnave . . . Séance du samedi 9 janvier 1790, *etc.* [1790.] 8°. R. **31**. (18.)

—— *See* Gariod (H.) Eloge de Barnave, *etc.* 1861. 8°. **10660**. cc. **13**.

—— *See* Heidenstam (O. G. von) Marie Antoinette, Fersen et Barnave. Leur correspondance. [1913.] 8°. **10909**. bbb. **36**.

—— *See* Heidenstam (O. G. von) The Letters of Marie Antoinette, Fersen and Barnave, *etc.* [With a portrait.] 1926. 8°. **010902**. **f**. **33**.

—— *See* Jacobite. Observations impartiales d'un Jacobite. [In reply to a denunciation by Barnave of a new club called: " Amis de la Constitution Monarchique."] [1791.] 8°. **F**. **808**. **(10.)**

—— *See* Lameth (C. M. F. de) *Count.* Grande dénonciation de MM. Charles & Alexandre de Lameth, Barnave . . . & autres, jockeis & aboyeurs à la suite de la conspiration. [1792 ?] 8°. **F**. **419**. **(6.)**

—— *See* Malouet (P. V. de) *Baron.* Réponse de M. Malouet à la dénonciation du Club de la constitution monarchique, par M. Barnave. [1791.] 8°. **R**. **673**. **(13.)**

—— *See* Malouet (P. V. de) *Baron.* Réponse . . . à la dénonciation du Club de la Constitution monarchique, par M. Barnave. [1791.] 8°. R. **81**. (15.)

—— —— [1791.] 8°. R. **81**. (14.)

—— *See* Mary Antoinette, *Queen Consort of Louis XVI., King of France.* Marie-Antoinette et Barnave: correspondance secrète, *etc.* 1934. 8°. **010920**. k. **41**

—— *See* Pétion de Villeneuve (J.) Lettre de MM. les Commissaires de l'Assemblée nationale à M. le Président. [Concerning the safe conduct of Louis XVI. on his return to Paris from Varennes. Signed: Pétion, La Tour-Maubourg, Barnave.] [1791.] *s. sh.* 8°. **F.R**. **118**. **(31.)**

—— *See* Tempête, *le Capitaine, pseud.* Le Capitaine Tempête à Barnave. [Warning him of the consequences of his policy.] [1792 ?] 8°. **T**. **444**. **(18.)**

BARNAVE (ANTOINE PIERRE JOSEPH MARIE)

—— *See* WELVERT (Eugène) Le Secret de Barnave, *etc.* 1920. 8°. **10657. aa. 13.**

—— Œuvres de Barnave, mises en ordre, et précédées d'une notice historique sur Barnave, par M. Bérenger de la Drome. [With a portrait.] 4 tom. *Paris*, 1843. 8°. **1339. e. 7, 8.**

—— Correspondance inédite de Barnave en 1792. *See* MICHON (Georges) Essai sur l'histoire du parti feuillant. Adrien Duport, *etc.* 1924. 8°. **09225. i. 52.**

—— Articles proposés à l'Assemblée nationale, sur le travail du comité de constitution. pp. 4. 1789. 8°. **F.R. 113. (3.)**

—— Coup d'œil sur la lettre de M. de Calonne [i.e. " Lettre adressés au Roi par M. de Calonne, le 9 février 1789 "]. pp. 29. *Dauphiné*, 1789. 8°. **F. 34. (15.)**

—— Esprit des édits, enregistrés militairement au Parlement de Grenoble le 10 Mai 1788. [By A. P. J. M. Barnave.] pp. 24. 1788. 8°. *See* DAUPHINY.—*Parlement.* **F.R. 6. (12.)**

—— L'Esprit des édits enrégistrés militairement aux Parlements de France, le 10 Mai 1788. [By A. P. J. M. Barnave.] pp. 26. 1788. 8°. *See* FRANCE.—*Parlements.* **910. b. 14. (5.)**

—— *See* BOURG-EN BRESSE.—*Grand Bailliage.* Jugement du Grand Bailliage de Bourg-en-Bresse qui supprime un ecrit [by A. P. J. M. Barnave] intitulé, " Esprit des édits enrégistrés militairement au Parlement de Grenoble." 1788. 8°. **F.R. 6. (21.)**

—— Grande dénonciation, faite à la tribune des Jacobins . . . d'une quantité étonnante de libelles répandus dans Paris. pp. 7. [*Paris*, 1791.] 8°. **F. 1193. (1.)**

—— [Another copy.] **F. 398. (7.)**

—— Instruction pour les colonies, présentée à l'Assemblée nationale, au nom du comité chargé de ce travail, le 23 Mars 1790. pp. 28. *Paris*, [1790.] 8°. **F. 713. (7.)**

—— Necrologie. Grande mort du petit Barnave. [A satire.] pp. 3. [1791.] 8°. **R. 207. (5.)**

—— Opinion de M. Barnave, prononcée à la Séance du 15 Juillet [1791. Concerning the flight of Louis XVI to Varennes]. pp. 19. [1791.] *See* FRANCE.—*Assemblée Nationale Constituante.* [1789–1791.] Procès-verbal de l'Assemblée . . . nationale. tom. 63. 1789, *etc.* 8°. **284. k. 33.**

—— Opinion de M. Barnave, prononcée à la séance du 15 juillet, *etc.* [*Paris*, 1791.] 8°. **R. 150. (5.)**

—— Opinion de M. Barnave, prononcée à la séance du quinze juillet [1791]. pp. 12. *Douay*, [1791.] 4°. **R. 690. (6.)**

—— [Another edition.] pp. 19. *Rouen*, [1791.] 8°. **F. 702. (6.)**

—— [Another edition.] pp. 20. *Toulouse*, [1791.] 8°. **8050. d. 61. (15.)**

—— Discours adressé aux Français, amis de la Constitution, contenant les principes qui ont dicté le décret du 16, relatif au Roi, *etc.* [A precis of the " Opinion de M. Barnave, prononcée à la Séance du 15 Juillet."] pp. 8. *Bordeaux*, 1791. 8°. **R. 3. (21.)**

—— Rapport fait à l'Assemblée nationale, le 8 Mars 1790, au nom du Comité des colonies. pp. 22. *Paris*, 1790. 8°. **F. 707. (14.)**

BARNAVE (ANTOINE PIERRE JOSEPH MARIE)

—— [Another issue.] 1790. *See* FRANCE.—*Assemblée Nationale Constituante.* [1789–1791.] Procès-verbal de l'Assemblée . . . nationale. tom. 14. 1789, *etc.* 8°. **283. k. 17.**

—— Rapport fait à l'Assemblée nationale, sur les colonies . . . le 23 Septembre 1791. 1791. *See* FRANCE.—*Assemblée Nationale Constituante.* [1789–1791.] Procès-verbal de l'Assemblée . . . nationale. tom. 72. 1789, *etc.* 8°. **283. l. 8.**

—— Rapport sur les affaires de Saint-Domingue, fait a l'Assemblée nationale, au nom du Comité des colonies, les 11 & 12 Octobre, 1790. pp. 103. *Paris*, [1790.] 8°. **F. 685. (11.)**

—— [Another issue.] [1790.] *See* FRANCE.—*Assemblée Nationale Constituante.* [1789–1791.] Procès-verbal de l'Assemblée . . . nationale. tom. 33. 1789, *etc.* 8°. **284. k. 3.**

—— *See* BRISSOT (J. P.) Lettre de J. P. Brissot à M. Barnave, sur ses rapports concernant les colonies, les décrets qui les ont suivis, leurs conséquences fatales, *etc.* 1790. 8°. **F. 672. (1.)**

—— *See* MILLET (T.) Nouvel examen du rapport de M. Barnave sur l'affaire de Saint-Domingue, d'après celui qu'il a fait imprimer. [1790 ?] 8°. **F. 710. (1.)**

—— Examen du rapport fait par M. Barnave à l'Assemblée nationale, sur l'affaire de Saint Domingue, *etc.* [By T. Millet. With the Report.] pp. 134. *Paris*, [1790.] 8°. **F. 700. (6.)**

—— Duel et funeste combat, arrivé au Bois de Boulogne, entre M.M. Barnave et Cazalès, *etc.* pp. 7. [1790.] 8°. **F. 415. (10.)**

—— Grand détail sur la conspiration de M. Barnave & Louis XVI, contre le peuple. Par un Garde natisnale [*sic*] de Varennes, qui accompagnoit le Roi, et qui a tout entendu. pp. 8. [1790 ?] 8°. **F. 887. (15.)**

—— Lettre à Messieurs Barnave et Cazalès . . . sur leur duel du 10 Aout 1790. pp. 22. *Paris*, [1790.] 8°. **F.R. 52. (1.)**

—— Le Réveil de Barnave. pp. 8. [*Paris*, 1792 ?] 8°. **F. 386. (10.)**

BARNAVELT (*Sir* JOHN VAN OLDEN) *See* OLDENBARNEVELD (Johan van)

BARNAVOL (EUGÈNE) Le Cosmos. Action sociale en 3 actes & 5 tableaux. Préface de Georges Eekhoud. Cinq croquis de l'auteur. pp. vii. 108. *Mons*, 1913. 8°. **11735. dd. 2.**

BARNAVOPHILE, *pseud.*

—— Lettre à Monsieur Barnave, par un habitant des montagnes du Dauphiné. [Signed : Barnavophile. An attack on A. P. J. M. Barnave.] pp. 7. [*Grenoble ?* 1791.] 8°. **R. 207. (2.)**

BARNAY (LUDWIG) *See* GELLERT (G.) Ludwig Barnay, *etc.* [With a portrait.] 1890. 8°. **10705. bbb. 50. (4.)**

—— Erinnerungen. 2 Bd. *Berlin*, 1903. 8°. **010708. k. 24.**

—— Über Theater und Anderes. pp. 176. *Berlin*, 1913. 8°. **11795. df. 7.**

BARNBARROCH, *Lairds of.* Royal Letters and other original documents addressed to the Lairds of Barnbarroch MDLIX—MDCXVIII. *See* GLASGOW.—*Maitland Club.* Miscellany of the Maitland Club, *etc.* vol. 1. pt. 2. 1834, *etc.* 4°. **Ac. 8253/25. (14.)**

BARNBY ( ) *Mrs., Author of "The Rock; or, Alfred and Anna."* *See* SOLANGES, *Marquis de.* Kerwald Castle, or Memoirs of the Marquis de Solanges. Translated from the French, by Mrs. Barnby. [1803.] 12°. **N. 1899.**

BARNBY (ADELINE) Michael Daenen. pp. 128. *Murray & Evenden: London,* [1920.] 8°. **012601. cc. 4.**

—— A Tropical Romance. pp. 320. *Murray & Evenden: London,* [1920.] 8°. **NN. 6113.**

BARNBY (HENRY GEORGE)

—— Poems 1938 to 1945. From Balgowan to Bologna. pp. 29. *Durban,* 1945. 8°. **11657. bb. 70.**

BARNBY (JOSEPH) *See* BIBLE.—*Old Testament.—Psalms.* [*English.—Prose versions.*] The Cathedral Psalter . . . pointed for chanting by S. F. Jones . . . and J. Barnby, *etc.* [1874.] 16°. **3434. aaaa. 47.**

BARNBY (LOUIS H.) Some Elementary Remarks on Musical Theory. pp. 26. *Weekes & Co.: London,* [1899.] 8°. **7807. i. 12. (4.)**

BARNCROFT MAGAZINE. *See* ENGLAND.—*Army.—Infantry.—Officer Cadet Battalions.—14th Battalion, D Company.*

BARNDT (ISIDOR) Blätter und Blumen. Gedichte. pp. 156. *Neisse,* 1867. 8°. **11528. aaa. 9.**

—— Herbstblumen. Gedichte, *etc.* pp. 99. *Schweidnitz,* 1864. 8°. **11525. cc. 46. (4.)**

—— Pius-Hymnen. Sonette . . . Ein Beitrag zum Peterspfennig. Zweite vermehrte Auflage. pp. 144. *Schweidnitz,* 1871. 8°. **11528. e. 11.**

—— Von Hindostan nach Preussen. Photographische Reisebilder in Versen, mit Anmerkungen. pp. 97. *Neisse,* 1868. 8°. **11528. aaa. 70. (3.)**

BARNE (EMILY) Henry Barne: a memoir by his widow (Emily Barne). pp. xvii. 473. *John Kensit: London,* 1887. 8°. **4907. aaa. 22.**

BARNE (FREDERICK) Selections. [An anthology.] By F. Barne. pp. 51. [*Printed for private circulation:*] *Leamington,* [1880?] 8°. **11601. f. 34.**

BARNE (GEORGE) The Three Orders of Perspective. pp. vii. 43. *Chatto & Windus: London,* 1924. 8°. **7859. e. 57.**

BARNE (H. H.) *See* CHESTER PLAYS. The Shepherd's Offering. One of the Chester Miracle Plays. Edited by H. H. Barne. 1906. 8°. **11774. b. 25.**

BARNE (HENRY) *See* BARNE (Emily) Henry Barne, *etc.* 1887. 8°. **4907. aaa. 22.**

—— A Letter addressed to the Rev. A. P. Cust . . . on the state of the Diocese of Oxford. pp. 16. *Seeley & Co.: London,* 1859. 8°. **4108. c. 7.**

BARNE (KITTY) *See* BARNE, afterwards STREATFEILD (Marion Catherine)

BARNE (LUCY)

—— The Boyhood of a Saint, Sadhu Sundar Singh. pp. 34. *Edinburgh House Press: London,* 1947. 8°. [*Everyland Plays.*] **W.P. 12949/20.**

—— Christians Courageous. An Indian village play in five scenes. pp. 31. *S.P.G.: London,* 1938. 8°. **11782. b. 22.**

BARNE, afterwards **STREATFEILD** (MARION CATHERINE)

—— Admiral's Walk . . . Illustrated by Mary Gurnat. pp. vi. 186. *J. M. Dent & Sons: London,* 1953. 8°. **12836. c. 17.**

—— Adventurers. A pageant play. pp. viii. 69. *H. F. W. Deane & Sons: London,* [1931.] 8°. **011779. i. 75.**

—— Young Adventurers . . . Illustrated, *etc.* (Based on the pageant play "Adventurers.") pp. x. 244. *London,* 1936. 8°. [*Nelsonian Library.*] **12827.aaa.1/36.**

—— The Amber Gate. A pageant-play, *etc.* pp. 45. *J. Curwen & Sons: London,* [1925.] 8°. **011779. ee. 52.**

—— The Amber Gate, *etc.* [A tale, based on the play of the same name.] pp. vi. 281. *T. Nelson & Sons: London,* [1933.] 8°. [*Nelsonian Library.* no. 4.] *12827.aaa.1/4.*

—— [A reissue.] The Amber Gate, *etc.* *London,* 1951. 8°. **12833. f. 18.**

—— Barbie . . . Illustrated by Marcia Lane Foster. pp. 255. *J. M. Dent & Sons: London,* 1952. 8°. **12830. f. 78.**

—— Bracken, my Dog. *See* infra: May I keep Dogs?

—— Celandine's Secret: a children's play . . . Verses by D. W. Wheeler. Illustrated by J. M. Saunders, with cover by D. Fitzherbert. [With musical notes.] pp. v. 49. *J. Curwen & Sons: London,* [1914.] 4°. **11771. l. 7.**

—— Days of Glory . . . A pageant-play. *H. F. W. Deane & Sons: London,* [1946.] 8°. **11783. bbb. 16.**

—— Duet for Sisters. pp. 281. *Chapman & Hall: London,* 1947. 8°. **NN. 37394.**

—— Dusty's Windmill. With line drawings . . . by Marcia Lane Foster. pp. 264. *J. M. Dent & Sons: London,* 1949. 8°. **12832. f. 4.**

—— The Easter Holidays. pp. 280. *William Heinemann: London. Toronto.* 1935. 8°. **20055. b. 25.**

—— [The Easter Holidays.] Secret of the Sandhills . . . Illustrated by Kiddell-Monroe. pp. vi. 258. *Thomas Nelson & Sons: London,* [1955.] 8°. **12826. l. 60.**

—— Elizabeth Fry. A story biography. pp. 191. *Penguin Books: Harmondsworth,* 1950. 8°. [*Puffin Story Books.* no. 65.] **W.P. 13534/65.**

—— Elizabeth Fry . . . Illustrated by Ruth Gervis. pp. 195. *Methuen & Co.: London,* 1953. 8°. [*Story Biographies.*] **W.P. 12668/11.**

—— Enter Two Musicians. pp. 228. *Chapman & Hall: London,* 1944. 8°. **NN. 34953.**

—— Family Footlights . . . Illustrated by Ruth Gervis. pp. vii. 244. *J. M. Dent & Sons: London,* 1939. 8°. **12825. bb. 22.**

—— Here Come the Girl Guides. [A short history of the Guide Movement. With plates.] pp. 100. 1946. 8°. *See* ENGLAND.—*Girl Guides Association.* **7916. e. 46.**

—— In the Same Boat, *etc.* pp. 218. *J. M. Dent & Sons: London,* 1945. 8°. **12830. b. 13.**

—— Introducing Handel . . . With drawings by J. J. Crockford. pp. v. 90. *J. M. Dent & Son: London,* 1955. 8°. **10712. aa. 7.**

—— Introducing Mozart . . . With drawings by J. J. Crockford. pp. vi. 89. *J. M. Dent & Sons: London,* 1955. 8°. **7901. a. 41.**

—— Listening to the Orchestra. [With plates.] pp. xvi. 205. *J. M. Dent & Sons: London,* 1941. 8°. **7891. a. 9.**

—— The 'Local Ass.' A documentary pageant play for Girl Guides. With alternative prologue: The Lion Gives a Party. pp. 16. *Girl Guides' Association: London,* 1947. 8°. **11783. ff. 2.**

BARNE, afterwards **STREATFEILD** (MARION CATHERINE)

—— Madge. A camp-fire play, *etc.* pp. 27. *Novello & Co.: London,* [1928.] 8°. **011781. ee. 49.**

—— May I Keep Dogs? . . . Illustrated by Arnrid Johnston. pp. 294. *Hamish Hamilton: London,* 1941. 8°. **012826. f. 7.**

—— [May I keep Dogs?] Bracken, my Dog . . . Illustrated by Alice Molony. pp. 279. *J. M. Dent & Sons: London,* 1948. 8°. [*Literature of Yesterday and To-day.*] **W.P. 13329/26.**

—— Bracken, my Dog, *etc.* [Another edition of " May I keep Dogs? "] pp. 270. *J. M. Dent & Sons: London,* 1949. 8°. **12832. e. 24.**

—— Mother at Large. [A novel.] pp. 348. *Chapman & Hall: London,* 1938. 8° **NN. 28969.**

—— Music perhaps. pp. 296. *Chapman & Hall: London,* 1953. 8°. **NNN. 4122.**

—— Musical Honours, *etc.* pp. v. 199. *J. M. Dent & Sons: London,* 1947. 8°. **12831. a. 40.**

—— Peter & the Clock: a play for three children. pp. 6. *J. Curwen & Sons: London,* [1919.] 8°. **11779. k. 52.**

—— Philemon and Baucis. A play in one act. pp. 28. *Gowans & Gray: London & Glasgow,* 1926. 16°. [*Plays for Children.* no. 7.] **W.P. 6569/7.**

—— Roly's Dogs . . . Illustrated by Alice Molony. pp. 235. *J. M. Dent & Sons: London,* 1950. 8°. **12833. b. 25.**

—— Rosina Copper . . . Illustrations by Alfons Purtscher. pp. 192. *Evans Bros.: London,* 1954. 8°. **NNN. 5807.**

—— Secret of the Sandhills. *See* supra: The Easter Holidays.

—— She Shall Have Music . . . Illustrated by Ruth Gervis. pp. x. 261. *J. M. Dent & Sons: London,* 1938. 8°. **12821. b. 24.**

—— Shilling Teas. A comedy for women in one act. pp. 22. *H. F. W. Deane & Sons: London,* [1938.] 8°. **011781. f. 79.**

—— Songs and Stories for Acting . . . Illustrated by Ruth Gervis. pp. vii. 151. *Brown, Son & Ferguson: Glasgow,* 1939. 8°. **11782. c. 7.**

—— Susie Pays a Visit . . . A play, with dance, for children. pp. 10. *J. Curwen & Sons: London,* [1921.] 8°. **11779. l. 33.**

—— Tann's Boarders . . . With drawings by J. J. Crockford. pp. 183. *J. M. Dent & Sons: London,* 1955. 8°. **12833. b. 23.**

—— They Made the Royal Arms. [A play.] pp. 37. *H. F. W. Deane & Sons: London,* [1937.] 8°. **11780. b. 55.**

—— Three and a Pigeon . . . Illustrated by Steven Spurrier. pp. 221. *Hamish Hamilton: London,* 1944. 8°. **12827. f. 37.**

—— Timothy's Garden. A children's play. Written and composed by K. Barne. Verses by D. W. Wheeler. Illustrations by Lucy Barne. pp. 45. *J. Curwen & Sons: London,* [1912.] 4°. **1874. b. 57.**

—— To-morrow . . . Illustrated by Ethel King-Martyn. [A tale founded on the children's play " To-morrow," by Kitty Barne and D. W. Wheeler.] pp. 243. *Hodder & Stoughton: London,* [1912.] 8°. **012809. aaa. 34.**

—— To-Morrow, *etc.* pp. 276. *T. Nelson & Sons: London,* 1939. 8°. [*Nelsonian Library.* no. 55.] 12827.aaa.1/35

BARNE, afterwards **STREATFEILD** (MARION CATHERINE)

—— Two Mimes . . . from Folk-Songs. The Frog and t[he] Mouse. The Flowers in the Valley. pp. 29. *J. Curwen & Sons: London,* [1937.] 8°. **011779. k. 12**

—— Two More Mimes from Folk-Songs. The Wraggle, Tagg[le] Gipsies, O! Robin-a-Thrush. pp. 45. *J. Curwen & Sons: London,* [1936.] 8°. **011779. k. 12**

—— Vespa. pp. 280. *Chapman & Hall: London,* 1950. 8°. **NNN. 9**

—— Visitors from London . . . With 40 drawings by Ru[th] Gervis. pp. vii. 262. *J. M. Dent & Sons: London,* 1940. 8°. **012826. aa.**

—— We'll Meet in England . . . Illustrated by Stev[en] Spurrier. pp. 260. *Hamish Hamilton: London,* 1942. 8°. **012826. f.**

—— We'll Meet in England . . . Illustrated by Stev[en] Spurrier. pp. 207. *Penguin Books: Harmondswor[th;] New York,* 1945. 8°. [*Puffin Story Books.* no. 21.] **W.P. 13534**

—— While the Music Lasted. [A novel.] pp. 224. *Chapman & Hall: London,* 1943. 8°. **NN. 3397**

BARNE, afterwards **STREATFEILD** (MARION CATHERINE) and **WHEELER** (D. W.)

—— To-morrow, *etc.* [A tale founded [on] the children's play " To-morrow," by Kitty Barne a[nd] D. W. Wheeler.] [1912.] 8°. **012809. aaa.**

—— To-morrow. A new version by K. Barne of the play [by] K. Barne and D. W. Wheeler. pp. 74. *Lond[on,]* [1941.] 8°. [*Nelson Theatre.* section 3. no. 17.] **W.P. 6834/**

BARNE (MARY) St. Anthony in Meneage, *etc.* [A poem.] pp. 19. *Poetry Publishing Co.: Exeter,* [1934.] 8°. **20017. cc. 3**

BARNE (MILES) The Authority of Church Guides Asserte[d.] *See* infra: A Sermon preached before the King at Whit[e] Hall, October 17. 1675.

—— A Discourse concerning the Nature of Christ's Kingdo[m] with relation to the kingdoms of this world; in t[wo] sermons preach'd at St. Maries, before the University [of] Cambridge. 2 pt. *J. Hayes; for R. Green: Cambrid[ge,]* 1682. 4°. **226. i. 12. (2**

—— [Another copy.] **694. g. 18. (1**
Imperfect; wanting the first sermon.

—— Second edition. pp. 59. *J. Hayes; for R. Gree[n:] Cambridge,* 1682. 4°. **4474. d.**

—— A Sermon preach'd at the Assizes at Hertford, July 1[?] 1684. pp. 24. *J. Hayes, for R. Green: Cambridge; s[old] by W. Davis: London,* 1684. 4°. **226. i. 2. (**

—— [Another copy.] **226. i. 12. (2**
The titlepage is cropped.

—— A Sermon preached before the King at Newmark[et,] April 24, 1670. pp. 34. *John Hayes; sold by Edw. Sto[rey:] Cambridge,* 1670. 4°. **226. h. 4. (**

—— A Sermon preached before the King at White-H[all,] October 17. 1675. pp. 44. *T. Milbourn, for W. Cadema[n:] London,* 1675. 4°. **695. e. 11. (1**

—— [Another copy.] **226. g. 12. (**

—— [Another edition.] The Authority of Church-Gui[des] Asserted in a sermon preach'd . . . at Whiteh[all,] Octob. 17. 1675 . . . The second edition. pp. 23. *For Richard Green: London,* 1685. 4°. **4474. d. 114. (**

BARNE (MILES)

—— A Sermon preach'd before the University of Cambridge on the 9th of September [1683], being the day of publick thanksgiving for the deliverance of His Majesties sacred person . . . from the late hellish fanatick conspiracy. pp. 34. *J. Hayes; for R. Green: Cambridge,* 1683. 4°. **226. i. 5. (11.)**

—— [Another copy.] **226. i. 12. (25.)**
This copy has the phrase " when Mercy was turn'd into Judgment " corrected to " when Judgment was turn'd into Mercy," on p. 28.

—— [Another edition.] pp. 34. *For R. Royston: London,* 1683. 4°. **696. f. 10. (1.)**
With the reading: " When Mercy was turn'd into Judgment."

—— [Another edition.] With His Majesty's Declaration (concerning the treasonable conspiracy . . . lately discovered). pp. 33. *H. Hills: London,* 1710. 8°. **T. 1815. (10.)**
With the reading: " When Judgment was turn'd into Mercy."

BARNEAUD (CHARLES) Origines et progrès de l'éducation en Amérique. Étude historique et critique. vol. 1. pp. 372. *Paris,* 1898. 8°. **8304. f. 20.**
No more published.

BARNEBEY (OSCAR LEONARD) *See* DALES (B.) and BARNEBEY (O. L.) Elementary Qualitative Analysis, *etc.* 1916. 8°. **8904. a. 35.**

BARNEBY (THOMAS) Catalogue of Popular Sidereal Objects, 150, in their order of right ascension on the 1st January, 1870. pp. 20. *For Private Circulation only: Worcester,* [1870.] 8°. **8560. dd. 11.**

BARNEBY (WILLIAM HENRY) Life and Labour in the Far, Far West: being notes of a tour in the Western States, British Columbia, Manitoba, and the North West Territory . . . With . . . map, *etc.* pp. xvi. 432. *Cassell & Co.: London,* 1884. 8°. **10408. f. 7.**

—— The New Far West and the Old Far East, being notes of a tour in North America, Japan, China, Ceylon . . . With maps and illustrations. pp. viii. 316. *E. Stanford: London,* 1889. 8°. **10028. ee. 19.**

BARNEDES (JOSEPH THOMAS MICHEL) De l'usage du quinquina et des règles de son administration dans les fièvres intermittentes. Essai présenté . . . pour obtenir le grade de Docteur en Médecine. pp. 20. *Montpellier,* 1811. 4°. **1180. g. 5. (9.)**

BARNEFIELD (GEORGE) *See* CARPENTER (Edward) *Social Reformer.* The Psychology of the Poet Shelley. By E. Carpenter and G. Barnefield. 1925. 8°. **011840. a. 29.**

BARNEFIELDE (RICHARD) *See* BARNFIELD.

BARNEHURST BULLETIN. *See* PERIODICAL PUBLICATIONS.— *Dartford.*

BARNEKOW, *Family of. See* BOHLEN-BOHLENDORF (J. von) *Baron.* Der Bishofs-Roggen . . . in erblichem Besitz der Barnekow und Umriss der Geschichte dieses adlichen . . . Geschlechts, *etc.* 1850. 8°. **10250. d. 11.**

BARNEKOW (KJELL RAGNAR MACDOUGALL)

—— Lunds domkyrkas historia, 1536–1680. *See* NEWMAN (Ernst) Lunds domkyrkas historia, *etc.* dl. 2. 1946. 4°. **4696. c. 7.**

BARNEKOW (RENÉ VON)

—— Jeg mødte en Viking. pp. 148. *København,* 1947. 8°. **9102. b. 5.**

BARNEL (F.) *See* SOLEILLET (J. J. M. M. P.) Les Voyages et decouvertes de Paul Soleillet, *etc.* [With a biographical sketch, signed: F. B., i.e. F. Barnel.] 1881. 12°. **10097. aaa. 35.**

BARNELL (E.)

—— *See* STUDIES. Studies in Tropical Fruits, *etc.* [By E. Barnell and others.] 1938, *etc.* 8°. [*Imperial College of Tropical Agriculture. Low Temperature Research Station. Memoir.* no. 9, 13, 19–22.] **Ac.3546.c.**

BARNELL (H. J.) Pitman's Illustrated Aids to Composition. 2 ser. *Sir I. Pitman & Sons: London,* 1905. 4°. **12984. f. 21.**

—— [Another edition.] 2 ser. *Sir I. Pitman & Sons: London,* [1905, 06.] 4°. **12985. f. 16.**

—— Practical Object Lessons from the Plant World. pp. 171. *London,* [1906.] 8°. [*Pitman's Object Lesson Books.*] **012203. f. 35. (2.)**

BARNELL (HERBERT REX)

—— *See* STUDIES. Studies in Tropical Fruits, *etc.* [By H. R. Barnell and others.] 1938, *etc.* 8°. [*Imperial College of Tropical Agriculture. Low Temperature Research Station. Memoir.* no. 9, 13, 19–22.] **Ac.3546.c.**

—— Metabolic and Storage Investigations of the Banana. By C. W. Wardlaw, E. R. Leonard and H. R. Barnell. 1939. 8°. [*Imperial College of Tropical Agriculture. Low Temperature Research Station. Memoir.* no. 11.] **Ac.3546.c.**

BARNÉOUD (F. MARIUS) Académie de Paris. Faculté des sciences. Mémoire de botanique. Recherches sur le développement, la structure générale et la classification des plantaginées et des plumbaginées . . . Mémoire de géologie. De l'origine des lacs. Thèses, *etc.* pp. 44. pl. 2. *Paris,* 1844. 4°. **1254. k. 29.**

—— [Another copy.] **1254. k. 7.**

—— Botanique. Monographie générale de la famille des plantaginées. pp. 52. *Paris,* 1845. 4°. **1253. h. 15.**

BÄRNER ( )

—— [For the German surname of this form:] *See* BAERNER. **W.P. 8978 2.**

BARNER (C.) I Thüringen. pp. 149. *Kjøbenhavn,* 1878. 8°. **10235. b. 19.**

BARNER (DIETERICUS CHRISTOPHORUS À)

—— Dissertatio juridica de promissionibus generosa fide vallatis, vulgò von der Cavaliers-Parole, oder dem Adel. Wort, *etc.* *Praes.* H. Zollius. pp. 90. *H. A. Enax: Rinthelii,* 1695. 4°. **1480. aa. 11.**

BARNER (G.) Denkschrift in Betreff der im Jahre 1861 im städtischen Waisenhause zu Elberfeld geschehenen Erweckung . . . von Barner, Dr. Hassencamp, Köllner, Krafft, Künzel, Lichtenstein, Rinck. pp. 29. *Elberfeld,* 1861. 8°. **4407. dd. 4.**

—— Synodalpredigt über Offenbarung Johannis 3, 7–12. *See* LUCASSEN (C.) Wupperthaler Zeugnisse, *etc.* 1861. 8°. **4424. b. 47.**

—— Zeugnisse von sieben evangelischen Pastoren über die Erweckung im städtischen Waisenhause zu Elberfeld [signed: Barner, Hassenkamp, *etc.*], nebst einer Beleuchtung derselben in einer Anzahl von Artikeln aus dem Kirchlichen Anzeiger. 2 pt. *Elberfeld,* 1861. 8°. **3910. bb. 25.**

BARNER (HANS) Zwei " theologische Schriften " Goethe's. Ein Beitrag zur Religiosität des jungen Goethe. [An essay on the " Brief des Pastors " and the " Zwo wichtige bisher unerörterte biblische Fragen " of Goethe.] pp. 163. *Leipzig,* 1931. 8°. **11822. v. 33.**

BARNER (Heinrich) Abriss des Neuen Menschen nach dem Ebenbild des Him̃lischen, *etc.* pp. 421. *A. Kolwalds sehl. Witwe: Halberstad,* 1665. 8°. **3908.** bb. **5. (1.)**

BARNER (Jacobus) *See* Becke (D. von der) David von der Becke . . . Barnerus leviter & amicè castigatus. 1675. 8°. **1033.** e. **16. (1.)**

—— Chymia philosophica perfecte delineata, docte enucleata, & feliciter demonstrata, *etc.* [With engraved plates.] pp. 560. *Sumptibus A. Ottonis: Noribergæ,* 1689. 8°. **1034.** f. **1.**

—— Jacobi Barneri Dissertatio epistolica ad . . . Joelem Langelot . . . seu prodromus vindiciarum experimentorum, ac dogmatum suorum, quæ David von der Becke . . . pro suis venditavit, *etc.* *Apud G. Gebelium: Augustæ Vindelicorum,* [1690 ?] 8°. **1032.** a. **27.**

—— Jacobi Barneri . . . Prodromus Sennerti novi, seu delineatio novi medicinæ systematis, in quo quicquid à primis seculis in hunc usque diem de arte prodiit, Hippocratis, Galeni, Paracelsi, Helmontij, Sylvij Willisii. &c. dogmata, ex principiis anatomico-chymicis examinantur. pp. 55. *Sumptibus T. Göbelii: Augustæ Vindelicorum,* 1674. 4°. **544.** e. **4. (3.)**

—— Jacobi Barneri D. Spiritus vini sine acido . . . Cum modo conficiendi salia volatilia oleosa, eorumqve usu. pp. 40. *Sumptibus J. Fritzschii: Lipsiæ,* 1675. 12°. **1033.** e. **16. (3.)**

BARNER (Jan)

—— *See* Bible. [*Czech.*] Biblj Czeská . . . podle . . . Latinského . . . přeloženj, *etc.* [Translated by J. Constantius, M. V. Steyer and J. Barner. 1771, *etc.* fol. **3015.** d. **10.**

—— *See* Bible. [Czech.] Druhý djl Biblij, *etc.* [Edited by the Jesuits J. Constantius, M. V. Steyer and J. Barner.] 1677. fol. **3035.** cc. **1.**

BARNER (Johannes) *pseud.* [i.e. Ulrik Peter Overby.] Digte, gamle og nye . . . Samlet Udgave. pp. 136. *Kjøbenhavn,* 1858. 8°. **11565.** aaa. **11.**

BARNER (Konrad) Familien Rosenkrantz's Historie, af K. Barner. 2 Bd.

1. Fra de ældste Tider til Begyndelsen af det 16de Aarhundrede. [With "Diplomatarium."] 2 pt. 1874.
2. Familien Rosenkrantz's Historie i det 16de Aarhundrede, af A. Heise . . . Første Halvbind. Hovedlinierne til c. 1550. Med Diplomatarium 1500–1572. 1882.

Kjøbenhavn, 1874, 82. fol. **9906.** cc. **1.**
No more published in this form. Heise's contribution was continued and completed in the "Historisk Tidsskrift" and in the "Personalhistorisk Tidsskrift," 1885–91.

BARNER (Leopold Theodor) Studier over nogle af vor tids vigtigste sociale og videnskabelige forholde, *etc.* pp. xi. 267. *Bergen,* 1853. 8°. **8007.** bb. **4.**

BARNER-AAGAARD (C.) Karen Munk. Et historisk Livsbillede fra Christian den Fjerdes Tid. pp. 230. *Kjøbenhavn,* 1883. 8°. **12582.** bbb. **36.**

BARNÉRIAS (J. S.)

—— L'Équilibre économique international. Nouveaux aspects de la théorie. pp. 223. *Paris,* 1952. 8°. [*Cahiers de la Fondation nationale des sciences politiques.* no. 29.] W.P. **14427/29.**

BÄRNERISCHE KRIEGS-POSAUN. *See* Bernese War Trumpet.

BARNERS, John, *Lord.* *See* Bourchier (J.) *2nd Baron Berners.*

BARNERUS (Jacobus) *See* Barner.

BARNES.—*Barnes Labour Party.*

—— Your Barnes . . . Prepared for the Barnes Labour Party by Douglas Frank, with the assistance of Hilary Bursill and Rose Albu . . . Edited by Leonard McNae. Maps by Norman Howard. pp. 31. *Jason Press: London,* [1946.] 8°. **8288.** eee. **74.**

Borough Council.

—— Barnes, Mortlake and East Sheen, and their residential advantages . . . Official handbook. pp. 42. *New Centurion & Publicity Co.: Derby & Cheltenham,* [1934.] 8°. **010352.** bbb. **14.**

—— The Tenant's Handbook. A reference book for municipal tenants in the Borough of Barnes, *etc.* pp. 28. *E. J. Burrow & Co.: Cheltenham & London,* [1939.] 8°. **8288.** eee. **12.**

—— The Tenant's Handbook for the Borough of Barnes . . . Second edition. pp. 32. *Ed. J. Burrow & Co.: Cheltenham & London,* [1950.] 8°. **8289.** a. **56.**

—— *Ranelagh Club.* Rules, Regulations, and List of Members, January, 1889. pp. 42. [*Printed for private circulation:*] *London,* 1889. 8°. **10348.** ccc. **41.**

Urban District Council.

—— Barnes, Mortlake & East Sheen. Written by Frederick Bingham. Official guide, *etc.* 4 pt. *E. J. Burrow & Co.: Cheltenham & London,* [1921–30.] 8°. **10354.** a. **54.**
Various editions. The original author's name is omitted after 1925.

BARNES JUNIOR SPORTS NOVEL SERIES. *See* Barnes (A. S.) and Company.

BARNES LABOUR PARTY. *See* Barnes.

BARNES ( ) *Satirist.* The treatyse answerynge the boke of Berdes [by Andrew Borde]. Compyled by Collyn clowte, dedycatyd to Barnarde barber dwellynge in Banbery. **B.L.** *R*[*obert*] *W*[*yer*]: [*London,* 1543 ?] 4°. **C. 40.** c. **6.**
The verso of the last leaf contains verses addressed to Barnes, with the heading: "Barnes in the defence of the Berde." There are woodcuts on the recto and verso of the titlepage, and on the verso of the last leaf. Imperfect; wanting Sig. A iiii.

—— [Another edition.] *See* Borde (Andrew) The fyrst Boke of the Introduction of Knowledge, *etc.* 1870. 8°. [*Early English Text Society.* Extra ser. no. 10.] Ac. **9926/7.**

BARNES ( ) *Song Writer.* *See* Weston ( ) and Barnes ( ) I Kept On. 1906. fol. **1875.** d. **9. (100.)**

BARNES (A.) *M.A.* *See* Consterdine (A.) and Barnes (A.) The Rudiments of Practical Mathematics. 1905. 8°. [*Murray's Home and School Library.*] **12200.** e. **9/15.**

BARNES (A. H.)

—— Structure of the X-Ray *K* Absorption Limits of the Elements Manganese to Zinc, *etc.* (Reprinted from the Physical Review.) [A thesis.] [*New York,* 1933.] 8°. **8710.** h. **45.**

BARNES (A. Lewis)

—— Woodbridge, Suffolk. Its topography and history, with notes of general interest for visitors and prospective residents. pp. 44. *E. J. Burrow & Co.: Cheltenham,* [1921.] 8°. **10354.** b. **31.**

BARNES (A. P.) *See* Periodical Publications.—*New York.* Brentano's Chess Monthly. Edited by H. C. Allen . . . A. P. Barnes. 1881, *etc.* 8°. P.P. **1831.** l.

BARNES (A. R.) *Mrs.* The South African Household Guide . . . Third edition . . . enlarged. pp. 255. *Darter Bros. & Walton: Cape Town,* 1899. 8°. **07943. g. 51.**

—— Fifth edition, revised and enlarged, by Allerley Glossop. pp. 348. *Darter Bros. & Co.: Cape Town,* 1913. 8°. **7945. c. 37.**

BARNES (A. S.) and **BURR,** *Publishers.* Illustrated Descriptive Catalogue of the National Series of Standard School Books . . . Published by A. S. Barnes and Burr. (Library of Miscellaneous Works.) 2 pt. *A. S. Barnes & Burr: New York,* 1862. 8°. **11901.** bbb. **32. (4.)**

BARNES (A. S.) **AND CO.**

—— Barnes's Elementary History of the United States. *See* BALDWIN (James) *Ph.D.*

—— Barnes' First Year Book. *See* KAHN (Amy)

—— The Barnes Junior Sports Novel Series. *A. S. Barnes & Co.: New York,* [1953– .] 8°. W.P. B. **701.**

—— Barnes's School History of the United States. *See* STEELE (Joel D.) and (E. B.)

—— The New Barnes Readers. *See* ROBBINS (May)

BARNES (ADOLPHUS WILLIAM) *See* NICLOUX (M. L.) A Week's Amusement, translated from the French . . . by A. W. Barnes. 1823. 12°. N. **191. (1.)**

BARNES (AL. G.)

—— Master Showman. [An autobiography. With plates.] pp. 288. *Jonathan Cape: London & Toronto,* 1938. 8°. **11797.** b. 3.

BARNES (ALBERT) *See* BIBLE. [*Welsh.*] Bibl yr Addoliad Teuluaidd . . . gyd a . . . nodiadau ac egluriadau gan . . . A. Barnes, *etc.* [1878.] 4°. **L.14.c.6.**

—— *See* BIBLE.—*Job.* [*English.*] Notes, critical, illustrative, and practical, on the Book of Job: with a new translation, and an introductory dissertation, By A. Barnes. 1844. 12°. **1215.** e. **9.**

—— —— 1847. 8°. **1217.** b. **17, 18.**

—— —— 1851. 12°. **03129.** de. **23.**

—— *See* BIBLE.—*Psalms.* [*English.—Prose Versions.*] Notes, critical, explanatory, and practical, on the Book of Psalms. By A. Barnes. [1868, *etc.*] 8°. **3089.** bb. **29.**

—— —— [1870, *etc.*] 8°. **03089.** h. **15.**

—— *See* BIBLE.—*Isaiah.* [*English.*] Notes: critical, explanatory, and practical on the Book of the Prophet Isaiah; with a new translation, by A. Barnes. 1840. 8°. **1215.** g. **1–3.**

—— —— 1845. 8°. **1107.** e. **25.**

—— —— 1847. 12°. **3165.** b. **29.**

—— —— 1847, *etc.* 8°. **1217.** b. **19–21.**

—— —— 1850, *etc.* 12°. **3165.** b. **28.**

—— *See* BIBLE.—*Daniel.* [*English.*] Notes, explanatory and practical, on the Book of Daniel. By the Rev. A. Barnes, *etc.* 1853. 8°. **3166.** b. **24.**

—— *See* BIBLE.—*New Testament.* [*English.*] Notes, explanatory and practical on the Gospels (the New Testament). By A. Barnes. 1841, *etc.* 12°. **1216.** c. **16–20.**

—— —— 1848. 4°. **3107.** de. **14.**

—— —— [1853.] 12°. **3225.** d. **1.**

—— —— [1884, *etc.*] 8°. **03129.** e. **45.**

BARNES (ALBERT)

—— *See* BIBLE.—*New Testament.* [*English.*] Notes on the New Testament . . . By A. Barnes, *etc.* [c. 1875.] 8°. **3130.** m. **9.**

—— *See* BIBLE.—*New Testament.* [*Gaelic.*] Mineachadh air an Tiomnadh Nuadh, air eadartheangachadh o Bharnes, Scott, *etc.* 1848, *etc.* 4°. **3051.** eee. **1.**

—— *See* BIBLE.—*New Testament.* [*Welsh.*] Esboniad (Sylwadau eglurhaol ac ymarferol) ar y Testament Newydd. Gan y Parch. A. Barnes. 1846, *etc.* 8°. **3224.** d. **18.**

—— —— 1853, *etc.* 8°. **3224.** d. **4.**

—— *See* BIBLE.—*New Testament.* [*Welsh.*] Y Testament Newydd, gyda sylwadau eglurhaol ac ymarferol. Gan y Parch. A. Barnes, *etc.* 1854, *etc.* 8°. **3070.** dd. **17.**

—— *See* BIBLE.—*Gospels.* [*English.*] Notes, explanatory and practical, on the Gospels . . . By A. Barnes. 1833. 12°. **843.** i. **5.**

—— —— [1835?] 12°. **863.** l. **22, 23.**

—— —— 1846. 12°. **1217.** b. **2.**

—— —— [1847.] 12°. **4413.** g. **7.**

—— *See* BIBLE.—*Gospels.—Selections.* [*English.*] Simple Readings on the Gospels . . . Compiled from the works of the Rev. J. C. Ryle . . . the Rev. A. Barnes, *etc.* 1871. 8°. **3224.** bb. **8.**

—— *See* BIBLE.—*Epistles.* [*English.*] Notes, explanatory and practical, on the Epistles of Paul to the Thessalonians, to Timothy, to Titus, and to Philemon. By A. Barnes. 1845. 12°. **1217.** b. **8.**

—— —— 1846. 12°. **1217.** b. **9.**

—— *See* BIBLE.—*Epistles.* [*English.*] Notes, explanatory and practical, on the Second Epistle to the Corinthians and the Epistle to the Galatians. By A. Barnes. 1846. 12°. **1217.** b. **6.**

—— *See* BIBLE.—*Epistles.* [*English.*] Notes, explanatory and practical, on the Epistles of Paul to the Ephesians, Philippians, and Colossians. By the Rev. A. Barnes. 1846. 12°. **1217.** b. **11.**

—— *See* BIBLE.—*Luke.* Questions on the Gospel of Luke . . . Compiled from the works of Barnes and other writers, *etc.* 1861. 12°. **3224.** bb. **15.**

—— *See* BIBLE.—*Acts.* [*English.*] Notes, explanatory and practical, on the Acts of the Apostles by A. Barnes. [1841.] 8°. **1126.** k. **16.** (2.)

—— —— 1846. 12°. **1217.** b. **13.**

—— *See* BIBLE.—*Romans.* [*English.*] Notes, explanatory and practical, on the Epistle to the Romans. By A. Barnes. 1846. 12°. **1217.** b. **4.**

—— *See* BIBLE.—*Corinthians.* [*English.*] Notes, explanatory and practical, on the Epistles of Paul to the Corinthians. By A. Barnes, *etc.* [1840.] 8°. **1126.** k. **13.** (2.)

—— *See* BIBLE.—*Corinthians.* [*English.*] Notes, explanatory and practical on the First Epistle of Paul to the Corinthians. By A. Barnes, *etc.* 1846. 8°. **1217.** b. **5.**

—— *See* BIBLE.—*Hebrews.* [*English.*] Notes, explanatory and practical, on the Epistle to the Hebrews. By A. Barnes. 1846. 8°. **1217.** b. **10.**

—— *See* BIBLE.—*Revelation.* [*English.*] Notes, explanatory and practical, on the Book of Revelation. By the Rev. A. Barnes, *etc.* 1852. 8°. **3186.** b. **32.**

—— See BUTLER (Joseph) successively *Bishop of Bristol* and *of Durham.* The Analogy of Religion . . . with an introductory essay by A. Barnes. 1851. 8°. **4376. b. 9.**

—— —— 1859. 12°. **4016. a. 13.**

—— —— 1867. 8°. **4016. aaa. 13.**

—— See BUTLER (Joseph) successively *Bishop of Bristol* and *of Durham.* The Analogy of Religion . . . With an introductory essay by A. Barnes, *etc.* 1875. 8°. 04018. h. 92. (1.)

—— See DAVIES (Samuel) *President of Princeton College, New Jersey.* Sermons on Important Subjects . . . With an essay on the life and times of the author by A. Barnes. 1851. 12°. **4485. b. 30.**

—— —— 1867. 8°. **4464. cc. 13.**

—— See MURDOCH (John) *LL.D.* Questions on the Gospel of Luke . . . Compiled . . . from the works of Barnes and other writers, *etc.* 1861. 8°. **3226. aa. 46.**

—— See ONDERDONK (Henry U.) *Bishop of the Protestant Episcopal Church in Pennsylvania.* Episcopacy Examined and Re-examined, comprising the tract " Episcopacy tested by Scripture," and the controversy [between H. U. Onderdonk and A. Barnes] concerning that publication. 1835. 12°. **4183. b. 13.**

—— See PHILIP (Robert) Experimental Guides. [With an introductory essay to each volume by A. Barnes.] 1872, *etc.* 8°. **4402. k. 37.**

—— See SMITH (Gerrit) Correspondence of Gerrit Smith with Albert Barnes. 1868. 8°. **4015. f. 28.**

—— Albert Barnes on the Maine Liquor Law. The Throne of Iniquity; or, Sustaining evil by law: a discourse in behalf of a law prohibiting the traffic in intoxicating drinks, *etc.* pp. 31. *T. B. Peterson: Philadelphia,* [1852.] 8°. **8435. d. 15.**

—— [Another edition.] pp. 24. *L. M. Guernsey: Springfield,* [1852?] 12°. **4485. bb. 6.**

—— [Another edition.] pp. 24. *American Temperance Union: New York,* 1852. 12°. **4486. aa. 65. (11.)**

—— [Another edition.] The Throne of Iniquity; or, Sustaining evil by law, *etc.* pp. 24. *W. Tweedie: London,* 1852. 12°. **8435. c. 66. (6.)**

—— [Another edition.] pp. 16. *Partridge & Oakey: London,* [1852.] 8°. **4476. c. 9.**

—— Tenth thousand. pp. 24. *George Lewis: Selkirk,* [1872.] 8°. **4486. a. 58. (13.)**

—— The Choice of a Profession: an address delivered before the Society of Inquiry in Amherst College, August 21, 1838. pp. 29. *J. S. & C. Adams: Amherst,* 1838. 8°. **8404. dd. 30. (4.)**

—— Christianity as applied to the Mind of a Child in the Sunday-School. Annual sermon in behalf of the American Sunday-School Union, delivered . . . May 12, 1850. pp. 54. *American Sunday-School Union: Philadelphia,* [1850.] 12°. **4486. aa. 68. (8.)**

—— The Church and Slavery. pp. 196. *Parry & McMillan: Philadelphia,* 1857. 8°. **8156. aa. 12.**

—— See ROSS (Frederick A.) Position of the Southern Church in relation to Slavery, as illustrated in a letter of Dr. F. A. Ross to Rev. A. Barnes [on the latter's work entitled: " The Church and Slavery "], *etc.* 1857. 12°. **8156. aa. 44.**

—— Development of the Christian Character. [A sermon.] See AMERICAN PULPIT. The American Pulpit, *etc.* 1852. 8°. **4485. d. 70.**

—— Essays on Science and Theology . . . arranged and revised by the Rev. E. Henderson. pp. viii. 376. *Knight & Son: London,* [1856.] 12°. **4377. f. 6.**

—— The Evidences of Christianity in the Nineteenth Century. See infra: Lectures on the Evidences of Christianity in the Nineteenth Century.

—— How shall Man be just with God? pp. 132. *Presbyterian Publication Committee: Philadelphia,* 1854. 12°. **4256. b. 2.**

—— The Immorality of the Traffic in Ardent Spirits: a discourse, delivered . . . April 13, 1834. pp. 44. *George, Latimer & Co.: Philadelphia,* 1834. 8°. **8435. b. 19**

—— An Inquiry into the Organization and Government of the Apostolic Church: particularly with reference to the claims of Episcopacy. pp. 251. *Perkins & Purves Philadelphia,* 1843. 12°. **4183. a. 61**

—— [Another edition.] pp. 252. *Presbyterian Publication Committee: Philadelphia,* [1855.] 12°. **4183. a. 62**

—— An Inquiry into the Scriptural Views of Slavery pp. 384. *Perkins & Purves: Philadelphia,* 1846. 12°. **8155. c. 9**

—— Lectures on the Evidences of Christianity in the Nineteenth Century. Delivered in the Mercer Street Church New York, January 21 to February 21, 1867, *etc.* pp. 451 *Harpers & Bros.: New York,* 1868. 8°. **4014. ee. 4**

—— [Another edition.] The Evidences of Christianity in the Nineteenth Century, *etc.* pp. 440. *Blackie & Son. London,* 1871. 8°. **4018. d. 18**

—— Life at Three-Score. [A sermon. With a portrait.] pp. 64. *Knight & Son: London,* [1859.] 8°. **4985. a. 19**

—— Third edition. pp. 78. *Parry & McMillan: Philadelphia,* 1859. 8°. **4486. aa. 58**

—— Miscellaneous Essays and Reviews. 2 vol. *Sampson Low & Co.: London; Philadelphia* [printed], 1855. 8°. **3756. c. 6**

Vol. 1 *has an additional titlepage bearing the imprint " Ivison & Phinney: New York."*

—— The Missionary Enterprise dependent on the Religion of Principle for Success. A Sermon preached . . . Sept. 1844, before the American Board of Commissioners for Foreign Missions, *etc.* pp. 43. *Crocker & Brewster. Boston,* 1844. 8°. **4193. g. 24**

—— [Another edition.] See ILLINGWORTH (William) *Rev.* A Voice from the Sanctuary, *etc.* 1845. 8°. **1354. i. 1**

—— [Another edition.] See AMERICAN PULPIT. The American Pulpit, *etc.* 1852. 8°. **4485. d. 70**

—— Notes, critical, explanatory and practical, on the Old Testament . . . The Book of the Prophet Isaiah. [With the text.] 2 vol. [1851.] 8°. See BIBLE.—*Isaiah.* [*English.*] **03129. e. 44**

—— Notes, critical, explanatory and practical, on the Old Testament . . . The Book of the Prophet Daniel [With the text.] 2 vol. [1853.] 8°. See BIBLE.—*Daniel.* [*English.*] **03129. e. 44***

—— An Oration on the Progress and Tendency of Science; delivered before the Connecticut Alpha of Phi, Beta, Kappa, at New Haven, August 18, 1840. pp. 40. *I. Ashmead: Philadelphia*, 1840. 8°. **8703. e. 15.**

—— Our Position. A sermon, preached before the General Assembly of the Presbyterian Church in the United States . . . May 20, 1852. pp. 39. *Newman & Ivison: New-York*, 1852. 8°. **4486.** d. **41.** (**11.**)

—— Second edition. pp. 29. *William Harned: New York*, 1852. 8°. **4486.** d. **41.** (**12.**)

—— Plea in behalf of Western Colleges. A discourse delivered before the Society for promoting Collegiate and Theological Education at the West . . . October 29, 1845, *etc.* pp. 28. *William Sloanaker: Philadelphia*, 1846. 8°. **8365.** d. 32. (3.)

—— The Position of the Evangelical Party in the Episcopal Church . . . Fourth edition. pp. 70. *Perkins & Purves: Philadelphia*, 1844. 12°. **4183. aa. 60.**

—— Remarks on Mr. Barnes' Inquiry into the Position of the Evangelical Party in the Episcopal Church. From the Episcopal Recorder. pp. 54. *R. S. H. George: Philadelphia*, 1844. 12°. **4183.** aa. **59.**

—— Practical Sermons: designed for vacant congregations and families . . . First English edition. With additional sermons. pp. vi. 443. *T. & T. Clark: Edinburgh*, 1854. 8°. **4485.** a. **55.**

—— [Another edition.] pp. vii. 312. *G. Routledge & Co.: London*, 1854. 8°. **4485.** a. **54.**

—— Prayers for the use of Families, chiefly selected from various authors; with a preliminary essay; together with a selection of hymns. pp. 360. *Thomas, Cowperthwait & Co.: Philadelphia*, 1850. 12°. **3455.** d. **37.**

—— Questions on the First Epistle to the Corinthians . . . Adapted to the author's notes on that Epistle. pp. 164. *Harper & Bros.: New York*, 1846. 12°. **1159.** g. **8.**

—— Questions on the Historical Books of the New Testament, designed for Bible classes and Sunday schools. (vol. 1. Questions on the Gospel of Matthew.) pp. 207. *J. Leavitt: New York*, 1830. 12°. **3225.** a. **4.**
Imperfect; wanting vol. 2–5.

—— [Another edition.] Questions on the Historical Books of the New Testament, designed for Bible classes and Sunday Schools. (vol. 5. Questions on the Epistle to the Romans.) 5 vol. *Harper & Bros.: New York*, [1846.] 12°. **1159.** g. **7.**

—— [Another edition.] Questions on the Four Gospels, *etc.* (Questions on the Acts of the Apostles.—Questions on the Epistle to the Romans.) 4 pt. *Blackie & Son: Glasgow*, 1847, 46. 8°. **3226.** c. **4.**

—— [Another edition.] Questions on the four Gospels, *etc.* (Questions on the Acts of the Apostles.—Questions on the Epistle to the Romans.—Questions on the First Epistle to the Corinthians.—Questions on the Epistle to the Hebrews.) 6 pt. *Blackie & Son: Glasgow*, [1852.] 8°. **3226.** c. **5.**

—— Revival Sermons . . . Edited by Rev. A. Weston. pp. viii. 392. *William Tegg: London*, 1865. 8°. **4485.** aa. **75.**
This collection includes the six sermons published in 1842 *under the title:* " *The Theory and Desirableness of Revivals.*"

—— The Theory and Desirableness of Revivals, being six sermons . . . With a preface by the Hon. & Rev. Baptist Wriothesley Noel. pp. 195. *R. B. Blackader: London*, 1842. 12°. **1357.** a. **19.**

—— The Throne of Iniquity. *See* supra: Albert Barnes on the Maine Liquor Law, *etc.*

—— The Way of Salvation; a sermon delivered at Morristown, New Jersey, February 8 1829 . . . Third edition. pp. 20. *Charles Whipple: Newburyport, Mass.*, 1831. 8°. **4485.** i. **24.**

—— *See* PHILADELPHIA, *Presbytery of.* A Report of the Debates in the Presbytery of Philadelphia (on the case of the Rev. Albert Barnes), *etc.* [With special reference to Barnes's sermon entitled: " The Way of Salvation."] 1831. 8°. **4183.** bb. **27.**

—— The Way of Salvation illustrated in a series of discourses . . . Revised by Rev. E. Henderson. [With a portrait.] pp. xii. 474. *Knight & Son: London*, [1855.] 12°. **3558.** b. **4.**

—— [A reissue.] *Parry & M'Millan: Philadelphia*, 1858. 8°. **4464.** d. **8.**

—— Thoughts for the Thoughtful. Selected from the writings of the Rev. A. Barnes. *Knight & Son: London*, [1864.] 12°. **3755.** a. **4.**

—— The Facts in the Case of the Rev. Albert Barnes fairly stated. Addressed to the ministers, elders, and people at large of the Presbyterian churches and congregations in the United States. By Members of the Presbytery and Synod of Philadelphia. pp. 20. *Philadelphia*, 1836. 8°. **4183.** cc. **21.**

—— Trial of the Rev. Albert Barnes, before the Synod of Philadelphia, in session at York, October 1835, on a charge of heresy, preferred against him by the Rev. Geo. Junkin: with all the pleadings and debate. As reported for the New York Observer, by A. J. Stansbury. (Appendix. Defence of Albert Barnes.—The Appeal of Mr. Barnes.) 2 pt. *Van Nostrand & Dwight: New York*, 1836. 12°. **5175.** de. **31.**

BARNES (ALBERT COOMBS) Art and Education. By John Dewey, A. C. Barnes [and others. Edited by A. C. Barnes]. pp. x. 349. *Barnes Foundation Press: Rahway*, [1929.] 8°. **07805.** aaa. **33.**

—— The Art in Painting, *etc.* [With illustrations.] pp. 530. Hartcourt, Brace & Co.: New York, [1927.] 8°. **7859.** bb. **34.**

BARNES (ALBERT COOMBS) and **DE MAZIA** (VIOLETTE)

—— The Art of Cézanne . . . With 171 illustrations [including portraits]. pp. xviii. 456. *Jonathan Cape: London; printed in U.S.A.*, 1939. 8°. **7865.** pp. **22.**

—— The Art of Henri-Matisse . . . One hundred and fifty-one illustrations. pp. xvi. 464. *C. Scribner's Sons: New York, London*, 1933. 8°. **7852.** pp. **28.**

—— The Art of Renoir . . . One hundred and fifty-eight illustrations. [With a portrait and a catalogue of the artist's works.] pp. xxi. 515. *Minton, Balch & Co.: New York*, 1935. 8°. **7862.** ppp. **16.**

BARNES (ALBERT THOMAS)

—— The Dahlia Grower's Treasury. [With plates.] pp. 160. *W. H. & L. Collingridge: London; Transatlantic Arts: New York*, 1954. 8°. **7036.** c. **4.**

BARNES (Albert William) Concerning Ourselves. A book of sexual instruction for girls, *etc.* pp. 40. *J. Bale & Co.: London*, 1929. 8°. **07001. e. 73.**

—— A Dickens Guide, together with true stories of the great novelist, *etc.* pp. 44. *J. Bale & Co.: London*, 1929. 8°. **010856. aaa. 73.**

—— Knowing Ourselves. A book of sexual instruction for boys, *etc.* pp. 40. *J. Bale & Co.: London*, 1929. 8°. **07580.** df. **67.**

BARNES (*Right Hon.* Alfred)

—— The Co-operator in Politics, *etc.* pp. 26. *London*, 1923. 8°. [*Fabian Tract.* no. 206.] **8275.dd.7/206.**

—— The Political Aspect of Co-operation, *etc.* pp. 50. *Co-operative Union: Manchester*, 1922. 8°. **08139.** aaa. **55.**

—— Revised and enlarged edition. pp. 84. *Co-operative Union: Manchester*, 1926. 8°. **08139.** aaa. **56.**

BARNES (Alfred Atkinson) Hydraulic Flow Reviewed. A book of reference of standard experiments on pipes, channels, notches, weirs and circular orifices, *etc.* pp. xi. 158. *E. & F. N. Spon: London*, 1916. 8°. **08776.** cc. **10.**

BARNES (Algernon Strange Valentine)

—— Afrikaanse spreekwoorde, gesegdes en ander uitdrukkinge, *etc.* pp. 294. *Bloemfontein*, 1949. 8°. **12974.** a. **15.**

—— English Readers for Southern Africa . . . Edited by G. H. Franz. 8 bk. *Via Afrika Book Store: Bloemfontein*, 1951–56. 8°. **012987.** l. **3.**
There are two editions of "Primer for Sub-Standard B."

BARNES (Algernon Strange Valentine) and **NIENABER** (Gabriël Stephanus)

—— Sonneblom-reeks. (Lees boekies.) [With Afrikaans-English vocabularies.] 7 bk. *Bloemfontein*, 1948. 8° **12974.** c. **10.**

BARNES (Alice Josephine Mary Taylor)

—— Gynaecological Histology. pp. xii. 242. *Harvey & Blythe: London*, 1948. 8°. **7423.** bb. **18.**

BARNES (Alison)

—— *See* Birt (Catherine) Royal Sisters. (vol. 3. By A. Barnes.) [1949, *etc.*] 8°. W.P. **9787/3.**

BARNES (Ambrose) *See* R., M. The Life of Ambrose Barnes, sometime Alderman of Newcastle. 1828. 8°. **1077. f. 22. (4.)**

—— —— 1867. 8°. Ac. **8045/41.**

BARNES (Anna) *See* Barnes (Earl) and (A.) A Case of Infantile Paralysis, *etc.* [1915?] 8°. **7581.** de. **56.**

BARNES (Annie) *See* Sessely, afterwards Barnes. **010655.** i. **3.**

BARNES (Annie E.) *See* Bunting (Evelyn M.) A School for Mothers. By E. M. Bunting . . . A. E. Barnes, *etc.* [1907.] 8°. **7580. ff. 26.**

BARNES (Annie Maria) An American Girl in Korea, *etc.* [A novel.] pp. 392. *Penn Publishing Co.: Philadelphia*, 1905. 8°. **012707.** d. **44.**

—— Mistress Moppet . . . Illustrated, *etc.* pp. 197. *Penn Publishing Co.: Philadelphia*, 1904. 8°. **012707.** c. **5.**

BARNES (Archie Fairbairn)

—— Practice in Modern Harmony. [With musical notes.] pp. 40. *Oxford University Press: London*, 1937. 8°. **07899.** df. **58.**

—— The Story of the 2/5th Battalion Gloucestershire Regiment, 1914–18. Edited by A. F. Barnes. [With plates.] pp. 192. 1930. 8°. *See* England.—*Army.—Infantry.—Gloucestershire Regiment.* **08821. aa. 69.**

BARNES (Arthur Alison Stuart) On Active Service with the Chinese Regiment. A record of the operations of the first Chinese regiment in North China from March to October 1900. pp. xv. 228. *Grant Richards: London*, 1902. 8°. **9055. a. 43.**

BARNES (Arthur Chapman)

—— Agriculture of the Sugar-Cane. [With plates.] pp. x. 392. *Leonard Hill: London*, 1953. 8°. **7081.** aa. **17.**

BARNES (Arthur Grafton) *See* Villiers (George) *2nd Duke of Buckingham.* The Rehearsal, by George Villiers, Duke of Buckingham, and The Critic, by . . . Sheridan. Edited by A. G. Barnes. 1927. 8°. **11770. c. 6.**

—— A Book of English Verse Satire. Chosen and annotated by A. G. Barnes. pp. xix. 172. *Methuen & Co.: London*, 1926. 8°. **11607. ccc. 30.**

—— Poems from Lakeland Fells. [With a portrait.] pp. 59. *A. H. Stockwell: London*, [1939.] 8°. **11656.** i. **4.**

BARNES (Arthur Stanley) *See* Vincent (Swale) and Barnes (A. S.) On the Structure of the Red Glands in the Swim-Bladder of certain Fishes, *etc.* [1896.] 8°. **7204. df. 6. (13.)**

BARNES (Arthur Stapylton)

—— Bishop Barlow and Anglican Orders. A study of the original documents. pp. xviii. 194. *Longmans & Co.: London*, 1922. 8°. **3940. i. 24.**

—— *See* Jenkins (Claude) Bishop Barlow's Consecration and Archbishop Parker's Register, *etc.* [A review of "Bishop Barlow and Anglican Orders: a study of the original documents," by A. S. Barnes.] 1935. 8°. **04429.dd.18/17.**

—— Blessed Joan the Maid. pp. 140. *Burns & Oates: London*, [1909.] 8°. **4827. df. 43.**

—— Catholic Oxford. pp. 36. *Catholic Truth Society: London*, 1933. 8°. **3943.** aa. **334**

—— The Catholic Schools of England. pp. xi. 255. *Williams & Norgate: London*, 1926. 8°. **8311. ff. 8.**

—— Christianity at Rome in the Apostolic Age. An attempt at reconstruction of history. pp. xiii. 222. *Methuen: London*, 1938. 8°. **20032.** a. **26.**

—— The Early Church in the Light of the Monuments. A study in Christian archæology . . . With illustrations. pp. xx. 223. *Longmans & Co.: London*, 1913. 8°. [*Westminster Library.*] **2206. a. 9/9.**

—— The English Liturgical Colours and recent writings thereon. pp. 54. *Church Printing Co.: London*, 1890. 8°. **3477. eeee. 24. (2.)**

—— Eton in the Olden Days. pp. 26. *Robert Browning: London*, [1898.] 8°. **8304. bb. 11. (5.)**

—— The Holy Shroud of Turin. [With plates.] pp. v. 70. *Burns, Oates & Co.: London*, 1934. 4°. **20088.** b. **27.**

BARNES (Arthur Stapylton)

—— Low Mass in England before the Reformation. A paper, *etc.* pp. 22. *Robert Browning: London,* [1905?] 8°. **3477.** dg. **36. (1.)**

—— The Man of the Mask: a study in the by-ways of history . . . With a frontispiece. pp. viii. 345. *Smith, Elder & Co.: London,* 1908. 8°. **10806.** ee. **10.**

—— Revised and cheaper edition. pp. viii. 345. *Smith, Elder & Co.: London,* 1912. 8°. **10806.** c. **33.**

—— The Martyrdom of St. Peter and St. Paul, *etc.* [With plates.] pp. x. 184. *Oxford University Press: London,* 1933. 8°. **04808.** f. **17.**

—— No Sacrifice—No Priest; or, Why Anglican orders were condemned. pp. 24. *Catholic Truth Society: London,* [1897.] 8°. **3943.** aa. **368.**

—— No Sacrifice—No Priest . . . New edition. pp. 32. *Catholic Truth Society: London,* 1933. 8°. **3943.** aa. **367**

—— The Popes and the Ordinal: a collection of documents bearing on the question of Anglican Orders. Second edition, enlarged, with a preface by H. E. Cardinal Vaughan. pp. 210. *Robert Browning: London,* 1898. 8°. **3940.** l. **2.**

—— St. Peter in Rome and his Tomb on the Vatican Hill . . . With . . . plates, *etc.* pp. viii. 395. *S. Sonnenschein & Co.: London,* 1900. 8°. **2208.** dd. **3.**

—— [Another copy.] **4808.** i. **25.**

BARNES (Barnabe)

—— *See* Dodds (Madeleine H.) Barnabe Barnes of Durham: author and playwright. 1946. 8°. [*Archaeologia Aeliana.* ser. 4. vol. 24.] Ac. **5675.**

—— *See* Eccles (Mark) Barnabe Barnes. 1933. 8°. [*Sisson* (*Charles J.*) *Thomas Lodge and other Elizabethans, etc.*] **20016.** h. **30.**

—— The Poems of Barnabe Barnes . . . Part i. Parthenophil and Parthenophe, 1593. From the only known exemplar in the possession of his Grace the Duke of Devonshire. Part ii. A Divine Centurie of spirituall sonnets, 1595. From the author's . . . gift-copy in the Cathedral Library, York. Edited, with introduction and notes, by the Rev. Alexander B. Grosart. 2 pt. *Charles Simms: Manchester,* 1875. 4°. [*Occasional Issues of Unique or Very Rare Books.* vol. 1.] **2326.** g. **1. (2.)**
No. 25 *of an edition of thirty copies, printed for the subscribers.*

—— The Divils Charter: a Tragædie conteining the Life and Death of Pope Alexander the sixt. As it was plaide before the Kings Maiestie . . . But more exactly reuewed [*sic*], corrected, and augmented since by the author, for the more pleasure and profit of the Reader. [In verse.] *G. E. for Iohn Wright: London,* 1607. 4°. C. **34.** c. **3.**
Imperfect; wanting the dedicatory epistle, which has been supplied from another copy in a photographic reproduction.

—— [Another copy.] **162.** c. **4.**
Imperfect; wanting the dedicatory epistle. Cropped.

—— [Another edition.] Edited from the quarto of 1607 by R. B. McKerrow. pp. xxiii. 144. *Louvain,* 1904. 8°. [*Materialien zur Kunde des älteren englischen Dramas.* Bd. 6.] **11853.v.1/6.**

—— [Another edition.] *J. C. Farmer: Amersham,* 1913. 4°. [*Tudor Facsimile Texts.*] Tab. **579.** a. **1.**

BARNES (Barnabe)

—— A Divine Centurie of Spirituall Sonnets. *See* Park (Thomas) Heliconia, *etc.* vol. 2. 1815. 4°. **77.** k. **12.**

—— Foure Bookes of Offices: enabling privat persons for the speciall seruice of all good Princes and Policies. pp. 210. **L.P.** *Printed at the Charges of G. Bishop, J. Adams & C. Burbie: London,* 1606. fol. C. **48.** k. **4.**
Without leaves a1 & 2.

—— Parthenophil and Parthenophe. Sonnets, *etc.* 1882. *See* Arber (Edward) An English Garner, *etc.* vol. 5. 1877, *etc.* 8°. **12269.** cc. **12.**

—— Parthenophil and Parthenophe. Sonnets, madrigals, elegies and odes, *etc.* 1904. *See* Arber (Edward) An English Garner. (Elizabethan Sonnets. vol. 1.) 1903, *etc.* 8°. **2324.** e. **9/11.**

—— Ten Poems from "Parthenophil and Parthenophe." With an introduction by Madeleine Hope Dodds. pp. vi. 10. *Priory Press: Tynemouth,* 1929. 8°. **11643.** cc. **59.**
No. 19 *of an edition of* 20 *copies printed on hand-made paper.*

BARNES (Benjamin Francis)

—— *See* Mathews (Oscar R.) and Barnes (B. F.) Dry Land Crops at the Dalhart—Texas—Field Station. 1940. 8°. [*U.S. Department of Agriculture. Circular.* no. 564.] A.S. **804/2.**

BARNES (Benjamin Thomas) *See* Liturgies.—*Church of England.—Common Prayer.—Catechism.* [*English.*] Easy Lessons on the Church Catechism . . . By the Rev. B. T. Barnes. 1886. 8°. **3504.** cc. **53.**

BARNES (Bertie Frank) *See* Vaughan (*Dame* Helen C. I. G.) *G.B.E.*, and Barnes (B. F.) The Structure and Development of the Fungi. 1927. 8°. **07028.** b. **10.**

—— —— 1930. 8°. **2028.b.**

—— *See* Vaughan (*Dame* Helen C. I. G.) *G.B.E.*, and Barnes (B. F.) The Structure & Development of the Fungi, *etc.* 1937. 8°. **7029.** pp. **27.**

BARNES (Bertram)

—— Goethe's Knowledge of French Literature. pp. viii. 172. *Clarendon Press: Oxford,* 1937. 8°. [*Oxford Studies in Modern Languages and Literature.*] **012902.w.18/8.**

BARNES (Bertram Herbert)

—— *See* O'Neil (Joseph A.) A Shona Grammar. Zezuru dialect . . . With notes on the Karanga and Manyika by . . . A. A. Louw . . . and . . . B. H. Barnes. 1935. 8°. **12911.** aa. **9.**

—— Johnson of Nyasaland. A study of the life and work of William Percival Johnson, D.D., Archdeacon of Nyasa, missionary pioneer, 1876–1928. [With plates, including portraits.] pp. 258. *Universities' Mission to Central Africa: London,* 1933. 8°. **4909.** c. **6.**

—— A Vocabulary of the Dialects of Mashonaland. In the new orthography. pp. ix. 213. *Sheldon Press: London,* 1932. 8°. **12911.** b. **12.**
Interleaved.

BARNES (Betty) The History of Betty Barnes. 2 vol. *D. Wilson & T. Durham: London,* 1753. 12°. **12612.** de. **12.**

BARNES (C. Burton) Sure Guide to Good Health. A lecture . . . on the most approved principles of drainage and sanitary fitments for dwelling houses. pp. 15. *Minchin & Gibbs: Gloucester,* 1905. 16°. **8777.** a. **15.**

BARNES (C. L.)

—— *See* DANTE ALIGHIERI. [*Divina Commedia.—Italian and English.*] La Divina Commedia . . . The Italian edited by H. Oelsner [and revised by C. L. Barnes], *etc.* 1933. 8°. **011420.** cc. **54.**

BARNES (CALVIN RANKIN)

—— Ethelbert Talbot, October 9, 1848—February 27, 1928, *etc.* [With plates, including portraits, and a bibliography.] *In:* Historical Magazine of the Protestant Episcopal Church. vol. 24. no. 2. pp. 141–185. 1955. 8°. P.P. 851. f.

BARNES (CARMAN DEE) Beau Lover. A novel. pp. 253. *T. Werner Laurie: London,* 1931. 8°. NN. **17451.**

—— Schoolgirl. [A novel.] pp. x. 236. *T. Werner Laurie: London,* 1930. 8°. **12813.** d. **21.**

—— Time Lay Asleep. pp. 243. *Harper & Bros.: New York, London,* [1946.] 8°. **12728.** d. **21.**

—— Young Woman. pp. 318. *T. Werner Laurie: London,* 1935. 8°. A.N. **2470.**

BARNES (CHARLES A.) *See* SCOTT (William) *Principal of the Toronto Normal School,* and BARNES (C. A.) Companion to the Public School Arithmetic, *etc.* 1901. 8°. **08533.** ee. **65.**

—— Algebraical Exercises and Examination Papers for public school leaving and primary examinations. pp. 121. *Copp Clark Co.: Toronto,* [1897.] 8°. **8533.** aaa. **46.**

BARNES (CHARLES BRINTON) The Longshoremen . . . A study carried on under the direction of Pauline Goldmark. [With illustrations.] pp. xx. 287. 1915. 8°. *See* NEW YORK, *City of.—Russell Sage Foundation.* **8276.** e. **76.**

BARNES (CHARLES C.) Directive Study Sheets in World History. pp. ix. 142. *Houghton Mifflin Co.: Boston,* [1929.] 8°. **09004.** a. **14.**

BARNES (CHARLES C.) and **DAIL** (JOHN B.)

—— American Life and Problems. [With plates.] pp. viii. 626. *Longmans & Co.: New York,* 1940. 8°. 8288. e. 34.

BARNES (CHARLES E.)

—— The King of the Rustlers. pp. 122. *C. A. Pearson: London,* [1941.] 8°. **012646.** aaa. **21.**

—— Lawless Range. pp. 126. *London,* [1940.] 8°. [*Pearson's Blue-Gun Library.*] 12730.k.36/3.

—— Rogues of the Range. A Western story. pp. 253. *Eldon Press: London,* 1936. 8°. A.N. **3218.**

—— Rogues of the Range. pp. 123. *C. A. Pearson: London,* [1941.] 8°. **012646.** aaa. **22.**

—— Sagebrush Knights. A western story. pp. 253. *Eldon Press: London,* 1936. 8°. A.N. **3362.**

—— Valley of Peril. pp. 126. *London,* [1940.] 8°. [*Pearson's Blue-Gun Library.*] **12730.k.36/2.**

BARNES (CHARLES LIGHTFOOT) Geology. With illustrations. pp. viii. 181. *Rivington, Percival & Co.: London,* 1896. 8°. [*Beginners' Text-Books of Science.*] **08708.** a. **7.**

—— Practical Acoustics. pp. x. 214. *Macmillan & Co.: London,* 1897. 8°. [*Lessons in Elementary Practical Physics.* vol. 3. pt. 1.] **08708.** aa. **19.**

—— [Another edition.] pp. x. 220. *Macmillan & Co.: London,* 1909. 8°. [*Lessons in Elementary Practical Physics, etc.* vol. 3. pt. 1.] **08708.** aa. **19.**

BARNES (CHARLES LIGHTFOOT)

—— Rock History: a concise note-book of Geology having special reference to the English and Welsh formations . . . With maps, *etc.* pp. vi. 117. *Edward Stanford: London,* 1884. 8°. **7202.** aaa. **22**

—— Sound: an elementary treatise. pp. 79. *London,* 1893. 8°. [*Nisbet's Elementary Science Manuals.*] **8708.** ee. **7**

BARNES (CHARLES RANDALL) The People's Bible Encyclopedia . . . Edited by . . . C. R. Barnes, *etc.* 1900. 8°. *See* ENCYCLOPAEDIAS. **03129.** g. **2**

BARNES (CHARLES REID) *See* ARTHUR (Joseph C.) Handbook of Plant Dissection. By J. C. Arthur, C. R. Barnes, *etc.* 1886. 8°. **7033.** cc. **21**

—— *See* COULTER (John M.) A Textbook of Botany . . . By J. M. Coulter . . . C. R. Barnes, *etc.* [1910, *etc.*] 8°. **7031.** pp. **1**

—— —— [1930, *etc.*] 8°. **07028.** b. **37**

—— Artificial Keys to the Genera and Species of Mosses recognised in Lesquereux and James's "Manual of the Mosses of North America." [With "Additions and Corrections."] 1892. *See* MADISON, *Wisconsin.—Wisconsin Academy of Sciences, etc.* Transactions, *etc.* vol. 8. 1872, *etc.* 8°. Ac. **1880/2**

—— [Another edition.] Analytic Keys . . . Revised and extended by F. de F. Heald, *etc.* 1896. *See* MADISON, *Wisconsin.—University of Wisconsin.* Bulletin, *etc.* Science Series. vol. 1. no. 5. 1894, *etc.* 8°. Ac. **179**

—— Plant Life considered with special reference to form and function. pp. vii. 428. *H. Holt & Co.: New York,* 1898. 8°. **7033.** aaa. **25**

BARNES (CHARLOTTE MARY SANFORD) Plays, Prose, and Poetry. pp. 489. *E. H. Butler & Co.: Philadelphia,* 1848. 12°. **12295.** d. **1**

—— The Night of the Coronation: written on reading the account of the coronation of Victoria I. [A poem.] ff. 7. [*New York,* 1838.] 8°. **11645.** bbb. **31**
Printed on one side of the leaf only.

BARNES (CLARE)

—— Home Sweet Zoo. [With illustrations.] pp. 75. *Methuen & Co.: London,* 1950. 8°. **07209.** aaa. **20**

—— White Collar Zoo. pp. 73. *Methuen & Co.: London,* 1949. 8°. **07209.** b. **18**

—— [A reissue.] White Collar Zoo. *Angus & Robertson: Sydney, London,* [1950.] 8°. **7209.** aaa. **34**

BARNES (CLAUDE T.) Mammals of Utah. pp. 166. *Salt Lake City,* 1922. 8°. **07207.** f. **25**
Vol. 12. *no.* 15 *of the Bulletin of the University of Utah.*

—— The Wending Year. [Verses.] pp. 59. [*Salt Lake City,* 1940.] 16°. **011645.** de. **22**

BARNES (CLIVE)

—— Ballet in Britain since the War. pp. 92. *Thrift Books: London,* 1953. 8°. [*Thrift Books.* no. 21.] **012213.p.7/21**

BARNES (CONSTANCE)

—— The Wise Grasshopper. [A tale for children.] pp. 37. *Art & Educational Publishers: London & Glasgow,* 1946. 8°. **12800.** i. **10**

BARNES (CULMER) *See* JEWETT (J. H.) The Bunny Stories . . . with . . . illustrations by C. Barnes. 1893. 8°. **12806.** p. **41**

BARNES (CULMER)

—— *See* JEWETT (J. H.) More Bunny Stories . . . With . . . illustrations by C. Barnes. [1900.] 8°. **12809. o. 23.**

BARNES (CYRIL CHARLES)

—— Choosing Electric Cables. A comparative analysis of cable structure in relation to installation conditions. pp. 40. *Emmott & Co.: Manchester*, 1954. 8°. [*Mechanical World Monographs.* no. 67.] W.P. **2806/67.**

—— The Current Rating of Paper Insulated Cables. pp. 44. *Draughtsman Publishing Co.: Rugeley*, [1945?] 8°. [*Association of Engineering and Shipbuilding Draughtsmen. Publications of the Technical Section.*] Ac. **4395. (163.)**

—— Power Cables: their design and installation, *etc.* [With plates.] pp. xvi. 272. *Chapman & Hall: London*, 1953. 8°. [*Series of Monographs on Electrical Engineering.* vol. 14.] W.P. **11335/14.**

—— Progress in Paper Insulated Power Cable Developments. pp. 37. *London*, [1950.] 8°. [*Association of Engineering and Shipbuilding Draughtsmen. Publications of the Technical Section.*] Ac. **4395. (245.)**

BARNES (CYRIL JOHN)

—— The Boy who didn't count: Theodore Hopkins Kitching. pp. 15. *Salvationist Publishing & Supplies: London*, [1954.] 8°. **4908. k. 60.**
Part of a series entitled "Liberty Booklets."

—— Called from the Plough: Charles Ward. pp. 15. *Salvationist Publishing & Supplies: London*, [1955.] 8°. **4194. b. 67.**
One of the "Liberty Booklets."

—— The Man with two Lives: Henry F. Milans, O.F. pp. 15. *Salvationist Publishing & Supplies: London*, 1946. 8°. **4431. a. 78.**
Part of the "Trophy Series."

—— The One-Legged Prophet—Thomas Robertson. pp. 15. [*Salvationist Publishing & Supplies: London*, 1952.] 8°. **4920. de. 49.**

—— Prophet in Prison and Park: Anker Deans. pp. 15. [*Salvationist Publishing & Supplies: London*, 1952.] 8°. **4431. a. 80.**

—— The White Castle. The story of Mary Lichtenberger. [With a portrait.] pp. 63. *Salvationist Publishing & Supplies: London*, 1954. 8°. **4921. aa. 1.**

—— You can't stop Lawrance! Harriet Lawrance. Edited by C. J. Barnes. pp. 15. *Salvationist Publishing & Supplies: London*, [1953.] 8°. **1856. g. 14. (89.)**

BARNES (DAVID) *D.D., of Scituate.* Sermons. pp. 142. *Munro & Co.: Boston*, 1815. 12°. **4486. b. 45.**

—— The Character and Duty of a Christian Minister: considered in a discourse delivered at Barnstable . . . Sept. 30. 1801. on the ordination of . . . J. Waterman. pp. 27. *Manning & Loring: Boston*, 1802. 8°. **4485. i. 25.**

—— A Discourse on Education, delivered before the Trustees of the Derby Academy, at Hingham, *etc.* pp. 27. *Manning & Loring: Boston*, 1805. 8°. **4485. f. 20.**

—— Thoughts on the Love of Life and Fear of Death: delivered in a sermon. pp. 23. *Samuel Hall: Boston*, 1795. 8°. **4485. c. 4.**

—— The Wisdom of God in appointing men, teachers of men. A sermon delivered . . . soon after the decease of . . . Rev. James Hawley, *etc.* pp. 20. *Manning & Loring: Boston*, 1801. 8°. **4985. bb. 47. (17.)**

BARNES (DAVID M.) The Draft Riots in New York. July, 1863. The Metropolitan Police: their services during Riot Week. Their honorable record. pp. 117. *Baker & Goodwin: New York*, 1863. 8°. **9602. dd. 23.**

BARNES (DEREK G.) *Writer of Verse.*

—— Young Man's Fancy. pp. 30. *Ernest Benn: London*, 1928. 8°. [*Shilling Books of Neu Poetry.* bk. 7.] **11613.bb.9/7.**

BARNES (DEREK GILPIN)

—— Bertram Mills' Circus in Story and Pictures. (Written and designed by D. G. Barnes.) [1948.] 8°. *See* BERTRAM W. MILLS' CIRCUS. **11798. bb. 1.**

—— Bertram Mills' Circus in Story and Pictures. Second edition. (Written and designed by D. G. Barnes.) [1949.] 8°. *See* BERTRAM W. MILLS' CIRCUS. **11798. bb. 2.**

—— Cloud Cover. Recollections of an intelligence officer . . . Illustrated by A. K. Lawrence. pp. 176. *Rich & Cowan: London*, [1943.] 8°. **9101. ff. 6.**

—— Lords of Life. An anthology of animal poetry of the last fifty years. Chosen, edited and with an introduction by D. G. Barnes. Illustrated by Kathleen Gardiner. pp. 175. *Rich & Cowan: London*, [1946.] 8°. **11605. cc. 20.**

BARNES (DJUNA)

—— Nightwood. [A novel.] pp. 239. *Faber & Faber: London*, 1936. 8°. **012604. k. 64.**

—— Nightwood. (Second edition.) pp. 239. *Faber and Faber: London*, 1950. 8°. **012635. bb. 31.**

BARNES (DONALD GROVE)

—— George III and William Pitt, 1783–1806. A new interpretation based upon a study of their unpublished correspondence. pp. xiii. 512. *Stanford University Press: Stanford University*, [1939.] 8°. **09525. h. 7.**

—— A History of the English Corn Laws from 1660–1846. [With a bibliography.] pp. xv. 336. *G. Routledge & Sons: London*, 1930. 8°. [*Studies in Economic and Social History.*] Ac. **2363/3. (2.)**

BARNES (DORA M.)

—— Edgar Allan Poe: impressions of his life and work, and his associations with Stoke Newington. [With plates, including a portrait.] pp. 58. *Inclusive Service: London*, 1949. 8°. **10890. ee. 29.**

BARNES (DOROTHY) A Kiss for Fun. pp. 80. *J. Leng & Co.: London*, 1932. 8°. [*Ivy Stories.* no. 246.] **12819. a. 1/246.**

BARNES (DWIGHT F.)

—— *See* STICKNEY (Fenner S.) Date Palm Insects in the United States. By F. S. Stickney, D. F. Barnes, *etc.* 1950. 8°. [*U.S. Department of Agriculture. Circular.* no. 846.] A.S. **804/2.**

BARNES (E. C.) *Artist.* *See* HOOD (Thomas) *the Younger.* From Nowhere to the North Pole . . . With illustrations by . . . E. C. Barnes. 1875. 8°. **12803. g. 24.**

—— A Model Child. *See* HALLIDAY (A.) The Savage-Club. Papers for 1868, *etc.* 1868. 8°. **12352. f. 13.**

BARNES (E. G.) *of the Aerodynamics Division, N.P.L.*

—— *See* NEWBY (K. W.) Model Tests on an Air Interchange System for removing Engine Exhaust Products from a Wind Tunnel. By K. W. Newby . . . E. G. Barnes, *etc.* 1954. 4°. [*Aeronautical Research Council. Reports and Memoranda.* no. 2639.] B.S. **2/2.**

BARNES (E. G.) *of the Aerodynamics Division, N.P.L.*

—— *See* THOMPSON (J. S.) *B.A.* Model Tests with Flow on the Gloster F. 9/40 . . . By J. S Thompson . . . E. G. Barnes. 1952. fol. [*Aeronautical Research Council. Reports and Memoranda.* no. 2517.] B.S. **2/2.**

BARNES (E. J.) Faithful and True; or, the Mother's legacy. pp. 155. *S.P.C.K.: London,* [1871.] 8°. **12806.** dd. **6.**

BARNES (E. W.)

—— The "Borough" Guide to Matlock, *etc.* pp. 44. *E. J. Burrow: Cheltenham,* [1919.] 8°. **10354.** a. **606.**

BARNES (EARL) [Articles on the education of children, reprinted from various periodicals.] 7 pt. [1898–1908.] 8°. **8385.** f. **34.**

—— The Celibate Woman of To-day. (Reprinted from The Popular Science Monthly.) [*New York,* 1915.] 8°. **8416.** h. **48.** (**2.**)

—— Child Study. (Saturday Teachers Class.) [Syllabus. With circulars relating to the same subject.] [1893–95.] 8° & 4°. **8308.** k. **4.**

—— Child Study in relation to elementary Art Education . . . Reprint from Art Education in the Public Schools of the United States. pp. 20. *American Art Annual: New York,* [1908.] 8°. **8307.** i. **21.** (**4.**)

—— Children's Ideals. pp. 12. [1900.] 8°. **8306.** g. **15.** (**12.**)

—— Children's Imaginary Companions . . . Reprinted from the Sequoia. [1894?] 8°. **8305.** f. **27.** (**6.**)

—— Corporal Punishment as a means of social control. (Reprinted from March "Education.") pp. 8. [1898.] 8°. **8306.** g. **15.** (**5.**)

—— Discipline in the Family and in the School. [1897?] 8°. **8304.** f. **7.** (**6.**)

—— The Education of a partially paralyzed Muscle . . . Reprinted from the Pedagogical Seminary, *etc.* [*Worcester, Mass.,* 1912.] 8°. **7660.** c. **29.**

—— Freedom in Education . . . Reprinted from "Child Life," *etc.* [*London,* 1900.] 4°. **8305.** ee. **40.** (**3.**)

—— Punishment as seen by Children . . . Reprinted from the Pedagogical Seminary, *etc.* pp. 11. [*Worcester, Mass.,* 1895.] 8°. **8304.** ee. **7.** (**4.**)

—— [Another edition.] (Reprinted from The Pacific Educational Journal.) pp. 13. [1898.] 8°. **8304.** f. **7.** (**10.**)

—— Six Lectures . . . on "The Development of Educational Control." Abstract. [1900.] 8°. **8306.** g. **15.** (**11.**)

—— A Study of Children's Drawings. Reprinted from the Pedagogical Seminary. pp. 8. [*Worcester, Mass.,* 1894.] 8°. **8305.** ee. **36.** (**8.**)

—— A Study of Children's Interests . . . Reprinted from the "Pacific Educational Journal," *etc.* pp. 11. [1893.] 8°. **8305.** ee. **36.** (**5.**)

—— A Study on Children's Property-Sense. Reprinted from "Child Life," *etc.* pp. 4. [*London,* 1899.] 4°. **8305.** ee. **40.** (**2.**)

—— Theological Life of a California Child. Reprinted from the Pedagogical Seminary, *etc.* pp. 7. [*Worcester, Mass.,* 1893.] 8°. **8305.** ee. **36.** (**9.**)

—— The University Extension Club of San Jose, Cal. . . . Syllabus of a course of eight lectures on "The History of European Civilization." [1897.] 8°. **8304.** d. **20.** (**4.**)

BARNES (EARL)

—— Where Knowledge Fails . . . With an introduction by the editor (E. H. Griggs). pp. ix. 50. *T. Fisher Unwin: London,* 1909. 8°. [GRIGGS (*E. H.*) *The Art of Life Series, etc.* vol. 2.] **8410.** ee. **1/2.**

—— Woman in Modern Society. pp. 257. *Cassell & Co.: London,* 1912. 8°. **08415.** de. **45.**

—— Woman's Place in the New Civilization. (Reprinted from the Annals of the American Academy of Political and Social Science.) [*Philadelphia,* 1914.] 8°. **8416.** h. **48.** (**1.**)

BARNES (EARL) and **BARNES** (ANNA)

—— A Case of Infantile Paralysis—anterior poliomyelitis. pp. 19. [1915?] 8°. **7581.** de. **56**

BARNES (EARL) and **BARNES** (MARY SHELDON)

—— Collections of Sources in English for History Teaching. (Reprinted from the Educational Review.) [1898.] 8°. **8306.** g. **15.** (**7.**

BARNES (EDGAR GEORGE) How to arrest Infectious Diseases. pp. 88. *J. & A. Churchill: London,* 1883. 16° **7442.** a. **11**

BARNES (EDWARD JOHN) Our Girls and Boys. Their future responsibility. pp. 20. *Elliot Stock: London* [1884.] 12°. **4422.** aaa. **62.** (**1.**

—— The People's Bible Finger-post. A novel and attractive guide to Bible subjects, with notes and anecdotes, in parallel columns. pp. vi. 89. *Elliot Stock: London* 1883. 8°. **3128.** ee. **29**

BARNES (EDWIN N. C.) *See* BARNES (Joshua N.) Lights and Shadows of Eighty Years . . . Revised and edited by . . . E. N. C. Barnes, *etc.* 1911. 8°. **4902.** de. **26.**

BARNES, afterwards **YARROW** (ELEANOR CECILIA) *Lady.* Alfred Yarrow, his life and work . . . Illustrated. [With portraits.] pp. xv. 328. *E. Arnold & Co.: London,* 1923. 8°. **010856.** dd. **8.**

—— Popular edition. pp. xii. 276. *E. Arnold & Co.: London,* 1928. 8°. **010855.** b. **72.**

—— As the Water Flows. A record of adventures in a canoe on the rivers and trout streams of southern England . . . With illustrations by Helen Stratton and . . . photographs, *etc.* pp. 189. *Grant Richards: London,* 1920. 4°. **010368.** i. **7.**

—— [Another edition.] pp. 158. *Clement Ingleby: London,* 1927. 4°. **10369.** pp. **26.**

BARNES (ELIZABETH) *Murderess.* Natures Cruell Step-Dames: or, Matchlesse Monsters of the female sex, Elizabeth Barnes and Anne Willis, who were executed . . . at Tyburne, for the unnaturall murthering of their owne children . . . Further, a relation of the wicked life and impenitent death of John Flood, who raped his own childe. pp. 20. *For Francis Coales: London,* 1637. 4°. **6485.** a. **1.**

BARNES (ELIZABETH) *Widow. See* ANDREWS (Thomas) *Tradesman, of Westminster.* To the Honourable the Knights, Citizens, and Burgesses in Parliament assembled The petition of T. Andrews . . . E. Barnes, *etc.* [1701.] fol. **816.** m. **17.** (**23.**)

BARNES (EMANUEL) Προσφωνησεις amicorum gratulantium . . . Emmanueli Baernesio Anglo, et . . . Paulo Crocio Cycnaeo, quum in sacrum theologorum doctorum ordinem in . . . Basiliensium Academia . . . cooptarentur. *Ex officina Oporiniana: Basileae,* 1582. 4°. **11408.** bb. **22.**

BARNES (Emma J.) A Needle and Thread: a tale for girls. pp. viii. 213. *W. P. Nimmo: Edinburgh,* 1873. 12°. **12803**. aaa. **54**.

BARNES (Eric Stephen) and **DYER** (Henry Peter Francis Swinnerton)

—— The Inhomogeneous Minima of Binary Quadratic Forms, *etc.* *In:* Acta mathematica. vol. 87. no. 3/4, *etc.* 1952– . 4°. P.P. **1582**. bb.

BARNES (Eric Wollencott)

—— Anna Cora. The life and theatre of Anna Cora Mowatt. [With plates, including portraits.] pp. 376. *Secker & Warburg: London,* 1954. 8°. **10892**. bb. **13**.

BARNES (Ern)

—— Easier Shearing. [With illustrations.] pp. xiv. 56. *Whitcombe & Tombs: Melbourne,* 1955. 8°. **07295**. bb. **26**.

BARNES (Ernest) *Ordnance Officer of Canterbury.*

—— Antient Blackfrerys Canterbury . . . A concise guide to Mother City. [With a map.] *Simpson & Turner: Margate,* [1935.] 16°. **010352**. a. **17**.

—— Antient Blakefrerys, Canterbury: Dominican Priory notes. A concise guide to Black Friars Monastery. *Simpson & Turner: Margate,* [1936.] 16°. **20029**. a. **34**.

BARNES (Ernest) *Translator.*

—— *See* Bailly (Auguste) The Divine Minstrels . . . Translated by E. Barnes. 1909. 8°. **04413**. h. **22**.

BARNES (Ernest William) *Bishop of Birmingham.* *See* Cohen (Chapman) An Open Letter to Bishop Barnes [on the relations of Christianity and science]. 1927. 8°. **4105**. aaa. **71**.

—— *See* Lawrence (William) *Bishop of Massachusetts.* Fifty Years . . . With a foreword by E. W. Barnes. 1924. 8°. **4744**. bb. **27**.

—— *See* Tremenheere (George H.) Dr. Barnes' Claim to dispense from Belief in the Creed, *etc.* 1934. 8°. **03504**. ff. **72**.

—— A Christian Approach to Peace . . . An address, *etc.* *National Peace Council: London,* 1945. 8°. [*Peace Aims Leaflet.* no. 5.] W.P. **15377**.

—— Freedom and Authority. pp. 15. *Hodder & Stoughton: London,* [1924.] 8°. [*Anglican Evangelical Group Movement Pamphlets.* no. 47.] **4107**. ff. **55/47**.

—— Man. [With a portrait.] pp. 14. [*Birmingham,*] 1932. 8°. [*Birmingham and Midland Institute. Presidential Addresses.* 1932.] Ac. **1193**. c.

—— Man, the Adolescent. The oration delivered . . . during the fiftieth Foundation Week on Thursday, 14th March, 1946, *etc.* [1949.] *See* London.—iii. *University College, etc.—Union Society.* [Foundation Week Orations.] [1897, *etc.*] 8°. Ac. **2666**. f/4. (24.)

—— Patriotism and Christianity. pp. 7. *Pacifist Council of the Christian Church: London,* [1945.] 8°. **08425**. g. **56**.

—— Religion amid Turmoil . . . The Rede Lecture, 1949, *etc.* pp. 36. *University Press: Cambridge,* 1949. 8°. **4381**. eee. **89**.

—— Religion and Science. pp. 15. *Hodder & Stoughton: London,* [1923.] 8°. [*Anglican Evangelical Group Movement Pamphlets.* no. 39.] **4107**. ff. **55/39**.

BARNES (Ernest William) *Bishop of Birmingham.*

—— The Rise of Christianity. pp. xx. 356. *Longmans, Green & Co.: London,* 1947. 8°. **2214**. c. **12**.

—— The Rise of Christianity. (Third impression [with corrections].) pp. xx. 356. *Longmans, Green & Co.: London,* 1948. 8°. **4536**. b. **7**.

—— *See* Dodd (Charles H.) Christian Beginnings. A reply to Dr. Barnes' 'The Rise of Christianity.' [1947.] 8°. **04018**. h. **76**.

—— *See* Fisher (Geoffrey F.) successively *Bishop of Chester and of London* and *Archbishop of Canterbury.* The Presidential Address to the Full Synod of the Convocation of Canterbury . . . Including a statement on the book entitled "The Rise of Christianity" [by Bishop E. W. Barnes], *etc.* [1947.] 8°. **4110**. a. **6**.

—— Scientific Theory and Religion. The world described by science and its spiritual interpretation . . . The Gifford Lectures at Aberdeen, 1927–1929. pp. xxiv. 685. *University Press: Cambridge,* 1933. 8°. **08710**. dd. **23**.

—— Should such a Faith offend? Sermons and addresses. pp. xxx. 330. *Hodder & Stoughton: London,* 1927. 8°. **04478**. ee. **48**.

—— Spiritualism and the Christian Faith. pp. 60. *Liverpool,* 1918. 8°. [*Liverpool Diocesan Board of Divinity.* Publications. no. 18.] **3606.aa.2/18.**

—— Second edition. pp. 61. *Student Christian Movement: London,* 1920. 8°. **8633**. aa. **17**.

BARNES (Esther) The Disengaged Fair. [A poem.] pp. 32. *S. Bonner: Bristol,* [1796.] 8°. **11641**. bb. **2**.

BARNES (Everett) American History for Grammar Grades . . . Revised edition. pp. xvi. 426. xxxii. *D. C. Heath & Co.: Boston,* [1923.] 8°. **9616**. cc. **2**.

BARNES (Everett) *pseud.* [i.e. Alfred Kenneth Boyd.]

—— A Housemaster's Case-Book. pp. 190. *W. & R. Chambers: London & Edinburgh,* 1955. 8°. **08368**. cc. **54**.

BARNES (F. F.)

—— Effect of Accelerated Erosion on Silting in Morena Reservoir, San Diego County, Calif. By F. F. Barnes . . . C. J. Kraebel . . . and R. S. La Motte. pp. 22. pl. 5. *Washington,* 1939. 8°. [*U.S. Department of Agriculture. Technical Bulletin.* no. 639.] A.S. **800**/2.

BARNES (F. J.)

—— *See* Bible.—*Mark.* [*Panaieti.*] Iesu Keriso wasana waiwasana Mareko wana leleli. (Revised version [prepared by F. J. Barnes].) 1918. 8°. **03068**. h. **65**.

BARNES (F. W.) How to Write for a Job. A concise guide to successful letter-writing. pp. 16. *Finchley Press: London,* [1929.] 8°. **08246**. ee. **41**.

BARNES (Fancourt) *See* Barnes (Robert S. F.)

BARNES (Florence M.)

—— A Child's Guide to the Bible. pp. 33. *C.S.S.M.: [London,]* 1947. 8°. **3130**. h. **12**.

BARNES (Francis) Twelve Sermons preached in Holy Trinity Church, Plymouth. pp. 189. *Longman & Co.: London; W. H. Luke: Plymouth,* 1860. 12°. **4464**. c. **6**.

BARNES (Francis Merriman) *See* Nitsche (Paul) and Wilmanns (C.) The History of the Prison Psychoses . . . Translation by F. M. Barnes, *etc.* 1912. 8°. **07660**. d. **4**.

BARNES (FRANCIS MERRIMAN)

—— An Introduction to the Study of Mental Disorders . . . Second edition [including "Notes on Mental Diseases"]. pp. 295. *Henry Kimpton: London; St. Louis*, printed, 1923. 8°. **07660**. cc. **3**.

BARNES (FRANK) *See* SCHUETZ (Heinrich) *Writer of Nature Stories*. [Der sterbende Gletscher.] When Mammoths roamed the Frozen Earth . . . Translated . . . by F. Barnes. [1930.] 8°. **012554**. dd. **20**.

BARNES (FRANK) *Historian*.

—— Fort Sumter. National monument, South Carolina. [With illustrations.] pp. 48. *Washington*, 1952. 8°. [*National Park Service. Historical Handbook Series*. no. 12.] A.S. **194/39**.

BARNES (FRANK EDWIN) Estimating Building Costs and Appraising Buildings. pp. xii. 822. *McGraw-Hill Book Co.: New York*, 1924. 8°. **07815**. e. **14**.

—— Third edition / fifth impression. pp. xv. 656. *McGraw-Hill Book Co.: New York & London*, 1931. 8°. **07816**. aa. **69**.

BARNES (FRED)

—— Barrow and District. An illustrated history . . . Compiled by F. Barnes. [With maps.] pp. 144. 1951. 8°. *See* BARROW-IN-FURNESS.—*Library and Museum Committee*. **010368**. pp. **51**.

BARNES (FRED ASA) *See* CRANDALL (C. L.) and BARNES (F. A.) Field Book for Railroad Surveying, *etc.* 1909. 8°. **8548**. cc. **40**. (**2**.)

—— —— 1910. 8°. **08767**. de. **69**.

—— *See* CRANDALL (C. L.) and BARNES (F. A.) Railroad Construction. 1913. 8°. **08767**. cc. **30**.

BARNES (FREDERICK) A Sermon preached before the Honourable House of Commons . . . January 30, 1807, *etc.* pp. 28. *L. Hansard & Sons: London*, 1807. 4°. **114**. b. **42**.

BARNES (FREDERICK K.) *See* RANKINE (W. J. M.) Shipbuilding, theoretical and practical . . . By J. Watts . . . F. K. Barnes, *etc.* 1866. fol. **1801**. b. **23**.

BARNES (FREDERICK P.) Ireland in the Present Century; with suggestions for the settlement of the landlord & tenant difficulty. pp. 15. *W. Ridgway: London*, 1881. 8°. **8145**. bbb. **3**. (**16**.)

BARNES (G. ATKINSON) George and Joseph, Maud of Ditchling and other poems. pp. 43. *Bemrose & Sons: London*, 1888. 8°. **11653**. m. **32**.

BARNES (G. FRANCES)

—— *See* BARNES (Kenneth C.) and (G. F.) Sex, Friendship and Marriage. 1938. 8°. **08416**. l. **20**.

BARNES (G. H.)

—— The Development of Unevenaged Stands of Engelmann Spruce and Probable Development of Residual Stands after Logging . . . Reprinted from The Forestry Chronicle, *etc.* pp. 47. [1937.] 8°. *See* COLUMBIA, *British*.—*Department of Lands*.—*Forest Branch*. C.S. E. **106/2**.

BARNES (GEORGE) *Archdeacon of Bombay*. A Sermon, *etc.* *See* BOMBAY, *City of*.—*Society for Promoting the Education of the Poor*. (The First Annual Report, *etc.*) 1816, *etc.* 8°. **08310.ee.96.**

—— A Sermon preached . . . at the anniversary of the Exeter Diocesan Committees of the Societies for Promoting Christian Knowledge and for the Propagation of the Gospel in foreign parts. pp. 23. *C. & J. Rivington: London*, 1828. 8°. **T. 1204**. (**17**.)

BARNES (GEORGE) *Archdeacon of Bombay*.

—— A Sermon preached in St. Thomas's Church, Bombay . . . April xxviii, MDCCCXXV, at the primary visitation of Reginald Heber DD., Bishop of Calcutta. pp. 32. *C. & J. Rivington: London*, 1826. 8°. **T. 1044**. (**1**.)

—— A Sermon preached in Bombay, St. Thomas's Church on November xiii., MDCCCXXV. being the Sunday preceding his resignation of the Archdeaconry. pp. 28. *C. & J. Rivington: London*, 1826. 8°. **T. 1044**. (**10**.)

BARNES (GEORGE) *Barrister at Law*. *See* CICERO (M. T.) [*De Oratore*.—*English*.] Cicero, on the Complete Orator . . . Translated with notes and illustrations by G. Barnes. 1762. 8°. **11805**. e. **34**

—— The Rights of the Imperial Crown of Ireland asserted and maintained, against Edward Cooke, Esq. reputed author of a pamphlet, entitled, "Arguments for and against an Union," &c. In a letter to that gentleman . . . The second edition, with additions. pp. 99. *W. Gilbert: Dublin*, 1799. 8°. **8145**. d. **3**

—— Letters on Ireland: to refute Mr. G. Barnes's statistical account, &c. By a Citizen of Waterford. pp. vii. 136. *William Smith: Waterford*, 1813. 8°. **8145**. dd. **3**

BARNES (*Sir* GEORGE)

—— *See* STAMP (Josiah C.) *Baron Stamp*. English Institutions. General editor: Lord Stamp (Sir George Barnes) 1938, *etc.* 8°. W.P. **3915**

BARNES (GEORGE CARNAC) Report on the Settlement in the District of Kangra in the Trans-Sutlej States. pp. iv. 233. "*The Chronicle*" *Press: Lahore*, 1855. 8° **10058**. k. **18**

BARNES (GEORGE G.) Enter China! A study in race contacts. pp. 168. *Edinburgh House Press: London*, 1928. 8°. **010055**. a. **6**

—— In the Furnace. Stories of Chinese Christians in revolution years. pp. 80. *Edinburgh House Press London*, 1928. 8°. [" *Youth* " *Series*. no. 2.] **4768.aaa.27/2**

—— Yarns from the Far East. pp. 72. *Edinburgh House Press: London*, 1933. 8°. **4765**. gg. **6**

BARNES (*Right Hon.* GEORGE NICOLL) From Workshop to War Cabinet, *etc.* [An autobiography. With portrait.] pp. xiii. 315. *Herbert Jenkins: London* 1924 [1923]. 8°. **010855**. aa. **7**

—— Henry George. pp. 20. *Independent Labour Party London*, [1909.] 12°. **10881**. aa. **4**

—— History of the International Labour Office, *etc.* [With portraits.] pp. 106. *Williams & Norgate: London* 1926. 8°. **08282**. a. **104**

—— Industrial Conflict. The way out, *etc.* pp. xi. 100 *Sir I. Pitman & Sons: London*, 1924. 8°. **08282**. ee. **36**

—— The Industrial Section of the League of Nations pp. 16. *Oxford University Press: London*, 1930. 8° [*Barnett House Papers*. no. 5.] **8295.f.23/5**

—— Karl Marx. pp. 21. *Independent Labour Party London*, [1909.] 12°. **10703**. aa. **43**

—— The Perils to the Workers from Materialism. *See* INTERNATIONAL CONFERENCE ON LABOUR AND RELIGION [London, 1919.] The Religion in the Labour Movement *etc.* [1919.] 8°. **08275**. aa. **70**

BARNES (*Right Hon.* GEORGE NICOLL)

—— The Problem of the Unemployed. [With a portrait.] pp. 16. *Independent Labour Party: London*, [1908.] 8°. **8287. df. 105.**

—— Robert Burns. pp. 12. *Independent Labour Party: London*, [1909.] 8°. **8282. tt. 8. (1.)**

—— The Unemployed Problem. pp. 12. *Independent Labour Party: London*, [1909.] 8°. **8282. tt. 8. (4.)**

BARNES (*Right Hon.* GEORGE NICOLL) and **HENDERSON** (*Right Hon.* ARTHUR)

—— Unemployment in Germany. A report of an inquiry into the methods adopted in Germany for dealing with unemployment, presented to the Labour Party. pp. 15. *Independent Labour Party: London*, [1908.] 8°. **8282. tt. 8. (3.)**

BARNES (GEORGE O.) *See* GUINNESS (Henry G.) *the Elder*. The Heresy taught by the Rev. G. O. Barnes . . . exposed, *etc.* [1884.] 8°. **4372. f. 12. (11.)**

—— Eureka! The Church of my fathers and how and where I found it; or rather, "was found of it." pp. 24. *S. Standring: London*, 1885. 8°. **4109. aa. 33. (15.)**

—— Second edition. pp. 16. *S. Standring: London*, [1885.] 8°. **4109. e. 6. (3.)**

—— 'The Gospel of the Grace'; or, the three-one parable, and the two salvations. pp. 86. *Elliot Stock: London*, 1892. 8°. **4257. f. 27.**

BARNES (GEORGE REGINALD) *See* MONTAGU (John) *Earl of Sandwich*. The Private Papers of John, Earl of Sandwich . . . 1771–1782. Edited by G. R. Barnes and J. H. Owen. 1932, *etc.* 8°. [*Publications of the Navy Records Society.* vol. 69, *etc.*] Ac. **8109.**

—— A List of Books printed in Cambridge at the University Press, 1521–1800. [Compiled by Francis J. H. Jenkinson, Sydney Castle Roberts, and G. R. Barnes, and edited by G. R. Barnes.] pp. 57. 1935. 8°. *See* CAMBRIDGE.—*University of Cambridge.—University Press.* **11912. aa. 77.**

BARNES (*Sir* GEORGE STAPYLTON) *K.C.B.* *See* BUXTON (S. C.) *Viscount Buxton* and BARNES (*Sir* G. S.) A Handbook to the Death Duties. 1890. 8°. **8228. aaa. 17.**

BARNES (GEORGE WILLIAM) Centenary History and Reminiscences of the Baptist Church, High Street, Ilford. pp. 64. *Manby & Co.: Ilford*, 1901. 8°. **4715. aaa. 53.**

BARNES (GERALD) Swimming and Diving. pp. x. 140. *C. Scribner's Sons: New York, London*, 1923 [1922]. 8°. **07911. de. 99.**

BARNES (GERARD C.)

—— Australia's Curse. Borrowed money and private bankers. (Second impression.) pp. 20. *Torch Newspaper: Bankstown*, [1932.] 8°. **8230. eee. 37.**

—— Banking Buccaneering. (The greatest crime in history.) pp. 20. *Sydney*, 1931. 8°. **8230. eee. 38.**

—— Mysteries of Ancient Egypt and modern freemasonry. Transaction no. 2 of Lodge Isis, Sydney, *etc.* pp. 22. *Epworth Press: Sydney*, [1932.] 8°. **20020. e. 15.**

BARNES (GILBERT HOBBS) *See* ARNESON (B. A.) A Gateway to the Social Sciences. By B. A. Arneson . . . G. H. Barnes, *etc.* [1926.] 8°. **08286. aa. 16.**

BARNES (GILBERT HOBBS)

—— The Antislavery Impulse, 1830–1844. pp. ix. 298. [1933.] 8°. *See* UNITED STATES OF AMERICA.—*American Historical Association.* Ac. **8504/17.**

BARNES (GILBERT HOBBS) and **DUMOND** (DWIGHT LOWELL)

—— Letters of Theodore Dwight Weld, Angelina Grimké Weld, and Sarah Grimké, 1822–1844. Edited by G. H. Barnes and D. L. Dumond. 2 vol. pp. xxxvii. x. 1023. [1934.] 8°. *See* UNITED STATES OF AMERICA.—*American Historical Association.* **010920. k. 35.**

BARNES (GRACE) and **SUTCLIFFE** (MARY JEAN)

—— On Stage, everyone. [On theatrical production. With plates.] pp. xii. 400. *Macmillan Co.: New York*, [1954.] 8°. **11799. d. 7.**

BARNES (H.) *English Master at the Central School, Morley.* A Book of Essays. Selected by H. Barnes. pp. 191. *London*, 1928. 8°. [*Harrap's Readers of To-day.*] W.P. **4918/17.**

—— Essays Old and New. Edited by H. Barnes. pp. 234. *London*, 1931. 8°. [*Harrap's Junior Modern English Series.*] W.P. **9661/10.**

BARNES (H. N.)

—— The People's Charter. "That men may live out their lives in freedom from fear and want," *etc.* pp. 163. *G. Allen & Unwin: London*, 1942. 8°. **8218. a. 11.**

BARNES (HAROLD)

—— Chemical Aspects of Oceanography. pp. 29. *London*, 1955. 8°. [*Royal Institute of Chemistry. Lectures, Monographs and Reports.* 1955. no. 4.] Ac. **3921/32.**

—— A Statistical Study of the Variability of Catches obtained with two models of the Hardy Plankton Indicator. *University College: Hull*, 1951. 4°. [*Hull Bulletins of Marine Ecology.* vol. 2. no. 16.] Ac. **2677. b.**

BARNES (HAROLD DOUGLAS)

—— *See* RONDELLE (M.) A Fifteenth Century Armourer's Letter, *etc.* [With a translation and a note by H. D. Barnes.] [1930?] 4°. **10921. l. 34.**

BARNES (HARRY) The Architect in Practice, *etc.* pp. 152. *Ernest Benn: London*, 1924. 8°. **07815. ee. 14.**

—— Housing. The facts and the future. pp. 450. *Ernest Benn: London*, 1923. 8°. **08282. d. 95.**

—— National Housing. A proposal for a national municipal house building service. With an examination of the new Housing Bill introduced . . . on June 3, 1924, *etc.* pp. 46. *Ernest Benn: London*, [1924.] 8°. **08248. c. 37.**

—— Rating of Coal Mines. By H. Barnes . . . Sir R. A. S. Redmayne . . . and Wilfrid Fordham. pp. xvii. 189. 17. *Butterworth & Co.; Shaw & Sons: London*, 1933. 8°. **6426. v. 15.**

—— The Slum: its story and solution. pp. xv. 398. *P. S. King & Son: London*, 1931. 8°. **8275. tt. 15.**

—— Valuation & Revaluation for Poor Rate and Income Tax (Post War). pp. ix. 223. *Poor-Law Publications: London*, 1923. 8°. **6426. r. 17.**

BARNES (HARRY ALDRICH) The Tonsils, facial, lingual and pharyngeal: with some account of the posterior and lateral pharyngeal nodules . . . Illustrated. pp. 168. *Henry Kimpton: London; A. Stenhouse: Glasgow; printed in America*, 1914. 8°. **07610. k. 26.**

—— Second edition. pp. 217. *Henry Kimpton: London; St Louis* printed, 1923. 8°. **07616. g. 4.**

BARNES (Harry Elmer) *See* Calverton (Victor F.) Sex Expression in Literature . . . With an introduction by H. E. Barnes. 1926. 8°. **20016. bb. 19.**

—— *See* Davis (Jerome D.) and Barnes (H. E.) An Introduction to Sociology, *etc.* [1927, *etc.*] 8°. **W.P. 8153/1.**

—— *See* Dunning (William A.) A History of Political Theories . . . Essays . . . Edited by . . . H. E. Barnes. 1924. 8°. **08007. f. 40.**

—— *See* Garnerin de Montgelas (M. M. C. D.) *Count.* British Foreign Policy under Sir Edward Grey . . . Edited . . . by H. E. Barnes. 1928. 8°. **09505. de. 12.**

—— *See* Knight (Melvin M.) Economic History of Europe, *etc.* (pt. 2. In modern times. By M. M. Knight . . . H. E. Barnes.) [1926, *etc.*] 8°. **08244. eee. 30.**

—— —— 1930. 8°. **08246. eee. 49.**

—— *See* Ploetz (C.) Ploetz' Manual of Universal History . . . Revised under the editorship of H. E. Barnes, *etc.* [1925.] 8°. **09009. c. 27.**

—— *See* Robinson (James H.) The Human Comedy . . . With an introduction by H. E. Barnes. 1937. 8°. **8287. c. 35.**

—— *See* Wegerer (A. von) A Refutation of the Versailles War Guilt Thesis . . . Introduction by H. E. Barnes. 1930. 8°. **08026. cc. 38.**

—— [Pamphlets on historical subjects.] 7 pt. [1917–20.] 8°. **09007. dd. 12.**

—— Battling the Crime Wave. Applying sense and science to the repression of crime. pp. vi. 245. *Stratford Co.: Boston,* [1931.] 8°. **06055. h. 26.**

—— Borzoi Historical Series. Edited by H. E. Barnes. 5 vol. *A. A. Knopf: New York,* 1926–30. 8°. **9012.b.7.**

—— The Evolution of Penology in Pennsylvania. A study in American social history . . . Illustrated. pp. 414. *Bobbs-Merrill Co.: Indianapolis,* [1927.] 8°. **6055. g. 12.**

—— The Genesis of the World War. An introduction to the problem of war guilt . . . New and revised edition. pp. xxvii. 754. *A. A. Knopf: New York & London,* 1929. 8°. **09083. dd. 49.**

—— The History and Prospects of the Social Sciences . . . [Articles] edited, with an introduction, by H. E. Barnes. pp. xxi. 534. *A. A. Knopf: New York,* 1925. 8°. **08282. dd. 80.**

—— History and Social Intelligence. pp. xviii. 597. *A. A. Knopf: New York,* 1926. 8°. **09007. b. 35.**

—— A History of Historical Writing. pp. x. 434. *University of Oklahoma Press: Norman,* 1937. 8°. **09004. de. 5.**

—— A History of the Penal, Reformatory and Correctional Institutions of the State of New Jersey, analytical and documentary. pp. 654. *MacCrellish & Quigley Co.: Trenton, N.J.,* 1918. 8°. **6055. ee. 22.**

—— The History of Western Civilization. By H. E. Barnes . . . with the collaboration of Henry David. [With plates and maps.] 2 vol. *Harcourt, Brace and Co.: New York,* [1935.] 8°. **09007. ccc. 27.**

—— An Economic History of the Western World. [Based on the economic parts of "The History of Western Civilization" by H. E. Barnes with the collaboration of Henry David. With plates.] pp. xvi. 790. *Harcourt, Brace & Co.: New York,* [1937.] 8°. **08230. bb. 23.**

BARNES (Harry Elmer)

—— Immediate Causes of the World War. *See* Ashley (*Sir* Percy W. L.) *K.B.E.* Europe from Waterloo to Sarajevo, *etc.* 1926. 8°. **9075. e. 1.**

—— An Intellectual and Cultural History of the Western World. [With plates.] pp. xx. 1250. *Random House: New York,* [1937.] 8°. **9010. cc. 14.**

—— An Introduction to the History of Sociology. (Edited by H. E. Barnes.) pp. xvi. 960. *University of Chicago Press: Chicago,* 1948. 8°. **2020.b.**

—— Living in the Twentieth Century. A consideration of how we got this way. pp. 392. *Bobbs-Merrill Co.: Indianapolis,* [1928.] 8°. **08248. h. 73.**

—— Money Changers vs. the New Deal. A candid analysis of the inflation controversy. pp. 150. *Ray Long & R. R. Smith: New York,* 1934. 8°. **8233. a. 7.**

—— The New History and the Social Studies. [With portraits.] pp. xvii. 605. *Century Co.: New York,* 1925. 8°. **09008. cc. 48.**

—— Prohibition versus Civilization. Analyzing the dry psychosis. pp. 128. *Viking Press: New York,* 1932. 8° **8436. d. 8**

—— The Repression of Crime. Studies in historical penology. pp. 382. *G. Allen & Unwin: London; printed in U.S.A.,* [1926.] 8°. **6055. s. 2**

—— The Social History of the Western World. An outline syllabus. pp. xii. 126. *D. Appleton & Co.: New York, London,* 1921. 8°. **08282. b. 47**

—— Social Institutions in an Era of World Upheaval. pp. xviii. 927. *Prentice-Hall: New York,* 1942. 8°. **08286. k. 5**

—— Society in Transition. Problems of a changing age. [With a bibliography.] pp. xviii. 999. xvii. *Prentice-Hall: New York,* 1940. 8°. **8289. dd.**

—— Sociology and Political Theory, *etc.* pp. xiii. 260. *A. A. Knopf: New York,* 1924. 8°. **08007. de. 21**

—— Sociology before Comte: a summary of doctrines and an introduction to the literature . . . Reprinted . . . from the American Journal of Sociology, *etc.* [*Chicago,*] 1917. 8°. **08285. c. 19**

—— The Story of Punishment, *etc.* pp. vii. 292. *Stratford Co.: Boston,* [1930.] 8°. **06055. f. 40**

—— The Twilight of Christianity. pp. xi. 470. *Vanguard Press: New York,* [1929.] 8°. **04018. g. 42**

—— [A reissue.] *R. R. Smith: New York,* 1931. 8°. **04018. g. 43**

—— World Politics in Modern Civilization. The contributions of nationalism, capitalism, imperialism and militarism to human culture and international anarchy. [With maps.] pp. xxi. 608. xliii. *A. A. Knopf: New York,* 1930. 8°. [*Borzoi Historical Series.*] **9012.b.7/4**

BARNES (Harry Elmer) and **BECKER** (Howard)

—— Social Thought from Lore to Science. By H. E. Barnes . . . and H. Becker . . . with the assistance of Émile Benoit-Smullyan and others. 2 vol. pp. xxiv. lxxxiv. viii. lxxvii. 1178. *D. C. Heath & Co.: Boston,* [1938.] 8°. **08286. e.**

BARNES (Harry Elmer) and **TEETERS** (Negley King)

—— New Horizons in Criminology. The American crime problem, *etc.* (Third printing.) pp. xxvi. 1069. *Prentice-Hall: New York,* 1944. 8°. **6058. r. 1**

BARNES (Harry Elmer) and **TEETERS** (Negley King)

—— New Horizons in Criminology . . . Second edition. (Fourth printing.) pp. xvi. 887. *Prentice-Hall: New York*, 1954. 8°. 6059. d. 42.
Part of the "Prentice-Hall Sociology Series."

BARNES (Helen Elcessor) A study of the Variations between the Original and the Standard Editions of Balzac's Les Chouans. pp. viii. 71. *University of Chicago Press: Chicago*, 1923. 8°. **011850.** aaa. **24.**

BARNES (Helen Virginia)

—— *See* Watrous (Roberta C.) and Barnes (H. V.) Bibliography on Cork Oak, *etc.* 1946. 8°. [*U.S. Department of Agriculture. Bibliographical Bulletin.* no. 7.]
A.S.859/8.

—— List of Bulletins of the Agricultural Experiment Stations for the calendar years 1941 and 1942. Compiled by H. V. Barnes. pp. 70. *Washington*, 1944. 8°. [*U.S. Department of Agriculture. Bibliographical Bulletin.* no. 4.]
A.S.859/8.

BARNES (Helen Virginia) and **ALLEN** (Jessie May)
—— A Bibliography of Plant Pathology in the Tropics and in Latin America. pp. vi. 78. *Washington*, 1951. 8°. [*U.S. Department of Agriculture. Bibliographical Bulletin.* no. 14.] A.S. **859/8.**

BARNES (Henry) *M.D., F.R.S.E.* Aikton Church . . . Reprinted from the Cumberland and Westmorland Antiquarian and Archæological Society's Transactions, *etc. Kendal*, 1913. 8°. **07816.** i. **39.** **(3.)**

—— Leprosy and Local Leper Hospitals . . . Reprinted from the Transactions of the Cumberland and Westmorland Antiquarian and Archæological Society. *Kendal*, 1889. 8°. **07305.** e. **24.** **(11.)**

—— On Quarter Sessions Orders relating to the Plague in the County of Durham in 1665 . . . Overprints from "Archaeologia Aeliana," *etc.* [*Newcastle-upon-Tyne*, 1890.] 8°. **07305.** e. **24.** **(13.)**

—— On Roman Medicine and Roman Medical Inscriptions found in Britain. (Reprinted from the Proceedings of the Royal Society of Medicine.) pp. 17. *J. Bale & Co.: London*, 1914. 8°. **7321.** i. **8.** **(7.)**

—— On Touching for the King's Evil . . . Reprinted from the Transactions of the Cumberland and Westmoreland Antiquarian and Archæological Society. *Kendal*, 1895. 8°. **07305.** m. **2.** **(5.)**

—— The President's Address on the Medical History of Carlisle . . . Reprinted from the British Medical Journal, *etc.* pp. 18. *British Medical Association: London*, 1896. 8°. **07306.** g. **9.** **(1.)**

—— Visitations of the Plague in Cumberland & Westmorland . . . Reprinted from the Transactions of the Cumberland and Westmorland Antiquarian and Archæological Society. *Kendall*, 1890. 8°. **07305.** e. **24.** **(14.)**

BARNES (Henry) *One of the Secondaries.* Notes of Cases in points of Practice: taken in the Court of Common Pleas . . . from Michaelmas Term . . . 1732 to Hillary Term . . . 1739. By a Gentleman of the Middle Temple [i.e. H. Barnes]. pp. 348. 1741. 8°. *See* England.—*Court of Common Pleas.—Reports.* **959.** b. **2.**

—— Notes of Cases in points of Practice taken in the Court of Common Pleas . . . from Michaelmas Term 1732 to Hilary Term 1756 inclusive . . . The second edition revised . . . To which is added a continuation of cases to the end of King George II . . . With a table . . . and an index. pp. 500. 1772. 4°. *See* England.—*Court of Common Pleas.—Reports.* **1243.** i. **5.**

BARNES (Henry) *One of the Secondaries.*

—— The third edition. pp. xxxii. 500. 1790. 8°. *See* England.—*Court of Common Pleas.—Reports.* **21.** a. **3.**

BARNES (Henry Broughton) A Sketch of Toppesfield Parish, Essex Co., England. By Rev. H. B. Barnes . . . and the History and Antiquities of Toppesfield Parish . . . By W. Morant . . . Annotated and edited by G. F. Don. pp. 30. 1905. *See* Toppesfield. The Register of Baptisms, *etc.* 1905. 8°. **9902.** c. **16.**

BARNES (Henry Frederick) The Faithful Steward Delineated. A sermon preached . . . at the visitation of the Venerable the Archdeacon of the East-Riding. pp. 23. *John Furby: Bridlington; Seeleys: London*, 1852. 8°. **4445.** b. **5.**

—— Spiritual Husbandry. A sermon preached . . . at the visitation of the . . . Archbishop of York. pp. 17. *Seeleys: London; John Furby: Bridlington*, 1853. 8°. **4445.** c. **9.**

BARNES (Henry Gorell) *Baron Gorell*, and **DE MONTMORENCY** (James Edward Geoffrey) The Divorce Commission. The majority and minority reports summarised, with appendices on the history of divorce; foreign and colonial divorce laws; proposed divorce circuits in England and Wales; names of women after divorce . . . With prefaces by the Hon. Lord Guthrie and Sir Lewis T. Dibdin. pp. xvi. 95. *P. S. King & Son: London*, 1912. 8°. **5175.** e. **43.**

BARNES (Herbert)

—— *See* Bible.—*Gospels.* [*Nyanja.—Eastern Nyanja dialect.*] Maevangel ya ambuye watu Yesu Kristo pamoji ndi Machitidwe ya Aapostolo woyera. [Revised by H. Barnes.] 1907. 8°. **03068.** e. **125.**

—— *See* Bible.—*Matthew.* [*Nyanja.—Eastern Nyanja dialect.*] Evangel ya W. Mattayo. [Revised by H. Barnes.] 1907. 8°. **03068.** e. **84.**

—— *See* Bible.—*Mark.* [*Nyanja.—Eastern Nyanja dialect.*] Evangel ya W. Marko. [Revised by H. Barnes.] 1907. 8°. **03068.** e. **83.**

—— *See* Woodward (M. E.) English-Nyanja Vocabulary . . . Enlarged and revised by the Rev. H. Barnes. 1913. 8°. **12910.** ccc. **27.**

—— *See* Woodward (M. E.) Nyanja-English Vocabulary. Enlarged and revised by the Rev. H. Barnes. 1902. 8°. **12910.** aaa. **81.**

—— —— 1929. 8°. **12911.** e. **46.**

BARNES (Herbert Charles) Mean Speed Tables for daily use. *J. Seager & Sons: London*, [1907.] 8°. **8548.** b. **70.**

BARNES (Homer Francis) Charles Fenno Hoffman. [With a selection of his correspondence, a number of uncollected poems, and a bibliography.] pp. viii. 361. *New York*, 1930. 8°. [*Columbia University Studies in English and Comparative Literature.*] R. Ac. **2688/12.** **(17.)**

BARNES (Horace Francis)

—— Gall Midges of Economic Importance, *etc. C. Lockwood & Son: London*, 1946– . 8°. [*Agricultural and Horticultural Handbooks.*] W.P. **4907/23.**

BARNES (Howard)

—— Your Boat, its Selection and Care . . . Illustrated by the author. pp. xiv. 111. *Charles Scribner's Sons: New York; London*, 1948. 8°. **8804.** h. **28.**

BARNES (Howard MacKent)

—— Mother's Millions. A comedy-drama in three acts. [With plates.] pp. 123. *New York*, [1934.] 8°. [*French's Standard Library Edition.*] **011781.** g. **1/369.**

BARNES (HOWARD TURNER) Ice Formation, with special reference to Anchor-Ice and Frazil. pp. x. 260. *J. Wiley & Sons: New York*, 1906. 8°. **08755. i. 23.**

—— Report on Ice Formation in the St. Lawrence River and a report on the influence of icebergs on the temperature of the sea as shown by the use of the micro-thermometer in a trip to Hudson Strait and Bay in July, 1910. [With charts.] pp. 60. 1911. 8°. [CANADA. *Department of Fisheries.*] C.S. E. **30/44.**

—— Report on the Influence of Icebergs and Land on the Temperature of the Sea, as shown by the use of the micro-thermometer, on a trip of the C.G.S. Montcalm in the Gulf of St. Lawrence and Coast of Labrador, *etc.* [With diagrams.] pp. 37. 1913. 8°. *See* CANADA.—*Department of Fisheries.* C.S. E. **30/45.**

BARNES (HOWARD TURNER) and **WHEELER** (N. E.)

—— Loose Leaf Laboratory Notes. Heat, Light and Sound. *Renouf Publishing Co.: Montreal*, [1914.] 4°. **8710. h. 14.**

BARNES (HUBERT DIXIE)

—— *See* QUINTON (Margaret H.) and BARNES (H. D.) The Serum Proteins of Healthy Bantu Males. [1942.] 8°. **7471. c. 10.**

—— [Articles reprinted from various periodicals.] [1935– .] 8°, *etc.* W.P. **2161.**

BARNES (HUBERT DIXIE) and **GORDON** (MARY S.)

—— Fractional Gastric Analysis in South African Bantu. [An offprint from the "South African Journal of Medical Science."] [*Johannesburg*, 1937.] 8°. **07630. f. 36.**

BARNES (HUGH)

—— *See* FREDRICSON (N.) Endless Voyage . . . Edited by H. Barnes. 1939. 8°. **010760.i.63.**

—— *See* GURCHAN SINGH. Singa, the Lion of Malaya . . . Edited by H. Barnes. 1948. 8°. **10608. dd. 29.**

—— *See* LENÔTRE (G.) *pseud.* The Tuileries . . . Translated . . . by H. Barnes. 1934. 8°. **010170. i. 43.**

—— *See* PETERS (Ernest W.) Shanghai Policeman . . . Edited by H. Barnes. 1937. 8°. **20031. b. 35.**

BARNES (INA G.) Rural School Management. pp. xv. 303. *Macmillan Co.: New York*, 1923. 8°. [*Rural Education Series.*] **08311.h.99/2.**

BARNES (IORWERTH) *See* HERVEY (James) Myfyrdodau a sylwiadau . . . A gyfieithwyd . . . gan Jorwerth Barnes. 1785. 12°. **872. f. 19. (1.)**

BARNES (IRENE H.) *See* BLACK (Margaret) and BARNES (I. H.) By Love serve one another, *etc.* 1901. 8°. **4907. de. 46.**

—— *See* JANVRIN (Alice J.) He Expecteth, and other poems . . . With introduction by I. H. Barnes. 1908. 8°. **11650. bbb. 40.**

—— Behind the Great Wall . . . With . . . illustrations. pp. viii. 179. *Marshall Bros.: London*, [1896.] 8°. **010057. e. 45.**

—— Behind the Pardah. The story of C.E.Z.M.S. work in India, *etc.* pp. xii. 264. *Marshall Bros.: London*, 1897. 8°. **4767. d. 30.**

—— Between Life and Death. The story of the C.E.Z.M.S. Medical Missions in India, China, and Ceylon . . . With illustrations, *etc.* pp. 302. *Marshall Bros.: London*, 1901. 8°. **4766. ee. 28.**

BARNES (IRENE H.)

—— The Church Missionary House, *etc.* pp. 55. *C.M.S.: London*, 1915. 8°. **4763. aaa. 4**

—— Doctor Alec, *etc.* pp. 200. *C.M.S.: London* 1907 [1906]. 8°. **04412. ee. 25**

—— Doctor Alec's Son . . . Illustrated by J. B. Greene pp. 192. *C.M.S.: London*, 1912 [1911]. 8°. **04413. de. 65**

—— Honeybun, others, and us. A play book for the pla hour, *etc.* pp. 87. *C.M.S.: London*, 1917 [1916]. 8°. **12800. dd.**

—— In Salisbury Square. [An account of the Churc Missionary House.] . . . With preface by the Right Ho Sir John H. Kennaway . . . Illustrated, *etc.* pp. viii. 23 *C.M.S.: London*, 1906 [1905]. 8°. **4764. g.**

—— Other People's Shoes. [Tales.] pp. 48. *C.M.S London*, [1914.] 8°. **04419. g. 5. (**

—— A Parable in Porcelain and other papers. pp. 80. *Marshall Bros.: London*, 1899. 8°. **4377. aa.**

—— A Peace Scout . . . Illustrated by J. B. Greene. pp. 1 *C.M.S.: London*, 1911 [1910]. 8°. **04413. de.**

—— Pip & Co . . . With preface by the Right Rev. t Lord Bishop of Durham, *etc.* pp. 206. *C.M. London*, 1908 [1907]. 8°. **04420. ff.**

—— Prisca . . . With introduction by the Rev. Ca R. B. Girdlestone. *Marshall Bros.: London*, [1908.] **012627. aa.**

—— Puck, M. P. . . . With preface by the Rt. Hon. John H. Kennaway, *etc.* pp. 206. *C.M.S.: Lond* 1910 [1909]. 8°. **04413. ee.**

BARNES (IRSTON ROBERT)

—— The Economics of Public Utility Regulation. pp. xxiv. 952. *F. S. Crofts & Co.: New York*, 1942. **8218. bb.**

—— Public Utility Control Massachusetts. A study in the commission regulatio security issues and rates. pp. x. 239. *New Ha* 1930. 8°. [*Yale Publications in Economics, Social Sci and Government.* vol. 2.] **Ac. 2692. ma**

BARNES (IRWIN JAMES)

—— Truth is Immortal. The story of Baptists in Eur pp. 127. *Carey Kingsgate Press: London*, 1955. 8°. **4716. aa.**

BARNES (ISMAY) Manual on Swimming Instruction, pp. 11. *Titus Wilson: Kendal*, 1914. 4°. **7905. f.**

BARNES (J. B. MORTON) The Last Flame of Hell. pp *John Heywood: Manchester & London*, [1901.] 8°. **011651. k.**

BARNES (J. EDMESTONE) The Economic Value of Native Races of Africa in relation to the developm of the resources of that continent. pp. 19. *Watts & London*, 1908. 8°. **8157. bbb.**

—— The Economy of Life. Some suggestions for w betterment. pp. xi. 131. *Universal Publishing Chorley*, [1921.] 8°. **08285. a.**

—— The Signs of the Times, touching the final suprem of nations. pp. 48. *H. F. Brion: London*, 1903. 8° **03128. g. 50.**

BARNES (J. H.) *of Manchester.* Equivalent Pr English-French. Per lb.=per 100 kilos. (Per cwt.= 100 kilos.) Card no. 1, 2. *Bednal Bros.: Manche* [1892.] 16°. **8533. a.**

BARNES (J. H.) *Writer of Songs. See* BODEN (Harry) W. H. Noel's Egg-centric Parody on the favourite Hunting Song " Gone Away " [by J. H. Barnes], *etc.* [1894.] 4°. **1875.** d. **9. (18.)**

BARNES (J. M.) *of St. John, N.B.* Maritime Provinces Road Book. pp. 82. *E. J. Armstrong : St. John, N.B.*, [1898.] *obl.* 8°. **10470.** de. **9.**

BARNES (J. S.) *Captain.* Il Futuro stato d'Albania. Con una cartina geografica. pp. 24. *Novara*, 1919. 8°. **08026.** aaa. **61.**

BARNES (JAMES) *Author of " For King or Country."*

—— *See* DEARBORN (Henry A. S.) The Life of William Bainbridge, Esq. of the United States Navy . . . Edited by J. Barnes. 1931. 8°. **10880.** tt. **15.**

—— *See* KEARTON (Cherry) and BARNES (J.) Through Central Africa from East to West, *etc.* 1915. 8°. **10094.** p. **13.**

—— The Blockaders, and other stories. pp. 244. *Harper & Bros.: New York & London*, [1925.] 8°. **12811.** bb. **35.**

—— The Clutch of Circumstance. pp. viii. 386. *D. Appleton & Co. : New York*, 1908. 8°. **012705.** aa. **32.**

—— David G. Farragut. pp. xviii. 132. *Kegan Paul & Co.: London; Boston* printed, [1899.] 16°. [*Beacon Biographies of Eminent Americans.*] **10883.** a. **37/1.**

—— Drake and his Yeomen, *etc.* [A tale.] pp. xiii. 415. *Macmillan Co. : New York*, 1899. 8°. **012641.** a. **27.**

—— From Then till Now. Anecdotal portraits and transcript pages from memory's tablets. [With plates, including portraits.] pp. xv. 535. *D. Appleton-Century Co.: New York, London*, 1934. 8°. **010885.** eee. **3.**

—— The Giant of Three Wars. A life of General Winfield Scott . . . Illustrated, *etc.* pp. xi. 241. *D. Appleton & Co. : New York*, 1903 8°. **010883.** e. **3.**

—— The Great War Trek. With the British Army on the veldt. pp. xii. 372. *D. Appleton & Co. : New York*, 1901. 8°. **09061.** aaa. **3.**

—— [Another copy.] **9060.** b. **2**

—— The Hero of Stony Point : Anthony Wayne, *etc.* pp. 209. *D. Appleton & Co. : New York, London*, 1916. 8°. **12800.** aaa. **18.**

—— Naval Actions of the War of 1812 . . . With 21 illustrations in color by C. T. Chapman. pp. xiv. 263. *Osgood, McIlvaine & Co. : London; [New York* printed,] 1897. 8°. **9615.** df. **11.**

—— Outside the Law. pp. 281. *D. Appleton & Co.: New York*, 1906 [1905]. 8°. **012706.** a. **2.**

—— A Princetonian. A story of undergraduate life at the College of New Jersey, *etc.* pp. viii. 431. *G. P. Putnam's Sons : New York*, 1896. 8°. **012707.** m. **1.**

—— Rifle and Caravan ; or, Two boys in East Africa . . . Illustrated. pp. 325. *D. Appleton & Co. : New York & London*, 1912. 8°. **012704.** d. **10.**

—— Ships and Sailors : being a collection of songs of the sea as sung by the men who sail it. With numerous illustrations in colour and black-and-white by Rufus F. Zogbaum. Edited and compiled by J. Barnes. pp. 124. *F. A. Stokes Co. : New York*, 1898. *obl.* fol. **1874.** b. **42.**

—— The Son of Light Horse Harry. pp. 242. *Harper & Bros.: London & New York*, 1904. 8°. **012707.** cc. **19.**

—— [A reissue.] *New York & London*, [1925.] 8°. **12810.** bbb. **20.**

BARNES (JAMES) *Author of " For King or Country."*

—— The Unpardonable War. pp. vi. 356. *Macmillan Co.: New York*, 1904. 8°. **012707.** c. **12.**

—— With the Flag in the Channel ; or, the Adventures of Captain Gustavus Conyngham, *etc.* pp. vii. 158. *D. Appleton & Co. : New York*, 1902. 8°. **012703.** l. **24.**

BARNES (JAMES) *Dramatic Writer.* The Dramatic Works of James Barnes. (Section 2. The Agitator.—William the Conqueror, part II.—Gessican, part I.) 3 pt. *James Ainsworth : Manchester*, 1854, 55. 12°. **11779.** c. **4.** *No more published.*

—— The Absent Man. A comic sketch, *etc.* pp. 16. *Manchester & London*, [1879.] 8°. [*Abel Heywood & Son's Series of Original Dramas.* no. 5.] **011779.** h. **101.**

—— The Barber's Courtship. A comic sketch, *etc.* pp. 16. *Manchester & London*, [1879.] 8°. [*Abel Heywood & Son's Series of Original Dramas.* no. 1.] **011779.** h. **101.**

—— The Bashful Man : a humorous dialogue, *etc.* pp. 16. *Manchester*, [1881 ?] 8°. [*Abel Heywood & Son's Series of Original Dramas.* no. 21.] **011779.** h. **101.**

—— The Black Box and Cox. A nigger farce for three male characters. pp. 16. *Manchester*, [1894.] 8°. [*Abel Heywood & Son's Series of Original Dramas.* no. 152.] **11778.** p. **1.**

—— The Black Rivals, a musical entertainment, *etc.* pp. 40. *Manchester*, [1884.] 8°. [*Abel Heywood's Musical Dramas.* no. 4.] **011779.** ee. **1.**

—— Choosing a Schoolmaster, a humorous dialogue, *etc.* pp. 16. *Manchester*, [1880 ?] 8°. [*Abel Heywood & Son's Series of Original Dramas.* no. 14.] **011779.** h. **101.**

—— A Comical Mistake. A musical entertainment, *etc.* pp. 32. *Manchester*, [1884.] 8°. [*Abel Heywood's Musical Dramas.* no. 3.] **011779.** ee. **1.**

—— Cross Purposes. A farce, *etc.* pp. 16. *Manchester*, [1889.] 8°. [*Abel Heywood & Son's Series of Original Dramas.* no. 114.] **011779.** h. **101.**

—— A Doctor pro tem. A humorous drama, *etc.* *Manchester*, [1881 ?] 8°. [*Abel Heywood & Son's Series of Original Dramas.* no. 19.] **011779.** h. **101.**

—— Making a Paper ; or, the Troubles of an editor, a comic sketch, *etc.* pp. 16. *Manchester & London*, [1879.] 8°. [*Abel Heywood & Son's Series of Original Dramas.* no. 6.] **011779.** h. **101.**

—— Money or Brains : a dramatic reading, *etc.* pp. 16. *Manchester*, [1885 ?] 8°. [*Abel Heywood & Son's Series of Original Dramas.* no. 8.] **011779.** h. **101.**

—— A Race for a Razor, a dialogue, *etc.* pp. 16. *Manchester*, [1880 ?] 8°. [*Abel Heywood & Son's Series of Original Dramas.* no. 18.] **011779.** h. **101.**

—— The Rival Tutors, a humorous dialogue, *etc.* pp. 15. *Manchester*, [1880 ?] 8°. [*Abel Heywood & Son's Series of Original Dramas.* no. 16.] **011779.** h. **101.**

—— Sea-side Lodgings. A musical entertainment. pp. 32. *Manchester*, [1884.] 8°. [*Abel Heywood's Musical Dramas.* no. 2.] **011779.** ee. **1.**

—— Surmounting a Difficulty. A musical entertainment, *etc.* pp. 40. *Manchester*, [1885.] 8°. [*Abel Heywood's Musical Dramas.* no. 7.] **011779.** ee. **1.**

—— There's Nothing like Business : a humorous drama, *etc.* pp. 16. *Manchester*, [1881 ?] 8°. [*Abel Heywood & Son's Series of Original Dramas.* no. 20.] **011779.** h. **101.**

BARNES (James) *Dramatic Writer.*

—— The Two Thompsons. A comic sketch, *etc.* pp. 16. *Manchester & London,* [1879.] 8°. [*Abel Heywood & Son's Series of Original Dramas.* no. 3.] **011779.** h. **101.**

—— The Village Rivals: a dramatic sketch, *etc.* pp. 16. *Manchester,* [1885?] 8°. [*Abel Heywood & Son's Series of Original Dramas.* no. 10.] **011779.** h. **101.**

BARNES (James) *Gardener. See* Johnson (George W.) *F.R.H.S.*, and Barnes (J.) The Pine Apple; its culture, *etc.* 1847. 16°. [*The Gardener's Monthly Volume.*] **1251.** a. **34.**

BARNES (James) *of Halifax.* On the Analysis of Bright Spectrum Lines . . . Dissertation, *etc.* (Reprinted from The Astrophysical Journal.) *University of Chicago Press: [Chicago,]* 1904. 8°. **8715.** i. **31.**

BARNES (James) *of the Ancient Order of Foresters.* Monetary Tables compiled from the Rates of Mortality and Sickness of the Ancient Order of Foresters' Friendly Society. Experience of 1871–1875, *etc.* 1885. 8°. *See* Foresters, *Ancient Order of.* **8277.** h. **22.**

BARNES (James Anderson)

—— Wealth of the American People. A history of their economic life. pp. x. 910. *Prentice-Hall: New York,* 1949. 8°. **8218.** f. **43.**

BARNES (James M.) A Guide to Good Golf, *etc.* pp. xiii. 137. *John Lane: London,* 1925. 8°. **7904.** f. **17.**

—— Picture Analysis of Golf Strokes . . . Photographs by L. F. Deming. pp. 252. *J. B. Lippincott Co.: Philadelphia & London,* 1919. 4°. **7911.** i. **7.**

BARNES (James Thomas Strachey) Fascism. pp. 251. *Thornton Butterworth: London,* 1931. 8°. [*Home University Library.* vol. 150.] **12199.** p. **1/167.**

—— Fascism and the International Centre of Fascist Studies. ff. 22. [1929.] 4°. *See* Lausanne.—*International Centre of Fascist Studies.* **8032.** m. **20.**

—— Half a Life . . . [An autobiography.] With portraits, *etc.* pp. vii. 342. *Eyre & Spottiswoode: London,* 1933. 8°. **2409.** e. **6.**

—— Half A Life Left. (With an account of the Abyssinian Campaign.) [Autobiographical reminiscences. With portraits.] pp. 329. *Eyre & Spottiswoode: London,* 1937. 8°. **010821.** g. 5.

—— The Universal Aspects of Fascism. [With portraits.] pp. xxi. 247. *Williams & Norgate: London,* 1928. 8°. **8033.** f. **51.**

—— (Second edition.) pp. xxix. 247. *Williams & Norgate: London,* 1929. 8°. **8033.** h. **45.**

BARNES (Jasper Converse) Voluntary Isolation of Control in a Natural Muscle Group. pp. 50. *New York,* 1916. 8°. [*Psychological Monographs.* vol. 22. no. 1.] P.P. **1247.** eb.

BARNES (Jean H.)

—— *See* Abravanel (J.) The Philosophy of Love . . . Translated . . . by F. Friedeberg-Seeley (Dialogues i and ii) and J. H. Barnes (Dialogue iii), *etc.* 1937. 8°. **8415.** i. **36.**

BARNES (Jessie Foster) Histoires et Jeux. A book of simple French stories, songs and games. [With musical notes.] pp. ix. 188. *Ginn & Co.: Boston,* [1922]. 8°. **12951.** b. **23.**

BARNES (John) *Benedictine Monk.*

—— *See* Nédoncelle (M.) Trois aspects du problème anglo-catholique au xviie siècle, *etc.* [With special reference to J. Barnes.] 1951. 8°. **3943.k.9.**

—— Catholico-Romanus pacificus. pp. 171. *E Theatro Sheldoniano: Oxoniae,* 1680. 12°. **3935.** a. **14.**

—— [Another edition.] *See* Gratius (O.) Fasciculus rerum expetendarum, *etc.* tom. 2. 1690. fol. **7.** c. **11.**

—— Johannis Barnesii . . . Sententia, de Ecclesiæ Britannicæ privilegiis. Ex Cathol. Rom. pacif. sect. 3. *See* Usher (James) successively *Bishop of Meath* and *Archbishop of Armagh.* Jacobi Usserii . . . opuscula duo, *etc.* 1687. 8°. G. **19844.**

—— [Another edition.] *See* Usher (James) successively *Bishop of Meath* and *Archbishop of Armagh.* Jacobi Usserii . . . opuscula duo, *etc.* 1688. 8°. **701.** b. **15.** (**2.**)

—— [Another edition.] *See* Usher (James) successively *Bishop of Meath* and *Archbishop of Armagh.* Jacobi Usserii . . . opuscula duo, *etc.* 1701. 8°. **4570.** a. **37.**

—— Three Chapters concerning the Priviledges of the Britannick Church . . . selected out of a Latin manuscript, entituled, Catholico-Romanus pacificus. *See* Basire (I.) The Ancient Liberty of the Britannick Church, *etc.* 1661. 8°. **701.** b. **17.** (**2.**)

—— Dissertatio contra æquivocationes. pp. 542. *R. Baragne & I. Villery: Parisiis,* 1625. 8°. **1020.** d. **14.**

BARNES (John) *Bookseller. See* Du Moulin (Pierre) *the Elder.* The Waters of Siloe . . . Translated . . . by I. B. [i.e. J. Barnes?] 1612. 8°. **3900.** a. **50.**

—— *See* France.—Louis xiii., *King.* The French Kinges declaration and confirmation of the proclamation of Nantes . . . Faythfully translated . . . by I. B. [i.e. J. Barnes?] 1613. 12°. **4629.** a. **43.**

BARNES (John) *Emigrant. Begin.* From John Barnes, *etc.* [Letters by J. Barnes and others on the prospects of emigrants to Canada.] pp. 12. *J. Phillips: Petworth,* [1840?] 8°. C.T. **240.** (**4.**)

BARNES (John) *of Pembroke.* The Christian's Pocket Companion: consisting of select texts of the New Testament, with suitable observations in prose and verse for every day in the year. [With a preface by John Wesley.] pp. 372. *The Author: Carmarthen,* 1765. *obl.* 16°. **3205.** a. **25.**

BARNES (John) *of Smedmore. See* Jenner, afterwards Jenner Fust (*Right Hon. Sir* H.) In the Prerogative Court of Canterbury. Sentence pronounced by the Judge . . . in a cause of J. Barnes . . . against L. Mansel, *etc.* 1836. 8°. **6495.** f. **13.**

BARNES (John) *of the Office of Ordnance in the Tower of London.* The Tradesman's Assistant: containing useful and exact tables, shewing the amount or value of any number or quantity of goods, *etc.* pp. xxiii. 251. *The Author: London,* 1755. 12°. **8506.** bbb. **13.**

BARNES (John) *Town Major in the E.I. Company's Service.* A Tour through the Island of St. Helena; with notices of its geology, mineralogy, botany, &c. &c. collected during a residence of twelve years; with some particulars respecting the arrival and detention of Napoleon Buonaparte. pp. xx. 239. *J. M. Richardson: London,* 1817. 12°. **279.** b. **8.**

—— A Tour throughout the whole of France, *etc.* [With plates and a map.] pp. 112. *William Darton: London,* 1815. 12°. **575.** e. **26.**

BARNES (JOHN ARUNDEL)

—— The Fort Jameson Ngoni. [With plates.] *In:* COLSON (Elizabeth) *Director, Rhodes-Livingstone Institute,* and GLUCKMAN (H. M.) Seven Tribes of British Central Africa, *etc.* pp. 194–252. 1951. 8º. **010097**. m. **8**.

—— Marriage in a Changing Society. A study in structural change among the Fort Jameson Ngoni. pp. ix. 136. *Oxford University Press: Cape Town,* 1951. 8º. [*Rhodes-Livingstone Papers.* no. 20.] W.P. **9478/20**.

—— [Another copy.] Marriage in a Changing Society, *etc. Cape Town,* 1951. 8º. W.P. **9478/20a**.

—— The Material Culture of the Fort Jameson Ngoni. pp. 13. pl. IV. *Rhodes-Livingstone Museum: Livingstone,* 1948. 8º. [*Occasional Papers of the Rhodes-Livingstone Museum.* New ser. no. 1.] W.P. **2964/1**.

—— Politics in a Changing Society. A political history of the Fort Jameson Ngoni. [With a bibliography.] pp. x. 220. *Oxford University Press: Cape Town,* 1954. 8º. **08004**. df. **42**.

BARNES (JOHN GORELL) *Baron Gorell. See* DE MONTMORENCY (J. E. G.) John Gorell Barnes . . . With portrait. 1920. 8º. **010855**. c. **44**.

BARNES (JOHN H.) *Actor.* Forty Years on the Stage: others, principally, and myself. [With portraits.] pp. vi. 320. *Chapman & Hall: London,* 1914. 8º. **011795**. bb. **28**.

BARNES (JOHN HINDMARSH) Notes on Surgical Nursing, being a short course of lectures, *etc.* pp. 72. *J. & A. Churchill: London,* [1874.] 8º. **7461**. b. **3**.

BARNES (JOHN LANDES)

—— *See* GARDNER (MURRAY F.) and BARNES (J. L.) Transients in Linear Systems, *etc.* 1942, *etc.* 8º. W.P. **2174**.

BARNES (JOHN MORRISON)

—— Toxic Hazards of Certain Pesticides to Man. Together with a select bibliography on the toxicology of pesticides in man and mammals. pp. 129. *Geneva,* 1953. 8º. [*World Health Organization. Monograph Series.* no. 16.] U.N. o. **104/2**.

BARNES (JOHN RONALD) and **SHARPLES** (ALEXANDER) Book-keeping for Commercial Classes. Elementary. [With a key.] 2 vol. *Macmillan & Co.: London,* 1914, 16. 8º. **8503**. ee. **33**.

—— Second edition, enlarged. 2 pt. *Macmillan & Co.: London,* 1928, 30. 8º. **08225**. aaa. **48**.

—— Book-keeping for Commercial Classes. Second edition, enlarged. pp. xii. 338. *Macmillan & Co.: London,* 1936. 8º. **8233**. a. **38**.

BARNES (JOHN SANFORD) *See* FANNING (Nathaniel) Fanning's Narrative . . . Edited and annotated by J. S. Barnes. 1912. 8º. Ac. **8426**. c. **(2.)**

—— *See* NEW YORK, *City of.—Naval History Society.* Catalogue of the Books, Manuscripts and Prints . . . in the John S. Barnes Memorial Library of the Naval History Society. 1915. 8º. Ac. **8426**. d/3.

—— The Logs of the Serapis—Alliance—Ariel under the command of John Paul Jones, 1779–1780. With extracts from public documents, unpublished letters, and narratives, and illustrated with reproductions of scarce prints. Edited by J. S. Barnes. pp. xliv. 138. *New York,* 1911. 4º. [*Publications of the Naval History Society.* vol. 1.] Ac. **8426**. c. **(1.)**

BARNES (JOHN SANFORD)

—— Submarine Warfare, offensive and defensive. Including a discussion of the offensive torpedo system . . . With illustrations. pp. 233. *D. Van Nostrand: New York,* 1869. 8º. **8805**. ee. **15**.

BARNES (JORWERTH) *See* BARNES (Iorwerth)

BARNES (JOSEPH) *Artist.* The Patriot's Companion; or, a selection of patriotic pieces in prose & verse. To which is added a . . . summary of the extent of territory . . . of the principal states of Europe . . . With the routes and distances from London to all the principal towns in . . . Europe. pp. 98. *J. Turner: Coventry,* 1813. 12º. **12350**. c. **46**.

—— The Young Artist's Companion: containing plain and easy directions for the acquirement of the art of drawing . . . To which are added, general rules of perspective . . . The third edition . . . enlarged, *etc.* pp. 46. *J. Aston: Coventry,* [1815.] 12º. **1422**. a. **4**.

BARNES (JOSEPH) *Attorney.* Remarks on Mr. John Fitch's Reply to Mr. James Rumsey's Pamphlet. [A reprint of the 1788 edition.] pp. 33. *Tarrytown,* 1928. 4º. [*Magazine of History.* Extra no. 139.] P.P. **3437**. bab.

BARNES (JOSEPH) *Science-Master at the Bolton High School.* Tables for the Qualitative Analysis of "Simple Salts" & "Easy Mixtures," *etc.* pp. 47. *Galt & Co.: Manchester,* [1882.] 16º. **8908**. a. **28**.

BARNES (JOSEPH) *Secretary of the American Council of the Institute of Pacific Relations.*

—— Empire in the East. [Essays by various authors.] Edited by J. Barnes, *etc.* (A coöperative attempt to state the problems of American policy in the Far East.) pp. vii. 322. *Doubleday, Doran & Co.: New York,* 1934. 8º. **8004**. f. **2**.

—— [Another issue.] Empire in the East, *etc. Kegan Paul & Co.: London,* 1934. 8º. **8004**. ee. **27**.

BARNES (JOSEPH) *Translator.*

—— *See* GARY (R.) [Le Grand vestiaire.] The Company of Men. Translated . . . by J. Barnes. 1950. 8º. **012550**. s. **7**.

BARNES (JOSEPH) *Vicar of Berwick.* The Assurance of Salvation by Faith in Jesus Christ; being a continuation of a former sermon on the same text. pp. 42. *Thomas Ramsey: Berwick-upon-Tweed,* 1836. 8º. **4473**. bb. **9**. **(10*.)**

—— Catechetical Lectures for Christmas, Easter, Whitsunday, and on other important subjects, *etc.* pp. 89. *C. Richardson: Berwick,* [1840.] 8º. **3505**. e. **3**.

—— Faith the Foundation of Christian Morality; being the last of a series of three sermons on the same text. pp. 44. *Thomas Ramsay: Berwick-upon-Tweed,* 1837. 8º. **4473**. bb. **9**. **(10**.)**

—— Faith, the Way of Salvation: a sermon, *etc.* pp. 31. *C. Richardson: Berwick,* 1833. 8º. **4473**. bb. **9**. **(10.)**

—— Observations on Clandestine, or Irregular Marriages; with a short account of the laws, both of England and Scotland affecting marriage. pp. 41. *W. Lochhead: Berwick,* 1812. 8º. **5176**. c. **1**. **(1.)**

—— The Origin, Increase, and Effects of Faith. 1845. *See* WATSON (Alexander) *Vicar of St. Marychurch.* Practical Sermons, *etc.* vol. 2. 1845, *etc.* 8º. **1358**. g. **5**.

BARNES (JOSEPH ANTHONY) *See* MOORHOUSE (Arthur) Arthur Moorhouse. Memories and aftermath. Edited by J. A. Barnes. 1905. 8º. **4907**. i. **24**.

BARNES (JOSEPH ANTHONY)

—— *See* PIVERT DE SENANCOUR (E.) Obermann . . . Translated, with introduction and notes, by J. A. Barnes. [1910, *etc.*] 8°. 012208.ee.2/56.

BARNES (JOSEPH K.)

—— *See* UNITED STATES OF AMERICA.—*Department of War.—Surgeon General's Office.* The Medical and Surgical History of the War of the Rebellion. 1861–65. Prepared . . . under the direction of . . . J. K. Barnes. 1870, *etc.* 4°. **7686.** i. **4.**

BARNES (JOSEPHINE) *See* BARNES (Alice J. M. T.)

BARNES (JOSHUA) *Professor of Greek at Cambridge.* *See* also PHILARGYRIUS, *Cantab.*, *pseud.* [i.e. J. Barnes.]

—— *See* ANACREON. [*Greek and Latin.*] Anacreon . . . ad fidem . . . vet. MS. Vatican. emendatus . . . opera et studio J. Barnes. 1705. 12°. **997.** a. **7.**

—— —— 1721. 12°. **997.** a. **8.**

—— —— 1734. 8°. **11335.** aa. **13.**

—— —— 1781. fol. **687.** l. **20.**

—— *See* ANACREON. [*Greek, Latin and Italian.*] Anacreonte tradotto in versi italiani . . . Con la giunta della versione latina di G. Barnes. 1736. 4°. **74.** f. **18.**

—— *See* EURIPIDES. [*Works.—Greek and Latin.*] *Εὐριπιδου σωζομενα ἁπαντα* . . . Euripidis quæ extant omnia . . . Operâ & studio J. Barnes. 1694. fol. **653.** g. **14.**

—— —— 1778, *etc.* 4°. **653.** c. **7–9.**

—— —— 1821. 8°. **998.** k. **1–9.**

—— *See* EURIPIDES. [*Alcestis.—Greek and Latin.*] *Εὐριπιδου Ἀλκηστις* . . . E recensione et cum notis I. Barnesii, *etc.* 1776. 8°. **999.** n. **2.**

—— —— 1789. 8°. **52.** m. **10.**

—— *See* EURIPIDES. [*Electra.—Greek.*] *Εὐριπιδου Ἠλεκτρα* . . . notis Porsoni . . . Barnesii . . . illustrata. 1820. 8°. **998.** f. **22.**

—— *See* EURIPIDES. [*Orestes.—Greek and Latin.*] *Ὁ του Εὐριπιδου Ὀρεστης* . . . Adjecta est ad finem versio latina, ex editione J. Barnes. 1753. 8°. **160.** c. **18.**

—— —— 1778. 8°. **999.** b. **25.**

—— *See* HOMER. [*Works.—Greek and Latin.*] *Ὁμηρου Ἰλιας και Ὀδυσσεια* . . . Homeri Ilias & Odyssea . . . Operâ, studio, & impensis J. Barnes. 1711. 4°. **54.** c. **12, 13.**

—— *See* THEOCRITUS. [*Greek.*] Theocriti . . . quae supersunt . . . Præmittuntur editoris dissertatio de bucolicis Græcorum, vita Theocriti a J. Barnesio scripta, *etc.* 1770, *etc.* 4°. **653.** d. **9.**

—— *Ἀνακρεων Χριστιανος.* Anacreon Christianus, hoc est parodiae duae Anacreonticae & alia poemata, Psalmique aliquot Davidici, omnia Anacreontis stylo & metro Graece & Latine, donata per Joshua Barnes. *Gr. & Lat.* pp. 35. *Typis Academicis : Cantabrigiae,* 1705. 8°. **11335.** b. **2.**

—— [Another copy.] **3504.** aaa. **40.** **(1.)**

—— *Αὐλικοκατοπτρον·* sive Estheræ historia, poetica paraphrasi idque Græco carmine, cui versio Latina opponitur, exornata : una cum scholiis seu annotationibus Græcis . . . Additur Parodia Homerica de eadem hac historia. pp. xlvii. 171. *Typis M. C. : Londini,* 1679. 8°. **1010.** a. **20.**

—— [Another copy.] **73.** i. **5.**

—— [Another copy.] G. **17247.**

BARNES (JOSHUA) *Professor of Greek at Cambridge.*

—— Gerania : a new discovery of a little sort of people anciently discoursed of, called Pygmies. With a lively description of their stature, habit, manners, buildings, knowledge, and government, being very delightful and profitable. pp. 110. *W. G. for Obadiah Blagrave : London,* 1675. 8°. **1080.** h. **35.**

—— [Another copy.] **244.** b. **6.**

—— [Another copy.] 1675. 8°. G. **18856.** **(2.)**

—— [Another edition.] A New Discovery of a Little Sort of People, anciently discoursed of, called Pygmies, *etc.* *R. Griffiths : London,* 1750. 8°. **8005.** f. **3.**
Imperfect ; wanting all after p. 72.

—— The Good Old Way : or, three brief discourses tending to the promotion of religion . . . I. The happy island, & II. A sure way to victory, &c. III. The case of the Church of England truly represented and fully vindicated. There is added, The character of an honest man. 3 pt. *W. Turner : London,* 1703. 8°. **4106.** a. **11.**

—— The History of that Most Victorious Monarch Edward III[d] King of England and France . . . together with that of his most renowned son Edward, Prince of Wales . . . sirnamed the Black-Prince, *etc.* [With portraits.] pp. 911. *John Hayes for the Author : Cambridge,* 1688. fol. **195.** g. **10.**

—— [Another copy.] 505.ff.13.
Imperfect ; wanting the titlepage and dedication, and the portraits.

—— [Another copy.] G. **5071.**
Imperfect ; wanting the portrait of Edward the Black-Prince.

—— An History of the Jaquerie in France in the year 1358 ; with an account of their horrid cruelties and final extirpation. Taken from Barnes's History of the most Victorious Monarch Edward III., to shew that the character of the French peasantry, when unrestrained by law, has ever been brutally ferocious. pp. 14. *John Stockdale : London,* 1798. 8°. **6495.** bb. **1.** **(12.)**

—— [Another copy.] E. **2176.** **(2.)**

—— A Pindarick Congratulatory Poem to the Right Honourable George, Lord Jeffreys, Baron of Wem, *etc.* pp. 7. *Walter Davis : London,* 1685. fol. **11626.** i. **4.**

—— A Sermon preach'd on St. Matthew's Day, at Christ's Church before the Right Honourable Sir William Gore, Kt., Lord Mayor, the aldermen and governours of the several hospitals of the City of London. With an apology of the orphans of Christ's Hospital. pp. 23. 14. *George Sawbridge : London,* 1703. 4°. **4474.** i. **7.**

BARNES (JOSHUA N.) Lights and Shadows of Eighty Years. An autobiography. By Rev. J. N. Barnes. Revised and edited by his son, Edwin N. C. Barnes . . . With an introduction by Rev. Joseph McLeod. pp. 6. 218. *Barnes & Co. : St. John, N.B.,* 1911. 8°. **4902.** de. **26.**

BARNES (JOSIAH) The Green Mountain Travellers' Entertainment. pp. 360. *Derby & Jackson : New York,* 1858. 8°. **12704.** f. **7**

BARNES (JULIA MAY) Chart of the Lives of the Patriarchs. Illustrating Gen. 47–9. *John Heywood : Manchester,* [1924.] *s. sh. obl.* fol. **1865.** c. **11.** **(11.)**

BARNES (JULIAN F.) The Genesis of the American First Army. pp. x. 81. *Washington,* 1929. 8°. [*U.S. Army War College. Monograph Series on the American Military Participation in the World War.* pt. 2. no. 8.] A.S. **585.**

BARNES (JULIANA) *Dame.* *See* BERNES.

BARNES (KATHLEEN)

—— *See* GREGORY (Homer E.) and BARNES (K.) North Pacific Fisheries, *etc.* 1939. 8°. **7290.** m. **1.**

BARNES (KENNETH CHARLES) and **BARNES** (G. FRANCES)

—— Sex, Friendship and Marriage. pp. 205. *G. Allen & Unwin: London,* 1938. 8°. **08416.** l. **20.**

BARNES (KENNETH K.)

—— *See* FREVERT (Richard K.) Soil and Water Conservation Engineering. [By] R. K. Frevert . . . K. K. Barnes. 1955. 8°. W.P. **14532/3.**

BARNES (L. C.) Petworth and its Surroundings, Bignor, Pulborough, *etc.* pp. 88. *London,* 1902. 8°. [*Homeland Association's Handbooks.* no. 26.] **10360.p.26.**

BARNES (LAVERNE ALMON)

—— *See* WHITE (Benjamin) *Ph.D.* The Biology of Pneumococcus . . . [By] B. White . . . with the collaboration of E. S. Robinson . . . and L. A. Barnes. 1938. 8°. **07560.** ee. **53.**

BARNES (LEOLA CHRISTIE)

—— Purple Petals. [With a portrait.] pp. 46. *London,* 1934. 8°. [*Channing Poets' Library.* no. 30.] W.P. **7136/30.**

BARNES (LEONARD JOHN)

—— Caliban in Africa. An impressior of colour-madness. [A study of the native problem in South Africa.] pp. 245. *Victor Gollancz : London,* 1930. 8°. **08157.** ee. **52.**

—— The Duty of Empire. pp. 318. *Victor Gollancz: London,* 1935. 8°. **20019.** f. **62.**

—— Empire or Democracy? A study of the colonial question. pp. 303. *Victor Gollancz: London,* 1939. 8°. **20032.** a. **46.**

—— The Future of Colonies. pp. 46. *L. & V. Woolf: London,* 1936. 8°. [*Day to Day Pamphlets.* no. 32.] **012211.bb.1/32.**

—— The New Boer War. pp. xii. 238. *L. & V. Woolf: London,* 1932. 8°. **08157.** df. **38.**

—— The Outlook for Youth Work. Report, *etc.* pp. 143. 1948. 8°. *See* LONDON.—III. *King George's Jubilee Trust.* **8289.** d. **39.**

—— Skeleton of the Empire. pp. 98. *London,* 1937. 8°. [*Fact.* no. 3.] P.P. **3558.** ica.

—— Soviet Light on the Colonies . . . Maps and diagrams by J. F. Horrabin. [With a portrait.] pp. 288. *Penguin Books: Harmondsworth, New York,* 1944. 8°. [*Penguin Special.* no. 131.] **12208.** a. **2/131.**

—— Youth at Arms. [Poems.] pp. 71. *Peter Davies: London,* 1933. 8°. **011641.** df. **34.**

—— Youth Service in an English County. Report prepared for King George's Jubilee Trust by L. J. Barnes . . . Maps and diagrams by J. F. Horrabin. pp. 122. [1945.] 8°. *See* LONDON.—III. *King George's Jubilee Trust.* **8287.** m. **15.**

—— Zulu Paraclete. A sentimental record. [A narrative of farming life in South Africa.] pp. 244. *Peter Davies: London,* 1935. 8°. **010094.** ee. **57.**

BARNES (LEONARD STEWART) *See* ARMITAGE (Doris M.) A Challenge to Neurasthenia. [A description of Dr. L. S. Barnes's treatment.] 1929. 8°. **07660.** ee. **75.**

—— —— 1931. 8°. **07660.** aa. **14.**

—— *See* MARTIN (John W.) and (J.) Martin's Questions & Answers on Home Nursing. Revised and brought up to date by L. S. Barnes, *etc.* 1916. 16°. **07686.** de. **42.**

—— *See* MARTIN (John W.) and (J.) Martin's Questions and Answers upon Ambulance Work. Revised . . . by L. S. Barnes, *etc.* 1915. 16°. **07686.** de. **39.**

BARNES (LIONEL HICKMAN) *See* CHALMERS (Dalzell H. J.) and BARNES (L. H.) Student's Guide to Roman Law—Justinian and Gaius. 1907. 8°. **5207.** b. **5.**

—— A Short History of the Grocers' Company. Together with a description of Grocers' Hall and the principal objects of interest therein. [A revised and expanded version by L. H. Barnes and J. Ellison-Macartney of an earlier pamphlet and catalogue by L. H. Barnes. With illustrations.] pp. viii. 78. 1950 [1951]. 4°. *See* LONDON.—II. *Livery Companies.—Grocers.* **8248.** h. **29.**

BARNES (M. G.)

—— More About Nursery Rhymes . . . Illustrated, *etc.* pp. 31. *Sir I. Pitman & Sons: London,* 1936. 4°. **20055.** e. **39.**

—— Rhyming Plays for Infants and Juniors. For reading or acting. [By M. G. Barnes and L. Inwood.] 9 pt. *Sir I. Pitman & Sons: London,* 1936–39. 8°. **11774.** ccc. **17.**

BARNES (M. L.) Happy Memories of Robert Barnes. pp. 31. *J. Parker & Co.: Oxford & London,* 1875. 8°. **4906.** aaaa. **6.**

BARNES (M. M.) *M.A. Oxon.*

—— *See* KHALĪFAH SHUJĀʻ AL-DĪN and BARNES (M. M.) Highroads of Islamic History. 1936. 8°. **9004.** d. **4.**

BARNES (MADELINE) Diana's Idea and After the Party, *etc.* pp. 47. *Blackie & Son: London & Glasgow,* [1928.] 16°. **012808.** e. **68.**

—— Fireside Stories . . . Pictured by Anne Anderson. pp. 95. *Blackie & Son: London,* 1922. 8°. **12801.** d. **50.**

—— [A reissue.] *London & Glasgow,* [1927.] 8°. **12805.** i. **67.**

—— The Lucky Bag . . . With verses by various authors. *Blackie & Son: London & Glasgow,* [1931.] 8°. **12801.** v. **16.**

—— Nannie's Big Story Book . . . With verses by various writers. *Blackie & Son: London & Glasgow,* [1928.] 4°. **012803.** i. **106.**

—— Nannie's Own Story Book . . . With verses by various writers. *Blackie & Son: London & Glasgow,* [1927.] 4°. **012802.** d. **47.**

—— Nannie's Treasure Box . . . With verses by various writers. *Blackie & Son: London & Glasgow,* [1928.] 4°. **012803.** i. **107.**

—— The Party Book, *etc.* pp. 80. *Blackie & Son: London & Glasgow,* [1930.] 4°. **12813.** b. **30.**

—— Stirabout Stories, *etc.* pp. 80. *Blackie & Son: London & Glasgow,* [1929.] 4°. **012803.** k. **36.**

—— Tub-time Tales, *etc.* pp. 79. *Blackie & Son: London,* 1920. 8°. **12802.** dd. **22.**

BARNES (MALCOLM)

—— *See* EVEREST, *Mount.* [Avant-premières à l'Everest.] Forerunners to Everest . . . English version by M. Barnes. 1954. 8° **7920. g. 43.**

—— *See* GOS (C.) [Notre-Dame des neiges.] Song of the High Hills . . . Translated . . . by Malcolm Barnes. 1949. 8°. **12730. f. 18.**

—— *See* GOS (C.) [Tragédies alpestres.] Alpine Tragedy . . . Translated . . . by M. Barnes. 1948. 8°. **10196. k. 8.**

—— *See* HARE (Augustus J. C.) In my Solitary Life . . . Edited with notes and introduction by M. Barnes. 1953. 8°. **10857. g. 50.**

—— *See* HARE (Augustus J. C.) The Years with Mother . . . Edited with notes and introduction by M. Barnes. 1952. 8°. **10863. c. 12.**

—— *See* LATTRE DE TASSIGNY (J. M. G. de) The History of the French First Army . . . Translated by M. Barnes, *etc.* 1952. 8°. **9102. p. 4.**

—— *See* LE GOLIF (L. A. T.) [Cahiers de Louis Adhémar Timothée Le Golif.] The Memoirs of a Buccaneer . . . Translated by M. Barnes. 1954. 8°. **010665. l. 46.**

—— *See* SENET (A.) [L'Homme à la recherche de ses ancêtres.] Man in search of his Ancestors . . . Translated by M. Barnes. 1955. 8°. **7211. c. 14.**

BARNES (MARGARET) *Writer of Children's Books.*

—— First Stories. (no. 5, *etc.* [By] Pat Devenport.) *E. J. Arnold & Son: Glasgow,* [1947– .] 16°. **W.P. 14031/8.**

From no. 5 *onward published in Leeds.*

—— [First stories.] Storiau cyntaf . . . Troswyd gan Gwladus Roberts. *E. J. Arnold & Son: Leeds,* [1948– .] 8°. **W.P. 3047.**

BARNES (MARGARET AYER)

—— *See* WEBSTER (Henry K.) The Alleged Great-Aunt . . . Completed by J. A. Fairbank and M. A. Barnes. [1935.] 8°. **A.N. 2492.**

—— *See* WEBSTER (Henry K.) The Alleged Great-Aunt. (Completed by J. A. Fairbank and M. A. Barnes.) [1935.] 8°. **A.N. 742.**

—— Edna his Wife. An American idyll. pp. 628. *Jonathan Cape: London,* 1936. 8°. **A.N. 2884.**

—— Prevailing Winds. [Tales.] pp. 297. *Constable & Co.: London; printed in U.S.A.,* 1929. 8°. **12715. b. 18.**

—— Westward Passage. pp. 323. *Houghton Mifflin Co.; Boston & New York,* 1931. 8°. **A.N. 1135.**

—— [Another edition.] pp. 336. *Jonathan Cape: London,* 1932. 8°. **A.N. 1356.**

—— Wisdom's Gate. pp. 370. *Houghton Mifflin Co.: Boston,* 1938. 8°. **12718. dd. 20.**

—— Wisdom's Gate. pp. 383. *Jonathan Cape: London,* 1939. 8°. **12719. cc. 6.**

—— Within this Present. pp. 611. *Houghton Mifflin Co.: Boston & New York,* 1933. 8°. **12709. eee. 1.**

—— [A reissue.] *Jonathan Cape: London,* 1934. 8°. **12709. g. 8.**

—— Years of Grace. pp. 581. *Constable & Co.: London: Cambridge, Mass.* printed, 1930. 8°. **A.N. 471.**

BARNES (MARGARET CAMPBELL)

—— Brief Gaudy Hour. A novel of Anne Boleyn. pp. 336. *Macdonald & Co.: London,* 1949. 8°. **NN. 39787.**

BARNES (MARGARET CAMPBELL)

—— Like Us, They Lived. A novel. pp. 268. *Macdonald & Co.: London,* [1944.] 8°. **NN. 34432.**

—— [Like us, they lived.] The Passionate Brood. (Revised and re-set.) pp. 296. *Macdonald: London,* 1954. 8°. **12654. d. 16.**

—— My Lady of Cleves. [A novel.] pp. 316. *Macdonald & Co.: London,* [1946.] 8°. **NN. 35971.**

—— The Passionate Brood. *See* supra: Like us, they lived.

—— The Tudor Rose. pp. 288. *Macdonald: London,* 1953. 8°. **NNN. 4296.**

—— With all my Heart. The love story of Catherine of Braganza. [A novel.] pp. 288. *Macdonald: London,* 1951. 8°. **NN. 8065.**

—— Within the Hollow Crown. pp. x. 366. *Macdonald & Co.: London,* 1948. 8°. **NN. 38097.**

BARNES (MARY DOWNING) *See* SHELDON, afterwards BARNES.

BARNES (MARY FRANCES HARTLEY) Feeding the Child from Two to Six, *etc.* pp. xiii. 206. *Macmillan Co.: New York,* 1928. 8°. **7383. cc. 48.**

BARNES (MARY MATHEWS) Epithalamium . . . With drawings by Dora Wheeler. pp. 31. *G. P. Putnam's Sons: New York & London,* 1889. *obl.* 8°. **11686. ee. 38.**

BARNES (MATTHEW) *pseud.* [i.e. ROBERT SEYMOUR BRIDGES and MARY MONICA BRIDGES.]

—— *See* also BRIDGES (Mary M.)

—— *See* also BRIDGES (Robert S.)

—— What is Pure French, by M. Barnes. Note on "as to", by H. W. Fowler, *etc.* pp. 11. *Clarendon Press: [Oxford,]* 1922. 8°. [*S.P.E. Tract.* no. 8.] **Ac. 9921.**

—— Words from the French, -é, -ée. *See* KURATH (H.) American Pronunciation, *etc.* 1928. 8°. [*S.P.E. Tract.* no. 30.] **Ac. 9921.**

BARNES (MAUD ELIZABETH FURSE) *Baroness Gorell. See* GORELL (Elizabeth) *pseud.* [i.e. M. E. F. Barnes, *Baroness Gorell.*]

BARNES (MAUDE FIERO) Renaissance Vistas. [Essays on art.] pp. vii. 223. *W. F. Payson: New York,* [1930.] 8°. **07807. i. 59.**

BARNES (MELVIN) A Few General and Unmethodized Remarks to a medical younger friend, on phrenology. pp. 16. *J. W. Tuttle: Platsburgh,* 1853. 8°. **7410. aaa. 41. (5.)**

—— Reprint of a Short Biography of Colonel Ebenezer Allen . . . [By "M. Rarnes," or rather, M. Barnes.] Also short biographies of Lieutenant Samuel Allen and Dr. Jacob Roebeck, *etc.* pp. 32. *J. W. Tuttle: Plattsburgh,* 1852. 8°. **10880. e. 53.**

BARNES (MICHAEL)

—— *See* also DRAYTON (Ricky) *pseud.* [i.e. M. Barnes.]

—— Landscape with Corpses. pp. 160. *Milestone Publications: London,* [1954.] 8°. [*Merit Books.*] **W.P. c. 343/6.**

BARNES (NATHANIEL WARING) *See* BROWN (Rollo W.) and BARNES (N. W.) The Art of Writing English, *etc.* 1913. 8°. **011852. b. 57.**

BARNES (NELLIE) American Indian Love Lyrics, and other verse . . . Selected by N. Barnes, *etc.* pp. 190. *Macmillan Co.: New York,* 1925. 8°. **011686. g. 84.**

BARNES (Nellie)

—— American Indian Verse. Characteristics of style. pp. 61. *Lawrence*, 1921. 8°. [*Bulletin of the University of Kansas. Humanistic Studies.* vol. 2. no. 4.] Ac. **2692**. i/**4**.

BARNES (Nettie)

—— For One Man's Love. pp. 35. *William Stevens: London*, [1944.] 8°. [*True Love Series.*] **12633**. p. **1/325**.

—— Love in Chains. pp. 36. *William Stevens: London*, [1942.] 8°. [*True Love Series.*] **12633**. p. **1/300**.

BARNES (Otis Tiffany) Children's Object Story-Sermons. pp. 159. *F. H. Revell Co.: New York*, [1916.] 8°. **04419**. g. **45**.

BARNES (P. E.)

—— Unbeaten Tracks around Bristol, Bath and Weston-super-Mare . . . Reprinted from "The Western Daily Press" and Bristol "Sports News." [With plates.] pp. ii. 298. *Western Daily Press: Bristol*, [1927.] 8°. **010368**. q. **28**.

BARNES (P. R.)

—— Crum Elbow Folks. [A novel.] pp. 283. *J. B. Lippincott Co.: Philadelphia*, [1938.] 8°. **12718**. cc. **15**.

BARNES (Parker Thayer) House Plants and how to grow them . . . Illustrated. pp. x. 236. *Doubleday, Page & Co.: London; New York* printed, 1909. 8°. [*Garden Library.*] **7033**. bb. **1/6**.

BARNES (Patricia) *See* Abercrombie (P. B.) *pseud.* [i.e. P. Barnes.]

BARNES (Patricia Mary)

—— *See* England.—*Exchequer.* The Great Roll of the Pipe for the fourteenth year of the reign of King John, Michaelmas 1212, Pipe Roll 58 . . . Edited by P. M. Barnes. 1955. 8°. [*Publications of the Pipe Roll Society.* New series. vol. 30.] **2082**. b.

BARNES (Peter)

—— The Trial of Peter Barnes and Others. The I.R.A. Coventry explosion of 1939. Edited by Letitia Fairfield. [With plates.] pp. xiii. 284. *William Hodge & Co.: London*, 1953. 8°. [*Notable British Trials Series.* vol. 77.] **6496**. d. **1/70**.

BARNES (Phil A.)

—— "Trespassers will be Prosecuted." Views of the forbidden moorlands of the Peak district. pp. 32. *P. A. Barnes: Sheffield*, 1934. 4°. **010360**. dd. **84**.

BARNES (Philip) Martyrs to Freedom; or, Struggles for national liberty, *etc.* pp. 360. *John Hogg: London*, [1889.] 8°. **10601**. cc. **13**.

BARNES (*Mrs.* Philip) Bingle's Widow. pp. 127. *S.P.C.K.: London*, [1907.] 8°. **04429**. ccc. **70**.

—— Kitty and Toddles, or, Two little tramps. pp. 160. *R.T.S.: London*, [1903.] 8°. **04429**. l. **16**.

—— Kitty and Toddles. pp. 32. [*R.T.S.: London*, 1908.] 8°. [*Bouverie Series of Penny Stories.* no. 47.] **4430**. ee. **18**.

—— Miss Cynthy's Experiment. pp. 128. *R.T.S.: London*, [1898.] 8°. **4430**. e. **13**.

BARNES (Philip Edward) *See* Belgium. [*Collections of Laws, etc.*] The Electoral Laws of Belgium . . . Translated . . . by P. E. Barnes. 1849. 16°. **8005**. e. **3**.

BARNES (Philip Edward)

—— *See* Félice (G. de) History of the Protestants of France . . . Translated . . . by P. E. Barnes. 1853. 8°. **4632**. c. **33**.

—— *See* Strype (John) Memorials of . . . Thomas Cranmer . . . A new edition . . . by P. E. Barnes. 1853. 8°. **4903**. f. **52**.

BARNES (Phineas) The Present Technical Condition of the Steel Industry of the United States. pp. 85. *Washington*, 1885. 8°. [*U.S. Geological Survey. Bulletin.* no. 25.] A.S. **212/2**.

BARNES (R. H.) [The "Nap" Selector Plan. An aid to successful betting and the winning of newspaper competitions.] [*R. H. Barnes: London*, 1933.] fol. **7912**. k. **33**.

Reproduced from typewriting.

BARNES (R. K.)

—— *See* Franklin (E.) *Physicist*, and Barnes (R. K.) The Radiometric Assay of Uranium and Thorium Ores, *etc.* 1953. fol. [*Atomic Energy Research Establishment. Report.* no. EL/R 1175.] B.S. **62/40**. (**4**.)

BARNES (Ralph) *See* Bible.—*Old Testament.—Selections.* [*English.*] The Sacred History of the Old Testament, abridged, in the language of the Bible . . . by R. Barnes. 1821. 12°. T. **868**. (**6**.)

—— *See* Exeter.—*Cathedral Church.—Chapter.* Report of the Case of the Queen v. the President and Chapter of the Cathedral Church of . . . Exeter . . . by R. Barnes. 1841. 8°. **1131**. g. **17**.

—— *See* Liturgies.—*Latin Rite.—Pontificals.*—ii. *Exeter.* Liber Pontificalis of Edmund Lacy, Bishop of Exeter . . . Edited by R. Barnes. 1847. 8°. **1220**. h. **20**.

—— *See* Rodd (Richard) A Faithful Statement of all the Facts . . . relative to . . . the burial ground . . . of Stoke-Damerell . . . Devon . . . with true copies of letters . . . on the subject between Dr. Philpotts, Bishop of Exeter, his secretary (R. Barnes) and Mr. Rodd. 1832. 8°. **796**. f. **18**.

—— An Appeal to the People of England on the proposed transfer of all testamentary business to London. pp. 48. *S. Sweet: London*, 1834. 12°. **4106**. aa. **75**. (**4**.)

—— An Inquiry into Equity-Practice, and the Law of Real Property, with a view to legislative revision. pp. x. 323. *J. & W. T. Clarke: London*, 1827. 8°. **514**. d. **4**.

—— A Letter on Church Rates. pp. 34. *Rivingtons: London*, 1837. 12°. T. **2156**. (**4**.)

—— [Another copy.] **4106**. aa. **75**. (**3**.)

—— A Letter to Sir John Campbell on the Law of Church Rates. [In reply to his letter to Lord Stanley.] pp. 19. *J. G. & T. Rivington: London*, 1937. 8°. T. **2133**. (**11**.)

—— A Letter to the Right Honourable Lord John Russell on the Commission of Inquiry into Episcopal and Capitular Estates. pp. 31. *F. & J. Rivington: London*, 1849. 8°. **4107**. d. **5**.

—— A Letter to the Right Honourable Lord John Russell on the First Report of the Episcopal and Capitular Revenues Commissioners. pp. 29. *F. & J. Rivington: London*, 1850. 8°. **4107**. c. **3**.

—— Observations on a Bill, introduced into Parliament in the Session of 1817, for the amendment of the law in respect of Modus for Tithes. [By R. Barnes.] pp. 63. [1817.] 8°. *See* England.—*Parliament.—Bills.*—II. [1817 June 20.] **5155**. aaa. **30**.

—— [Another edition.] pp. 63. *University Press: Cambridge*, 1818. 8°. **5155**. c. **93**. (**1**.)

BARNES (RALPH)

—— The Papal Brief [of 29 Sept. 1850] considered with reference to the Laws of England. pp. 91. *F. & J. Rivington; Stevens & Norton: London*, 1850. 8°. **3938**. e. **9**.

—— Remarks on the Judgment of the Judicial Committee in the case of the Bishop of Natal. pp. 95. *W. Roberts: Exeter*, 1866. 8°. **4106**. bb. **55**. **(1.)** *Printed for private circulation.*

—— [Another edition.] pp. 99. *Hatchard & Co.: London*, 1866. 8°. **5155**. aa. **29**.

—— Remarks on the Tithe Commutation Act, *etc.* pp. 24. *J. G. & T. Rivington: London*, 1836. 8°. T. **2133**. **(3.)**

—— Second edition, with an appendix. pp. 36. *J. G. & T. Rivington: London*, 1836. 8°. **4108**. f. **18**. **(3.)**

—— A Summary of the Proceedings and Right of Voting at County Elections. pp. 39. *Trewman & Co.: Exeter*, 1818. 8°. **6325**. c. **1**.

—— Thoughts on Mr. Gladstone's Chapter of Autobiography, in its legal aspect. pp. 40. *Hatchard & Co.: London*, 1869. 8°. **8138**. bbb. **6**.

BARNES (RALPH C.)

—— The Pipers' Drums. [Elementary instructions for making drums.] pp. 24. *J. B. Cramer & Co.: London*, [1935.] 4°. **7894**. tt. **29**.

BARNES (RALPH MOSSER) Industrial Engineering and Management. Problems and policies. pp. vii. 366. *New York & London*, 1931. 8°. [*McGraw-Hill Industrial Management Series.*] W.P. **9221/7**.

—— Motion and Time Study. pp. ix. 285. *J. Wiley & Sons: New York*, 1937. 8°. **8712**. b. **29**.

—— Motion and Time Study . . . Second edition, twelfth printing. pp. xi. 390. *John Wiley & Sons: New York*, 1947. 8°. **8713**. b. **29**.

—— Motion and Time Study . . . Third edition. pp. xii. 559. *John Wiley & Sons: New York*, [1949.] 8°. **08535**. h. **167**.

—— Motion and Time Study Applications . . . Revised printing, *etc.* pp. 188. *John Wiley & Sons: New York*, 1946. 4°. **8235**. t. **45**.

—— Motion and Time Study Applications . . . Second edition. pp. 188. *John Wiley & Sons: New York*, 1953. 4°. **8234**. d. **75**.

—— Motion and Time Study Problems and Projects. pp. 222. *John Wiley & Sons: New York*, [1949.] 4°. **8223**. dd. **27**.

—— Studies of One and Two-Handed Work . . . By R. M. Barnes, Marvin E. Mundel, John M. MacKenzie. pp. 67. *Iowa City*, 1940. 8°. [*University of Iowa Studies. Studies in Engineering.* no. 21.] Ac. **2692**. f/**17**.

—— Work Methods Manual. pp. vii. 136. *J. Wiley & Sons: New York*, [1944.] 8°. **7947**. aaa. **40**.

BARNES (RALPH MOSSER) and **MUNDEL** (MARVIN E.)

—— Studies of Hand Motions and Rhythm appearing in Factory Work. pp. 62. *Iowa City*, 1938. 8°. [*University of Iowa Studies in Engineering.* Bulletin 12.] Ac. **2692**. f/**17**.

—— A Study of Simultaneous Symmetrical Hand Motions. pp. 39. *Iowa City*, 1939. 8°. [*University of Iowa Studies. Studies in Engineering.* Bulletin 17.] Ac. **2692**. f/**17**.

BARNES (RALPH MOSSER) and **PERKINS** (JAMES S.)

—— A Study of the Effect of Practice on the Elements of a Factory Operation. By R. M. Barnes . . . and J. S. Perkins . . . with the assistance and collaboration of J. M. Juran. pp. 95. *Iowa City*, 1940. 8°. [*University of Iowa Studies in Engineering.* Bulletin no. 22.] Ac. **2692**. f/**17**.

BARNES (REGINALD HENRY)

—— *See* PHILLPOTTS (Henry) *Bishop of Exeter.* Addresses delivered to the Clergy of the Diocese of Exeter . . . Compiled . . . by . . . R. H. Barnes. 1863. 8°. **4446**. c. **49**.

—— *See* TOMKINS (Henry G.) The Church of the First-born, and the Spirits of the Just. A sermon . . . with a preface by . . . R. H. Barnes. 1863. 16°. **4478**. a. **126**. **(16.)**

—— "Asa's Victory." *See* EXETER, *Diocese of.* Ordination Sermons, *etc.* 1869. 8°. **4463**. g. **11**.

BARNES (REGINALD HENRY) and **BROWN** (CHARLES EDWARD)

—— Charles George Gordon. A sketch . . . With facsimile letter. pp. 106. *Macmillan & Co.: London*, 1885. 8°. **10817**. aaa. **16**.

—— Spurgeon, the People's Preacher. By the authors of "The Life of General Gordon." [i.e. R. H. Barnes and C. E. Brown.] pp. 330. [1892.] 8°. *See* SPURGEON (C. H.) [*Appendix.*] **4906**. df. **17**.

BARNES (RICHARD) *Accountant.* 1808. Government Life Annuities. Table of annuities granted on single lives, at every age, from 35 to 75 for each £100 Stock, *etc.* *Cadell & Davies: London*, 1808. 8°. **8506**. c. **14**.

BARNES (RICHARD) *Bishop of Durham.* Bishop Barnes's Injunctions to the Clergy of the Diocese of Durham. pp. 32. 1849. *See* REPRINTS. Reprints of Rare Tracts, *etc.* vol. 2. 1847, *etc.* 8°. **1077**. f. **85**.

—— The Injunctions and other Ecclesiastical Proceedings of Richard Barnes. [Edited by James Raine.] pp. xix. 142. clxix. 1850. 8°. *See* DURHAM.—*Surtees Society.* Ac. **8045/21**.

BARNES (RICHARD H.) and **MAACK** (JEAN E.)

—— Review of the Literature on the Nutritive Value of Soybeans. pp. 63. 1943. 8°. *See* MINNEAPOLIS.—*University of Minnesota.—Hormel Institute.* **Ac.2692.krb.**

BARNES (RICHARD JONES) Chrysanthemums. A manual for exhibitors and all growers . . . Illustrated. pp. 112. *Maclaren & Sons: London*, [1914.] 8°. **07029**. e. **43**.

BARNES (RICHARD LANGLEY)

—— Devotions to the Lord Christ. pp. 53. *A. R. Mowbray & Co.: London & Oxford*, 1936. 8°. **03456**. ee. **107**.

—— An Introduction to Worship. Written for those in the family of Toc H who love the Church of England, *etc.* pp. xi. 74. *A. R. Mowbray & Co.: London, Oxford*, 1932. 12°. **03456**. df. **119**.

—— The Priest and his Priesthood. A devotional commentary on the principles of the sacred ministry. pp. 96. *A. R. Mowbray & Co.: London & Oxford*, 1940. 8°. **4498**. c. **44**.

—— A War-Time Chaplaincy. pp. 80. *A. R. Mowbray & Co.: London & Oxford*, 1939. 8°. **4498**. p. **21**.

BARNES (RICHARD WILLIAM) *See* also ALAZON, *pseud.* [i.e. R. W. Barnes.]

—— Appendix and Imaginary Criticisms. [By R. W. Barnes.] pp. 132. 1865. 8°. *See* APPENDIX. **4377**. cc. **5**.

—— The Authority due to the Opinions of the Revd. H. E. Head . . . on Apostolic Succession, and other theological subjects, considered. pp. 81. *G. Spurway: Honiton*, 1839. 8°. T. **2441**. **(8.)**

—— [Another copy.] **4107**. cc. **49**. **(3.)**
In this copy there is no date on the titlepage.

—— Christmas Day Sermons preached . . . Christmas Day, 1864. pp. 26. *Rivingtons: London; J. R. Netherton: Truro*, 1864. 8°. **4478**. cc. **66**. **(6.)**

—— Confirmation—Holy Communion—Ordination. Four sermons. pp. 64. *Longman & Co.: London*, 1860. 8°. **4325**. c. **10**.

—— Four Sermons preached in the Parish Church of Probus, Cornwall, *etc.* pp. 57. *Netherton & Worth: Truro*, 1879. 8°. **4475**. f. **52**. **(15.)**

—— New Year's Day Sermons preached . . . on New Year's Day, 1865. pp. 35. *Rivingtons: London; J. R. Netherton: Truro*, 1865. 8°. **4478**. cc. **67**. **(8.)**

—— Public Opinion considered in letters between one of his friends and R. W. Barnes. pp. 238. *J. N. Netherton: Truro; J. & C. Mozley: London*, 1855. 8°. **8006**. c. **7**.

—— The Repentance of Judas. A sermon, *etc.* pp. 15. *Rivingtons: London; J. R. Netherton: Truro*, 1865. 8°. **4477**. bb. **76**. **(5.)**

—— A Sermon, preached at the Visitation of . . . the Lord Bishop of Exeter, at the Cathedral Church of St. Peter, Exeter, on St. Peter's Day, 1842. pp. 23. *P. A. Hannaford: Exeter; J. G. F. & J. Rivington: London*, 1842. 8°. **1358**. h. **21**. **(1.)**

—— Sermon preached in the Mission Chapel at Tresillian, *etc.* pp. 27. *Netherton & Worth: Truro*, 1879. 8°. **4475**. f. **52**. **(16.)**

—— Three Sermons, preached in Exeter Cathedral . . . on 7th, 8th, and 9th Sundays after Trinity, *etc.* pp. 75. *Rivingtons: London*, 1869. 8°. **4477**. bb. **76**. **(18.)**

BARNES (ROBERT) *Artist.* *See* GREY (Sidney) Story-land . . . With . . . illustrations by R. Barnes. [1884.] 4°. **12805**. w. **16**.

—— *See* PICTURE BOOK. My Own Picture Book. With . . . engravings by R. Barnes [and others], *etc.* [1880.] 4°. **12806**. g. **1**.

—— *See* PICTURES. Idyllic Pictures. Drawn by Barnes [and others], *etc.* 1867. 4°. **11651**. h. **8**.

—— *See* WATTS (John G.) Pictures of English Life, after original studies by R. Barnes and M. Wimperis. 1865. fol. **1751**. a. **27**.

BARNES (ROBERT) *Baptist Minister.* The Reasons of Spiritual Declension negatively and positively stated. pp. iv. 124. *Shearcroft: Clare*, [1833.] 12°. **4402**. f. **31**.

BARNES (ROBERT) *Chaplain to Henry VIII.* *See* also ANTONIUS, *Anglus, pseud.* [i.e. R. Barnes.]

—— *See* COVERDALE (Miles) *Bishop of Exeter.* A Confutacion of that treatise, which one J. Standish made against the protestacion of D. Barnes, *etc.* [1541?] 8°. C. **25**. b. **6**.

BARNES (ROBERT) *Chaplain to Henry VIII.*

—— *See* MORE (*Sir* Thomas) *Lord High Chancellor of England.* The second parte of the Cōfutacion of Tyndal's Answere. In whyche is also confuted . . . the chyrche that frere Barnes devyseth, *etc.* 1533. fol. C.111.g.10.(2.)

—— The Workes of Doctour Barness. *See* TYNDALE (William) The Whole Workes of W. Tyndall, Iohn Frith, and Doct. Barnes, *etc.* 1573, *etc.* fol. **6**. f. **18**.

—— Vitæ Romanorum pontificum . . . collectæ, per D. R. Barns . . . Eiusdem Sententiæ, siue præcipui Christianæ religionis articuli, *etc.* [With a prefatory epistleby Martin Luther.] pp. 406. FEW MS. NOTES. *Basileæ*, [1555.] 8°. **4855**. a. **3**.

—— [Another copy.] G. **19555**. **(1.)**

—— Scriptores duo Anglici, coætanei ac conterranei; de vitis pontificum Romanorum. Videlicet: Robertus Barns, & Iohannes Baleus, quos a tenebris vindicavit, veterum testimonijs ne quis de fide illorum dubitaret confirmavit, & vsque ad Paulum Quintum . . . continuavit Iohannes Martini Lydius. 3 pt. *G. A. a Marsse; sumptibus H. Laurentij: Lugduni Batavorum*, 1615. 8°. **484**. a. **21**.

—— [Another copy.] G. **19554**.
With the arms of G. A. de Thou on the binding.

—— Bapst trew Hadriani iiij. vnd Alexanders III. gegen Keyser Friderichen Barbarossa geůbt. Aus der Historia [i.e. the Vitae Romanorum Pontificum of R. Barnes] zusamen gezogen . . . Mit einer Vorrhede D. M. Luthers. 1545. 4°. *See* ADRIAN IV., *Pope.* [Nicholas Breakspere.] **3905**. cc. **24**.

—— Bapsttrew Hadriani iiij. vnd Alexanders iij. gegen Keyser Friderichen Barbarossa geůbt. Aus der Historia [i.e. the Vitae Romanorum Pontificum of R. Barnes] zusamen gezogen . . . Mit einer Vorrhede D. Mar. Luthers. 1545. 4°. *See* ADRIAN IV., *Pope.* [Nicholas Breakspere.] **3905**. cc. **23**.

—— A Supplicatyon made by Robert Barnes . . . vnto the most excellent and redoubted prince kinge henrye the eyght. The articles for which this forsayde doctoure Barnes was condemned of oure spiritualtye, are confirmed by the scripture, doctoures and their awne lawe. After that he disputeth certayne comen places which also he confermeth with the scripture, holye doctoures and their awne lawe. **B.L.** ff. clij. [*London*, 1531?] 8°. C. **53**. h. **25**.

—— [Another edition.] **B.L.** MS. NOTE [by Francis Hargrave]. *John Byddell: London*, 1534. 4°. C. **37**. d. **1**. **(2.)**

—— [Another copy.] FEW MS. NOTES. C. **37**. e. **22**.
Imperfect; wanting sig. F and I.

—— [Another edition.] **B.L.** *Hugh Syngelton: London*, [1550?] 8°. **227**. a. **37**.

—— [Another copy.] G. **19927**.
Imperfect; wanting the titlepage.

—— A Treatise on Justification . . . appended to a Supplication unto . . . King Henry VIII. *See* TYNDALE (William) The Writings of Tindal, Frith, and Barnes. [1830?] 12°. 865.b.2.(1–2.)

—— Bekantnus dess Glaubens, die Doctor Robertus Barus [*sic*] . . . in Teütschen landen D. Antonius Anglus genant, zu Lunden in Engelland gethon hat, im Jar M.D.XL. am XXX. dess Monats Julij, do er zum Fewr, on Vrtel vñ Recht, vnschuldig, vnuerhörter sach, gefürt, vñ verbrēdt wordē ist. Auss der Englischen Sprach verteutscht. *M. Ramīnger: Augspurg*, 1540. 4°. **3932**. dd. **11**.

—— [Another edition.] [1540?] 4°. **3906**. aaa. **75**.

BARNES (Robert) *Chaplain to Henry* VIII.

—— [Another edition.] Mit einer Vorrhede D. M. Luthers. *Wittenberg*, 1540. 4°. **3906**. cc. **10**.

—— [Another edition.] 1541. 4°. **3906**. cc. **11**.

—— [Another edition.] *M. Kriestein: Augspurg*, [1545?] 4°. **3932**. dd. **12**.

—— The Life and Selections from the Writings of R. Barnes. *See* Richmond (Legh) The Fathers of the English Church, *etc.* vol. 1. 1807, *etc.* 8°. **478**. b. **5**.

—— The Metynge of Doctor Barons and doctor Powell at Paradise gate ⁊ of theyr communicacion bothe drawen to Smithfydle frō the Towar. The one burned for Heresye as the papistes do saye truly and the other quartered for popery and all within one houre. [In verse.] **B.L.** *Wyllyam Hill: London*, [1548.] 8°. **C. 37**. a. **40**.

BARNES (Robert) *M.D.* *See* London.—III. *New Sydenham Society.* A Biennial Retrospect of Medicine, *etc.* (1865–6, 1867–8, 1869–70. Report on midwifery and the diseases of women and children. By R. Barnes.) 1867, *etc.* 8°. Ac. **3838/16**.

—— Clinical and Critical Contributions to Obstetric Science and Practice. I. On Uterine Polypus, *etc.* pp. 44. *John Churchill: London*, 1854. 12°. **1177**. d. **31**.

—— A Clinical History of the Medical and Surgical Diseases of Women. pp. xviii. 916. *J. & A. Churchill: London*, 1873. 8°. **7580**. cc. **13**.

—— Second edition. pp. xix. 918. *J. & A. Churchill: London*, 1878. 8°. **07581**. ee. **27**.

—— Lectures on Obstetric Operations, including the treatment of hæmorrhage, *etc.* pp. xxiii. 526. *J. Churchill & Sons: London*, 1870. 8°. **7581**. cc. **9**.

—— Second edition, revised and extended. pp. xxiii. 508. *J. & A. Churchill: London*, 1871. 8°. **7581**. c. **2**.

—— Third edition, revised and extended. pp. xxiii. 606. *J. & A. Churchill: London*, 1876. 8°. **7580**. df. **12**.

—— Fourth edition. pp. xxiii. 503. *J. & A. Churchill: London*, 1886. 8°. **07481**. h. **42**.

—— The Physiology and Treatment of Placenta Præira. Being the Lettsomian lectures on midwifery, for 1857. pp. xii. 208. *John Churchill: London*, 1858. 8°. **7580**. b. **6**.

—— A Synoptical Guide to the Study of Obstetrics, *etc.* pp. vi. 122. *Smith, Elder & Co.: London*, 1883. 8°. **7581**. b. **21**.

BARNES (Robert) *M.D.*, and **BARNES** (Robert Sydenham Fancourt)

—— A System of Obstetric Medicine and Surgery, *etc.* 2 vol. *Smith, Elder & Co.: London*, 1884, 85. 8°. **07581**. ee. **35**.

BARNES (Robert) *Mayor of Manchester.* *See* Barnes (M. L.) Happy Memories of Robert Barnes. 1875. 12°. **4906**. aaaa. **6**.

BARNES (Robert) *of Greys.* A Sermon preached at Henly at the Visitation on the 27. of Aprill, 1626, *etc.* pp. 30. *Printed by J. L.* [*John Lichfield*] *and W. T.* [*William Turner*]: *Oxford*, 1626. 4°. **4473**. f. **23**. (**2**.)

BARNES (Robert Bowling)

—— Infrared Spectroscopy. Industrial applications and bibliography. [By] R. B. Barnes, Robert C. Gore, Urner Liddel and Van Zandt Williams. pp. v. 236. *Reinhold Publishing Corporation: New York*, 1944. 8°. **08715**. cc. **60**.

BARNES (Robert Bowling)

—— [A reissue.] Infrared Spectroscopy, *etc.* (Second printing.) *New York*, 1944. 8°. **8716**. dd. **41**.
The date on the verso of the titlepage is 1946.

BARNES (Robert Freeman) The Dry Collodion Process. pp. 31. *G. Knight & Co.: London*, 1856. 8°. **787**. d. **37**.

—— Second edition . . . augmented. pp. xi. 42. *R. F. Barnes & Co.: London*, 1857. 8°. **787**. c. **51**.

BARNES (Robert Money)

—— A History of the Regiments & Uniforms of the British Army. pp. 335. pl. XXIV. *Seeley Service & Co.: London*, [1950.] 8°. **8832**. dd. **17**.

BARNES (Robert Sydenham Fancourt) *See* Barnes (Robert) *M.D.*, and Barnes (R. S. F.) A System of Obstetric Medicine, *etc.* 1884, *etc.* 8°. **07581**. ee. **35**.

—— *See* Chavasse (P. H.) Chavasse's Advice to a Wife . . . Revised by F. Barnes, *etc.* [1898.] 8°. **7581**. de. **13**.

—— *See* London.—III. *British Gynaecological Society.* The British Gynæcological Journal . . . Edited by F. Barnes. 1885, *etc.* 8°. Ac. **3829**.

—— *See* London.—III. *New Sydenham Society.* Selected Monographs . . . Neugebauer on Spondyl-Olisthesis. (Translated by F. Barnes.) 1888. 8°. Ac. **3838/50**.

—— *See* Martin (Eduard A.) Martin's Atlas of Obstetrics . . . Translated . . . by F. Barnes. 1880. 4°. **7580**. h. **2**.

—— A German-English Dictionary of Words and Terms used in Medicine and its cognate sciences. pp. viii. 300. *H. K. Lewis: London*, 1881 [1880]. 8°. **07305**. f. **34**.

—— [A reissue.] *Toeplitz & Deuticke: Vienna*; [*London* printed,] 1882. 8°. **12963**. bbb. **36**.

—— A Manual of Midwifery for Midwives . . . With illustrations. pp. x. 177. *Smith, Elder & Co.: London*, 1879. 8°. **7581**. df. **18**.

—— Second edition. pp. xiii. 181. *Smith, Elder & Co.: London*, 1883. 8°. **7580**. df. **8**.

—— Third edition. pp. xii. 185. *Smith, Elder & Co.: London*, 1886. 8°. **7581**. aa. **2**.

—— Fifth edition. pp. xii. 187. *Smith, Elder & Co.: London*, 1891. 8°. **07581**. de. **16**.

—— Sixth edition. pp. xii. 189. *Smith, Elder & Co.: London*, 1893. 8°. **07581**. de. **31**.

—— Seventh edition. pp. xii. 189. *Smith, Elder & Co.: London*, 1896. 8°. **07581**. de. **46**.

—— Eighth edition. pp. xii. 191. *Smith, Elder & Co.: London*, 1899. 8°. **07581**. de. **67**.

—— Ninth edition. pp. xii. 191. *Smith, Elder & Co.: London*, 1902. 8°. **07581**. f. **64**.

BARNES (Robert Yallowley) A New and Improved System of Book-Keeping, suitable to be used in all businesses, and effecting a combination of accuracy and completeness with simplicity and ease, *etc.* pp. xii. 443. iv. *J. Haddon & Co.: London*, 1869. 8°. **8505**. bbb. **23**.

—— A Treatise on Book-Keeping; showing the advantages of a clear, distinct, and accurate method of accounts; and explaining the principles of a new and improved system, *etc.* pp. 44. *J. Haddon & Co.: London*, 1867. 8°. **8247**. bb. **40**. (**8**.)

BARNES (Roger William)

—— Endoscopic Prostatic Surgery . . . With 104 illustrations. pp. 232. *Henry Kimpton: London; St. Louis* printed, 1942. 8º. **7484**. c. **6**.

BARNES (Roland B.)

—— Customers' Complaints: how to deal with them. pp. 31. *Efficiency Magazine: London*, [1938.] 8º. [*Up-to-Date Bulletins for Business Men*. no. 82.] W.P. **78/82**.

—— How to get More Interviews. pp. 32. *Efficiency Magazine: London*, [1935.] 8º. [*Up-to-date Bulletins for Business Men*. no. 61.] W.P. **78/61**.

—— How to Make the Most of your Territory. pp. 32. *Efficiency Magazine: London*, [1936.] 8º. [*Up-to-date Bulletins for Business Men*. no. 69.] W.P. **78/69**.

—— Selling to our Seniors. pp. 32. *Efficiency Magazine: London*, [1935.] 8º. [*Up-to-date Bulletins for Business Men*. no. 58.] W.P. **78/58**.

—— Stand up to Him, Man! pp. 32. *Efficiency Magazine: London*, [1939.] 8º. [*Up-to-Date Bulletins for Business Men*. no. 93.] W.P. **78/93**.

BARNES (Ronald Gorell) *Baron Gorell*. *See* Characters. Characters and Observations . . . [By Alexander Pope ?] With a foreword by Lord Gorell. 1930. 8º. **12354**. v. **23**.

—— *See* De Montmorency (J. E. G.) John Gorell Barnes . . . With an introduction by Ronald, third Lord Gorell, *etc.* 1920. 8º. **010855**. c. **44**.

—— *See* Encyclopaedias. Odhams Encyclopaedia, Illustrated. General advisory editor: Lord Gorell, *etc.* 1953. 8º. **12224**. e. **8**.

—— *See* England.—*Committee on the Regent's Park Terrace.* Report of the Committee on the Regent's Park Terraces, *etc.* [Chairman, Lord Gorell.] 1947. 8º. B.S. **68/25. (7.)**

—— Although. pp. 396. *John Murray: London*, 1932. 8º. NN. **19946**.

—— Babes in the African Wood . . . [A narrative of big-game hunting in British East Africa.] With 69 illustrations and a map. pp. xv. 247. *Longmans & Co.: London*, 1911. 8º. **07906**. g. **14**.

—— D. E. Q. pp. vi. 308. *John Murray: London*, 1922. 8º. NN. **8242**.

—— Days of Destiny. War poems at home and abroad. pp. x. 36. *Longmans & Co.: London*, 1917. 8º. **011648**. df. **29**.

—— Devil's Drum. pp. 318. *John Murray: London*, 1929. 8º. NN. **15524**.

—— The Devouring Fire. pp. 351. *John Murray: London*, 1928. 8º. NN. **13826**.

—— Earl's End. pp. 191. *Ward, Lock & Co.: London, Melbourne*, 1951. 8º. NNN. **2198**.

—— Education and the Army. An essay in reconstruction. pp. 291. *Humphrey Milford: London*, 1921. 8º. **08821**. d. **4**.

—— Elizabeth Star. pp. 363. *John Murray: London*, 1933. 8º. NN. **20438**.

—— Fact and Fancy. A lecture, *etc.* pp. 15. *C. Tinling & Co.: Liverpool*, [1928.] 8º. **12301**. s. **56**.

—— The Failure of Self-Disinfection. An address, *etc.* pp. 10. *London*, 1921. 8º. [*National Council for Combating Venereal Diseases.* N.C. 61.] **7642.de.1/61.**

BARNES (Ronald Gorell) *Baron Gorell.*

—— Gauntlet. pp. 358. *John Murray: London*, 1931. 8º. NN. **17658**.

—— He walked in Light. The story of Our Lord. pp. 240. *Odhams Press: London*, 1954. 8º. **4227**. l. **20**.

—— "He Who Fights ——." pp. 320. *John Murray: London*, 1928. 8º. NN. **14701**.

—— In the Days of his Youth, and other poems. pp. 103. *John Murray: London*, 1950. 8º. **11658**. f. **43**.

—— In the Night. pp. viii. 244. *Longmans & Co.: London*, 1917. 8º. NN. **4314**.

—— (Popular edition.) pp. 250. *T. Fisher Unwin: London*, 1925. 8º. NN. **11138**.

—— In the Potter's Field, & other new poems. pp. viii. 98. *John Murray: London*, 1936. 8º. **11655**. bb. **15**.

—— John Keats: the principle of beauty. [With a portrait.] pp. 126. *Sylvan Press: London*, 1948. 8º. **11859**. a. **29**.

—— Last of the English, & other new poems. pp. x. 148. *John Murray: London*, 1939. 8º. **2290**. c. **16**.

—— Let not thy Left Hand. pp. 222. *Ward, Lock & Co.: London & Melbourne*, 1949. 8º. NN. **39356**.

—— Love Triumphant, and other poems. pp. viii. 54. *Longmans & Co.: London*, 1913. 8º. **11649**. h. **43**.

—— Luck, and other new stories. pp. 222. *Ward, Lock & Co.: London & Melbourne*, 1948. 8º. NN. **38396**.

—— Many Mansions. [Poems.] pp. viii. 112. *John Murray: London*, 1926. 8º. **011645**. h. **39**.

—— Murder at Manor House. pp. 190. *Ward, Lock & Co.: London & Melbourne*, 1954. 8º. NNN. **4920**.

—— Murder at Mavering. pp. 208. *John Murray: London*, 1943. 8º. NN. **34248**.

—— New Educational Library. Advisory editor: Lord Gorell. *Odhams Press: London*, 1947– . 8º. W.P. **999**.

—— 1904–1936. Poems, *etc.* [With a portrait.] pp. xv. 592. *John Murray: London*, 1937. 8º. **2292**. g. **31**.

—— Not for an Hour. [Poems.] pp. xi. 126. *John Murray: London*, 1955. 8º. **11657**. l. **83**.

—— Out of the Blue. pp. v. 311. *Longmans & Co.: London*, 1913. 8º. NN. **771**.

—— Pilgrimage. [Poems.] pp. xii. 135. *Longmans & Co.: London*, 1920. 8º. **011648**. f. **147**.

—— Plush. A romance of the House of Lords. pp. 280. *T. Fisher Unwin: London*, 1924. 8º. NN. **9937**.

—— Red Lilac. pp. 315. *John Murray: London*, 1935. 8º. NN. **23889**.

—— Rosamund. pp. vii. 344. *John Murray: London*, 1923. 8º. NN. **9022**.

—— The Spirit of Happiness. [A poem.] pp. 137. *T. Fisher Unwin: London*, 1925. 8º. **11643**. cc. **18**.

—— Unheard Melodies. [In verse.] pp. viii. 111. *John Murray: London*, 1934. 8º. **011641**. df. **120**.

—— Venturers All. pp. viii. 332. *John Murray: London*, 1927. 8º. NN. **13133**.

—— Warrior's Way. [A novel.] pp. 287. *John Murray: London*, 1945. 8º. NN. **35344**.

BARNES (RONALD GORELL) *Baron Gorell.*

—— We Go a Journey. [On the Christian way of life.] pp. 119. *Hutchinson & Co.: London*, [1944.] 8°. **4379. ee. 38.**

—— The Well of Life, *etc.* [On the Christian way of life.] pp. xi. 111. *John Murray: London*, 1951. 8°. **4397. f. 47.**

—— Where there's a Head. pp. 216. *Ward, Lock & Co.: London & Melbourne*, 1952. 8°. NNN. **2688.**

—— Wild Thyme, and other stories. pp. 256. *John Murray: London*, 1941. 8°. NN. **32366.**

—— Wings of the Morning, and other new poems of peace and war. pp. viii. 71. *John Murray: London*, 1948. 8°. **11658. ee. 34.**

BARNES (ROSEMARY)

—— Wigley, *etc.* [A tale.] pp. 112. *Ward Lock & Co.: London & Melbourne*, [1949.] 4°. **12828. bbb. 83.**

BARNES (RUTH A.)

—— I Hear America Singing. An anthology of folk poetry. Collected by R. A. Barnes. Illustrated by Robert Lawson, *etc.* pp. xix. 346. *J. C. Winston Co.: Chicago*, [1937.] 8°. **2290. h. 8.**

BARNES (SIDNEY FRANCIS)

—— The Ashes ablaze. The M.C.C. Australian tour, 1954–55. [With plates.] pp. 192. *William Kimber: London*, 1955. 8°. **7920. l. 64.**

—— It isn't Cricket, *etc.* [An autobiography. With plates, including portraits.] pp. 175. *William Kimber: London*, 1953. 8°. **7920. b. 94.**

—— It isn't Cricket. pp. 192. *Hamilton & Co.: London*, 1955. 8°. [*Panther Books.* no. 515.] W.P. B. **29/515.**

BARNES (SIDNEY WILLSON)

—— *See* RAHN (O.) Invisible Radiations of Organisms . . . With an introduction to the Physics of Radiation by S. W. Barnes, *etc.* 1936. 8°. **08712. c. 5.**

BARNES (STANLEY) *Angler.*

—— Anglers' Knots in Gut and Nylon. pp. 158. *Cornish Bros.: Birmingham*, [1947.] 8°. **7916. ee. 48.**

—— Anglers' Knots in Gut and Nylon . . . Second edition, revised and enlarged. pp. 262. *Cornish Bros.: Birmingham*, 1951. 8°. **7919. e. 33.**

BARNES (STANLEY) *M.D.*

—— The Birmingham Hospitals Centre, *etc.* [With illustrations and plans.] pp. xxi. 144. *Stanford & Mann: Birmingham*, 1952. 8°. **7689. d. 23.**

BARNES (SUSAN B.)

—— *See* ANDERSON GALLERIES, *New York.* Catalogue of Art Objects, Bronzes, Georgian Silver, Chinese Rugs and Porcelains from the estates of the late J. D. Crimmins and S. B. Barnes and other consignors, *etc.* [1918.] 8°. **07806. h. 53. (2.)**

BARNES (SYDNEY FRANCIS)

—— *See* WHITE (Wilfrid S.) Sydney Barnes, *etc.* [1937.] 8°. **07908. e. 33.**

—— Eyes on the Ashes. [A report of the 1953 Test Matches. With plates.] pp. 206. *William Kimber: London*, 1953. 8°. **7919. f. 52.**

BARNES (T. E.)

—— *See* ROGERS (O. C.) Soil Survey of Fulton County, Indiana. By O. C. Rogers . . . T. E. Barnes, *etc.* 1946. 8°. [*U.S. Department of Agriculture. Soil Survey.* ser. 1937. no. 17.] A.S. **881/2.**

BARNES (T. H.)

—— Catching Trout . . . Illustrated by Joy Barnes. pp. 111. *Herbert Jenkins: London*, [1946.] 8°. **7918. aa. 57.**

BARNES (T. WALLIS) Hints to Prospectors, a series of easy tests for metals, *etc.* [Reprinted from the "Australian Mining Standard."] pp. xii. 121. *Australian Mining Standard: Sydney*, 1892. 8°. **7105. aa. 4.**

BARNES (THOMAS) *D.D. See* YATES (John) *Dissenting Minister.* A Funeral Discourse occasioned by the death of the Rev. Dr. Barnes, *etc.* 1810. 8°. **4476. f. 117. (2.)**

—— A Discourse delivered at the Commencement of the Manchester Academy, *etc.* pp. 37. 19. *W. Eyres: Warrington*, [1786.] 8°. **8306. de. 20. (1.)**

—— [Another issue.] *See* HARRISON (Ralph) A Sermon preached at the Dissenting Chapel in Cross-street, Manchester, *etc.* [1786.] 8°. **4476. b. 129. (4.)**

—— A Sermon, preached at Rochdale, April 13, 1806, on occasion of the death of the Rev. Thomas Threlkeld . . . To which is added an appendix, containing some account of the life and character of Mr. Threlkeld, *etc.* pp. 56. *S. Russell: Manchester*, 1806. 8°. **4804. h. 5. (1.)**

BARNES (THOMAS) *Editor of the Times. See* also CRITICUS, *pseud.* [i.e. T. Barnes.]

—— *See* FUNNEFELLO (Abel) pseud. The Blue-Coat Boy; or, domestic reminiscences of Mister Thomas Bounce, driver of "The Turnabout" [i.e. T. Barnes], *etc.* 1837. 8°. **838. h. 19.**

—— *See* HUDSON (Derek) Thomas Barnes of the Times . . . With selections from his critical essays, never before reprinted, edited by Harold Child. [With portraits.] 1943. 8°. **10861. b. 3.**

—— *See* PERIODICAL PUBLICATIONS.—London.—*The Times.* Thomas Barnes, 1785–1841, *etc.* [Reprinted from "The History of The Times." With a portrait.] 1935. 8°. **Cup.510.b.2/5.**

BARNES (THOMAS) *Gardener.* A New Method of Propagating Fruit-trees, and Flowering Shrubs . . . Second edition. pp. 40. pl. 7. *R. Baldwin & J. Jackson: London*, 1759. 8°. **235. k. 12. (1.)**

—— [Another copy.] **116. k. 6.**

—— The third edition. pp. 40. pl. 2. *R. Baldwin & J. Jackson: London*, 1762. 8°. **7073. b. 6.**

—— [Another issue.] *See* HILL (John) *M.D., etc.* Botanical Tracts, *etc.* 1762. 8°. **447. b. 7. (8.)**

BARNES (THOMAS) *M.D.* Account of Mr. Robert Bowman of Irthington in Cumberland, who has completed his 115th year. pp. 6. 1820. 8°. **1414. d. 1.**

—— Dissertatio medica inauguralis de erysipelate, *etc.* pp. 29. *Abernethy & Walker: Edinburgi*, 1817. 8°. **1184. b. 11. (6.)**

—— Observations on the Expediency and Advantage of establishing a General Infirmary at Carlisle . . . Second edition, with an appendix. pp. 64. *Charles Thurnam: Carlisle*, 1831. 8°. **7687. e. 18.**

BARNES (THOMAS) *Minister of St. Margaret's, New Fish Street, London.* The Gales of Grace; or, the Spirituall Winde: wherein the mysterie of sanctification is opened and handled. pp. 249. *H. L. [Humphrey Lownes] for Nathanael Newbery: London*, 1622. 8°. **4257. aaa. 4**

BARNES (THOMAS) *Minister of St. Margaret's, New Fish Street, London*

—— Needfull Helpes: against Desperate Perplexitie; and Deepe Securitie. As they haue beene delivered in sundry Sermons, *etc.* (Cure for the Comfortles, *etc.*—The Wise-Mans Forecast against the Evill Time.—Sions Sweets: or the Spouses spikenard; and mysticall myrrhe.) 3 pt. *I. D.* [*John Dawson*] *for Nathaniell Newbery: London,* 1624. 4°. **4452. d. 4.**
In this copy the general titlepage has been misbound at the beginning of the third part.

—— Vox Belli, or, an Alarum to Warre. pp. 41. *Printed by H. L.* [*Humphrey Lownes*] *for Nathanael Newbery: London,* 1626. 4°. **1471. aa. 4. (1.)**

—— [Another copy.] Vox Belli, *etc.* *London,* 1626. 4°. **8026. a. 23.**
Mutilated.

BARNES (THOMAS) *Minister of the Gospel.* Safe Conduct to the Christians Resting-Place. In a discourse . . . With a preface by Timothy Rogers. pp. 251. *W. & J. Marshall: London,* 1702. 12°. **4409. d. 10.**

BARNES (THOMAS) *Westminster-Scholar.* See ISOCRATES. [*Archidamus.—English.*] Archidamus, or, the Councill of Warre . . . Translated by T. Barnes. 1624. 4°. **834. g. 30. (3.)**

BARNES (THOMAS SCOTT) and **BARNES** (WALTER SCOTT)

—— A Unit Building. Report on (A) the necessity for the early erection of the unit building outlined herein . . . as a proof of the usefulness of multi-storey tenements . . . and (B) the conditions under which such a unit building can be erected so as to yield a reasonable return on its capital cost. [With plans.] ff. 12. *London,* 1934. fol. **1736. e. 11.**
Reproduced from typewriting.

BARNES (THURLOW WEED) Memoir of Thurlow Weed. 1884. *See* WEED (T.) Autobiography, *etc.* 1883, *etc.* 8°. **010882. m. 9.**

BARNES (URIAH)

—— *See* UNITED STATES OF AMERICA.—*Laws and Statutes.*—I. Barnes' Federal Code . . . Edited by U. Barnes, *etc.* (1923 Supplement . . . Edited by U. Barnes.) [1921, *etc.*] 8°. **6618. c. 4.**

BARNES (VIOLA FLORENCE) The Dominion of New England. A study in British Colonial policy. pp. viii. 303. *New Haven,* 1923. 8°. [*Yale Historical Publications.* Miscellany. vol. 11.] **Ac. 2692. md/3.**

—— Land Tenure in English Colonial Charters of the Seventeenth Century . . . Reprinted from "Essays in Colonial History." pp. 40. *Yale University Press:* [*New Haven,*] 1931. 8°. **9555. df. 23.**

—— Sir William Phips, first Royal Governor of the Province of Massachusetts Bay, 1691–1695. (The Rise of William Phips.—Phippius Maximus.) [Articles extracted from "The New England Quarterly."] 2 pt. [*Baltimore,* 1928.] 8°. **010885. eee. 26.**

BARNES (W. C.) Potiphar's Wife. [A tale.] pp. 149. *S. C. Brown & Co.: London,* 1903. 8°. **012643. aaa. 28.**

BARNES (W. G.) Prices of Trunk Telephone Calls from London. [With "Scottish Supplement."] 2 pt. *Telecost Co.: London,* 1924. 8°. **08244. e. 19.**

BARNES (W. L.) An Essay on the Ancient Greek Heroes. *See* PERIODICAL PUBLICATIONS.—London.—*Boys' Own Magazine.* Prize Papers . . . for the Boys' Own Magazine. 1864. 8°. **12273. d. 5.**

BARNES (WALLEY)

—— Captain of Wales, *etc.* [Reminiscences. With plates, including portraits.] pp. 208. *Stanley Paul & Co.: London,* 1953. 8°. **10864. aa. 15.**

BARNES (WALTER) *See* CHURCHILL (Winston) The Crisis . . . Edited by W. Barnes. 1921. 16°. **12199.a.1/124.**

—— The Children's Poets. Analyses and appraisals of the greatest English and American poets for children, *etc.* pp. vi. 264. *World Book Co.: Yonkers-on-Hudson,* 1924. 8°. **011850. aaa. 66.**

—— English for American High Schools. A book of language activities. pp. xvi. 646. *Rand, McNally & Co.: New York,* [1931.] 8°. **12985. dd. 27.**

—— The Realm of Reading. [By W. Barnes and others.] 6 vol. *American Book Co.: New York,* [1941,] 1940. 8°. **12299. bb. 10.**

BARNES (WALTER) and **LANE** (MARTHA ALLEN LUTHER)

—— An Easy Primer, *etc.* [A reading book for children.] pp. 124. *Ginn & Co.: Boston,* [1920.] 8°. **12980. cc. 15.**

BARNES (WALTER J.)

—— Income Tax Handbook. pp. xiv. 222. *Natal Witness: Pietermaritzburg,* 1925. 8°. **6605. d. 28.**

—— Income Tax Handbook . . . Second edition, revised. pp. xxiv. 284. *Natal Witness: Pietermaritzburg,* 1929. 8°. **6605. d. 29.**

—— Income Tax Handbook . . . Third edition, revised. pp. xxxii. 374. *Natal Witness: Pietermaritzburg,* 1933. 8°. **06605. bb. 33.**

—— Income Tax Handbook. By W. J. Barnes . . . assisted by A. W. Osborn . . . Fourth edition, revised. pp. xl. 464. *Butterworth & Co.: Durban; printed in Great Britain,* 1939. 8°. **06605. bbb. 8.**

—— Barnes' Income Tax Handbooks. By A. W. Osborn . . . assisted by H. Rothschild . . . Fifth edition. pp. xxiii. 308. *Butterworth & Co.: Durban,* 1944. 4°.

—— 1944 Supplement, *etc.* (Second [*etc.*] Cumulative Supplement, 1945 [*etc.*]). *Butterworth & Co.: Durban,* 1944– . 4°. **6608. d. 3.**

—— Income Tax Handbook . . . Sixth edition by A. W. Osborn. pp. xxxii. 331. *Butterworth & Co.: Durban,* 1947. 8°. **6608. dd. 1.**

—— 1948 Supplement, *etc.* pp. 31. *Butterworth & Co.: Durban,* 1948. 8°. **6608. dd. 1a.**

—— Barnes' Income Tax Handbook. A commentary on the Income Tax Act, 1949. By B. E. J. Blann . . . Incorporating a cumulative supplement to the sixth edition. pp. 65. *Butterworth & Co.: Durban,* 1949. 8°. **6608. dd. 1/b.**

—— Income Tax Handbook . . . Seventh edition. Edited by B. E. J. Blann. pp. xxxiii. 275. *Butterworth & Co.: Durban,* 1951. 8°. **8232. k. 4.**

—— Questions & Answers on Income Tax. Issued as a supplement to Barnes' Income Tax Handbook. 3 pt. *Butterworth & Co.: Durban,* [1951.] 8°. **8232. k. 4a.**

—— South African Income Tax Tables and Table of Rates and Rebates from 1941. Compiled by B. E. J. Blann . . . Issued as a supplement to Barnes' Income Tax Handbook. *Butterworth & Co.: Durban,* [1951.] 8°. **8232. k. 4b.**

BARNES (WALTER J.)

—— A Commentary on the Income Tax Act, 1952, by B. E. J. Blann . . . being a Supplement to the seventh edition, *etc.* pp. 29. *Butterworth & Co.: Durban,* 1952. 8°. **8232. k. 4c.**

—— Income Tax Practice in South Africa. [With a table.] pp. xxviii. 291. *Hortors: Johannesburg & Capetown,* 1919. 8°. **06605. c. 30.**

—— Income Tax Simplified . . . Second edition. pp. xiv. 184. *Natal Witness: Pietermaritzburg,* 1920. 8°. **6606. c. 28.**

BARNES (WALTER J.) and **OSBORN** (A. W.) *Chartered Accountant.*

—— Excess Profits Duty Handbook. pp. x. 112. 13. *Butterworth & Co.: Durban,* 1940. 8°.

—— Supplement, 1941. pp. 31. *Butterworth & Co.: Durban,* 1941. 8°. **6428. tt. 15.**

The second edition is entered under OSBORN *(A. W.) Chartered Accountant, and* CORNISH *(C. Saint-R.).*

BARNES (WALTER SCOTT)

—— *See* BARNES (Thomas S.) and (W. S.) A Unit Building, *etc.* 1934. fol. **1736. e. 11.**

BARNES (WALTON MARSH)

—— The Favourable Soil for Tuberculosis. A theory, with suggestions for treatment . . . Part I. pp. xii. 138. *Ebenezer Baylis: Worcester,* 1931. 8°. **7612.d.30.**
Printed for private circulation.

BARNES (WENDY)

—— The Adventures of Timothy and Peter . . . Illustrations by George Brook. *J. Fairston: London,* [1944.] 8°. [" *Tally-Ho " Books for Children.* no. 2.] W.P. **784/2.**

—— The " Deserted Fishing Village " . . . Illustrated by George Brook. *London,* [1946.] 8°. [' *Tally-Ho ' Books for Children.* no. 11.] W.P. **784/11.**

—— The Ocean Princess . . . With pictures by L. David Harris. pp. 46. *J. Fairston: London,* [1944.] 8°. [" *Tally-Ho " Books for Children.*] W.P. **784/5.**

BARNES (WILFRID J.) *See* RUSSIA.—*Orthodox Church: Synod.* Russian Observations upon the American Prayer Book. Translated by W. J. Barnes, *etc.* 1917. 8°. [*Alcuin Club Tracts.* no. 12.] Ac. **2066.**

BARNES (WILFRID JOHN)

—— Portugal, Gateway to Greatness. [With portraits.] pp. xii. 188. pl. XII. *Edward Stanford: London,* 1950. 8°. **9196. b. 16.**

BARNES (WILLIAM) *Cavalier.* A True and Perfect Relation of the seizing the House of one Master William Barnes a Cavalier, and apprehending him neer Wollage in Kent, by Captaine Willoughby and his company of volunteers . . . And likewise of the seizing of threescore and fifteene peeces of ordnance, by the said Captain and his company in the woodyard at Wollage . . . on Friday the 26 of August, 1642, *etc.* pp. 6. *For T.S.: London,* 1642. 4°. **E. 115. (13.)**

BARNES (WILLIAM) *Cowkeeper.* A Few Suggestions as to the Cause and Cure of Typhoid Engorgement, or Congestion of the Lungs in Cattle, *etc.* pp. 14. *Leath & Ross: London,* 1858. 8°. **7295. d. 2.**

BARNES (WILLIAM) *Dorsetshire Poet. See* BAXTER (Lucy E.) The Life of William Barnes, *etc.* [With a portrait.] 1887. 8°. **10826. df. 15.**

—— *See* BIBLE.—*Song of Solomon. [English, Dialects.]* The Song of Solomon in the Dorset Dialect . . . By W. Barnes. 1859. 16°. **3050. a. 41. (4.)**

BARNES (WILLIAM) *Dorsetshire Poet.*

—— *See* DUGDALE (Arthur G.) William Barnes of Dorset, *etc.* [With portraits.] 1953. 8°. **10863. f. 24.**

—— *See* HARDY (Thomas) *O.M.* William Barnes: a biographical note. 1894. 8°. [JOHNSON *(Lionel P.) The Art of Thomas Hardy.*] **11853. e. 9.**

—— *See* JACOBS (Willis D.) William Barnes, Linguist. 1952. 8°. [*University of New Mexico Publications in Language and Literature.* no. 9.] Ac. **2685. f/9.**

—— *See* POOLE (Jacob) A Glossary . . . of the Old Dialect of the English Colony in the Baronies of Forth and Bargy . . . Edited . . . by W. Barnes. 1867. 8°. **12985. bb. 55.**

—— *See* UDAL (John S.) Dorsetshire Folk-lore . . . With a fore-say by . . . W. Barnes [and a portrait of W. Barnes]. 1922. 8°. **12431. ppp. 30.**

—— An Arithmetical and Commercial Dictionary, containing a simple explanation of commercial and mathematical terms and arithmetical operations, *etc.* pp. 76. *Longman & Co.: London,* 1840. 12°. **717. b. 54.**

—— Early England and the Saxon English; with some notes on the father-stock of the Saxon-English, the Frisians. pp. 178. *J. R. Smith: London,* 1869. 12°. **12984. aaa. 37.**

—— The Elements of English Grammar, with a set of questions and exercises. pp. viii. 112. *Longman & Co.: London,* 1842. 16°. **1212. i. 38.**

—— [Another copy.] **828. a. 7.**

—— The Elements of Linear Perspective and the Projection of Shadows, *etc.* pp. 57. *Longman & Co.: London,* 1842. 12°. **1043. d. 42.**

—— [Another copy.] **786. d. 16.**

—— A Few Words on the Advantages of a more common Adoption of the Mathematics as a Branch of Education, or subject of study. pp. 23. *Whittaker & Co.: London,* 1834. 12°. **8536. a. 18.**

—— Se Gefylsta—the Helper: an Anglo-Saxon Delectus. Serving as a first class-book of the language. pp. vi. 78. *J. R. Smith: London,* 1849. 12°. **12260. c. 10.**

—— A Glossary of the Dorset Dialect, with a grammar of its word shapening and wording. pp. vii. 124. *M. & E. Case: Dorchester; Trübner & Co.: London,* 1886. 8°. **2278. d. 15.**

—— A Grammar and Glossary of the Dorset Dialect, with the history, outspreading, and bearings of South-Western English. pp. 103. 1863. *See* LONDON.—III. *Philological Society.* Transactions, *etc.* 1864. [1854, *etc.*] 8°. Ac. **9930/3.**

—— A Guide to Dorchester and its Neighbourhood, *etc.* [By W. Barnes.] pp. iv. 30. [1864?] 8°. *See* DORCHESTER. Cup. **401. c. 16.**

—— A Guide to Dorchester and its Neighbourhood, *etc.* [By W. Barnes.] pp. iii. 31. [1884.] 8°. *See* DORCHESTER. **10351. aaa. 56. (4.)**

—— [Another copy.] A Guide to Dorchester, *etc.* [1884.] 8°. *See* DORCHESTER. **10347. c. 13. (4.)**

—— A Guide to Dorchester and its Neighbourhood . . . [By W. Barnes.] Revised from the original edition. pp. 30. 1887. 8°. *See* DORCHESTER. **10347. c. 17. (12.)**

—— An Investigation of the Laws of Case in Language, exhibited in a system of natural cases; with some observations on prepositions, tense and voice, *etc.* pp. 49. *Longman & Co.: London*, 1840. 12°. **828**. d. **9**.

—— Notes on Ancient Britain and the Britons. pp. viii. 167. *J. R. Smith: London*, 1858. 12°. **1303**. a. **41**.

—— Orra: a Lapland tale . . . The wood-cuts engraved by the author. pp. viii. 30. *J. Criswick: Dorchester*, 1822. 8°. C. **100**. h. **29**.

—— An Outline of English Speech-Craft. pp. viii. 92. *C. Kegan Paul & Co.: London*, 1878. 8°. **12985**. ccc. **34**.

—— An Outline of Rede-Craft—Logic, with English wording. pp. viii. 56. *C. Kegan Paul & Co.: London*, 1880. 8°. **8469**. bb. **19**.

—— A Philological Grammar grounded upon English, and formed from a comparison of more than sixty languages. Being an introduction to the science of grammar, and a help to grammars of all languages, especially English, Latin, and Greek. pp. x. 312. *J. R. Smith: London*, 1854. 8°. **012902**. h. **18**.

—— Poems of Rural Life in Common English. pp. xii. 200. *Macmillan & Co.: London*, 1868. 8°. **11647**. bbb. **2**.

—— Poems of Rural Life, in the Dorset Dialect: with a dissertation and glossary. pp. vii. 373. *J. R. Smith: London*, 1844. 12°. **1077**. i. **39**.

—— Second edition. The dissertation and glossary enlarged, *etc.* pp. viii. 411. *J. R. Smith: London*, 1848. 12°.. **1077**. h. **76**.

—— Third edition. pp. xii. 211. *J. R. Smith: London*, 1862. 12°. **1077**. h. **78**.
This edition does not include the Dissertation.

—— Hwomely Rhymes. A second collection of poems in the Dorset dialect. pp. viii. 208. *J. R. Smith: London*, 1859. 12°. **1077**. h. **77**.

—— Poems of Rural Life in the Dorset Dialect. Second collection. Second edition. pp. viii. 212. *J. R. Smith: London*, 1863. 8°. **11649**. aaa. **10**.

—— Poems of Rural Life in the Dorset Dialect. Third collection. pp. viii. 133. *J. R. Smith: London*, 1862. 12°. **1077**. h. **79**.

—— Poems of Rural Life in the Dorset Dialect . . . Third collection. Second edition. pp. viii. 140. *John Russell Smith: [London,]* 1869. 8°. **11661**. b. **3**.
With an additional titlepage dated 1870.

—— Poems of Rural Life in the Dorset Dialect. (First—third collection.) pp. xi. 467. *C. Kegan Paul & Co.: London*, 1879. 8°. **2292.f.1.**

—— Poems, partly of Rural Life, in national English. pp. vii. 144. *J. R. Smith: London*, 1846. 12°. **11644**. eeee. **13**.

—— "Ruth," a short drama from the Bible. With a dissertation on the law of the Goel-ha-dom. pp. 28. *Henry Ling: Dorchester*, [1881.] 8°. **11783**. bb. **31**.

—— Tiw; or, a View of the roots and stems of the English as a Teutonic tongue. pp. xxiv. 324. *J. R. Smith: London*, 1862 [1861]. 12°. **12982**. aa. **44**.

—— Views of Labour and Gold. pp. 190. *J. R. Smith: London*, 1859. 12°. **8275**. a. **41**.

—— [Selections, edited by C. Sayle.] [1891.] *See* MILES (Alfred H.) The Poets and the Poetry of the Century, *etc.* vol. 2. [1891, *etc.*] 8°. **11603.cc.20/2.**

—— Select Poems . . . Chosen and edited with a preface and glossarial notes by Thomas Hardy. [With a portrait.] pp. xvi. 196. *Henry Frowde: London*, 1908. 8°. **11611**. df. **21**.

—— A Selection of Poems of Rural Life in the Dorset Dialect. By William Barnes. Edited by his son [i.e. W. M. Barnes]. pp. viii. 132. *Kegan Paul & Co.: London*, 1909. 16°. **011653**. i. **55**.

—— Twenty Poems in Common English. With an introduction by John Drinkwater. pp. 45. *Basil Blackwell: Oxford*, 1925. 8°. [*Little Nineteenth Century Classics.* no. 3.] **012202**. a. **3/3**.

—— Poems Grave and Gay . . . Selected and edited with foreword and biographical notes by Giles Dugdale. [With a portrait.] pp. xix. 116. *Longmans: Dorchester*, 1949. 8°. **11605**. cc. **31**.

—— Selected Poems of William Barnes, 1800–1886. Edited with an introduction by Geoffrey Gregson. [With a portrait.] pp. x. 296. *Routledge & Kegan Paul: London*, 1950. 8°. [*The Muses' Library.*] **W.P.3362/6.**

BARNES (WILLIAM) *M.I. Mech. E.* Excavating Machinery, as represented by power shovels, drag lines & grabbing cranes. pp. xvi. 247. *Ernest Benn: London*, 1928. 8°. **8769**. cc. **8**.

BARNES (WILLIAM) *of Albany, N.Y.* *See* NEW YORK, *State of.* [*Public Documents, etc.*] General Statute Laws of the State of New York relating to Fire, Marine, Life and Casualty Insurance Companies, and all miscellaneous insurance laws passed by the legislature from 1859 to and including 1871, *etc.* 1871. 8°. **6736**. bb. **4**.

—— New York Insurance Reports. Condensed edition. 1830 (–1863). vol. 1, 2. *Weed, Parsons & Co.: Albany; C. & E. Layton: London*, 1873. 8°. **6736**. g. **4**.

—— The Settlement and Early History of Albany. pp. 100. *J. Munsell: Albany*, 1864. 8°. **10411**. cc. **14**.

BARNES (WILLIAM) *of Salisbury, Mass.* *See* HOYT (David W.) Hoyt Family . . . with . . . an appendix, containing the family history of W. Barnes of Salisbury, *etc.* 1857. 8°. **9914**. a. **12**.

BARNES (WILLIAM) *of Trowbridge.* *See* BARTLETT (George) *of Trowbridge.* Death versus Life . . . To which is appended, a few words in reference to an unmanly assertion in a lecture on "Manliness," read by Mr. Barnes. 1858. 8°. **4374**. e. **11**.

—— Sprinkling not Christian Baptism; in reply to a tract entitled "Immersion not Christian Baptism." pp. 15. *Simpkin, Marshall & Co.: London*, 1851. 8°. **4325**. e. **5**.

BARNES (WILLIAM) *Pastor of the Congregational Church in Hampton.* American Slavery. A sermon preached at Hampton, Conn. . . . the day of the annual public fast. pp. 23. *Elihu Geer: Hartford*, 1843. 8°. **4486**. f. **15**.

BARNES (WILLIAM) *Rector of Brixton Deverill.* Evidences of the Truth and Certainty of the Christian Religion contrasted with the evils of infidelity, *etc.* pp. xv. 416. *Bell & Daldy: London*, 1858. 8°. **4016**. b. **5**.

—— The Faithful Pastor. A sermon, *etc.* pp. 37. *G. L. Dinsdale: Warminster*, [1840.] 8°. **908**. d. 2. (5.)

—— A Few Words in defence of that reformed part of the Catholic Church established in these realms. A sermon, *etc.* pp. 45. *M. Bell: Richmond* [*Yorks.*], 1831. 8°. **908**. d. 2. (6.)

BARNES (WILLIAM) *Rector of Brixton Deverill.*

—— A Funeral Sermon preached in the parish church of Horningsham . . . on the death of the late Rev. F. Skurray, *etc.* pp. 23. *W. H. Taylor: Warminster,* [1848.] 8°. **908.** d. **2.** (**7.**)

—— Remarks on the Rev. Lord Charles Thynne's recent letter to his late parishioners. pp. 50. *J. H. Parker: Oxford,* 1853. 8°. **3940.** f. **14.**

—— A Selection of Psalms and Hymns, intended for public worship, as well as for the use of families/. . . Second edition. pp. 417. *T. & A. Bowman: Richmond* [*Yorks.*], 1833. 24°. **3435.** aaa. **24.**
See BIBLE.—Psalms.—Selections. [English.]

—— A Selection of Psalms and Hymns, intended for public worship, as well as for the use of families and individuals . . . A new edition, revised. pp. 451. 1840. 12°. *See* BIBLE.—*Psalms.—Selections.* [*English.*] **3440.** ppp. **12.**

—— A new edition revised, with an appendix selected by the Rev. Lawrence Ottley. pp. vii. 398. *John Bell: Richmond* [*Yorks.*], 1852. 12°. **3436.** d. **6.**
See BIBLE.—Psalms.—Selections.[English.]

—— A Sermon on Confirmation. A sermon preached at Richmond, *etc.* pp. 25. *M. Bell: Richmond* [*Yorks.*], 1832. 16°. **908.** b. **9.** (**2.**)

—— A Sermon on Confirmation. A sermon preached in the parish churches of Hill and Brixton Deverill, *etc.* pp. 28. *G. L. Dinsdale: Warminster,* [1840.] 12°. **908.** b. **1.** (**5.**)

BARNES (WILLIAM) *Teacher of Singing.* How to improve the Voice. A treatise, *etc.* pp. 13. *John Guest: London,* 1874. 8°. **7897.** g. **12.**

BARNES (WILLIAM CROFT) *See* RAINE (William M.) and BARNES (W. C.) Cattle. 1930. 8°. **07295.** ee. **43.**

—— The Story of the Range, *etc.* [With plates.] pp. iii. 60. 1926. 8°. *See* UNITED STATES OF AMERICA.—*Department of Agriculture.—Forest Service.* A.S. **851/8.**

BARNES (WILLIAM EMERY) *See* ABRAHAM, *the Patriarch.* The Testament of Abraham . . . With an appendix containing extracts from the Arabic version . . . by W. E. Barnes. 1892. 8°. [*Texts and Studies.* vol. 2. no. 2.] **03605.h.21/2.**

—— *See* BIBLE. [*English.*] The Cambridge Bible for Schools, *etc.* (The Two Books of Kings, in the Revised Version. With introduction and notes by W. E. Barnes.) 1877, *etc.* 8°. **2200.** aa. **7.**

—— *See* BIBLE. [*English.*] The Cambridge Bible for Schools, *etc.* (The Books of Chronicles. With maps, notes, and introduction by W. E. Barnes.) 1877, *etc.* 8°. **03107.** e. **3/16.**

—— *See* BIBLE. [*English.*] The Cambridge Bible for Schools and Colleges. (Haggai and Zechariah. With notes and introduction by W. E. Barnes.) 1877, *etc.* 8°. **2200.** aa. **21.**

—— *See* BIBLE. [*English.*] Oxford Commentaries (Westminster Commentaries), *etc.* (The Psalms. With introduction and notes by W. E. Barnes.) 1899, *etc.* 8°. **03126.** i. **35.**

—— *See* BIBLE.—*Pentateuch.* [*Syriac.*] Pentateuchus Syriace. Post S. Lee recognovit emendavit edidit G. E. Barnes, *etc.* 1914. 4°. **753.** c. **40.**

—— *See* BIBLE.—*Psalms.* [*Syriac.*] The Peshitta Psalter . . . Edited with an apparatus criticus by W. E. Barnes. 1904. 4°. **753.i.29.**

BARNES (WILLIAM EMERY)

—— *See* BIBLE.—*Isaiah.* [*English.*] Isaiah . . . Explained by W. E. Barnes. 1901, *etc.* 8°. **03107.** e. **2/5.**

—— *See* BIBLE.—*Appendix.* [*Miscellaneous.*] A Companion to Biblical Studies: being a revised and re-written edition of the Cambridge Companion to the Bible. Edited by W. E. Barnes. 1916. 8°. **03128.** k. **33.**

—— *See* MACCABEES. The Fourth Book of Maccabees and kindred documents in Syriac . . . With an introduction and translations by W. E. Barnes. 1895. 8°. **753.** hh. **8.**

—— After the Celebration of the Oxford Movement. Some considerations. pp. 23. *Bowes & Bowes: Cambridge,* 1933. 8°. **4106.** cc. **20.**

—— An Apparatus criticus to Chronicles in the Peshitta version, with a discussion of the value of the Codex Ambrosianus. pp. xxxiv. 62. *University Press: Cambridge,* 1897. 8°. **3165.** e. **37.**

—— Canonical and Uncanonical Gospels. With a translation of the recently discovered fragment of the Gospel of Peter, and a selection from the sayings of Our Lord not found in the Four Gospels. pp. xii. 112. *Longmans & Co.: London,* 1893. 8°. **3226.** de. **29.**

—— The Creed of St. Athanasius. A lecture, *etc.* pp. 31. *Macmillan & Bowes: Cambridge,* 1905. 8°. **4109.** i. **19.** (**2.**)

—— Early Christians at Prayer, 1–400 A.D., *etc.* pp. xi. 180. *Methuen & Co.: London,* 1925 [1924]. 8°. **03456.** e. **19.**

—— The Forgiveness of Jesus Christ. A study in the Gospels. pp. ix. 134. *S.P.C.K.: London,* 1936. 8°. **03226.** ff. **39.**

—— Gospel Criticism and Form Criticism. pp. ix. 83. *T. & T. Clark: Edinburgh,* 1936. 8°. **03226.** e. **78.**

—— Hermas . . . A lecture, *etc.* pp. 24. *Bowes & Bowes: Cambridge,* 1922. 8°. **04530.** g. **10.**

—— The Last Supper and the Lord's Supper. A lecture, *etc.* pp. 31. *Bowes & Bowes: Cambridge,* 1927. 8°. **03226.** de. **30.**

—— Lex in Corde—the Law in the Heart. Studies in the Psalter. pp. xii. 264. *Longmans & Co.: London,* 1910. 8°. **03089.** h. **23.**

—— The Permanent Value of the Old Testament. *See* SWETE (Henry B.) Essays on some Theological Questions of the Day, *etc.* 1905. 8°. **4379.** h. **33.**

—— Peterhouse, Domus Divi Petri, 1280–1931. A sketch. pp. 15. *Bowes & Bowes: Cambridge,* 1931. 8°. **08364.** ee. **79.**

—— The Revision of the Lectionary. pp. 30. *J. Nisbet & Co.: London,* 1910. 8°. [*Prayer-Book Revision Series.* no. 4.] **3476.** c. **78/4.**

—— The Testimony of Josephus to Jesus Christ. pp. 22. *S.P.C.K.: London,* 1920. 8°. [*Biblical Studies.*] **03127.de.80/3.**

BARNES (WILLIAM ENGLISH) *See* BAYLEY (*Sir* John) *Bart.* A Summary of the Law of Bills of Exchange . . . The third edition, by W. E. Barnes. 1812. 8°. **515.** c. **6.**

BARNES (*Mrs.* WILLIAM G.) *See* BARNES (A. R.) *Mrs.*

BARNES (WILLIAM GEORGE) *See* BURNET (Gilbert) *Vicar of Coggeshall.* Practical Sermons, *etc.* [Edited by W. G. Barnes.] 1747. 8°. **1021.** h. **16, 17.**

BARNES (WILLIAM GEORGE)

—— Charity and Charity Schools defended. A sermon, *etc.* pp. 28. *John Wyat: London*, 1727. 8°. **693. d. 23.**

—— The Nature of Offences. A sermon, *etc.* pp. vii. 24. *Joseph Smith: London*, 1728. 8°. **693. d. 24.**

—— On the Annunciation of the Virgin Mary. [A sermon.] *See* FAMILY CHAPLAIN. The Family Chaplain, *etc.* vol. 1. 1775. 8°. **4455. cc. 10.**

—— On the Epiphany. [A sermon.] *See* FAMILY CHAPLAIN. The Family Chaplain, *etc.* vol. 1. 1775. 8°. **4455. cc. 10.**

—— On the Holy Innocents Day. [A sermon.] *See* FAMILY CHAPLAIN. The Family Chaplain, *etc.* vol. 2. 1775. 8°. **4455. cc. 10.**

—— The Powers that be, how ordained of God; and the duty of magistrate and subject to answer the ends of such institutions. A sermon, *etc.* pp. 18. *London*, 1738. 8°. **693. d. 25.**

—— [Another copy.] **225. h. 2. (19.)**

—— A Sermon preached on occasion of the present unnatural Rebellion, *etc.* pp. 16. *J. Clarke: London*, 1745. 4°. **225. i. 2. (13.)**

—— *Begin.* To the Worthy Inhabitants of St. James's, Clerkenwell, *etc.* [An address by Barnes in support of his candidature to succeed Gilbert Burnet as minister of that parish.] [1745.] *s. sh.* fol. **1855. c. 4. (42.)**

BARNES (WILLIAM GEORGE KYNASTON) How to Keep "Fit"; or, the Sailor's guide to health in all parts of the world, *etc.* pp. 37. *London*, 1905. 16°. [*Gale & Polden's Naval Series.*] **8807. aaaa.**

BARNES (WILLIAM GOODMAN) Business in the Bible. pp. 42. *A. H. Stockwell: London*, [1924.] 8°. **03126. df. 13.**

—— Women in the Bible. pp. 79. *Marshall Bros.: London & Edinburgh*, [1928.] 8°. **03127. de. 50.**

BARNES (WILLIAM HARRISON)

—— The Contemporary American Organ. Its evolution, design and construction . . . Illustrated. (Fifth edition.) pp. 358. *J. Fisher & Bro.: New York*, 1952. 4°. **7901. c. 20.**

BARNES (WILLIAM HENRY) The Call of the World. S.P.G. Birthday Pageant, 1701–1927 . . . Words by W. H. Barnes, *etc.* pp. 39. [1927.] 8°. *See* ENGLAND.—*Church of England.—Church Societies.—Society for the Propagation of the Gospel in Foreign Parts.* **011779. f. 91.**

—— Second edition, *etc.* pp. 39. 1927. 8°. *See* ENGLAND.—*Church of England.—Church Societies.—Society for the Propagation of the Gospel in Foreign Parts.* **011779. f. 104.**

—— Peace in Bethlehem. A modern mystery. pp. 16. *Missionary Literature Supply: London*, 1918. 8°. **011779. g. 48. (1.)**

BARNES (WILLIAM HORATIO) The Body Politic. [An account of the United States of America.] pp. 309. *Moore & Co.: Cincinnati*, 1866. 8°. **8175. aa. 20.**

—— History of the Thirty-Ninth Congress of the United States . . . With portraits. pp. 636. *Harper & Bros.: New York*, 1868. 8°. **8177. c. 5.**

—— History of Congress. The fortieth Congress of the United States. 1867–1869 . . . With portraits on steel. 2 vol. *W. H. Barnes & Co.: New York*, 1871. 8°. **10881. f. 1.**
With an additional titlepage, engraved, dated 1869.

BARNES (WILLIAM LAWSON) Visitations and Visitation Fees examined, and shown to be uncanonical & arbitrary exactions on the clergy and churchwardens. pp. 36. *Jarrold & Sons: London*, 1861. 8°. **5157. aaa. 12.**

BARNES (WILLIAM MILES) *See* BARNES (William) *Dorsetshire Poet.* A Selection of Poems of Rural Life in the Dorset Dialect. By William Barnes. Edited by his son [W. M. Barnes], *etc.* 1909. 16°. **011653. i. 55.**

BARNES (WILLIAM MORRIS) Rolling Home. When ships were ships and not tin pots. pp. vi. 471. *Cassell & Co.: London*, 1931. 8°. **010815. g. 37.**

BARNES (WILLIAM RICHARD) and **LONGBOTHAM** (ILONA MARY)

—— Halifax Parish Church, *etc.* [With illustrations.] pp. 27. *British Publishing Co.: Gloucester*, [1955.] 8°. **010368. k. 227.**

BARNES (WILLIAM WRIGHT)

—— The Southern Baptist Convention 1845–1953. pp. x. 330. *Broadman Press: Nashville, Tenn.*, [1954.] 8°. **4745. h. 27.**

BARNES (WILLIS) Dame Fortune smiled. The doctor's story. pp. 335. *Arena Publishing Co.: Boston*, 1896. 8°. **012705. k. 52.**

—— Doctor Josephine. A love story of profit-sharing. pp. 321. *Abbey Press: New York*, [1901.] 8°. **012703. h. 8.**

BARNES (WINIFRED)

—— English Explained . . . Edited by F. H. Mackay . . . Sketches by R. Charles Roylance. *Schofield & Sims: Huddersfield*, 1952– . 8°. **W.P. A. 267.**

—— Marking Guide. *Schofield & Sons: Huddersfield*, 1952– . 8°. **W.P. A. 267a.**

—— Jenny at St. Julien's . . . Illustrations by W. Lindsay Cable. pp. 240. *Schofield & Sims: Huddersfield*, [1949.] 8°. **12832. c. 30.**

—— The Jewels and Jenny . . Illustrations by W. Lindsay Cable. [A novel.] pp. 200. *Schofield & Sims: Huddersfield*, 1948. 8°. **12829. b. 19.**

—— Shortened Classics. (W. Barnes, — Oswald Harland — editor.) *Schofield & Sims: Huddersfield*, 1954– . 8°. **W.P. c. 273.**

BARNES (WINSTON HERBERT FREDERICK)

—— The Philosophical Predicament. pp. 184. *Adam & Charles Black: London*, 1950. 8°. **08464. df. 11.**

BARNESBY (GEORGE J.) *See* BECHSTEIN (J. M.) Chamber and Cage Birds . . . New edition revised and partly re-written . . . by G. J. Barnesby. 1871. 8°. **7295. bb. 3.**

—— —— 1892. 8°. **7293. bbb. 35.**

—— —— [1905.] 8°. **7285. cc. 16.**

—— The Canary: its management, habits, breeding & training with directions for preparing show-birds. pp. 87. *G. Routledge & Sons: London*, [1877.] 8°. **7295. b. 1.**

BARNESBY (NORMAN) Medical Chaos and Crime. pp. 384. *Mitchell Kennerley: London & New York*, 1910. 8°. **7680. b. 18.**

BARNES-GRUNDY (MABEL SARAH) *See* GRUNDY.

BARNESIUS (JOANNES) *Benedictine Monk. See* BARNES (John)

BARNESIUS (Joshua) *See* Barnes.

BARNES-LAWRENCE (Arthur Evelyn) *See* Lawrence.

BARNES-LAWRENCE (Ashley Lawrence) *See* Lawrence.

BARNESLEY (William) An Authentick Account of the proceedings in Law and Equity, between William Barnesley, Esq., plaintiff, and Mansell Powell, Esq. and others, defendants. pp. 227. *The Author: London,* 1750. 8°. **518**. k. **8**. (**1**.)

—— [Another copy.] **113**. h. **6**.

BARNESMORE. The Gap of Barnesmore: a tale of the Irish Highlands, and the Revolution of 1688. [By Isaac Butt.] 3 vol. *Smith, Elder & Co.: London,* 1848. 8°. N. **2707**.

BARNESTAPOLIUS (Obertus) *pseud.* [i.e. Robert Turner.] Maria Stuarta Regina Scotiae . . . Martyr Ecclesie, innocens à caede Darleana. pp. 71. *Ex officina W. Ederi: Ingolstadii,* 1588. 8°. **600**. b. **42**.

—— [Another copy.] C. **46**. b. **9**.

—— [Another copy.] G. **1740**.

—— [Another copy.] G. **1742**. (**1**.)

—— [Another copy.] **600**. b. **48**.
Slightly mutilated.

—— [Another edition.] pp. 68. *Apud A. Crinesium, sumptibus P. Henningii: Bambergæ,* 1627. 8°. **600**. b. **45**.

—— [Another copy, with a different titlepage.] *Sumptibus P. Henningii: Coloniæ,* 1627. 8°. **288**. a. **33**. (**2**.)

—— [Another copy.] G. **1744**. (**2**.)

—— [Another edition.] *See* Jebb (Samuel) De vita & rebus gestis . . . Mariæ Scotorum Reginæ, *etc.* vol. 1. 1725. fol. **1321**. l. **2**.

—— L'Histoire et Vie de Marie Stuart, Royne d'Escosse, d'Oiriere de France, heritiere d'Angleterre & d'Ibernye, en laquelle elle est clairement iustifiee de la mort du Prince d'Arlay son mary . . . faicte Françoise, par Gabriel de Gutterry Clunisois. pp. 208. *G. Iulien: Paris,* 1589. 12°. C. **38**. a. **51**.

BARNET. [For works relating to the parish of Chipping Barnet:] *See* Chipping Barnet.

—— Official Guide to Barnet & East Barnet, Hertfordshire . . . (Barnet and East Barnet, Hertfordshire. The official guide.—Barnet Urban District, Hertfordshire. The official guide.) Third [*etc.*] edition. *Home Publishing Co.: Croydon,* [1952- .] 8°. **010360**. p. **61**.

—— Strange and wonderfull Newes from Barnet. Being an exact and true relation of an apparition which hath several times appeared to Henry Taylor parish Clark of East-Barnet, *etc.* [With a woodcut.] pp. 4. *P. L.: London,* 1668. 4°. C. **40**. d. **63**.

Barnet and District Record Society.

—— Twenty-Fourth [*etc.*] Annual Report of the Executive Committee for the year ended 30th September 1955 [*etc.*]. [*Barnet,* 1955- .] 8°. P.P. **3410**. cac.

—— Half-Yearly Bulletin. [*Barnet,*] 1949- . 8°. P.P. **3410**. c.

BARNET.—*Barnet Division Conservative Association.*

—— The Right Voice. The official organ of the Barnet Division Conservative Association. Nov. 1955, *etc.* *Barnet,* 1955- . fol. P.P. **3558**. lbb/**32**.

BARNET, *East.*—*East Barnet Valley Urban Sanitary District.*

—— Nineteenth Annual Report of the Sanitary Condition of the East Barnet Valley Urban Sanitary District, for the year 1892, by Walter Roughton . . . Medical Officer of Health. pp. 12. [*New Barnet,*] 1893. 8°. A.R. **967**.

Urban District Council.

—— District A. Civil Defence . . . September 3rd 1939 to May 8th 1945. *J. Swain & Son: London & Barnet,* [1945.] *obl.* 8°. **8839**. b. **33**.

BARNET, *a Converted Indian.* *See* Newcomb (Harvey) The Wyandot Chief: or the history of Barnet, *etc.* 1839. 12°. **4986**. b. **2**.

BARNET AND DISTRICT RECORD SOCIETY. *See* Barnet.

BARNET BOOK. The Barnet Book of Photography. A collection of practical articles by Capt. W. de W. Abney . . . Charles H. Bothamley, *etc.* [With plates.] pp. 287. *Elliott & Son: Barnet,* 1898. 8°. **8909**. dd. **5**.

—— Barnet Book of Photography. New edition, illustrated. Edited by W. L. F. Wastell. [A different collection of articles from the preceding.] 1922. 8°. *See* Wastell (William L. F.) **8910**. df. **25**.

BARNET DIVISION CONSERVATIVE ASSOCIATION. *See* Barnet.

BARNET DIVISION YOUNG CONSERVATIVE ASSOCIATION. *See* England.—*National Union of Conservative and Constitutional Associations.—Young Conservatives.*

BARNET (Elizabeth) *See* Rouvellet (J. D. R.) Trial of J. D. R. Rouvellet . . . Also of E. Barnet for felony, *etc.* [1806.] 8°. **8155**. ee. **8**. (**3**.)

BARNET (Enrique B.)

—— Manual de Practica Sanitaria . . . Dirigido y anotado por el Dr. E. B. Barnet. pp. xvi. 1114. x. 1905. 8°. *See* Cuba, *Republic of.*—*Secretaría de Gobernación.*—*Departamento de Sanidad de la Habana.* **7382**. r. **2**.

BARNET (Henri Depont) *See* Depont-Barnet.

BARNET (Jacob) Remarks upon Dr. Priestley's Letters to the Jews, upon his Discourse on the Resurrection of Jesus, and upon his Letters to the Members of the New Jerusalem, introductory to an address to the Jews. pp. 36. *R. Hindmarsh: London,* 1792. 8°. **105**. c. **39**.

BARNET (James) The Martyrs and Heroes of Illinois in the great Rebellion. Biographical sketches. Edited by J. Barnet . . . Illustrated with portraits. pp. xvi. 263. *J. Barnet: Chicago,* 1865. 8°. **10882**. d. **11**.

BARNET (Jean) *See* Du Duc (F.) L'Histoire tragique de la Pucelle d'Orléans . . . représentée à Pont-à-Mousson . . . publiée en M.D.LXXXI par J. Barnet. 1859. 4°. **11739**. f. **20**.

BARNET (John) *Clerk in the Custom House at Newcastle.* Report of the Trial of John Barnett for Forgery . . . at the Durham Assizes, Feb. 26th, 1830. (Taken from the Durham Chronicle of March 6.) pp. 23. *R. Stobbs: Durham,* [1830.] 12°. **6496**. aa. **13**. (**4**.)

BARNET (John) *Clerk in the Custom House at Newcastle.*

—— Trial of Mr. John Barnet at the Durham Spring Assizes . . . on a charge of forging a codicil to the will of the late John Marley, *etc.* pp. 40. *W. Fordyce: Newcastle upon Tyne,* 1830. 8°. **6496.** bbb. **10.** **(1.)**

BARNET (John) *Curate of Whickham.* A Sermon, preached in the Parish Church of Whickham, *etc.* pp. 12. *Matthew Brown: Newcastle upon Tyne,* [1800.] 12°. **4473.** e. **8.** **(6.)**

BARNET (John) *of Dunston Lodge, Durham.* A Letter on the Ascension of Jesus Christ into Heaven, *etc.* pp. 30. *The Author: Newcastle upon Tyne,* 1827. 8°. **4226.** g. **7.**

BARNET (John Guthrie) *See* Bruce (Michael) *Poet.* Life and Complete Works of Michael Bruce . . . By [i.e. edited by] J. G. Barnet, *etc.* 1927. 8°. **011645.** h. **88.**

BARNET (Nehemiah) *See* Barnett.

BARNET (Robert Ayres) "Baron Humbug": a Hungarian musical play, in two acts. ff. 87. [*E. B. Kinsila: London,* 1903.] 4°. **11779.** l. **10.** *Typewritten.*

BARNET (Thomas) *See* MacCoy (John) The Last Speech . . . of J. Mc.Coy, T. Barnet, *etc.* 1725. *s. sh.* fol. **C.133.g.7.(37.)**

—— *See* MacCoy (John) The Last Speeches and Dying Words of J. Mc.Coy, T. Barnet, *etc.* [1725.] *s. sh.* fol. **C.133.g.7.(59.)**

—— *See* MacCoy (John) The Tryal and Examination of J. MaCoy . . . T. Barret [*sic*], *etc.* [1725.] *s. sh.* fol. **C.133.g.7.(49.)**

—— *See* MacCoy (John) The Whole and True Tryal of J. MCoy, T. Barnet, *etc.* [1725.] *s. sh.* fol. **C.133.g.7.(50.)**

BARNET (*Mrs.* William) *See* Guerini (G.) Fireside Entertainments. [Translated from the Italian by Mrs. W. Barnet and others.] 1874. 8°. **12470.** i. **17.**

BARNETCHE (Louis Jean) Essai sur la nostalgie. Tribut académique, *etc.* pp. 30. *Montpellier,* 1831. 4°. **1181.** f. 4. **(1.)**

BARNETH (John Charles) *See* Scott (Thomas) *Rector of Aston Sandford, Bucks.* The Spirit and Principles of a Genuine Missionary. A sermon occasioned by the death of . . . J. C. Barneth. 1810. 8°. **4903.** eee. **2.** **(7.)**

BARNET LYON (John James) *See* Lyon.

BARNETSON (James) *Assistant Pathologist, South African Institute for Medical Research.*

—— *See* Simson (Frank W.) and Barnetson (J.) Histoplasmosis, *etc.* [1942.] 8°. **7689.** bb. **15.**

—— Undulant Fever: its incidence in South Africa . . . Reprinted from the South African Medical Journal, *etc.* pp. 10. *Cape Town,* [1939.] 8°. **7563.** bb. **2.**

BARNETSON (James) *Head Teacher, Regent Road Evening School, Edinburgh.*

—— McDougall's Exercises in Book-keeping. 2 pt. *McDougall's Educational Co.: Edinburgh,* [1899.] 8°. **08533.** df. **14.** (3.)

BARNETT HOUSE. *See* Oxford.

BARNETT (A.) *of Paris.* *See* Noel (F. J. M.) and Chapsal (C. P.) A New French Grammar upon very methodical principles . . . Translated . . . by A. Barnett. 1864. 8°. **12954.** bbb. **19.**

BARNETT (Ada) *See* also Cardella (G.) *pseud.* [i.e. A. Barnett.]

—— *See* Forbes (Robert E.) *pseud.* [i.e. Ralph Straus.] Mrs. Holmes, Commandant. [By R. Straus in collaboration with A. Barnett.] 1918. 8°. NN. **4734.**

—— Here is Freedom. [A novel.] pp. 352. *Grayson & Grayson: London,* [1935.] 8°. NN. **23869.**

—— The Joyous Adventurer. pp. 381. *G. Allen & Unwin: London,* 1923. 8°. NN. **9188.**

—— The Man on the Other Side. pp. 248. *G. Allen & Unwin: London,* 1921. 8°. NN. **7132.**

—— Mary's Son. pp. 320. *G. Allen & Unwin: London,* 1927. 8°. NN. **12481.**

BARNETT (Adam)

—— *See* Alexander (Lawrence) The Iron Cradle. By L. Alexander as told to A. Barnett. [1954.] 8°. **7643.** ee. **11.**

—— *See* Alexander (Lawrence) The Iron Cradle . . . As told to A. Barnett. 1955. 8°. **7662.** e. 5.

BARNETT (Adam John Guilbert)

—— Silage Fermentation. pp. x. 208. *Butterworths Scientific Publications: London,* 1954. 8°. **08777.** f. **7.**

BARNETT (Albert)

—— Historical and other Articles, contributed . . . in The Optician, *etc.* pp. 213. [1944.] 8°. **12359.** h. **23.**

BARNETT (Albert Edward)

—— Paul becomes a Literary Influence. [With special reference to the Epistles of St. Paul.] pp. xiii. 277. *University of Chicago Press: Chicago,* 1941. 8°.

Reproduced from typewriting. **3268. c.12.**

BARNETT (Albert I.) *See* Montalvo (Berita de) *Countess.* "The Diamond Lady" . . . With an introduction by A. I. Barnett. [1913.] 8°. **07106.** e. **12.**

BARNETT (Andrew Ketchan) Observations on the Elvan Courses, Greenstones, and Sandstones of Cornwall . . . Reprinted from the (Royal Cornwall Polytechnic) Society's 41st Annual Report, *etc.* pp. 41. *F. H. Earle: Falmouth,* 1873. 8°. **07109.** m. **3.** **(3.)**

—— [Another edition.] From the Report of the Miners' Association of Cornwall and Devon for 1873. pp. 26. *Lake & Co.: Falmouth,* 1874. 8°. **7106.** f. **25.** **(6.)**

BARNETT (Andrew Philip) and **LLOYD** (David Willson) The South Wales Coalfield. [With illustrations.] pp. 114. *Business Statistics Co.: Cardiff,* [1921.] fol. **7105.** i. **28.**

BARNETT (Ann) Late, but not too late. A tale. pp. iv. 335. *Williams & Norgate: London, Edinburgh,* 1865. 8°. **12620.** bb. **8.**

BARNETT (Annie) *See* Andersen (H. C.) *the Novelist.* [*Eventyr.—English.*] Stories from Hans Andersen. Selected and arranged by Mrs. P. A. Barnett, *etc.* 1911. 8°. **012273.** de. **43.**

—— The Children's Way. A book of verses about children, selected and arranged by Mrs. P. A. Barnett. pp. 221. *Jarrold & Sons: London,* [1910.] 8°. **11604.** dg. **5.**

—— Drifting Thistledown. By Mrs. P. A. Barnett and another. pp. 157. *Longmans & Co.: London,* 1910. 8°. **012623.** a. 6.

BARNETT (Annie)

—— Golden Numbers. A book of verse for boys and girls. Selected and arranged by Mrs. P. A. Barnett. pp. viii. 166. *Longmans & Co.: London,* 1906. 8°. **11604.** c. **14.**

—— A Little Book of English Prose. Selected and arranged by A. Barnett, *etc.* pp. xi. 335. *Methuen & Co.: London,* 1900. 8°. [*Little Library.*] **012208.** df. **7/22.**

—— Song and Story. Selections of verse. (Black's School Poetry.) 3 bk. *A. & C. Black: London,* [1907.] 8°. **11603.** i. **30.**

BARNETT (Annie) and **DALE** (Lucy)

—— An Anthology of English Prose (1332 to 1740) . . . With a preface by Andrew Lang. pp. xii. 247. *Longmans & Co.: London,* 1912. 8°. **012273.** ff. **1.**

—— An Anthology of Modern English Prose (1741 to 1892). pp. xii. 450. *Longmans & Co.: London,* 1911. 8°. **12272.** pp. **4.**

BARNETT (Annie A.) The Penlee Recipe Book. A comprehensive cookery book containing 490 approved recipes on food reform lines. pp. viii. 232. *G. Bell & Sons: London,* 1915. 8°. **07943.** f. **97.**

BARNETT (Anthony)

—— The Fight against Infection. pp. 20. *Bureau of Current Affairs: London,* 1947. 8°. [*Current Affairs.* no. 30.] P.P. **3610.** gkl.

—— The Human Species. A biology of man. pp. x. 280. pl. 16. *Macgibbon & Kee: London,* 1950. 8°. **7008.** e. **21.**

—— No Two Alike. (A survey of human diversity.) pp. 16. *Bureau of Current Affairs: London,* 1946. 8°. [*Current Affairs.* no. 5.] P.P. **3610.** gkl.

BARNETT (Arthur James) *See* Sallustius Crispus (C.) [*Catilina.—Latin.*] The Catiline of Sallust. By A. J. Barnett. 1911. 8°. **9041.** eee. **23.**

BARNETT (Arthur Thomas) The Purpose of Life. Addresses given in Holy Week. pp. 54. *Skeffington & Son: London,* 1903. 8°. **4479.** e. **42.**

—— The Shadow of Heaven. Sermons. pp. x. 145. *Skeffington & Son: London,* 1896. 8°. **4479.** ee. **15.**

—— Why are Betting and Gambling wrong? pp. 23. *S.P.C.K.: London,* 1897. 8°. **4430.** aaa. **56.** (**1.**)

BARNETT (Avrom)

—— Foundations of Feminism. A critique. pp. 245. *Robert M. McBride & Co.: New York,* 1921. 8°. **8417.** aa. **50.**

BARNETT (B.) *Dramatic Writer. See* Barnett (Morris) and (B.) Out on the Loose, *etc.* [1850.] 12°. [*Lacy's Acting Edition.* vol. 2.] **2304.** d. **6.**

BARNETT (B.) *of Banbury.* Out of the Deep. [Poems.] pp. 40. *The Author: Banbury,* [1917.] 8°. **011648.** ee. **19.**

BARNETT (Burgess) The Terrarium. Tortoises, other reptiles and amphibians in captivity, *etc.* pp. 57. *Poultry World: London,* [1934.] 8°. **07290.** de. **13.**

BARNETT (C. J.) *See* Barnett (Charles Z.)

BARNETT (Cecil Guy)

—— Note on the Protective Embankments in the Irrawaddy Delta, 1862–1912, *etc.* [With a map.] pp. 142. 1914. fol. *See* Burma.—*Public Works Department.* I.S. bu. **53/14.**

BARNETT (Cefni)

—— Illustrated Handbook to the Roman Caerwent Collection. [With plates.] pp. 28. 1954. 8°. *See* Newport, *Monmouthshire.—Public Libraries, Museum and Art Gallery.* **07705.** c. **17.**

BARNETT (Charles)

—— "Cavalcade of a Crook." [A film scenario.] ff. 14. *C. Barnett: London,* 1935. fol. **11795.** tt. **37.** *Typewritten.*

—— Fine Feathers. A film fantasy, featuring Mr. and Mrs. Feather. [A film scenario.] ff. 10. *National Progress Film Co.: London,* [1938.] fol. Cup. **1252.** a. **67.** *Typewritten.*

—— Lucky Star. [A film scenario.] ff. 7. *National Progress Film Co.: London,* [1935.] fol. Cup. **1252.** a. **66.** *Typewritten.*

BARNETT (Charles Zachary)

—— The Bohemians of Paris . . . A drama, in three acts, *etc.* pp. 52. *London,* [1843?] 12°. [*Duncombe's Edition of the British Theatre.* vol. 48.] **2304.** a. **24.**

—— The Bravo, or, the Bridge of Sighs. A melo-drama, in two acts, *etc.* pp. 34. *London,* [1833?] 12°. [*Duncombe's Edition of the British Theatre.* vol. 11.] **2304.** a. **6.**

—— Cæsar Borgia; the Scourge of Venice. An historical drama in three acts, *etc.* pp. 28. *London,* [1833?] 12°. [*Duncombe's Edition of the British Theatre.* vol. 11.] **2304.** a. **6.**

—— A Christmas Carol; or, the Miser's Warning! Adapted from Charles Dickens's celebrated work. pp. 26. *London,* [1871?] 12°. [*Lacy's Acting Edition of Plays.* vol. 94.] **2304.** g. **12**

—— A Christmas Carol, *etc.* (Adapted from Charles Dickens' work.) pp. 11. *London,* [1886.] 8°. [*Dicks' Standard Plays.* no. 722.] **11770.** bbb. 4.

—— Dominique, the Deserter. pp. 10. *London,* [1877?] 8°. [*Dicks' Standard Plays.* no. 256.] **11770.bbb.4.**

—— Dominique the Possessed: a melo drama, in two acts, *etc.* pp. 24. *London,* [1833?] 12°. [*Duncombe's Edition of the British Theatre.* vol. 9.] **2304.** a. **5.**

—— Don Cæsar de Bazan . . . A drama, in three acts, *etc.* pp. 48. *London,* [1844?] 12°. [*Duncombe's Edition of the British Theatre.* vol. 51.] **2304.** a. **26.**

—— The Dream of Fate: or, Sarah, the Jewess. A melo drama, in three acts, *etc.* pp. 38. *London,* [1838?] 12°. [*Duncombe's Edition of the British Theatre.* vol. 30.] **2304.** a. 15.

—— The Dream of Fate, *etc.* pp. 15. *London,* [1886.] 8°. [*Dicks' Standard Plays.* no. 771.] **11770.** bbb. **4.**

—— The Dream of Fate, or Sarah the Jewess. A tale . . . founded on the . . . drama. By C. Z. Barnett. pp. 34. *J. Duncombe & Co.: London,* [1840?] 16°. [*Dramatic Tales.* New ser. no. 1.] **12601.** aa. **5.**

—— Farinelli, a serio comic opera, in two acts, *etc.* pp. 46. *London,* [1839?] 12°. [*Duncombe's Edition of the British Theatre.* vol. 33.] **2304.** a. **17.**

—— The Songs, Duetts, Trios, &c. in Farinelli, a serio comic opera in two acts, *etc.* [By C. Z. Barnett.] pp. 32. [1839?] 8°. *See* Broschi Farinelli (C.) **11782.** cc. **32.** (**5.**)

BARNETT (CHARLES ZACHARY)

—— Linda, the Pearl of Savoy. A . . . drama, in three acts, *etc.* pp. 42. *London,* [1843 ?] 12°. [*Duncombe's Edition of the British Theatre.* vol. 47.] **2304. a. 24.**

—— Linda, the Pearl of Savoy, *etc.* pp. 16. *London,* [1886 ?] 8°. [*Dicks' Standard Plays.* no. 704.] **11770.** bbb. **4.**

—— The Loss of the Royal George . . . A nautico-domestic drama, in two acts, *etc.* pp. 46. *London,* [1840 ?] 12°. [*Duncombe's Edition of the British Theatre.* vol. 42.] **2304.** a. **21.**

—— The Loss of the Royal George, *etc.* pp. 19. *London,* [1886.] 8°. [*Dicks' Standard Plays.* no. 775.] **11770.** bbb. **4.**

—— Midnight! or, the Sentinel and the hour, a melo drama, in three acts, *etc.* pp. 35. *London,* [1845 ?] 12°. [*Duncombe's Edition of the British Theatre.* vol. 53.] **2304. a. 27.**

—— [Another edition.] Midnight: the thirteenth chime; or Old Saint Paul's, *etc.* pp. 32. *London,* [1875.] 12°. [*Lacy's Acting Edition of Plays.* vol. 101.] **2304.** g. **19.**

—— The Minute Gun at Sea! A drama, in three acts, *etc.* pp. 45. *London,* [1845 ?] 12°. [*Duncombe's Edition of the British Theatre.* vol. 55.] **2304. a. 28.**

—— Mrs. Caudle! or, Curtain Lectures! A dramatic sketch, in one act, *etc.* pp. 16. *London,* [1845 ?] 12°. [*Duncombe's Edition of the British Theatre.* vol. 53.] **2304. a. 27.**

—— Oliver Twist . . . A domestic drama, in three acts, *etc.* pp. 38. *London,* [1838 ?] 12°. [*Duncombe's Edition of the British Theatre.* vol. 29.] **2304. a. 15.**

—— The Phantom Bride; or, the Castilian Bandit: a melo-drama, in two acts, *etc.* pp. 32. *London,* [1830 ?] 12°. [*Duncombe's Edition of the British Theatre.* vol. 7.] **2304. a. 4.**

—— La Polka . . . A farce, in one act, *etc.* pp. 21. *London,* [1844 ?] 12°. [*Duncombe's Edition of the British Theatre.* vol. 50.] **2304. a. 25.**

—— "Swing!" A farce, in one act, *etc.* pp. 24. *London,* [1830 ?] 12°. [*Duncombe's Edition of the British Theatre.* vol. 8.] **2304. a. 4.**

—— Victorine; or, the Orphan of Paris. A melo-drama in three acts, *etc.* pp. 24. *London,* [1833 ?] 12°. [*Duncombe's Edition of the British Theatre.* vol. 9.] **2304. a. 5.**

—— William the Fourth, an historical melo-drama, in two acts, *etc.* pp. 24. *London,* [1831 ?] 12°. [*Duncombe's Edition of the British Theatre.* vol. 8.] **2304. a. 4.**

BARNETT (DAVID) Guide to Edinburgh Castle. pp. 31. *David Macdonald: Edinburgh,* 1928. 8°. **010370.** eee. **81.**

BARNETT (DENIS OLIVER) *See* MATHESON (Annie) Our Hero of the Golden Heart, *etc.* [With a biography and portrait of D. O. Barnett.] [1920.] 8°. **W.P. 6293/3.**

—— Denis Oliver Barnett . . . His letters from France and Flanders October 1914—August 1915. [The preface signed: F. H. D., i.e. Frank Harry Busbridge Dale. With portraits.] pp. xi. 238. *Privately printed: Stratford-upon-Avon,* 1915. 8°. **10922.** d. **20.**

BARNETT (E. A.) *Campanologist.*

—— Collection of Plain Major Methods. Second edition [of "Collection of Plain Major and Cater Methods"]. Issued under the authority of the Council by E. A. Barnett, *etc.* pp. 60. 1952. 8°. *See* LONDON.—III. *Central Council of Church Bell Ringers.* **3479.** aa. **71.**

BARNETT (EDITH A.) *See* O'NEILL (Hannah C.) and BARNETT (E. A.) New Life . . . A book for young mothers. 1890. 8°. **07581. de. 9.**

—— *See* O'NEILL (Hannah C.) and BARNETT (E. A.) Our Nurses, *etc.* [1888.] 8°. **7391. aaa. 4.**

—— A Champion in the Seventies, being the true record of some passages in a conflict of social faiths. pp. viii. 360. *William Heinemann: London,* 1898. 8°. **012623. g. 52.**

—— Common-sense Clothing. pp. 150. *Ward, Lock & Co.: London,* [1882.] 8°. **7743. bbb. 33.**

—— The Cookery Instructor; containing full explanations on the science and practice of cookery, *etc.* pp. 192. *Ward, Lock & Co.: London,* [1881.] 8°. **7945.** b. **8.**

—— Dr. and Mrs. Gold. An episode in the life of a cause. [A novel.] pp. 287. *Swan Sonnenschein & Co.: London,* 1891. 8°. **012632.** h. **51.**

—— The Fetich of the Family. A record of human sacrifice. pp. vi. 348. *William Heinemann: London,* 1902. 8°. **012638** aa. **23.**

—— A Garden of Eden. Kempton Park once upon a time. pp. vii. 147. *A. Constable & Co.: London,* 1905. 8°. **012631.** aaa. **2.**

—— A Healthy Home in one or two rooms. pp. 16. *Allman & Son: London,* [1888.] 8°. **8776.** aa. **13.** (**3.**)

—— National Health Society's Penny Cookery Book. pp. 35. *London,* 1879. 16°. [*Allman's Penny School Series.*] **12204.** a. **10.**

—— Sunningham and the Curate, *etc.* pp. vi. 353. *Chapman & Hall: London,* 1899. 8°. **012642.** bb. **14.**

—— The Training of Girls for Work. An expression of opinions. pp. viii. 215. *Macmillan & Co.: London,* 1894. 8°. **8415.** de. **39.**

—— A Wilderness Winner. pp. vi. 333. *Methuen & Co.: London,* 1907. 8°. **012634.** aa. **11.**

BARNETT (EDITH A.) and **O'NEILL** (HANNAH COX)

—— Primer of Domestic Economy. pp. x. 130. *Macmillan & Co.: London,* 1892. 8°. **7942. a. 61.**

BARNETT (EDWARD) *See* ENGLAND.—*Admiralty.—Hydrographic Department.—Sailing Directions.* [*West India Islands.*] The West India Pilot. Vol. I. . . . Compiled by . . . E. Barnett. 1861. 8°. **10496.** i. **14.**

—— *See* ENGLAND.—*Admiralty.—Hydrographic Department.—Sailing Directions.* [*West India Islands.*] The West India Pilot. Vol. II. . . . Compiled by . . . E. Barnett. 1859. 8°. **10496.** i. **14*.**

BARNETT (EDWARD DE BARRY) *See* RIDEAL (Samuel) Industrial Chemistry . . . Edited by S. Rideal (E. de B. Barnett). 1918, *etc.* 8°. 8711.bb.1/1–22.

—— Anthracine and Anthraquinone. pp. xi. 436. *Baillière & Co.: London,* 1921. 8°. **8903.** c. **29.**

—— Coal Tar Dyes and Intermediates. pp. xvi. 213. *Baillière & Co.: London,* 1919. 8°. [*Industrial Chemistry.*] **8711.** bb. **1/5.**

—— Explosives. pp. xv. 241. *Baillière & Co.: London,* 1919. 8°. [*Industrial Chemistry.*] **8711.** bb. **1/6.**

—— The Preparation of Organic Compounds . . . With 50 illustrations. pp. xvi. 310. *J. & A. Churchill: London,* 1912. 8°. **08909.** a. **15.**

—— Second edition. pp. xiv. 273. *J. & A. Churchill: London,* 1920 [1919]. 8°. **8903.** aaa. **18.**

BARNETT (Edward de Barry)

—— A Textbook of General Organic Chemistry. Stereochemistry. pp. ix. 169. *Sir Isaac Pitman & Sons: London,* 1950. 8°. **8896**. e. **23**.

—— A Text-Book of Organic Chemistry . . . With 15 illustrations. pp. xii. 380. *J. & A. Churchill: London,* 1920. 8°. **08909**. b. **51**.

BARNETT (Edward de Barry) and **THORNE** (Percy Cyril Lesley)

—— Organic Analysis, qualitative and quantitative. pp. xi. 168. *University of London Press: London,* 1921. 8°. **8903**. d. **33**.

BARNETT (Edward de Barry) and **WILSON** (Cecil Leeburn)

—— Inorganic Chemistry. A text-book for advanced students. pp. xiv. 512. *Longmans, Green & Co.: London,* 1953. 8°. **08909**. p. 25.

BARNETT (F. Mary) Our Dogs' Birthday Book. Arranged by Mrs. F. M. Barnett. With twelve pictures of champion dogs. pp. 144. *George Allen: London,* 1902. *obl.* 8°. **12274**. de. **16**.

BARNETT (F. S. A.) Sprott: an autobiography. Edited [or rather, written] by F. S. A. B. [i.e. F. S. A. Barnett.] pp. 104. 1884 [1883]. 8°. *See* Sprott. **12805**. s. **23**.

BARNETT (Francis) *See* also Lefèvre, *pseud.* [i.e. F. Barnett.]

—— Memoirs of Francis Barnett, the Lefevre of "No Fiction" [a novel by Dr. Andrew Reed] and a review of that work. With letters, and authentic documents. 2 vol. *Francis Barnett: London,* 1823. 12°. **491**. a. **5**.

—— A Reply to Mr. Reed's Advertisement to the seventh edition of "No Fiction." With a review of "Martha." pp. 48. *Francis Barnett: London,* 1823. 12°. **491**. a. **26**.

BARNETT (Frederic) The Prince of Darkness and the Curse of War. (In aid of the Turkish Compassionate Fund for the relief of all creeds.) [In verse.] pp. 23. *Elzevir Press: London,* 1877. 8°. **11601**. h. **29**. (2.)

BARNETT (Frederick Oswald)

—— Happy Endings to Old Nursery Rhymes. Rhymes by F. O. Barnett, pictures by Dorothy Dibdin. *George G. Harrap & Co.: London,* 1947. 4°. **12828**. dd. **45**.

BARNETT (Frieda) *See* Washburne (Carleton W.) Washburne Individual Arithmetic . . . By C. W. Washburne . . . F. Barnett, *etc.* 1925, *etc.* 8°. 08535.dd.13.

BARNETT (George DeForest) *See* Hewlett (Albion W.) Pathological Physiology of Internal Diseases . . . Revised . . . under the editorial supervision of G. D. Barnett, *etc.* [1928.] 8°. **7439**. h. **22**.

BARNETT (George Ernest) *See* Baltimore.—*Johns Hopkins University.—Economic Seminary.* A Trial Bibliography of American Trade-Union Publications prepared by the Economic Seminary of the Johns Hopkins University. Edited by G. E. Barnett. 1904. 8°. [*Johns Hopkins University Studies in Historical and Political Science.* ser. 22. no. 1, 2.] Ac. **2689**.

—— *See* Evans (George H.) and Barnett (G. E.) Principles of Investment, *etc.* [1940.] 8°. **08230**. f. 36.

—— *See* Hollander (J. H.) and Barnett (G. E.) Studies in American Trade Unionism. 1906. 8°. **2240**. d. **20**.

BARNETT (George Ernest)

—— *See* King (Gregory) Two Tracts . . . Edited with an introduction by G. E. Barnett. 1936. 8°. **8286**. i. **58**.

—— Chapters on Machinery and Labor. pp. vi. 161. *Harvard University Press: Cambridge, Mass.,* 1926. 8°. **08286**. b. **7**.

—— The Printers. A study in American Trade Unionism. pp. vii. 387. *Saratoga,* 1909. 8°. [*American Economic Association Quarterly.* ser. 3. vol. 10. no. 3.] Ac. **2388**.

—— State Banking in the United States since the passage of the National Bank Act. pp. 117. *Baltimore,* 1902. 8°. **08229**. i. **4**.

—— [Another issue.] *Baltimore,* 1902. 8°. [*Johns Hopkins University Studies in Historical and Political Science.* ser. 20. no. 2, 3.] Ac. **2689**. *Without the last leaf containing the author's Vita.*

—— State Banks and Trust Companies since the passage of the National-Bank Act. pp. 366. 1911. 8°. *See* United States of America.—*National Monetary Commission.* A.S. **937/38**.

BARNETT (George Ernest) and **MAC CABE** (David Aloysius)

—— Mediation, Investigation and Arbitration in Industrial Disputes. pp. viii. 208. *D. Appleton & Co.: New York, London,* 1916. 8°. **08226**. aa. **57**.

BARNETT (George Henry) With the 48th Division in Italy, *etc.* [With plates and maps.] pp. xi. 162. *W. Blackwood & Sons: Edinburgh & London,* 1923. 8°. **09084**. cc. **11**.

BARNETT (George J.)

—— *See* Vehanen (Kosti) Marian Anderson, *etc.* (Written with the collaboration of G. J. Barnett.) [1941.] 8°. **10888**. h. **11**.

BARNETT (Gilbert) V.C.'s of the Air . . . With an additional chapter on heroes of America . . . Pictured by Dudley Tennant. pp. 36. *E. J. Burrow & Co.; Simpkin, Marshall & Co.: London,* [1918.] 8°. **9082**. d. 3.

BARNETT (Glyn)

—— The Call-Box Murder. pp. vi. 346. *Sampson Low & Co.: London,* [1935.] 8°. NN. **24590**.

—— Death Calls Three Times. pp. vi. 410. *Sampson Low & Co.: London,* [1936.] 8°. NN. **25718**.

—— Find the Lady. pp. vi. 218. *Sampson, Low & Co.: London,* [1946.] 8°. NN. **36044**.

—— I Knew Mrs. Lang. pp. vi. 346. *Sampson Low & Co.: London,* [1937.] 8°. NN. **28169**.

—— Murder on Monday. pp. vi. 409. *Sampson Low & Co.: London,* [1937.] 8°. NN. **26996**.

—— There's Money in Murder. pp. 343. *Chapman & Hall: London,* 1939. 8°. NN. **30482**.

BARNETT (Grace Treleven) and **BARNETT** (Olive Elizabeth)

—— The Cock that Crowed at Two. [A tale. With illustrations.] *Lothrop, Lee & Shepard Co.: Boston, New York,* [1937.] 4°. **012808**. d. **53**.

—— Dark Island Mystery. pp. 181. *Oxford University Press: New York,* 1949. 8°. **12832**. cc. **37**.

BARNETT (Grace Treleven) and **BARNETT** (Olive Elizabeth)

—— Ghost Town Mystery. pp. 221. *Oxford University Press: New York*, 1953. 8°. **12836**. cc. **23**.

—— Silver in the Teapot. *Lothrop, Lee & Shepard Co.: Boston, New York*, [1938] 4°. **12822**. bb. **1**.

—— They Hunted High and Low . . . Illustrated by the authors. *Lothrop, Lee & Shepard: Boston, New York*, [1939.] 8°. **12825**. c. **16**.

BARNETT (H. L.)

—— *See* Dukes (*Mrs.* Marcus) Coconut Recipes . . . Third edition revised by H. L. Barnett. 1947. 8°. **7948**. aa. **25**.

BARNETT (H. M.) *Writer of Verse.* The Mermaids' Retreat, and other poems. pp. 24. *A. H. Stockwell: London*, [1928.] 8°. **011645**. i. **132**.

BARNETT (Harold Montgomery)

—— Studies in Leucine and Dileucine Hydrochloride and a New Method for the Isolation of Leucine from Proteins. A thesis, *etc.* (Reprinted from the Journal of Biological Chemistry.) [*New York*, 1933.] 8°. **8899**. ff. **68**.

BARNETT (Harold R.) Man Management in Chain Stores, *etc.* pp. x. 252. *Harper & Bros.: New York & London*, 1931. 8°. **08246**. i. **16**.

BARNETT (Harry Theodore) Up-to-date "Gramophone Tips." 1924 edition, *etc.* pp. 44. *H. T. Barnett: Southsea*, 1924. 8°. **07896**. de. **22**.

—— Second 1924 edition, *etc.* pp. 43. *H. T. Barnett: Southsea*, [1924.] 8°. **07896**. de. **49**.

—— 1925 edition. pp. 76. *Gramophone Publications: Guernsey*, [1924.] 8°. **07896**. de. **30**.

—— Gramophone Tips. 1927 edition, *etc.* pp. 46. *H. T. Barnett: Old Portsmouth*, 1927 [1926]. 8°. **07896**. de. **81**.

BARNETT (Harry Villiers) *See* Massenet (J. E. F.) My Recollections . . . Authorized translation . . . by . . . H. V. Barnett. [1919.] 8°. **010662**. c. **17**.

BARNETT (*Dame* Henrietta Octavia Weston) *D.B.E.* *See* Barnett (Samuel A.) Practicable Socialism . . . By the Rev. and Mrs. S. A. Barnett. 1888. 8°. **8282**. b. **61**.

—— —— 1894. 8°. **08275**. ee. **8**.

—— *See* Barnett (Samuel A.) Practicable Socialism. New series. By Canon S. A. Barnett . . . and Mrs. S. A. Barnett, *etc.* 1915. 8°. **08248**. cc. **23**.

—— *See* Barnett (Samuel A.) Vision and Service . . . Edited . . . by . . . H. O. Barnett. [1917.] 8°. **3755**. h. **5**.

—— *See* Barnett (Samuel A.) Worship and Work. Thoughts from the unpublished writings of the late Canon S. A. Barnett . . . Selected and edited by his wife (H. O. Barnett). 1913. 8°. **4379**. de. **10**.

—— *See* Barnett (Samuel A.) and (*Dame* H. O. W.) *D.B.E.* Towards Social Reform. 1909. 8°. **08276**. a. **40**.

—— *See* Mallam (Kathleen) Destitute, Neglected, and Delinquent Children . . . Edited by Mrs. S. A. Barnett. 1908. 8°. [*Pan-Anglican Papers.* S.G. 5c.] **4108**. cc. **35**.

—— *See* Stephens (Margaret) Woman and Marriage . . . With . . . an introduction by Mrs. S. A. Barnett. 1910. 8°. **07580**. e. **15**.

BARNETT (*Dame* Henrietta Octavia Weston) *D.B.E.*

—— Canon Barnett. His life, work, and friends . . . With thirty-nine illustrations. 2 vol. *John Murray: London*, 1918. 8°. **4908**. g. **8**.

—— [Another edition.] pp. xxvi. 805. *John Murray: London*, 1921. 8°. **4908**. h. **9**.

—— How to mind the Baby. pp. 12. *Cassell & Co.: London*, [1887.] 8°. **7306**. df. **6**. (**4**.)

—— The Making of the Body. A children's book on anatomy and physiology, *etc.* pp. 288. *Longmans & Co.: London*, 1894. 8°. **7419**. aa. **7**.

—— New edition, thoroughly revised by A. H. Thompson. pp. xii. 271. *Longmans & Co.: London*, 1901. 8°. **7419**. aa. **12**.

—— The Making of the Home. A reading-book of domestic economy, *etc.* pp. xii. 206. *Cassell & Co.: London*, [1885.] 8°. **7945**. b. **45**.

—— Matters that Matter. [With plates, including a portrait.] pp. xi. 429. *John Murray: London*, 1930. 8°. **8276**. ppp. **14**.

—— Reverence the Child. pp. 21. *Shaftesbury Society: London*, [1921.] 8°. [*Shaftesbury Lecture.* no. 3.] W.P. **7538/3**.

—— Science and City Suburbs. *See* Hand (James E.) Science in Public Affairs, *etc.* 1906. 8°. **8138**. aaa. **51**.

—— What has the Charity Organisation Society to do with Social Reform. pp. 8. *London*, [1884.] 8°. [*Miscellaneous Papers of the Charity Organisation Society.*] **8277**. dd.

BARNETT (Henry Martyn) The Test of Truth applied to some statements against the Free Church of England in "An Exposure" &c. thereof, by M. A. Gathercole . . . With which is embodied a Lecture on the origin, nature, doctrines, and objects of the Free Church of England, by T. E. Thoresby. pp. 81. *G. J. Stevenson: London*, 1873. 8°. **4109**. a. **44**.

BARNETT (Henry N.) *Religious Writer.* After Thoughts: or Reflections on the recent election for the Borough of Evesham; its virtues, its immoralities and its results. pp. 24. *Richard Bult: Evesham; A. Hall & Co.: London*, 1852. 8°. **8138**. c. **7**.

—— A Discourse of Faith in the Living and the Reigning God, *etc.* pp. 16. *George Manwaring: London*, 1860. 8°. **4478**. c. **4**.

—— The Great Contrast; or, the Czar in life and death. A discourse, *etc.* pp. 16. *W. Freeman: London; Evans & Arrowsmith: Bristol*, [1855.] 8°. **10790**. c. **5**.

—— The Late Theodore Parker: a discourse, *etc.* pp. 16. *George Manwaring: London*, 1860. 8°. **4986**. dd. **21**. (**15**.)

—— Religious Enthusiasm: notes of a discourse, *etc.* pp. 11. *J. Burbidge: Bristol*, [1858.] 12°. **4355**. bb. **20**. (**1**.)

—— The Victor vanquished: a discourse occasioned by the death of the Duke of Wellington, *etc.* pp. 23. *A. Hall & Co.: London; R. Bult: Evesham*, [1852.] 8°. **10815**. b. **3**.

—— The Youthful Inquirer counselled and encouraged. pp. 148. *W. Freeman: London*, 1853. 12°. **4407**. d. **29**.

BARNETT (Henry Norman) Accidental Injuries to Workmen, with reference to Workmen's Compensation Act, 1906 . . . With article on injuries to the organs of special sense by Cecil E. Shaw . . . and legal introduction by Thomas J. Campbell. pp. vii. 376. *Rebman: London*, 1909. 8°. **6325**. v. 3.

—— Drunkenness: sin or disease? pp. 13. *Mayne & Boyd: Belfast*, 1907. 8°. **8436**. f. **30**. (3.)

—— Legal Responsibility of the Drunkard . . . With an introduction by Sir Andrew Reed. pp. 64. *Baillière & Co.: London*, 1908. 8°. **6095**. de. **32**.

—— Sea-Sickness. Its true cause and cure. pp. vi. 39. *Baillière & Co.: London*, 1907. 8°. **7640**. ee. **29**.

—— The Student's Textbook of Surgery. pp. xix. 794. pl. LXXIX. *William Heinemann: London*, 1916. 8°. **07481**. i. **16**.

BARNETT (Herbert) Glympton. The history of an Oxfordshire manor. [With "The Registers of the Parish, 1567–1812," and with plates and a map.] pp. 141. *Oxford*, 1923. 8°. [*Oxfordshire Record Series.* vol. 5.] Ac. **8127**.

—— [Another copy, with a different titlepage.] *Humphrey Milford: London*, 1923. 8°. **010368**. g. **6**.

BARNETT (Herbert Arthur)

—— *See* Bible.—*Appendix.*—*Old Testament.* [*Miscellaneous.*] The Old Testament. By H. A. Barnett . . . L. W. Grensted, *etc.* 1938. 8°. W.P. **7178/1**.

BARNETT (Homer Garner)

—— Culture Element Distributions: IX. Gulf of Georgia Salish. *Berkeley, Cal.*, 1939. 4°. [*Anthropological Records.* vol. 1. no. 5.] Ac. **2689**. g/**47**.
Reproduced from typewriting.

—— Culture Element Distributions: VII. Oregon Coast. *Berkeley, Cal.*, 1937. 4°. [*Anthropological Records.* vol. 1. no. 3.] Ac. **2689**. g/**47**.
Reproduced from typewriting.

—— Innovation: the basis of cultural change. pp. xi. 462. *McGraw-Hill Book Co.: New York*, 1953. 8°. [*McGraw-Hill Series in Sociology and Anthropology.*] W.P. **9223/47**.

BARNETT (Horace Leslie)

—— *See* Lilly (Virgil G.) and Barnett (H. L.) Physiology of the Fungi. 1951. 8°. **07030**. d. **14**.

BARNETT (I. D.) Open Letter to President McKinley by colored people of Massachusetts. [Signed by I. D. Barnett and others.] pp. 11. [1899.] 8°. **8176**. ee. **18**. (3.)

BARNETT (Israel Albert) Plane Analytic Geometry. pp. ix. 269. *J. Wiley & Sons: New York*, 1926. 8°. **8507**. ccc. **19**.

—— Analytic Geometry . . . Second edition [of "Plane Analytic Geometry"]. pp. xii. 345. *J. Wiley & Sons: New York*, 1928. 8°. **08531**. ee. **39**.

BARNETT (James) *Hon. Sec. to the National Poultry Association. See* Doyle (Martin) *pseud.* The Illustrated Book of Domestic Poultry, *etc.* (no. 1. Edited by J. Barnett.) 1854. 8°. **7294**. f. **12**.

BARNETT (James) *M.P. See* England.—*Parliament.*—*House of Commons.*—*Proceedings.*—II. Proceedings of a Select Committee of the House of Commons, on the petition against the return of James Barnett, Esq. for the representation of . . . Rochester, which commenced February 19, 1807, *etc.* 1808. 8°. **10368**. e. **2**. (**4**.)

—— *See* England.—*Parliament.*—*House of Commons.*—*Proceedings.*—II. Proceedings of a Select Committee of the House of Commons, on the petition against the return of James Barnett, Esq. as one of the representatives of . . . Rochester, which commenced . . . February 21 . . . 1817, *etc.* 1817. 8°. **10368**. e. **2**. (**7**.)

BARNETT (James Duff) The Operation of the Initiative, Referendum, and Recall in Oregon. pp. xi. 295. *Macmillan Co.: New York*, 1915. 8°. **8175**. aaa. **65**.

BARNETT (James Harwood)

—— The American Christmas. A study in national culture. pp. xi. 173. *Macmillan Co.: New York*, 1954. 8°. **10414**. aa. **27**.

BARNETT (James Rennie) Modern Motor Lifeboats of the Royal National Lifeboat Institution. [With illustrations.] pp. 79. *Blackie & Son: London & Glasgow*, 1933. 8°. **8808**. df. **20**.

—— Modern Motor-Lifeboats of the Royal National Lifeboat Institution . . . Second edition. pp. 78. *Blackie & Son: London & Glasgow*, 1950. 8°. **08809**. b. **9**.

BARNETT (Joel)

—— Gipsy Morrow. pp. 448. *Victor Gollancz: London*, 1937. 8°. NN. **27893**.

BARNETT (John) *Clerk in the Custom House at Newcastle. See* Barnet.

BARNETT (John) *Musician. See* Rogers (Henry M.) John Barnett, Musician, *etc.* [1925.] 8°. **010856**. f. **45**.

—— Systems & Singing Masters: an analytical comment upon the Wilhem system as taught in England, with letters, authenticated anecdotes, and critical remarks upon Mr. John Hullah's Manual, and the prefatory minute of the Council of Education. pp. iv. 60. *W. S. Orr & Co.: London*, 1842. 8°. **7896**. c. **9**.
Imperfect; wanting pp. 57, 58.

BARNETT (John) *pseud.* [i.e. John Reginald Stagg.] Barry and a Sinner. pp. 307. *Smith, Elder & Co.: London*, 1913. 8°. NN. **904**.

—— Eve in Earnest. pp. 307. *Smith, Elder & Co.: London*, 1910. 8°. **012623**. aa. **37**.

—— Fighting Admirals . . . With portraits, and a frontispiece, *etc.* pp. viii. 309. *Smith, Elder & Co.: London*, 1910. 8°. **08806**. aa. **5**.

—— Geoffrey Cheriton. pp. 316. *Smith, Elder & Co.: London*, 1909. 8°. **012625**. a. **20**.

—— Joseph: a dancing bear . . . With twenty-one illustrations by L. Leslie Brooke. pp. x. 274. *Eveleigh Nash: London*, 1908. 8°. **012626**. aa. **19**.

—— The Luck of the Lanes. pp. viii. 256. *Cassell & Co.: London*, 1907. 8°. **012627**. b. **21**.

—— The New Guv'nor. pp. 303. *Wells, Gardner & Co.: London*, [1913.] 8°. NN. **1043**.

—— The Prince's Valet. pp. 304. *Smith, Elder & Co.: London*, 1907. 8°. **012627**. aa. **42**.

BARNETT (John) *pseud.* [i.e. John Reginald Stagg.]

—— A Queen of Castaways. pp. 308. *Methuen & Co.: London,* 1912. 8°. **012618. aaa. 12.**

—— The Rebel Lady. pp. viii. 344. *Nisbet & Co.: London,* 1915. 8°. **NN. 3349.**

—— The Skipper of the XI, *etc.* pp. 255. *Blackie & Son: London,* [1915.] 8°. **012804. d. 14.**

—— [A reissue.] The Skipper of the XI, *etc.* *London & Glasgow,* [1936.] 8°. **20055. ff. 21.**

—— Trader Carson. pp. 303. *Ward, Lock & Co.: London,* 1914. 8°. **NN. 1806.**

BARNETT (John) *Rev., of Blaby.* "Faithful unto Death." Memorials of the late John Barnett, of Blaby . . . with extracts from his correspondence. Edited by his son [John Barnett]. pp. 222. *Grattan, Marshall & Co.: London; James Vice: Leicester,* 1878. 8°. **4920. bb. 41.**

BARNETT (John) *Son of Rev. John Barnett of Blaby. See* Barnett (John) *Rev., etc.* "Faithful unto Death." Memorials of . . . John Barnett, of Blaby . . . Edited by his son [J. Barnett]. 1878. 8°. **4920. bb. 41.**

BARNETT (John Francis) Musical Reminiscences and Impressions . . . Illustrated. pp. xvi. 341. *Hodder & Stoughton: London,* 1906. 8°. **7899. pp. 1.**

BARNETT (John Pyer) *See* Bailhache (C.) Sermons selected from the papers of . . . C. Bailhache. Edited by . . . J. P. Barnett. 1880. 8°. **4465. k. 6.**

—— The Duty of Dissenters at the Present Crisis. pp. 14. *A. Hall & Co.: London,* 1847. 8°. **4135. a. 10.**

—— Helps to Faith and a Holy Life. pp. viii. 219. *Hodder & Stoughton: London,* 1870. 8°. **4463. dd. 9.**

—— Life and Immortality. A reply to Mr. Robert Roberts . . . with remarks on some other parts of Mr. R.'s religious teaching, as embodied in his "Twelve Lectures." pp. 54. *Morris & Watkins: Swansea,* 1868. 16°. **4374. cc. 6. (2.)**

—— *See* Roberts (Robert) *Christadelphian.* A Defence of the Faith proclaimed in ancient times . . . being a rejoinder to the . . . criticisms of the Rev. J. P. Barnett . . . on "Twelve Lectures." 1868. 8°. **4374. cc. 6. (3.)**

—— —— 1874. 8°. **4139. aaa. 7.**

—— "To whom shall I go?" A review of Dr. Pusey's sermon, entitled: "God and human independence," *etc.* pp. 34. *E. C. Alden: Oxford,* 1876. 8°. **4479. bbb. 2. (14.)**

BARNETT (Joseph)

—— Transition Curves for Highways. pp. 211. 1938. 8°. *See* United States of America.—*Department of Agriculture.—Bureau of Public Roads.* **08535. dd. 8.**

BARNETT (Kennet Bruce) Handbook on Military Sanitation for Regimental Officers . . . With an introduction by Lt.-General Sir Horace L. Smith-Dorrien. pp. xxii. 176. *Forster Groom & Co.: London,* 1912. 8°. **8823. aaa. 9.**

BARNETT (Leonard Palin)

—— Adventure with Youth. A handbook for Church club leaders. pp. 272. *Methodist Youth Department: London,* [1952.] 8°. **4194. e. 31.**

BARNETT (Leonard Palin)

—— The Church Youth Club, *etc.* pp. 190. *Epworth Press: London,* 1951. 8°. **4194. aa. 107.**

—— For Christian Beginners . . . A guide. pp. 92. *Methodist Youth Department: London,* 1955. 8°. [*Ludgate Series.* no. 2.] **W.P. D. 201/2.**

—— A Parson at the Pictures. Talks, *etc.* pp. 56. *Epworth Press: London,* 1949. 8°. **4397. f. 2.**

—— A Prayer Diary for Youth. pp. 77. *Epworth Press: London,* 1953. 8°. **3458. e. 25.**

—— Prayer-Time with Youth. Thirty orders of worship for youth groups. pp. 74. *Epworth Press: London,* 1955. 8°. **3458. c. 18.**

—— Redeeming Feature. A war-time play in three acts. pp. 63. *Epworth Press: London,* 1946. 8°. **11783. aaa. 85.**

—— "Ten to Twelve." A glimpse of an idea in two acts. pp. 31. *Methodist Youth Department: London,* [1955.] 8°. **11785. c. 17.**

—— Twice Twenty Questions on Church Youth Club Work, *etc.* pp. 32. *Methodist Youth Department: London,* 1952. 8°. **4194. aa. 128.**

—— What's the Use of Youth Clubs? M.A.Y.C. clubs suggest an answer. A survey reported by L. P. Barnett. pp. 38. *Methodist Youth Department: London,* 1955. 8°. **08282. f. 131.**

BARNETT (Lincoln Kinnear)

—— The Universe and Dr. Einstein. With a foreword by Albert Einstein. [With plates, including a portrait.] pp. 127. *William Sloane Associates: New York,* [1948.] 8°. **08710. b. 5.**

—— The Universe and Dr. Einstein . . . Illustrated by Anthony Sodaro. pp. 112. *Victor Gollancz: London,* 1949. 8°. **8713. a. 55.**

—— The Universe and Dr. Einstein, *etc.* (New and revised edition.) pp. 112. *Victor Gollancz: London,* 1950. 8°. **08710. bb. 54.**

—— Writing on Life. Sixteen close-ups. pp. 383. *William Sloane Associates: New York,* [1951.] 8°. **10890. e. 33.**

BARNETT (Lionel David) *C.B., Keeper of Oriental Printed Books and Manuscripts, British Museum.*

—— *See* Aeschylus [*Eumenides.—Greek.*] The Eumenides of Aeschylus Edited . . . by L. D. Barnett, *etc.* 1901. 8°. **11306. bb. 29/1.**

—— *See* Hitopadeṣa. Hitopadeṣa . . . Translation . . . by F. Johnson. Revised and in part re-written, with an introduction, by L. D. Barnett, *etc.* 1928. 8°. **14005. ff. 5.**

—— *See* Joachim (Hermann) A Brief History of Roman Literature . . . Translated by L. D. Barnett. 1904. 8°. **012200. e. 7/33.**

—— *See* Kavichakravarti, *Author of the Pakhal Inscription.* Pakhāl Inscription of the Reign of the Kākatīya Ganapatidēva. [Edited and translated by L. D. Barnett.] 1919. fol. [*Hyderabad Archaeological Series.* no. 4.] **7705.tt.3/4.**

BARNETT (LIONEL DAVID) *C.B., Keeper of Oriental Printed Books and Manuscripts, British Museum.*

— *See* KOCH (Julius) Roman History. (Translated from the German . . . by L. D. Barnett.) 1900. 8°. **012200. e. 7/8.**

— *See* LALLĀ, *Poetess.* Lallā-Vākyāni . . . Edited with translation, notes, and a vocabulary by Sir G. Grierson . . . and L. D. Barnett. 1920. 8°. **14005. b. 18.**

— *See* LONDON.—III. *British Museum.—Department of Oriental Printed Books and Manuscripts.* An Alphabetical Index to the Chinese Encyclopaedia, *etc.* [With a preface by L. D. Barnett.] 1911. 4°. Circ. **91.** b.

— *See* LONDON.—III. *British Museum.—Department of Oriental Printed Books and Manuscripts.* A Catalogue of the Armenian Manuscripts in the British Museum, *etc.* [With a preface by L. D. Barnett.] 1913. 4°. Circ. **35.** b.

— *See* LONDON.—III. *British Museum.—Department of Oriental Printed Books and Manuscripts.* A Descriptive List of the Arabic Manuscripts acquired by the Trustees of the British Museum since 1894, *etc.* [With a preface by L. D. Barnett.] 1912. 8°. **Circ.86.b.**

— *See* LONDON.—III. *British Museum.—Department of Oriental Printed Books and Manuscripts.* A Supplementary Catalogue of Bengali Books in the Library of the British Museum, *etc.* [With a prefatory note by L. D. Barnett.] 1910. 4°. **Circ.90.b.**

— *See* LONDON.—III. *Spanish and Portuguese Jews' Congregation.* Bevis Marks Records . . . Edited by L. D. Barnett. 1940, *etc.* 4°. **4517.d.1.**

— *See* LONDON.—III. *Spanish and Portuguese Jews' Congregation.* El Libro de los Acuerdos . . . Translated . . . by L. D. Barnett. 1931. 4°. **04515. g. 19.**

— *See* MAHĀBHĀRATA.—*Bhagavadgītā.* Bhagavadgita: or, the Lord's Song. Translated by L. D. Barnett. [1905.] 8°. **012200.de.8/123.**

— *See* MAHENDRA-VIKRAMA-VARMĀ, *Pallava, King of Conjevaram.* Matta-Vilasa . . . Translated by L. D. Barnett, *etc.* [1930.] 8°. **14079. d. 44. (3.)**

— *See* MAISCH (R.) A Manual of Greek Antiquities. (Translated by L. D. Barnett.) 1903. 8°. **012200. e. 7/30.**

— *See* PLAUTUS (T. M.) [*Mostellaria.—Latin and English.*] The Haunted House . . . With a translation . . . by . . . L. D. Barnett, *etc.* 1890. 8°. **11707. ccc. 11. (2.)**

— *See* SANDBERG (S. L. G.) Tibet and the Tibetans. [With a note by L. D. Barnett.] 1906. 8°. **4429. dd. 30.**

— *See* ŚĀNTI-DEVA. The Path of Light. Rendered . . . into English . . . by L. D. Barnett. 1909. 8°. **14003. a. 27.**

— *See* SOMADEVA BHAṬṬA. The Golden Town and other tales from Soma-Deva's "Ocean of Romance-Rivers." By L. D. Barnett. 1909. 8°. **14005. d. 2.**

— *See* STEUDING (H.) Greek and Roman Mythology and Heroic Legend. (Translated and edited by L. D. Barnett.) 1901. 8°. **012200. e. 7/19.**

— *See* STRONG (Herbert A.) and BARNETT (L. D.) Historical Reader of Early French, *etc.* 1901. 8°. **12954. dd. 23.**

BARNETT (LIONEL DAVID) *C.B., Keeper of Oriental Printed Books and Manuscripts, British Museum.*

— *See* SWOBODA (H.) Greek History. (Translated from the German by L. D. Barnett.) 1900. 8°. **012200. e. 7/14.**

— *See* UPANISHADS. Some Sayings from the Upanishads. Done into English with notes by L. D. Barnett. 1905. 8°. **14007. b. 24.**

— Alphabetical Guide to Sinhalese Folklore from ballad sources . . . Reprinted from the "Indian Antiquary." pp. 120. *British India Press: Bombay,* 1917. 8°. **12450. l. 21.**

— Antiquities of India. An account of the history and culture of ancient Hindustan . . . With numerous illustrations and a map. pp. xvi. 306. *Macmillan & Co. & P. L. Warner: London,* 1913. 8°. [*Handbooks to Ancient Civilizations Series.*] **2259. d. 1/3.**

— Brahma-Knowledge. An outline of the philosophy of the Vedānta as set forth by the Upanishads and by Śankara. pp. 113. *Orient Press: London,* 1907. 8°. [*Wisdom of the East.*] **14003. a. 19.**

— A Catalogue of the Burmese Books in the British Museum. pp. vii. coll. 346. 1913. 4°. *See* LONDON.—III. *British Museum.—Department of Oriental Printed Books and Manuscripts.* **Circ.91.b.14.**

— [Another copy.] **11925.dd.11.**

— A Catalogue of the Kannada, Badaga, and Kurg Books in the Library of the British Museum. pp. iv. coll. 278. 1910. 4°. *See* LONDON.—III. *British Museum.—Department of Oriental Printed Books and Manuscripts.* Circ. **90. b.**

— A Catalogue of the Telugu Books in the Library of the British Museum. pp. v. coll. 444. 1912. 4°. *See* LONDON.—III. *British Museum.—Department of Oriental Printed Books and Manuscripts.* **Circ.91.b.12.**

— [Another copy.] **11925.dd.18.**

— The Early History of Southern India.—The Early History of Ceylon. *See* INDIA. The Cambridge History of India. vol. 1. 1922, *etc.* 8°. W.P. **5616.**

— Edward James Rapson, 1861–1937. From the Proceedings of the British Academy, *etc.* pp. 14. *Humphrey Milford: London,* [1938.] 8°. **10857.** g. 3.

— The Greek Drama. pp. x. 114. *J. M. Dent & Co.: London,* 1900. 8°. [*Temple Primers.*] **012200. e. 7/2.**

— The Heart of India: sketches in the history of Hindu religion and morals. pp. 122. *Orient Press: London,* 1908. 8°. [*Wisdom of the East.*] **14003. a. 22.**

— Hindu Gods and Heroes. Studies, *etc.* pp. 120. *Orient Press: London,* 1922. 8°. [*Wisdom of the East.*] **14003. a. 57.**

— Hinduism. pp. vi. 66. *A. Constable & Co.: London,* 1906. 8°. [*Religions: Ancient and Modern.*] **4505. de. 23/6.**

— Index der Abteilung mDo des handschriftlichen Kanjur im Britischen Museum—Or. 6724. [An offprint from "Asia Major."] *Leipzig,* 1930. 8°. **Oriental Students Room.**

— Inscriptions at Palampet and Uparpalli. [Edited by L. D. Barnett.] pp. 19. *Calcutta,* 1919. fol. [*Hyderabad Archaeological Series.* no. 3.] **7705.tt.3.**

BARNETT (LIONEL DAVID) *C.B., Keeper of Oriental Printed Books and Manuscripts, British Museum.*

—— A Supplementary Catalogue of Sanskrit, Pali, and Prakrit Books in the Library of the British Museum acquired during the years 1892–1906. pp. iv. coll. 1096. 1908. 4°. *See* LONDON.—III. *British Museum.—Department of Oriental Printed Books and Manuscripts.* Circ.90.b.

—— [Another copy.] **11925.dd.21.**

—— A Supplementary Catalogue of the Sanskrit, Pali, and Prakrit Books in the Library of the British Museum, acquired during the years 1906–1928. pp. vii. 1694. 1928. 4°. *See* LONDON.—III. *British Museum.—Department of Oriental Printed Books and Manuscripts.* **Circ.90.b.**

—— [Another copy.] A Supplementary Catalogue of the Sanskrit, Pali, and Prakrit Books in the Library of the British Museum, acquired during the years 1906–1928. 1928. 4°. *See* LONDON.—III. *British Museum.—Department of Oriental Printed Books and* MSS. **11906.** dd. **19.**

—— A Supplementary Catalogue of the Tamil Books in the Library of the British Museum. pp. viii. coll. 696. 1931. 4°. *See* LONDON.—III. *British Museum.—Department of Oriental Printed Books and Manuscripts.* **Circ.90.b.**

—— [Another copy.] **11925.dd.20.**

BARNETT (LIONEL DAVID) *C.B., Keeper of Oriental Printed Books and Manuscripts, British Museum,* and **POPE** (GEORGE UGLOW)

—— A Catalogue of the Tamil Books in the Library of the British Museum. pp. viii. coll. 590. 1909. 4°. *See* LONDON.—III. *British Museum.—Department of Oriental Printed Books and Manuscripts* **Circ.90.b.**

—— [Another copy.] **11925.dd.19.**

BARNETT (M. J.) *Author of "Practical Metaphysics.* The Five Redeemers. [Essays.] pp. 166. *H. H. Carter & Co.: Boston,* 1890. 8°. **8411.** cc. **9.**

BARNETT (MARGARET) The Dream-Village, and other poems. pp. 12. *A. H. Stockwell: London,* [1933.] 8°. **011641.** df. **75.**

—— Short Stories and Verse for Children. pp. 52. *A. H. Stockwell: Ilfracombe,* [1945.] 8°. **12830.** aaa. **10.**

BARNETT (MARY)

—— Flights of Fancy. Stories for children. pp. 40. *Arthur H. Stockwell: Ilfracombe,* 1954. 8°. **12837.** ff. **33.**

BARNETT (MARY G.) Young Delinquents. A study of reformatory and industrial schools . . . With an introduction by the Right Hon. Sir John Gorst. pp. xiv. 222. *Methuen & Co.: London,* 1913. 8°. **08248.** aaa. **17.**

BARNETT (MATILDA J.) Tontine. [A novel.] pp. 505. *F. Pitman: London,* [1883.] 8°. **12643.** bbb. **16.**

BARNETT (MATTHEW) A Sermon preached at . . . Barton upon Humber . . . when the Volunteer Infantry of that place . . . were present. pp. iv. 16. *J. Asperne: London,* 1804. 8°. **4473.** e. **11.** **(13.)**

BARNETT (MAURICE) *LL.B.*

—— *See* AFRICA, *South.—Union of South Africa.—Supreme Court.* Rules of the Supreme Court of South Africa . . . By A. L. Arenhold . . . and P. Fisher . . . assisted by M. Barnett. 1938. 8°. **06605.** bbb. **10.**

BARNETT (MAURICE) *LL.B.*

—— *See* AFRICA, *South.* [Union of South Africa.]—*Supreme Court.* Rules of the Supreme Court of South Africa . . . Second edition by M. Barnett. 1949. 8°. **6609.** b. **2.**

—— *See* BISSET (Murray) and SMITH (P. F.) Index and Digest of the South African Law Reports, 1946–1949 . . . Edited by G. Duncan . . . M. Barnett, *etc.* 1951. 8°. **6608.** bb. **26**

—— *See* INGRAM (Charles J.) and DE VILLIERS (J. E.) Rules, Orders, &c., *etc.* (Supplement to the second edition, by J. E. de Villiers and M. Barnett.) [1935.] 8°. **06605.** bb. **42.**

BARNETT (MAURICE) *M.A., B.D.*

—— The Living Flame. Being a study of the Gift of the Spirit in the New Testament. With special reference to prophecy, glossolalia, Montanism and perfection. pp. xvi. 152. *Epworth Press: London,* 1953. 8°. **3228** de. **13.**

—— This Concerns You. pp. 21. *Epworth Press: London,* [1947.] 8°. [*The Message and Mission of Methodism.* no. 2.] W.P. **15530/2.**

—— What next? An approach to young people on joining the Church. pp. 8. *Epworth Press: London,* 1950. 8°. **4194.** c. **14.**

BARNETT (MILES AYLMER FULTON)

—— The Cyclonic Storms in Northern New Zealand on the 2nd February and the 26th March, 1936, *etc.* pp. 34. *Wellington,* 1938. 8°. [*New Zealand. Meteorological Office Note.* no. 22.] C.S. G. **696/2.**

BARNETT (MORRIS) The Bold Dragoons. An original comic drama in two acts. pp. 29. *London,* [1853.] 12°. [*Lacy's Acting Edition of Plays.* vol. 9.] **2304.** d. **13.**

—— The Bold Dragoons, *etc.* pp. 14. *London,* [1884.] 8° [*Dicks' Standard Plays.* no. 509.] **11770.** bbb. **4**

—— Circumstantial Evidence! A comic piece, in one act. pp. 15. *London,* [1852.] 12°. [*Lacy's Acting Edition of Plays.* Supplementary vol. 3.] **2304.** i. **3.**

—— Lilian Gervais. A drama, in three acts. [Adapted from "Marie Simon," by J. E. Alboize de Pujol and E. de Saint-Yves.] pp. 39. *London,* [1857.] 12°. [*Lacy's Acting Edition of Plays.* vol. 31.] **2304.** e. **5.**

—— Married Un-married. A drama, in two acts. pp. 23. *London,* [1854.] 12°. [*Lacy's Acting Edition of Plays.* vol. 14.] **2304.** d. **18.**

—— Monsieur Jacques: a musical piece, *etc.* pp. 22. *John Miller: London,* 1836. 12°. **841.** b. **11.** **(12.)**

—— [Another edition.] pp. 22. *London,* [1857.] 12°. [*Lacy's Acting Edition of Plays.* vol. 28.] **2304.** e. **2.**

—— "Monsieur Jacques," and "Plot and Counterplot." Written respectively by M. Barnett and C. Kemble, *etc.* 2 pt. *London,* [1883.] 8°. [*Dicks' Standard Plays.* no. 503.] **11770.** bbb. **4.**

—— Mrs. G. of the Golden Pippin, a petite opera, in two acts, *etc.* pp. 26. *London,* [1830.] 12°. [*Duncombe's Edition of the British Theatre.* vol. 8.] **2304.** a. **4.**

—— Power and Principle. A drama, in three acts, founded upon von Schillers "Kabale und Liebe." pp. 31. *London,* [1850.] 12°. [*Lacy's Acting Edition of Plays, etc.* vol. 2.] **2304.** d. **6.**

BARNETT (MORRIS)

—— Sarah the Creole; or, a Snake in the grass. A drama in five acts. pp. 51. *London*, [1858.] 12°. [*Lacy's Acting Edition of Plays.* vol. 31.] **2304**. e. **5**.

—— The Serious Family. A comedy, in three acts, *etc.* pp. 40. *Chapman & Hall: London*, [1849.] 12°. [WEBSTER (*Benjamin N.*) *The Acting National Drama.* vol. 16.] **2304**. b. **19**.

—— [Another edition.] pp. 16. *London*, [1896.] 8°. [*Dicks' Standard Plays.* no. 1007.] **11770.bbb.4.**

—— The Spirit of the Rhine, a petite opera, in two acts, *etc.* pp. 25. *London*, [1835?] 12°. [*Duncombe's Edition of the British Theatre.* vol. 19.] **2304**. a. **10**.

—— Tact; or, the Wrong Box. A farce, in two acts, *etc.* pp. 34. *London*, [1830?] 12°. [*Duncombe's Edition of the British Theatre.*] **2304**. a. **7**.

—— Yankee Peddler; or, Old Times in Virginia. A farce, in one act, *etc.* pp. 16. *Samuel French: New York*, [1868?] 12°. **11770**. bb. **3**.

—— The Yellow Kids; a farce, in one act, *etc.* pp. 22. *London*, [1835?] 12°. [*Duncombe's Edition of the British Theatre.*] **2304**. a. 9.

—— The Yellow Kids, *etc.* *See* MILLINGEN (John G.) "Borrowed Feathers," *etc.* [1888.] 8°. [*Dicks' Standard Plays.* no. 967.] **11770**. bbb.

BARNETT (MORRIS) and **BARNETT** (B.) *Dramatic Writer.*

—— Out on the Loose. A farce. In one act. pp. 22. *London*, [1850.] 12°. [*Lacy's Acting Edition of Plays.* vol. 2.] **2304**. d. **6**.

BARNETT (MORRIS) and **MATHEWS** (CHARLES JAMES)

—— Serve him right! A comic drama, in two acts. pp. 44. *London*, [1850.] 12°. [*Lacy's Acting Edition of Plays.* vol. 3.] **2304**. d. **7**.

—— [A reissue.] Serve him right! *etc.* *London*. [1872.] 12°. [*Lacy's Acting Edition.* no. 31.] **11791**. t. **1/1208**.

BARNETT (MURIELLE I.) Browns' Mental Arithmetic Tests for Group Work in Infant Schools. Arranged by M. I. Barnett. [Cards, in packets.] 5 pt. *A. Brown & Sons: London*, [1932.] *obl.* 8°. **8503**. df. **34**.

BARNETT (NEHEMIAH) God's Lift up Hand for Lancashire, presented in a sermon preached before the Honorable Committee of the County at Lancaster upon the 18th December 1645, being a solemne day of thanksgiving to God for clearing of the county in subduing the enemies thereof. pp. 47. *W. Wilson for John Williams: London*, 1648. 8°. E. **1165**. **(2.)**

—— The Regenerate Man's Growth in Grace . . . Preached in a sermon at Lancaster upon a day of humiliation. pp. 78. *John Dawson for John Williams: London*, 1646. 8°. E. **1165**. **(1.)**

BARNETT (OLIVE ELIZABETH)

—— [For works written by O. E. Barnett in collaboration with Grace T. Barnett:] *See* BARNETT (Grace T.) and BARNETT (O. E.)

BARNETT (PAUL)

—— Business-Cycle Theory in the United States, 1860–1900. pp. ix. 129. *University of Chicago Press: Chicago*, 1941. 8°. [*Studies in Business Administration.* vol. 11. no. 3.] Ac. **2691**. e/5.

BARNETT (PERCY ARTHUR) *See* BURRELL (Arthur) Clear Speaking and Good Reading . . . With a preface by P. A. Barnett. 1898. 8°. **011824**. g. **70**.

—— *See* CARPENTER (George R.) Longmans' English Classics . . . With a preface by P. A. Barnett. 1896, *etc.* 8°. **12274.bbb.15**.

—— *See* DEFOE (Daniel) The Story of Robinson Crusoe in Latin. Adapted . . . by G. F. Goffeaux. Edited, amended and rearranged by P. A. Barnett. 1907. 8°. **012612**. ff. **15**.

—— *See* DUMVILLE (B.) Elements of French Pronunciation and Diction . . . With introduction by P. A. Barnett. 1904. 8°. **12215.e.1/20.**

—— *See* MORELL (John D.) The New Morell; being a grammar of the English language . . . Based on the work of . . . J. D. Morell, re-written under the revision of P. A. Barnett. 1893. 8°. **12981**. ccc. **20**.

—— Common Sense Grammar, *etc.* pp. 51. *Christophers: London*, 1923. 8°. **12980**. df. **16**.

—— Common Sense in Education. An introduction to practice. pp. ix. 321. *Longmans & Co.: London*, 1899. 8°. **8307**. ccc. **38**.

—— The Little Book of Health & Courtesy. Written for boys and girls. pp. 24. *Longmans & Co.: London*, 1905. 8°. **8408**. aa. **40**.

—— Second edition. pp. 24. *Longmans & Co.: London*, 1906. 8°. **08407**. ee. **9**.

—— New edition. pp. 24. *Longmans & Co.: London*, 1925. 8°. **8405**. aa. **48**.

—— Teaching and Organisation . . . A manual of practice. Edited by P. A. Barnett. pp. xix. 419. *Longmans & Co.: London*, 1897. 8°. **8311**. aaa. **44**.

BARNETT (PERCY ARTHUR) and **SWEENEY** (GEORGE WILLIAM)

—— Natal. The state and the citizen. pp. xi. 128. *Longmans & Co.: London*, 1904. 8°. **8156**. de. **39**.

BARNETT (*Mrs.* PERCY ARTHUR) *See* BARNETT (Annie)

BARNETT (PERCY NEVILLE)

—— [A collection of Australian bookplates, formed by P. N. Barnett.] [c. 1952.] 8° & 12°. **Cup.500.d.11.**

—— The Bookplate in Australia. Its inspiration and development. (Reprinted from the 1929 Year Book of the American Society of Bookplate Collectors and Designers.) [With illustrations.] pp. 29. *Tyrrell's Galleries: Sydney*, 1930. 8°. **011903**. bb. **127**.

—— Japanese Colour-Prints. [With plates.] pp. 109. *Privately printed: Sydney*, 1936. fol. **7861**. v. 21.

—— P. Neville Barnett and his Books. [By various authors. With illustrations, including portraits.] [1951.] 4°. 7868. f. 63.

BARNETT (Percy William)

—— *See* Bagenal (Philip H. E.) and Barnett (P. W.) The Reduction of Noise in Buildings, *etc.* 1933. 8°. [*Building Research Board. Bulletin.* no. 14.] B.S. **38.** a/**5.**

—— *See* Glanville (Sir William H.) and Barnett (P. W.) Mechanical Properties of Bricks and Brickwork Masonry. 1934. 8°. [*Building Research Board. Special Report.* no. 22.] B.S. **38.** a/**3.**

—— Jointless—Magnesium Oxychloride—Floors. (pt. 1 by P. W. Barnett. pt. 2 by B. Bakewell.) pp. iii. 26. *London,* 1925. 8°. [*Building Research Board. Bulletin.* no. 1.] B.S. **38.** a/**5.**

BARNETT (R.) *Rev.* Catechism on the Creed. pp. 16. *Hatchards: London,* 1884. 16°. **3505.** df. **40.** (**2.**)

BARNETT (Reginald) The Devil's Whisper. pp. 249. *Walter Scott: London,* [1889.] 8°. [*Novocastrian Novels.*] **012600.** e. **1.**

—— Police Sergeant C 21. The story of a crime. pp. 305. *Walter Scott: London,* [1888.] 8°. [*Novocastrian Novels.*] **012600.** e. **1.**

—— Rubbed Out. pp. 283. *R. A. Everett & Co.: London,* [1904.] 8°. **012621.** e. **55.**

BARNETT (Richard David) *Keeper of Western Asiatic Antiquities, British Museum.*

—— *See* Dupont-Sommer (A.) [Nouveaux aperçus sur des manuscripts de la Mer Morte.] The Jewish Sect of Qumran and the Essenes . . . Translated . . . by R. D. Barnett. 1954. 8°. **4508.** bb. **11.**

—— *See* London.—iii. *British Museum.* Carchemish. Report on the excavations at Djerabis, *etc.* (pt. 3. The Hittite Inscriptions. By R. D. Barnett.) 1914, *etc.* 4°. **7705.** i. **31.**

—— *See* Woolley (*Sir* Charles L.) Alalakh. An account of the excavations at Tell Atchana . . . With sections by . . . R. D. Barnett. 1955. 4°. Ac. **5665**/**11.**

—— Karatepe, the Key to the Hittite Hieroglyphs. *In:* Anatolian Studies. vol. 3. pp. 53–95. 1953. 8°. Ac. **5198**/**2.**

BARNETT (Richard Whieldon) The White Cockade. A Jacobite opera in three acts, *etc.* pp. 32. [*Printed for private circulation: London,* 1889?] 8°. **11778.** aaa. **11.** (**2.**)

—— [Another edition.] pp. 32. *Printed for private circulation: London,* 1889. 8°. **906.** i. **8.** (**8.**)

BARNETT (Robert Edward) *See* Bottomley (Samuel E.) Photography in Principle and Practice . . . With an introduction by Mr. R. E. Barnett. 1909. 8°. **08909.** b. **9.**

BARNETT (Robert W.) The Practical Hand-book to the Bills of Exchange Act, 1882. pp. 88. *Blades & Co.: London,* 1883. 8°. **6376.** cc. **7.**

BARNETT (Rupert Noel)

—— Memorandum on the Use of Machines in Accounting. *See* Back (William J.) Standard Practice in Auditing, *etc.* 1937. 8°. **8231.** ee. **16.**

BARNETT (Samuel Anthony)

—— Survey of Human Biology. *Routledge & Kegan Paul: London,* 1953– . 8°. W.P. b. **527.**

BARNETT (Samuel Augustus) *See* Aitken (William F.) Canon Barnett, Warden of Toynbee Hall: his mission and its relation to social movements. 1902. 8°. **10601.** e. **22/3.**

—— *See* Barnett (*Dame* Henrietta O. W.) *D.B.E.* Canon Barnett. His life, work, and friends, *etc.* 1918. 8°. **4908.** g. **8.**

—— —— 1921. 8°. **4908.** h. **9.**

—— *See* England.—*Royal Commission on the Poor Laws and Relief of Distress.* New Poor Law or No Poor Law . . . With an introductory note by Canon Barnett. 1909. 8°. **6426.** eee. **21.**

—— *See* Gamon (Hugh R. P.) The London Police Court, to-day & to-morrow. (Introduction by Canon Barnett.) 1907. 8°. **6056.** r. **1.**

—— *See* Lewis (George G.) *Headmaster, etc.* Typical School Journeys . . . With foreword by the Rev. Canon Barnett. [1909.] 8°. **7006.** aaa. **47.**

—— *See* Peppin (Talbot S.) Club-Land of the Toilers . . . With a preface by Canon Barnett. 1895. 8°. **08277.** ee. **18.**

—— *See* Robertson (Frederick W.) F. W. Robertson's Sermons. With a commendation by Canon Barnett. [1906.] 8°. 12206.p.1/23.

—— *See* Russell (Charles) *Principal of Patna College.* The Jew in London . . . With an introduction by Canon Barnett, *etc.* 1900. 8°. **04034.** ee. **33.**

—— *See* Thompson (Rosalie B.) Peter Thompson . . . With foreword by Rev. Canon Barnett. 1910. 8°. **4902.** ee. **25.**

—— *See* Washburn (Henry B.) The Religious Motive in Philanthropy, *etc.* (Samuel Barnett.—Vincent de Paul, *etc.*) 1931. 8°. [*George Dana Boardman Lectures.* no. 14.] Ac. **2692.** p/**21.**

—— The Ideal City. pp. 32. *Arrowsmith: Bristol,* [1894.] 16°. **08275.** de. **25.** (**1.**)

—— Perils of Wealth and Poverty . . . Edited by . . . V. A. Boyle, *etc.* pp. 93. *G. Allen & Unwin: London,* 1920. 8°. **08282.** aa. **59.**

—— Practicable Socialism. Essays on social reform. By the Rev. and Mrs. S. A. Barnett. pp. viii. 212. *Longmans & Co.: London,* 1888. 8°. **8282.** b. **61.**

—— Second edition . . . enlarged. pp. viii. 328. *Longmans & Co.: London,* 1894. 8°. **08275.** ee. **8.**

—— Practicable Socialism. New series. By Canon S. A. Barnett . . . and Mrs. S. A. Barnett, *etc.* pp. xiv. 338. *Longmans & Co.: London,* 1915. 8°. **08248.** cc. **23**

—— Religion and Politics. Lectures given in Westminster Abbey. pp. viii. 184. *Wells Gardner & Co.: London,* 1911. 8°. **04403.** ee. **74.**

—— Religion and Progress. pp. 59. *A. & C. Black: London,* 1907. 8°. **08275.** i. **77.**

—— St. Jude's, Whitechapel. Seventeenth Pastoral Address and Report of the Parish Work. Accounts for the year 1889–1890. pp. 64. [1890.] 8°. *See* Jude, *Saint and Apostle, Church of, Whitechapel, London.* **4192.** aaa. **45.**

—— Sermon . . . preached before the University of Oxford, on June 15th, 1884. pp. 8. [1884.] 8°. **4478.** f. **70.** (**3.**)

BARNETT (Samuel Augustus)

—— The Service of God. Sermons, essays, and addresses. pp. viii. 346. *Longmans & Co.: London*, 1897. 8°. **4477.** ee. **31.**

—— The Temperance Question. *See* Hocking (William J.) The Church and New Century Problems, *etc.* [1901.] 8°. **08275.** f. **59.**

—— Vision and Service: being sermons, papers, letters, and aphorisms . . . Selected, edited, and introduced by . . . Henrietta O. Barnett. [With a portrait.] pp. 79. *London*, [1917.] 8°. **3755.** h. **5.**

—— The Witness of the Past. *See* Bristol.—*Cathedral Church.* Octave Sermons, *etc.* [1895.] 8°. **4478.** de. **11.**

—— Worship and Work. Thoughts from the unpublished writings of the late Canon S. A. Barnett . . . Selected and edited by his wife (Henrietta O. Barnett). pp. xix. 219. *Garden City Press: Letchworth*, 1913. 8°. **4379.** de. **10.**

—— Second edition. pp. xix. 219. *Garden City Press: Letchworth*, 1913. 8°. **4379.** de. **11.**

BARNETT (Samuel Augustus) and **BARNETT** (*Dame* Henrietta Octavia Weston) *D.B.E.*

—— Towards Social Reform. pp. 359. *T. Fisher Unwin: London, Leipsic*, 1909. 8°. **08276.** a. **40.**

BARNETT (*Mrs.* Samuel Augustus) *See* Barnett (*Dame* Henrietta O. W.) *D.B.E.*

BARNETT (Samuel Jackson) Elements of Electromagnetic Theory. pp. 480. *Macmillan Co.: New York*, 1903. 8°. **08755.** h. **1.**

—— Evidence on the Nature of the Elementary Magnet from Researches on Gyromagnetic Phenomena. pp. 43. [*Los Angeles*,] 1930. 8°. [*University of California at Los Angeles. Faculty Research Lectures.* no. 4.] Ac. **2689.** gk. (**7.**)

BARNETT (Stanley)

—— God Be at My End. pp. 23. *Society for Promoting Christian Knowledge: London*, 1946. 8°. **4398.** aa. **132.**

BARNETT (Thomas) The Niagara Falls Museum . . . near Table Rock, Ontario, Canada. [A folder.] [1880?] 8°. **10470.** aa. **62.**

BARNETT (Thomas Duff) *See* Shakespeare (William) [*Julius Caesar.*] Shakespeare's Julius Caesar. Edited by T. D. Barnett. 1893. 8°. **012272.aaaa.1/2.**

—— *See* Shakespeare (William) [*Merchant of Venice.*] Shakespeare's Merchant of Venice. Edited by T. D. Barnett. 1893. 8°. **012272.aaaa.1/3.**

—— *See* Shakespeare (William) [*Tempest.*] Shakespeare's The Tempest. Edited by T. D. Barnett. 1893. 8°. **012272.aaaa.1/4.**

—— Notes on Shakespeare's play of "As You Like It." pp. 71. *G. Bell & Sons: London*, 1895. 8°. **11763.** aaa. **19.**

—— Notes on Shakespeare's play of Hamlet. pp. 100. *G. Bell & Sons: London*, 1889. 8°. **11766.** bb. **27.**

—— Notes on Shakespeare's play of King Lear. pp. 75. *G. Bell & Sons: London*, 1891. 8°. **11764.** ccc. **12.** (**4.**)

—— Notes on Shakespeare's play of King Richard III. pp. 81. *G. Bell & Sons: London*, 1895. 8°. **11765.** aaa. **33.**

—— Notes on Shakespeare's play of the Merchant of Venice. pp. 71. *G. Bell & Sons: London*, 1889. 8°. **11762.** df. **9.** (**5.**)

BARNETT (Thomas Duff)

—— Notes on Shakespeare's play of Much Ado about Nothing. pp. 71. *G. Bell & Sons: London*, 1895. 8°. **11765.** aa. **44.**

—— Notes on Shakespeare's play of Richard II. pp. 67. *G. Bell & Sons: London*, 1890. 8°. **11762.** df. **9.** (**7.**)

—— [Another copy.] **11764.** bb. **50.** (**4.**)

—— Notes on Shakespeare's play of Twelfth Night, *etc.* pp. 71. *G. Bell & Sons: London*, 1895. 8°. **011765.** f. **8.**

—— Questions on "The Tempest," *etc.* pp. 52. *Relfe Bros.: London*, [1897.] 8°. **11764.** ccc. **12.** (**7.**)

BARNETT (Thomas Henry) Lessons on the Children of the Bible. pp. xii. 184. *Church of England Sunday School Institute: London*, [1886.] 8°. **4804.** aa. **16.**

—— The Strong and the Stronger. A series of forty short readings upon the temptation of our Lord in the wilderness. pp. 156. *Wells Gardner & Co.: London*, [1889.] 8°. **4465.** f. **16.**

BARNETT (Thomas Ratcliffe) Autumns in Skye, Ross and Sutherland, *etc.* [With plates.] pp. 187. *R. Grant & Son: Edinburgh*, 1930. 8°. **010369.** f. **52.**

—— The Blessed Ministry of Childhood. pp. 64. *Oliphant & Co.: Edinburgh & London*, 1906. 8°. **04402.** ee. **48.**

—— Border By-ways & Lothian Lore . . . With 16 illustrations. pp. xii. 208. *R. Grant & Son: Edinburgh*, [1925.] 8°. **010369.** f. **9.**

—— Border By-Ways & Lothian Lore . . . New and enlarged edition. pp. xii. 252. *Moray Press: Edinburgh & London*, 1937. 8°. **010369.** f. **71**

—— Border By-Ways & Lothian Lore, *etc.* (Fifth edition revised.) pp. xii. 227. *John Grant: Edinburgh, London*, 1943. 8°. **010370.** aa. **5**

—— The Cradle of Christianity. A pilgrimage to the Holy Places . . . With drawings by John Spencer. pp. 166 *J. Clarke & Co.: London*, [1936.] 8°. **010076.** de. **63**

—— Fairshiels. Memories of a Lammermoor parish. pp. 127 *Oliphant & Co.: Edinburgh & London*, 1906. 8°. **10369.** f. **22**

—— The Finest Baby in the World: being letters from a man to himself about his child. [By T. R. Barnett.] pp. 61. 1904. 8°. *See* Baby. **012330.** i. **52**

—— Highland Harvest. [With plates.] pp. 198. *J. Clarke & Co.: London*, [1938.] 8°. **010369.** h. **55**

—— The Land of Lochiel and the Magic West . . . With 2[illegible] illustrations. pp. 193. *R. Grant & Son: Edinburgh*, 1927. 8°. **010369.** f. **24**

—— The Land of Lorne and the Isles of Rest, *etc.* [With plates.] pp. 199. *W. & R. Chambers: London & Edinburgh*, 1933. 8°. **010390.** f. **23**

—— The Makers of the Kirk. [With illustrations.] pp. 311 *T. N. Foulis: London*, 1915. 8°. **4956.** i. **14**

—— Margaret of Scotland, Queen and Saint: her influence on the early Church of Scotland. [With plates.] pp. xi. 183. *Oliver & Boyd: Edinburgh, London*, 1926. 8°. **4830.** bbb. **25**

—— Reminiscences of Old Scots Folk . . . With ten illustrations in colour by R. Gemmell Hutchison. pp. 205. *T. N. Foulis: London & Edinburgh*, 1913. 8°. **012354.** f. **41**

BARNETT (THOMAS RATCLIFFE)

—— The Road to Rannoch and the Summer Isles . . . With 16 illustrations. pp. xv. 200. *R. Grant & Son: Edinburgh,* 1924. 8°. **10369. dd. 24.**

—— [A reissue.] *Edinburgh,* 1930. 8°. **010369. f. 49.** *In this issue one illustration is omitted and the rest are re-arranged.*

—— The Road to Rannoch and the Summer Isles . . . With 22 illustrations, *etc.* (New and revised edition.) pp. xv. 184. *John Grant: Edinburgh, London,* 1944. 8°. **010370. aa. 12.**

—— [A reissue.] The Road to Rannoch and the Summer Isles, *etc. Edinburgh, London,* 1946. 8°. **010370. a. 18.**

—— Scottish Pilgrimage in the Land of Lost Content. [With plates.] pp. 207. *John Grant: Edinburgh, London,* 1942. 8°. **010370. aa. 4.**

—— The Story of the Covenant. Fifty years of fighting faith. [With plates.] pp. xii. 298. *Oliver & Boyd: Edinburgh, London,* 1928. 8°. **9510. cc. 27.**

—— The Winds of Dawn, and other parables from nature. pp. vi. 87. *J. Nisbet & Co.: London,* 1914. 8°. **04376. e. 26.**

BARNETT (TILLY)

—— *See* MAYBAUM (I.) The Jewish Home. (Translated . . . by T. Barnett and L. V. Snowman.) [1946.] 8°. **4035. aa. 45.**

BARNETT (V. H.) *See* CALVERT (William R.) Geology of the Standing Rock and Cheyenne River . . . By W. R. Calvert . . . V. H. Barnett, *etc.* 1914. 8°. [*U.S. Geological Survey. Bulletin.* no. 575.] A.S. **212/2.**

BARNETT (WALTER LEIGH)

—— Grasses and Forage Crops in Jamaica. pp. 16. [1926.] 8°. *See* JAMAICA.—*Department of Science and Agriculture.* C.S. F. **166/2.**

—— Notes on Jamaica Rum. pp. 8. *Kingston,* 1951. 8°. [*Jamaica. Department of Government Chemist. Bulletin.* no. 1.] C.S. F. **156/13.**

BARNETT (WILLIAM) *of Sutton Coldfield.* New Form of Rent-Book by Double Entry; with an abstract of the Act of Parliament, also an important decision at the Public Office, Birmingham, between landlord and tenant. *The Author: Birmingham,* 1856. 12°. **712. b. 71.**

BARNETT (WILLIAM) *Poisoner. See* CURREN (William) An Account of the Trial, Execution, &c. of W. and J. Curren . . . and of W. Barnett, for the poisoning of his wife, *etc.* 1822. fol. **1889. d. 3. (206.)**

BARNETT (WINIFRED)

—— A Posy of Poems. pp. 15. *Arthur H. Stockwell: Ilfracombe,* [1952.] 8°. **11659. aaa. 14.**

BARNETT-BENTLIF (PHILIP) *See* BENTLIF.

BARNETT-CLARKE (CHARLES WILLIAM) *Dean of Capetown. See* CLARKE.

BARNETT-CLARKE (H. P.) *See* CLARKE.

BARNETTE (IDA MILLICENT)

—— Innocence. [A novel.] pp. 252. *Wright & Brown: London,* [1934.] 8°. NN. **22950.**

BARNETTE (IDA MILLICENT)

—— Innocence. pp. 254. *Mellifont Press: London & Dublin ; Dublin* printed, [1935.] 8°. **12626. t. 21.**

—— Love may not last. pp. 160. *Wright & Brown: London,* [1953.] 8°. NNN. **4441.**

—— Love me for ever. pp. 189. *Wright & Brown: London,* [1950.] 8°. NNN. **982.**

—— Lover, come back. pp. 190. *Wright & Brown: London,* 1955. 8°. NNN. **6682.**

—— Maiden in Danger. pp. 192. *Wright & Brown: London,* 1951. 8°. NNN. **2211.**

—— Maiden in doubt. pp. 160. *Wright & Brown: London,* [1953.] 8°. NNN. **3693.**

—— The Orange Shop. [A novel.] pp. 254. *Wright & Brown: London,* [1935.] 8°. NN. **23731.**

—— Pretence and Peril. pp. 252. *Wright & Brown: London,* 1935. 8°. NN. **24917.**

—— Pretence and Peril. pp. 128. *Mellifont Press: London ; Dublin* printed, [1938.] 8°. **12643.y.2**

BARNEVAL (L. TACHET DE) *See* TACHET DE BARNEVAL.

BARNEVELDIST. Den berouden Bernevellist, sijn leetwesen ende bekentenisse. Ghedaen door eenen die gheweest is van des Advocaets Factie. *A. Meuris: s' Graven-haghe,* 1620. 4°. T. **2250. (1.)**

—— [Another copy.] T. **2422. (32.)**

BARNEVELDT (DE) *Madame.* Memoirs of Madame de Barneveldt. [By Jean Du Castre d'Auvigny and Pierre François Guyot Desfontaines.] Translated from the French by Miss Gunning. 2 vol. *S. Low; E. Booker: London,* 1795. 8°. **12510. e. 16.**

—— Second edition . . . with . . . portrait of the translator by Bartolozzi. 2 vol. *Vernor & Hood; H. Lowndes: London,* 1796. 8°. **12511. g. 13.**

BARNEVELDT (HENRICUS VAN) Catalogus variorum & insignium in quavis facultate librorum . . . ex bibliotheca . . . Henrici van Barneveldt . . . qui publica auctione distrahetur [*sic*] . . . ad diem 4. Octobris 1703. pp. 30. *Lugduni Batavorum,* 1703. 12°. S.C. **84. (2.)**

BARNEVELDT (JOHAN VAN OLDEN) *See* OLDENBARNEVELD.

BARNEVELT, *Family of.* Genealogie van het geslacht van Barnevelt, *etc.* pp. 98. 1877. *See* SCHEFFER (J. H.) Nederlands familie-archief. 1878, *etc.* 8°. **9905. bb. 38.**

BARNEVELT (GEORGE) *See* BARNWELL.

BARNEVELT (HENRICUS À) Disputationum physico-astronomicarum secunda, de sole, *etc. Praes.* J. Luyts. *M. à Dreunen: Ultrajecti,* 1678. 4°. **531. l. 2. (20.)**

BARNEVELT (JAN VAN OLDEN) *See* OLDENBARNEVELD (Johan van)

BARNEVELT (JOHAN VAN) *See* OLDENBARNEVELD.

BARNEVILLE ( ) *Commissaire des Guerres.* Observations . . . sur l'évacuation des ville et château de Namur, et les bateaux pris par l'ennemi, près de Dinant ; suivies de pièces justificatives. pp. 52. [1793.] 4°. F. **43*. (4.)**

BARNEVILLE ( ) *Inventor.* *See* MOREAU (M. F.) Convention Nationale. Rapport fait . . . sur l'invention du citoyen Barneville, qui a pour objet d'établir en France des manufactures de mousselines superfines, *etc.* [1794.] 8°. **F. 485/15.**

BARNEVILLE (CHARLES BRISOUT DE) *See* BRISOUT DE BARNEVILLE.

BARNEVILLE (LOUIS BRISOUT DE) *See* BRISOUT DE BARNEVILLE.

BARNEVILLE (MATTHIEU DE)

—— *See* BIBLE.—*New Testament.* [*French.*] Le Nouveau Testament, *etc.* [Translated by M. de Barneville.] 1720. 12°. **1159.** i. **6.**

—— *See* BIBLE.—*New Testament.* [*French.*] Le Nouveau Testament . . . Traduit selon la Vulgate [by M. de Barneville]. 1731. 12°. **1017.** a. **7.**

BARNEVILLE (PIERRE DE) Au seuil du siècle. Esquisses contemporaines. pp. 294. *Paris,* 1902. 8°. **012356.** ee. **82.**

—— Les Ombres sur la mur. [Poems.] pp. 184. *Paris,* 1908. 8°. **011483.** ee. **55.**

—— Le Rythme dans la poésie française. pp. 149. *Paris,* 1898. 8°. **011824.** g. **69.**

—— Tiburce. [A novel.] pp. 224. *Paris,* [1922.] 8°. **012547.** b. **69.**

BARNEWALL (ALICIA) *Baroness Trimlestown.* *See* LLOYD (Evan) *Major General.* In the Court of King's Bench in Ireland. Lloyd and wife versus Trimlestown. Evidence, *etc.* 1819. 8°. **6573.** aaa. **16.**

BARNEWALL (HENRIETTA) A Hundred Years Ago; or, a Narrative of events leading to the marriage and conversion to the Catholic faith of Mr. and Mrs. Marlow Sidney . . . By their grand-daughter [i.e. H. Barnewall]. pp. 128. 1877. 8°. *See* SIDNEY (Marlow) **4903.** b. **63.**

—— [Another edition.] pp. iii. 126. [1887.] 8°. *See* SIDNEY (M.) **4903.** b. **69.**

BARNEWALL (JOHN THOMAS) *Baron Trimlestown.* *See* LLOYD (Evan) *Major General.* In the Court of King's Bench in Ireland. Lloyd and wife versus Trimlestown. Evidence, *etc.* 1819. 8°. **6573.** aaa. **16.**

BARNEWALL (NICHOLAS) *Viscount Barnewall of Kingsland.* An Elegy on the much lamented Death of . . . the Lord Viscount Kingsland . . . By R. U. 1725. *s. sh.* fol. *See* U., R. **1881.** c. **6.** (**60.**)

—— Nicholas, Lord Viscount Kingsland . . . appellant. Frances Countess Dowager of Tyrconnell . . . respondent. et è contra. The case of the respondent, *etc.* pp. 4. [*London,* 1725.] fol. **19.** h. **2.** (**121.**)

—— The Right Honourable Nicholas Lord Viscount Kingsland, appellant. Frances Countess Dowager of Tyrconnell respondent. et è contra. The appellants case. pp. 4. [*London,* 1724.] fol. **19.** h. **2.** (**120.**)

BARNEWALL (RICHARD VAUGHAN) [For editions of Reports of Cases in the Court of King's Bench, 1817–1834, edited by R. V. Barnewall and others:] *See* ENGLAND.—*Court of King's Bench.* [*Reports.*]

BARNEWALL (ROBERT)

—— [A report by R. Barnewall on the introduction of the Aumany revenue system into the Neriad Pergunna. Dated 1 Aug. 1816.] *See* BOMBAY, *Presidency of.* [*Miscellaneous Public Documents, etc.*] [1830?] fol. **793.** m. **17.** (5.)

BARNEWALL (ROBERT)

—— [Another copy.] **793.** m. **17.** (**20.**)

BARNEWALLUS (JOANNES) *Praes.* *See* BRINAN (P.) Sententia D. Augustini . . . de gratia, lib. arbit. prædestinatione et reprobatione, publice defensa, *etc.* 1641. 4°. **4256.** c. **69.** (**2.**)

BARNEWITZ (FRIEDRICH) Geschichte des Hafenorts Warnemünde, unter besonderer Berücksichtigung der Volks- und Bodenkunde . . . Mit 96 Abbildungen und einer Beilage. pp. 294. *Rostock,* 1919. 8°. **10230.** ee. **22.**

BARNEY. Barney. A Soldier's Story. By E. A. B. D. [i.e. E. A. Bland.] 1887. 8°. *See* D., E. A. B. **4413.** n. **18.**

BARNEY, *Family of.* *See* ADAMS (William F.) Commodore Joshua Barney. Many interesting facts connected with the life of Commodore Joshua Barney . . . also a compilation of genealogical material relating to Commodore Barney's ancestors and descendants, with valuable records for those in search of Barney family connections. 1912. 8°. **010880.** i. **2.**

BARNEY (A. M.) *Miss.* The Star in the East. An account of the Church Missionary Society's work in North India; with sketches of the country and people. With a preface by the Rev. W. Knight. pp. vii. 224. *J. F. Shaw & Co.: London,* 1860. 8°. **4766.** c. **44.**

BARNEY (C.) Recollections of Field Service with the Twentieth Iowa Infantry Volunteers; or, What I saw in the Army, *etc.* pp. 323. *The Author: Davenport,* 1865. 8°. **9602.** bb. **9.**

BARNEY (C. G.) Bibliotheca Americana. Catalogue of a private library [that of Dr. C. G. Barney] comprising . . . rare and valuable books relating to America. Also, local histories . . . to be sold . . . January 17th, 1870, *etc.* pp. 174. [1870.] 4°. *See* LEAVITT, STREBEIGH AND CO. **11903.** e. **30.**

BARNEY (CHARLES NORTON) Circumcision and Flagellation among the Filipinos . . . Reprint from the Journal of the Association of Military Surgeons of the United States. pp. 6. *Carlisle, Pa.,* 1903. 8°. **10057.** df. **25.** (**6.**)

BARNEY (DANFORD) Chords from Albireo, *etc.* [Poems.] pp. 100. *John Lane: New York, London,* 1920. 8°. **011686.** h. **14.**

—— In the Comet's Hair. [Poems.] pp. 63. *Elkin Mathews: London,* 1921. 4°. **011645.** e. **13.**

BARNEY (EVERETT HOSMER) *See* ADAMS (William F.) Everett Hosmer Barney; his family connections. A record of his life's work, *etc.* 1912. 4°. **L.R. 30.** a. **14.**

BARNEY (GEORGE MURRAY) *See* ADAMS (William F.) Everett Hosmer Barney; his family connections. A record of his life work. George Murray Barney. 1912. 4°. **L.R. 30.** a. **14.**

BARNEY (GRACE)

—— A Ghostly Evening. A merry comedy in one act. pp. 49. *Samuel French: New York,* [1940.] 8°. **011791.** aa. **40.**

—— You ain't heard the Half of it. A bright and merry comedy for an all female cast in one act. pp. 39. *Samuel French: New York,* [1944.] 8°. **011791.** b. **59.**

BARNEY (HELEN CORSE)

—— A Wilderness to conquer. [A novel.] pp. 254. *Bannisdale Press: London,* 1955. 8°. NNN. **7470.**

BARNEY (IDA)

—— *See* SCHLESINGER (Frank) and BARNEY (I.) Catalogue of the Positions and Proper Motions of 8563 Stars. Reobservation . . . of the Astronomische Gesellschaft zone between declinations —14° and —18°, *etc.* 1940. 4°. [*Transactions of the Astronomical Observatory of Yale University.* vol. 12. pt. 1.] **8565**. d.

—— *See* SCHLESINGER (Frank) and BARNEY (I.) Catalogue of the Positions and Proper Motions of 4553 Stars. Reobservation . . . of the Astronomische Gesellschaft zone between declinations —18° and —20°, *etc.* 1940. 8°. [*Transactions of the Astronomical Observatory of Yale University.* vol. 12. pt. 2.] **8565**. d.

—— *See* SCHLESINGER (Frank) and BARNEY (I.) Catalogue of the Positions and Proper Motions of 4292 Stars. Reobservation . . . of the Astronomische Gesellschaft zone between declinations -20° and -22°, *etc.* 1943. 4°. [*Transactions of the Astronomical Observatory of Yale University.* vol. 13. pt. 1.] **8565**. d.

—— *See* SCHLESINGER (Frank) and BARNEY (I.) Catalogue of the Positions and Proper Motions of 15110 Stars. Reobservation . . . of the Cordoba Zone between declinations -22° and -27°, *etc.* 1943. 4°. [*Transactions of the Astronomical Observatory of Yale University.* vol. 14.] **8565**. d.

—— *See* SCHLESINGER (Frank) and BARNEY (I.) Catalogue of the Positions and Proper Motions of 9455 Stars. Reobservation . . . of the Cordoba Zone between declinations -27° and -30°, *etc.* 1943. 4°. [*Transactions of the Astronomical Observatory of Yale University.* vol. 13. pt. 2.] **8565**. d.

—— Catalogue of the Positions and Proper Motions of 8108 Stars. Re-observation by photography of the Astronomische Gesellschaft Zone between declinations —2° and —6°, *etc.* pp. 8. 166. *New Haven,* 1945. 4°. [*Transactions of the Astronomical Observatory of Yale University.* vol. 17.] **8565**. d.

—— Catalogue of the Positions and Proper Motions of 8248 Stars. Re-observation by photography of the Astronomische Gesellschaft Zone between declinations —6° and —10°, *etc.* pp. 14. 169. *New Haven,* 1945. 4°. [*Transactions of the Astronomical Observatory of Yale University.* vol. 16.] **8565**. d.

—— Catalogue of the Positions and Proper Motions of 8967 Stars. Re-observation by photography of the Astronomische Gesellschaft Zone between Declinations + 10° and 15°, reduced to 1950.0 without applying Proper Motions. pp. 185. *New Haven,* 1948. 4°. [*Transactions of the Astronomical Observatory of Yale University.* vol. 19.] **8565**. d.

—— Catalogue of the Positions and Proper Motions of 9092 stars. Re-observation by photography of the Astronomische Gesellschaft Zone between declinations +15° and +20°, reduced to 1950.0 without applying proper motion. pp. 187. *New Haven,* 1947. 4°. [*Transactions of the Astronomical Observatory of Yale University.* vol. 18.] **8565**. d.

—— Revised Catalogue of the Positions and Proper Motions of 8703 Stars, contained in the Astronomische Gesellschaft Zone between declinations +20° and +25°, on the system of the FK3, *etc.* pp. 9. 176. *New Haven,* 1954. 4°. [*Transactions of the Astronomical Observatory of Yale University.* vol. 25.] **8565**. d.

—— Revised Catalogue of the Positions and Proper Motions of 10358 Stars, contained in the Astronomische Gesellschaft Zone between declinations +25° and +30°, on the system of the FK3, *etc.* pp. 10. 209. *New Haven,* 1953. 4°. [*Transactions of the Astronomical Observatory of Yale University.* vol. 24.] **8565**. d.

BARNEY (IDA) and **VAN WOERKOM** (A. J. J.)

—— Catalogue of the Positions and Proper Motions of 1031 Stars between declinations +85° and +90°, reduced without applying proper motions to the equinox 1950. 0. pp. 9. 44. *New Haven,* 1954. 8°. [*Transactions of the Astronomical Observatory of Yale University.* vol. 26. pt. 1.] **8565**. d.

BARNEY (J. A.)

—— *See* BIBLE.—*Matthew.* [*Ngala.—Uele dialect.*] Matayo. [Translated by A. B. Buxton and J. A. Barney.] 1927. 8°. **03068**. ee. 105.

—— *See* BIBLE.—*Mark.* [*Momvu.*] Lio Lembe Mako itendi waraga ke. [Translated by J. A. Barney.] 1931. 8°. **3061**. de. 30.

BARNEY (JOSHUA) *See* ADAMS (William F.) Commodore Joshua Barney. Many interesting facts connected with the life of Commodore Joshua Barney, hero of the United States Navy, 1776–1812, also a compilation of genealogical material relating to Commodore Barney's ancestors and descendants, *etc.* 1912. 8°. **010880**. i. 2.

—— *See* ADAMS (William F.) A Few Facts in connection with the "Life of Commodore Joshua Barney, 1759–1818" [by Mary Barney]. 1910. 8°. **10882**. c. 27.

—— *See* BARNEY (Mary) A Biographical Memoir of . . . Commodore J. Barney, *etc.* [With a portait.] 1832. 8°. **1453**. i. 7.

—— *See* PAINE (Ralph D.) Joshua Barney, *etc.* [With portraits.] [1924.] 8°. **010884**. e. 4.

BARNEY (LAURA CLIFFORD) *See* 'ABD AL-BAHĀ IBN BAHĀ ALLĀH. Les Leçons de Saint Jean d'Acre. Recueillies par L. C. Barney, *etc.* 1908. 8°. **757**. b. 64.

—— *See* 'ABD AL-BAHĀ IBN BAHĀ ALLĀH. Some Answered Questions. Collected and translated from the Persian . . . by L. C. Barney. 1908. 8°. **757.f.51.(1.)**

—— *See* 'ABD AL-BAHĀ IBN BAHĀ ALLĀH. Some Christian Subjects. Collected and translated from the Persian . . . by L. C. Barney, *etc.* [1946.] 8°. **3228**. aa. 29.

—— God's Heroes. A drama in five acts. pp. xii. 108. *Kegan Paul & Co.: London; J. B. Lippincott Co.: Philadelphia,* [1910.] 8°. **11773**. i. 6.

BARNEY (MAGINEL WRIGHT) The Baby's Record. Through the first year in song and story. Designed and illustrated by M. W. Barney. [With musical notes.] pp. 61. *Harper & Bros.: New York & London,* 1928. 4°. **7581**. h. 27.

BARNEY (MARY) A Biographical Memoir of the late Commodore J. Barney, *etc.* [With a portrait.] pp. xvi. 328. *Gray & Bowen: Boston,* 1832. 8°. **1453**. i. 7.

—— *See* ADAMS (William F.) A Few Facts in connection with the "Life of Commodore Joshua Barney 1759–1818" [by Mary Barney]. 1910. 8°. **10882**. c. 27.

—— Mrs. Barney's Letter to President Jackson. [Concerning his refusal to reinstate Major William Bedford Barney.] pp. 4. [*Baltimore,* 1829.] 8°. **8052**. i. 1. (66.)

BARNEY (NATALIE CLIFFORD) Aventures de l'esprit. [Essays on contemporary writers.] pp. 278. *Paris,* 1929. 8°. **11824**. ppp. 25.

—— Nouvelles pensées de l'Amazone. pp. 214. *Paris,* 1939. 8°. **12359**. c. 26.

BARNEY (NATALIE CLIFFORD)

—— The One who is Legion; or, A. D.'s after-life, *etc.* pp. 160. *Eric Partridge: London,* 1930. 8°. **08632.** ff. **22.**

—— Pensées d'une amazone, *etc.* pp. vii. 210. *Paris,* 1920. 8°. **012305.** m. **90.**

BARNEY (RICHARD WILLIAM DURBIN) Crustacea. Part v.—Ostracoda, *etc. London,* 1921. 4°. [*British Antarctic Expedition,* 1910. *Natural History Report. Zoology.* vol. 3. no. 7.] **7006.w.1/3.**

BARNEY (STEPHEN) *See* BOUNTY, *H.M.S.* Minutes of the Proceedings of the Court-Martial held at Portsmouth, August 12, 1792. On ten persons charged with mutiny on board His Majesty's ship the Bounty, *etc.* [Compiled by S. Barney.] 1794. 4°. **6875.** ee. **23.**

—— *See* BOUNTY, *H.M.S.* Minutes of the Proceedings of the Court Martial . . . on . . . mutiny on board . . . the Bounty . . . By S. Barney. 1938. 8°. [BLIGH (*William*) *A Book of the Bounty.*] **12206.p.1/736.**

BARNEY (SYDNEY DAVID)

—— Clothes and the Horse. A guide to correct dress for all riding occasions . . . With an historical introduction by James Laver, *etc.* [With plates.] pp. 123. *Vinton & Co.: London,* 1953. 8°. **7744.** df. **15.**

—— Clothes and the Man. A guide to correct dress for all occasions, *etc.* pp. 124. *Sir Isaac Pitman & Sons: London,* 1951. 8°. **7744.** df. 5.

BARNEY (THOMAS) *See* BEDDINGFIELD (Thomas) An Elegy on the death of T. Beddingfield, Esq.; who was murdered by Mr. T. Barney, *etc.* 1684. *s. sh.* fol. Lutt. I. 8.

—— *See* BEDDINGFIELD (Thomas) A Full Relation of a Barbarous Murther, committed upon the body of Esq; Beddingfield . . . by Mr. Barney: as also The further account of the tryal and conviction of the said Mr. Barney, *etc.* 1684. *s. sh.* fol. **515.** l. **2.** (**93.**)

BARNEY (WILLIAM BEDFORD) *See* BARNEY (Mary) Mrs. Barney's Letter to President Jackson. [Concerning his refusal to reinstate Major W. B. Barney.] [1829.] 8°. **8052.** i. **1.** (**66.**)

BARNEY (WINFIELD SUPPLY) Premier livre de lecture. pp. ix. 129. *D. Appleton & Co.: New York,* [1928.] 8°. **12951.** ee. **16.**

BARNFEILD (RICHARD) *See* BARNFIELD.

BARNFIELD (RICHARD) *See* NICHOLSON (Samuel) *Poetical Writer.* Acolastus, his after-witte, 1600. A poem . . . containing quotations and adaptations from Shakespeare and Barnfield, *etc.* 1876. 4°. **2326.** g. **2.** (3.)

—— *See* SHAKESPEARE (William) [*Works attributed to Shakespeare.—Passionate Pilgrim.*] The Passionate Pilgrim. By Shakspere, Marlowe, Barnfield, Griffin, and other writers . . . The First Quarto, 1599, a facsimile, *etc.* [1883.] 4°. **11764.** k. **13.**

—— *See* SHAKESPEARE (William) [*Works attributed to Shakespeare.—Passionate Pilgrim.*] The Passionate Pilgrime . . . With a preface, in which the claims of R. Barnfield to the authorship of two of the pieces are vindicated from the objections of Mr. J. Payne Collier. By Charles Edmonds. 1870. 12°. [*Isham Reprints.*] **11633.i.18/1.**

BARNFIELD (RICHARD)

—— The Complete Poems of Richard Barnfield. Edited, with introduction and notes, by the Rev. Alexander B. Grosart. pp. xlv. 240. 1876. 4°. *See* LONDON.—III. *Roxburghe Club.* C. **101.** d. **6.**

—— Poems. 1594–1598. Edited by Edward Arber. pp. xxiv. 124. *Birmingham,* 1882. 8°. [*English Scholar's Library.* no. 14.] **12205.ee.1/14.**

—— [Another copy, with a different titlepage.] **L.P.** *Birmingham,* 1883. 4°. [*English Scholar's Library.* Limited Library Edition. no. 14.] **2324.** f. **14.**

—— The Poems of Richard Barnfield. [Edited by Montague Summers.] pp. xxxii. 135. *Fortune Press: London,* [1936.] 8°. **2292.** g. **23.**

—— The Affectionate Shepheard, *etc.*—Cynthia, *etc.*—The Encomion of Lady Pecunia, *etc.*—The Complaint of Poetrie, for the Death of Liberalitie.—The Combat, betweene Conscience and Couetousnesse, in the Minde of Man.—Poems: in diuers humors. 1903. *See* ARBER (Edward) An English Garner. (Some Longer Elizabethan Poems.) 1903, *etc.* 8°. **2324.** e. **9/9.**

—— The Encomion of Lady Pecunia: or, the praise of Money. (The Complaint of Poetrie, for the Death of Liberalitie. —The Combat, betweene Conscience and couetousnesse, in the minde of Man.—Poems: in diuers humors.) [Reprint from the 1598 editions. Edited by James Boswell the Younger.] 4 pt. [*Alexander Boswell: Auchinleck,* 1816.] 4°. **1077.** e. **11.**

—— [Another issue.] Poems. (The Encomion of Lady Pecunia, *etc.*) 1816. 4°. *See* LONDON.—III. *Roxburghe Club.* C. **101.** a. **4.**

—— [Another edition.] pp. ii. 49. *See* COLLIER (John P.) Illustrations of Old English Literature. vol. 1. 1866. 4°. **2326.** c. **6.**

—— The Affectionate Shepherd . . . A.D. 1594. Edited by James Orchard Halliwell. pp. iv. 51. *London,* 1847. 8°. [*Percy Society. Early English Poetry, etc.* vol. 20.] Ac. **9480.**

—— [Cynthia. With Certaine Sonnets, and the Legend of Cassandra.] [*Printed for Humfrey Lownes: London,* 1595.] 8°. C. **60.** b. 5.
Imperfect; wanting all before sig. B; *also sig.* D 2. *The contents of the missing leaves have been supplied in* MS.

—— Cynthia; and the Legend of Cassandra. [Reprinted from the 1595 edition with notes by Edward Vernon Utterson.] pp. 44. *Beldornie Press:* [*Ryde,*] 1841. 12°. C. **32.** b. **10.**
One of an edition of sixteen copies.

—— Greenes Funeralls. By R. B. Gent. [i.e. Richard Barnfield?] *See* R., B. B. R.—R. B. Greenes Newes both from Heauen and Hell, 1593, and Greenes Funeralls, 1594, reprinted . . . with notes, &c., by R. B. McKerrow. 1911. 4°. **12316.** v. **11**

—— Greenes Funeralls. By R. B. Gent. [i.e. R. Barnfield? A photostat copy of the original edition of 1594.] [1923.] 4°. *See* B., R., *Gent.* **L.R.263.aa.11.**

—— Lady Pecunia; or, the Praise of Money. Also a Combat betwixt Conscience and Covetousnesse. Together with The Complaint of Poetry for the death of Liberality Newly corrected and inlarged, &c. [A reprint of the 1605 edition.] pp. iv. 38. *See* COLLIER (John P.) Illustrations of Old English Literature. vol. 1. 1866. 4°. **2326.** c. **6**

BARNFIELD (Richard)

—— [Orpheous his Journey to Hell, and his Music to the Ghosts, by R. B., i.e. R. Barnfield?] [1595.] 4°. *See* B., R. C. **38**. c. **12**.

BARNGOL'TS (S. B.) and **KHAVIN** (I. E.)

—— Пути ускорении оборачиваемости оборотных средств в машиностроении. pp. 157. *Москва*, 1950. 8°. **08773**. d. **16**.

BARNHAM (Alice) *See* Bacon (Alice) *Viscountess St. Albans.*

BARNHAM (Henry Dudley) *See* Nasreddin, *Hoca.* Tales . . . Translated . . . by H. D. Barnham, *etc.* 1923. 8°. **14469**. c. **3**.

BARNHAM (James Calthrop) A Series of Questions on the most important points connected with a Legal Education, *etc.* pt. 1–3. *Stevens & Sons: London; John Stacy: Norwich*, 1836. 8°. **1129**. e. **16**.

—— Fourth edition, entirely remodelled and considerably enlarged, by Edward Ings. pp. xii. 340. *V. & R. Stevens & G. S. Norton: London*, 1840. 12°. **1129**. d. **30**.

—— Some Talk about Pears and Pear-Trees . . . A paper, *etc.* pp. 23. *Goose & Co.: Norwich*, [1881.] 8°. **7033**. aaa. **13**. (**5**.)

BARNHARDT (William Newton) *See* Periodical Publications.—*Toronto.* The Journal of Psychosophy. Edited by W. N. Barnhardt, *etc.* 1899, *etc.* 8°. P.P. **1247**. l.

BARNHART (Belle)

—— *See* Harper (Martha B.) Winter Wedding. [A biography of Belle Barnhart.] 1950. 8°. **10889**. aaa. **26**.

BARNHART (Clarence Lewis)

—— *See* Encyclopaedias. The New Century Cyclopedia of Names. Edited by C. L. Barnhart, *etc.* [1954.] 8°. **2050.d.**

—— Thorndike-Barnhart Comprehensive Desk Dictionary. Edited by C. L. Barnhart. pp. 896. *Hodder & Stoughton: London; Garden City, N.Y.* printed, 1952. 8°. **012987**. c. **20**.

—— Thorndike-Barnhart Handy Pocket Dictionary. Edited by C. L. Barnhart. pp. 523. *Hodder & Stoughton: London*, 1952. 8°. **12986**. a. **58**.

BARNHART (Earl W.) An Analysis of the Work of a Stenographer. pp. 36. *New York*, [1927.] 8°. [*Gregg's Educational Monographs.*] W.P. **6357/5**.

BARNHART (Edward Norton)

—— *See* Chandler (Albert R.) A Bibliography of Psychological and Experimental Aesthetics, 1864–1937. By A. R. Chandler . . . and E. N. Barnhart, *etc.* 1938. 8°. **B.B.c.f.17.**

—— *See* TenBroek (J.) Prejudice, War and the Constitution. [By] J. tenBroek, E. N. Barnhart, *etc.* 1954. 8°. W.P. d. **304**/2.

BARNHART (Jesse M.) *See* Lee (Carl E.) and Barnhart (J. M.) Composition of Market Butter. 1909. 8°. [*University of Illinois Agricultural Experiment Station Bulletin.* no. 139.] **A.S.i.22/2.**

BARNHART (John Donald)

—— Valley of Democracy. The frontier versus the plantation in the Ohio valley, 1775–1818. [With a map and a bibliography.] pp. x. 338. *Indiana University Press: Bloomington*, 1953. 8°. [*Indiana University Publications. Social Science Series.* no. 11.] Ac. **2692**. w/**10**.

—— [Another issue.] Valley of Democracy, *etc.* *Bloomington*, 1953. 8°. **9617**. d. **14**.

BARNHART (John Hendley)

—— *See* Merrill (Elmer D.) Biographical Memoir of Nathaniel Lord Britton . . . With bibliography by J. H. Barnhart, *etc.* 1938. 8°. [*National Academy of Sciences. Biographical Memoirs.* vol. 19.] A.S. **939/2**.

BARNHART (Percy Spencer)

—— Marine Fishes of Southern California. [With illustrations.] pp. iv. 209. *University of California Press: Berkeley*, 1936. fol. **07290**. h. **12**.

BARNHART (Thomas Frederick)

—— *See* Nafziger (Ralph O.) Red Wing and its Daily Newspaper . . . Management Problems, by T. F. Barnhart. 1946. 4°. [*Community Basis for Postwar Planning.* no. 9.] Ac. **2692**. k./**16**.

—— Weekly Newspaper Makeup and Typography. [With illustrations.] pp. ix. 267. *University of Minnesota Press: Minneapolis*, [1949.] 8°. **11868**. h. **15**.

—— Weekly Newspaper Management. pp. viii. 444. *D. Appleton-Century Co.: New York, London*, 1936. 8°. **11857**. aa. **46**.

BARNHELM (Minna von) Minna von Barnhelm, oder das Soldatenglück. Ein Lustspiel in fünf Aufzügen. [By Gotthold Ephraim Lessing.] 1791. *See* German Stage. Deutsche Schaubühne. Bd. 28. 1788, *etc.* 8°. **752**. a. **1/28**.

BARNHILL (James) *the Elder.* A Plea for the Advancement of Hebrew Literature in Scotland to the position claimed for it by the first Scottish Reformers. Originally addressed to the Free Presbytery of Glasgow, at their meeting on 6th Feb., 1861. pp. 16. *David Bryce: M. Ogle & Son: Glasgow*, 1861. 16°. **8364**. a. **26**. (**2**.)

BARNHILL (James) *the Younger.* The Statics of Harmony; with an appendix on anticipations, suspensions, & transitions, illustrated by examples from the great masters . . . Re-published from the "Choir and Musical Record," *etc.* pp. v. 80. *Metzler & Co.: London*, 1865. 8°. **7895**. a. **54**. (**5**.)

—— Testimonials in favour of Mr. J. Barnhill, M.A. [as candidate for an appointment in the Education Department]. pp. 12. [*Glasgow?* 1874?] 8°. **1414**. h. **9**. (**14**.)

BARNHILL (John Basil) Gounod's opera, "Faust": a plea for the lyric drama. A sermon, *etc.* pp. 17. *M'Caw & Co.: Belfast*, 1894. 8°. **4473**. h. **19**. (**8**.)

BARNHILL (John Finch) The Nose, Throat and Ear, *etc.* pp. xxxvii. 604. *D. Appleton & Co.: New York, London*, 1928. 8°. **07611**. i. **13**.

—— Principles and Practice of Modern Otology. By John F. Barnhill . . . and Ernest de Wolfe Wales, *etc.* pp. 575. *W. B. Saunders Co.: Philadelphia & London*, 1907. 8°. **07610**. k. **5**.

—— Surgical Anatomy of the Head and Neck, *etc.* pp. xiii. 921. *Baillière & Co.: London; printed in U.S.A.*, 1937 [1938]. 8°. **7421**. i. **33**.

BARNHILL (W. W.)

—— West African Rhymes. pp. 79. *Arthur H. Stockwell: Ilfracombe*, 1948. 8°. **11658**. ee. **61**.

BARNHOLT (HENNINGIUS) *Resp.* *See* HOFFIUS (P.) Dissertatio de τῳ scheva Ebræorum, *etc.* 1686. 4°. **12903**. c. **13**.

BARNHOLTH (HENNINGIUS) *See* BARNHOLT.

BARNHOUSE (DONALD GREY)

—— God's Methods for Holy Living. pp. 93. *Pickering & Inglis: London*, [1937.] 8°. **04400**. f. **45**.

—— Happy though Poor. A series of heart messages, *etc.* pp. 95. *Pickering & Inglis: London*, [1937.] 8°. **04400**. ff. **27**.

—— His Own Received Him Not, but . . . The turning point in the ministry of Christ. pp. 185. *Pickering & Inglis: London; printed in U.S.A.*, [1936.] 8°. **4226**. de. **22**.

—— Life by the Son. Practical lessons in experimental holiness. pp. 127. *Pickering & Inglis: London; printed in U.S.A.*, [1939.] 8°. **04400**. g. **84**.

—— Teaching the Word of Truth. pp. 189. *Children's Special Service Mission: London; Philadelphia* printed, [1940.] 8°. **4192**. g. **13**.

—— [A reissue.] Teaching the Word of Truth. *London*, [1948.] 4°. **4193**. l. **16**.

BARNI (GIANLUIGI)

—— *See* ALCIATUS (A.) Le Lettere di Andrea Alciato giureconsulto. [Edited by G. L. Barni.] 1953. 8°. **010921**. l. **19**.

—— La Formazione interna dello Stato Visconteo. 1941. *See* MILAN.—*Società Storica Lombarda.* Archivio storico lombardo, *etc.* (Nova serie.) anno 6. fasc. 1/4. 1874, *etc.* 8°. Ac. **6525**.

—— I Rapporti internazionali dello Stato di Milano in Italia durante il periodo della preponderanza straniera. Note di storia giuridica. 1943. *See* MILAN.—*Società Storica Lombarda.* Archivio storico lombardo, *etc.* (Nuova serie.) anno 8. fasc. 1/4. 1874, *etc.* 8°. Ac. **6525**.

BARNI (JULES ROMAIN) *See* DIDE (A.) Jules Barni, sa vie et ses œuvres. 1891. 8°. **010662**. g. **2**.

—— *See* FICHTE (J. G.) [Beitrag zur Berichtigung der Urtheile über die Französische Revolution.] Considérations destinées à rectifier les jugements du public sur la Revolution française . . . Traduit . . . par J. Barni, *etc.* 1859. 8°. **8008**. f. **19**.

—— *See* KANT (I.) Éléments métaphysiques de la doctrine du droit, première partie de la Métaphysique des mœurs . . . Traduit . . . par J. Barni . . . avec une introduction . . . du traducteur. 1853. 8°. **6025**. c. **24**.

—— *See* KANT (I.) Critique de la raison pratique . . . Traduit . . . par J. Barni. 1848. 8°. **8465**. cc. **33**.

—— *See* KANT (I.) Critique du jugement . . . Traduit . . . par J. Barni. 1846. 8°. **1248**. e. **18**.

—— L'Instruction républicaine. pp. 35. *Paris*, 1872. 16°. **8308**. a. **56**. (**7**.)

—— Manuel républicain. pp. vi. 120. *Paris*, 1872. 12°. **8051**. aaa. **31**.

—— Les Martyrs de la libre pensée. Cours public, *etc.* pp. 301. *Genève*, 1862. 8°. **10602**. c. **24**.

BARNI (JULES ROMAIN)

—— La Morale dans la démocratie. pp. xi. 266. *Paris*, 1868. 8°. **08276**. g. **47**.

—— Deuxième édition, augmentée d'une notice sur la vie et les travaux de l'auteur par M. D. Nolen. pp. xxxi. 265. *Paris*, 1885. 8°. **8205**. g. **9**.

—— Les Moralistes français au dix-huitième siècle . . . Vauvenargues — Duclos — Helvétius — Saint-Lambert — Volney. pp. vii. 234. *Paris*, 1873. 18°. **8406**. cc. **32**.
The half-title reads: "Histoire des idées morales et politiques en France au dix-huitième siècle."

—— Napoléon Ier et son historien M. Thiers. pp. xvi. 370. *Paris*, 1869. 8°. **10661**. ccc. **11**.

—— Napoléon 1er. [Extracted from the author's "Napoléon Ier et son historien M. Thiers."] pp. ii. 186. *Paris*, 1870. 8°. **10660**. bbb. **12**.

—— [Another edition.] pp. 186. *Paris*, [1880.] 8°. **10658**. a. **17**.

—— [Another copy.] **12206**. b. **53**.

—— Philosophie de Kant. Examen des Fondements de la métaphysique des moeurs, et de la Critique de la raison pratique. pp. vii. 336. *Paris*, 1851. 8°. **1248**. h. **9**.

—— Les Principes et les mœurs de la République. pp. 36. *Paris*, 1873. 16°. **8051**. a. **92**. (**5**.)

BARNICH (GEORGES) Comment faire payer l'Allemagne. Erreurs d'hier, solutions de demain. pp. 231. *Paris*, [1923.] 8°. **08028**. de. **116**.

—— Essai de politique positive basée sur l'Énergétique sociale de Solvay, *etc.* [With a bibliography.] pp. 411. *Bruxelles*, 1918. 8°. **08282**. dd. **17**.

BARNICKEL (HEINRICH CARL THEODOR) *See* SELBITZ (Heinrich von) *pseud.* [i.e. H. C. T. Barnickel.]

BARNICKEL (JOHANN BAPTIST) Grundzüge zur Geschite der zum Erzbisthume Bamberg gehörigen Pfarrei Rodheim, im k. Landgerichte Uffenheim, *etc.* 1846. *See* BAMBERG.—*Historischer Verein.* Bericht, *etc.* no. 9. Beilage 3. 1834, *etc.* 8°. Ac. **7014**.

—— Michael von Deinlein, Erzbischof von Bamberg. [With a portrait.] 1874. *See* GERMANY. [*Appendix.—Religion.*] Deutschlands Episcopat in Lebensbildern. Bd. 3. Hft. 4. 1873, *etc.* 8°. **4887**. bb. **39**.

BARNICLE (MARY ELIZABETH) *See* TROY. The Seege or Batayle of Troy . . . Edited . . . by M. E. Barnicle. 1927. 8°. Ac. **9925/128**.

BARNICOAT, afterwards **GRANDE** (CONSTANCE ALICE) *See* FINOT (Jean) The Death-Agony of the "Science" of Race . . . Translated . . . by C. A. Grande. 1911. 8°. **10007**. a. **8**.

—— *See* GRANDE (Julian) Constance Grande, *etc.* [With portraits.] 1925. 8°. **010856**. i. **35**.

—— *See* NICOLAI (Georg F.) The Biology of War . . . Translated by C. A. Grande, *etc.* 1919. 8°. **8425**. g. **65**.

—— Where's Where. A new guide for tourists and travellers. Part I.—France. pp. xxvi. 104. *"Review of Reviews": London*, 1905. 8°. **010026**. ee. **60**.
No more published.

BARNICOAT, afterwards **GRANDE** (CONSTANCE ALICE) and **GRANDE** (JULIAN)

—— Geneva: its place in the world. [With plates.] pp. 156. *T. Fisher Unwin: London; Geneva* [printed], 1920. 8°. **10195**. df. **19**.

BARNICOAT (Cuthbert Richmond)

—— The Determination of Diacetyl and Acetyl Methyl Carbinol . . . Reprinted from The Analyst, *etc.* *W. Heffer & Sons: Cambridge*, [1935.] 8°. 8900. k. 37.

BARNICOAT (Cuthbert Richmond) and **PALMER** (Leroy Sheldon)

—— A Study of the Chemistry of Incipient Oxidation Defects in Butter. pp. 63. [*Minneapolis*,] 1939. 8°. [*University of Minnesota Agricultural Experimental Station. Technical Bulletin.* no. 134.] A.S.M.204/2.

BARNICOT (A. M.) The Shadow of the Woman. [A novel.] pp. 287. *Grayson & Grayson: London*, 1934. 8°. NN. 22372.

BARNICOTT AND PEARCE. Specimens of Type: being a selection from the numerous founts used by Barnicott & Pearce. pp. 51. *Barnicott & Pearce: Taunton*, 1898. 4°. 11899. k. 21.
Printed on one side of the leaf only.

BARNICOTT (Olinthus Roberts) Old Testament History. pp. xii. 138. *J. M. Dent & Co.: London; J. B. Lippincott Co.: Philadelphia*, [1903.] 16°. [*Temple Series of Bible Characters and Scripture Handbooks.*] 03128.ee.63/1.

—— Old Testament History for use in schools. pp. xiv. 157. *J. M. Dent & Co.: London*, 1904. 8°. 03166. de. 13.

BARNICOTT (Roger) Plymouth in History . . . With many illustrations by W. S. Lear. pp. 114. *Cornubian Press: London*, 1906. 8°. 10368. ccc. 35.

BARNIER (Charles) Du ténia inerme et de son expulsion par les principes actifs de l'écorce de grenadier. Thèse, *etc.* pp. 58. *Montpellier*, 1870. 4°. 7379. l. 17. (9.)

BARNIER (J. B. T. Séraphin) Des pessaires, de leur mode d'action et de leurs indications. pp. 50. *Paris*, 1855. 4°. [*Collection des thèses soutenues à la Faculté de Médecine de Paris.* An 1855. tom. 1.] 7372. h. 1.

BARNIER (L. A.) Compulsory Service; or, la Conscription, *etc.* [A peace tract.] *Wisbech Local Peace Association Depôt: Wisbech*, [1890.] 8°. 8425. c. 70. (9.)

BARNIER (M.) Des tubercules du testicule. pp. 45. *Paris*, 1873. 4°. [*Collection des thèses soutenues à la Faculté de Médecine de Paris.* An 1873. tom. 1.] 7373. o.

BARNIER (S.) Des paralysies sans lésions organiques appréciables . . . Thèse, *etc.* pp. 88. *Paris*, 1857. 8°. 7630. f. 41. (7.)

BARNIER (Th. L.) Au service de la chose publique. Contribution à l'étude d'un meilleur outillage administratif. pp. xviii. 337. *Paris*, 1926. 8°. 08052. d. 11.

BARNIKELIUS (Christophorus) *See* Specnerus (J. G.) Auspiciis Rectoris . . . cetera paradoxa physico-mathematica praeses Io. Guilelmus Specnerus . . . examinanda proponit . . . respondentis munere nixus, quo functurus est C. Barnikelius. [1714?] 4°. 529. g. 15. (23.)

BARNIKOL (Ernst)

—— Apostolische und Neutestamentliche Dogmengeschichte als Vor-Dogmengeschichte . . . Vierte, erweiterte Auflage. [A new edition of "Zurück zum alten Glauben Jesus der Christus."] pp. 101. *Halle*, 1938. 8°. 3205. ff. 28.

—— Die Christwerdung des Paulus in Galiläa und die Apostelberufung vor Damaskus und im Tempel. pp. 64. *Halle*, 1935. 8°. 03265. h. 20.

BARNIKOL (Ernst)

—— Das entdeckte Christentum im Vormärz. Bruno Bauers Kampf gegen Religion und Christentum und Erstausgabe seiner Kampfschrift. pp. viii. 177. *Jena*, 1927. 8°. 3914. e. 35.

—— Studien zur Geschichte der Brüder vom gemeinsamen Leben. Die erste Periode der deutschen Brüderbewegung: Die Zeit Heinrichs von Ahaus. Ein Beitrag zur Entwicklung und Organisation des religiösen Lebens auf deutschem Boden im ausgehenden Mittelalter . . . Ergänzungsheft zur Zeitschrift für Theologie und Kirche, 1917. pp. xii. 215. 1917. 8°. *See* Periodical Publications.—Tubingen.—*Zeitschrift für Theologie und Kirche.* P.P. 89. k.

BARNILS GIOL (Pere)

—— *See* Arteaga y Pereira (J. M. de) Textes catalans avec leur transcription phonétique . . . Ordenats i publicats per Pere Barnils. 1915. 8°. [*Biblioteca filològica de l'Institut de la Llengua Catalana.* no. 5.] Ac. 138. d/2.

—— *See* CATALAN - GERMAN VOCABULARY. Vocabulari català-alemany de l'any 1502. Ediciò facsímil . . . acompanyada de la transcripció, d'un estudi preliminar i de registres alfabètics per Pere Barnils. 1916. 8°. [*Biblioteca filològica de l'Institut de la Llengua Catalana.* no. 7.] Ac. 138. d/2.

—— Estudis fonètics. Publicats sota la direcció del Dr. P. Barnils. vol. 1. pp. 329. 1917. 8°. *See* Barcelona.—*Institut d'Estudis Catalans.—Laboratori de Fonètica Experimental.* 12944. i. 30.

—— Die Mundart von Alacant. Beitrag zur Kenntnis des Valencianischen . . . Memoria doctoral, *etc.* [With a map.] pp. 119. *Barcelona*, 1913. 8°. [*Biblioteca filològica de l'Institut de la Llengua Catalana.* no. 2.] Ac. 138. d/2.

BARNIM XII., *Duke of Pomerania. See* Medem (F. L. C. von) *Baron.* Die Universitäts-Jahre der Herzoge Ernst Ludwig und Barnim von Pommern, *etc.* 1867. 8°. 10706. h. 6.

BARNIM (Adalbert Johann Baptist von) *Baron. See* Hartmann (Robert) Reise des Freiherrn A. von Barnim durch Nord-Ost-Afrika in den Jahren 1859 und 1860, *etc.* 1863. 4°. 1785. a. 20.

BARNIMUS HAGIUS, *pseud.* [i.e. Andreas Mueller, *of Greiffenhagen.*] *See* Hagius (B.) *pseud.*

BARNITZ (David Park)

—— The Book of Jade. [Verses. By D. P. Barnitz.] pp. 131. 1901. 8°. *See* Book. 11687. dd. 31.

BARNIVELT (Esdras) *Apoth., pseud.* [i.e. Alexander Pope.] A Key to the Lock. Or, a treatise proving, beyond all contradiction, the dangerous tendency of a late poem [by Alexander Pope], entituled, the Rape of the Lock, to Government and Religion. By E. Barnivelt, Apoth. pp. 32. *J. Roberts: London*, 1715. 8°. 994. c. 42.

—— The second edition. To which are added commendatory copies of verses, *etc.* pp. 32. *J. Roberts: London*, 1715. 8°. 11840. ccc. 12.

—— The third edition, *etc.* pp. 32. *J. Roberts: London*, 1718. 8°. 12274. h. 3. (2.)

—— A Key to the Lock . . . Fourth edition, *etc.* pp. 32. [*London*,] 1723. 8°. 11634. b. 5. (2.)

BARNKOINIGOS (   ) *See* Warnkoenig (L. A.)

BARNLEY (George) Kenooshao. A Red Indian tragedy. pp. 112. *C. H. Kelly: London,* [1899.] 8°. **012804.** de. **6.**

BARNLEY (John)

—— A Copy of Verses for 1811, humbly presented to all my worthy masters and mistresses in the liberty of Saffron Hill, Hatton Garden, & Ely Rents, in the parish of St. Andrew, Holborn, by John Barnley, night beadle and bellman. *T. Bayley: London,* [1811.] *s. sh.* fol. **1875.** d. **8.** (**17.**)

BARNOLA (Antoine Guillaume) De l'influence atmosphérique sur l'économie animale. Tribut académique, *etc.* pp. 21. *Montpellier,* 1811. 4°. **1180.** g. **5.** (**3.**)

BARNOLDSWICK.

—— Barnoldswick. Official guide, *etc.* *E. J. Burrow & Co.: Cheltenham,* [1925– .] 8°. **10354.** a. **53.**
Various editions.
(The Official Guide to Barnoldswick.)

BARNOSCHI (D. V.)

—— Originile democrației române. "Cărvunarii." Constituția Moldovei dela 1822, *etc.* [With the text.] pp. viii. 330. v. *Iași,* 1922. 8°. **9134.** aaa. **31**

BARNOUIN (Jacques Fr.) *See* Bible.—*Selections.* [*French.*] Recueil de passages de la Sainte Écriture sur les véritez et les devoirs de la religion. Par J. F. Barnouin. 1750. 12°. **861.** i. **20.**

BARNOUIN (Th.) Jésus-Christ et M. Renan, ou la vérité et l'erreur devant le peuple. pp. 245. *Avignon,* 1865. 12°. **4824.** bb. **8.**

BARNOUT (Hippolyte) Le Monde sans Dieu, et le dernier mot de tout. pp. 396. *Paris,* 1890. 18°. **4018.** c. **15.**

—— Système rationnel de navigation aérienne, à circulation stable, fondé sur le principe de la séparation des appareils, ainsi que sur l'emploi du point d'appui, et pratiqué au moyen d'un propulseur rotatif à effet alterno-continu. pp. 15. *Paris,* 1857. 8°. **8755.** h. **45.** (**1.**)

BARNOUW (Adriaan Jacob) *See* Beatrice, *a Nun.* Beatrijs: a Middle Dutch legend. Edited . . . with a grammatical introduction, notes and a glossary by A.J. Barnouw. [1914.] 8°. [*Publications of the Philological Society.* vol. 3.] **Ac. 9930/9.**

—— *See* Bible.—*Gospels.—Harmonies.* [*Polyglott.*] The Liège Diatessaron . . . English translation of the Dutch text by A. J. Barnouw. 1929, *etc.* 8°. [*Verhandelingen der Koninklijke Akademie van Wetenschappen.* Afd. letterkunde. Nieuwe reeks. dl. 31.] **Ac. 944/3.**

—— *See* Bruegel (P.) The Fantasy of Pieter Brueghel. [With introduction and notes by A. J. Barnouw.] [1947.] *obl.* 8°. Cup. **1252.** a. **80.**

—— *See* Chaucer (Geoffrey) [*Canterbury Tales.—Prioress's Tale.*] De Vertelling van de Priores. Uit Chaucer's Canterbury Tales. Door A. J. Barnouw. [1909.] 8°. **11641.** g. **37.** (**4.**)

—— *See* Esmoreit. An Ingenious Play of Esmoreit . . . With an introduction by A. J. Barnouw. 1924. 8°. **20020.cc.3/2.**

—— *See* Kipling (Rudyard) Vertellingen van "The Trade" . . . Vertaald door A. J. Barnouw. [1916.] 8°. **9081.** aa. **9.**

—— *See* Marieken, *van Nijmegen.* A Marvelous History of Mary of Nimmegen . . . With an introduction by A. J. Barnouw. 1924. 8°. **20020.cc.3/3.**

BARNOUW (Adriaan Jacob)

—— *See* Marieken, *van Nijmegen.* Mary of Nimmegen. A facsimile reproduction of the copy of the English version in the Huntington Library. With an introduction by H. M. Ayres . . . and A. J. Barnouw. 1932. 8°. W.P. **9803/6.**

—— *See* New York.—*Metropolitan Museum of Art.* Dutch Paintings. A picture book. [With an introduction by A. J. Barnouw.] 1944. 4°. **7866.** ppp. **24.**

—— *See* Noyes (Alfred) Open Booten . . . Vertaald door A. J. Barnouw. [1918.] 8°. **09083.** c. **42.**

—— *See* Vogel (J. P.) Buddhist Art in India, Ceylon and Java . . . Translated . . . by A. J. Barnouw. 1936. 8°. **07805** f. **75.**

—— The Dutch, *etc.* pp. xi. 297. *Columbia University Press: New York,* 1940. 8°. **010271.** ee. **29.**

—— Echoes of the Pilgrim Fathers' Speech. [Vindicating the validity of the transcription of the names of the English colonists in the Leyden Townhall register.] pp. 51. *Amsterdam,* 1923. 8°. [*Mededeelingen der Koninklijke Akademie van Wetenschappen.* Afd. Letterkunde. dl. 55. ser. A. no. 6.] **Ac. 944.**

—— Holland under Queen Wilhelmina, *etc.* [With a portrait.] pp. ix. 321. *C. Scribner's Sons: New York, London,* 1923. 8°. **09406.ff.4.**

—— The Land of William of Orange, *etc.* [With plates.] pp. 104. *J. B. Lippincott Co.: Philadelphia & New York,* [1944.] 4°. **010271.** pp. **2.**

—— The Land of William of Orange, *etc.* (Revised edition.) pp. 108. *J. B. Lippincott Co.: Philadelphia & New York,* [1953.] 8°. [*Portraits of the Nations Series.*] W.P. **2475/23.**

—— Language and Race Problems in South Africa. pp. 71. *Martinus Nijhoff: The Hague,* 1934. 8°. **20018.** bb. **15.**

—— The Making of Modern Holland. A short history. pp. 224. *George Allen & Unwin: London,* 1948. 8°. **9415.** f. **17.**

—— The Pageant of Netherlands History. pp. xi. 370. *Longmans, Green & Co.: New York,* 1952. 8°. **09406.** f. **5.**

—— Textkritische Untersuchungen nach dem Gebrauch des bestimmten Artikels und des schwachen Adjectivs in der altenglischen Poesie. Proefschrift, *etc.* pp. 236. *Leiden,* 1902. 8°. **12985.** g. **16.**

—— A Trip through the Dutch East Indies. [With plates and a map.] pp. 73. *Koch & Knuttel: Gouda,* [c. 1930.] 8°. **010057.** df. **19.**

—— Vondel, *etc.* pp. ix. 227. *C. Scribner's Sons: New York, London,* 1925. 8°. [*Great Hollanders.*] **010760.e.48/2.**

BARNOUW (Adriaan Jacob) and **LANDHEER** (Bartholomew)

—— The Contribution of Holland to the Sciences. A symposium edited by A. J. Barnouw and B. Landheer . . . With 13 illustrations. pp. xvii. 373. *Querido: New York,* 1943. 8°. **11865.** h. **11.**

BARNOUW (Erik)

—— Handbook of Radio Writing. An outline of techniques and markets in radio writing in the United States. pp. x. 306. *Little, Brown & Co.: Boston,* 1945. 8°. **11867.** f. **29.**

BARNOUW (Erik)

—— Open Collars. A play of undergraduate life in Kingston University, in three acts. pp. 82. *Princeton University Press: Princeton*, 1928. 8°. **11791**. e. **21**.

BARNOUW (Victor)

—— Acculturation and Personality among the Wisconsin Chippewa. pp. 152. *Menasha*, 1950. 8°. [*American Anthropological Association. Memoir Series.* no. 72.] Ac. **6239/2**.

—— Ruth Benedict: Apollonian and Dionysian. (Reprinted from the University of Toronto Quarterly.) [1949.] 8°. **11860**. ff. **12**

BARNOVUS (Consalvus) *See* Barnuevo (Gonsalvo)

BARNOWSKY (Victor)

—— *See* Berstl (J.) 25 Jahre Berliner Theater und Victor Barnowsky, *etc.* [Tributes and congratulations from various persons connected with the theatre. With a portrait.] 1930. 8°. **11796**. c. **10**.

BARNOYA (Narciso F. J. Viñas y) *See* Viñas y Barnoya.

BARNS (Chancy R.) The Commonwealth of Missouri; a centennial record . . . Edited by C. R. Barns. [With illustrations.] pp. xxiv. 936. *Bryan, Brand & Co.: St. Louis*, 1877. 8°. **10409**. g. **12**.

—— Switzler's Illustrated History of Missouri, from 1541 to 1877, *etc.* [Edited by C. R. Barns. From the larger work edited by him, entitled: "The Commonwealth of Missouri."] pp. xviii. 601. *C. R. Barns: Saint Louis*, 1879. 8°. **9615**. ee. **6**.

BARNS (Charles Edward) The Amaranth and the Beryl, an elegy. pp. 248. *Willard Fracker: New York*, 1889. 8°. **11688**. i. **12**.

—— A Disillusioned Occultist. A drama-novel. pp. 146. *W. Fracker & Co.: New York*, 1889. 8°. **012705**. g. **15**.

—— Solitarius to his Dæmon. Three papers. pp. 237. *W. Fracker & Co.: New York*, 1889. 8°. **12350**. f. **31**.

—— A Venetian Study in Black and White . . . Third edition. pp. 172. *Welch, Fracker Co.: New York*, 1890. 8°. **012705**. k. **7**.

BARNS (Glenn Miller)

—— Murder is a Gamble, *etc.* [A novel.] pp. 192. *W. Foulsham & Co.: London*, 1954. 8°. NNN. **5786**.

—— Murder walks the Stairs, *etc.* pp. 192. *W. Foulsham & Co.: London*, 1955. 8°. NNN. **6721**.

BARNS (H. E.) Naju of the Nile . . . Illustrations by Warwick Reynolds. pp. 277. *G. P. Putnam's Sons: London & New York*, 1924. 8°. **012630**. m. **42**.

BARNS (John) *Benedictine Monk.* *See* Barnes.

BARNS (John) *Wesleyan Minister.* *See* Periodical Publications.—*Penzance.* The Cornish Methodist Church Record. [Edited by J. H. Harris and J. Barns.] [1893, *etc.*] 4°. P.P. **441**. i.

BARNS (John Wintour Baldwin)

—— *See* Merton (Wilfred) A Descriptive Catalogue of the Greek Papyri in the Collection of Wilfred Merton, *etc.* (vol. 2. Edited by B. R. Rees, H. I. Bell, J. W. B. Barns.) 1948, *etc.* 4°. W.P. **14320**.

BARNS (John Wintour Baldwin)

—— *See* Oxyrhynchus Papyri. The Oxyrhynchus Papyri, *etc.* (pt. 24. Edited by J. W. B. Barns [and others].) 1898, *etc.* 4°. **7705**. s.

—— The Ashmolean Ostracon of Sinuhe. [With the text and a transcription.] pp. 33. 1952. fol. *See* Oxford.—*University of Oxford.—Ashmolean Museum.* L.R. **273** d. **12**.

BARNS (Joseph Henry) Estimating for Builders. pp. viii. 166. *The Builder: London*, [1925.] 8°. **08244**. e. **55**.

—— Notes on Estimating for Builders' Work. [A revised edition of "Estimating for Builders."] pp. viii. 168. *The Builder: London*, [1939.] 8°. **08230**. b. **33**.

BARNS (Lucy) The Female Christian; containing a selection from the writings of Miss L. Barns; who departed this life, August 27th, 1809. pp. 71. *Francis Douglas: Portland*, [1809.] 8°. **3751**. aaa. **5**.

BARNS (Margarita D.)

—— India Today and Tomorrow. [With plates.] pp. 303. *G. Allen & Unwin: London*, 1937. 8°. **20030**. h. **13**.

—— The Indian Press. A history of the growth of public opinion in India. pp. xv. 491. *G. Allen & Unwin: [London,]* 1940. 8°. **11864**. cc. **9**.

BARNS (Robert) *See* Barnes (Robert) *Chaplain to Henry VIII.*

BARNS (Stephen J.) *See* Buckhurst Hill.—*Epping Forest and County of Essex Naturalists' Field Club.* Transactions, *etc.* (General Index to volumes i. to xxii. 1887–1930. Compiled and edited by S. J. Barns.) 1880. *etc.* 8°. Ac. **3013**. b.

—— *See* Walthamstow. Calendar of Deeds relating to Walthamstow . . . By S. J. Barns. 1923, *etc.* 4°. [*Walthamstow Antiquarian Society. Official Publication.* no. 11, 21,] *33.* Ac. **5646**.

—— *See* Walthamstow. Walthamstow Vestry Minutes, Churchwardens' and Overseers' Accounts, 1710–1794. By S. J. Barns. 1925, *etc.* 4°. [*Walthamstow Antiquarian Society. Official Publication.* no. 13, 14, 16.] Ac. **5646**.

BARNS (Thomas) *See* Francis [de Sales], *Saint, Bishop of Geneva.* Introduction to the Devout Life . . . Translated with notes and introduction by the Rev. T. Barns. 1906. **03605**. de. **2/23**.

—— *See* Scupoli (L.) The Spiritual Combat . . . Translated from the Italian with notes and introduction by the Rev. T. Barns. 1909. 8°. **03605**. de. **2/29**.

BARNS (Thomas Alexander) An African Eldorado: the Belgian Congo . . . With . . . illustrations and . . . maps. pp. xv. 229. *Methuen & Co.: London*, 1926. 8°. **010094**. h. **46**.

—— Angolan Sketches . . . With 20 illustrations and 3 maps. pp. xi. 206. *Methuen & Co.: London*, 1928. 8°. **10094**. aaa. **10**.

—— Tales of the Ivory Trade. pp. 223. *Mills & Boon: London*, 1923. 8°. NN. **8938**.

—— The Wonderland of the Eastern Congo . . . With an introduction by Sir H. H. Johnston. [With illustrations and a map.] pp. xxxv. 288. *G. P. Putnam's Sons: London & New York*, 1922. 8°. **010094**. l. **13**.

—— Across the Great Craterland to the Congo. A sequel to "The Wonderland of the Eastern Congo" . . . With an introduction by J. W. Gregory. [With plates.] pp. 276. *Ernest Benn: London*, 1923. 8°. **10094**. d. **5**.

BARNS (William) The Bristol Bridegroom: or, the Weding Garland of Joy and Delight. Containing five new songs . . . Collected by W. Barns. pp. 8. *E. Brooksby: [London,* 1680?] 8°. **11621.** e. **7.**

BARNS (William) *Minister of the Methodist Episcopal Church in the United States of America.* The Ne plus ultra, or Lay representation in the general government of the church, proven to be unscriptural, unreasonable, and contrary to sound ecclesiastical policy. pp. 32. *C. Sherman, Son & Co.: Philadelphia,* 1863. 8°. **4183.** e. **52. (10.)**

BARNS (William E.) The Labor Problem. Plain questions and practical answers. Edited by W. E. Barns, with an introduction by R. T. Ely . . . and special contributions by J. A. Waterworth and F. Woodrow. pp. 330. *Harper & Bros.: New York,* 1886. 8°. **8276.** aa. **28.**

BARNS (William Everard Cecil) Meditations on the Crown of Thorns . . . With preface by the Rev. G. Body. pp. 59. *W. Clowes & Sons: London,* 1909. 8°. **3457.** f. **37.**

—— [Another edition.] The Thorn Crown. pp. 58. *S.P.C.K.: London,* 1929. 16°. **4225.** df. **24.**

BARNSBURIAN. *See* London.—iii. *Barnsbury Park Commercial and Science and Art Centre.* Journal, *etc.*

BARNSBURY. [For institutions, etc. situated within the parish of Barnsbury:] *See* London.—iii.

BARNSCHEUER (Gustav) Deutsch. Eine Sammlung von falschen Ausdrücken die in der deutschen Sprache vorkommen. pp. xv. 194. *Bonn,* 1895. 8°. **12962.** c. **37.**

BARNSDALE (Barnish) Elocution for the Masses, with humorous, serious & dramatic pieces . . . Edited and selected . . . by B. Barnsdale. pp. 80. *Simpkin, Marshall & Co.: London,* 1890. 12°. **11805.** b. **49.**

BARNS-GRAHAM (John Wedderburn) *See* Graham.

BARNSHAW (Charles) High Drafting in Cotton Spinning. pp. 127. *Ernest Benn: London,* 1930. 8°. **07742.** c. **35.**

BARNSLEY. Barnsley Ta'an Ca'ancel. [A poem in the Yorkshire dialect.] pp. 4. [1850?] 8°. **10347.** e. **37. (4.)**

—— Barnsley, West Riding, Yorkshire . . . Official guide, etc. *E. J. Burrow & Co.: Cheltenham,* [1925– .] 8°. **10354.** a. **76.**
Various editions. Incorporates material from the "Borough" Pocket Guide to Barnsley.

—— The "Borough" Pocket Guide to Barnsley. Containing a street plan, *etc.* pp. 44. *E. J. Burrow: Cheltenham,* [1919.] 8°. **10354.** a. **77.**
Material from this guide was later incorporated in "Barnsley, West Riding, Yorkshire. Official guide."

—— [Charters, court-rolls and estreats.] *See* Hall (Thomas W.) Worsborough, Eckington and Sheffield, *etc.* 1924. 4°. **010368.** i. **27.**

—— A Historical Account of Barnsley, its industries, and principal objects of interest, *etc.* pp. 27. *T. & C. Lingard: Barnsley,* 1878. 8°. **10347.** d. **7. (3.)**

Barnsley Agricultural Society.

—— Annual Show . . . to be held . . . on Saturday, 16th July 1949 [*etc.*] . . . Catalogue, *etc.* [*Barnsley,* 1949– .] 8°. P.P. **2487.** mbl.
Wanting the catalogue for 1951.

BARNSLEY.

Conference of Ladies' Associations for the Care of Friendless Girls.

—— Friends in Need. Some papers read at a Conference of Ladies' Associations for the Care of Friendless Girls, held at Barnsley, April 3rd and 4th, 1889. pp. vi. 88. *Hatchards: London,* 1889. 8°. **08416.** k. **120.**

Midland Institute of Mining Engineers.

Midland Institute of Mining Engineers, 1869–75.
Midland Institute of Mining, Civil and Mechanical Engineers, 1875–1923.
Midland Institute of Mining Engineers, 1923– .

—— Rules, List of Officers, (Rules and List of Members.—Rules, List of Members, Abstracts of Papers, etc. . . . and List of Members, *etc.* Year Book.—Annual Report of the Council, *etc.*) *Newcastle-upon-Tyne & London,* 1897[–1927]. 8°. Ac. **3234/2.**
The issues for 1920–21 *and subsequent years contain the Annual Report of the Council.*

—— [Notices of Meetings.] *Sheffield,* 1936– . 8°. W.P. **2168.**

—— Transactions, *etc.* *Barnsley,* 1869– . 8°. Ac. **3234.**
Imperfect; wanting pt. 8, 9, 13–17, 19–21, 29, 33. *An alternative title "Proceedings" appears first on the wrapper of vol.* 12. *no.* 105.

—— Memorandum prepared by the Joint Committee of the Midland Institute of Mining, Civil, and Mechanical Engineers and the Yorkshire Branch of the National Association of Colliery Managers on the Education of Colliery Officials in Yorkshire. (From the Transactions of the Institution of Mining Engineers.) [With a diagram.] pp. 35. *London,* 1920. 8°. Ac. **3234/4.**

—— Sections of Strata of the Coal Measures of Yorkshire . . . Compiled from records of borings and sinkings by a Committee of the Midland Institute of Mining Engineers. [With a map.] pp. 399. *Sheffield,* 1927. 8°. Ac. **3234/3.**

—— Rules governing the Examination for Certificated Studentship and Guide to Candidates, *etc.* pp. 19. *Wakefield,* 1943. 8°. Ac. **3234/6.**

Midland Institute of Mining Engineers.—Advisory Committee on Research.

—— Summary of Mining Research, including coal and coal products, 1934–35 [*etc.*]. *Sheffield,* 1936– . 8°. W.P. **3644.**

Midland Institute of Mining Engineers.—Control of Roof and Support of Mine Workings Committee, afterwards *Safe Working of Mines Committee.*

—— Third [*etc.*] Progress Report. *A. Reid & Co.: Newcastle-upon-Tyne,* 1931– . 8°. Ac. **3234/5.**
The first and second reports were printed in the Transactions of the Midland Institute of Mining Engineers.

Midland Institute of Mining Engineers.—Library.

—— Catalogue of Library. Subject-matter index of papers, and of articles on mining and allied subjects contained in the books, transactions, &c. in the Library, on December 31st, 1915. Compiled by the librarian [i.e. F. Oxley]. pp. 232. *Loxley Bros.: Sheffield,* 1916. 8°. **11917.** aa. **35.**

BARNSLEY.—*Town Council.*

—— Report on the Sanitary Condition of Barnsley . . . in 1919, *etc.* (Report of the Medical Officer of Health for the year 1920[-36].—Report of the Medical Officer of Health and School Medical Officer . . . for the year 1937 [*etc.*].) *Barnsley*, 1920– . 8°. A.R. **363.**

—— Public Health Services. [By] J. L. Burn . . . Official handbook, second edition. pp. 26. *E. J. Burrow & Co.: Cheltenham*, [1940.] 8°. **7391.** v. **22.**

Town Council.—Education Committee.

—— Report of the School Medical Officer for the year 1920 (-23, 25 [*etc.*]). *Barnsley*, 1921– . 8°. A.R. **360.**

Town Council.—Housing and Welfare Services Committee.

—— Municipal Tenants' Handbook, *etc.* [With illustrations.] *British Publishing Co.: Gloucester*, [1955–]8°. *Various editions.* **8295.** g. **8.**

BARNSLEY AGRICULTURAL SOCIETY. *See* BARNSLEY.

BARNSLEY AND VILLAGE RECORD. *See* PERIODICAL PUBLICATIONS.—*Barnsley.* Bairnsla Foaks Annual, *etc.*

BARNSLEY BRITISH CO-OPERATIVE SOCIETY, LIMITED.

—— The Coronation History of the Barnsley British Co-operative Society Limited. 1862–1902. [With illustrations, including portraits.] pp. 207. *Co-operative Wholesale Society's Printing Works: Manchester*, 1903. 8°. **8286.** aa. **40.**

BARNSLEY CHURCH AND SCHOOL NEWS. *See* PERIODICAL PUBLICATIONS.—*Barnsley.*

BARNSLEY ILLUSTRATED ANNUAL BUSINESS REVIEW. *See* PERIODICAL PUBLICATIONS.—*Barnsley.*

BARNSLEY (ALAN) *See also* FIELDING (Gabriel) *pseud.* [i.e. A. Barnsley.]

—— The Frog Prince, and other poems. *Hand & Flower Press: Aldington*, 1952. 8°. [*Poems in Pamphlet.* 1952. no. 9.] P.P. **5126.** bbt.

BARNSLEY (EDWARD ROBERTS)

—— Major Thomas Barnsley of the Royal American Regiment of Foot. A paper . . . Reprinted . . . from the Bristol Courier, *etc.* pp. 8. [*Bristol, Pa.*, 1934.] 8°. **010886.** eee. **32.**

BARNSLEY (SIDNEY HOWARD) *See* SCHULTZ (Robert W.) and BARNSLEY (S. H.) The Monastery of Saint Luke of Stiris, in Phocis, *etc.* 1901. 8° **L.R.404.e.15.**

BARNSLEY (THOMAS)

—— *See* BARNSLEY (Edward R.) Major Thomas Barnsley of the Royal American Regiment of Foot, *etc.* [1934.] 8°. **010886.** eee. **32.**

BARNSTABLE, *Massachusetts, City of.* The Cape Cod Centennial Celebration at Barnstable, Sept. 3, 1839, of the incorporation of that town, Sept. 3. 1639, *etc.* pp. 92. *S. B. Phinney: Barnstable*, 1840. 8°. **8176.** aaa. **14.** (**13.**)

—— Three hundredth Anniversary of the Founding of the first Congregational Church in London. Exercises in celebration held by the Congregational Church in West Barnstable and the Congregational Church and Society in the East Precinct . . . 1916, *etc.* [With plates.] pp. 16. *Montague Press: [Barnstable,]* 1916. 8°. **4745.** ee. **23.**

BARNSTABLE, *Massachusetts, County of.* A Description of the Eastern Coast of the County of Barnstable, from Cape Cod, or Race Point . . . to Cape Mallebarre, or the Sandy Point of Chatham, pointing out the spots on which the trustees of the Humane Society have erected huts . . . By a member of the Humane Society. pp. 15. *Hosea Sprague: Boston*, 1802. 8°. **10410.** d. **37.** (**1.**)

BARNSTAIR (HENRY)

—— Amateur Songwriters' Vade-Mecum. pp. 6. *London*, [1947.] 4°. **7892.** s. **2.**
Reproduced from typewriting.

BARNSTAPLE. Barnstaple Parish Register of Baptisms Marriages and Burials, 1538 A.D. to 1812 A.D. Edited by Thos. Wainwright. 3 pt. *J. G. Commin: Exeter*, 1903. 4°. **9902.** i. **5.**

—— Reprint of the Barnstaple Records, published by J. R. Chanter and Thos. Wainwright. With corrections and additions by Thos. Wainwright. 2 vol. *A. E. Barnes: Barnstaple*, 1900. 8°. **10351.** dd. **15.**

—— Barnstaple. The official guide, *etc.* [With illustrations.] pp. 111. *Century Press: London*, [1947.] 8°. **10359.** c. **27.**

—— Barnstaple. The official guide, *etc.* [With maps and illustrations.] pp. 127. *Century Press: London*, [1949.] 8°. **010368.** s. **1.**

—— Guide Book to Barnstaple, Ilfracombe and North Devon, *etc.* (Revised edition.) pp. 52. *H. A. Foyster: Barnstaple*, [1886.] 8°. **10347.** cc. **14.** (**1.**)

—— Historical Pageant of Old Barnstaple. Five scenes performed in the Theatre Royal, at Barnstaple, on Wednesday, January 28th, 1914. [Edited by R. J. E. Boggis.] *Percival Harris: Barnstaple, Braunton*, 1914. 8°. **11778.** l. **47.**

—— Rambles around Barnstaple, in the year 1865. By A. M. L. [1865.] 8°. *See* L., A. M. **10352.** bb. **36.**

—— *Barnstaple Grammar School.* Barnstaple Grammar School Magazine. vol. 1. no. 1. *Barnstaple*, 1912. 8°.
[Continued as:]
Rock Magazine. vol. 1. no. 2, *etc.* *Barnstaple*, 1913– . 8°. P.P. **6152.** ck.

—— *Barnstaple Literary and Scientific Institution.* Rules and Regulations, *etc.* pp. xii. 15. *Barnstaple*, 1845. 12°. **8308.** b. **49.** (**1.**)

—— *North Devon Athenæum.* Rules of the North Devon Athenæum. 1888. pp. 8. *Barnstaple*, [1888.] 8°. **011899.** h. **31.** (**1.**)

—— Catalogue of the Circulating and Reference Department of the Library. pp. 350. *Percival Hunter: Barnstaple*, 1898. 8°. **11917.** e. **71.**

BARNSTAPLE, *Rural District of.*

—— The Official Guide to Barnstaple Rural District. With . . . map and . . . illustrations. pp. 47. *Century Press: London*, [1947.] 8°. [*Rural England.*] **W.P.1324/55**
Later editions are entered under BARNSTAPLE, *Rural District of.—Council.*

Council.

—— North Devon. The Official Guide of the Barnstaple Rural District Council . . . Second (—Fifth) edition. 4 pt. *Century Press: London*, [1948–55.] 8°. [*Rural England Series.* no. 55.] W.P. **1324/55a.**
The first edition is entered under BARNSTAPLE, *Rural District of.*

BÄRNSTEIN (ADOLF PERNWERTH VON) *See* PERNWERTH VON BAERNSTEIN.

BARNSTEIN (HEINRICH) *Doctor, of Erfurt, the Elder.* Kurtze Beschreibung dess Tabacks. Wo er seinen Namen her habe . . . wo, wann vnnd wie er gepflantzet . . . vnd zugerichtet werde . . . in vielen Figuren abgebildet, vnd beschrieben. *T. Fritzschen: Erffurdt,* 1645. 4°. **12316. f. 26. (10.)**

—— Extract aus Henrici Barnsteinii . . . Tractat vom Taback. *See* THEBESIUS (G. D.) Georg Daniel Thebesii . . . Deutliche und ausführliche Nachricht vom Rauch- und Schnupf-Taback, *etc.* 1751. 4°. **778. e. 39. (5.)**

BARNSTEIN (HEINRICH) *Doctor, of Erfurt, the Younger.* Exercitatiuncula de synocha imputri, *etc. Praes.* J. Rehefeldius. *Erfurti,* 1734. 4°. **T. 551. (36.)**

BARNSTEIN (HENRY) The Targum of Onkelos to Genesis. A critical enquiry into the value of the text exhibited by Yemen MSS. compared with that of the European recension. Together with some specimen chapters of the Oriental text. pp. ix. 100. *D. Nutt: London,* 1896. 8°. **03128. i. 16. (4.)**

BARNSTEINIUS (HENRICUS) *See* BARNSTEIN (Heinrich)

BARNSTORF (ERNESTUS) Disputatio medica inauguralis de catarrho. *Apud viduam & hæredes J. Elsevirii: Lugduni Batavorum,* 1672. 4°. **1185. k. 12. (8.)**

—— [Another copy.] **1185. g. 12. (6.)**

—— Disputatio medica pathologica de comate et caro, *etc. Praes.* J. Tappius. *Typis H. Mülleri: Helmestadii,* 1668. 4°. **1179. b. 6. (20.)**

BARNSTORFF (BERNHARDUS) *See* DETHARDING (Georg) *the Younger.* Programma qvo ad justa solemnia . . . B. Barnstorffio . . . instituenda . . . invitat Georg Detharding, *etc.* 1704. 4°. **731. f. 4. (38.)**

—— *See* DOEBEL (J. J.) Programma quo . . . ad disputationem inauguralem . . . Bernhardi Barnstorffii . . . invitat J. J. Döbelius. 1670. 4°. **1179. e. 17. (4.)**

—— *See* HOFFMANN (Friedrich) *of Halle, the Younger.* Epistola gratulatoria ad . . . B. Barnstorffium. 1696. 4°. **1179. c. 18. (10.)**

—— *See* KLEIN (Johann) *J.U.D.* Programma quo . . . Johannes Klein . . . ad exequias quas . . . Bernhardo Barnstorffio . . . vidua ac liberi . . . D. vi. Maji A. 1704 . . . parant, proceres ac cives academicos . . . invitat. [1704.] 4°. **731. f. 4. (42.)**

—— *Resp. See* SCHÖN (C.) Disputatio physica quâ qualitates occultas in Academia Wittebergensi ad examen publicum revocat præses M. Caspar Schön, *etc.* 1665. 4°. **536. f. 16. (21.)**

—— Disputatio medica inauguralis de morbo virgineo, seu fœdis virginum coloribus, *etc. Praes.* J. J. Döbelius. *Typis J. Kilii: Rostochii,* 1670. 4°. **1179. e. 17. (3.)**

—— [Another copy.] **T. 543. (32.)**

—— Dissertatio physica de filis meteoricis, vulgo filamentis Mariæ, *etc. Praes.* S. Kirchmajerus. *Typis J. Haken: Wittebergæ,* 1666. 4°. **700. h. 13. (2.)**

—— Programma funebre quo Rector Academiæ Rostochiensis D. Bernhardus Barnstorff . . . exsequias præstantissimæ matronæ Annæ Magdalenæ gente Hilleniæ conjugio Steveriæ . . . eundas indicit. *Rostochii,* [1703.] 4°. **731. f. 4. (34.)**

BARNSTORFF (BERNHARDUS)

—— Programma qvo ad funus qvod . . . Caspar. Matthæus Mullerus . . . unicæ . . . filiolæ Margaretæ Catharinæ . . . paratum habet patres ac cives Academiæ . . . invitat D. B. Barnstorff, *etc. Rostochii,* [1703.] 4°. **731. f. 4. (35.)**

—— Programma quo Universitatis Rostochiensis Rector D. B. Barnstorff . . . festum Paschale civibus suis indicit ac de resuscitatione plantarum tractat. *Rostochii,* 1703. 4°. **B. 129. (13.)**

—— Programma qvo Rector Academiæ Rostochiensis B. Barnstorff . . . ad exeqvias qvas . . . Barbaræ Karstens conjugi suæ . . . paratas cupit viduus . . . Johannes Sibrandus . . . omnes & singulos Universitatis hujus cives . . . invitat. *Typis J. Wepplingii: Rostochii,* 1697. 4°. **731. f. 4. (8.)**

BARNSTORFF (D.) *See* SHAKESPEARE (William) [*Sonnets.*] Schlüssel zu Shakspeare's Sonnetten. Von D. Barnstorff. [With the English text.] 1860. 8°. **11765. b. 23.**

—— *See* SHAKESPEARE (William) [*Sonnets.*] A Key to Shakespeare's Sonnets by D. Barnstorff, *etc.* 1862. 8°. **11765. c. 10.**

BARNSTORFF (FRIDERICUS ANDREAS) Dissertatio inauguralis medica de mensium fluxu nimio, *etc. Praes.* G. D. Coschwitz. pp. 34. *Halæ-Magdeb.,* 1723. 4°. **1179. f. 15. (9.)**

—— [Another copy.] **T. 585. (16.)**

BARNSTORFF (HERMANN)

—— Die soziale, politische und wirtschaftliche Zeitkritik im Werke Gerhart Hauptmanns. pp. 155. *Jena,* 1938. 8°. **011850. k. 74.**

BARNSTORFF (JOHANNES) *of Munich.* Youngs Nachtgedanken und ihr Einfluss auf die deutsche Litteratur . . . Mit einem Vorwort von F. Muncker. pp. vi. 87. *Bamberg,* 1895. 8°. **011851. h. 13. (3.)**

BARNSTORFF (JOHANNES) *Rector of the University of Rostock. See* MUELLER (C. M.) Programma qvo ad exeqvias . . . J. Barnstorffii . . . paratas freqventi præsentia condecorandas . . . invitat Casp. Matthæus Müller. [1705.] 4°. **731. f. 4. (49.)**

—— *See* SCHAPER (J. E.) Rector Universitatis Rostochiensis Johannes Ernestus Schaperus ad memoriam . . . J. Barnstorffii . . . in illius funere . . . debito cum studio hodiè adornando freqventi comitatu recolendam . . . cives academicos . . . invitat. [1705.] 4°. **731. f. 4. (48.)**

—— Amplissimo . . . domino Dno. Jacobo Diestelero . . . parantur exeqviæ, qvas ut frequenter eant proceres ac cives Academiæ Rostochiensis humanissime rogo J. Barnstorff . . . Universitatis Rector. *Rostochii,* [1702.] 4°. **731. f. 4. (29.)**

—— J. Barnstorffius . . . Academiae Rector ad exeqvias . . . Henrici Ernesti de Cramm . . . freqventandas, proceres civesque ac fautores reipubl. literariæ . . . invitat. *Rostochii,* [1702.] 4°. **731. f. 4. (28.)**

—— Maxime reverendum . . . dominum, Dn. Ioh. Nicolaum Qvistorpium . . . filio desideratissimo Hugon[i] Qvistorpio . . . exeqvias parare significat, omnesque . . . proceres ac cives Academiæ Rostochiensis ad easdem . . . invitat J. Barnstorff . . . Academiæ Rector. *Rostochii,* [1701.] 4°. **731. f. 4. (25.)**

BARNSTORFF (Johannes) *Rector of the University of Rostock.*

—— Rector Academiæ J. Barnstorffius . . . ad exeqvias . . . Sophiae Casparæ Mülleriæ . . . paratas, proceres, cives ac fautores reip : literariæ . . . invitatos cupit. *Rostochii*, [1702.] 4°. . **731. f. 4. (27.)**

BARNSTORFF (Johannes Georgius) Dissertatio circularis medica, sistens medicinæ curiosæ specimen duabus quæstionibus enodatum, *etc.* *Praes.* J. E. Schaperus. *Rostochii*, 1711. 4°. **1179. d. 18. (1.)**

—— [Another copy.] **7306. i. 15. (29.)**

—— Dissertatio solennis medica, de tympanite, *etc.* *Praes.* J. E. Schaperus. pp. 34. *Rostochii*, 1712. 4°. **T. 575. (4.)**

—— [Another copy.] **1179. d. 18. (3.)**

—— [Another copy.] **7306.h.5.(23*.)**

BARNSTORFFIUS (Bernhardus) *See* Barnstorff.

BARNSTORFFIUS (Eberhardus) *See* Pfeiffer (S. A.) Disquisitio de imperio phantasmiæ in sensus, *etc.* *Praes.* E. Barnstorffius. 1707. 4°. **1185. b. 9. (19.)**

BARNSTORFFIUS (Ernestus) *See* Barnstorf.

BARNSTORFFIUS (Johannes) *See* Barnstorff (J.) *Rector of the University of Rostock.*

BARNSTORMER PLAYS. Barnstormer Plays. 2 vol. *Gerald Howe: London*, 1928. 8°. **011779. k. 81.**
No more published.

—— Barnstormer Plays. [1943– .] *See* Slater (Montagu)

BARNUEVO (Diego Nicolás de Heredia) *See* Heredia Barnuevo.

BARNUEVO (Francisco de la Pradilla) *See* Pradilla Barnuevo.

BARNUEVO (Francisco Mosquera de) *See* Mosquera de Barnuevo.

BARNUEVO (Gonsalvo)

—— *See* Álvarez de Paz (J.) De quotidiana virtutum exercitatione, *etc.* [Edited by G. Barnuevo.] 1613. 8°. **1483. b. 32.**

BARNUEVO (Rodrigo) *Begin.* Señor, R. Barnueuo de la Compañia de Iesus, *etc.* [A memorial of his services in the Spanish Indies, etc. addressed to the king of Spain.] [*Madrid?* 1630?] fol. **1324. i. 2. (38.)**

BARNUEVO DE PERALTA (Geronimo) *See* Barrionuevo de Peralta (Jerónimo)

BARNUEVO ROCHA Y BENAVIDES (Pedro de Peralta) *See* Peralta Barnuevo Rocha y Benavides (P. J. de)

BARNUEVO Y ROCHA (Pedro de Peralta) *See* Peralta Barnuevo Rocha y Benavides (P. J. de)

BARNUM AND BAILEY. The Barnum and Bailey Songster. Railway tour, Great Britain, 1899. pp. 32. *Barnum & Bailey: London*, [1899.] 8°. **11603. bbb. 38. (4.)**

—— The Barnum-Bailey Illustrated Hand-book of Natural History, *etc.* pp. 31. [1899.] 8°. **07001. h. 9.**

—— The Official Guide. Book of Marvels in the Barnum & Bailey Greatest Show on Earth. With full description of the human prodigies and rare animals by Clarence L. Dean. pp. 44. *Barnum & Bailey: London*, 1899. 4°. **7208. dd. 6.**
The last page is mutilated.

BARNUM AND BAILEY.

—— Official Programme of the Barnum & Bailey Greatest Show on Earth, *etc.* pp. 20. *Barnum & Bailey: London*, [1899.] 8°. **7956. h. 17.**

—— (Fifth edition.) pp. 28. *W. Hill & Co.: London*, [1899.] 8°. **07958. f. 35.**

BARNUM (Daniel) *See* Wilson (James G.) *of New York.* Circuit Court . . . for the Eastern District of Pennsylvania. J. G. Wilson vs. D. Barnum. Opinion of . . . Judge Kane, *etc.* 1849. 8°. [Seward (*William H.*) *Opinion . . . on the Rights of the Patentee during the third term of Woodworth's patent, etc.*] **6616. ccc. 6.**

BARNUM (Francis) Grammatical Fundamentals of the Innuit Language as spoken by the Eskimo of the Western Coast of Alaska. pp. xxv. 384. *Ginn & Co.: Boston & London*, 1901. 8°. **12910. v. 23.**

BARNUM (H. L.) The Spy Unmasked; or, Memoirs of Enoch Crosby, alias Harvey Birch, the hero of Mr. Cooper's tale of the Neutral Ground [i.e. "The Spy"] . . . Taken from his own lips, in short-hand. Containing many . . . facts . . . never before published . . . By H. L. Barnum [i.e. compiled by him]. Embellished with engravings [including a portrait]. pp. 206. *J. & J. Harper: New York*, 1828. 8°. **10881. dd. 22.**

—— [Another edition.] 2 vol. *J. & J. Harper: New York; A. K. Newman & Co.: London*, 1829. 12°. **N. 670.**

—— [Another edition, without the appendix.] pp. 231. *Rebellion Record: New York*, 1864. 12°. **12705. b. 6.**

BARNUM (Madalene Demarest) *See* Maxwell (William Henry) *M.A., LL.D.* Speaking and Writing . . . By W. H. Maxwell . . . M. D. Barnum. [1910, *etc.*] 8°. **12984. df. 8.**

—— Our Aunt from California. A farce in one act. pp. 16. *New York & London*, [1903.] 12°. [*French's Acting Edition.*] **2304. h. 41.**

—— School Plays for all Occasions. pp. 186. *Barse & Hopkins: New York, Newark, N.J.*, [1922.] 8°. **11791. df. 47.**

BARNUM (Phineas Taylor) *See* Ab, *o' th'-Yate, pseud.* Ab-o' th'-Yate and Barnum, *etc.* [1889.] 8°. **12316. ee. 17. (3.)**

—— *See* Jefferson (Caleb) Life and History of P. T. Barnum, *etc.* [1889.] 8°. **10602. aaaa. 24. (5.)**

—— *See* Kiralfy (Imre) Nero . . . A grandly realistic . . . spectacle . . . associated with P. T. Barnum's Greatest Show on Earth. [1889.] 8°. **11779. dd. 2. (3.)**

—— *See* Root (Harvey W.) The Boy's Life of Barnum . . . Illustrated. [1926.] 8°. **010884. de. 9.**

—— *See* Root (Harvey W.) The Unknown Barnum. [With portraits.] 1927. 8°. **010884. ee. 39.**

—— *See* Rourke (Constance M.) Trumpets of Jubilee. H. W. Beecher . . . P. T. Barnum. [With portraits.] 1927. 8°. **010884. f. 22.**

—— *See* Werner (Morris R.) P. T. Barnum. [With a portrait.] 1923. 8°. **10883. e. 15.**

—— The Art of Money-Getting; or, hints and helps how to make a fortune. pp. 60. *Ward, Lock & Co.: London, New York*, [1883.] 8°. **8244. aaa. 23.**

—— Barnum and Jumbo's A.B.C. [In verse. With coloured illustrations.] *F. Warne & Co.: London & New York*, [1890.] 4°. **12807. s. 54.**

BARNUM (Phineas Taylor)

—— Barnum's New Year's Address. pp. 17. [*New York*, 1851.] 8°. **12330. h. 7.**

—— Barnum's Parnassus, being confidential disclosures of the Prize Committee on the Jenny Lind song, with specimens of the leading American poets in the happiest effulgence of their genius. pp. 52. *D. Appleton & Co.: New York; G. S. Appleton: Philadelphia*, 1850. 12°. **11686. e. 3.**

—— Second edition. pp. 52. *D. Appleton & Co.: New York; G. S. Appleton: Philadelphia*, 1850. 12°. **11688. bbb. 45. (5.)**

—— Barnum's Show and Circus. [With coloured illustrations.] *F. Warne & Co.: London & New York; printed in Holland*, [1890.] 4°. **7959. k. 11.**

—— Dollars and Sense; or, how to get on . . . To which is added sketches of the lives of successful men . . . By Henry M. Hunt: and an appendix containing . . . Money, Banks and Banking by Selden R. Hopkins, *etc.* [With a portrait.] pp. 488. *Sampson Low & Co.: London*, 1890. 8°. **12331. i. 14.**

—— Funny Stories told by P. T. Barnum. [With a portrait.] pp. xvi. 374. *G. Routledge & Sons: London*, 1890. 8°. **012314. i. 15.**

—— The Great Composite Novel. His Fleeting Ideal. A romance of baffled hypnotism. The joint work of P. T. Barnum, John L. Sullivan, Bill Nye, Ella Wheeler Wilcox, Maj. Alfred C. Calhoun, Howe & Hummel, Inspector Byrnes, Pauline Hall, Miss Eastlake, W. H. Ballou, Nell Nelson, Alan Dale. pp. 187. *J. S. Ogilvie: New York*, [1890.] 8°. **012705. f. 45.**

—— The Humbugs of the World. pp. vi. 315. *J. C. Hotten: London*, 1866 [1865]. 8°. **12352. cc. 22.**

—— [Another edition.] pp. x. 424. *Carleton: New York*, 1866. 12°. **12352. bbbb. 38.**

—— Les Blagues de l'univers. pp. 367. *Paris*, 1866. 12°. **12352. bbbb. 13.**

—— The Life of P. T. Barnum, written by himself. Author's edition. [With illustrations and a portrait.] pp. 404. *Sampson Low, Son & Co.: London*, 1855. 8°. **10881. b. 3.**

—— [Another copy, with a different titlepage.] *Redfield: New York*, 1855. 8°. **010883. ee. 34.**

—— [Another edition.] pp. viii. 372. *Sampson Low: London*, 1855. 8°. **10881. aa. 5.**

—— [Another edition.] pp. viii. 332. *Willoughby & Co.: London*, [1855.] 8°. **10881. b. 2.**

—— The Life of P. T. Barnum, written by himself, *etc.* pp. 246. *Sampson Low, Son, & Co.: London*, 1855. 8°. **10890. a. 21.**

—— [Another edition.] The Autobiography of P. T. Barnum, *etc.* pp. 160. *Ward & Lock: London*, 1855. 8°. **10881.b.17.**

—— [Another edition.] Barnum, the Yankee showman, *etc.* [Slightly abridged.] pp. 171. *Clarke & Beeton: London*, [1855.] 8°. **10881. a. 2.**

—— [Another edition.] Barnum, or, the Life of a humbug, *etc.* pp. 1–16. *L. T. Holt: London*, [1855.] 8°. **10882. ff. 39.**

Imperfect; wanting all after p. 16.

BARNUM (Phineas Taylor)

—— [Another edition.] The Autobiography of P. T. Barnum. [Much abridged.] pp. 16. *H. Elliot: London*, [1855?] 8°. **10881.d.33.(9.)**

—— [Another edition.] Diprose's Sixpenny Edition of Barnum, the great American Showman, written by himself. pp. 80. *J. Diprose: London*, [1856.] 8°. **10882. aaa. 36. (3.)**

—— Lion Jack: a story of perilous adventures among wild men and the capturing of wild beasts, *etc.* [With illustrations.] pp. iv. 308. *Sampson Low & Co.: London*, 1877 [1876]. 8°. **12808. bb. 27.**

—— Routledge's Barnum's Show. [Coloured illustrations.] *G. Routledge & Sons: [London;] printed in Holland*, [1889.] 4°. **7959. k. 7.**

—— Struggles and Triumphs: or, forty years' recollections of P. T. Barnum. Written by himself. [With illustrations, including a portrait.] pp. 780. *Sampson Low & Co.: London*, 1869. 8°. **010882. h. 32.**

—— [Another edition, brought up to 1882.] pp. 367. *Ward, Lock & Co.: London*, [1882.] 8°. **10882. aa. 24.**

—— [Another edition.] Life of P. T. Barnum . . . Brought up to 1888. Illustrated. pp. 357. *Courier Co.: Buffalo*, 1888. 8°. **10883. aaa. 14.**

—— [Another edition.] Life of P. T. Barnum . . . including his Golden Rules for Money-making, brought up to 1888. pp. 379. *G. Routledge & Sons: London*, 1889. 8°. **10883. b. 13.**

—— [Another edition.] Illustrated and brought up to 1889, *etc.* pp. viii. 398. *Ward, Lock & Co.: London*, 1889. 8°. **10883. aaa. 28.**

—— Struggles and Triumphs . . . illustrated and brought up to 1889, *etc.* [With a portrait.] pp. 360. *Courier Co.: Buffalo*, 1889. 8°. **10889. aa. 4.**

—— [Another edition.] Edited, with an introduction, by George S. Bryan. Illustrated from contemporary prints. 2 vol. pp. lxvi. 879. *A. A. Knopf: New York & London*, 1927. 8°. **010884. f. 20.**

—— Yankee Barnum's Songster, *etc.* *W. S. Fortey: London*, [1890.] 8°. **11602. ee. 27. (3.)**
The title is taken from the wrapper.

—— [Another copy, with a different wrapper.] The New Pavilion Songster. (Barnum's Songster.) *See* Pavilion Songster. **11602. ee. 27. (5.)**

—— Here Comes Barnum. P. T. Barnum's own story collected from his books and introduced by Helen Ferris. Illustrated, *etc.* [With portraits.] pp. xiii. 368. *Harcourt, Brace & Co.: New York*, [1932.] 8°. **11796. bb. 2**

—— The Life of Barnum, *etc.* [By an anonymous author.] pp. 16. *General Publishing Co.: London*, [1891.] 8°. **10881. dd. 24. (6**

—— Life, Ventures and Funny Hoaxes of P. T. Barnum the Yankee showman, in all his ups and downs in fortune and failure. [By Henry Llewellyn Williams.] pp. 3 *General Publishing Co.: London*, [1889.] 8°. **10603. dd. 4. (3**

BARNUM (Phineas Taylor) and **BURKE** (Sarah J.)

—— P. T. Barnum's Circ Text and illustrations arranged for little people. *White & Allen: New York*, 1888. 4°. **7955. f.**

BARNUM (PHINEAS TAYLOR) and **BURKE** (SARAH J.)

—— P. T. Barnum's Museum. Text and illustrations arranged for little people. *White & Allen: New York*, 1888. 4°. **7955. f. 25.**

BARNUM (RICHARD) Kneetime Animal Stories. 17 vol. *Barse & Hopkins: New York*, 1915–22. 8°. **012804.** eee. **1.**

—— [Another copy of vol. 1–5, with different titlepages.] *Simpkin, Marshall & Co.: London*, [1916.] 8°. **012804.** eee. **2.**

BARNUM (SAMUEL WEED) See SMITH (*Sir* William) *LL.D.* A Comprehensive Dictionary of the Bible. Mainly abridged from Dr. W. Smith's Dictionary of the Bible . . . Edited by Rev. S. W. Barnum, *etc.* 1871. 8°. **3126. g. 23.**

—— Romanism as it is: an exposition of the Roman Catholic system, for the use of the American people; embracing a full account of its origin and development . . . and its special relations to American institutions and liberties . . . An appendix of matters from 1871 to 1876. pp. 848. *Connecticut Publishing Co.: Hartford*, 1878. 8°. **4182. f. 13.**

—— A Vocabulary of English Rhymes arranged on a new plan [after MS. notes of L. Case] . . . Second edition. pp. xviii. 767. *T. R. Barnum: New Haven*, 1896. 8°. **011824.** ee. **29.**

BARNUM (VANCE) Joe Strong, the boy wizard. pp. 188. *G. G. Harrap & Co.: London*, 1921. 8°. NN. **7081.**

BARNUTIU (SIMEONE)

—— *See* BOGDAN-DUICĂ (G.) Viața și ideile lui Simion Bărnuțiu. 1924. 8°. [*Academia Română. Studii și cercetări.* no. 8.] Ac. **743/43.**

—— *See* MARCU (A.) Simion Bărnuțiu, Al. Papiu Ilarian și Iosif Hodoș la studii în Italia, *etc.* 1934, *etc.* 8°. [*Academia Română. Memoriile secțiunii literare.* ser. 3. tom. 7.] Ac. **743.** (**4.**)

—— Dereptulu naturale privatu. pp. 300. *Iașii*, 1868. 8°. **6006. b. 20.**

BARNWAL (ROBERT) *See* ENGLAND.—*Year Books.*—Henry VI. [*Years* 21, 22, 27, 28, 30–39.] La Premiere Part des ans du roy Henry le VI, *etc.* (Les Reports des Cases . . . communement appeles, The Second Part of Henry the Sixth . . . avec une table [by R. Barnwal].) 1679. fol. **17. e. 3. (2.)**

BARNWALL (NICHOLAS) *Viscount Barnewall of Kingsland.* *See* BARNEWALL.

BARNWELL ABBEY. *See* GILES, *Saint*, and ANDREW, *Saint and Apostle, Priory of, Barnwell.*

BARNWELL (ARTHUR) The Hibernian Sunday School Hymn Book. pp. 208. *G. Healy: Dublin*, [1870?] 12°. **3438.** df. **29.**

BARNWELL (CHARLES FREDERICK) *See* ARCHIMEDES. [*Arenarius.*] Θεωρημα ῳ κεχρηται, ἐν τῳ Ψαμμιτῃ, ὁ Ἀρχιμηδης, *etc.* MS. NOTE [by C. F. Barnwell]. [1755?] fol. **715. k. 2.**

BARNWELL (CHARLES H.) *of Hull.* Anecdotes of Celebrities, historical, biographical and humorous. Compiled by C. H. Barnwell. pp. viii. 104. *Elliot Stock: London; Walker & Brown: Hull*, 1878. 8°. **10602. d. 11.**

BARNWELL (CHARLES HEYWARD) *See* SHAKESPEARE (William) [*Works.*] The Tudor Shakespeare, *etc.* (The second part of Henry the Sixth. Edited by C. H. Barnwell.) 1911, *etc.* 16°. **11764.** tt. **1/37.**

BARNWELL (EDWARD LOWRY) Perrot Notes; or, some account of the various branches of the Perrot family. [With illustrations.] pp. iv. 216. 1867. 8°. *See* ENGLAND. —*Cambrian Archaeological Association.* **9903. g. 13.**

BARNWELL (F. S.) Aeroplane Design, by F. S. Barnwell, and A Simple Explanation of Inherent Stability, by W. H. Sayers. pp. 102. *McBride, Nast & Co.: London*, 1916. 8°. **08768.** aa. **64.**

BARNWELL (GEORGE) An Excellent Ballad of G. Barnwel, an Apprentice of London, who was undone by a strumpet, who having thrice robbed his master, and murdered his uncle in Ludlow, was hanged in chains in Polonia, *etc.* B.L. 2 pt. *F. Coles, T. Vere, J. Wright & J. Clarke: London*, [1680?] fol. Rox. III. **26.**

—— [Another edition.] 2 pt. *W. O.* [*William Onley*]: *London*, [1710?] fol. C. **40.** m. **10.** (**109.**)

—— [Another copy.] C. **40.** m. **9.** (**42.**)

—— [Another edition.] [*London*, 1720?] *s. sh.* fol. **C.116.i.2.(15.)**

—— [Another edition.] 2 pt. *M. Deacon: London*, [1725?] fol. **C.116.i.4.(99.)**

—— [Another edition.] [*London*, 1810?] *s. sh.* fol. **1876.** e. **1.** (**7.**)

—— [Another edition.] The History of G. Barnwell, in two parts, *etc.* pp. 16. *J. Evans & Son: London*, [1810?] 12°. **11621.** b. **27.** (**2.**)

—— [Another edition.] pp. 24. *J. Pitts: [London*, 1810?] 8°. **12331.** i. **7.** (**4.**)

—— [Another edition.] The Life of George Barnwell. [*London?* 1830?] *s. sh. obl.* fol. **11602.** i. **12.** (**28.**)

—— Barnwell. [A novel, by Thomas Skinner Surr.] Traduit de l'anglais par Jean François André. 3 tom. *Paris*, l'an VII [1799?]. 12°. **12808.** o. **17.**

—— George Barnwell. [A ballad, based on the traditional one.] *See* KILFANE. The Joys of Kilfane, *etc.* [1820?] 16°. **1078.** k. **12.** (**30.**)

—— George Barnwell. The Comic Phiz, &c. Anthony Brown. Fair Young Phœbe. [Songs.] pp. 8. *Printed for the Booksellers: Edinburgh*, [1820?] 12°. **11621.** b. **9.** (**35.**)

—— Georgy Barnwell.—Free and easy. [Songs.] [*London*, 1846?] *s. sh.* 4°. **11621.** k. **4.** (**23.**)

—— Lettre de Barnevelt dans sa prison à Truman son ami [in verse], précédée d'une lettre de l'auteur [Claude Joseph Dorat]. Quatrième édition. [With a frontispiece.] pp. 34. *Paris*, 1766. 4°. **11481.** f. **37.** (**1.**)

—— Memoirs of George Barnwell, the unhappy subject of Lillo's . . . tragedy . . . By a descendant of the Barnwell family. pp. 142. *B. Flower: Harlow; M. Jones: London*, 1810. 12°. **10854.** aa. **24.** (**1.**)

—— [Another edition.] pp. 141. *Sherwood, Neely & Jones: London*, 1817. 12°. **10827.** a. **22.**

—— The Life and History of G. Barnwell, *etc.* [Abridged from the "Memoirs."] pp. 34. *Dean & Munday: London*, [1820.] 8°. **10803.** aa. **3.** (**1.**)

—— Pathetic History of George Barnwell, *etc.* pp. 24. *W. & T. Fordyce: Newcastle & Hull*, [1840?] 8°. **11621.** aaa. **1.** (**16.**)

BARNWELL (George)

—— [Another edition, abridged.] *J. Wrigley: Manchester*, [1840?] 12°. **11621**. b. **21**. (**18**.)

—— The 'Prentice's Tragedy: or, the History of George Barnwell: being a fair warning to young men to avoid the company of lewd women. [Including the ballad. With woodcuts.] pp. 24. *W. O. [William Onley]: London*, [1700?] 4°. C. **56**. d. **31**.

—— The Tragical History of George Barnwell. pp. 24. *Falkirk*, 1821. 12°. **1076**. l. **20**. (**18**.)
Imperfect; wanting pp. 7–18.

—— Youth's Warning-Piece; or, the Tragical history of George Barnwell who was undone by a strumpet, that caused him to rob his master, and murder his uncle. pp. 24. *London*, [1730?] 12°. T. **1854**. (**10**.)

—— [Another edition, containing the ballad.] pp. 24. *London*, [1750?] 12°. **1079**. i. **13**. (**5**.)

—— [Another edition.] pp. 23. *R. Christopher: Stockton*, [1795?] 12°. **1076**. l. **24**. (**3**.)

—— [Another edition.] pp. 24. *Printed for the Purchaser: Warrington*, [1810?] 12°. **1078**. i. **23**. (**3**.)

—— [Another edition.] pp. 24. *J. Turner: Coventry*, [1815?] 12°. **1078**. i. **28**. (**29**.)

—— [Another copy.] **1078**. i. **25**. (**10**.)

—— [Another edition.] pp. 15. *A. Swindells: Manchester*, [1820?] 12°. **11621**. b. **16**. (**16**.)

BARNWELL (James G.) Reading Notes on the Constitution of the United States. (From the Bulletin of the Library Company.) pp. xv. *Philadelphia*, 1887. 8°. **8177**. df. **21**. (5.)

BARNWELL (Patrick Joseph)

—— Visits and Despatches, Mauritius, 1598–1948. pp. 296. *Standard Printing Establishment: Port Louis*, 1948. 8°. **010096**. i. 65.

BARNWELL (Patrick Joseph) and **TOUSSAINT** (Auguste)

—— A Short History of Mauritius, *etc.* pp. viii. 268. 1949. 8°. *See* Mauritius, *Island of.* [*Miscellaneous Official Publications.*] **09062**. aa. **27**

BARNWELL (Robert Gibbes) *See* Girardin (M.) called Saint-Marc Girardin. Lectures on Dramatic Literature . . . First series. Translated . . . by R. G. Barnwell. 1849. 8°. **11795**. e. **58**.

—— The New-Orleans Book. [A selection of pieces in prose and verse.] Edited by R. G. Barnwell. pp. xii. 384. *New-Orleans*, 1851. 8°. **12352**. cc. **26**.

BARNWELL (V. T.) *See* Directories.—*Atlanta*. Barnwell's Atlanta City Directory . . . Compiled . . . by V. T. Barnwell. 1867. 12°. P.P. **2534**. f.

BÄRNWICK (   )

—— [For the German surname of this form:] *See* Baernwick.

BARNY (Alexis) Heures de loisir. Théories et problèmes sur tous les genres de jeux d'esprit. [In verse. With "solutions."] pp. 84. *Limoges*, 1889. 18°. **11483**. cc. **30**.

BARNY (Eugène) Considérations sur quelques maladies des femmes en couches, et sur leur hygiène; thèse, *etc.* pp. 61. *Paris*, 1829. 4°. **1184**. c. **13**. (2.)

BARNY (Pierre) Défenses des Jésuites contre les requêtes et plaidoyers de l'Université et des curés de Paris. *See* Jesuits. [*Appendix.*] Annales de la Société des soi-disans Jésuites, *etc.* tom. 1. 1764, *etc.* 4°. **1485**. **s**. **3**.

BARNY DE ROMANET (J. A. A.) Histoire de Limoges et du Haut et Bas Limousin, *etc.* pp. xiv. 496. *Limoges*, 1821. 8°. **10173**. cc. **18**.

BARNY DE ROMANET (Jean Baptiste Auguste) Du régime des eaux en Algérie . . . De l'organisation des irrigations. Des routes. pp. iv. 59. *Alger*, 1860. 8°. **8777**. bbb. **30**. (**1**.)

—— Traité historique des poids et mesures et de la vérification depuis Charlemagne jusqu'à nos jours, complété par le recueil annoté des lois, *etc.* pp. 301. *Paris, Alger*, 1863. 8°. **8504**. e. **24**.

BARO. Du baro mors et vis, conte du xiie siècle; publié par Gh. [or rather, Ch.] J. Richelet [or rather, written by him. In verse]. pp. 15. *Paris*, 1832. 8°. **11475**. d. **46**. (**2**.)
No. 17 *of an edition of twenty-nine copies.*

—— Incominzano li prouerbii de lo Schiauo de Baro. E la b c disposto. E sonetti morali. [With a woodcut.] 𝕲.𝕷. [*Venice*, 1500?] 8°. IA. **25160**.
4 *leaves. Sig.* a⁴. 35 *lines to a page. Another edition of this work was published under the title of* "*El Savio Romano.*"

—— *Begin.* [fol. 1 *recto*:] Liber baronis de clauibus sapiētie siue de documētis prīs ad filiū Feliciter īcipit. 𝕲.𝕷. [*Jean Bouyer and Guillaume Bouchet: Poitiers*, 1500?] 4°. IA. **42839**.
18 *leaves. Sig.* A⁸ B¹⁰. 22–26 *lines to the page. Imperfect; wanting the last leaf, the contents of which are not known.*

BARO (Antonius) Triumviratus Sanctimoniæ Societatis Jesu, tribus epigrammatum libris ad imitationem propositus. pp. 170. *De Bonis: Neapoli*, 1695. 8°. **11405**. d. **5**.

BARO (Balthasar) [For editions of Honoré d'Urfé's "L'Astrée," the last two parts of which were edited by B. Baro:] *See* Urfé (H. d')

—— Les Poésies de Balthazar Baro, le continuateur d'Astrée, académicien; recueillies pour la première fois, sur des documents inédits et d'après des ouvrages oubliés, par Leon Côte et Paul Berthet. pp. 82. *Grenoble*, 1913. 8°. C. **57**. f. **7**.
One of an edition of thirty copies.

—— [La Clarimonde, tragedie.] [In verse.] pp. 112. [*A. de Sommaville: Paris*, 1643.] 4°. **164**. c. **27**.
Imperfect; wanting the titlepage and the following leaf.

—— [La Clorise . . . pastorale.] [In verse.] pp. 139. [*F. Pomeray: Paris*, 1634.] 8°. **164**. a. **9**.
Imperfect; wanting the titlepage.

—— [Parthenie.] [In verse.] pp. 112. [*A. de Sommaville: Paris*, 1642.] 4°. **164**. c. **28**.
Imperfect; wanting the titlepage.

—— Extrait de Parthenie, tragedie, *etc.* *See* Bibliothèque. Bibliothèque poëtique, *etc.* tom. 1. 1745. 4°. **84**. h. **1**.

—— Sainct Eustache martyr, poëme dramatique. [In verse.] pp. 94. *A. de Sommaville: Paris*, 1649. 4°. **164**. c. **29**.

—— [Another edition.] pp. 72. [*G. de Luyne: Paris*, 1666.] 12°. **163**. e. **12**.
Imperfect; wanting the titlepage.

BARO (Bonaventura) *See* Baronius.

BARO (Camille) Deux mots sur l'Italie. pp. 30. *Paris,* 1859. 8°. **8033**. c. **37**. (**1**.)

BARO (Eguinarius) *See* Baron (Éguinaire)

BARO (Joannes) *See* Pigna (G. B.) Io. Bapt. Pignæ De principibus Atestinis historiarum libri VIII . . . Ex Italica in Latinam linguam conuersi a I. Barone. 1585. fol. C. **75**. e. **3**.

BARO (Marcus) Incipit liber Marci Baronis. De geometria. De casis litterarum. *See* Goesius (W.) Rei agrariæ auctores, *etc.* 1674. 4°. **441**. b. **16**.

BARO (Peter) *See* L., T. A Voyce out of the Wildernes, *etc.* (De fide ejusque ortu, et naturâ: contra P. Baronis . . . prælectionem in Cap. 3. ad Rom. vers. 28.—Of Faith, and the Originall and Nature thereof . . . Against the lecture of P. Baro, *etc.*) 1651, *etc.* 8°. **3185**. a. **85**.

—— —— 1653. 8°. **702**. b. 9. (5.)

—— Fower Sermons and two Questions. As they were vttered and disputed . . . in Cambridge . . . Englished by I. L. [i.e. John Ludham.] *See* Treatise. A speciall Treatise of Gods Prouidence, *etc.* [1600?] 8°. **857**. b. **3**.

—— Petri Baronis Stempani . . . In Jonam Prophetam Prælectiones 39 . . . Adjecta sunt etiam, & alia quædam ejusdem authoris . . . Operâ & studio Osmundi Laki . . . collecta, & ab authore ipso recognita. (Doctissimi cujusdam viri tractatus contra Missæ sacrificium, & transubstantiationem Papistarum.) 2 pt. *Apud Joannem Dayum: Londini,* 1579, 78. fol. **1408**. l. **17**.

—— De Fide eiusque ortu, & natura. Contra P. Baronis Stempani . . . prælectionem. In Cap. 3. ad Rom. vers. 28. Editio secunda. pp. 67. *Apud Petrum Cole: Londini,* 1644. 12°. E. **1187**. (**1**.)

BARO (Robertus) *See* Baron (Robert) *Professor of Divinity in Marischal College, Aberdeen.*

BARO (Roulox) Relation du Voyage de R. Baro . . . au pays des Tapuies dans la terre ferme du Brasil . . . Traduict d'Hollandois . . . par Pierre Moreau, *etc. See* Morisot (C. B.) Relations veritables et curieuses de l'Isle de Madagascar et du Bresil, *etc.* 1651. 4°. **982**. f. **24**.

BARÓ (Teodoro) *See* Bastinos (A. J.) Arte Dramático Español Contemporáneo . . . Con la colaboración de D. T. Baró y D. R. Pomés. 1914. 8°. **11791**. ccc. **15**.

—— *See* Coll y Vehí (J.) Dialogos literarios, *etc.* [With a biographical notice of the author by T. Baró.] 1882. 8°. **11853**. p. **22**.

—— —— 1885. 8°. **012356**. f. **8**.

—— *See* Fabra (C.) Código, ó deberes de buena sociedad. [With a preface by T. Baró.] 1883. 8°. **8411**. aaa. **36**.

—— Cuentos del Ampurdán. pp. 64. *Barcelona,* 1896. 8°. **12489**. dd. **4**.

—— Cuentos y Novelas. pp. vii. 231. *Madrid,* 1887. 8°. **12489**. f. 35.

—— Juan Alcarreño. [A novel. With illustrations.] pp. 438. *Madrid,* 1889. 8°. **12489**. k. **23**.

BAROALDUS (Philippus) *See* Beroaldus.

BAROCCI (Federigo) *See* Farabulini (D.) Sopra una sacra famiglia di F. Barocci nell' Esposizione Romana, ragionamento. 1870. 8°. **7857**. bb. **41**. (**12**.)

—— *See* Olsen (H.) Federico Barocci. A critical study, *etc.* 1955. 4°. [*Figura.* no. 6.] Ac. **1077**. nc.

—— *See* Pietro (F. di) Disegni . . . di Federigo Barocci negli Uffizi, *etc.* 1913. fol. **7858**. t. **31**.

BAROCCI (Federigo)

—— *See* Schmarsow (A.) Federigo Barocci, *etc.* (F. Barocci's Zeichnungen.) 1909, *etc.* 8°. [*Abhandlungen der philologisch-historischen Klasse der königlich Sächsischen Gesellschaft der Wissenschaften.* Bd. 26. no. 4, 5; Bd. 28. no. 3.] Ac. **700/4**.

—— Nozze Vaccaj-Gennari. (Lettere di F. Barocci . . . non . . . mai stampate. [Edited with a preface by G. Grossi.]) pp. 22. *Pesaro,* 1883. 8°. **10905**. e. **9**. (**1**.)

BAROCCI (Luigi) *See* Fabi-Montani (F.) *Count.* Collezione di quaranta sacre ceremonie usate principalmente in Roma, incise . . . dal Professore L. Barocci, *etc.* [1841, *etc.*] *obl.* fol. **1860**. c. **7**.

BAROCCIAN MANUSCRIPT. [For editions of the Baroccian manuscript first edited by Humphrey Hody with the title "Anglicani novi schismatis redargutio," and ascribed by him to Nikephoros Kallistos Xanthopoullos:] *See* Xanthopoullos (N. K.)

—— [For controversial works relating to "Anglicani novi schismatis redargutio" and to the translation thereof by H. Hody:] *See* Hody (Humphrey)

BAROCCIO (Alfonso) *See* Hippocrates. [*Aphorismi.—Greek and Latin.*] Alfonsi Baroccii . . . In primam magni Hippocratis aphorismorum sectionem . . . lectiones. [With the text.] 1593. 4°. **1165**. g. **4**. (**2**.)

—— Alfonsi Baroccii . . . Lectionum de febribus liber primus, qui est de febre generatim. Cum triplici indice . . . Nunc primum opera Ioannis Libioli . . . exceptus ac editus. pp. 116. *Apud V. Baldinum: Ferrariæ,* 1606. fol. **1167**. eee. **21**. (**3**.)

BAROCCIO (Giacomo) *See* Barozzi (G.) called Il Vignola.

BAROCCIUS (Alphonsus) *See* Baroccio (Alfonso)

BAROCCIUS (Franciscus) *See* Barozzi (Francesco)

BAROCCIUS (Petrus) successively *Bishop of Belluno* and *of Padua.* *See* Barozzi (P.)

BAROCELLI (Piero)

—— Augusta Praetoria. Curavit P. Barocelli. [With plates.] pp. xix. 68. *Roma,* 1932. 4°. [*Inscriptiones Italiae.* vol. 11. fasc. 1.] Ac. **67**.

—— Augusta Praetoria. *Ital.* coll. lxxx. 232. pl. 28. v. *Roma,* 1948. fol. [*Forma Italiae.* Regio XI. Transpadana. vol. 1.] W.P. **8562/11**. (**1**.)

—— Il Piemonte dalla capanna neolitica ai monumenti di Augusto. [With plates.] *See* Turin. Studi su Torino e il Piemonte. 1933. 8°. [*Biblioteca della Società Storica Subalpina.* vol. 139.] Ac. **6536**.

—— Il Regio Museo di Antichità di Torino. Collezioni preistoriche e greco-romane. 84 illustrazioni. pp. 50. 1931. 8°. *See* Turin.—*Regio Museo di Antichità.* W.P. **8625/6**.

—— Il Regio Museo Preistorico-Etnografico "Luigi Pigorini" di Roma, *etc.* [By P. Barocelli, R. Boccassino and M. Carelli. With illustrations.] pp. 85. 1937. 8°. *See* Rome.—*The City.—Museo Preistorico-Etnografico "Luigi Pigorini."* W.P. **8625/58**.

—— Tradizione etnica e realtà culturale del Piemonte e della Liguria prima della unificazione augustea. XVIII E.F. [1940.] *See* Rome.—*The City.—Società Italiana per il Progresso delle Scienze.* Relazioni, *etc.* (XXVIII riunione.) vol. 5. XVIII E.F. [1940], *etc.* 8°. Ac. **2804**. d.

BAROCHE (Céleste) Second Empire. Notes et souvenirs, *etc.* pp. xi. 661. *Paris*, 1921. 8°. **10657.** dd. **26.**

BAROCHE (Ernest) *See* Ozou de Verrie ( ) Les Trois journées du Bourget. La mort du Commandant Baroche. 1871. 8°. **9077.** ee. **32.** (**3.**)

—— Rapport sur l'industrie de la laine.—Rapport sur la filature du coton.—Rapport sur les tissus de coton.—Rapport sur les sucres raffinés. *See* France.—*Ministère de l'Agriculture et du Commerce.—Conseil supérieur de l'Agriculture, du Commerce et de l'Industrie.* Enquête, *etc.* 1862. 4°. S. **169.** a.

BAROCHE (Jules) *See* Baroche (Pierre J.)

BAROCHE (*Mme.* Jules) *See* Baroche (Céleste)

BAROCHE (Pierre Jules) *See* Bouhier de l'Écluse (R. C.) La Lettre de M. Baroche . . . et l'Encyclique [of 8 Dec. 1864]. 1865. 8°. **5107.** dd. **15.**

—— *See* Castille (H.) Portraits politiques, *etc.* 1856, *etc.* 8°. **10603.** a. **18.**

—— *See* Colin (A.) Barreau de Paris. Éloge de Baroche. 1888. 8°. **10602.** k. **10.** (**3.**)

—— *See* Duvergier (J. B.) Consultation pour la Compagnie des mines de la Loire . . . suivie des adhésions motivées de MM. Paillet . . . et Baroche. 1846. 4°. **1377.** k. **3.** (**2.**)

—— *See* Jauffret (A.) Mémoire en réponse aux consultations de MM. Duvergier . . . et Baroche. 1846. 8°. **1132.** k. **32.**

—— *See* Maurain (J.) Baroche, ministre de Napoléon III, d'après ses papiers inédits. [With a portrait.] 1936. 8°. **010665.** ff. **61.**

—— Traité de commerce avec l'Angleterre. Discours . . . au Corps législatif, *etc.* pp. 43. *Paris*, 1861. 8°. **8244.** d. **33.** (**7.**)

BAROCIO (Alberto)

—— *See* Mexico.—*Secretaría de Educación Pública.* México y la cultura. [Essays by A. Barocio and others.] 1946. 8°. L.A.S. **525/19.**

BAROCIO (Giacomo) *See* Barozzi (G.) called Il Vignola.

BAROCIUS (Franciscus) *See* Barozzi (Francesco)

BAROCKMUSEUM. *See* Vienna.—*Belvedere.*

BÁRÓCZY (Sándor) *See* Freemasons. [*Appendix.*] [L'Adepte moderne.] A' mostani Adeptus . . . Frantziából fordította Bárótzi S. 1810. 8°. **12512.** bbb. **27.**

BARODA. *Baroda State Museum.*

—— Bulletin of the Baroda State Museum and Picture Gallery. [*Baroda*,] 1944– . 8°. Ac. **1941.** d.

—— Catalogue of the European Pictures. [By Ernst Cohn-Wiener. With plates.] pp. 42. *Baroda State Press:* [*Baroda*,] 1935. 8°. **7866.** ppp. **6.**

—— Descriptive Guide to the Baroda Museum and Picture Galleries. By S. Ganguli. [*Baroda*, 1930– .] *obl.* fol. W.P. **15090.**

—— Travelling Report for . . . February–April 1936. By Dr. Ernst Cohn-Wiener, *etc.* pp. 37. pl. XVI. [*Baroda*,] 1937. 8°. **7813.** b. **22.**

BARODA.—*Central Library of Baroda.*

Formerly the Laxmi-Vilasa Palace Library.

—— An Index Catalogue of Books in the Laxmi-Vilasa Palace Library, *etc.* (Author catalogue of books added to the Central Library, *etc.*) pp. 270. cccxx. *Times Press: Bombay*, 1910. 8°. **11908.** e. **28.**

—— Author Catalogue of Books added to the Central Library . . . from January 1910 to October 1911. pp. 61. *Baroda Printing Works: Baroda*, 1912. 8°. **11908.** e. **26.**

—— Central Library, Baroda. Bulletin of New Books. 26 December 1911(—January 1918). 29 pt. [*Baroda*,] 1911–17. fol. & 8°. **11908.** k. **33.**

—— The Baroda Library System. A paper [on the Baroda Library Department] . . . By Newton M. Dutt. pp. 13. *Baroda*, 1917. 8°. **011903.** bb. **71.**

—— A Handbook of the Baroda Library Department. By Newton M. Dutt. [Being the second edition of "The Baroda Library System."] pp. 41. *Baroda*, 1921. 8°. **11908.** a. **32.**

—— Gaekwad's Oriental Series. Edited under the supervision of the Curator of State Libraries, Baroda. *Baroda*, 1916– . 8°. **14003.** pp. **1**, *etc.*
From 1927 *onwards published by the Oriental Institute, Baroda, formerly the Sanskrit Section of the Central Library.*

—— The Library System of the Baroda State. By Newton M. Dutt. Third edition [of "The Baroda Library System"]. With six illustrations. pp. iv. 44. *Baroda*, 1924. 8°. **11908.** a. **38.**

—— The Baroda Library Hand-book. By Newton Mohun Dutt . . . Fourth edition [of "The Baroda Library System"]. With 15 illustrations, *etc.* pp. xii. 64. *Baroda*, 1926. 8°. **011899.** c. **35.**

—— Baroda and its Libraries. By Newton Mohun Dutt . . . With three addresses on libraries and literature by H. H. the Maharaja Gaekwad . . . 34 illustrations . . . and a . . . map, *etc.* [A revised and enlarged edition of "The Baroda Library System."] pp. xxxvi. 191. *Baroda*, 1928. 8°. **11907.** d. **16.**

Kala Bhavan.

—— Second Annual Report and Statement of Accounts for . . . 1891–92. pp. xlii. 57. *Bombay*, 1894. 8°. **7808.** df. **17.**

Laxmi-Vilasa Palace Library. See supra: *Central Library of Baroda.*

Maharaja Sayajirao University of Baroda.

—— Journal of the Maharaja Sayajirao University of Baroda, *etc.* vol. 2. no. 2, *etc.* Oct. 1953, *etc.* *Baroda*, 1953– . 8°. Ac. **2696.** e.

—— M.S. University Archaeology Series. *Baroda*, 1953– . 4°. Ac. **2696.** e/**2.**

Museum and Picture Gallery. See supra *Baroda State Museum.*

Oriental Institute.

—— Gaekwad's Oriental Series. [From 1927 onwards published by the Oriental Institute, formerly the Sanskrit Section of the Central Library.] *See* supra: *Central Library of Baroda.* Gaekwad's Oriental Series, *etc.* 1916, *etc.* 8°. **14003.** pp. **1**, *etc.*

BARODA.—*University of Baroda. See* supra: *Maharaja Sayajirao University of Baroda.*

BARODA, *State of.*

LAWS.—II. COLLECTIONS OF LAWS ON SPECIAL SUBJECTS.

Military Law.

—— The Discipline Act for the Baroda Army. ff. 20. *Bombay,* 1887. fol. I.S. c. **3.**
Printed on one side of the leaf only.

MISCELLANEOUS OFFICIAL PUBLICATIONS.

—— Ancient Vijñatipatras. By . . . Hirananda Sastri. pp. ix. 80. pl. XXVIII. [*Baroda,*] 1942. 4°. **15010.i.13.**
Memoir no. 1 *of the series* " *Srī-Pratapasiṁha Mahārāja Rājyābhisheka Granthamālā.*"

—— Beautiful Baroda. [An illustrated guide to the state. Edited by C. A. Mehta.] pp. 19. [*Baroda,*] 1940. 8°. **10055.** w. **14.**

—— Important Inscriptions from the Baroda State. vol. 1. [With translations and a commentary by A. S. Gadre.] pp. viii. 112. pl. XVI. [*Baroda,*] 1943. 4°. **15010.i.13.**
Memoir no. 2 *of the series* " *Srī-Pratāpasiṁha Mahārāja Rājyābhisheka Granthamālā.*"

—— Investigations in Prehistoric Archæology of Gujarat. Being the official report of the First Gujarat Prehistoric Expedition, 1941–42. By Hasmukh D. Sankalia. pp. xviii. 336. pl. v. XXXI. [*Baroda,*] 1946. 4° **15010.i.13.**
Śrī-Pratāpasiṁha Mahārāja Rājyābhisheka Granthamālā. Memoir. no. 4. *A label bearing the word* " *into* " *has been pasted over the word* " *in* " *on the titlepage.*

—— Report on the Administration of the Baroda State for 1875–76(—1880–81). 6 pt. *Calcutta,* 1876–83. 8°. [*Selections from the Records of the Government of India.* no. 132, *etc.*] I.S. **358.**

—— [Another edition of the report for 1875–76.] pp. 60. *Bombay,* [1876.] 8°. I.S. c. **20/2.**
Without the appendices.

—— Report on the Administration of the Baroda State for 1881–82[—1886–87]. 6 pt. *Bombay,* 1883–88. 8°. I.S. c. **20.**
The reports for 1887–88 *to* 1889–90 *were not published.*

—— Report on the Census of the Baroda Territories, 1881. By Gajânan Krishna Bhâtavadékar. pp. xxiv. 291. 503. *Bombay,* 1883. fol. I.S. c. **5/2.**

—— Report on the Further Development of the Fishery Resources of Baroda State. By James Hornell. pp. 26. *Baroda,* 1918. fol. I.S. c. **10.**

—— Report on the Political Administration of the Baroda State for 1890–91(—1903–1904). 14 pt. *Calcutta,* 1891–1904. fol. [*Selections from the Records of the Government of India.* no. 279, *etc.*] I.S. **133.**

—— A Scheme of Sanskrit Education in the Baroda State. [Signed: J. C. Chatterji.] pp. 42. *Bombay,* [1917.] fol. I.S. c. **8.**

DEPARTMENTS OF STATE AND PUBLIC INSTITUTIONS.

Archaeological Department.

—— Annual Report of the Director of Archæology, Baroda State, 1934–35 [*etc.*]. [*Baroda,*] 1936– . 4°. I.S. c. 2.

BARODA, *State of.*

—— Archæology in Baroda, 1934–1947. A brief review. By A. S. Gadre. [With a map.] pp. iv. 39. pl. XXXVI. [*Baroda,*] 1947. 8°. I.S. c. **22/4.**

—— Gaekwad's Archaeological Series. *Baroda,* 1936– . 4°. I.S. c. **2/2.**

Department of Commerce, Industries, and Labour.

—— Report on the Marine Fisheries of the Baroda State in 1930 with suggestions for their further developments. By James Hornell. [With plates.] pp. v. 22. *Baroda,* 1930. fol. I.S. c. **6.**

APPENDIX.

—— The Gaikwari Raj. Being a reprint of the notices which appeared in the " Hitechhu " of Ahmedabad. (Baroda, 1873–1874. With suggestions for the improvement of the administration.) pp. 116. *Hitechhu Press: Ahmedabad,* 1875. 12°. **8022.** bb. **3.**

—— The Rulers of Baroda. pp. iii. 392. *Education Society's Press: Bombay,* 1879. 12°. **9056.** aa. **21.**

BARODA, CHIMNABAI, *Maharani of. See* CHIMṆĀ-BĀI, *Maharani of Baroda.*

BARODA, SAYAJI RAJ, *Maharaja Gaekwar of. See* SAYĀJĪ RĀU, *Maharajah Gaekwar of Baroda.*

BARODA GOODS TERMINUS. *See* BROOKE (Charles L.) Remarks on the pamphlet entitled " Reasons why the Baroda Goods Terminus should not be at Colaba," *etc.* 1868. 8°. **8235.** b. **58.** (**7.**)

BARODA STATE MUSEUM. *See* BARODA, *City of.*

BARODET (ALFRED)

—— Un Noble caractère: Alfred Barodet. Lettres, notes et pensées, suivies d'un journal du siège de Belfort. [With a portrait.] pp. 256. *Lyon & Villeurbanne,* 1932. 8°. **010920.** a. **46.**

BARODET (DÉSIRÉ) *See* EMION (P.) and PALLIER (T.) Barodet, candidat de Paris. [A biography.] 1873. 16°. **8051.** a. **78.**

—— *See* LYON ESE. Le Candidat Barodet. Sa vie . . . par un Lyonnais. 1873. 12°. **10662.** df. **5.**

—— Biographie de M. Barodet, ex-Maire de Lyon, candidat de la Démocratie républicaine. pp. 28. *Paris,* [1873.] 16°. **10661.** aa. **27.** (**3.**)

BARODET (G. A.) De la Banque en Angleterre. Aperçu sur son organisation et son fonctionnement dans le Royaume-Uni. pp. 161. iii. *Librairie du Courrier de l'Europe: Londres,* [1876.] 8°. **8229.** bb. **17.**

BARODIA (U. D.) *See* UMED-CHAND DOLAT-CHAND BAROḌIYĀ.

BAROETA Y ALDAMAR (JOAQUIN) *See* SANCHEZ SILVA (M.) Critica de los fueros de los Provincias de Alava, Guipuzcoa y Vizcaya. Discursos pronunciados . . . por . . . M. Sanchez Silva . . . y J. Baroeta y Aldamar, *etc.* 1864. 8°. **5384.** ff. **21.**

—— Barroeta Aldamar en el Senado, 1864. (Los Fueros y sus defensas. tom. 7.) [Speeches.] pp. xcvi. 127. *Bilbao.* 1898. 8°. [*Biblioteca Bascongada.* tom. 25.] **12231.ee.21.**

BAROFFIO (Felice) and **QUAGLIOTTI** (Alessandro) Alimentazione del soldato. Memoria onorata del primo premio al concorso Riberi, *etc.* 2 vol. pp. xxvi. 1199. 1860. 8°. *See* Italy.—*Ministero della Guerra.* **7390.** bb. **4.**

BAROGO. *See* Barogo-Niaizet.

BAROGO-NIAIZET ( )

—— Je n'dis qu'-ça', ou Y-a-gros, C.A.D. lettre particulière au Roi, par le facétieux Barogo, sur les deux traits historiques [*sic*] rappellés à S.M. par la Nation Françoise. *See* Louis xvi., *King of France.* [*Appendix.*] Dernière lettre du peuple au Roi, *etc.* 1787. 8°. **F. 864. (15.)**

—— [Another edition.] Je n'-dis qu'-ça, ou Y-a-gros, *etc.* *See* Louis xvi., *King of France.* [*Appendix.*] Lettre du peuple au roi, *etc.* [1787.] 8°. **R. 1. (1.)**

—— [Another copy.] Je n'dis qu'-ça', *etc.* *See* Louis xvi., *King of France.* [*Appendix.*] Dernière lettre du peuple au Roi, *etc.* 1787. 8°. **F.R. 4. (32.)**

—— Lettre de Barogo et consors, maîtres ramoneurs au Palais-Royal, à M. Figaro & Compagnie, négocians au Fauxbourg Saint-Germain. [An attack on the Italian comedians in Paris.] pp. 35. *Amsterdam,* 1786. 8°. **R. 185. (2.)**

BAROHN (Olof A.) *Resp.* *See* Bring, afterwards Lagerbring (S.) Monumenta Scanensia, *etc.* vol. 2. pt. 1. [1745, *etc.*] 4°. **152. b. 26.**

—— Dissertatio gradualis de territorio Oxie, *etc.* *Praes.* Dns. Svenbring. pp. 36. *Londini Gothorum,* 1754. 4°. **150. b. 21. (6.)**

BAROIS (Jean)

—— La Mecque, ville interdite. [With a portrait.] pp. 162. [*Paris,*] 1938. 8°. **010076. g. 43.**

BAROIS (Julien) L'Irrigation en Égypte . . . Extrait du Bulletin de la Direction de l'Hydraulique agricole. (Planches.) 2 pt. 1887. 8°. *See* France.—*Ministère de l'Agriculture et du Commerce.* **8777. i. 12.**

—— Irrigation in Egypt . . . Translated by Major A. M. Miller. [With maps.] pp. 113. 1889. 4°. [*U.S. House Miscellaneous Documents.* 50th Congress, 2nd Session. vol. 9.] *See* France.—*Ministère de l'Agriculture et du Commerce.* **A.S. 10/3.**

—— Les Irrigations en Égypte. pp. iv. 386. *Paris,* 1904. 8°. **8775. f. 39.**

—— Deuxième édition, revue et augmentée. pp. xvi. 422. *Paris,* 1911. 8°. **8776. ff. 48.**

—— Rapport sur les travaux géodésiques et topographiques de la Mission, *etc.* *See* France.—*Ministère des Travaux Publics.* Chemin de Fer Transsaharien. Documents relatifs à la Mission dirigée au Sud de l'Algérie, *etc.* vol. 1. 1890, *etc.* 4°. **08235. m. 28.**

BAROIS (Léon) Étude de diagnostic sur un cas de paralysie du grand oblique de l'œil droit. pp. 35. *Paris,* 1874. 4°. [*Collection des thèses soutenues à la Faculté de Médecine de Paris.* An 1874. tom. 1.] **7374. a. 6.**

BAROIS (Paul) Des accidents cérébraux dans le rhumatisme articulaire aigu. pp. 50. *Paris,* 1871. 4°. [*Collection des thèses soutenues à la Faculté de Médecine de Paris.* An 1871. tom. 1.] **7373. m. 15.**

BAROJA (Julio Caro) *See* Caro Baroja.

BAROJA (Pío) *See* Baroja y Nessi.

BAROJA (Ricardo) *See* Baroja y Nessi.

BAROJA (Serafín) *See* Baroja y Zornoza.

BAROJA DE CARO (Carmen)

—— El Encaje en España. pp. 197. pl. xxxi. *Barcelona, Buenos Aires,* 1933. 8°. **7742. aa. 55.**

BAROJA FERNANDEZ DE JUBERA (Manuel de) *See* Sanchez Pereyra (D.) Por el alferez D. M. de Baroja Fernandez de Jubera, preso en la Real Carcel de esta Corte, *etc.* 1721. fol. **6785. k. 2. (1.)**

BAROJA Y NESSI (Pío)

—— *See* Balseiro (J. A.) Blasco Ibáñez, Unamuno, Valle Inclán, Baroja. Cuatro individualistas, *etc.* [1949.] 8°. **11869. ff. 78.**

—— *See* Granjel (L. S.) Retrato de Pío Baroja. [1953.] 8°. **10635. i. 44.**

called Azorin

—— *See* Martínez Ruiz (J.) La Fuerza del Amor . . . Prólogo de P. Baroja. [1901.] 8°. **11725. df. 10.**

—— *See* Pérez Ferrero (M.) Pío Baroja en su Rincón . . . Biografía. 1941. 8°. **10633. r. 36.**

—— *See* Pina (F.) Pío Baroja. 1928. 8°. **10634. df. 29.**

—— Ein Gerechter.—Der Abgrund. [" Un Justo " and " La Sima," translated by M. Spiro.] *See* Spiro (M.) Meisternovellen spanischer Autoren, *etc.* [1915.] 8°. **12491. s. 40.**

—— Los Espectros del Castillo. Las Familias Enemigas. La Caja de Música. Los Herejes Milenaristas. La Pasión Igualitaria. pp. 183. *Barcelona,* 1941. 8°. **12332. a. 44.**

—— Los Impostores Joviales, y el Tesoro del Holandés, Yan-Si-Pao o la svástica de oro, los Buscadores de tesoros, *etc.* [With illustrations and a portrait.] pp. 431. *Madrid,* 1941. 8°. **12492. a. 5.**

—— Los Amores de Antonio y Cristina. pp. 64. *Madrid,* 1953. 8°. [*La Novela del sábado.* año 1. no. 5.] **P.P. 4075. dcd.**

—— Los Amores Tardíos. Novela. (Agonías de nuestro tiempo.) pp. 213. *Madrid,* [1927.] 8°. **12490. w. 22.**

—— El Aprendiz de Conspirador. (Memorias de un hombre de acción.) pp. 291. *Madrid,* 1913. 8°. **12489. r. 39.**

—— Aquí París. (Recuerdos.) pp. 267. *Madrid,* 1955. 8°. **10636. a. 19.**
Colección " El Grifón." vol. 22.

—— El Arbol de la Ciencia. Novela. (La Raza.) pp. 355. *Madrid,* 1911. 8°. **12489. s. 14.**

—— The Tree of Knowledge . . . Translated . . . by Aubrey F. G. Bell. pp. 329. *A. A. Knopf: New York,* 1928. 8°. **12489. t. 25.**

—— Aurora Roja. Novela. (La Lucha por la vida.) pp. 370. *Madrid,* 1904. 8°. **12489. g. 33.**

—— Aventuras, inventos y mixtificaciones de Silvestre Paradóx. (Novela.) pp. 284. *Madrid,* [1902.] 8°. **12489. cccc. 11.**

—— Aviraneta, o la vida de un conspirador. [With a portrait.] pp. 328. *Madrid*, 1931. 8°. **10633**. pp. **33**.

—— La Busca. Novela. (La Lucha por la vida.) pp. 321. *Madrid*, 1917. 8°. **12490**. r. **8**.

—— Los Buscadores de Tesoros. pp. 16. [*Madrid*,] 1940. 8°. **12492**. b. **5**.

—— El Caballero de Erlaiz. [With a portrait.] pp. 395. *Madrid*, [1943.] 8°. **12491**. a. **47**.

—— El Cabo de las Tormentas. Novela. (La Selva oscura.) pp. 300. [*Madrid*, 1932.] 8°. **12488**. s. **33**.

—— Camino de perfección. Novela. (Pasión mística.) pp. 251. *Madrid*, 1913. 8°. **12489**. s. **36**.

—— Los Caminos del Mundo. (Memorias de un hombre de acción.) pp. 391. *Madrid, Buenos Aires*, 1914. 8°. **12490**. pp. **7**.

—— Canciones del Suburbio, *etc.* [With a portrait.] pp. 324. *Madrid*, 1944. 8°. **11453**. b. **21**.

—— La Canóniga. Novela. pp. 93. *Madrid*, [1929.] 8°. **12488**. p. **18**.

—— El Cantor vagabundo, *etc.* (Saturnales.) pp. 317. *Madrid*, 1950. 8°. **12942**. aaa. **27**.

—— El Capitán Mala Sombra. pp. 159. *Madrid*, 1953. 16°. **12489**. a. **52**.
Colección " *Más allá*." vol. 101.

—— La Casa de Aizgorri. Novela en siete jornadas. pp. 227. *Bilbao*, 1900. 8°. [*Biblioteca Bascongada*. tom. 52.] **12231**.ee.*21*

—— [Another edition.] pp. 234. *Madrid*, 1911. 8°. **12489**. s. **13**.

—— Los Caudillos de 1830. Novela. pp. 290. [*Madrid*,] 1918. 8°. **12489**. p. **38**.

—— La Caverna del Humorismo. pp. 352. *Madrid*, 1919. 8°. **012350**. ff. **10**.

—— César ó nada. Novela. (Las Ciudades.) pp. 468. *Madrid*, 1910. 8°. **12489**. s. **8**.

—— Caesar or Nothing . . . Translated . . . by Louis How. pp. 337. *Jonathan Cape: London; printed in U.S.A.*, 1922. 8°. **12489**. ppp. **11**.

—— Chopin y Jorge Sand, y otros ensayos. pp. 248. *Barcelona*, 1941. 8°. **10797**. a. **15**.

—— La Ciudad de la Niebla. Novela. (La Raza.) pp. 314. *Madrid*, 1909. 8°. **12489**. r. **15**.

—— [Another edition.] pp. 283. *Lóndres, Paris*, [1912.] 8°. [*Collección Española Nelson*.] **012200**. k. **6/2**.

—— Comunistas, Judíos y Demás Ralea . . . Segunda edición. pp. 286. *Valladolid*, 1939. 8°. **08042**. b. **62**.

—— Con la Pluma y con el Sable. Crónica de 1820 á 1823. (Memorias de un hombre de acción.) pp. 430. *Madrid, Buenos Aires*, 1915. 8°. **12489**. tt. **16**.

—— Los Confidentes audaces. Novela. (Memorias de un hombre de acción.) pp. 305. *Madrid*, 1931. 8°. **12488**. s. **13**.

—— Los Contrastes de la Vida. (Memorias de un hombre de acción.) pp. 241. *Madrid*, [1920.] 8°. **12490**. tt. **1**.

—— Crítica arbitraria. [Articles published by Baroja as dramatic critic of " El Globo " in the year 1902.] pp. 63. *Madrid*, 1924. 16°. **11795**. a. **47**.

—— Crónica escandalosa. (Memorias de un hombre de acción.) pp. 266. *Madrid*, [1935.] 8°. **12488**. ppp. **22**.

—— Cuentos. tom. 1–4. *Madrid*, [1919.] 16°. **12490**. de. **12**.
No more published.

—— El Cura Santa Cruz y su partida. (Folletos de Actualidad.) pp. 29. [*Madrid*,] 1918. 8°. **10634**. aa. **10**.

—— La Dama de Urtubi, y otras historias. pp. 170. *Madrid*, [c. 1953.] 16°. **12489**. a. **51**.
Colección " *Más allá*." vol. 100.

—— La Dama Errante. Novela. (La Raza.) pp. 274. *Madrid*, 1908. 8°. **12489**. p. **9**.

—— [Another edition.] pp. 283. *Paris*, [1916.] 8°. [*Colección Española Nelson*.] **012200**. k. **6/19**.

—— Desde el Principio hasta el Fin. (Memorias de un hombre de acción.) pp. 256. *Madrid*, [1935.] 8°. **12488**. ppp. **24**.

—— Desde la última vuelta del camino. Memorias. 7 vol. *Madrid*, 1944–49. 8°. **10636**. e. **7**.
Vol. 3 *is of the second edition.*

—— El Diablo a Bajo Precio. Prólogo de Federico de Onis. [Essays. With portraits.] pp. 125. *Barcelona*, [1942.] 16°. **12352**. a. **74**.

—— Divagaciones apasionadas. pp. 241. *Madrid*, [1924.] 8°. **12490**. t. **27**.

—— Divagaciones sobre la cultura. pp. 127. *Madrid*, [1920.] 8°. **12350**. b. **9**.

—— Los Enigmáticos. Historias. pp. 159. *Madrid*, [1952.] 8°. **12487**. p. **33**.
Colección Escritores célebres. no. 24.

—— Entretenimientos. Dos sainetes y una conferencia. pp. 181. *Madrid*, [1926.] 8°. **11725**. df. **19**.

—— El Escuadrón del Brigante. Novela. (Memorias de un hombre de acción.) pp. 407. *Madrid*, 1913. 8°. **12490**. pp. **3**.

—— La Estrella del Capitán Chimista. Novela. (El Mar.) pp. 334. *Madrid*, [1930.] 8°. **12488**. pp. **15**.

—— Fantasías Vascas. pp. 160. *Buenos Aires, México*, 1941. 8°. **12489**. r. **32**.

—— La Feria de los Discretos. Novela. (El Pasado.) pp. 346. *Madrid*, 1917. 8°. **12490**. r. **2**

—— Las Figuras de Cera. Novela. (Memorias de un hombre de acción.) pp. 290. *Madrid*, [1924.] 8°. **12490**. t. **26**.

—— El Gran Torbellino del Mundo. Novela. (Agonías de nuestro tiempo.) pp. 359. *Madrid*, [1926.] 8°. **12490**. dd. **37**.

—— Las Horas Solitarias. Notas de un aprendiz de psicólogo. pp. 413. *Madrid*, 1918. 8°. **012350**. ff. **1**.

—— El Horroroso Crimen de Peñaranda del Campo y otras historias. pp. 184. *Madrid*, [1928.] 8°. **11728**. ccc. **11**.

—— El Hotel del Cisne. pp. 104. *Madrid*, 1954. 8°. **12489**. t. **36**.

Revista literaria. no. 1197.

—— Humano Enigma. Novela. (Memorias de un hombre de acción.) pp. 326. *Madrid*, 1928. 8°. **12489**. w. **16**.

—— Idilios y Fantasías. pp. 236. *Madrid*, 1918. 8°. **012354**. df. **35**.

—— Las Inquietudes de Shanti Andía. Novela. (El Mar.) pp. 381. *Madrid*, 1911. 8°. **12489**. s. **12**.

—— [Another edition.] Edited with introduction, notes, and vocabulary by Laurence D. Bailiff . . . and Maro Beath Jones. pp. xii. 222. *Chicago*, 1930. 8°. [*University of Chicago Junior College Series.* Spanish.] Ac. **2691**. d/**35**. (C. **6**.)

—— [Las Inquietudes de Shanti Andía.] De Onrust van Shanti Andía. (Vertaling: E. Straat.) *In:* De Gids. jaarg. 118. no. 1, *etc.* 1955– . 8°. P.P. **4595**.
Printed on green paper.

—— Intermedios. pp. 348. *Madrid*, [1931.] 8°. **12488**. t. **22**.

—— La Isabelina. (Memorias de un hombre de acción.) pp. 330. *Madrid*, 1919. 8°. **12489**. p. **41**.

—— Juan van Halen, el oficial aventurero. [With plates, including a portrait.] pp. 359. *Madrid*, 1933. 8°. **10633**. s. **32**.

—— Juventud, egolatría. pp. 348. *Madrid*, 1917. 8°. **12354**. s. **32**.

—— La Juventud Perdida. Las noches del buen retiro. Novela. pp. 320. *Madrid*, [1934.] 8°. **12488**. ppp. **10**.

—— El Cura de Monleón, *etc.* (La juventud perdida.) pp. 359. *Madrid*, [1936.] 8°. **12491**. t. **51**.

—— El Laberinto de las Sirenas. Novela. (El Mar.) Segunda edición. pp. 356. *Madrid*, [1924.] 8°. **12491**. dd. **34**.

—— Laura, o la Soledad sin remedio. Novela. pp. 414. *Buenos Aires*, 1939. 8°. **12492**. a. **3**.

—— La Leyenda de Jaun de Alzate. pp. 308. *Madrid*, 1922. 8°. **11726**. bbb. **35**.

—— Locuras de carnaval. pp. 160. *Madrid*, [1952.] 8°. **12487**. p. **29**.

Colección Escritores célebres. no. 4.

—— Mala Hierba. Novela. (La Lucha por la vida.) pp. 336. [*Madrid*,] 1918. 8°. **12470**. p. **29**.

—— Las Mascaradas sangrientas. Novela. (Memórias de un hombre de acción.) pp. 334. *Madrid*, [1927.] 8°. **12490**. w. **40**.

—— El Mayorazgo de Labraz. pp. 303. *Barcelona*, 1903. 8°. **12489**. dd. **18**.
Part of the " Biblioteca de Novelistas del siglo xx."

—— [Another edition.] pp. 270. *Madrid*, 1919. 8°. **12489**. pp. **9**.

—— The Lord of Labraz . . . Translated . . . by Aubrey F. G. Bell. pp. xv. 251. *A. A. Knopf: New York & London*, 1926. 8°. **12491**. d. **38**.

—— Momentum Catastrophicum. (Los mitos de los aliadófilos.) pp. 90. *Madrid*, 1919. 8°. **8042**. e. **53**.

—— El Mundo es ansí. Novela. (Las Ciudades.) pp. 322. *Madrid*, 1912. 8°. **12490**. cc. **7**.

—— La Nave de los Locos. Novela. (Memorias de un hombre de acción.) pp. 395. *Madrid*, 1925. 8°. **12490**. tt. **42**.

—— El Nocturno del Hermano Beltrán. pp. 272. *Madrid*, 1929. 8°. **12488**. p. **27**.

—— Nuevo Tablado de Arlequín. [Literary sketches, followed by a collection of articles entitled " Alrededor de la Guerra."] pp. 240. [*Madrid*,] 1917. 8°. **012350**. df. **17**.

—— La Obsesión del misterio, *etc.* pp. 80. *Madrid*, [1952.] 8°. **12487**. p. **35**.
Novelistas de hoy. vol. 1.

—— El País vasco. [With illustrations and maps.] pp. 519. *Barcelona*, 1953. 8°. **10163**. ee. **10**
Part of the series: " Guías de España."

—— Paradox, Rey. Novela. pp. 286. *Madrid*, 1906. 8°. **12489**. cccc. **36**

—— Paradox, King. A novel . . . Translated by Nevil Barbour. pp. viii. 260. *Wishart & Co.: London* 1931. 8°. **12488**. s. **9**

—— Pequeños ensayos. pp. 299. *Buenos Aire* 1943. 8°. **12360**. de.

—— Los Pilotos de Altura. Novela. (El Mar.) pp. 332 *Madrid*, [1929.] 8°. **12488**. pp. **14**

—— Rapsodias. pp. 260. *Madrid*, [1936.] 8°. **12357**. s. **32**

—— Los Recursos de la Astucia. (Memorias de un hombr de acción.) pp. 354. *Madrid*, 1915. 8°. **12490**. pp. **1**

—— La Ruta del Aventurero. Novela. (Memorias de u hombre de acción.) pp. 428. *Madrid*, 1916. 8°. **12490**. r.

—— El Sabor de la Venganza. Segunda edición. (Memori de un hombre de acción.) pp. 255. *Madrid*, [1921.] 8 **12490**. p. **2**

—— La Selva Oscura. La Familia de Errotacho. pp. 30 *Madrid*, [1932.] 8°. **12488**. t. **2**

—— La Senda dolorosa. Novela. (Memorias de un homb de acción.) pp. 348. *Madrid*, 1928. 8°. **12489**. w. **1**

—— La Sensualidad pervertida, *etc.* (Las Ciudades.) pp. 393. *Madrid*, [1920.] 8°. **12489**. p. **4**

—— Siluetas Románticas, y otras historias de pillos y extravagantes. pp. 308. *Madrid*, [1934.] 8°. **12356**. ppp.

—— Susana. Novela. pp. 212. *San Sebastián*, 1938. 8° **12491**. t.

—— El Tablado de Arlequín. [Miscellaneous essays.] pp. 2 *Madrid*, [1928.] 8°. **012352**. bb.

—— Las Tragedias Grotescas. Novela. (El Pasad pp. 274. *Madrid*, 1920. 8°. **12489**. p.

—— Un Trepador. pp. 15. *Madrid*, [1950.] 8°. **12492**. aa.

La novela corta. no. 41.

BAROJA Y NESSI (Pío)

—— Los Últimos Románticos. Novela. (El Pasado.) pp. 318. *Madrid*, 1906. 8°. **12489**. g. **37**.

—— [Another edition.] pp. 315. *Madrid*, 1919. 8°. **12490**. p. **18**.

—— Las Veleidades de la Fortuna. Novela. (Agonías de nuestro tiempo.) pp. 299. *Madrid*, [1926.] 8°. **12490**. w. **23**.

—— La Veleta de Gastizar. Novela. (Memorias de un hombre de acción.) pp. 238. [*Madrid*,] 1918. 8°. **12490**. p. **15**.

—— La Venta de Mirambel. Novela. (Memorias de un hombre de acción.) pp. 269. *Madrid*, 1931. 8°. **12488**. s. **14**.

—— Vidas Sombrías. pp. 236. *Madrid*, [1925.] 8°. **12491**. d. **36**.

—— Los Visionarios. (La Selva oscura.) pp. 315. *Madrid*, [1932.] 8°. **12488**. t. **16**.

—— Vitrina Pintoresca. pp. 284. *Madrid*, [1935.] 8°. **12488**. t. **33**

—— Zalacaín el Aventurero, *etc.* pp. 278. *Madrid*, 1919. 8°. **12490**. ppp. **2**.

—— Zalacaín el Aventurero . . . Illustrated by R. Baroja. pp. xxxv. 292. *London*, 1935. 8°. [*Black's Spanish Readers.*] W.P. **10452/3**.

—— Zalacaín el Aventurero, *etc.* (Reprinted, with corrections.) pp. xxxv. 292. *London*, 1945. 8°. [*Black's Spanish Readers.*] W.P. **10452/5**.

—— Páginas escogidas. Selecciones y notas del autor . . . Edited with introduction, notes and vocabulary by S. L. Millard Rosenberg and Laurence D. Bailiff. [With a portrait.] pp. xxiv. 173. *A. A. Knopf: New York*, 1928. 8°. **012942**. bb. **20**.

BAROJA Y NESSI (Ricardo)

—— Bienandanzas y Fortunas. Novela histórica. pp. 244. *Barcelona*, 1941. 8°. **12492**. a. **4**.

—— Clavijo. Tres versiones de una vida. pp. 190. *Barcelona*, 1942. 8°. **010632**. b. **21**.

—— Gente del 98. pp. 188. *Barcelona*, 1952. 8°. **11869**. ff. **25**.

—— La Nao "Capitana." Cuento español del mar antiguo. Dibujos del autor. pp. 214. *Madrid*, 1935. 8°. **12470**. t. **6**.

—— Pasan y se van. Narración novelesca. pp. 241. *Barcelona*, 1941. 8°. **12491**. aaaa. **40**.

—— El Pedigree. Tres jornadas y un epílogo, *etc.* pp. 270. *Madrid*, [1926.] 8°. **11726**. d. **55**.

—— La Tribu del Halcón: cuento prehistórico de actualidad, y El Coleccionista de Relámpagos: novela. pp. 266. *Zaragoza*, [1940.] 8°. **12492**. a. **1**.

BAROJA Y ZORNOZA (Serafín) Hirni, ama alabac; drama en dos actos en vascuence y en verso . . . con su traduccion en prosa castellana. pp. 31. *Pamplona*, 1882. 8°. **11725**. ee. **14**. **(1.)**

BAROLA (Paolo) Ave Maris Stella esposto in versi, *etc.* pp. 35. *Roma*, 1844. 16°. **12314**. aa. **39**. **(3.)**

BAROLI (Pietro) Il Progresso, considerato nei suoi rapporti scientifici e sociali. Memoria religioso-filosofico-storico-politica. pp. viii. 343. *Milano*, 1842. 8°. **1389**. b. **21**.

BAROLIN (Johannes C.) Der Hundertstundentag. Vorschlag zu einer Zeitreform unter Zugrundelegung des Dezimalsystems, im Anschluss an ein analoges Bogen- und Längenmass. pp. 142. *Wien & Leipzig*, 1914. 8°. **8560**. c. **62**.

—— Nationality and Peace. pp. 7. [*Vienna*, 1922.] 8°. **8425**. s. **31**.

BAROLITANUS (Marianus Sanctus) *See* Sanctus (M.)

BAROLLI (Girolamo) Orazione panegirica pel Padovano Santuario volgarmente detto Arcella. Con relative annotazioni del C. P. M. Pier Giuseppe Casser, *etc.* pp. 35. *Padova*, 1814. 8°. **4605**. aaa. **27**.

BAROLO, Giulia Falleti, *Marchioness di.* *See* Falleti (Julie Victoire Françoise)

BAROLO, Julie Victoire Françoise Falletti, *Marchioness di.* *See* Falletti.

BAROM (Thomas) Mr. Thomas Barom, Esquire, his Relation of the state of Bandonbridge in Ireland, *etc.* *See* London.—iii. *Tower of London.* Divers Remarkable Occurrences . . . in the Tower, *etc.* 1642. 4°. E. **154**. **(20.)**

BAROMETER. The Aneroid Barometer, how to buy and how to use it. By a Fellow of the Meteorological Society. pp. 32. *Houlston & Wright: London*, 1869. 8°. **8755**. aaa. **40**. **(4.)**

—— Forty-fifth thousand. pp. 32. *Houlston & Sons: London*, 1902. 8°. **8758**. bb. **30**.

BAROMETER CHART. Barometer and Thermometer Chart. *E. G. Wood: London*, [1864.] *s. sh.* 4°. **1811**. a. **1**. **(15.)**

BAROMETERS. Economic Barometers, *etc.* pp. 56. *Geneva*, 1924. 8°. [*International Labour Office. Studies and Reports.* ser. N. no. 5.] **U.N.H.17.**

BARON.

—— Baron and Feme. A treatise of the common law concerning husbands and wives . . . The second edition, with large additions. pp. 422. *John Walthoe: London*, 1719. 8°. **1479**. aaa. **15**.

—— Baron and Feme. A treatise of law and equity, concerning husbands and wives . . . The third edition; in which are added many cases in law and equity, from the best books of reports. pp. 485. *T. Waller: London*, 1738. 8°. **515**. d. **29**.

—— [Another copy.] **228**. g. **27**.

—— The Baron's Daughter. A ballad by the author of Poetical Recreations [i.e. William C. Hazlitt]. pp. 20. F.P. *Ballantyne, Hanson & Co.: Edinburgh*, 1877. 4°. **11651**. h. **6**.

—— Songs, Duets, Chorusses &c. in the Musical Comedy of the Baron [by Miles P. Andrews]. pp. 22. *T. Cadell: London*, 1781. 8°. **11777**. c. **7**.

BARON, *pseud.* [i.e. Baron Stirling Henry Nahum.]

—— Baron at the Ballet. Introduction and commentary by Arnold L. Haskell, *etc.* [Photographs.] pp. 222. *Collins: London*, 1950. 4°. **7920**. k. **12**.

—— Have you a Camera? [With illustrations.] pp. 71. *Frederick Muller: London*, 1955. 8°. **8913**. d. **29**.

BARON, *pseud.* [i.e. BARON STIRLING HENRY NAHUM.]

—— Our Young Prince. A Royal Family Album, *etc.* *Country and Sporting Publications: [London*, 1949–] fol. **W.P.3791.**

BARON, *pseud.* [i.e. BARON STIRLING HENRY NAHUM], and **GRAHAM** (CLIVE)

—— Great Horses of the Year 1954-1955 [*etc.*]. 1954– . 8°. *See* PERIODICAL PUBLICATIONS.—*London.* P.P. **2489**. dgb.

BARON BRUKENTHALISCHES MUSEUM. *See* HERMANSTADT.—*Brukenthal'sches Museum.*

BARON ( ) [For the Lettish surname in this form:] *See* BARONS.

BARON ( ) *Chef du deuxième Bataillon de la Charente Inférieure.* Aux vrais et fidelles défenseurs de la patrie. (Qualités que doit avoir un général, et ses devoirs.) pp. 12. [1795?] 8°. F. **940**. **(24.)**

—— Précis, justificatif de l'innocence opprimée & persécutée par la tyrannie et l'arbitraire, quoiqu'elle devroit avoir disparue [*sic*] du sol de la liberté. [In defence of his military conduct.] pp. 11. [1793?] 8°. F. **1004**. **(12.)**

BARON ( ) *Mrs. See* BIESENTHAL (J. H. R.) "Aus dem Cheder" . . . Translated from the German by Mrs. Baron, *etc.* [1903.] 8°. **4033**. df. **57**.

BARON (ACARIE) *See* ACARIE-BARON.

BARON (A.) *Journalist.*

—— Le Petit homme rouge. [Edited by M. Fournier and A. Baron.] 1848. fol. **Hendon.**

BARON (ABRAHAM LOUIS)

—— Handbook of Antibiotics. pp. viii. 303. *Reinhold Publishing Corporation: New York*, 1950. 8°. **7511**. cc. **12**.

BARON (ADOLPHE PIERRE) Essai sur la métrite aiguë. Tribut académique, *etc.* pp. 15. *Montpellier*, 1833. 4°. **1181**. f. **13**. (**14**.)

BARON (ALBERT HEYEM NACHMEN) *See* RIBOT (T. A.) Essay on the Creative Imagination . . . Translated . . . by A. H. N. Baron. 1906. 8°. **08461**. g. **45**.

BARON (ALEXANDER) *Novelist. See* BARON (Joseph A.)

BARON (ALEXANDER) *Scotus.*

—— Disputatio inauguralis medica, de tussi convulsiva. pp. 51. *Balfour, Auld & Smellie: Edinburgi*, 1768. 8°. T. **264**. (**1**.)

BARON (ALFRED) Der Haus- und Grundbesitzer in Preussens Städten, einst und jetzt. Unter Berücksichtigung von Steins Städteordnung. pp. xii. 154. *Halle*, 1911. 8°. [*Sammlung nationalökonomischer und statistischer Abhandlungen.* Bd. 65.] Ac. **2320**.

BARON (ANDRÉ) *See* also DASTÉ (Louis) *pseud.* [i.e. A. Baron.]

—— Les Sociétés secrètes, leurs crimes depuis les initiés d'Isis jusqu'aux Francs-Maçons modernes. pp. xi. 383. *Paris*, 1906. 8°. **04785**. l. **22**.

BARON (ANTOINE) De l'éclampsie puerpérale. pp. 26. *Paris*, 1853. 4°. [*Collection des thèses soutenues à la Faculté de Médecine de Paris.* An 1853. tom. 1.] **7372**. f. **3**.

—— Mémoire sur trente-sept cas de maladies utérines recueillies et traitées aux Eaux de La Motte, Isère. pp. 26. *Grenoble*, 1861. 8°. **7580**. d. **5**.

BARON (ARNAUD) *See* COSTE (Adolphe) Les Questions sociales contemporaines . . . Observations de MM. A. Baron, E. Chevalet, *etc.* 1886. 8°. **8277**. cc. **40**.

—— L'Idée de la commune. pp. 164. *Paris*, 1879. 12°. **8051**. a. **46**. (**12**.)

—— Le Paupérisme. Ses causes et ses remèdes. (Premier prix du concours Pereire.) pp. xii. 326. *Paris; Lausanne* [printed], 1882. 8°. **8276**. ff. **21**.

BARON (AUGUSTE) *Dramatist.* Le Chevalier coquet, comédie-vaudeville en un acte. pp. 34. *Paris*, [1853.] 8°. [*Bibliothèque dramatique.* tom. 52.] **2296**. c. **21**.

—— [Another edition.] pp. 10. *Paris*, [1855.] fol. [*Théâtre contemporain illustré.* livr. 178, 179.] **2296**. h.

BARON (AUGUSTE) *of Limoges.* Excursions de pélerins et voyageurs en Asie, à la Terre-Sainte, en Chine, dans l'Inde, etc., etc. pp. 163. *Limoges*, [1869.] 8°. **10027**. f. **15**.

—— Naufrage de la Méduse. pp. 72. *Limoges*, [1869.] 8°. **10027**. bb. **12**.

BARON (AUGUSTE) *of Lyons.* Histoire de Lyon pendant les journées des 21, 22 et 23 novembre 1831, contenant les causes, les conséquences et les suites de ces déplorables événements, *etc.* pp. 288. *Lyon*, 1832. 8°. **10171**. ccc. **13**.

BARON (AUGUSTE ALEXIS FLORÉAL) *See* BELGIANS. Les Belges illustres. Par J. Altmeyer, A. Baron, F. Carron, *etc.* 1844, *etc.* 8°. **1321**. f. **2**, **3**.

—— *See* BELGIUM. [*Appendix.—Historical.*] Gloires nationales. Album biographique de Belges célèbres, texte par Messieurs Gachard . . . A. Baron, *etc.* [1860.] 4°. **10760**. g. **10**.

—— *See* BIOGRAPHIE. Biographie universelle, *etc.* [Edited by A. A. F. Baron.] 1843, *etc.* 8°. **1330**. h. **1**.

—— *See* CALLINUS. Poésies militaires de l'antiquité, ou Callinus et Tyrtée, texte grec, traduction . . . prolégomènes et commentaires; par A. Baron. 1835. 8°. **11335**. f. **15**.

—— *See* HEEREN (A. H. L.) Manuel de l'histoire ancienne . . . Traduction entièrement refondue et augmentée d'une introduction sur l'étude de l'histoire ancienne par M. Baron. 1834. 12°. **1432**. b. **5**.

—— *See* HOPE (Thomas) *Esq.* Histoire de l'architecture . . . Traduite . . . par A. Baron. 1839. 8°. **1264**. d. **9**.

—— *See* MEENEN (P. F. van) Lettre de M. van Meenen . . . sur la philosophie. 1818. De la construction française, par M. van Meenen . . . Précédées d'un avant-propos de l'éditeur (A. Baron). 1840. 12°. **8469**. aa. **22**.

—— *See* NOËL (François J. M.) and LA PLACE (G. F. M. J. de) Leçons françaises de littérature et de morale . . . Vingt-deuxième édition. Augmentée . . . d'un résumé de l'histoire de la littérature française, par A. Baron. 1848. 8°. **12239**. h. **9**.

—— *See* NOËL (François J. M.) and LA PLACE (G. F. M. J. de) Leçons françaises de littérature et de morale . . . Vingt-huitième édition, augmentée . . . par A. Baron. 1862. 8°. **12236**. g. **12**.

—— Œuvres complètes. tom. 1–5. *Bruxelles*, 1853–60. 8°. **830**. d. **19**.

No more published.

BARON (AUGUSTE ALEXIS FLORÉAL)

—— Coup d'œil sur l'état actuel des arts, des sciences, etc. en Belgique. *See* BELGIUM. La Belgique monumentale, *etc.* 1844. 8°. [*Panthéon National.* vol. 5, 6.] [Appendix.-Topography.] **1321. f. 4.**

—— Discours prononcé à la séance publique de la Classe des Beaux-Arts de l'Académie Royale de Belgique, le 25 septembre 1850. (Extrait du tome XVII. n° 9, des Bulletins.) pp. 20. [*Brussels*, 1850.] 8°. **7857. bbb. 37. (7.)**

—— Discours prononcé par M. Baron, à l'installation de l'Université Libre. pp. 30. *See* BRUSSELS.—*Université Libre de Belgique.* Université Libre. Procès-verbal de la séance d'installation, *etc.* 1834. 8°. **T. 2100. (6.)**

—— Histoire abrégée de la littérature française depuis son origine jusqu'au XVIIe siècle. 2 tom. *Bruxelles*, 1841. 8°. **818. f. 21.**

—— Lettres et entretiens sur la danse, *etc.* pp. 344. *Paris*, 1824. 8°. **7907. bbb. 13.**

—— Lettres à Sophie sur la danse, suivies d'entretiens sur les danses ancienne, moderne, religieuse, civile et théatrale . . . Avec planche. pp. 344. *Paris*, 1825. 8°. Hirsch **1721.**

—— Le Marquis de Sy et M. Poupar. [A letter from A. A. F. Baron to S. van de Weyer on the relation between the translation of Horace's Ars Poetica by the Marquis de Sy, published in 1816, and that published under the name of J. B. Poupar in 1828, with van de Weyer's reply.] pp. 70. [1857.] *See* LONDON.—III. *Philobiblon Society.* Bibliographical and Historical Miscellanies. vol. 3. 1854, *etc.* 8°. Ac. **9120.**

—— [Another copy, with a different titlepage.] *Londres*, 1857. 8°. **11385. bb. 8.**

—— Mosaïque belge, mélanges historiques et littéraires. pp. xxviii. 284. *Bruxelles*, 1837. 8°. **12356. aa. 34.**

BARON (AUGUSTE FERDINAND JOSEPH) Les Derniers jours d'un soldat (J.-B. Racth) condamné à mort, publiés [from a letter of A. Baron] par M. le comte Anatole de Ségur . . . Quatrième édition. pp. 65. *Paris*, 1860. 24°. **4866. a. 6.**

—— Le Directoire des aumôniers de l'armée française pour le temps de paix et le temps de guerre établi d'après la loi du 20 mai 1874, *etc.* pp. xi. 550. *Paris*, [1874.] 12°. **8825. bbb. 10.**

—— L'Aumônerie militaire. Aux nouveaux aumôniers militaires, *etc.* (Resneignements [*sic*] et avis . . . extraits par une réunion d'aumôniers . . . du Directoire des aumôniers . . . de M. l'abbé Baron.) pp. 16. *Paris*, [1874.] 12°. **8831. aaa. 1. (6.)**

BARON (BARCLAY) *See* CLAYTON (Philip T. B.) Letters from Flanders . . . With a preface and notes by B. Baron. 1932. 8°. **010905. e. 72.**

—— The Doctor. The story of John Stansfeld of Oxford and Bermondsey, *etc.* [With a portrait.] pp. xi. 228. pl. VIII. *Edward Arnold & Co.: London*, 1952. 8°. **10863. bb. 25.**

—— Girolamo Mocetto, painter-engraver. (Estratto da "Madonna Verona.") [With plates.] 2 pt. *Verona*, 1909, 10. 8°. **07808. ee. 18. (6.)**

—— The Growing Generation: a study of working boys and girls in our cities. pp. xiv. 192. *Student Christian Movement: London*, [1911.] 8°. **08282. ff. 30.**

BARON (BARCLAY)

—— The Light of the Lamp. As produced at the 11th Toc H Birthday Festival, *etc.* (pt. 2. Abridged and adapted from "The Unknown Warrior," by the authors M. Creagh Henry and D. Marten.) [With musical notes.] 2 pt. *Toc H British Headquarters: London*, 1926. 4°. M.F. **690. xx. (1.)**

BARON (C.) *F.C.W.A.*

—— *See* BARRETT (G. E.) and BARON (C.) Consumers' Master Record: a suggested model. 1946. 4°. W.P. **9138/207.**

BARON (CARL MORITZ) Geschichte der Leibesübungen. Eine kurze und populäre Darstellung der Gymnastik bei den Alten und ihrer Weiterentwickelung bis auf die Gegenwart . . . Zweiter unveränderter Abdruck. pp. 86. *Chemnitz*, 1868. 8°. **7908. aa. 6.**

BARON (CASIMIR) Faculté de Droit de Paris. Thèse pour le doctorat. (Droit romain. De captivis et postliminio reversis.) pp. 47. *Versailles*, 1858. 8°. **5406. aaa. 2. (23.)**

BARON (CHARLES) *Médecin du Bureau Central des Hôpitaux.* De la pleurésie dans l'enfance, *etc.* pp. 186. *Paris*, 1841. 4°. [*Collection des thèses soutenues à la Faculté de Médecine de Paris.* An 1841. tom. 1.] **7371. c. 1.**

—— Mémoires sur la nature et le développement des produits accidentels. (Extrait du tome XI des Mémoires de l'Académie Royale de Médecine.) pp. vi. 160. *Paris*, 1845. 4°. **7410. e. 9.**

BARON (CHARLES) *Officier d'administration*, and **LASSALLE** (CHARLES JEAN)

—— Dictionnaire des communes . . . 22e édition [of the work by C. J. Lassalle] . . . entièrement mise à jour par le commandant Repain. pp. 1681. *Paris*, 1938. 8°. **10175. c. 5.**

—— Dictionnaire des communes . . . Édition 1949, entièrement mise à jour par le Commandant Repain. pp. 1531. *Paris*, 1949. 8°. **10175. ff. 25.**

BARON (CHARLES) *Président de la Commission des Mines et de la Force motrice.*

—— Au pays de l'or noir. Bakou—Grozny—le pétrole russe. [With plates and maps.] pp. 174. *Paris, Liège*, 1934. 8°. **07104. ee. 18.**

BARON (CHARLES) *Professor at Clermont-Ferrand.* De Platonis dicendi genere. Facultati litterarum Parisiensi thesim proponebat C. Baron, *etc.* pp. 75. *Paris*, [1891.] 8°. **8460. ee. 44.**

—— Le Pronom relatif et la conjonction en grec et principalement dans la langue homérique, *etc.* pp. 188. *Paris*, 1891. 8°. **12923. de. 2.**

BARON (CHARLOTTE ELIZABETH) Archie's King, *etc.* pp. 217. *Gall & Inglis: London*, [1903.] 8°. **04412. f. 59.**

—— Phil's Hero; or, a Street Arab's resolve, *etc.* pp. 248. *R.T.S.: London*, [1907.] 8°. **04429. e. 21.**

—— Rebels. [A tale.] pp. 142. *Gall & Inglis: London & Edinburgh*, [1902.] 8°. **012803. b. 29.**

BARON (CL. CHIVAS) *See* CHIVAS-BARON.

BARON (DAVID)

—— *See* SAPHIR (A.) Christ and Israel: lectures and addresses on the Jews . . . Collected and edited by D. Baron, *etc.* 1911. 8°. **04034. eee. 47.**

BARON (DAVID)

—— The Ancient Scriptures and the Modern Jew. pp. 342. *Hodder & Stoughton: London*, 1900. 8°. **04034**. eee. **22**.

—— Fifth edition. pp. xv. 305. *Morgan & Scott: London*, [1918.] 8°. **4034**. e. **4**.

—— A Divine Forecast of Jewish History. A proof of the supernatural element in Scripture. pp. 89. *Morgan & Scott: London*, [1905.] 8°. **03128**. f. **43**.

—— The History of Israel: its spiritual significance. A series of connected expositions. pp. viii. 310. *Morgan & Scott: London*, [1925.] 8°. **03149**. f. **48**.

—— The History of the Ten " Lost " Tribes: Anglo-Israelism examined. pp. 85. *Morgan & Scott: London*, 1915. 8°. **04034**. eee. **66**.

—— Israel's Inalienable Possessions, *etc.* pp. 93. *Morgan & Scott: London*, [1906.] 8°. **4033**. de. **33**.

—— The Jewish Problem, its solution; or, Israel's present and future . . . Introduction by Rev. A. T. Pierson. pp. 78. *F. H. Revell Co.: Chicago, New York*, [1891.] 8°. **4034**. de. **37**.

—— New edition . . . revised. pp. 70. *Morgan & Scott: London*, [1894.] 8°. **4034**. i. **41**.

—— La Question juive et sa solution . . . Traduit par D. Lortsch. pp. viii. 79. *Lyon*, [1900.] 8°. **04034**. ee. **36**.

—— Jews and Jesus . . . Being a study of Dr. Joseph Klausner's " Jesus of Nazareth—His Time, His Life, and His Teaching." pp. 62. *Hebrew Christian Testimony to Israel: Northwood*, [1927.] 8°. **4807**. aaa. **40**.

—— Rays of Messiah's Glory; or, Christ in the Old Testament. pp. 274. *Hodder & Stoughton: London*, 1886. 8°. **4227**. f. **26**.

—— The Servant of Jehovah: the sufferings of the Messiah and the glory that should follow. An exposition of Isaiah LIII. pp. xii. 158. *Morgan & Scott: London*, 1922. 8°. **03187**. i. **54**.

—— The Servant of Jehovah . . . An exposition of Isaiah LIII. (New edition.) pp. xiv. 158. *Marshall, Morgan & Scott: London, Edinburgh*, [1954.] 8°. **3228**. b. **54**.

—— The Shepherd of Israel and his scattered flock. A solution of the enigma of Jewish history. pp. xii. 133. *Morgan & Scott: London*, 1910. 8°. **4516**. bbb. **14**.

—— Types, Psalms, and Prophecies: being a series of Old Testament studies. pp. xi. 377. *Hodder & Stoughton: London*, 1906. 8°. **03149**. f. **9**.

—— Third, revised, edition. pp. xv. 377. *Morgan & Scott: London*, [1924.] 8°. **3149**. ddd. **28**.

—— The Visions & Prophecies of Zechariah . . . An exposition. pp. xii. 554. *Morgan & Scott: London*, 1918. 8°. **03187**. ee. **42**.

BARON (DENIS)

—— *See* KAPLAN (Louis) and BARON (D.) Mental Hygiene and Life, *etc.* [1952.] 8°. W.P. **13777/2**.

BARON (EDGAR) Lettre ouverte à Édouard Drumont. [On his anti-semitic principles. Together with " Protestation d'un propriétaire contre l'extension abusive donnée à son droit."] 2 pt. *Fontenay-le-Comte*, 1896. 8°. **4034**. k. **42**.

—— Suite aux lettres ouvertes à Édouard Drumont. Lettre ouverte à l'Abbé * * *. pp. 126. *Fontenay-le-Comte*, 1897. 8°. **4034**. k. **43**.

BARON (EDGAR)

—— Suite aux lettres ouvertes à Drumont et à l'Abbé * * *. Lettre ouverte au T. R. P. Ollivier des Frères Prêcheurs. pp. 121. *Fontenay-le-Comte*, 1898. 8°. **4034**. k. **44**.

—— Suite aux lettres ouvertes à Drumont, à l'Abbé * * * et au R. P. Ollivier. Deuxième lettre ouverte à l'Abbé * * *. pp. 91. *Fontenay-le-Comte*, 1899. 8°. **04034**. ee. **26**.

BARON (ÉGUINAIRE) *See* BRITTANY. Coustumes generalles des Pays et Duche de Bretaigne, *etc.* (Index rerum insigniorum consuetudinem [*sic*] Britanniæ celticæ [by E. Baron], *etc.*) 1540. 4°. **5423**. b. **5**.

—— *See* HENRYSON (E.) Eduardi Henrysonis pro E. Barone aduersus A. Goueanum de iurisdictione libri II, *etc.* 1555. 8°. **5255**. a. **20**

—— —— 1752. fol. [MEERMAN (G.) *Novus thesaurus juris civilis.* tom. 3.] **18**. h. **8**.

—— De diuiduis et indiuiduis obligationibus commentarii, *etc.* *See* TRACTATUS. Primum [*etc.*] volumen tractatuum, *etc.* vol. 5. 1549. fol. **5305**. i.

—— [Another edition.] *See* TRACTATUS. Tractatus vniuersi iuris, *etc.* tom. 6. pt. 2. 1584. fol. **499**. f. **8**.

—— De ratione docendi, discendique juris civilis. *See* OPUSCULA. Variorum opuscula ad cultiorem jurisprudentiam adsequendam pertinentia. tom. 1. 1769, *etc.* 8°. **1375**. c. **1**.

BARON (ÉMILE) Faculté de Droit de Paris. Thèse pour la licence, *etc.* (Jus Romanum. De contrahenda emptione. —Droit français. De la nature et de la forme de la vente.) pp. 51. *Paris*, 1859. 8°. **5406**. b. **8**. **(18.)**

BARON (ERNST GOTTLIEB) Ernst Gottlieb Barons . . . Abriss einer Abhandlung von der Melodie. pp. 12. *Berlin*, 1756. 4°. **7898**. g. **15**.

—— Ernst Gottlieb Barons . . . Historisch-theoretisch und practische Untersuchung des Instruments der Lauten, *etc.* [With a portrait.] pp. 218. *Nürnberg*, 1727. 8°. **785**. c. **45**

—— [Another copy.] Ernst Gottlieb Barons . . . Historisch theoretisch und practische Untersuchung des Instrument der Lauten, *etc.* *Nürnberg*, 1727. 8°. Hirsch IV. **1471**

BARON (ÉTIENNE)

—— Les Principales puissances économiques du monde, *etc.* [With illustrations and maps.] pp. 477. *Paris*, 1946. 8°. **010004**. g. **57**.

BARON (F.) *Writer for Children.*

—— Chums Divided. pp. 19. *Gerald G. Swan: London* [1947.] 8°. [*Schoolgirls' Pocket Library.* no. 25.] **012643**. t. **1/25**.

—— The Dragon Contest, and other stories [by variou authors]. pp. 32. *London; Dublin* printed, [1945.] 8° [*Mellifont Press Children's Series.*] W.P. **9916/95**

—— The Flodden Rubies. pp. 180. *Gerald G. Swan London*, 1947. 8°. **12830**. eee. **2**

—— The King Works Magic. pp. 32. *London & Dublin Dublin* printed, [1947.] 8°. [*Mellifont Press Children Series.*] W.P. **9916/11**

—— The Mystery of the Silver Statuette. pp. 192. *Gerald G. Swan: London*, 1948. 8°. **12827**. e. **9**

—— Olive Dawson's Secret. *G. G. Swan: London* [1946.] 16°. **12638**. a. **8**

BARON (F.) *Writer for Children.*

—— Pip Kin Seeks the Wizard (by F. Baron), and other stories. pp. 32. *London; Dublin* printed, [1946.] 8°. [*Mellifont Children's Series.*] W.P. **9916/97.**

—— Prince Bigfrown's Spell (by F. Baron), and other stories [by various authors]. pp. 32. *London & Dublin; Dublin* printed, [1947.] 8°. [*Mellifont Press Children's Series.*] W.P. **9916/116.**

BARON (F. POCHAT) *See* POCHAT-BARON.

BARON (FÉLIX) De la glucosurie ou diabète sucré. pp. 30. *Paris,* 1853. 4°. [*Collection des thèses soutenues à la Faculté de Médecine de Paris.* An 1853. tom. 1.] **7372.** f. **3.**

BARON (FRANÇOIS) *Archiviste.* Le Cardinal Pierre de Foix le vieux, 1386–1464, et ses légations. pp. 205. *Amiens,* 1920. 8°. **4863.** g. **3.**
The wrapper bears the date 1920–1922.

BARON (FRANÇOIS) *Colonial Administrator.*

—— Les Frontières du bonheur. pp. 308. [*Paris,*] 1954. 8°. **012551.** t. **26.**
Part of the series "*L'Air du temps.*"

BARON (FRANÇOIS) *of La Lozère.* Quelques soldats lozériens de 1805 à 1813. Extrait du Moniteur de la Lozère, *etc.* pp. 31. *Mende,* 1915. 8°. **010168.** e. **42.**

BARON (FRANÇOIS) *of the Compagnie des Indes Orientales.*

—— *See* BOUREAU DESLANDES (A.) Les Premières relations de la Compagnie française des Indes et du Siam au XVIIe siècle, *etc.* (Lettre écrite de Siam à M. le Directeur Général Baron par le Sieur Deslandes Boureau le 26 décembre 1682.) [1942.] 8°. **8232.** i. **30.**

BARON (FRANÇOIS) *Rev., of Weybridge.* Parents: their position, privileges, and prospects. A New Year's address, *etc.* pp. 16. *Sunday School Union: London,* [1875.] 8°. **4193.** a. **1.** **(5.)**

BARON (FRANÇOIS DÉSIRÉ) Traité théorique et pratique de la fabrication des draps unis et nouveautés, *etc.* pp. 103. pl. 15. *Paris,* [1860?] 4°. **7953.** l. **6.**

BARON (FRANÇOIS LOUIS JÉRÔME) Projet de l'organisation, de l'administration des Eaux et Forêts, proposé au Comité des Domaines, *etc.* pp. 30. *Paris,* 1790. 8°. **F.R. 243.** **(5.)**

BARON (FRANÇOIS MARIE) Dissertation sur quelques points de l'histoire du traitement des hernies étranglées avec gangrène; thèse, *etc.* pp. 22. *Paris,* 1836. 4°. **1184.** g. **16.** **(4.)**

BARON (FRANK) *Novelist.*

—— George Waring's Choice. [A novel.] pp. viii. 306. *Ward & Downey: London,* 1892. 8°. **012641.** k. **23.**

BARON (FRANK) *of Truro.*

—— The City of Truro . . . The official handbook of the Truro City Council. pp. 36. [1917.] 8°. *See* TRURO. **10354.** a. **913.**

—— Cornish Yarns, *etc.* pp. 88. *John W. Saundry: Penzance,* [1953.] 8°. **12646.** i. **39.**

—— Ma'tha Madder. A Cornish character. (Reprinted.) pp. 87. *John W. Saundry: Penzance,* [1952.] 8°. **12699.** b. **1.**

BARON (GEORGE) No-Body his Complaint. A dialogue between Master No Body, and Doctour Some-Body. A delightfull discourse. **B.L.** *B. Alsop: London,* 1652. 8°. **E. 1351.** **(5.)**

BARON (GEORGE) *Organizing Tutor, University of London Institute of Education.*

—— A Bibliographical Guide to the English Educational System. pp. 70. *Athlone Press: London,* 1951. 8°. **B.B.c.e.7.**

—— [Another copy.] A Bibliographical Guide to the English Educational System. *London,* 1951. 8°. **2744.s.1.**

BARON (GODOFREDUS) Disputationem juridicam de jure domesticorum . . . subjicit G. Baron . . . M.DC.LXXII. . . . Denuo edita. *Praes.* S. Strykius. pp. 43. *Sumptibus J. Schrey & H. J. Meyer: Francofurti ad Viadrum,* 1683. 4°. **5510.** aa. **5.**

—— [Another edition.] 1743. *See* STRYKIUS (S.) Viri . . . illustris . . . S. Strykii . . . opera omnia. vol. 2. 1743, *etc.* fol. **498.** g. **4.**

BARON (GUILLAUME CASIMIR) Considérations générales sur les maladies catarrhales, *etc.* pp. 23. *Montpellier,* an VII [1799]. 4°. **1180.** d. **5.** **(5*.)**

BARON (H.) *Ingénieur en chef.* École Nationale des Ponts et Chaussées. Catalogue descriptif des modèles, instruments et dessins des galeries de l'École. pp. x. 557. 1873. 8°. *See* PARIS.—*École des Ponts et Chaussées.* **08768.** dd. **5.**

BARON (HANS)

—— *See* BRUNI (L.) *Aretino.* [*Two or more Works.*] Leonardo Bruni Aretino. Humanistisch-philosophische Schriften, mit einer Chronologie seiner Werke und Briefe. Herausgegeben und erlaütert von Dr. H. Baron. 1928. 8°. **012227.** d. **8.**

—— *See* TROELTSCH (E.) Deutscher Geist und Westeuropa . . . Herausgegeben von H. Baron. 1925. 8°. **08072.** a. **80.**

—— *See* TROELTSCH (E.) Spektator-Briefe . . . Herausgegeben von H. Baron. 1924. 8°. **08072.** a. **71.**

—— Calvins Staatsanschauung und das konfessionelle Zeitalter. pp. viii. 121. *Berlin, München,* 1924. 8°. [*Historische Zeitschrift.* Beiheft 1.] **P.P. 3548.** ac.

—— Cicero and the Roman Civic Spirit in the Middle Ages and the Early Renaissance . . . Reprinted from the "Bulletin of the John Rylands Library," *etc.* pp. 28. *Manchester University Press: Manchester,* 1938. 8°. **11312.** m. **73.**

—— The Crisis of the Early Italian Renaissance. Civic humanism and republican liberty in an age of classicism and tyranny. [With plates.] 2 vol. pp. xxix. 656. *Princeton University Press: Princeton,* 1955. 8°. **9169.** e. **24.**

—— [Another copy.] **9171.** d. **1.**

—— Humanistic and Political Literature in Florence and Venice at the Beginning of the Quattrocento. Studies in criticism and chronology. pp. x. 223. *Harvard University Press: Cambridge,* Mass. 1955. 8°. **11871.** ee. **25.**

—— [Another copy.] **11870.** bb. **40.**

BARON (HAROLD) Chemical Industry on the Continent. A report to the electors to the Gartside Scholarships. pp. xi. 71. *Manchester,* 1909. 8°. [*University of Manchester Publications.* Economic series. no. 11.] **Ac. 2671/2.**

BARON (HARRY)

—— Magic Simplified. [With illustrations.] pp. 112. *Nicholas Kaye: London*, [1954.] 8°. **7950**. b. **30**.

—— My Best Card Trick . . . Edited by H. Baron. [With illustrations.] pp. 31. *Ridgmount Books: London*, 1953. 8°. **7917**. bbb. **39**.

BARON (HAYM SALOMON) Haym Salomon, immigrant and financier of the American Revolution. pp. 107. *Bloch Publishing Co.: New York*, 1929. 8°. **10885**. aa. **6**.

BARON (HEINRICH)

—— Mit Karl Roos—dem Blutzeugen des deutschen Elsass—die letzten Tage in der Todeszelle. Bericht. [With plates, including a portrait.] pp. 45. [*Strasburg*,] 1940. 8°. **010709**. l. **61**.

BARON (HENRI) Li Banquet d'Warfusaie. Drame historique ès cinq akes . . . d'après Weustenrad . . . Li scinne si passe à Lîge en 1637. pp. 88. *Liége*, 1899. 8°. **11740**. ee. **56**.

—— Les Deux cusennes. Comèdeie è deux ackes. pp. 54. *Liége*, 1884. 8°. **11740**. aaa. **28**. (**3**.)

—— Houbert et Jenniton. Vaudeville-opérette ès in' ake. pp. 28. *Liége*, 1884. 8°. **11740**. aaa. **28**. (**4**.)

BARON (HENRI CHARLES ANTOINE) *See* ARIOSTO (L.) [*Orlando Furioso.—French.*] Roland Furieux . . . Illustrations par T. Johannot, Baron, *etc.* 1864. 8°. **11426**. k. **13**.

—— *See* ARTISTES. Les Artistes anciens et modernes. [Lithographs by H. Baron and others.] [1848, *etc.*] fol. Dept. of Prints & Drawings.

—— *See* CASTELLAN (T.) Le Roi des Albums . . . Dessins de Alophe, Baron, *etc.* [1860.] *obl.* 4°. **1754**. a. **16**.

—— *See* CHALLAMEL (J. B. M. A.) Les Français sous la Révolution . . . Avec . . . scènes . . . dessinés par H. Baron. [1843.] 8°. **1442**. k. **14**.

—— *See* LURINE (L.) and BROT (C. A.) Les Couvents . . . Illustrés par MM. T. Johannot, Baron, *etc.* 1846. 8°. **4071**. f. **16**.

—— *See* PAULIN (V.) Guerre d'Italie en 1859; tableau historique . . . Illustré de . . . gravures sur bois d'après . . . des dessins . . . par MM. Bahers, Baron, *etc.* 1859. fol. **1781**. a. **26**.

—— *See* PHILIPON DE LA MADELAINE (V.) L'Orléanais. Histoire des ducs et du duché d'Orléans . . . Illustrée par MM. Baron, Français, *etc.* 1845. 4°. **10171**. h. **11**.

—— *See* TASSO (T.) [*La Gerusalemme Liberata.—French.*] La Jérusalem délivrée . . . Édition illustrée par MM. Baron et C. Nanteuil. 1841. 8°. **1463**. k. **13**.

BARON (HENRY)

—— Martin Claims Damages. A sporting romance . . . Illustrated by Michael Lyne. pp. vii. 266. *Country Life: London*, 1937. 8°. NN. **28067**.

BARON (HENRYK WŁADYSŁAW) *See* ORWID (Wł.) Henryk Baron. Życiorys. 1910. 8°. **10600**. aaa. **4**. (**4**.)

BARON (HERBERT S.)

—— *See* BLUM (Arno A.) and ROSENBAUM (M.) The Law relating to Trading with the Enemy. By A. Blum . . . and M. Rosenbaum . . . with the collaboration of H. S. Baron. 1940. 8°. **6428**. ppp. **15**.

BARON (HYACINTHE THÉODORE) *the Elder*. [For dissertations at which H. T. Baron acted as Praeses:] *See* BARON D'HÉNOUVILLE (T.) LE MONNIER (L. G.) COCHON DU PUY (G.)

—— Quæstio medica, an dysentericis affectibus sanguinis missio? *Praes.* L. de Mondières Dugué. pp. 4. [*Paris*, 1709.] 4°. **1182**. e. **4**. (**96**.)

—— Question de médecine, dans laquelle on examine, si c'est aux médecins qu'il appartient de traiter les maladies vénériennes . . . Par M***, Docteur Régent de la Faculté de Médecine de Paris [i.e. H. T. Baron]. pp. 28. 1735. 4°. *See* M***, *Docteur Régent de la Faculté de Médecine de Paris*. **551**. d. **2**. (**4**.)

BARON (HYACINTHE THÉODORE) *the Younger*. *See* BOUVART (M. P.) Consultation contre la légitimité des naissances prétendues tardives. [By Bouvart, Baron and others.] 1765. 8°. T. **1069**. (**13***.)

—— *Praes.* *See* GAUTIER DU ROCHER (F. N.) Quaestio medica, an, vt sanandis, sic et praecauendis pluribus morbis, aquae nouae minerales Passiacae? *etc.* 1760. 4°. [SIGWART (*G. F.*) *Quaestiones medicae Parisinae*, *etc.* fasc. 2.] **1179**. b. **18**.

—— *Praes.* *See* HAZON (J. A.) Quæstio medica . . . An solvendis pertinacibus sanguinis in cerebro congestionibus, *etc.* 1734. 4°. **1182**. e. **5**. (**76**.)

—— Quæstio medica, an longior jucundiorque vita sobrietatis obligata legibus? *Praes.* F. Afforty. pp. 4. [*Paris*,] 1731. 4°. **1182**. e. **4**. (**76**.)

—— Quæstio medica, an variolis narcotica? *Praes.* C. Vergne. pp. 4. [*Paris*,] 1731. 4°. **1182**. e. **4**. (**37**.)

—— [Another copy.] **1182**. e. **4**. (**73**.)

—— Quæstio medico-chirurgica . . . an fracto cranio semper admovenda terebra? *Praes.* P. Le Tonnelier. pp. 4. [*Paris*,] 1732. 4°. **1182**. e. **4**. (**50**.)

—— [Another edition.] *Resp.* T. Baron d'Hénouville. *See* SIGWART (G. F.) Quaestiones medicae Parisinae, *etc.* fasc. 1. 1759, *etc.* 4°. **1179**. b. **17**.

—— Catalogue de différens objets de curiosité, qui composoient le cabinet de feu M. Baron. pp. 12. *Paris*, 1788. 8°. **439**. l. **16**. (**2**.)

—— Catalogue de la bibliothèque de feu M. Baron. [Preceded by a biographical sketch.] pp. xx. 349. 142. *Paris*, 1788. 8°. **439**. l. **16**. (**1**.)

BARON (J. F.) Dissertation sur l'air des hôpitaux, *etc.* pp. 36. *Paris*, 1808. 4°. **1182**. h. **1**. (**4**.)

BARON (J. M. A. AUGUSTE) Thèse pour le doctorat en médecine, *etc.* (Essai sur les luxations incomplètes de la hanche.) pp. 27. *Paris*, 1838. 4°. **1184**. i. **5**. (**1**.)

BARON (JACQUES) *Licencié ès droits*. Origine, genealogie, et demonstration: de ceste excellente, et heroyque maison de Lorraine, et Guyse en dependente, *etc.* [By J. Baron.] pp. 30. 1589. 8°. *See* LORRAINE, *House of*. **9200**. aaa. **50**.

BARON (JACQUES) *Writer of Verse*. Peines perdues, *etc.* pp. 116. *Paris*, 1933. 8°. **011482**. de. **75**.

BARON (JAMES) *B.D.* *See* BARRON.

BARON (JAMES W.) Vagabonds and Rogues. pp. 29. *M. Waller: Hull*, [1889.] 8°. **8411**. aaa. **54**. (**4**.)

BARON (JAUME) Tresor pera als vius, y almoyner del purgatori lo rosari de Maria Santissima que componguè en castellà lo M. R. P. M. Fr. J. Baron . . . Traduhit en català per lo M. R. Francisco Roca, *etc.* pp. 276. FEW MS. NOTES. *Vich*, [1752.] 8°. **1360**. a. **8**.

BARON (JEAN). Description de l'église cathédrale Notre-Dame d'Amiens . . . Publiée par Edmond Soyez, *etc.* pp. ix. 244. *Amiens,* 1900. 8°. **7814.** i. **11.**

BARON (JOHANNES) J. Z. Barons. Rododaphnée ofte: Persiaensche heldinne. Treur-spel. [In verse.] pp. 37. *Voor den Autheur: Leyden,* 1651. 4°. **11755.** aa. **3.** *Slightly cropped.*

BARON (JOHN) *Fellow of Balliol College, Oxford.* The Case of Glocester Hall, in Oxford, rectifying the false stating thereof by Doctor Woodroffe. [By J. Baron.] pp. 57. [1702?] 4°. *See* WOODROFFE (Benjamin) **731.** k. 8. (1.)

—— A Sermon preach'd June 1. 1699. at Feckenham, Worcester-shire, before the Trustees appointed by Sir Thomas Cookes . . . to manage his charity given to that place. pp. 37. *Leon. Lichfield: Oxford,* 1699. 4°. **694.** g. **6.** (**2***.)

BARON (JOHN) *M.D.* Delineations of the Origin and Progress of various Changes of Structure which occur in man, and some of the inferior animals; being the continuation of works already published on this subject. pp. 56. pl. 4. *Longman & Co.: London,* 1828. 4°. **784.** n. **7.**

—— An Enquiry illustrating the Nature of Tuberculated Accretions of Serous Membranes; and the origin of tubercles and tumours in different textures of the body. With engravings. pp. viii. 6–307. 2. *Longman & Co.: London,* 1819. 8°. **549.** g. **25.** (**4.**)

—— [Another copy.] **956.** k. **16.**

—— Illustrations of the Enquiry respecting Tuberculous Diseases. [With plates.] pp. xxxii. 233. 3. *T. & G. Underwood: London,* 1822. 8°. **1187.** f. **9.**

—— [Another copy.] MS. MEMORANDUM [by Edward Jenner]. C. **61.** h. **6.**

—— The Life of Edward Jenner . . . with illustrations of his doctrines, and selections from his correspondence. [With portraits.] 2 vol. *Henry Colburn: London,* 1827, 38. 8°. **551.** c. **7, 8.**

—— *See* VIGORNIENSIS, *pseud.* An Historical Review of the Nature and Results of Vaccination, as unfolded in Dr. Baron's Life of Jenner. 1838. 8°. **551.** a. **30.**

—— —— 1869. 8°. **7561.** d. **31.**

BARON (JOHN) *Rector of Upton Scudamore. See* ENGLAND.—*Church of England.* [*Constitutions and Canons.—Constitutiones Provinciales.*] A Collection of the Laws and Canons of the Church of England . . . A new edition. [With notes and a preface by J. Baron.] 1850, *etc.* 8°. **2204.** d. **12.**

—— Anglosaxon Witness on Four Alleged Requisites for Holy Communion, Fasting, Water, Altar Lights, and Incense. [With illustrations.] pp. viii. 121. *Rivingtons: London,* 1869. 8°. **4326.** cc. **7.**

—— The Greek Origin of the Apostles' Creed illustrated by ancient documents and recent research. [With plates.] pp. xix. 95. *Parker & Co.: Oxford & London,* 1885. 8°. **3506.** f. **41.**

—— Report on the Anglosaxon Documents in Wilkins's Concilia. pp. 40. *Printed for private circulation: Oxford,* 1859. 8°. **4110.** b. **21.** (**4.**)

BARON (JOHN) *Rector of Upton Scudamore.*

—— Scudamore Organs, or practical hints respecting organs for village churches and small chancels, on improved principles . . . With designs by George Edmund Street. pp. 67. pl. 7. *Bell & Daldy: London,* 1858. 8°. **7895.** c. **2.**

—— Second edition revised, with postscript, and further steps. pp. xxii. 112. 8. pl. 7. *Bell & Daldy: London,* 1862. 8°. **7896.** c. **30.**

—— Scudamore Organs: Further Steps. Part I. Containing notices—extracts from reviews—letter to the "Ecclesiastic." (Part II. Containing letter to the "Ecclesiologist"—quotations in support of the principles of Scudamore Organs, &c.—Mr. Willis's Prospectus.) 2 pt. *J. Wright & Co.: Bristol,* 1858. 8°. **7896.** c. **37.** (**7.**)

BARON (JOSEPH) *of Blackburn.* All about the English Lakes. A cyclopedia of places, persons, myths and happenings. [With plates.] pp. 194. *Atkinson & Pollitt: Kendal,* 1925. 8°. **010368.** g. **27.**

—— Blackburn Rovers: the Blackburn Weekly Telegraph's handy history of the famous "Blue and Whites" from origin to 1906–7. pp. ii. 62. [*Blackburn,* 1906.] 16°. **07905.** de. 9.

—— James Sharples, blacksmith and artist. pp. 59. *Jarrold & Sons: London,* [1894.] 8°. **10827.** a. 30.

—— The Lancashire Almanack for 1917. In the Lancashire dialect. By J. Baron. [1916.] 8°. *See* EPHEMERIDES. P.P. **2507.** ui.

—— A Lankisher Dickshonary. Revised version . . . Fourth edition. [With a portrait.] pp. 154. *Advance Press: Blackburn,* 1907. 8°. **12987.** a. 40.

BARON (JOSEPH) *of Montpellier.* De la pneumonie typhoïde. Thèse, *etc.* pp. 64. *Montpellier.* 1876. 4°. **7379.k.14.(15.)**

BARON (JOSEPH ALEXANDER)

—— From the City, from the Plough. [A novel.] pp. 224. *Jonathan Cape: London,* 1948. 8°. NN. **38244.**

—— The Golden Princess. pp. 402. *Jonathan Cape: London,* 1954. 8°. NNN. **6132.**

—— The Human Kind, *etc.* pp. 187. *Jonathan Cape: London,* 1953. 8°. **10863.** aa. **41.**

—— Rosie Hogarth. pp. 342. *Jonathan Cape: London,* 1951. 8°. NNN. **1996.**

—— There's no Home. pp. 223. *Jonathan Cape: London,* 1950. 8°. NNN. **140.**

—— With Hope, Farewell. pp. 256. *Jonathan Cape: London,* 1952. 8°. NNN. **2726.**

BARON (JOSEPH STÉPHANE) De la ménopause—age critique. pp. 31. *Paris,* 1851. 4°. [*Collection des thèses soutenues à la Faculté de Médecine de Paris.* An 1851. tom. 1.] **7372.** d. **8.**

BARON (JULIUS) *Avocat en Parlement.* L'Art heraldique, contenant la maniere d'apprendre facilement la blason. Enrichy des figures necessaires pour l'intelligence des termes . . . Derniere edition, plus ample . . . que l[es] [p]recedentes impressions. pp. 199. *C. Osmont: Paris,* 1681. 8°. **9904.** aa. **11.** *With an additional titlepage, engraved. The printed titlepage is slightly mutilated.*

—— Nouvelle édition, revûë, corrigée & augmentée. Par A. Playne. pp. 291. *Paris,* 1717. 8°. **9904.** b. **24.** *With an additional titlepage, engraved.*

BARON (JULIUS) *Professor an die Universität Berlin.* Abhandlungen aus dem preussischen Recht. pp. iv. 143. *Berlin,* 1860. 8°. **5655.** bb. **3.**

—— Abhandlungen aus dem römischen Civilprozess. 3 vol. *Berlin,* 1881–87. 8°. **5254.** c. **3.**

—— Angriffe auf das Erbrecht. Mit einer Nachschrift über die social-democratischen Wahlen. pp. 39. *Berlin,* 1877. 8°. [*Deutsche Zeit- und Streit-Fragen.* Jahrg. 6. Hft. 85.] **12209.** f.

—— Das Budgetrecht des Reichstages. Von einem Conservativen [i.e. J. Baron]. pp. 28. 1867. 8°. *See* KONSERVATIVER. **8227.** bbb. **16.**

—— Die Gesammtrechtsverhältnisse im Römischen Recht. pp. xvi. 536. *Marburg & Leipzig,* 1864. 8°. **5207.** bb. **3.**

—— Geschichte des Römischen Rechts. Tl. 1. Institutionen und Civilprozess. pp. xii. 471. *Berlin,* 1884. 8°. **5254.** cc. **5.**

No more published.

—— Das Heirathen in alten und neuen Gesetzen. pp. 44. *Berlin,* 1874. 8°. [*Sammlung gemeinverständlicher wissenschaftlicher Vorträge.* Ser. 9. Hft. 211.] **12249.** l. **9.**

—— Pandekten. pp. xxv. 949. *Leipzig,* 1872 [1871, 72]. 8°. **5206.** bb. **4.**

Published in parts.

—— Siebente, verbesserte Auflage. pp. xx. 776. *Leipzig,* 1890. 8°. **5206.** d. **10.**

—— Peregrinenrecht und Ius gentium. Festschrift zum fünfzigjährigen Doctorjubiläum von Rudolph von Jhering am 6. August 1892 dargebracht von J. Baron. pp. 40. *Leipzig,* 1892. 8°. **6005.** h. **26.** (**6.**)

BARON, afterwards **BETTERTON** (KATHLEEN DIANA)

—— *See* EDWARD (William A.) Teach Yourself Latin . . . Completely revised by K. Baron. 1938. 8°. W.P. **706/7.**

—— *See* EDWARD (William A.) Teach yourself Latin . . . Based on the work of W. A. Edward, revised by K. Baron, *etc.* 1948. 8°. W.P. **706/93.**

—— *See* THORNTON (G. H.) Teach Yourself Good English . . . Completely revised and enlarged by K. Baron. 1938. 8°. W.P. **706/6.**

—— Bringing up Children. pp. 192. *English Universities Press: London,* 1951. 8°. [*Teach yourself Books.*] W.P. **706/121.**

—— Teach Yourself to Spell. A guide to good spelling, *etc.* pp. 238. *English Universities Press: London,* 1939. 8°. [*E.U.P. Books.*] W.P. **706/20.**

—— Teach Yourself to Write. pp. 208. *London,* 1942. 8°. [*E.U.P. Teach Yourself Books.*] W.P. **706/39.**

BARON (L.) *Agronome.* La Science des campagnes. Terres cultivables, amendements et engrais. pp. viii. 135. *Paris,* [1861?] 16°. **7075.** a. **12.**

BARON (L. J.) Aperçu sur les phlegmasies considérées en général, et sur la puogénie ou formation du pus, considérée en particulier. Tribut académique, *etc.* pp. 142. *Montpellier,* 1811. 4°. **1180.** g. **3.** (**12.**)

BARON (LAZAR' IZRAILEVICH)

—— Вторичное дробление и выпуск руды. pp. 284. *Москва,* 1950. 8°. **7112.** b. **2.**

BARON (LEO) and **MEREDITH** (ADAM)

—— The Baron System of Contract Bridge. pp. 180. *Contract Bridge Equipment: Leeds,* 1948. 8°. **7917.** e. **69.**

—— Contract Bridge. The Baron system outlined, *etc.* pp. 32. *Nicholson & Watson: London,* 1946. 8°. **7918.** b. **25.**

BARON (LÉONCE) Coudekerque. Coudekerque-Branche. Essai de monographie. [With plates and maps.] pp. xvi. 178. xxxiv. *Dunkerque,* 1923. 8°. **010169.** h. **21.**

BARON (M. A.)

—— Реактивные структуры внутренних оболочек—серозных, мозговых, синовиальных, эндокарда и амниона. pp. 463. *Ленинград,* 1949. 8°. **7407.** tt. **7.**

BARON (MARGARET)

—— The Mechanical Properties of Cheese and Butter. pp. 106. *Dairy Industries: London,* 1952. 8°. **7295.** pp. **17.**

BARON (MELVIN L.)

—— *See* SALVADORI (Mario G.) Numerical Methods in Engineering . . . With a collection of problems by M. L. Baron. 1952. 8°. **08774.** c. **41.**

BARON (MICHEL) *See* BOYRON.

BARON (P. ALEXIS) Flore des départemens méridionaux de la France, et principalement de celui de Tarn-et-Garonne, ou description des plantes qui croissent naturellement dans ces départemens, et de celles qu'on cultive communément dans les jardins, disposées suivant le système sexuel de Linné, *etc.* pp. xxxvi. 468. *Montauban,* 1823. 8°. **1145.** f. **6.**

BARON (P. J. B. LEGALCHER) *See* LEGALCHER BARON.

BARON (PETER) *D.D. See* BARO.

BARON (PETER) *Dissenting Minister.* A Sermon preach'd in Exeter, August the 24th, 1742. Being Bartholomew-Day, *etc.* pp. 23. *Aaron Tozer: Exon:,* 1742. 8°. **4474.** bbb. **6.**

BARON (PETER) *pseud.* [i.e. LEONARD WORSWICK CLYDE.] Jerry the Lag. pp. 329. *Selwyn & Blount: London,* 1928. 8°. NN. **15316.**

—— The Poacher. pp. 288. *Selwyn & Blount: London,* [1929.] 8°. NN. **16067.**

—— Who? pp. 304. *Selwyn & Blount: London,* [1927.] 8°. NN. **12841.**

BARON (PIERRE) *Abbé.*

—— Un Théologien laïc orthodoxe russe au XIXe siècle: Alexis Stépanovitch Khomiakov, 1804–1860. Son ecclésiologie —exposé et critique. pp. 293. *Roma,* 1940. 8°. [*Orientalia Christiana Analecta.* no. 127.] Ac. **2002.** bb.

BARON (PIERRE) *M.D.* Dissertation sur l'hygiène des nourrices, précédée de quelques considérations générales sur les avantages de l'allaitement maternel, *etc.* pp. 25. *Paris,* 1818. 4°. **1183.** e. **2.** (**21.**)

BARON (PIERRE) *Mayor of Étampes.* La Prise d'Étampes. Poëme latin inédit de Pierre Baron, maire de la ville en 1652. Traduit en français, avec le texte en regard & des notes & précédé d'une notice biographique sur l'auteur par Paul Pinson. pp. 45. *Paris,* 1869. 12°. **11405.** aaa. **16.**

BARON (PROSPER ANTOINE FRANÇOIS VIEILLARD) *See* VIEILLARD BARON.

BARON (R.) *Writer of Verse.*

—— England, Home and Other Poems. pp. 15. *Arthur H. Stockwell: Ilfracombe*, 1947. 8°. **11658.** ee. **11.**

BARON (R. J. B. A. M. A. ADOLPHE) Considérations générales sur le régime alimentaire dans les maladies, thèse, *etc.* pp. 21. *Paris*, 1833. 4°. **1184.** e. **15. (23.)**

BARON (RAOUL) Méthodes de reproduction en zootechnie. pp. vii. 500. *Paris*, 1888. 8°. **7291.** aaa. **26.**

BARON (REGINALD RUSSELL NEEDHAM) Exercises in French Free Composition for upper classes. pp. vii. 167. *Mills & Boon: London*, 1912. 8°. **12952.** s. **25.**

—— French Prose Composition. pp. viii. 125. *Methuen & Co.: London*, 1902. 8°. **12953.** df. **40.**

—— Eighth edition, enlarged. pp. vii. 152. *Methuen & Co.: London*, 1923. 8°. **12951.** b. **41.**

—— A Junior French Prose. pp. viii. 192. *London*, 1905. 8°. [*Methuen's Junior School Books.*] **012202.** aaa. **1/10.**

—— Eleventh edition, enlarged. pp. viii. 208. *London*, 1922. 8°. [*Methuen's Junior School Books.*] **012202.** aaa. **1/21.**

—— Key to a Junior French Prose. pp. 59. *Methuen & Co.: London*, 1921. 8°. **12951.** cc. **16.**

—— Mills & Boon's Direct Method French Texts. Edited by R. R. N. Baron. 5 pt. *Mills & Boon: London*, [1912–16.] 8°. **12951.** cc. **15.**

—— Tristapatte et Goret et autres contes tirés des Livres Roses Larousse. Edited by R. R. N. Baron. pp. vii. 129. *Mills & Boon: London*, [1915.] 8°. [*Direct Method French Texts.*] **12951.** cc. **15/5.**

BARON (RENÉ DIEUDONNÉ DENNE) *See* DENNE-BARON.

BARON (RICHARD) *Diakonus in Löwen. See* KRAUSE (C. W. A.) Die protestantischen Freunde und ihre erste Hauptversammlung in Breslau vertheidigt gegen den Herrn Diaconus Baron . . . Ein offenes Sendschreiben an denselben auf Veranlassung seines Berichtes in Nr. 33 des kirchlichen Anzeigers. 1845. 8°. **3910.** e. **64.**

—— Das Princip und die Versammlungen der protestantischen Freunde beleuchtet von Richard Baron . . . Offene Antwort auf das Sendschreiben an den Verfasser: Die protestantischen Freunde und ihre erste Hauptversammlung in Breslau &c. von C. W. A. Krause. pp. 29. *Breslau*, 1845. 8°. **3910.** e. **3.**

—— Zum confessionellen Frieden! Ein Neujahrsgruss an Katholiken und Protestanten. pp. 32. *Breslau*, 1845. 8°. **3910.** b. **8.**

BARON (RICHARD) *Dissenting Minister. See* BARRON.

BARON (RICHARD) *Missionary. See* PERIODICAL PUBLICATIONS.—*Antananarivo.* The Antananarivo Annual and Madagascar Magazine, *etc.* [no. 5–7 edited by R. Baron. no. 8–11, 13–24 edited by J. Sibree and R. Baron.] 1875, *etc.* 8°. P.P. **3800.** fg.

—— Botany, na filazana ny amy ny zara-maniry sy ny fombany . . . Notontaina fanindroany. pp. iv. 165. *Antananarivo*, 1888. 8°. **884.** h. **37.**

—— Geology. *Malagasy.* vol. 1. pp. vii. 191. *Antananarivo*, 1896. 8°. **07108.** g. **59.**

BARON (RICHARD) *of Oppeln. See* DANTE ALIGHIERI. [*Divina Commedia.—German.*] Dante Alighieri's Göttliche Comödie. Erste Abtheilung. Die Hölle. Neu metrisch übertragen mit Erläuterungen, von R. Baron. 1870. 8°. **11421.** ccc. **18.**

BARON (RICHARD) *of Oppeln.*

—— Der Deutschen Krieg und Sieg in Frankreich. 1870. 1871. Ein Buch für Volk, Heer und Schule. pp. 203. *Oppeln*, 1871. 8°. **9078.** cc. **24.**

—— Der deutsche Knabe in Amerika. Hold-Else's Wunderaugen. Zwei Erzählungen . . . Zweite Auflage. Mit 4 Stahlstichen. pp. 151. *Breslau*, 1866. 16°. **12803.** aaa. **10.**

—— Ein Landwehrmann. Eine Erzählung aus dem Sommerkriege von 1866 . . . Mit vier Stahlstichen. pp. 115. *Breslau*, 1867. 8°. **12808.** ff. **7.**

—— Preussens Krieg gegen Oesterreich und dessen Verbündete im Jahre 1866. Ein Gedenkbüchlein für Schule, Volk und Heer. pp. 85. *Oppeln*, 1866. 8°. **9386.** aaa. **19.**

BARON (ROBERT) *of Gray's Inn.* An Apologie for Paris. For rejecting of Juno, and Pallas, and presenting of Ate's golden ball to Venus, *etc.* pp. 96. *Th. Dring: London*, 1649. 8°. **112.** a. **53.**

—— Ἐροτοπαίγνιον or the Cyprian Academy. 2 pt. *Printed by W. W.; sold by J. Hardesty, etc.*: [*London*,] 1647. 8°. **643.** b. **19.**

With an additional titlepage, engraved. Imperfect; wanting the engraved portrait of Robert Baron.

—— [Another copy.] E. **1147. (1.)** *Imperfect; wanting the printed titlepage.*

—— [Another issue.] *London*, 1648. 8°. C. **71.** cc. **4.**

—— [Another copy.] G. **18846.** *Imperfect; wanting the engraved titlepage.*

—— Mirza. A tragedie, really acted in Persia, in the last age. Illustrated with historicall annotations. pp. 264. *Humphrey Moseley; T. Dring: London*, [1647.] 8°. E. **1449. (1.)**

—— [Another copy.] **643.** b. **20.**

—— [Another copy.] **162.** c. **5.**

—— Pocula Castalia. The Authors Motto, Fortunes Tennis-Ball. Eliza. Poems. Epigrams, &c. pp. 137. *W. H. for Thomas Dring: London*, 1650. 8°. E. **1221. (1.)**

BARON (ROBERT) *Professor of Divinity in Marischal College, Aberdeen. See* MICHEL (William) *Student in Divinity at Aberdeen.* Epitaphs vpon the vntymelie death of . . . William Michel, *etc.* (An Epitaph, or Consolatorie Epistle upon the death of the sayd young man . . . By M. R. B. Preacher of the Evangel [i.e. R. Baron].) 1634. 4°. **4902.** d. **46.**

—— Ad Georgii Turnebulli Tetragonismum pseudographum apodixis catholica, sive apologia pro disputatione de formali objecto fidei, *etc.* pp. 808. *Edwardus Rabanus: Abredoniæ*, 1631. 8°. **3902.** a. **4.**

—— Ad Georgii Turnebulli Tetragonismum pseudographum apodixis catholica, *etc.* pp. 522. *Excudebat R.N. pro Jos. Kirton: Londini*, 1657. 12°. **1481.** a. **35.**

—— *See* TURNEBULLUS (G.) In sacræ scholæ calumniatorem & calumniæ duplicatorem sententiæ iuris. Pro Tetragonismo G. Turnebulli . . . De obiecto, & regula fidei. [A reply to R. Baron's "Ad Georgii Turnebulli Tetragonismum pseudographum apodixis catholica."] 1632. 8°. **4091.** e. **1.**

—— Disputatio theologica, de formali objecto fidei, hoc est, de sacræ Scripturæ divina, & canonica autboritate, *etc.* *Praes.* J. Forbesius. pp. 43. *Eduardus Rabanus: Abredoniæ*, 1627. 4°. **3103.** bb. **24.**

BARON (ROBERT) *Professor of Divinity in Marischal College, Aberdeen.*

—— Disputatio theologica, de vero discrimine peccati mortalis & venialis, deq: impossibilitate implendi legem Dei ob quotidianam peccatorum venalium incursionem, *etc.* pp. 176. *Edwardus Rabanus: Abredoniæ*, 1633. 8°. **699. a. 5.**

—— [Another edition.] pp. 148. *J. Schulperoort: Amstelodami*, 1649. 12°. **4372. a. 13. (3.)**

—— Rob. Baronii . . . Metaphysica generalis; accedunt nunc primùm quæ supererant ex parte speciali . . . Opus postumum, *etc.* pp. 437. 66. *Ex officinâ F. Moyardi: Lugduni Batavorum*, 1657. 8°. **8462. aa. 13.**

—— [Another edition.] pp. 479. *Ex officina R. Danielis, & væneunt apud Th. Robinson & Ri. Davis: Londini*, 1658. 12°. **8466. aa. 43.**

—— [Another edition.] pp. 479. MS. NOTES [by Samuel Parr]. *Ex off. J. Redmayne: Londini*, [1670?] 12°. **1386. b. 15.**

—— [Another copy.] **231. k. 7.**

—— [Another edition.] pp. 479. *Ex officina Johan. Hayes: Cantabrigiæ; impensis H. Sawbridge: Londini*, 1685. 12°. **528. e. 4.**

—— Philosophia theologiæ ancillans; hoc est, pia & sobria explicatio quæstionum philosophicarum in disputationibus theologicis subinde occurrentium. pp. 341. *Eduardus Rabanus: Andreapoli*, 1621. 8°. **4018. a. 29.**

—— Editio priori correctior. pp. 202. *Impensis T. Robinson & R. Davis: [Oxford,]* 1658. 12°. **1112. a. 32.**

—— A Sermon, preached at the funerall of the R. R. Father in God, Patricke Forbes, late Lord Bishop of Aberdene, *etc. See* FORBES (Patrick) *Bishop of Aberdeen.* Funerals of a Right Reverend Father in God Patrick Forbes, *etc.* 1635. 4°. **696. d. 30.**

BARON (ROBERT BENJAMIN) *See* SODOR AND MAN, *Diocese of.* The Sodor and Man Diocesan Calendar. (R. B. Baron, J. Kewley, editors.) 1894, *etc.* 8°. P.P. 2506. enb.

BARON (ROBERT WEBB STONE) Mayor-Choosing Day; or, the Lambertine of the Angels: and Bishop Saint Lambert re-martyred; or, the adoption of the Mayor-Elect: with other poems. pp. xv. 112. *H. C. Creagh: Plymouth*, 1824. 8°. **11645. aaa. 40.**

—— Mayors and Mayoralties: or, the Annals of the Borough [Plymouth]. pp. 112. *Amelia Arliss: [Plymouth,]* 1846. 12°. **10360. d. 23.**

BARON (RONALD)

—— Am I a Real Catholic? (Reprinted from The Pilot.) pp. 7. *Coelian Press: Loughlinstown*, [1950.] 8°. 3943. b. 29.

BARON (S.) *Dr., Oriental Student. See* BIBLE.—*Psalms.* ^Selections [*Polyglott.*] Saadia Al-fajjûmi's arabische Psalmenübersetzung und Commentar . . . Herausgegeben, übersetzt und mit Anmerkungen versehen von Dr. S. Baron. 1900. 8°. Psalm 50-72. Arab. & Germ. **754. e. 28. (2.)**

BARON (SALO WITTMAYER)

—— *See* JANOWSKY (Oscar I.) The JWB Survey . . . With the report of the JWB Survey Commission by S. W. Baron, *etc.* [1948.] 8°. 04034. p. 58.

BARON (SALO WITTMAYER)

—— American and Jewish Destiny: a semimillennial experience. pp. 12. 1942. 8°. *See* UNITED STATES OF AMERICA.—*Synagogue Council of America.* **04516. aaa. 12.**

—— Essays on Maimonides. An octocentennial volume. Edited by Salo Wittmayer Baron. pp. 316. *Columbia University Press: New York*, 1941. 8°. **20035. cc. 29.**

—— Freedom and Reason. Studies in philosophy and Jewish culture in memory of Morris Raphael Cohen. Edited by S. W. Baron, Ernest Nagel, and Koppel S. Pinson. [With a portrait.] pp. 468. *Free Press: Glencoe, Ill.*, 1951. 8°. 12361. cc. 8.

—— Die Judenfrage auf dem Wiener Kongress, *etc.* pp. 211. *Wien & Berlin*, 1920. 8°. **04034. k. 43.**

—— Modern Nationalism and Religion. pp. x. 363. *Harper & Bros.: New York & London*, [1947.] 8°. **4381. d. 25.**

—— Die politische Theorie Ferdinand Lassalle's. pp. v. 122. *Leipzig*, 1923. 8°. [*Beihefte zum Archiv für die Geschichte des Sozialismus und der Arbeiterbewegung.* Hft. 2.] PP. **1423.** hae.

—— Saadia's Communal Activities. *See* UNITED STATES OF AMERICA.—*American Academy for Jewish Research.* Saadia Memorial Volume. 1943. 8°. **1986.h.5/2.**

—— A Social and Religious History of the Jews. 3 vol. *Columbia University Press: New York*, 1937. 8°. **20029.** h. 39.

—— A Social and Religious History of the Jews . . . Second edition, revised and enlarged. 8 vol. *Columbia University Press: New York*, 1952–58. 8°. **04034. t. 16.**

—— Index to Volumes I–VIII. pp. xi. 163. *Columbia University Press: New York*, 1960. 8°. **04034. t. 16a.**

BARON (SALO WITTMAYER) and **MARX** (ALEXANDER) *Professor in the Jewish Theological Seminary of America.*

—— Jewish Studies in memory of George A. Kohut, 1874–1933. Edited by S. W. Baron and A. Marx. [With a section in Hebrew, a portrait and a bibliography compiled by E. D. Coleman.] 2 pt. 1935. 8°. *See* ALEXANDER KOHUT MEMORIAL FOUNDATION. **04034. k. 51.**

BARON (SAMUEL) A Description of the Kingdom of Tonqueen. *See* CHURCHILL (Awnsham) and (J.) A Collection of Voyages and Travels, *etc.* vol. 6. 1732. fol. **566. k. 11.**

—— [Another edition.] 1746. *See* CHURCHILL (Awnsham) and (J.) A Collection of Voyages and Travels, *etc.* vol. 6. 1744, *etc.* fol. **455. f. 6.**

—— [Another edition.] *See* CHURCHILL (Awnsham) and (J.) A Collection of Voyages and Travels, *etc.* vol. 6. 1752. fol. **215.** e. **6.**

—— [Another edition.] 1811. *See* PINKERTON (John) *Antiquary.* A General Collection of the best and most interesting Voyages, *etc.* vol. 9. 1808, *etc.* 4°. L.R. **80.** c. **1.**

BARON (STANLEY)

—— *See* LONDON.—III. Town and Country Planning Association. Country Towns in the Future England . . . Edited by S. Baron, *etc.* 1944. 8°. **8288.** aa. **84.**

—— *See* MACKAY (Ian) The Real Mackay . . . Edited by S. Baron, *etc.* 1953. 8°. **12357.** tt. **28.**

BARON (STANLEY R.) News-Chronicle Cycling Annual and Resthouse List (News-Chronicle Cycling & Open Road Annual), 1931 [*etc.*]. [1931– .] 8°. *See* PERIODICAL PUBLICATIONS.—London.—*News-Chronicle.* P.P. **2489.** dph.

—— Westward Ho! From Cambria to Cornwall, *etc.* [With illustrations by Reginald Gammon.] pp. 294. *Jarrolds: London,* 1934. 8°. **010360.** aa. **78.**

BARON (STANLEY WADE)

—— All my Enemies. A novel. pp. 286. *Rupert Hart-Davis: London,* 1952. 8°. **12701.** df. **34.**

—— End of the Line. A novel. pp. 319. *Rupert Hart-Davis: London,* 1951. 8°. NNN. **2218.**

—— People and Americans. A memoir of transatlantic tourists. pp. 223. *Rupert Hart-Davis: London,* 1953. 8°. **10888.** a. **51.**

BARON (STEPHEN) Sermones Declamati corã alma vniuersitate Cãtibrigiẽsi, *etc.* **B.L.** *p wynandũ de Worde: lõdonijs,* [1510?] 8°. C. **53.** h. **27.**

—— Sermones Declamati coram alma vniuersitate Cantabrigiensi, *etc.* (Incipit tractatulus eiusdem venerandi patris De regimine principum, *etc.*) **G.L.** 2 pt. *In achademia parrhisiẽsi,* [1510?] 8°. **3832.** aa. **27.**

BARON (THÉODORE) *See* BARON D'HÉNOUVILLE.

BARON (V.) *See* CARASI ( ) *pseud.* [i.e. V. Baron.]

BARON (WALTER) *pseud.*

—— Devil-Brother . . . [A diary of adventures in Brazil.] Edited by H. Howard Taubman. [With a portrait.] pp. 286. *Hurst & Blackett: London,* 1935. 8°. **10482.** cc. **28.**

BARON (WILLIAM) calling himself "*Bill o' Jack's.*" *See* PERIODICAL PUBLICATIONS.—*Manchester.* Bill o' Jack's Monthly . . . Edited by W. Baron—"Bill o' Jack's." 1897. 4°. **1865.** a. **16.** (**20.**)

—— "Beneath Dark Skies." An original drama, in five acts. pp. 52. *Ormerod Bros.: Rochdale,* 1901. 8°. **11778.** f. **23.** (**2.**)

BARON (WILLIAM) *Chaplain to the Earl of Clarendon.* The Dutch Way of Toleration, most proper for our English Dissenters, *etc.* [Signed: ——M——n, i.e. W. Baron.] pp. 23. 1698. 4°. *See* ——M——N. T. **995.** (**12.**)

—— The second edition. pp. 23. 1699. 4°. *See* ——M——N. **4135.** c. **60.**

—— An Historical Account of Comprehension, and Toleration. From a general retrospect on the several reformations at first . . . Part I. By the author the Dutch Way of Toleration [i.e. W. Baron]. pp. 72. 1705. 4°. *See* ACCOUNT. T. **749.** (**6.**)

—— An Historical Account of Comprehension, and Toleration. From the old Puritan to the new Latitudinarian . . . Part II. [By W. Baron.] pp. 84. 1706. 4°. *See* ACCOUNT. **116.** d. **3.**

—— A Just Defence of the Royal Martyr K. Charles I. from the many false and malicious aspersions in Ludlow's Memoirs, and some other virulent libels of that kind. 2 pt. 1699. 8°. *See* LUDLOW (Edmund) **808.** e. **17.**

—— Separation and Sedition inseparable, whilst Dissenters and Commonwealthsmen are permitted to controll in all publick administrations of Church and State: being a farther prosecution of the Dutch toleration. In a letter to a Member of Parliament. [Signed: ——M——n, i.e. W. Baron.] pp. 29. 1703. 4°. *See* ——M——N. **4135.** a. **53.**

BARON (WILLIAM PERCY)

—— *See* JOHNSTON (W. D.) *B.A.*, and BARON (W. P.) Matriculation and Junior Certificate Revision Notes in Geography. [1939.] 4°. **010004.** ff. **56.**

—— *See* WHEATON (A.) AND CO. Wheaton's Atlas Geographies . . . Revised by W. P. Baron, *etc.* 1936, *etc.* 4°. W.P. **4514.**

—— School Certificate Revision Notes in Geography. pp. 63. *A. Wheaton & Co.: Exeter,* 1935. 4°. **010004.** h. **32.**

BARON (WILLIAM RUSSELL NEEDHAM) The Story of the Church of St. Michael the Archangel at Kirby in Malhamdale, Craven, Yorkshire. (Second edition.) [With plates.] pp. 27. *John Bellows: Gloucester,* 1926. 8°. **04705.** a. **52.**

BARONAS (ALOYZAS)

—— Antrasis krantas. Novelis. pp. 132. *Nida Press: London,* 1954. 8°. [*Nidos knygų klubo leidinys.* no. 5.] W.P. **2080/5.**

BARONAS (J.)

—— Rusiškai lietuviškas žodynas. Русско-литовскiй словарь. pp. 576. *Kaunas,* 1924. 8°. **12975.** aaa. **29.**

BARONA Y LOAYSA (GASPAR SANCHO) *Begin.* Señor, Don Gaspar Sancho Barona y Loaysa, vezino de la ciudad de Santiago, de la Prouincia de Guatemala. Dize, *etc.* [A memorial, addressed to the King of Spain, setting forth his services to the Crown.] [1640?] fol. **1324.** i. **2.** (**37.**)

—— [Another copy.] **1324.** i. **2.** (**119.**)

BARÓN CASTRO (RODOLFO)

—— La Población de El Salvador. Estudio acerca de su desenvolvimiento desde la época prehispánica hasta nuestros días . . . Prólogo de Carlos Pereyra. [With a bibliography.] pp. 644. pl. CXXV. *Madrid,* 1942. 8°. Ac. **132/4**

—— La Población hispano-americana a partir de la Independencia. [With maps.] *In:* Instituto "Balmes," de Sociologia. Estudios demográficos. vol. 1. pp. 185–245. 1945. 8°. **8286.** h. **78.**

BARON CAZAUX (DOMINIQUE) Faculté de Droit de Paris. Thèse pour la licence. (Jus romanum. De substitutionibus.—Droit français. Des testaments). pp. 44. *Paris,* 1857. 8°. **5406.** aa. **1.** (**20.**)

BARONCELLI, *Family of.* *See* AMMIRATO (Scipione) *the Elder.* Baroncelli et Bandini. [A genealogical tree.] 1585. *s. sh.* fol. **131.** h. **5.** (**32.**)

—— *See* FLANDREYSY (J. de) and BARONCELLI-JAVON (A. de) *Viscount.* La Maison de Baroncelli en Italie du Xe au XVe siècle. 1924, *etc.* fol. W.P. **8903.**

BARONCELLI (ADRIEN DE) *Baron.* *See* PERIODICAL PUBLICATIONS.—*Paris.* Annuaire de la vélocipédie pratique, par A. de Baroncelli. 1883. 8°. P.P. **1857.** f.

—— Guide des environs de Paris détaillé dans un rayon de 140 kilomètres avec l'itinéraire abrégé de la France, *etc.* pp. xl. 538. *Paris,* [1894.] 8°. **10174.** aa. **42.**

—— Guide routier du vélocеman en France & en Europe; indicateur des distances avec annotations, *etc.* pp. vii. 352. *Paris,* 1891. 8°. **10106.** de. **3.**

BARONCELLI (COSIMO)

—— *See* GUEVARA (A. de) successively *Bishop of Guadix* and *of Mondoñedo.* Il Dispregio della corte, e lode della villa . . . Traslatato . . . da C. Baroncelli. 1601. 8°. **1478.** c. **44.**

BARONCELLI (Cosimo)

—— *See* Guevara (A. de) successively *Bishop of Guadix* and *of Mondoñedo.* Il Dispregio della corte, e lode della villa . . . Traslatato dalla lingua spagnuola . . . da C. Baroncelli, *etc.* 1602. 12°. **1030**. a. **7**.

BARONCELLI (Jacopo) *See* Pontanus (J. J.) Trattato dell'obedienza di M. G. Pontano . . . Tradotto da M. I. Baroncelli, *etc.* 1568. 8°. **230**. k. **50**.

BARONCELLI (Jean de)

—— [Vingt-six hommes.] Seksogtyve Mand. [A novel.] (Oversættelse af William Jensen.) pp. 240. *København,* 1942. 8°. **12519**. e. **66**.

BARONCELLI (Ugo)

—— Bibliografia della storia bresciana. Quinquennio 1930–1934. 1936. *See* Brescia.—*Accademia di Scienze, Lettere, Agricultura ed Arti del Dipartimento del Mella,* afterwards *Ateneo Brescia.* Commentarj dell'Ateneo. anno accademico 134. 1814, *etc.* 8°. Ac. **28**.

—— Catalogo degli incunaboli della Biblioteca Ugo da Como di Lonato, *etc.* [With plates.] pp. 172. 1953. 8°. [*Biblioteca di bibliografia italiana.* vol. 25.] *See* Lonato.—*Biblioteca Ugo da Como.* P.P. **6476**. en.

BARONCELLI-JAVON (Adrien de) *Viscount.* *See* Flandreysy (J. de) and Baroncelli-Javon (A. de) *Viscount.* La Maison de Baroncelli en Italie, *etc.* 1924, *etc.* fol. W.P. **8903**.

BARONCELLI-JAVON (Folcó de) *Marquis.* Babali. Nouvello prouvençalo, emé la traducioun en francés. Ilustracioun pèr R. Blanchard. pp. 54. *Avignoun,* 1890. 8°. **12518**. cc. **36**.

—— Blad de Luno. Recuei de pouèsio prouvençalo emé la traducioun en francés e 155 ilustracioun retrasènt lou biòu e lou chivau dins l'art au courrènt dis age. Prefàci pèr Frederi Mistral. Blé de Lune. Recueil de poésies provençales, *etc.* pp. 239. *Paris; Avignoun,* 1909. 4°. **11498**. m. **23**.

BARONCHELLI-GROSSON (Paola) La Donna nella nuova Italia: documenti del contributo femminile alla guerra, maggio 1915—maggio 1917, *etc.* pp. 334. *Milano,* 1917. 8°. **8416**. h. **44**.

BARONCINIUS (Purpurinus) *à Faventia.* *See* Baroncino (Porporino)

BARONCINO (Giuseppe) [Poems.] 1551. *See* Domenichi (L.) Rime diuerse di molti excellentiss. auttori nuouamente raccolte, *etc.* vol. 4. 1546, *etc.* 8°. **240**. d. **7**.

—— La Fante. Comedia. ff. 55. [*Ercole Bottrigaro*:] *Bologna,* 1547. 8°. **11712**. a. **33**.

BARONCINO (Porporino) P. D. Purpurini a Faventia . . . . Ad kalendarium romanum Amiterni effossum minuscula commentaria. Ludicrum geniale, *etc.* 1719. *See* Sallengre (A. H. de) Novus thesaurus antiquitatum romanarum, *etc.* tom. 3. 1716. fol. **588**. l. **16**.

—— [Another edition.] *See* Sallengre (A. H. de) Novus thesaurus antiquitatum romanarum, *etc.* tom. 3. 1735. fol. **145**. i. **4**.

BARONCOURT (Petit de) *See* Petit de Baroncourt.

BARON DE SAINT GIRONS ( ) Discours de M. Baron de S.-Giron, représentant à la Commune . . . en présentant M. Beaulieu. pp. 10. [*Paris,*] 1789. 8°. **F. 1058**. **(17.)**

—— Discours prononcé par le C^n Baron de S-Girons, commandant en chef le bataillon des vétérans volontaires du département de la Seine, sur la tombe de Caillieres de Létang, leur instituteur. pp. 3. [*Paris,* 1795.] 4°. **936**. f. **17**. (68.)

—— [Another copy.] F. **19***. (11.)

BARON D'HÉNOUVILLE (Théodore) *Resp.* *S*[ee] Baron (Hyacinthe T.) *the Younger.* Quaestio medic[o]-chirurgica, an fracto cranio semper admouenda terebra 1759. 4°. [*Sigwart* (*G. F.*) *Quaestiones medica[e] Parisinae, etc.* fasc. 1.] **1179**. b. **1**

—— *Praes.* *See* Gautier du Rocher (F. N.) Quaesti[o] medica, an humor perspiratorius sit excrementicius? *et[c.]* 1759. 4°. [*Sigwart* (*G. F.*) *Quaestiones medica[e] Parisinae.* fasc. 1.] **1179**. b. **1**

—— *See* Lémery (N.) Cours de chymie . . . Nouvel[le] édition, revue, corrigée & augmentée . . . par M. Baro[n] 1756. 4°. **45**. h. **1**

—— *See* Model (J. G.) Johann Georg Models . . . Versuc[h] und Gedanken über ein natürliches oder gewachsen[es] Salmiak, nebst Erörterung einiger vom Hrn. Baron g[e]machten Einwürfe über das persische Salz. 1758. 8°. **725**. c.

—— Quaestio medica, an raro hemorrhagiis adstringentia *etc.* *Praes.* I. de Diest. *See* Sigwart (G. F.) Quae[s]tiones medicae Parisinae, *etc.* fasc. 1. 1759, *etc.* 4°. **1179**. b. **1**

—— Quæstio medica . . . An dùm contrahitur cor, dilatent[ur] arteriæ coronariæ. *Praes.* H. T. Baron. pp. 4. [*Paris*] 1741. 4°. **1182**. e. **6**. (14

—— [Another edition.] 1747. *See* Haller (A. von) *Baro[n]* Disputationum anatomicarum selectarum volumen I [*etc.*] vol. 2. 1746, *etc.* 4°. **45**. e. **1**

—— Quæstio medica . . . An prolem lactare matrib[us] saluberrimum? *Praes.* H. T. Baron. pp. 4. [*Paris*] [1741.] 4°. T. **642**. (32

—— [Another copy.] **1182**. e. **6**. (33

BARON DU TAYA (Aimé Marie Rodolphe) Broceliand[e] ses chevaliers et quelques légendes, *etc.* (La présen[te] compilation a été publiée aux frais et par les soins de Bar[on] du Taya.) pp. 358. **L.P.** *Rennes,* 1839. 8°. **12450**. g.

BARONE. Il Barone deluso, opera-buffa in due atti. I[l] Baron trompé, opéra-bouffon . . . représenté pour [la] première fois à Paris . . le 13 thermidor an 13. [In] verse. Adapted from " Il Fanatico burlato " by Saver[io] Zini.] *Ital. & Fr.* pp. 36. 36. *Paris,* 1805. 12°. **905**. i. **1**. (2

BARONE (Alfredo) La Vita di Gesù Cristo ossia l'armon[ia] degli Evangeli, di Barone Alfredo, evangelista. pp. 313. 1895. 8°. *See* Bible.—*Gospels.*—*Harmonies.* [*Italian*] **03225**. df.

BARONE (Allen G.)

—— Cosmogony. A study of the origin of the worl[d] pp. 134. *Meador Publishing Co.*: *Boston,* 1937. 8°. **08560**. b.

BARONE (Enrico) *See* Mantegazza (V.) Storia del[la] Guerra mondiale. Con note militari di E. Barone. [1915, *etc.*] 8°. **9085**. bb.

—— " Opera omnia "—postuma. Studi sulla condotta de[lla] guerra. A cura del tenente colonnello di fanteria Sand[ro] Piazzoni. 3 vol.

1. I grandi capitani sino alla rivoluzione francese. pp. viii. 398. pl. 15. 1928.
2. Le campagne per l'indipendenza e l'unità d'Italia, 1848—1859–66. pp. 329. pl. xxiv. 1929.
3. Le campagne del generale Bonaparte in Italia, 1796–e 1800. [With plans.] pp. 338. 1932.

Torino, 1928–32. 8°. **8838**. g. **1**

BARONE (ENRICO)

—— The Ministry of Production in the Collectivist State. *See* HAYEK (F. A. von) Collectivist Economic Planning, *etc.* 1935. 8°. **8286. f. 27.**

—— Principi di economia politica. Quinta ristampa (semplificata). pp. vi. 269. *Roma*, 1920. 8°. **8205. ff. 16.**

—— La Storia militare della nostra guerra fino a Caporetto. pp. 222. *Bari*, 1919. 8°. **09083. bb. 61.**

—— Studi sulla condotta della guerra. 6 pt.

1806 in Germania. 2 pt.
1814 in Francia. 2 pt.
1866 in Boemia. 2 pt.

Torino, 1900. 8°. **09078. c. 57.**

BARONE (FRANCESCO) calling himself *lu Sulitariu.*

—— Martiriu di S. Agata, virgini, e martiri Palermitana. Poema epicu, *etc.* pp. 150. *Per Anglese, e di Leoni: Palermu*, 1692. 8°. **241. e. 38.**

BARONE (FRANCESCO) *Writer on Philosophy.*

—— Assiologia e ontologia. Etica ed estetica nel pensiero di Nicolai Hartmann. *In:* Atti dell'Accademia delle Scienze di Torino. Classe di scienze morali, storiche e filologiche. vol. 88. pp. 217–334. 1954. 8°. **Ac. 2816/4.**

BARONE (FRANCESCO P.) La Stella della Daunia. Memorie storiche del Santuario Mariano di Valleverde. Raccolte, documentate ed illustrate da Monsignor F. P. Barone . . . Sesta edizione, *etc.* pp. 384. *Lucera*, 1910. 8°. **4606. i. 2.**

BARONE (GIOVANNI) *See* BARO (Joannes)

BARONE (GIUSEPPE) *See* CEBES. [*Greek.*] *Κεβητος Πιναξ.* La Tavola di Cebete, con prefazione e note . . . e con un saggio bibliografico. Per cura di G. Barone. 1883. 8°. **8470. cc. 6. (3.)**

—— *See* JENNARO (P. J. de) Il Canzoniere di Pietro Jacopo de Jennaro . . . Pubblicato . . . con prefazione e note da G. Barone. 1883. 8°. **11429. g. 3.**

—— D'un antenato italiano di Falstaff. pp. 29. *Roma*, 1895. 8°. **11763. dd. 4. (10.)**

—— Epimenide di Creta e le credenze religiose de' suoi tempi. Studio storico-critico-filologico. pp. 201. *Napoli*, 1880. 8°. **4503. f. 18.**

—— Reminiscenze etiche e pedagogiche nello studio della Divina Commedia. pp. 47. *Napoli*, 1906. 8°. **11421. b. 22. (1.)**

BARONE (MARIO) Sull'uso dell'aoristo nel *Περι της ἀντιδοσεως* di Isocrate, con una introduzione intorno al significato fondamentale dell'aoristo greco. pp. 107. *Roma*, 1907. 8°. **12924. ff. 35.**

BARONE (NICOLA) Le Filigrane delle antiche cartiere ne' documenti dell'Archivio di Stato in Napoli dal XIII al XV secolo. [With plates.] 1889. *See* NAPLES.—*Società della Storia Patria.* Archivio storico, *etc.* anno 14. 1876, *etc.* 8°. **Ac. 6534.**

—— Notizie storiche raccolte dai Registri Curiae della Cancelleria Aragonese. 7 pt. 1888–90. *See* NAPLES.—*Società della Storia Patria.* Archivio storico, *etc.* anno 13–15. 1876, *etc.* 8°. **Ac. 6534.**

—— Paleografia latina, diplomatica e nozioni di scienze ausiliarie. Manuale ad uso delle scuole universitarie. [With a chart.] pp. 369. *Potenza*, 1910. 8°. **07703. ee. 2.**

BARONE (NICOLA)

—— Terza edizione. (Atlante di facsimili.) pp. 351. pl. XXVIII. *Napoli*, 1923. 8° & fol. [*Biblioteca di Μουσειον.* vol. 1.] **20092.c.5/1.**

—— Il R. Archivio di Stato di Napoli. pp. 36. pl. XXII. *Napoli*, 1923. 8°. [*Biblioteca di Μουσειον.* vol. 2.] **20092.c.5/2.**

—— Sommario di lezioni di paleografia. Con due tavole. pp. 91. *Napoli*, 1902. 8°. **07708. de. 15.**

BARONE (VINCENZO) *See* NICOLA DI NAPOLI, afterwards BARONE.

BARONESS. The Baroness. A tale. Dedicated to the daughters of rank and affluence in Great Britain. pp. 479. *Seeley, Burnside & Seeley: London*, 1843. 8°. **1362. i. 2.**

BARONET. The Baronet's Sunbeam . . . By A. C. W. 1870. 8°. *See* W., A. C. **12627. f. 16.**

—— Thoughts upon the Causes of the Present Distress of the Country, and upon their remedy. By a Baronet. pp. 24. *Richard Cruttwell: Bath*, 1816. 8°. **08227. aaa. 25. (1.)**

—— The Young Baronet. A novel. By the author of "The Scottish Heiress" [i.e. Robert Mackenzie Daniel], *etc.* 3 vol. *T. C. Newby: London*, 1846. 12°. **N. 2621.**

—— The Young Baronet; or, the Broken Leg. pp. 178. *Harvey & Darton: London*, 1830. 12°. **941. a. 29.**

BARONETS.

—— More Baronets made, 1642. (A Catalogue of the Nobility, Baronets, and Knights that the King made after his going from London all the time of the Warre.) pp. 7. [1650?] *See* W., T. A Catalogue of the Dukes, *etc.* 1642. 8°. **607. d. 2. (3.)**

BARON-GUIHOMARD (MARGUERITE)

—— *See* DYGASIŃSKI (A.) [Beldonek.] Le Banquet de la vie. Traduit . . . par M. Baron-Guihomard, *etc.* 1937. 8°. **12593.k.7**

BARONI. I Due baroni. A comic opera, in two acts. As performed at the King's Theatre in the Haymarket, *etc.* [By G. Palomba.] *Ital. & Eng.* pp. 67. *J. Brettell: London*, [1803.] 8°. **907. k. 9. (11.)**

BARONI (A.) *of Piacenza.* Ricordi di un garibaldino. pp. 148. *Torino*, 1911. 8°. **9166. c. 41.**

BARONI (ALBERTO) Tito Livio nel Rinascimento. pp. vii. 77. *Pavia*, 1889. 8°. **11312. p. 2. (4.)**

BARONI (ALESSANDRO) La Scuola Francescana guidata dal suo serafico dottore S. Bonaventura da Bagnorea, in conformità dei principii del dottore angelico S. Tommaso d'Aquino, nella questione scolastica sulla composizione sostanziale dei corpi. Cenni dialettici. 3 vol. *Firenze*, 1886, 85. 8°. **3836. df. 5.**

BARONI (C. A.) *See* GIANI (E.) L'Antico teatro di Verona . . . Con XIX tavole fuori testo di C. A. Baroni. 1908. 8°. **7705. e. 50.**

BARONI (CALOANDRO) I Lombardi nelle guerre italiane, 1848–49. Memorie. 2 vol. *Torino*, 1856. 8°. **9165. b. 42.**

BARONI (CAROLUS) De mira potus aquosi virtute dissertatio inauguralis, *etc.* pp. 15. *Patavii*, 1830. 8°. **7306. b. 7. (6.)**

BARONI (CLEMENTE) *See* BARONI CAVALCABÒ.

BARONI (COSTANTINO)

—— Bramante, *etc.* pp. 57. pl. 134. *Bergamo*, 1944. 4°. **7822. cc. 45.**

Part of a series entitled "I Grandi artisti italiani."

BARONI (Costantino)

—— Ceramiche italiane minori del Castello Sforzesco, *etc.* [A catalogue.] pp. 437. 1934. 8°. *See* Milan.—*Museo Archeologico.* **07805.** d. **62.**

—— Documenti per la storia dell'architettura a Milano nel Rinascimento e nel barocco. *Firenze,* 1940– . 8°. [*Raccolta di fonti per la storia dell'arte.* vol. 4, *etc.*] W.P. **6793/4.**

—— Maioliche di Milano. pp. 71. pl. 98. *Milano,* 1940. 8°. **07805.k.66.**

—— Scultura gotica lombarda. [With plates.] pp. 181. *Milano,* 1944. 8°. **7877.** bb. **11**

BARONI (Constantino) and **SAMEK LUDOVICI** (Sergio)

—— La Pittura lombarda del Quattrocento. [With plates.] pp. 282. *Messina, Firenze,* 1952. 8°. **7870.** aa. **65.** *Biblioteca di cultura contemporanea.* vol. 31.

BARONI (Eugenio) Guida botanica, ossia chiavi analitiche per determinare le piante spontanee che vivono principalmente nell'Italia media, *etc.* pp. xxiv. 574. *Rocca S. Casciano,* 1907. 8°. **07029.** eee. **29.**

—— Supplemento generale al "Prodromo della flora toscana di T. Caruel." 6 fasc. pp. 635. *Firenze,* 1897–1908. 8°. **07031.h.49.**

BARONI (Francesco) *See* Rosellini (M.) Odi due dell' egregia signora Massimina Rosellini fantastici. [Edited by F. Baroni.] 1809. 4°. L.R. **233.** b. **24.**

BARONI (Francesco) *Canon and Professor.*

—— Il Volto Santo di Lucca. [With plates and a bibliography.] pp. 210. *Lucca,* 1932. 8°. **010151.** ee. **23.**

BARONI, afterwards **CASTELLANI** (Leonora) *See* Ademollo (A.) La Leonora di Milton e di Clemente ix. [1885.] 8°. **10601.** c. **15.** (**13.**)

BARONI (Leopoldo)

—— I Maggi, *etc.* [On the popular dramatic dialogues of Tuscany. With three 'maggi' by Pietro Frediani.] pp. 213. *Pisa,* 1954. 8°. **11436.** m. **34.**

BARONI (Luigi) *Professore di Matematiche e d'Idraulica. See* Libes (A.) Trattato completo ed elementare di fisica . . . Tradotto . . . e corredato di note e illustrazioni da L. Baroni. 1814, *etc.* 8°. **8705.** c. **16.**

BARONI (Luigi) *Servite. See* Boccaccio (G.) [*Filostrato.* —*Italian.*] Il Filostrato . . . ora per la prima volta dato in luce. [The editor's dedicatory epistle signed: F. L. B. S., i.e. Fra L. Baroni, Servita.] 1789. 8°. **671.** e. **9.**

BARONI (Pandolfo Ricasoli) *See* Ricasoli Baroni.

BARONI (Paulus) *See* Caruel (T.) and Baroni (P.) Enumeratio Seminum, *etc.* [1867, *etc.*] 8°. **7055.** l. **5.**

BARONI (Pietro) Sesostri. Dramma per musica, diviso in tre atti, da rappresentarsi nel Teatro Contavalli la primavera dell' 1842. pp. 35. *Bologna,* [1842.] 8°. **906.** c. **10.** (**5.**)

BARONI (Stefano) Il Sacro oratore secondo Dante Alighieri al Canto xxix del Paradiso. Osservazioni di S. B. [i.e. S. Baroni.] pp. 40. 1874. 8°. *See* B., S. **11422.** ff. **29.** (**12.**)

BARONI (Vincenzo) San Ciriaco principale protettore di Ancona inventore della croce l'anno cccxxvi. indi vescovo di detta città e martire in Gerusalemme l'anno ccclxiii . . . Dissertazione, *etc.* [With plates.] 2 pt. *Ancona,* 1813. fol. **4827.** h. **6.**

BARONIAN (Hagop H.) *See* Paronean (Yakob Y.)

BARONIAN (L.) *See* Paronean.

BARONIAN (Sukias) *See* Paronean (Soukhias)

BARONIBUS (Pandulfus de Ricasulis) *See* Ricasoli Baroni (Pandolfo)

BARONI CAVALCABÒ (Clemente) *See* Barbieri (L.) *Count.* Dissertazione, e parere . . . su la controversia tra li signori C. Baroni de Cavalcabò, e F. M. Zanotti intorno la natura della felicità. 1763. 8°. T. **2362.** (**2.**)

—— *See* Chiaramonti (G. B.) Discorso filosofico-morale . . . in cui si esamina l'opinione intorno alla felicità del sig. C. Baroni de' Marchesi Cavalcabò esposta e difesa nelle sue lettere, *etc.* 1759. 8°. **232.** a. **11.**

—— *See* Rosmini (C. de') Memorie intorno alla vita e agli scritti di C. Baroni Cavalcabò. 1798. 8°. **10629.** cc. **7.**

—— Idea della storia, e delle consuetudini antiche della Valle Lagarina, ed in particolare del Roveretano, di un Socio dell' Imp. Reg. Accademia degli Agiati. [i.e. C. Baroni Cavalcabò]. pp. viii. 295. [1776?] 4°. *See* Lagarina, *Valley of.* **9150.r.13.**

—— Dissertazione contro l'operetta del signor C. Baroni, intitolata L'Impotenza del Demonio di trasportare a talento per l'aria da un luogo all'altro i corpi umani. [By Gaetano Locatelli.] *See* Calogierà (A.) Nuova raccolta d'opuscoli scientifici e filologici, *etc.* tom. 1. 1755, *etc.* 12°. **247.** a. **1.**

—— [Another edition.] Detta dal P. Lett. N. N. Domenicano [i.e. Gaetano Locatelli], *etc.* 1765. 4°. [*Chiaramonti (G. B.) Dissertazioni istoriche, scientifiche, erudite recitate . . . in Brescia, etc.* tom. 1.] *See* N., N., *P. Lett., Domenicano.* **8356.** c. **8.**

BARONI CAVALCABÒ (Gaspare Antonio) *See* Vannetti (C.) Notizie intorno al pittore Gasparantonio Baroni Calvalcabò di Sacco. 1781. 4°. **786.** g. **6.**

BARONIES.

—— Baronies by Writ devolving upon Coheirs, *etc.* [Eight pedigrees, together with a legal opinion on baronies in fee.] [1700?] 4°. **1482.** d. **19.** (**7.**)

BARONIGIAN (Armenag S.) *See* Paronikean (Armenak S.)

BARONI-GUARINONI (Bernardino) Osservazioni sostenute da documenti officiali contro la proposta di decretare la nuova strada ferrata da Parma per Borgotaro e Pontremoli a Spezia . . . Con una carta topografica. pp. 51. *Lucca,* 1865. 4°. **8235.** l. **45.**

BARONIO (Angelo Cipriano) [Leaflets on pantelegraphy and stenotelegraphy.] 9 pt. *London,* 1903–06. 8°, *etc.* **1879.** b. **28.**

—— Pantelegraphy. A system profitable to telegraph administrations and economical to their patrons. Rudimentary section. pp. 10. *The Author: San Diego, Cal.,* 1899. 4°. **8756.** f. **84.**

—— Pantelegraphy, or a Universal Language and a Universal Code . . . Section Pape. pp. 273. *Pantelegraphic Publishing Co.: New York, London,* [1902.] 4°. **8756.** f. **55.**

BARONIO (Angelo Cipriano)

—— Papa. The polyglot stenocode, *etc.* *The Author: London*, [1908.] fol. **8758. h. 24.**

—— The Rudimentary Section of the Polyglot Stenocode, *etc.* *The Author: London & San Diego, Cal.*, [1909.] 4°. **8754. ddd. 13.**

—— Stenotelegraphy, or the Polyglot Spelling Code, *etc.* pp. vii. ff. 12. *Pantelegraphy Publishing Co.: London*, 1904. fol. **8758. eee. 7.**

—— Symbolo Pantelegraphy; or, a Simplified system for constructing telegraph codes, *etc.* pp. 4. *Nissen & Arnold: London*, [1880.] 4°. **8807. g. 18.**

BARONIO (Cesare) *Cardinal. See* Baronius (Caesar)

BARONIO (Giorgio) Orazione delle lodi di S. Chiara d'Assisi, *etc.* pp. 32. *Ferrara*, 1742. 4°. T. **78*. (1.)**

BARONIO (Giuseppe) Ricerche critiche sui varj metodi di cura per le morsicature dei cani arrabbiati.—Lettera . . . intorno alla regenerazione di tutto il gran tendine d'Achille osservata in un uomo. 1786. *See* Amoretti (C.) and Soave (F.) Opuscoli scelti sulle scienze, *etc.* tom. 9. 1778, *etc.* 4°. **981. h. 9.**

—— Degli innesti animali. [With an engraved portrait.] pp. 78. pl. ii. *Milano*, 1804. 8°. **990. i. 2.**

—— [Another copy.] T. **2127. (1.)**
Imperfect; wanting the portrait.

—— Istruzione del sig. dott. Giuseppe Baronio . . . intorno al modo di conciliare in grande colla maggiore economia possibile la macerazione del lino e della canapa. 1788. *See* Amoretti (C.) and Soave (F.) Opuscoli scelti sulle scienze, *etc.* tom. 11. 1778, *etc.* 4°. **981. h. 11.**

—— Notizie per servire alla storia de' veleni. 1787. *See* Amoretti (C.) and Soave (F.) Opuscoli scelti sulle scienze, *etc.* tom. 10. 1778, *etc.* 4°. **981. h. 10.**

—— Saggio del dottore Giuseppe Baronio sulla corrente epidemia delle pollastre nella Lombardia. 1789. *See* Amoretti (C.) and Soave (F.) Opuscoli scelti sulle scienze, *etc.* tom. 12. 1778, *etc.* 4°. **981. h. 12.**

BARONIO (Teodoro) *See* Baronius (Theodorus)

BARONIO (Vincenzio) *See* Baronius (Vincentius)

BARONIO MANFREDI (Francesco) D. Francisci Baronii ac Manfredis De maiestate Panormitana libri iv. 4 pt. *A. de Isola: Panormi*, 1630. fol. **664. e. 11.**

—— D. Francisci Baronii ac Manfredis . . . De Panormitana majestate libri iv. . . . Editio novissima, emendatior, auctior, *etc.* coll. 460. 1725. *See* Graevius (J. G.) Thesaurus antiquitatum et historiarum Italiæ, *etc.* tom. 10. (Siciliæ. vol. 13.) 1704, *etc.* fol. **L.R.302.a.2/10.**

—— D. D. Francisci Baronii, ac Manfredis, Historicæ et chronologicæ dissertationis Antonini de Amico . . . de antiquo urbis Syracusarum archiepiscopatu ac de ejusdem in universa Sicilia metropolico jure judicium. Editio novissima, diligenter recognita, *etc.* coll. 46. 1723. *See* Graevius (J. G.) Thesaurus antiquitatum et historiarum Italiæ, *etc.* tom. 10. (Siciliæ. vol. 2.) 1704, *etc.* fol. **L.R.302.a.2/10.**

—— Palermo glorioso, *etc.* pp. 238. *Nella stamperia d'Alfonso dell'Isola: Palermo*, [1645?] 4°. **665. c. 24.**

BARONIS (Stephanus) *See* Baron (Stephen)

BARONIUS (Bonaventura) Opuscula prosa et metro, argumento etiam varia. *E. M. Zinck: Herbipoli*, 1666. fol. **G. 5857.**
In this copy is inserted a portrait taken from the author's "Scotus per universam philosophiam defensus."

—— Fr. Joan. Duns Scotus . . . per universam philosophiam, logicam, physicam, metaphysicam, ethicam, contra adversantes defensus, quæstionum novitate amplificatus, *etc.* 3 tom. *Apud I. Busæum: Coloniæ Agrippinæ*, 1664. fol. **8464. g. 3.**

—— Ioannes Duns Scotus . . . De Deo Trino, contra aduersantes quosque defensus, quæstionum nouitate amplificatus. pp. lvj. 212. lxxv. *M. Liberal: Lugduni*, 1668. fol. **3559. f. 3.**

—— Metra miscellanea. Epigrammatum libri tres. Sylvarum totidem. Accesserunt eulogia aliquot illustrium heroum . . . Editio altera, auctior, *etc.* pp. 250. *Apud I. Busæum: Coloniæ Agrippinæ*, 1657. 12°. **1213. b. 12.**
With an additional titlepage, engraved.

—— Trias tusca, sive totidem servi Dei nuper in Hetruria vitis functi & defuncti. pp. xv. 224. *B. ab Egmond & Socios: Coloniæ Agrippinæ*, 1676. 8°. **1370. d. 7.**

BARONIUS (Caesar) *Cardinal.*

ANNALES ECCLESIASTICI.

—— Annales ecclesiastici. tom. 2, 4. *Ex Typographia Vaticana: Romæ*, 1590, 93. fol. **692. g. 10, 11.**
Imperfect; wanting vol. 1, 3, 5–12. *The imprint of tom.* 4 *reads: Ex Typographia Congreg. Oratorij apud S. Mariam. The titlepages are engraved.*

—— Annales ecclesiastici auctore Cæsare Baronio . . . Editio postrema ab ipsomet aucta et recognita. 12 tom. *Sumptibus I. Gymnici & A. Hierati: Moguntiæ*, 1601–08. fol. **481. i. 1–6.**
The titlepages are engraved. In a note at the end of the prefatory matter in tom. 1–3 *this is described as "Quinta & postrema editio."*

—— Editio nouissima ab ipsomet antè obitum aucta & recognita. 12 tom. *Sumptibus I. Gymnici & A. Hierati: Coloniæ Agrippinæ*, 1609. fol. **480. h. 1–6.**
The titlepages are engraved. The date in the colophon of tom. 11 *is* 1605.

—— Nouissima editio, postremùm ab auctore aucta et recognita. 12 tom. *Ex officina Plantiniana: Antuerpiæ*, 1612, 1597–1609. fol. **480. g. 1–12.**
The titlepages are engraved. The words "Nouissima editio . . . recognita" occur only in tom. 1; *tom.* 2–7 *are described as "Editio nouissima"; tom.* 8–12 *have no such description. The volumes are dated as follows: The general titlepage to tom.* 1, 1612, *the special titlepage and the colophon,* 1610; *tom.* 2 *&* 3, *described in the text as "Quarta editio,"* 1597, 1598 *respectively; tom.* 4 *&* 5, 1601; *tom.* 6 *&* 7, 1603; *tom.* 8, 1600; *tom.* 9, 1601; *tom.* 10, 1603; *tom.* 11, 1608; *tom.* 12, 1609.

—— Annales ecclesiastici . . . una cum critica historico-chronologica P. Antonii Pagii . . . Additur præterea dissertatio hypatica ejusdem Pagii; & epistola consularis Henrici Card. Norisii. In hac vero editione Fasti consulares ab A. U. C. 709. ad annum Christi 567. illustrantur . . . Accedunt animadversiones in Pagium, *etc.* (Annales ecclesiastici ab anno mcxcviii. ubi desinit Cardinalis Baronius, auctore Odorico Raynaldo . . . Accedunt in hac editione notæ . . . quibus Raynaldi annales . . . emendantur, auctore Joanne Dominico Mansi.—Annalium ecclesiasticorum Cæsaris Baronii . . . cum critice subjecta P. Antonii Pagi, continuatione Odorici Raynaldi, notisque Dominici Georgii & P. Joannis Dominici Mansi . . . in Pagium & Raynaldum apparatus, *etc.*—Index universalis rerum omnium, quæ in Baronii, ac Pagii apparatibus, in Baronii Annalibus, Pagii critica, Annalibus Raynaldi, notisque Georgii, & Mansi continentur, *etc.*) [Edited by G. D. Mansi and D. Georgius.] 38 tom. *Lucæ*, 1738–59. fol. **L.2.a.1.**

— [Another copy.] **202. h. 11–205. h. 8.**

— Cæsario S. R. E. Card. Baronii, Od. Raynaldi et Jac. Laderchii . . . Annales ecclesiastici denuo excusi et ad nostra usque tempora perducti ab Augustino Theiner. 37 tom. *Barri-Ducis, Parisiis*, 1864–83. 4°. **4532. h.**

— Thesaurus antiquitatum ecclesiasticarum, ex septem prioribus tomis Annalium ecclesiasticorum Cardinalis Cæsaris Baronii . . . collectus. Adiunctis singularibus scholijs aduersus Centurias Magdeburgensium & Caluinistas. Studio & industria Cornelii Schultingii Steinwichii. 7 tom. *S. Hemmerden: Coloniæ Agrippinæ*, 1601. 8°. **4532. aa. 6.**
The titles of tom. 2–7 *read: "Thesauri antiquitatum ecclesiasticarum . . . tomus secundus(—septimus)."*

— Annales ecclesiastici ex XII. tomis Cæsaris Baronii . . . in epitomen redacti, opera Henrici Spondani . . . & eiusdem illustrissimi Cardinalis auctoritate editi. pp. 1080. *Impensis I. T. Schönwetteri: Moguntiæ*, 1614. fol. **4520. h. 1.**
The titlepage is engraved.

— [Another edition.] Accedit hac postrema editione appendix ex Bzouio. pp. 1086. *Impensis A. Hierati: Moguntiæ*, 1618. fol. **209. g. 1.**
The titlepage is engraved.

— Editio altera, priori longè accuratior. Vna cum vita eiusdem illustrissimi Cardinalis; ac nonnullis posthumis lucubrationibus, ad Annales pertinentibus: necnon & notis ad eosdem Annales . . . ac breui auctario ab eo tempore quo Baronius cessavit, vsque ad ann. 1622. Operâ Henrici Spondani. 3 pt. *Impensis A. Hierati: Moguntiæ*, 1623. fol. **4533. g. 4.**
The titlepage is engraved.

— Editio postrema, prioribus longè accuratior. Opera Henrici Spondani. 2 pt. *D. de la Noüe: Lutetiæ Parisiorum*, 1639. fol. **4520. h. 2.**
The titlepage is engraved.

— Compendium Annalium ecclesiasticorum . . . Cardinalis Cæsaris Baronii (Odorici Raynaldi) . . . Authore P. Augustino Sartorio. (tom. 15–20. Continuatore P. Eustachio Janka.) 20 tom. *Pragæ*, 1721–27. 8°. **4531. a. 3.**

— Legationes Alexandrina et Ruthenica ad Clementem VIII. Pont. Max. pro vnione et communione cum Sede Apostolica. Anno Domini M.D.XCV., *etc.* [Reprinted from tom. 6 and 7 of the "Annales ecclesiastici" of Baronius.] pp. 54. *Ex typographia A. Sartorii: Ingolstadii*, 1598. 4°. **4695. b. 32.**

— Añaliũ ecclesiasticoꝝ Cæsaris Baronii . . . arabica epitome. Pars prima (secunda) labore F. Britij, *etc.* (Continuationis Annalium ecclesiasticorum . . . Card. Baronii ab anno 1198 vsque ad annum 1646. per Henricum Spondanum . . . factæ & protractæ arabica epitome. Pars tertia. Opera & labore P. F. Britii.) 3 pt. *Typis & sumptibus S. Cong. ꝑdæ̃ Fidej: Romæ*, 1653–71. 4°. **14501.c.2–4.**

— [Another copy.] **864. m. 1–3.**
Imperfect; wanting the titlepage and the prefaces of pt. 1 *and the titlepage of pt.* 2.

— [Another copy of pt. 3.] **864. m.**
Imperfect; wanting the titlepage, preface, and s xxxxxx.

— Abrégé des Annales ecclesiastiques de Cesar Baron . . . Composé en latin, par le R. P. Aurele Perusin . et traduit . . . par Me Charles Chaulmer. 8 tom. *I. Cochart: Paris*, 1673. 12°. **1366. a.**

— Gli Annali ecclesiastici del R. P. Cesare Baronio; rido in compendio da Monsig. Revermo Panigarola, *etc.* pp. 104–376 [382]. *Appresso la Minima Compagn Venetia*, 1593. 4°. **858. h.**

— Rocznedźieie Kośćielne od národzenia Páná . . . Jes Christusa, wybráne z rocznychdzieiow kośćieln C. Baroniusza . . . názwánych Annales Ecclesiastici pr X. P. Skarge . . . Te kśięgi zamykáią w sobie . . . tyśiąc y dwieśćie. Wtorym wydaniem. [Translated Skarga.] pp. iij. iij. 1202. *W drukárn Andrzeiá Piotrkowczyká: w Krakowie*, 1607. fol. **491. k.**
This copy contains the autograph of J. U. Niemcewicz.

— [For separate editions of the treatise "De monarc Siciliae," originally published in vol. 11 of the "Ann ecclesiastici":] *See* infra: OTHER WORKS.

— Vita Sancti Niconis . . . ex actis ejus ab abb monasterii S. Niconis anno 1150 Græcè scriptis, interpr Jacobo Sirmundo Arverno . . . ex Cæsaris Baronii nalium tomo decimo collecta, *etc.* 1864. *See* MIG (J. P.) Patrologiæ cursus completus, *etc.* Series græ tom. 113. 1857, *etc.* 4°. **2001.**

Appendix.

— *See* BASNAGE (S.) Samuelis Basnagii . . . Ann politico-ecclesiastici annorum DCXLV. a Cæsare Aug ad Phocam usque. In quibus res imperii ecclesia observatu digniores subjiciuntur oculis, errores evelluntur Baronio. 1706. fol. **4533.**

— *See* BASNAGIUS (S.) De rebus sacris & ecclesias exercitationes historico-criticæ. In quibus Cardin Baronii Annales, ab anno Christi XXXV, in quo Casaubo desiit, expenduntur, *etc.* 1692. 4°. **490. b.**

— *See* BENI (P.) Pauli Benii . . . De ecclesiasticis Bar Cardinalis Annalibus disputatio, *etc.* 1596. 4°. **698. k.**

— *See* BERNEGGERUS (M.) Hypobolimæa divæ M deiparæ camera, seu idolum Lauretanum, eversis Bar Cardinalis, Canisii . . . fulcimentis dejectum, *etc.* 1619. 4°. **4808. bbb.**

— *See* BLONDEL (D.) De la primauté en l'Eglise: tr ou sont confrontées, auec la response du serenissime de la grand' Bretagne, les Annales du Card. Baronius Controuerses du Cardinal Bellarmin, *etc.* 1641. fol. **L.7.e.**

— *See* BOULENGER (J. C.) Iulii Cæsaris Bulengeri Diat ad Isaaci Casauboni Exercitationes aduersus Illu simum Cardinalem Baronium, *etc.* 1617. fol. **C. 110.**

— *See* BRANCATUS (L.) *Cardinal.* Index alphabe rerum, & locorum omnium memorabilium ad An Cardinalis Baronii, *etc.* 1694. 4°. **690.**

— *See* BZOVIUS (A.) Annalium ecclesiasticorum illustriss. et reuerendiss. D.D. C. Baronium t XIII.(—XVIII.), *etc.* 1616, *etc.* fol. **481. i.**

BARONIUS (CAESAR) *Cardinal*.—[ANNALES ECCLESIASTICI. —*Appendix*.]

—— *See* BZOVIUS (A.) Historiæ ecclesiasticæ ex illustriss. C. Baronii . . . Annalibus aliorumque viror. illust. ecclesiasticis historicisq; monumentis tomus I [*etc*.]. 1617. fol. **1232**. k. **1**.

—— *See* CASAUBON (I.) [*Works*.] Casauboniana, sive Isaaci Casauboni varia de scriptoribus librisque judicia . . . ut & animadversiones in Annales Baronii ecclesiasticos ineditæ, *etc*. 1710. 8°. **678**. a. **16**.

—— *See* CASAUBON (I.) [*Works*.] Isaaci Casauboni De rebus sacris et ecclesiasticis exercitationes XVI. Ad Cardinalis Baronii Prolegomena in Annales, & primam eorum partem, De Domini nostri Iesu Christi natiuitate, vita, passione, assumtione, *etc*. 1614. fol. C. **24**. c. **3**.

—— —— 1655. 4°. **205**. c. **2**.

—— *See* COMBER (Thomas) *D.D., Dean of Durham*. Roman Forgeries in the Councils during the First Four Centuries . . . With an appendix concerning the forgeries and errors in the Annals of Baronius. 1689. 4°. **701**. e. **12**. (**1**.)

—— —— 1738. fol. [*A Preservative against Popery, etc.* vol. 3.] **478**. f. **13**.

—— —— 1849. 8°. [GIBSON (*Edmund*) *A Preservative against Popery, etc.* vol. 15.] **3940**. k.

—— *See* CONTELORI (F.) Concordiæ inter Alexandrum III. . . . et Fridericum I. . . . Venetiis confirmatæ narratio . . . Cæsaris Cardinalis Baronii authoritas a calumnijs vindicata, *etc*. 1632. fol. **1852**. d. **6**.

—— *See* COOKE (Alexander) Pope Ioane . . . Manifestly prouing, that a woman called Ioane was Pope of Rome: against the surmises and obiections made to the contrarie, by Robert Bellarmine and C. Baronius, *etc*. 1610. 4°. **226**. a. **22**.

—— —— 1625. 4°. **861**. b. **6**.

—— —— 1745. 4°. [*Harleian Miscellany*. vol. 4.] **185**. a. **8**.

—— —— 1809. 4°. [*Harleian Miscellany*. vol. 4.] **2072.g.**

—— *See* COOKE (Alexander) La Papesse Ieanne, ou dialogue . . . prouuant manifestement qu'vne femme nommée Ieanne a esté pape de Rome: contre les suppositions & objections faictes au contraire, par Robert Bellarmin & C. Baronius, *etc*. 1633. 8°. **484**. a. **28**.

—— *See* COUNCILS OF THE CHURCH. Summa conciliorum omnium, ordinata, aucta, illustrata ex Merlini . . . Baronii . . . aliorumque collectionibus, *etc*. 1675. fol. **2012.h.**

—— —— 1701. fol. **689.ee.1.**

—— —— 1723. fol. **5005**. f. **7**.

—— *See* CRAKANTHORP (Richard) Iustinian the Emperor defended, against Cardinal Baronius. 1616. 4°. **4825**. c. **9**.

—— *See* CRAKANTHORP (Richard) Vigilius dormitans . . . A treatise of the fift generall Councell held at Constantinople, anno 553 . . . Wherein . . . the exceeding frauds of Cardinall Baronius and Binius are clearely discovered, *etc*. 1631. 8°. **3936**. i. **19**.

—— —— 1634. fol. **3936**. i. **21**.

BARONIUS (CAESAR) *Cardinal*.—[ANNALES ECCLESIASTICI. —*Appendix*.]

—— *See* DU MOULIN (L.) A Short and True Account of the Several Advances the Church of England hath made towards Rome, *etc*. (A New Essay towards a True Ecclesiastical History, which may serve as a key to the Annalls of Baronius.) 1680. 4°. **702**. e. **3**. (**6**.)

—— *See* EUDAEMON-IOANNES (A.) *Cydonius*. Defensio Annalium ecclesiasticorum C. Baronii . . . adversus falsas calumnias, errores, ac mendacia Isaaci Casauboni, *etc*. 1617. 4°. **858**. b. **1**.

—— *See* FERNANDEZ DE VELASCO (J.) *Duke de Frias, etc.* Dos Discursos en que se defiende la Venida y Predicacion del Apostol Santiago en España, *etc*. [With reference to the "Annales ecclesiastici" of C. Baronius.] 1605. 4°. **4808**. g. **15**.

—— *See* FERNANDEZ DE VELASCO (J.) *Duke de Frias, etc.* Hispaniarum vindiciæ tutelares . . . venisse in hæc Regna Iacobum apostolum, fideſque lumen intulisse, adversus Cardinalis Baronii, aliorúmque opinionem, *etc*. 1608. 4°. **1124**. h. **16**. (**9**.)

—— *See* FRANGIPANE (C. C.) Per la historia di Papa Alessandro III. . . . Allegatione in iure . . . contra la narratione contenuta nel duodecimo tomo delli Annali ecclesiastici. 1615. 4°. **175**. d. **20**. (**3**.)

—— —— [1616.] 4°. **175**. d. **20**. (**2**.)

—— —— 1685. 12°. [*Opere del Padre Paolo dell'ordine de' Servi*. vol. 6.] **1223**. a. **6**.

—— *See* GIEFERS (W. E.) Das ungarische Fluchformular und das Leben der h. Jungfrau Synoris nach Baronius und Andreä, beleuchtet von W. E. Giefers, *etc*. 1866. 8°. **4887**. aa. **33**.

—— *See* GRETSER (J.) Jacobi Gretseri . . . Opera omnia, *etc*. (tom. 6. Cæsar Baronius . . . a rationalis calviniani criminationibus vindicatus, *etc*.) 1734, *etc*. fol. **12**. f. **6**.

—— *See* HOSPINIANUS (R.) De Templis: hoc est, de origine, progressu . . . templorum . . . libri V. Editio secunda . . . locupletata, cum integris capitibus, tum responsionibus ad Rob. Bellarmini, C. Baronii . . . sophismata & argumenta, quibus idololatriam romanam defendere conantur, *etc*. 1603. fol. **482**. d. **10**.

—— —— 1672. fol. **3477**. f. **8**. (**3**.)

—— *See* IGNATIUS, *Saint, Bishop of Antioch*. [*Greek and Latin*.] *Τα του άγιου Ἰγνατιου . . . εὑρισκομενα ἁπαντα* . . . Cum XII. exercitationibus in eundem Ignatium, pro antiquitate catholicâ aduersus Baronium & Bellarminum, *etc*. 1623. 4°. **473**. b. **14**.

—— *See* JOAN, *Pope*. Johanna Papissa toti orbi manifestata. Adversus scripta Bellarmini, C. Baronii, *etc*. [By Alexander Cooke.] 1619. 8°. **4856**. a. **21**.

—— *See* KORTHOLT (C.) *the Elder*. Christiani Kortholti . . . Disquisitiones anti-Baronianæ, *etc*. 1677. 4°. **210**. b. **23**. (**3**.)

—— *See* KREBS (J. F.) Joh. Friderici Krebsii . . . De jure alienandi imperia, schediasma cum animadversionibus . . . ad C. Baronii Annalium ecclesiasticorum tom. IX., *etc*. 1709. 4°. **1054**. i. **25**. (**11**.)

—— *See* LADERCHI (G.) Annales ecclesiastici ab anno 1556, *etc*. [A continuation of the "Annales" of C. Baronius and O. Raynaldus.] 1728, *etc*. fol. **L.2.a.1.**

BARONIUS (CAESAR) *Cardinal.*—[ANNALES ECCLESIASTICI. —*Appendix.*]

—— *See* LADERCHI (G.) Annales ecclesiastici ab anno, quo post Card. C. Baronium desinit O. Raynaldus . . . usque ad annum 1567 continuati, *etc.* 1733. fol. **480.** h. **11.** (**2.**)

—— *See* LYDIAT (T.) Recensio et explicatio argumentorum productorum libello Emendationis temporum compendio factæ, cum additamento plurimum, quibus confirmatur paradoxa . . . sententia de annis natiuitatis, baptismatis & cruciatus . . . Domini Iesu Christi. Insertis breuibus confutationibus contrariarum opinionum, Scaligeranæ, Baronianæque, *etc.* 1613. 12°. **847.** a. **10.**

—— *See* MAYER (Johann F.) *Professor of Theology at Wittenberg.* Jo. Frid. Mayeri . . . De fide Baronii & Bellarmini ipsis pontificiis ambigua eclogæ, *etc.* 1697. 8°. **1012.** a. **21.** (**1.**)

—— *See* MONTAGU (Richard) successively *Bishop of Chichester,* and *of Norwich.* Analecta ecclesiasticarum exercitationum. [In answer to the "Annales ecclesiastici" of C. Baronius.] 1622. fol. **696.** m. **22.**

—— *See* MORNAY (P. de) *Seigneur du Plessis Marly.* [*Separate Works.*] Mysterium iniquitatis seu, historia papatus . . . Asseruntur etiam jura imperatorum, regum, & principum christianorum adversus Bellarminum & Baronium, *etc.* 1611. fol. **478.** g. **9.**

—— —— 1612. 8°. **3901.** bbb. **30.**

—— —— 1662. 4°. **3901.** ee. **14.**

—— *See* MORNAY (P. de) *Seigneur du Plessis Marly.* [*Separate Works.*] Le Mystère d'iniquité . . . Ou sont . . . defendus les droicts des empereurs rois & princes Chrestiens, contre les assertions des Cardinaux Bellarmin & Baronius. 1611. fol. **699.** m. **15.**

—— —— 1612. 8°. **223.** d. **19.**

—— *See* MORNAY (P. de) *Seigneur du Plessis Marly.* [*Separate Works.*] The Mysterie of Iniquitie: that is to say, the historie of the Papacie . . . Where is also defended the right of emperours, kings, and Christian princes, against the assertions of the Cardinals, Bellarmine and Baronius. 1612. fol. **4570.** f. **9.**

—— *See* OTTE (J. B.) Editio scriptorum posthumorum Joh. Henrici Ottii in Annales C. Baronii . . . epistolâ responsoriâ . . . exposita, *etc.* [1687.] 8°. **619.** b. **2.** (**3.**)

—— *See* PAGI (A.) Critica historico-chronologica in universos Annales ecclesiasticos . . . Cæsaris Cardinalis Baronii, in qua rerum narratio defenditur, illustratur, suppletur, ordo temporum corrigitur, *etc.* 1727. fol. **4533.** g. **3.**

—— *See* RAINOLDS (John) Iohannis Rainoldi . . . Sex theses de Sacra Scriptura & Ecclesia . . . recognitæ, & apologia contra Pontificios Elymas, Stapletonum . . . Baronium . . . auctæ. 1602. 8°. **1020.** d. **9.**

—— *See* RAUSCHEN (G.) Jahrbücher der christlichen Kirche unter dem Kaiser Theodosius dem Grossen. Versuch einer Erneuerung der Annales ecclesiastici des Baronius für die Jahre 378–395. 1897. 8°. **4532.** ee. **25.**

—— *See* RAYNALDUS (O.) Annales ecclesiastici ab anno quo desinit Card. C. Baronius M.C.XCVIII. usque ad annum M.D.XXXIV. continuati, *etc.* 1694, *etc.* fol. **480.** h. **7–11.**

—— *See* REDING (A.) Vindex veritas Annalium ecclesiasticorum . . . Cardinalis C. Baronij, adversus arrogatum J. H. Ottij . . . Examen perpetuum. 1680. fol. **480.** g. **14.**

BARONIUS (CAESAR) *Cardinal.*—[ANNALES ECCLESIASTICI. —*Appendix.*]

—— *See* ROESCHIUS (G.) Exercitatio historico-philologica de cultu Simonis Magi apud Romanos, contra Baronium, *etc.* [1663.] 4°. **1012.** d. **45.**

—— *See* ROSSI (Filippo) *Artist.* Descrizione di Roma antica, *etc.* (Descrizione di Roma moderna . . . con le auttorità del Card. C. Baronio, A. Ciaconio, *etc.*) 1707. 8°. **575.** b. **6.**

—— —— 1719. 8°. **10131.** aa. **28.**

—— —— 1739. 12°. **658.** a. **13.**

—— *See* ROSWEYDUS (H.) Lex talionis XII. tabularum Cardinali Baronio ab I. Casaubono dicta. 1614. 8°. **877.** h. **14.**

—— *See* SAUR (J. B. A.) Fixio certa anni, quo conditus est episcopatus Bambergensis contra lapsus Sigeberti . . . Cardin. Baronii, *etc.* [1783.] 4°. **4660.** b. **3.**

—— *See* SCULTETUS (A.) Confutatio prolixæ disputationis C. Baronii . . . de baptismo Constantini Romano, quam tertio Annalium ecclesiasticorum tomo inseruit, *etc.* 1607. 4°. **700.** g. **11.** (**2.**)

—— *See* SCULTETUS (A.) Medullæ theologiæ Patrum syntagma. In quo theologia priscorum . . . doctorum . . . methodo analyticâ . . . expressa, atq; à R. Bellarmini, C. Baronii . . . aliorumq; . . . corruptelis . . . vindicatur, *etc.* 1634. 4°. **474.** b. **3.**

—— *See* SPANHEIM (F.) *the Younger.* Friderici Spanhemii Introductio ad chronologiam, et historiam sacram . . . Cum necessariis castigationibus C. Baronii. 1683. 4°. **4534.** aa. **16.**

—— *See* SPONDE (H. de) *Bishop of Pamiers.* Annalium emin[mi] Cardinalis Cæs. Baronii continuatio ab anno M.C.XCVII. quo is desiit, ad finem M.DC.XL. 1641. fol. **1232.** k. **2–4.**

—— —— 1647. fol. **4520.** h. **7.**

—— *See* SURIUS (L.) De vitis sanctorum omnium nationum . . . ex VII. tomis R. P. F. Laurentij Surij . . . compendium . . . Opus nouum . . . illustratum . . . notationibus varijs ex scriptis . . . C. Baronii . . . & aliorum, *etc.* 1605. fol. C. **79.** g. **11.**

—— *See* THEINER (A.) Annales ecclesiastici quos post Caesarem S. R. E. Card. Baronium, O. Raynaldum ac I. Laderchium . . . ab an. MDLXXII. ad nostra usque tempora continuat A. Theiner. 1856. fol. **481.** k. **11–13.**

—— *See* TRIBBECHOV (A.) Adami Tribbechovii . . . Exercitationes ad Baronii Annales ubi desiit I. Casaubonus, *etc.* [1677.] 4°. **700.** h. **7.** (**13.**)

—— *See* VOIGT (Gottfried) De sacrosancta unius divinitatis Triade . . . exercitatio historica . . . intermixtis argumentis aliis, de versione græca librorum Mosaicorum ante LXX, contra Baronium & Waltonum, *etc.* 1675. 4°. **479.** a. **27.** (**3.**)

—— *See* WENDLER (J. C.) Dissertationem præliminarem qua asseritur adversus Stanislaum Rescium, Baronium . . . Lutheranos præiudicium doctrinæ purioris neque supprimere neque corrumpere scriptores ecclesiasticos . . . submittit . . . I. C. Wendler, *etc.* [1713.] 4°. T. **2171.** (**11.**)

—— *See* WIDEKIND (M. L.) Dissertatio antibaroniana prima in nummum argenteum Imperatoris Nervæ Cocceii de fisco judaico eiusque calumnia S.C. sublata, *etc.* [1732.] 4°. **602.** c. **34.** (**6.**)

BARONIUS (CAESAR) *Cardinal*.

OTHER WORKS.

—— Venerabilis Caesaris Baronii . . . Epistolae et opuscula, pleraque nunc primum ex archetypis in lucem eruta. Novam eiusdem Baronii vitam operi praeposuit recensuit et adnotationibus illustravit Raymundus Albericius. 3 tom.

tom. 1 continens ven. auctoris et clarorum virorum ad eum epistolas selectas ab anno MDLXXIX. ad annum MDC. pp. xxiii. 479. 1759.
tom. 2 continens eiusdem Baronii et clarorum virorum ad eum epistolas selectas ab anno M.DC. ad annum M.DC.VII. ac vitam S. Gregorii Nazianzeni. pp. xxii. 396. 1759.
tom. 3 continens ven. auctoris et clarorum virorum ad eum epistolas selectas novissime repertas. pp. xxvi. 348. 1770.

Romae, 1759–70. 4°. **3678**. e. **9**.

—— [For editions of " De martyrologio Romano " by Cardinal C. Baronius included in the Martyrologium Romanum :] *See* LITURGIES.—*Latin Rite.*—*Martyrologies.*—I.

—— Cæsaris Cardinalis Baronii Tractatus de monarchia Siciliæ. Accessit Ascanii Cardinalis Columnæ de eodem tractatu iudicium. Cum eiusdem Cardinalis Baronii responsione apologetica aduersus Cardinalem Columnam, & epistola ad Philippum III. regem Hispaniæ. Nunc primum editi. pp. 239. *H. Beys: Parisiis*, 1609. 8°. **1195**. b. **28**.
The treatise " De monarchia Siciliae " was originally published in vol. 11 *of " Annales ecclesiastici."*

—— Editio novissima prioribus auctior ac emendatior. coll. 74. 1723. *See* GRAEVIUS (J. G.) Thesaurus antiquitatum et historiarum Italiæ, *etc.* vol. 10. (Siciliæ. vol. 3.) 1704, *etc.* fol. **L.R.302.a.2/10.**

—— *See* SPAIN. [*Laws, etc.*—II. Philip III., *King*. 1598–1621.] Edicto del Rey Don Phelippe d'España contra el tractado della monarchia de Sicilia enxerido por C. Baronio en el tomo vndecimo de sus Annales Ecclesiasticos. 1611. 8°. **857**. g. **11**. **(2.)**

—— —— 1612. 4°. [*Recueil de plusieurs actes et mémoires remarquables, etc.*] **1195**. c. **4**. **(2, 3.)**

—— Duo vota, hoc est, ex animo voto prolatæ sententiæ. Vnum . . . Cæsaris Baronii . . . contra serenissimam Rempublicam Venetam. Alterum . . . Ioannis Marsilii . . . pro eadem serenissima Republica. pp. 22. 1606. 4°. **175**. f. **15**. **(17.)**

—— [Another edition.] pp. 23. 1607. 12°. C. **79**. a. **5**. **(3.)**

—— [Another edition.] *See* GERARDUS, *Loppersius*. Gerardi Loppersii . . . Sententiæ ill[mi] ac reu[m] Card. Baronii in sacro consistorio dictæ propugnatio, *etc.* 1607. 4°. **4051**. e. **17**.

—— *See* MILENSIO (F.) Pro voto illustrissimi ac reuerendissimi Cardinalis Cæsari Baronii in causa Sanctæ Matris Ecclesiæ Catholicæ cum Republica Venetorum scrutinium . . . contra votum D. Ioannis Marsilii, *etc.* 1607. 8°. **175**. f. **10**. **(2.)**

—— *See* VIGNIER (Nicolas) *the Younger*. De Venetorum excommunicatione adversus C. Baronium . . . dissertatio, *etc.* [With the text of the decree.] 1606. 8°. **8073**. aaa. **1**. **(5.)**

—— —— 1607. 4°. **3908**. d. **7**.

—— *See* VIGNIER (N.) *the Younger*. Concerning the Excommunication of the Venetians. A discourse against C. Baronius, *etc.* [With a translation of the text of the decree.] 1607. 4°. **3908**. c. **8**.

—— Historica relatio de Ruthenorum origine, eorumque miraculosa conversione, & quibusdam alijs ipsorum regum rebus gestis. Item quomodo progressu temporis ab agnita veritate defecerint ; a modo vero partim ad communionem S. Sedis Apostolicæ recepti fuerint, *etc.* *Sumptibus N. Steinij : Coloniae*, 1598. 8°. **698**. c. **6**. **(3.)**

—— Legationes Alexandrina et Ruthenica ad Clementem VIII. Pont. Max. pro vnione et communione cum sede Apostolica, anno domini M.D.XCV. die 15. Ianuarij & 23. Decembris. Nunc primùm separatim excusæ. pp. 54. *Ex typographia A. Sartorii : Ingolstadii*, 1598. 4°. T. **1567**. **(3.)**

—— [Another edition.] pp. xi. 130. *Parisiis*, 1860. 8°. **4605**. bb. **16**.

—— Discours de l'origine des Russiens et de leur miraculeuse conversion . . . Traduict en françois par Marc Lescarbot. Nouvelle édition revue et corrigée par le prince Augustin Galitzin. pp. xiv. 60. *Paris*, 1856. 12°. **9455**. a. **28**.

—— Aus der Relation des Cardinal Baronius über die Bekehrung der Russinen. *See* GAGARIN (J.) Wird Russlands Kirche das Papstthum anerkennen ? *etc.* 1857. 8°. **3926**. g. **16**.

—— Cæs. Baronii . . . Parænesis ad Rempublicam Venetam. pp. 50. *Romæ*, 1606. 4°. **4051**. c. **5**. **(1.)**

—— [Another copy.] **3902**. f. **8**. **(12.)**

—— [Another edition.] pp. 60. *Romæ, Ferrariæ*, 1606. 8°. **175**. f. **10**. **(1.)**

—— [Another edition.] pp. 76. *Apud D. Francum : Augustæ Vindelicorum*, 1606. 8°. **8073**. aaa. **1**. **(4.)**

—— [Another edition.] pp. 28. *Apud V. Benatium : Bononiæ*, 1606. 4°. **805**. c. **29**.

—— [Another edition.] *See* ROME, *Church of*.—[*Popes*.]—*Paul* V. Controversiæ memorablis inter Paulum V. . . . & Venetos . . . acta et scripta varia, *etc.* 1607. 8°. **1008**. a. **12**.

—— Esortatione alla Republica Venetiana . . . Tradotta di latino in volgare. pp. 51. *S. Marchetti : Siena*, 1606. 4°. **175**. f. **6**. **(4.)**

—— *See* CRASSO (Niccolo) *Veneziano, the Younger*. Nicolai Crassi Iunioris . . . Antiparænesis ad C. Baronium Cardinalem pro seren. Veneta Republica. 1606. 4°. **4051**. c. **6**. **(1.)**

—— —— [1607.] 4°. [*Raccolta degli scritti . . . nella causa del P. Paolo* V. *co' Signori Venetiani, etc.*] **1010**. d. **3**. **(1.)**

—— Ad illustrissimum Cæsarem Baronium Cardinalem epistola. Incerti auctoris. [A reply to his " Paraenesis ad Rempublicam Venetam." By Alexander Lysca.] pp. 15. [*Venice*,] 1606. 4°. **175**. f. **14**. **(8.)**

—— Christianorum Reipublicæ Venetæ civium et amicorum, ad antichristianam Cardinalis Baronii Paræenesin, responsio. [By Niccolo Crasso.] pp. 66. 1607. 8°. **8073**. aaa. **1**. **(7.)**

—— Vita Sancti Ambrosii . . . a C. Baronio . . . collecta. 1587. *See* AMBROSE, *Saint, Bishop of Milan*. [*Works*.] Operum Sancti Ambrosii . . . tomus primus, *etc.* tom. 6. 1580, *etc.* fol. **L.19.k.1.**

—— [Another edition.] *See* AMBROSE, *Saint, Bishop of Milan*. [*Works*.] Sancti Ambrosii . . . Opera, *etc.* tom. 1. 1603. fol. **474**. i. **1**, **2**.

BARONIUS (CAESAR) *Cardinal.*

WORKS TRANSLATED OR WITH NOTES BY BARONIUS.

—— [For editions of the " Martyrologium Romanum " containing the notes of C. Baronius and his treatise " De Martyrologio Romano " :] *See* LITURGIES.—*Latin Rite.*—*Martyrologies.*—I.

—— *See* ROME. [*Emperors.*]—Constantine I., [324-337.] *Κωνσταντινου . . . ἐπιστολη Ἀρειῳ και Ἀρειανοις.* Contantini [*sic*] Imp. rescriptum ad Arium & Arianos. [The Latin version by C. Baronius.] 1595. 8°. **857.** c. **3.**

APPENDIX.

—— *See* BARNABEUS (H.) Vita Cæsaris Baronii, *etc.* 1651. 4°. **486.** c. **9.**

—— —— 1718. 8°. **4863.** ccc. **18.**

—— *See* BEDE, *the Venerable,* Saint. Venerabilis Bedæ . . . opera, *etc.* (Vita Venerabilis Bedæ . . . ex Annalibus Cardin. C. Baronij & alijs desumpta.) 1612. fol. **474.** f. **11.**

—— —— 1688. fol. **10.** e. **4.**

—— *See* CALENZIO (G.) La Vita e gli scritti del Cardinale Cesare Baronio, *etc.* 1907. 4°. **4864.** f. **6.**

—— *See* KERR (*Lady* Amabel) The Life of Cesare Cardinal Baronius, *etc.* 1898. 8°. **4863.** ccc. **32.**

—— *See* LAEMMER (H.) De Cæsaris Baronii literarum commercio diatriba. 1903. 8°. **10905.** i. **28.**

—— *See* LE FÈVRE (T.) La Vie de César, Cardinal Baronius. 1668. 12°. **862.** h. **14.**

—— *See* SIMONCELLI (V.) Per Cesare Baronio. Scritti vari nel terzo centenario della sua morte, *etc.* 1911. 8°. **4864.** f. **19.**

—— *See* VITE. Vite di pii letterati. [Containing the lives of C. Baronius and others.] 1780. 8°. **4865.** c. **48.**

BARONIUS (JACOBUS) *See* BARRON (James) *B.D.*

BARONIUS (JOANNES DECIUS) *See* DÉCSI (János) *Baronyai.*

BARONIUS (JOHANNES CALVINUS) *See* BARONIUS (Justus)

BARONIUS (JUSTUS) Iusti Baronii . . . Epistolarum sacrarum ad pontificem max. et amplissimos cardinales &c. libri VI. Quibus quæ ad causam abiectæ à se hæreseos pertinent, ordine quasi historico complexus est, *etc.* pp. 392. *E Typographeo I. Albini: Moguntiæ,* 1605. 8°. **1020.** d. **11.**

BARONIUS (MARTINUS) Iasna pochodnia zyćia apostolskiego, *etc.* [Being a translation into Polish of the " Vita, gesta et miracula B. Stanislai Casimiritani " attributed to M. Baronius.] pp. 78. 1660. 4°. *See* STANISLAUS, *of Casimir, Saint.* **4823.** d. **43.**

BARONIUS (OCTAVIUS) Ad pontificem maximum Urbanum VIII., panegyris abb. Octauij Baronij. pp. 11. *Apud hæredem B. Zannetti: Romæ,* 1627. 4°. **11405.** e. **5.**

BARONIUS (ROBERTUS) *See* BARON (Robert) *Professor of Divinity in Marischal College, Aberdeen.*

BARONIUS (THEODORUS) Theodori Baronii . . . De operationis meiendi triplici læsione, & curatione libri duo, *etc.* pp 294. *Apud A. Vianum: Papiæ,* 1609. 4°. **781.** c. **4.**

BARONIUS (VINCENTIUS) Vincentij Baronij . . . de pleuripneumonia, anno Domini M.DC.XXXIII. et alij temporibus Flaminiam aliasq; regiones popularite infestante, ac a nemine hactenus obseruata. Libri duo *etc.* pp. 378. *Apud I. Cimattium: Foroliuij,* 1636. 4°. **806.** dd. **4.** (2.

The titlepage is engraved.

BARONIUS AC MANFREDUS (FRANCISCUS) *See* BARONIO MANFREDI (Francesco)

BARONIUSZ (CESAR) *Cardinal.* *See* BARONIUS (Caesar)

BARONNAT ( ) *Abbé.* Histoire impartiale et critique du rigorisme moderne en matière de prêt de commerce, ou la législation française et la doctrine de l'église catholique sur le prêt à intérêt, justifiées des imputations de la plupar des séminaires de France. Réfutation des erreurs de M. l'abbé Combalot sur l'autorité du Pape, et sur l'indépendance des rois, quant au temporel. pp. xlviii. 602. 18 *Paris,* 1842. 8°. **1391.** d. **18**

—— Le Prétendu mystère de l'usure dévoilé, ou le plaiemen d'argent, connu sous le nom de prêt à intérêt, démontr légitime par l'autorité civile et par l'autorité ecclésiastique *etc.* 2 tom. *Paris,* 1822. 8°. **1391.** d. **15**

BARONNET (E.) La Banque de France. Pour elle ou contre elle. pp. 47. *Paris,* 1865. 8°. **8227.** g. **45.** (12.

—— Le Crédit général pour tous non remboursable. Spécialement applicable aux finances de la ville de Paris. pp. 92 *Paris,* 1870. 4°. **8228.** i. **2**

—— Système des bons de délégation pour assurer l'exécutio prompte et rapide des grands travaux de Paris et de principales villes de la France. Mémoire présenté à M. l baron Haussmann, *etc.* pp. 61. *Paris,* 1867. 8°. **8225.** eee. **42.** (3.

BARONNIERE-LEDOUX (J. B.) Essai sur l'hémorrhagi utérine pendant et après l'accouchement, *etc.* pp. 19. *Paris,* 1809. 4°. **1182.** h. **5.** (2

BARONS. The Last of the Barons. By the author o " Rienzi." [The preface signed: E. L. B., i.e. Edwar G. E. L. Bulwer, afterwards Bulwer-Lytton.] 1843. 12° *See* B., E. L. N. **2281**

BARONS (KRIŠJĀNIS)

—— *See* BAUMANIS (A.) Krišjānis Barons, *etc.* [With portrait.] 1946. 8°. **10794.** b. **1**

—— *See* BĒRZKALNS (A.) Typenverzeichnis lettischer Volks romanzen in der Sammlung Kr. Barons' Latvju Dainas. 1938. 8°. [*FF Communications.* no. 123.] Ac. **9883.**

—— *See* KLAUSTIŅŠ (R.) Latvju tautas daiņas, *etc.* [Co taining material drawn from the collection of K. Baror and other sources.] 1928, *etc.* 8°. **2286.** g.

—— *See* ŠMITS (P.) Tautas dziesmas. Papildinājums K Barona " Latvju Dainām," *etc.* 1936, *etc.* 8°. Ac. **988**

—— Latwju dainas Kr. Barona kopojum . . . 2. eefpoedums. (Chansons nationales latvienne *etc.*) [With the editor's portrait.] *Lett.* 6 vol. *Rig* 1922. 8°. **011586.** m. **2**

Vol. 3 is in 3 pt. The first edition is entered und BARONS (*K.*) *and* WISSENDORFFS (*H.*)

BARONS (KRIŠJĀNIS) and **WISSENDORFFS** (H.)

—— Латышскія народн пѣсни. (Chansons nationales lataviennes.—Latwju dain *etc.*) [Edited by K. Barons and H. Wissendorffs.] *L* 4 том. *Jelgawā, С.-Петербургъ,* 1894–1910. 8°. **011586.** cc.

Том. 3 *is in* 3 *pt.*

BARONS (PERCY ALFRED)

—— Backwardness in School. Its diagnosis and treatment. pp. viii. 182. *Blackie & Son: London & Glasgow*, 1938. 8°. **8312**. a. **10**.

—— Forward to Arithmetic. [With teachers' books.] 8 pt. *Blackie: London*, [1939.] 8°. **08535**. a. **12**.

—— Forward to Reading. 4 bk. *Blackie & Son: London & Glasgow*, 1938. 8°. **12986**. d. **15**.

—— Our Wondrous World. (A first nature book for primary schools.) [With illustrations.] pp. 112. *Blackie & Son: London & Glasgow*, 1948. 8°. **7008**. aa. **46**.

—— Tiger Hunt. pp. 63. *London & Glasgow*, 1939. 8°. [*Blackie's Graded Story Readers*.] W.P. **10279/76**.

—— Tiger Hunt . . . Illustrated by Raymond Sheppard. pp. v. 50. *Blackie & Son: London & Glasgow*, 1952. 8°. [*Crusader Series*. no. 12.] W.P. **4024/12**.

BARONS (ROBERT) *See* BARNES (Robert) *Chaplain to Henry VIII.*

BARONSFEATHER (CHARLES GILBERT STENHOUSE) Medical Missionary Language Study as it is and as it ought to be. (Together with a literal translation of St. Mark's Gospel in Cantonese [i.e. a word for word translation of the Cantonese version].) pp. 218. *Kelly & Walsh: Hongkong*, 1914. 8°. **11094**. d. **14**.

BARONSFEATHER (WILLIAM N.) Tables for the Multiplication of Fractions, of one pound sterling at thirty-two different rates. pp. 8. *F. C. Mathieson & Sons: London*, 1898. 8°. **08548**. f. **2**.

BARONTE (GERVÉE) *See* BARONTI.

BARONTI, afterwards **BRECKENRIDGE** (GERVÉE) *See also* MILES (Arthur) *pseud.* [i.e. G. Baronti, afterwards Breckenridge.]

—— The Bracelet, and other stories. pp. 126. *Morgan, Laird & Co.: London*, 1946. 8°. **12642**. a. **70**.

—— Dying Flame. A novel. pp. 288. *Hurst & Blackett: London*, [1932.] 8°. NN. **19967**.

—— The History of the Soul. [On the doctrine of re-incarnation.] pp. 72. [*The Author*:] *Chesham*, [1937.] 8°. **8634**. cc. **31**.

—— Life and Loves of a Prodigal Daughter. Being the intimate memoirs of Gervée Baronte. [With a portrait.] pp. 384. *Baronte Press: London*, 1935. 8°. **010822**. e. **20**.

—— More Truth than Poetry. pp. 181. *Morgan, Laird & Co.: London*, 1944. 8°. **012643**. pp. **71**.

—— The Scent of the Aloe. [Poems.] pp. 63. *Selwyn & Blount: London*, 1921. 8°. **011648**. g. **59**.

—— You Have Lived Before! [Articles on reincarnation reprinted from Pearson's Weekly. With a portrait.] pp. 186. *C. A. Pearson: London*, 1936. 8°. **8634**. ccc. **4**.

—— Your Previous Life on Earth. Reincarnation simplified. pp. 215. *Herbert Jenkins: London*, 1938. 8°. **8634**. ccc. **76**.

BARONUS (VINCENTIUS) *See* BARONIUS.

BARON VAN DEDEM (ALEXANDER) *See* DEDEM.

BARON-WILSON (MARGARET) *See* HARRIES, afterwards BARON-WILSON.

BARONYAI DECSI (JÁNOS) *See* DÉCSI (J.) *Baronyai.*

BARÓN Y TORRES (LEOPOLDO) *Duke de Maqueda.*

—— Don Gutierre de Cárdenas, íntimo confidente y consejero de los Reyes Católicos. pp. 207. [*Madrid*,] 1945. 8°. **010632**. a. **5**.

BARONZI (GEORGE A.) Barba luĭ Stefan cel Mare. Comedia intr' un act. pp. 55. *Craiova*, 1882. 8°. **11758**. bbb. **40**. (**2**.)

—— Бѣтрѫnȣл mistepiosȣ, tpadȣsȣ din францозеще de Ȣ. B. [i.e. G. A. Baronzi.] (Фantasmeле nonтȣpne.—Кънътжiȣл din Lord Byron.—Вокабȣлар, *etc.*) pp. 31. 1851. 8°. *See* B., G. **12513**. c. **32**.

—— Comedia Stelelor. Feeria intr'un act şi un prolog. pp. 32. *Craiova*, 1882. 8°. **11758**. bbb. **39**. (**1**.)

—— Daciada, poemă epică in opt cânturi. pp. 90. *Braila*, 1890. 8°. **11586**. bbb. **21**. (**3**.)

—— Legenda Romanieĭ. [A poem.] pp. 56. *Bucurescĭ*, 1862. 8°. **11586**. dd. **11**. (**2**.)

—— Limba Română şi tradiţiunile eĭ. pp. 280. *Galaţi*, 1872. 8°. **12264**. k. **7**.
Vol. 1 *of an edition of the author's "Opere complecte."*

—— Matei Basarabu; saŭ, Dorobanţi şi Seimeni. Dramă în cincĭ acte şi în versurĭ, *etc.* pp. 152. *Bucurescĭ*, 1858. 8°. **11758**. bbb. **11**. (**2**.)

—— Muncitori statului. (Roman original.) pp. 372. *Galaţĭ*, [1880?] 8°. **12589**. m. **7**.

—— Orele Dalbe. [A collection of short poems.] pp. 68. *Bucurescĭ*, 1864. 8°. **11586**. bb. **13**. (**4**.)

—— Satire. pp. 58. *Bucuresci*, 1867. 16°. **11586**. a. **1**. (**1**.)

BARONZIO (AMLETO) La Morale positiva. pp. 88. v. *Mantova*, 1890. 8°. **8408**. h. **29**.

BAROOAH (NARENDRA NATH SHARMA) *See* NARENDRANĀTHA ŚARMĀ BAṚUYĀ.

BAROOAH (U.) *See* UPENDRANĀTHA BAṚUYĀ.

BAROPIUS (WOLFGANGUS) Disputatio v. de adiaphoris, seu ritibus ecclesiasticis, pro Augustanæ Confessionis articulo XIV. adversus Calvinianos, pontificios & Photinianos, *etc.* 1610. *See* FRANTZE (W.) Augustanæ Confessionis articuli fidei XXI . . . disputationibus . . . confirmati, *etc.* 1611, *etc.* 4°. **1353**. e. **2**.

BARORS (JOAQUIM SERGIO DE) *See* BARROS.

BAROS (GYULA) Madách nyomai szépirodalmunkban. pp. 35. *Budapest*, 1923. 8°. **011840**. bb. **19**.

BAROS (JAN)

—— *See* BAŤA (T.) How I began. [Translated by J. Baros.] 1934. 8°. **10795**. pp. **13**.

—— *See* BAŤA (T.) How I began. Translated by J. Baros, *etc.* 1941. 8°. **10798**. d. **2**.

BAROS (NEMESIO) *See* BOLLO (Luis C.) South America Past and Present . . . Translated . . . by N. Baros, *etc.* 1919. 8°. **9773**. ee. **4**.

BAROSCHI (J. B.) Quelques considérations sur la kératite. Thèse, *etc.* pp. 48. *Montpellier*, 1865. 4°. **7379**. f. **12**. (**14**.)

BAROSIA.—*Ἀναγνωστηριον "Ἡ Σαλαμις." Κανονισμος του ἐν Βαρωσιοις-Ἀμμοχωστῳ Ἀναγνωστηριον "Ἡ Σαλαμις."* pp. 12. *Ἐν Λευκωσιᾳ*, 1892. 8º **11904**. e. **41**. (**6**.)

Ἀνωτερα Ἐμπορικη Σνολη Σιακαλλη.

—— *Κανονισμος Ἀνωτερας Ἐμπορικης Σχολης Σιακαλλη.* (English High School Shacallis.) *Mod. Gr.* pp. 12. *Βαρωσια*, [1934.] 8º. **8355**. d. **47**.

—— *Κανονισμος Ἀνωτερας Ἐμπορικης Σχολης Σιακαλλη, etc.* [New edition, with additions.] pp. 12. *Βαρωσια*, [1935.] 8º. **8355**. d. **48**.

—— *Οἰκοτροφειον Ανωτερας Ἐμπορικης Σχολης Σιακαλλη, etc.* pp. 4. *Βαρωσια*, [1935.] 16º. **8356**. aa. **42**.

—— *Μουσικοφιλολογικος και Φιλαθλητικος Συλλογος "Ἀνορθωσις."*

—— *Ἐκδοσεις Μ. Φ. Α. Σ. "Ἀνορθωσις." Λευκωσια*, 1933– . 8º. W.P. **11394**.

—— *Ταμιευτηριον "Ἡ Σαλαμις." Καταστατικον του ταμιευτηριου "Ἡ Σαλαμις."* pp. 14. *Ἐν Λεμησσῳ*, 1900. 16º. **8282**. aa. **63**.

BAROSIA (ANTIFOR DI) *See* ANTAFOR, *di Barosia.*

BAROSS (GÁBOR) *See* PETROVICS (L.) Bellusi Baross Gábor volt Magyar kereskedelmi miniszter élete, *etc.* 1892. 8º. **10795**. d. **36**.

BAROSS (GYÖRGY)

—— A Külügyi Szemle a második világháborúban. Egy fejezet a szellemi ellenállás történetéből. pp. 31. *Budapest*, 1946. 8º. **11867**. g. **35**.

BAROSS (JÁNOS) Agrár öröklési jog . . . Az előszót irta: Széchényi I. gr. köt. 1. Általános tanok és a német törzsöröklés. pp. vii. 420. *Budapest*, 1902. 8º. **05551**. i. **22**.

BAROSS (KÁROLY) *See* SAJÓ (K.) Peronospora Viticola. [With a preface by K. Baross.] 1890. 8º. **07076**. e. **15**.

—— Magyarország földbirtokosai. Az összes 100 holdnál többel biró magyar birtokosok névsora, a tulajdonukban levő földterületek mivelési ágak szerinti feltüntetésével . . . sajtó alá rendezte és kiadta . . . Baross K. . . . Az egyes vármegyék gazdasági leirását szerkesztette dr. Németh J. pp. 885. 155. *Budapest*, 1893. 4º. **8223**. f. **34**.

—— Szöleink újjáalakitása . . . Jelentések az Országos Magyar Gazdasági Egyesület által Peér . . . Kecskemétre rendezett szöllészeti tanulmány-útról. pp. 148. *Budapest*, 1890. 8º. *A "Borászati Lapok" Kiadasa.* Munka 2. **7078**. bbb. **47**.

BAROSSO (MARIA) Foro Romano. I monumenti forensi e notizie sugli ultimi scavi. (In occasione del v. Congresso dell'Associazione italiana per gli studi sui materiali da costruzione.) [With illustrations and a plan.] pp. 96. *Roma*, 1907. 8º. **07703**. ee. **34**.

BAROSSO (PIETRO ANTONIO) Proverbj e detti proverbiali scelti e ristampati per cura di P. A. Barosso con gli equivalenti latini. pp. 90. *Torino*, 1837. 8º. **1074**. k. **18**.

BAROSSO Y POSSO (JUAN) *See* BELLE (P. van) Pertinent en waarachtig verhaal van alle de handelingen en directie van P. van Belle ontrent den slavenhandel, ofte, het assiento de negros, eerst door D. J. Barosso y Posso . . . aangegaan, *etc.* 1689. fol. **8223**. d. **56**. (**4**.)

BAROT (ALEXANDRE) L'Ortie, sa valeur alimentaire, fourragère, textile . . . sa culture en France et en Suède. pp. 106. *Paris*, 1891. 8º. **7075**. de. **21**.

BAROT (FIRMIN) De l'angine couenneuse, pseudomembraneuse, ou mieux pseudoméningée. pp. 31. *Paris*, 1848. 4º. [*Collection des thèses soutenues à la Faculté de Médecine de Paris.* An 1848. tom. 1.] **7372**. b. **4**.

BAROT (FRANÇOIS ODYSSE) *See* CARLYLE (Thomas) [*The French Revolution.*] Histoire de la Révolution française . . . Traduit . . . par E. Regnault et O. Barot. 1865, *etc.* 12º. **9220**. bb. **31**.

—— *See* PERIODICAL PUBLICATIONS.—*Paris.* Revue des cours littéraires de la France et de l'étranger, *etc.* (Redacteur en chef, M. Odysse-Barot.) 1863, *etc.* 4º. P.P. **4290**. d.

—— *See* PERIODICAL PUBLICATIONS.—*Paris.* Revue des cours scientifiques de la France et de l'étranger, *etc.* (Redacteur en chef, M. Odysse-Barot.) 1863, *etc.* 4º. P.P. **1614**. ea.

—— L'Agonie de la papauté. pp. 32. *Paris*, 1868. 8º. **8033**. b. **68**. (**10**.)

—— Histoire de la littérature contemporaine en Angleterre 1830–1874. pp. 511. *Paris*, 1874. 8º. [*Histoire de la littérature contemporaine dans les différents états de l'Europe.*] **2310**. b. **9/2**.

—— Histoire des idées au XIXᵉ siècle. Émile de Girardin. Sa vie, ses idées, son œuvre, son influence. pp. 342. *Paris*, 1866. 8º. **12237**. bb. **2**.

—— L'Inceste. Troisième édition. pp. 414. *Paris*, 1883. 18º. **12518**. d. **17**.

—— Lettres sur la philosophie de l'histoire. pp. 242. *Paris*, 1864. 8º. **9005**. bb. **6**.

—— Madame la Présidente. Quatrième édition. pp. 338. *Paris*, 1883. 8º. **12510**. k. **26**.

—— La Naissance de Jésus. Fragment d'une histoire du Christ publié en 1857. pp. 33. *Paris*, 1864. 8º. **4825**. aa. **4**.

BAROT (LOUIS JOSEPH) Guide pratique de l'Européen dans l'Afrique Occidentale . . . Préface de M. Binger. pp. xxiv. 487. *Paris*, [1902.] 8º. **010097**. g. **35**.

BAROT (ODYSSE) *See* BAROT (François O.)

BAROT (P. DESIRÉ) Dissertation sur l'apoplexie, *etc.* pp. 45. *Paris*, 1818. 4º. **1183**. d. **15**. (**30**.)

BAROT-FORLIÈRE (L.)

—— *See* BAROT-FORLIÈRE (M.) and (L.) Notre sœur, la Pologne, *etc.* 1928. 8º. **10292**. p. **14**.

BAROT-FORLIÈRE (M.) and (L.)

—— Notre sœur, la Pologne—. Notes et impressions, septembre 1927, *etc.* pp. 237. *Paris*, 1928. 8º. **10292**. p. **14**.

BARÓTHY (BÁLINT) *See* ANDREWS (Charles) *Representative for Maine.* Ismeretlen levelek Kossuth amerikai szerepléséről. Andrews Károly . . . bezséde . . . Sajtó alá rendezte és a bevezetést irta: Baróthy B. 1925. 8º. **8027**. g. **13**.

—— Halleluja—Regény. . . Második kiadás. pp. 93. *Budapest*, 1933. 8º. **12590**. w. **17**.

BARÓTI (COLOMANNUS) Exercitatio theologica de auri generatione, locis, nominibus, generibus, atque allegorica eorum significatione, *etc.* *Praes.* R. Andala. pp. 32. *Franequeræ*, 1716. 4º. **4371**. e. **2**. (**3**.)

ARÓTI (DEZSŐ)

— Juhász Gyula. Tanulmány. [With a bibliography.] pp. 80. *Szeged*, 1933. 8°. **11855**. aaa. **23**.

ARÓTI (LAJOS) *See* PERIODICAL PUBLICATIONS.—*Pest.* Bolond Istók. Kiadó-tulajdonos és felelős szerkesztő Baróti L. 1905, *etc.* 4°. P.P. **4834**. pu.

— *See* PETŐFI (S.) [*Prose Works.*] Petőfi ujabb reliquiái . . . Gyüjtötte Baróti L. 1887. 8°. Ac. **8983/16**.

— Petőfi költeményeinek első kritikai kiadásáról . . . Különnyomat a " Philologiai Közlöny " ből. pp. 44. *Budapest*, 1894. 8°. **011851**. ee. **6**. **(3.)**

ARÓTI (LAJOS) and CSÁNKI (DEZSŐ)

— Magyarország története középiskolák alsó osztályai és polgári fiúiskolák számára . . . Térképekkel, *etc.* pp. 192. *Budapest*, 1891. 8°. **09315**. e. **5**.

BARÓTI SZABÓ (DAVID) *See* SZABÓ (D.) *Baróti.*

BAROTS (F. H.) Manuel des familles, contenant dictionnaire de droit français . . . augmenté d'un dictionnaire d'agriculture et de la médecine vétérinaire . . . par Roche, Lubin. pp. 664. *Paris*, 1858. 8°. **5405**. e. **8**.

BAROTSI-LAND. Barotsi-Land Sketches. [Photographs, with descriptive letterpress.] *Impression Sadag: Genève*, [1905.] 8°. **4766**. aaa. **18**.

BAROTSI-LAND MISSION. [For publications of the Barotsi-Land Mission of the Société des Missions Évangéliques :] *See* PARIS.—*Société des Missions Évangéliques.*

BAROTT (HERBERT G.)

— Effect of Temperature, Humidity, and other Factors on Hatch of Hens' Eggs and on Energy Metabolism of Chick Embryos. pp. 46. *Washington*, 1937. 8°. [*United States Department of Agriculture.* Technical Bulletin. no. 553.] A.S. **800/2**.

BAROTTE (JEAN) *See* VELU (H.) and BAROTTE (J.) Éléments pratiques de la pathologie vétérinaire exotique, *etc.* 1924. 8°. **7295**. h. **30**.

— Les Trypanosomiases de l'Afrique du Nord. [With a bibliography.] pp. viii. 183. pl. XVII. *Rabat; Rochefort-sur-Mer* [printed], 1925. 8°. **07687**. k. **6**.
The date in the colophon is 1926.

BAROTTI (CESARE) Pitture e scolture che si trovano nelle chiese, luoghi pubblici, e sobborghi della città di Ferrara. [With a plan.] pp. 223. *Ferrara*, 1770. 8°. **10130**. b. **34**.

BAROTTI (GIOVANNI ANDREA) *See* ARIOSTO (L.) [*Works.*] Opere in versi, e in prosa, *etc.* [Edited by G. A. Barotti.] 1741. 12°. **1063**. c. **1–4**.

— *See* ARIOSTO (L.) [*Orlando Furioso.*] L'Orlando Furioso di L. Ariosto e le dichiarazioni di G. Barotti . . . al poema. 1840. 8°. [*I quattro poeti italiani coi migliori comenti, etc.* tom. 1. pt. 2.] **11421**. i. **16**.

— — 1900. 8°. **11426**. i. **13**.

— *See* BERTOLDO. Traduzion dal toscan in lengua veneziana de Bertoldo, Bertoldin e Cacasseno, *etc.* (Dichiarazioni d'alquanti vocaboli contenuti nel testo toscan della presente opera, ricavate in parte dalle copiose annotazioni fatte alla prima edizione della medesima dal dottore G. A. Barotti.) 1747. 8°. **84**. b. **33**.

BAROTTI (GIOVANNI ANDREA)

— *See* BERTOLDO. Bertoldo, con Bertoldino e Cacasenno, in ottava rima. Con . . . annotazioni [by G. A. Barotti], *etc.* 1736. 4°. **639**. l. **17**.

— — 1737. 8°. **11431**. bb. **19**.

— — [1737.] 12°. **1063**. f. **3**.

— — 1739. 8°. **1063**. f. **4**.

— *See* BOUHOURS (D.) La Maniera di ben pensare ne componimenti. Dialoghi tradotti . . . nella lingua italiana dal Signor G. A. Barotti. 1735. 4°. [*Considerazioni del marchese G. G. Orsi . . . sopra la Maniera di ben pensare, etc.* tom. 1.] **89**. g. **13**.

— *See* GUARINI (G. B.) Il Pastor fido, *etc.* (Delle opere del Cavalier B. Guarini tomo 2–4.) [Edited by G. A. Barotti and A. Zeno.] 1737, *etc.* 4°. **639**. k. **15–18**.

— *See* GUSTA (F.) De vita et scriptis J. A. Barotti . . . commentarius, *etc.* [1780.] 8°. **10631**. c. **28**.

— *See* TASSONI (A.) *Count.* La Secchia rapita. Poema eroicomico . . . S'aggiungono la prefazione, e le annotazioni di G. Barotti, *etc.* 1744. 4°. **79**. k. **8**.

— — 1813. 16°. **1464**. a. **2**.

— Del dominio delle donne. Discorsi accademici. [Edited by G. P. Zanotti.] pp. 56. *Bologna*, 1745. 8°. **8415**. ee. **27**. **(1.)**

— Delle chiome bionde, e ciglia nere d'Alcina. Discorso accademico, *etc.* pp. 48. *Padova*, [1747.] 8°. **161**. k. **41**.

— Difesa degli scrittori ferraresi . . . da quanto ha pubblicato contro di loro l'autore delle Osservazioni al terzo libro dell' Eloquenza italiana di Monsignor G. Fontanini. pp. 166. *See* FONTANINI (G.) *Archbishop of Ancyra.* Esami di varj autori sopra il libro intitolato l'Eloquenza italiana, *etc.* 1739. 4°. **617**. k. **17**.

— Memorie intorno alla vita del padre Giacomo Sanvitali, della Compagnia di Gesù. pp. viii. 66. *Venezia*, 1757. 4°. **4865**. ff. **12**.

— Memorie istoriche di letterati ferrares [*sic*]. Opera postuma. [With portraits. Edited by Lorenzo Barotti.] vol. 1. pp. viii. 343. *Ferrara*, 1777. fol. **663**. l. **15**.
No more published in this edition. The titlepage is engraved. The date in the colophon is 1774.

— [Another copy.] **821**. eee. **3**.

— [Another copy.] **134**. f. **9**.

— Edizione seconda. (Volume secondo. Dell' abate Lorenzo Barotti.) [The whole edited by Lorenzo Barotti.] *Ferrara*, 1792, 93. 4°. **617**. l. **18**. & **617**. l. **19**. **(1.)**
Vol. 1 *only is of the second edition.*

— [Another copy.] **1321**. f. **11**.

— *See* BARUFFALDI (Girolamo) *the Younger.* Continuazione delle Memorie istoriche di Letterati ferraresi [by G. A. and L. Barotti], *etc.* 1811. 4°. **617**. l. **19**. **(2.)**

— Notizia intorno alla vita di Monsignor Bonaventura Barberini, arcivescovo di Ferrara, *etc.* 1753. *See* CALOGIERÀ (A.) Raccolta d'opuscoli scientifici e filologici. tom. 49. 1728, *etc.* 12°. **247**. c. **18**.

— Prose italiane. 3 tom. *Ferrara*, 1770. 4°. **12227**. d. **4**.

BAROTTI (GIOVANNI ANDREA)

—— [For editions of the "Vita di Messer Lodovico Ariosto" by G. A. Barotti included in editions of the "Orlando Furioso":] *See* ARIOSTO (L.) [*Orlando Furioso.*]

BAROTTI (LORENZO) *See* BAROTTI (G. A.) Memorie istoriche di letterati ferrares [*sic*], *etc.* [Edited by L. Barotti.] 1777. fol. **663.** l. **15.**

—— *See* BAROTTI (G. A.) Memorie istoriche di letterati ferraresi, *etc.* (Volume secondo. Dell' abate L. Barotti.) [The whole edited by L. Barotti.] 1792, *etc.* 4°. **617.** l. **18.** & **617.** l. **19.** (**1.**)

—— Il Caffè. Canti due. pp. 38. **L.P.** *Parma,* 1781. 4°. **11431.** f. **40.** (**1.**)

—— [Another copy.] **11429.** k. **10.** (**4.**)

—— La Fisica. Poemetto. *See* ITALIAN POEMS. Poemetti italiani. vol. 11. 1797. 12°. **1062.** f. **11.**

—— Lezioni sacre . . . su i libri di Tobia, di Giuditta, di Ester. (vol. 2. Lezioni sacre . . . su i libri de' Maccabei.) 2 vol. *Parma,* 1785, 86. 4°. **5.** f. **14.**

—— Memorie istoriche intorno a Cornelio Bentivoglio, cardinale. *See* BENTIVOGLIO (C.) *Cardinal.* La Tebaide di Stazio. 1821. 8°. [*Collezione de' classici italiani.* vol. 290.] **12201.p.1/290.**

—— Serie de' vescovi ed arcivescovi di Ferrara, *etc.* pp. 159. *Ferrara,* 1781. 4°. **659.** e. **17.**

—— Vita di Guido Bentivoglio, cardinale. *See* BENTIVOGLIO (G.) *Cardinal.* Opere storiche del cardinal Bentivoglio. vol. 1. 1806, *etc.* 8°. [*Collezione de' classici italiani.* vol. 184.] **12201.p.1/184.**

BAROTTUS (JOANNES ANDREAS) *See* BAROTTI (Giovanni A.)

BÁRÓTZI (SÁNDOR) *See* BÁRÓCZY.

BAROU (NOAH ISAACOVITCH) *See* BARU.

BAROUCHAS (ATHANASIOS) *See* ATHANASIUS, *Monk, of Crete.*

BAROUD (CLAUDE ODILE JOSEPH) *See* DUVEYRIER (H.) *pseud.* [i.e. C. O. J. Baroud.]

BAROU DU SOLEIL (PIERRE ANTOINE) Discours prononcé . . . en présentant à l'enregistrement la Déclaration qui annonce les États-Généraux, & rétablit les Cours & Tribunaux au même . . . état qu'ils étoient avant le 8 mai. *See* LYONS, *Grand-Bailliage de.* Récit de ce qui s'est passé au Grand Bailliage de Lyon, *etc.* [1788.] 8°. **911.** b. **10.** (**28.**)

—— [Another edition.] *See* LYONS, *Grand-Bailliage de.* Récit de ce qui c'est passé au Grand-Bailliage de Lyon, *etc.* [1788.] 8°. F.R. **7.** (**13.**)

—— Éloge de M. Prost de Royer . . . Prononcé à l'ouverture des Audiences de la Sénéchaussée de Lyon, le 30 novembre 1784. pp. 68. 1785. 8°. **10664.** bb. **24.** (**3.**)

BAROUILLE (ÉMILE EUGÈNE) Emploi thérapeutique des plantes de la famille des labiées. pp. 38. *Paris,* 1865. 4°. [*Collection des thèses soutenues à la Faculté de Médecine de Paris.* An 1865. tom. 1.] **7373.** f. **7.**

BAROUILLET (J. MARTIN) *See* also MARTIN, *pseud.* [i.e. J. M. Barouillet.]

—— *See* ALCIBIADES. Alcibiade solitaire, opéra, *etc.* [By J. G. A. Cuvelier de Trie and J. M. Barouillet.] 1814. 8°. **11738.** c. **34.** (**11.**)

BAROUILLET (J. MARTIN)

—— *See* CUVELIER DE TRIE (J. G. A.) L'Officier cosaque, comédie . . . paroles de J. G. A. Cuvelier [assisted by "B.," i.e. J. M. Barouillet], *etc.* 1803. 8°. **11738.** c. **34.** (**5.**)

—— *See* CUVELIER DE TRIE (J. G. A.) and B * * *, J. M. A-t-il deux femmes? ou les corsaires barbaresques, mélodrame . . . paroles de J. G. A. Cuvelier, et J. M. B * * * [i.e. J. M. Barouillet], *etc.* 1803. 8°. **11738.** c. **40.** (**6.**)

BAROUKAS (ATHANASIUS) *See* BAROUCHAS.

BAROUNCELLI-JAVOUN (FOLCÓ DE) *Marquis. See* BARONCELLI-JAVON.

BARO URBIGERUS, *pseud. See* URBIGERUS (Baro) *pseud.*

BAROUSSE (G.) Essai sur la cataracte. Thèse, *etc.* pp. 19. *Montpellier,* 1839. 4°. **1181.** i. **10.** (**10.**)

BAROUX (J. B.) Dissertation sur l'hydropisie de l'articulation du bras avec l'épaule, *etc.* pp. 25. *Paris,* 1804. 4°. **1182.** f. **6.** (**4.**)

BAROUX (J. B. F.) De la dysphagie, ou considérations générales sur les causes qui gênent ou empêchent la déglutition. Thèse, *etc.* pp. 21. *Paris,* 1837. 4°. **1184.** h. **13.** (**7.**)

BAROUX (L.) Lettre de M. l'abbé Baroux à M. J. Deneve. [An account of the tribe of the Potowatomies.] pp. 67. *Orléans,* 1863. 12°. **4745.** aaa. **24.**

BĂROV (D.)

—— Учебник по гражданско право с увод в правото. pp. lx. 943. *Свищов,* 1948. 8°. **5759.** ee. **1.**
Висше Училище за Стоп. и Социални Науки "Д. А. Ценов." Библиотека Научни трудове и помагала. no. 49.

BAROVIUS (JOANNES DECIUS) *See* DÉCSI (János) *Baronyai.*

BAROVIUS (JOHANNES GEORGIUS) Ex Theologiæ theoretico-practicæ, parte posteriore, jam exituræ, caput postremum. De dispensatione fœderis gratiæ, sub æternitate, quod . . . publicè tueri conabitur, J. G. Barovius, *etc. Praes.* P. van Mastricht. *Ultrajecti,* 1686. 4°. **1014.** b. **11.** (**16.**)
An extract, before publication, from "Theoretico-practica theologia" by P. van Mastricht.

BAROVIUS (SAMUEL) Dissertatio theologica de primogeniti adoratione angelis imperata, ad locum ex Epistolâ Pauli ad Hebræos cap 1. vs. 6. prima, secunda & tertia, *etc. Praes.* J. Wesselius. pp. 22. *Lugduni Batavorum,* 1729. 4°. T. **2183.** (**26.**)

BARÔZAI. Ein Barôzai de lai rue Saint-Felebar es barôzai ses aimins, su lés aifaire du tan; d'aivô ein dialôgue su lés aifaire qui son airivé ai Dijon dan lai septeime semaigne aipré lai Pentecôte. [In verse. By —— Berger.] pp. 12. *Dijon,* 1845. 12°. **11498.** e. **48.** (**2.**)

BARÔZAI (GUI) *pseud.* [i.e. BERNARD DE LA MONNOYE.] Noei Borguignon de Gui Barôzai. Quatreime édicion, *etc.* [Edited by J. Bouhier.] pp. 416. *Dioni,* 1720. 8°. **241.** g. **32.**

—— [Another copy.] G. **18200.**

—— [Another edition.] [With two appendices, the first containing musical notes, the second a Latin elegy on La Monnoye, by F. Oudin and a French translation of the elegy, signed R. de R., i.e. R. de Ruffey.] 3 pt. *Dioni,* 1720 [1730?]. 8°. **11498.** cc. **5.**
Pt. 1 containing the text is a duplicate of the preceding. The imprint at the end of the musical notes reads: "De l'imprimerie, du Mont-parnasse."

BARÔZAI (GUI) *pseud.* [i.e. BERNARD DE LA MONNOYE.]

—— Cinqueime édicion. Reveue, & augmentée de la nôte de l'ar, de chécun de Noei, *etc.* 2 pt. *Bregogne,* 1738. 12°. **1464.** b. **2.**

—— Cinqueime édicion, *etc.* pp. 422. *Dioni,* 1776. 12°. **11498.** bb. **49.**
A different edition from the preceding.

—— [Another edition.] Aivô queique aj utorion. pp. 101. [1780?] 12°. **11498.** a. **17.**

—— [Another edition.] Suivis de quelques poësies du même genre et d'un abrégé du glossaire alphabétique. Quatorzième édition. [Edited by L. Du Bois de Lisieux.] pp. xix. 144. *Châtillon-sur-Seine,* 1825 2°. **11498.** bb. **37.**

BAROZZI, *Family of.*

—— *See* BAROZZI (Pietro) *of Modena.* Vita e opere di Jacopo Barozzi detto il Vignola, con cenni sui suoi antenati e discendenti. [With genealogical tables.] 1949. 8°. **010632.** bbb. **35.**

BARÒZZI (A. E.) De la pleurésie purulente, et de sa terminaison par fistule pleuro-cutanée. pp. 55. *Paris,* 1853. 4°. [*Collection des thèses soutenues à la Faculté de Médecine de Paris.* An 1853. tom. 1.] **7372.** f. **3.**

BAROZZI (CARLO) *See* SINTHERN (P.) Roma Sacra . . . Versione italiana di C. Barozzi. 1925. 4°. **7815.** w. **17.**

BAROZZI (FRANCESCO) *See* HERO, *of Alexandria.* Heronis Mechanici liber de machinis bellicis, necnon liber de geodæsia. A F. Barocio . . . latinitate donati, multis mendis expurgati, & figuris, ac scholijs illustrati. 1572. 4°. **8461.** e. **2.** (**2.**)

—— *See* PROCLUS, *Diadochus.* [*Commentarii in Euclidem.*] Procli Diadochi . . . In primum Euclidis Elementorum librum commentariorum . . libri IIII. a F. Barocio . . . summa opera . . . expurgati: scholiis, & figuris . . . aucti: primùm iā romanę linguę venustate donati, *etc.* 1560. fol. **530.** k. **3.**

—— Admirandum illud geometricum problema tredecim modis demonstratum. Quod docet duas lineas in eodem plano designare, quæ nunquam inuicem coincidant, etiam si in infinitum protrahantur, *etc.* pp. 269. *Apud G. Perchacinum, sumptibus I. B. Fantini: Venetiis,* 1586. 4°. **530.** i. **4.**

—— Francisci Barocii . . . Commentarius in locum Platonis obscurissimum, & hactenus a nemine rectè expositum in principio dialogi octaui de Rep. ubi sermo habetur de numero geometrico, de quo prouerbium est, quòd numero Platonis nihil obscurius, *etc.* ff. 34. *Typis A. Benacii: Bononiæ,* 1566. 4°. **8461.** e. **2.** (**1.**)

—— Cosmographia in quatuor libros distributa . . . Cum præfatione eiusdem autoris . . . Præcesserunt etiam quædam communia mathematica, *etc.* pp. 349. *Ex officina G. Perchacini: Venetiis,* 1585. 8°. **533.** b. **10.**

—— Cosmografia in quattro libri divisa, *etc.* ff. 230. *G. Perchacino: Venetia,* 1607. 8°. **8562.** a. **10.**

—— Nobili nozze. Elisabetta Barozzi, Cesare Foscari. (Descrittione dell' Isola di Creta, composta da Francesco Barozzi fu figliuolo di messer Jacomo Nobile Venetiano l'anno 1777 [*sic*] ritrovandosi nella detta Isola.) [Edited by Giuseppe Nicoletti.] pp. 20. [*Venice,* 1898.] fol. **10125.** g. **22.**

—— Il Nobilissimo et antiquissimo giuoco Pythagoreo nominato Rythmomachia cioè battaglia de consonantie de numeri, *etc.* ff. 24. *G. Perchacino: Venetia,* 1572. 4°. **1040.** e. **37.** (**1.**)

BAROZZI (FRANCESCO)

—— Rythmomachia. Ein vortrefflich, und uhraltes Spiel, dess Pythagoræ: welches Gustavus Selenus, auss des Francisci Barozzi . . . welschem Tractätlein, ins Deutsche ubergesetzet, *etc.* *See* SELENUS (Gustavus) *pseud.* Das Schach- oder König-spiel, *etc.* 1616. fol. **61.** f. **22.**

BAROZZI (GIACINTO) *See* SPINELLI (A. G.) Bio-bibliografia dei due Vignola [Giacomo and Giacinto Barozzi]. 1908. 8°. [*SORBELLI (A.) Memorie e studi intorno a Jacopo Barozzi.*] **10633.** ccc. **1.**

BAROZZI (GIACOMO) called *Il Vignola.*

—— *See* BAROZZI (Pietro) *of Modena.* Vita e opere di Jacopo Barozzi detto il Vignola, con cenni sui suoi antenati e discendenti. [With plates.] 1949. 8°. **010632.** bbb. **35.**

—— *See* LOTZ (W.) Vignola-Studien, *etc.* 1939. 8°. **07815.** aa. **67.**

—— *See* SORBELLI (A.) Memorie e studi intorno a Jacopo Barozzi, pubblicati nel iv centenario dalla nascita, *etc.* [With plates, including a portrait and a bibliography.] 1908. 8°. **10633.** ccc. **1.**

—— *See* WILLICH (H.) Giacomo Barozzi da Vignola . . . Mit 38 Abbildungen im Text und 22 Tafeln. 1906. 8°. **7803.** t. **20.** (**2.**)

—— Il Vignola illustrato. Proposto da Giambattista Spampani, e Carlo Antonini, *etc.* [Containing the " Regola delli cinque ordini d'architettura " and the " Due regole della prospettiva pratica."] pp. 58. xxviii. pl. XXXXI. [7.] 3. *Roma,* 1770. fol. **L.R.294.b.9.**

—— Le Regole de' cinque ordini di architettura civile di M. Iacopo Barozzio da Vignola. Corredate delle aggiunte fattevi nell' edizione Romana dell'anno 1770 dagli architetti Gio. Batista Spampani e Carlo Antonini, che comprendono un saggio di geometrica; il comento al testo; il parallelo della proporzioni degli ordini . . . e le Due regole di prospettiva pratica . . . colle note del P. Gaudio; ed in questa ultima edizione Napolitana ricorrette, ed accresciutte di una dissertazione intorno a' medesimi ordini architettonici. pp. xii. 58. xx. viii. pl. LV. *Napoli,* 1795. fol. **7814.** d. **6.**

—— Le Due regole della prospettiva pratica . . . con i comentarij del R. P. M. Egnatio Danti, *etc.* pp. 145. *F. Zannetti: Roma,* 1583. fol. **48.** h. **20.**
The titlepage is engraved.

—— [Another edition.] pp. 145. *Nella Stamparia Camerale: Roma,* 1611. fol. **1259.** aa. **3.**
The titlepage is engraved.

—— [Another edition.] pp. 145. *Nella Stamparia del Mascardi: Roma,* 1644. fol. **560*.** e. **34.**

—— Regole della prospettiva prattica . . . con i commentarj del Rev. Padre M. Egnatio Danti . . . ora in questa quarta edizione diligentemente migliorata. [Edited by Francesco Veniero. With plates.] pp. 79. *Venezia,* 1743. fol. **60.** i. **22.**

—— Prospettiva pratica . . . Conforme l'edizione di Lelio dalla Volpe. pp. 30. pl. LXIV. **F.P.** *Milano,* 1830. 8°. **1259.** c. **15.**

—— *See* MALTON (James) The Young Painter's Maulstick; being a practical treatise on perspective . . . founded on the . . . process of Vignola and Sirigatti, *etc.* 1800. 4°. **1259.** c. **16.**

—— Regola delli cinque ordini d'architettura. pl. XXXII. *G. Porro: Venetia,* 1596. fol. **7815.** e. **21.**
The titlepage is engraved.

—— [Another edition.] Con vn ragionamento alli architeti di M. Ottaviano Ridolfi intorno alla perfetione di tutti gli cinque ordini di detta architetura. *G. Franco: Venetia,* 1603. fol. **559*. f. 4.**
Engraved throughout.

—— Regola delli cinque ordini d'architettura . . . Libro primo et originale. (Nuoua et vltima aggiunta delle porte d'architet[a] di Michel Angelo Buonaroti, *etc.*) pl. i–xxxxi, xxxxiiii, xxxxv. *A. Vaccarius: Romæ,* 1607. fol. **7815. e. 45.**
Engraved throughout. The date in the imprint of the second part containing the additional plates, is 1610. *Imperfect; wanting pl. xxxxii, xxxxiii. In this copy are inserted a number of architectural drawings and engravings.*

—— [Another edition.] pl. xxxxvi. *M. G. Rossi: Romæ,* 1617. fol. **559*. f. 5.**
Engraved throughout. The imprint of the second part containing pl. xxxx–xxxxvi reads: "G. B. de Rossi: Roma."

—— [Another edition.] pl. xxxxvi. *G. B. Rossi: Roma,* [1620?] 8°. **1043. f. 15.**
Engraved throughout.

—— [Another edition.] pl. xxxxv. *P. Marchetti: Siena,* [1635.] fol. **60. h. 18.**
Engraved throughout.

—— Regola delli cinque ordini d'architettura, *etc.* pl. xxxxv. *Bernardo Oppi: Siena,* [1635.] fol. **1483. dd. 4.**
Engraved.

—— [Another edition.] Gli Ordini di architettura . . . pubblicati da Carlo Amati. pp. 56. pl. xxxviii. *Milano,* 1805. fol. **559*. g. 16.**
The titlepage is engraved.

—— [Another edition.] I Cinque ordini d'architettura. pp. 17. pl. xxx. *Firenze,* 1806. fol. **7814. d. 7.**

—— [Another edition.] Gli Ordini di architettura. *Verona,* 1811. 4°. **7816. aaa. 4.**

—— [Another edition.] Accresciuti di altre interessanti tavole ed ombreggiati secondo il recente metodo de' licei. Quarta edizione, *etc.* pp. 36. pl. xxxix. *Milano,* 1846. 4°. **7820. c. 21.**

—— [Another edition.] Gli Ordini d'architettura civile . . . Corredati delle aggiunte fattevi dagli architetti Gio. Battista Spampani e Carlo Antonini ed ombreggiati secondo il nuovo metodo delle accademie delle belle arti d'Italia. Quarta edizione Milanese nuovamente accresciuta e migliorata per cura di Giuseppe Vallardi. pp. 102. xliv. *Milano,* 1850. fol. **7814. d. 8.**

—— [Another edition.] Regola dei cinque ordini di architettura . . . Riprodotti con aggiunte per cura e col disegno di Adriano de Bonis. pp. 24. pl. xxxii. *Firenze,* 1851. 8°. **7820. f. 6.**

—— [Another edition.] Gli Ordini d'architettura civile . . . Intagliati in rame e semplici contorni. Terza edizione eseguita sopra quelle ombreggiate pubblicate per cura di Giuseppe Vallardi. pp. 24. pl. xxix. *Milano,* 1854. fol. **7816. c. 4.**

—— Reigles des cinq ordres d'architecture . . . Avec une augmentation nouvelle de Michel Angelo Bonaroti et autres. Le Regole dei cinque ordini d'architettura, *etc.* *Ital. & Fr.* pp. 87. *Paris,* [1780?] 8°. **7815. aa. 6.**
Engraved throughout. Cropped.

—— Vignola: or the Compleat Architect. Shewing in a plain and easie way the rules of the five orders in architecture . . . Translated into English, by Joseph Moxon. pp. 80. pl. lv. *J. Moxon: London,* 1655. 8°. **1043. c. 43.**
With an additional titlepage, engraved.

—— The second edition, with additions. pp. 80. pl. lvi. *W. Leybourn, for Joseph Moxon: London,* 1665. 8°. **7815. a. 6.**

—— The fourth edition, with additions. pp. 80. pl. xlix. *J. Moxon: London,* 1694. 8°. **52. b. 10.**

—— The Regular Architect: or the General Rule of the Five Orders of Architecture of M. Giacomo Barozzio da Vignola. With a new addition of Michael Angelo Buonaroti. Rendred [*sic*] into English . . . and explained by John Leeke, *etc.* ff. 40. pl. 40. *John Marshall: London,* [1700?] fol. **7815. df. 25.**

—— Vignola: or, the Compleat Architect . . . Translated into English, by Joseph Moxon. The fifth edition, with additions. pp. 80. pl. l. *See* Vitruvius Pollio (M.) The Theory and Practice of Architecture, *etc.* 1703. 8°. **7815. aa. 35.**

—— [Another edition.] pp. 98. pl. l. *See* Vitruvius Pollio (M.) The Theory and Practice of Architecture, *etc.* 1729. 8°. **957. l. 36.**

—— The Five Orders of Architecture according to Vignola. Arranged by Pierre Esquié, *etc.* [Edited by Arthur Stratton.] pp. 26. pl. 66. *J. Tiranti & Co.: London,* [1926.] 4°. **7814. r. 39.**

—— Règles des cinq ordres d'architecture de M. Iacques Barozzio de Vignole. Traduction nouuelle, & augmentation de ses œuures [by B. Menessier]. pp. 93. *Paris,* 1665. 8°. **1474. aa. 23.**

—— Le Vignole des architectes et des élèves en architecture, ou nouvelle traduction des Règles des cinq ordres d'architecture de Jacques Barrozzio de Vignole . . . Suivie d'une méthode abrégée du tracé des ombres dans l'architecture. Par Charles Normand, *etc.* 2 pt. *Paris,* 1842, 36. 4°. **7815. cc. 2.**
Pt. 2 is of the second edition.

—— Traité élémentaire pratique d'architecture, ou Étude des cinq ordres d'après Jacques Barozzio de Vignole . . . Composé, dessiné et mis en ordre par J.-A. Leveil . . . Nouvelle édition. pl. lxxii. *Paris,* [1875?] fol. **7820. s. 31.**

—— Vignole des propriétaires, ou les cinq ordres d'architecture d'apres J. Barozzio . . . par Moisy, suivi de la charpente, menuiserie et serrurerie par Thiollet. pp. 48. pl. 48. *Paris,* [1873.] 4°. **7814. e. 1.**

—— *See* Aviler (A. C. d') Cours d'architecture, qui comprend les ordres de Vignole, *etc.* 1696, *etc.* 4°. **557*. b. 19.**

—— —— 1760. 4°. **59. c. 11.**

—— *See* Coll y March (J.) Tratado práctico de arquitectura, con los órdenes según Vignola, Palladio, *etc.* [1932.] fol. **L.R. 252. a. 9.**

—— *See* Durelli (F.) I Cinque ordini d'architettura di Serlio, Vignola, *etc.* 1841. fol. **1730. b. 32.**

—— *See* Fréart de Chambray (R.) Parallèle de l'architecture antique et de la moderne: avec vn recueil des dix principaux autheurs qui ont écrit des cinq ordres; sçauoir, Palladio et Scamozzi, Serlio et Vignola, *etc.* 1650. fol. **560*. e. 1.**

—— —— 1702. fol. **60. g. 3. (2.)**

BAROZZI (GIACOMO) called *Il Vignola.*

—— —— 1766. 8°. [*ERRARD* (*C.*) *and FRÉART DE CHAMBRAY* (*R.*) *Parallèle de l'architecture, etc.*] 7820. cc. 7.

—— *See* FRÉART DE CHAMBRAY (R.) A Parallel of the Antient Architecture with the Modern, in a collection of ten principal authors who have written upon the five orders, viz. Palladio and Scamozzi, Serlio and Vignola, *etc.* 1664. fol. 60. h. 6.

—— *See* GARNERI (A.) Gli Ordini di architettura civile di G. Barozzi, *etc.* [1924.] 8°. 7817. aa. 24.

—— *See* RENARD (F. A.) Architecture décimale. Parallèle des ordres d'architecture et de leurs principales applications suivant Palladio . . . Vignole, *etc.* 1845. fol. 1268. i. 10.

—— —— 1854. fol. 1732. d. 26.

BAROZZI (GIUSEPPE) Esortazione allo studio del patrio dialetto . . . Indirizzata alla gioventù trivigiana. pp. 31. *Venezia,* 1874. 8°. 12902. d. 1. (18.)

BAROZZI (JACOPO) *See* BAROZZI (Giacomo) called *Il Vignola.*

BAROZZI (JACQUES) *See* BAROZZI (Giacomo) called *Il Vignola.*

BAROZZI (LUCIANO) Legge storica del perfezionamento umano. Pensieri di Luciano Barozzi pubblicati da Giandomenico Belletti. pp. viii. 30. *Sassuolo,* 1876. 8°. 12225. bb. 3.

—— Lorenzo Valla. *See* SABBADINI (R.) Studi sul Panormita e sul Valla, *etc.* 1891. 8°. [*Pubblicazioni del R. Istituto di Studi Superiori Practici e di Perfezionamento. Sezione di filosofia e filologia.* no. 25.] Ac. 8848.

BAROZZI (MICHELE) *See* PIAZZA (A.) *Consigliere dell'Istituto dei Ciechi in Milano.* Per la solenne inaugurazione del busto . . . del Cavaliere Barozzi, fondatore dell' Istituto dei Ciechi in Milano. 1868. 8°. 10631. cc. 46. (7.)

BAROZZI (NICOLÒ) *See* BALLARINI (L.) I Conti del Nord a Venezia, *etc.* [Edited by N. Barozzi.] 1870. 8°. 10708. g. 28. (7.)

—— *See* BERLAN (F.) Statuti italiani. Saggio bibliografico . . . Con giunte di N. Barozzi, *etc.* 1858. 8°. 11900. dd. 16. (3.)

—— *See* DONATO (L.) *Doge of Venice.* Viaggio da Venezia a Roma . . . l'anno 1592. [Edited by N. Barozzi.] 1866. 8°. 10132. c. 13.

—— *See* FRANCISCUS, *de Crema.* L'Assedio di Cividale dell' anno 1509. [Translated from the Latin by N. Barozzi.] 1859. 8°. 9150. g. 7.

—— *See* LUNZI (E.) *Count.* Della condizione politica delle Isole Ionie sotto il dominio veneto . . . Versione con note di M. Dr. Typaldo-Foresti e N. Barozzi, *etc.* 1858, *etc.* 8°. 9135. e. 8.

—— *See* PERIODICAL PUBLICATIONS.—*Venice.* Raccolta Veneta, *etc.* [Edited by N. Barozzi.] 1866, *etc.* 8°. P.P. 1899. c.

—— *See* VENICE.—Senato. Relazioni degli stati europei lette al senato dagli ambasciatori veneti . . . raccolte ed annotate da N. Barozzi e G. Berchet. 1856, *etc.* 8°. 9073. e.

—— *See* VYAZEMSKY (P. A.) *Prince.* Fotografia di Venezia. [The translator's preface signed: N. B., i.e. N. Barozzi.] 1864. 8°. 11585. h. 35. (6.)

BAROZZI (NICOLÒ)

—— Accenni a cose venete nel poema di Dante. Discorso. 1866. *See* DANTE ALIGHIERI. [*Appendix.—Miscellaneous.*] Dante e il suo secolo. vol. 2. 1865, *etc.* 4°. 1871. d. 9. (38.)

—— Dello amore dei Veneziani per lo studio di Dante.—Intorno ai codici delle opere minori di Dante conservati in Venezia. Cenni. *See* DANTE ALIGHIERI. [*Appendix.—Bibliography.*] I Codici di Dante Alighieri in Venezia, *etc.* 1865. 4°. 11422. g. 12.

—— Intorno all'opera Collezione di piombi istoriati rinvenuit nella Senna, e raccolti da Arturo Forgeais. Cenni, *etc.* [*Milan,* 1864.] 8°. 7755. bb. 39. (15.)

—— Relazione degli studii nelle scienze morali e nelle lettere dell'Ateneo di Venezia negli anni accademici 1858–60–61–62, letta nella pubblica adunanza del giorno 6 di dicembre 1863, *etc.* (Dagli Atti dell'Ateneo Veneto.) pp. 11. *Venezia,* 1864. 12°. 8355. dd. 43. (10.)

—— Gli Scavi di Concordia nel febbraio 1873. Rapporto alla R. Commissione consultiva per la Conservazione dei Monumenti della città e provincia di Venezia. (Estratto dalla Gazzetta di Venezia.) pp. 17. *Venezia,* 1873. 8°. 7705. b. 56.

BAROZZI (PIETRO) successively *Bishop of Belluno* and *of Padua.* *See* CANIS (J. J.) *Begin.* D. Ioannis Iacobi Caius in aduētu. D. Petri Barocij . . . oratio, *etc.* [1487.] 4°. IA. 30035.

—— Patriciorum aliquot Venetorum orationes. Tres in primis Petri Barrocii . . . nunquam antehac editæ. *See* VALIERO (A.) *Cardinal.* Augustini Valerii . . . Opusculum . . . de cautione adhibenda in edendis libris, *etc.* 1719. 4°. 72. f. 20.

—— Petri Barrocii . . . pro Christophoro Mauro, Venetiarum Duce . . . oratio.—Petri Barrocii . . . In morte Joannis patrui Patriarchæ Venetiarum pro se, proque tota familia ad Paulum II. Pontificem Maximum oratio. [With an Italian translation by Girolamo Ascanio Molin.] 1795. *Ital. & Lat.* *See* MOLIN (G. A.) Orazioni, elogi e vite, *etc.* tom. 1. 1795, *etc.* 4°. 1200. cc. 5.

BAROZZI (PIETRO) *Capitano.* *See* MENGOZZI (G. M.) Memorie d'alcuni uomini illustri della famiglia Malvezzi, *etc.* [Compiled by G. M. Mengozzi, P. Barozzi and others.] [1770.] 4°. 9915. c. 18.

—— *See* MENGOZZI (G. M.) Memorie di alcune nobilissime donne maritate nella famiglia Malvezzi, *etc.* [Edited by G. M. Mengozzi, P. Barozzi and others.] 1772. 4°. 10630. ee. 25.

BAROZZI (PIETRO) *of Modena.*

—— Vita e opere di Jacopo Barozzi detto il Vignola, con cenni sui suoi antenati e discendenti. [With plates.] pp. 114. *Modena,* 1949. 8°. 010632. bbb. 35.

BAROZZI (SERAFINO) Pianta e spaccato della celebre chiesa di S. Vitale di Ravenna, *etc.* [With plates.] pp. 16. *Bologna,* 1782. 4°. 4605. e. 6.

BAROZZIO (GIACOMO) called *Il Vignola.* *See* BAROZZI.

BAROZZIO (JAMES) *See* BAROZZI (Giacomo) called *Il Vignola.*

BAROZZIO DE VIGNOLE (JACQUES) *See* BAROZZI (Giacomo) called *Il Vignola.*

BAROZZUS (FRANCISCUS) *See* BAROZZI (Francesco)

BARPAS (THEOPHANES L.)
—— " Universal Reconciliation " Exposed. (Reprinted from " The Bible Witness.") [A study of the meaning of αἰων and of αἰωνιος in the Bible.] pp. 11. *Dundee*, [1935.] 8°. **04374**. de. **30**.

BARPETRI ( ) Clef universelle des langues par ordre alphabétique et technique, pour enseigner et apprendre aisément toute sorte de langues et de jargon. pp. xiv. 177. *Ph. Le Boussonier: Londres*, 1801. 8°. **12902**. aaa. **18**. *Interleaved.*

BARPI (ANTONIO) La Pastorizia del Cadore. Studii statistici, zootecnici, igienici ed agricolo-veterinarii. pp. 119. *Cadore*, 1876. 8°. **7293**. b. **3**.

BARPO (GIOVANNI BATTISTA) Le Delitie, & i frutti dell'agricoltura, e della villa, libri tre, spiegati in ricordi particolari, *etc.* [Edited by Tomaso Barpo.] pp. 268. *Presso il Sarzina: Venetia*, 1634. 4°. **441**. d. **5**. (**1**.)

BARPO (TOMASO) *See* BARPO (G. B.) Le Delitie, & i frutti dell'agricoltura, e della villa, libri tre, *etc.* [Edited by T. Barpo.] 1634. 4°. **441**. d. **5**. (**1**.)

BARPTHOLEMAEUS (NICOLAUS) *See* BARPTOLEMAEUS.

BARPTOLEMAEUS (NICOLAUS) *See* ROLLAND (Joachim) Nicolas Barthélemy de Loches, *etc.* 1920. 12°. **011903**. aa. **29**.

—— Nicolai Barptholemæi . . . Christus Xylonicus. [A tragedy. In verse.] *Ex officina S. Colinæi: Parisiis*, 1531. 8°. **11409**. aa. **43**. (**6**.)

—— [Another copy.] **11409**. aa. **41**. (**1**.)

—— Nicolai Barptolemæi . . . Christus Xylonicus. Tragœdia, *etc.* *Excudebat vidua M. Cæsaris; impensis I. Coccij: Antuerpiæ*, 1537. 8°. **11712**. aaa. **6**.

—— [Another copy.] Nicolai Barptolemæi . . . Christus Xylonicus, *etc.* *Antwerpiæ*, 1537. 8°. **11712**. aa. **1**. (**6***.)

—— Tragœdia Nicolai Barptolomæi . . . Christus Xilonicus, *etc.* *I. Gymnicus: Coloniæ*, 1541. 8°. **11409**. e. **7**.

—— Nicolai Bartolomæi Christus Xylenicus. Tragoedia. *See* COMOEDIAE. Comoediæ ac tragoediæ aliquot ex Novo et Vetere Testamento desumptæ, *etc.* 1542. 8°. **636**. d. **1**.

—— Nicolai Barptholemæi . . . Ennœæ. [In verse.] *Ex officina S. Colinæi: Parisiis*, 1531. 8°. **11409**. aa. **43**. (**5**.)

—— [Another copy.] **11409**. aa. **41**. (**2**.)

BARQUE.
—— La Barque du pêcheur, *etc.* 1868. 8°. *See* F., L. **04422**. c. **27**.

BARQUEBOIS (DE) *pseud.* [i.e. JACQUES ROBBE.] La Rapiniere, ou l'interessé, comédie, *etc.* pp. 102. *E. Lucas: Paris*, 1683. 12°. **163**. c. **3**. *The leaves of the preface are cropped.*

BARQUERA (JUAN MARÍA WENCESLAO) A la Exaltación al Trono de N. C. M. el Sr. D. Fernando VII de Borbon, Rey de España y de las Indias. Oda sáfico-adónica, *etc.* [*Mexico*, 1808.] 4°. **11451**. bbb. **43**. (**6**.)

—— Aviso patriótico de un Americano imparcial [i.e. J. M. W. Barquera]. pp. 4. 1821. fol. *See* AMERICAN. **9770**. k. **5**. (**91**.)

BARQUERA (JUAN MARÍA WENCESLAO)

—— Los Delirios de Napoleon, contrapuestos a la verdadera, y mas sana política. Dialogo entre un Español y un Frances contertulios de una casa de campo en las inmediaciones de México. pp. 16. *México*, 1809. 4°. **9180**. e. **6**. (**8**.)

—— Discurso patriótico que en celebridad del glorioso grito de independencia dado en el pueblo de Dolores . . . el 16 de setiembre de 1810, pronunció el ciudadano J. W. Barquera, *etc.* pp. 10. *Tlalpam*, 1827. 8°. **12301**. d. **5**. (**12**.)

—— Discurso patriótico que en el aniversario del primer grito de nuestra independencia, solemnizado en la ciudad de Toluca . . . dijo el sr . . . J. W. Barquera, *etc.* pp. 24. *Toluca*, 1830. 8°. **12301**. d. **5**. (**1**.)

—— Oración patriotica, que pronunció . . . J. W. Barquera, el 16 de septiembre de 1825 por encargo de la junta cívica, reunida . . . con el preciso objeto de celebrar con la debida solemnidad el primer grito de libertad en el Pueblo de Dolores, *etc.* pp. 33. *México*, 1825. 16°. **8005**. a. **5**.

—— Reflexiones filosófopolíticas sobre los últimos sucesos de la Francia, heroísmo de la España y fidelidad de la América. [*Mexico*, 1808.] 4°. **9180**. c. **10**. (**19**.)

—— El Triunfo de la Religion, oda heroica, *etc.* [Signed: J. W. B., i.e. J. M. W. Barquera.] 1808. 4°. *See* B., J. W. **9180**. d. **1**. (**28**.)

—— [Another copy.] **11451**. bbb. **6**. (**37**.)

BARQUERA (JUAN WENCESLAO) *See* BARQUERA (Juan M. W.)

BARQUERO (FRANCISCO) *See* ÁGUILA (A. de) Por Andres de Azeytuna, como padre, y administrador . . . de sus hijos . . . Con el Fiscal desta Corte . . . y F. Barquero su yerno, *etc.* [1630?] fol. **1322**. l. **10**. (**25**.)

BARQUI (F.) L'Architecture moderne en France. Maisons les plus remarquables des principales villes des départements . . . Cent vingt planches in-folio accompagnés d'un texte descriptif. *Paris*, 1864–[68]. fol. **1733**. b. **17**.

BARQUI (F.) and **DOREN** (M^{US} VAN)

—— Cours de dessin industriel. Enseignement de l'École La Martinière. 2 pt. *Lyon*, 1874, 75. 8°. **1803**. a. **24**.

—— [Plates.] 2 pt. *obl.* fol. **1803**. d. **4**.

BARQUÍN (JUAN BENAVENTE) *See* BENAVENTE BARQUÍN.

BARQUISIMETO, *City of.* Certámen literario celebrado et 5 de Julio de 1874 en Barquisimeto, para solemnizar el 63° aniversario de la independencia de Venezuela. pp. 51. [*Barquisimeto*, 1874.] 16°. **8180**. a. **9**.

Centro Histórico Larense.

—— Boletín del Centro Histórico Larense. no. 1–20, 24–33/34, 37/40, 41/44. enero/mar. 1942—oct./dic. 1946; oct./dic. 1947—enero/jun. 1950; enero/dic. 1951; enero/dic. 1952. *Barquisimeto*, 1942–52. 8°. P.P. **4099**. eh.

—— Discurso de recepción del Dr. David Anzola . . . y contestación por Hno. Nectario María . . . 24 de julio de 1944. Tema: Médicos y cirujanos que prestaron sus servicios en la guerra de la independencia de Venezuela. Las enfermedades y la guerra. pp. 27. *Barquisimeto*, 1944. 8°. **12302**. bb. **155**.

BARQUISIMETO, *City of.*

—— Discurso de recepción del Dr. Eladio A. del Castillo . . . y contestación por E. Macías Mujica . . . Tema: La astronomía americana en sus orígenes. Estudio particular de ella referente a Venezuela, *etc.* pp. 38. *Barquisimeto,* 1945. 8°. **12302.** bb. **156.**

—— Discurso de recepción del señor Rafael Rodríguez Ortiz . . . 5 de diciembre de 1946. [On the part played by lawyers in the struggle of Venezuela for independence.] pp. 16. [*Barquisimeto,* 1946.] 8°. **12302.** bb. **157.**

—— *Church of Saint Antony of Padua. See* ANTONY, *of Padua, Saint* [Fernando Bulhon].—*Church of, at Barquisimeto.*

Concejo Municipal.

—— Antología cabudareña . . . Selección, notas biográficas y prólogo de Carlos Felice Cardot. pp. xiii. 73. *Barquisimeto,* 1944. 8°. **12231.** v. **6.**

BARQUISIMETO, *State of.—Secretaría de Gobierno y Guerra.* Memoria que dirige el Secretario de Gobierno y Guerra á la Asamblea Legislativa del Estado di Barquisimeto. pp. 69. *Cabudare,* 1865. 8°. **8180.** bb. **52. (7.)**

BARQUISIMETO AUTHORS.

—— Autores barquisimetanos. [An anthology.] *See* PRISCO C. (R. di)

BARQUISSAU (J.) Examen des principaux caractères de l'opium, et de son emploi dans le traitement du tétanos. These, *etc.* pp. 16. *Montpellier,* 1831. 4°. **1181.** f. **2. (1.)**

BARQUISSAU (RAPHAËL) *See* FOUCQUE (H.) L'Île de La Réunion . . . Par H. Foucque, R. Barquissau, *etc.* 1923. 8°. **010094.** l. **18.**

—— —— 1925. 8°. **010094.** m. **15.**

—— A Tananarive pendant la foire. Carnet de route. pp. 66. *Paris, St. Denis de la Réunion,* 1924. 8°. **10167.** cc. **13.**

—— L'Asie française et ses écrivains, *etc.* pp. 246. *Paris,* 1947. 4°. **10493.** h. **20.**

—— Les Poètes créoles du XVIIIe siècle. Parny, Bertin, Léonard. pp. 249. *Paris,* 1949. 8°. **11858.** h. **2.**

BARQUISSAU (STÉPHANE) De l'éclampsie puerpérale. pp. 80. *Paris,* 1871. 4°. [*Collection des thèses soutenues à la Faculté de Médecine de Paris.* An 1871. tom. 1.] **7373.** m. **15.**

BARR.—*Realschule.*

—— Jahresbericht mit welchem zugleich zu der öffentlichen Prüfung und zur Schlussfeier . . . 1875 . . . die hohen Behörden . . . einladet W. Cramer . . . Inhalt: 1. Germanische Mythe bei Shakespeare. Von W. Dahlem. 2. Schulnachrichten. Vom Direktor. pp. 103. *Strassburg,* 1875. 8°. **11766.** k. **15. (1.)**

BARR, *Saint, Bishop of Cork. See* FINBARR.

BARR AND SUGDEN. Barr & Sugden's Autumnal Catalogue, comprising choice selections of Dutch, Cape flowering bulbs, &c. (1861.) pp. 32. *Barr & Sugden: London,* 1861. 8°. **7055.** f. **6.**

—— Barr & Sugden's Guide to the Kitchen Garden, and descriptive priced list of vegetable seeds . . . gladioli, *etc.* (1863. Third edition.) pp. 48. *Barr & Sugden: London,* [1863.] 8°. **7055.** cc. **1.**

BARR AND SUGDEN.

—— Barr & Sugden's Illustrated Guide to the Flower Garden, and descriptive priced list of choice seeds, canna roots, *etc.* (1863.) pp. 112. *Barr & Sugden: London,* [1863.] 8°. **7055.** cc. **2.**

—— Barr & Sugden's Spring Seed Catalogue, and guide to the flower and kitchen garden, *etc.* (1862.) pp. 116. *Barr & Sugden: London,* 1862. 8°. **7055.** h. **11.**
The cover bears the title "Barr & Sugden's Guide to the Flower Garden, &c."

BARR ( ) *of Glasgow,* and **BROWN** (JAMES) *Council Officer.* Biographical Sketches of the Hon. the Lord Provosts of Glasgow, *etc.* [Compiled by —— Barr and J. Brown.] pp. v. 381. 52. *John Tweed: Glasgow,* 1883. 8°. **10816.** g. **15.**

BARR (A. G.)

—— *See* TANNER (Arthur E.) Tobacco . . . Revised by A. G. Barr, *etc.* 1950. 8°. **07077.** f. **1/154.**

BARR (A. J.) Let Tomorrow Come. [Sketches of American prison-life.] pp. 269. *W. W. Norton & Co.: New York,* [1929.] 8°. **06055.** df. **9.**

BARR (ALEXANDER DAVID ST. CLAIR) *See* JODHPUR.—*Legislative Department.* The Marwar Penal Code. 1914. Compiled by A. D. C. Barr. 1915. 8°. **5310.** cc. **16.**

BARR (ALFRED HAMILTON)

—— *See* CAHILL (Holger) and BARR (A. H.) Art in America in Modern Times, *etc.* [1934.] 4°. **7817.** r. **14.**

—— *See* CAHILL (Holger) and BARR (A. H.) Art in America. A complete survey, *etc.* 1939. 4°. **7811.** v. **2.**

—— *See* JOHNSON (Philip) *Writer on Architecture.* Machine Art . . . Foreword by A. H. Barr. [1934.] 4°. **7959.** g. **32.**

—— *See* NEW YORK, *City of.—Museum of Modern Art.* Henri Matisse. [A catalogue of an exhibition held at the Museum of Modern Art.] Introduction by A. H. Barr, *etc.* [1931.] 4°. **7852.** t. **16.**

—— *See* NEW YORK, *City of.—Museum of Modern Art.* Modern German Painting and Sculpture. Introduction and notes by A. H. Barr. [1931.] 4°. **7853.** t. **33.**

—— *See* NEW YORK.—*Museum of Modern Art.* Painting and Sculpture in the Museum of Modern Art. [1948.] 8°. **7869.** ppp. **13.**

—— *See* RUIZ PICASSO (P.) Picasso. Forty years of his art. Edited by Alfred H. Barr, *etc.* [1939.] 8°. **7867.** c. **5.**

—— *See* SOBY (James T.) Twentieth-Century Italian Art. By J. T. Soby and A. H. Barr. [1949.] 8°. **7813.** i. **34.**

—— Cubism and Abstract Art. pp. 249. [1936.] 4°. *See* NEW YORK.—*Museum of Modern Art.* **07804.** bb. **24.**

—— Masters of Modern Art. Edited by A. H. Barr. [With reproductions.] pp. 239. [1954.] 4°. *See* NEW YORK.—*Museum of Modern Art.* **7871.** d. **22**

—— Modern Architects. By A. H. Barr, Jr., Henry Russell Hitchcock, Jr., Philip Johnson and Lewis Mumford. [With illustrations.] pp. 199. [1932.] 4°. *See* NEW YORK, *City of.—Museum of Modern Art.* **07816.** d. **12.**

BARR (ALFRED HAMILTON)

—— Vincent Van Gogh. With an introduction and notes selected from the letters of the artist, edited by Alfred H. Barr, Jr. [Catalogue of an exhibition. With reproductions.] pp. 193. 1936. 4°. *See* NEW YORK.—*Museum of Modern Art.* **7864.** r. **36.**

BARR (ALLAN)

—— A Diagram of Synoptic Relationships. [Illustrating the relations between the Synoptic Gospels.] pp. 7. *T. & T. Clark: Edinburgh,* [1938.] 8°. **03226.** h. **51.**

—— The Ecumenical Church and the Ecumenical State. pp. 30. *Scottish Voluntary Churches Association: Glasgow,* [1954.] 8°. **4193.** l. **24.**

BARR (AMELIA EDITH) All the Days of my Life: an autobiography, *etc.* [With plates, including portraits.] pp. vii. 528. *D. Appleton & Co.: New York & London,* 1913. 8°. **010881.** k. **20.**

—— The Beads of Tasmer. [A novel.] pp. 320. *J. Clarke & Co.: London,* 1893. 8°. **012630.** ee. **47.**

—— The Belle of Bowling Green, *etc.* pp. 342. *B. F. Stevens & Brown: London; New York* printed, 1904. 8°. **012707.** cc. **53.**

—— [Another edition.] pp. 314. *John Long: London,* 1906. 8°. **012632.** b. **15.**

—— Bernicia. pp. v. 306. *B. F. Stevens: London,* 1895. 8°. **012706.** l. **3.**

—— [A reissue.] *Sampson Low & Co.: London,* 1896. 8°. **012705.** i. **52.**

—— Between Two Loves. A tale of the West Riding. pp. 311. *J. Clarke & Co.: London,* 1886. 8°. **12625.** g. **24.**

—— The Black Shilling. pp. 350. *T. Fisher Unwin: London,* 1904. 8°. **012629.** bbb. **46.**

—— A Border Shepherdess. A romance of Eskdale. pp. 323. *J. Clarke & Co.: London,* 1887. 8°. **12611.** l. **5.**

—— The Bow of Orange Ribbon. A romance of New York. pp. 445. *Dodd, Mead & Co.: New York,* 1886. 8°. **12704.** m. **20.**

—— [Another edition.] pp. 309. *J. Clarke & Co.: London,* 1886. 8°. **12613.** m. **31.**

—— Cecilia's Lovers. pp. viii. 389. *T. Fisher Unwin: London; New York* printed, [1905.] 8°. **012706.** a. **18.**

—— [Another edition.] pp. v. 311. *T. Fisher Unwin: London,* 1906. 8°. **012632.** cc. **32.**

—— Christine, a Fife fisher girl, *etc.* pp. 372. *D. Appleton & Co.: New York, London,* 1917. 8°. **12702.** a. **8.**

—— Cluny Macpherson. A tale of brotherly love, *etc.* pp. 311. *Hodder & Stoughton: London,* 1884. 8°. **12624.** i. **28.**

—— A Daughter of Fife. pp. 335. *J. Clarke & Co.: London,* 1886. 8°. **12624.** m. **20.**

—— Feet of Clay. pp. 360. *J. Clarke & Co.: London,* 1889. 8°. **012632.** i. **6.**

—— The Flower of Gala Water, and other stories. pp. 392. *Sampson Low & Co.: London,* 1895. 8°. **012628.** m. **1.**

BARR (AMELIA EDITH)

—— Friend Olivia. pp. 455. *Dodd, Mead & Co.: New York,* [1890.] 8°. **012631.** g. **50.**

—— [Another edition.] pp. 448. *J. Clarke & Co.: London,* 1890. 8°. **012631.** i. **19.**

—— The Hallam Succession. A tale of Methodist life in two countries. pp. 256. *T. Woolmer: London,* 1885. 8°. **4412.** d. **23.**

—— [A reissue.] *C. H. Kelly: London,* [1906.] 8°. **4408.** ff. **3**

Without the head- and tailpieces to the chapters.

—— The Hands of Compulsion, *etc.* pp. 311. *Cassell & Co.: London,* 1910. 8°. **012623.** aa. **38.**

—— The Harvest of the Wind, and other stories. pp. 149. *J. Clarke & Co.: London,* 1886. 8°. **12620.** b. **4.**

—— The Heart of Jessy Laurie, *etc.* pp. 319. *Curtis Brown: London; printed in U.S.A.,* 1907. 8°. **012706.** bb. **34.**

—— [Another edition.] pp. 287. *J. Clarke & Co.: London,* [1908.] 8°. **012627.** aaa. **31.**

—— The House on Cherry Street, *etc.* pp. 375. *B. F. Stevens & Brown: London; printed in U.S.A.,* 1909. 8°. **012705.** cc. **15.**

—— [A reissue.] *T. Werner Laurie: London,* [1912.] 8°. **012704.** a. **5.**

—— The Household of McNeil. pp. 319. *J. Clarke & Co.: London,* 1888. 8°. **012633.** l. **57.**

—— I, Thou, and the Other One. A love story, *etc.* pp. 354. *T. Fisher Unwin: London,* 1899. 8°. **012631.** i. **38.**

—— In Spite of Himself. A tale of the West Riding. pp. 293. *J. Clarke & Co.: London,* 1888. 8°. **012633.** g. **32.**

—— Jan Vedder's Wife. pp. 329. *J. Clarke & Co.: London,* [1885.] 8°. **12600.** o. **23**

—— [A reissue.] *London,* 1892. 8°. [*Warne's Star Series.*] **12600.** m. **4/26.**

—— Joan. A romance of an English mining village, *etc.* pp. viii. 325. *D. Appleton & Co.: New York, London,* 1917. 8°. **NN. 4034.**

—— A Knight of the Nets. pp. 314. *William Briggs: Toronto,* [1896.] 8°. **12704.** k. **23.**

—— [Another issue.] *B. F. Stevens: London; Cambridge, U.S.A.* printed, 1896. 8°. **012705.** i. **60.**

—— [A reissue.] *Hutchinson & Co.: London,* 1897. 8°. **012623.** eee. **14.**

—— The Last of the Macallisters. pp. 304. *J. Clarke & Co.: London,* [1890.] 8°. **012631.** i. **16.**

—— The Lion's Whelp. A story of Cromwell's time, *etc.* pp. v. 383. *T. Fisher Unwin: London,* 1902. 8°. **012637.** aaa. **1.**

—— The Lone House. pp. 235. *Hodder & Stoughton: London; New York* printed, 1894. 8°. **012705.** eee. **1.**

—— The Lost Silver of Briffault. pp. 318. *Hodder & Stoughton: London,* 1886. 8°. **12624.** n. **20.**

—— Love for an Hour is Love Forever. pp. 306. *Hutchinson & Co.: London,* [1892.] 8°. **012706.** f. **49.**

—— Love Will Venture In. *See* infra: The Man Between.

BARR (Amelia Edith)

—— The Maid of Maiden Lane. A love story. pp. 338. *T. Fisher Unwin: London*, 1901. 8°. **012640**. c. **38**.

—— A Maid of Old New York. A romance of Peter Stuyvesant's time. pp. 377. *B. F. Stevens & Brown: London; printed in U.S.A.*, 1911. 8°. **012704**. aa. **14**.

—— The Man Between. An international romance, *etc.* pp. 323. *McLeod & Allen: Toronto*, [1906.] 8°. **012706**. aaa. **41**.

—— [Another edition.] Love Will Venture In, *etc.* pp. 311. *Chatto & Windus: London*, 1907. 8°. **012634**. ccc. **7**.

—— The Measure of a Man, *etc.* pp. vii. 316. *D. Appleton & Co.: New York & London*, 1915. 8°. NN. **2909**.

—— Michael and Theodora. A Russian story. pp. 168. *Bradley & Woodruff: Boston*, [1892]. 8°. **012618**. f. **33**.

—— An Orkney Maid, *etc.* pp. 307. *D. Appleton & Co.: New York, London*, 1918. 8°. **12702**. a. **18**.

—— The Paper Cap, *etc.* pp. xi. 354. *D. Appleton & Co.: New York, London*, 1918. 8°. NN. **5088**.

—— Paul and Christina. pp. 222. *J. Clarke & Co.: London*, 1887. 8°. **4414**. i. **3**.

—— Playing with Fire, *etc.* pp. 329. *D. Appleton & Co.: New York & London*, 1914. 8°. **04413**. i. **23**.

—— The Preacher's Daughter. A domestic romance. pp. 297. *Sampson Low & Co.: London*, 1893 [1892]. 8°. **012706**. h. **27**.

—— The Price She Paid. [An offprint from a periodical, mounted.] 2 pt. [*Gay & Bird: London*, 1896.] 8°. **012627**. m. **13**.

—— Prisoners of Conscience. pp. 240. *Century Co.: New York*, 1897. 8°. **012705**. k. **53**.

—— [Another issue.] pp. 240. *T. Fisher Unwin: London*, 1897. 8°. **012628**. n. **16**.

—— Profit & Loss, *etc.* pp. 307. *D. Appleton & Co.: New York, London*, 1916. 8°. NN. **3669**.

—— A Reconstructed Marriage. pp. 350. *T. Fisher Unwin: London*, 1911. 8°. **012618**. aaa. **13**

—— Remember the Alamo. pp. 431. *Dodd, Mead & Co.: New York*, 1888. 8°. **012705**. e. **58**.

—— Romances and Realities: tales of truth and fancy. pp. 432. *J. B. Ford & Co.: New York*, 1876. 8°. **12704**. ccc. **9**.

—— A Rose of a Hundred Leaves. A love-story. pp. 238 *J. Clarke & Co.: London*, 1893. 8°. **012706**. g. **49**.

—— Scottish Sketches. pp. 320. *Oliphant, Anderson & Co.: Edinburgh*, 1890. 8°. **4408**. k. **5**.

—— She Loved a Sailor. pp. 459. *J. Clarke & Co.: London*, [1892.] 8°. **012706**. f. **46**.

—— Sheila Vedder, *etc.* pp. 341. *T. Fisher Unwin: London*, 1912. 8°. NN. **7**.

—— A Singer from the Sea. pp. iv. 346. *B. F. Stevens: London; New York* printed, [1893.] 8°. **012706**. h. **35**.

—— [Another issue.] *Hutchinson & Co.: London; Nimeguen* printed, [1893.] 8°. **012706**. m. **7**.

—— A Sister to Esau. pp. 341. *B. F. Stevens: London; Rahway, N.J.* printed, [1891]. 8°. **012705**. f. **37**.

—— [Another edition.] pp. 341. *J. Clarke & Co.: London*, [1892.] 8°. **012634**. i. **53**.

BARR (Amelia Edith)

—— A Song of a Single Note. ff. 330. *B. F. Steevens* [sic] *& Brown: London; printed in U.S.A.*, 1902. 8°. **012703**. k. **33**.

Printed on one side of the leaf only.

—— [Another edition.] pp. vii. 328. *T. Fisher Unwin: London*, 1905. 8°. **012630**. bbb. **38**.

—— Songs in the Common Chord, *etc.* pp. xix. 293. *D. Appleton & Co.: New York, London*, 1919. 8°. **011686**. ee. **97**.

—— Souls of Passage. pp. 319. *T. Fisher Unwin: London*, 1901. 8°. **012639**. a. **38**.

—— The Squire of Sandal-Side. pp. 276. *J. Clarke & Co.: London*, 1887. 8°. **12613**. l. **20**.

—— Three Score and Ten. A book for the aged. pp. 326. *D. Appleton & Co.: New York*, 1915. 8°. **04403**. f. **24**.

—— Thyra Varrick. A love story, *etc.* pp. 343. *J. F. Taylor & Co.: New York*, 1903. 8°. **012707**. aa. **17**.

—— [Another edition.] pp. vii. 337. *T. Fisher Unwin: London*, 1904. 8°. **012628**. d. **28**.

—— Trinity Bells. A tale of old New York, *etc.* pp. viii. 278. *B. F. Stevens & Brown: London; Cambridge, Mass.* printed, 1899. 8°. **012707**. ee. **23**.

—— [A reissue.] *T. Fisher Unwin: London*, 1900. 8°. **012707**. ee. **29**.

—— Was It Right To Forgive? A domestic romance. pp. 294. *H. S. Stone & Co.: Chicago & New York*, 1899. 8°. **012707**. g. **7**.

—— [Another issue.] pp. 294. *T. Fisher Unwin: London*, 1900. 8°. **012641**. a. **10**.

—— The Winning of Lucia. A love story, *etc.* pp. 334. *D. Appleton & Co.: New York & London*, 1915. 8°. NN. **2505**.

—— Woven of Love and Glory. pp. 431. *J. Clarke & Co.: London*, 1890. 8°. **012705**. g. **8**.

BARR (Archibald) *See* Thomson (William) *Baron Kelvin*, and Barr (A.) The Horsfall Destructors, *etc.* [1899.] fol. **8777**. k. **21**.

—— Address on the Application of the Science of Mechanics to Engineering Practice. pp. 23. 1899. 8°. *See* London.—iii. *Institution of Civil Engineers*. **8707**. e. **26**. (5.)

—— Physics and Engineering Science, with special reference to Mechanical Engineering, *etc.* 1923. *See* London.—iii. *Institute of Physics*. Physics in Industry, *etc.* vol. 1. 1923, *etc.* 8°. W.P. **4549/1**.

BARR (Arvil Sylvester) *See* Anderson (Charles J.) Visiting the Teacher at Work . . . By C. J. Anderson . . . A. S. Barr, *etc.* [1925.] 8°. **8314.b.1/1.**

—— *See* Ayer (Fred C.) and Barr (A. S.) The Organization of Supervision, *etc.* [1928.] 8°. **8314.b.1/3.**

—— *See* Good (Carter V.) The Methodology of Educational Research. By C. V. Good . . . A. S. Barr, *etc.* [1936.] 8°. **8314.b.1/12.**

—— *See* Supervision. Supervision. Principles and practices in the improvement of instruction. By A. S. Barr . . . W. H. Burton, *etc.* [1938.] 8°. **8314.b.1/15.**

BARR (Arvil Sylvester)

—— *See* Supervision. Supervision . . . By A. S. Barr . . . W. H. Burton . . . L. J. Brueckner, *etc.* [1947.] 8°. **8314.b.1/18.**

—— An Introduction to the Scientific Study of Classroom Supervision. pp. xxv. 399. *New York, London,* [1931.] 8°. [*Appleton Series in Supervision & Teaching.*] **8314.b.1/7.**

—— The Supervision of Instruction, *etc.* pp. xiv. 626. *New York, London,* [1926.] 8°. [*Appleton Series in Supervision and Teaching.*] **8314.b.1/2.**

BARR (Arvil Sylvester) and **BURTON** (William Henry)

—— The Appleton Series in Supervision and Teaching. Edited by A. S. Barr . . . W. H. Burton. 19 vol. *D. Appleton & Co.: New York, London,* [1925–50.] 8° & 4°. **8314. b. 1.**

Containing two editions of "Supervision," and "The Child and his Curriculum."

BARR (Carolyn) Suzanna Skids. A one-act comedy, *etc.* pp. 26. *Longmans & Co.: New York,* 1931. 8°. **11791. de. 74.**

BARR (Catherine) Verses by Catherine Barr, a poor blind woman, better known in the Church Militant as "Kitty." pp. 23. *Rixon & Arnold: London,* 1859. 16°. **11601. aa. 61. (1.)**

BARR (Catherine M.)

—— Scripture Snapshots. 8 no. *Stirling Tract Enterprise: Stirling,* [1947.] 12°. **4431. a. 4.**

—— Simple Scripture Stories. Retold by C. M. Barr. 6 pt. *Stirling Tract Enterprise: Stirling,* [1942.] 24°. **944. c. 39.**

BARR (Cathrine)

—— *See* Preston (Hall) and Barr (C.) Smokey's Big Discovery. 1950. 8°. **012802. d. 56.**

—— *See* Preston (Hall) and Barr (C.) The Bear Cubs escape. 1953. 4°. **12836. e. 4.**

—— The Runaway Chimps. *Oxford University Press: New York,* 1954. 4°. **12833. dd. 36.**

—— Sammy Seal of the Circus. [With illustrations.] *Oxford University Press: New York,* 1955. 4°. **12837. l. 25.**

BARR (Cecil) *pseud.* [i.e. Jack Kahane.] *See also* Kahane (Jack)

—— Suzy Falls Off. [A novel.] pp. 253. *John Long: London,* 1928. 8°. NN. **13686**

BARR (Charles John Henry) A Preparatory Geometry. pp. viii. 152. *Methuen & Co.: London,* 1927. 8°. **08531. de. 70.**

BARR (David) Climbing the Ladder: the struggles and successes of a village lad. Autobiography of D. Barr. pp. 132. *Robert Culley: London,* 1910. 8°. **4908. aa. 25**

BARR (Dennis) A Dock Brief. A novel. pp. 254. *Jonathan Cape: London,* 1928. 8°. NN. **13685.**

—— A Rope Broke. pp. 286. *Jarrolds: London,* [1932.] 8°. NN. **19271.**

BARR (Densil Neve)

—— The Man with only one Head. [A novel.] pp. 192. *Rich & Cowan: London,* 1955. 8°. NNN. **7465.**

BARR (Donald) The Fernland Story Book. Edited by D. Barr. pp. 87. *Whitcombe & Tombs: Melbourne,* [1923.] 4°. **12801. d. 44.**

BARR (Edward) Elevations, Sections, and Details, of Strixton Church, Northamptonshire. pp. 8. pl. xii. *J. H. Parker: Oxford & London,* 1849. fol. **1261. i. 4.**

BARR (Estelle De Young)

—— A Psychological Analysis of Fashion Motivation. pp. 100. *New York,* 1934. 8°. [*Archives of Psychology.* no. 171.] P.P. **1247. gb.**

BARR (F. Mary)

—— Bapu. Conversations and correspondence with Mahatma Gandhi. [With portraits.] pp. ix. 214. *International Book House: Bombay,* 1949. 8°. **10607. ee. 78.**

BARR (Finn) *Brother.* *See* Finn Barr.

BARR (Francis) *See* Smith (William) *of Sheriff Hutton.* The Village Cooper. Memoirs of the life, character and labours of F. Barr, *etc.* 1849. 12°. **4905. a. 55.**

BARR (Frank Stringfellow) *See* Smith (Charles A.) Southern Literary Studies . . . With a biographical study by F. S. Barr. 1927. 8°. **011840. cc. 15.**

BARR (Frederick) Love Letters of Jews in Exile. [Original poems.] pp. 77. *Morland: Amersham,* 1921. 8°. **011645. df. 39.**

—— The Prince—Judah. pp. xi. 217. *Kegan Paul & Co.: London,* 1912. 8°. **4804. f. 23.**

BARR (Glenn) *See* Palacio Valdés (A.) A Cara o Cruz . . . Edited with notes, direct-method exercises, and vocabulary by G. Barr. 1932. 8°. **11567.g.1/12.**

—— *See* Palacio Valdés (A.) Selections from Armando Palacio Valdés. Edited by G. Barr and H. J. Russell. [1935.] 8°. **012942. c. 34.**

—— Cuatro cuentos rioplatenses. Adapted and edited by G. Barr. pp. iv. 60. *D. C. Heath & Co.: Boston,* [1950.] 8°. [*Heath-Chicago Spanish Series. Graded Spanish Readers.* bk. 6: alternate.] W.P. **13317/3a. (6.)**

BARR (Guy) *See* Graetz (L.) Recent Developments in Atomic Theory . . . Translated by G. Barr, *etc.* 1923. 8°. **8710. aa. 8.**

—— *See* Nernst (W.) The New Heat Theorem . . . Translated . . . by G. Barr. 1926. 8°. **8716. h. 7.**

—— A Monograph of Viscometry. pp. xiv. 318. *Oxford University Press: London,* 1931. 8°. **8710. g. 8.**

BARR (H. Macdonald) Libretto of Audrey. Musical comedy in two acts, *etc.* pp. 51. *Barr & Clements: Brooklyn,* [1921.] 8°. **11791. de. 10.**

BARR (Hugh) *M.I.Mar.E.* *See* MacGibbon (William C.) B.O.T. Orals and Marine Engineering Knowledge . . . By W. C. MacGibbon . . . H. Barr. [1934.] 8°. **2246. c. 23.**

—— *See* Macgibbon (William C.) B.O.T. Orals and Marine Engineering Knowledge . . . By W. C. Macgibbon . . . H. Barr. [1938.] 8°. **08805. aaa. 24.**

BARR (Hugh) *M.I.Mar.E.*

—— *See* MacGibbon (William C.) B. O. T. Orals and Marine Engineering Knowledge . . . By W. C. MacGibbon . . . H. Barr. [1941.] 8°. **8809.** aa. **9.**

—— *See* MacGibbon (William C.) B.O.T. Orals and Marine Engineering Knowledge . . . By W. C. MacGibbon . . . H. Barr. [1950.] 8°. **08809.** b. **7.**

—— *See* MacGibbon (William C.) Indicator Diagrams, Steam and Oil, for Marine Engineers, *etc.* [Edited by A. Martin and H. Barr.] [1936.] 8°. **08806.** cc. **28.**

—— *See* MacGibbon (William C.) MacGibbon's M.o.T. Orals and Marine Knowledge. By . . . H. Barr. [1954.] 8°. **08805.** bb. **16.**

—— *See* MacGibbon (William C.) Marine Engineers' Pictorial Drawing Book for Board of Trade Examinations . . . By W. C. MacGibbon . . . in collaboration with . . . H. Barr. 1931. *obl.* 4°. **8804.** e. **7.**

—— *See* MacGibbon (William C.) Marine Engineers' Pictorial Drawing Book . . . By W. C. MacGibbon . . . in collaboration with . . . H. Barr. 1939. *obl.* 8°. **Cup.1246.aa.29.**

—— *See* MacGibbon (William C.) [Questions & Answers for B.O.T. Examinations on Marine Oil Engines.] Macgibbon's Questions & Answers for Ministry of Transport Examinations on Marine Oil Engines . . . By H. Barr. [1955.] 8°. **08774.** ff. **1.**

—— *See* Tod (John) *M.I.M.E.*, and MacGibbon (W. C.) Tod & MacGibbon's Elementary Questions and Answers in Engineering Knowledge for Marine Engineers . . . Fully illustrated and explained. By A. Martin . . . and H. Barr. [1941.] 8°. **8809.** a. **4.**

BARR (Hugh) *Presbyterian Minister, of Kingskettle.* Asleep in Jesus; and The Service of the Saints. Sermons. pp. 32. *W. Oliphant & Co.: Edinburgh,* 1864. 12°. **4478.** a. **126.** (**18.**)

—— Too Late for Martyrdom: memorials of the Rev. H. Barr . . . (Sermons.—Poems.) Memoir by the Rev. Thomas Dunlop. pp. xiv. 192. *Andrew Elliot: Edinburgh,* 1875. 8°. **4955.** aaa. **41.**

BARR (Hy Max) *See* Barry (J. N.) and Barr (H. M.) Redskin and Pioneer, *etc.* [1932.] 8°. W.P. **4942/7.**

BARR (Isaac M.) British Settlements in North Western Canada on Free Grant Lands, *etc.* pp. 15. [*London,* 1902.] 8°. **10470.** e. **33.**

BARR (James)

—— Quatrefoil. [A novel.] pp. 373. *Vision: London,* 1953. 8°. **12732.** bb. **9.**

BARR (James) *Architect.* Anglican Church Architecture, with some remarks upon ecclesiastical furniture. pp. 126. *J. H. Parker: Oxford,* 1842. 8°. **1043.** f. **34.**

—— Second edition. pp. 8. 216. *J. H. Parker: Oxford* 1843. 8°. **1043.** f. **37.**

—— Third edition. pp. xii. 220. *J. H. Parker: Oxford,* 1846. 8°. **1043.** f. **42.,**

BARR (James) *Captain.* A Correct and Authentic Narrative of the Indian War in Florida, with a description of Maj. Dade's massacre, *etc.* pp. 32. *J. Narine: New York,* 1836. 8°. **9602.** a. **31.**

BARR (James) *D.D.* *See* Scott (John) *D.D., Minister of the New Church, Greenock.* Sermons . . . To which is prefixed a memoir of the author by J. Barr. 1839. 8°. **1113.** e. **15.**

BARR (James) *Novelist.* Laughing through a Wilderness. pp. vii. 296. *Methuen & Co.: London,* 1906. 8°. **012633.** b. **5.**

—— [Another edition.] Illustrated by Thomas Kinsella. pp. vi. 114. *Amalgamated Press: London,* [1912.] 8°. [" *Daily Mail* " *Sixpenny Novels.* no. 159.] **012604.e.1/136.**

—— The Witchery of the Serpent. pp. 315. *Gay & Bird: London,* 1907. 8°. **012634.** d. **21.**

BARR (James) *of the Detroit Free Press.* American Humorous Verse. Selected and edited, with introduction and notes, by J. Barr. pp. xxiv. 314. *Walter Scott: London,* [1891.] 8°. [*Canterbury Poets.*] **11604.** aa. **4.**

—— The Humour of America. Selected, with an introduction and index of American humorists, by J. Barr. Illustrations by C. E. Brock. pp. xiii. 462. *Walter Scott: London,* 1893. 8°. [*International Humour.*] **012314.** g.

BARR (James) *Rev., of Glasgow.*

—— Capital Punishment from the Christian Standpoint . . . The third Roy Calvert Memorial Lecture. pp. 17. *National Council for the Abolition of the Death Penalty: London,* [1940.] 8°. **8435.** e. **59.**

—— Christianity and War: a series of lectures delivered in Rutherford United Free Church, Glasgow, during the course of the South African War. pp. 191. *Simpkin Marshall & Co.: London; C. L. Wright: Glasgow,* 1903. 8°. **8425.** de. **22.**

—— Lang Syne. Memoirs of the Rev. J. Barr. [With plates.] pp. 384. *William Maclellan & Co.: Glasgow,* 1949. 8°. **4957.** b. **24.**

—— Religious Liberty in the Totalitarian States. The challenge to the Church of Communism, Fascism, Nazism. pp. 64. *Allenson & Co.: London,* 1938. 8°. **20032.** f. **22.**

—— The Scottish Church Question. pp. 308. *J. Clarke & Co.: London,* 1920. 8°. **4165.** e. **22.**

—— The Scottish Covenanters. [With illustrations.] pp. 245. *J. Smith & Son: Glasgow,* 1946. 8°. **04735.** f. **19.**

—— The Scottish Covenanters . . . Second edition. pp. 266. *John Smith & Son: Glasgow,* 1947. 8°. **04735.** h. **15**

—— The United Free Church of Scotland. [With a portrait.] pp. 302. *Allenson & Co.: London,* 1934. 8°. **4175.** cc. **45.**

BARR (*Sir* James) Abrams' Methods of Diagnosis & Treatment. [By various authors.] Edited by Sir J. Barr. [With a portrait.] pp. xxxi. 122. *William Heinemann: London,* 1925. 8°. **7439.** h. **5.**

—— The Treatment of Typhoid Fever, and reports of fifty-five consecutive cases with only one death, *etc.* pp. x. 212. *H. K. Lewis: London,* 1892 [1891]. 8°. **7561.** k. **3.**

BARR (James Craig) Home Service. The recollections of a commanding officer serving in Great Britain during the war, 1914–1919 . . . With photographs and sketches [including a portrait of the author], *etc.* pp. 365. *Alexander Gardner: Paisley,* 1920. 8°. **09082.** d. **57.** *Printed for private circulation.*

BARR (James Robertson) Principles of Direct-Current Electrical Engineering, *etc.* pp. viii. 551. *Whittaker & Co.: London,* 1908. 8º. [*Specialists' Series.*] **08709.h.1/84.**

—— [Another edition.] By . . . J. R. Barr . . . and D. J. Bolton . . . Second edition [of the work originally written by J. R. Barr alone]. pp. x. 486. *Sir I. Pitman & Sons: London,* 1934. 8º. **2246.** c. **22.**

BARR (James Robertson) and **ARCHIBALD** (Robert Douglas)

—— The Design of Alternating Current Machinery, *etc.* pp. 496. *Whittaker & Co.: London,* 1913. 8º. [*Specialists' Series.*] **08709.h.1/79.**

BARR (James William H.) A New and Improved System of Freight Transport by Rail and Road, *etc.* [With plates.] pp. 16. *Pardy & Son: Bournemouth,* 1931. fol. **1884.** b. **9.**

BARR (Janet Rhoda)

—— Within Sound of the Bell. [An autobiography. With portraits.] pp. 98. *Whitcombe & Tombs: Christchurch,* 1953. 8º. **10863.** ff. **12.**

BARR (Jean) Pride of Race. [A novel.] pp. 287. *Andrew Melrose: London,* 1929. 8º. NN. **14847.**

—— Rabbits in Fate's Hat. pp. 320. *Andrew Melrose: London,* 1930. 8º. NN. **16796.**

—— Restive Lovers. pp. 287. *Andrew Melrose: London,* [1930.] 8º. NN. **16148.**

—— Summer in Brittany. pp. 288. *Andrew Melrose: London,* [1929.] 8º. NN. **15646.**

BARR (John) *Chief Librarian, Auckland, N.Z.*

—— *See* Munn (Ralph) and Barr (J.) New Zealand Libraries, *etc.* 1934. 4º. **11912.** d. **16.**

—— Auckland Public Libraries, 1880–1950. A brief historical description. [With illustrations.] pp. 38. 1950. 8º. *See* Auckland.—*City Council.—Library Committee.* **11916.** i. **38.**

—— [Another copy.] pp. 38. 1950. 8º. *See* Auckland.—*City Council.—Library Committee.* **011903.** f. **40.**

—— The City of Auckland, New Zealand, 1840–1920 . . . Preceded by a Maori history of the Auckland Isthmus by George Graham, *etc.* [With plates.] pp. 255. *Whitcombe & Tombs: Auckland,* 1922. 8º. **10493.** bb. **1.**

BARR (John) *D.D. See* Stark (James) *Minister of Cartsdyke Church, Greenock.* The Church Question Briefly Considered: with special reference to the "Church Politics" of the Rev. Mr. Morren, and the "Address" of the Rev. Dr. Barr. 1843. 8º. **4175.** d. **110.**

BARR (John) *Laureate to the Caledonian Society.*

—— Poems and Songs, descriptive and satirical. pp. 254. *John Greig & Son: Edinburgh,* 1861. 8º. **11658.** aaa. **248.**

BARR (John) *of Leeds. See* A——, T., *of K——, East-Riding of Yorkshire.* Letter i. to Mr. T. A——, of K——, *etc.* [By Thomas Galland. A criticism of "A Statement of Facts," by J. Barr, on the introduction of an organ into Brunswick Chapel, Leeds.] [1827.] 8º. **4135.** b. **6.**

BARR (John) *of Leeds.*

—— *See* Galland (Thomas) Letter ii. from a Minister in, Leeds, to his Friend in the Country. Subject. The Conference defended from the imputation cast upon it in "a Statement of Facts" [by J. Barr]. [1827.] 8º. **4135.** b. **32.**

—— *See* Keeling (Isaac) A Reply to the Pamphlet intituled "A Statement of Facts, &c." [by J. Barr], in reference to the introduction of an organ into Brunswick Chapel, and the dissensions connected with that proceeding. 1827. 8º. **4135.** b. **46.**

BARR (John) *Paymaster of the Dutchess County Militia.*

—— Ensign John Barr's Book . . . 1779 . . . 1781, *etc. See* United States of America.—*Army.—Fourth New York Regiment.* Orderly Books of the Fourth New York Regiment, *etc.* 1932. 8º. **9615.** r. **2.**

BARR (John) *Rector of Oumby.* A Sermon, preach'd on the Ninth of October, being the day appointed to be observ'd as the day of a General Thanksgiving, for the suppression of the late unnatural Rebellion. pp. 20. *R. Dodsley: London,* [1746.] 8º. **225.** f. **25.** (**2.**)

BARR (John) *Rev., of Glasgow.* Christ the Desire of all Nations. [A sermon.] *See* S., J. The Relief Preacher, *etc.* 1836. 12º. **4461.** c. **29.**

—— A Help to Professing Christians, in judging their spiritual state and growth in grace. pp. viii. 336. *Blackie, Fullarton & Co.: Glasgow,* 1831. 12º. **4406.** ee. **6.**

—— Plain Catechetical Instructions on Christian Baptism . . . Third edition, corrected, and enlarged. pp. 72. *Blackie, Fullarton & Co.: Glasgow,* 1829. 12º. **4326.** aa. **9.**

—— Leabhar Ceasnachaidh mu Ordugh a Bhaistidh . . . A'chuid is mò dheth air eadar-theangachadh o Bheurla an Urramaich Iain Barr [i.e. "Plain Catechetical Instructions on Christian Baptism"] . . . agus a chuid eile air atharrachadh agus air a dhealbh as ùr, le aon de Mhinisteirean Mhuile. pp. 72. *Clo-Bhuailte le Deorsa Brookman: Glaschu,* 1836. 12º. **4405.** aaa. **21.**

—— The Scripture Student's Assistant; being a complete index, and concise dictionary to the Holy Bible, *etc.* pp. iv. 177. *Blackie, Fullarton & Co.: Glasgow,* 1829. 12º. **861.** i. **3.**

—— New edition, *etc.* pp. v. 284. *Blackie & Son: London,* 1854. 8º. **3127.** f. **24.**

—— [A reissue.] 1858. *See* Bible.—*Appendix.—Concordances.* [*English.*] The Twofold Concordance to the Words and Subjects of the Holy Bible, *etc.* 1858. 8º. **3129.** c. **31.**

—— [Another edition.] A Complete Index, and Concise Dictionary of the Holy Bible, *etc. See* Bible. [*English.*] The Self-Interpreting Family Bible, *etc.* [1862.] 4º. **3052.** ee. **5.**

—— [Another edition.] The Bible-Reader's Assistant . . . A new edition, revised and enlarged by the Rev. M. G. Easton, *etc.* pp. viii. 276. *Blackie & Son: London,* 1875. 8º. **3103.** b. **1.**

—— [Another edition.] The Bible-Reader's Assistant, *etc. See* Bible. [*English.*] The Pew and Study Bible, *etc.* [1876.] 4º. **3050.** cc. **3.**

BARR (JOHN) *Writer on Currency.* Labour and the Money Problem. pp. 16. *Labour Pioneer Press: Merthyr Tydvil,* 1920. 8°. **08285. a. 60.**

BARR (JOHN HENRY) *See* KIMBALL (Dexter S.) the Elder, and BARR (J. H.) Elements of Machine Design. 1909. 8°. **08767. d. 16.**

— — 1923. 8°. **8763. ee. 8.**

— *See* KIMBALL (Dexter S.) the Elder, and BARR (J. H.) Elements of Machine Design, *etc.* 1935. 8°. **08770. c. 43.**

— Kinematics of Machinery. A brief treatise on constrained motions of machine elements, *etc.* pp. v. 247. *J. Wiley & Sons: New York,* 1899. 8°. **08766. d. 9.**

— (Second edition.) Revised by Edgar H. Wood, *etc.* pp. vii. 264. *J. Wiley & Sons: New York,* 1911. 8°. **08766. d. 50.**

BARR (JOHN STODDART) *See* BARR (Thomas) *M.D.* Manual of Diseases of the Ear . . . By T. Barr . . . and J. S. Barr, *etc.* 1909. 8°. **2256. g. 17.**

BARR (JOHN T.) Chapters for the Young. pp. 180. *Partridge & Oakey: London,* 1851. 12°. **4415. f. 9.**

— The Cottage of Content; or, Incidents in the life of a Birmingham man. pp. 24. *S. W. Partridge: London,* [1863.] 12°. **4417. aaa. 11.**

— Recollections of a Minister; or, Sketches drawn from life and character. pp. 132. *John Snow: London,* 1838. 12°. **1117. h. 14.**

— Story of the Two Apprentices. pp. 30. *S. W. Partridge: London,* [1862.] 8°. **12806. dd. 7.**

— The Wesleyan Church-Member's Pocket Companion: being a practical guide to members of the Wesleyan-Methodist Society. pp. 92. *John Mason: London,* 1849. 12°. **4405. e. 4.**

BARR (JOSEPH ROBERT) The Golden Pelt. A tale of black foxes whose silver tips are worth their weight in gold. [With illustrations.] pp. 27. [*Charlottetown, P.E.I.,* 1913.] 8°. **07207. i. 9.**

BARR (KAJ)

— *See* ANDREAS (F. C.) Iranische Dialektaufzeichnungen aus dem Nachlass von F. C. Andreas. Zusammen mit K. Barr . . . bearbeitet und herausgegeben von A. Christensen. 1939, *etc.* 8°. [*Abhandlungen der Gesellschaft der Wissenschaften zu Göttingen.* Phil.-hist. Klasse. Folge 3. no. 11.] **Ac. 670. (1.)**

BARR (KNUT AUGUST) *See* SWEDBERG, afterwards SWEDENBORG (E.) [*Drömmar.*] Swedenborgs Drömmar . . . Utgiven och kommenterad med förklarande noter samt med bibliografiska och biografiska essayer av K. Barr. 1924. 8°. **3716. b. 30.**

— Arbetets söner. Ett illustrationsverk öfver den svenska arbetsklassen. Med text af D:r. K. Barr. pp. 696. *Stockholm,* [1907.] *obl.* 8°. **1884. aa. 1.**

— Bellman . . . Bearbetad av Leon Fried. [With illustrations, including portraits.] pp. 258. *Stockholm,* 1930. 8°. **10760. aa. 15.**

— Olof Broman, författaren till vår första roman. Akademisk afhandling, *etc.* pp. 90. *Upsala,* 1898. 8°. **10761. h. 24.**

BARR (LOCKWOOD)

— A Brief, but most complete & true account of the settlement of the Ancient Town of Pelham, Westchester County, State of New York . . . Also the story of the three modern villages called The Pelhams, *etc.* pp. xv. 190. pl. XXVIII. *Dietz Press: Richmond, Va.,* 1946. 8°. **10414. bb. 22.**

BARR (LOUISE FARROW)

— Presses of Northern California and their Books, 1900–1933. pp. xxii. 276. *Book Arts Club, University of California: Berkeley,* 1934. 8°. **11914. d. 23.**

BARR (MARGARET)

— *See* FINDLOW (Bruce) Kharang . . . An eye-witness account of the work of M. Barr, *etc.* 1955. 8°. **4768. bbb. 69.**

— *See* SPARHAM (Griffith J.) Khasi Calls . . . Edited and enlarged by M. Barr. 1945. 8°. **4768. aaa. 11.**

— The Great Unity. A new approach to religious education. pp. 95. *Lindsey Press: London,* 1937. 8°. **20033. aa. 14.**

BARR (MARTIN W.) The King of Thomond. A story of yesterday. pp. xix. 218. *Chatto & Windus: London,* 1907. 8°. **012706. d. 33.**

BARR (MARTIN W.) and **MALONEY** (EARLE FRANCIS) 88

— Types of Mental Defectives, *etc.* pp. ix. 179. pl. XXXI. *H. K. Lewis & Co.: London; printed in America,* 1921. 8°. **7660. g. 41.**

BARR (MARY MARGARET HARRISON)

— Bibliographical Data on Voltaire from 1926 to 1930 . . . Reprinted from "Modern Language Notes." [*Baltimore,* 1933.] 8°. **11911.b.58.**

— A Century of Voltaire Study. A bibliography of writings on Voltaire, 1825–1925. pp. xxiii. 123. *New York,* 1929. 8°. [*Publications of the Institute of French Studies.*] **Ac. 2688. k. (7.)**

— Voltaire in America, 1744–1800, *etc.* (Reprinted from the Johns Hopkins Studies in Romance Literatures and Languages.) [A thesis. With a bibliography.] pp. 150. *Baltimore,* 1941. 8°. **11865. d. 12.**

BARR (MATTHIAS) *See* also DUNKELMANN (H.) *pseud.* [i.e. M. Barr.]

— The Child's Garland of Little Poems . . . With illustrative borders by Giacomello. pp. 100. *Cassell, Petter, & Galpin: London,* [1866.] 4°. **11651. h. 15.**

— Hours of Sunshine, *etc.* [Verses for children.] pp. 96. *Cassell, Petter, & Galpin: London,* [1869.] 8°. **12808. ff. 35.**

— New edition, *etc.* pp. 96. *Hodder Bros.: London,* 1894. 8°. **011652. ee. 1.**

— Little Willie, and other poems on children. pp. 25. *Longmans, Green & Co.: London,* 1867. 12°. **11648. a. 85. (10.)**

— (Third edition.) pp. 36. *Cassell, Petter, & Galpin: London,* [1871.] 8°. **11652. a. 72. (3.)**

— (Fourth edition.) pp. 36. *Barr & Co.: London,* [1879.] 8°. **11653. a. 30.**

BARR (Matthias)

—— Poems. pp. viii. 154. *Longman & Co.: London,* 1865. 8°. **11649**. bb. **37**.

—— Revised and enlarged edition. pp. 190. *Cassell, Petter, & Galpin: London,* 1870. 8°. **11648**. ee. **27**.

—— New edition. 2 pt. pp. 190. *Cassell, Petter, & Galpin: London,* [1872.] 8°. **11652**. a. **64**.

—— [A reissue in one volume.] *Barr & Co.: London,* [1879.] 8°. **11653**. a. **32**.

BARR (Maurice) Mémoires d'une poule noire, *etc.* [With illustrations.] pp. 296. *Paris,* 1882. 4°. **12805**. n. **47**.

—— Visites au Jardin zoologique d'acclimatation. Illustration par Freeman et Yan'Dargent. [With a plan.] pp. xxii. 208. *Tours,* 1867. 8°. **7206**. k. **29**.

BARR (Noel)

—— Beaky, the Greedy Duck . . . Illustrations by P. B. Hickling. *Wills & Hepworth: Loughborough,* [1951.] 8°. [*Ladybird Book.*] W.P. **9629/54**.

—— Cocky, the Lazy Rooster . . . Illustrations by P. B. Hickling. *Wills & Hepworth: Loughborough,* 1953. 8°. [*Ladybird Book.* ser. 497.] W.P. **9629/65**.

—— The Conceited Lamb . . . Illustrations by P. B. Hickling. *Wills & Hepworth: Loughborough,* 1951. 8°. [*Ladybird Series.* no. 497.] W.P. **9629/55**.

—— The Discontented Pony . . . Illustrations by P. B. Hickling. *Wills & Hepworth: Loughborough,* [1951.] 8°. [*Ladybird Book.*] W.P. **9629/53**.

—— The Inquisitive Harvest Mouse. A story . . . Illustrated by P. B. Hickling. *Wills & Hepworth: Loughborough,* [1949.] 8°. **12831**. de. 49.

—— Mick the Disobedient Puppy . . . Illustrations by P. B. Hickling. *Wills & Hepworth: Loughborough,* 1952. 8°. [*Ladybird Book.* ser. 497.] W.P. **9629/61**.

—— Ned the Lonely Donkey . . . Illustrations by P. B. Hickling. *Wills & Hepworth: Loughborough,* 1952. 8°. [*Ladybird Books.*] W.P. **9629/59**.

—— The Sleepy Water Vole . . . Illustrations by P. B. Hickling. *Wills & Hepworth: Loughborough,* [1955.] 8°. [*Ladybird Books.* ser. 497.] W.P. **9629/75**.

—— Tiptoes: the mischievous kitten . . . Illustrations by P. B. Hickling. *Wills & Hepworth: Loughborough,* 1949. 8°. [*Ladybird Book.*] W.P. **9629/43**.

—— We Four and the King's Treasure. pp. 156. *George G. Harrap & Co.: London,* 1950. 8°. **12833**. e. **18**.

—— We Four on Mouse Island. pp. 140. *George G. Harrap & Co.: London,* 1950. 8°. **12833**. e. **12**.

—— The Wise Robin . . . Illustrations by P. B. Hickling. *Wills & Hepworth: Loughborough,* 1950. 8°. [*Ladybird Books.*] W.P. **9629/49**.

BARR (Peter) *Novelist.*

—— King of the Clouds. pp. 254. *Columbine Publishing Co.: London,* [1939.] 8°. NN. 30167.

BARR (Peter) *V.M.H., London.*

—— Reading on the Cultivation of the Daffodil . . . Delivered at the monthly meeting of the Sea Point Horticultural Society. (Reprinted from the Cape Times, with sundry corrections.) pp. 46. *J. C. Juta & Co.: Cape Town,* 1901. 8°. **7030**. de. **17**.

—— [Another copy.] **7030**. de. **15**. **(2.)**

—— Readings on the Lilies of the World, *etc.* (Reprinted from The Cape Times, with sundry corrections.) pp. 30. *Cape Times: [Cape Town,* 1901.] 8°. **7030**. de. **15**. **(3.)**

BARR (R. A. Byers) *See* Dansey (Roger) All Blacks in England . . . Edited by R. A. Byers-Barr. [1924.] 4°. **7904**. dd. **20**.

BARR (Richard Alexander) *See* Douglas (Richard) Surgical Diseases of the Abdomen . . . Edited by R. A. Barr. 1909. 8°. **2256**. h. **10**.

BARR (Robert) *Novelist. See* also Sharp (Luke) *pseud.* [i.e. R. Barr.]

—— *See* Crane (Stephen) *Novelist,* and Barr (R.) The O'Ruddy, *etc.* [1903.] 8°. **012707**. a. **22**.

—— —— [1913.] 8°. **012600**. c. 5.

—— *See* Periodical Publications.—*Coventry.* The Lady's Idler. Edited by R. Barr. 1894. 16°. **1866**. a. **15**. **(9.)**

—— *See* Periodical Publications.—*London.* The Idler. Edited by J. K. Jerome and R. Barr. 1892, *etc.* 8°. P.P. **6004**. gmi.

—— Cardillac, *etc.* pp. 306. *Mills & Boon: London,* 1909. 8°. **012624**. d. **14**.

—— [Another edition.] pp. 128. *Hodder & Stoughton: London,* [1914.] 8°. **012600**. b. **77**.

—— A Chicago Princess, *etc.* pp. 306. *F. A. Stokes Co.: New York,* 1904. 8°. **012707**. cc. **38**.

—— The Face and the Mask. pp. 304. *Hutchinson & Co.: London,* 1894. 8°. **012629**. ee. **46**.

—— From Whose Bourne, *etc.* [Three tales.] pp. 277. *Chatto & Windus: London,* 1893. 8°. **012641**. f. 57.

—— The Girl in the Case: being the manœuvres of the inadvertent Mr. Pepperton . . . Third impression. pp. 256. *Eveleigh Nash: London,* 1910. 8°. **012623**. aa. **39**.

—— [Another edition.] pp. 94. *Hodder & Stoughton: London,* [1914.] 8°. **012600**. b. **94**.

—— The Helping Hand, and other stories. pp. 247. *Mills & Boon: London,* 1920. 8°. NN. **6390**.

—— I Travel the Road. [On touring in Great Britain. With illustrations.] pp. 172. *Quality Press: London,* 1945. 8°. **10360**. s. 13.

—— In a Steamer Chair, and other shipboard stories. pp. 264. *Chatto & Windus: London,* 1892. 8°. **012634**. i. **64**.

—— In the Midst of Alarms. pp. 352. *Methuen & Co.: London,* 1894. 8°. **012629**. ee. **43**.

—— Jennie Baxter, Journalist. pp. 128. *Methuen & Co.: London,* 1899. 8°. **012614**. i. **7**.

—— [Another edition.] pp. 128. *Copp, Clark Co.: Toronto,* 1899. 8°. **12706**. h. **44**.

BARR (Robert) *Novelist.*

—— The King Dines. pp. 8. *S. S. McClure Co.: London,* 1901. 8°. **12623. f. 60.**

—— The Lady Electra. pp. 313. *Methuen & Co.: London,* 1904. 8°. **012630. aa. 31.**

—— Lord Stranleigh Abroad. pp. 304. *Ward, Lock & Co.: London,* 1913. 8°. NN. **905.**

—— Lord Stranleigh, Philanthropist . . . Fully illustrated. pp. 320. *Ward, Lock & Co.: London,* 1911. 8°. **012618. aaa. 15.**

—— [A reissue.] *London,* [1913.] 8°. NN. **906.**

—— The Measure of the Rule. pp. 308. *A. Constable & Co.: London,* 1907. 8°. **012627. aa. 21.**

—— [Another edition.] pp. 127. *London,* [1909.] 8°. [*Constable's Sixpenny Series.*] **012604.g.1/4.**

—— The Mutable Many. pp. 394. *Methuen & Co.: London,* 1897. 8°. **012625. i. 50.**

—— My Enemy Jones. An extravaganza. pp. 225. *Eveleigh Nash: London,* 1913. 8°. NN. **1218.**

—— [Another edition.] Unsentimental Journey, *etc.* pp. 95. *Hodder & Stoughton: London,* [1915.] 8°. **012600. c. 42.**

—— Over the Border. pp. viii. 400. *Isbister & Co.: London,* 1903. 8°. **012628. d. 31.**

—— [Another edition.] pp. 192. *Sir I. Pitman & Sons: London,* 1907. 8°. **012625. ee. 96.**

—— The Palace of Logs. pp. 316. *Mills & Boon: London,* 1912. 8°. NN. **169.**

—— A Prince of Good Fellows . . . Illustrated by E. J. Sullivan. pp. x. 340. *Chatto & Windus: London,* 1902. 8°. **012637. c. 28.**

—— The Purser's Story. *See* Wagner (L.) xx Stories by xx Tellers, *etc.* 1895. 8°. **C.132.g.63.**

—— Revenge! *etc.* [Short stories.] pp. 344. *Chatto & Windus: London,* 1896. 8°. **012626. ee. 48.**

—— A Rock in the Baltic . . . Illustrated in water-colors by Hermann Heyer. pp. 321. *Mcleod & Allen: Toronto,* [1906.] 8°. **012706. aaa. 39.**

—— [Another edition.] pp. 326. *Hurst & Blackett: London,* 1907. 8°. **012633. bb. 19.**

—— The Speculations of John Steele. pp. 344. *Chatto & Windus: London,* 1905. 8°. **012631. bbb. 36.**

—— Stranleigh's Millions. pp. 344. *Eveleigh Nash: London,* 1909. 8°. **012624. d. 15.**

—— Second impression. pp. 344. *Eveleigh Nash: London,* 1911. 8°. **012618. aaa. 14.**

—— The Strong Arm. [Short stories.] pp. 336. *William Briggs: Toronto,* 1899. 8°. **012622. f. 48.**

—— [Another edition.] pp. 336. *Methuen & Co.: London,* 1900. 8°. **012641. b. 33.**

—— The Sword Maker. A romance of love and adventure . . . Second edition. pp. vii. 415. *Mills & Boon: London,* 1910. 8°. **012623. aa. 40.**

—— [Another edition.] pp. 144. *Hodder & Stoughton: London,* [1913.] 8°. **012600. c. 23.**

—— Tales of Two Continents. pp. 252. *Mills & Boon: London,* 1920. 8°. NN. **6063.**

BARR (Robert) *Novelist.*

—— Tekla. A romance of love and war. pp. 437. *G. N. Morang: Toronto,* 1898. 8°. **012643. f. 18.**

—— [A reissue.] The Countess Tekla. *Methuen & Co.: London,* 1899. 8°. **012642. aa. 22.**

—— [Another edition.] pp. 320. *London,* [1913.] 8°. [*Everett's Library.*] **12209.k.1/76.**

—— The Tempestuous Petticoat, *etc.* pp. 306. *Methuen & Co.: London,* 1905. 8°. **012630. c. 30.**

—— The Triumphs of Eugène Valmont. pp. 307. *Hurst & Blackett: London,* 1906. 8°. **012632. c. 19.**

—— The Unchanging East, *etc.* [Travel impressions of Northern Africa and Palestine.] pp. x. 321. *Chatto & Windus: London,* 1900. 8°. **10077. cc. 7.**

—— Unsentimental Journey. *See* supra: My Enemy Jones.

—— The Victors. A romance of yesterday morning and this afternoon. pp. ix. 567. *Methuen & Co.: London,* 1902. 8°. **012639. ccc. 44.**

—— A Woman in a Thousand. pp. 315. *Hodder & Stoughton: London,* [1913.] 8°. NN. **907.**

—— A Woman Intervenes . . . Illustrations by H. Hurst. pp. 352. *Chatto & Windus: London,* 1896. 8°. **012628. l. 44.**

—— The Woman Wins. pp. 313. *F. A. Stokes Co.: New York,* 1904. 8°. **012707. cc. 14.**

—— Young Lord Stranleigh . . . Illustrated by Gilbert Holiday. pp. 302. *Ward Lock & Co.: London,* 1908. 8°. **012627. aa. 41.**

BARR (Robert) *of Australia.*

—— Spoken English as an Auxiliary World Language. The printed word reformed and a universal alphabet. pp. 23. *W. Barr: Melbourne,* 1945. 8°. **12987. bb. 12.**

BARR (Robert) *Rev., of Capetown.* Born King, *etc.* [Religious meditations.] pp. 110. *Oliphants: London, Edinburgh,* [1933.] 8°. **04402. g. 48.**

—— In Sweet Remembrance. A book of Communion addresses. pp. 128. *Oliphants: London; Edinburgh,* [1938.] 8°. **4480. df. 36.**

—— [A reissue.] In Sweet Remembrance, *etc.* *London. Edinburgh,* 1948. 8°. **4480. e. 58.**

—— Speak, Precious Stones. [Sermons on the precious stones mentioned in the Bible.] pp. 128. *Oliphants: London. Edinburgh,* 1953 [1954]. 8°. **4481. a. 52.**

—— With the Psalmist at Bain's Kloof. (Meditations in and around the Peninsula.) pp. 11. *Maskew Miller: Cape Town,* [1929.] 8°. **04400. de. 2.**

BARR (Robert M.) *See* Pennsylvania, *State of.—Supreme Court.* Pennsylvania State Reports, *etc.* (vol. 1–10. By R. M. Barr.) 1846, *etc.* 8°. **6622.k.16.**

BARR (Samuel)

—— The Theory and Practice of Harmony and Composition: being a manual for the use of students. pt. 1. pp. 39. ms. notes. *J. H. De Monti: Glasgow,* 1859. 8°. **4431. e. 1. (8.)**

BARR (Stringfellow)

—— Citizens of the World, *etc.* [Proposing the establishment of an International Development Authority.] pp. 285. *Doubleday & Co.: Garden City, N.Y.*, 1952. 8°. **8289**. m. **20**.

—— Citizens of the World, *etc.* [On U.S. policy on world poverty.] pp. 285. *Victor Gollancz: London*, 1953. 8°. **8290**. aa. **13**.

—— Copydog in India . . . Illustrated by Kurt Wiese. pp. 127. *Viking Press: New York*, 1955. 8°. **12837**. l. **22**.

—— Let's join the Human Race. pp. 19. *Bureau of Current Affairs: London*, 1951. 8°. [*Current Affairs.* no. 134.] P.P. **3610**. gkl.

—— Let's join the Human Race. (Sixth impression.) pp. 30. *University of Chicago Press: Chicago*, 1951. 8°. **8177**. l. **22**.

—— Mazzini. Portrait of an exile. [With a portrait.] pp. viii. 308. *H. Holt & Co.: New York*, [1935.] 8°. **20030**. c. **29**.

—— The Pilgrimage of Western Man. pp. xiii. 369. *Victor Gollancz: London*, 1950. 8°. **09077**. ee. **75**.

BARR (Thomas) *Head of Mathematical Department, Hutcheson's' Grammar School, Glasgow.* Practical Mathematics for Continuation Classes, embodying a preparatory technical course for craftsmen. pp. viii. 232. *Blackie & Son: London*, 1910. 8°. **8507**. dd. **33**.

BARR (Thomas) *M.D.* Manual of Diseases of the Ear, *etc.* pp. xxvii. 529. *J. Maclehose & Sons: Glasgow*, 1884. 8°. **07610**. de. **39**.

—— Second edition, entirely revised and extensively re-written. pp. xxiii. 415. *J. Maclehose & Sons: Glasgow*, 1896. 8°. **7610**. d. **3**.

—— Third edition, revised and partially re-written, *etc.* pp. xxiii. 429. *J. Maclehose & Sons: Glasgow*, 1901. 8°. **07610**. f. **11**.

—— Fourth edition, entirely revised and largely re-written, *etc.* (By T. Barr . . . and J. Stoddart Barr.) pp. xxvii. 477. *J. Maclehose & Sons: Glasgow*, 1909. 8°. **2256**. g. **17**.

BARR (Thomas E.) The Gist of it : a philosophy of human life, *etc.* pp. xxxiii. 350. *A. C. Armstrong & Son: New York*, 1887. 8°. **8463**. ccc. **23**.

BARR (W. T.)

—— For a Web begun. The story of Dunfermline. pp. xii. 186. *Oliver & Boyd: Edinburgh, London*, 1947. 8°. **010370**. b. **30**.

BARR (Walter) Shacklett. The evolution of a statesman. [A novel.] pp. viii. 392. *D. Appleton & Co.: New York*, 1901. 8°. **012707**. l. **18**.

—— [A reissue.] *T. Fisher Unwin: London*, 1902. 8°. **012707**. m. **44**.

BARR (William) *A.R.T.C.*, and **HONEYMAN** (Allan James Knox) Steel and its Practical Applications. pp. xiv. 125. pl. xxiv. *London & Glasgow*, 1932. 8°. [*Blackie's "Technique" Series.*] W.P. **535/4**.

—— Steel and its Practical Applications . . . Second edition. pp. xii. 156. pl. 35. *London & Glasgow*, 1945. 8°. [*Blackie's "Technique" Series.*] W.P. **535/15**.

BARR (William) *Lieutenant, Bengal Horse Artillery.* Journal of a March from Delhi to Peshâwur, and from thence to Câbul, with the Mission to Lieut-Col. Sir C. M. Wade, *etc.* [With plates.] pp. xvi. 410. *J. Madden & Co.: London*, 1844. 12°. **1425**. e. **15**.

BARR (William) *M.D.*

—— Gangrel Verses. In the Scots of the south-west. pp. 72. *William MacLellan: Glasgow*, 1949. 8°. **11657**. cc. **110**.

—— I. K. Therapy, Immunkörper, Immune Substances, in Pulmonary Tuberculosis. With a summary of cases and forty-two illustrated charts. pp. 82. *J. Wright & Sons: Bristol; Simpkin, Marshall & Co.: London*, 1916. 8°. **7616**. cc. **9**.

—— Passing Songs. pp. vi. 57. *Grant Richards: London*, 1922. 8°. **011645**. eee. **15**.

BARR (William) *Minister of the Relief Synod.* The Perpetuity of the Gospel. [A sermon.] *See* S., J. The Relief Preacher, *etc.* 1836. 12°. **4461**. c. **29**.

BARR (William Miller) A Catechism on the Combustion of Coal and the Prevention of Smoke. A practical treatise, *etc.* pp. 349. *N. W. Henley & Co.: New York*, 1901. 8°. **8716**. aa. **37**.

—— A Practical Treatise on the Combustion of Coal, including descriptions of various mechanical devices for the economic generation of heat by the combustion of fuel, whether solid, liquid or gaseous. pp. viii. 306. *Yohn Brothers: Indianapolis*, 1879. 8°. **8716**. bbb. **15**.

—— Pumping Machinery. A practical hand-book relating to the construction and management of steam and power pumping machines, *etc.* pp. 447. *J. B. Lippincott Co.: Philadelphia*, 1893. 8°. **8768**. e. **29**.

—— Second edition, *etc.* pp. 483. *J. B. Lippincott Co.: Philadelphia & London*, 1908. 8°. **08767**. h. **29**.

BARR (William Monfort)

—— An Analysis of the Current Expenditures of Selected Indiana High Schools. pp. 30. *Bloomington*, 1954. 8°. [*Bulletin of the School of Education, Indiana University.* vol. 30. no. 3.] Ac. **2692**. wa.

BARR (William Norbert)

—— *See* Lee (Henry I.) and Barr (W. N.) Practical Secretarial Work, *etc.* 1929. 8°. **6376**. w. **23**.

—— *See* Lee (Henry I.) and Barr (W. N.) Practical Secretarial Work, *etc.* [1947.] 8°. **08246**. eee. **75**.

—— *See* Lee (Henry I.) and Barr (W. N.) Practical Secretarial Work, *etc.* 1950. 8°. **08223**. e. **75**.

BARRA. Barra ; or, the Lord of the Isles. A tragedy. In five acts. [In verse.] pp. 122. *Richard Welch: Reading*, 1845. 8°. **11781**. f. **2**.

BARRA (Antonio) [Selected poems.] *See* Acampora (G.) Raccolta di rime di poeti napoletani, non più ancora stampate, *etc.* 1701. 12°. **240**. e. **32**.

BARRA (Bruno Larrain) *See* Larrain Barra.

BARRA (Eduardo de la) *See* Darío (R.) *pseud.* Azul, *etc.* [With a preface by E. de la Barra.] 1888. 8°. **12489**. k. **36**.

—— *See* Eliz (L.) D. Eduardo de la Barra. Rasgos biográficos, *etc.* 1889. 8°. **10881**. dd. **24**. (**5**.)

—— Elementos de Métrica Castellana. *See* Varela (F.) Certámen Varela, *etc.* tom. 2. 1887. 8°. **11450**. g. **4**.

BARRA (EDUARDO DE LA)

—— [Another issue.] pp. 104. *Santiago de Chile*, 1887. 8°. **2310**. h. **4**.

—— Estudios Críticos. Restauración de el Misterio de los Reyes Magos. La página más antigua del teatro español. pp. 43. *Santiago de Chile*, 1898. 8°. **11853**. a. **24**. (**1**.)

—— Estudios sobre la Versificación Castellana. pp. 101. *Santiago de Chile*, 1889. 8°. **011824**. i. **2**.

—— Francisco Bilbao ante la Sacristía. Refutación de un folleto. pt. 1. *Santiago*, 1872. 8°. **10632**. cc. **6**. *Imperfect; wanting all after pt.* 1.

—— La Hoja Perdida del Poema del Cid. pp. 11. *Rosario de Santa Fé*, 1894. 8°. **11852**. i. **32**. (**2**.)

—— Literatura Arcaica. Estudios críticos, *etc.* pp. viii. 373. *Valparaiso*, [1898.] 8°. **011851**. g. **40**.

—— Ortografía Fonética, *etc.* pp. 82. *Santiago de Chile*, 1897. 8°. **12942**. aa. **49**.

—— Poesías. 2 tom. *Santiago de Chile*, 1889. 8°. **11451**. cc. **14**.

—— El Problema de los Andes. pp 416. *Buenos Aires*, 1895. 8°. **10480**. df. **10**.

—— Problemas de Fonética, resueltos según un nuevo método. pp. 192. *Buenos Aires*, 1894. 8°. **12943**. ee. **25**.

—— Restauracion de la Gesta del Cid Campeador, *etc.* pp. 27. *Santiago de Chile*, 1896. 8°. **11851**. ee. **21**. (**5**.)

—— Rimas Chilenas . . . Precedidas de la biografía del autor por Leonardo Eliz. [With a portrait.] pp. lv. 331. *Paris*, 1890. 18°. **11450**. cc. **18**.

BARRA (FEDERICO DE LA) Intereses Nacionales. Coleccion de artículos publicados en " La Capital." pp. 31. *Rosario*, 1871. 8°. **8180**. a. **12**.

BARRA (FRANCESCH) Brev Tractat De Artilleria, recopilat de diversos autors y treballat per F. Barra, *etc.* pp. 130. *I. Mathevat: Barcelona*, 1642. 4°. **8826**. g. **6**.

BARRA (FRANCISCO SUBIRÁS Y) *See* SUBIRÁS Y BARRA.

BARRA (FRANCISCO XAVIER) Memoria sobre la construccion del pavimento ó firme de los caminos. pp. 88. *Madrid*, 1826. 4°. **8776**. cc. **10**. (**1**.)

—— Proyecto y memoria de Don F. X. Barra . . . sobre la conduccion de aguas á Madrid, *etc.* [With charts.] pp. 103. *Madrid*, 1832. fol. **8776**. g. **25**.

BARRA (GIOVANNI) *Priest, of Naples.*

—— Argomenti sul Purgatorio. pp. 413. *Napoli*, 1868. 8°. **3902**. aa. **7**.

BARRA (JACOBUS) Disputatio inauguralis de calculo renum, *etc.* *Henricus Ludovici ab Haestens: Lugduni Batavorum*, 1610. 4°. **1185**. g. **1**. (**38**.)

BARRA (JEAN BAPTISTE) *See* BARA.

BARRA (JOSEP VICENÇ AMORÓS) *See* AMORÓS BARRA.

BARRA (JOSEPH)

—— *See* DAVID (J. L.) Convention Nationale. Rapport sur la fête héroique pour les honneurs du Panthéon à décerner aux jeunes Barra & Viala, *etc.* [1794.] 8°. R. **179**. (**31**.)

BARRA (JOSEPH) Discours prononcés sur l'autel de la patrie de la commune d'Avignon. Le jour de la fête des jeunes Barra et Viala. pp. 16. *Avignon*, [1794.] 4°. **936**. f. **7**. (**11**.)

—— Procès-verbal, de la fête qui eût lieu dans cette commune d'Avignon le 30 Messidor [1794], en l'honneur de Barra et Viala. pp. 4. *Avignon*, [1794.] 4°. **936**. f. **7**. (**12**.)

BARRA (LIAM DE)

—— The Irish Revival—do we mean it? pp. 64. *Paramount Printing House: Cork*, [1943.] 8°. **12979**. a. **12**.

BARRA (LUIS LEÓN DE LA) *See* LEÓN DE LA BARRA (L.)

BARRA (OSCAR PINOCHET DE LA) *See* PINOCHET DE LA BARRA.

BARRA (PIERRE) L'Abus de l'antimoine et de la saignée ; demonstré par la doctrine d'Hippocrate. pp. 192. *C. Fourmy: Lyon*, 1664. 12°. **783**. b. **21**.

—— Les Abus de la theriaque, et de la confection d'hyacinthe, *etc.* pp. 75. *A. Valançol: Lyon*, 1667. 8°. **1038**. a. **32**.

—— De veris terminis partus humani libri tres ex Hippocrate. Authore P. Barrá . . . Accessit historia mulieris Romanæ jam ab annis quatuor grauidæ, cum responsione vaticinia eiusdem authoris, & explicatione responsionis. pp. 101. *C. Fourmy: Lugduni*, 1666. 8°. **774**. b. **26**.

—— L'Usage de la glace, de la neige et du froid. pp. 249. *A. Cellier fils: Lyon*, 1675. 12°. **774**. b. **27**.

BARRA (UINSIONN DE) *See* BARRY (Vincent C.)

BARRABÉ (A. J. M.) Essai sur l'usage médical de la glace, *etc.* pp. 36. *Paris*, 1817. 4°. **1183**. d. **7**. (**20**.)

BARRABINI (FRANCESCO) Per i fluidi. pp. 52. *Trapani*, 1915. 8°. **08709**. bb. **15**.

BARRACAND (LÉON) *See* also GRANDET (L.) *pseud.* [i.e. L. Barracand.]

—— Poêmes. Jeannette—L'Enragé. 2 pt. *Paris*, 1878. 12°. **11483**. bb. **23**.

—— L'Adoration. [Short stories.] pp. ii. 302. *Paris*, 1895. 8°. **012551**. f. **14**.

—— La Belle Madame Lenain. Mœurs politiques contemporaines. pp. iv. 314. *Paris*, 1893. 12°. **012550**. df. **10**.

—— Le Bonheur au village. pp. 224. *Paris*, 1883. 8°. **12510**. o. **9**.

—— Le Cheval blanc. pp. 119. *Paris*, [1907.] fol. [*Le Monde illustré.* Supplements. Novels.] P.P. **4283**. n. (**1**.)

—— Les Hésitations de Madame Planard. pp. 271. [A novel.] *Paris*, 1886. 8°. **12491**. n. **18**.

—— L'Invasion, 4 août, 1870–16 septembre 1873. Illustrations de Paul Leroy. pp. v. 490. *Paris*, [1903.] 8°. **9076**. h. **15**.

—— Le Manuscrit du sous-lieutenant. [Short stories.] pp. 308. *Paris*, [1887.] 8°. **12491**. q. **29**.

—— Mariage mystique. [A novel.] pp. 283. *Paris*, 1895. 12°. **012550**. i. **25**.

—— Romans dauphinois . . . Avec huit compositions de Tofani. pp. 370. *Paris*, 1882. 8°. **12518**. n. **28**.

BARRACAND (Léon)

—— Servienne. Histoire d'une servante. pp. 236. *Paris*, 1886. 8°. **12514**. i. **23**.

—— Théâtre. Morgana, La Comtesse de Châteaubriant, Chalais, Tristan. pp. 349. *Paris*, 1878. 12°. **11736**. ccc. **1**.

—— Un Village au XIIe siècle et au XIXe. Récit comparatif des mœurs du moyen âge et des mœurs modernes. (Troisième édition.) [On the village of Blatigny. With plates.] pp. 206. *Paris*, 1883. 8°. **12510**. o. **12**.

BARRACAND (Paul Auguste) Considérations sur le tænia de l'espèce humaine. Thèse, *etc.* pp. 39. *Montpellier*, 1863. 4°. **7379**. f. **4**. (**2**.)

BARRACCO (Giovanni) La Collection Barracco. Publiée par Frédéric Bruckmann d'après la classification et avec la texte de G. Barracco et Wolfgang Helbig. [Reproductions of the sculpture in the collection, with explanatory text.] 2 vol. *Munich*, [1892–94.] fol. **1705**. b. **20**.

—— Regalia. [Poems.] pp. 74. *Roma*, 1908. 8°. **11436**. r. **25**.

Printed on one side of the leaf only.

BARRACCO (Mauricio)

—— Le Sorelle. Comedia. pp. 165. *Leonardo Angrisano: Cosenza*, 1596. 8°. C. **107**. aa. **22**.
The pagination is irregular.

BARRACH (Siegmund) Ueber spekulative Aesthetik und Kritik. Ein Sendschreiben an Herrn Dr. Robert Zimmermann. pp. 47. *Wien*, 1854. 8°. **11826**. e. **23**. (**1**.)

—— *See* Drbal (M. A.) Die absolute Kritik. Antwort auf das Sendschreiben des Herrn S. Barrach an Herrn Dr. R. Zimmermann. 1854. 8°. **11825**. d. **43**.

BARRACHIN (L. G.) Dissertation sur la fièvre adéno-nerveuse, dite peste orientale, *etc.* pp. 23. *Strasbourg*, 1823. 4°. [*Collection générale des dissertations de la Faculté de Médecine de Strasbourg*. vol. 30.] **7381*.b.**

—— M. de Lamartine apprécié comme homme politique. Lettre adressée du député de Macon . . . 2e edition, augmentée d'une réfutation du manifeste de l'illustre poète, sur les mariages espagnols. pp. 75. *Paris*, 1846. 8°. **1250**. l. **12**. (**2**.)

BARRACHINA (Pascual Boronat y) *See* Boronat y Barrachina.

BARRACHINA Y PASTOR (Federico)

—— Derecho Foral Español en sus relaciones con el Código Civil, la jurisprudencia del Tribunal Supremo y doctrina de la Dirección general de los registros y del notariado. 3 vol. *Castellón*, 1911, 12. 8°. **05385**. eee. **8**.

BARRACK (Gulielmus) *See* Barrack (William)

BARRACK (William) *See* Horatius Flaccus (Q.) [*Works.—Latin.*] Q. Horatii Flacci Opera. Ex recensione novissima J. C. Orellii, accurante Gul. Barrack. 1864. 16°. **11385**. a. **8**.

—— Lexicon to Xenophon's Anabasis, for the use of schools. pp. x. 164. *Longmans, Green & Co.: London*, 1872. 8°. **12924**. aaa. **40**.

BARRACKS. The Royal Barracks: a poem. pp. 84. *Hodges, Smith & Co.: Dublin*, 1859. 8°. **11651**. c. **9**.

BARRACLIFFE (Frederick) A Still Tongue. A screaming farce. pp. 15. *H. Lodge & Sons: Dewsbury*, [1930.] 8°. **011781**. de. **116**.

BARRACLOUGH (Alfred) The Owner of Gethsemane, and other sermons. pp. 130. *A. H. Stockwell: London*, [1910.] 8°. **4473**. i. **7**.

BARRACLOUGH (Arthur) Observations on the Physical Education of the Vocal Organs. pp. 22. *Cramer & Co.: London*, 1876. 8°. **7807**. c. **15**. (**8**.)

BARRACLOUGH (Augustus) *See* Cracknell (Alfred G.) and Barraclough (A.) Junior Algebra. 1915. 8°. **8505**. de. **12**.

—— Preliminary Arithmetic. pp. viii. 216. *W. B. Clive: London*, 1913. 8°. **8504**. aaaa. **46**.

BARRACLOUGH (Christine)

—— Songs of the Countryside. [Verses.] pp. 16. *Arthur H. Stockwell: Ilfracombe*, [1948.] 8°. **11658**. ee. **87**.

BARRACLOUGH (Edward Murray Conrad)

—— Yacht Flags and Ensigns. Regulations, customs, traditions, and recommendations for wearing and flying flags, other than signal flags, in British yachts. [With illustrations.] pp. 53. *Iliffe & Sons: London*, 1951. 8°. **08805**. aa. **19**.

BARRACLOUGH (Frank)

—— *See* Alexander (Sir William P.) and Barraclough (F.) County and Voluntary Schools. 1949. 8°. **08368**. b. **28**.

—— *See* Alexander (Sir William P.) and Barraclough (F.) County and Voluntary Schools, *etc.* 1953. 8°. **08368**. ee. **23**.

—— *See* Alexander (Sir William P.) and Barraclough (F.) The Establishment, Maintenance and Management of County and Voluntary Schools, *etc.* 1946. 8°. **08368**. b. **34**.

—— *See* Holmyard (Eric J.) and Barraclough (F.) Heat, Light and Sound for Beginners. 1931. 8°. W.P. **9581/15**

—— Elementary Mechanics and Hydrostatics. pp. vi. 282. *University Tutorial Press: London*, 1934. 8°. **08769**. aa. **18**.

—— Sound and Light for Schools, *etc.* pp. vii. 311. *W. B. Clive: London*, 1932. 8°. [*School Examinations Series.*] **12207.aaa.1/5.**

BARRACLOUGH (Frank) and **HOLMYARD** (Eric John)

—— Mechanics for Beginners. [With plates.] pp. viii. 214. *London*, 1931. 8°. [*Dent's Modern Science Series.*] W.P. **9581/14**

BARRACLOUGH (Fred) Housing Policy in the City of Leeds. By . . . F. Barraclough . . . Francis H. O'Donnell and . . . Charles Jenkinson . . . Being a minority report of a sub-committee of the Improvements Committee of the City Council, *etc.* pp. v. 90. 1933. 8°. *See* Leeds.—*City Council.—Improvements Committee.* **8277**. r. **11**

BARRACLOUGH (Frederick) A New System of Short-Hand. *W. N. Sharpe: Bradford*, 1906. *obl.* 8°. **1865**. c. **1**. (**10**.)

BARRACLOUGH (GEOFFREY)

—— *See* LAPSLEY (Gaillard T.) Crown, Community and Parliament in the later Middle Ages . . . Edited by H. M. Cam & G. Barraclough. 1951. 8°. W.P. **12243** 6.

—— *See* ROME, *Church of.*—*Curia Romana.* Public Notaries and the Papal Curia. A calendar and a study of a "Formularium Notariorum Curie" . . . By G. Barraclough. 1934. 4°. Ac. **5232**. b/3.

—— The Chancery Ordinance of Nicholas III., a Study of the Sources. By G. Barraclough. [With the text of the ordinance.] 1933–34. 8°. [*Quellen und Forschungen aus italienischen Archiven und Bibliotheken.* Bd. 25.] *See* ROME, *Church of.*—[*Popes.*]—NICHOLAS III. [1277–1280.] Ac. **6545**/3.

—— The Earldom and County Palatine of Chester. (Reprinted from the Transactions of the Historic Society of Lancashire and Cheshire.) [With illustrations.] pp. 39. *Basil Blackwell: Oxford,* 1953. 8°. **09506**. ee. 2.

—— Factors in German History. pp. vii. 165. *Basil Blackwell: Oxford,* 1946. 8°. **09327**. c. 32.

—— The Mediaeval Empire. Idea and reality. pp. 27. *George Philip & Son:* [*London.*] 1950. 8°. [*Historical Association. General Series.* G. 17.] W.P. **3175** 17.

—— Mediaeval Germany, 911–1250. Essays by German Historians. Translated with an introduction by G. Barraclough. 2 vol. *Basil Blackwell: Oxford,* 1938. 8°. [*Studies in Mediaeval History.* vol. 1, 2.] W.P. **12243** 1. 2.

—— [A reissue.] Mediaeval Germany, 911–1250, *etc.* (Second impression.) *Oxford,* 1948. 8°. **2088.b.**

—— The Origins of Modern Germany. [With maps.] pp. x. 481. *Basil Blackwell: Oxford,* 1946. 8°. **9365**. e. 27.

—— The Origins of Modern Germany. (Second revised edition.) pp. xi. 481. *Basil Blackwell: Oxford,* 1947. 8°. **9385**. bb. 23.

—— Papal Provisions. Aspects of Church history constitutional, legal and administrative in the later Middle Ages. [With a bibliography.] pp. xvi. 187. *Basil Blackwell: Oxford,* 1935. 8°. **20019**. b. 8.

—— Studies in Mediaeval History. Edited by G. Barraclough. *Basil Blackwell: Oxford,* 1938– . 8°. W.P. **12243**.

BARRACLOUGH (GEORGE) Morphology of the Calcareous Skeleton, as manifested in silicious rocks. pp. 12. *Lamley & Co.: London,* [1892.] 8°. **07109**. m. 3. (**11**.)

BARRACLOUGH (J.) *Corporal.*

—— Melodies for the March. Pointed for singing. [Compiled by J. Barraclough.] pp. 23. *E. R. Cousans: Lincoln,* 1861. 12°. **11650**. cc. 24. (7.)

BARRACLOUGH (JUNE)

—— *See* CARITAT (M. J. A. N.) *Marquis de Condorcet.* Sketch for a Historical Picture of the Progress of the Human Mind. Translated by J. Barraclough, *etc.* 1955. 8°. W.P. c. **691** 3.

BARRACLOUGH (PETER)

—— Vocation for the Ministry. pp. 15. *Independent Press: London,* [1955.] 8°. **4499**. p. 32.

BARRACLOUGH (TITUS) The 1892 "Eclipse" Mental . . . Standards I., II. and III. [A textbook in arithmetic.] pp. 48. *John Wilson: Bradford,* 1892. 8°. **8532**. aaa. 25.

—— The 1892 "Eclipse" Mental . . . Standards II., III. & IV. pp. 48. *G. Bell & Sons: London,* [1893.] 8°. **8530**. bbb. 27. (13.)

BARRACLOUGH (W. H.)

—— Butler Wood. An appreciation . . . With bibliographical references by Mabel Dawes. [With a portrait.] (Overprint from the "Bradford Antiquary.") pp. 7. *Bradford,* 1936. 8° **010822**. i. **46**.

BARRACO (FRANCESCO) *See* COSTANTINI (P. L.) Scelta di prose italiane . . . Terza edizione . . . pubblicata da F. Barraco. 1822. 12°. **12226**. aa. **13**.

BARRADA (HASSAN) *See* ḤASAN BARRĀDAH.

BARRADALE (VICTOR ARNOLD) Pearls of the Pacific: being sketches of missionary life and work in Samoa and other islands in the South Seas . . . With ninety-three illustrations. pp. 192. *London Missionary Society: London,* 1907. 4°. **10492**. d. **45**.

—— Pearls of the Southern Seas. An illustrated handbook of life in Polynesia. pp. 95. *Livingstone Press: London,* 1922. 8°. **10493**. de. **24**.

BARRADALL (EDWARD) *See* VIRGINIA, *Colony of.*—*General Court.* Virginia Colonial Decisions . . . The reports by Sir J. Randolph and by E. Barradall of decisions of the General Court of Virginia, 1728–1741, *etc.* 1909. 8°. **06614**. f. 7.

BARRADAS (ANTÓNIO) *See* VIEIRA BARRADAS.

BARRADAS (BALTASAR DE) Feliz Victoria que Don Baltasar de Barradas . . . ha tenido en los presidios y fuerças de la Baltolina, contra vn exercito de Franceses y Saboyanos, que estauan de guarnicion, passando a cuchillo casidos mil dellos, y les ganò dos fuerças de mucha consideracion, *etc. S. Faxardo: Seuilla,* 1625. fol. **593**. h. **17**. (33.)

BARRADAS (EMMANUEL) P. Emmanuelis Barradas . . . Tractatus tres historico-geographici. *Port.* pp. xxxii. 402. *Roma,* 1906. 4°. [*Rerum Aethiopicarum scriptores occidentales inediti.* vol. 4.] **9060**. i. **1**.

—— Il Tigrè, descritto da un missionario gesuita del secolo XVII. ["Do Rémo de Tyrê e seus Mandos em Ethiopia" of E. Barradas, translated and edited by Camillo Beccari.] pp. 114. 1909. 8°. *See* ROME, *the City.*—*Istituto Coloniale Italiano.* **010075**. i. **8**.

—— 2ª edizione, con illustrazioni e nuove note. pp. xiv. 180. *Roma,* 1912. 8°. **010075**. i. **14**.

BARRADAS (ISIDRO) *See* PALACIOS (M.) Noticia estraordinaria. Parte oficial del comandante en gefe de la division de operaciones contra los invasores, en que detalla la accion del dia 1. dada en el Paso de los Corchos, y en que anuncia la muerte de Barradas. 1829. *s. sh.* fol. **9770**. k. 9. (**103**.)

—— Proclama del General de Vanguardia del ejército invasor, Isidro Barradas. [With notes in criticism of the proclamation.] *México,* 1829. *s. sh.* fol. **9770**. k. 9. (**125**.)

BARRADAS (JOSÉ PÉREZ DE) *See* PÉREZ DE BARRADAS.

BARRADAS (MANOEL) Discriçaõ da cidade de Columbo. *See* GOMES DE BRITO (B.) Historia tragico-maritima, *etc.* tom. 1. 1735, *etc.* 4°. **1424**. g. 1.

BARRADAS (Manuel) *Historical Writer.* O Infante D. Henrique. pp. 149. *Lisboa,* 1894. 8°. **10632**. bb. **50**.

BARRADAS (Manuel) *Jesuit Missionary to Ethiopia. See* Barradas (Emmanuel)

BARRADAS (Manuel) *Jesuit Missionary to India. See* Barradas (Manoel)

BARRADAS (Rafael) *See* Martínez Sierra (G.) Un Teatro de Arte en España. [With designs by R. Barradas.] 1926. fol. L.R. **262**. c. **5**.

BARRADAS (Sebastianus) Sebastiani Barradas . . . Tomus I. Commentariorum in concordiam, et historiā euangelicam. *A. de Maris : Conimbricæ,* 1599. fol. pp. 924. **3125**. g. **2**.
The titlepage is engraved.

—— Sebastiani Barradas . . . Tomus II. Commentariorum in concordiam, et historiam quatuor euangelistarum. *Apud P. Crasbeeck: Olisipone,* 1605. fol. pp. 1255. **3125**. g. **13**.
The titlepage is engraved. The date in the colophon is 1604.

—— R. P. Sebastiani Barradii . . . Tomus III. Commentariorum in concordiam et historiam quatuor Euangelistarum, *etc. Sumptibus H. Mylii, excudebat B. Lippius : Moguntiæ,* 1609. fol. **L.7.b.9.**

—— [Another edition.] R. P. Sebastiani Barradii . . . Tomus III. (Tomus IV. et ultimus) Commentariorum in concordiam et historiam quatuor Euangelistarum, *etc. Sumptibus H. Mylii, excudebat B. Lippius: Moguntiæ,* 1611, 12. fol. **3225**. g. **15**.

—— [Another edition.] R. P. Sebastiani Barradii . . . Commentaria in concordiam et historiam evangelicam. tom. 1, 2. *Sumptibus H. Mylii, excudebat B. Lippius: Moguntiæ,* 1618. fol. **L.7.b.8.**
Imperfect; wanting tom. 3, 4. *The imprint in the colophon of tom.* 1 *is "Typis H. Meresii" and the date* 1631. *The imprint on the titlepage of tom.* 2 *is "Sumptibus H. Mylii, excudebat H. Meresius."*

—— Sebastiani Barradas . . . Itinerarium filiorum Israel ex Ægypto in terra repromissionis, *etc.* pp. 890. *Apud H. Verdussium: Antuerpiæ,* 1621. fol. **690**. h. **12**.

—— [Another edition.] pp. 824. *Apud G. Valentinum: Venetiis,* 1623. 8°. **483**. b. **6**.

BARRADAS DE OLIVEIRA ( )

—— Roteiro do Oriente na viagem do Ministro do Ultramar, Comandante Sarmento Rodrigues, às províncias portuguesas da Índia, Timor e Macau, no ano de 1952. pp. 249. 1953. 8°. *See* Portugal.—*Ministério do Ultramar.—Agência Geral do Ultramar.—Divisão de Publicações e Biblioteca.* S. L. **201 15**.

BARRADAS MUITO PAM E MORATO (João Vaz) *See* Vaz Barradas Muito Pam e Morato.

BARRADELL (Eric)

—— Thirty-One Days. A story. pp. 46. *A. H. Stockwell: London,* 1936. 8°. **012601**. aa. **49**.

BARRADELL-SMITH (Walter) *See* Smith.

BARRADIUS (Sebastianus) *See* Barradas.

BARRADO (Moises Sánchez) *See* Sánchez Barrado.

BARRAGAN (Gregorio) *See* Pino (F. del) Diccionario Popular Enciclopédico de la Lengua Española . . . Redactado por . . . F. del Pino . . . G. Barragán, *etc.* 1900, *etc.* 4°. **12943**. s. **2**.

BARRAGAN (Joaquin) Relacion subsinta de algunos hechos de la administracion del gobernador de Tamaulipas D. Vital Fernandez en los años de 832 y 833. *Monterrey,* 1834. fol. **9770**. k. **12**. (**86**.)

BARRAGÁN (José Vicente)

—— *See* Palmer (Harold E.) [The International English-Course.] Curso Internacional de Inglés . . . Versión española adaptada y traducida por J. V. Barragán, *etc.* 1944. 8°. **12987**. a. **43**.

BARRAGAN (Miguel) *See* Lopez de Santa-Anna (A.) *President of the Republic of Mexico.* Prision de los generales Santa-Ana y Barragan en la plaza de Veracruz. 1827. *s. sh.* fol. **9770**. k. **9**. (**53**.)

—— [For official documents issued by M. Barragan as Acting President of the Republic of Mexico:] *See* Mexico.—Barragan (M.) *Acting President.* [1835, 1836.]

—— [For official documents issued by M. Barragan as Governor of the State of Vera Cruz :] *See* Vera Cruz, *State of.*—Barragan (M.) *Governor.*

—— *Begin.* Buscar la salud de la Patria es el primer deber de todo Ciudadano, *etc.* [Report of a meeting of officers called by M. Barragan in support of the Provisional Government. Dated : 1 July 1823.] *Querétaro,* [1823.] *s. sh.* fol. **9770**. k. **7**. (**28**.)

—— El Comandante General á los militares de esta provincia. [Exhorting them to obedience. Dated : Mexico, 18 Jan. 1824.] [*Mexico,* 1824.] *s. sh.* fol. **9770**. k. **8**. (**82**.)

—— El Presidente interino de los Estados-Unidos Mexicanos á sus compatriotas. [On assuming office. Dated: 31 Jan. 1835.] *México,* 1835. fol. **9770**. k. **12**. (**139**.)

BARRAGÁN (Nereo Rodríguez) *See* Rodríguez-Barragán.

BARRAGÁN (Pedro)

—— La Verdad acerca de la busca del tesoro de Poblet. (La dictadura pintoresca.) pp. 30. *Tarragona,* 1931. 8°. **10163**. f. **10**.

BARRAGE. [i.e. John Austin.]

—— Grand Barrage. By Gun Buster. pp. 185. *Hodder & Stoughton: London,* 1944. 8°. NN. **34850**.

BARRAGO (Francesco) L'Uomo fatto ad imagine di Dio fu anche fatto ad imagine della scimia. Lettura pubblica, *etc.* pp. 100. *Cagliari,* 1869. 8°. **7001**. bb. **9**.

BARRAGRY (John)

—— *See* Congregatio Bonae Mortis. Confraternity of the Bona Mors. Devotions, prayers, etc. Compiled by Rev. J. Barragry. 1939. 16°. **04402**. ff. **121**.

BARRAIL (Henri)

—— L'Autonomie régionale en Espagne. Étude de droit constitutionnel comparé. pp. 197. *Lyon,* 1933. 8°. **05385**. eee. **9**.

BARRAIL (Jean Prosper) De la délivrance artificielle. pp. 41. *Paris,* 1866. 4°. [*Collection des thèses soutenues à la Faculté de Médecine de Paris.* An 1866. tom. 1.] **7373**. g. **4**.

BARRAILLER LAPLANTE (PIERRE) *See* BARAILLER LAPLANTE.

BARRAK. Barrak: the official organ of the Imperial Camel Corps. *See* AUSTRALIA.—*Military Forces.—Australian Contingent, British Expeditionary Force.—Imperial Camel Corps.*

BARRAL, *Family of.* *See* MARY, *the Blessed Virgin.—Orders and Associations.—Sisters of the Presentation of Mary.* La Famille De Barral et la Présentation à Castres, 1760–1802. 1877. 8°. **4864**. ccc. **2.**

BARRAL (DE) *Abbé.* *See* BARRAL (L. M. de) *successively Bishop of Troyes, Meaux,* and *Archbishop of Tours.* Défense des libertés de l'église gallicane . . . Ouvrage posthume de M. L. M. de Barral . . . Précédée d'une notice sur sa vie publique et sur ses écrits ; par l'abbé de Barral, son frère. 1817. 4°. **700**. i. **19.**

BARRAL (ADRIEN DE) *See* AUGUSTINE, *Saint, Bishop of Hippo.* [*Confessiones.—French.*] Les Confessions de Saint Augustin. Traduction nouvelle par M. l'abbé Barral. 1884. 12°. **3805**. aaa. **18.**

—— *See* BARRAL (A. H. F. de) *Count.* Notices sur les châteaux, abbayes & monuments du département du Cher . . . Publiées avec des notes . . . par . . . M. le Comte E. de Barral . . . et M. l'Abbé A. de Barral. 1898. 8°. **07708**. f. **51.**

—— Autour du Clocher. Coutumes et fêtes chrétiennes. pp. 300. *Paris, Lyon,* 1893. 8°. **3478**. bb. **2.**

—— Les Chroniques de l'histoire de France. Légendes capétiennes. Les premiers Capétiens. pp. x. 224. *Tours,* 1884. 12°. **9210**. bb. **22.**

BARRAL (ANDRÉ HORACE FRANÇOIS DE) *Count.* Notices sur les châteaux, abbayes & monuments du département du Cher. Par le Général Comte de Barral . . . Publiées avec des notes par son petit-fils M. le Comte E. de Barral . . . et M. l'Abbé A. de Barral. [With a portrait.] pp. 288. *Paris, Lyon,* 1898. 8°. **07708**. f. **51.**

BARRAL (CLAUDE MATHIAS JOSEPH DE) *Bishop of Troyes.* Mandement de Monsieur l'éveque de Troyes, qui ordonne des prières publiques dans toutes les églises de la ville d'Aurillac, conformément aux intentions du roi, exprimées dans la lettre de Sa Majesté, en date du deux septembre 1789. [*Aurillac,* 1789.] *s. sh.* fol. Tab. **443**. a.3(75.)

BARRAL (DOMINIQUE DE) *Count.* *See* BARRAL-MONTFERRAT (H. D. de) *Marquis.*

BARRAL (E. A.) Observations et réflexions sur quelques points de la pathologie et de la physiologie des centres nerveux. (Thèse.) pp. 46. *Paris,* 1838. 4°. **1184**. h. **18**. (**12**.)

BARRAL (EDGARD DE) *Count.* *See* BARRAL (A. H. F. de) *Count.* Notices sur les châteaux, abbayes & monuments du département du Cher . . . Publiées avec des notes par . . . M. le Comte E. de Barral . . . et M. l'abbé A. de Barral. 1898. 8°. **07708**. f. **51.**

—— *See* BARRAL (P. A. A. O.) *Count.* Souvenirs de guerre et de captivité d'un page de Napoléon . . . Publiés par . . . le comte E. de Barral. [1925.] 8°. **10656**. e. **8.**

—— Les Zouaves pontificaux, 1860–1870, *etc.* [With plates.] pp. 317. *Paris,* 1932. 8°. **9168**. cc. **20.**

BARRAL (ÉTIENNE) Précis d'analyse chimique quantitative, *etc.* pp. xii. 864. *Paris,* 1905. 8°. **08909**. h. **31.**

—— Recherches sur quelques dérivés surchlorés du phénol et du benzène. pp. 128. *Paris,* 1895. 8°. [*Annales de l'Université de Lyon.* fasc. 17.] Ac. **365.**

BARRAL (FRANCISCO ANTONIO) Considérations sur les moyens proposés pour constater l'empoisonnement par les substances végétales ; thèse, *etc.* pp. 47. *Paris,* 1826. 4°. **1183**. i. **1**. (**22**.)

—— Noticia sobre o clima do Funchal, e sua influencia no tratamento da tisica pulmonar, *etc.* pp. 257. 1854. *See* LISBON.—*Academia das Sciencias de Lisboa.* Memorias, *etc.* Nova ser. classe 1. tom. 1. pt. 1. 1854, *etc.* 4°. **Ac.190/10.a.(1.)**

—— Le Climat de Madère, et de son influence thérapeutique sur la phthisie pulmonaire . . . Traduit . . . refondu et augmenté de notes . . . par . . . P. Garnier. pp. 308. *Paris,* 1858. 8°. **7686**. d. **4.**

BARRAL (GEORGES) *See* BERNARD (Claude) of the Académie Française. Arthur de Bretagne . . . Précédé d'une préface historique de M. G. Barral. 1887. 8°. **11740**. g. **2.**

—— *See* CARNOT (L. N. M.) *Count.* Don Quichotte . . Précédé d'une étude littéraire & historique par G. Barral, *etc.* 1891. 8°. **11483**. ccc. **29.**

—— *See* NAPOLEON I., *Emperor of the French.* [*Letters, Despatches, etc.*] Messages et discours politiques. Publiés . . . par G. Barral. [1896.] 8°. **9230**. aaa. **13.**

—— *See* RAMBAUD (Y.) *pseud.,* and DUBUT DE LAFOREST (J. L.) Le Faiseur d'hommes . . . Avec une préface de . . . G. Barral. 1884. 8°. **12510**. r. **1.**

—— *See* REYNOSO (A.) Essai sur la culture de la canne à sucre par M. A. Reynoso. Résumés critiques de MM. Bobierre, Girard, et Barral. 1865. 8°. **7076**. g. **44**. (**2**.)

—— Collection des poètes français à l'étranger. Publiée sous la direction littéraire de G. Barral. 15 vol. *Paris,* 1897–1910. 8°. **011433**. d. **1.**

—— L'Épopée de Waterloo, *etc.* pp. 328. *Paris,* [1895.] 8°. **9079**. e. **9.**

—— Les Frances littéraires de l'étranger. *See* SEVERIN (F.) Poèmes ingénus, *etc.* 1899. 8°. **011483**. d. **1/7.**

—— Histoire d'un inventeur. Exposé des découvertes et des travaux de M. Gustave Trouvé dans le domaine de l'électricité, *etc.* [With a portrait.] pp. xvi. 610. *Paris,* 1891. 8°. **8757**. i. **16.**

—— Histoire des sciences sous Napoléon Bonaparte. pp. ix. 290. *Paris,* 1889. 18°. **8708**. a. **3.**

—— Impressions aériennes d'un compagnon de Nadar. Suivies de la note lue à l'Observatoire Impérial sur la troisième ascension du Géant, avec une carte du voyage. pp. 20. *Paris,* 1864. 8°. **8755**. cc. **51**. (**3**.)

—— Itinéraire illustré de l'épopée de Waterloo, *etc.* pp. 165. *Paris,* [1896.] 8°. **9077**. aaa. **12.**

—— Le Livre de l'épouse. Missel de l'amour sentimental. Édition elzévirienne. pp. 221. *Paris,* 1884. 16°. **8416**. a. **45.**

BARRAL (GEORGES) and **BARRAL** (JACQUES)

—— Histoire populaire des 72 savants dont les noms sont inscrits sur la grande frise de la Tour Eiffel . . . Édition ornée de portraits. pp. 146. *Paris,* [1889.] 8°. **10664**. aaa. **43.**

BARRAL (HENRI ÉMILE) Quelques mots sur les luxations de l'astragale. Thèse, *etc.* pp. 96. *Montpellier,* 1868. 4°. **7379**. h. **5**. (**4**.)

BARRAL (J. DE SAINT-MAURICE JOLEAUD) *See* JOLEAUD-BARRAL.

BARRAL (JACQUES) *See* BARRAL (G.) and (J.) Histoire populaire des 72 savants dont les noms sont inscrits sur la grande frise de la Tour Eiffel, *etc.* [1889.] 8°. **10664**. aaa. **43**.

BARRAL (JEAN AUGUSTIN) *See* ARAGO (D. F. J.) Œuvres complètes de François Arago . . . Publiées . . . sous la direction de M. J. A. Barral. 1854, *etc.* 8°. **830**. h. **5–17**.

—— *See* ARAGO (D. F. J.) Astronomie populaire . . . Publiée . . . sous la direction de M. J. A. Barral. 1854, *etc.* 8°. **830**. h. **1–4**.

—— *See* ENCYCLOPAEDIAS. Encyclopédie technologique. Dictionnaire des arts et manufactures . . . Par . . . Messieurs Alcan . . . Barral, *etc.* 1845, *etc.* 8°. **7955**. eee. **1**.

—— —— 1853, *etc.* 8°. **1396**. k. **1**.

—— *See* G - - - -, L. Précis de l'histoire de la botanique. Suivi d'un apppendice de géographie botanique avec cartes, par J. A. Barral. [1869.] 8°. [*DUPUIS* (*A.*) *Le Règne végétal, etc.*] **7055**. l. **7**.

—— *See* PERIODICAL PUBLICATIONS.—*Paris.* Journal de l'agriculture, fondé et dirigé par J. A. Barral, *etc.* 1866, *etc.* 8°. P.P. **2332**. ae.

—— *See* PERIODICAL PUBLICATIONS.—*Paris.* Presse scientifique des deux mondes, *etc.* [Edited by J. A. Barral.] 1860, *etc.* 8°. P.P. **1613**. c.

—— Agriculture. 1862. *See* PARIS.—*Association Polytechnique.* Conférences, *etc.* (Entretiens populaires.) sér. 2. 1860, *etc.* 8°. Ac. **4417/2**

—— L'Agriculture. (Exposition nationale agricole de 1860.) *See* PARIS.—*Association Polytechnique.* Conférences, *etc.* sér. 1. 1860, *etc.* 8°. Ac. **4417/2.**

—— L'Agriculture en 1789 et en 1864. 1865. *See* PARIS.—*Association Polytechnique.* Conférences, *etc.* (Entretiens populaires.) sér. 5. 1860, *etc.* 8°. Ac. **4417/2.**

—— Avenir de grandes exploitations agricoles établies sur les côtes du Vénézuéla. pp. 164. *Paris,* 1881. 8°. **7078**. bb. **6**.

—— Le Blé et le pain. Liberté de la boulangerie. pp. 697. *Paris,* 1863. 12°. **8247**. bbb. **32**.

—— De l'air au point de vue de la physique du globe et de l'hygiène. 1864. *See* PARIS.—*Association Polytechnique.* Conférences, *etc.* (Entretiens populaires.) sér. 4. 1860, *etc.* 8°. Ac. **4417/2.**

—— De l'influence exercée par l'atmosphère sur la végétation, *etc.* 1861. *See* PARIS.—*Société Chimique.* [de France.] Leçons de chimie, professées en 1860, *etc.* 1861, *etc.* 8°. Ac. 3895/4.

—— Dictionnaire d'agriculture. Encyclopédie agricole complète. (Continué sous la direction de H. Sagnier.) 4 tom. *Paris,* 1885–92. 8°. **7055**. i. **8**.

—— Drainage des terres arables . . . Seconde édition. 4 tom. *Paris,* 1856–60. 12°. **7073**. aa. **5**.

—— Les Irrigations dans le département de Vaucluse. Rapport sur le concours ouvert en 1876 (1877) pour le meilleur emploi des eaux d'irrigation. 2 vol. 1877, 78. 4°. *See* FRANCE.—*Ministère de l'Agriculture et du Commerce.*—*—Direction de l'Agriculture.* S. **194/2.**

—— Les Irrigations dans le département des Bouches-du-Rhône. Rapport sur le concours ouvert en 1875 pour le meilleur emploi des eaux d'irrigation. [With maps.] pp. 548. pl. IV. 1876. 4°. *See* FRANCE.—*Ministère de l'Agriculture et du Commerce.—Direction de l'Agriculture.* S. **194**.

BARRAL (JEAN AUGUSTIN)

—— La Lutte contre le phylloxera . . . Deuxième édition, *etc.* pp. x. 283. *Paris,* 1883. 12°. **7078**. bb. **22**.

—— Metz et le maréchal Bazaine . . . Deuxième édition. pp. 39. *Paris,* 1870. 8°. **9078**. g. **15**. (**1**.)

—— L'Œuvre agricole de M. de Béhague. Compte rendu d'une visite faite par une délegation de la Société Centrale d'Agriculture de France sur le domaine de Dampierre . . . Par J.-A. Barral . . . Précédé d'un discours et d'un tableau par M. E. Chevreul. [With a portrait and a plan.] pp. 204. 1875. 18°. *See* PARIS.—*Société Centrale d'Agriculture de France.* **7074**. c. **3**.

—— Programme d'un cours de chimie appliquée à l'agriculture. pp. 16. *Paris,* [1849.] 8°. **1142**. h. **20**.

—— Revue de l'Exposition de Londres. 1863. *See* PARIS.—*Association Polytechnique.* Conférences, *etc.* (Entretiens populaires.) sér. 3. 1860, *etc.* 8°. Ac. **4417/2.**

—— Situation actuelle de l'agriculture en France. 1867. *See* PARIS.—*Association Polytechnique.* Conférences, *etc.* (Entretiens populaires.) sér. 7. 1860, *etc.* 8°. Ac. **4417/2.**

—— Barral's kurzgefasste Agricultur-Chemie. *See* THURN (J. H. im) Das landwirthschaftliche Düngerwesen, *etc.* 1866. 8°. **7077**. dd. **14**.

BARRAL (JEAN AUGUSTIN) and **SAGNIER** (HENRI)

—— Notions d'agriculture et d'horticulture . . . Cours élémentaire, *etc.* pp. 111. *Paris,* 1883. 8°. **7078**. b. **48**.

—— Notions d'agriculture et d'horticulture . . . Cours supérieur, *etc.* pp. 320. *Paris,* 1883. 8°. **07077**. ee. **20**.

BARRAL (JEAN AUGUSTIN) and **TISSERANT** (EUGÈNE) *Professeur à l'École Vétérinaire de Lyon.*

—— Concours international de machines à moissonner, tenu sur le domaine impérial de Fouilleuse, les 19, 20 et 21 juillet 1859. Rapport du jury, suivi de la description et des gravures des machines primées. (Les rapporteurs, J. A. Barral, E. Tisserant.) pp. 62. 1860. 8°. *See* FRANCE.—*Ministère de l'Agriculture de Lyon et du Commerce.* **7076**. g. **45**. (**1**.)

BARRAL (JEAN J.) *See* BARRAL (Jean Augustin)

BARRAL (JEAN SÉBASTIEN DE) *Bishop of Castres. See* COMBES (A.) Étude historique sur Jean-Sébastien de Barral, évêque de Castres, *etc.* 1843. 8°. **4867**. cc. **26**.

—— Lettre de Monseigneur l'évêque de Castres à M. le Procureur Genéral du Parlement de Toulouse. [On the "Assertions dangereuses et pernicieuses en tous genres, que les soi-disants Jésuites ont, dans tous les temps et persévéramment, soutenues, enseignées et publiées dans leur livres, *etc.*"] 1828. *See* JESUITS. [*Appendix.*] Documents historiques, critiques, apologétiques, concernant la Compagnie de Jésus. tom. 2. 1827, *etc.* 8°. **04785**. i. **42**.

—— Brief des Herrn Bischof von Castres an den Herrn Generalprokurator des Parlaments zu Toulouse. 1842. *See* JESUITS. [*Appendix.*] Dokumente zur Geschichte, Beurtheilung und Vertheidigung der Gesellschaft Jesu, *etc.* no. 16. 1841, *etc.* 8°. **1367**. h. **30**.

BARRAL (L.) *Translator.*

—— *See* KIRIŢESCU (C.) La Roumanie dans la guerre mondiale, 1916–1919. Traduit . . . par L. Barral, *etc.* 1934. 8°. **09081**. bb. **58**.

BARRAL (L. M.) *See* NORIE (John W.) Sailing Directions for the Rio de la Plata . . . Compiled from surveys and observatinos [*sic*] made during the years 1831 and 1832, by Captain Barral, *etc.* 1854. 8°. **10496**. b. **24**.

—— *See* ROUSSIN (A. R.) *Baron.* Sailing Directions for the Coast of Brazil . . . Compiled chiefly from the surveys made by Baron Roussin and M. Barral. 1856. 8°. **10496**. aa. **30**.

BARRAL (LOUIS)

—— La Grotte Barriéra. Un gisement énéolithique dans les Alpes-Maritimes. pp. 83. pl. XXIX. *Monaco,* 1954. 8°. **07708**. g. **100**.
Publications du Musée d'Anthropologie Préhistorique de Monaco. fasc. 1.

BARRAL (LOUIS MATHIAS DE) successively *Bishop of Troyes* and *of Meaux,* and *Archbishop of Tours.* Défense des libertés de l'église Gallicane, et de l'assemblée du clergé de France, tenue en 1682 ; ou réfutation de plusieurs ouvrages, publiés récemment en Angleterre, sur l'infaillibilité du Pape ; ouvrage posthume de M. L. M. de Barral . . . Précédée d'une notice sur sa vie publique et sur ses écrits ; par l'abbé de Barral, son frère. pp. 441. *Paris,* 1817. 4°. **700**. i. **19**.

—— Éloge funèbre de M. le maréchal Duc de Biron. (Observations historiques sur les grands hommes de la maison de Biron, & particulièrement sur Louis-Antoine.) pp. 32. *Paris,* 1788. 8°. R. **177**. (**6**.)

—— Lettre d'un évêque de France, à un de ses collègues, sur la démission de leur siége, demandée par le bref de Pie VII, en date du 15 août 1801. [By L. M. de Barral.] pp. 42. 1801. 8°. *See* ROME, *Church of.—[Popes.]*—Pius VII. [1806–1823.] F. **139**. (**1**.)

—— Lettre de M. l'évêque de Troyes à M. Sibille, se disant évêque du département de l'Aube. pp. 45. *Paris,* [1791.] 8°. F. **106**. (**2**.)

—— Lettre de M. l'évêque de Troyes, à MM. les électeurs du département de l'Aube. [On the civil constitution of the clergy.] pp. 55. [*Paris,* 1791.] 8°. F. **116**. (**1**.)

—— Lettre de M. l'évêque de Troyes, à MM. les vicaires généraux de son diocèse. [On his resignation of the Bishopric of Troyes.] pp. 21. *Paris,* 1801. 8°. F. **175**. (**13**.)

—— Mandement pour la renouvellement des pouvoirs dépendans de la jurisdiction épiscopale, *etc.* pp. 15. *Paris,* 1791. 8°. F.R. **130**. (**7**.)

BARRAL (M.) *Docteur en Médecine.*

—— Fièvre jaune de Marseille, observée au lazaret. Thèse, *etc.* pp. 51. *Montpellier,* 1827. 4°. **1181**. d. **15**. (**9**.)

BARRAL (PHILIPPE ANNE AMÉDÉE OCTAVE) *Count.* Souvenirs de guerre et de captivité d'un page de Napoléon (Vicomte de Barral), 1812–1815. Publiés par . . . le comte E. de Barral. [With a portrait.] pp. 267. *Paris,* [1925.] 8°. **10656**. e. **8**.

BARRAL (PIERRE) *Abbé. See* GOUJET (C. P.) Mémoires historiques & littéraires de M. l'abbé Goujet, *etc.* [Edited by P. Barral.] 1767. 12°. **4863**. bbb. **21**.

BARRAL (PIERRE) *Abbé.*

—— *See* SÉVIGNÉ (M. de) *Marchioness.* Sevigniana, *etc.* [Compiled by P. Barral.] 1756. 12°. **1088**. a. **33**.

—— —— 1768. 12°. **97**. a. **10**.

—— —— 1787. 12°. **10910**. aa. **7**.

—— —— [1799.] 8°. [*Ana, ou collection de bons mots, etc.* tom. 10.] **248**. g. **34**.

—— Dictionnaire portatif, historique, théologique, géographique, critique et moral, de la Bible, pour servir d'introduction à la science de l'Écriture-Sainte. Nouvelle édition. Revuë, corrigée & augmentée. [By P. Barral.] 2 tom. 1760. 8°. *See* BIBLE.—*Appendix.* [*Miscellaneous.*] **3107**. aaa. **25**

—— Dizionario portatile della Bibbia. Tradotto . . . nell' Italiano idioma, ed arricchito di moltissime note, di nuovi articoli, e di varie carte topografiche dal P. D. Prospero dell'Aquila . . . Edizione novissima, accresciuta, ed emendata. [By P. Barral.] 4 tom. 1768. 8°. *See* BIBLE. *Appendix.*—[*Miscellaneous.*] **3125**. cc. **14**.

—— Nuova edizione emendata. 3 tom. 1833, 34. 8°. *See* BIBLE.—*Appendix.* [*Miscellaneous.*] **689**. d. **12**, **13**.

BARRAI (PIERRE) *Colonel.* Mémoire sur l'histoire naturelle de l'isle de Corse, avec un catalogue lythologique de cette isle, & des reflexions sommaires sur l'existence physique de nostre globe. [With a map.] pp. viii. 126. *Londres, et se trouve à Paris,* 1783. 8°. **953**. g. **3**.

BARRA LASTARRIA (LUIS DE LA)

—— *See* PANAMERICAN RED CROSS CONFERENCE. [Santiago de Chile, 1940.] Cuarta Conferencia Panamericana de la Cruz Roja, *etc.* [Proceedings. Edited by L. de la Barra Lastarria.] 1941. 8°. **7689**. dd. **13**.

BARRALET (ALFRED G.) Camping and Caravanning, *etc.* pp. 127. *Fleetgate Publications : London,* 1926. 8°. **7911**. f. **52**.

—— The Machinery of Business. pp. xii. 226. *London,* [1925.] 8°. [*Philips' New Era Library.*] W.P. **5729/8**.

BARRA-LÉVY (JOSEPH) De l'hydrothorax et de la thoracenthèse. Thèse, *etc.* pp. 40. *Montpellier,* 1845. 4°. **1182**. d. **11**. (**13**.)

BARRALIER (EMMANUEL) *See* LAISANT (C.) Guide du touriste aux Antilles françaises, par MM. C. Laisant . . . E. Barralier, *etc.* 1913. 8°. **10480**. aa. **46**.

BARRALIS (ANTONIO) Catechismus zum Gebrauch dern Königlichen Walonischen Garden wie auch dern in Spanien, wohnhaften Ausländern, *etc.* pp. 304. *Madrid,* 1777. 8°. **3505**. de. **45**.

BARRALIS (GIOVANNI BATTISTA) Quaresimale. pp. 672. *Torino,* 1717. 4°. **4426**. i. **11**.

BARRALIS (J. B. ÉDOUARD) De la commotion de la moelle épinière. Thèse, *etc.* pp. 53. *Montpellier,* 1879. 4°. **7379**. l. **17**. (**2**.)

BARRALI SALERNA (VINCENTIUS) Chronologia sanctorum & aliorum virorum illustrium, ac abbatum sacræ Insulæ Lerinensis. a . . . V. Barrali Salerno [*sic*] . . . in vnum compilata. Cum annotationibus eiusdem. pp. 396. 3–466. *Sumptibus P. Rigaud : Lugduni,* 1613. 4°. **485**. d. **18**.
The titlepage is engraved.

BARRALLIER (Auguste Marie) Des accidents tertiaires de la syphilis. Thèse, *etc.* pp. 58. *Montpellier,* 1847. 4°. **7379**. a. **3**. (**3**.)

—— Du typhus épidémique et histoire médicale des épidémies de typhus observées au bagne de Toulon en 1855 et 1856. pp. 384. *Paris,* 1861. 8°. **7560**. bb. **7**.

BARRALLIER (Joseph Étienne Antoine) Des luxations de la clavicale. Thèse, *etc.* pp. 60. *Montpellier,* 1854. 4°. **7379**. c. **5**. (**1**.)

—— Essai sur les ophthalmies purulentes. Thèse, *etc.* pp. 56. *Montpellier,* 1853. 4°. **7379**. c. **1**. (**14**.)

BARRAL-MONTFERRAT (Henri Dominique de) *Marquis.*

—— Étude sur l'histoire diplomatique de l'Europe. 2 vol. *Paris,* 1880, 85. 8°. **9080**. d. **20**.

BARRAL-MONTFERRAT (Horace Dominique de) *Marquis.* De Monroe à Roosevelt. 1823–1905. Avec une préface de M. le Comte d'Haussonville. pp. xv. 356. *Paris,* 1905. 8°. **8175**. ee. **18**.

—— Dix ans de paix armée entre la France et l'Angleterre, 1783–1793. tom. 1. pp. xii. 374. *Paris,* 1893. 8°. **09077**. f. **42**.

No more published.

BARRAMEDA.—*Convento de nuestra Señora de Barrameda. See* Mary, *the Blessed Virgin.—Churches and Institutions.*

BARRAN (   ) *Abbé.* Exposition raisonnée des dogmes et de la morale du Christianisme dans les entretiens d'un professeur de théologie avec un docteur en droits . . . Seconde édition, revue, corrigée et augmentée. 3 tom. *Paris,* 1845. 8°. **3557**. c. **5**.

BARRAN (Joseph Nicolas Barbeau du) *See* Barbeau du Barran.

BARRANCA (José S.) *See* Valdez de Sicuani (   ) Ollanta . . . Traducido del Quichua al Castellano . . . por J. S. Barranca. 1868. 8°. **11726**. h. **5**.

BARRANCO (Antonio Casero y) *See* Casero y Barranco.

BARRANCO (Mariano) *See* Barranco y Caro.

BARRANCO (Pedro Cano) *See* Cano Barranco.

BARRANCO Y CARO (Mariano) Las Hormigas ; comedia en un acto y en prosa, tomada del Francés. pp. 26. *Madrid,* 1883. 8°. **11728**. bbb. **12**. (**2**.)

—— ¡ Pobres hombres ! Proverbio en un acto y en prosa. pp. 30. *Madrid,* 1883. 8°. **11728**. bbb. **12**. (**3**.)

—— La Receta ; juguete cómico en dos actos y en verso. pp. 50. *Madrid,* 1883. 8°. **11728**. bbb. **12**. (**1**.)

—— La Valverde. *See* Jones (Willis K.) and Da Cruz (D.) Five Spanish Plays for Study and Stage, *etc.* 1930. 8°. **11567.g.1/10.**

BARRANCO Y CATALÁ (José) *See* Tejera y Magnin (L. de la) and Barranco y Catalá (J.) Proyectores de Luz Eléctrica. 1898, *etc.* 4°. **8757**. l. **25**.

BARRAND (Arthur Rhys) *See* Bunyon (Charles J.) Bunyon on the Law of Life Assurance. Fifth edition by J. V. V. Fitzgerald . . . A. R. Barrand, *etc.* 1914. 8°. **6405**. tt. **20**.

BARRAND (Elizabeth) The Willows of Amwell. By a Lady. [Poems. The dedication signed : E. Barrand.] *G. & S. E. Simson : Hertford,* 1853. 8°. **11645**. bbb. **48**.

BARRAND (François Hippolyte) Du favus. Sa nature, son traitement. pp. 38. *Paris,* 1854. 4°. [*Collection des thèses soutenues à la Faculté de Médecine de Paris.* An 1854. tom. 1.] **7372**. g. **1**.

BARRAND (O. A.) and **GREEN** (G. A.) Life-Saving Appliances on Merchant Ships, *etc.* [With illustrations.] pp. 64. *London,* [1932.] 8°. [*Royal Society of Arts. Thomas Gray Lectures.*] Ac. **4470/40**.

BARRANDE (Joachim) *See* Wentzel (J.) Ueber die Beziehungen der Barrande'schen Etagen C, D und E zum britischen Silur. 1891. 4°. [*Jahrbuch der Kaiserlich-Königlichen Geologischen Reichsanstalt.* Bd. 41. Hft. 1.] Ac. **3132**.

—— Défense des Colonies. pt. 1. *Prague, Paris,* 1861. 8°. **7107**. aaa. **55**. (**1**.)

Imperfect ; wanting all after pt. 1.

—— Du maintien de la nomenclature établie par M. Murchison. Extrait du compte rendu sténographique du Congrès International de Géologie . . . à Paris . . . 1878. pp. 8. *Paris,* 1880. 8°. **7109**. f. **2**. (**6**.)

—— Notice préliminaire sur le système silurien et les trilobites de Bohême. pp. vi. 97. *Leipsic.* 1846. 8°. **7203**. c. **3**.

—— i. Réapparition du genre Arethusina Barr . . . ii Faune Silurienne des environs de Hof, en Bavière, *etc.* pp. 110. *Prague, Paris,* 1868. 8°. **7202**. c. **15**.

—— Systême silurien du centre de la Bohême. (Vol. vii. Ouvrage posthume de feu J. Barrande, publié par W Waagen. Vol. viii. Par Philippe Počta.) 29 pt. *Prague, Paris,* 1852–1911. 4°. **7203**. g.

—— Céphalopodes siluriens de la Bohême. Introduction. Extrait du "Syst. Silur. du centre de la Bohême, Vol. ii." pp. 48. *Prague, Paris,* 1867. 8°. **7202**. b. **17**. (**2**.)

—— Ptéropodes siluriens de la Bohême. Introduction. Extrait du Syst. Silur. du centre de la Bohême, Vol. iii. pp. 16. *Prague, Paris,* 1867. 8°. **7202**. b. **17**. (**3**.)

—— *See* Perner (J.) Études sur les graptolites de Bohême . . . Suite de l'ouvrage : Système silurien du centre de la Bohême, par J. Barrande, *etc.* 1894, *etc.* 4°. **7203.1.40.**

—— *See* Potonié (G. E. H.) and Bernard (C.) *of Geneva.* Flore dévonienne de l'étage H. de Barrande, *etc.* (Suite de l'ouvrage : Système silurien du centre de la Bohême, par J. Barrande.) [1903.] 4°. **7203**. f. **38**.

—— Versuch einer Classification der Trilobiten . . . Aus dem October-Hefte des Jahrganges 1850 der Sitzungsberichte der mathem.-naturw. Classe der kaiserl. Akademie der Wissenschaften besonders abgedruckt. pp. 22. [*Vienna,* 1850.] 8°. **7203**. c. **4**.

BARRANDON (Auguste) *See* Loret (H.) and Barrandon (A.) Flore de Montpellier, *etc.* 1876. 8°. **7074**. a. **6**.

BARRANDON (François Xavier Louis) Quelques considérations sur les affections dites tumeurs blanches. Thèse, *etc.* pp. 62. *Montpellier,* 1836. 4°. **1181**. g. **16**. (**11**.)

BARRANGEARD (Antoine) Considérations générales sur les sympathies, envisagées surtout sous le point de vue pathologique. Thèse, *etc.* pp. 62. *Paris*, 1816. 4°. **1183.** d. **4. (28.)**

—— Extrait de divers mémoires publiés depuis très-longtemps par le docteur Barrangeard, sur le danger des inhumations précipitées, et sur la nécessité de constater avec soin tous les décès, sans aucune exception, *etc.* pp. 12. *Lyon*, [1863.] 8°. **7686.** aa. **57. (5.)**

BARRANGER (Antoine) Étude d'archéologie celtique gallo-romaine et franque, appliquée aux antiquités de Seine-et-Oise, 1864. pp. 51. *Paris*, 1864. 8°. **7707.** c. **33. (10.)**

—— Étude de théodicée, d'androsie, de psychologie, adressée à l'école anthropologique, aux libres-penseurs, à la morale indépendante, par les poètes et les philosophes de l'antiquité. pp. 63. *Paris*, 1869. 8°. **8467.** bbb. **42. (5.)**

BARRANTES, Adela Antoine Álvarez de Lorenzana, *Viscountess de.* *See* Álvarez de Lorenzana.

——, Juan Álvarez de Lorenzana, *Viscount de.* *See* Álvarez de Lorenzana.

BARRANTES (Francisco Montero) *See* Montero Barrantes.

BARRANTES (Vicente) *See* Alarcón y Meléndez (J.) Recuerdo de Recuerdos . . . 1858–1912. (Sentimientos . . . Con un prólogo de Don V. Barrantes.) 1912. 8°. **11452.** ee. **39.**

—— *See* Alarcón y Meléndez (J.) Sentimientos . . . Con un prólogo de Don V. Barrantes. 1865. 8°. **11436.** aaa. **44.**

—— *See* Cortijo y Valdés (A.) Biografía del Excmo. Sr. D. Vicente Barrantes, *etc.* [With a portrait.] 1873. 8°. **10602.** h. **8. (8.)**

—— *See* Padecopeo (G.) *pseud.* Soliloquios Amorosos de un Alma á Dios . . . Con un prólogo y notas de D. V. Barrantes. 1863. 8°. **4409.** h. **25.**

—— *See* Philippine Islands. Guerras piráticas de Filipinas contra mindanaos y joloanos, corregidas é ilustradas por . . . V. Barrantes. 1878. 8°. **9771.** ee. **18.**

—— *See* Sanchez (D.) Recopilacion en metro del Bachiller D. Sanchez . . . Reimpresa del ejemplar único por . . . V. Barrantes. 1882, *etc.* 8°. **12230.** bbb. **14.**

—— Aparato Bibliográfico para la Historia de Extremadura. 3 tom. *Madrid*, 1875–77. 8°. **11905.** i. **40.**

—— Baladas Españolas . . . Con un prologo de D. Luis de Eguilaz. pp. xxiii. 222. *Madrid*, 1853. 8°. **11451.** b. **13.**

The cover bears the date 1854.

—— Barros Emeritenses. Estudio sobre los restos de cerámica romana que suelen hallarse en las ruinas de Mérida . . . Tercera impresion. pp. 42. *Madrid*, 1877. 8°. **7704.** g. **17. (7.)**

—— Catálogo razonado y crítico de los libros, memorias y papeles, impresos y manuscritos, que tratan de las provincias de Extremadura, así tocante á su historia, religion y geografía, como á sus antigüedades, nobleza y hombres célebres, *etc.* pp. viii. 320. *Madrid*, 1865. 8°. **11902.** h. **21.**

—— Coronacion del eminente poeta D. Manuel José Quintana, celebrada en Madrid, á 25 de Marzo de 1855. [Edited by V. Barrantes. With a portrait.] pp. 96. *Madrid*, 1855. 8°. **10632.** e. **26.**

BARRANTES (Vicente)

—— Cúentos y Leyendas. pp. viii. 382. *Madrid*, 1875. 8°. **12356.** aa. **12.**

—— Del Estilo y de los Conceptos de Nuestros Filósofos Contemporáneos. Discorso. 1886. *See* Madrid.—*Real Academia Española.* Memorias, *etc.* tom. 5. 1870, *etc.* 8°. Ac. **144/10.**

—— Dias sin Sol . . . Con una carta de Don Antonio de Trueba. [Poems.] pp. 229. *Madrid*, 1875. 8°. **11450.** c. **10.**

—— La Instruccion Primaria en Filipinas. pp. 174. *Madrid*, [1869.] 8°. **8365.** aaa. **38.**

—— La Joven España. Folleto dedicado a la Asamblea Constituyente. pp. 77. *Madrid*, 1854. 8°. **8042.** a. **57. (4.)**

—— Juan de Padilla. Novela historica . . . Ilustrada con láminas, *etc.* 2 tom. *Madrid*, 1855, 56. 4°. **12491.** g. **29.**

—— Las Jurdes y sus Leyendas. Conferencia, *etc.* [With a map.] pp. 96. *Madrid*, 1891. 8°. **10160.** dd. **3.**

—— Nicolás i., Czar. 1854. *See* Herrero (J. B.) Reyes Contemporaneos, *etc.* tom. 3. 1855, *etc.* 4°. **9077.** h. **12**

—— San Pedro de Alcántara, cristiano romance . . . Reimpreso por un devoto del Santo. [In verse.] pp. 71. *Madrid*, 1880. 16°. **11450.** a. **15.**

—— Siempre tarde. Novela original. pp. 305. *Madrid*, 1852. 8°. **12490.** b. **2.**

—— El Teatro Tagalo. pp. 199. *Madrid*, 1889. 8°. **011795.** g. **12.**

—— La Viuda de Padilla, novela historica . . . Ilustrada con láminas, *etc.* pp. 476. *Madrid*, 1857. 4°. **12491.** g. **15.**

BARRANTES MALDONADO (Pedro) Crónica del Rey Don Enrique Tercero deste nombre en la casa de Castilla y de Leon. pp. 125. *Madrid*, 1868. 8°. **9180.** c. **14.**

—— Dialogo entre Pedro Barrantes Maldonado, y un cavallero estrangero : en que cuenta el saco que los turcos hizieron en Gibraltar. Y el vencimiento y destruycion que la armada de España hizo en la de los turcos. Año 1540. **G.L.** *S. Martinez : Alcala de Henares*, 1566. 8°. G. **6112.**

—— Dialogo entre Pedro Barrantes Maldonado y un caballero extranjero en que cuenta el saco que los turcos hicieron en Gibraltar, *etc.* *See* Relaciones. Tres relaciones históricas, *etc.* 1889. 8°. [*Coleccion de libros españoles raros ó curiosos.* tom. 19.] **12230.** aa.

BARRANX (Serge)

—— L'Homme qui regarda la vie. Gustave Geffroy. Études et extraits. [With illustrations, including a portrait.] pp. 320. *Poitiers*, [1935.] fol. **10657.** i. **19.**

BARRAQUÉ (A. Nicolau) *See* Nicolau-Barraqué.

BARRAQUÉ (J. B. Nicolau) *See* Nicolau-Barraqué.

BARRAQUÉ (Oscar Nicolau) *See* Nicolau-Barraqué.

BARRAQUER (Joaquin) and **CABELLO** (Francisco) *Teniente Coronel.*

—— Memoria sobre la compensacion general de los errores en la Red Geodésica de España. Por D. J. Barraquer, D. F. Cabello. pp. 58. 1874. 8°. *See* Spain.—*Instituto Nacional de Estadística.* **10160.** ff. **3.**

BARRAQUER Y ROVIRALTA (CAYETANO) Las Casas de Religiosos en Cataluña durante el primer tercio del siglo XIX. 2 tom. *Barcelona,* 1906. 8°. **4625**. g. **8**.

BARRAS (ETHEL) A Day in the Country. A childrens play, *etc.* pp. 21. *Forsyth Bros.: London, Manchester,* [1922.] *obl.* 8°. **11779**. ff. **68**.

BARRAS (FRANCISCO DE LAS) *See* BARRAS DE ARAGÓN.

BARRAS (JEAN PIERRE TOBIE) Traité sur les gastralgies et les entéralgies, ou maladies nerveuses de l'estomac et des intestins . . . Troisième édition, revue, corrigée et considérablement augmentée. pp. 637. *Paris,* 1829. 8°. **7442**. cc. **17**.

—— Supplément au Traité sur les gastralgies et les entéralgies, *etc.* pp. 346. *Paris,* 1838. 8°. **7442**. cc. **23**.

—— Traité sur les gastralgies et les entéralgies . . . Tome II. Deuxième édition, revue, corrigée et considérablement augmentée [of the "Supplément"]. pp. 650. *Paris,* 1839. 8°. **7442**. cc. **22**.

BARRAS (JULIUS) The Beautiful Miss Vivian; or, Society in the Colonies. pp. 378. *Simpkin, Marshall & Co.: London,* [1887.] 8°. **12618**. n. **30**.

—— India and Tiger-Hunting. 2 vol. *Rastall & Son: London,* 1883, [84.] 8°. **7908**. bb. **24**.

—— [A reissue.] *Swan Sonnenschein & Co.: London,* 1885. 8°. **7908**. b. **45**.

—— The New Shikari at our Indian Stations. 2 vol. *Swan Sonnenschein & Co.: London,* 1885. 8°. **10056**. b. **5**.

—— Rama. A sensational story of Indian village life. pp. iv. 103. *Simpkin, Marshall & Co.: London,* 1886. 8°. **12637**. aa. **2**.

BARRAS (LIONEL WILFRED) Uncle Lionel's Children's Hour / 8pt. *Evangelistic Association: London,* [1929–35.] 8°. **12813.h.4.**

—— Uncle Lionel's New Bed Time Stories. pp. 67. *Cities Evangelistic Association: London,* 1927. 8°. **12801**. r. **17**.

—— Uncle Lionel's New Stories. pp. 67. *Evangelistic Association: London,* [1928.] 8°. **04419**. h. **37**.

BARRAS (LOUIS) Souvenirs d'un médecin sur la plus grande guerre. Essais psycho-physiologiques. pp. iii. 206. *Paris,* 1925. 8°. **7679**. a. **33**.

BARRAS (MOSES) The Stage Controversy in France from Corneille to Rousseau, *etc.* [With a bibliography.] pp. 358. *New York,* [1933.] 8°. [*Publications of the Institute of French Studies.*] Ac. **2688**. k. (**38**.)

BARRAS (PAUL FRANÇOIS JEAN NICOLAS DE) *Viscount.* *See* ALMÉRAS (H. d') Barras et son temps, *etc.* [1930.] 8°. **10655**. bb. **4**.

—— *See* CAMBYSE, *pseud.* Les Trois rois de la France, Barras, Lareveillère-Lépeaux et Rewbell. [1797.] 8°. F. **423**. (**4**.)

—— *See* DESPAZE (J.) Les Cinq hommes. (Letourneur, Barras, *etc.*) 1796. 8°. T. **1104**. (**8**.)

—— *See* DESPAZE (J.) The Five Men . . . S. F. L. H. Letourneur . . . P. F. I. N. Barras, *etc.* 1797. 8°. **1137**. e. **17**.

—— *See* FRANCE.—*Directoire Exécutif.* Détails officiels de l'audience du 20 frimaire, an VI. Grand discours prononcé par le général Buonaparte . . . et réponse du C. Barras. [1797.] 8°. F. **1190**. (**9**.)

BARRAS (PAUL FRANÇOIS JEAN NICOLAS DE) *Viscount.*

—— *See* FRANCE.—*Directoire Exécutif.* Vie privée des cinq membres du Directoire. (Rewbel, Barras, *etc.*) [By Joseph Despaze.] [1796.] 8°. F. **55****. (**2**.)

—— *See* GRABIT ( ) *pseud.* [i.e. Joseph Despaze.] Vie secrète et privée des cinq membres du Directoire. [1797?] 8°. F. **1308**. (**2**.)

—— *See* MARQUISET (A.) Quand Barras était roi, *etc.* 1911. 8°. **09225**. g. **25**.

—— *See* ROUSSET (S.) Quelques vérités frappantes sur le directeur Barras, et conduite de ce membre du Directoire envers un malheureux artiste, *etc.* [1799?] 8°. R. **114**. (**21**.)

—— *See* TREILHARD (J. B.) *Count.* Convention Nationale, Rapport sur quelques pièces relatives à Barras et Fréron, *etc.* [Dismissing charges of peculation against them.] [1794.] 8°. F. **1258**. (**7**.)

—— *See* UDRAND ( ) Détails exacts et circonstanciés, de l'assassinat prêmédité commis hier, sur le directeur Barras, *etc.* [1797.] 8°. F. **972**. (**16**.)

—— *See* VERITÉ, La Vérité au peuple français sur les intrigues de Barras et de ses favorites, *etc.* [1799.] 8°. F. **1120**. (**8**.)

—— *See* VIVENT (J.) Barras, le "roi" de la République, *etc.* 1937. 8°. **010665**. d. **30**.

—— Lettres de Barras et de Fréron en mission dans le Midi. [Mainly concerning their relations with Moÿse Bayle. Edited by Edmond Poupé.] pp. ix. 222. *Draguignan,* 1910. 8°. **10902**. f. **28**.

—— Compte rendu par Barras, représentant du peuple, le premier vendémiaire, an III, *etc.* pp. 6. *Paris,* an IV [1795]. 8°. F. **1552**. (**48**.)

—— Discours prononcé . . . le 2 pluviôse an 6, jour de l'anniversaire du supplice du dernier tyran des Français. pp. 6. *Paris,* an VI [1778]. 8°. F. **863**. (**15**.)

—— Mémoires de Barras . . . Publiés avec une introduction générale, des préfaces et des appendices par George Duruy, *etc.* [With portraits, facsimiles and maps.] *Paris,* 1895, 96. 8°. **2402**. c. **3**.

—— Memoirs of Barras . . . Edited with a general introduction, prefaces and appendices, by George Duruy. Translated by Charles E. Roche. With seven portraits, *etc.* 4 vol. *Osgood McIlvaine & Co.: London,* 1895, 96. 8°. **010663**. k. **3**.

—— Memoiren . . . Mit einer allgemeinen Einleitung, Vorworten und Anhängen herausgegeben von George Duruy. Autorisirte Uebersetzung. Bd. 4. pp. xxxviii. 522. *Stuttgart,* 1896. 8°. M.L. g. **67**.
Imperfect; wanting Bd. 1–3.

—— Le IX thermidor. Fragments des Mémoires de Barras. 1875. *See* BARRIÈRE (J. F.) Biliothèque des mémoires relatifs à l'histoire de France pendant le 18me siècle, *etc.* tom. 29. 1846, *etc.* 12°. **10662**. bb. **23**. (**4**.)

—— Rapport fait à la Convention Nationale le 30 vendémiaire, an 4, sur la conspiration et la rebellion qui ont éclaté dans les journées des 13 et 14 vendémiaire, et sur les opérations militaires exécutées par l'armée républicaine, *etc.* pp. 20. *Paris,* [1795.] 8°. **935**. b. **13**. (**18**.)

—— [Another copy.] F. **833**. (**25**.)

—— Amours et aventures du vicomte de Barras . . . Par M. le baron de B*** [i.e. Charles Doris], *etc.* 1816, *etc.* 12°. *See* B***, *M. le Baron de.* **839**. b. **33**.

BARRAS (Paul François Jean Nicolas de) *Viscount.*

—— Les Crimes de Barras pour servir de base à son acte d'accusation. [A eulogy.] pp. 8. [*Paris*, 1795?] 8°. F. **972.** (**15.**)

BARRAS (Paul François Jean Nicolas de) *Viscount*, and **FRÉRON** (Louis Stanislaus)

—— Convention Nationale. Compte rendu . . . par P. Barras et Fréron des dépenses qu'ils ont faites pendant les différentes missions qu'ils ont remplies dans les départemens des Hautes et Basses Alpes, du Var, des Alpes-Maritimes, des Bouches-du-Rhône, et auprès de l'Armée d'Italie et de celle dirigée contre Toulon. pp. 3. *Paris*, an III [1795]. 8°. F. **1552.** (**46.**)

BARRAS (Robert Thomas) Specimen Pages of the Sheffield Illustrated List of prices of machinery, files, rasps, saws, & joiners' tools, *etc.* *R. T. Barras : Sheffield*, 1862. *obl.* fol. **1803.** a. **33.**

—— The Sheffield Standard List, illustrated ; containing prices and patterns of machinery, files, rasps, saws, joiners' tools, *etc.* *R. T. Barras : Sheffield*, 1862. *obl.* fol. **1803.** a. **32.**
An enlarged edition of the preceding.

BARRAS (Sébastien) *See* Boyer (J. B.) *Marquis d'Aguilles.* Première partie des tableaux du cabinet de Mre I. B. Boyer, Chevalier seigneur D'Aguilles . . . Gravez par S. Barras et Iac. Coelemans. [1709.] fol. **559*.** g. **9.**

BARRAS (T.) Dissertation sur les luxations spontanées de fémur, *etc.* pp. 32. *Paris*, 1801. 8°. **1182.** b. **6.** (**3.**)

BARRAS (William) The Duties of Protestants. (Ninth thousand.) pp. 11. *Scottish Protestant Alliance : Glasgow*, [1880?]. 8°. **4165.** e. **24.**

—— Proposed Canonisation of Mary Queen of Scots, Cardinal Beaton, and Archbishop Hamilton. pp. 15. *Scottish Protestant Alliance : Glasgow*, 1887. 8°. **3939.** i. **19.**

BARRAS (William David)

—— Modern Science Studies. *A. Wheaton & Co. : Exeter*, 1954– . 8°. W.P. c. **771.**

BARRASA (Joseph) *Begin.* El Padre Maestro Fray Ioseph Barrasa de la orden de Nuestra Señora de la merced, y fu Procurador General de la Prouincia de Lima . . . para la pretension que tiene, de que el Consejo Real de las Indias sea seruido de permitir a la dicha religion, y prouincia el vso del colegio fundado en la Ciudad de los Reyes, con vocacion de San Pedro Nolasco, *etc.* ff. 10. [1665?] fol. **1324.** i. **1.** (**32.**)

BARRASA ENRIQUEZ (Melchor de) *Begin.* Señor. El capitan Melchior de Barrasa Enriquez, procurador general de la . . . ciudad de Mexico, *etc.* [A memorial to the king of Spain, on the services, privileges, administration and commerce of the city of Mexico.] ff. 22. [1650?] fol. **1324.** i. **9.** (**30.**)

—— [Another copy.] **1324.** i. **9.** (**26.**)
Imperfect ; wanting the last leaf.

BARRAS DE ARAGÓN (Francisco de las)

—— *See* Azara (F. de) Viajes por la América Meridional . . . Traducida . . . por F. de las Barras de Aragón. 1941. 8°. **10482.** i. **26.**

—— *See* Barras y Prado (A. de las) La Habana a mediados del siglo xix. Memorias de A. de las Barras y Prado, las publica . . . F. de las Barras de Aragón. 1925. 8°. **9773.** aa. **23.**

BARRAS DE ARAGÓN (Francisco de las)

—— [Articles reprinted from various periodicals.] 18 pt. *Madrid*, 1939–46. 8°. **7711.** dd. **26.**

—— Algunos índices de la serie de cráneos de papúas, donativo de D. Ignacio Baüer al Museo de Antropología. [An offprint from the "Memorias" of the Sociedad Española de Antropología, Etnografía y Prehistoria.] [*Madrid*, 1930?] 8°. **10008.** pp. **34.**

—— Algunos Indices de la serie de cráneos del Africa tropical existentes en el Royal College of Surgeons of England de Londres. pp. 14. *Madrid*, [1913.] 8°. **7001.** t. **8.** (**12.**)

—— Andalucía, como región natural : discurso, *etc.* pp. 23. *Sevilla*, 1916. 8°. **10162.** h. **11.**

—— Aplicación de la hoja craneométrica de Mónaco a cuatro gorilas y un chimpancé. [An offprint from the "Memorias" of the Sociedad Española de Antropología, Etnografía y Prehistoria.] *Madrid*, [1927.] 8°. **10008.** pp. **39.**

—— Apuntes para una descripción geológico-mineralógica de la provincia de Sevilla, *etc.* [With a bibliography.] pp. 355. *Palencia*, 1899. 8°. **07108.** h. **24.**

—— Un Cráneo de negro papúa. [An offprint from the "Corona de estudios," published by the Consejo Superior de Investigaciones Cientificas, 1941.] *Madrid*, 1941. 8°. **10008.** pp. **38.**

—— Cráneo procedente de una antigua necrópolis de Cervera de Pisuerga . . . y noticia de otros descubrimientos análogos en la misma región. [Extracted from the "Memorias" of the Sociedad Española de Antropología, Etnografía y Prehistoria.] [*Madrid*, 1928.] 8°. **10006.** t. **1.**

—— Cráneos de Filipinas. pp. 187. pl. 31. *Madrid*, 1942. 8°. **010055.** aa. **108.**
Ser. A, no. 2 *of the Publications of the Instituto Bernardino de Sahagún.*

—— Cráneos del Museo de Niebla—Huelva. [An offprint from the "Memorias de la Sociedad Española de Antropología, Etnografía y Prehistoria."] [1930?] 8°. **7422.** s. **14.**

—— Cráneos procedentes de las islas Marianas y Carolinas, del Museo de Antropología de Madrid. [Reprinted from "Las Ciencias."] pp. 16. *Madrid*, 1939. 8°. **10008.** pp. **36.**

—— D. Alberto Lista y don Rafael de Aragón. Ocho cartas inéditas de Lista. Del Boletín de la Real Academia Sevillana de Buenas Artes. pp. 16. *Sevilla*, 1917. 8°. **10905.** i. **31.**

—— Discursos leidos ante la Real Academia Hispano Americana en la recepción pública del Sr. D. F. de las Barras de Aragón el día 8 de diciembre de 1912. (Primeros pasos de España en América. [By F. de las Barras de Aragón.] Contestación por el académico Don Juan Reina.) pp. 53. 1912. 8°. *See* Cadiz.—*Real Academia Hispano Americana de Ciencias y Artes.* **09009.** c. **19.** (**3.**)

—— Discursos leídos ante la Real Academia Sevillana de Buenas Letras en la recepción pública del Sr. D. F. de las Barras de Aragón el día 6 de diciembre de 1914. (Discurso del Sr. D. F. de las Barras de Aragón.—Discurso del Sr. D. G. Lupiáñez Estévez.) pp. 39. 1914. 8°. *See* Seville.—*Real Academia Sevillana de Buenas Letras.* **7005.** dd. **19.**

—— Documentos Referentes a Mutis y su Tiempo, recolectados en el Archivo de Indias de Sevilla. pp. 35. *Madrid*, 1933. 8°. **20001.** h. **49.**

BARRAS DE ARAGÓN (FRANCISCO DE LAS)

—— Dos notas craniométricas sobre habitantes protohistóricos de la península ibérica. [Reprinted from the "Memorias" of the Sociedad Española de Antropologia, Etnografia y Prehistoria.] *Madrid*, 1924. 8°. **7002**. gg. **28**.

—— Ensayo de aplicación de la hoja craneométrica del Congreso de Antropología de Mónaco a un cráneo de gorila. [An offprint.] *Madrid*, [1929?] 8°. **10008**. pp. **37**.

—— Estudio de los cráneos antiguos de Canarias, existentes en el Museo Antropológico Nacional. [With illustrations. An offprint from the "Memorias de la Sociedad Española de Antropología, Etnografía y Prehistoria."] pp. 153. *Madrid*, [1928?] 8°. **7422**. s. **13**.

—— Estudio de los cráneos procedentes de tres necrópolis visigodas. [An offprint from the "Memorias" of the Sociedad Española de Antropología, Etnografía y Prehistoria.] *Madrid*, [1927.] 8°. **10008**. pp. **40**.

—— Estudio de varios craneos procedentes de una cueva próxima a Torrelaguna—Madrid—existentes en el Museo de Antropología. [An offprint from the "Memorias" of the Sociedad Española de Antropología, Etnografía y Prehistoria.] *Madrid*, [1928.] 8°. **10008**. pp. **41**.

—— Helechos del África tropical. (Datos procedentes de los herbarios de Kew Gardens y South Kensington Museum of N. H. de Londres.) pp. 15. *Madrid*, [1913.] 8°. **7033**. g. **19**. (**3**.)

—— Historia natural. pp. 250. [*Madrid*,] 1916. 8°. **7006**. de. **8**.

—— Indices craneales medios obtenidos de cinco yacimientos visigodos de España. [Reprinted from "Las Ciencias."] [*Madrid*, 1942.] 8°. **10008**. pp. **35**.

—— Medidas e índices de varios cráneos procedentes de la zona española de Marruecos. [An offprint from the Proceedings of the Asociación Española para el Progreso de las Ciencias.] *Madrid*, [1927?] 8°. **7422**. s. **15**.

—— Los Naturalistas del distrito universitario de Sevilla. [Reprinted from "Anales de la Universidad Hispalense."] pp. 133. *Sevilla*, 1945. 8°. **010632**. bbb. **8**.

—— Notas para un curso de antropología. pp. 531. *Madrid*, 1927. 8°. **010006**. f. **32**.

—— Notas para una historia de la expedición botánica de Nueva España. *In*: Anuario de estudios americanos. tom. 7. pp. 411–469. 1950. 8°. Ac. **161**. a/**2**.

—— Notas sobre índices obtinidos de medidas tomadas en vivo, de sujetos naturales de la provincia de Sevilla y sus limítrofes. pp. 68. *Madrid*, [1924?] 8°. **010007**. h. **20**.

—— Notas sobre restos humanos prehistóricos, protohistóricos y antiguos de España. [A series of offprints from the "Memorias" of the Sociedad Española de Antropología, Etnografía y Prehistoria.] 8 pt. *Madrid*, [1930–]42. 8°. **10008**. n. **8**.

—— Notas tomadas en Inglaterra, Escocia e Irlanda, en 1909. pp. 111. *Sevilla*, 1915. 16°. **10348**. aaa. **64**.

—— Noticia de algunos sevillanos que intervinieron en la gesta española del Océano Pacífico. pp. 35. *Sevilla*, 1945. 8°. **010632**. bbb. **6**.

—— Noticias y documentos referentes al insigne gaditano y alumno de esta Universidad de Sevilla, Don José Celestino Mutis. [With a portrait.] pp. 63. *Sevilla*, 1941. 8°. **010632**. bbb. **5**.

BARRAS DE ARAGÓN (FRANCISCO DE LAS)

—— Tres notas sobre restos humanos prehistóricos y antiguos de Andalucía. Carmona—Arva—Cueva de la Mora. [Reprinted from "Anales de la Universidad Hispalense."] pp. 35. *Sevilla*, 1939. 8°. **07708**. c. **9**.

—— Viaje a Colombia con motivo del centenario de Mutis, 1932. *In*: Boletín de la Real Sociedad Geográfica. tom. 91. no. 1/3, 4/6. 1955. 8°. Ac. **6018**.

—— Viaje de Cádiz a Manila tocando en Anger y Singapoore, por Rafael de Aragón. pp. 42. 1945. 8°. *See* MADRID. *Sociedad Geográfica Nacional*. **10028**. s. **6**.

BARRAS DE LA PENNE (JEAN ANTOINE DE) Lettre critique de M. de Barras de la Penne . . . écrite à M. Le Bailly de * * *. à Marseille le dernier decembre 1725, au sujet d'un livre intitulé, Nouvelles découvertes sur la guerre &c. avec des remarques critiques sur les trois nouveaux systemes des Triremes . . . [By Jean Charles de Folard.] Imprimez dans les Mémoires de Trevoux . . . 1722. pp. 60. *Marseille*, 1727. fol. **533**. l. **16**. (**3**.)

BARRASFORD (THOMAS) The Barrasford Alphabetical Index Racing Guide . . . July, 1902. Being a compilation of all races run from November 22nd, 1901, to June 28th, 1902. coll. 475. pp. 105. *Thomas Barrasford: Leeds*, [1902.] 8°. **7908**. a. **10**.

BARRASS (ALEXANDER) The Pitman's Social Neet. [Poems.] pp. 96. *J. Dent: Consett*, 1897. 8°. **011652**. g. **63**.

BARRASS (EDWARD) A Gallery of Distinguished Men. pp. xi. 346. *Printed for the Author: Napanee*, [1870.] 8°. **4902**. bbb. **20**.

BARRASS (MARY PATRICIA FRENCH)

—— Fifty Years in Midwifery. The story of Annie McCall. [With a portrait.] pp. 122. *Health for All Publishing Co.: London*, 1950. 8°. **07580**. bbb. **98**.

BARRASS (PATRICIA) *See* BARRASS (Mary P. F.)

BARRAS Y PRADO (ANTONIO DE LAS) La Habana a mediados del siglo XIX. Memorias de A. de las Barras y Prado, las publica su hijo Francisco de las Barras de Aragón. pp. 287. *Madrid*, 1925. 8°. **9773**. aa. **23**.

BARRAT (ENID MARY)

—— *See* MARSHALL (Vera M.) and BARRAT (E. M.) Arithmetic for Girls, *etc.* [1930.] 8°. **08534**. df. **3**.

BARRAT (JEAN) Observations sur un cas de cirrhose. Thèse, *etc.* pp. 50. *Montpellier*, 1874. 4°. **7379.k.4.(9.)**

BARRAT (PIERRE MARIE) Contribution à l'étude du cancer du nez. pp. 100. *Bordeaux*, 1924. 8°. **7620**. g. **41**.

BARRAT (PIERRE PHILIPPE CELESTIN) Différences entre l'empoisonnement et l'étranglement interne, *etc.* pp. 23. *Paris*, 1840. 4°. [*Collection des thèses soutenues à la Faculté de Médecine de Paris.* An 1840. tom. 1.] **7371**. b. **2**.

BARRATIN (ANNE) *See* DIEULAFOY (Jeanne P. H. R.) L'Œuvre littéraire de Madame Barratin. 1912. 8°. **011852**. aaa. **49**. (**4**.)

—— De toutes les paroisses. [Aphorisms.] pp. 240. *Paris*, 1913. 8°. **12305**. k. **18**.

—— De vous à moi. Feuilles noires. pp. 211. *Paris*, 1902. 8°. **12305**. l. **22**.

BARRATIN (ANNE)

—— Heures de brume. Poésies, *etc.* pp. xii. 259. *Paris*, 1908. 8°. **011483**. ee. **59**.

—— Lueurs du soir. Poésies. pp. 304. *Paris*, 1911. 8°. **011483**. aaa. **46**.

—— Œuvres posthumes. Théâtre—pensées—poésies. pp. 329. *Paris*, 1920. 8°. **012238**. bb. **17**.

BARRATT (AGNES STEPHANIE)

—— *See* STRONG (Pitt) Der grosse Unbekannte . . . Edited by A. S. Barratt, *etc.* 1937. 8°. W.P. **10834/9**.

BARRATT (ALFRED) Physical Ethics; or, the Science of action. An essay. pp. vi. 387. *Williams & Norgate: London*, 1869. 8°. **8404**. f. **17**.

—— Physical Metempiric. [Edited with a memoir by Dorothea Barratt.] pp. xviii. 311. *Williams & Norgate: London*, 1883. 8°. **8468**. g. **8**.

BARRATT (CHARLES)

—— Your Local Authority. pp. vi. 201. *Sir Isaac Pitman & Sons: London*, 1946. 8°. **8288**. f. **77**.

—— Your Local Authority . . . Second edition. pp. x. 213. *Sir Isaac Pitman & Sons: London*, 1949. 8°. **8288**. aaa. **103**.

BARRATT (DOROTHEA) *See* BARRATT (Alfred) Physical Metempiric. [Edited with a memoir by D. Barratt.] 1883. 8°. **8468**. g. **8**.

BARRATT (DOROTHY MARY)

—— *See* WORCESTER, *Diocese of.* Ecclesiastical Terriers of Warwickshire Parishes . . . Transcribed and edited by D. M. Barratt. 1955, *etc.* 8°. [*Publications of the Dugdale Society.* vol. 22, *etc.*] Ac. **8024**.

BARRATT (EDITH) Edith Barratt. Her life and thoughts. pp. 204. *C. H. Kelly: London*, 1913. 8°. **4908**. de. **13**.

BARRATT (*Mrs.* FRANCIS) *See* LAYLAND (Frances) afterwards LAYLAND-BARRATT (F.) *Lady.*

BARRATT (GEOFFREY)

—— *See* ENGLAND. [*Laws and Statutes.—*IV. *Workmen's Compensation.*] The Workmen's Compensation Acts, 1925 to 1934 . . . By W. A. Willis . . . assisted by G. Barratt. 1938. 8°. **6326**. ee. **7**.

—— *See* ENGLAND. [*Laws and Statutes.—*IV. *Workmen's Compensation.*] The Workmen's Compensation Acts, 1925–1938 . . . By W. A. Willis . . . assisted by G. Barratt. 1939. 8°. **6326**. gg. **30**.

BARRATT (GEORGE) Recollections of Methodism and Methodists in the City of Lincoln, *etc.* pp. 94. *Charles Akrill: Lincoln*, 1866. 8°. **4139**. bb. **4**.

BARRATT (HERBERT OSBORN)

—— *See* BLAKE (Walter H.) The Place of Force in Human Government . . . Edited by the Rev. H. O. Barratt. [1942.] 8°. **8425**. tt. **45**.

—— Landewednack Church, The Lizard. pp. 8. [*The Author: Landewednack*,] 1934. 12°. **07816**. e. **58**.

—— The Wreck of the Titanic . . . April 14th, 1912. [A poem.] *J. Pratt: Shipston-on-Stour*, 1912. 8°. **011604**. ff. **5**. (**4**.)

BARRATT (JAMES) Report on the Iron Works: iron, copper, lead, ores, coal & lime, of Beerbhoom. pp. 17. *P. M. Cranenburgh: Calcutta*, 1857. 8°. **7106**. c. **1**. (**2**.)

BARRATT (JOHN BERNHARD STEINLEN) *See* HEYWOOD (Henry R.) Sermons and Addresses, *etc.* [With a preface by J. B. S. Barratt.] 1896. 8°. **4473**. bb. **40**.

BARRATT (JOHN C.) *See* POPE (William B.) Die Person Christi, *etc.* [Edited and translated by J. C. Barratt.] 1874. 8°. **4226**. g. **35**.

BARRATT (JOSEPH) *M.D.* The Indian of New-England, and the North-Eastern Provinces; a sketch of the life of an Indian hunter, ancient traditions relating to the Etchemin tribe . . . With vocabularies in the Indian and English . . . Derived from Nicola Tenesles. By a Citizen of Middletown, Conn. [The preface signed: J. B., i.e. J. Barratt.] pp. 24. 1851. 8°. *See* B., J. **10408**. bb, **33**. (**1**.)

—— Report on the Season of 1846, with a table showing the flowering of fruit trees . . . from 1837 to 1846 . . . Being an abstract of the report made on gardens, by the Chairman. Published by request of the Middlesex County Agricultural Society. pp. 14. *C. H. Pelton: Middletown*, 1846. 8°. **7073**. cc. **9**.

BARRATT (JOSEPH) *of Sheffield.* Scripture Arithmetic: or, the Jewish and Roman coins, weights, and measures mentioned in Scripture, reduced to English standards. pp. 16. *Saxton & Chaloner: Sheffield*, 1837. 16°. **1392**. a. **15**. (**2**.)

BARRATT (KATHLEEN)

—— The Bright Lantern. pp. 198. *Herbert Jenkins: London*, 1954. 8°. NNN. **4861**.

—— The Fault Undone. pp. 256. *Herbert Jenkins: London*, [1949.] 8°. NN. **39243**.

—— To Fight Another Day. [A novel.] pp. 276. *Chapman & Hall: London*, 1947. 8°. **12830**. eee. **40**.

BARRATT (KATHLEEN IRENE) Visions & Fancies, in verse. pp. 16. *A. H. Stockwell: London*, [1926.] 8°. **011644**. e. **124**.

BARRATT (LOUISE BASCOM) *See* DAYTON (Helena S.) and BARRATT (L. B.) New York in Seven Days, *etc.* [1926.] 8°. **010409**. e. **8**.

BARRATT (NORRIS STANLEY) Address of Past Master Brother N. S. Barratt . . . November 16, 1914, upon the death of Past Master Brother Joseph S. Miller, *etc.* pp. 16. 1915. 8°. *See* FREEMASONS.—*Lodge No. 2, F. and A. M. of Philadelphia.* **010880**. i. **19**.

—— Address of Hon. N. S. Barratt . . . Wednesday, May 1, 1918 . . . on the Trained Nurse and the Doctor as seen with the eyes of the dove, *etc.* pp. 46. *New Era Printing Co.: Lancaster, Pa.*, 1918. 8°. **07686**. i. **15**.

—— Outline of the History of Old St. Paul's Church, Philadelphia, *etc.* [With plates.] pp. vi. 327. 1917. 8°. *See* PHILADELPHIA.—*Colonial Society of Pennsylvania.* **4744**. k. **16**.

BARRATT (NORRIS STANLEY) and **SACHSE** (JULIUS FRIEDRICH)

—— Freemasonry in Pennsylvania, 1727–1907, as shown by the records of Lodge no. 2, F. and A. M. of Philadelphia from the year A.L. 5757, A.D. 1757. 2 vol. 1908, 09. 8°. *See* FREEMASONS.—*Grand Lodge of Pennsylvania.* **4782**. cc. **11**.

BARRATT (RAYMOND W.) and **HORSFALL** (JAMES GORDON)

—— Fungicidal Action of Metallic Alkyl Bisdithiocarbamates. pp. 51. *New Haven*, 1947. 8°. [*Connecticut Agricultural Experiment Station. Bulletin.* no. 508.] A.S. c. **91/2**.

BARRATT (Reginald) *See* De Sélincourt (Beryl D.) and Henderson, afterwards Gretton (M. S.) Venice . . . Illustrated by R. Barratt. 1907. 8°. **10151**. dd. **28**.

—— *See* Margoliouth (David S.) Cairo, Jerusalem and Damascus . . . With . . . additional plates by R. Barratt. 1907. 4°. K.T.C. **107**. a. **10**.

BARRATT (Robert C.) "Long Life and Peace." Memorials of Mrs. Elizabeth Shaw, *etc.* [With extracts from her journal, and correspondence, and with a portrait.] pp. ix. 227. *Wesleyan Conference Office: London,* 1875. 16°. **4903**. bb. **3**.

BARRATT (Stanley G. R.)

—— A Short History of Totteridge in the County of Hertford. Edited by S. G. R. Barratt. [With a transcript of the parish registers from 1570 to 1837.] pp. 153. *Elliot Stock: London,* 1934. 4°. **10350**. i. **3**.

BARRATT (Thomas Ball) In the Days of the Latter Rain. pp. viii. 224. *Simpkin, Marshall & Co.: London,* 1909. 8°. **4380**. ee. **20**.

—— Revised edition. pp. 222. *Elim Publishing Co.: London,* 1928. 8°. **04375**. g. **79**.

BARRATT (Thomas James) The Annals of Hampstead . . . With over five hundred illustrations. (Introduction by Sir W. Robertson Nicoll.) 3 vol. *A. & C. Black: London,* 1912. 4°. Tab. **502**. b. **6**.

BARRATTE (Gustave) *See* Barratte (Jean F. G.)

BARRATTE (Jean François Gustave)

—— *See* Bonnet (Edmond) *Botanist*. Catalogue raisonné des plantes vasculaires de la Tunisie. Par E. Bonnet et G. Barratte, *etc.* 1896. 8°. **10105.ff.16/2.**

—— *See* Bonnet (Edmond) *Botanist*, and Barratte (J. F. G.) Illustrations des espèces nouvelles, rares ou critiques de phanérogames de la Tunisie, *etc.* 1895. fol. [*Exploration scientifique de la Tunisie. Illustrations de la partie botanique.*] **10105**. h.

—— *See* Durand (E.) *Botanist*, and Barratte (J. F. G.) Floræ Libycæ prodromus, *etc.* 1910. 4°. **7028.h.33.**

—— *See* Patouillard (N.) Catalogue raisonné des plantes cellulaires de la Tunisie. Par N. Patouillard . . . Avec la collaboration de Bescherelle . . . Barratte, *etc.* 1897. 8°. **10105.ff.6/21.**

BARRAU (Adolphe Édouard de) Essai sur le scorbut. Thèse, *etc.* pp. 15. *Montpellier,* 1830. 4°. **1181**. e. **13**. (**12**.)

BARRAU (Albert) Étude sur quelques tendances du mysticisme avant la Réformation. Thèse, *etc.* pp. 48. *Strasbourg,* 1868. 8°. **3678**. bb. **20**. (**5**.)

BARRAU (Antonio de) *See* Lull (Ramón) Livre de l'ami et de l'aimé: petits cantiques . . . Traduits . . . par A. de Barrau et Max Jacob. 1919. 16°. **3834**. a. **30**.

BARRAU (Charles) Essai sur la vie et les travaux de Cyrille Lucaris, patriarche de Constantinople au XVIIe siècle. Thèse, *etc.* pp. 34. *Strasbourg,* 1853. 8°. **3678**. bb. **4**. (**4**.)

BARRAU (Charles Félix) Questions tirées au sort. Sciences médicales. Faire connaître les maladies de la peau qui sont contagieuses . . . Thèse, *etc.* pp. 38. *Montpellier,* 1839. 4°. **1181**. i. **14***. (**27**.)

BARRAU (David) *See* England.—*Parliament.—House of Commons.—Proceedings.*—II. The Report of the Committee of the House of Commons, to whom the petition of the Royal Lustring-Company of England, was referred. . . . Also, the articles of impeachment exhibited . . . against J. Goudet, D. Barrau . . . for high crimes and misdemeanors; with their answers to the same; and the replication of the House of Commons to the said answers, *etc.* 1698. fol. **522**. l. **6**.

BARRAU (Eugène de) 1789 en Rouergue. Étude historique et critique des institutions électorales de l'ancien et du nouveau régime. 1er volume. Sénéchaussée de Rodez. pp. ccx. 417. *Rodez,* 1873. 8°. **9225**. h. **31**. *No more published.*

BARRAU (H. C.)

—— *See* Cavallos (A. de) New Light from Spanish Archives on the Voyage of Olivier van Noort . . . Dutch translation of the Spanish document by . . . Dr. C. F. A. van Dam and Dr. H. C. Barrau, *etc.* 1937. 8°. **9551**. m. **13**.

BARRAU (Hippolyte de) Documens historiques et généalogiques sur les familles et les hommes remarquables du Rouergue dans les temps anciens et modernes. 4 tom. *Rodez,* 1853–60. 8°. **9914**. aa. **23**.

BARRAU (J. J.) *Historian*. Histoire politique des peuples Musulmans depuis Mahomet jusqu'à nos jours, suivie de considérations sur les destinées futures de l'Orient. 2 tom. *Paris,* 1842. 8°. **1434**. c. **7**.

BARRAU (J. J.) *Historian*, and **DARRAGON** (B.)

—— Histoire des croisades contre les Albigeois. (Nouveaux documens sur l'histoire de France aux 11e, 12e et 13e siècles.) 2 tom. *Paris,* 1840. 8°. **1123**. e. **23**.

—— Montfort et les Albigeois. 2 tom. *Bruxelles,* 1840. 24°. **4629**. a. **58**.

BARRAU (Jean Baptiste) *Abbé*. Notice historique sur la vraie croix de Baugé. pp. vii. 142. *Angers,* 1874. 8°. **7709**. bb. **32**.

BARRAU (Jean Baptiste) *Surgeon*. Dissertation sur les fractures du sternum, *etc.* pp. 19. *Strasbourg,* 1815. 4°. [*Collection générale des dissertations de la Faculté de Médecine de Strasbourg.* vol. 20.] **7381*.b.**

BARRAU (Jean Félix) Petitions, la première sur l'organisation de la conservation du cadastre, et la seconde sur la nécessité de renouveler les évaluations cadastrales, adressés à la Chambre des Deputés dans les sessions 1844 et 1845. pp. 15. *Paris,* 1845. 8°. **8205**. c. **2**.

BARRAU (Jean François) La Mort de Marat, tragédie en trois actes, et en vers, suivie de son apothéose, en un acte, et en vers. pp. 48. *Toulouse,* [1794.] 8°. **11738**. aaa. **26**. (**2**.)

BARRAU (Jean Joseph) Considérations générales sur l'empoisonnement par l'oxyde blanc d'arsénic, *etc.* *Paris,* 1821. 4°. **1183**. g. **1**. (**3**.)

BARRAU (Joannes Maria) Tentamen medicum de hepatitide, *etc.* pp. 8. *Monspelii,* 1784. 4°. T. **19**. (**36**.)

BARRAU (Pierre Bernard) Traité des assurances réciproques ou mutuelles contre les fléaux et les cas fortuits . . . ou Manuel des propriétaires de toutes les classes . . . Deuxième édition [of "Manuel des propriétaires de toutes les classes"], *etc.* pp. xxiv. 607. *Paris,* 1827. 8°. **1140**. g. **15**.

BARRAU (Théodore Henri) Amour filial. Récits à la jeunesse . . . Ouvrage illustré de 41 vignettes par Ferogio. pp. 401. *Paris,* 1862. 8°. **12206**. i. **1**. (**1**.)

BARRAU (Théodore Henri)

—— Amour filial . . . Quatrième édition. pp. 318. *Paris*, 1872. 8°. **012550**. n. **31**.

—— Tales of Filial Love. With sixteen full-page illustrations by P. Ferogio. pp. 256. *Darton & Hodge: London*, 1865. 8°. **12805**. ccc. **13**.

—— [Another edition.] Eight full-page illustrations. pp. 256. *Gall & Inglis: Edinburgh*, [1870.] 8°. **12637**. aa. **16**.

—— Choix gradué de 50 sortes d'écritures pour exercer les enfants à la lecture des manuscrits. Nouvelle édition, entièrement refondue. pp. 126. *Paris*, [1854.] 8°. **12952**. bb. **15**.

Engraved throughout.

—— Conseils aux ouvriers sur les moyens d'améliorer leur condition . . . Nouvelle édition, revue et augmentée. pp. iii. 302. *Paris*, 1867. 12°. **8276**. aaa. **28**.

—— De l'éducation dans la famille et au collége. pp. vi. 269. *Paris*, 1852. 8°. **8308**. f. **35**.

—— [Félix, ou le jeune cultivateur.] Felix, the Young Gardener. Illustrated. pp. 64. *Gall & Inglis: London*, [1887.] 8°. **12806**. n. **18**.

—— Histoire de la Révolution française, 1789–1799. pp. 536. *Paris*, 1857. 12°. **1320**. c. **26**.

—— [Another copy.] **1322**. a. **7**.

—— Législation de l'instruction publique. Contenant les lois, décrets, ordonnances, règlements et arrêtés actuellement en vigueur. Recueillis et mis en ordre par T. H. Barrau. pp. iv. 452. *Paris*, 1851. 8°. **1376**. g. **5**.

—— Livre de morale pratique, ou choix de préceptes et de beaux exemples destiné à la lecture courante dans les écoles et dans les familles . . . Nouvelle édition, *etc.* pp. viii. 472. *Paris*, 1863. 12°. **8407**. aaa. **10**.

—— Morceaux choisis des auteurs français, à l'usage des écoles normales primaires, des instituteurs et des institutrices. pp. xiv. 401. *Paris*, 1860 [1859]. 12°. **12235**. a. **3**.

—— La Patrie. Description et histoire de la France, *etc.* pp. vii. 464. *Paris*, 1860. 12°. **9210**. b. **18**.

—— Nouvelle édition. pp. vii. 464. *Paris*, 1865. 8°. **9200**. bbb. **1**.

—— Simples notions sur l'agriculture . . . Nouvelle édition, refondue . . . et contenant 78 vignettes et une carte de la France agricole par Gustave Heuzé. pp. iv. 280. *Paris*, 1868. 8°. **7077**. bbb. **5**.

BARRAUD (Allan) *See* Brown (John) *of Bunyan Meeting, Bedford.* Bunyan's Home . . . Illustrated by A. Barraud. [1890.] *obl.* 4°. **4902**. e. **29**.

—— *See* Corkran (Alice) The Poets' Corner . . . Illustrated by A. Barraud, *etc.* [1892.] 4°. **10347**. d. **6**.

—— *See* L'Estrange (C. J.) Familiar London . . . With sketches in colour by A. Barraud. [1890.] *obl.* 4°. **10349**. f. **5**.

—— —— [1892.] *obl.* 4°. **10350**. de. **45**.

BARRAUD (Alphonse) Observations et réflexions sur les suites des opérations chirurgicales. Thèse, *etc.* pp. 52. *Paris*, 1837. 4°. **1184**. h. **11**. **(30.)**

BARRAUD (Clement William) Lays of the Knights. pp. viii. 164. *Longmans & Co.: London*, 1898. 8°. **011651**. f. **15**.

BARRAUD (Clement William)

—— Richard Wynn—White—Schoolmaster. Martyred October 15, 1584. pp. 24. *Catholic Truth Society: London*, [1912.] 8°. **3943**. aa. **346**.

—— Saint Thomas of Canterbury and Saint Elizabeth of Hungary. Historical dramas. pp. 196. *Longmans & Co.: London*, 1892. 8°. **11781**. g. **44**.

BARRAUD (Daniel Bertrand) *See* Bertrand-Barraud.

BARRAUD (Élie) Essai sur l'accouchement naturel. Thèse, *etc.* pp. 17. *Paris*, 1819. 4°. **1183**. e. **12**. **(13.)**

BARRAUD (Enid Mary)

—— Set my Hand upon the Plough. (Second impression.) [An account of the author's experiences in the Women's Land Army. With plates, including a portrait.] pp. 91. *Littlebury & Co.: Worcester*, 1946. 8°. **07078**. i. **5**.

—— Tail Corn. [With plates.] pp. 221. *Chapman & Hall: London*, 1948. 8°. **7080**. aa. **44**.

—— "What Flower is that?" . . . Illustrated by the author. pp. 126. *Littlebury & Co.: Worcester*, 1952. 8°. **7035**. bbb. **45**.

BARRAUD (Étienne) Recueil de poésies populaires, religieuses, politiques et satiriques. [With a preface by Claudius Hébrard.] pp. xxxi. 263. *Lyon*, 1853. 12°. **11482**. d. **9**.

BARRAUD (Félix) Des poussières; leur influence sur la santé, spécialement sur les fonctions respiratoires, *etc.* pp. 46. *Paris*, 1860. 4°. [*Collection des thèses soutenues à la Faculté de Médecine de Paris.* An 1860. tom. 1.] **7373**. c. **9**.

BARRAUD (Francis Alban) A Table shewing the Interest at the rate of two and three quarters per cent. per annum on sums varying from £1 to £10,000 for all periods from 1 to 364 days, and from 1 to 12 months, *etc.* pp. iv. 64. *Waterlow & Sons: London*, 1889. 8°. **8548**. bbb. **51**.

BARRAUD (George)

—— "Accused." Synopsis of the film based upon the French film entitled: "Accusée levez-vous." pp. 14. *Criterion Film Productions: London*, [1936.] 8°. **011794**. aa. **12**.

BARRAUD (Georges)

—— Touristes de jadis. L'évolution du "sens touristique" jusqu'au XVIIIe siècle . . . Orné de huit gravures hors texte. pp. 135. *Paris; La Rochelle*, 1937. 8°. **010026**. f. **53**.

BARRAUD (Hermann) Gedichte. pp. 114. *Posen*, 1858. 8°. **11526**. b. **54**. **(9.)**

BARRAUD (J. F.)

Le Spartacus, *etc.* [Edited by J. F. Barraud.] 1848. fol.

Hendon.

BARRAUD (Jacques) *See* Poitou. Coustumes du comté et pays de Poictou . . . Avec les annotations sommaires faictes sur icelles . . . par M. I. Barraud, *etc.* 1625. 4°. C. **69**. ee. **4**.

BARRAUD (Jean) Vieux papiers bordelais. Études sur Bordeaux sous la Terreur. [Edited by Paul Courteault. With illustrations.] pp. vi. 190. *Paris*, 1910. 8°. **010171**. i. **25**.

BARRAUD (L. I. C.) Essai sur l'emploi des bains en hygiène, *etc.* pp. 50. *Paris*, 1856. 4°. [*Collection des thèses soutenues à la Faculté de Médecine de Paris.* An 1856. tom. 2.] **7372**. i. **2**.

BARRAUD (Louis Victor) Du ramollissement du cerveau chez l'enfant et le vieillard, thèse, *etc.* pp. 34. *Paris*, 1825. 4°. **1183.** h. **13.** (**17.**)

BARRAUD (Marcel) Les Chambres de métiers en France. pp. 429. iv. *Paris*, 1925. 8°. **08229.** dd. **35.**

BARRAUD (Maurice) *See* Carco (F.) *pseud.* Au coin des rues. Contés ornés de dessins par M. Barraud. 1919. 8°. **12548.** v. **2.**

—— *See* Mérimée (P.) Carmen and Letters from Spain . . . With ten monochrome water-colours by M. Barraud. 1931. 8°. **12239.** cc. **7.**

BARRAUD (P. B.) Recherches historiques sur l'ancienne abbaye de N.-D. de Chastres. pp. 35. *Cognac*, 1870. 12°. **4535.** bb. **2.** (**2.**)

BARRAUD (P. J. Lucien) De l'accouchement naturel par l'extrémité pelvienne, *etc.* pp. 30. *Paris*, 1853. 4°. [*Collection des thèses soutenues à la Faculté de Médecine de Paris.* An 1853. tom. 1.] **7372.** f. **3.**

BARRAUD (Philip J.) *See* Blanford (William T.) The Fauna of British India, *etc.* (Diptera. vol. 5. Family Culicidæ. Tribes Megarhinini and Culicini. By P. J. Barraud.) 1888, *etc.* 8°. **2251.f.19.**

BARRAUD (Phillip) A New Book of Single Cyphers, comprising six hundred; invented & engraved by P. Barraud. ff. 100. [*London*,] 1782. 4°. **556.** b. **5.**

BARRAUD (Pierre Constant) and **MARTIN** (Arthur Marie) Le Bâton pastoral. Étude archéologique . . . Extrait du tome iv. des Mélanges d'archéologie, d'histoire et de littérature, *etc.* [With plates.] pp. 112. *Paris*, 1856. fol. **L.18.e.4.**

BARRAU DE GIRAC (François) successively *Bishop of Saint Brieue* and *of Rennes.* Lettre de M. l'Évêque de Rennes à Messieurs les électeurs du département d'Isle et Vilaine. [On the election of a constitutional bishop. Dated: 18 Feb. 1791.] pp. 16. [*Paris*,] 1791. 8°. F.R. **130.** (**8.**)

BARRAU-DIHIGO (Louis) *See* Barcelona, *Counts of.* Gesta Comitum Barcinonensium. Textos llatí i català editats i anotats per L. Barrau Dihigo, *etc.* 1925. 4°. Ac. **138/5.**

—— *See* Foulché-Delbosc (R.) and Barrau-Dihigo (L.) Manuel de l'hispanisant. 1920, *etc.* 8°. **B.B.gf.27.**

—— *See* Joly (B.) Voyage de Barthélemy Joly en Espagne . . . Publié par L. Barrau-Dihigo. 1909. 8°. [*Revue Hispanique.* tom. 20.] P.P. **4331.** aea.

—— *See* Valpuesta. Chartes de l'église de Valpuesta du ixe au xie siècle, publiées par L. Barrau-Dihigo. 1900. 8°. [*Revue Hispanique.* tom. 7.] P.P. **4331.** aea.

—— *See* Verardus (C.) Historia Bætica. Rééditée par L. Barrau-Dihigo. 1920. 8°. [*Revue Hispanique.* tom. 47.] P.P. **4331.** aea.

—— Catalogue de la Bibliothèque Gaston Paris. livr. 1. 1912. 8°. [*Bibliothèque de l'École des Hautes Études. Sciences historiques et philologiques.* fasc. 200.] *See* Paris (G.**B.P.**) Ac. **8929.**

—— Recherches sur l'histoire politique du Royaume Asturien, 718–910. Extrait de la "Revue Hispanique," *etc.* pp. 360. *New York, Paris*, 1921. 8°. **9181.** aa. **11.**

BARRAULT (d'Émery de) *Count de Blagnac. See* Émery de Barrault.

BARRAULT (Alexis) *See* Flachat (E.) Traité de la fabrication du fer et de la fonte . . . Par E. Flachat, A. Barrault, *etc.* 1842. 4°. **8768.** m. **6.**

BARRAULT (Alexis) and **BARRAULT** (Pierre Ange Casimir Émile)

—— Le Canal de Suez et la question du tracé . . . Extrait de la Revue des Deux Mondes, *etc.* [With a map.] pp. 40. *Paris*, 1856. 8°. **8235.** c. **59.** (**3.**)

—— [Another copy.] **8235.** f. **2.** (**3.**)

—— Politique du canal de Suez. Questions techniques et économiques. [With a map.] pp. 79. *Paris*, 1856. 8°. **8235.** d. **55.** (**7.**)

BARRAULT (Alexis) and **BRIDEL** (G.) *Ingénieur.*

—— Le Palais de l'Industrie et ses annexes. Description raisonnée du système de construction en fer et en fonte adopté dans ces bâtiments, avec dessins d'exécution et tableaux des poids. pp. vi. 45. pl. xxviii. *Paris*, 1857. fol. **1800.** c. **7.**

BARRAULT (E.) *Ancien Professeur au Collége Stanislas et au Lycée Napoléon.* Traité des synonymes de la langue latine. Composé sur un plan nouveau d'après les travaux des grammairiens, des commentateurs et des synonymistes anciens et modernes, et principalement d'après le grand travail de M. Dœderlein. Par E. Barrault . . . avec la collaboration, pour la 2e partie, de M. Ernest Grégoire, *etc.* pp. xxxii. 768. *Paris*, 1853. 8°. **12932.** d. **15.**

BARRAULT (Émile) *Civil Engineer.* Les Inventeurs et la loi des États-Unis modifiée en 1861. Texte, documents et commentaire de la législation des brevets d'inventions, dessins et modèles de fabriques aux États-Unis. pp. 54. *Paris*, 1861. 12°. **6625.** a. **2.**

—— Marques de fabrique et noms commerciaux. Guide pratique du fabricant, du négociant et du commerçant, *etc.* pp. 160. *Paris*, 1859. 12°. **7953.** b. **10.**

BARRAULT (Émile) *Saint-Simonian. See* Barrault (Pierre A. C. E.)

BARRAULT (Ernest) De la splénotomie chez l'homme. Avec une étude sur la physiologie de la rate d'après un récent mémoire de M. Ch. Robin, et une nouvelle observation de splénotomie pratiquée avec succès par M. le Dr. Péan, *etc.* pp. 76. *Paris*, 1876. 8°. **7306.** c. **5.** (**5.**)

BARRAULT (François) *See* Rinuccini (G. B.) *Archbishop of Fermo.* Le Capucin escossois. Histoire merveilleuse . . . Traduitte . . . par le R. P. F. Barrault, *etc.* 1650. 12°. **4955.** a. **32.** (**1.**)

—— —— 1652. 12°. **4051.** aa. **38.**

—— —— 1664. 12°. **4955.** a. **31.**

—— —— 1682. 12°. **4863.** b. **27.**

—— —— 1689. 12°. G. **16133.**

BARRAULT (Henry Émile) *See* Gidel (G.) and Barrault (H. E.) Le Traité de paix avec l'Allemagne du 28 juin 1919 et les intérêts privés, *etc.* 1921. 8°. **6916.** ee. **32.**

—— Le Droit d'association en Angleterre. pp. 309. *Paris*, 1908. 8°. **6006.** h. **28.**

BARRAULT (Jean) Essai sur le rôle du silence créateur d'obligations. pp. viii. 161. *Dijon*, 1912. 8°. **05402.** aaa. **48.**

BARRAULT (Jean Louis)

—— *See* Claudel (P. L. C. M.) [*Selections.*] Connaissance de Paul Claudel. (Textes de présentation de J.-L. Barrault.) [1955.] 8°. [*Cahiers de la compagnie Madeleine Renaud-Jean-Louis Barrault.* no. 12.] **W.P.1447/12.**

BARRAULT (JEAN LOUIS)

—— *See* GIDE (A. P. G.) and BARRAULT (J.-L.) [Le Procès.] The Trial, *etc.* 1950. 8°. **11741. aa. 38.**

—— A propos de Shakespeare et du théâtre. [Three lectures.] pp. 107. [*Paris*,] 1949. 8°. **11768.** cc. **6.**

—— Je suis homme de théâtre. pp. 146. *Paris*, 1955. 8°. **11797. a. 119.**
Part of the series " Mon métier."

—— Réflexions sur le théâtre, *etc.* [With illustrations.] pp. 202. *Paris*, 1949. 4°. **11798.** b. **25.**

—— Reflections on the Theatre, *etc.* (Translated by Barbara Wall.) [With portraits.] pp. xi. 185. pl. VIII. *Rockliff: London*, [1951.] 8°. **11798.** c. **11.**

BARRAULT (PIERRE ANGE CASIMIR ÉMILE) *See* also CASAMAJOR (A. de) *Madame, pseud.* [i.e. P. A. C. E. Barrault.]

—— *See* BARRAULT (A.) and BARRAULT (P. A. C. E.) Le Canal de Suez et la question du tracé, *etc.* 1856. 8°. **8235.** c. **59.** (**3.**)

—— *See* BARRAULT (A.) and BARRAULT (P. A. C. E.) Politique du canal de Suez, *etc.* 1856. 8°. **8235.** d. **55.** (**7.**)

—— *See* CADALVÈNE (E. de) and BARRAULT (P. A. C. E.) Deux années de l'histoire d'Orient, *etc.* 1840. 8°. **802.** i. **27.**

—— *See* CADALVÈNE (E. de) and BARRAULT (P. A. C. E.) Histoire de la guerre de Méhémed-Ali contre la Porte Ottomane, *etc.* 1837. 8°. **1053.** g. **27.**

—— *See* ENFANTIN (B. P.) Religion saint-simonienne. Procès en la Cour d'Assises de la Seine, les 27 et 28 août 1832. [An account of the trial of B. P. Enfantin, P. A. C. E. Barrault and others.] 1832. 8°. **5423.** dd. **8.** (**1.**)

—— Le Chemin de fer du Nord en Espagne. [With a map.] pp. 207. *Paris*, 1858. 8°. **8235.** b. **42.**

—— Le Christ. pp. 488. *Paris*, 1865. 8°. **4806.** h. **14.**

—— Lettres contemporaines. [Addressed to various French statesmen.] livr. 1–5. *Paris*, 1848. fol. **1851.** b. **23.**
Imperfect; wanting all after livr. 5. The series title first appears in livr. 3. Livr. 1 and 2 are entitled : " Lettre à M. Lamartine " and " Lettre à M. Thiers " respectively.

—— [Another copy of livr. 1.] **1880.** c. **1.** (**168.**)

—— Occident et Orient. Études politiques, morales, religieuses, pendant 1833–1834, *etc.* pp. 498. *Paris*, 1835. 8°. **8028.** bb. **20.**

—— Le Tocsin des travailleurs. [Edited by P. A. C. E. Barrault and F. Delente.] 1848. fol. **Hendon.**

BARRAULT (PIERRE CONSTANT) *See* BARRAUD.

BARRAULT (SERGE)

—— Scènes et tableaux. Le règne de Louis XIV. [With plates, including portraits.] pp. 249. *Paris*, 1938. 8°. **09226.** c. **10.**

BARRAULT (SIGMUND) Die Ausbildung der Rekruten bei den k. k. Fusstruppen in einer achtwöchentlichen Unterrichtsperiode ; anschaulich gemacht durch Beispiele für das Gefecht in zerstreuter Ordnung, *etc.* pp. 96. *Wien*, 1870. 8°. **8829.** bbb. **46.** (**3.**)

BARRAUT (FRANÇOIS) *See* BARRAULT.

BARRAZA (CARLOS F.)

—— Brown y Garibaldi. Las luchas por el dominio del rio Paraná durante la guerra entre Rosas y Rivera. 1943. *See* BUENOS AYRES.—*Sociedad de Historia Argentina.* Anuario de Historia Argentina. año 1942. 1942, *etc.* 4°. Ac. **8592.** d/**2.**

BARRAZA (GABRIEL DE) *See* HERRERA (F. M. de) Por la casa, hijos, y herederos de el Señor Don Geronimo de Estrada, Marqués, que fue, de Casa-Estrada ; contra los hijos, y herederos de Don G. de Barraza, *etc.* 1713. fol. **707.** h. **27.** (**1.**)

BARRAZA (JOSÉ LORETO) *See* LORETO BARRAZA.

BARRE, *Saint, Bishop of Cork. See* FINBARR.

BARRÉ ( ) *Auditeur des Comptes.* Catalogue des livres de feu M. Barré . . . dont la vente se fera en détail lundy 13. janvier 1744. & jours suivans, *etc.* 2 tom. *Paris*, 1743. 8°. **270.** d. **15, 16.**

BARRÉ ( ) *of Rouen.* Dissertation sur le mal vertébral, *etc.* pp. 13. *Paris*, 1816. 4°. **1182.** h. **9.** (**12.**)

BARRÉ ( ) *Resident of the King of France in the Netherlands. See* NETHERLANDS.—*United Provinces.—Staten Generaal.* Extract uyt het Register der resolutien vande . . . Staeten Generael . . . behelsende het antwoort op de memorie van den Heer Barré. [1702.] 4°. **107.** g. **9.** (**31.**)

BARRÉ (A. R.) Essai sur les polypes utérins. Tribut académique, *etc.* pp. 19. *Montpellier*, 1823. 4°. **1181.** c. **12.** (**7.**)

BARRÉ (ALBERT) *See* ADELY (P.) and BARRÉ (A.) L'Escargot, *etc.* [1884.] 8°. **11739.** g. **96.** (**4.**)

—— *See* HENNEQUIN (M.) Le Paradis, *etc.* [By M. Hennequin, P. Bilhaud and A. Barré.] **11740.** bbb. **57.**

—— *See* KÉROUL (H.) and BARRÉ (A.) Le Chopin, *etc.* 1905. 8°. **11736.** f. **36.**

—— *See* KÉROUL (H.) and BARRÉ (A.) Une Nuit de noces, *etc.* 1905. 8°. **11736.** i. **6.**

—— Les Gilets jaunes. Comédie en trois actes. pp. 120. *Paris*, 1880. 12°. **11740.** f. **19.** (**1.**)

BARRÉ (ALBERT EDMOND) Des transactions en droit romain et en droit français. (Thèse.) pp. 138. *Paris*, 1855. 8°. **5406.** a. **8.** (**2.**)

BARRE (ANDRÉ) *See* PLATO. [*Selections.—French.*] Platon. Choix de textes avec étude du système philosophique et notices biographique et bibliographique par A. Barre, *etc.* [1909.] 8°. **8459.** aa. **14/1.**

—— La Bosnie-Herzégovine. Administration autrichienne de 1878 à 1903. pp. v. 290. *Paris*, [1906.] 8°. **9134.** e. **21.**

—— L'Esclavage blanc. Arménie et Macédoine. pp. 320. *Paris*, [1909.] 8°. **8026.** de. **26.**

—— La Menace allemande. pp. 282. *Paris*, [1907.] 8°. **8027.** bb. **42.**

—— Le Symbolisme. Essai historique sur le mouvement symboliste en France de 1885 à 1900, suivi d'une bibliographie de la poésie symboliste. pp. ix. 411. xii. 294. *Paris*, 1911. 8°. **011852.** d. **16.**

—— La Tragédie serbe. [On the assassination of King Alexander and Queen Draga.] pp. 278. *Paris*, [1906.] 8°. **9134.** e. **22.**

BARRÉ (ANTOINE) Essai sur les affections scrophuleuses ; thèse, *etc.* pp. 59. *Paris*, 1817. 4°. **1183.** d. **10.** (**7.**)

BARRÉ (ANTOINE OCTAVE) L'Architecture du sol de la France. Essai de géographie tectonique. pp. iii. 393. *Paris*, 1903. 8°. **07107.** l. **29.**

—— La Géographie militaire et les nouvelles méthodes géographiques. Introduction à l'étude de l'Europe centrale, *etc.* pp. 79. *Paris*, 1899. 8°. **10107.** gg. **3.**

BARRE (AUGUSTE) Du diagnostic des lésions profondes de l'œil à l'aide de l'ophthalmoscope et des phosphènes. pp. 150. *Montpellier*, 1857. 8°. **7610.** b. **48.** (**3.**)

—— Essai sur la péritonite tuberculeuse. Thèse, *etc.* pp. 61. *Montpellier*, 1852. 4°. **7379.** b. **8.** (**9.**)

BARRÉ (CAROLUS) Étude sur la bourgeoisie au moyen-âge. Une famille de tabellions royaux : les de Kerromp. [With plates and genealogical tables.] pp. 248. *Paris*, 1930. **8°**. **09915.** h. **14.**

BARRÉ (CHARLES AMBROISE EDMOND) De l'eutocie par la face, ou de l'accouchement considéré comme naturel dans cette position, *etc.* pp. 23. *Paris*, 1833. 4°. **1184.** f. **2.** (**14.**)

BARRE (CHARLES GUSTAVE) Hygiène du premier âge. Des soins que réclame l'enfant depuis la naissance jusqu'après le sevrage. pp. 90. *Paris*, 1861. 4°. [*Collection des thèses soutenues à la Faculté de Médecine de Paris.* An 1861. tom. 1.] **7373.** d. **2.**

BARRE (CHARLES JOSEPH) *Count de La Garde.* Un Bouquet littéraire, ou huit jours dans l'île du bois de Boulogne. pp. 448. *Paris*, 1857. 12°. **12513.** c. **24.**

—— De l'organisation sociale, ou théorie sur les passions et les institutions humaines, l'économie politique, les récompenses, les délits et les peines. pp. viii. 504. *Paris*, 1868. 8°. **8006.** ee. **7.**

—— Du crédit et des banques hypothécaires. pp. 367. *Paris*, 1849. 8°. **5423.** bb. **21.**

BARRE (ERNST) Gedichte. pp. 123. *Leipzig*, 1869. 8°. **11521.** cc. **37.** (**4.**)

—— Der ländliche Wucher, *etc.* pp. 56. *Berlin*, 1890. 8°. **8226.** f. **60.** (**5.**)

—— Der Prozess Ziethen in Elberfeld. pp. 105. *Berlin*, 1893. 8°. **5604.** d. **4.**

—— Ueber die Bruderschaft der Pfeifer im Elsass, ein Vortrag . . . nebst urkundlichen Beilagen. pp. 54. *Colmar*, 1873. 8°. **7896.** b. **48.** (**11.**)

BARRÉ (EUGÈNE) *Dramatist.* *See* LUCAS (Hippolyte J. J.) and BARRÉ (E.) Le Ciel et l'enfer, *etc.* 1853. 8°. [*La Bibliothèque dramatique.* tom. 51.] **2296.** c. **20.**

—— —— 1854. fol. [*Théâtre contemporain illustré.* livr. 138, 139.] **2296.** h.

—— *See* MESTÉPÈS (E.) and BARRÉ (E.) Christophe Colomb, *etc.* [1861.] 4°. **11739.** k. **9.**

BARRE (EUGÈNE) *M.D.* Quelques considérations sur le siége et la nature de l'hystérie. Thèse, *etc.* pp. 52. *Montpellier*, 1863. 4°. **7379.** f. **2.** (**8.**)

BARRÉ (FRANÇOIS THÉOPHILE) English Accentuation. pp. v. 78. *Librairie Beauchemin : Montréal*, 1909. 8°. **12983.** dd. **12.**

—— English Accentuation. Abridged speller and reader. pp. 48. "*La Croix*": *Montreal*, 1912. 8°. **012901.** ff. **40.** (**2.**)

BARRÉ (FRÉDÉRIC) Chansons de vingt ans. pp. 140. *Paris*, 1865. 12°. **11482.** b. **12.**

—— Rimes d'escolier. pp. 176. *Paris*, 1867. 12°. **11482.** bb. **2.**

BARRÉ (GEORGES) *Docteur en Médecine de la Faculté de Paris.*

—— *See* GALIPPE (M. L. V.) and BARRÉ (G.) Le Pain. Aliment minéralisateur, *etc.* [1894.] 8°. **08709.** f. **58.**

—— *See* GALIPPE (M. L. V.) and BARRÉ (G.) Le Pain. Technologie, *etc.* [1895.] 8°. **08709.** f. **60.**

BARRÉ (GEORGES) *Général.*

—— Tunisie, 1942–1943. Avec 10 croquis. [With a map.] pp. xii. 322. *Paris*, 1950. 8°. **9102.** n. **4.**
Part of a series entitled "La seconde guerre mondiale: histoire et souvenirs."

BARRÉ (GUILLAUME VINCENT) *See* BARRÉ (William V.)

BARRE (H. CHR.)

—— *See* MYKLEBOST (H.) Drammen . . . Med bidrag av . . . H. C. Barre, *etc.* 1949. 4°. **10281.** k. **35.**

BARRE (HENRI) Réflexions sur divers points de médecine et de chirurgie. Thèse, *etc.* pp. 26. *Montpellier*, 1845. 4°. **1182.** d. **15.** (**2.**)

BARRÉ (HENRI) *Bibliothécaire de la Bibliothèque de Marseille.* *See* BOUCHES-DU-RHÔNE, *Département des.—Conseil Général.* Les Bouches-du-Rhône, *etc.* (Tome XI. Biographies. Par H. Barré.) 1913, *etc.* fol. **10167.** r. **1/11.**

—— *See* BOUCHES-DU-RHÔNE, *Département des.—Conseil Général.* Les Bouches-du-Rhône, *etc.* (Tome XIII. Demographie. Par H. Barré, *etc.*) 1913, *etc.* fol. **10167.** r. **1/13.**

—— *See* GIBERTI (J. J.) L'Histoire de la ville de Pernes . . . Publiée . . . par Hubert Giraud [assisted by H. Barré]. 1923. 8°. **10167.** m. **10.**

—— Catalogue des incunables de la Bibliothèque de la Ville de Marseille, *etc.* pp. vii. 71. 1897. 8°. *See* MARSEILLES.—*Bibliothèque de la Ville.* **011901.** ee. **39.**

BARRÉ (HENRI) *Inspecteur des Forêts.* Notions pratiques de constructions forestières. pp. 111. 1857. fol. *See* NANCY.—École Nationale des Eaux et Forêts. **7816.** c. **5.**

BARRE (HENRY JOHN) and **SAMMET** (LOY LUTHER)

—— Farm Structures. pp. xi. 650. *John Wiley & Sons: New York; Chapman & Hall: London*, 1950. 8°. [*Ferguson Foundation Agricultural Engineering Series.*] W.P. **14532/1**

BARRÉ (ISAAC) *Lieut.-Colonel.* *See* BRITTON (John) The Authorship of the Letters of Junius elucidated : including a biographical memoir of Lieut. Col. I. Barré. 1848. 4°. **8007.** f. **13.**

BARRÉ (ISAAC) *Teacher of French.* Stances sur la mort de son Altesse Frederic Henri, Prince Palatin du Rhin . . . esleu & designé Roy de Boheme, *etc.* *A. Meuris : La Haye*, 1629. 4°. **1161.** h. **28.** (**1.**)

BARRE (J. A.) *Professeur de Neurologie.*

—— *See* BABINSKI (J. F. F.) Œuvre scientifique. Recueil des principaux travaux publié par les soins de J.-A. Barré [and others], *etc.* 1934. 4°. **7320.tt.2.**

BARRÉ (J. J. HENRI) Dissertations sur la nature des affections dites scrofuleuses, *etc.* pp. 50. *Paris*, 1852. 4°. [*Collection des thèses soutenues à la Faculté de Médecine de Paris.* An 1852. tom. 1.] **7372.** e. **5.**

BARRÉ (JACQUES) Dissertation sur l'apoplexie, considérée comme hémorrhagie cérébrale ; thèse, *etc.* pp. 33. *Paris*, 1828. 4°. **1184.** c. **2.** (**23.**)

BARRE (JEAN) *See* also LINDSAY (Lee) *pseud.* [i.e. J. Barre.]

—— A Hunting We Will Go. pp. 287. *Wright & Brown: London,* [1934.] 8°. **NN. 21572.**

—— All Sorts of Rebels. pp. 283. *Wright & Brown: London,* [1933.] 8°. **NN. 20267.**

—— Chivalrous Quest. pp. 284. *Wright & Brown: London,* [1939.] 8°. **NN. 31032.**

—— Chivalrous Quest. pp. 96. *Mellifont Press: London; Dublin* printed, [1954.] 8°. **12653.** bb. **41.**

—— Code of Honour. pp. 284. *Wright & Brown: London,* [1940.] 8°. **NN. 31418.**

—— The Crusader's Secret. pp. 288. *Wright & Brown: London,* [1937.] 8°. **NN. 28346.**

—— The Crusader's Secret. pp. 112. *Mellifont Press: London; Dublin* printed, [1944.] 8°. [*Mellifont Library.*] W.P. **10045/60.**

—— The Dark Hunter. pp. 287. *Wright & Brown: London,* [1932.] 8°. **NN. 19300.**

—— Darke Ladyes. pp. 287. *Wright & Brown: London,* [1933.] 8°. **NN. 20799.**

—— The Desert Son. pp. 352. *Wright & Brown. London,* [1935.] 8°. **NN. 23618.**

—— Elusive Romance. pp. 287. *Wright & Brown: London,* [1939.] 8°. **NN. 29917.**

—— Gallantry Fights On. pp. 284. *Wright & Brown: London,* [1940.] 8°. **NN. 31883.**

—— Gallantry fights on. pp. 96. *Mellifont Press: London; Dublin* printed, [1954.] 8°. **12653.** bb. **19.**

—— Gather Ye Rosebuds. pp. 286. *Wright & Brown: London,* [1937.] 8°. **NN. 27357.**

—— Glorious Life. pp. 320. *Wright & Brown: London,* [1935.] 8°. **NN. 24919.**

—— Hawk's Last Flight. pp. 288. *Wright & Brown: London,* [1936.] 8°. **NN. 25349.**

—— Hawk's Last Flight. [An abridgment.] pp. 128. *Mellifont Press: London; Dublin* printed, [1944.] 8°. [*Mellifont Library.*] W.P. **10045/46.**

—— The Ivory Goddess. pp. 286. *Wright & Brown: London,* [1938.] 8°. **NN. 28781.**

—— The Jester of Mayfair. pp. 283. *Wright & Brown: London,* [1939.] 8°. **NN. 30208.**

—— The Judgment of Paris. pp. 320. *Wright & Brown: London,* [1934.] 8°. **NN. 23105.**

—— The Judgment of Paris. [An abridgment.] pp. 128. *Mellifont Press: London; Dublin* printed, [1944.] 8°. [*Mellifont Library.*] W.P. **10045/65.**

—— The King's Pearl. pp. 280. *Wright & Brown: London,* [1934.] 8°. **NN. 22421.**

—— The Lady Escapes. pp. 284. *Wright & Brown: London,* [1939.] 8°. **NN. 30609.**

—— Light and Shade. pp. 284. *Wright & Brown: London,* [1942.] 8°. **NN. 33063.**

—— Lover Awake! pp. 286. *Wright & Brown: London,* [1938.] 8°. **NN. 29311.**

—— Lover awake! pp. 96. *Mellifont Press: London; Dublin* printed, [1953.] 8°. **012635.** h. **75.**

—— Lover's Pride. pp. 282. *Wright & Brown: London,* [1940.] 8°. **NN. 32523.**

—— The Mill of Happiness. pp. 288. *Wright & Brown: London,* 1931. 8°. **NN. 18038.**

—— The Mill of Happiness. pp. 128. *Mellifont Press: London; Dublin* printed, [1952.] 8°. [*Mellifont Romances.* no. 1.] W.P. A. **335/1.**

—— Spanish Secret. pp. 286. *Wright & Brown: London,* [1935.] 8°. **NN. 24275.**

—— Spanish Secret. pp. 128. *Mellifont Press: London; Dublin* printed, [1952.] 8°. [*Mellifont Romances.* no. 3.] W.P. A. **335/3.**

—— Storms of Spring. pp. 287. *Wright & Brown: London,* [1932.] 8°. **NN. 19375.**

—— The Swiftest Thing in Life, *etc.* pp. 326. *Wright & Brown: London,* [1931.] 8°. **NN. 18037.**

—— Take Your Choice. [Tales.] pp. 236. *Wright & Brown: London,* [1942.] 8°. **NN. 33600.**

—— The Tarnished Shield. pp. 279. *Wright & Brown: London,* [1932.] 8°. **NN. 22683.**

—— The Twisted Stair. pp. 320. *Wright & Brown: London,* [1936.] 8°. **NN. 26583.**

—— The Twisted Stair. [Abridged.] pp. 128. *Mellifont Press: London; Dublin* printed, [1945.] 8°. [*Mellifont Library.*] W.P. **10045/82.**

—— Wild Legacy. pp. 288. *Wright & Brown: London,* [1936.] 8°. **NN. 25992.**

—— The Wilful Jade. pp. 318. *Wright & Brown: London,* [1936.] 8°. **NN. 26178.**

—— The Wilful Jade. [An abridgment.] pp. 128. *Mellifont Press: London; Dublin* printed, [1944.] 8°. [*Mellifont Library.*] W.P. **10045/78.**

—— Youth's in the Saddle. pp. 202. *Wright & Brown: London,* 1943. 8°. **NN. 34488.**

BARRÉ (JEAN)

—— *See* TYRWHITT, afterwards TYRWHITT-WILSON (G. H.) *Baron Berners.* [The Camel.] Le Chameau . . . Traduit . . . par J. Barré. 1951. 8°. [*Les Œuvres libres. Nouvelle série.* no. 60.] **12208.ee.285.**

BARRÉ (JEAN ALEXANDRE) *See* GUILLAIN (G.) and BARRÉ (J. A.) Travaux neurologiques de guerre, *etc.* 1920. 8°. **07660.** i. **44.**

BARRÉ (JEAN AUGUSTE) *See* REY (J.) Traité complet d'éducation . . . Par J. Rey . . . avec la coopération de M. J. A. Barré. 1852. 8°. **8355.** dd. **39.**

BARRÉ (JOANNES) Dissertatio medica inauguralis de venæ sectione, *etc.* pp. 8. *Lugduni Batavorum,* 1712. 4°. **1185.** h. **10.** (**14.**)

BARRE (JOSEPH) Histoire générale de l'Allemagne. 10 tom. *Paris,* 1748. 4°. **157. f. 1-11.**

—— Allgemeine Geschichte von Deutschland vor und nach Errichtung des Kaiserthums bis auf itzige Zeiten . . . Aus dem Französischen übersetzt. 8 Bd. *Leipzig,* 1749-52. 4°. **9340.** cc. **2.**

—— Vie de M. le marquis de Fabert, Maréchal de France. 2 tom. *Paris,* 1752. 12°. **613.** b. **11, 12.**

—— [Another copy.] **275.** c. **2, 3.**

BARRE (JOSEPH)

—— Vindiciæ librorum deutero-canonicorum Veteris Testamenti, in quibus traditionis et concilii Tridentini mens de eorum autoritate accuratè elucidatur. Autore uno è Canonicis regularibus Congregationis Gallicanæ. [The dedication signed: Josephus Barre.] pp. xxiii. 359. *Parisiis*, 1730. 8°. **3125. a. 37.**

BARRE (JULES) Étude sur les déviations magnétiques des compas aux approches des volcans, courants marins sur les côtes de Madagascar et de Bourbon . . . perte du croiseur britannique le "Warren-Hastings," *etc.* pp. 56. *Paris*, 1899. 8°. **08805. f. 33.**

BARRE (LIDUVINE) Précieux souvenir pour la Congregation de Saint-Charles. [Selections from the writings of L. Barre, preceded by an "Exhortation adressée à la Communauté par M. l'abbé Maslats."] 2 pt. *Nancy*, 1858. 12°. **4408. bb. 10.**

BARRE (LOUIS) Recherches cliniques et philosophiques pour servir à l'histoire de la maladie de Bright. Thèse, *etc.* pp. 120. *Montpellier*, 1842. 4°. **1182. c. 13. (1.)**

BARRÉ (LOUIS) *See* ARNAULD (Antoine) *Doctor of the Sorbonne*, and NICOLE (P.) La Logique . . . par MM. de Port-Royal . . . Nouvelle édition précédée d'une introduction . . . par L. Barré. 1864. 12°. **8466. aaa. 2.**

—— *See* BOISTE (P. C. V.) Dictionnaire universel de la langue française . . . Neuvième édition . . . comparée avec le dictionnaire de l'Académie de 1835, par MM. Ch. Nodier . . . et L. Barré. 1839. 4°. **12951.i.14.**

—— —— 1851. 4°. **12952. g. 16.**

—— —— 1857. 4°. **12952. f. 5.**

—— *See* DANTE ALIGHIERI. [*Divina Commedia.—French.*] Œuvres de Dante Alighieri. La Divine Comédie . . . Avec des notes d'après les meilleurs commentaires par L. Barré, *etc.* 1854. 4°. **11420. gg. 32.**

—— *See* ENCYCLOPAEDIAS. Encyclopédie nationale des sciences, des lettres et des arts . . . Redigé par une société de savants et d'hommes de lettres, sous la direction de MM. J.-P. Houzé et L. Barré. 1853, *etc.* 4°. **012221. c. 2.**

—— *See* ENCYCLOPAEDIAS. Encyclopédie nationale des sciences, des lettres et des arts . . . Rédigée par une société de savants et d'hommes de lettres, sous la direction de MM. J.-P. Houzé et L. Barré, *etc.* 1857, *etc.* 8°. **735. g. 10 & 10*.**

—— *See* LANDAIS (N.) Dictionnaire général et grammatical des dictionnaires français, *etc.* (Complément . . . rédigé . . . sous la direction de MM. D. Chésurolles et L. Barré.) 1850, *etc.* 4°. **1331. k. 6–8.**

—— —— 1854. 4°. **12952.w.4.**

—— —— 1862. 8°. **12952. h. 3.**

—— *See* LANDAIS (N.) and BARRÉ (L.) Dictionnaire des rimes françaises, *etc.* 1859. 16°. **12953. a. 46.**

—— *See* MAZOIS (F.) Les Ruines de Pompéi. (Le texte de la quatrième partie a été rédigé par M. Barré.) 1824, *etc.* fol. **744. g. 4.**

—— *See* PARIS.—*Académie Française.* Complément du Dictionnaire de l'Académie . . . Précédé d'une préface par L. Barré. 1842. 4°. **12954. h. 10.**

—— *See* RABELAIS (F.) Œuvres de F. Rabelais . . . Nouvelle édition . . . accompagnée de notes succinctes et d'un glossaire par L. Barré, *etc.* [1854.] 4°. **12236. i. 2.**

—— —— [1856?] 12°. **12235. c. 14.**

BARRÉ (LOUIS)

—— *See* SCARRON (P.) Le Roman comique de Scarron . . . Conclusion par L. Barré, *etc.* 1858. 8°. **012548. ccc. 18.**

—— Herculaneum et Pompéi. Recueil général des peintures bronzes, mosaïques etc. découverts jusqu'à ce jour, et reproduits d'après le Antichita di Ercolano, il Museo Borbonico, et tous les ouvrages analogues; augmenté de sujets inédits, gravés au trait sur cuivre par H. Roux ainé, et accompagné d'un texte explicatif par M. L. Barré. 8 tom. *Paris*, 1840, 39, 40. 8°. **Cup.363.bb.2.**
The titlepage of tom. 2, *dated* 1839, *bears the words: "Accompagné d'un texte explicatif par MM. L. Barré et J. Bories."*

—— [Another edition.] 8 tom. *Paris*, 1870–72. 8°. **Cup.363.bb.1.**

—— Nouvelle biographie classique, contenant jusqu'à l'année 1840, la liste des principaux personnages de tous les pays . . . Seconde édition. pp. 555. *Paris*, 1844. 12°. **609*. a. 26.**

—— La Suite de l'École des vieillards. *See* RASTOUL DE MONGEOT (A. S.) Soirées à la campagne, *etc.* 1835. 12°. **10172. c. 28. (3.)**

BARRÉ (LOUIS) and **LANDOIS** (NARCISSE)

—— Complément du Dictionnaire de l'Académie française . . . Publié sous la direction d'un membre de l'Académie française, par M. Louis Barré . . . et M. Narcisse Landois, *etc.* pp. xxxvi. 1082. 1839. *See* PARIS.—*Académie Française.* Dictionnaire de l'Académie française, *etc.* pt. 2. 1845, *etc.* 4°. **12950. v. 6.**

BARRÉ (LOUIS AUGUSTE) *See* DOULIOT (J. P.) Traité spécial de coupe des pierres . . . Deuxième édition . . . augmentée . . . les XXIII derniers chapitres par J. Claudel et L. A. Barré, *etc.* 1869. 4°. **7814. f. 19.**

—— Memento de l'architecte et de l'entrepreneur. Théorie, pratique et législation du bâtiment . . . Par L.-A. Barré . . . Avec la collaboration d'architectes, de spécialistes et de Paul Barré, fils. pp. vii. 1032. *Paris*, 1896. 8°. **7815. a. 38.**

—— Ancien Memento Barré. Notes & formules de l'architecte. Par un comité de spécialistes sous la direction du lieutenant-colonel G. Espitallier. [tom. 1 and part of tom. 2 edited by Commandant Baudran.] 2 tom. *Paris*, 1919, 20. 8°. **07816. aa. 33.**

—— Ponts métalliques. Théorie & construction. pp. 106. *Paris*, 1894. 4°. [*VIGREUX (L.) and RAUX (A.) Théorie et pratique de l'art de l'ingénieur.*] **08766. dd. 10.**

BARRÉ (LOUIS AUGUSTE) and **BARRÉ** (PAUL)

—— Manuel de génie sanitaire. La ville salubre. Avec une préface par Louis Masson, *etc.* pp. viii. 340. *Paris*, 1897. 18°. **8777. aaa. 48.**

BARRÉ (LOUIS CAROLUS) *See* CAROLUS-BARRÉ (L.)

BARRE (MARIE JEANNE VON) *Countess. See* DU BARRY.

BARRÉ (MARIO RAVELO) *See* RAVELO BARRÉ (M.)

BARRÉ (NICOLAS) *of the Order of Minims.*

—— *See* CORDONNIER (Ch.) Le R.P. Nicolas Barré, *etc.* 1938. 8°. **20043. e. 5.**

—— *See* GRÈZES (H. de) Vie du R. P. Barré, religieux minime, *etc.* 1892. 8°. **4864. e. 17.**

BARRÉ (NICOLAS) *of the Order of Minims.*

—— Lettres spirituelles du R. père Nicolas Barré, *etc.* (Recueillies par les soins du sieur abbé N.) pp. 310. *J. B. Besongne: Rouen,* 1697. 12°. **872.** d. **37.**

BARRÉ (NICOLAS) *Traveller.*

—— Copie de quelques letres sur la navigation du chevallier de Villegaignon es terres de l'Amerique oultre l'æquinoctial. *See* TERNAUX-COMPANS (H.) Archives des voyages, *etc.* tom. 1. [1841, *etc.*] 8°. **10028.pp.9.**

—— Exemplar duarum litterarum, quibus breuiter explicantur, et nauigatio Nicolai Villagagnonis . . . in illam Americæ prouinciam, quæ vltra Æquatorem . . . extenditur: & mores . . . incolarum eius regionis. Scriptæ quidem illæ ad flumen Ganabara . . . & in Galliam missæ . . . Nunc Latio donatæ a C. C. A. [Carolus Clusius Atrebatensis, i.e. C. de l'Écluse.] *See* BRY (T. de) [America. pt. 3.] Americæ tertia pars, *etc.* 1592. fol. **C.115.h.2.(3.)**

—— [Another edition.] *See* BRY (T. de) [America. pt. 3.] Americæ tertia pars, *etc.* 1605. fol. C. **74.** g. **4.** (**3.**)

—— [Another edition.] *See* BRY (T. de) [America. pt. 3.] Historiæ Antipodum . . . pars tertia, *etc.* 1630. fol. **215.** c. **14.** (**4.**)

BARRÉ (OCTAVE) *See* BARRÉ (Antoine O.)

BARRÉ (OSCAR ÉLIE) Essai sur la typhlite. pp. 54. *Paris,* 1873. 4°. [*Collection des thèses soutenues à la Faculté de Médecine de Paris.* An 1873. tom. 1.] **7373.** o.

BARRÉ (PAUL) *See* BARRÉ (L. A.) Memento de l'architecte . . . Par L.-A. Barré . . . Avec la collaboration . . . de P. Barré, fils. 1896. 8°. **7815.** a. **38.**

—— *See* BARRÉ (L. A.) and BARRÉ (P.) Manuel de génie sanitaire. La ville salubre, *etc.* 1897. 18°. **8777.** aaa. **48.**

BARRÉ (PAUL ALPHONSE) De l'action de l'émétique sur l'économie animale . . . Thèse, *etc.* pp. 27. *Paris,* 1824. 4°. **1183.** h. **2.** (**30.**)

BARRÉ (PIERRE YON) *See* ARISTOTLE. [*Appendix.—Miscellaneous.*] Aristote amoureux . . . opéra-comique, *etc.* [By A. P. A. de Piis and P. Y. Barré.] 1780. 8°. **11738.** l. **20.** (**2.**)

—— *See* ARLEQUIN CRUELLO. Arlequin Cruello, parodie d'Othello, *etc.* [By J. B. Radet, F. G. Desfontaines and P. Y. Barré.] [1794,95.] 8°. **11738.** b. **37.** (**3.**)

—— *See* COUPIGNY (A. F. de) Hommage du petit vaudeville au grand Racine, *etc.* [By A. F. de Coupigny, P. Y. Barré and others.] [1798.] 8°. **11738.** b. **38.** (**5.**)

—— *See* DESFONTAINES (F. G.) *pseud.* Le Pari, divertissement . . . Par . . . Desfontaines, Barré, *etc.* 1797. 8°. **11738.** d. **18.** (**7.**)

—— *See* DOCTEURS. Les Docteurs modernes, comédie-parade, *etc.* [By J. B. Radet and P. Y. Barré.] 1785. 8°. **11738.** m. **6.** (**6.**)

—— *See* FEMME. La Bonne femme . . . parodie d'Alceste, *etc.* [By A. P. A. de Piis, P. Y. Barré and others.] 1776. 8°. **11738.** l. **19.** (**1.**)

—— *See* LÉANDRE-CANDIDE. Léandre-Candide . . . comédie, *etc.* [By A. P. A. de Piis, P. Y. Barré and J. B. Rozières.] 1784. 8°. **11736.** cc. **1.** (**1.**)

—— —— 1786. 8°. **11738.** l. **20.** (**3.**)

BARRÉ (PIERRE YON)

—— *See* MERCURE. Les Étrennes de Mercure . . . opéra-comique, *etc.* [By A. P. A. de Piis and P. Y. Barré.] 1781. 8°. **11738.** l. **19.** (**4.**)

—— *See* OPERA. L'Opéra de province, nouvelle parodie d'Armide, *etc.* [By A. P. A. de Piis, P. Y. Barré and J. B. D. Després.] 1777. 8°. **11738.** l. **20.** (**6.**)

— *See* PERIODICAL PUBLICATIONS.—*Paris.* Les Diners du vaudeville. [By P. Y. Barré and others.] [1797, *etc.*] 12°. P.P. **4299.** e.

—— *See* PIIS (A. P. A. de) La Vallée de Montmorency . . . opéra-comique . . . Par . . . Piis, Barré [and others], *etc.* [1799.] 8°. **11738.** b. **38.** (**6.**)

—— *See* PIIS (A. P. A. de) Voltaire . . . comédie . . . Par . . . Piis, Barré, *etc.* 1802. 8°. **11738.** l. **18.** (**12.**)

—— *See* PIIS (A. P. A. de) and BARRÉ (P. Y.) Théâtre de MM. de Piis et Barré, *etc.* 1785. 12°. **241.** a. **27.**

—— *See* PIIS (A. P. A. de) and BARRÉ (P. Y.) Les Amours d'été, divertissement, *etc.* 1781. 8°. **11740.** e. **11.** (**1.**)

—— —— 1788. 8°. **11738.** l. **18.** (**10.**)

—— *See* PIIS (A. P. A. de) and BARRÉ (P. Y.) Cassandre astrologue . . . comédie-parade, *etc.* 1781. 8°. **11738.** l. **20.** (**7.**)

—— *See* PIIS (A. P. A. de) and BARRÉ (P. Y.) Cassandre oculiste . . . comédie-parade, *etc.* 1781. 8°. **11738.** l. **19.** (**3.**)

—— *See* PIIS (A. P. A. de) and BARRÉ (P. Y.) Le Gâteau à deux fèves, divertissement, *etc.* 1782. 8°. **11738.** l. **19.** (**5.**)

—— *See* PIIS (A. P. A. de) and BARRÉ (P. Y.) La Matinée et la veillée villageoises . . . divertissement, *etc.* 1781. 8°. **11738.** l. **18.** (**7.**)

—— *See* PIIS (A. P. A. de) and BARRÉ (P. Y.) L'Oiseau perdu et retrouvé . . . opéra-comique, *etc.* 1782. 8°. **11738.** l. **20.** (**8.**)

—— *See* PIIS (A. P. A. de) and BARRÉ (P. Y.) Le Printemps, divertissement pastoral, *etc.* 1781. 8°. **11738.** l. **18.** (**8.**)

—— *See* PIIS (A. P. A. de) and BARRÉ (P. Y.) Les Quatre coins, opéra-comique, *etc.* 1783. 8°. **11738.** l. **20.** (**5.**)

—— *See* PIIS (A. P. A. de) and BARRÉ (P. Y.) Les Vendangeurs . . . divertissement, *etc.* 1781. 8°. **11738.** l. **18.** (**11.**)

—— *See* PIIS (A. P. A. de) and BARRÉ (P. Y.) Les Voyages de Rosine, opéra-comique, *etc.* 1783. 8°. **11738.** l. **19.** (**8.**)

—— *See* PROJET. Le Projet manqué, ou Arlequin taquin, parodie . . . Par les auteurs d'Arlequin afficheur [i.e. J. B. Rader and P. Y. Barré], *etc.* 1792. 8°. **11738.** b. **37.** (**2.**)

—— *See* RADET (J. B.) Abuzar . . . Parodie d'Abufar . . . Par Radet, Barré et Desfontaines. [1797.] 8°. **11738.** b. **37.** (**10.**)

—— *See* RADET (J. B.) Arlequin afficheur, comédie parade . . . Par M. M. Radet, Desfontaines et Barré. 1792. 8°. **640.** g. **12.** (**3.**)

—— —— [1795.] 8°. **11738.** b. **37.** (**1.**)

—— *See* RADET (J. B.) Favart aux Champs-Élysées, *etc.* [By J. B. Radet, F. G. Desfontaines and P. Y. Barré.] 1793. 8°. **640.** g. **13.** (**3.**)

—— *See* RADET (J. B.) and BARRÉ (P. Y.) Candide marié . . . comédie, *etc.* 1788. 8°. **11738**. m. **6**. (**2**.)

—— *See* RADET (J. B.) and BARRÉ (P. Y.) La Négresse . . . comédie, *etc.* 1787. 8°. **11738**. m. **6**. (**5**.)

—— *See* RADET (J. B.) and BARRÉ (P. Y.) Renaud d'Art, comédie, *etc.* 1788. 8°. **11738**. m. **3**. (**3**.)

—— *See* SUSANNA. La Chaste Suzanne, pièce, *etc.* [By J. B. Radet, F. G. Desfontaines and P. Y. Barré.] [1793.] 8°. **11738**. b. **37**. (**4**.)

—— *See* UNION. L'Union villageoise, scène patriotique, *etc.* [By F. G. Desfontaines, A. P. A. de Piis and P. Y. Barré.] [1794.] 8°. **11738**. b. **37**. (**8**.)

—— Les Amazones et les Scythes ; ou sauter le fossé, comédie en deux actes et en prose, mêlée de vaudevilles. Par MM. Barré, Radet et Desfontaines. pp. 51. *Paris*, 1812. 8°. **11738**. b. **42**. (**4**.)

—— Bertrand Duguesclin et sa soeur, comédie en deux actes et en prose, mêlée de vaudevilles, par MM. Barré, Radet et Desfontaines. pp. 59. *Paris*, 1804. 8°. **11738**. b. **40**. (**5**.)

—— Cassandre-Agamemnon et Colombine-Cassandre, parodie d'Agamemnon, en un acte, en prose, mêlée de vaudevilles ; by MM. Barré, Radet, Desfontaines et Armand-Gouffé. pp. 26. *Paris*, 1804. 8°. **11738**. b. **40**. (**2**.)

—— [Another copy.] **11738**. f. **36**. (**7**.)

—— Chapelain, ou la ligue des auteurs contre Boileau, comédie-vaudeville, en un acte et en prose ; par MM. Barré, Radet et Desfontaines. pp. 40. *Paris*, 1804. 8°. **11738**. b. **40**. (**1**.)

—— Le Château et la chaumière, ou les arts et la reconnaissance, comédie en trois actes et en prose, mêlée de vaudevilles, par MM. Barré, Radet et Desfontaines. pp. 68. *Paris*, 1814. 8°. **11738**. b. **41**. (**2**.)

—— Colombine mannequin, comédie-parade, en un acte, en prose, mêlée de vaudevilles ; par les cc. Barré, Radet et Desfontaines. pp. 48. *Paris*, an II [1793,94]. 8°. **11738**. b. **37**. (**6**.)

—— Les Deux Edmon, comédie en deux actes et en prose, mêlée de vaudevilles ; par MM. Baré [*sic*], Radet et Desfontaines. pp. 58 [59]. *Paris*, 1811. 8°. **11738**. b. **42**. (**2**.)

—— [Another edition.] *In :* La France dramatique au dix-neuvième siècle. tom 7. pp. 723–744. 1837. 8°. **2296**. f. **7**. (**33**.)

—— Les Deux lions, vaudeville en un acte, par MM. Barré, Picard, Radet et Desfontaines. pp. 45. *Paris*, 1810. 8°. **11738**. b. **41**. (**10**.)

—— Les Deux n'en font qu'un, comédie en un acte et en prose, mêlée de vaudevilles, suivie d'un divertissement à l'occasion de la paix ; par MM. Barré, Radet et Desfontaines. pp. 56. *Paris*, 1806. 8°. **11738**. b. **40**. (**9**.)

—— Dugai-Trouin, prisonier à Plymouth, fait historique en deux actes, par MM. Barré, Radet, Desfontaines et Saint-Félix. pp. 43. *Paris*, 1804. 8°. **11738**. b. **40**. (**4**.)

—— [Another copy.] **11738**. e. **36**. (**1**.)

—— Les Écriteaux, ou René le sage à la foire Saint-Germain, pièce anecdotique en deux actes et en prose, mêlée de vaudevilles ; par MM. Barré, Radet et Desfontaines. pp. 64. *Paris*, 1806. 8°. **11738**. b. **40**. (**8**.)

—— Enfin nous y voilà, divertissement en un acte, par les auteurs des Diners du vaudeville [i.e. P. Y. Barré, J. B. Radet and F. G. Desfontaines]. pp. 49. [1801.] 8°. *See* ENFIN. **11738**. b. **39**. (**5**.)

—— Gaspard l'avisé, comédie-anecdote en un acte, en prose et en vaudeville, par MM. Barré, Radet et Desfontaines. pp. 36. *Paris*, 1812. 8°. **11738**. b. **42**. (**6**.)

—— Gessner, comédie en deux actes et en prose, mêlée de vaudevilles, par les c^ens^ Barré, Radet, Desfontaines, Bourgueil. pp. 79. *Paris*, 1800. 8°. **11738**. b. **39**. (**4**.)

—— [Another copy.] **11738**. bbb. **8**. (**3**.)

—— La Girouette de Saint-Cloud, impromptu en un acte, en prose, mêlé de vaudevilles, par les cc. Barré, Radet [and others], *etc.* pp. 32. *Paris*, an VIII [1800]. 8°. **11738**. b. **39**. (**1**.)

—— [Another copy.] **11738**. e. **1**. (**10**.)

—— [Another copy.] F. **434**. (**2**.)

—— L'Heureuse décade, divertissement patriotique, en un acte et en vaudevilles, des citoyens Barré, Léger et Rosières . . . Seconde édition. pp. 31. *Paris*, an II [1794]. 8°. **11738**. h. **13**. (**11**.)

—— [Another copy.] **11738**. b. **37**. (**5**.)

—— L'Hôtel de la Paix, rue de la Victoire, à Paris, comédie-vaudeville en un acte, suivie d'un divertissement de circonstance ; par MM. Barré, Radet, Desfontaines et Dieu-la-foi. pp. 53. *Paris*, 1807. 8°. **11738**. b. **41**. (**5**.)

—— [Another copy.] **11738**. bbb. **8**. (**5**.)

—— L'Isle de la mégalanthropogénésie, ou les savans de naissance, vaudeville en un acte. Par MM. Barré, Radet, Desfontaines et Dieulafoi. pp. 43. *Paris*, 1807. 8°. **11738**. b. **41**. (**4**.)

—— La Megalantropogenesia, ossia l'Isola sapiente : commedia . . . trasportata ad uso del teatro italiano dal signor L. Bossi. pp. 48. *Venezia*, 1807. 8°. [*Terza Raccolta in continuazione all' Anno teatrale.* tom. 6.] **639**. d. **11**. (**5**.)

—— Lantara, ou le peintre au cabaret. Vaudeville en un acte, par MM. Y. Barré, L. Picard, J. Radet, et F. Desfontaines . . . Seconde édition. pp. 40. *Paris*, 1812. 8°. **11738**. b. **41**. (**8**.)

—— Laujon de retour à l'ancien caveau, vaudeville . . . par les convives du caveau moderne [i.e. P. Y. Barré, J. B. Radet and F. G. Desfontaines]. pp. 47. 1811. 8°. *See* LAUJON (P.) **11738**. b. **42**. (**3**.)

—— Les Limites, comédie en un acte mêlée de vaudevilles ; par MM. Barré, Radet et Desfontaines. pp. 32. *Paris*, 1812. 8°. **11738**. b. **42**. (**5**.)

—— M. Durelief, ou petite revue des embellissemens de Paris ; en prose et en vaudevilles ; par MM. Barré, Radet et Desfontaines. pp. 32. *Paris*, 1810. 8°. **11738**. b. **41**. (**9**.)

—— M. Guillaume, ou le voyageur inconnu, comédie en un acte et en prose, mêlée de vaudevilles . . . Par les c^ens^ Barré, Radet, Desfontaines, Bourgueil. Troisième édition. pp. 80. *Paris*, 1801. 8°. **11738**. b. **39**. (**3**.)

—— [Another edition.] pp. 48. *Paris*, 1818. 8°. **11738**. bbb. **8**. (**2**.)

BARRÉ (Pierre Yon)

—— De Heer Willem, ofde Onbekende reiziger. Blijspel naar het Fransche van Barré, Radet, Desfontaines en Bourgueil. *In:* Spectatoriaale Schouwburg. dl. 27. pp. 269–338. 1800. 8°. **11754. c. 4.**

—— Il Signor Guglielmo Farsa . . . Traduzione inedita del signor G. Piazza. pp. 41. *Venezia,* 1804. 8°. [*Anno teatrale.* Anno 1. tom. 4.] **639. b. 22.**

—— Le Mai des jeunes filles, ou un passage de militaires, divertissement en un acte. Par MM. Barré, Radet et Desfontaines. pp. 40. *Paris,* 1807. 8°. **11738. b. 41. (3.)**

—— Le Mariage de Scarron, comédie en un acte et en prose, mêlée de vaudevilles. Par MM. Barré, Radet et Desfontaines. pp. 48. *Paris,* 1809. 8°. **11738. b. 38. (3.)**

—— Monet, Directeur de l'Opéra-Comique, comédie en un acte et en vaudevilles ; par les citoyens Baré [*sic*], Radet et Desfontaines. pp. 40. *Paris,* 1802. 8°. **11738. b. 38. (8.)**

—— La Nouvelle télegraphique, vaudeville en un acte, de MM. Barré, Radet et Desfontaines. pp. 38. *Paris,* 1811. 8°. **11738. b. 42. (1.)**

—— Omazette, ou Jozet en Champagne. Parodie d'Omasis, ou Joseph en Égypte, vaudeville en un acte, par MM. Barré, Radet, Desfontaines et Dieulafoy. pp. 36. *Paris,* 1807. 8°. **11738. b. 40. (10.)**

—— Le Peintre français à Londres, comédie anecdotique en un acte et en prose, mêlée de vaudevilles. Par les cens Barré, Radet, Desfontaines et Bourgueil. pp. 40. *Paris,* 1802. 8°. **11738. b. 39. (7.)**

—— Nouvelle édition. pp. 32. *Paris,* 1814. 8°. **11738. b. 42. (8.)**

—— [Another copy.] **11738. bbb. 8. (4.)**

—— Le Peintre français en Espagne, ou le dernier soupir de l'Inquisition, comédie-vaudeville, en un acte, par MM. Barré, Radet, Desfontaines. pp. 39. *Paris,* 1809. 8°. **11738. b. 41. (6.)**

—— Un Petit voyage du Vaudeville, divertissement en un acte, pour le retour de la paix . . . Par MM. Baré [sic], Radet et Desfontaines, etc. pp. 35. *Paris,* 1814. 8°. **11738. b. 42. (7.)**

—— Le Procès du fandango, ou la fandangomanie, comédie-vaudeville en un acte ; par MM. Barré, Radet et Desfontaines . . . Seconde édition. pp. 31. *Paris,* 1810. 8°. **11738. b. 41. (7.)**

—— La Récréation du monde, suite de la Création, mélodrame, musique d'Haydn, mêlée de vaudevilles, par les . . . CC. Barré, Radet et Desfontaines. pp. 25. *Paris,* an IX [1800, 01.] 8°. **11738. b. 39. (2.)**

—— René le sage, ou C'est bien la Turcaret, comédie en un acte, en prose et en vaudevilles. Des citoyens Barré, Radet, Deschamps, D * * [i.e. J. B. D. Desprès]. pp. 43. *Paris,* 1802. 8°. **11738. b. 39. (8.)**

—— Le Rêve, ou la colonne de Rosbach, divertissement en un acte, en prose et en vaudevilles, par MM. Barré, Radet, Desfontaines. pp. 24. *Paris,* 1808. 8°. **11738. b. 41. (1.)**

—— Sophie Arnould, comédie en trois actes et en prose, mêlée de vaudevilles, par MM. Barré, Radet et Desfontaines. pp. 83. *Paris,* 1805. 8°. **11738. b. 40. (6.)**

—— La Tapisserie de la reine Mathilde, comédie, en un acte, en prose, mêlée de vaudevilles ; par MM. Barré, Radet et Desfontaines . . . Seconde édition. pp. 28. *Paris,* 1804. 8°. **11738. b. 40. (3.)**

BARRÉ (Pierre Yon)

—— La Tragédie au Vaudeville, en un acte, mêlée de couplets ; suivie de Après la confession, la pénitence : petit épilogue, *etc.* [By P. Y. Barré, J. B. Radet and F. G. Desfontaines.] pp. 49. [1801.] 8°. *See* Tragédie. **11738. b. 39. (6.)**

—— Les Trois Saphos lyonnaises, ou une cour d'amour, comédie-vaudeville, en deux actes, par MM. Barré, Radet et Desfontaines. pp. 46. *Paris,* 1815. 8°. **11738. b. 42. (9.)**

—— Le Vaudeville au camp de Boulogne, prologue-impromptu, par MM. Barré, Radet et Desfontaines. pp. 23. *Boulogne* [c. 1805.] 8°. **11738. b. 40. (7.)**

BARRÉ (Pierre Yon) and BOURGUEIL (N.)

—— Le Mur mitoyen, ou le divorce manqué, comédie-vaudevilles [*sic*] en un acte. pp. 40. *Paris,* 1802. 8°. **11738. b. 38. (2.)**

BARRÉ (Pierre Yon) and LÉGER (François Pierre Auguste)

—— Le Sourd guéri, ou les tu et les vous, comédie en un acte, mêlée de vaudevilles. pp. 36. *Paris,* an III [1795]. 8°. **11738. b. 37. (9.)**

—— [Another copy.] **11738. h. 13. (10.)**

BARRÉ (Pierre Yon) and OURRY (E. T. Maurice)

—— La Danse interrompue, vaudeville en un acte. pp. 35. *Paris,* an IX [1801]. 8°. **11738. k. 25. (4.)**

—— [Another edition.] pp. 32. *Paris,* 1805. 8°. **11738. b. 38. (1.)**

BARRÉ (René François Jacques) Corps Législatif. Conseil des Anciens. Rapport fait . . . sur l'application des dispositions de la loi du 24 messidor, sur la répression du brigandage, au département de la Sarthe. Séance du premier jour complémentaire. pp. 4. *Paris,* an 7 [1799]. 8°. **R. 652. (7.)**

BARRE (S. M.) A New Plan of Creamery Work and the Patron's Hand Book. How centralization and farm pasteurization will solve the creamery problem. pp. 93. [*Winnipeg,* 1903.] 8°. **07945. i. 40.**

—— The Twentieth Century Creamery. How centralization and pasteurization will solve the creamery problem. (Manitoba special edition.) pp. 64. [*Winnipeg,*] 1903. 8°. **07293. k. 34.**

—— Plan de centralisation de l'industrie laitière applicable à la province de Québec, *etc.* [1908.] 8°. **7074. l. 16. (4.)**

BARRE (Uttere) Avondale of Avondale. A political romance. 3 vol. *Remington & Co.: London,* 1877. 8°. **12634. b. 1.**

BARRE (W. L.) The Life and Public Services of Millard Fillmore. pp. 408. *Wanzer, McKim & Co.: Buffalo,* 1856. 8°. **10882. b. 4.**

BARRE (William) Apologues, or moral tales, fables, &c. in verse. pp. 108. *The Author: London,* 1815. 12°. **11643. f. 46.**

—— The Months ; a rural poem ; and other pieces : with illustrative notes. pp. 71. *The Author: London,* 1813. 12°. **T. 409. (9.)**

—— [Another copy.] **11642. aa. 62. (2.)**

—— Second edition. pp. 47. *The Author: London,* 1825. 12°. **4422. h. 23. (6.)**

BARRE (WILLIAM)

—— Original Hymns, for the use of infants' schools. pp. 38. *Houlston & Son: Wellington, Salop,* 1829. 24°. **T. 1433. (2.)**

—— Poems, sacred and serious. With occasional notes. pp. 90. *The Author: London,* 1812. 12°. **11642. aa. 62. (1.)**

—— Tales, Fables, &c. [In verse.] pp. 104. *The Author: London,* 1814. 12°. **11642. aa. 62. (3.)**

BARRE (WILLIAM H.)

—— Poems, sacred and serious, *etc.* pp. 94. *J. Briscoe: London,* 1842. 12°. **11603. i. 47.**

BARRÉ (WILLIAM VINCENT) History of the French Consulate under Napoleon Buonaparte: being an authentic narrative of his administration . . . including a sketch of his life. The whole interspersed with curious anecdotes and a faithful statement of interesting transactions until the renewal of hostilities in 1803. [With an engraved portrait of Napoleon.] pp. viii. 535. *Thomas Hurst: London,* 1804. 8°. **285. l. 27.**

—— Monologue de l'empereur jaune, le nommé Napoleone Buonaparte . . . sur la destruction de son digne émule et rivale, l'empereur noir, le nommé Jacques Dessalines, par la légion d'honneur de l'armée noire de St. Domingue, le 16 octobre, 1806. Traduit du Corse par Guillaume Barré. [An original composition in verse by W. V. Barré.] [1806.] fol. *See* NAPOLEON I., *Emperor of the French.* [*Appendix.*] **1870. d. 1. (206.)**

—— The Rise, Progress, Decline and Fall of Buonaparte's Empire in France. [With a portrait of Napoleon.] pp. xvi. 590. *J. Badcock: London,* 1805. 8°. **8026. c. 12.**

BARREAU. Barreau Français. *See also* FRANCE.—*Barreau.*

—— Barreau français. Annales de l'éloquence judiciaire en France. *See* PERIODICAL PUBLICATIONS.—*Paris.*

BARREAU (CLAUDE FRANÇOIS) *See* PERÉE ( ) Tribunat. Rapport fait . . . sur la réclamation du citoyen Barreau, *etc.* [1801.] 8°. **F.R. 99. (46.)**

BARREAU (DAVID) *See* BARRAU.

BARREAU (FÉLIX CONSTANT) De l'avantage sous le rapport hygiénique de l'emploi de l'armée aux travaux d'utilité publique. Thèse, *etc.* pp. 58. *Montpellier,* 1847. 4°. **7379. a. 2. (11.)**

BARREAU (FERDINAND) Le Magnétisme humain en cour de Rome et en cour de cassation, sous le rapport religieux, moral et scientifique, suivi d'une méthode pratique, *etc.* pp. 308. *Paris,* 1845. 12°. **1404. b. 13.**

BARREAU (FRANÇOIS HAMPTONNE)

—— *See* ENGLAND. [*Miscellaneous Public Documents.*—I.] Documents relatifs aux Iles de la Manche tirés des rôles des Lettres closes . . . 1205–1327. Édités par F. H. Barreau et H. M. Godfray. 1891, *etc.* 4°. [*Société Jersiaise. Publication.* no. 9.] **Ac. 8140.**

BARREAU (JACQUES) Réflexions sur la catalepsie, *etc.* pp. 18. *Montpellier,* 1805. 4°. **1180. f. 2. (9.)**

BARREAU (JULES LOUIS) Guide du voyageur dans la ville de Bourges et spécialement dans la cathédrale. pp. iv. 128. *Bourges,* 1863. 12°. **4632. aaa. 17.**

BARREAU (RENÉ) Les Obligations de conscience en droit civil. Doctrine, législation, jurisprudence. pp. x. 306. *Angers,* 1915. 8°. **5408. aa. 22.**

BARREAU (ROBERT)

—— Le Syndicalisme en Espagne. pp. 146. *Toulouse,* 1934. 8°. **8042. i. 39.**

BARRECHEGUREN (CONCHITA) *See* BARRECHEGUREN Y GARCÍA (M. de la C.)

BARRECHEGUREN Y GARCÍA (MARÍA DE LA CONCEPCIÓN)

—— *See* ITÚRBIDE (D. de F.) Flor de Granada. Historia documentada y completa de Conchita Barrecheguren seguida de sus escritos. [With portraits.] 1935. 8°. **010160. g. 11.**

BARREDA (ANTONIO) *See* SÁNCHEZ FEIJOO (J.) Vindicacion del corredor de número J. Sanchez Feijoo sobre las injurias que le infirió D. A. Barreda. 1840. 4°. **8244. bbb. 37. (10.)**

BARREDA (ANTONIO DE LA TORRE Y) *See* TORRE Y BARREDA.

BARREDA (CÁSTULO) Alegato de bien probado hecho por el Licenciado Don C. Barreda en el juicio promovido por el representante de . . . Francisca Villanueva y Zaldivar de Sevilla contra . . . Eugenia Ouvrard é hijo, sobre indemnizacion de los perjuicios causados por el incendio de la casa num. 3 de la 1ª Calle de Plateros, *etc.* pp. 51. *México,* 1865. 8°. **6784. b. 7. (11.)**

—— Oracion cívica pronunciada en la noche del 15 de Setiembre de 1853. pp. 11. *México,* 1853. 8°. **12301. d. 3. (19.)**

BARREDA (CONSALVUS) Consalvi Barredae . . . De vini temperatura præmissam Fracastorij sententiam perpendens libellus. *See* FRACASTORO (G.) Hieronimi Fracastorii . . . De temperatura vini sententia, *etc.* 1553. 4°. **7942. bbb. 52.**

BARREDA (DOMINGO) Prevencion conveniente que habiendose hecho a los Religiosos del Orden de Santo Domingo, la dirige ahora . . . al juicioso público . . . Fr. D. Barreda. pp. 28. *México,* 1810. 4°. **9770. aaa. 13. (17.)**

BARREDA (FELIPE A.)

—— Manuel Pardo Ribadeneira, regente de la Real Audiencia del Cuzco. [With plates, including a portrait.] pp. 152. *Lima,* 1954. 8°. **10634.h.35.**

BARREDA (FERNANDO)

—— *See* CAGIGAS (D. de las) El Ataque de Nelson a Tenerife, *etc.* [Edited by F. Barreda.] 1936. 8°. **09077. aaa. 52.**

—— Comercio marítimo entre los Estados Unidos y Santander, 1778–1829. pp. 99. [*Santander*], 1950. 8°. **08229. p. 85.**

One of the "Publicaciones del Centro de Estudios Montañeses."

BARREDA (FRANCISCO DE) *See* LEÓN PINELO (A. de) Tratado de Confirmaciones Reales de Encomiendas, *etc.* [With an introduction by F. de Barreda.] 1630. 4°. **C.96.b.8.**

BARREDA (GABRIEL DE) Por el Estado Eclesiastico destos Reynos con el señor Fiscal [in a suit relating to the payment of tithes]. ff. 4. [*Mexico,* 1650?] fol. **5125. g. 7. (8.)**

BARREDA (IÑIGO DE) Oña y su Real Monasterio, hoy Colegio de PP. Jesuitas, según la descripción inédita del monje de Oña Fr. I. de Barreda. Introducción y notas históricas y artísticas por el P. E. Herrera y Oria . . . 43 fotograbados, *etc.* pp. viii. 193. *Madrid,* 1917. 8°. **07816. aa. 17.**

BARREDA (JOSÉ MANUEL DE GOYENECHE Y) *Count de Guaqui.* *See* GOYENECHE Y BARREDA.

BARREDA (JOSÉ PARDO Y) *See* PARDO Y BARREDA.

BARREDA (JOSÉ SEBASTIAN DE GOYENECHE Y) *Archbishop of Lima.* *See* GOYENECHE Y BARREDA.

BARREDA (LUIS) Cancionero Montañés. pp. 59. *Madrid*, 1898. 8º. **011451**. de. **2**.

—— Romancero de Carlos Quinto. pp. 192. *Madrid*, 1918. 8º. **011451**. eee. **63**.

BARREDA BRACHO (ROQUE JACINTO DE LA) *See* PÉREZ DE VILLA REAL (C. F.) Por D. Roque Jacinto de la Barredo Bracho [and others] . . . en la causa criminal, que contra ellos se ha seguido, por la muerte à azotes de B. de la Concepcion, *etc.* [1700?] fol. **6785**. k. **2**. (**5**.)

BARREDA LAOS (FELIPE)

—— Dos Américas: dos mundos. pp. 165. *Madrid*, 1952. 8º. **8008**. dd. **64**.
Part of the "Colección Hombres e Ideas."

—— Segunda emancipación de América Hispana. pp. 360. *Buenos Aires*, 1947. 8º. **9773**. aaa. **25**.

BARREDA LYNCH (JULIO) *See* PELLIZA (M. A.) La Organización Nacional. Con una introducción de J. Barreda Lynch. 1923. 8º. **9774**. c.1/15.

BARRÉ DE SAINT-VENANT (ADHÉMAR JEAN CLAUDE) *See* CLEBSCH (R. F. A.) Théorie de l'élasticité des corps solides . . . Traduite par MM. Barré de Saint-Venant . . . et Flamant . . . Avec des notes . . . de M. de Saint-Venant. 1883. 8º. **8705**. ff. **7**.

—— Résistance des fluides: considérations historiques, physiques et pratiques rélatives au problème de l'action dynamique mutuelle d'un fluide et d'un solide, *etc.* (Mémoire sur la perte de force vive d'un fluide aux endroits où sa section d'écoulement augmente brusquement ou rapidement.—Mémoire sur la prise en considération de la force centrifuge dans le calcul du mouvement des eaux courantes, *etc.* [With a preface by J. Boussinesq.] pp. 280. 1888. *See* PARIS.—*Académie des Sciences.* Mémoires, *etc.* sér. 2. tom. 44. 1833, *etc.* 4º. **Ac.424/2.(2.)**

—— De la torsion des prismes, avec des considérations sur leur flexion, ainsi que sur l'équilibre des solides élastiques en général, et des formules pratiques pour le calcul de leur résistance à divers efforts s'exerçant simultanément. pp. xx. 332. *Paris*, 1855. 4º. **8715**. f. **30**.

—— Saint Benezet, patron des ingénieurs. Par A. Barré de Saint-Venant . . . Œuvre posthume publiée par ses enfants. pp. xiii. 154. *Bourges*, 1889. 8º. **4829**. df. **15**.

BARREIRA (ISIDORO DE) Tractado das significacoens das plantas, flores, e fructos que se referem na Sagrada Escriptura, *etc.* pp. 582. *P. Craesbeec: Lisboa*, 1622. 4º. **1010**. c. **7**.

BARREIRA (JOÃO)

—— Arte portuguesa. *Lisboa*, [1948?– .] fol. W.P. **3204**.
Published in parts.

BARREIRO (AGUSTÍN JESÚS)

—— *See* ANDRÉS (M.) Relación del Viaje de Marcelino Andrés por las Costas de África . . . Publícalo . . . A. J. Barreiro. 1932. 8º. **010028**. k. **28**.

—— See CALDAS Y TENORIO (F. J. de) Relación de un Viaje hecho a Cotacache, *etc.* [Edited by A. J. Barreiro.] 1933. 8º. **10482**. dd. **11**.

BARREIRO (AGUSTÍN JESÚS)

—— *See* HEULAND (C.) E Viaje científico de Conrado y Cristián Heuland a Chile y Peru . . . Publícalo . . . A. Barreiro. 1929. 8º. **10482**. h. **24**.

—— *See* JIMÉNEZ DE LA ESPADA (M.) Diario de la Expedición al Pacífico . . . Publícalo . . . adicionado con notas, el P. A. J. Barreiro. 1928. 8º. Ac. **6018/12**.

—— *See* RUIZ LOPEZ (H.) Relación del Viaje hecho a los Reynos del Perú y Chile . . . Revisada y anotada por . . . A. J. Barreiro. 1931. 8º. Ac. **2825**. b.

—— **See RUIZ LÓPEZ (H.) Relación histórica del viage, que hizo a los reynos del Perú y Chile el botánico D. Hipólito Ruiz . . . Hallado y revisado por . . . A. J. Barreiro . . . Segunda edición, emendada y completada . . . por el Dr. Jaime Jaramillo-Arango. 1952. 8º.** **10481**. w. **12**.

—— *See* RUIZ LOPEZ (H.) Travels of Ruiz, Pavón, and Dombey in Peru and Chile, 1777–1788 . . . With an epilogue and official documents added by A. J. Barreiro, *etc.* 1940. 8º. [*Field Museum of Natural History. Botanical Series.* vol. 21.] Ac. **1738/2**.

—— *See* SANTA CRUZ Y CÁRDENAS (J. de) *Count de San Juan de Jaruco* and *de Mopox.* Documentos relativos a la Expedición del Conde de Mopox a la Isla de Cuba durante los años 1796 a 1802. Publicados . . . por el P. Barreiro. 1933. 8º. **10482**. cc. **23**.

—— Discurso leído en el acto de su recepción por . . . A. J. Barreiro (Características de la Fauna y de la Flora filipinas y labor española en el estudio de las mismas) . . . y Contestación del académico D. Ignacio Bolívar, *etc.* pp. 126. 1928. 8º. *See* MADRID.—*Real Academia de Ciencias exactas, físicas y naturales.* Ac. **2825/5**. (**4**.)

—— Discurso leído en la Universidad Central para obtener el grado de Doctor en Ciencias Naturales. (Estudio psicológico y antropológico de la raza malayo-filipina desde el punto de vista de su lenguaje.) pp. 134. *Valladolid*, [1910.] 8º. **10006**. r. **8**.

—— Historia de la Comisión Científica del Pacífico, 1862 a 1865 . . . Con 47 laminas y 3 mapas. pp. xvi. 525. 1926. 8º. *See* MADRID.—*Instituto Nacional de Ciencias físico-naturales.—Museo de Ciencias naturales.* **07001**. h. **33**.

—— El Origen de la raza indígena de las Islas Carolinas, *etc.* pp. 131. *Madrid*, 1920. 8º. **010007**. ee. **39**.

—— Los Trabajos inéditos del Dr. Francisco Hernández sobre la gea y la fauna mejicanas. [Extracted from the proceedings of the Asociación Española para el Progreso de las Ciencias.] *Madrid*, [1929.] 8º. **7208**. g. **39**.

BARREIRO (ALEJO) *See* MEXICO. [*Appendix.*] Apuntes para la Historia de la Guerra entre Mexico y los Estados-Unidos. (Redactores: Alcaraz . . . Barreiro . . . Castillo.) 1848. 4º. **9771**. f. **20**.

BARREIRO (ANTONIO) *See* PINO (P. B.) Noticias historicas . . . del Nuevo-México . . . Adicionadas por . . . A. Barreiro, *etc.* 1849. 8º. **10480**. bb. **13**.

—— Ojeada sobre Nuevo-México, *etc.* [A facsimile of the edition of 1832.] pp. 42. 10. *See* PINO (P. B.) Three New Mexico Chronicles. The Exposición of Don P. B. Pino 1812; the Ojeada of Lic. A. Barreiro 1832; and the additions by Don J. A. de Escudero, 1849. Translated . . . by H. B. Carroll, J. V. Haggard. 1942. 8º. Ac. **8534/3**.

BARREIRO (JUAN MANUEL DÍAZ) *See* DÍAZ BARREIRO.

BARREIRO (LISARDO R.) Esbozos y Siluetas de un viaje por Galicia. pp. 270. *Coruña*, 1890. 8°. [*Biblioteca Gallega*. no. 24.] **12231**. g.

BARREIRO (LUIS MARÍA)

—— Educación integral o alfabetización? pp. 17. *Instituto Social: Santa Fe*, 1947. 8°. **8313**. aa. **21**.

BARREIRO (MIGUEL) Discurso pronunciado . . . la noche del 15 de Setiembre de 1865, *etc*. pp. 9. *Mérida*, 1865. 8°. **12301**. d. **9**. (**20**.)

—— Porvenir de Yucatan, y ligera ojeada sobre su situacion actual. pp. 76. *Mérida*, 1864. 16°. **8179**. a. **15**.

BARREIRO DE V. V. (BERNARDO) *See* MACIÑEIRA Y PARDO (F.) Crónicas de Ortigueira. [With a preface by B. Barreiro de V. V.] 1892. 8°. **10161**. bbb. **24**.

—— Brujos y Astrólogos de la Inquisicion de Galicia, y el famoso Libro de San Cipriano. pp. lxii. 162. *Coruña*, 1885. 8°. **4071**. bbb. **25**.

BARREIROS (EDUARDO MONTUFAR) *See* MONTUFAR BARREIROS.

BARREIROS (FORTUNATO JOZE) Ensaio sobre os principios geraes de strategia e de grande tactica. pp. viii. 191. 1837. 8°. *See* LISBON.—*Academia das Sciencias de Lisboa*, *etc*. **717**. d. **49**.

—— Memoria sobre os pesos e medidas de Portugal, Espanha, Inglaterra e França, que se empragão nos trabalhos do Corpo de Engenheiros, *etc*. pp. xii. 80. 1838. 4°. *See* LISBON.—*Academia das Sciencias de Lisboa, etc.* **1397**. g. **25**.

—— Principios geraes de Castrametaçao, *etc*. [With plates.] pp. viii. 128. 1838. 8°. *See* LISBON.—*Academia das Sciencias de Lisboa, etc.* **1397**. g. **14**.

BARREIROS (GASPAR) Chorographia de alguns lugares que stam em hum caminho, que fez G. Barreiros ó anno de M.D.XXXXVJ. começãdo na cidade de Badajoz em Castella, te á de Milam em Italia, cõ algũas outras obras, *etc*. (Censuras . . . sobre quatro liuros intitulados em M. Portio Catam de Originibus, em Beroso Chaldæo, em Manethon Ægyptio, & em Q. Fabio Pictor Romano.—Commentarius de Ophyra regione apud diuinam scripturam cõmemorata, *etc*.—Garsias Manesius Eborensis præsul, quum Lusitaniæ regio inclyti legatus, & regiæ classis aduersus Turcas Hydruntē in Apulia pręsidio tenentes præfectus ad Vrbem accederet, in tēplo diui Pauli publicè exceptus, apud Xistũ .iiij. Ponti. Max. & apud sacrum Cardinalium senatum, huiuscemodi orationem habuit.) 4 pt. *I. Aluarez: Coimbra*, 1561. 4°. C. **62**. b. **35**.

—— [Another copy of pt. 1.] G. **7308**.

—— Censura in quendam auctorem, qui sub falsa inscriptione Berosi Chaldaei circunfertur. pp. 73. *Romæ*, 1565. 4°. **1103**. c. **16**. (**1**.)

The titlepage and last leaf are slightly mutilated.

—— [Another edition.] pp. 46. *Apud H. Commelinum: [Heidelberg,]* 1598. 8°. **1089**. k. **31**.

—— [A reissue.] *See* BONUTIUS (J.) Historia antiqua, *etc*. 1599. 8°. **802**. d. **31**.

—— [Another edition.] 1622. *See* LA BIGNE (M. de) Magna bibliotheca veterum patrum, *etc*. tom. 15. 1618, *etc*. fol. **469.e.15.**

—— [Another edition.] 1677. *See* LA BIGNE (M. de) Maxima bibliotheca veterum patrum, *etc*. tom. 12. pt. 1. 1677, *etc*. fol. **464**. f. **2**.

—— [Another edition.] *See* COLLECTIO. Nova librorum rariorum conlectio. fasc. 1. 1709, *etc*. 8°. **271**. a. **1**.

BARREIROS (GASPAR)

—— Censura contro un certo autore che va circolando sotto la falsa denominazione di Beroso Caldeo. [With notes and commentaries by G. G. Martinetti.] *Lat. & Ital.* 1827. *See* MARTINETTI (G. G.) Collezione classica, ossia tesoro delle antichità giudaiche, *etc*. tom. 4. 1824, *etc*. 8°. **1305**. c. **7**.

—— De Ophira regione in Sacris Literis disputatio. *See* CANINIUS (A.) De locis S. Scripturæ Hebraicis A. Caninii commentarius, *etc*. 1600. 8°. **1006**. c. **3**.

—— [Another edition.] *See* AMERICA. Novus Orbis, *etc*. 1616. 8°. **1060**. a. **23**. (**1, 2**.)

—— [Another edition.] *See* PONTANUS (J. I.) Joh. Isacii Pontani discussionum historicarum libri duo, *etc*. 1637. 8°. **1128**. b. **2**.

—— [Another edition.] *See* PEARSON (John) *Bishop of Chester*. Critici sacri, *etc*. tom. 8. 1660. fol. **C.80.k.8.**

—— [Another edition.] *See* PEARSON (John) *Bishop of Chester*. Critici sacri, *etc*. tom. 2. 1698. fol. **4**. f. **3**.

BARREIROS (JOAQUIM ANTONIO VELLEZ) *See* VELLEZ BARREIROS.

BARREIROS (MANUEL DE AGUIAR) *See* AGUIAR BARREIROS.

BARREIROS E SANTOS ( )

—— O Exercício da medicina e os planos que sobre ele se anunciam. (Separata da revista A Medicina contemporânea.) *Lisboa*, 1946. 8°. **7681**. b. **52**.

—— Medicina social. Algumas palavras . . . Separata da revista A Medicina contemporânea, *etc*. [*Lisboa*, 1945.] 8°. **7383**. p. **18**.

BARREL DE PONTEVÈS (JOSEPH ÉMILE DE) Des nerfs vaso-moteurs et de la circulation capillaire, *etc*. pp. 114. *Paris*, 1864. 4°. [*Collection des thèses soutenues à la Faculté de Médecine de Paris*. An 1864. tom. 1.] **7373**. e. **12**.

BARRELET (TH.) Das Liebeswesen der Diakonie in der franz.-reformierten Gemeinde zu Hamburg, 1686–1750. Von Pastor Th. Barrelet, mit der gütigen Mitwirkung von O. Vigouroux. pp. 24. *Magdeburg*, 1906. 8°. [*Geschichtsblätter des Deutschen Hugenotten-Vereins*. Bd. 13. Hft. 3, 4.] Ac. **2032**.

—— Zur Geschichte der französisch-reformierten Gemeinde in Hamburg, *etc*. pp. 42. *Magdeburg*, 1904. 8°. [*Geschichtsblätter des Deutschen Hugenotten-Vereins*. Bd. 12. Hft. 7, 8.] Ac. **2032**.

BARRELIER (JACQUES) *See* BARRELIERUS (Jacobus)

BARRELIERUS (JACOBUS) Plantæ per Galliam, Hispaniam et Italiam observatæ, iconibus æneis exhibitæ . . . Opus posthumum, accurante Antonio de Jussieu . . . Cui accessit ejusdem auctoris Specimen de insectis quibusdam marinis, mollibus, crustaceis & testaceis. MS. NOTES. *Parisiis*, 1714. fol. **438**. m. **12**.

With an additional titlepage, engraved.

—— [Another copy.] **449**. k. **17**.

—— [Another copy.] **36**. g. **10**.

BARRELL (FRANCIS RICHARD) *See* ALDOUS (John C. P.) An Elementary Course of Physics, *etc*. (Magnetism, Electricity, by F. R. Barrell.) 1898. 8°. **8771.aa.20/7.**

—— Elementary Geometry. 3 pt. pp. ix. 360. *Longmans & Co.: London*, 1903, 04. 8°. **8529**. de. **36**.

BARRELL (George) The Pedestrian in France and Switzerland. pp. 312. *G. P. Putnam & Co.: New York,* 1853. 8°. **10105**. c. **28**.

BARRELL (Gilbert) *See* Grant (William) *Vicar of Isleworth, Middlesex.* The Vindication of the Vicar of Istleworth . . . Whereunto are likewise added, Certaine notorious impieties and misdemeanours of G. Barrell, *etc.* 1644. 4°. E. **170**. (**9**.)

BARRELL (Joseph) *Merchant, of Boston. See* Ford (Worthington C.) Boston in 1775. Letters from General Washington . . . Joseph Barrell. 1892. 8°. **10902**. f. **33**. (**2**.)

BARRELL (Joseph) *Professor of Philosophy, Beloit College.*

—— A Philosophical Study of the Human Mind. pp. xii. 575. pl. 5. *Philosophical Library: New York,* [1954.] 8°. **8475**. bb. **35**.

BARRELL (Joseph) *Professor of Structural Geology in Yale College.*

—— *See* Schuchert (Charles) Biographical Memoir of Joseph Barrell, 1869–1919, *etc.* [With a portrait and a bibliography.] 1929. 8°. [*National Academy of Sciences. Biographical Memoirs.* vol. 12.] A.S. **939/2**.

—— Central Connecticut in the Geologic Past. pp. 44. *Hartford,* 1915. 8°. [*Connecticut State Geological and Natural History Survey. Bulletin.* no. 23.] **A.S.c.94.**

—— Geology of the Marysville Mining District, Montana, *etc.* pp. x. 178. *Washington,* 1907. 4°. [*U.S. Geological Survey. Professional Paper.* no. 57.] A.S. **209/6**.

—— The Nature and Environment of the Lower Cambrian Sediments of the Southern Appalachians. (From The American Journal of Science.) pp. 20. [*New Haven, Connecticut,*] 1925. 8°. **07106**. ee. **47**.

—— Origin and Significance of the Mauch Chunk Shale. 1907. *See* United States of America.—*Geological Society of America.* Bulletin, *etc.* vol. 18. 1890, *etc.* 8°. Ac. **3187**.

—— The Origin of the Earth. *See* Lull (Richard S.) The Evolution of the Earth and its Inhabitants, *etc.* 1918. 8°. **7001**. s. **22**.

—— [Another edition.] *See* Lull (Richard S.) The Evolution of the Earth and Man, *etc.* 1929. 8°. **7002**. cc. **12**.

BARRELL (Joseph) *Professor of Structural Geology in Yale College,* and **LOUGHLIN** (Gerald Francis)

—— The Lithology of Connecticut. pp. 207. *Hartford,* 1910. 8°. [*Connecticut State Geological and Natural History Survey. Bulletin.* no. 13.] **A.S.c.94.**

BARRELL (Joseph) *of the Yale Graduate School.*

—— Shelley and the Thought of his Time. A study in the history of ideas. pp. viii. 210. *Yale University Press: New Haven,* 1947. 8°. [*Yale Studies in English.* vol. 106.] Ac. **2692**. ma/3.

BARRELL (Maria) British Liberty Vindicated; or, a Delineation of the King's Bench. pp. 22. *The Author: London,* 1788. 4°. **643**. k. **16**. (**5**.)

—— The Captive. [A play.] pp. 31. *London,* 1790. 8°. **11777**. c. **8**.

BARRELL (P.) Riches and Poverty: a tale. pp. 212. *Samuel Tipper; Joseph Robins: London,* 1808. 12°. **12611**. bbb. **4**.

—— The Test of Virtue, and other poems. *C. Chapple; T. Boosey: London,* 1811. 12°. **11645**. aa. **8**.

BARRELL (Robert) The Spirituall Architecture . . . A sermon preached at Pauls Crosse, *etc.* pp. 68. *Augustine Matthewes & Iohn Norton: London,* 1624. 4°. **873**. e. **98**.

BARRELLA (Marcella Bottiglioni) *See* Bottiglioni-Barrella.

BARRELLAS (Estevan) Semanario curioso historico, erudito, comercial, publico, y economico. El Blason de Cataluña, deducido de los echos heroycos . . . de los nobles, cavalleros . . . en el siglo octavo y siguientes, en defensa de la santa fé Catholica, y libertad de la patria, contra la multitud horrorosa de Africanos, que inundaron la España. Lo saca à luz . . . Don P. A. de Tarazona, *etc.* 5 tom. *Barcel[ona,* 1775 ?] 12°. **1323**. a. **3–7**.

BARRELLE (Georges)

—— Le Pèlerin lyrique. Entretiens avec Louis Le Cardonnel au Palais du Roure. Notes et souvenirs. [With a portrait.] pp. 90. [*Paris,*] 1937. 8°. **11863**. b. **28**.

BARRELLE (Jean François Joseph Adorateur) *See* Chayournes (L. de) Vie du Revérénd Père Joseph Barrelle, *etc.* [With a portrait.] 1868. 8°. **4867**. dd. **42**.

BARRELLE (Joseph) *See* Barrelle (Jean F. J. A.)

BARRELLE (Jules) and **LE BRET** (Arthur) La Défense nationale dans les Deux-Sèvres pendant la guerre de 1870–71. [With illustrations.] pp. 236. *Niort,* 1907. 8°. **09231**. l. **11**.

—— Les Mobiles des Deux-Sèvres pendant la guerre de 1870–71. [With maps.] pp. ix. 204. *Niort,* 1904. 8°. **09077**. f. **18**.

BARRÊME (Edmond) Éloge de J.-I. Saurin, avocat au Parlement de Provence, *etc.* pp. 32. *Aix,* 1861. 8°. **10660**. cc. **53**. (**11**.)

BARRÊME (Eugène) *See* Periodical Publications.—*Aix, Bouches du Rhône.* Revue Sextienne, *etc.* (Directeurs: E. Barrême, F. Chavernac.) 1880, *etc.* 8°. P.P. **4367**. c.

BARRÊME (François) [Le Grand banquier, ou le livre des monnoyes étrangères réduites en monnoyes de France.] pp. xxiii. 216. [*The Author: Paris,* 1690 ?] 8°.

Imperfect; wanting the titlepage. **1028.c.19.(2.)**

—— Le Grand commercé, ou le nouveau livre des changes estrangers, de tous les païs de l'Europe, *etc.* tom. 1. pp. 664. *Paris,* 1709. 8°. **8504**. d. **23**.
The titlepage is engraved.

—— Le Livre des comptes-faits, *etc.* *Paris,* 1766. 12°. **8503**. bbb. **28**. (**1**.)

—— [Another edition.] *Paris,* 1771. 8°. **8529**. a. **14**.
With an additional titlepage, engraved.

—— [Le Livre facile pour apprendre l'aritmétique.] L'Arithmetique du s[r] Barreme, ou le Livre facile pour apprendre l'arithmetique de soi-même, & sans maître. Augmenté dans cette nouvelle édition de plus de 190 pages ou regles differentes, par N. Barreme . . . Avec la Geometrie servant au mesurage, *etc.* pp. 437. *Paris,* 1732. 12°. **8503**. bbb. **38**.

—— Le Livre necessaire à toute sorte de conditions . . . Corrigé . . . et augmenté de 460 tarifs, *etc.* pp. 576. *Paris,* 1708. 8°. C. **48**. c. **12**.
With the arms of Louis Phélypeaux, Count de Pontchartrain, stamped on the cover.

BARRÈME (JULES) Faculté de Droit de Paris. Thèse pour la licence. (Jus romanum. De actionibus empti et venditi.—Droit français De la vente et de l'échange.) pp. 43. *Paris*, 1860. 8°. **5406. c. 2. (5.)**

BARRÈME (LOUIS MARIE JOSEPH EDMOND HÉLION DE) *Viscount. See* HÉLION DE BARRÈME.

BARRÊME (NICOLAS) *See* BARRÊME (F.) [Le Livre facile pour apprendre l'aritmétique.] L'Arithmetique du s[r] Barreme . . . Augmenté . . . par N. Barreme, *etc.* 1732. 12°. **8503. bbb. 38.**

BARRENECHE (ANTONIO B.) El César Adriano. Narración del siglo II del Cristianismo. pp. 287. *Madrid*, 1926. 8°. **12490. ppp. 6.**

BARRENECHEA (EADBERTO) Colección de fábulas en verso para el uso de las escuelas de 1ª enseñanza. pp. ii. 185. *Durango*, 1900. 12°. **012305. e. 29.**

—— Mesa Revuelta. Colección de cuentos morales. pp. 149. *Durango*, 1900. 12°. **04412. g. 4.**

BARRENECHEA (JOSÉ ANTONIO)

—— Conmemoración del Primer Centenario del Nacimiento del Doctor Don José Antonio Barrenechea, 1829—Abril 24—1929. pp. 44. 1929. 8°. *See* LIMA.—*Universidad Nacional Mayor de San Marcos.* **010885. de. 63.**

BARRENECHEA (JUAN DE) Reloj astronomico de temblores de la tierra, *etc. See* ODRIOZOLA (M. de) Terremotos, *etc.* 1863. 4°. **7108. aaa. 38.**

BARRENECHEA (MARIANO ANTONIO)

—— Historia Estética de la Música. Con dos estudios más sobre consideraciones históricas y técnicas acerca del arte del canto y la obra maestra del teatro melodramático. (Tercera edición.) pp. 535. *Buenos Aires*, [1941.] 8°. **7890.aa.19.**

BARRENECHEA (RAÚL PORRAS) *See* PORRAS BARRENECHEA.

BARRENECHEA Y RAYGADA (ÓSCAR)

—— Bartolomé Herrera, educador y diplomático peruano, 1808–1864. [With illustrations including portraits.] pp. 91. *Buenos Aires*, 1947. 8°. **10890. f. 20.**

—— Congresos y conferencias internacionales celebrados en Lima, 1847–1894. pp. 406. *Buenos Aires*, 1947. 8°. **9773. p. 15.**

BARRENGER (MICHAEL)

—— *See* BARKAS (Natalie) The Quest of the Bellamy Jewels . . . From an original play by M. Barrenger, *etc.* [1949.] 8°. **12651. e. 35.**

BARRER (RICHARD MALING)

—— Diffusion in and through Solids. pp. xiii. 464. *University Press: Cambridge*, 1941. 8°. [*Cambridge Series of Physical Chemistry.*] **W.P. 9347/8.**

BARRERA, *Tratado de la.* [For editions of the text of and works relating to the "Barrier Treaty" of 29 Oct. 1709, concluded between England and the Netherlands:] *See* ENGLAND.—*Treaties.*—II. Anne.

BARRERA (A. DE) *Madame.* Gems and Jewels: their history, geography, chemistry, and ana. From the earliest ages down to the present time. [With a preface by J. Babinet.] pp. xxxii. 382. *Richard Bentley: London*, 1860. 8°. **7106. aaa. 3.**

—— Memoirs of Rachel [i.e. Élisabeth Rachel Félix, the actress]. By Madame de B—— [i.e. A. de Barrera]. 2 vol. 1858. 8°. *See* B——, *Madame de.* **10663. b. 3.**

BARRERA (ALFREDO)

—— *See* ALICANTE (M. M.) Soil Survey of Iloilo Province. By M. M. Alicante . . . A. Barrera, *etc.* 1947. 8°. [*Philippine Islands. Department of Agriculture and Natural Resources. Soil Report.* no. 9.] **S. T. 256/2.**

BARRERA (ALOYSIO DE LA) *See* PÉREZ DE VARGAS (J. I.) Synopsis rerum quas pro latinae linguae examine subeundo explanandas exhibebunt . . . J. I. Perez de Vargas . . . A. de la Barrera, *etc.* 1829. 4°. **731. f. 35.**

BARRERA (ANTONIO CORZO Y) *See* CORZO Y BARRERA.

BARRERA (CARLO) Storia della Valsolda, con documenti e statuti. pp. 404. *Pinerolo*, 1864. 8°. **10129. bb. 34.**

BARRERA (CARLOS ARNICHES Y) *See* ARNICHES Y BARRERA (C.)

BARRERA (CAYETANO ALBERTO DE LA) *See* BARRERA Y LEIRADO.

BARRERA (CLAUDI OMAR Y) *See* OMAR Y BARRERA.

BARRERA (CLÉMENT) Analogie du scorbut avec la fièvre putride. Tribut académique, *etc.* pp. 28. *Montpellier*, 1810. 4°. **1180. g. 1. (28.)**

BARRERA (DANIEL) *See* HUTCHINSON (Thomas J.) Two Years in Peru . . . With map by D. Barrera, *etc.* 1873. 8°. **010480. ee. 43.**

BARRERA (DOMINICUS LOPEZIUS DE) *See* LOPEZIUS DE BARRERA.

BARRERA (EMILIO) *See* BARRERA LUYANDO.

BARRERA (EMILIO DE LA) Los Equinos, Auquénidos y Estadística Ganadera de la Provincia de Chumbivilcas. [With a portrait.] pp. xviii. 220. *Lima*, 1930. 8°. **07293. m. 50.**

—— Informes ilustrativos sobre la provincia Rodríguez de Mendoza y los distritos de Vitulla, Sonche . . . del departamento de Amazonas . . . Años 1932–1933. [With a portrait.] pp. 30. ii. *Lima*, [1934.] 8°. **010480. h. 18.**

—— Mi Labor de Estudio como miembro de la Comisión de Demarcarción Territorial de la Sociedad Geográfica de Lima . . . Años 1932–1933. [With a portrait.] pp. 93. iii. *Lima*, [1934.] 8°. **010480. h. 19.**

BARRERA (ENRIQUE ANIBAL DE LA) Universidad Mayor de San Marcos. Facultad de Ciencias políticas y administrativas. Corso maritimo. Tesis, *etc.* pp. 18. *Lima*, 1878. 8°. **06955. de. 5. (1.)**

BARRERA (FRANCISCO) *Licenciado.* Satisfacción que da á este ilustre pueblo la oficialidad del Regimiento de Ordenes militares, *etc.* [Signed: J. A. A., i.e. F. Barrera ?] 1821. 4°. *See* A., J. A. **9770. bb. 9. (5.)**

—— *See* A., J. M. Contra los enemigos del Regimiento de Ordenes militares. [Occasioned by the pamphlet entitled: "Satisfacción, *etc.*," signed: J. A. A., i.e. F. Barrera ?] 1821. 4°. **9770. bb. 9. (6.)**

—— *See* C., A. R. El Regimiento . . . de Ordenes militares . . . se justifica de la supuesta satisfacción dada . . . por algun intruso [i.e. F. Barrera ? signing himself: J. A. A.]. [1821.] 4°. **9770. bb. 9. (4.)**

—— *See* R., J. Ataque á los serviles, *etc.* [A reply to the pamphlet, signed: A. R. C., entitled: "El Regimiento . . . de Ordenes militares . . . se justifica de la supuesta satisfacción dada . . . por algun intruso," i.e. F. Barrera ? signing himself: J. A. A.] [1821.] 4°. **9770. bb. 9. (8.)**

BARRERA (FRANCISCO) *Licenciado.*

—— *See* R., J. El Honor marcial sostenido, *etc.* [A reply to the pamphlet, signed: A. R. C., entitled: "El Regimiento . . . de Ordenes militares . . . se justifica de la supuesta satisfacción dada . . . por algun intruso," i.e. F. Barrera? signing himself J. A. A.] 1821. 4°. **9770.** bb. **7.** (**39.**)

—— Breves reflexiones sobre el papel anónimo [by F. Barrera?] que con las iniciales de J. A. A. se ha impreso á nombre de la oficialidad del regimiento de Ordenes Militares. 1821. 4°. *See* A., J. A. **9770.** bb. **9.** (**7.**)

BARRERA (FRANCISCO) *of Lima. Resp. See* LIMA.—*Real Universidad de San Marcos.* Tabla de las materias . . . de las matematicas puras que han cursado . . . 1805 y 6; y presentan a examen D. M. Lopez, D. F. Barrera [and others], *etc.* [1807.] fol. B. **263.** (**9.**)

BARRERA (FRANCISCO XAVIER DE LA) *Ex-diputado en Córtes. See* BARRERA Y CARRIGAL.

BARRERA (FRANCISCO XAVIER DE LA) *Licenciado.* Representacion que dirige al respetable publico el licenciado F. X. de la Barrera para que en el Tribunal de la Razon, donde no hay intrigas ni acepcion de personas, le haga la justicia que le asiste en el negocio que dentro se espresa. pp. 20. *México,* 1826. 4°. **9770.** bb. **17.** (**30.**)

BARRERA (IGNACIO DÍEZ DE LA) *See* DÍEZ DE LA BARRERA.

BARRERA (ISAAC J.)

—— Estudios de Literatura Castellana. El siglo de oro. pp. 404. 1935. 8°. *See* QUITO.—*Academia Ecuatoriana.* **11863.** b. **16.**

—— Historia de la literatura ecuatoriana. 4 vol. *Casa de la Cultura Ecuatoriana: Quito,* 1953–55. 8°. **11870.** h. **25.**

—— Literatura Ecuatoriana. Apuntaciones históricas, *etc.* pp. 119. *Quito,* 1924. 8°. **011824.** d. **23.**

—— Quito colonial, siglo XVIII comienzos del siglo XIX. (Tres escritores del siglo XVIII. Espejo, Velasco, Aguirre.) 2 pt. *Quito,* 1922. 8°. [*Memorias de la Academia Nacional de Historia.* vol. 1.] Ac. **8589/2.**

—— Simón Bolívar. Libertador y creador de pueblos. [With portraits.] pp. 102. 1930. 8°. *See* ECUADOR.—*Ministerio de Educación.* **10899.** aa. **3.**

BARRERA (JAUME) *See* BARCELONA.—*Real Academia de Buenas Letras de Barcelona.* Discursos llegits . . . en la solemne recepció pública del Iltre. Sr. D. Eduart Toda, *etc.* (Contestació de D. J. Barrera.) 1930. 8°. Ac. **8884/4.** (**2.**)

—— *See* BIBLE.—*Psalms.* [*Catalan.*] Psalteri, trelladat . . . per . . . J. Roiç de Corella. (Amb una nota editorial de D. Jaime Barrera.) 1928. 8°. **03089.** e. **52.**

—— *See* MILÁ Y FONTANALÓ (M.) Obres Catalanes. [With a preface by J. Barrera.] 1908. 8°. **12231.** b. **2.**

BARRERA (JOAQUÍN GUICHOT Y) *See* GUICHOT Y BARRERA.

BARRERA (JOAQUÍN LÓPEZ) *See* LÓPEZ BARRERA.

BARRERA (JOSÉ DE LA) Orat[io] ad Augusti[nian]æ patres Er[emi] Comitia Bæticæ Provincialia Granatæ celebrantes. Die 28. Aprilis. Anni 1635. ff. 15. *Apud Salvatorem de Cea Tesa: Cordubæ,* 1635. 4°. **4071.** i. **2.** (**12.**)
The first leaf is mutilated.

BARRERA (JOSÉ MARÍA) *See* MEXICO, *City of.—Ayuntamiento.* Bases de la contrata de Limpia de calles y barrios, celebrada entre el . . . Ayuntamiento de esta capital y los contratistas Don L. Bracho y Don J. M. Barrera, *etc.* 1844. 12°. **8775.** a. **6.**

BARRERA (JOSÉ MARÍA AQUIRRE DE LA) *See* AQUIRRE DE LA BARRERA.

BARRERA (MANUEL DE LA) *See* ACCIONISTA. Voy a que el señor Barrera devuelve la entrada y vuela, ó sea reseña sobre la conducta de este personage en la funcion aerostática de D. A. Theodore. [Signed: Un Accionista.] 1833. *s. sh.* fol. **9770.** k. **11.** (**263.**)

—— *See* GONZALES (B.) Satisfaccion al público sobre la libertad de los Barreras [i.e. M. de la Barrera and others]. [1823.] *s. sh.* fol. **9770.** h. **8.** (**24.**)

—— *See* THEODORE (Adolfo) Ejecucion de justicia en el pícaro estrangero (A. Theodore) y en el general Trapero [i.e. M. de la Barrera]. 1833. *s. sh.* fol. **9770.** k. **11.** (**48.**)

—— Al respetable público. [On the writer's differences with certain comedians of the Mexican stage.] pp. 9. [*Mexico,* 1826.] 4°. **9770.** bb. **17.** (**31.**)

—— Contestacion á las medidas que inició el Síndico Buenrostro al Ayuntamiento, contra el propietario de la plaza principal de toros. [Occasioned by the publication entitled: "Medidas iniciadas por el Ayuntamiento al Sr. Gobernador del distrito, sobre la ascension aerostática ofrecida y no ejecutada por Mr. A. Theodore."] pp. 8. *México,* 1833. 4°. **9770.** bb. **22.** (**29.**)

—— Esposicion que acerca de la contrata de vestuarios para los cuerpos del Ejército hace el que suscribe. pp. 30. *México,* 1837. 4°. **9770.** bb. **24.** (**23.**)

—— Grito de la libertad. pp. 4. [*Mexico,* 1821.] fol. **9770.** k. **5.** (**132.**)

BARRERA (MIGUEL DE LA) Aduana Critica . . . Hebdomadario . . . Su autor don M. de la Barrera. 1763. 8°. *See* PERIODICAL PUBLICATIONS.—*Madrid.* P.P. **4053.** ac.

BARRERA (OLIVA SABUCO DE NANTES) *See* SABUCO DE NANTES BARRERA.

BARRERA (PANTALEON) Á los SS. EE. del Siglo XIX. los diputados por Yucatan. [Signed: "P. Barrera, Isidro Rejon" [and others]. A reply to articles in the "Siglo Diez y Nueve" on the relations of Yucatan to the Supreme Government of the Republic of Mexico.] 2 pt. [*Mexico,* 1843.] 8°. **9770.** bb. **26.** (**6.**)

BARRERA (PEDRO MARÍA) El Arco-Iris: cuentos y artículos. pp. 187. *Madrid,* 1885. 16°. [*Biblioteca Universal.* tom. 102.] **739.** b. **23.**

—— Soll ich heirathen? von P. M. Barrera und andere Novellen von H. Pontoppidan, F. Anstey, Pedro Ivo. pp. 167. *Stuttgart,* 1893. 8°. **12205.** de. **6.**

BARRERA (PIERO)

—— *See* PIGNATA (G.) Una Fuga dalle prigioni del Sant' Uffizio, 1693. [Edited by P. Barrera.] 1934. 8°. **20002.** g. **2.**

—— *See* YOUNG (Norwood) [The Story of Rome.] Rome and its Story . . . Revised by P. Barrera, *etc.* 1953. 8°. **2360.** b. **9/45.**

BARRERA LUYANDO (EMILIO)

—— *See* MILEGO (J.) El General Barrera. De Cataluña al 10 de Agosto. Prólogo y epílogo del General . . . E. Barrera. 1936. 8°. **8042.** k. **41.**

BARRERA PARRA (JAIME) Notas del Week-End. [With a portrait.] pp. xii. 168. *Bucaramanga,* 1933. 8°. [*Biblioteca Santander.* vol. 6.] W.P. **5549/6.**

BARRERA PEZZI (CARLO) Di Giovanni Cabotto, rivelatore del settentrionale emisfero d'America, con documenti inediti esistenti nei RR. Archivj di Stato di Milano, raccolti da C. Barrera Pezzi. pp. 50. *Venezia*, 1881. 4°. **10629**. f. **16**.

BARRERAS (ANTONIO) *See* SILVELA (Manuel) *Dramatist*, and BARRERAS (A.) Negro y Blanco. Juguete, *etc.* 1851. 8°. **11726**. bb. **46**. (**2**.)

—— El Espadachin; narracion histórica del motin de Madrid en 1766. pp. 260. *Madrid*, 1880. 8°. **12491**. l. **27**.

BARRERAS (GASPAR AGÜERO Y) *See* AGÜERO Y BARRERAS.

BARRERAS (JUAN GARCÍA) *See* GARCÍA BARRERAS.

BARRERAS Y FERNÁNDEZ (ANTONIO) Estudio medico legal del garrote en Cuba . . . Publicado en la " Revista de Medicina Legal de Cuba." [With plates.] pp. 105. *Habana*, 1927. 8°. **6055**. g. **19**.

BARRERA VÁSQUEZ (ALFREDO)

—— *See* BRINTON (Daniel G.) El Folk-Lore de Yucután . . . Con una breve noticia y nuevas notas por A. Barrera Vásquez. 1937. 8°. **4507**. a. 8.

—— *See* CHILAM BALAM. El Libro de los Libros de Chilam Balam. Tradución de sus textos paralelos por A. Barrera Vásquez y Silvia Rendón, basada en el estudio, cotejo y reconstrucción hechos por el primero, con introducciones y notas. 1948. 8°. **4506**. h. **37**.

—— Cuadernos Mayas. 2 pt.

1. Algunos datos acerca del arte plumaria entre los Mayos. pp. 15.
2. La identificación de la Deidad " E " de Schelhas. pp. 18.

Mérida, Yucatán, 1939. 8°. **07708**. b. **24**.

BARRERA VÁSQUEZ (ALFREDO) and **MORLEY** (SYLVANUS GRISWOLD) *Archaeologist*.

—— The Maya Chronicles. *In:* Contributions to American Anthropology and History. vol. 10. no. 48. pp. 1–85. 1949. 4°. [*Carnegie Institution. Publications.* no. 585.] Ac. **1866**.

BARRERA Y CARRAGAL (FRANCISCO XAVIER DE LA) *See* BARRON (Juan J.) and BARRERA Y CARRAGAL (F. X. de la) Representacion dirigida al . . . Congreso Constituyente por . . . J. J. Barron y . . . F. J. de la Barrera, *etc.* 1823. 4°. **9770**. bb. **14**. (**46**.)

BARRERA Y LEIRADO (CAYETANO ALBERTO DE LA) *See* CALDERÓN DE LA BARCA (P.) [*Separate Plays.*] La Vida es Sueño; comedia . . . Biografía del autor por D. C. A. de la Barrera. 1881. 8°. **11726**. b. **5**.

—— *See* CHORLEY (John R.) Catálogo de Comedias y Autos de . . . Lope Féliz de Vega' Carpio . . . Corregido y adicionado por . . . C. A. de la Barrera. [1861.] 8°. **11908**. k. **8**. (**1**.)

—— *See* GALLARDO (B. J.) Catálogo . . . de los principales artículos que componían la selecta librería de D. J. N. Böhl de Faber . . . Enmendado y anotado por D. C. A. de la Barrera. 1923. 4°. **11902**. r. 3.

—— *See* RIOJA (F. de) *Poet.* Poesias de D. Francisco de Rioja. Corregidas . . . añadidas é ilustradas con la biografía y la bibliografía del poeta por D. C. A. de la Barrera y Leirado. 1867. 8°. Ac. **8886/2**.

—— *See* RIOJA (F. de) *Poet.* Adiciones á las poesías de D. F. de Rioja . . . por . . . D. C. A. de la Barrera y Leirado. 1872. 4°. Ac. **8890/10**.

BARRERA Y LEIRADO (CAYETANO ALBERTO DE LA)

—— El Cachetero del Buscapié. (Resumen de las pruebas de hecho y de las razones críticas que evidencian la falsedad del " Buscapié " de Don Adolfo de Castro [attributed by him to Cervantes].) Prólogo del Excmo Sr. D. Francisco Rodríguez Marín, *etc.* pp. xi. 282. *Santander*, 1916. 8°. **011853**. r. 4.

One of the " Publicaciones de la Biblioteca Menéndez y Pelayo."

—— Segunda edición. pp. xi. 282. [1926.] 8°. *See* SANTANDER.—*Sociedad Menéndez Pelayo.* Ac. **9536/4**.

—— Catálogo bibliográfico y biográfico del teatro antiguo Español, desde sus origenes hasta mediados del siglo XVIII, *etc.* pp. xiii. 724. *Madrid*, 1860. 8°. **2043.b.**

—— [Another copy.] **11907**. s. 8.

—— [Another copy.] MS. NOTES [by J. R. Chorley]. **11725**. h. **7**.

—— Nueva Biografía de Lope Félix de Vega Carpio. [With " Apéndice bibliográfico."] pp. 718. *Madrid*, 1890. 4°. [*Obras de Lope de Vega publicados por la Real Academia Española.* tom. 1.] **11726**. m.

—— Nuevas Investigaciones acerca de la vida y obras de Cervantes.—Notas a las Nuevas Investigaciones. 1863. *See* CERVANTES SAAVEDRA (M. de) [*Works.—Spanish.*] Obras Completas. tom. 1. 1863, *etc.* 8°. **638.1.10.**

BARRERA Y LUYANDO (ANGEL) *See* GÓNGORA ECHENIQUE (M.) Angel Barrera y los posesiones españolas del Golfo de Guinea, *etc.* [With a portrait.] 1923. 8°. **10634**. aaa. **31**.

BARRERA Y TRONCOSO (MANUEL) Romance endecasílabo. *See* MEXICO, *City of.—Academia de Derecho teórico-practico.* Coleccion de piezas literarias, *etc.* 1835. 4°. **6785**. aaa. **13**. (**1**.)

BARRÈRE (ALAIN)

—— Les Crises de reconversion et la politique économique d'après-guerre. pp. 230. *Paris*, 1947. 8°. **08225**. l. **64**.

Part of " Bibliothèque générale d'économie politique."

BARRÈRE (ALBERT MARIE VICTOR) *See* DUMAS (A.) *the Elder.* [*Vingt ans après.*] L'Évasion du Duc de Beaufort. From Vingt ans après . . . Edited . . . by A. Barrère. 1913. 16°. **12199**. d. **1/11**.

—— *See* ERCKMANN (E.) and CHATRIAN (P. A.) L'Invasion . . . Edited . . . by A. Barrère. 1905. 8°. **012548**. aaa. **28**.

—— *See* GAUDICHOT-MASSON (A. M. B.) Les Enfants célèbres . . . Edited with a full French-English vocabulary . . . by A. Barrère. 1905. 8°. **10602**. aa. **40**.

—— *See* GORSSE (H. J. A. de) and JACQUIN (J.) La Jeunesse de Cyrano de Bergerac: la Bataille de Beaugency, le Cabaret des poètes. Edited with introduction . . . by A. Barrère. 1905. 8°. **12199**. d. **1/6**.

—— *See* GOZLAN (L.) Polydore Marasquin . . . Edited with introduction . . . notes . . . by A. Barrère. 1904. 8°. **12199**. d. **1/2**.

—— *See* HUGO (V. M.) *Viscount.* [*Les Misérables.*] Waterloo, from Les Misérables. Edited . . . by A. Barrère. 1907. 8°. **12199**. d. **1/8**.

—— *See* HUGO (V. M.) *Viscount.* [*Notre-Dame de Paris.*] La Esmeralda et Gringoire. Edited with introduction . . . notes . . . by A. Barrère. 1904. 8°. **12199**. d. **1/3**.

BARRÈRE (Albert Marie Victor)

—— *See* Labrunie de Nerval (G.) La Main enchantée . . . Edited, with an introduction . . . by A. Barrère. 1909. 8°. **12551**. tt. **33**.

—— *See* Le Sage (A. R.) [*Gil Blas.—French.*] Gil Blas chez les brigands. Edited . . . by A. Barrère. 1904. 8°. **12199**. d. **1/23**.

—— *See* Mairet (Jeanne) *pseud.* La Tâche du petit Pierre. Edited with grammatical and explanatory notes . . . by A. Barrère. 1905. 8°. **012548**. aa. **52**.

—— *See* Mérimée (P.) Tamango. José Maria le Brigand. Edited . . . by A. Barrère. 1906. 8°. **12239**. de. **4**.

—— *See* Mouton (E.) Le Supplice du ballon. Edited . . . by A. Barrère. 1905. 8°. **12199**. d. **1/5**.

—— *See* Scribe (A. E.) Une Chaîne . . . Edited by A. Barrère. 1895. 8°. **11740**. aa. **52/22**.

—— *See* Scribe (A. E.) La Verre d'eau . . . With an introduction and notes by A. Barrère. 1887. 8°. **12204**. de. **3/6**.

—— Argot and Slang. A new French and English dictionary of the cant words, quaint expressions, slang terms and flash phrases used in the high and low life of old and new Paris, *etc.* [With a collection of pieces in English and French slang.] pp. lxxxiv. 495. *Privately printed: London*, 1887. 8°. **12954**. e. **18**.

—— [Another copy.] **12952**. dd. **6**.

—— New and revised edition. pp. lx. 483. *Whittaker & Co.: London*, 1889. 8°. **12954**. e. **20**.

—— Chronicles of War, Aghrim, 1691, to Dahomey, 1890. Selected from standard English authors for translation into French . . . Edited, with . . . notes . . . and an English-French vocabulary of military terms, by A. Barrère. pp. viii. 228. *Hachette & Cie: London*, 1892. 8°. **9025**. bb. **15**.

—— A Dictionary of English and French Military Terms. 2 pt. *Hachette & Cie: London*, 1895, 96. 8°. **8823**. h. **49**.

—— (New edition.) pt. 2. pp. 140. *Hachette & Co.: London*, 1914. 8°. **8825**. aaaa. **52**.
Imperfect; wanting pt. 1.

—— A Dictionary of English and French Military Terms . . . Fifth revised edition with supplement containing the latest terms and expressions. 2 pt. *Hachette & Co.: London*, 1918. 8°. **08820**. a. **23**.
Pt. 2 *is of the fourth edition.*

—— Elements of French Grammar and first steps in idioms, *etc.* pp. vi. 124. *Whittaker & Co.: London*, [1886.] 8°. **12950**. bbb. **28**.

—— Graduated French Course in the form of examination papers . . . Third edition, improved and enlarged, *etc.* pt. 1, 2. *Hachette & Cie: London*, [1894.] 4°. **12952**. g. **22**.
Imperfect; wanting pt. 3.

—— Hachette's French Directory. 1909–1910 (1916–1917). Guide-Addresses des Français dans le Royaume-Uni et manuel de renseignements, *etc.* [Compiled by A. M. V. Barrère.] 2 pt. 1909, 16. 8°. *See* Directories.—*Great Britain and Ireland.* **P.P.2405.bg.**

—— Hachette's Popular French Authors. (General editor: A. Barrère.) 23 pt. *Hachette & Co.: London, Paris*, 1903–20. 8°. **12199**. d. **1**.

BARRÈRE (Albert Marie Victor)

—— Junior Graduated French Course, affording materials for translation, grammar and translation, with a vocabulary. pp. 73. *Whittaker & Co.: London; Naumburg a. S.* [printed, 1886.] 8°. **12950**. bbb. **27**.

—— Graduated French Course in the form of examination papers . . . Junior part . . . Second edition, revised [of " Junior Graduated French Course "]. pp. 83. *Hachette & Cie: London*, [1898.] 8°. **12950**. bbb. **47**.

—— New Grammatical French Course, *etc.* 2 vol. *Whittaker & Co.: London*, 1897. 8°. **12952**. df. **35**.

—— Précis of Comparative French Grammar and Idioms . . . Second . . . enlarged edition. pp. xiii. 319. *Whittaker & Co.: London*, 1888. 8°. **12950**. c. **25**.

—— Récits militaires. From Valmy, 1792, to the Siege of Paris, 1870. Edited, with notes and biographical notices, by A. Barrère. pp. viii. 232. *Whittaker & Co.: London*, 1889. 8°. **9080**. aaa. **24**.

—— Whittaker's French Series. For the use of schools and private students. Edited by A. Barrère. 6 pt. *Whittaker & Co.: London*, [1887.] 8°. **12204**. de. **3**.

BARRÈRE (Albert Marie Victor) and **LELAND** (Charles Godfrey)

—— A Dictionary of Slang, Jargon & Cant, embracing English, American, and Anglo-Indian Slang, Pidgin English, Tinkers' Jargon, *etc.* 2 vol. *Ballantyne Press: [Edinburgh,]* 1889, 90. 8°. **12981**. h. **3**.

—— Revised edition. 2 vol. *Bell & Sons: London*, 1897. 8°. **2051.d.**

BARRÈRE (Albert Marie Victor) and **SORNET** (Léon A.)

—— Short Passages for French Composition. An intermediate graduated course for the translation of English into French. With a vocabulary. pp. 164. *Whittaker & Co.: London*, 1895. 8°. **12950**. cc. **29**.

BARRÈRE (Bernard) *See* Taylor (John) *Lieutenant-Colonel, E.I.C. Service.* Lettres politiques commerciales et littéraires . . . sur l'Inde . . . Ouvrage traduit de l'anglais [by B. Barrère and others]. 1801. 8°. **583**. e. **7**.

BARRÈRE (Camille) *See* Barrère (P. E. C.)

BARRÈRE (Bertrand) *See* Barère de Vieuzac.

BARRÈRE (Jacques) *See* Barère.

BARRÈRE (Jean) *Chirurgien-Major.* Essai sur le plomb et préparations médicinales tirées de ce métal. pp. 19. *Paris*, 1811. 4°. **1182**. h. **12**. (**11**.)

BARRÈRE (Jean) *de Sainte-Maure-de-Peyriac.* De la méningite aiguë considérée dans son état de simplicité. Thèse, *etc.* pp. 16. *Montpellier*, 1831. 4°. **1181**. f. 5. (**11**.)

BARRÈRE (Jean Bertrand)

—— Hugo, l'homme et l'œuvre. pp. 255. *Paris*, [1952.] 8°. [*Connaissance des lettres.* no. 35.] W.P. **5820/35**.

BARRÈRE (Joseph) *Abbé.* Le Général de Tartas et récit de ses expéditions militaires en Afrique d'après sa correspondance et d'après le témoignage des documents officiels, *etc.* pp. 224. *Paris; Bordeaux*, 1860. 12°. **10662**. bbb. **2**.

BARRÈRE (Joseph) *Abbé.*

—— Histoire religieuse & monumentale du diocèse d'Agen, depuis les temps les plus reculés jusqu'à nos jours . . . enrichie de lithographies à deux teintes et d'un grand nombre de sujets iconographiques. 2 tom. *Agen,* 1855, 56. 4°. **4630**. e. **8**.

BARRÈRE (Joseph) *Avocat.*

—— *See* Armaingaud (A.) La Boétie et Machiavel d'après une publication récente [i.e. " Estienne de La Boëtie contre Nicolas Machiavel," by J. Barrère], *etc.* 1909. 8°. **11859**. d. **27**.

—— Le Droit et la vie du palais dans Rabelais. Discours, *etc.* pp. 48. *Bordeaux,* 1892. 8°. **5425**. m. **11**.

—— Estienne de la Boëtie contre Nicolas Machiavel. Étude sur les mobiles qui ont déterminé Estienne de la Boëtie à écrire le ' Discours de la servitude volontaire.' pp. 98. *Bordeaux,* 1908. 8°. **8008**. h. **32**.

—— Une Filleule de Bordeaux. Rions. Souvenirs historiques par J. Barrère, Th. Durepaire et G. Videau. Avec une préface de M. Francisque Habasque. [With plates.] pp. xi. 109. *Bordeaux,* 1910. 8°. **010171**. l. **10**.

—— L'Humanisme et la politique dans le Discours de la servitude volontaire. Étude sur les origines du texte et l'objet du discours d'Estienne de la Boétie. pp. 244. *Paris,* 1923. 8°. **8007**. f. **42**.

—— Une Promenade dans Bordeaux en 1550. Conférence, *etc.* pp. 34. *Bordeaux,* 1895. 8°. **10106**. de. **13**. (4.)

BARRÈRE (Pierre) *M.D.* Des plaies pénétrantes de la poitrine. pp. 28. *Paris,* 1843. 4°. [*Collection des thèses soutenues à la Faculté de Médecine de Paris.* An 1843. tom. 1.] **7371**. d. **11**.

BARRÈRE (Pierre) *Professor of French.* Les Écrivains français, leur vie et leurs œuvres, ou histoire de la littérature française. pp. 563. *Williams & Norgate: Londres; Bruxelles* [printed], 1863. 8°. **11851**. bb. **32**.

BARRÈRE (Pierre) *Professor of Medicine at Perpignan.* Diverses observations anatomiques, tirées des ouvertures d'un grand nombre de cadavres ; propres à découvrir les causes des maladies et leurs remèdes. pp. 66. *Perpignan,* 1751. 4°. **1405**. d. **12**.

—— Essai sur l'histoire naturelle de la France Equinoxiale . . . ou dénombrement des plantes, des animaux, & des minéraux qui se trouvent dans l'Isle de Cayenne, les Isles de Remire, sur les Côtes de la Mer, et dans le continent de la Guyane. Avec leurs noms differens, latins, françois, & indiens, *etc.* pp. xxiv. 215. *Paris,* 1741. 12°. **978**. a. **9**.

—— [Another copy.] **972**. a. **5**.

—— Nouvelle relation de la France Equinoxiale, contenant la description des Côtes de la Guiane ; de l'Isle de Cayenne ; le commerce de cette colonie . . . avec des figures, *etc.* pp. 250. *Paris,* 1743. 12°. **979**. d. **33**.

—— Observations sur l'origine et la formation des pierres figurées et sur celles qui, tant extérieurement qu'intérieurement, ont une figure régulière & déterminée. Avec figures. pp. 67. *Paris,* 1746. 8°. **953**. a. **13**.

—— [Another copy.] **444**. c. **45**.

—— [Another copy.] **233**. k. **36**.

BARRÈRE (Pierre) *Professor of Medicine at Perpignan.*

—— Ornithologiæ specimen novum, sive series avium in Ruscinone, Pyrenæis montibus, atque in Gallia Æquinoctiali observatarum in classes, genera & species . . . digesta, *etc.* pp. 84. *Perpiniani,* 1745. 4°. B. **337**. (**2**.)

—— [Another copy.] **235**. e. **37**.

—— Question de médecine, dans laquelle on examine, si la théorie de la botanique ou la connoissance des plantes est nécessaire à un médecin? Par M***, docteur en médecine [i.e. P. Barrère], *etc.* pp. 16. 1740. 4°. *See* M***, *Docteur en Médecine de l'Université de Perpignan.* B. **40**. (**6**.)

BARRÈRE (Pierre Eugène Camille)

—— *See* Charles-Roux (F.) Trois ambassades françaises à la veille de la guerre, *etc.* [An account of the work of P. Cambon, P. E. C. Barrère and J. Cambon.] 1928. 8°. **9081**. a. **13**.

—— *See* Delescluze (C.) From Paris to Cayenne . . . Translated by C. Barrère, *etc.* 1872. 8°. **10661**. b. **23**.

—— *See* Hill (William Henry) *Violin-Maker.* [Antonio Stradivari.] Antoine Stradivarius, sa vie et son œuvre . . . Avec une introduction de . . . Camille Barrère, *etc.* 1908. 4°. Hirsch **1584**.

—— *See* Laroche (J.) Quinze ans à Rome avec Camille Barrère, 1898–1913. [With a portrait.] 1948. 8°. **09101**. d. **3**.

—— *See* Noël (Léon) *Ambassadeur de France.* Camille Barrère, ambassadeur de France. [With a portrait.] 1948. 8°. **10656**. n. **46**.

—— *See* Serra (E.) Camille Barrère e l'intesa italo-francese, *etc.* 1950. 8°. **9170**. ee. **9**.

—— The Story of the Commune. By a Communalist [i.e. P. E. C. Barrère?]. Republished from the " Pall Mall Gazette " with additional matter. pp. xii. 93. 1871. 8°. *See* Communalist. **9230**. dd. **21**. (3.)

BARRÈRE (Simone)

—— *See* Moutet (A.) and Barrère (S.) Spectrographie d'émission. 1950. 4°. [*Office National d'Études et de Recherches Aéronautiques. Publication.* no. 46.] S. E. **220**.

BARRÈRE DE VIEUZAC (Bertrand) *See* Barère de Vieuzac.

BARRÈS (Auguste Maurice)

—— Maurice Barrès, ami des jeunes. Quelques lettres politiques inédites. Présentées par J. Caplain. [With a facsimile.] pp. 29. *Paris,* 1924. 8°. **8052**. i. **46**. *Âmes et choses.* no. 1.

—— L'Abdication du poète. Portrait de Lamartine gravé par P.-E. Vibert. [On the last years of Lamartine.] pp. 91. *Paris,* 1914. 8°. **010662**. df. 5.

—— Adieu à Moréas. pp. 18. *Paris,* 1910. 8°. **11850**. bb. 46. (5.)

—— Alsace-Lorraine. pp. 96. *Paris,* 1906. 8°. **8027**. a. **28**.

—— L'Âme française et la Guerre. [Being articles contributed to " L'Écho de Paris."] 11 tom.

L'Union sacrée.	Pour les mutilés.
Les Saints de la France.	Sur le chemin de l'Asie.
La Croix de Guerre.	Le Suffrage des morts.
L'Amitié des tranchées.	Pendant la bataille de Verdun.
Les Voyages de Lorraine et d'Artois.	Voyage en Angleterre.
	Les Tentacules de la Pieuvre.

Paris, 1915–20. **9085**. a. **4**.

For another collection, see ***infra*** *: Chronique de la Grande Guerre.*

BARRÈS (AUGUSTE MAURICE)

—— The Soul of France. Visits to invaded districts. [Selected and translated from tom. 1–5 of " L'Âme française et la Guerre."] pp. 41. *T. Fisher Unwin: London,* [1916.] 8°. **9081. de. 20.**

—— Les Amitiés françaises. Notes sur l'acquisition par un petit Lorrain des sentiments qui donnent un prix à la vie. pp. 270. *Paris,* [1907.] 8°. **12352. s. 1.**

—— [Another edition.] Ornées de bois gravés par Achille Ouvré. pp. 188. *Paris,* 1919. 8°. **012352. ee. 10.**

—— Amori et Dolori sacrum. La Mort de Venise. pp. 311. *Paris,* [1903.] 8°. **012355. de. 42.**

—— L'Angoisse de Pascal. pp. 59. *Paris,* 1910. 4°. **10658. t. 15.**

—— [Another edition.] Édition suivie d'une étude sur les deux maisons de Pascal à Clermont-Ferrand. Avec un portrait de Blaise Pascal gravé sur bois. pp. vi. 138. *Paris,* 1918. 12°. **10658. ee. 7.**

—— L'Appel au soldat. *See* infra: Le Roman de l'énergie nationale.

—— Autour de Jeanne d'Arc. pp. 86. *Paris,* 1916. 4°. **4830. e. 9.**

—— Les Bastions de l'Est. Au service de l'Allemagne. Illustrations, *etc.* pp. 125. *Paris,* [1905.] 8°. **012552. bb. 2.**

—— Les Bastions de l'Est. Colette Baudoche. Histoire d'une jeune fille de Metz. pp. 258. *Paris,* 1909. 8°. **12551. r. 33.**

—— Colette Baudoche . . . suivie d'un Discours à Metz (15 août 1911). pp. 204. *Paris; Édimbourg* [printed], [1919.] 8°. [*Collection Nelson.*] **012199. g. 1/134.**

—— Les Bastions de l'Est. Colette Baudoche . . . Nouvelle édition, augmentée de quelques pages inédites. pp. ix. 289. *Paris,* 1923. 8°. **012547. a. 40.**

—— Colette Baudoche . . . Translation and foreword by Frances Wilson Huard. pp. xii. 180. *G. H. Doran Co.: New York,* [1918.] 8°. **12547. ppp. 8.**

—— *See* FRONDAIE (P.) Colette Baudoche . . . D'après le roman de M. M. Barrès. 1920. fol. [*Petite Illustration Théâtrale.* Nouvelle série. no. 25.] **P.P. 4283. m. (2.)**

—— Les Bastions de l'Est. Le Génie du Rhin. pp. xxix. 259. *Paris,* 1921. 8°. **012350. ff. 58.**

—— La Bataille sous Nancy. (1914–1916.) Frontispice de Adolphe Giraldon. pp. ix. *Paris,* 1916. fol. [*Pages de guerre.*] **1869. d. 34.**

—— Le Bi-centenaire de Jean-Jacques Rousseau. (Observation présentée à la Chambre des Députés le 11 juin 1912.) pp. 23. *Paris,* 1912. 12°. **10658. ee. 2.**

—— Le Blason de la France, ou ses traits éternels dans cette guerre et dans les vieilles épopées. pp. 22. *London,* 1916. 8°. [*British Academy. Annual Lecture on Aspects of Art, etc.* no. 1.] **Ac. 1186/8.**

—— [Another edition.] Les Traits éternels de la France. pp. 55. *Paris,* 1916. 4°. **010169. ee. 24.**

—— The Undying Spirit of France—Les Traits éternels de la France . . . Translated by Margaret W. B. Corwin. With a foreword by Theodore Stanton. pp. xv. 58. *Yale University Press: New Haven; Humphrey Milford: London,* 1917. 12°. **010169. e. 9.**

—— Ce que j'ai vu au temps du Panama. pp. 160. *Paris,* 1906. 8°. **8027. a. 27.**

BARRÈS (AUGUSTE MAURICE)

—— Colette Baudoche. *See* supra: Les Bastions de l'Est.

—— La Colline inspirée. pp. 424. *Paris,* 1913. 8°. **4784. df. 34.**

—— Chronique de la Grande Guerre. vol. 1–13. *Paris,* 1931–39. 8°. **9196. l. 17.**
Imperfect; wanting vol. 14.

—— Le Culte du Moi.

Sous l'œil des Barbares.
Un Homme libre.
Le Jardin de Bérénice.

Editions of the various volumes are entered separately.

—— Dans le cloaque. Notes d'un membre de la Commission d'enquête sur l'affaire Rochette. (Cinquième édition.) pp. 120. *Paris,* 1914. 8°. **5408. de. 9.**

—— Dante, Pascal et Renan. [Three addresses.] pp. 78. *Paris,* 1923. 16°. **11825. a. 20.**

—— De la sympathie à la fraternité d'armes. Les États-Unis dans la guerre. pp. ii. 96. *Paris,* 1919. 8°. **08027. aaa. 151.**

—— Les Déracinés. *See* infra: Le Roman de l'énergie nationale.

—— Un Discours à Metz (15 août 1911). pp. 23. *Paris,* 1911. 8°. **012301. ee. 25. (2.)**

—— Les Diverses familles spirituelles de la France. pp. 316. *Paris,* 1917. 8°. **08052. a. 32.**

—— (Édition définitive, avec des textes inédits.) pp. iv. 278. *Paris,* 1930. 8°. **08486. de. 50.**

—— Dix jours en Italie. pp. 182. *Paris, Zurich,* 1916. 12°. **9083. df. 8.**

—— Dieci giorni in Italia. Testo francese e traduzione . . . Ornata da Emilio Mantelli, *etc.* pp. 83. 83. 1917. 8°. *See* GRENOBLE.—*Université de Grenoble.—Institut Français de Florence.* **010136. e. 23.**

—— Du sang, de la volupté, et de la mort. pp. 326. *Paris,* 1894. 12°. **8411. e. 7.**

—— En Provence. pp. 134. *Paris,* 1930. fol. **010170. f. 15.**

—— En regardant au fond des crevasses. [An attack on L. J. Malvy.] pp. 110. *Paris,* 1917. 8°. **08052. aaa. 7.**

—— L'Ennemi des lois. Troisième édition. pp. 302. *Paris,* 1893. 8°. **012548. eeee. 60.**

—— [Another edition.] pp. viii. 215. *Paris; Londres,* [1913.] 8°. [*Collection Gallia.*] **012210.bb.1/7.**

—— Une Enquête aux pays du Levant. [With plates.] 2 vol. *Paris,* [1923.] 8°. **10024. a. 29.**

—— *See* FRANDON (I. M.) " Assassins " et " Danseurs mystiques " dans " Une enquête aux pays du levant " de Maurice Barrès. 1954. 8°. [*Société de publications romanes et françaises.* no. 41.] **Ac. 9807.**

—— Ernest Renan . . . Discours, *etc.* pp. 19. *Abbeville,* 1923. 16°. [*Les Amis d'Édouard.* no. 47.] **012207.p.1/47.**

—— Faut-il autoriser les congrégations ? 3 pt.

1. Les Frères des Écoles chrétiennes.
2. Les Pères blancs.
3. Les Missionaires africains de Lyon.

Paris, 1923. 8°. **04784. de. 6.**

—— La Folie de Charles Baudelaire. pp. 104. *Paris*, 1926. 8°. **11825. aa. 38.**

—— La France dans les pays rhénans—une tâche nouvelle. (L'Appel du Rhin.) pp. 96. *Paris*, 1919. 16°. **8052. aaa. 44.**

—— Der Genius des Rheins. Eine Reihe freier Vorträge gehalten an der Universität Strassburg. 3 pt. *Strasbourg*, [1925.] 8°. **08072. a. 78.**

—— *See* BERTRAM (Ernst) Rheingenius und Génie du Rhin. [A reply to "Der Genius des Rheins" by A. M. Barrès.] 1922. 8°. **08027. c. 108.**

—— La Grande pitié des églises de France. pp. 419. *Paris*, 1914. 8°. **3902. ee. 42.**

—— Les Grands problèmes du Rhin. [With a map.] pp. iv. 471. *Paris*, 1930. 8°. **08027. ff. 45.**

—— Greco, ou le secret de Tolède. (Avec vingt-quatre illustrations. Vingt-huitième édition) pp. 187. *Paris*, 1912. 8°. **7857. r. 17.**

—— Un Homme libre. pp. 297. *Paris*, 1889. 8°. **012548. eee. 48.**

—— Nouvelle édition. pp. xxiii. 271. *Paris*, 1912. 8°. **12548. ppp. 19.**

—— (Edition définitive.) pp. xxi. 259. *Paris*, [1922.] 8°. **012547. b. 75.**

—— Huit jours chez M. Renan. (Dialogues parisiens.) pp. 55. *Paris*, 1888. 12°. **10661. a. 30.**

—— Deuxième édition. pp. 58. *Paris*, 1890. 12°. **10659. aa. 39.**

—— [Another edition.] Suivi de M. Renan au purgatoire. Troisième édition. [Containing also "Le Regard de M. Renan. D'après M. Charles Laurent."] *Paris*, 1904. 12°. **10663. a. 46.**

—— Huit jours chez M. Renan. Trois stations de psychothérapie. Toute licence sauf contre l'amour. (Quatrième édition.) pp. xiii. 248. *Paris*, 1913. 8°. **010662. a. 19.**

—— [Another edition.] pp. xvi. 262. *Paris*, 1923. 8°. **012352. g. 12.**

—— Le Jardin de Bérénice. pp. 296. *Paris*, 1891. 8°. **012548. eee. 49.**

—— [Another edition.] Pointes sèches en couleurs de Malo Renault. pp. xiii. 171. *Paris*, 1922. 8°. K.T.C. **28. b. 27.**

—— Un Jardin sur l'Oronte. pp. 241. *Paris*, 1922. 8°. **012547. bb. 31.**

—— Une Journée parlementaire. Comédie de mœurs en trois actes. pp. iii. 85. *Paris*, 1894. 8°. **11740. g. 21.**

—— Le Jubilé de Jeanne d'Arc. Orné de six compositions d'Angel. pp. 28. *Paris*, 1912. 4°. **4827. h. 16.**

—— Leur figures. *See* infra: Le Roman de l'énergie nationale.

—— La Lorraine devastée. Avec 8 planches et 1 carte hors texte. Sixième édition. pp. iii. 3. 176. *Paris*, 1919. 8°. **9083. a. 54.**
One of the "Collection 'La France Devastée.'"

—— Les Maîtres. [Literary studies.] pp. ii. 326. *Paris*, 1927. 8°. 011840. cc. 55.

—— La Maîtresse servante [by Jérôme et Jean Tharaud]. [A review.] pp. 23. *Abbeville*, 1911. 16°. [*Les Amis d'Édouard.* no. 1.] **012207.p.1/1.**

BARRÈS (AUGUSTE MAURICE)

—— Mes Cahiers. 14 Tom. *Paris*, 1929–57. 8°. **12240.p.2.**

—— La Voix intérieure de Maurice Barrès, d'après ses cahiers. [Extracts, edited, with a running commentary, by F. Duhourcau.] pp. 243. *Paris*, 1929. 8°. **10656. df. 7.**

—— La Minute sacrée, *etc.* (L'Appel du Rhin.) [On the liberation of Alsace-Lorraine, 1918.] pp. 84. *Paris*, 1919. 8°. **9084. e. 4.**

—— Le Mystère en pleine lumière. [Essays.] pp. ii. 281. *Paris*, 1926. 8°. **012352. c. 61.**

—— La Politique rhénane. Discours parlementaires. *Paris*, 1922. 8°. **8027. aa. 50.**

—— Pour la haute intelligence française. Préface de M. Charles Moureu. pp. xxvi. 282. *Paris*, 1925. 8°. **8355. aaa. 69.**

—— Le Printemps en Provence. pp. 92. *Liège*, *Paris* [printed], 1926. 16°. [*A la lampe d'Aladdin.* vol 9.] **012208.d.1/9.**

—— Un Renovateur de l'occultisme. Stanislas de Guaita, 1861–1898. Souvenirs, *etc.* pp. 32. *Paris*, 1898. 8°. **010664. m. 45.**

—— Le Roman de l'énergie nationale. L'Appel au soldat, *etc.* pp. 552. *Paris*, 1900. 18°. **012550. l. 37.**

—— [Another edition.] pp. 576. *Paris; Édimbourg* [printed], [1919.] 8°. [*Collection Nelson.*] **012199. g. 1/135.**

—— Le Roman de l'énergie nationale. Les Déracinés, *etc.* pp. 491. *Paris*, 1898. 18°. **012551. df. 22.**

—— [Another edition.] pp. 473. *Paris; Édimbourg* [printed], [1919.] 8°. [*Collection Nelson.*] **012199. g. 1/136.**

—— Le Roman de l'énergie nationale. Leurs figures. (Nouvelle édition.) pp. 331. *Paris*, 1917. 8°. **12547. tt. 7.**

—— [Another edition.] pp. 379. *Paris; Édimbourg* [printed], [1920.] 8°. [*Collection Nelson.*] **012199. g. 1/146.**

—— Scènes et doctrines du nationalisme. pp. 518. *Paris*, [1902.] 8°. **8050. bbb. 43.**

—— Séance de l'Académie Française du 17 janvier 1907. Discours de réception de Maurice Barrès [on J. M. de Hérédia the younger]. pp. 48. *Paris*, 1907. 8°. **010663. f. 63**

—— Sensations de Paris. Le Quartier Latin, *etc.* pp. 35. *Paris*, 1888. 12°. **12315. ccc. 41. (5.)**

—— Une Soirée dans le silence et le vent de la mort. (Fragment d'un livre abandonné sur La mort de Venise.) pp. 20. *Paris*, 1901. 8°. **10136. f. 27**

—— Sous l'œil des Barbares . . . Nouvelle édition, augmentée d'un examen des trois volumes (Sous l'Œil des Barbares, Un Homme libre, Le Jardin de Bérénice) pp. 308. *Paris*, 1892. 8°. **012548. eee. 47**

—— Stockholm. *See* WAHL (M.) Alger, *etc.* [1892.] 4° [*Les Capitales du monde.* no. 14.] **10025. g. 4**

—— Taine et Renan. Pages perdues. Recueillies et commentées par Victor Giraud, *etc.* pp. 46. *Paris*, 1922. 8° **11840. aaa. 43**

—— La Terre & les morts. Sur quelles réalités fonder la conscience française. pp. 36. *Paris*, [1899.] 12°. [*La Patrie française. Troisième conférence.*] **8051. a. 74.**

BARRÈS (AUGUSTE MAURICE)

—— Le Tombeau d'Ernest Psichari au seuil de la forêt des Ardennes. pp. 14. *Paris*, 1920. 8°. **10657. bb. 12.**

—— Toute licence sauf contre l'amour. pp. 86. *Paris*, 1892. 12°. **12357. a. 43.**

—— Les Traits éternels de la France. *See* supra: Le Blason de la France, *etc.*

—— Trois stations de psychothérapie. pp. xx. 68. *Paris*, 1891. 12°. **8411. aa. 52.**

—— Une Visite à l'armée anglaise. pp. 109. *Paris, Nancy*, 1915. 8°. **9083. gg. 22.**

—— [Another copy.] Une Visite à l'armée anglaise, *etc.* **F.P.** *Paris, Nancy*, 1915. 8°. File **726.**

—— Le Voyage de Sparte. pp. 300. *Paris*, 1906. 8°. **10126.df.6.**

—— Nouvelle édition, augmentée d'un chapitre. pp. v. 288. *Paris*, 1922. 8°. **10127. de. 8.**

—— Vingt-cinq années de vie littéraire. Pages choisies. Introduction de H. Bremond. pp. xcii. 442. *Paris*, 1908. 8°. **11850. p. 19.**

—— Pages choisies. [Edited by F. Baldensperger.] pp. 149. *Paris*, [1915.] 8°. **9083. ff. 14.**
One of the series "Écrivains français pendant la guerre."

—— L'Esprit de Barrès. Pages choisies avec une introduction par Fernand Cauët. pp. xxviii. 259. *Paris*, 1938. 8°. **12238. bbb. 3.**

WORKS EDITED OR WITH CONTRIBUTIONS BY BARRÈS.

—— *See* ALSACE. [*Appendix.*] L'Alsace et la Lorraine. Préface: M. Barrès. [1916, *etc.*] fol. **1783. cc. 17.**

—— *See* ARGUROGLOS-KALLIAS (G.) L'Allemagne ennemie de l'Hellénisme. Préface de M. Barrès, *etc.* 1916, *etc.* 8°. **08026. aa. 66.**

—— *See* BARRÈS (J. B. A.) Souvenirs d'un officier de la Grande Armée. Publiés par M. Barrès, *etc.* 1923. 8°. **10657. a. 17.**

—— *See* BARRÈS (J. B. A.) Memoirs of a Napoleonic Officer . . . Edited, with an introduction, by . . . M. Barrès, *etc.* 1925. 8°. **10657. bbb. 12.**

—— *See* BEAUBOURG (M.) Contes pour les assassins . . . Préface de M. Barrès. 1890. 8°. **012547. l. 53.**

—— *See* BEAUVAU-CRAON (C. L. J. E. M. J. V. de) *Prince.* La Survivance française au Canada . . . Préface de M. M. Barrès. 1914. 8°. **10470. ppp. 23.**

—— *See* BELLOUARD (J.) Un Chant de consolation. Avec préface de M. Barrès. [1916.] 8°. **011483. bbb. 70.**

—— *See* BEYLE (M. H.) Correspondance de Stendhal . . . Préface de M. Barrès. 1908. 8°. **10902. f. 14.**

—— *See* BIBIKOV (M.) Our Indians at Marseilles . . . With an introduction by M. Barrès, *etc.* 1915. 8°. **9082. f. 44.**

—— *See* BOGLIONE (A.) Le Secret de Cybèle. Préface de M. Barrès. 1910. 8°. **11735. f. 14.**

—— *See* BONNARD (F.) Au pays de Saint Pierre Fourier. Historie du village de Mattaincourt en Lorraine . . . Avec une lettre de M. Barrès, *etc.* 1910. 8°. **010170. g. 3.**

—— *See* BOUDON (V.) Avec Charles Péguy de la Lorraine à la Marne . . . Préface de M. Barrès, *etc.* 1916. 8°. **9081. de. 36.**

—— *See* BRENIER (F.) L'Allemagne occulte, *etc.* (Préface de M. Barrès.) 1915. 8°. **4504. g. 44.**

—— *See* BUCHON (J. A. C.) Voyage dans l'Eubée, les Îles Ioniennes et les Cyclades en 1841 . . . Préface de M. Barrès. 1911. 8°. **10126. dd. 27.**

—— *See* CAZALS (F. A.) and LE ROUGE (G.) Les Derniers jours de Paul Verlaine . . . Avec une préface de M. Barrès, *etc.* 1911. 8°. **10661. ppp. 30.**

—— *See* CHENU (C.) La Ligue des patriotes . . . Avec une préface de M. Barrès, *etc.* 1916. 8°. **08052. a. 40.**

—— *See* CLERMONT (Louise) Émile Clermont . . . Préface de M. Barrès. 1919. 8°. **010662. cc. 26.**

—— *See* COLIN (Louis) Les Barbares à la Trouée des Vosges. Récits des témoins . . . Préface de M. M. Barrès. 1915. 8°. **9083. gg. 10.**

—— *See* COLLIN (Rémy) Les Foyers nouveaux. Préface de M. Barrès. 1912. 8°. **08275. e. 85.**

—— *See* CROUVEZIER (G.) L'Aviation pendant la Guerre . . . Préface de M. Barrès. 1915. 8°. **9082. ee. 13.**

—— *See* DELAIRE (A.) Au lendemain de la victoire . . . Préface de M. Barrès, *etc.* 1916. 8°. **08027. d. 94.**

—— *See* DÉPAGNIAT (R.) Les Martyres de l'aviation . . . Introduction de M. Barrès, *etc.* 1912. 8°. **10600. ccc. 15.**

—— *See* DUCRAY (C.) Paul Déroulède . . . Préface de M. Barrès. [1914.] 8°. **010662. bb. 24.**

—— *See* ESCHEVANNES (C. d') *Count.* Un Explorateur français. Henry Moll d'après sa correspondance. Préface de M. Barrès. [1912.] 8°. **010920. i. 29. (2.)**

—— *See* ESPARTES (G. d') Le Roi . . . Précédé d'une préface de M. Barrès. 1901. 12°. **012550. a. 36.**

—— *See* FLAT (P.) Les Premiers Vénitiens. Préface de M. M. Barrès, *etc.* 1899. 4°. Tab. **438. c. 2.**

—— *See* FLORENT-MATTER (E.) L'Alsace-Lorraine de nos jours. Préface de M. Barrès. 1908. 8°. **10255. de. 10.**

—— *See* FOROT (V.) Architecture religieuse. Les églises de la Corrèze. (Préface de M. M. Barrès.) 1913. 8°. **07816. h. 45. (4.)**

—— *See* GAUSSERON (B. M. H.) Un Français au Sénégal. Abel Jeandet. Préface par M. Barrès, *etc.* 1913. 8°. **010662. dd. 27.**

—— *See* GAUTIER (Philippe) Quatre ans à la cour de Saxe. Nouvelle édition, précédée d'une préface de M. Barrès. 1919. 8°. **10657. aa. 9.**

—— *See* HELMER (P. A.) France-Alsace . . . Préface de M. Barrès. [1916.] 8°. **08052. a. 15.**

—— *See* HINZELIN (E.) L'Alsace sous le joug. Préface de M. Barrès. [1914.] 8°. **08052. aa. 1.**

—— *See* HOUDAILLE (O.) Les Énergies mystérieuses. Le Mannequin d'amour. Introduction par M. Barrès. 1914. 12°. **12548. r. 37.**

—— *See* IBAÑEZ DE IBERO (C.) Une Enquête en Allemagne. La situation . . . de l'Empire allemand pendant la Guerre. Préface de M. M. Barrès, *etc.* 1915. 8°. **08027. d. 51.**

—— *See* LA FAYE (J. de) Élisabeth de Bavière, impératrice-reine d'Autriche-Hongrie. Préface de M. M. Barrès, *etc.* 1913. 8°. **010705. ee. 29.**

BARRÈS (AUGUSTE MAURICE)—[WORKS EDITED OR WITH CONTRIBUTIONS BY BARRÈS.]

—— *See* LAFOND (Georges) Avec les mitrailleurs de la coloniale. Ma mitrailleuse. Préface de M. M. Barrès. [1917.] 8°. **09082. bbb. 6.**

—— *See* LARRONDE (C.) Anthologie des écrivains français morts pour la patrie . . . Préface par M. Barrès. [1916.] 8°. **012238. bb. 4.**

—— *See* LAUMONIER (D.) Sang d'Argonne. Épisodes de 1792. Préface de M. Barrès. 1910. 8°. **12551. v. 15.**

—— *See* LORRAIN (Jean) *pseud.* La Petite classe. Préface de M. Barrès, *etc.* 1895. 12°. **012550. i. 48.**

—— *See* MADELIN (L.) Croquis lorrains. Préface de M. M. Barrès. 1907. 8°. **10169. ee. 11.**

—— *See* MARCHAND (Louis) L'Offensive morale des Allemands, en France, pendant la guerre . . . Préface de M. M. Barrès. 1920. 8°. **9083. dd. 4.**

—— *See* MATHIEU (François D.) *Cardinal.* Œuvres oratoires . . . Avec . . . le discours prononcé aux obsèques par M. Barrès. 1910, *etc.* 8°. **4498. ff. 20.**

—— *See* MÉNARD (Louis) *Historical Writer.* Rêveries d'un päien mystique. Préface de M. Barrès, *etc.* 1909. 8°. **08461. f. 31.**

—— *See* METZ-NOBLAT (A. de) *the Younger.* A l'ombre des cyprès. Avec une préface de M. M. Barrès. 1908. 8°. **011483. g. 68.**

—— *See* MEUNIER (G.) En lisant l'histoire de Jeanne d'Arc. Préface de M. Barrès, *etc.* 1913. 8°. **12548. pp. 15.**

—— *See* MOLL (Henry) Une Âme de colonial. Lettres du lieutenant-colonel Moll. Avec une préface de M. M. Barrès. 1912. 8°. **10905. c. 18.**

—— *See* NOUSSANNE (H. de) *pseud.* Des faits, des hommes, des idées, 1905–1906. Préface de M. Barrès. 1907. 8°. **8028. aaa. 31.**

—— *See* PERROUT (R.) Les Images d'Épinal. Préface de M. Barrès. 1912. 4°. **10171. i. 18.**

—— *See* PHELIP (G.) Voix d'Alsace et de Lorraine. Préface de M. Barrès. [1911.] 8°. **8074. bbb. 38.**

—— *See* PILANT (P.) Le Patriotisme en France et à l'étranger. Précédé d'une lettre ouverte à M. Gabriel Hanotaux par M. Barrès. 1912. 8°. **08007. df. 61.**

—— *See* POILAY (M.) Souvenirs d'un engagé volontaire. Belfort, 1870–1871. Préface de M. Barrès. 1907. 8°. **09077. ee. 32.**

—— *See* POMAIROLS (C. de) Poèmes choisis . . . Avec une préface de M. Barrès. 1913. 8°. **011483. c. 24.**

—— *See* RACHILDE, *pseud.* Monsieur Vénus . . . Précédé d'une preface et d'une lettre autographe . . . de M. Barrès. 1926. 8°. **12516. pp. 25.**

—— *See* RIVASSO (R. de) L'Unité d'une pensée. Essai sur l'œuvre de M. Paul Bourget. Précédé d'une lettre de M. M. Barrès. 1914. 8°. **011853. aa. 46.**

—— *See* ROLLIN (E. A. G.) Le Drapeau . . . Lettre-préface de M. Barrès. 1910. 8°. **11482. aaa. 34.**

—— *See* SAVINIAN (   ) La Lionide . . . Lettre de M. Barrès, *etc.* 1911. 8°. **11498. l. 14.**

—— *See* SÉRIS (R.) and AUBRY (J.) Les Parisiens pendant l'état de siège. Préface de M. Barrès, *etc.* 1915. 8°. **9082. ee. 8.**

BARRÈS (AUGUSTE MAURICE)—[WORKS EDITED OR WITH CONTRIBUTIONS BY BARRÈS.]

—— *See* TANET (J.) Les Défenseurs . . . Préface de M. Barrès. 1909. 8°. **010170. e. 1/7.**

—— *See* TOUSSAINT (M.) Writer on Gallo-Roman History. Les Étapes de l'Est . . . Préface de M. Barrès. 1910. 8°. **010170. e. 1/18.**

—— *See* WETTERLÉ (E.) Propos de guerre . . . Préface de M. M. Barrès. [1915.] 8°. **08027. a. 60.**

APPENDIX.

—— *See* BEAUSIRE (P.) D'un certain esprit français. (Notes sur Barrès, Maurras, le surréalisme.) 1930. 8°. **11822. v. 20.**

—— *See* BENJAMIN (René) Barrès. Joffre. (Grandes figures.) 1931. 8°. **10655. aaa. 24.**

—— *See* BENJAMIN (René) Le Soliloque de Maurice Barrès, *etc.* 1933. 8°. [*Les Œuvres libres, etc.* no. 29.] **12208. ee. 29.**

—— *See* BENJAMIN (René) Le Soliloque de Maurice Barrès. Orné d'une eau-forte de Renefer d'après un portrait de Maurice Barrès, *etc.* [1924.] 8°. **012548. ccc. 41.**

—— *See* BÉRARD (Léon) *Ancien Sous-Secrétaire d'État aux Beaux-Arts.* Maurice Barrès . . . Discours, *etc.* 1923. 16°. 012207. p. 1/58.

—— *See* BERLET (C.) Un Ami de Barrès, Stanislas de Guaita. 1936. 4°. **010665. i. 78.**

—— *See* BLANCHE (J. E.) De Barrès à Gide. Souvenirs. [1948.] 8°. [*Les Œuvres libres. Nouvelle série.* no. 28 (254).] **12208. ee. 254.**

—— *See* BLANC-PÉRIDIER (A.) La Route ascendante de Maurice Barrès, *etc.* 1925. 8°. **010662. cc. 61.**

—— *See* BOISDEFFRE (P. de) Barrès parmi nous, *etc.* 1952. 8°. **10666. a. 50.**

—— *See* BONNEFON (M. F. J. J. de) La Douzaine. (no. 1. M. A. M. Barrès.) 1908. 12°. **010662. df. 10.**

—— *See* BORDEAUX (H.) L'Appel du divin, ou Maurice Barrès en Orient. 1925. 8°. **11826. aaa. 41.**

—— *See* BORDEAUX (H.) Voyageurs d'Orient. (Barrès.) 1926. 8°. **010026. f. 26.**

—— *See* BORDEAUX (H.) Le Retour de Barrès à sa terre, *etc.* [With a portrait.] 1924. 8°. **10656. a. 14.**

—— *See* BORDEAUX (H. C.) Fragments de mémoires. La mort de Maurice Barrès. 1953. 8°. [*Les Œuvres libres.* Nouvelle série. no. 83.] **12208. ee. 308.**

—— *See* BOYER DE SAINTE-SUZANNE (R. de) L'Idéologie religieuse de Maurice Barrès et le catholicisme, d'après ses cahiers. 1935. 8°. **3900. ccc. 32.**

—— *See* BREMOND (H.) Maurice Barrès. 1924. 16°. **011852. f. 48.**

—— *See* CLOUARD (H.) La "Cocarde" de Barrès [i.e. the journal of that name directed by Barrès], *etc.* 1910. 8°. **11735. f. 11.**

—— *See* COCTEAU (J.) La Noce massacrée—souvenirs. I. Visites à Maurice Barrès. 1921. 8°. **10656. a. 28.**

—— *See* COHEN (Gustave) Le Dernier projet littéraire de Maurice Barrès : Descartes et la princesse Élisabeth. 1929. 16°. **012207.p.1/143.**

BARRÈS (AUGUSTE MAURICE)—[APPENDIX.]

—— *See* CORPECHOT (L.) Souvenirs d'un journaliste. (tom. 2. Barrès. Bourget.) 1936, *etc.* 8°. **10656.n.27.**

—— *See* CURTIUS (E. R.) Maurice Barrès und die geistigen Grundlagen des französischen Nationalismus. 1921. 8°. **08052. c. 17.**

—— *See* DECAHORS (E.) Trois Messages. Maurice Barrès, André Gide, François Mauriac. 1939. 8°. **8473.bb.33.**

—— *See* DUQUAIRE (H.) Dans Tolède avec Barrès et le Greco, *etc.* 1938. 8°. **10162. l. 17.**

—— *See* EBERT (J.) Maurice Barrès und die Rheinfrage. 1936. 8°. **08028. cc. 42.**

—— *See* EMPAYTAZ (F.) Chroniques barrésiennes. 1928, *etc.* 8°. **P.P. 4331. emb.**

—— *See* ENGERAND (R.) Aux fontaines de Barrès. 1929. 8°. **10655. aaa. 32.**

—— *See* FAURE-BIGUET (J. N.) Maurice Barrès, son œuvre. Portrait, *etc.* 1924. 8°. **011824. a. 70.**

—— *See* FERNANDEZ (Ramon) *Literary Critic.* Barrès. [With a portrait.] 1943. 8°. **11864. bb. 14.**

—— *See* FRANDON (I. M.) L'Orient de Maurice Barrès, *etc.* 1952. 8°. [*Société de publications romanes et françaises.* no. 35.] **Ac. 9807.**

—— *See* GAUBERT (E. A.) Figures françaises . . . A. de Rivarol . . . M. Barrès. 1910. 8°. **11851. w. 14.**

—— *See* GAULTIER (Paul) Les Maîtres de la pensée française. Paul Hervieu . . . Maurice Barrès. 1921. 8°. **011853. a. 68.**

—— *See* GILLOUIN (R.) Maurice Barrès. 1907. 8°. **010661. a. 67.**

—— *See* GIRAUD (Victor) *Professor, etc.* Les Maîtres de l'heure. M. Barrès. [1922.] 8°. **011851. b. 39.**

—— *See* GOUHIER (H.) Notre ami Maurice Barrès. 1928. 8°. **10656. de. 13.**

—— *See* GUÉRARD (Albert L.) Five Masters of French Romance : Anatole France . . . Maurice Barrès, *etc.* 1916. 8°. **011853. ppp. 15.**

—— *See* HERLUISON (J.) Maurice Barrès et le problème de l'ordre. [1911.] 8°. [*Études sociales et politiques.* no. 3.] **08052. b. 2.**

—— *See* HILL (Georges Chatterton) Lettre ouverte à M. Maurice Barrès. [In reply to the latter's defence of the Allies.] 1916. 8°. **08027. aaa. 111.**

—— *See* JACQUET (R.) Notre maître Maurice Barrès. 1900. 8°. **010662. f. 56.**

—— *See* JARY (J.) Essai sur l'art et la psychologie de M. Barrès. 1912. 8°. **011853. p. 13.**

—— *See* KING (Sylvia M.) Maurice Barrès. La pensée allemande et le problème du Rhin. [With a bibliography.] 1933. 8°. **11870.d.1/92.**

—— *See* LALONDE (M. B.) Les Origines, la formation et les années de jeunesse de M. Barrès, 1862–1895, *etc.* [1935.] 8°. **010665. f. 52.**

—— *See* LIONNET (J.) L'Évolution des idées chez quelques-uns de nos contemporains. Zola . . . Barrès, *etc.* 1903. 8°. **011853. g. 44.**

BARRÈS (AUGUSTE MAURICE)—[APPENDIX.]

—— *See* LYAUTEY (H.) Hommage d'un lorrain à un lorrain [A. M. Barrès]. 1923. 16°. **012207.p.1/57.**

—— *See* MASSIS (H.) Jugements. (sér. 1. Maurice Barrès, ou la génération du relatif.) 1923, *etc.* 8°. **11824. pp. 1.**

—— *See* MASSIS (H.) La Pensée de Maurice Barrès, *etc.* 1909. 8°. **11850. aaa. 1. (3.)**

—— *See* MERCANTON (J.) Poésie et religion dans l'oeuvre de Maurice Barrès. 1940. 8°. **11866. cc. 42.**

—— *See* MIÉVILLE (H. L.) La Pensée de Maurice Barrès. 1934. 8°. **11856. aaa. 16.**

—— *See* MOREAU (P.) *Professeur à l'Université de Fribourg.* Maurice Barrès. 1946. 8°. **010665. de. 91.**

—— *See* PICA (V.) Letteratura d'eccezione. (M. Barrès.) 1898. 8°. **011851. de. 66.**

—— *See* ROSS (Flora E.) Goethe in Modern France. With special reference to M. Barrès, *etc.* 1937. 8°. [*Illinois Studies in Language and Literature.* vol. 21. no. 3/4.] **Ac. 2692. u/15.**

—— *See* SADLER (Georges) Sur le vif. Maurice Barrès à Charmes-sur-Moselle, *etc.* 1938. 8°. **10655. h. 42.**

—— *See* THARAUD (Jérôme) and (Jean) Un Grand maître (M. Barrès) n'est plus. 1924. 16°. **012207.p.1/60.**

—— *See* THARAUD (Jérôme) and (Jean) Mes années chez Barrès. 1928. 8°. **10656. de. 7.**

—— *See* THARAUD (Jérôme) and THARAUD (Jean) Le Roman d'Aïssé. [On Countess A. de Noailles and Maurice Barrès.] 1946. 8°. **10656. k. 37.**

—— *See* THIBAUDET (A.) Les Princes lorrains. (Cahier de la mort de M. Barrès.) 1924. 8°. **12237. ppp. 1/35.**

—— *See* THIBAUDET (A.) Trente ans de vie française. (II. La Vie de M. Barrès.) 1920, *etc.* 8°. **011853. t. 37.**

—— *See* VENZAC (G.) De Chateaubriand à Barrès. Aux pays de leur enfance. (Barrès.) [With a portrait.] 1936. 4°. **010665. i. 45.**

—— *See* ZARACH (A.) Bibliographie barrésienne, *etc.* 1951. 8°. **11927. c. 22.**

—— Maurice Barrès. [A bibliography.] ff. 5. *La Rochelle,* [1924.] *obl.* 8°. **11901. a. 26.**
Cards.

BARRÈS (FRANÇOIS) Considérations générales sur le traitement de l'hydropisie ascite ; thèse, *etc.* pp. 19. *Paris,* 1825. 4°. **1183. h. 13. (26.)**

BARRÈS (H. DE) *Docteur-en-Droit.* Les Secours publics à Paris sous Louis XIV. Thèse pour le doctorat, *etc.* pp. 303. *Paris,* 1909. 8°. **08276. c. 33.**

BARRÈS (HENRI DE) Essai sur le croup. Thèse, *etc.* pp. 55. *Montpellier,* 1841. 4°. **1182. c. 9. (6.)**

BARRÈS (JEAN BAPTISTE AUGUSTE) Souvenirs d'un officier de la Grande Armée (J. B. A. Barrès). Publiés par Maurice Barrès, son petit-fils. pp. xix. 331. *Paris,* 1923. 8°. **10657. a. 17.**

—— Memoirs of a Napoleonic Officer, J. B. Barrès. Edited, and with an introduction, by his grandson Maurice Barrès. Translated by B. Miall. pp. 316. *G. Allen & Unwin : London,* 1925. 8°. **10657. bbb. 12.**

BARRÈS (MAURICE) *See* BARRÈS (Auguste M.)

BARRÈS (PHILIPPE)

—— *See* CURIE (E.) They Speak for a Nation. Letters from France. Edited . . . by E. Curie, P. Barrès, *etc.* 1941. 8°. **9100.** f. 12.

—— Ainsi que l'albatros. pp. 251. *Paris,* 1933. 8°. **12356.** p. **23.**

—— Charles de Gaulle. [With a portrait.] *Eng.* pp. 172. *Hutchinson & Co.: London,* [1942.] 8°. **010655.** ee. **31.**

—— Charles de Gaulle. pp. 316. *Montréal,* 1941. 8°. **10655.** v. 45.

—— Charles de Gaulle. [With plates, including a portrait.] pp. 255. *Continental Publishers & Distributors: London,* [1941.] 8°. **010655.** h. **6.**

—— La Guerre à vingt ans. pp. 316. *Paris,* 1924. 8°. **012551.** ee. **63.**

—— Sous la vague hitlérienne, octobre 1932—juin 1933. pp. 312. *Paris,* 1933. 8°. **08072.** b. **103.**

—— La Victoire au dernier tournant. pp. 225. *Paris,* 1932. 8°. **08028.** a. **9.**

BARRES (VINCENT) Essai sur les passions, considérées sous leur rapport médical, *etc.* pp 42. *Montpellier,* 1820. 8°. **1180.** i. **10.** (**6.**)

BARRÈS DU MOLARD (ALPHONSE) *Viscount.* Mémoires sur la guerre de la Navarre et des provinces basques, depuis son origine en 1833, jusqu'au traité de Bergara en 1839, accompagnés du portrait de Maroto. [With a map.] pp. x. 427. *Paris,* 1842. 8°. **1445.** g. **13.**

BARRESWIL (CHARLES LOUIS) *See* PARIS.—*Société chimique.* Répertoire de chimie pure et appliquée. (Compte rendu des applications de la chimie . . . par . . . C. Barreswil, *etc.*) 1858, *etc.* 8°. Ac. **3895.**

—— Documents académiques et scientifiques . . . sur le tannate de quinine. pp. 59. *Paris,* 1852. 8°. **7460.** aa. **55.** (**2.**)

—— Parfumerie. [A report.] *See* PARIS.—*Exposition Universelle de* 1867. Exposition . . . Rapports du Jury International, *etc.* tom. 3. 1868. 8°. **7956.i.9.**

BARRESWIL (CHARLES LOUIS) and **DAVANNE** (LOUIS ALPHONSE)

—— Chimie photographique . . . Quatrième édition, revue, augmentée, *etc.* pp. xx. 520. *Paris,* 1864. 8°. **1399.** e. **1.**

BARRESWIL (CHARLES LOUIS) and **GIRARD** (AIMÉ)

—— Dictionnaire de chimie industrielle. Par MM. Barreswil et A. Girard, avec la collaboration de M. de Luca, et MM. Aubergier, Balard [and others], *etc.* 3 tom. *Paris,* 1861–64. 8°. **8907.** cc. **4.**

Tom. 2 *is in* 2 *pt.* ; *tom.* 3 *in* 3 *pt.*

—— Introduction au dictionnaire de chimie industrielle. Par MM. Barreswil et A. Girard, avec la collaboration de M. de Luca, et MM. Barthelot, Bessand [and others], *etc.* pp. viii. 511. *Paris,* 1861. 8°. **8909.** ccc. **46.**

BARRESWIL (CHARLES LOUIS) and **SOBRERO** (ASCANIO)

—— Appendice à tous les traités d'analyse chimique. Recueil des observations publiées depuis dix ans, *etc.* pp. vi. 547. *Paris,* 1843. 8°. **1143.** e. **13.**

BARRET ( ) *Curé d'Amblainville. See* MANNEVILLE (C. A. A.) De l'état des terres et des personnes dans la paroisse d'Amblainville, *etc.* [Edited by —— Barret.] 1887, *etc.* 8°. [*Mémoires de la Société Académique d'Archéologie, Sciences et Arts du Département de l'Oise.* tom. 13, 14.] Ac. **278/2.**

BARRET ( ) *Member of the House of Assembly, Jamaica.* A Reply to the Speech of Dr. Lushington, in the House of Commons, on the 12th June, 1827, on the condition of the free-coloured people of Jamaica. pp. 58. *Shackell & Baylis : London,* 1828. 8°. **8156.** c. **74.** (**6.**)

—— The Speeches of Mr. Barrett and of Mr. Burge at a general meeting of Planters . . . and others, interested in the West India Colonies . . . 1833. pp. 114. *A. J. Valpy : London,* 1833. 8°. **8156.** c. **9.**

BARRET ( ) *Rédacteur du Courrier de l'Escaut.* Adresse au rédacteur du Courier de l'Escaut, Barret ; au Sr Mauson . . . Le Brun, *etc.* [On their vituperation of the Belgian revolutionists.] [*Brussels,* 1789.] *s. sh.* fol. **112.** f. **43.** (**35.**)

BARRET (ABEL) L'Intendance militaire. Son organisation, ses attributions, sa mission. pp. 48. *Paris,* 1871. 8°. **8829.** h. **35.** (**6.**)

BARRET (ALEXANDER) *See* CONYBEARE (C. A. V.) The Rosemellyn China Clay Lease . . . Correspondence relating to the transactions between Capt. S. E. Serjeant . . . and . . . A. Barret, *etc.* [1886.] 4°. **1417.** k. **56.** (**4.**)

BARRET (ANDREW)

—— Old Andrew Barrett, Esq; his Will, *etc.* (Here followeth the several opinions of Sir John Maynard, Sir William Jones [and others] . . . in the cause wherein John St. Leger is plaintiff, and John Barrett and others defendant, *etc.*) pp. 4. [1685.] fol. **1474.** d. **26.** (**5.**)

—— The Pedigree from old Andrew Barret, Esq., *etc.* (The will of Sir William Barret. The case of John Barret Esq. ; appellant, from a decree made by the High Court of Chancery in Ireland, in a cause there depending, wherein J. A. Leger Esq. is plantiff against the said J. Barret, defendant.) [*London,* 1678.] *s. sh.* fol. **816.** m. **5.** (**11.**)

—— The Pedigree from Old Andrew Barrett, Esq., *etc.* (The Case of John Barrett, Esq; appellant from a decree made . . . in a cause . . . wherein John St. Leger, Esq; is plaintiff.) pp. 4. [1685.] fol. **1474.** d. **26.** (**4.**)

BARRET (CH.) *Abbé.*

—— Études philosophiques sur Dieu et la Création d'après la Somme de Saint Thomas d'Aquin, Contra Gentes ; précédées de quelques notions sur la philosophie en général. Thèse, *etc.* pp. 293. *Paris,* 1848. 8°. **8460.** dd. **43.**

BARRET (CHARLES)

—— *See* PRINCE (JOHN D.) Grammaire pratique de la langue latvienne, *etc.* [A translation of the work by J. D. Prince, with adaptations by C. Barret and E. Blese.] 1928. 8°. **12977.** b. **2.**

BARRET (E.) *Conservateur au Musée du Limousin.* Géologie du Limousin. [With maps and plates.] pp. vi. 208. *Limoges,* 1892. 8°. **07108.** k. **6.**

BARRET (EUGÈNE) De la coxalgie. Thèse, *etc.* pp. 59. *Montpellier,* 1870. 4°. **7379.** h. **12.** (**12.**)

BARRET (FRANÇOIS)

—— L'Évolution du capitalisme japonais. 3 tom. *Paris,* [1946–48.] 8°. **8236.** h. **16.**

BARRET (FRANÇOIS)

—— Histoire du développement de la politique des prix imposés en France. pp. 283. 1935. 8°. *See* LYONS.—*Université de Lyon.—Institut de Droit Comparé.* **5423.** df. **14.**

—— La Politique des prix imposés en droit français et en droit anglais, *etc.* pp. xxiv. 308. 1935. 8°. *See* LYONS. —*Université de Lyon.—Institut de Droit Comparé.* **5423.** df. **15.**

BARRET (GEORGE) *See* BODKIN (Thomas) Four Irish Landscape Painters. George Barret, *etc.* 1920. 8°. **7859.** de. **45.**

—— The Theory and Practice of Water Colour Painting, *etc.* pp. viii. 123. *Ackermann & Co.: London,* 1840. 8°. **1044.** k. **11.**

BARRET (GULIELMUS) *Anglus.* *See* BARRET (William) *Fellow of Caius College, Cambridge.*

BARRET (HENRY) The Armyng of a Christen Warrier readie to fyghte with the enemies of our captain and Sauioure Iesus Christe, *etc.* B.L. [*T. Berthelet: London,*] 1549. 12°. **3932.** a. **30.**

BARRET (J.) *Juge de Paix.* Usages locaux du canton de Saint-Genest-Malifaux, Loire, recueillis et mis en ordre par M. J. Barret. [With a prefatory letter by B. Terrat.] pp. viii. 68. *Versailles,* 1872. 8°. **5423.** de. **6.**

BARRET (J. V.)

—— *See* CORNER (Julia) and BARRET (J. V.) The Children in the Wood. Edited by Miss Corner and J. V. Barret. [1854.] 16°. **011779.** k. **163/4.**

—— Shakspere fresh chiselled on stone, by J. V. Barret. [Humorous drawings.] *Dean & Son: London,* [1859.] 12°. **1266.** a. **22.**

—— Echoes. [Humorous drawings.] *Dean & Son: London,* [1860.] 8°. **1266.** b. **23.**

—— Reflections. [Humorous drawings.] *Dean & Son: London,* [1859.] 8°. **1266.** a. **18.**

BARRET (JACQUES)

—— Le Chant du coq, ou Prophéties mémorables, recueillies au commencement du quatorzième siècle, pour la fin du dix-huitième. [By J. Barret.] pp. 61. 1793. 8°. *See* CHANT. F. **448.** (**17.**)

BARRET (JEAN ADOLPHE) De la phthisie pulmonaire, *etc.* pp. 35. *Paris,* 1851. 4°. [*Collection des thèses soutenues à la Faculté de Médecine de Paris.* An 1851. tom. 1.] 1839, *etc.* 4°. **7372.** d. **8.**

BARRET (JOHN) *Author of the "Alvearie."* *See* BARET.

BARRET (JOHN) *Esq.*

—— *See* BARRET (Andrew) Old Andrew Barrett, Esq; his Will, *etc.* (Here followeth the several opinions of Sir John Maynard, Sir William Jones [and others] . . . in the cause wherein John St. Leger is plaintiff, and John Barrett and others defendant, *etc.*) [1685.] fol. **1474.** d. **26.** (**5.**)

—— *See* SAINT LEGER (John) *Captain.* The Judges Opinions delivered before His Grace the Lord Chancellor of Ireland, in the cause between John St. Leger, Esq; plaintiff, and John Barrett, Esq; defendant, *etc.* [1685.] fol. **1474.** d. **26.** (**6.**)

—— The Case of John Barret, appellant, from a decree made by the High Court of Chancery in Ireland, in a cause there depending wherein J. St. Leger Esq., is plantiff against the said J. Barret defendant. *See* BARRET (Andrew) The Pedigree from old Andrew Barret, *etc.* [1678.] fol. **816.** m. **5.** (**11.**)

BARRET (JOHN) *Esq.*

—— The Case of John Barrett, Esq; appellant from a decree made . . . in a cause . . . wherein John St. Leger, Esq; is plaintiff. *See* BARRET (Andrew) The Pedigree from Old Andrew Barrett, Esq; *etc.* [1685.] fol. **1474.** d. **26.** (**4.**)

—— The Case of John St. Leger Esq; respondent in the appeal of John Barret, from a decree in the Chancery of Ireland. pp. 3. [1685.] fol. L.R. **305.** a. **8.** (**6.**)

BARRET (JOHN) *M.A., of Nottingham.* *See* G., T. The Quæries Examined . . . Occasioned by the publication of Fifty Queries, gathered out of the works of Mr. Rich. Baxter, by J. B. [i.e. J. Barret], *etc.* 1676. 4°. **4325.** aaa. **32.**

—— *See* RYTHER (J.) A Defence of the Glorious Gospel of the Blessed God, attempted against the New Law: with an answer to thirteen arguments of . . . Mr. Barret, *etc.* 1703. 8°. **4256.** aa. **50.**

—— The Evil and Remedy of Scandal. A practical discourse on Psalm CXIX. CLXV. [Edited by J. Billingsley.] pp. 28. *N. Cliff & D. Jackson: London,* 1711. 8°. **4474.** c. **28.**

—— A Funeral-Sermon preached at Nottingham, occasioned by the death of Mr. John Whitlock, sen. December 8th, 1708. With another discourse partly upon the same occasion, *etc.* pp. 40. *N. Cliffe: London,* 1709. 8°. **1419.** i. **16.**

—— Much in a Little; or, an Abstract of Mr. Baxter's plain Scripture-Proof for Infants Church-Membership or Baptism. With a few notes upon the anti-queries of T. G. [i.e. on "The Quæries Examined," by Thomas Grantham.] By the same hand that wrote the Fifty Queries [i.e. J. Barret. The preface signed: J. B.]. pp. [70]. 1678. 8°. *See* B., J. **4325.** a. **5.**

—— *See* GRANTHAM (Thomas) *Baptist Minister.* The Controversie about Infants Church-Membership and Baptism, epitomized. In two treatises . . . The second, being a plain confutation of Mr. J. B. his second book of more than 60 queries, about Infants Church-Membership and Baptism [i.e. of "Much in a Little," by J. Barret], *etc.* 1680. 4°. **4325.** aaa. **35.**

—— The Rector of Sutton committed with the Dean of St. Paul's, or, a Defence of Dr. Stillingfleet's Irenicum, his Discourses of Excommunication of Idolatry, and other writings; against his late sermon, intituled, The Mischief of Separation. By the author of the Christian Temper [i.e. J. Barret], *etc.* pp. 80. 680. 4°. *See* STILLINGFLEET (E.) *Bishop of Worcester.* **699.** f. **27.**

—— [Another copy.] **110.** f. **8.**

—— Reliquiæ Barretteanæ. Or, Select sermons on sundry practical subjects. pp. 212. *John Collyer: Nottingham; R. Robinson; N. Cliff & D. Jackson: London,* 1714. 8°. **4461.** aaa. **3.**

—— A Sermon preach'd at the Funeral of . . . W. Reynolds. *See* WHITLOCK (John) *the Elder.* A Short Account of the Life of . . . W. Reynolds, *etc.* 1698. 8°. G. **14385.** (**2.**)

BARRET (JOHN) *of Boston, Mass.* Proposals for carrying on a Manufacture in the Town of Boston, for employing the poor of said town. [Signed: J. Barret, E. Goldthwait, and others.] [*Boston,* 1768.] *s. sh.* fol. **8223.** e. **1.** (**170.**)

BARRET (KATHARINE ELLIS) *See* BARRETT (K. R. S.)

BARRET (L.) *Ingénieur.*

—— Note sur l'aménagement des ports de commerce. pp. viii. 341. pl. LXII. [1875.] 8°. *See* MARSEILLES.—*Société Scientifique Industrielle.* Ac. **4411.**

BARRET (L. H.) Propositions de médecine et de chirurgie ; thèse, *etc.* pp. 16. *Paris,* 1833. 4°. **1184.** f. **3.** (**34.**)

BARRET (LEIGHTON)

—— Though Young. [A novel.] pp. 251. *Random House: New York,* [1938.] 8°. **12717.** bb. **5.**

BARRET (LE ROY CARR)

—— *See* VEDAS.—*Atharvaveda.* The Kashmirian Atharva Veda, Book one(–five, seven–fifteen, eighteen). Edited with critical notes by L. C. Barret. 1906, *etc.* 8°. [*Journal of the American Oriental Society.* vol. 26, 30, 32, 35, 37, 40–44, 46–48, 50, 58.] Ac. **8824.**

—— *See* VEDAS.—*Atharvaveda.* The Kashmirian Atharva Veda. Books sixteen and seventeen (nineteen and twenty). Edited with critical notes by L. C. Barret. 1936, *etc.* 8°. [*American Oriental Series.* vol. 9, 18.] **14005.** aa. **2.**

BARRET (LOUIS FRANÇOIS ANDRÉ) Discours pour la bénédiction des drapeaux de la Garde nationale parisienne, *etc.* pp. 32. *Paris,* 1789. 8°. F. **1067.** (**5.**)

BARRET (MARIE ANTOINE) Thèse pour le doctorat en médecine, *etc.* (Questions sur diverses branches des sciences médicales.) pp. 37. *Paris,* 1847. 4°. [*Collection des thèses soutenues à la Faculté de Médecine de Paris.* An 1847. tom. 1.] **7372.** a. **9.**

BARRET (MARY LÆTITIA)

—— *See* PARREL (C. de) L'Idylle d'un prisonnier de guerre français à Wantage, 1809. M. L. Barret et le lieutenant-colonel Chalot, *etc.* 1934. 8°. **010825.** ee. **19.**

BARRET (NARCISSE) Nouméa. Aller et retour. (Voyage du Navarin en Nouvelle Calédonie.) pp. 215. *Paris,* 1880. 12°. **10097.** aa. **14.**

BARRET (P.) *Attaché de recherches.*

—— La Mesure des températures des flammes. pp. 41. *Paris,* 1950. fol. [*France. Ministère de l'Air. Notes techniques.* no. 33.] S. E. **58/3.**

—— Un Nouveau manographe photo-électrique. pp. 14. *Paris,* 1950. fol. [*France. Ministère de l'Air. Notes techniques.*] S. E. **58/3.**

BARRET (PAUL) De la lumière naturelle envisagée comme modificateur physiologique, hygide et thérapeutique. Thèse, *etc.* pp. 56. *Montpellier,* 1870. 4°. **7379.** h. **12.** (**13.**)

—— Sénégambie et Guinée.—La Région gabonaise. L'Afrique occidentale. La nature et l'homme noir. Avec 2 cartes. 2 tom. *Paris,* 1888. 8°. **10095.** ee. **6.**

BARRET (RICHARD)

—— *See* SANDERS (Nicholas) De iustitia Britannica, *etc.* [With a prefatory letter by R. Barret.] 1584. 8°. **808.** c. **14.**

BARRET (ROBERT) *Brother of Surgeons Hall.* A Companion for Midwives, childbearing women, and nurses, directing them how to perform their respective offices. Together with an essay, endeavouring to shew the influence of moral abuses upon the health of children. pp. 111. *For Tho. Ax: London,* 1699. 8°. **1177.** h. **2.**

BARRET (ROBERT) *of Esborn in Sussex.* The Perfect and Experienced Farrier . . . shewing a most exact . . . way of curing all sorances and diseases incident to horses, and other cattle, *etc.* pp. 31. *T. Fawcet for Fr. Coles: London,* 1660. 4°. E. **1022.** (**3.**)

—— [Another copy.] **C.31.f.16.(4.)**
The titlepage and following leaf are mutilated.

BARRET (ROBERT) *Soldier of Fortune.* The Theorike and Practike of moderne Warres, discoursed in dialogue wise, *etc.* pp. 247. [*R. Field*] *For William Ponsonby, London:* 1598. fol. **534.** l. **1.**

BARRET (THOMAS) *See* BARNET.

BARRET (WILLIAM) *Consul in Aleppo.* The Money and Measures of Babylon, Balsara, and the Indies, with the customes, &c. Written from Aleppo in Syria An. 1584. 1598. *See* HAKLUYT (R.) The Principal Navigations, *etc.* vol. 2. pt. 1. 1598, *etc.* fol. **683.** h. **5.**

—— [Another edition.] 1810. *See* HAKLUYT (R.) Hakluyt's Collection of the Early Voyages, *etc.* vol. 2. 1809, *etc.* 4°. **208.** h. **11.**

BARRET (WILLIAM) *See* HELIODORUS, *Bishop of Tricca.* Heliodorus his Æthiopian History done out of Greeke [by T. Underdowne and revised by W. Barret], *etc.* 1622. 4°. **1074.** l. **10.**

—— *See* S., R. St. Peters Complainte . . . Wth other workes of the author R. S. [i.e. Robert Southwell], *etc.* [Edited by W. Barret.] 1620. 12°. **11623.** aa. **35.**

—— —— 1630. 12°. **C.118.a.27.**

BARRET (WILLIAM) *Fellow of Caius College, Cambridge.* *See* ANDREWES (Lancelot) successively *Bishop of Chichester, of Ely, etc.* [*Miscellaneous Writings.*] Lanceloti Andrewes de Synodo oblatis articulis judicium ; unà cum ejusdem censurâ censuræ D. Barreti, de certitudine salutis, *etc.* 1631. 12°. [*Articuli Lambethani.*] **C.110.a.13.(3.)**

—— —— 1696. 12°. [*Articulorum* XXXIX *Ecclesiæ Anglicanæ defensio.*] **843.** b. **19.**

—— —— 1700. 12°. **3505.** d. **39.** (**1.**)

—— *See* ANDREWES (Lancelot) successively *Bishop of Chichester, of Ely, etc.* [*Miscellaneous Writings.*] The Judgement of . . . Dr. L. Andrewes . . . concerning the Articles which were offered to the Assembly, together with his review of the censure passed upon Dr. Barret, concerning certainty of salvation. 1700. 12°. [*A Defence of the Thirty-nine Articles.*] **3505.** d. **39.** (**2.**)

—— A Coppie of a Recantation of certaine errors . . . made by Maister Barret . . . in . . . 1595 . . . Translated out of Lattine into English. *See* PRYNNE (W.) God no Impostor nor Deluder. 1629. 4°. **702.** f. **27.**

—— [Another edition.] *See* PRYNNE (W.) God no Impostor, *etc.* 1630. 4°. **700.** g. **6.** (**4.**)

BARRET (WILLIAM) *Fellow of Caius College, Cambridge.*

—— Ius Regis, siue de absoluto & independenti Secularium Principum dominio & obsequio eis debito, *etc.* pp. 543. *Apud H. Pistum: Basileiæ* [*N. Okes: London*], 1612. 8°. C. **64.** c. **4.**

—— [Another copy.] **522.** b. **16.**
Imperfect, and mutilated at the end.

BARRET (*Sir* WILLIAM)

—— The several Depositions taken about the Proof of Sir William Barret's Will in Bristoll, *etc.* pp. 4. [1685.] fol. **1474.** d. **26.** (**6.**)

BARRET (*Sir* William)

—— The Will of Sir William Barret. *See* Barret (Andrew) The Pedigree from old Andrew Barret, *etc.* [1678.] *s. sh.* fol. **816. m. 5. (11.)**

BARRET DE NAZARIS (Esther) *See* Bolívar (Simón) *President of the Republic of Colombia.* Cartas del Libertador, *etc.* (Indice analítico . . . formado con la colaboración de . . . E. Barret de Nazaris.) 1929, *etc.* 8°. **010920.dd.20.**

—— *See* Bolívar (S.) *President of the Republic of Colombia.* Simón Bolívar. Obras completas . . . Compilación y notas de V. Lecuna, con la colaboración de . . . E. Barret de Nazaris. 1947. 8°. **12230. e. 17.**

—— *See* Bolívar (S.) *President of the Republic of Colombia.* Simón Bolívar. Obras completas. Compilación y notas de Vicente Lecuna, con la colaboración de la señorita Esther Barret de Nazaris. 1950. 8°. **12232. e. 4.**

—— *See* Lecuna (Vicente) *of Caracas.* La Entrevista de Guayaquil . . . Por V. Lecuna . . . Con la cooperación de E. Barret de Nazaris. 1952. 8°. W.P. **B. 547/5.**

—— *See* Lecuna (V.) *of Caracas.* Relaciones diplomáticas de Bolívar con Chile y Buenos Aires . . . Obra preparada con la colaboración de la señorita E. Barret de Nazaris, *etc.* 1954. 8°. **9774. e. 16.**

BARRET DE NAZARIS (V.) El General Venancio Pulgar, Presidente constitucional del Estado soberano del Zulia, ante la nacion. [With a portrait.] pp. 203. *Carácas,* 1873. 8°. **8180. dd. 3.**

BARRETIER (Francis) *See* Baratier (François)

BARRETIER (John Philip) *See* Baratier (Jean P.)

BARRETO ( )

—— *See* Farias Brito (R. de) Obras de Farias Brito . . . Introdução de Barreto Filho. 1951, *etc.* 8°. W.P. **838.**

BARRETO (Adriano Ernesto de Castilho) *See* Castilho Barreto.

BARRETO (Affonso Henrique Lima) *See* Lima Barreto (A. H.)

BARRETO (Benjamin Muniz) *See* Muniz Barreto.

BARRETO (Domingos Alves Branco Moniz) *See* Alves Branco Moniz Barreto.

BARRETO (Francisco) *Bishop of Algarve. See* Algarve, *Diocese of.* Constituiçoens Synodaes do bispado do Algarve novamente feytas . . . pelo . . . Senhor Dom F. Barreto, *etc.* 1674. fol. **5107. g. 6.**

BARRETO (Francisco) *Governor of Pernambuco.* Relaçam diaria do sitio, e tomada da forte praça do Recife, recuperação das Capitanías de Itamaracà, Paraiba, Rio grande, Ciará, & Ilha de Fernão de Noronha, por F. Barreto, *etc.* *Na officina Craesbeeckiana : Lisboa,* 1654. 4°. **9195. c. 22. (3.)**

BARRETO (Francisco de) *Governor of India.*

—— *See* Monclaro (F.) Relaçaõ da Viagem q̃ fizeraõ os Pes da Companhia de Jesus com F. Barretto na conquista de Monomotapa no anno de 1569. 1899. 8°. [Theal (*George M.*) *Records of South-Eastern Africa, etc.* vol. 3.] **09061. aa.**

BARRETO (Francisco Xavier Paes) *See* Paes Barreto.

BARRETO (G. Moniz) *See* Moniz Barreto.

BARRETO (Gianfrancesco) *See* Barreto (João F.)

BARRETO (Honório Pereira) *See* Pereira Barretto.

BARRETO (Isabel)

—— *See* Bosch Barrett (M.) Doña Isabel Barreto, *etc.* 1943. 8°. **010632. b. 29.**

BARRETO (J. A. da Graça) *See* Graça Barreto.

BARRETO (Jeronimo) *Bishop of Funchal. See* Funchal, *Diocese of.* Constituicões Synodaes do bispado do Funchal [promulgated by J. Barreto], *etc.* 1601. 4°. **5107. ee. 16.**

BARRETO (João)

—— História da Guiné, 1418–1918, *etc.* [With illustrations.] pp. 452. *Lisboa,* 1938. 8°. **10483. d. 2.**

BARRETO (João de Barros) *See* Barros Barreto.

BARRETO (João Franco) *See* Camoens (L. de) Obras de L. de Camoens . . . Com os argumentos do Lecenceado J. F. Barreto, *etc.* 1669, *etc.* 4°. **1072. g. 14.**

—— —— 1720. fol. **85. l. 7.**

—— —— 1670. 12°. **11452. a. 6.**

—— —— 1721. 16°. **11452. aa. 43.**

—— —— 1731, *etc.* 4°. **11452. k. 7.**

—— *See* Camoens (L. de) La Lusiade . . . Tradctta . . . da N. N. Piemontese . . . con gli argomenti aggiunti al poema da G. Barreto. 1772. 12°. **243. a. 18.**

—— *See* Virgilius Maro (P.) [*Aeneis.—Portuguese.*] Eneida Portugueza. Por J. F. Barreto. 1664, *etc.* 12°. **238. i. 30.**

—— —— 1808. 8°. **11355. b. 32.**

—— Relação da Embaixada [of Francisco de Mello and Antonio Coelho de Carvalho] a França em 1641 . . . Reimpressa com noticias e documentos elucidativos por Carlos Roma du Bocage e Edgar Prestage. pp. cxxxviii. 381. 1918. 8°. *See* Lisbon.—*Academia das Sciencias de Lisboa.* **9180. ee. 15.**

BARRETO (João Nunes) *Patriarch of Ethiopia. See* Nunes Barreto.

BARRETO (José María) Sin Réplica. Cartas diplomáticas. pp. ii. 66. *La Paz, Bolivia,* 1919. 8°. **8180. bb. 66.**

BARRETO (José Teixeira) *See* Teixeira Barreto.

BARRETO (José Trazimundo Mascarenhas) *Marquis de Fronteira* and *d'Alorna. See* Mascarenhas Barreto.

BARRETO (Joseph G.)

—— An Adventure in Mexico. pp. 216. *Cosmic Age Press: [San Diego;] printed in Mexico,* 1952. 8°. **010481. a. 67.**

BARRETO (L. P.) Ordem e Progresso. As Tres Philosophias. 2 pt. *Rio de Janeiro,* 1874, 76 [77]. 8°. **8464. bbb. 35.**

BARRETO (Luiz do Rego) *See* Rego Barreto.

BARRETO (M. de Barros) *See* Barros Barreto.

BARRETO (M. P. dos Santos) *See* Santos Barreto.

BARRETO (Nicolás) *Count de Casa Barreto.* Contestacion al manifiesto que ha dado . . . F. de Arango sobre la Junta proyectada en la Habana en Julio . . . 1808. pp. 31. *Habana,* 1821. 8°. **8155. b. 24.**

—— Contestacion que dá el Conde de Casa Barreto, al papel del . . . Señor D. F. de Arango ; contrayendose en parte a los publicados por el Señor D. José del mismo apellido. pp. 18. *Habana,* 1821. 8°. **8155. b. 23.**

BARRETO (Paulo) *See* Rio (J. do) *pseud.* [i.e. P. Barreto.]

BARRETO (Rozendo Moniz) *See* Moniz Barreto.

BARRETO (Sebastiano) *See* Jesuits. [*Letters from Missions.*] Histoire de ce qui s'est passé en Éthiopie, Malabar, Brasil, et és Indes Orientales. Tirée des lettres escrites [by S. Barreto and others] és années 1620. jusques à 1624, *etc.* 1628. 8°. **867. d. 18.**

—— Lettera della provintia di Goa. Dell' anno 1624. *See* Jesuits. [*Letters from Missions.*] Lettere annue, *etc.* 1627. 8°. **4766. aaa. 8. (2.)**

BARRETO CORTE REAL (Antonio Moniz) *See* Moniz Barreto Corte Real.

BARRETO DE MENESES (Tobias) Brasilien wie es ist in literarischer Hinsicht betrachtet, *etc.* pp. 38. *Pernambuco,* 1876. 8°. **011850. g. 6. (1.)**

—— Estudos allemães. Publicação posthuma dirigida por S. Roméro. pp. xxiv. 710. *Rio de Janeiro,* 1892. 8°. **10235. cc. 9.**

BARRETO DE OLIVEIRA ( )

—— *See* Lapie (P. O.) [La Légion Étrangère à Narvik.] A Epopeia de Narvik . . . Tradução do Brigadeiro Barreto de Oliveira. 1941. 8°. **09101. a. 16.**

BARRETO FEIO (Joze Victorino) *See* Camoens (L. de) Die Lusiaden, *etc.* (Kritische Einleitung zu den Lusiaden. Von Barreto Feio und G. Monteiro.) 1857. 8°. **11452. a. 18.**

—— *See* Michael, calling himself *King of Portugal.* Dom Miguel, ses aventures scandaleuses . . . Traduit [and augmented, mainly from the notes of J. V. Barreto Feio] par J. B. Mesnard. 1833. 8°. **9195. bb. 13.**

—— *See* Sallustius Crispus (C.) [*Works.—Latin and Portuguese.*] Sallustio em Portuguez por J. V. Barreto Feio. 1825. 12°. **587. a. 18.**

—— *See* Sines (J. D. de) Biographia posthuma do eximio patriota J. V. Barreto Feio. 1850. 8°. **10632. bb. 13.**

—— *See* Vicente (G.) Obras . . . Correctas . . . pelo ciudado . . . de J. V. Barreto Feio e J. G. Monteiro. 1843. 8°. **11726. g. 19.**

—— —— 1834. 8°. **839. e. 21.**

BARRETO FILHO (Mello) *See* Mello Barreto Filho ( )

BARRETO PEREIRA DE CAMPOS (Affonso) Classes das penas, sua graduacão, e differentes especies de applicação, ou Mapa de classificação, e graduação duplice correlativa das penas do Codigo penal portuguez, e da Reforma penal do 1°. de julho de 1867, *etc.* [With tables.] pp. 71. *Lisboa,* 1875. 8°. **6056. df. 5.**

BARRET-PRAHEL (François) Considérations médico-légales sur l'ecchymose. pp. 20. *Strasbourg,* 1829. 4°. [*Collection générale des dissertations de la Faculté de Médecine de Strasbourg.* vol. 40.] **7381*.b.**

BARRETT'S GENERAL AND COMMERCIAL DIRECTORY.

—— Barrett's General and Commercial Directory of Burnley. *See* Directories.—*Burnley.* Directory and Topography of Burnley.

—— Barrett's General & Commercial Directory of Preston and District. *See* Directories.—*Preston.* General and Commercial Directory of Preston.

BARRETT'S LONDON AND PROVINCIAL TRADES REGISTER. *See* Directories.—*Commerce.*

BARRETT'S PUBLICATIONS LTD.

—— Barrett's Derby County Borough Directory. *See* Directories.—*Derby, County of.*

BARRETT, *Family of.* *See* Lennard (T. B.) An Account of the Families of Lennard and Barrett, *etc.* 1908. 8°. **9904. r. 5.**

—— *See* Marks (Jeannette) The Family of the Barrett, *etc.* [On Elizabeth Barrett Browning and the Barrett family. With portraits.] 1938. 8°. **9915. s. 6.**

BARRETT ( ) *Member of the House of Assembly, Jamaica.* *See* Barret.

BARRETT ( ) *Mrs.* Practical Illustrations on fitting and making Dresses in the French and English styles. [With a folding plate.] pp. 16. *The Author: London,* [1854.] 8°. **1269. b. 13.**

—— Second edition. [With plates.] pp. 16. *Harrisons: London,* [1856.] 8°. **1269. e. 41.**

BARRETT (A. N.) Inspection of Aero-Engines after Overhaul. *See* Aero-Engines. Aero-Engines, *etc.* 1934. 8°. **08773.e.21/4.**

—— Aero-Engines, inspection of, during manufacture, overhaul and test. "D." Licence . . . Second edition. pp. viii. 77. *Sir I. Pitman & Sons: London,* 1935. 8°. [*Aeronautical Engineering Series. Ground Engineers.*] **08773.e.21/6.**

—— Aero-Engines, inspection of, during manufacture, overhaul, and test. "D" Licence. . . . Third edition. pp. viii. 117. *Sir I. Pitman & Sons: London,* 1935. 8°. [*Aeronautical Engineering Series. Ground Engineers.*] **08773.e.21/10.**

—— Aero-Engines, inspection of, during manufacture, overhaul, and test. "D" licence . . . Fourth edition. pp. viii. 123. *Sir I. Pitman & Sons: London,* 1936. 8°. [*Aeronautical Engineering Series. Ground Engineers.*] **08773.e.21/11.**

—— Aero-Engines . . . "D" Licence . . . Fifth edition. pp. viii. 128. *Sir I. Pitman & Sons: London,* 1937. 8°. [*Aeronautical Engineering Series. Ground Engineers.*] **08773.e.21/15.**

—— Aero-Engines . . . Sixth edition. pp. viii. 136. *Sir I. Pitman & Sons: London,* 1939. 8°. [*Aeronautical Engineering Series.* Ground Engineers.] **08773.e.21/20.**

—— Aero-Engines . . . Seventh edition. pp. viii. 140. *Sir I. Pitman & Sons: London,* 1940. 8°. [*Aeronautical Engineering Series. Ground Engineers.*] **08773.e.21/25.**

—— Aero-Engines . . . Eighth edition. pp. viii. 140. *Sir I. Pitman & Sons: London,* 1941. 8°. [*Aeronautical Engineering Series. Ground Engineers.*] **08773.e.21/27.**

—— Aero-Engines . . . Ninth edition. pp. viii. 160. *Sir I. Pitman & Sons: London,* 1942. 8°. [*Aeronautical Engineering Series. Ground Engineers.*] **08773.e.21/32.**

BARRETT (Ada Louise)

—— George Stephenson, Father of Railways. [With plates, including a portrait.] pp. vii. 287. *Paebar Co.: New York,* [1948.] 8°. **10863. f. 91.**

BARRETT (ALBERT R.) Modern Banking Methods and practical bank bookkeeping . . . Illustrated with over two hundred forms of bank books, *etc.* pp. 325. *Bradford Rhodes & Co.: New York,* 1902. 8°. **8229.** h. **28.**

BARRETT (ALEXANDER) Essay on Conciliation, or Review of the Viceroyalty of the Marquis Wellesley, *etc.* pp. 142. *The Author: Dublin,* 1823. 8°. **8145.** e. **4.**

BARRETT (ALFRED) *M.A., of Worcester College, Oxford.* Latin Exercises for the Lowest Form. pp. vii. 188. *Longman & Co.: London,* 1854. 12°. [*New Series of Latin Exercises.* no. 2.] **12934.** b. **38.**

—— Little Arthur's Latin Primer; or, Latin etymology and syntax for little boys. pp. 56. *Longman & Co.: London,* 1854. 12°. [*New Series of Latin Exercises.* no. 1.] **12934.** b. **38.**

—— Waste of Mental Labour. *See* YATES (James) *F.R.S.* International Association for obtaining a uniform Decimal System, *etc.* 1860. 8°. **8504.** d. **37.** (**6.**)

BARRETT (ALFRED) *Wesleyan Minister. See* BURTON, afterwards CRYER (Mary) The Devotional Remains of Mrs. Cryer. With an introduction by the Rev. A. Barrett. 1854. 12°. **4906.** d. **48.**

—— —— [1862.] 12°. **4407.** aaa. **34.**

—— *See* HAY (David) Home: or, the Way to make home happy . . . With an introduction by the Rev. A. Barrett. 1854. 12°. **4406.** a. **89.**

—— *See* STEWARD (George) *Independent Minister.* The Farewell to Wesleyan Controversy: being a defence of the principles of Church Government in reply to the "Wesleyan Magazine," and the Rev. A. Barrett. 1854. 8°. **4135.** e. **31.**

—— The Boatman's Daughter: a narrative for the learned and unlearned. pp. 180. *John Mason: London,* 1847. 12°. **1362.** a. **37.**

—— Catholic Evangelical Principles, viewed in their present application to the Church of God, in a series of letters to a friend. pp. viii. 263. *Hamilton, Adams & Co.: London,* 1843. 12°. **1352.** f. **17.**

—— Christ in the Storm: or, the World pacified. pp. vii. 271. *For the Author: London,* 1849. 16°. **4375.** a. **7.**

—— Consolator: or, Recollections of a departed friend, the Rev. John Pearson. pp. 186. *Hamilton, Adams & Co.: London,* 1856. 8°. **4906.** c. **29.**

—— Discourse on the Modern Mental Philosophy, viewed in its aspects on Christianity: with strictures on that exposition of it presented by Mr. J. D. Morell, in his Philosophy of religion, *etc.* pp. 64. *For the Author: London,* 1850. 16°. **4375.** a. **8.**

—— Essay on the Pastoral Office, as a divine institution in the Church of Christ: containing a particular reference to the manner in which it is exercised amongst the Wesleyan Methodists. pp. 370. *John Mason: London,* 1839. 16°. **1115.** g. **17.**

—— Holy Living: exemplified in the life of Mrs. Mary Cryer . . . With the extracts from her papers and correspondence. pp. iv. 326. *John Mason: London,* 1825. 12°. **1373.** g. **14.**

—— The Life of the Rev. John Hewgill Bumby who was drowned in the river Thames, New Zealand, June 26th, 1840. With a brief history of the commencement and progress of the Wesleyan mission in that country. pp. vi. 374. *J. Mason: London,* 1852. 12°. **4903.** c. 87.

BARRETT (ALFRED) *Wesleyan Minister.*

—— Longing for Spiritual Light. A sermon. *See* WESLEYAN METHODIST MINISTERS. Sermons by Wesleyan Methodist Ministers. vol. 1. 1850, *etc.* 12°. **4461.** f. **24.**

—— The Ministry and Polity of the Christian Church: viewed in their scriptural and theological aspects; and in relation to principles professed by the Wesleyan Methodists. pp. xvi. 453. *John Mason: London,* 1854. 8°. **4139.** d. **10.**

—— Mr. Barrett's New Pastoral Addresses. [Being a reply to his two letters "On the Theory of two Wesleyan parties, and a compromise between them."] pp. 8. 1851. 8°. **4139.** g. **1.** (**14.**)

BARRETT (ALFRED MOUAT) Notes on the various Arms of the Service, their characteristics and employment in the five principal tactical operations of war. pp. 32. *Gale & Polden: Aldershot,* 1927. 8°. **8832.** c. **15.**

BARRETT (ALFRED WALTER) *See* ANDOM (R.) *pseud.* [i.e. A. W. Barrett.]

BARRETT (ALFRED WILSON) The Blue Taxi. pp. 320. *Ward, Lock & Co.: London,* 1915. 8°. NN. **2808.**

—— [Another edition.] pp. 112. *Aldine Publishing Co.: London,* [1920.] 8°. ["*Goodship*" *Sixpennies.*] **012603.** c. **1/13.**

—— Father Pink . . . Illustrated. pp. 285. *Ward, Lock & Co.: London,* 1907. 8°. **012627.** aaa. **27.**

—— The French Master, *etc.* pp. 251. *Ward, Lock & Co.: London,* [1903.] 8°. **012638.** b. **33.**

—— The Golden Lotus. [A tale.] pp. 306. *J. Macqueen: London,* 1901. 8°. **012640.** c. **10.**

—— The House over the way, *etc.* pp. 320. *Ward, Lock & Co.: London,* 1906. 8°. **012633.** aaa. **27.**

—— [Another edition.] pp. 128. *Aldine Publishing Co.: London,* [1915.] 8°. [*Mascot Novels.* no. 23.] **12644.** a. **1/23.**

—— The Jew of Prague. pp. 311. *F. V. White & Co.: London,* 1912. 8°. NN. **1311.**

—— [Another edition.] *Aldine Publishing Co.: London,* [1921.] 8°. [*Mascot Novels.* no. 155.] **12644.** a. **1/155.**

—— Justus Wise. pp. 320. *Ward, Lock & Co.: London,* 1911. 8°. **012618.** aaa. **16.**

—— The Secret Marriage. pp. 302. *Ward, Lock & Co.: London,* 1912. 8°. NN. **170.**

—— [Another edition.] *Aldine Publishing Co.: London,* [1921.] 8°. [*Mascot Novels.* no. 171.] **12644.** a. **1/171.**

—— The Shadow on the House. pp. 284. *Everett & Co.: London,* [1909.] 8°. **012624.** aa. **7.**

—— The Silver King . . . Founded on the famous play by Henry Arthur Jones and Henry Herman. pp. 303. *Everett & Co.: London,* [1914.] 8°. NN. **2003.**

—— [Another edition.] pp. 253. *Playtime Press: London,* [1920.] 8°. **12600.** h. **51.**

—— [Another edition.] pp. 128. *George Newnes: London,* [1929.] 8°. **012604.** bbb. **14.**

—— The Silver Pin. pp. 320. *Ward, Lock & Co.: London,* 1905. 8°. **012631.** a. **16.**

—— A Soldier's Love. pp. 318. *Everett & Co.: London,* [1912.] 8°. **012623.** a. **51.**

BARRETT (ALFRED WILSON)

—— The Third Mistake. pp. 127. *Aldine Publishing Co.: London*, [1917.] 8°. [*Mascot Novels.* no. 52.] **12644.** a. **1/52.**

—— The Tower Hill Mystery. pp. 320. *Ward, Lock & Co.: London*, 1912. 8°. **012618.** aaa. **17.**

BARRETT (ALFRED WILSON) and **FRYERS** (AUSTIN) *pseud.* [i.e. WILLIAM AUSTIN CLERY.]

—— The Man with the Opals . . . Illustrations, *etc.* pp. 312. *Ward, Lock & Co.: London*, 1906. 8°. **012632.** bb. **17.**

BARRETT (AMOS) Concord and Lexington Battle . . . Written . . . 1825. 1900. *See* TRUE (Henry) *Rev., of Hampstead, New Hampshire.* Journal and Letters, *etc.* 1900. 8°. **4985.** ee. **24.**

BARRETT (ANDREW) *See* BARRET.

BARRETT (ANNE)

—— Caterpillar Hall . . . With drawings by Catherine Cummins. [A tale.] pp. 158. *Collins: London*, 1950 8°. **12831.** cc. **50.**

—— The Dark Island. pp. 191. *Collins: London*, 1952. 8°. **12829.** aa. **79.**

—— The Journey of Johnny Rew. pp. 254. *Collins: London*, 1954. 8°. **12836.** h. **8.**

—— Stolen Summer . . . With drawings by John Robinson. pp. 256. *Collins: London*, 1951. 8°. **12834.** cc. **2.**

BARRETT (ARTHUR) *See* GOLDSMITH (O.) *the Poet.* [*Poems.*] The Traveller and The Deserted Village. Edited with introduction and notes by A. Barrett. 1888. 8°. **11612.** bb. **22.**

BARRETT (ARTHUR CHARLES) Companion to the New Testament. Designed for the use of theological students, *etc.* pp. vii. 304. *Deighton, Bell & Co: Cambridge*, 1861. 8°. **3226.** a. **3.**

—— Companion to the Greek Testament . . . Second edition, revised and enlarged. pp. xii. 315. *Deighton, Bell & Co.: Cambridge*, 1867. 8°. **3021.** aa. **27.**

—— Third edition, revised and enlarged. pp. xiv. 325. *Deighton, Bell & Co.: Cambridge*, 1873. 8°. [*Cambridge School and College Text Books.*] **8703.bbb.21/1.**

—— Fourth edition, revised and enlarged. pp. xiv. 336. *Deighton, Bell & Co.: Cambridge*, 1878. 8°. [*Cambridge School and College Text Books.*] **8703.bbb.21/2.**

—— The Propositions in Mechanics and Hydrostatics, which are required of questionists, not candidates for honours [in the University of Cambridge]. pp. viii. 188. *J. & J. J. Deighton: Cambridge*, 1847. 8°. **8765.** c. **19.**

—— Second edition, with additions and corrections. pp. viii. 192. *Deighton, Bell & Co.: Cambridge*, 1855. 8°. **8765.** c. **18.**

—— Third edition, with additions and corrections. pp. viii. 199. *Deighton, Bell & Co.: Cambridge*, 1862. 8°. **8766.** b. **19**

BARRETT (ARTHUR RUSSELL) Some Records of "Ye Chapel of Marsden." Compiled by A. R. Barrett. pp. xi. 291. *Coates & Bairstow: Huddersfield*, 1910. 8°. **4707.** df. **36.**

BARRETT (ASHLEY WILLIAM) Dental Surgery for General Practitioners, *etc.* pp. xii. 83. *London*, 1885. 8°. [*Lewis's Practical Series.*] **07481.** a. **1.**

BARRETT (ASHLEY WILLIAM)

—— Dental Surgery for Medical Practitioners . . . Second edition, with illustrations. pp. xii. 136. *London*, 1890. 8°. [*Lewis's Practical Series.*] **07481.** a. **10.**

—— Third edition, *etc.* pp. xii. 54. *London*, 1897. 8°. [*Lewis's Practical Series.*] **07481.** a. **29.**

—— Fourth edition, *etc.* pp. xii. 159. *London*, 1905. 8°. [*Lewis's Practical Series.*] **07481.** a. **42.**

BARRETT (BASIL RICHARD) The Life of Cardinal Ximenes. pp. 396. *J. Booker: London*, 1813. 8°. **1124.** f. **21.**

BARRETT (BENJAMIN FISK) *See* BUSH (George) *Swedenborgian*, and BARRETT (B. F.) "Davis' Revelations" Revealed, *etc.* 1847. 8°. **8465.** d. **11.**

—— *See* NEW JERUSALEM CHURCH. Rev. Mr. Barrett and the General Convention Report of the Committee of Investigation, *etc.* 1867. 8°. **4183.** aa. **51.**

—— *See* WHITE (William) *Swedenborgian.* Life of Emanuel Swedenborg . . . With an introduction by B. F. Barrett, *etc.* 1866. 12°. **4885.** aaa. **59.**

—— Beauty for Ashes ; or, the Old and the new doctrine concerning the state of infants after death, contrasted. pp. 108. *D. Appleton & Co.: New York*, 1855. 12°. **4183.** b. **14.**

—— Catholicity of the New Church ; and Uncatholicity of New-Churchmen. pp. 312. *Mason Bros.: New York*, 1863. 12°. **4183.** aaa. **81.**

—— [Another copy, with a different titlepage.] *Longman & Co.: London ; Thomas Robinson: Manchester*, 1864. 12°. **4183.** b. **15.**

—— The Corner-Stone of the New Jerusalem. pp. 57. *Bartlett & Welford: New York*, 1845. 12°. **4183.** aa. **90.** (3.)

—— The End of the World, or, Consummation of the Age. Tract no. VI. For the New Church in the United States. pp. 54. *Otis Clapp: Boston*, 1843. 12°. **3166.** aa. **17.**

—— Episcopalianism. pp. 180. *J. B. Lippincott & Co.: Philadelphia*, 1871. 16°. **4182.** aa. **32.**

—— The Golden Reed ; or, the True measure of a true church. pp. 311. *D. Appleton & Co.: New York*, 1855. 8°. **4373.** d. **2.**

—— Heaven Revealed. Being a popular presentation of Swedenborg's disclosures about Heaven, *etc.* pp. 382. *Porter & Coates: Philadelphia*, 1885. 8°. **3716.** d. **1.**

—— Letters on the Divine Trinity, addressed to Henry Ward Beecher. pp. 160. *J. B. Lippincott & Co.: Philadelphia*, 1869. 8°. **4225.** aaa. **2.**

—— Letters on the Future Life, addressed to Henry Ward Beecher. [In reply to his sermon entitled "On the Hereafter."] pp. 191. *Claxton & Co.: Philadelphia*, 1873. 8°. **4380.** e. **21.**

—— The Lord's Prayer briefly explained. Tract no. XII. For the New Church in the United States. pp. 28. *Otis Clapp: Boston*, 1846. 12°. **3225.** aa. **31.**

—— The New Church : its nature and whereabout, *etc.* pp. 213. *Claxton & Co.: Philadelphia*, 1877. 8°. **4182.** bbb. **5**

—— The New View of Hell, showing its nature, whereabouts, duration, and how to escape it. pp. 215. *J. B. Lippincott & Co.: Philadelphia*, 1872. 8°. **4380.** a. **13.**

BARRETT (BENJAMIN FISK)

—— Den Nya läran om helvetet . . . Öfversättning [by Herrman I. Carlson]. pp. iii. 128. *Wexjö*, 1874. 8°. **4257**. m. **12**.

—— Swedenborg and Channing. Showing the many and remarkable agreements in the beliefs and teachings of these writers. pp. 288. *Claxton, Remsen & Co.: Philadelphia*, 1879. 8°. **4182**. bbb. **10**.

BARRETT (BENJAMIN HILTON) *See* GREGORY (John W.) and BARRETT (B. H.) General Stratigraphy, *etc.* 1931. 8°. W.P. **8325**/**6**.

BARRETT (BENJAMIN HILTON) and **RICHEY** (JAMES ERNEST)

—— Economic Geology of Canonbie Coalfield . . . By B. H. Barrett . . . and J. E. Richey . . . with assistance from W. E. Graham, *etc.* pp. 52. *South Kensington*, 1945. fol. [*Geological Survey of Great Britain. Wartime Pamphlet.* no. 42.] B.S. **38**. g/**8**.
Reproduced from typewriting.

BARRETT (BRYANT) *See* FRANCE. [*Laws, etc.—I.—Code Civil.*] The Code Napoléon, verbally translated from the French, to which is prefixed an introductory discourse . . . By B. Barrett. 1811. 8°. **5425**. g. **5**.

BARRETT (BYRON SIMEON) Book of Homonyms, *etc.* pp. vii. 196. *Sir I. Pitman & Sons: London*, [1914.] 8°. **12980**. a. **9**.

—— English Exercises. A book of homonyms. [A revised edition of "Book of Homonyms."] pp. viii. 157. *Sir I. Pitman & Sons: London*, 1927. 8°. **12980**. ee. **34**.

BARRETT (C. F.) The Benevolent Jew. [A song, with patter.] *See* LAUGH. Laugh when you can, *etc.* [1795?] 12°. **012314**. e. **35**. **(2.)**

—— The Great Devil's Tale. *See* CANTERBURY TALES. Canterbury Tales, *etc.* 1802. 12°. **12614**. b. **12**.

—— Mary Queen of Scots, or, the Royal captive of Fotheringay Castle: a Scottish legendary tale, *etc.* (Parental Avarice, the source of Filial Misery.) pp. 36. *Tegg & Castleman: London*, [1810?] 12°. **12611**. df. **8**.

BARRETT (C. J.) The History of Barn Elms and the Kit-Cat Club now the Ranelagh Club . . . Second edition. [With illustrations.] pp. 287. *London*, 1889. 8°. **010349**. l. **12**.
Mostly printed on one side of the leaf only.

BARRETT (C. P.) The Overseer's Guide and Assistant, containing plain instructions to overseers of parishes in Poor Law Unions. pp. 71. *Shaw & Sons: London*, 1840. 12°. **1130**. c. **34**.

BARRETT (CECIL JEREMIAH)

—— Adoption. The parent, the child, the home. pp. 97. *Clonmore & Reynolds: Dublin*, 1952. 8°. **8289**. de. **89**.

BARRETT (CHARLES) *Schoolmaster.* A Retrospect of the Year 1879 in Verse. pp. 8. *"News": Bridport*, [1880.] 12°. **11602**. ee. **9**. **(4.)**

BARRETT (CHARLES GOLDING) The Lepidoptera of the British Islands. A descriptive account of the families, genera and species indigenous to Great Britain and Ireland, *etc.* [With coloured plates.] 11 vol. *L. Reeve & Co.: London*, 1892–1907. 8°. 7298.r.17.

BARRETT (CHARLES KINGSLEY)

—— *See* HOWARD (Wilbert F.) The Fourth Gospel in Recent Criticism and Interpretation . . . Revised by C. K. Barrett. 1955. 8°. **3228**. de. **22**.

—— The Gospel according to St. John. An introduction with commentary and notes on the Greek text. pp. xii. 531. *S.P.C.K.: London*, 1955. 8°. **3053**. f. **17**.

—— The Holy Spirit and the Gospel Tradition. pp. viii. 176. *Society for Promoting Christian Knowledge: London*, 1947. 8°. **3228**. d. **6**.

BARRETT (CHARLES LESLIE)

—— *See* GULLETT (*Sir* Henry S.) and BARRETT (C. L.) Australia in Palestine. (H. S. Gullett, Chas Barrett, editors.) 1919. 4°. **9085**. ff. **24**.

—— *See* LEACH (John A.) An Australian Bird Book . . . Revised and edited by C. Barrett, *etc.* 1939. 8°. **2250**. b. **19**.

—— Across the Years. The lure of early Australian books. Edited by C. Barrett. [By various authors. With plates, including portraits.] pp. 148. *N. H. Seward Pty.: Melbourne*, 1948. 8°. **11911**. d. **45**.

—— Art of the Australian Aboriginal. By C. Barrett and Robert Henderson Croll. With a foreword by A. P. Elkin. [With plates.] pp. 94. *Bread & Cheese Club: Melbourne*, 1943. 8°. **7812**. s. **23**.

—— Australia: My Country. [With plates.] pp. 136. *Oxford University Press: Melbourne, London*, 1941. 8°. **10492**. bb. **68**.

—— An Australian Animal Book. (Revised edition.) [With plates.] pp. 374. *Oxford University Press: Melbourne*, 1947. 8°. **07209**. bb. **24**.

—— An Australian Animal Book. (Second edition.) pp. xii. 325. pl. 64. *Oxford University Press: Melbourne, Wellington*, 1955. 8°. **7211**. c. **19**.

—— Australian Bird Life. (Reprinted.) [With plates.] pp. 239. *Oxford University Press: Melbourne*, 1947. 8°. **7286**. p. **78**.

—— An Australian Wild Flower Book, *etc.* [With plates.] pp. 205. *Oxford University Press: Melbourne*, 1947. 8°. **7035**. a. **76**.

—— Australian Wild Life. [With plates.] pp. 116. *Georgian House: Melbourne*, 1943. 8°. **07209**. ee. **13**.

—— The Bird Man. A sketch of the life of John Gould. [With plates, including a portrait.] pp. 51. *Whitcombe & Tombs: Melbourne*, 1938. 8°. **10858**. a. **38**.

—— Gold in Australia. Edited by C. Barrett. [With plates.] pp. 100. *Cassell & Co.: London; Melbourne printed*, 1951. 4°. **07107**. m. **43**.

—— The Island World. An anthology of the Pacific. Edited by C. Barrett. [With plates.] pp. 185. *Oxford University Press: Melbourne*, 1944. 8°. **010493**. a. **12**.

—— Isle of Mountains. Roaming through Tasmania. (Fourth edition.) [With plates.] pp. xiii. 263. *Cassell & Co.: London; Melbourne* printed, 1950 [1951]. 8°. **010493**. aa. **6**.

—— Isles of the Sun, *etc.* [An account of the author's experiences in New Guinea and neighbouring islands. With plates and maps.] pp. xiv. 258. *William Heinemann: London: Melbourne* printed, 1954. 8°. **010493**. e. **7**.

BARRETT (CHARLES LESLIE)

—— Koala. The story of Australia's native bear. [With plates.] pp. 31. *Robertson & Mullens: Melbourne,* 1937. 8º. **7211.** b. **29.**

—— Koonwarra. A naturalist's adventures in Australia. [With plates.] pp. xii. 315. *Oxford University Press: London,* 1939. 8º. **7002.** s. **19.**

—— The Pacific, Ocean of Islands. [By various authors.] Edited by C. Barrett. [With plates.] pp. 176. *N. H. Seward Pty.: Melbourne,* [1950.] 8º. **10493.** h. **33.**

—— Parrots of Australasia, *etc.* [With plates and illustrations.] pp. v. 106. *N. H. Seward Pty.: Melbourne,* 1949. 4º. **7286.** d. **30.**

—— The Penguin People. (Drawings by R. Malcolm Warner.) pp. 64. *Cassell & Co.: London; Melbourne* printed, 1948. 4º. **7286.** v. **27.**

—— The Platypus. (The world's wonder animal.) [With illustrations.] pp. 62. *Robertson & Mullens: Melbourne,* 1944. 8º. **07209.** aaa. **11.**

—— Ralph in the Bush. pp. 61. *Melbourne,* [1922.] 8º. [*Australian Nature Story Readers.*] **7002.** p. **7/3.**

—— Rambles Round the Zoo. [With plates.] pp. 123. *Whitcombe & Tombs: Melbourne,* 1923. 8º. **7203.** a. **8.**

—— The Sunlit Land. Wanderings in Queensland. [With plates.] pp. xiii. 306. *Cassell & Co.: London,* 1947. 8º. **10493.** fff. **29.**

—— Wanderer's Rest. pp. 119. *Cassell & Co.: London; Melbourne* printed, 1946. 8º. **12360.** e. **32.**

—— Wild Life of Australia and New Guinea, *etc.* [With plates.] pp. xi. 229. *William Heinemann: London: Melbourne* printed, 1954 [1955]. 8º. **7211.** c. **13.**

BARRETT (CHARLES LESLIE) and SHEAD (ISOBEL ANN)

—— Kooborr the Koala . . . Decorations by Joan Kiddell-Monroe. pp. 48. *Oxford University Press: London.* [1941.] 8º. **12824.** e. **46.**

BARRETT (CHARLES RAYMOND) *See* KNOWLSON (T. S.)

Money-Making by Short-Story Writing. [Based on C. R. Barrett's "Short Story Writing."] 1904. 8º. **11826.** m. **5.**

BARRETT (CHARLES RAYMOND BOOTH) *See* also SANTOS, *pseud.* [i.e. C. R. Barrett.]

—— *See* ENGLAND.—*Army.—Infantry.—King's Shropshire Light Infantry.* The 85th King's Light Infantry, now 2nd Battn. The King's Shropshire Light Infantry. By "One of Them." Edited by C. R. B. Barrett. 1913. 8º. **8832.** dd. **8.**

—— *See* HUEFFER (Joseph L.F.H.M.) The Queen Who Flew . . . With . . . border design by C. R. B. Barrett. 1894. 4º. **12410.** eee. **24.**

—— *See* MACCALMONT (Rose E.) Memoirs of the Binghams . . . Edited by C. R. B. Barrett. 1915. 4º. **9906.** p. **9.**

—— Barrett's Illustrated Guides. no. 1–9. *Lawrence & Bullen: London,* 1892–94. 8º. **010360.** e. **35.**

—— Battles and Battlefields in England . . . Illustrated by the author. With an introduction by H. D. Traill. pp. xxviii. 458. *Innes & Co.: London,* 1896. 8º. **9503.** ee. **19.**

BARRETT (CHARLES RAYMOND BOOTH)

—— Caister Castle and Sir John Fastolfe, K.G. [An extract from the Journal of the British Archaeological Association.] [*London,* 1895.] 8º. **07709.** cc. **33.**

—— The Chapel of Lede or Lead, in the Parish of Ryther-cum-Ozendyke, Yorks. [An extract from The Journal of the British Archaeological Association.] [*London,* 1895 ?] 8º. **07709.** cc. **32.**

—— Charterhouse. 1611–1895, in pen and ink . . . With a preface by G. E. Smythe. *Bliss & Co.: London,* 1895. 4º. **10349.** pp. **2.**

—— Essex: highways, byways and waterways. Written and illustrated by C. B. R. Barrett. 2 ser. **L.P.** *Lawrence & Bullen: London,* 1892, 93. 8º. **10352.** i. **42.**

—— Hippo-Sandals. [An extract from The Journal of the British Archaelogical Association.] [*London,* 1894.] 8º. **7704.** cc. **34. (5.)**

—— The History of the Society of Apothecaries of London . . . Illustrated by the author. pp. xxxix. 310. *Elliot Stock: London,* 1905. 4º. **7680.** f. **14.**

—— History of the XIII. Hussars . . . With illustrations. 2 vol. *See* ENGLAND.—*Army.—Cavalry.—Thirteenth Hussars.* 1911. 4º. **8833.** cc. **1.**

—— The Missing Fifteen Years, 1625–1640, in the life of Robert Blake, Admiral and General at Sea. [An extract from The Journal of the Royal United Service Institution. [*London,* 1917.] 8º. **10816.** h. **17.**

—— "Riding Skimmington" and "Riding the Stang." [An extract from the Journal of the British Archaeological Association.] [*London,* 1894.] 8º. **12430.** l. **23. (3.)**

—— The 7th, Queen's Own, Hussars. [With illustrations and maps.] 2 vol. 1914. 8º. *See* ENGLAND.—*Army.—Cavalry.—Seventh (Queen's Own) Hussars.* **L.R. 33.** b. **1.**

—— Somersetshire: highways, byways, and waterways. Written and illustrated by C. R. B. Barrett. [With plates.] 2 pt. **L.P.** *Bliss & Co.: London,* 1894. 4º & fol. **L.R.404.h.11.**
No. 43 *of an edition of* 65 *copies.*

—— Surrey: highways, byways and waterways. Written and illustrated by C. R. B. Barrett. pp. xv. 251. *Bliss & Co.: London,* 1895. 4º. **10352.** dd. **13.**

—— The Tower: a series of etchings with vignettes, descriptive letterpress &c., by C. R. B. Barrett. *Catty & Dobson: London,* [1889.] fol. **Cup.1247.ccc.16.**

—— The Trinity House of Deptford Strond. Written and illustrated by C. R. B. Barrett. pp. x. 159. *Lawrence & Bullen: London,* 1893. 4º. **8807.** g. **30.**

BARRETT (CHARLES ROBIN)

—— Studies in the Word-Order of Ælfric's Catholic Homilies and Lives of the Saints. Inaugural-Dissertation der philosophisch-historischen Fakultät der Universität Bern, *etc.* pp. ix. 135. *Cambridge,* 1953. 8º. [*University of Cambridge. Museum of Archaeology and Ethnology. Department of Anglo-Saxon. Occasional Papers.* no. 3.] Ac. **5626.** c.

BARRETT (CHARLES SANBORN)

—— Structure of Metals. Crystallographic methods, principles, and data. pp. xiii. 567. *McGraw-Hill Book Co.: New York & London,* 1943. 8º. [*Metallurgy and Metallurgical Engineering Series.*] W.P. **13077/4.**

—— Structure of Metals . . . Second edition. pp. xvi. 661. *McGraw-Hill Book Co.: New York,* 1952. 8º. [*Metallurgy and Metallurgical Engineering Series.*] W.P. **13077/16.**

BARRETT (CHARLES SANBORN)

—— Structure of Metals . . . Second edition. pp. xvi. 659. *McGraw-Hill Publishing Co.: London; printed in U.S.A.,* [1953.] 8°. [*Metallurgy and Metallurgical Engineering Series.*] W.P. **13077/17.**

BARRETT (CHARLOTTE FRANCES) *See* BURNEY, afterwards D'ARBLAY (Frances) Diary and Letters of Madame d'Arblay . . . Edited by her Niece [i.e. C. F. Barrett]. 1842, *etc.* 8°. **010854.** df. **1.**

—— *See* BURNEY, afterwards D'ARBLAY (Frances) Diary and Letters . . . Edited by her niece [C. F. Barrett], *etc.* 1854. 8°. **10824.** a. **29.**

—— —— 1891. 8°. **10855.** e. **16.**

—— —— 1904, *etc.* 8°. **10863.ff.1.**

BARRETT (CHRISTOPHER MERIFIELD) A Poem . . . entitled: "The Ghost of Gas Hill," a legend of Truro. pp. 8. *Lake & Lake: Truro,* [1881.] 8°. **11602.** ee. **30. (4.)**

BARRETT (CLIFFORD L.)

—— Contemporary Idealism in America . . . [Essays by various authors.] Edited by Clifford Barrett. pp. ix. 326. *Macmillan Co.: New York,* 1932. 8°. **08458.** b. **53.**

—— Ethics. An introduction to the philosophy of moral values. [With a bibliography.] pp. xi. 484. *Harper & Bros.: New York & London,* 1933. 8°. **8411.** d. **15.**

—— Philosophy. An introductory study of fundamental problems and attitudes. [With a bibliography.] pp. xiii. 395. *Macmillan Co.: New York,* 1935. 8°. **08459.** e. **37.**

BARRETT (CLYDE) The Fourteenth Guest. A comedy of superstition in one act. pp. 31. *Samuel French: New York, London,* [1927.] 8°. **11791.** ee. **41. (10.)**

—— [Another edition.] pp. 32. *London, New York,* 1931. 8°. [*French's Acting Edition.*] **11791.** t. **1/221.**

BARRETT (DANIEL WILLIAM) Life and Work among the Navvies . . . Second edition. pp. xv. 157. *Wells Gardner & Co.: London,* 1880. 8°. **8277.** bbb. **35.**

—— Third edition. pp. xvi. 162. *S.P.C.K.: London,* 1883. 8°. **8277.** bbb. **34.**

—— The Royal Prisoner of Holdenby. (King Charles I at "Holmby House.") [With plates, including a portrait.] pp. 16. *The Author: [Holdenby,* 1910?] 8°. **10807.** h. **11.**

—— Sketches of Church Life in the counties of Essex and Hertfordshire forming the Diocese of St. Albans . . . With map. pp. xvi. 447. *Skeffington & Son: London,* 1902. 8°. **4707.** f. **25.**

BARRETT (DANIEL WILLIAM) and **WORDSWORTH** (CHRISTOPHER) *Fellow of Peterhouse, Cambridge.*

—— A Catalogue of the Library at King's Cliffe, Northamptonshire, founded by William Law, *etc.* pp. viii. 39. [1886.] 8°. *See* KING'S CLIFFE, *Northamptonshire.—Parish Library.* **11904.** e. **39. (5.)**

BARRETT (DAVID)

—— *See* TOMPURI (E.) Voices from Finland, *etc.* [Translations by D. Barrett, J. M. Crawford and others.] 1947. 8°. **12260.** e. **16.**

BARRETT (DON CARLOS) The Greenbacks and Resumption of Specie Payments, 1862–1879. pp. x. 259. *Cambridge, Mass.,* 1931. 8°. [*Harvard Economic Studies.* vol. 36.] Ac. **2692/11.**

—— [Another copy.] **8224.** de. **13.**

BARRETT (DOROTHEA) Neither Citizen nor Freewoman. vol. 1. pp. 410. *H. & C. Treacher: Brighton,* [1915.] 8°. **08416.** aaa. **12.**

No more published.

—— Three Travellers, *etc.* pp. 148. *Hazell & Co.: London,* [1924.] 8°. **010025.** de. **29.**

BARRETT (DOROTHY MOSS)

—— Memory in Relation to Hedonic Tone. pp. 61. *New York,* 1938. 8°. [*Archives of Psychology.* no. 223.] P.P. **1247.** gb.

BARRETT (DOUGLAS ERIC)

—— Islamic Metalwork in the British Museum. pp. xxiii. pl. 40. 1949. 8°. *See* LONDON.—III. *British Museum.—Department of Oriental Antiquities.* **7813.** ee. **14.**

—— Persian Painting of the 14th Century. With an introduction and notes by D. Barrett. pp. 24. *Faber & Faber: London,* 1952. fol. [*Faber Gallery of Oriental Art.*] W.P. **12866/7.**

—— Sculptures from Amaravati in the British Museum. [With a catalogue and reproductions.] pp. 75. pl. XLVIII. 1954. 4°. *See* LONDON.—III. *British Museum.—Department of Oriental Antiquities.* **07705.** k. **9.**

BARRETT (E. E.) Camilla de Solys. [A novel.] pp. 219. *S. B. Barrett: London,* 1893. 8°. **012630.** f. **23.**

BARRETT (E. J.)

—— Valley of the Giants. pp. 71. *John Crowther: London & Bognor Regis,* [1941.] 8°. **012826.** de. **15.**

BARRETT (E. R.) *Head of the English Department, Kansas State Teachers' College.*

—— Barrett-Ryan-Schrammel English Test. By E. R. Barrett . . . Teresa M. Ryan . . . and H. E. Schrammel. 9 pt. *World Book Co.: Yonkers-on-Hudson,* [1938, 39.] 4°. **012986.** dd. **17.**

Slips bearing the imprint "George G. Harrap & Co.: London" have been pasted over the original imprint.

—— Barrett-Ryan-Schrammel English Test. New edition, *etc.* *World Book Co.: Yonkers-on-Hudson,* [1954– .] 4°. W.P. c. **898.**

BARRETT (EATON STANNARD) *See* also HOGG (Cervantes) *pseud.* [i.e. E. S. Barrett.]

—— *See* also POLYPUS, *pseud.* [i.e. E. S. Barrett.]

—— The Comet; by the author of All the Talents [i.e. E. S. Barrett]. Second edition. pp. 86. 1808. 8°. *See* COMET. **12331.** bbb. **42. (8.)**

—— The Heroine, or Adventures of a fair romance reader. 3 vol. *Henry Colburn: London,* 1813. 12°. **012635.** d. **8.**

—— The Heroine, or Adventures of Cherubina. Second edition, with considerable additions and alterations. 3 vol. *Henry Colburn: London,* 1814. 12°. **12614.** aaa. **3.**

—— Third edition. 3 vol. *Henry Colburn: London,* 1815. 12°. **12614.** eee. **4.**

—— [Another edition.] With an introduction by Walter Raleigh. pp. xv. 298. *Henry Frowde: London,* 1909. 8°. **012618.** ee. **30.**

BARRETT (Eaton Stannard)

—— [Another edition.] With an introduction by Michael Sadleir. pp. 364. *E. Matthews & Marrot: London,* 1927. 8°. [*Rescue Series.* no. 2.] **012208.** b. **1/2.**

—— The Miss-led General; a serio-comic . . . romance. By the author of the Rising Sun [i.e. E. S. Barrett]. [A satire on Frederick, Duke of York.] pp. 197. 1808. 12°. *See* General. **12612.** df. **13.**

—— The Miss-led General . . . By the author of The Rising Sun [i.e. E. S. Barrett]. Second edition. pp. 200. 1808. 12°. *See* General. **012642.** π.**232.**

—— "My Wife! What Wife?" A comedy, in three acts. pp. 60. *C. Chapple: London,* 1815. 8°. **643.** f. **17.** **(2.)**

—— [Another copy.] **643.** f. **14.** **(3.)**

—— The Second Titan War against Heaven; or, the Talents buried under Portland-Isle. A satirical poem. By the author of the Rising Sun [i.e. E. S. Barrett]. pp. 63. 1807. 8°. *See* Titan War. **11641.** e. **62.**

—— Six Weeks at Long's. By a late resident [i.e. E. S. Barrett]. Third edition. 3 vol. 1817. 12°. *See* Long's Hotel. **N. 2326.**

—— The Talents Run Mad; or, Eighteen Hundred and Sixteen. A satirical poem . . . With notes. By the author of "All the Talents" [i.e. E. S. Barrett]. pp. 70. 1816. 8°. *See* Talents. **992.** i. **18.** **(6.)**

—— The Tarantula; or, the Dance of Fools. A satirical work . . . By the author of the "Rising Sun," &c. [i.e. E. S. Barrett]. 2 vol. 1809. *See* Tarantula. **12314.** df. **47.**

—— Woman, a poem. pp. xv. 85. *John Murray: London,* 1810. 8°. **11643.** aa. **36.**

—— Woman, a poem. Occasional Poems. pp. 121. *Henry Colburn: London,* 1818. 12°. **994.** e. **7.**

—— Third edition. pp. 121. *Henry Colburn: London,* 1819. 8°. **11644.** bb. **47.**

—— A new edition. With engravings from designs by R. Westall, *etc.* pp. 117. *H. Colburn & Co.: London,* 1822. 12°. **11646.** ccc. **19.**

—— A new edition. With four engravings, *etc.* pp. xxx. 23–117. *Henry Colburn: London,* 1841. 12°. **11646.** aaa. **37.**

BARRETT (Edmund Howard) The Family Doctor: a dictionary of domestic medicine and surgery, *etc.* pp. 329. *G. Routledge & Sons: London,* 1909. 8°. **7391.** cc. **24.**

BARRETT (Edward) *See* Carlyle (Thomas) [*Selections.*] The Carlyle Anthology . . . Selected and arranged . . . by E. Barrett. 1867. 8°. **012272.** de. **26.**

—— Gunnery Instructions, simplified for the Volunteer Officers of the U.S. Navy, *etc.* pp. 88. *D. Van Nostrand New York,* 1862. 12°. **8806.** c. **32.**

—— Temporary Fortifications: prepared for the Naval Service. pp. 14. *For the Author: New York,* 1863. 8°. **8806.** bb. **23.** **(4.)**

BARRETT (Edward John Boyd) Absolution. pp. xiii. 253. *Geoffrey Bles: London,* 1932. 8°. **08458.** bb. **47.**

—— Ex-Jesuit. pp. v. 263. *Geoffrey Bles: London,* 1931. 8°. **4908.** i. **17.**

—— The Great O'Neill . . . With illustrations [including a portrait]. pp. xxi. 443. *Hale, Cushman & Flint: Boston,* 1939. 8°. **10859.** r. 4.

BARRETT (Edward John Boyd)

—— The Jesuit Enigma. [With portraits.] pp. 351. *Jonathan Cape: London; printed in U.S.A.,* 1928. 8°. **04785.** l. **57.**

—— Life begins with Love. pp. 96. *Clonmore & Reynolds: Dublin,* 1953. 8°. **8412.** df. **25.**

—— Motive-Force and Motivation-Tracks: a research in will psychology. pp. xiv. 225. *Longmans & Co.: London; Louvain* printed, 1911. 8°. **8459.** dd. **2.**

—— The New Psychology. How it aids and interests. pp. ix. 358. *Harding & More: London,* 1925. 8°. **08465.** ee. **43.**

—— Psycho-analysis and Christian Morality. pp. 16. *Catholic Truth Society: London,* [1921.] 8°. **08462.** e. **77.**

—— The Quest of Honour. pp. 96. *Clonmore & Reynolds: Dublin,* 1954. 8°. **4409.** t. 5.

—— Shepherds in the Mist. [On the author's abandonment of and return to the Roman Catholic faith.] pp. x. 102. *Burns Oates & Washbourne: London,* 1950. 8°. **3943.** e. **7.**

—— Strength of Will. pp. 263. *P. J. Kenedy & Sons: New York,* 1919. 8°. **08467.** de. 45.

—— While Peter Sleeps. [Maintaining the need of reform in the Roman Catholic Church.] pp. 321. *Ives Washburn: New York,* 1929. 8°. **3940.** i. **29.**

BARRETT (Edward L.)

—— The Tenney Committee. Legislative investigation of subversive activities in California. pp. xi. 400. *Cornell University Press: Ithaca, N.Y.,* 1951. 8°. [*Cornell Studies in Civil Liberty.*] Ac. **2692.** g/**14.** (4.)

BARRETT (Edward P.) *Metallurgist. See* Williams (Clyde E.) Production of Sponge Iron. By C. E. Williams, E. P. Barrett, *etc.* 1927. 8°. [*U.S. Bureau of Mines. Bulletin.* no. 270.] A.S. **229.**

BARRETT (Edward Peter) "Spiritualism." A sermon, *etc.* pp. 18. *Elliot Stock: London,* [1872.] 8°. **8631.** ee. **29.**

BARRETT (Edward Ware)

—— Truth is our Weapon. [A work on American propaganda. With plates.] pp. xviii. 355. *Funk & Wagnalls Co.: New York,* 1953. 8°. **8177.** k. 25.

BARRETT (Edwin G.) Principles and Processes of Metal Plate Work . . . With numerous examples, illustrations, plates and tables. pp. vii. 124. *C. Lockwood & Son: London,* 1914 [1913]. 8°. **08768.** cc. **3.**

—— Screw-cutting on the Lathe. With examples, formulæ, gauges, tools, and tables, *etc.* pp. 44. *London,* 1913. 8°. ["*Practical Engineer*" *Handbooks.* no. 3.] **08771.a.19/3.**

BARRETT (Edwin Ralph) The Truth about Intoxicating Drinks: or, the Scientific, social, and religious aspects of total abstinence. A prize essay. pp. viii. 226. *National Temperance Publication Depot: London,* [1889.] 8°. **8436.** bb. **32.**

—— Third edition, revised and enlarged. pp. xii. 252. *Ideal Publishing Union: London,* 1899. 8°. **8436.** g. **3.**

BARRETT (Eliza) *See* Olivier, *de Castile.* The History of Oliver and Arthur . . . Now done into English by W. Leighton and E. Barrett. 1903. 4°. C. **100.** k. **8.**

BARRETT (ELIZABETH) *Writer of Verse.*

—— Sussex Gleanings. [Verses, reprinted from various periodicals.] pp. 16. *W. E. Baxter: Lewes,* [1944.] 8°. **11657**. c. **95**.

—— Sussex Secrets. [Verses. With illustrations.] pp. 16. *W. E. Baxter: Lewes,* [1938?] 8°. **11657**. c. **96**.

BARRETT, afterwards BROWNING (ELIZABETH BARRETT)

COLLECTED POEMS.

—— Elizabeth Barrett Browning's Poetical Works. Seventh edition. [With a portrait.] 5 vol. *Chapman & Hall: London,* 1866. 8°. Ashley **220**.
Earlier editions, with the title "Poems," are entered below under the heading SINGLE WORKS.

—— The Poetical Works of Elizabeth Barrett Browning. Complete. With a memoir [and a portrait]. 2 vol. *James Miller: New York,* 1871. 8°. **11612**. ee. **18**.

—— The Poetical Works of Elizabeth Barrett Browning . . . Corrected by the last London edition. pp. 533. *James Miller: New York,* 1877. 8°. **11611**. bb. **29**.

—— The Poetical Works of Elizabeth Barrett Browning . . . From the last London edition. pp. 624. *Belford, Clarke & Co.: Chicago,* [1880?] 8°. **11654**. bb. **82**.

—— The Poetical Works of Elizabeth Barrett Browning, *etc.* pp. 533. *James Miller: New York,* [c. 1880.] 16°. 11607. aa. 35.

—— The Poetical Works of Elizabeth Barrett Browning. [With a prefatory note signed: R. B., i.e. Robert Browning.] 6 vol. **L.P.** *Smith, Elder & Co.: London,* 1889, 90. 8°. **11612**. h. **2**.

—— The Poems of Elizabeth Barrett Browning. With memoir, etc. pp. xxiv. 551. *F. Warne & Co.: London,* 1893. 8°. **11611**. cc. **2**.

—— The Poetical Works of Elizabeth Barrett Browning. With a portrait. [Edited by Sir F. G. Kenyon.] pp. xxi. 667. *Smith, Elder & Co.: London,* 1897. 8°. **2290**. g. **2**.

—— The Complete Poetical Works of Elizabeth Barrett Browning. [Edited by H. W. Preston.) pp. xviii. 548. *Houghton Mifflin Co.: Boston & New York,* [1900.] 8°. [*Cambridge Edition of the Poets.*] **011604**. ff. **13/9**.

—— The Poetical Works of Elizabeth Barrett Browning, *etc.* pp. xxiv. 551. *S.P.C.K.: London,* [1900?] 8°. **11657**. ee. **55**.
A reissue of the edition of 1893.

—— The Complete Poems of Elizabeth Barrett Browning. 2 vol. *George Newnes: London,* [1904.] 8°. **11611**. df. **12**.

—— The Poetical Works of Elizabeth Barrett Browning. (Oxford complete edition.) pp. viii. 667. *Henry Frowde: London,* 1904. 8°. **11650**. dd. **23**.

—— [A reissue.] The Poetical Works of Elizabeth Barrett Browning. (Oxford complete edition.) *London,* 1906. 8°. **11603**. ccc. **32**.

—— Complete Poetical Works of Elizabeth Barrett Browning . . . With an introduction . . . by Lilian Whiting. 2 vol. *T. Nelson & Sons: New York,* [1919.] 8°. [*New Century Library.*] **012209**. de. **19/1**.
The half-title reads: "Complete Works of Elizabeth Barrett Browning."

SMALLER COLLECTIONS.

—— Miscellaneous Poems. *See* AESCHYLUS. [*Prometheus Vinctus.—English.*] Prometheus Bound, translated from the Greek, *etc.* 1833. 12°. **997**. e. **18**.

BARRETT, afterwards BROWNING (ELIZABETH BARRETT)—[SMALLER COLLECTIONS.]

—— A Selection from the Poetry of Elizabeth Barrett Browning. [With a prefatory note signed: R. B., i.e. Robert Browning. With a portrait.] pp. ix. 319. *Chapman & Hall: London,* 1866. 8°. **11612**. c. **24**.
With an additional titlepage, engraved.

—— A Selection from the Poetry of E. B. Browning. Second edition. *Chapman & Hall: London,* 1866. 8°. pp. ix. 319. **C.117.c.15.**
A presentation copy to F. T. Palgrave from Robert Browning, with his autograph inscription.

—— Poems of Childhood, *etc.* pp. 162. *James Miller: New York,* 1867. 12°. **11650**. bbb. **28**.

—— Poems of Memory and Hope, *etc.* [With a portrait.] pp. 162. *James Miller: New York,* 1873. 12°. **11651**. e. **20**.
A reissue of "Poems of Childhood," with two additional poems substituted for the first poem in that collection. With an additional titlepage, engraved.

—— Life, Letters and Essays of Elizabeth Barrett Browning. 2 vol.

1. Letters . . . addressed to R. H. Horne.
2. The Book of the Poets.

James Miller: New York, 1877. 8°. **12274**. aaa. **26**.
No more published.

—— A Selection from the Poetry of Elizabeth Barrett Browning. Seventh edition. pp. xi. 319. *Smith, Elder & Co.: London,* 1877. 8°. **11630**. bb. **48**.
With an additional titlepage, engraved. First edition, 1866.

—— The Earlier Poems of Elizabeth Barrett Browning, 1826–1833. [Edited by R. H. Shepherd.] pp. xiii. 239. *Bartholomew Robson: London,* 1878 [1877]. 12°. **11644**. ccc. **2**.

—— A Selection from the Poetry of Elizabeth Barrett Browning. Second series. pp. viii. 349. *Smith, Elder & Co.: London,* 1880. 8°. **11612**. c. **24***.

—— The Poetical Works of Elizabeth Barrett Browning, from 1826 to 1844. Edited, with a memoir by J. H. Ingram. pp. xvi. 400. *Ward, Lock & Co.: London,* [1887]. 8°. **11644**. ccc. **51**.

—— Poems, *etc.* pp. 356. *Smith, Elder & Co.: London,* 1887. 8°. **11606**. aa. 28.

—— [Another copy.] Poems, *etc.* *London,* 1887. 8°. Ashley **221***.

—— [Another copy.] Poems, *etc.* *London,* 1887. 8°. Ashley **221**.
This copy contains two inserted leaves which bear a "Prefatory Note" by Robert Browning, contradicting statements made by John H. Ingram in a memoir prefixed to the volume of E. B. Browning's poems edited by him in 1887.

—— The Seraphim, and other poems, *etc.* pp. 282. *Ward, Lock & Co.: London, New York,* [1888.] 8°. **11612**. aa. **21**.

—— The Poetical Works of Elizabeth Barrett Browning, from 1826 to 1844. pp. xviii. 432. *Griffith, Farran & Co.: London & Sydney,* [1891.] 8°. [*Newbery Classics.*] **012202**. f. **8/1**.
Previous edition, 1887.

—— Prometheus Bound, and other poems . . . With an introduction by Alice Meynell. [With a portrait.] pp. xix. 330. *Ward, Lock & Co.: London,* 1896. 8°. [*XIXth Century Classics.*] **012202**. g. **7/2**.

—— Aurora Leigh, and other poems. (The Oxford miniature edition.) [With a portrait.] pp. xi. 948. *Henry Frowde: London*, 1902. 16°. **11607**. cc. **15**.

—— Love Poems of Elizabeth Barrett Browning, including the Sonnets from the Portuguese. pp. viii. 133. *John Lane: London & New York*, 1902. 12°. [*Lover's Library*.] **11607**. aaaa. **1/6**.

—— Poems by Elizabeth Barrett Browning. With an introduction by Alice Meynell. pp. xi. 278. *Blackie & Son: London*, 1903. 8°. [*Red Letter Library*.] **012209**. fff.1/**16**.

—— Casa Guidi Windows, and other poems. (The Oxford miniature edition.) [With a portrait.] pp. xv. 936. *Henry Frowde: London*, 1904. 16°. **11607**. cc. **17**.

—— Selected Poems . . . Edited with introduction and notes by Elizabeth Lee. pp. xxix. 173. *Ginn & Co.: Boston*, 1904. 8°. **11611**. de. **7**.

—— Sonnets. pp. 89. *Astolat Press: London*, 1904. 16°. **11647**. dg. **3**.

—— Sonnets from the Portuguese, and other sonnets. pp. 95. *S. Bagster & Sons: London*, [1909.] 16°. **11647**. dg. **10**.

—— Sonnets. pp. 94. *Siegle, Hill & Co.: London*, [1910.] 16°. [*Queen's Library of Literary Treasures*.] **012199**. de. **2/1**.

Previous edition, 1904.

—— The Romaunt of the Page [and other poems]. [With plates.] *Collins' Clear-Type Press: London & Glasgow*, [c. 1910.] 8°. **11661**. a. **17**.

—— Love Sonnets. pp. vii. 63. *A. L. Humphreys: London*, 1911. 16°. **11612**. dg. **12**.

—— Poems. pp. viii. 428. *Oxford University Press: London*, 1912. 8°. [*World's Classics*.] **012209**. df. **90**.

—— Sonnets from the Portuguese, and other poems. [With a portrait.] pp. 87. *W. P. Nimmo & Co.: Edinburgh*, 1912. 16°. **11607**. aaa. **23**.

—— Hitherto unpublished Poems and Stories. With an inedited autobiography. [With portraits.] 2 vol. 1914. 8°. *See* BOSTON, *Mass.—Bibliophile Society*. Ac. **9719/32**.

—— Poems by Elizabeth Barrett Browning. [With a portrait.] See BROWNING (Robert) New Poems by Robert Browning and Elizabeth Barrett Browning, *etc.* 1914. 8°. **2344**. a. **6**.

—— The Poets' Enchiridion. A hitherto unpublished poem. With an inedited address to Uvedale Price on his eightieth birthday, an early Invocation to Sleep, and a preliminary draft of the renowned poem Catarina to Camoens. (Elizabeth Barrett Browning : new data. A centennial address to the Bibliophile Society spoken across the Atlantic by H. Buxton Forman.) pp. 53. 1914. 8°. *See* BOSTON, *Mass.—Bibliophile Society*. Ac. **9719/30**.

—— Les Quarante-quatre "Sonnets portugais." (Poésies diverses.) *See* DES GUERROIS (C.) Étude sur Mistress Elizabeth Browning, *etc.* 1885. 8°. **11840**. bb. **29**.

—— [Selected poems.] *See* BROWNING (Robert) *the Poet*. [*Smaller Collections*.] The Poetry of the Brownings, *etc.* [With a portrait.] 1947. 8°. **11605**. c. **9**.

—— Poems by Elizabeth Barrett Browning. Selected with an introduction by Samuel J. Looker. pp. 64. *Grey Walls Press: London; The Hague* printed, 1948. 8°. [*Crown Classics*.] W.P. **2809/12**.

—— Poèmes et poésies. Traduction de l'anglais et étude par Albert Savine. pp. lxxiii. 317. *Paris*, 1905. 8°. **11648**. eee. **5**.

—— Die Sonette aus dem Portugiesischen und andere Gedichte. In deutscher Uebertragung von Helene Scheu-Riesz . . . Zweite Auflage. [With a portrait.] pp. 91. *Berlin*, [1921.] 8°. **011645**. f. **6**.

—— Poesie scelte . . . Versione libera di Tullo Massarani. pp. li. 326. *Milano*, 1898. 16°. **11611**. a. **29**.

LETTERS.

—— The Religious Opinions of Elizabeth Barrett Browning (as expressed in three letters, addressed to Wm. Merry). *In:* NICOLL (*Sir* William R.) and WISE (T. J.) Literary Anecdotes of the Nineteenth Century. vol. 2. pp. 121–142. 1896. 8°. **011852**. g. **61**.

—— [Another issue.] The Religious Opinions of Elizabeth Barrett Browning, as expressed in three letters addressed to Wm. Merry, Esq., J.P. Edited by the Rev. W. Robertson Nicoll. pp. 28. *Privately printed: London*, 1896. 4°. Ashley **2520**.

One of an edition of thirty copies.

—— The Letters of Elizabeth Barrett Browning. Edited with biographical additions by F. G. Kenyon, *etc.* 2 vol. *Smith, Elder & Co.: London*, 1897. 8°. **010910**. b. **6**.

—— Letters of Elizabeth Barrett Browning addressed to R. H. Horne . . . With comments on contemporaries. [With a connecting narrative by R. H. Horne.] Edited by S. R. T. Mayer. 2 vol. *R. Bentley & Son: London*, 1877[1876]. 8°. **10921**. e. **1**.

—— Kind Words from a Sick Room. [Four letters addressed to A. P. Paton.] pp. 10. *William Hutchison: Greenock*, 1891. 8°. **010910**. cc. **2**. **(5.)**
Privately printed.

—— [Letters.] *See* BROWNING (Robert) [*Letters, etc.*] The Letters of Robert Browning and E. B. Barrett, *etc.* 1899. 8°. **2410**. b. **3**.

—— The Religious Opinions of Elizabeth Barrett Browning. [Three letters addressed by her to William Merry on his pamphlet "Predestination and Election."] pp. 56. *Hodder & Stoughton: London*, 1906. 8°. **10910**. dd. **31**.

—— The Art of Scansion . . . (A letter to Uvedale Price.) With an introduction by Alice Meynell. [With a foreword by Clement K. Shorter.] pp. ix. 11. *Privately printed by Clement Shorter: London*, 1916. 4°. Tab. **578**. a. **41**.

One of an edition of twenty-five copies.

—— Letters to Robert Browning and other correspondents . . . Edited by Thomas J. Wise. pp. 53. *For Thomas J. Wise: London*, 1916. 8°. C. **57**. d. **36**.
One of an edition of thirty copies printed for private circulation.

—— Alfred Tennyson : notes and comments ; with a defence of the rhyme system of "The Dead Pan." (Two letters to R. H. Horne.) pp. 19. *For T. J. Wise: London*, 1919. 8°. C. **57**. d. **39**. **(2.)**
One of an edition of thirty copies printed for private circulation.

—— Charles Dickens and other 'Spirits of the Age' discussed and analysed. [Two letters to R. H. Horne.] pp. 18. *For T. J. Wise: London*, 1919. 8°. C. **57**. d. **39**. **(4.)**
One of an edition of thirty copies printed for private circulation.

—— Edgar Allan Poe: a criticism; with remarks on the morals and religion of Shelley and Leigh Hunt. (Two letters to R. H. Horne.) pp. 15. *For T. J. Wise: London*, 1919. 8°. C. **57**. d. **39**. (**1**.)
One of an edition of thirty copies printed for private circulation.

—— A Note on William Wordsworth; with a statement of her views on spiritualism. By E. B. Browning. [Two letters.] pp. 17. *For T. J. Wise: London*, 1919. 8°. C. **57**. d. **39**. (**3**.)
One of an edition of thirty copies printed for private circulation.

—— Elizabeth Barrett Browning: letters to her sister, 1846–1859. Edited by Leonard Huxley . . . With portraits. pp. xxv. 344. *John Murray: London*, 1929. 8°. **010920**. bb. **2**.

—— Twenty-two Unpublished Letters of Elizabeth Barrett Browning and Robert Browning addressed to Henrietta and Arabella Moulton-Barrett. [With a portrait of E. B. Browning.] pp. x. 89. *United Feature Syndicate: New York*, 1935. 8°. **010921**. g. **8**.

—— [Letters from Italy.] *See* BROWNING (Robert) [*Letters, Prefaces, etc.*] From Robert & Elizabeth Browning. A further selection of the Barrett-Browning family correspondence, *etc.* 1936. 8°. **010910**. aa. **56**.

—— Letters from Elizabeth Barrett to B. R. Haydon. Edited by Martha Hale Shackford. pp. lxxii. 78. *Oxford University Press: New York*, 1939. 8°. **10922**. c. **8**.

—— Twenty Unpublished Letters of Elizabeth Barrett to Hugh Stuart Boyd. [Edited by Bennett Weaver.] (Reprinted from PMLA.) [*New York*, 1950.] 8°. **10922**. g. **7**.

—— Elizabeth Barrett to Miss Mitford. The unpublished letters of Elizabeth Barrett Barrett to Mary Russell Mitford. Edited and introduced by Betty Miller. [With plates, including portraits.] pp. xviii. 284. *John Murray: London*, 1954. 8°. **10922**. b. **28**.

—— [Letters.] *In*: Unpublished Letters of Thomas De Quincey and E. B. Browning, *etc.* pp. 20–37. 1954. 8°. [*Auckland University College. Bulletin.* no. 44.] Ac. **1988**. b/2.

SINGLE WORKS.

—— Aurora Leigh. pp. 403. *Chapman & Hall: London*, 1857 [1856]. 8°. **11649**. d. **1**.

—— Second edition. pp. 403. *Chapman & Hall: London*, 1857. 8°. **11649**. d. **2**.

—— Aurora Leigh. pp. 351. *C. S. Francis & Co.: New York, Boston*, 1857. 16°. **11658**. de. **16**.

—— Fourth edition. Revised. [With a portrait.] pp. 403. *Chapman & Hall: London*, 1859. 8°. **11647**. df. **25**.

—— Aurora Leigh . . . Fifth edition. [With a portrait.] pp. 403. *Chapman & Hall: London*, 1860. 8°. **11658**. a. **103**.

—— Aurora Leigh . . . Copyright edition. pp. 334. *Bernhard Tauchnitz: Leipzig*, 1872. 8°. [*Collection of British Authors. Tauchnitz Edition.* vol. 1248.] **12267**. a. **1/389**.

—— Aurora Leigh . . . Twentieth edition. [With a portrait.] pp. 403. *Smith, Elder, & Co.: London*, 1887. 8°. **11660**. e. **1**.

—— New edition, with prefatory note by A. C. Swinburne. pp. xiv. 377. *Smith, Elder & Co.: London*, 1898. 8°. **11647**. cc. **46**.

—— [Another edition.] (Edited by H. Buxton Forman.) [With a portrait.] pp. 366. *J. M. Dent & Co.: London*, 1899. 8°. [*Temple Classics.*] **012200.de.8/8.**

—— [Another edition.] With an introduction by E. Wingate Rinder. [With a portrait.] pp. xxii. 342. *Walter Scott: London*, [1899.] 8°. [*Canterbury Poets.*] **11604**. aa. **11**.

—— [Another edition.] With introduction by Charlotte Porter and Helen A. Clarke. pp. xxviii. 354. *G. Bell & Sons: London*, 1902. 8°. **11647**. df. **10**.
One of the "Life and Light Books."

—— (India paper edition.) pp. 489. *H. R. Allenson: London*, 1905. 16°. **11646**. de. **41**.

—— Aurora Leigh. Traduit de l'anglais, *etc.* [The translator's preface signed: A. B.] pp. 326. *Paris*, 1890. 12°. **11647**. ccc. **40**.

—— Aurora Leigh. Traduzione di Elisa Ghislanzoni. Prefazione di Antonio Fogazzaro. pp. vi. 275. *Roma*, 1908. 8°. **11646**. f. **73**.

—— *See* COUPLAND (William C.) Aurora Leigh. A discourse, *etc.* [1887.] 8°. [*South Place Religious Society. Publications.* no. 17.] **4109**. f. **44**. (**17**.)

—— The Battle of Marathon. A poem written in early youth by E. B. Browning. Printed for her father in 1820 and now reprinted in type-fac-simile. With an introduction by H. Buxton Forman. pp. 16. xv. 72. *For private distribution only: London*, 1891. 8°. **T.C.4.b.5.**
One of an edition of fifty copies.

—— The Battle of Marathon. A poem. pp. xv. 72. *W. Lindsell: London*, 1820. 8°. Ashley **2512**.
A presentation copy from the author.

—— Casa Guidi Windows. A poem. pp. vii. 140. *Chapman & Hall: London*, 1851. 8°. **11646**. d. **30**.

—— [Another edition.] With introduction by A. M. F. Robinson. pp. xvi. 88. *John Lane: London & New York*, 1901. 8°. **11646**. ee. **46**.

—— A Drama of Exile: and other poems. *See* infra: Poems.

—— The Enchantress, and other poems. pp. 28. *For T. J. Wise: London*, 1913. 8°. C. **57**. d. **38**. (**1**.)
One of an edition of thirty copies printed for private circulation.

—— Epistle to a Canary, 1837 . . . Edited by Edmund Gosse. pp. 19. *For T. J. Wise: London*, 1913. 8°. C. **57**. d. **38**. (**2**.)
One of an edition of thirty copies printed for private circulation.

—— An Essay on Mind, with other poems. [By E. B. Barrett, afterwards Browning.] pp. xiii. 152. 1826. 12°. *See* ESSAY. **994**. f. **42**.

—— The Greek Christian Poets and the English Poets. [Two essays.] pp. iv. 211. *Chapman & Hall: London*, 1863. 8°. **11335**. b. **9**.

—— Lady Geraldine's Courtship. *See* infra: Poems.

—— Last Poems. [Edited by Robert Browning.] pp. xi. 142. *Chapman & Hall: London*, 1862. 8°. C. **58**. d. **3**.
With a facsimile of the MS. *of Elizabeth Browning's last poem, "The North and the South," inserted.*

BARRETT, afterwards **BROWNING** (ELIZABETH BARRETT)—[SINGLE WORKS.]

—— Second edition. pp. xi. 142. *Chapman & Hall: London,* 1862. 8°. 11660. b. 14.
Imperfect; wanting pp. 55, 56.

—— [Another copy.] Last Poems . . . Second edition. *London,* 1862. 8°. **11650.** bbb. **27.**
Imperfect; wanting pp. 55, 56.

—— My Kate. [From "Last Poems."] *Henry Frowde and Hodder & Stoughton: London,* [1911.] 16°. **11607.** dd. **8.** (**3.**)

—— Leila. A tale. [In verse.] pp. 35. *For T. J. Wise: London,* 1913. 8°. C. **57.** d. **38.** (**3.**)
One of an edition of thirty copies printed for private circulation.

—— Napoleon III in Italy, and other poems. *See* infra: Poems before Congress.

—— Poems. 2 vol. *Edward Moxon: London,* 1844. 8°.
C.117.a.45.

—— [Another edition.] A Drama of Exile: and other poems. [With a portrait.] 2 vol. *H. G. Langley: New-York,* 1845. 8°. **11644.** d. **46.**

—— Poems . . . New edition. 2 vol. *Chapman & Hall: London,* 1850. 12°. **11611.** e. **1, 2.**

—— Third edition. 2 vol. *Chapman & Hall: London,* 1853. 8°. **11611.** e. **3, 4.**

—— [Another copy.] Poems . . . Third edition. *London,* 1853. 8°. **11660.** aa. **15.**

—— [Another edition.] 2 vol. *C. S. Francis & Co.: New York,* 1854. 8°. **011641.** df. **1.**

—— Fourth edition. 3 vol. *Chapman & Hall: London,* 1856. 8°. **11611.** de. **16.**

—— Poems . . . Fifth edition. 3 vol. *Chapman & Hall: London,* 1862. 8°. Ashley **218.**

—— Poems . . . Sixth edition. [With a portrait.] 4 vol. *Chapman & Hall: London,* 1864. 8°. Ashley **219.**
Subsequent editions, with the title "Poetical Works," are entered above under the heading COLLECTED POEMS.

—— [Another edition, abridged.] *G. Routledge & Sons: London,* 1887. 16°. **12208.** aaaa. **2.**

—— [Another edition, abridged.] pp. 315. *G. Routledge & Sons: London,* 1887. 8°. **11609.** g. **23.**

—— [Another edition, abridged.] pp. 315. *G. Routledge & Sons: London,* 1887. 8°. **11612.** e. **14.**

—— [Another edition, abridged.] [With a prefatory note signed: R. B., i.e. Robert Browning.] pp. 356. *Smith, Elder & Co.: London,* 1890. 16°. **11612.** de. **18.**
Different from the abridged edition first published in 1887.

—— The Rhyme of the Duchess May. [From "Poems"] . . . Illustrated by Charlotte M. B. Morrell. pp. vi. 20. *Sampson Low & Co.: London,* 1873. 4°. **11651.** k. **23.**

—— [Another edition.] (Illustrations by Katharine Cameron.) *T. N. Foulis: London & Edinburgh,* [1907.] 8°. [*Envelope Books.* no. 2.] **012202.** e. **10.**

—— Lady Geraldine's Courtship. [From "Poems"] . . . Illustrated. pp. 90. *J. R. Osgood & Co.: Boston,* 1876. 24°. **12209.** a. **27.**
Part of the "Vest-Pocket Series of Standard and Popular Authors."

—— [Another edition.] Illustrated by Charles Pears. pp. 46. *T. C. & E. C. Jack: London & Edinburgh,* [1906.] 8°. **11646.** de. **50.**

BARRETT, afterwards **BROWNING** (ELIZABETH BARRETT)—[SINGLE WORKS.]

—— [Another edition.] Illustrations by G. C. Wilmshurst, and decorations by Franklin Booth. pp. 107. *D. Appleton & Co.: New York,* 1907. 8°. **11648.** i. **24.**

—— [Another edition.] pp. 96. *Siegle, Hill & Co.: London,* [1911.] 32°. [*Langham Booklets.*] **944.** b. **57.**

—— Sonnets from the Portuguese. [From "Poems," 1850 edition] . . . Illustrated by Ludvig Sandöe Ipsen. *Ticknor & Co.: Boston,* [1887.] *obl.* fol. **1869.** a. **31.**
Lithographed.

—— Sonnets. By E. B. B. [i.e. E. B. Browning.] [Purporting to be the first edition of "Sonnets from the Portuguese, first published in the 1850 edition of "Poems."] pp. 47. 1847 [c. 1890]. 8°. *See* B., E. B. Ashley **223.**

—— [Another copy.] Sonnets. By E. B. B. [i.e. E. B. Browning.] 1847 [c. 1890]. 8°. *See* B., E. B. Ashley **4715.**
Preserved in wrappers in a volume bound in gold-tooled red morocco by Sangorski & Sutcliffe, lettered "A Memento of Mr & Mrs Robert Browning." Locks of E. B. and Robert Browning's hair are mounted in the doublures, and the volume also contains documents authenticating them.

—— [Another edition.] Illustrated by C. E. Brock and Jessie Bayes. pp. 47. *Ernest Nister: London; E. P. Dutton & Co.: New York; printed in Bavaria,* 1891. 16°. [*Laurel Wreath Series.*] **012201.de.6/10.**

—— [Another edition.] With decorative settings by Frederick Colin Tilney, and an introduction by Edmund Gosse. pp. 22. *J. M. Dent & Co.: London; Vienna printed,* 1894. 4°. **11642.** eee. **31.**
The sonnets are printed on one side of the leaf only.

—— [Another edition.] pp. 51. *Copeland & Day: Boston,* 1896. 8°. **11647.** ee. **38.**

—— [Another edition.] pp. 46. *Hacon & Ricketts: London,* 1897. 4°. C. **99.** a. **14.**

—— [Another edition.] *G. Bell & Sons: London,* 1898. 4°. K.T.C. **38.** a. **2.**
One of an edition of twenty-five copies on Japanese vellum.

—— [Another edition.] *O. Schulze & Co.: Edinburgh,* 1901. 4°. **11647.** e. **57.**

—— Sonnets from the Portuguese. pp. 96. *Anthony Treherne & Co.: London,* 1904. 32°. **945.** f. **6.**

—— [Another edition.] pp. 32. *Gowans & Gray: London, Glasgow,* 1905. 16°. [*Cadogan Booklets.* no. 1.] **944.** bb. **3.**

—— [Another edition.] pp. 47. *G. Routledge & Sons: London; E. P. Dutton & Co.: New York,* [1905.] 16°. [*Broadway Booklets.*] **12204.** p. **8/28.**

—— Sonnets from the Portuguese. By E. B. Browning. One Word More and other poems by Robert Browning. With an introduction by R. Watson Gilder. pp. li. 136. *Century Co.: New York,* 1905. 8°. **11646.** de. **39.**

—— Sonnets from the Portuguese. *Chapman & Hall: London,* [1906.] 16°. **11648.** de. **19.**

—— [Another edition.] Illustrated by Herbert Cole. pp. 48. *T. C. & E. C. Jack: London,* [1907.] 8°. **11646.** de. **59.**

—— [Another edition.] pp. 91. *Siegle, Hill & Co.: London,* 1908. 32°. [*Langham Booklets.*] **944.** b. **8.**

BARRETT, afterwards BROWNING (Elizabeth Barrett)—[Single Works.]

—— [Another edition.] *Henry Frowde: London,* [1909.] 32°. [*Moment Series.*] 944. ccc.

—— [Another edition.] pp. 95. *John Ouseley: London,* [1909.] 32°. 944. ee. 2.

—— Sonnets from the Portuguese. [With a portrait.] pp. 92. *Barse & Hopkins: New York,* [c. 1910.] 8°. 11657. i. 110.

—— [Another edition.] pp. 52. *St. Catherine Press: London,* [1912.] 16°. [*Arden Books.* no. 2.] 12209. a. 35/2.

—— [Another edition.] pp. 27. *P. L. Warner: London,* 1914. fol. [*Riccardi Press Booklets.*] 012210.c.1/5.

—— [Another edition.] With photographic illustrations, etc. *Dodge Publishing Co.: New York,* [1920.] 4°. 11646. t. 14.
Printed on one side of the leaf only.

—— [Another edition.] Illustrated by Nestore Leoni. *T. Fisher Unwin: London,* [1924.] 4°. 11642. h. 46.

—— Sonnets. By E. B. B. [i.e. E. B. Browning.] [A facsimile of the edition of "Sonnets from the Portuguese" purporting to have been printed at Reading in 1847.] pp. 47. 1927. 8°. *See* B., E. B. C. 98. a. 2.

—— Sonnets from the Portuguese . . . With some observations and a bibliographical note by William Andrews Clark, *etc.* pp. xxxi. 45. *J. H. Nash: San Francisco,* 1927. fol. C. 98. gg. 21.

—— [Another edition.] pp. xi. 26. *Basil Blackwell: Oxford,* 1933. 4°. [*Shakespeare Head Quartos.* no. 6.] W.P. 8217/6a.

—— Sonnets from the Portuguese. pp. 95. *R. Rivière & Son: London,* 1936. 16°. 011651. h. 201.

—— Sonnets from the Portuguese. [Edited by Adrian S. Mott.] pp. xi. 26. *Basil Blackwell: Oxford,* 1946. 8°. [*Shakespeare Head Quartos.* no. 6.] W.P. 8217/6. b.

—— Sonnets from the Portuguese . . . Centennial variorum edition. Edited with an introduction by Fannie Ratchford, and notes by Deoch Fulton. pp. 123. *Philip C. Duschnes: New York,* 1950. 8°. C. 106. c. 3.
Designed and printed by Peter Beilenson.

—— Les Sonnets du Portugais . . . Traduits en vers français, avec préface, texte anglais en regard, et notes par Léon Morel. pp. xv. 94. *Paris,* 1903. 8°. 11646. ff. 34.

—— Les Sonnets portugais d'Elizabeth Barrett Browning. Traduits en sonnets français, avec notice, texte anglais, commentaire et notes par Fernand Henry. pp. lxiv. 137. *Paris,* 1905. 8°. 11649. cc. 53.

—— Sonnets de la portuguaise . . . Traduction d'Émile B. d'Erlanger . . . suivie d'une conférence sur E. B. Browning et Marceline Desbordes-Valmore. pp. 40. *Paris, Londres,* [1935.] 8°. 011653. o. 55.

—— Sonnets de la Portugaise . . . Traduits . . . par le Baron Émile B. d'Erlanger. pp. 24. *Paris, Strasbourg,* [1938.] 8°. 11656. b. 13.

—— Sonnets. Sonnets from the Portuguese. Traduits . . . par Alliette Audra. *Fr.* pp. 95. *Paris,* 1945. 8°. 11658. aa. 130.

—— Sonnets from the Portuguese. (Sonette aus dem Portugiesischen. Nachdichtung von Hans Wolfgang von Herwarth.) *Eng. & Ger.* pp. 93. *München,* 1920. 8°. 011645. e. 9.

BARRETT, afterwards BROWNING (Elizabeth Barrett)—[Single Works.]

—— Sonette aus dem Portugiesischen. [Translated by Rainer Maria Rilke.] *See* Rilke (R. M.) Gesammelte Werke. Bd. 6. 1927. 8°. 012251. aa. 5.

—— Sonette aus dem Portugiesischen. Übertragen durch Rainer Maria Rilke. pp. xlvi. *Leipzig,* [1931.] 8°. [*Insel-Bücherei.* no. 252.] 012213. de. 1/252.

—— *See* Saludok (E.) Stilkritische Untersuchungen der Sonette der Elizabeth Barrett-Browning im Verhältnis zu Rainer Maria Rilkes Übertragung, *etc.* 1933. 8°. 11855. b. 42.

—— I Sonetti portoghesi di Elisabetta Barrett-Browning. Studio e versione italiana di Teresa Venuti de Domenicio. pp. 134. *Roma,* 1902. 8°. 11647. df. 14.

—— Love Sonnets of E. B. Browning. [A selection from "Sonnets from the Portuguese."] pp. 23. *T. N. Foulis: Edinburgh & London,* [1906.] 12°. [*Roses of Parnassus.* no. 15.] 11604. dg. 17/15.

—— Sonnets from the Portuguese. [Selections. With illustrations.] *Hodder & Stoughton: London,* [1911.] 12°. 11603. i. 35. (1.)

—— Плачъ дѣтей. Изъ поэмы. "The Cry of the Children." [From "Poems."] *See* England. [*Appendix.—Miscellaneous.*] Избранные поэты Англiи, *etc.* no. 1. 1864, *etc.* 8°. 11603. bb. 17.

—— Poems before Congress. pp. viii. 65. *Chapman & Hall: London,* 1860. 8°. 11651. c. 38.

—— [Another edition.] Napoleon III in Italy, and other poems. pp. 72. *C. S. Francis & Co.: New York,* 1860. 12°. 11649. b. 44.

—— Psyche Apocalypté: a lyrical drama. Projected by E. B. Browning and R. H. Horne. Reprinted from the St. James's Magazine and United Empire Review for February, 1876. [Drafts and correspondence concerning the play, with a connecting narrative by R. H. Horne.] pp. 19. *Hazell, Watson, & Viney: London & Aylesbury,* 1876. 8°. Ashley 2518.
Printed for private circulation.

—— The Runaway Slave at Pilgrim's Point. [In verse.] pp. 26. *Edward Moxon: London,* 1849. 8°. [1888?] C. 39. g. 30.
The imprint is fictitious.

—— The Seraphim, and other poems. pp. xxi. 360. *Saunders & Otley: London,* 1838. 12°. 994. f. 3.

—— The True Mary: being Mrs. Browning's poem: "The Virgin Mary to the Child Jesus" [from "The Seraphim, and other poems"], with comments and notes . . . Edited by W. A. Muhlenberg. [The annotator's preface signed: A. A.] pp. 45. *Thomas Whittaker: New-York,* 1868. 8°. 11650. g. 6.

—— Two Poems. By Elizabeth Barrett and Robert Browning. (A Plea for the Ragged Schools of London. [By E. B. Barrett, afterwards Browning.]—The Twins. "Give" and "It-shall-be-given-unto-you." [By R. Browning.]) pp. 15. *Chapman & Hall: London,* 1854. 8°. C. 59. c. 27.

—— [Another copy.] Two Poems, *etc.* *London,* 1854. 8°. Ashley 2527.

—— The Sleep. [From "The Seraphim, and other poems."] *See* Gems. Gems of Devotional Poetry, *etc.* [1897.] 8°. 11601. k. 7.

—— [Another edition.] *A. Fairbairns & Co.: London,* 1907. 16°. 11603. de. 10. (1.)

BARRETT, afterwards **BROWNING** (ELIZABETH BARRETT)—[SINGLE WORKS.]

—— A Song. [" Is't loving, to list to the night guitar," *etc.*] pp. 4. *Privately printed: [London,]* 1907. 8°. **1875**. d. **9**. (**66**.)

One of an edition of twenty copies.

—— Sonnets from the Portuguese. *See* supra: Poems.

—— The Virgin Mary to the Child Jesus. *See* supra: The Seraphim, and other poems.

SELECTIONS.

—— Mrs. Browning's Birthday Book. Edited by R. H. Stoddard. [With a portrait.] pp. vi. 375. *James Miller: New York,* 1882. 16°. **11601**. bbb. **37**.

—— The Mrs. Browning Birthday Book. Compiled by E. W. H. With a preface by the Rev. Charles Mackeson. pp. 250. *Griffith, Farran & Co.: London,* [1889.] 16°. **11612**. aa. **29**.

—— [Selections, edited by J. A. Noble.] [1892.] *See* MILES (Alfred H.) The Poets and the Poetry of the Century, *etc.* (Baillie to Blind.) [1891, *etc.*] 8°. **11603.cc.20/7.**

—— [Sixteen poems.] *See* BROWNING (Robert) [*Selections.*] The Brownings for the Young, *etc.* 1896. 8°. **11612**. a. **33**.

—— Poems of Elizabeth Barrett Browning. *See* BROWNING (Robert) [*Selections.*] Poems of Robert and Elizabeth Barrett Browning, *etc.* 1901. 8°. **11609**. bb. **33**.

—— [Selected poems.] *Eng.* *See* JIRICZEK (O. L.) Viktorianische Dichtung, *etc.* 1907. 8°. **11603**. dd. **12**.

—— An E. B. Browning Birthday Book. *Siegle, Hill & Co.: London,* [1914.] 16°. [*Langham Birthday Books.*] **012305**. de. **73/4**.

—— [Twenty-four poems.] *See* BROWNING (Robert) [*Selections.*] Selections from the Brownings, *etc.* 1933. 8°. W.P. **6815/30**.

—— [Selections.] *Fr.* *See* BUISSON DU BERGER (A.) Poètes anglais contemporains. Robert Burns . . . Élisabeth Browning . . . Traduction inédite par A. Buisson du Berger. [1890.] 8°. **11601**. ee. **34**. (**6**.)

—— Hommage français à Elizabeth Barrett Browning à l'occasion de son centenaire, *etc.* [Selected poems, translated by various writers. Edited by Hedgar Pluviannes.] pp. 26. *Vals-les-Bains,* 1906. 8°. **10602**. g. **18**. (**1**.)

—— [Another copy.] **10600**. bb. **26**. (**3**.)

—— Due poesie di Elizabeth Barrett Browning [" The Romaunt of the Page " and " Bianca among the Nihgtingales "] e due poesie di * * * tradotte dall'inglese da Miss Kate Davis e Francesco di Silvestri Falconieri. pp. 24. *Roma,* 1906. 8°. **11604**. ee. **6**. (**4**.)

WORKS TRANSLATED, ETC., BY MRS. BROWNING.

—— *See* AESCHYLUS. [*Prometheus Vinctus.—English.*] Prometheus Bound, translated from the Greek . . . and Miscellaneous Poems, by the translator, author of an " Essay on Mind " [i.e. E. B. Barrett, afterwards Browning], *etc.* 1833. 12°. **997**. e. **18**.

—— *See* CHAUCER (Geoffrey) [*Works.*] The Poems of Geoffrey Chaucer, modernized [by R. H. Horne, E. B. Barrett, afterwards Browning, and others]. 1841. 8°. **1066**. f. **12**.

BARRETT, afterwards **BROWNING** (ELIZABETH BARRETT)—

APPENDIX.

—— *See* ASOLO. Municipio della città di Asolo. Pel cinquantesimo anniversario delle nozze di Roberto Browning con Elisabetta Barrett, *etc.* 1896. fol. **10804**. f. **7**. (**3**.)

—— *See* BAYNE (Peter) Two Great Englishwomen, Mrs. Browning & Charlotte Brontë, *etc.* 1881. 8°. **11840**. e. **23**.

—— *See* BOAS (Louise S.) Elizabeth Barrett Browning. [With portraits.] 1930. 8°. **010826**. ee. **58**.

—— *See* BROWNING (Robert) [*Letters, etc.*] The Death of Elizabeth Barrett Browning. [The letter written by R. Browning to his sister describing the death of his wife.] 1916. 8°. C. **57**. d. **13**.

—— *See* BROWNING (Robert) Edward Fitzgerald and Elizabeth Barrett Browning. 1919. 8°. C. **57**. i. **11**. (**1**.)

—— *See* BURDETT (Osbert H.) The Brownings. 1928. 8°. **010855**. h. **32**.

—— —— 1933. 8°. **2408**. b. **13**.

—— *See* BUYS (R. van Brakell) Drie dichteressen uit het Victoriaanse tijdperk. Christina Rossetti, Emily Brontë, Elizabeth Barrett Browning. [With a portrait.] [1947.] 8°. **011840**. m. **67**.

—— *See* CLARKE (Isabel C.) Elizabeth Barrett Browning, *etc.* [With plates, including portraits.] [1929.] 8°. **10824**. g. **14**.

—— *See* CRESTON (Dormer) *pseud.* Andromeda in Wimpole Street. The romance of E. B. Browning. 1929. 8°. **10824**. i. **3**.

—— *See* DES GUERROIS (C.) Étude sur Mistress Elizabeth Browning, *etc.* 1885. 8°. **11840**. bb. **29**.

—— *See* DRUSKOWITZ (H.) Drei englische Dichterinnen. Essays [on Joanna Baillie, E. B. Browning and George Eliot]. 1885. 8°. **11840**. ccc. **30**.

—— *See* ELTON (Oliver) The Brownings. 1924. 8°. **011840**. a. **8**.

—— *See* FLECKENSTEIN (E.) Die literarischen Anschauungen und Kritiken Elizabeth Barrett Brownings. 1911. 8°. **11865.cc.28/3.**

—— *See* FORMAN (Harry B.) Elizabeth Barrett Browning and her scarcer books. A bio-bibliographical note. 1896. 8°. **C.116.e.9.**

—— *See* GILLINGTON, afterwards BYRON (May C.) A Day with Elizabeth Barrett Browning. [1911.] 8°. **10600**. bbb. **2/11**.

—— *See* GOULD (Elizabeth P.) The Brownings and America. 1904. 8°. **10854**. de. **4**.

—— *See* HEWLETT (Dorothy) Elizabeth Barrett Browning, *etc.* [A biography. With portraits.] 1953. 8°. **10863**. ee. **4**.

—— *See* INGRAM (John H.) Elizabeth Barrett Browning. 1888. 8°. **2407**. b. **8**.

—— *See* JANNATTONI (L.) Elizabeth Barrett Browning. Con un saggio di bibliografia italiana. [With portraits.] 1953. 8°. **11926**. e. **62**.

BARRETT, afterwards BROWNING (ELIZABETH BARRETT)—[APPENDIX.]

—— *See* JONES (*Sir* Henry) *Professor of Moral Philosophy at the University of Glasgow.* Robert Browning and Elizabeth Barrett Browning. 1916. 8°. [*Cambridge History of English Literature.* vol. 13.] 11870.g.1.

—— *See* KESSEL (E.) Elisabeth Barrett-Browning, *etc.* [With a portrait.] [1939.] 8°. 10857. f. 15.

—— *See* LOTH (D. G.) The Brownings, *etc.* [With a portrait.] 1929. 8°. 10824. bb. 14.

—— *See* LUBBOCK (Percy) Elizabeth Barrett Browning in her Letters, *etc.* 1906. 8°. 10905. ccc. 20.

—— *See* MARKS (Jeannette) The Family of the Barrett, *etc.* [On E. B. Browning and the Barrett family. With portraits.] 1938. 8°. 9915. s. 6.

—— *See* MAUROIS (A.) *K.B.E.* Robert et Elizabeth Browning. Portraits, *etc.* 1955. 8°. 11870. df. 20.

—— *See* MERLETTE (G. M.) La Vie et l'œuvre d'Elizabeth Barrett Browning. 1905. 8°. 10854. h. 21.

—— *See* MONTÉGUT (E.) Écrivains modernes de l'Angleterre. (sér. 2. Mistress Gaskell, Mistress Browning, *etc.*) 1885, *etc.* 8°. 11840. p. 11.

—— *See* NICATI (A. B.) Femme et poète. Elizabeth Browning. 1912. 8°. 010854. de. 28.

—— *See* ROBINSON, afterwards DARMESTETER, afterwards DUCLAUX (Agnes M. F.) Grands écrivains d'Outre-Manche . . . Les Browning, *etc.* [1901.] 8°. 011853. e. 3.

—— *See* ROYDS, afterwards INNES (Kathleen E.) Elizabeth Barrett Browning & her Poetry. 1912. 8°. 11863.a.11/10.

—— *See* SARRAZIN (G.) Poètes modernes de l'Angleterre. (E. B. Browning.) 1885. 18°. 11851. cc. 9.

—— *See* SHACKFORD (Martha H.) E. B. Browning; R. H. Horne. Two studies. [1935.] 8°. 11857. b. 59.

—— *See* SELDEN (Camille) *pseud.* Portraits de femmes, *etc.* (Elizabeth Browning.) 1877. 8°. 10602. d. 8.

—— *See* SIM (Frances M.) Robert Browning and Elizabeth Barrett. 1930. 8°. 10824. d. 11.

—— *See* STEDMAN (Edmund C.) Elizabeth Barrett Browning. 1877. 16°. 12206. aaa. 51.

—— *See* THACKERAY (Anne I.) afterwards RITCHIE (~~Anne~~ I.) *Lady.* Records of Tennyson, Ruskin and Browning. (Robert & Elizabeth Browning.) 1892. 8°. 10803. e. 8.

—— *See* THACKERAY (Anne I.) afterwards RITCHIE (A. I.) *Lady.* Records of Tennyson . . . (Robert and Elizabeth) Browning, *etc.* 1892. 8°. 10804. c. 33.

—— *See* VITERBI (B. B.) Elisabetta Barrett-Browning. 1913. 8°. 10827. a. 64.

—— *See* WHITING (Lilian) The Brownings: their life and art, *etc.* 1911. 8°. 010827. ee. 36.

—— *See* WHITING (Lilian) A Study of Elizabeth Barrett Browning. 1899. 8°. 10856. a. 23.

—— *See* WILLIS (Irene C.) Elizabeth Barrett Browning. 1928. 8°. 010855. b. 71.

—— *See* WINWAR (Frances) pseud. The Immortal Lovers: Elizabeth Barrett and Robert Browning, *etc.* [With a portrait.] [1950.] 8°. 10862. f. 43.

BARRETT, afterwards BROWNING (ELIZABETH BARRETT)—[APPENDIX.]

—— *See* WINWAR (Frances) *pseud.* [i.e. F. Grebanier.] The Immortal Lovers: Elizabeth Barrett & Robert Browning. A biography. [With portraits.] 1950. 8°. 10862. c. 20.

—— *See* WISE (Thomas J.) A Bibliography of the Writings in prose and verse of E. B. Browning. 1918. 8°. 11927.b.20.

—— *See* WISE (Thomas J.) A Browning Library. A catalogue of printed books, manuscripts and autograph letters by R. Browning and E. B. Browning, *etc.* [With portraits.] 1929. 4°. C. 57. f. 19.

—— *See* ZAMPINI-SALAZAR (F.) Roberto ed Elisabetta Browning, *etc.* 1896. 16°. 10855. a. 35.

—— *See* ZAMPINI-SALAZAR (F.) La Vita e le opere di Roberto Browning ed Elisabetta Barrett-Browning, *etc.* 1907. 8°. 010827. e. 8.

—— *See* ZIMMERN (Helen) The Brownings. 1906. 8°. [*Homes and Haunts of Famous Authors, etc.*] 010347. f. 29.

—— Elizabeth Barrett Browning. A biographical and critical study. [Signed: R.] 1899. 8°. *See* R. 10856. aa. 18.

BARRETT (ELIZABETH GERTRUDE BARBER) *See* BARBER, afterwards BARRETT (E. G.)

BARRETT (ELLIOTT PIERCE)

—— Toward a Method for the Investigation of the Thermal Effects produced by the Exposure of Metals to Vapors. Dissertation, *etc.* pp. 15. *New York*, 1931. 8°. 08710. d. 37.

BARRETT (ENA CONSTANCE) Rainbow Lyrics. pp. 104. *Erskine Macdonald: London* [1922.] 8°. 011645. ee. 38.

BARRETT (ERNEST) *B.Sc.*

—— A Second Class-Book of Chemistry, *etc.* pp. viii. 272. *London*, 1920. 8°. [*Black's Elementary Science Series.*] 8709.aa.31/6.

BARRETT (ERNEST) *B.Sc.* and NUNN (*Sir* THOMAS PERCY)

—— A First Class-Book of Chemistry, *etc.* pp. iv. 123. *London*, 1912. 8°. [*Black's Elementary Science Series.*] 8709.aa.31/1.

—— (Second edition.) pp. iv. 125. *London*, 1920. 8°. [*Black's Elementary Science Series.*] 8709.aa.31/3.

—— Third edition, *etc.* pp. iv. 125. *London*, 1923. 8°. [*Black's Elementary Science Series.*] 8709.aa.31/4.

—— Fourth edition, *etc.* pp. iv. 128. *London*, 1931. 8°. [*Black's Elementary Science Series.*] 8709.aa.31/5.

BARRETT (ERNEST) *Methodist Minister.*

—— Hugh Bourne. pp. 16. *Epworth Press: London*, 1936. 8°. [*Little Books of the Kindly Light.* no. 13.] 3628.aa.7/13.

BARRETT (ERNEST PRIESTLEY)

—— Hints & Aids for Science Teachers. pp. 92. *Educational Company of Ireland: Dublin & Cork*, [1936.] 8°. 08310. de. 17.

BARRETT (FLORENCE ELIZABETH) *Lady.* *See* WILLEY (Florence E.) afterwards BARRETT (F. E.) *Lady.*

BARRETT (Francis) *See* Raphael, *pseud.* The Art of Talismanic Magic: being selections from the works of Rabbi Solomon . . . F. Barrett, *etc.* 1880. 4°. **8630.** h. **3.**

—— The Lives of Alchemystical Philosophers; with a critical catalogue of books in occult chemistry, and a selection of the most celebrated treatises on the theory and practice of the hermetic art. [By F. Barrett?] pp. 384. 1815. 8°. *See* Lives. **275.1.5.**

—— The Lives of Alchemystical Philosophers, *etc.* [By F. Barrett? A facsimile of the edition of 1815.] pp. 384. 1955. 8°. *See* Lives. **08909.** ss. **38.**

—— *See* Waite (Arthur E.) Lives of Alchemystical Philosophers. Based on materials collected in 1815 [by F. Barrett?], and supplemented by recent researches, *etc.* 1888. 8°. **10602.** i. **25.**

—— The Magus, or Celestial Intelligencer; being a complete system of occult philosophy. In three books, *etc.* [With a portrait.] 2 pt. *Lackington, Allen & Co.: London,* 1801. 4°. G. **1521. (1.)**

—— [A facsimile of the edition of 1801.] *Knight & Compton: [London,* 1875.] 4°. **8630.** k. **8.**

BARRETT (Francis Thornton)

—— *See* Glasgow.—*Royal Glasgow Institute of the Fine Arts.* Memorial Catalogue of the Burns Exhibition, *etc.* (Books: F. T. Barrett.) 1898. 4°. K.T.C. 29. b. 12.

—— On the Selection of Books for a Reference Library, *etc.* pp. 9. *J. Bale & Sons: London,* 1896. 8°. **11899.** dd. **8. (10.)**

BARRETT (Frank) *Novelist.*

—— John Ford . . . and, His Helpmate. A new edition. pp. 283. *Chatto & Windus: London,* 1892. 8°. **012641.** ee. **5.**

—— The Admirable Lady Biddy Fane, her surprising, curious adventures in strange parts, *etc.* 3 vol. *Cassell & Co.: London,* 1888. 8°. **012638.** m. **11.**

—— [Another edition.] pp. viii. 352. *Cassell & Co.: London,* [1889.] 8°. **012633.** m. **41.**

—— Illustrated edition. pp. viii. 352. *Cassell & Co.: London,* 1894. 8°. **012618.** h. **50.**

—— [Another edition.] pp. 160. *Cassell & Co.: London,* 1902. 8°. **12624.** f. **53.**

—— Between Life and Death. A novel. 3 vol. *Chatto & Windus: London,* 1890. 8°. **012640.** h. **11.**

—— Breaking the Shackles. pp. 338. *John Macqueen: London,* 1900. 8°. **012641.** dd. **16.**

—— [Another copy.] **012640.** a. **7.**

—— The Error of her Ways. pp. viii. 321. *Chatto & Windus: London,* 1905. 8°. **012631.** a. **38.**

—— Fantoccini. 2 vol. *Tinsley Bros.: London,* 1874. 8°. **12628.** dd. **1.**

—— Fettered for Life. A novel. 3 vol. *Chatto & Windus: London,* 1889. 8°. **012639.** f. **10.**

—— Folly Morrison. A novel. 3 vol. *R. Bentley & Son: London,* 1881 [1880]. 8°. **12640.** bb. **8.**

—— New edition. pp. xii. 356. *Ward & Downey: London,* 1885 [1884]. 8°. **12622.** e. **1.**

—— For Love and Honour. A novel . . . A new edition. pp. iv. 288. *Chatto & Windus: London,* 1892. 8°. **012641.** ee. **2.**

BARRETT (Frank) *Novelist.*

—— Found Guilty. A novel. 3 vol. *Ward & Downey: London,* 1887 [1886]. 8°. **12636.** k. **17.**

—— A new edition. pp. iv. 330. *Chatto & Windus: London,* 1892. 8°. **012634.** h. **18.**

—— The Great Hesper, *etc.* pp. 171. *Ward & Downey: London,* 1887. 8°. **12619.** aaa. **30.**

—— The Harding Scandal. 2 vol. *Chatto & Windus: London,* 1896. 8°. **012643.** m. **10.**

—— Hidden Gold, *etc.* pp. 245. *Digby, Long & Co.: London,* 1904. 8°. **012628.** a. **44.**

—— [Another edition.] pp. 96. *Aldine Publishing Co.: London,* [1919.] 8°. [*Mascot Novels.* no. 117.] **12644.** a. **1/117.**

—— His Helpmate. pp. 256. *Ward & Downey: London,* 1887. 8°. **12618.** n. **14.**

—— His Own Law. pp. 302. *Ward, Lock & Co.: London,* 1914. 8°. NN. **2004.**

—— Honest Davie. A novel. 3 vol. *R. Bentley & Son: London,* 1883. 8°. **12643.** l. **6.**

—— New edition. pp. 356. *Ward & Downey: London,* 1885. 8°. **12622.** n. **15.**

—— Jockey Club Stories. Illustrated, *etc.* pp. 148. *"Fun": London,* [1888.] 8°. **012633.** f. **25.**

—— John Ford: his faults and his follies. 2 vol. *Ward & Downey: London,* 1885 [1884]. 8°. **12619.** t. **1.**

—— The Justification of Andrew Lebrun. pp. vi. 277. *William Heinemann: London,* 1894. 8°. **012630.** h. **52.**

—— Kitty's Father. 3 vol. *William Heinemann: London,* 1893. 8°. **012637.** e. **21.**

—— Lady Judas: a drama in a prologue and three acts. [A novel.] pp. vi. 307. *Chatto & Windus: London,* 1903. 8°. **012628.** bb. **25.**

—— Lieutenant Barnabas. A novel. 3 vol. *R. Bentley & Son: London,* 1881. 8°. **12642.** aa. **2.**

—— Little Lady Linton. A novel. 3 vol. *R. Bentley & Son: London,* 1884. 8°. **12636.** s. **4.**

—— A new edition. pp. iv. 314. *Chatto & Windus: London,* 1893. 8°. **012641.** ee. **6.**

—— Maggie? A novel. 3 vol. *Tinsley Bros.: London,* 1876. 8°. **12621.** l. **6.**

—— A Missing Witness, *etc.* pp. 282. *Chatto & Windus: London,* 1897. 8°. **012626.** e. **60.**

—— The Night of Reckoning. pp. 318. *John Long: London,* 1905. 8°. **012630.** c. **3.**

—— New edition. pp. 126. *John Long: London,* [1916.] 8°. **012600.** c. **95.**

—— The Obliging Husband, *etc.* pp. vi. 354. *Chatto & Windus: London,* 1907. 8°. **012634.** a. **2.**

—— Out of the Jaws of Death. 3 vol. *Cassell & Co.: London,* 1892. 8°. **012637.** k. **1.**

—— [Another edition.] pp. vii. 472. *Cassell & Co.: London,* 1893. 8°. **012641.** l. **47.**

—— [Another edition.] pp. 158. *Cassell & Co.: London,* 1901. 8°. **012624.** k. **44.**

BARRETT (Frank) *Novelist.*

—— Perfidious Lydia, *etc.* pp. viii. 306. *Chatto & Windus: London*, 1910. 8°. **012623. aa. 41.**

—— A Prodigal's Progress. 3 vol. *R. Bentley & Son: London*, 1882. 8°. **12642. c. 7.**

—— A new edition. pp. vi. 323. *Chatto & Windus: London*, 1892. 8°. **012641. ee. 3.**

—— A Recoiling Vengeance. 2 vol. *Ward & Downey: London*, 1888. 8°. **012633. k. 9.**

—— A new edition. With . . . illustrations by E. F. Brewtnall. pp. viii. 280. *Chatto & Windus: London*, 1892. 8°. **012641. ee. 4.**

—— A Set of Rogues, *etc.* pp. 346. *A. D. Innes & Co.: London*, 1895. 8°. **012628. m. 51.**

—— Second impression. pp. 130. *A. D. Innes & Co.: London*, 1899. 8°. **012624. k. 15.**

—— The Sin of Olga Zassoulichi. A novel. 3 vol. *Chatto & Windus: London*, 1891. 8°. **012640. k. 13.**

—— The Smuggler's Secret. A romance. pp. 278. *Griffith & Farran: London*, [1893.] 8°. **012618. e. 47.**

—— Two Knaves and a Queen. A novel. 3 vol. *Tinsley Bros.: London*, 1877. 8°. **12639. aaa. 5.**

—— Under a Strange Mask. Illustrated. 2 vol. *Cassell & Co.: London*, 1889. 8°. **012632. e. 13.**

—— [Another edition.] pp. viii. 307. *Cassell & Co.: London*, 1890. 8°. **12621. dd. 21.**

—— New edition, *etc.* pp. viii. 307. *Chatto & Windus: London*, 1899. 8°. **012642. aaa. 29.**

—— [Another edition.] pp. 138. *Cassell & Co.: London*, 1910. 8°. **012640. bb. 59.**

—— Was She Justified? pp. viii. 309. *Chatto & Windus: London*, 1898. 8°. **012623. ff. 10.**

—— The Woman of the Iron Bracelets. 3 vol. *Chatto & Windus: London*, 1893. 8°. **012642. f. 2.**

BARRETT (*Mrs.* **Frank**) *See* **Barrett (Joan)**

BARRETT (Frank Wilson) *See* Thomas (Jevan B.) and Barrett (F. W.) Patchwork, *etc.* [1927.] 8°. **11791. t. 1/98.**

BARRETT (Franklin Allen)

—— Caughley and Coalport Porcelain, *etc.* [With plates.] pp. 108. *F. Lewis: Leigh-on-Sea*, 1951. 4°. **7812. c. 10.**

—— Worcester Porcelain. pp. xiv. 53. pl. A–D. 96. *Faber & Faber: London*, 1953. 8°. [*Faber Monographs on Pottery and Porcelain.*] W.P. **2171/13.**

BARRETT (Franklin T.) Catalogue of the Library of the Institute of Accountants and Actuaries in Glasgow, *etc.* ff. 113. 1889. 4°. *See* Glasgow.—*Institute of Accountants and Actuaries.* **11903. c. 24.**

—— Catalogue of the Library of Thos. A. Mathieson. pp. 122. 1891. 4°. *See* Mathieson (T. A.) **11903. cc. 30.**

—— Fulham Public Libraries. Catalogue of the Central Libraries—Lending and Reference. pp. xvi. 437. 1899. 8°. *See* London.—ii. *Borough Councils.—Fulham.—Fulham Public Libraries.* **11900.ee.90.**

BARRETT (Frederick Charles)

—— *See* Brimley (Robert C.) and Barrett (F. C.) Practical Chromatography, *etc.* 1953. 8°. **8774. ee. 21.**

BARRETT (G.) *Chaplain of the Connecticut State Prison.* The Boy in Prison. Written for the American S. Union and revised by the Committee of Publication. pp. 22. *American Sunday-School Union: Philadelphia*, [1830?] 12°. **864. h. 47. (2.)**

BARRETT (G. E.) and **BARON** (C.)

—— Consumers' Master Record: a suggested model. pp. 11. *London*, 1946. 4°. [*British Electrical and Allied Industries Research Association. Technical Report.* Reference K/T 120.] W.P. **9138/207.**

BARRETT (G. E.) and **PRIDMORE** (W. A.)

—— A Trial Sampling-Survey of Domestic-Supply Conditions. pp. 11. *London*, 1946. 4°. [*British Electrical and Allied Industries Research Association. Technical Report.* Reference K/T 119.] W.P. **9138/208.**

BARRETT (George) *Anarchist.* The Anarchist Revolution. pp. 22. *Freedom Press: London*, 1915. 8°. **08248. b. 37.**

BARRETT (George) *Artist.* A Catalogue of the Collection of Pictures and Drawings . . . and Studies from Nature, by Mr. G. Barrett . . . which will be sold . . . the 9th of this instant May 1771, *etc.* pp. 4. [*London*, 1771.] 4°. **7854. i. 17. (7.)**

BARRETT (George) *Ironfounder. See* Fox (Henry H.) *Ironfounder*, and Barrett (G.) On the Construction of Public Buildings . . . on a fire-proof principle, *etc.* 1849. 12°. **1400. b. 81. (4.)**

BARRETT (George) *of Godalming.* An Essay towards establishing a System of Police, on constitutional principles, *etc.* pp. 62. *G. & T. Wilkie: London*, 1786. 8°. **103. l. 3.**

BARRETT (George) *of Spring Valley, Greene County, Ohio.* The Poor Man's Home, and the Rich Man's Palace. Or, the application of the gravel wall cement to the purposes of building. pp. 60. *Applegate & Co.: Cincinnati*, 1856. 8°. **07822.pp.68.**

BARRETT (George F.)

—— The Waterway from the Great Lakes to the Gulf of Mexico. America's greatest need. Facts and records of a century. pp. v. 194. xxi. 1926. 8°. *See* Chicago.—*Sanitary District.* **08809. b. 22.**

BARRETT (George Slatyer)

—— *See* Hymnals. [*English.*] The Book of Praise for Children. (G. S. Barrett, editor.) [1881.] 16°. **3440. e. 13.**

—— *See* Hymnals. [*English.*] The Book of Praise for Children. (G. S. Barrett, editor.) [1881.] 32°. **3438. ee. 4.**

—— The Bible and its Inspiration, with some reference to the higher criticism. pp. 171. *Jarrold & Sons: London*, 1897. 8°. **03128. g. 12.**

—— The Burden of Souls . . . Sermon, *etc.* pp. 16. *J. Clarke & Co.: London*, [1891.] 8°. **4473. bb. 36. (9.)**

—— Christian Nurture: a homily for parents. pp. 16. *Sunday School Union: London*, [1883.] 8°. **4422. bbb. 35. (2.)**

—— The Conflict of Rome with Civil and Religious Liberty. pp. 39. *R.T.S.: London*, [1900.] 8°. [*Present Day Papers on Romanism.* no. 3.] **3939. ccc. 43/3.**

—— *See* Manning (Bernard L.) The Hymns of Wesley and Watts, *etc.* [With some remarks on G. S. Barrett's "Congregational Church Hymnal."] 1942. 8°. **20046. aaa. 26.**

BARRETT (GEORGE SLATYER)

—— The Congregational Mission Hymnal and week-night service book. Edited for the Congregational Union by G. S. Barrett. pp. 255. *Congregational Union: London,* 1890. 16°. **3434**. de. **34**.

—— The Earliest Christian Hymn. pp. 207. *J. Clarke & Co.: London,* 1897. 8°. **4224**. a. **47**.

—— Family Worship: morning and evening. pp. 248. *Jarrold & Sons: London,* 1889. 8°. **3457**. g. **30**.

—— Second edition. pp. 248. *Jarrold & Sons: London,* 1894. 8°. **3456**. ee. **32**.

—— Family Worship, including special war prayers by the Archbishop of Canterbury, Bishop Boyd Carpenter, and the Bishop of Newcastle. [Extracts from the preceding.] pp. 64. *Jarrold & Sons: London,* [1915.] 8°. **3457**. ff. **56**.

—— The First Epistle General of St. John. A devotional commentary. pp. 219. *R.T.S.: London,* 1910. 8°. [*A Devotional Commentary.*] **04429**. k. **1/14**.

—— A Form for the Admission of Members into the Fellowship of a Congregational Church. pp. 7. *J. Clarke & Co.: London,* [1897.] 8°. **3456**. ee. **56**. **(2.)**

—— The Influence of the late Dr. Pusey, and of the Oxford Movement . . . on the English Nation and the English Church. A sermon, *etc.* pp. 20. *Jarrold & Sons: Norwich & London,* [1882.] 8°. **4106**. h. **32**. **(10.)**

—— The Intermediate State and the Last Things. pp. vi. 275. *Elliot Stock: London,* 1896. 8°. **4256**. de. **9**.

—— Cheap edition. pp. vi. 275. *Elliot Stock: London,* 1898. 8°. **4257**. d. **26**.

—— Musings for Quiet Hours. pp. 128. *R.T.S.: London,* [1898.] 8°. **4430**. de. **25**.

—— [Another edition.] pp. vi. 122. *R.T.S.: London,* [1907.] 8°. **04429**. g. **62**.

—— An Office for the Administration of Christian Baptism. pp. 8. *J. Clarke & Co.: London,* [1897.] 8°. **3456**. ee. **56**. **(3.)**

—— Religion in Daily Life. pp. 186. *Elliot Stock: London,* 1893. 8°. **4371**. c. **2**.

—— A Service Book for Church and School. pp. 64. 1891. 8°. *See* LONDON.—III. *Sunday School Union, etc.* **3406**. de. **36**. **(4.)**

—— The Seven Words from the Cross. pp. 131. *Jarrold & Sons: London,* 1902. 8°. [*Christian Workers' Series.* no. 1.] **4225.df.66.**

—— The Temptation of Christ. pp. ix. 243. *Macniven & Wallace: Edinburgh,* 1883. 8°. [*Household Library of Exposition.*] **3605**. d. **4**.

—— The Vitality and Value of the Bible. *See* BUCKLAND (Augustus R.) Words of Help on Belief and Conduct, *etc.* 1905. 8°. **04429**. l. **36**.

—— The Whole Armour of God. pp. xii. 102. *National Council of Evangelical Free Churches: London,* 1905. 8°. [*Little Books on the Devout Life.* no. 7.] **04402**. de. **80**.

BARRETT (GEORGE WEST) and **CASSERLEY** (JULIAN VICTOR LANGMEAD)

—— Dialogue on Destiny. [Based on four dialogue sermons given at Trinity Church, New York.] pp. 96. *Longmans, Green & Co.: London,* 1955. 8°. **4499**. p. **34**.

BARRETT (GLADYS M.)

—— A Brief History of Fuller Church, Kettering. [With plates.] pp. 26. *Parker Bros.: St. Albans,* [1946.] 8°. **7822**. bb. **33**.

BARRETT (HAROLD JAMES) How to Sell more Goods: secrets of successful salesmanship. pp. 213. *Harper & Bros.: New York & London,* 1918. 8°. **08245**. ee. **7**.

—— Modern Methods in the Office, *etc.* pp. 208. *Harper & Bros.: New York & London,* 1918. 8°. **08228**. b. **3**.

—— Patricia's Awakening. pp. 419. *T. Y. Crowell Co.: New York,* [1924.] 8°. **12702**. bbb. **23**.

BARRETT (HELEN MARJORIE)

—— Boethius. Some aspects of his times and work. pp. ix. 179. *University Press: Cambridge,* 1940. 8°. **10608**. b. **10**.

BARRETT (HENRY) *Engineer.*

—— *See* ENGLAND.—*Commissioners appointed to inquire into the Municipal Corporations in England and Wales.* Great Yarmouth Corporation. A report of the investigation before His Majesty's Municipal Commissioners . . . appointed to examine into, and report on the corporate affairs of this borough, compiled by H. Barrett, *etc.* 1834. 8°. **10352**. c. **45**.

—— Observations on Railways, addressed to the nobility, gentry, clergy, agriculturists . . . particularly to those situate on the line and connected with the Grand Northern and Eastern Railroad, projected by N. W. Cundy . . . Second edition. [By H. Barrett.] pp. 59. 1835. 8°. *See* CUNDY (Nicholas W.) **8235**. c. **93**. **(1.)**

—— A Treatise on the Formation of Harbours and Bars. pp. vi. 26. *Printed for the Author: London,* [1844.] 8°. **8776**. c. **41**. **(3.)**

BARRETT (HENRY) *Perpetual Curate of Pelton.* Christian Progress: a sermon, *etc.* pp. 15. *W. Douglas: Gateshead,* 1842. 8°. **4473**. f. **7**. **(10.)**

—— Church Purposes v. Clergy Purposes: a letter to the Venerable Charles Thorpe, D.D., and the Rev. John Davies, D.D., Canons of Durham. pp. 40. *Emerson Charnley: Newcastle-upon-Tyne; Simpkin & Marshall: London,* 1853. 8°. **4107**. c. **21**.

—— Second edition . . . With an appendix, containing a report of the late Church Meeting at Durham, *etc.* pp. 57. *Emerson Charnley: Newcastle-upon-Tyne; Simpkin & Marshall: London,* 1853. 8°. **4108**. c. **8**.

—— "Judge, therefore, yourselves, Brethren, that ye be not judged of the Lord." A sermon. pp. 16. *Rivingtons: London,* 1857. 8°. **4477**. d. **8**.

BARRETT (HENRY GEORGE SCOTT)

—— *See* OXFORD.—*University of Oxford.—University Observatory.* Astrographic Catalogue, 1900.0. Potsdam-Oxford section. Dec. +31° to +34°. From photographs taken by F. A. Bellamy and H. G. S. Barrett, *etc.* 1953, *etc.* 4°. **8561**. m. **59**.

—— *See* SHAW (Harold K.) and BARRETT (H. G. S.) The Radcliffe Catalogue of Proper Motions in the Selected Areas 1 to 115, *etc.* 1934. 4°. **8565**. cc. **17**.

BARRETT (HENRY JOHN) Fifteen Years among the Zulus and the Boers, with . . . accounts of the natives . . . the circumstances which have led up to the present war, and its probable results. pp. 59. *M. C. Peck & Son: Hull,* 1879. 8°. **10097**. b. **10**. **(7.)**

BARRETT (Herbert Raymond)

—— Corrected Times by the T.C.F. or T.H.C.F. [With score cards.] [*The Author: Southampton*, 1953.] 8°. **08548**. i. **63**.

BARRETT (Herbert Stanley) A.B.C. History of Antique English Furniture . . . Illustrated . . . Second edition. pp. 164. *Old-World Galleries: London*, 1923. 8°. **07805**. b. **21**.

—— Third edition. pp. 200. *Old-World Galleries: London*, [1926.] 8°. **07805**. h. **37**.

BARRETT (Howard) The Management of Infancy and Childhood, in health and disease. pp. xxviii. 627. *G. Routledge & Sons: London*, 1875 [1874]. 8°. **7581**. df. **38**.

—— [A reissue.] pp. xxiv. 627. *London*, 1883. 8°. **7580**. df. **6**.

With the preliminaries differently arranged.

—— [Another edition.] pp. xx. 653. *G. Routledge & Sons: London*, 1906. 8°. **07581**. df. **45**.

—— Our Medical Missions. pp. 37. *Wesleyan Mission House: London*, [1912.] 8°. [*Centenary Pamphlets*. no. 5.] **4763**. aaaa. **7/5**.

BARRETT (I. Casebow) *See* Barrett (John C.)

BARRETT (J.) *Rev., of Colwall.* A Description of Malvern, and its environs, *etc.* pp. 90. ii. *Printed for the Author: Worcester*, 1796. 12°. G. **3106**.

BARRETT (J. O.) *Writer on Spiritualism*, and **PEEBLES** (James Martin) The Gadarene: or, Spirits in prison. pp. 232. *Colby & Rich: Boston*, 1874. 12°. **8631**. b. **34**.

BARRETT (J. P.) A History of the Ville of Birchington, Thanet, Kent. pp. 8. 227. "*Keble's Gazette*": *Margate*, 1893. 8°. **010358**. f. **46**.

BARRETT (J. W.) *of Arklow ?*

—— Arklow, Co. Wicklow . . . Official guide, *etc.* [Various editions.] [1927– .] 8°. *See* Arklow, *Co. Wicklow*. **10354**. a. **42**.

BARRETT (J. W.) *Teacher.* Our Bible. A few words to my young friends from J. W. Barrett. pp. 16. *Christian Book Society: London*, 1877. 16°. **4422**. b. **3**. **(10.)**

BARRETT (Jack)

—— The New Crossword Book, *etc.* *F. Warne & Co.: London & New York*, [1937.] 8°. **7915**. ppp. **44**.

—— The Premier Cross Word Puzzle Book, *etc.* 4 ser. *F. Warne & Co.: London*, [1925–32.] 8°. **07908.e.23.**

BARRETT (James) *See* Hoffmann (Franz) *Novelist.* Captal . . . From the German . . . By J. Barrett. [1876.] 8°. **4418**. cc. **22**.

BARRETT (James Arthur Samuel) *See* Carlyle (Thomas) [*Sartor Resartus.*] Sartor Resartus . . . Edited, with introduction and notes, by J. A. S. Barrett. 1897. 8°. **12354**. de. **34**.

—— —— 1905. 8°. **12357**. df. **7**.

—— The Principal Portraits and Statues of Thomas Carlyle. A list compiled by J. A. S. Barrett, with the assistance of James L. Caw and Stanley Cursiter . . . With a commentary by James L. Caw. Excerpt from: A Bibliography of Thomas Carlyle's Writings and Ana. By Isaac W. Dyer, *etc.* pp. 21. *Spurr & Swift: London*, [1928.] 8°. **10823**. h. **13**.

BARRETT (James Joseph) Ivy of Sorrow. [Poems.] pp. 40. *J. J. Barrett: London*, [1896.] 16°. **011652**. h. **16**.

BARRETT (*Sir* James William) *K.B.E.*

—— *See* Daley (Charles) Victorian Historical Memorials to Explorers and Discoverers. (Prepared by C. Daley in collaboration with Sir J. Barrett.) [1944.] 8°. **10028**. pp. **25**.

—— Imperial Federation: the educational factor. pp. 12. *Melbourne*, 1909. 8°. [*Imperial Federation League of Australia. Addresses and Proceedings.* 1909. no. 5.] **8157**. e.

—— Save Australia. A plea for the right use of our flora and fauna. By various writers. Edited by Sir J. Barrett. [With illustrations.] pp. viii. 231. *Macmillan & Co.: Melbourne*, 1925. 8°. **7006**. de. **31**.

—— The Twin Ideals: an educated commonwealth. [Essays on Australian affairs.] 2 vol. *H. K. Lewis & Co.: London*, 1918. 8°. **8154**. bb. **71**.

—— Typhoid Fever in Victoria . . . Section I. pp. 44. *George Robertson: Melbourne*, 1883. 8°. **7561**. bbb. **20**.

—— A Vision of the Possible: what the R.A.M.C. might become, *etc.* pp. xx. 182. *H. K. Lewis & Co.: London*, 1919. 8°. **9081**. g. **24**.

—— The War Work of the Y.M.C.A. in Egypt. [With illustrations.] pp. xx. 212. *H. K. Lewis & Co.: London*, 1919. 8°. **09082**. c. **30**.

BARRETT (*Sir* James William) *K.B.E.*, and **DEANE** (P. E.)

—— The Australian Army Medical Corps in Egypt: an illustrated and detailed account of the . . . work . . . in Egypt in 1914–1915. pp. xiv. 259. *H. K. Lewis & Co.: London*, 1918. 8°. **9081**. g. **9**.

BARRETT (James Wyman)

—— *See* Moore (Herbert) *Publicist*, and Barrett (J. W.) Who Killed Hitler? *etc.* 1947. 8°. **010704**. k. **7**.

—— The End of "The World." A post-mortem . . . James W. Barrett . . . editor. [With plates.] pp. ix. 273. *Harper & Bros.: New York & London*, 1931. 8°. **11822**. pp. **14**.

BARRETT (Jane W.) A Long Letter from Ilfracombe, to my pupil, J. N. containing an account of the illness and death of C. Tartakover, a converted Jewess. pp. 36. *Hamilton, Adams & Co.: London*, 1853. 18°. **4903**. b. **33**.

BARRETT (Jay Amos) Evolution of the Ordinance of 1787. With an account of the earlier plans for the government of the Northwest Territory. pp. 94. *G. P. Putman's Sons: New York, London*, 1891. 8°. [*University of Nebraska. Departments of History and Economics. Seminary Papers.* no. 1.] Ac. **2692**. 1/2.

BARRETT (Jean)

—— Ward Management and Teaching. pp. xvii. 399. *Appleton-Century-Crofts: New York*, [1949.] 8°. **7689**. c. **17**.

—— Ward Management and Teaching . . . Second edition. pp. xiv. 440. *Appleton-Century-Crofts: New York*, [1954.] 8°. **7689**. n. **7**.

BARRETT (Jean Jacques de) *See* Cicero (M. T.) [*Two or more Works.—Latin and French.*] Les Livres . . . de la vieillesse, de l'amitié; les paradoxes . . . Traduction . . . avec le latin revu . . . par M. de Barrett. 1776. 12°. **525**. b. **28**.

BARRETT (JEAN JACQUES DE)

—— *See* CICERO (M. T.) [*Two or more Works.—French.*] Les Livres de Cicéron De la vieillesse, De l'amitié, Les Paradoxes, Le Songe de Scipion. Traduction nouvelle . . . Par M. Debarrett. 1768. 12°. **1396. a. 17.**

—— *See* CICERO (M. T.) [*De Officiis.—Latin and French.*] Les Offices de Cicéron. Traduction . . . avec le latin revu . . . par M. de Barrett. 1768. 12°. **11305.** bbb. **7.**

—— *See* ERASMUS (D.) [*Moriae Encomium.*] L'Éloge de la folie; traduction nouvelle . . . par M. Barrett. 1789. 12°. **12330.** bb. **25.**

—— De la loi naturelle, par M***. [i.e. J. J. de Barrett.] 2 tom. 1790. 8°. *See* M***. **521. h. 14.**

BARRETT (JERRY) "Mrs. Fry reading to the Prisoners in Newgate in 1816." A grand historical picture, by Jerry Barrett, *etc.* pp. 18. *J. Miles & Co.: London,* [1861.] 12°. **7856. a. 37. (7.)**

BARRETT (JOAN) Monte Carlo Stories. pp. 162. *Chatto & Windus: London,* 1896. 8°. **012628. e. 45.**

—— The Pretty Nobody. pp. 160. *D. C. Thomson & Co.: London,* 1927. 8°. [*Red Letter Novels.* no. 173.] **012604.** l. **1/173.**

—— The Story of a Cat and Two Naughty Magpies. (The Magic Doll's House. By Isla Glen.) pp. 118. *T. Nelson & Sons: London,* [1923.] 8°. **12802.** aaa. **50.**

BARRETT (JOHN) *Esq.* *See* BARRET.

BARRETT (JOHN) *M.A., of Nottingham.* *See* BARRET.

BARRETT (JOHN) *Minister of Sutton in Ashfield, Nottinghamshire.* The Dying Christian's Triumph in a Living Redeemer exemplified in a sermon . . . occasioned by the death of Matthew Butcher, jun., *etc.* pp. 48. *A. Bell: London,* [1777.] 8°. **1416. d. 60.**

BARRETT (JOHN) *Schoolmaster.* A Grammar of the English Language . . . The second edition, enlarged, *etc.* pp. 214. *The Author: Boston,* 1819. 12°. **12983. a. 55.**

BARRETT (JOHN) *U.S. Minister to Colombia.*

—— *See* PAN AMERICAN COMMERCIAL CONFERENCE. [Washington, 1919.] Pan American Commerce . . . Report of the Second Pan American Commercial Conference . . . Prepared by J. Barrett . . . assisted by Professor J. Moreno-Lacalle. 1919. 8°. **U.N.P.86/3.**

—— Colombia, her resources and prospects. *See* ALDANA (A.) "Colombia," *etc.* [1906.] 8°. **8180.** bb. **54.**

—— Latin America, the land of opportunity. A reprint of official reports and special articles, prepared by J. Barrett. pp. 104. 1909. 8°. See INTERNATIONAL BUREAU OF THE AMERICAN REPUBLICS. 010480. f. 19. (1.)

—— Panama Canal. What it is; what it means. [Edited by J. Barrett.] pp. 120. 1913. 8°. See PAN AMERICAN UNION. **U.N.P.86/21.**

BARRETT (JOHN) *Vice-Provost of Trinity College, Dublin.* *See* BIBLE.—*Matthew.* [*Greek.*] Evangelium secundum Matthaeum ex codice rescripto in Bibliotheca Collegii SS^ae Trinitatis . . . Descriptum opera et studio J. Barrett, *etc.* 1801. 4°. **1. b. 5.**

—— *See* TREGELLES (Samuel P.) The Dublin Codex Rescriptus. A supplement to Dr. Barrett's transcript of the Codex Dublinensis Rescriptus, *etc.* 1863. 4°. **3109. g. 5.**

BARRETT (JOHN) *Vice-Provost of Trinity College, Dublin.*

—— An Essay on the Earlier Part of the Life of Swift . . . To which are subjoined several pieces ascribed to Swift; two of his original letters; and extracts from his remarks on Bishop Burnet's History. pp. viii. 4–232. *J. Johnson, etc.: London,* 1808. 8°. **633. h. 12.**

—— [Another copy.] G. **1417.**

BARRETT (JOHN CASEBOW) The Bible the only safe Basis of National Education. A sermon, *etc.* pp. 34. *L. & G. Seeley & Co.: London; J. H. Beilby: Birmingham,* 1838. 8°. **4477. e. 106. (6.)**

—— The Christian Patriot's Duty at the Present Crisis. A sermon, *etc.* pp. 39. *L. & G. Seeley & Co.: London,* 1839. 8°. **4475. f. 57. (3.)**

—— [Another copy.] **4475. k. 8. (10.)**

—— The Claims of God, as the Father and Guide of Youth, considered and enforced. A sermon . . . Second edition. pp. 40. *John Hutchinson: Hull,* 1838. 8°. **10347. f. 10. (17.)**

—— "England and her Volunteers." An address, delivered before the Birmingham companies of the Warwickshire Rifle Corps, *etc.* pp. 24. *John Henderson: Birmingham,* 1860. 12°. **4477.** bb. **74. (5.)**

—— Ministerial Caution. A sermon, *etc.* pp. 27. *R. Groombridge & Sons: London,* 1849. 8°. **4475. e. 4.**

—— The Protestant Bible Burnt: a sermon, *etc.* pp. 27. *R. Groombridge & Sons: London,* 1848. 16°. **3938. c. 3.**

—— Psalms and Hymns, selected and arranged according to the services of the Church of England. pp. 447. xviii. *Wertheim & Macintosh: London,* 1853. 18°. **3436. f. 17.**

—— Purgatory, a Popish Figment, not a Scriptural Truth. *See* D., W. A Course of Sermons on the Creed of Pope Pius IV., *etc.* 1841. 8°. **1352. e. 10.**

—— Romanism Hostile to the Intellectual Advancement of a People, *etc.* pp. 31. *T. Hatchard: London,* [1850.] 8°. [*Birmingham Protestant Lectures.* Lecture 2.] **3942. b. 90.**

—— The Saints Preserved. *See* GRANGE, *in Cartmel.* Twenty-two Sermons, *etc.* 1854. 12°. **4455. h. 8.**

—— The Teacher: his influence upon scholars and their parents: his intercourse with fellow-teachers. *See* BIRMINGHAM.—*Birmingham Church of England Young Men's Christian and Missionary-Aid Association.* A Course of Lectures to Sunday School Teachers, *etc.* 1854. 8°. **4462. b. 18.**

BARRETT (JOHN I.) and **FANNING** (MARY F.) Ave Maria Readers. 4 vol. *American Book Co.: New York,* [1931.] 8°. **12980.** l. **12.**

BARRETT (JOHN LIONEL MACKENZIE) Practical Horsemanship. A book for the novice of all ages, *etc.* pp. 159. pl. 16. *H. F. & G. Witherby: London,* 1929. 4°. **7904.** cc. **14.**

—— Practical Horsemanship, *etc.* (First cheap edition.) pp. 191. pl. 12. *H. F. & G. Witherby: London,* 1935. 8°. **7915.** ppp. **5.**

—— Practical Jumping . . . Illustrated by Charles Simpson. pp. x. 164. *Country Life: London,* 1930. 8°. **7915. e. 39.**

—— Practical Jumping and Schooling . . . Illustrated, *etc.* pp. x. 107. *Country Life: London,* 1937. 8°. **7915. w. 26.**

BARRETT (John Oliver)

—— The Book of the Revelation. pp. 123. *Carey Press: London*, 1947. 8°. [*The Missionary Message of the New Testament.*] 03226. ff. **28.**

—— By Life and by Pen. Talks on translators of the Bible. pp. 59. *Carey Press: London*, [1939.] 8°. [*Furnival Library of Talks to Boys and Girls.* no. 2.] W.P. **10799/2.**

—— For the Baptist Minister. A denominational guide. pp. 28. *Carey Kingsgate Press: London*, 1953. 8°. **4716.** aa. **43.**

—— Rawdon College—Northern Baptist Education Society—1804–1954. A short history. pp. vi. 58. *Carey Kingsgate Press: London*, 1954. 8°. **8369.** de. **50.**

BARRETT (John Oliver) and **SHIELDS** (Robert W.)

—— Your Marriage, *etc.* pp. 23. *Carey Kingsgate Press: London*, 1949. 12°. **08416.** e. **123.**

BARRETT (Jonathan) Observations on Endowments for Charitable Purposes. [Signed: J. B., i.e. J. Barrett.] pp. 23. 1852. 8°. *See* B., J. **8277.** aa. **43.** (**1.**)

BARRETT (Jonathan Tyers) *See* Bible.—*Psalms.—Selections.* [*English.*] Select Portions of the New Version of the Psalms of David, adapted to the services of the Church of England . . . By J. T. Barrett. 1816. 12°. **855.** b. **23.**

—— *See* Bible.—*Psalms.—Selections.* [*English.*] [Another edition.] A Course of Psalms, selected from the New Version, for the services of the United Church of England and Ireland . . . By the Rev. J. T. Barrett, *etc.* 1816. 12°. **852. f. 1.**

—— —— 1820. 12°. **3435.** e. **41.**

—— —— 1824. 12°. **3433.** bbbb. **49.**

—— —— 1826. 12°. **3435.** d. **21.**

—— —— 1848. 12°. **3433.** c. **61.**

—— *See* Liturgies.—*Church of England.—Common Prayer.—Baptismal Office.* [*English.*] The Ministration of Publick Baptism of Infants . . . and the Form of Receiving Children who have been privately Baptized into the Congregation of Christ's Flock, arranged as one service [by J. T. Barrett], *etc.* 1840. 8°. **3406.** c. **46.**

—— *See* Liturgies.—*Church of England.—Common Prayer.—Family and School Prayers.* A Daily Prayer Book, for families and schools, arranged from the services of the United Church of England and Ireland . . . by J. T. Barrett. 1834. 24°. **3456.** b. **31.**

—— Christ anointed to preach the Gospel to the Poor. A sermon, *etc.* pp. 28. *F. C. & J. Rivington: London*, 1821. 12°. **695.** b. **6.** (**1.**)

—— The Importance of Early Instruction in Chief Truths. 1834. *See* Family Sermons. Original Family Sermons. vol. 4. 1833, *etc.* 8°. **694.** b. **4.**

—— A Letter to the Ecclesiastical Commissioners for England, upon the apportionment proposed by them of episcopal patronage between the dioceses of London and Rochester. pp. 19. *J. W. Parker: London*, 1837. 8°. **4109.** h. **6.** (**9.**)

—— Memorials of the Parochial Church, the Collegiate Chantry, and the Chapel of St. Mary, commonly called Mortimer's Chapel, in the parish of Attleborough . . . together with some account of the services used at the consecration of churches, from the Anglo-Saxon to the present time. [With plates.] pp. xv. 246. *J. W. Parker: London*, 1848. 8°. **4705.** g. **12.**

BARRETT (Jonathan Tyers)

—— "The Signs of the Times." A sermon, *etc.* pp. 21. *C. Muskett: Norwich; J. W. Parker: London*, 1845. 8°. **1358.** h. **99.**

—— [Another edition.] *See* Watson (Alexander) *Vicar of St. Marychurch.* Practical Sermons, *etc.* vol. 1. 1845, *etc.* 8°. **1358.** g. **5.**

—— The Temptation of Christ in the Wilderness; considered as a guide to us in the knowledge of our Christian calling, *etc.* pp. viii. 94. *F. C. & J. Rivington: London*, 1821. 12°. **700.** c. **35.**

BARRETT (Joseph) *of Nottingham.* A Funeral Sermon upon the Death of Mr. Joseph Barrett . . . Preached Aug. 30th. By J. W. Junior [i.e. John Whitlock] . . . To which is added, an account of his holy life, his evidences . . . and his constant course of self-examination. Being part of an exact diary written by his own hand. 1699. 8°. *See* W., J., *Junior.* **857.** h. **27.** (**1.**)

—— The Remains of Mr. Joseph Barrett . . . Being the second part taken out of an exact diary written by his own hand. [Edited by John Whitlock the elder and John Whitlock the younger.] pp. 216. *Tho. Parkhurst: London*, 1700. 8°. **857.** h. **27.** (**2.**)

BARRETT (Joseph) *Presbyterian Minister.* *See* Rees (Abraham) A Sermon preached . . . upon occasion of the . . . death of the Rev. James Lindsay . . . To which is added the address delivered at the interment of the deceased . . . by J. Barrett. 1821. 8°. T. **1038.** (**8.**)

—— The Duty of Britons to promote, by safe, gradual, and efficacious means, the progress of Christianity and Civilization in India. A sermon, *etc.* pp. 21. *J. Johnson & Co.: London*, 1813. 8°. **4766.** f. **20.** (**2.**)

—— Moral Reflections and Anticipations on the Opening of the Present Year. A sermon, addressed principally to young persons, *etc.* pp. 31. *T. Bensley: London*, 1806. 8°. **4476.** cc. **2.**

BARRETT (Joseph Hartwell) Abraham Lincoln and his Presidency . . . Illustrated. 2 vol. *R. Clarke Co.: Cincinnati*, 1904. 8°. **010881.** k. **14.**

—— Life of Abraham Lincoln, *etc.* [With plates, including a portrait.] pp. 842. *Moore, Wilstach & Baldwin: Cincinnati, New York*, 1865. 8°. **10881.** cc. **3.**

BARRETT (Joseph O.) History of "Old Abe," the live War Eagle of the Eighth Regiment Wisconsin Volunteers. pp. 71. *A. L. Sewell: Chicago*, 1865. 8°. **9602.** cc. **32.** (**7.**)

BARRETT (Katharine Ruth Ellis) *See* also Ba, *Lady, pseud.* [i.e. K. R. E. Barrett.]

—— *See* Barrett (Robert Le M.) and (K. R. E.) Cloudtop Mosaics. 1932. 8°. **010094.** de. **57.**

—— *See* Barrett (Robert Le M.) and (K. R. E.) A Yankee in Patagonia, *etc.* 1931. 8°. **10482.** bb. **10.**

—— Girls in the High Sierras. pp. xii. 335. *William Heinemann: London; printed in U.S.A.*, 1924. 8°. **7904.** b. **14.**

—— Red Shoes. Thoughts by Carlisle Ellis. Verses by K. E. Barrett. Drawings by Dorothy Fuller Odell. pp. viii. 77. *Womans Press: New York*, 1930. 8°. **011686.** h. **88.**

—— Small Flora Ann. A young pioneer. Jingles about her . . . Pictures by Harold W. Miles. pp. 65. *Privately printed*, 1934. 8°. **11688.** r. **8.**

BARRETT (Katharine Ruth Ellis)

—— The Trenchant Wind. Poems of Patagonia. pp. xii. 73. *W. Heffer & Sons: Cambridge,* 1932. 8°. **11640**. g. **83**.

BARRETT (Lawrence) *See* Barron (Elwyn A.) The Viking . . . With preface by L. Barrett. 1888. 8°. **11791**. b. **10**.

—— *See* Dehn (Adolf) How to Draw and Print Lithographs . . . Printing from the stone, by L. Barrett. [1950.] fol. 7871. d. 3.

—— Edwin Forrest. [A biography. With plates, including portraits.] pp. 171. *David Bogue: London; Cambridge* [*Mass.* printed, 1882]. 8°. [*American Actor Series.*] 11794.g.34/1.

BARRETT (Lillian) Gibbeted Gods. [A novel.] pp. 321. *Century Co.: New York,* [1921.] 8°. NN. **7337**.

BARRETT (Linton L.)

—— *See* Verissimo (E.) Time and the Wind . . . Translated by L. L. Barrett. 1954. 8°. **12492**. c. **26**.

BARRETT (Lucas) *See* England.—*Geological Survey of the United Kingdom.* Memoirs, *etc.* (Reports on the Geology of Jamaica . . . By T. G. Sawkins . . . with contributions from G. P. Wall . . . L. Barrett, *etc.*) 1846, *etc.* 8°. B.S.38.Ga/1.(7.)

—— Report on the Copper Veins of the Parish of Portland, Jamaica, *etc.* pp. 24. pl. 2. *Taylor & Francis: London,* 1861. 8°. **7105**. bb. **7**.

BARRETT (Manuel Bosch) *See* Bosch Barrett.

BARRETT (Marianne) *See* Edington (Arlo C.) and (C. B.) Drum Madness. By the Edingtons and M. Barrett. 1934. 8°. NN. **21981**.

BARRETT (Mary) *pseud.* [i.e. Mary Olivia Nutting.] Our Summer at Hillside Farm. pp. 256. *American Tract Society: Boston,* [1867.] 8°. **12705**. bbb. **13**.

—— Steps in the Upward Way: the story of Fanny Bell. pp. 279. *American Tract Society: Boston,* [1866.] 8°. **12706**. aaa. **11**.

—— The Story of William the Silent and the Netherland War. 1555–1584. [With a map.] pp. 480. *Warren & Blakeslee: Boston,* [1869.] 12°. **10760**. aaa. **13**.

BARRETT (Mary Constance)

—— An Experimental Study of the Thomistic Concept of the Faculty of Imagination. pp. vi. 51. *Catholic University of America Press: Washington,* 1941. 8°. [*Studies in Psychology and Psychiatry.* vol. 5. no. 3.] Ac. **2692**. y/7.

BARRETT (Maude T.)

—— Social Welfare Programmes in El Salvador. Prepared for the Government of El Salvador. pp. 18. *New York,* 1954. 4°. [*United Nations Technical Assistance Programme.* no. ST/TAA/El Salvador/1.] U.N. a. **403/27**.

BARRETT (Michael) *O.S.B.*

—— Footprints of the Ancient Scottish Church. pp. xi. 264. *Sands & Co.: London & Edinburgh; B. Herder: St. Louis,* 1914. 8°. **4735**. d. **27**.

—— The Pre-Reformation Church of Scotland. (Reprinted from the American Catholic Quarterly Review.) pp. 31. *Catholic Truth Society: London,* [1906.] 8°. **3943**. aa. **403**. (**1**.)

BARRETT (Michael) *O.S.B.*

—— The Scottish Monasteries of old. A brief account of the houses which existed in Scotland, before the Protestant Reformation, for monks following the rule of St. Benedict. pp. x. 224. *O. Schulze & Co.: Edinburgh,* 1913. 8°. **04785**. i. **56**.

—— Sidelights on Scottish History. pp. 244. *Sands & Co.: Edinburgh, London,* 1918. 8°. **9510**. dd. **7**.

BARRETT (Michael John)

—— The Reward. [A novel.] pp. 187. *Longmans, Green & Co.: London,* 1955. 8°. NNN. **6647**.

BARRETT (Monte) Knotted Silk. pp. 287. *Stanley Paul & Co.: London,* [1932.] 8°. A.N. **1360**.

—— Murder at Belle Camille. pp. 288. *Bobbs-Merrill Co.: Indianapolis, New York,* [1943.] 8°. **12726**. bb. **10**.

—— Murder at Belle Camille. pp. 143. *T. V. Boardman & Co.: London,* 1946. 8°. **12650**. e. **11**.

—— Murder Off Stage. pp. 320. *Bobbs-Merrill Co.: Indianapolis,* [1931.] 8°. A.N. **942**.

—— Smoke up the Valley. pp. 319. *Hodder & Stoughton London,* 1950. 8°. **12730**. i. **9**

—— Sun in their Eyes. A novel of Texas in 1812. pp. 319. *Bobbs-Merrill Co.: Indianapolis, New York,* [1944.] 8°. **12726**. c. **17**.

—— Sun in their Eyes, *etc.* pp. 236. *Stanley Paul & Co.: London,* [1946.] 8°. **12729**. aa. **42**.

—— Tempered Blade. pp. 288. *Stanley Paul & Co.: London,* [1948.] 8°. **12725**. aa. **29**.

—— The Wedding March Murder. pp. 314. *Bobbs-Merrill Co.: Indianapolis,* [1933.] 8°. A.N. **1462**.

—— [Another edition.] pp. 288. *Stanley Paul & Co.: London,* [1933.] 8°. **12708**. eee. **2**.

BARRETT (Olga)

—— The Harvest of the Mystic. Echoes of worlds unknown to men. By O. Barrett. [Inspirational writing purporting to be dictated by Ted Barrett to O. Barrett. With a portrait.] pp. 144. [1944.] 8°. *See* Barrett (Ted) **8633**. de. **41**.

BARRETT (Oliver Rogers) *See* Lincoln (Abraham) *President of the United States of America.* Lincoln's Last Speech in Springfield in the Campaign of 1858. [Edited by O. R. Barrett.] 1925. 4°. **8177**. i. **3**.

BARRETT (Otis Warren)

—— *See* Verrill (Alpheus H.) Foods America gave the World . . . By A. H. Verrill . . . in collaboration with O. W. Barrett. 1937. 8°. **07032**. tt. **7**.

—— The Animals on Postage Stamps. [With illustrations.] pp. vi. 90. *Scott Stamp & Coin Co.: New York,* [1938.] 8°. **20033**. cc. **19**.

—— The Changa, or Mole Cricket —Scapteriscus didactylus Latr.—in Porto Rico. pp. 19. *Washington,* 1902. 8°. [*Porto Rico Agricultural Experiment Station. Bulletin.* no. 2.] A.S. **871**.

—— La Changa, ó Grillotalpa—Scapteriscus didactylus Latr. —en Puerto Rico. pp. 19. *Washington,* 1902. 8°. [*Estación de Experimentos Agriculturales de Puerto Rico. Boletín.* no. 2.] A.S. **871/5**.

BARRETT (OTIS WARREN)

—— The Tropical Crops. A popular treatment of the practice of agriculture in tropical regions, *etc.* pp. xviii. 445. pl. XXIV. *Macmillan Co.: New York*, 1928. 8°. [*Rural Science Series.*] **07073.** k. **1/6.**

—— The Yautias or Taniers of Porto Rico. pp. 27. *Washington*, 1905. 8°. [*Porto Rico Agricultural Experiment Station. Bulletin.* no. 6.] A.S. **871.**

BARRETT (P.) AND CO. Barrett's General and Commercial Directory of Blackpool. *See* DIRECTORIES.—*Blackpool.*

—— Directory and Topography of Burnley. (General and Commercial Directory of Burnley.) By P. Barrett & Co. *See* DIRECTORIES.—*Burnley.*

—— Directory of the Boroughs of Blackburn, Accrington and Darwen . . . By P. Barrett & Co. *See* DIRECTORIES.—*Blackburn.*

—— General and Commercial Directory of Preston . . . By P. Barrett & Co. *See* DIRECTORIES.—*Preston.*

BARRETT (PAUL) *Dramatist.* *See* BARET (P.) *Dramatist.*

BARRETT (PAUL) *O.F.M.Cap.*

—— *See* GUIBERT (Joseph de) *S.J.* [Theologica spiritualis ascetica et mystica.] The Theology of the Spiritual Life . . . Translated by P. Barrett. 1954. 8°. **4383.** e. **14.**

BARRETT (PERCY REGINALD)

—— *See* CHAUNDY (Theodore W.) and BARRETT (P. R.) Recommendations to Mathematical Authors. 1954. 8°. [*The Printing of Mathematics.*] **11916.m.43.**

BARRETT (PHINEAS) Tables of the Several European Exchanges . . . Shewing, by inspection, the value of any sum of money in all the principal places of Europe, *etc.* pp. xvi. 1044. *Blyth & Beevor: London*, 1771. 4°. **29.** e. **10.**

BARRETT (R.) AND SONS. Information for Authors on Printing and Publishing . . . Third edition, with additions. pp. 23. *R. Barrett & Sons: London*, 1873. 8°. **11899.** bbb. **14.**

—— A Guide to Authors: or, Information on printing and publishing . . . Fourth edition [of "Information for Authors on Printing and Publishing"]. pp. 23. *R. Barrett & Sons: London*, 1874. 8°. **11899.** bbb. **15.**

BARRETT (RAFAEL)

—— Páginas selectas. pp. 93. *México*, 1947. 8°. [*Biblioteca enciclopédica popular.* no. 137.] **12214.** ee. **1/137.**

BARRETT (RALPH ELLIOTT)

—— An Annotated List of the Insects and Arachnids affecting the various Species of Walnuts or Members of the Genus Juglans Linn. *Berkeley*, 1932. 8°. [*University of California Publications in Entomology.* vol. 5. no. 15.] Ac. **2689.** g/**31.**

BARRETT (RAYMOND EDWARD)

—— A Guide to Health Education in Tropical Primary Schools. pp. 109. *Longmans, Green & Co.: London*, 1947. 8°. **7393.** aa. **81.**

—— A Guide to Health Education in Tropical Primary Schools. (Second edition.) pp. 111. *Longmans, Green & Co.: London*, 1950. 8°. **7391.** v. **49.**

BARRETT (RICARDUS) Dissertatio medica inauguralis de compressione quam patitur pulmo in expiratione, *etc.* pp. 14. *Lugduni Batavorum*, 1720. 4°. **1185.** h. **15.** (**11.**)

BARRETT (RICHARD) *See* SHAW (Henry) *Stationer.* Shaw's Authenticated Report of the Irish State Trials, 1844 [i.e. of the trial of R. Barrett and others on a charge of conspiring to raise disaffection amongst the Queen's subjects]. [1844.] 8°. **6495.** b. **46.**

—— History of the Irish Confederation. pp. 23. *George Mason: Dublin*, 1849. 8°. **8145.** cc. **4.**

BARRETT (RICHARD ARTHUR FRANCIS) A Synopsis of Criticisms upon those Passages of the Old Testament, in which modern Commentators have differed from the Authorized Version; together with an explanation of various difficulties in the Hebrew and English texts. vol. 1, 2; vol. 3. pt. 1. *Longman & Co.: London*, 1847. 8°. **1107.** i. **7.**
No more published.

BARRETT (RICHARD HENRY) A Refutation of Mr. W. H. Gillespie's Argument a priori for the existence of a Great First Cause. By R. H. B. [i.e. R. H. Barrett.] pp. 20. 1868. 8°. *See* B., R. H. **4014.** aaa. **48.** (**3.**)

BARRETT (RICHARD REGIS GORDON) Motoring in France . . . With . . . illustrations . . . maps and plans. pp. xiv. 206. *Methuen & Co.: London*, 1925. 8°. **010168.** e. **49.**

—— Motoring in Italy . . . With . . . illustrations . . . maps and plans. pp. xvii. 223. *Methuen & Co.: London*, 1928. 8°. **010151.** de. **39.**

BARRETT (RICHARD WARREN) Business Law. pp. xxi. 349. *Alexander Hamilton Institute: New York*, [1927.] 8°. [*Modern Merchandising Texts.* vol. 10.] **08230.aa.28/10.**

BARRETT (RICHMOND BROOKS) The Enemy's Gates. pp. 352. *Jonathan Cape: London*, 1926. 8°. **12710.** c. **18.**

—— Good Old Summer Days. Newport, Narragansett Pier Saratoga, Long Reach, Bar Harbor . . . Illustrated pp. xvii. 338. *D. Appleton-Century Co.: New York London*, 1941. 8°. **10413.** m. **26**

—— Madam. pp. 332. *Jonathan Cape: London*, 1932. 8°. A.N. **1390.**

—— Rapture. pp. 310. *Jonathan Cape: London; printed in U.S.A.*, [1924.] 8°. **12636.** m. **29.**

BARRETT (ROBERT) *Vicar of Barnham.* The Corpus of Dogmatic Theology of the Church. pp. 13. MS. NOTES. 1913. 8°. **4380.** df. **22.** (**5.**)

—— Epistola Cantabrigiensis. MDCCCCVI. [A letter describing a conference of clergy held at Cambridge.] pp. 16. *West Sussex Gazette & South of England Advertiser: Arundel & Horsham*, [1906.] 8°. **4373.** cc. **21.** (**1.**)

—— Fact in Dogma. A paper published by request of the Association for Mutual Counsel. pp. 16. *J. W. Moore: Chichester*, 1914. 8°. **4015.** i. **13.**

BARRETT (ROBERT JOHN) *See* PERIODICAL PUBLICATIONS.—*London.* The Anglo-African Who's Who . . . Edited by W. H. Wills and R. J. Barrett. 1905, *etc.* 4°. P.P. **2501.** ech.

—— Canada's Century: progress and resources of the great Dominion. Notes, with snapshots and other illustrations, of an extensive tour in British North America . . . With an introduction by the Right Hon. Lord Strathcona and Mount Royal. pp. xiv. 538. *Financier & Bullionist: London*, 1907. 8°. **010470.** i. **11.**

—— Canadian Securities Handbook. Companies' record. Directors list. Canadian-controlled companies. [The issues for 1906 and 1907.] 2 pt. *Financier & Bullionist: London*, [1906,] 07. 12° & 8°. **08226.** a. **22.**

BARRETT (Robert John)

—— Germany's Debt Problems . . . Reprinted from "The Financial Times." pp. 47. *London*, [1932.] 8°. **8224**. w. **26**.

—— Russia's New Era. Being notes, impressions and experiences . . . of an extended tour in the empire of the Tsar. With statistical tables, portraits, snapshots and other illustrations. pp. vii. 292. *Financier & Bullionist: London*, 1908. 8°. **8228**. r. **4**.

BARRETT (Robert Le Moyne) *See* also Davy (Gypsy) *pseud.* [i.e. R. Le M. Barrett.]

BARRETT (Robert Le Moyne) and **BARRETT** (Katharine Ruth Ellis)

—— Cloudtop Mosaics. [Notes on a visit to Tenerife.] pp. ix. 176. *W. Heffer & Sons: Cambridge*, 1932. 8°. **010094**. de. **57**.

—— A Yankee in Patagonia. Edward Chace . . . 1898–1928, *etc.* [With a portrait.] pp. 349. *W. Heffer & Sons: Cambridge*, 1931. 8°. **10482**. bb. **10**.

BARRETT (Robert S.) *Commercial Agent.* Brazilian Markets for Paper, Paper Products, and Printing Machinery. [With illustrations.] pp. 77. *Washington*, 1918. 8°. [*U.S. Bureau of Foreign and Domestic Commerce. Special Agents Series.* no. 171.] A.S. **130**.

BARRETT (Robert S.) *of Mexico.* The Standard Guide to the City of Mexico and Vicinity . . . Illustrated. pp. 152. *Modern Mexico Publishing Co.: City of Mexico; St. Louis* [printed], 1901. 8°. **010480**. g. **8**.

—— Modern Mexico's Standard Guide to the City of Mexico and Vicinity . . . Third edition. pp. 186. *Modern Mexico: City of Mexico & New York; New York* [printed, 1903]. 8°. **010480**. ee. **17**.

BARRETT (Robert S.) *Rev.* Thought Seed for Holy Seasons. pp. 162. *Griffith, Farran & Co.: London*, [1892.] 8°. **4371**. aa. **1**.

BARRETT (Robina)

—— Changed Horizon. A play of New Testament times, *etc.* pp. 47. *H. V. Capsey: London*, [1938.] 8°. **011781**. k. **42**.

BARRETT (Rosa Mary) *See* Barrett (*Sir* William F.) The Religion of Health. An examination of Christian Science . . . Completed by R. M. Barrett. 1925. 8°. **4183**. de. **37**.

—— *See* Lascelles, *Dr.* Beyond . . . Edited by R. M. Barrett. 1929. 8°. **08632**. g. **39**.

—— *See* Lascelles, *Dr.* The Seekers . . . Edited by R. M. Barrett. 1928. 8°. **08632**. g. **10**.

—— —— 1930. 8°. **08632**. g. **41**.

—— Ellice Hopkins: a memoir . . . With introduction by H. Scott Holland. pp. xi. 276. *Wells Gardner & Co.: London*, 1907. 8°. **010827**. e. **12**.

—— Foreign Legislation on behalf of Destitute and Neglected Children. Being a paper read before the Statistical and Social Inquiry Society of Ireland . . . Second edition. pp. 76. *Sealy & Co.: Dublin*, 1896. 8°. **8282**. df. **29**.

—— Guide to Dublin Charities. 3 pt. *Hodges & Co.: Dublin*, 1884. 8°. **8277**. dd. **16**.

BARRETT (S. A.) *Poetical Writer.* Maintonomah, and other poems. pp. 209. *Cady & Burgess: New York*, 1849. 12°. **11686**. d. **21**.

BARRETT (Samuel) *See* Pray (Lewis G.) Memoir of the Rev. Samuel Barrett, D.D., with a select series of his discourses. 1867. 8°. **4986**. aaa. **41**.

—— Apologies for Indifference to Religion and its Institutions Examined. pp. 24. *American Unitarian Association: Boston*, 1834. 12°. **4378**. bbb. **5**.

—— A Discourse, delivered before the Ancient and Honorable Artillery Company, June 6, 1831, *etc.* pp. 19. *E. W. Metcalf & Co.: Cambridge* [*Mass.*], 1831. 8°. **4486**. e. **51**. **(5.)**

—— A Discourse, delivered in the Twelfth Congregational Church, Boston, on Fast Day, April 10, 1851. pp. 15. *Eastburn's Press: Boston*, 1851. 8°. **4486**. e. **51**. **(9.)**

—— One Hundred Scriptural Arguments for the Unitarian Faith. [By S. Barrett.] pp. 23. 1827. 12°. *See* Unitarian Faith. **4224**. b. **81**. **(3.)**

—— [Another copy.] **1481**. d. **26**. **(9.)**

—— Fifth edition. pp. 16. 1830. 12°. *See* Unitarian Faith. **4225**. a. **67**.

—— Refutation of a Tract [by S. Barrett] entitled, "One Hundred Scriptural Arguments for the Unitarian Faith." [With the text of the tract.] pp. iv. 59. 1855. 8°. *See* Unitarian Faith. **4226**. b. **67**.

—— A Sermon delivered at the Installation of the Rev. George R. Noyes, as pastor of the First Congregational Society in Petersham, *etc.* pp. 24. *Charles Bowen: Boston*, 1834. 12°. **4486**. aa. **64**. **(10.)**

—— A Sermon, preached in the Twelfth Congregational Church, Boston . . . August 9, 1832, the day appointed for fasting . . . on account of the approach of the cholera, *etc.* pp. 18. *Hilliard, Gray & Co.: Boston*, 1832. 8°. **4486**. e. **49**. **(14.)**

—— "Thou shall not Kill." A sermon, preached . . . in consequence of the late duel in Washington. pp. 18. *I. R. Butts: [Boston,]* 1838. 8°. **4486**. e. **50**. **(8.)**

—— Two Discourses, preached in the Twelfth Congregational Church, Boston . . . February 10, 1850, on the completion of the twenty-fifth year of his ministry, by S. Barrett. pp. 40. *Tuttle & Dennett: Boston*, 1850. 8°. **4486**. e. **52**. **(11.)**

—— "What Thinkest Thou?" A sermon, *etc.* pp. 24. *Tuttle & Dennett: Boston*, 1843. 8°. **4486**. g. **19**.

—— Youths Void of Understanding. A discourse, *etc.* pp. 28. *Crosby, Nichols & Co.: Boston*, 1857. 8°. **4486**. e. **52**. **(19.)**

BARRETT (Samuel Alfred) Ancient Aztalan. By S. A. Barrett. S. A. Barrett: editor. Ira Edwards: assistant editor. [With maps.] pp. 602. pl. 100. *Milwaukee*, 1933. 8°. [*Bulletin of the Public Museum of the City of Milwaukee.* vol. 13.] Ac. **1793/2**.

—— The Cayapa Indians of Ecuador. 2 pt. pp. xvi. viii. 476. pl. cxlii. *New York*, 1925. 8°. [*Indian Notes and Monographs.* no. 40.] Ac. **1818**. b.

—— The Ethno-Geography of the Pomo and Neighboring Indians. 1908. *See* Berkeley, *Cal.—University of California.* Publications. American Archaeology and Ethnology. vol. 6. no. 1. 1903, *etc.* 8°. Ac. **2689**. g/3.

—— The Geography and Dialects of the Miwok Indians. 1908. *See* Berkeley, *Cal.—University of California.* Publications. American Archaeology and Ethnology. vol. 6. no. 2. 1903, *etc.* 8°. Ac. **2689**. g/3.

BARRETT (SAMUEL ALFRED)

—— The Material Culture of the Klamath Lake and Modoc Indians of Northeastern California and Southern Oregon. [With plates.] 1910. *See* BERKELEY, *Cal.—University of California.* Publications. American Archaeology and Ethnology. vol. 5. no. 4. 1903, *etc.* 8°. Ac. **2689**. g/**3**.

—— Pomo Indian Basketry. [With plates.] [1909.] *See* BERKELEY, *Cal.—University of California.* Publications. American Archaeology and Ethnology, *etc.* vol. 7. no. 3. 1903, *etc.* 8°. Ac. **2689**. g/**3**.

—— Pomo Myths . . . By S. A. Barrett. S. A. Barrett: editor. Ira Edwards: assistant editor. pp. 608. *Milwaukee,* 1933. 8°. [*Bulletin of the Public Museum of the City of Milwaukee.* vol. 15.] Ac. **1793/2**.

BARRETT (SAMUEL ALFRED) and **GIFFORD** (EDWARD WINSLOW)

—— Miwok Material Culture. [With plates.] *Milwaukee,* 1933. 8°. [*Bulletin of the Public Museum of the City of Milwaukee.* vol. 2. no. 4.] Ac. **1793/2**.

BARRETT (SAMUEL ALFRED) and **SKINNER** (ALANSON BUCK)

—— Certain Mounds and Village Sites of Shawano and Oconto Counties, Wisconsin. [With plates.] *Milwaukee,* 1932. 8°. [*Bulletin of the Public Museum of the City of Milwaukee.* vol. 10. no. 5.] Ac. **1793/2**.

BARRETT (SELAH HIBBARD) Memoirs of Eminent Preachers in the Freewill Baptist Denomination. [With a portrait.] pp. 304. *S. H. Barrett: Rutland, O.,* [1874.] 12°. **4985**. bbb. **8**.

BARRETT (SERENUS) Prove all Things. A sermon, *etc.* pp. 24. *J. Roberts: London,* 1722. 4°. **226**. g. **17**. (**20**.)

—— A Reply to the Catholic Answer. In defence of a sermon, lately publish'd against the errors of the Church of Rome [entitled "Prove all Things"], *etc.* pp. 83. *Printed for the Author: London,* 1725. 8°. **3935**. b. **2**.

—— A Sermon prearh'd [*sic*] . . . at the funeral of the Reverend Mr. Philip Thorne, *etc.* pp. 20. *Philip Barrett: London,* 1715. 4°. **226**. g. **23**. (**15**.)

BARRETT (SIDNEY)

—— Three Poems . . . "The Great Moving Picture." "The World's a Stage." "That Wooden Suit." *Sidney Barrett: Cowes,* [1938.] 8°. **11655**. aaa. **82**.

—— The Great Moving Picture. [In verse.] *Cowes,* [1938.] 8°. **11655**. ff. **63**.

—— [Another edition.] "The Great Moving Picture." [*Cowes,* 1938.] 8°. **11656**. a. **17**.

—— That Wooden Suit. [Verses.] [*The Author*: *Cowes,* 1936. 8°. **11655**. bbb. **15**.

—— The World's a Stage. [Verses.] [*The Author*: *Cowes,* 1936. 8°. **11655**. bbb. **16**.

—— [Another edition.] The World's a Stage. [*The Author*: *Cowes,* 1936.] 8°. **11655**. bbb. **23**.

BARRETT (SOLOMON) The Principles of Grammar: being a compendious treatise on the languages, English, Latin, and Greek . . . Revised edition. pp. 239. *Joel Munsell: Albany,* 1849. 8°. **12901**. c. **28**.

—— The Principles of Language: containing a full grammatical analysis of English poetry, *etc.* pp. 120. *O. Steele: Albany,* 1837. 12°. **1331**. a. **22**.

BARRETT (STEPHEN) *See* OVIDIUS NASO (P.) [*Epistolae Heroïdum.—English.*] Ovid's Epistles. Translated into English verse . . . by S. Barrett. 1759. 8°. **11355**. e. **6**.

—— *See* POPE (Alexander) *the Poet.* [*Two or more Works.—English and Latin.*] Bucolica Alexandri Popii . . . Latine reddita: interprete S. Barrett. 1746. 4°. **11630**. c. **5**. (**10**.)

—— War, an epic-satyr. Setting forth the nature of Fr - - ch policy, and the true cause of the present commotions in Europe. In four canto's. [By S. Barrett.] pp. ix. 80. 1747. 8°. *See* WAR. **11657**. c. **84**.

—— [Another copy.] T. **1551**. (**1**.)

BARRETT (STEPHEN J.) *See* DUBLIN.—*Gaelic League.* Imṫeaċta an Oireaċtais, *etc.* (1899. Edited by S. J. Barrett). 1897, *etc.* 8°. Ac. **9954**. d.

—— *See* O DUBHGHAILL (S.) Leaḃar Cainta . . . S. Bairead do ċuir ⁊ n-eagar, *etc.* 1904. 8°. Ac. **9954**. e.

BARRETT (STEPHEN MELVIL) *See* GERONIMO, *Apache Chief.* Geronimo's Story of his Life, taken down and edited by S. M. Barrett. 1906. 8°. **010883**. f. **27**.

—— Sociology of the American Indians . . . Illustrated, *etc.* pp. 142. *Burton Publishing Co.: Kansas City,* [1946.] 8°. **10009**. ppp. **33**.

BARRETT (STORRS BARROWS) *See* FROST (Edwin B.) Radial Velocities of 500 Stars of Spectral Class A. By E. B. Frost, S. B. Barrett, *etc.* 1929. fol. [*Publications of the Perkes Observatory.* vol. 7. pt. 1.] Ac. **4186**. e.

—— *See* PERIODICAL PUBLICATIONS.—*Northfield, Minn.* The Sidereal Messenger. (The Astrophysical Journal. A general index by authors and subjects to volumes I to XXV . . . Compiled by S. B. Barrett.) 1883, *etc.* 8°. P.P. **1565**. e.

BARRETT (T.) *of Skipton.* The Wreck of the "London." January 4, 1866. [In verse.] *Edmondson & Co.: Skipton,* 1866. *s. sh.* 4°. **1872**. a. **1**. (**132**.)
Printed on satin.

BARRETT (TED)

—— The Harvest of the Mystic. Echoes of worlds unknown to men. By Olga Barrett. [Inspirational writing purporting to be dictated by T. Barrett to Olga Barrett. With a portrait.] pp. 144. *A. H. Stockwell: Ilfracombe,* [1944.] 8°. **8633**. de. **41**.

BARRETT (THOMAS) Advice on the Management of Children in Early Infancy. pp. viii. 86. *Binns & Goodwin: Bath,* [1851.] 18°. **1178**. b. **37**.

BARRETT (THOMAS BARRETT BRYDGES)

—— List of Pictures at the Seat of T. B. Brydges Barrett, Esq. at Lee Priory . . . Kent. [By Sir S. E. Brydges, Bart. With a plate.] pp. 69. *Privately printed: Lee Priory,* 1817. 8°. **7857**. dd. **4**.
One of an edition of sixty copies.

BARRETT (THOMAS FERDINAND) Nouvelle méthode pratique anglaise, avec la prononciation représentée par des lettres françaises ayant les mêmes sons que les lettres correspondantes en anglais, *etc.* pt. 1. pp. viii. 96. *Lyon,* 1861. 8°. **12982**. cc. **10**.
No more published.

—— Rapport à Son Excellence le Ministre de l'Instruction Publique . . . sur la méthode naturelle et sur l'enseignement des langues vivantes dans les lycées impériaux et dans les maisons d'éducation. Réponse à sa circulaire du 27 septembre 1863. pp. 31. *Lyon,* 1863. 8°. **8309**. c. **51**. (**11**.)

BARRETT (THOMAS J.)

—— Harnessing the Earthworm. A practical inquiry into soil-building . . . with instructions for intensive propagation and use of domesticated earthworms, *etc.* pp. xvi. 166. pl. VII. *Faber & Faber: London*, 1949. 8°. **07078. i. 27.**

BARRETT (THOMAS JAMES ALFRED)

—— Hotel Accounts. [With charts.] pp. 84. *Gee & Co.: London*, 1951. 8°. **8219. h. 55.**

BARRETT (THOMAS KENNETH)

—— Psychology and Philosophy. The world of thought . . . Edited by T. K. Barrett. pp. 512. *Odhams Press: London*, [1936.] 8°. [*Standard University.*] **12212. aa. 2/8.**

BARRETT (THOMAS LENNARD) *Baron Dacre.* *See* ROPER (Anne) *Baroness Teynham*, afterwards MOORE (A.) *Baroness Dacre.* Anne, Lady Teynham, appellant. Dacre Barret Lennard, Esq; respondent. The appellant's case. [In the matter of the guardianship of T. L. Barrett, afterwards Baron Dacre.] [1724.] fol. **19. h. 2. (77.)**

—— *See* ROPER (Anne) *Baroness Teynham*, afterwards MOORE (A.) *Baroness Dacre.* Anne Lady Teynham, widow, appellant. Dacre Barrett Lennard, Esq; respondent. The respondent's case. [In the matter of the guardianship of T. L. Barrett, afterwards Baron Dacre.] [1724.] fol. **816. m. 5. (144.)**

BARRETT (THOMAS SQUIRE) *See* G., G. F. Satire: its nature and effects . . . Edited by T. S. Barrett. 1865. 12°. **11825. cc. 11.**

—— *See* OZANAM (J.) Magic Squares and how to make them . . . A new and revised edition . . . by T. S. Barrett. 1894. 8°. **8535. ccc. 48.**

—— *See* PERIODICAL PUBLICATIONS.—*London.* The Present Day, *etc.* [From no. 37 edited by T. S. Barrett.] 1883, *etc.* 4°. **P.P. 5857. eb.**

—— *See* PERIODICAL PUBLICATIONS.—*London.* The Present Day, *etc.* [A reissue of no. 37–40, issued under T. S. Barrett's editorship.] 1887. 4°. **8282. f. 22.**

—— *See* SQUARES. Magic Squares . . . Translated [by C. Hutton] from the French [of J. Ozanam], with numerous corrections and additions [by T. S. Barrett], *etc.* 1893. 8°. **8535. ccc. 43.**

—— An Examination of Mr. W. H. Gillespie's Argument à priori for the Existence of a Great First Cause. By T. S. B. [i.e. T. S. Barrett.] pp. 48. 1869. 8°. *See* B., T. S. **4014. ee. 3.**

—— Examination of Gillespie: being an analytical criticism of the Argument a priori for the Existence of a Great First Cause . . . Second edition. pp. 48. *Provost & Co.: London*, 1871. 8°. **4017. aa. 7.**

—— An Introduction to the Study of Logic and Metaphysics. pp. viii. 48. *Provost & Co.: London*, 1875. 8°. **8467. cc. 16.**

—— A New View of Causation. pp. xxiv. 213. *Provost & Co.: London*, 1871. 8°. **8468. aaa. 19.**

—— [Another edition.] The Philosophy of Science . . . Second edition. pp. xxiii. 213. *Provost & Co.: London*, 1872. 12°. **846. aaa. 20.**

—— Who wrote "Shakspeare"? pp. 12. *Privately printed: [London,]* 1896. 8°. **11763. cc. 18. (12.)**

—— [Another copy.] **11761. bbb. 8. (2.)**

BARRETT (TIMOTHEUS) *See* GURY (J. P.) Compendium theologiæ moralis . . . Editio . . . recognita a T. Barrett. 1915. 8°. **4061. f. 18.**

—— —— 1919. 8°. **4061. g. 11.**

BARRETT (UNWIN SANKEY) [Laws.-IV. Separate Laws.]

—— *See* AFRICA, *South.—Union of South Africa.* The Insolvency Act, 1916 . . . Reprinted with amendments and additions as provided by the Insolvency Act 1916 Amendment Act, 1926 . . . An edition of the text of the two acts by U. S. Barrett. 1926. 8°. **6605. aaa. 43.**

—— *See* VIRGILIUS MARO (P.) [*Aeneis.—English.*] The Aeneid of Virgil. Books I–IX translated by U. S. Barrett, *etc.* 1937. 8°. **11386. b. 48.**

BARRETT (URBANE)

—— Natural Eyesight System . . . Eighth edition. Illustrated. 5 pt. [*Natural Eyesight Institute: Los Angeles*, 1935.] 4°. **7611. r. 4.**

BARRETT (VERNON) *See* HARDY (Florence) Look Inside. Pictured by F. Hardy and V. Barrett. [1902.] 4°. **12812. c. 4.**

BARRETT (VICTOR)

—— Let's dance, *etc.* [With illustrations, including portraits.] pp. 70. *Frederick Muller: London*, 1955. 8°. **7922. aa. 55.**

BARRETT (WALTER) *pseud.* [i.e. JOSEPH A. SCOVILLE.] The Old Merchants of New York City. ser. 1–4. *Carleton: New York*, [1862]–66. 8°. **8247. bb. 30.** *Imperfect; wanting ser.* 5.

—— [A reissue.] 5 pt. *M. Doolady: New York*, 1870. 8°. **8275. bbb. 26.**

—— Vigor. A novel. pp. 428. *Carleton: New-York*, 1864. 8°. **12705. bb. 7.**

BARRETT (WALTER HENRY)

—— A Fisherman's Methods & Memories. [With plates, including a portrait.] pp. 175. *Seeley Service & Co.: London*, [1953.] 8°. **7921. c. 43.**

BARRETT (WILFRED PHILLIP) *See* CONGREVE (William) The Way of the World . . . Edited, with an introduction and explanatory notes, by W. P. Barrett. 1933. 16°. **11771. a. 18/29.**

—— *See* DALLINGTON (*Sir* Robert) The View of Fraunce, 1604. With an introduction by W. P. Barrett. 1936. 8°. [*Shakespeare Association Facsimiles.* no. 13.] **Ac. 9489. b/8.**

—— *See* JOAN [d'Arc], *Saint.* [*Biography.—II. Special.*] The Trial of Jeanne d'Arc. A complete translation of the text of the original documents, with an introduction by W. P. Barrett. 1931. 8°. **012210.c.3/9.**

—— *See* REMEDIES. Present Remedies against the Plague, etc. With an introduction by W. P. Barrett. 1933. 8°. [*Shakespeare Association Facsimiles.* no. 7.] **Ac. 9489. b/8.**

—— Chart of Plays, 1584 to 1623. Compiled by W. P. Barrett, *etc.* pp. 39. *University Press: Cambridge*, 1934. 4°. **011904. a. 92.**

BARRETT (WILLIAM) *Barrister-at-Law*, and **MAC CANN** (HUGH J.) The Law of the Labourers and the Labourers Question . . . Including the full text of the Labourers —Ireland—Acts, *etc.* pp. 250. *Sealy & Co.: Dublin*, 1906. 8°. **6503. a. 14.**

BARRETT (WILLIAM) *Fellow of Caius College, Cambridge.* *See* BARRET.

BARRETT (WILLIAM) *Instructor at the City College, New York City.*

—— Aristotle's Analysis of Movement: its significance for its time, *etc.* [A thesis.] pp. 69. *New York*, 1938. 8°. **8472. b. 5.**

BARRETT (WILLIAM) *Master Mariner.* Errors of the Compass. Geometrical diagram for obtaining the heeling error by eccentric circles. [*London ?*] 1874. *s. sh.* fol. **1801**. d. **1**. (**41**.)

—— Errors of the Compass. A graphic representation of the terms into which the deviation of the compass in an iron ship may be separated. MS. CORRECTIONS. [*London*, 1874.] 4°. **1801**. d. **1**. (**40**.)

BARRETT (WILLIAM) *Nonconformist.* Bonasus vapulans: or, Some Castigations given to Mr. John Durell, for fouling himself and others in his English and Latin book [entitled, Sanctæ Ecclesiæ Anglicanæ . . . Vindiciæ]. By a Country Scholar (W. B. [i.e. W. Barrett or Henry Hickman ?]). pp. 150. 1672. 12°. *See* B., W. **873**. h. **18**.

—— The Nonconformists vindicated from the abuses put upon them by Mr. Durel and Scrivener. Being some short animadversions on their books . . . In two letters to a friend . . . Containing some remarques upon the celebrated Conference at Hampton-Court. By a Country Scholar (W. B. [i.e. W. Barrett or Henry Hickman ?]). pp. 230. 1679. 8°. *See* B., W. **699**. c. **44**. (**2**.)

BARRETT (WILLIAM) *Surgeon.* The History and Antiquities of Bristol . . . Illustrated with copper-plate prints. pp. xix. 704. *William Pine: Bristol*, [1789.] 4°. **579**. h. **10**.

—— [Another copy.] **192**. b. **18**.

—— [Another copy.] G. **4073**.

—— [Another copy.] 10 vol. C. **55**. k. **1**.
In this copy numerous maps, plans, portraits and documents, collected by Miss S. S. Fripp, are inserted.

—— [Another copy.] MS. NOTES AND ADDITIONS [by R. Southey and J. Cottle]. C. **60**. m. **2**. (**1**.)
Imperfect; wanting pp. 245, 246, 567, 568, 593–616, 627-630, *and a plate at p.* 636.

BARRETT (WILLIAM ALEXANDER) *See* MORO (Antonio) Moro . . . Translated and adapted [from F. M. Piave's "Pittore e duca"] by W. A. Barrett. 1882. 8°. **11715**. cc. **7**. (**6**.)

—— *See* STAINER (*Sir* John) and BARRETT (W. A.) A Dictionary of Musical Terms. [1876.] 8°. **R.M.5.i.10.**

—— —— [1880.] 8°. [*Novello, Ewer and Co.'s Music Primers.* no. 21.] **W.P.A.900/21.**

—— —— [1888.] 8°. **2034.e.**

—— *See* STAINER (*Sir* John) and BARRETT (W. A.) Stainer and Barrett's Dictionary of Musical Terms, *etc.* 1898. 8°. Hirsch 134.

—— *See* WASIELEWSKI (J. W. von) Life of Robert Schumann . . . With preface by W. A. Barrett, *etc.* 1878. 8°. **10704**. bb. **26**.

—— Balfe: his life and work, *etc.* pp. 313. *Remington & Co.: London*, 1882. 8°. **10855**. de. **13**.

—— [A reissue.] Balfe: his Life and Work. pp. 312. *William Reeves: London*, [c. 1890.] 8°. Hirsch **2239**.
Without the plates. Imperfect; wanting the last leaf. A cutting of a newspaper article on M. W. Balfe, dated May 16, 1908, *has been pasted over some of the advertisements.*

—— The Chorister's Guide. pp. x. 126. *Rivingtons: London*, 1873. 8°. **7897**. aaa. **57**.

—— English Church Composers. pp. vii. 179. *Sampson Low & Co.: London*, 1882. 8°. [*Great Musicians.*] **07899**. de. **4**. (**3**.)

BARRETT (WILLIAM ALEXANDER)

—— [Another copy.] English Church Composers. *London*, 1882. 8°. R.M. **5**. c. **14/6**.

—— [A reissue.] English Church Composers. *Sampson Low, Marston & Co.: London*, [1899.] 8°. [*Great Musicians.*] **07899**. de. **4/3**a.

—— English Glee and Madrigal Writers. Two lectures, *etc.* pp. 42. *William Reeves: London*, [1877.] 8°. **7891.bbb.20.**

—— English Glees and Part-Songs. An enquiry into their historical development. pp. xii. 358. *Longmans & Co.: London*, 1886. 8°. **7898**. bb. **18**.

—— Flowers and Festivals; or, Directions for the floral decoration of churches. pp. viii. 176. pl. 24. *Rivingtons: London*, 1868 [1867]. 8°. **3475**. aaa. **49**.

—— Second edition. pp. viii. 173. pl. 24. *Rivingtons: London*, 1873. 8°. **3475**. aa. **68**.

—— An Introduction to Form and Instrumentation for the use of Beginners in Composition. pp. xi. 88. *Rivingtons: London*, 1879. 8°. **7898**. aa. **18**.

BARRETT (WILLIAM EDMUND)

—— The Evil Heart. pp. 165. *Peter Davies: London*, 1946. 8°. **12727**. aaa. **33**.

—— Flight from Youth. [A novel.] pp. 214. *Peter Davies: London*, 1940. 8°. **12721**. aaa. **16**.

—— The Left Hand of God. pp. 255. *Hodder & Stoughton: London*, 1952. 8°. **04422**. bb. **21**.

—— The Left Hand of God. pp. 255. *Transworld Publishers: London*, 1955. 8°. [*Corgi Books.* no. T 107.] W.P. **12745/242**.

—— The Number of My Days. pp. 201. *Peter Davies: London*, 1946. 8°. **12729**. e. **29**.

—— The Shadows of the Images. pp. xiv. 522. *William Heinemann: London*, 1954. 8°. NNN. **5428**.

—— To the Last Man, *etc.* pp. 133. *The World's Work: Kingswood*, 1947. 8°. **12650**. b. **16**.

—— Woman on Horseback. The biography of Francisco Lopez and Eliza Lynch. pp. ix. 360. *F. A. Stokes Co.: New York*, 1938. 8°. **010885**. eee. **72**.

—— Woman on Horseback, *etc.* pp. 352. *Peter Davies: London*, 1938. 8°. **010886**. g. **42**.

BARRETT (*Sir* WILLIAM FLETCHER) *See* AWDRY (Frances E.) Early Chapters in Science . . . Edited by W. F. Barrett, *etc.* 1899. 8°. **08708**. d. **5**.

—— *See* DALLAS (Helen A.) Mors Janua Vitae? . . . With an introduction by Professor W. F. Barrett. 1910. 8°. **08631**. eee. **19**.

—— *See* HOLE (Donald) Love and Death . . . With preface by Sir W. F. Barrett. 1922. 8°. **4257**. aaa. **55**.

—— *See* LONDON.—III. *Society for Psychical Research.* Journal of the Society for Psychical Research. [1884–1899. Edited by W. F. Barrett.] 1884, *etc.* 8°. Ac. **3834/2**.

—— *See* MASSEY (Charles C.) Thoughts of a Modern Mystic . . . Edited by W. F. Barrett. 1909. 8°. **4373**. df. **16**.

—— *See* REDGROVE (Herbert S.) The Magic of Experience . . . With an introduction by Sir W. F. Barrett. 1915. 8°. **08462**. e. **26**.

BARRETT (*Sir* WILLIAM FLETCHER)

—— *See* SWEDBERG, afterwards SWEDENBORG (E.) [*Opera Philosophica et Mineralia.*] The Principia . . . the Minor Principia and Summary of the Principia . . . With a foreword by Sir W. F. Barrett. 1912. 8°. **08709**. c. **14**.

—— *See* THOMAS (Charles D.) Some New Evidence for Human Survival . . . With an introduction by Sir W. F. Barrett. [1922.] 8°. **8633**. f. **27**.

—— *See* WILLSON (Beckles) Occultism and Common-Sense . . . With an introduction by Prof. W. F. Barrett. [1908.] 8°. **08631**. eee. **14**.

—— Creative Thought and the Problem of Evil . . . Second edition, revised and enlarged. pp. 71. *J. M. Watkins: London*, 1914. 8°. **08462**. ff. **31**.

—— Death-Bed Visions. [The editor's preface signed: F. E. B., i.e. Florence Elizabeth, Lady Barrett.] pp. xi. 116. *Methuen & Co.: London*, 1926. 8°. **08632**. de. **20**.

—— Easy Lessons in Science. Edited by . . . W. F. Barrett. 2 pt. *Macmillan & Co.: London*, 1880. 8°. **8709**. aaa. **9**.

—— Edison, and some of his inventions. 1879. *See* SCIENCE LECTURES. Science Lectures for the People, *etc.* ser. 10. 1866, *etc.* 8°. **8708**. h. **30**. **(9.)**

—— A Fragment of Faraday's Electrical Discoveries. A lecture, *etc.* pp. 20. [1873.] *See* SCIENCE LECTURES. Science Lectures for the People, *etc.* ser. 4. 1866, *etc.* 8°. **8708**. h. **28**. **(29.)**

—— On the Threshold of a New World of Thought: An examination of the phenomena of spiritualism. pp. xv. 127. *Kegan Paul & Co.: London*, 1908. 8°. **08464**. e. **83**.

—— On the Threshold of the Unseen. An examination of the phenomena of spiritualism and of the evidence for survival after death. pp. xx. 336. *Kegan Paul & Co.: London*, 1917. 8°. **08631**. ee. **65**.
Based on the preceding.

—— Second edition, revised. pp. xx. 336. *Kegan Paul & Co.: London*, 1917. 8°. **8633**. bbb. **3**.

—— Personality Survives Death. Messages from Sir W. Barrett. [A record of spiritualistic séances.] Edited by his wife . . . With a portrait. pp. xlvi. 203. *Longmans & Co.: London*, 1937. 8°. **8634**. ccc. **38**.

—— Psychical Research. pp. 255. *Williams & Norgate: London*, [1911.] 8°. [*Home University Library of Modern Knowledge.*] **12199**. p. **1/1**.

—— The Religion of Health. An examination of Christian Science . . . Completed by Rosa M. Barrett. [With a portrait.] pp. xiv. 149. *J. M. Dent & Sons: London & Toronto*, 1925. 8°. **4183**. de. **37**.

—— Seeing without Eyes. [An address delivered to the conference of the Spiritualists' National Union, 1910.] pp. 47. *Spiritualists' National Union: Halifax*, 1911. 8°. **8634**. ccc. **10**. **(4.)**

—— Sensitive Flames as illustrative of Sympathetic Vibration. 1879. *See* LONDON.—III. *South Kensington Museum.* Science Lectures, *etc.* vol. 2. 1878, *etc.* 8°. **7959**. aaa. **67**.

—— Swedenborg: the savant & the seer. pp. 70. *J. M. Watkins: London*, 1912. 16°. **3716**. aa. **31**.

BARRETT (*Sir* WILLIAM FLETCHER) and **BESTERMAN** (THEODORE)

—— The Divining-Rod. An experimental and psychological investigation . . . With 12 plates [and a bibliography], *etc.* pp. xxiii. 336. *Methuen & Co.: London*, 1926. 8°. **8633**. bb. **42**.

BARRETT (*Sir* WILLIAM FLETCHER) and **BROWN** (WILLIAM) *Professor of Physics, etc.*

—— Practical Physics. An introductory handbook for the physical laboratory. Part 1. Physical processes and measurements. The properties of matter. pp. xii. 284. *Percival & Co.: London*, 1892. 8°. **8703**. b. **54**.
No more published.

—— Introductory Practical Physics . . . New edition. pp. xii. 284. *Simpkin, Marshall & Co.: London; Sealy & Co.: Dublin*, [1906.] 8°. **08708**. ccc. **15**.

BARRETT (*Sir* WILLIAM FLETCHER) and **MYERS** (FREDERIC WILLIAM HENRY)

—— Intorno alla vita di Daniele Dunglas Home, pubblicata dalla sua vedova. Rivista, *etc.* [Translated by F. Rossi-Pagnoni.] pp. viii. 62. *Pesaro*, 1890. 8°. **8631**. eee. **38**.

BARRETT (WILLIAM GARLAND) *See* GREEN (Samuel) *Rev., of Walworth.* Baptist Mission in Jamaica. A review of . . . W. G. Barrett's pamphlet entitled, A Reply to the Circular of the Baptist Missionary Committee. 1842. 8°. **1369**. f. **21**.

—— *See* MONOD (A. L. F. T.) [La Femme.] Woman: her mission and her life . . . Translated by . . . W. G. Barrett. [1851.] 8°. **8415**. g. **23**.

—— —— 1858. 18°. **8415**. a. **46**.

—— *See* MONOD (A. L. F. T.) Saint Paul. Five discourses . . . translated by . . . W. G. Barrett. 1853. 18°. **4805**. b. **31**.

—— *See* WALLBRIDGE (Edwin A.) The Demerara Martyr . . . With a preface by W. G. Barrett. 1828. 8°. **1373**. f. **12**.

—— Emigration, in its moral and religious aspects. A sermon, *etc.* pp. 16. *A. Hall & Co.: London*, [1852.] 16°. **4475**. a. **13**.

—— Geological Facts; or, the Crust of the earth, what it is, and what are its uses. pp. xv. 288. *A. Hall & Co.: London*, 1855. 8°. **7107**. a. **13**.

—— Hints and Examples for an Improved Family Worship on the Liturgical Model. pt. 1. pp. 71. *A. Hall & Co.: London*, 1854. 12°. **3456**. d. **71**.
No more published.

—— Immigration to the British West Indies. Is it the slave-trade revived or not? pp. 32. *A. W. Bennett: London*, [1859.] 8°. **8156**. c. **10**.

—— New Sketches and Skeletons of Sermons devout and practical, *etc.* 2 ser. *Thomas Jepps: London*, 1859. 12°. **4498**. b. **5**.

—— Two Discourses; the first occasioned by the death of Mr. John Butler, of Royston . . . the second preached . . . on the removal of Mrs. Elizabeth Butler, *etc.* pp. 62. *Printed for private circulation: London*, [1849.] 16°. **4906**. a. **30**.

BARRETT (WILLIAM HENRY)

—— *See* LOCKET (George H.) and BARRETT (W. H.) Examples in Physical Chemistry. 1949. 8°. **8896**. de. **22**.

BARRETT (WILLIAM HENRY) *Actor.* *See* BARRETT (Wilson)

BARRETT (WILLIAM HENRY) *M.A., of Balliol College, Oxford.*

—— Chemistry. pp. viii. 151. *Clarendon Press: Oxford*, 1927. 8°. [*Clarendon Science Series.*] W.P. **7632/3**.

BARRETT (William Henry) *M.A., of Balliol College, Oxford.*

—— Elementary Organic Chemistry. pp. 256. *Clarendon Press: Oxford,* 1922. 8°. **8903. a. 41.**

—— Elementary Physical Chemistry. pp. viii. 247. *E. Arnold & Co.: London,* [1923.] 8°. **8903. ff. 30.**

—— Periodic Table & Atomic Numbers, *etc.* (Periodic table & atomic weights.—Periodicity of atomic volumes.—Melting points & atomic numbers.) *John Murray: London,* [1930.] *s. sh.* fol. Cup. **651. e. 1. (24.)**

BARRETT (William John) Andreas : a tragedy, in five acts. [In verse.] pp. 106. *Thomas Sanderson: London,* 1857. 8°. **11781. c. 37.**

—— Leoni. A play in five acts. [In verse.] pp. v. 84. *Thomas Hurst: London,* 1841. 8°. **841. f. 43.**

BARRETT (William Morgan) Soon and Safe : a short life well spent. [A memoir of W. M. Barrett.] pp. vi. 85. *Wesleyan Conference Office: London,* 1864. 12°. **4920. aaa. 30.**

BARRETT (Wilson) *See* Foote (George W.) The Sign of the Cross. A candid criticism of Mr. Wilson Barrett's play. 1896. 8°. **011795. bb. 59.**

—— *See* Lyne (Joseph L.) The Theatre ; with special reference to " The Sign of the Cross " [by Wilson Barrett]. [1896.] 8°. **04478. h. 36.**

—— *See* Shakespeare (William) [*Hamlet.*] Shakespeare's Tragedy of Hamlet, as arranged for the stage by W. Barrett, *etc.* [1884.] 8°. **11766. e. 8. (6.)**

—— —— [1886.] 8°. **11766. f. 20. (3.)**

—— The Never-Never Land. pp. vi. 368. *Eveleigh Nash: London,* 1904. 8°. **012630. dd. 26.**

—— On Stage for Notes. The story of the Wilson Barrett Company. [With plates, including portraits.] pp. ix. 266. *William Blackwood & Sons: Edinburgh & London,* 1954. 8°. **11794. l. 33.**

—— The Sign of the Cross. [A novel, based on the play of the same name.] pp. x. 291. *John Macqueen: London,* 1897 [1896]. 8°. **4414 dd. 1.**

—— [Another edition.] pp. x. 291. *John Macqueen: London,* 1902. 8°. **04412. f. 10.**

—— [Another edition.] pp. 323. *Eveleigh Nash: London,* 1904. 8°. [*Collection of Popular Novels.*] **012602. de. 7/2.**

—— [A reissue.] pp. 323. *Eveleigh Nash: London,* 1905. 8°. **012631. bb. 2.**

—— [Another edition.] pp. 316. *Queensway Library: London,* [1934.] 8°. **12601. r. 10.**

—— Souvenir of " The Sign of the Cross." by Mr. Wilson Barrett. *W. & D. Downey : London,* [1896.] 8°. **11795. f. 52.**

—— Souvenir of " The Christian King "—or Alfred of " Engle-Land " . . . Illustrated, *etc.* [*London,*] 1903. fol. **1874. b. 19.**

—— Souvenir of " The Daughters of Babylon." By Wilson Barrett. Illustrated, *etc.* [*London,* 1897.] 4°. **11795. k. 29.**

—— The Wilson Barrett Birthday Book. Illustrated. *W. & D. Downey: London,* [1899.] 4°. **12272. g. 3.**

BARRETT (Wilson) and **BARRON** (Elwyn Alfred)

—— In Old New York. A romance (founded on the play of the same name). pp. 410. *John Macqueen : London,* 1900. 8°. **012641. dd. 15.**

BARRETT (Wilson) and **HICHENS** (Robert Smythe)

—— The Daughters of Babylon. A novel. [Based on the play of the same name by W. Barrett alone.] pp. 332. *John Macqueen: London,* 1899. 8°. **012642. aa. 44.**

BARRETTA (Alphonsus Maria) Apparatus ad Sacra Biblia. pp. xiv. 579. *Neapoli,* 1883. 8°. **3125. bb. 18.**

—— [Another copy.] **3109. de. 8.**

BARRETTA (Ch. Joseph) Manuel complet théorique et pratique du chocolatier, limonadier . . . suivi d'un traité sur l'art de faire . . . les vins, *etc.* pp. iv. 814. pl. vii. *Paris, Lyon,* 1841. 8°. **7945. gg. 40.**

BARRETTA (Charles) Essai sur les piqûres des tissus . . . Dissertation, *etc.* pp. 36. *Paris,* 1827. 4°. **1183. i. 13. (2.)**

BARRETTE (Guillaume) Ecclesiastical Relations between the Old Catholics of America and Foreign Churches. [Edited by G. Barrette, E. Debecker, and A. Marchand.] pp. 27. [1892.] 8°. **4182. e. 34.**

BARRETT-GREY (Laurence) *See* Grey.

BARRETT-HAMILTON (Gerald Edwin Hamilton) *See* Hamilton.

BARRETT-LENNARD (Charles Edward) *See* Lennard.

BARRETT-LENNARD (Emma) *Lady. See* Lennard.

BARRETT-LENNARD (Thomas) *See* Lennard.

BARRETT-LENNARD (*Sir* Thomas) *2nd Bart. See* Lennard.

BARRETTO (Castro) *See* Castro Barretto.

BARRETTO (F. F.) Barretto's 12 Figure System Code, *etc.* pp. 22. *Guedes & Co.: Hongkong,* [1911.] fol. **1804. b. 33.**

—— Pamphlet Code. Containing nearly 3,000 words and short phrases, &c., and Lloyd's Register Table. To be used in conjunction with F. F. Barretto's 12-figure system code. pp. 14. *Guedes & Co. : Hongkong,* 1911. fol. **1804. b. 34.**

BARRETTO (Fernardo de Castro Paes) *See* Paes Barretto.

BARRETTO (Francesco) Relatione delle missioni e christianità che appartengono alla Prouincia di Malavar della Compagnia di Giesu. pp. 132. *F. Cavalli: Roma,* 1645. 8°. **4766. aaa. 12.**

—— Relation des missions de la province de Malabar, de la Compagnie de Jesus, *etc. See* Cardim (A. F.) Relation de ce qui s'est passé . . . au Japon, *etc.* 1646, *etc.* 8°. **4767. c. 4.**

BARRETTO (Francisco) *See* Barreto.

BARRETTO (Honorio Pereira) *See* Pereira Barretto.

BARRETTO (Joaõ Franco) *See* Barreto.

BARRETTO (Joseph) A Dictionary of the Persian and Arabic Languages. 2 vol. *S. Greenway: Calcutta,* 1804, 06. 8°. **622. h. 18, 19.**

—— [Another copy.] **64. a. 11.**

—— Shums—ool—loghat ; or, a Dictionary of the Persian and Arabic Languages the interpretation being in Persian, *etc.* 2 vol. *Hindustanee Press: Calcutta,* 1806. 4°. **435. e. 17, 18.**

BARRETTO (Larry) *See* Barretto (Laurence B.)

BARRETTO (LAURENCE BREVOORT)

—— Bright Mexico . . . [Reminiscences of travel.] Illustrated by Ann Barretto. pp. viii. 236. *Farrar & Rinehart: New York*, [1935.] 8°. **10482. aaa. 25.**

—— Children of Pleasure. pp. 288. *Jarrolds: London*, 1932. 8°. **NN. 22590.**

—— [Another edition.] pp. 253. *Readers Library Publishing Co.: London*, [1933.] 8°. **012600. e. 54.**

—— A Conqueror Passes. pp. 309. *Little, Brown & Co.: Boston*, 1924. 8°. **012705. aa. 53.**

—— Horses in the Sky. pp. 338. *J. Day Co.: New York*, [1929.] 8°. **A.N. 33.**

—— The Indiscreet Years. pp. 329. *Farrar & Rinehart: New York*, [1931.] 8°. **A.N. 722.**

—— [Another edition.] pp. 288. *Jarrolds: London*, [1932.] 8°. **A.N. 2174.**

—— Journey Through Time. pp. 256. *Jarrolds: London*, [1941.] 8°. **12723. aaa. 21.**

—— Old Enchantment. pp. 319. *J. Day Co.: New York*, 1928. 8°. **12713. c. 11.**

—— [Another copy, with a different titlepage.] *G. Allen & Unwin: London*, 1928. 8°. **12715. aa. 2.**

—— Three Roads from Paradise. pp. 305. *Farrar & Rinehart: New York*, [1933.] 8°. **12708. f. 23.**

—— [Another edition.] pp. 288. *Jarrolds: London*, 1934. 8°. **12709. i. 23.**

—— To Babylon. pp. 322. *Little, Brown & Co.: Boston*, 1925. 8°. **12708. cc. 3.**

—— Tomorrow will be different. pp. 310. *Farrar & Rinehart: New York*, [1936.] 8°. **A.N. 3041.**

—— Walls of Glass. pp. 319. *Little, Brown & Co.: Boston*, 1926. 8°. **12711. aa. 7.**

—— [Another edition.] pp. 319. *Leonard Parsons: London*, 1927. 8°. **12712. a. 20.**

BARRETTO (LUIZ DO REGO) *See* REGO BARRETTO.

BARRETTO (LUIZ PEREIRA) *See* PEREIRA BARRETTO.

BARRETTO (MANOEL)

—— *Praes.* *See* PINTO (A.) Conclusiones theologicas de essentia Dei et attributis, tuebitur A. Pinto. 1657. fol. **731. l. 6. (4.)**

—— Informaçaõ do estado e conquista dos rios de Cuama, vulgar e verdadeiramente chamados Rios do Ouro. (Report upon the State and Conquest of the Rivers of Cuama, *etc.*) *Port. & Eng.* 1899. *See* THEAL (George M.) Records of South-Eastern Africa, *etc.* vol. 3. 1898, *etc.* 8°. **09061. aa.**

BARRETTO (MELCHIOR PEREIRA) *See* PEREIRA BARRETTO.

BARRETTO (ROZENDO MONIZ) *See* MONIZ BARRETO.

BARRETTO (WILLIAM LOUIS)

—— Heroes of Burma, *etc.* [With portraits.] pp. 122. *Burma Union Press: Rangoon*, [1934 ?] 8°. **10602. pp. 18.**

—— King Mindon . . . A compilation of lectures. [A biography of Min Htôn Min, King of Burma. With plates, including portraits of Min Htôn Min and of the author.] pp. x. 127. *Rangoon*, [1935.] 8°. **20031. ee. 24.**

BARRETTO (WILLIAM LOUIS)

—— A Manual of Meeting Method; or, Procedure of conducting business in democratic assemblies. pp. iv. 76. *British Burma Press: Rangoon*, 1924. 8°. **8006. aa. 49.**

—— A Primer of World History with Burma Background. Being a compilation of lectures, *etc.* [With plates.] pp. v. 288. *Burma Union Press: Rangoon*, [1938.] 8°. **9004. a. 19.**

—— [Another copy.] A Primer of World History, *etc.* *Rangoon*, [1938.] 8°. **9004. aaa. 33.**

BARRETTO FUZEIRO (NUNO) Vida da gloriosa Virgem a Madre Santa Thereza de Jesus, Fundadora e Reformadora de Carmelitas Descalças, *etc.* pp. 432. *F. Villela: Lisboa*, 1691. fol. **487. i. 37.**

BARRETTUS (EMMANUEL) *See* BARRETTO (Manoel)

BARRETTUS (LUCIUS) *pseud.* [i.e. ALBERTUS CURTIUS] *See* BRAHE (T.) Historia cælestis. [Edited by L. Barrettus.] 1666. fol. **47. f. 13.**

BARRETTUS (RICHARDUS) *See* BARRET (Richard)

BARRETT-WATSON (ROBERT) *See* WATSON.

BARRETUS (GULIELMUS) *Fellow of Caius College, Cambridge.* *See* BARRET (William)

BARRETUS (JOANNES NUNNEZ) *Patriarch of Ethiopia.* *See* NUNES BARRETO.

BARRETUS (SEBASTIANUS) *See* BARRETO.

BARREY (CLAUDE ANTOINE) Dissertation sur les dangers des ouvrages de médecine, écrits à la portée de tout le monde, *etc.* pp. 18. *Paris*, 1803. 4°. **1182. f. 2. (7.)**

BARREY (H. G.) Pre-Historic Lymington and People: with brief notices of other places and times. pp. x. 92. *H. F. Bull: Devizes*, 1885. 8°. **7708. aa. 40.**

BARREY (LORDING) *See* BARRY.

BARREY (PHILIPPE) *See* BRÉARD (C.) and BARREY (P.) Documents relatifs à la marine normande aux XVe et XVIe siècles. 1906. 8°. [*Mélanges.* sér. 6.] **Ac. 6890/23.**

—— Le Havre maritime. La batellerie et les transports par terre du XVIe au XIXe siècle. 1921. *See* HAYEM (J.) Mémoires et documents pour servir à l'histoire du commerce et de l'industrie en France. sér. 6. 1913, *etc.* 8°. **W.P. 7356/6.**

—— Le Havre translantique de 1571 a 1610—Le Havre et la navigation aux Antilles sous l'ancien régime. La question coloniale en 1789–1791. 1917. *See* HAYEM (J.) Mémoires et documents pour servir à l'histoire du commerce et de l'industrie en France. sér. 5. 1913, *etc.* 8°. **W.P. 7356/5.**

BARREY (PIERRE EDMOND DE) *Baron.*

—— Le Cri de l'indignation. Réponse à M. Méhée de la Touche [to "Dénonciation au Roi"] . . . Seconde édition. pp. 16. *Paris*, 1814. 8°. **R. 128. (10.)**

—— Précis historique sur la maison du Roi, depuis sa formation en 1814, jusqu'à sa réforme en 1815. pp. 55. *Paris* 1816. 8°. **R. 128. (12.)**

BARREY (THÉOPHILE) Thèse pour le doctorat en médecine, *etc.* (Questions sur les diverses branches des sciences médicales.) pp. 28. *Strasbourg*, 1841. 4°. [*Collection générale des dissertations soutenues à la Faculté de Médecine de Strasbourg.* Année 1841.] **7381.* d.**

BARREYRE (Jean)

—— Amour et nouveautés. Nouvelle. *In:* Les Œuvres libres. Nouvelle série. no. 67. dec. 1951. pp. 95–160. 1951. 8°. **12208. ee. 292.**

—— La Confidence inavouable. Nouvelle. *In:* Les Œuvres libres. Nouvelle série. no. 31. pp. 111–164. 1948. 8°. **12208. ee. 256.**

—— Un Homme court après lui-même. Roman. *In:* Les Œuvres libres. Nouvelle série. no. 42. pp. 71–168. 1949. 8°. **12208.ee.267.**

—— Le Navire aveugle. [A novel.] pp. 228. *Paris,* 1925. 8°. **12516. pp. 30**

—— The Blind Ship . . . Translation and foreword by Beckles Willson. pp. 254. *T. Fisher Unwin: London,* 1926. 8°. **12515. pp. 2.**

BARREYRE (P.) Dressage pratique et perfectionné du chien d'arrêt anglais. pp. 215. *Paris,* 1881. 12°. **7908. aaaa. 43.**

—— Les Grands veneurs de l'époque. Souvenirs de chasse. pp. iii. 275. *Saint-Amand,* 1882. 8°. **7908. bb. 19.**

BARREYROS (Gaspar) *See* Barreiros.

BARR-HAMILTON (Alec) *See* Hamilton (A. B.)

BARRHEAD.

—— Barrhead, Renfrewshire. The official guide, *etc.* (The official handbook.) *E. J. Burrow & Co.: Cheltenham,* [1938– .] 8°. **10354. a. 71.**
Various editions.

Town Council.

—— Municipal Tenants' Handbook, *etc.* pp. 47. *British Publishing Co.: Gloucester,* [1954.] 8°. **8289. p. 4.**

BARRI, *Family of.* *See* Barry.

BARRI (Christophoro) *See* Borri (Cristoforo)

BARRI (Gabbriello) *See* Barrius.

BARRI (Giacomo) Viaggio pittoresco, in cui si notano distintamente tutte le pitture famose . . . che si conseruano in qualsiuoglia città dell'Italia. pp. 120. *G. G. Herz: Venetia,* 1671. 12°. **683. b. 30.**

—— [Another copy.] **1044. b. 38. (1.)**

—— The Painter's Voyage of Italy. In which all the famous paintings of the most eminent masters are particularised, as they are preserved in the several cities of Italy . . . Whereunto is added, that excellent collection of Signior Septale . . . illustrated with the heads of some of the most renowned painters . . . Englished by W. L. of Lincolns Inn [i.e. William Lodge]. pp. 159. *For Tho. Flesher: London,* 1679. 8°. **786. d. 1.**

—— [Another copy.] **52. c. 8.**

BARRI (Giraldus de) *Cambrensis.* *See* Giraldus [de Barri], *Cambrensis, etc.*

BARRI (Paul de) *See* Barry.

BARRIA (J. M.) Hombres de la Independencia de América, o sea el Almanaque del Centenario. [With portraits.] pp. 289. *Buenos Aires,* [1923.] 8°. **010885. g. 3.**

BARRIAL POSADA (Clemente) Origin of the Auriferous Region of Tacuarenbó, its analogy and concordance with others on the American Continent. *See* London.—iii. *International Exhibition of Mining and Metallurgy,* 1890. Republic of Uruguay. International Exhibition, *etc.* 8°. **07109. h. 5.**

BARRIAS (Félix) *See* Saintine (X. B.) *pseud.* Picciola . . . Vingt-quatrième édition . . . illustrée . . . sur les dessins de F. Barrias. 1854. 8°. **12512. i. 19.**

—— *See* Horatius Flaccus (Q.) [*Works.—Latin.*] Q. Horatii Flacci Opera, *etc.* [With engraved vignettes from designs by F. Barrias.] 1855. 16°. **11388. a. 6.**

—— *See* Sepet (M.) Jeanne d'Arc. [With illustrations by F. Barrias and others.] 1885. 8°. **10663. i. 11.**

—— *See* Shakespeare (William) [*Works.—French.*] Oeuvres complètes . . . Édition illustrée de gravures . . . sur des dessins originaux de F. Barrias. [1856.] 8°. **1343. n. 10.**

BARRIBALL (Alfred) *See* Wightman and Co., *Publishers, London.* Wightman's Arithmetical Tables. Revised by A. Barriball. [1899.] 16°. **8548. aa. 50. (2.)**

—— —— [1920.] 16°. **8548. aa. 98.**

—— The Essentials of French Grammar. pp. iii. 230. *E. Ralph & Co.: London,* 1899. 8°. [*Royal Standard Series.*] **012200. gg. 9/12.**

—— Helps to the Study of Coppée's Le Trésor, *etc.* pp. 75. *E. Ralph & Co.: London,* 1899. 8°. [*Royal Standard Series.*] **012200. gg. 9/1.**

BARRICADES. Les Barricades, scènes historiques. Mai 1588. [By Louis Vitet.] Troisième édition, revue et augmentée. pp. xv. 456. *Paris,* 1827. 8°. **1343. f. 15.**

—— Les Barricades, scènes les plus saisissantes de la révolution de 1848 ; illustrées d'un dessin representant la barricade du Faubourg Montmartre, *etc.* pp. 14. *Paris,* 1848. 8°. **8052. f. 54. (2.)**

—— Les Barricades de 1830. Drame historique en trois journées. pp. 14. *Paris,* 1830. 8°. **11738. aaa. 7. (3.)**

BARRICELLI (Giovanni Alphonso) *See* Bianchi (L.) Foundations of Mental Health . . . Translation . . . by G. A. Barricelli, *etc.* 1930. 8°. **07660. b. 33.**

BARRICK (Richard) *See* Hilliard (Timothy) Paradise promised by a dying Saviour to the penitent Thief on the Cross. A sermon . . . on the execution of A. White, R. Barrick, *etc.* 1785. 8°. **4485. c. 43.**

BARRIE (Alexander) The Child's Assistant . . . A new edition. pp. 24. *George Cameron: Glasgow,* 1856. 12°. **12983. a. 68. (2.)**

—— A Collection of English Prose and Verse for the use of Schools, selected from different authors . . . The second edition. pp. xvi. 272. *The Compiler & W. Coke: Edinburgh,* 1781. 12°. **992. e. 1.**

—— A Spelling and Pronouncing Catechism. pp. 36. [*Edinburgh?*] 1796. 12°. **1212. h. 15. (1.)**

—— A Spelling and Pronouncing Dictionary of the English Language . . . To which are added, the principles of English grammar. pp. iv. 312. *The Author: Edinburgh,* 1794. 12°. **1212. l. 9.**

BARRIÉ (André) Des eaux minérales sulfureuses de Bagnères de Luchon, *etc.* pp. 106. *Paris,* 1853. 4°. [*Collection des thèses soutenues à la Faculté de Médecine de Paris.* An 1853. tom. 1.] **7372. f. 3.**

BARRIE (Andrew D.) Away from Ice and Snow ; or, To Manilla in winter. pp. 70. *Anderson & Son: Dumfries,* [1890.] 4°. **10470. g. 27.**

BARRIE (C. D. O.) *See* LAMB (Charles) The Essays of Elia. [With an introduction by C. D. O. Barrie.] 1904, 05. 8°. **12271**. v. **5**.

BARRIE (*Sir* CHARLES) *See* DAVIDSON (Thomas M.) In Memoriam Sir Charles Barrie, *etc.* [With portraits.] 1922. 4°. **10825**. k. **21**.

BARRIE (DAVID) The City of Dundee illustrated: containing reminiscences and remarks . . . relating to Dundee and neighbourhood, and to certain events . . . during the last sixty years, and relating to local government in Scotland . . . With views, *etc.* pp. xx. 306. *Winter, Duncan & Co.: Dundee,* 1890. 4°. **10370**. g. **25**.

BARRIE (DEREK STIVEN MAXWELTON)

—— The Euston and Crewe Companion. [With plates.] pp. 42. *Oakwood Press: South Godstone,* 1947. 8°. **8236**. de. **16**.

—— Modern Locomotives of the L.M.S. [With plates.] pp. 34. [1937.] *obl.* 8°. *See* LONDON MIDLAND AND SCOTTISH RAILWAY. **08769**. a. **49**.

—— The Rhymney Railway. *Oakwood Press: South Godstone,* 1952. 8°. [*Oakwood Library of Railway History.* no. 9.] W.P. **865/10**.

—— The Taff Vale Railway. [With plates.] pp. 35. *Oakwood Press: Sidcup,* 1939. 8°. [*Oakwood Library of Railway History.* no. 2.] W.P. **865/2**.

—— The Taff Vale Railway. (Second edition.) [With plates.] pp. 43. *Oakwood Press: South Godstone,* 1950. 8°. [*Oakwood Library of Railway History.* no. 2.] W.P. **865/7**.

BARRIE (DEREK STIVEN MAXWELTON) and **CLINKER** (CHARLES RALPH)

—— The Somerset & Dorset Railway. [With plates.] pp. 73 *Oakwood Press: South Godstone,* 1948. 8°. [*Oakwood Library of Railway History.*] W.P. **865/6**.

BARRIE (DEREK STIVEN MAXWELTON) and **LEE** (CHARLES EDWARD)

—— The Sirhowy Valley and its Railways. pp. 36. *Railway Publishing Co.: London,* 1940. 8°. **20034**. d. **3**.

BARRIE (FRED)

—— Helen of Chitor. The tale of the most beautiful Princess of Rajasthan. [With plates.] pp. 145. *Modern Press: Agra,* [1940.] 8°. **012634**. p. **27**.

BARRIE (HEATHER)

—— Practical Homecraft. pp. 167. *Thorsons Publishers: London,* 1950. 8°. **7949**. aa. **47**.

BARRIE (JAMES) A New Collection of Poems on Various Subjects. [With a life of the author.] pp. iv. 124. *For the Author: Kleso* [*Kelso*], 1824. 16°. **1467**. a. **14**.

—— Poems on Various Subjects. pp. 124. *For the Author: Kelso,* 1815. 18°. **11602**. aa. **38**. (**5**.

BARRIE (*Sir* JAMES MATTHEW) *Bart.*

WORKS.

—— The Novels, Tales, and Sketches of J. M. Barrie. 8 vol. *C. Scribner's Sons: New York,* 1896. 8°. K.T.C. **26**. a. **15**.

—— The Plays of J. M. Barrie. (Uniform edition.) 12 vol. *Hodder & Stoughton: London,* 1918–38. 8°. **11780**. a. 5.
"*The Boy David*" *was published by Peter Davies, London.*

BARRIE (*Sir* JAMES MATTHEW) *Bart.*

—— The Plays of J. M. Barrie. [With a portrait.] pp. v. 844. *Hodder & Stoughton: London,* 1928. 8°. **011779**. i. **51**.

—— The Works of J. M. Barrie. (Uniform edition.) 4 vol.
The Little Minister.
Sentimental Tommy.
Tommy and Grizel.
Farewell Miss Julie Logan.
Cassell & Co.; Hodder & Stoughton: London, [1925–32.] 8°. **12274**. c. **13**.
No more published.

—— M'Connachie and J. M. B. Speeches, *etc.* pp. xv. 275. *Peter Davies: London,* 1938. 8°. **12302**. a. **2**.

—— The Plays of J. M. Barrie . . . Edited by A. E. Wilson. pp. xii. 1272. *Hodder & Stoughton: London,* 1942. 8°. **011781**. m. **9**.

LETTERS.

—— Letters of J. M. Barrie. Edited by Viola Meynell. [With a portrait.] pp. vii. 311. *Peter Davies: London,* 1942. 8°. **10922**. e. **2**.

SINGLE WORKS.

—— The Admirable Crichton . . . Illustrated by Hugh Thomson. pp. 234. *Hodder & Stoughton: London,* [1914.] 4°. K.T.C. **102**. b. **3**.

—— The Admirable Crichton. A fantasy in four acts. pp. 98. *London,* [1946.] 8°. [*French's Acting Edition.*] **11791**. tt. **1/431**.

—— The Admirable Crichton . . . Illustrated by Hugh Thomson. pp. 142. *University of London Press: London,* 1951. 8°. [*Pilot Books.*] W.P. **1272/22**.

—— L'Admirable Crichton . . . Adaptation française de Alfred Athis. pp. 31. *Paris,* 1920. fol. [*La Petite Illustration Théâtrale.* Nouvelle série. no. 22.] P.P. **4283**. m. (**2**.)

—— *See* BHŪSHAṆA, *V.N.* The Hawk over Heron. Notes on comedy . . . with . . . chapters on Congreve's "Way of the World" and Barrie's "Admirable Crichton." 1944. 8°. **11798**. a. **32**.

—— The Allahakbarrie Book of Broadway Cricket for 1899. [By Sir James Barrie. With illustrations.] pp. 33. [1899.] 16°. *See* ALLAHAKBARRIE BOOK. Ashley **64**.

—— J. M. Barrie's Allahakbarries C.C. 1899, *etc.* [With illustrations.] pp. 40. *James Barrie Publishers: London,* 1950. 8°. **7920**. aa. **53**.

—— Auld Licht Idylls. pp. 250. *Hodder & Stoughton: London,* 1888. 8°. **12357**. d. **14**.

—— [Another edition.] Illustrated by W. Hole. pp. xii. 232. *Hodder & Stoughton: London,* 1895. 8°. **012634**. n. **16**.

—— Eleventh edition. pp. 250. *Hodder & Stoughton: London,* 1898. 8°. **012618**. g. **8**.

—— Better Dead. pp. 145. *S. Sonnenschein & Co.: London,* 1888. 8°. **012625**. k. **53**.

—— Second edition. pp. 145. *S. Sonnenschein & Co.: London,* 1888. 8°. **12629**. a. **12**.

—— The Boy David. A play in three acts. pp. 87. *Samuel French: London,* [1948.] 8°. [*French's Acting Edition.* no. 360.] **11791**. t. **1/861**.

—— Charles Frohman: a tribute. [Reprinted from the "Daily Mail."] [*Privately printed for Clement Shorter: London*, 1915.] 4°. Ashley **2335**.
No. 7 of an edition of twenty copies.

—— Courage. (The Rectorial Address delivered at St. Andrews University, May 3rd, 1922.) pp. 47. *Hodder & Stoughton: London*, [1922.] 8°. **08408**. e. **30**.

—— [Another edition.] Courage. pp. 47. *Hodder & Stoughton: Toronto*, [1922.] 8°. **012301**. eee. **34**.

—— Courage, *etc.* pp. 59. *St. Hugh's Press: London*, 1950. 16°. **8403**. de. **3**.

—— Cricket . . . Being a speech delivered . . . on the occasion of the luncheon given to the Australian Cricket Eleven . . . April 20, 1926. pp. 8. *Privately printed for Clement Shorter: London*, 1926. 4°. **7904**. dd. **24**.
One of an edition of 25 *copies.*

—— Echoes of the War. pp. 168. *Hodder & Stoughton: London*, [1918.] 8°. **012603**. g. **44**.

—— An Edinburgh Eleven. Pencil portraits from College life. pp. 115. *London*, 1889. 8°. ["*British Weekly*" *Extras*. no. 3.] **012356**. ee. **51**.

—— An Edinburgh Eleven . . . Third edition. pp. 115. *Hodder & Stoughton: London*, 1896. 8°. **12361**. a. **23**.

—— The Entrancing Life. (Address delivered on installation as Chancellor of Edinburgh University, October 25, 1930.) pp. 22. *Hodder & Stoughton: London*, [1930.] 8°. **012301**. eee. **30**.

—— Farewell Miss Julie Logan. A wintry tale . . . As published in The Times, Thursday, December 24 1931. pp. 8. *The Times Publishing Co.: London*, 1931. fol. Ashley **5663**.

—— Farewell Miss Julie Logan, *etc.* pp. 103. *Charles Scribner's Sons: New York*, 1933. 8°. **12654**. f. **23**.

—— George Meredith, 1909. pp. 15. *Constable & Co.: London*, 1909. 16°. **10855**. a. **48**.

—— [Another copy.] **10855**. a. **49**.
Imperfect; wanting pp. 5, 6.

—— The Greenwood Hat, being a memoir of James Anon, 1885–1887, *etc.* [Articles written by Barrie under the pseudonym James Anon. With plates, including a portrait.] pp. xi. 285. *Peter Davies: London*, 1937. 8°. **12358**. c. **1**.

—— Half Hours. [Four one-act plays: Pantaloon, The Twelve-Pound Look, Rosalind, The Will.] pp. 207. *Hodder & Stoughton: London*, [1914.] 8°. **11774**. bb. **44**.

—— A Holiday in Bed, and other sketches . . . With a short biographical sketch of the author. [Articles, reprinted from various periodicals. With a portrait.] pp. 180. *New York Publishing Co.: New York*, [1892.] 4°. **12362**. b. **15**.

—— "The Ladies' Shakespeare" . . . Being the substance of a speech by Sir James Matthew Barrie, O.M., delivered at Stationers' Hall upon the occasion of his receiving the Freedom of the Stationers' Company, 3rd July, 1925. [Reprinted from "The Times."] pp. 7. *Privately printed by Clement Shorter: London*, 1925. 4°. Ashley **4690**.
One of an edition of twenty-five copies.

—— A Lady's Shoe. *See* Russell (William C.) Miss Parson's Adventure, *etc.* [1893.] 8°. **012630**. ee. **57**.

BARRIE (*Sir* James Matthew) *Bart.*

—— The Little Minister. 3 vol. *Cassell & Co.: London*. 1891. 8°. **C.131.e.1.**

—— Second edition. 3 vol. *Cassell & Co.: London*, 1891. 8°. **012640**. l. **23**.

—— Third edition. pp. xii. 464. *Cassell & Co.: London*, 1892. 8°. **012634**. k. **25**.

—— [A reissue.] **012630**. g. **24**.
Without the illustrations.

—— The Little Minister. [With plates.] pp. vii. 375. *Grosset & Dunlap: New York*, [1897.] 8°. **012635**. bb. **35**.

—— Popular edition. pp. xii. 340. *Cassell & Co.: London*, 1903. 8°. **012622**. ee. **49**.

—— [Another edition.] pp. viii. 375. *Cassell & Co.: London*, 1905. 8°. **012621**. de. **3**.

—— [Another edition.] pp. 302. *Cassell & Co.: London*, 1908. 8°. [*People's Library*. vol. 51.] **012206**. de.**1/48**.

—— Malý Farář . . . Přeložil Jos. Bartoš. pp. 488. [*Prague*,] 1900. 8°. [*Anglická Knihovna*.] **12203**. s. **1/4**.

—— *See* London.—iii. *Haymarket Theatre*. The Little Minister. By J. M. Barrie. [Drawings, etc. illustrating a performance of the dramatized version.] [1898.] 8°. **11795**. s. **3**.

—— The Little White Bird. pp. viii. 312. *Hodder & Stoughton: London*, 1902. 8°. **012638**. a. **25**.

—— [Another edition.] pp. iv. 349. *Copp, Clark Co.: Toronto*, 1902. 8°. **012622**. l. **31**.

—— Peter Pan in Kensington Gardens . . . From 'The Little White Bird.' With drawings by Arthur Rackham. pp. xii. 126. pl. 50. *Hodder & Stoughton: London*, 1906. 4°. **12812**. bb. **21**.

—— *See* Edmondston (Maysie) The Duke of Christmas Daisies (adapted from "The Little White Bird" . . . of Sir J. M. Barrie), *etc.* [1914.] 16°. **11781**. aa. **72**.

—— *See* Gillington, afterwards Byron (May C.) J. M. Barrie's Peter Pan in Kensington Gardens. Retold by M. Byron for little people, *etc.* [1929.] 8°. **12816**. d. **24**.

—— Margaret Ogilvy. By her son, J. M. Barrie. pp. viii. 204. *Hodder & Stoughton: London*, 1896. 8°. **10826**. bb. **34**.

—— [Another copy.] Margaret Ogilvy, *etc.* *London*, 1896. 8°. Ashley **63**.

—— Mary Rose. A play in three acts. pp. 79. *Samuel French: London*, [1947.] 8°. [*French's Acting Edition*. no. 1734.] **11791**. tt. **1/460**.

—— [Mary Rose.] *See* Goitein (Percy L.) A New Approach to an analysis of "Mary Rose," *etc.* [1926.] 8°. **11824**. s. **28**.

—— My Lady Nicotine. pp. 265. *Hodder & Stoughton: London*, 1890. 8°. **012356**. k. **48**.

—— Second thousand. pp. 265. *Hodder & Stoughton: London*, 1890. 8°. **12356**. cc. **29**.

—— Neil and Tintinnabulum. (An interlude for parents.) pp. 31. *Privately printed*: [*London*,] 1925. 4°. Ashley **4691**.
One of an edition of twelve copies.

BARRIE (*Sir* James Matthew) *Bart.*

—— Peter and Wendy . . . Illustrated by F. D. Bedford. pp. vii. 267. *Hodder & Stoughton: London,* [1911.] 8°. **012809. aaa. 3.**

—— [Another edition.] Illustrated . . . by Mabel Lucie Attwell. pp. vii. 185. *Hodder & Stoughton: London,* [1921.] 4°. **012802. d. 34.**

—— [Another edition.] Decorated by Gwynedd M. Hudson. pp. 271. *Hodder & Stoughton: London,* 1931. 4°. **012803. l. 29.**

—— Peter Pan and Wendy, *etc.* (New edition, reset.) pp. 127. *Oxford University Press: London,* 1934. 8°. **20053. eee. 24.**

—— The Blampied Edition of Peter Pan. The original text of Peter & Wendy . . . Newly illustrated by Edmund Blampied. pp. viii. 215. *Hodder & Stoughton: [London,]* 1939. 4°. L.R. **276. d. 10.**

—— J. M. Barrie's Peter Pan and Wendy. [With illustrations.] *Juvenile Productions: London,* [1955.] 4°. **12838. i. 6.**

—— Peter Pan . . . Illustrations by John Morton-Sale. pp. 192. *Hodder & Stoughton: London,* 1942. 8°. **11783. aa. 46.**

—— Peter Pan . . . Illustrated by Nora S. Unwin. pp. 192. *Hodder & Stoughton: London,* 1951. 8°. **12836. k. 40.**
Part of a series entitled "The Peter Pan Books."

—— Tír na Deó. (Peter Pan and Wendy.) Máiréad Ní Ġráda do ċuir Gaeḋilg air. [With plates.] pp. 192. Oifig Díolta Foillseaċáin Rialtais: Baile Áṫa Cliaṫ, 1938. 8°. **12825. b. 11.**

—— Peter Pan y Wendy . . . Traducción se María Luz Morales. pp. 320. *Barcelona,* [1925.] 8°. **012808. i. 50.**

—— Peter Pan and Wendy. [The story of "Peter Pan" extracted from "Peter and Wendy."] . . . Illustrated by F. D. Bedford. Authorised school edition. pp. 126. *Henry Frowde; Hodder & Stoughton: London,* [1915.] 8° **012807. a. 8.**

—— *See* Bedford (Annie N.) Walt Disney's Peter Pan and Wendy, *etc.* [Based on "Peter and Wendy" by Sir J. M. Barrie.] 1953. 8°. **12836. l. 3.**

—— *See* Disney (Walter E.) Walt Disney's Peter Pan. Based on the play by Sir J. M. Barrie, *etc.* [1952.] 4°. **11798. dd. 31.**

—— *See* Disney (Walter E.) Walt Disney's Peter Pan. Based on the story by J. M. Barrie, *etc.* 1953. 8°. **12836. l. 4.**

—— *See* Disney (Walter E.) Walt Disney's Peter Pan. From the original story by J. M. Barrie. Retold by Irene Pearl. 1953. *obl.* 8°. **12830. a. 150.**

—— *See* Disney (Walter E.) Walt Disney's Peter Pan. From the motion picture "Peter Pan," based on the story by Sir J. M. Barrie, *etc.* [1953.] 4°. **12811. h. 3.**

—— *See* Disney (Walter E.) Walt Disney's Peter Pan. From the motion picture "Peter Pan," based on the story by Sir J. M. Barrie, *etc.* [1953.] fol. **12844.b.4.**

—— *See* Drennan (G. D.) Peter Pan. Retold in story form from J. M. Barrie's dramatic fantasy by G. D. Drennan, *etc.* [1912.] 8°. **012808. a. 20.**

—— *See* Green (Roger L.) Fifty Years of Peter Pan, *etc.* 1954. 8°. **11798. bb. 32.**

BARRIE (*Sir* James Matthew) *Bart.*

—— *See* Hassall (John) The Peter Pan Painting Book. [Illustrations of the play by J. M. Barrie. 1915.] 4°. **1874. a. 40.**

—— *See* Herford (O.) The Peter Pan Alphabet. 1907. 4°. **12813. s. 12.**

—— *See* O'Connor (Daniel S.) The Peter Pan Picture Book. By A. B. Woodward and D. O'Connor, *etc.* 1907. 4°. **12812. bb. 20.**

—— —— 1911. 4°. **12803. w. 27.**

—— —— 1923. 8°. **12803. w. 53.**

—— *See* O'Connor (Daniel S.) [The Peter Pan Picture Book.] L'Histoire de Peter Pan. Par D. O'Connor, *etc.* 1916. 8°. **012807. dd. 23.**

—— *See* O'Connor (Daniel S.) The Story of Peter Pan. A reading book for use in schools, *etc.* 1912. 8°. **012809. aa. 37.**

—— —— 1914. 8°. **012807. c. 15.**

—— —— 1918. 8°. **12800. bbb. 20.**

—— —— 1926. 8°. **12813. aaa. 3.**

—— *See* O'Connor (Daniel S.) The Story of Peter Pan . . . Simplified from Daniel O'Connor's story of Sir J. M. Barrie's fairy play, *etc.* [1919.] 16°. **12801. a. 30.**

—— *See* Winn (Alison) Walt Disney's Peter Pan. Retold by A. Winn from the original story by J. M. Barrie. 1953. 8°. **12810. aa. 98.**

—— Peter Pan Keepsake. (The Story of Peter Pan. Retold from Mr. Barrie's fantasy.) Edited by Daniel S. O'Connor. With a foreword by W. T. Stead. pp. 32. *Chatto & Windus: London,* 1907 [1906]. 4°. **11795. pp. 1.**
^[by D. S. O'Connor]

—— [Another edition.] pp. 32. *Chatto & Windus: London,* 1908. 4°. **11795. g. 35.**

—— Peter Pan. Retold in story form from J. M. Barrie's dramatic fantasy. Edited^ by G. D. Drennan. pp. 38. *Mills & Boon: London,* 1909. 4°. **11795. p. 3.**
^[or rather, retold]

—— J. M. Barrie's Peter Pan & Wendy. Retold by May Byron for boys and girls . . . Pictures by Mabel Lucie Attwell. pp. 128. *Hodder & Stoughton: London,* [1925.] 8°. **012803. n. 30.**

—— J. M. Barrie's Peter Pan & Wendy. Retold by May Byron for little people . . . Pictures by Mabel Lucie Attwell. pp. 134. *Hodder & Stoughton: London,* [1925.] 8°. **12801. ee. 20.**

—— The Littlest Ones Peter Pan & Wendy. (Retold for the nursery by May Byron. Illustrated by Kathleen Atkins.) *Hodder & Stoughton: London,* [1930.] 16°. **012808. e. 80.**

—— J. M. Barrie's Peter Pan & Wendy retold by May Byron for little people with the approval of the author. Pictures by Mabel Lucie Attwell. pp. 144. *Hodder & Stoughton: London,* [1932.] 8°. **20053. h. 7.**

—— J. M. Barrie's Peter Pan and Wendy. Retold by May Byron for little people, *etc.* pp. 128. *University of London Press: London,* 1935. 8°. **20054. ff. 26.**

—— The Nursery Peter Pan and Wendy . . . Retold for the Nursery by May Byron. Illustrated by Kathleen Atkins. pp. 46. *Hodder & Stoughton: [London,* 1938.] 16°. [*Nursery Books.*] **12821. a. 6/6.**

—— J. M. Barrie's Peter Pan & Wendy. Retold by May Byron for boys and girls . . . Pictures by Mabel Lucie Attwell. pp. 188. *London*, 1938. 8°. [*Hodder & Stoughton's Colour Books.*] **12824.** f. **1/2.**

—— The Nursery Peter Pan and Wendy . . . Retold . . . by May Byron. Illustrated by Kathleen Atkins. pp. 62. *Brockhampton Book Co.: London*, [1943.] 16°. **12830.** e. **16.**

—— The Nursery Peter Pan and Wendy . . . Illustrated by Jeanne Farrar. Retold . . . by May Byron. pp. 61. *Brockhampton Press: Leicester*, [1946.] 16°. **12830.** e. **48.**

—— Peter Pan . . . Retold for the nursery by May Byron. Illustrated by Mabel Lucie Attwell. pp. 46. *Brockhampton Press: Leicester*, [1952.] 16°. [*Nursery Series.*] W.P. **14056/7.**

—— The Walt Disney Illustrated Peter Pan and Wendy . . . Retold by May Byron, *etc.* pp. 130. *Brockhampton Press: Leicester*, [1953.] 8°. **12834.** p. **13.**

—— Peter Pan and Wendy . . . Retold by Arthur Groom. (With five pop-up pictures.) *Birn Bros.: London*, [1955.] *obl.* 4°. **12830.** h. **48.**

—— Peter Pan and Wendy. A poem on the play [of J. M. Barrie]. By E. E. L. [1912.] 8°. *See* L., E. E. **011650.** f. **87.** **(9.)**

—— Peter Pan in Kensington Gardens. *See* supra: The Little White Bird.

—— Peter Pan's Play Book. *Humphrey Milford: [London*, 1929.] 8°. **12805.** i. **69.**

—— Quality Street, a comedy in four acts . . . Illustrated by Hugh Thomson. pp. vii. 197. *Hodder & Stoughton: [London*, 1913.] 4°. **11779.** l. **26.**

—— Scotland's Lament. A poem on the death of Robert Louis Stevenson, December 3rd, 1894. [With a portrait.] pp. 7. *Privately printed for T. J. Wise: London*, [1895.] 8°. Ashley **2334.**
One of an edition of twelve copies.

—— Scotland's Lament: Robert Louis Stevenson. [A poem. With a note by Clement Shorter.] pp. 10. *Privately printed by Clement Shorter: London*, 1918. 4°. Tab. **578.** a. **55.**
No. 21 *of an edition of twenty-five copies.*

—— Sentimental Tommy. The story of his boyhood. pp. viii. 452. *Cassell & Co.: London*, 1896. 8°. **012626.** g. **35.**

—— Forty-third thousand. pp. 452. *Cassell & Co.: London*, 1897. 8°. **012624.** ee. **24.**

—— Sentimentální Tommy . . . Přeložil Jos. Bartoš. pp. 443. [*Prague*,] 1902. 8°. [*Anglická Knihovna.*] **12203.** s. **1/21.**

—— Shakespeare's Legacy. [A farce.] *London*, 1916. 4°. Tab. **578.** a. **35.**
One of twenty-five copies printed for private circulation.

—— Speech by Sir James Barrie at the dinner to Rhodes Scholars, Oxford, June 20th, 1928. pp. 4. [1928.] 8°. Ashley **2337.**

—— Der Tag. A play. pp. 39. *Hodder & Stoughton: London*, 1914. 8°. **11774.** bb. **43.**

—— [A reissue.] Der Tag. A play. *London*, 1915. 8°. Ashley **68.**

—— Tommy and Grizel. pp. viii. 431. *Cassell & Co.: London*, 1900. 8°. **012641.** d. **42.**

—— [Another edition.] pp. vi. 509. *Copp, Clark Co.: Toronto*, 1900. 8°. **012622.** ee. **43.**

—— Walker, London. A farcical comedy in three acts. pp. 67. *Samuel French: New York, London*, [1921.] 8°. **011779.** e. **70.**

—— Walker, London, *etc.* pp. 70. *Samuel French: London, New York*, [1927.] 8°. [*French's Acting Edition.* no. 1337.] **11791.** t. **1/1190.**

—— What Every Woman Knows. A comedy in four acts. pp. 96. *London*, [1946.] 8°. [*French's Acting Edition.*] **11791.** tt. **1/433.**

—— What Every Woman knows. pp. 127. *University of London Press: London*, 1954. 8°. [*Pilot Books.*] W.P. **1272/33.**

—— When a Man's Single. A tale of literary life. pp. 289. *Hodder & Stoughton: London*, 1888. 8°. **012633.** f. **55.**

—— A Window in Thrums. pp. 7. 217. *Hodder & Stoughton: London*, 1889. 8°. **012633.** m. **55.**

—— [Another edition.] Illustrated by W. Hole. pp. xiv. 217. **L.P.** *Hodder & Stoughton: London*, 1892. 8°. **012634.** n. **8.**

—— Sixteenth edition. pp. vii. 217. *Hodder & Stoughton: London*, 1898. 8°. **012618.** g. **7.**

—— The Sabbath Day. [From "A Window in Thrums."] pp. 11. *Hodder & Stoughton: London*, 1895. 8°. **04410.** k. **30.** **(3.)**

WORKS WRITTEN IN COLLABORATION.

—— Jane Annie; or, the Good Conduct Prize. A . . . comic opera. Written by J. M. Barrie and A. Conan Doyle, *etc.* pp. 48. *Chappell & Co.: London*, 1893. 8°. **11779.** dd. **2.** **(5.)**
With four additional pages numbered 40a–d *inserted and a leaf numbered* 49 *pasted over page* 48.

—— [Another issue.] Jane Annie, *etc.* pp. 52. *London*, 1893. 8°. Ashley **2333.**
In this issue the inserted leaves are incorporated in the text.

SELECTIONS.

—— Selections from the Plays of J. M. Barrie (for use in schools). pp. 174. *University of London Press: London*, 1929. 8°. [*Treasuries of Modern Prose.*] W.P. **9720/2.**

—— Selections from the Prose Works of J. M. Barrie. pp. 174. *University of London Press: London*, 1929. 8°. [*Treasuries of Modern Prose.*] W.P. **9720/4.**

WORKS WITH PREFACES, ETC., BY BARRIE.

—— *See* ASHFORD (Daisy) The Young Visiters . . . With a preface by J. M. Barrie. 1919. 8°. **012603.** e. **23.**

—— *See* BALLANTYNE (R. M.) The Coral Island . . . With preface by J. M. Barrie, *etc.* 1913. 8°. **1874.** a. **4.**

—— *See* CABLE (G. W.) The Grandissimes . . . With an introductory note by J. M. Barrie. 1898. 8°. **012704.** f. **63.**

—— *See* CLEMENS (Samuel L.) [*Single Works.*] Who was Sarah Findlay? With a suggested solution . . . by J. M. Barrie. 1917. 4°. Tab. **578.** a. **49.**

BARRIE (*Sir* JAMES MATTHEW) *Bart.*

—— *See* MARCOSSON (Isaac F.) and FROHMAN (D.) Charles Frohman . . . With an appreciation by J. M. Barrie. 1916. 8°. **010880. f. 25.**

—— *See* MERRICK (Leonard) The Works of Leonard Merrick. (Conrad in Quest of his Youth . . . With an introduction by J. M. Barrie.) [1918, *etc.*] 8°. **012272. aa. 13/1.**

—— *See* OLIPHANT (Margaret A.) A Widow's Tale . . . With an introductory note by J. M. Barrie. 1898. 8°. **012643. bbb. 42.**

—— *See* SCOTT (Robert F.) The Voyages of Captain Scott . . . With an introduction by Sir J. M. Barrie, *etc.* 1914. 8°. **10460. de. 22.**

APPENDIX.

—— *See* ASQUITH (*Lady* Cynthia M. E.) Portrait of Barrie. [With portraits.] 1954. 8°. **10864. cc. 7.**

—— *See* BLAKE (George) *Novelist.* Barrie and the Kailyard School. 1951. 8°. **11873.a.15/18.**

—— *See* BLOCK (Andrew) Sir J. M. Barrie. His first editions: points and values. [A bibliography.] 1933. 8°. **W.P. 10036/3.**

—— *See* BRAYBROOKE (Patrick) J. M. Barrie, *etc.* [With a portrait.] [1924.] 8°. **11853. h. 5.**

—— *See* CHALMERS (Patrick R.) The Barrie Inspiration. [With portraits.] 1938. 8°. **11858. c. 94.**

—— *See* CUTLER (Bradley D.) Sir James M. Barrie. A bibliography, with full collations of the American unauthorized editions. [1931.] 8°. **011904. eee. 23.**

—— *See* DARLINGTON (William A. C.) J. M. Barrie. [A biography. With portraits.] 1938. 8°. **10856. m. 7.**

—— *See* DARTON (Frederick J. H.) J. M. Barrie. [With a portrait.] [1929.] 8°. **11863.aa.13/14.**

—— *See* ESCHENAUER (W.) Sir James Barrie als Dramatiker. 1929. 8°. **11823. r. 25.**

—— *See* GARLAND (Herbert) A Bibliography of the Writings of Sir James Matthew Barrie, *etc.* 1928. 8°. **011900. bb. 71.**

—— *See* HAMMERTON (John A.) Barrie. The story of a genius. [With portraits.] 1929. 8°. **10824. k. 9.**

—— *See* HAMMERTON (John A.) Barrieland, *etc.* [1929.] 8°. **011850. cc. 63.**

—— *See* HAMMERTON (John A.) J. M. Barrie and his Books, *etc.* 1900. 8°. **10827. cc. 17.**

—— *See* KENNEDY (John) *B.D.*. Thrums and the Barrie Country, *etc.* 1930. 8°. **010369. ff. 44.**

—— *See* LONDON.—II. *Livery Companies.—Stationers.* A Short Account of the Enrolment of . . . Sir J. Barrie, *etc.* [With a portrait.] [1925.] 4°. **10349. gg. 8.**

—— *See* MACKAIL (Denis G.) The Story of J. M. B., *etc.* [With a portrait.] 1941. 8°. **10859. b. 24.**

—— *See* MOULT (Thomas) Barrie. 1928. 8°. **010855. df. 10.**

—— *See* MUNDELL (Mary R. M.) Der Humor in der Gestaltenwelt Barries als Ausdruck seines Weltgefühls. 1938. 8°. **11859. ff. 25.**

—— *See* ROY (James A.) James Matthew Barrie. An appreciation, *etc.* [With portraits.] 1937. 8°. **010821. g. 15.**

BARRIE (*Sir* JAMES MATTHEW) *Bart.*

—— *See* SIBLEY (Carroll) Barrie and his Contemporaries, *etc.* [With a portrait.] 1936. 8°. **W.P.12220/a4.**

—— *See* WALBROOK (Henry M.) J. M. Barrie and the Theatre, *etc.* [With a portrait.] 1922. 8°. **11795. aaa. 36.**

BARRIE (JANE) *pseud.* [i.e. MILDRED SAVAGE.]

—— The Lumberyard and Mrs. Barrie. pp. 224. *Hammond, Hammond & Co.: London,* 1953. 8°. **012332. b. 21.**

BARRIE (JANE ANN) *Lady.*

—— *See* DAVIDSON (Thomas M.) In Memoriam Lady Barrie, 1845–1922. [With a portrait.] 1924. 4°. **10826. i. 56.**

BARRIÉ (M. ÉMILE) Des plaques muqueuses de la peau. pp. 34. *Paris,* 1866. 4°. [*Collection des thèses soutenues à la Faculté de Médecine de Paris.* An 1866. tom. 4.] **7373. g. 4.**

BARRIE (MARGARET) and **ROBERTS** (JOHN EDWARD) Emblems of Christ. An exercise for Junior Christian Endeavour Societies. pp. 16. *British National Council of Christian Endeavour: London,* [1902.] 8°. **04420. i. 33. (3.)**

—— The Good Ship Christian Endeavour. (An exercise for junior rallies.) pp. 16. *Christian Endeavour Council: London,* [1902.] 8°. **3435. k. 4.**

BARRIE (MARY W.) Gnosticism, *etc.* pp. vi. 114. *Theosophical Publishing House: Adyar,* 1926. 8°. [*Brahmavidya Library.* no. 4.] **W.P. 8119/4.**

BARRIÉ (NESTOR) Des dartres ; thèse, *etc.* pp. 55. *Paris,* 1818. 4°. **1183. e. 3. (21.)**

BARRIE (SUSAN)

—— Carpet of Dreams. pp. 187. *Mills & Boon: London,* 1955. 8°. **NNN. 6814.**

—— The Gates of Dawn. pp. 190. *Mills & Boon: London,* 1954. 8°. **NNN. 4950.**

—— Hotel Stardust. pp. 187. *Mills & Boon: London,* 1955. 8°. **NNN. 6150.**

—— Marry a Stranger. pp. 190. *Mills & Boon: London,* 1954. 8°. **NNN. 5491.**

—— Mistress of Brown Furrows. pp. 190. *Mills & Boon: London,* 1952. 8°. **NNN. 3220.**

BARRIE (V. H.)

—— Waskunde. pp. 175. *Bloemfontein,* 1948. 8°. [*Collegium-reeks.* no. 24.] **W.P. D. 864/24.**

BARRIENTOS (ANTONIO JOAQUÍN DE RIBADENEYRA Y) *See* RIBADENEYRA Y BARRIENTOS.

BARRIENTOS (BALTASAR DE ALAMOS Y) *See* ALAMOS Y BARRIENTOS.

BARRIENTOS (BARTOLOMÉ) *See* BARRIENTUS (Bartholomaeus)

BARRIENTOS (FERNANDO UGARTE) *See* UGARTE BARRIENTOS.

BARRIENTOS (JOSÉ MARÍA) Sermon del Santo Niño Jesus, llamado de San Juan, que se venera en la iglesia de Religiosas Clarisas de San Juan de la Penitencia en esta Corte. pp. 22. *México,* 1818. 4°. **4425. aaa. 9.**

BARRIENTOS (JOSEFA UGARTE) *See* UGARTE BARRIENTOS.

BARRIENTOS (Lope de) *Bishop of Cuenca.*

—— *See* Carrillo de Albornoz (P.) Refundición de la Crónica del Halconero por el obispo Don Lope Barrientos. *etc.* 1946. 8°. **9088.n.6/9.**

—— *See* Pérez de Guzmán (F.) Comiença la Cronica del . . . Rey Don Iuan Segundo, *etc.* [In part a compilation from works by L. de Barrientos and others.] 1517. fol. C. **62.** g. **1.**

—— Vida y Obras de Fr. Lope de Barrientos. [Edited by L. G. Alonso Getino.] pp. xcvi. 245. *Salamanca,* 1927. 8°. [*Anales Salmantinos.* vol. 1.] W.P. **4688/1.**

BARRIENTOS (Luis) Doctrina Cristiana en Lengua Chiapaneca. *See* Pinart (A. L.) Bibliothèque de linguistique et d'ethnographie américaines, *etc.* tom. 1. 1876, *etc.* 4°. **12907.** h. **9.**

BARRIENTOS CONTO (Alberto) Anotaciones a la Criminalidad Infantil. Casas y juzgados de menores. Tesis, *etc.* pp. 36. 1926. 8°. *See* Bogotá.—*Universidad Nacional.—Facultad de Derecho y Ciencias Políticas.* Ac. **2191/2.**

BARRIENTUS (Bartholomaeus) *See* Calvete de Estrella (J. C.) Ioannis Christophori Calueti Stellae de Aphrodisio expugnato . . . cōmentarius, cum scholiis B. Barrienti. 1566. 8°. C. **64.** cc. **1.**

—— Annotationum Sylua. ff. 48. *I. B. à Terranoua: Salmanticæ,* 1570. 8°. **12935.** a. **9.** (**2.**)

—— [Another edition.] 1604. *See* Gruterus (J.) Lampas, siue fax artium liberalium, *etc.* tom. 3. 1602, *etc.* 8°. **1087.** i. **3.**

—— Barbariei Lima agens de verborum constructionibus vocibusq; barbaris & parum vsitatis quæ latina censentur, *etc.* ff. 80. *Expensis S. à Portonarijs; excudebat M. Mares: Salmanticæ,* 1570. 8°. **12935.** a. **9.** (**1.**)

—— Breuissimæ in Somnium Scipionis explanationes. ff. 28. *Expensis S. à Portonarijs: Salmanticæ,* 1570. 8°. **12935.** a. **9.** (**4.**)

—— Cometarum explicatio atque prædictio. pp. 64. *Impensis S. Portanarij; excudebat P. Lasus: Salmanticæ,* 1574. 8°. **531.** e. **27.**

—— Partium orationis Syntaxeos liber, *etc.* pp. 85. *In ædibus D. a Portonarijs;* [*sold by*] *S. de Portonarijs: Salmanticæ,* 1571. 8°. **12935.** a. **9.** (**3.**)

—— Dos antiguas relaciones de la Florida. Publícalas por primera vez Genaro García. (Vida y hechos de Pero Menéndez de Auilés . . . Conpuesta por el maestro Barrientos.—Relación de los trabajos que la gente de vna nao . . . padeció . . . Escrita por fray Andres de San Miguel.) pp. cii. 226. *México,* 1902. 4°. **9770.** i. **11.**

BARRIER TREATY. *See* England.—*Treaties, etc.*—ii. Anne. [1702–1714.]

BARRIER (Albert) Quelques mots sur la chorée. Thèse, *etc.* pp. 34. *Montpellier,* 1856. 4°. **7379.** d. **1.** (**5.**)

BARRIER (Antoine Gilbert Eugène) Essai sur l'attaque régulière de la goutte des articulations. Tribut académique, *etc.* pp. 23. *Montpellier,* 1827. 4°. **1181.** d. **12.** (**2.**)

—— Traitement des maladies scrofuleuses et cancéreuses par les méthodes iatraleptiques. pp. 302. *Paris,* 1856. 8°. **7630.** e. **28.**

BARRIER (Claude)

—— Des campeurs ont vu—les Châteaux de la Loire, *etc.* [With illustrations.] *Paris,* 1946. 8°. **010171.** n. **26.**
Part of a series entitled "Des campeurs ont vu."

BARRIER (Éléanor Hippolyte) Répertoire général de voirie vicinale, ou guide . . . de législation, de jurisprudence et d'administrations des chemins vicinaux. 2 pt. *Paris,* 1866. 8°. **5423.** bb. **22.**

BARRIER (François Marguerite) *See* Periodical Publications.—*Paris.* Annuaire de l'Association . . . Par Barbier [i.e. Barrier], *etc.* 1867, *etc.* 8°. P.P. **1423.** km.

—— Considérations sur l'établissement des crèches dans la ville de Lyon. pp. 34. *Lyon, Paris,* 1847. 24°. **1390.** a. **35.**

—— Considérations sur la question du vitalisme et de l'animisme, à propos du livre de M. le professeur Bouillier, intitulé : Du principle vital et de l'âme pensante, *etc.* pp. 16. *Lyon,* 1862. 8°. **07305.** k. **15.** (**2.**)

—— Éloge d'Amédée Bonnet . . . Discours de réception prononcé à la séance publique de l'Académie des Sciences, Belles-Lettres et Arts de Lyon. pp. 36. *Lyon,* 1859. 8°. **10662.** g. **33.** (**12.**)

—— Esquisse d'une analogie de l'homme et de l'humanité. pp. 48. *Lyon,* 1846. 8°. **1248.** g. **8.**

—— Observation et remarques sur la rupture de l'ankylose de la hanche. pp. 16. *Lyon,* 1859. 8°. **7481.** g. **38.** (**3.**)

—— Principes de sociologie. tom. 1. pp. xxxii. 391. *Paris,* 1867. 8°. **8206.** g. **10.**
Imperfect; wanting tom. 2.

—— Thèse pour le doctorat en médecine, *etc.* (De la tumeur hydatique du foie.—Questions sur diverses tranches des sciences médicales.) pp. 103. *Paris,* 1840. 4°. [*Collection des thèses soutenues à la Faculté de Médecine de Paris.* An 1840. tom. 1.] **7371.** b. **2.**

—— Traité pratique des maladies de l'enfance, fondé sur de nombreuses observations cliniques. Deuxième édition, revue et augmentée. 2 tom. *Paris,* 1845. 8°. **1178.** d. **16, 17.**

BARRIER (Georges)

—— Dans Marrakech la rouge. [Autobiographical reminiscences. Edited by Raymond Boissier.] pp. 300. *Paris,* 1930. 8°. **010093.** de. **68.**

BARRIER (Gustave) *Abbé.* Un Ami de Rome et du pape au xixe siècle. Mgr. H. Sauvé. 2 tom. *Laval, Paris,* [1898.] 8°. **4866.** i. **16.**

BARRIER (Gustave) *Professeur à l'École vétérinaire d'Alfort.* *See* Goubaux (A.) and Barrier (G.) De l'Extérieur du cheval, *etc.* 1884. 8°. **7291.** g. **13.**

—— —— 1890. 8°. **7291.** ccc. **1**

—— *See* Goubaux (A.) and Barrier (G.) The Exterior of the Horse, *etc.* 1892. 8°. **07291.** ee. **4**

BARRIER (Jean) *See* Grangeon (L. P.) Jean Barrier . . . Vie et lettres, *etc.* 1889. 8°. **4867.** de. **33.**

BARRIER (Jean Anet) *See* Frachon (V.) Notice médicale sur les eaux minérales de Celles-les-Bains, Ardèche, principalement au point de vue des affections lymphatiques et tuberculeuses . . . et de leur traitement minéral par les méthodes du Dr. J. A. Barrier. 1860. 8°. **7470.** e. **20.**

—— Ma profession de foi en médecine. Dissertation inaugurale, *etc.* pp. 125. *Montpellier,* 1820. 4°. **1180.** i. **9.** (**14.**)

BARRIER (Jean Élysée Saint-Ange) Le Tubercule et la phthisie. Étude historique et analytique. pp. 74. *Paris,* 1868. 4°. [*Collection des thèses soutenues à la Faculté de Médecine de Paris.* An 1868. tom. 1.] **7373.** i. **5.**

—— [Another edition.] pp. 74. *Paris,* 1868. 8°. **7615.** bb. **37.** (**7.**)

BARRIER (SAINT-ANGE) *See* BARRIER (Jean E. St.-A.)

BARRIERA (ATTILIO) *See* SENECA (L. C.) [*De Ira.—Latin.*] L. Annaei Senecae De ira . . . Recensuit, praefatus est, appendice critica instruxit A. Barriera. [1920.] 8°. **011306.aa.2/21.**

BARRIERA (EUGÈNE) Emploi de l'eau froide en chirurgie. Thèse, *etc.* pp. 39. *Montpellier,* 1870. 4°. **7379. h. 13. (16.)**

BARRIÈRE (A.) *M.D.* Considérations générales sur la métrorrhagie. Dissertation, *etc.* pp. 18. *Montpellier,* 1821. 4°. **1181. c. 1. (18.)**

BARRIÈRE (ACHILLE ÉTIENNE) Essai sur quelques effets thérapeutiques de l'eau. Thèse, *etc.* pp. 102. *Montpellier,* 1850. 4°. **7379. b. 1. (12.)**

BARRIÈRE (ALEXIS) La Sainte Catherine, ou un bienfait n'est jamais perdu, à-propos vaudeville en un acte. pp. 56. *Paris,* [1861.] 24°. **11739. a. 46. (3.)**

BARRIÈRE (DANIEL ALEXANDRE FRANÇOIS) *See* GENTIL DE CHAVAGNAC (M. J.) La Vendange normande . . . vaudeville . . . par Gentil et * * * [i.e. D. A. F. and P. J. L. Barrière], *etc.* 1817. 8°. **11738. f. 27. (6.)**

BARRIÈRE (ERNEST) De l'embolie. pp. 31. *Paris,* 1861. 4°. [*Collection des thèses soutenues à la Faculté de Médecine de Paris.* An 1861. tom. 1.] **7373. d. 2.**

BARRIÈRE (FRANÇOIS) *Historical Writer. See* BARRIÈRE (Jean F.)

BARRIÈRE (FRANÇOIS) *M.D. See* BARRIÈRE (Pierre A. J. F.)

BARRIÈRE (JEAN FRANÇOIS) *See* BERVILLE (St.-A.) and BARRIÈRE (J. F.) Collection des mémoires relatifs à la Révolution française, *etc.* 1820, *etc.* 8°. **910.f.1–h.12.**

—— *See* BESENVAL (P. J. V. de) *Baron.* Mémoires du Baron de Besenval. Avec une notice sur sa vie, des notes et des éclaircissemens historiques par MM. Berville et Barrière. 1823. 8°. **010664. de. 4.**

—— *See* DU HAUSSAY (N.) Mémoires de Madame Du Hausset, *etc.* (Mis en ordre par M. Barrière.) 1825. 12°. **010663. de. 1.**

—— *See* LOMÉNIE DE BRIENNE (L. H. de) *Count.* Mémoires inédits . . . Avec un essai sur les moeurs et sur les usages du XVIIe siècle par F. Barrière. 1828. 8°. **1201. g. 2.**

—— Bibliothèque des mémoires relatifs à l'histoire de France pendant le 18me siècle, avec avant-propos et notices par F. Barrière. (Nouvelle série avec introductions, notices et notes par M. de Lescure.) 37 tom. *Paris,* 1846–81. 12°. **10662. bb. 1–31.**

—— *See* MARQUISET (A.) Table alphabétique des noms propres cités dans les " Mémoires relatifs à l'histoire de France," *etc.* 1913. 8°. [*Revue des Bibliothèques.* supp. 9.] P.P. **6475. i.**

—— La Cour et la ville sous Louis XIV, Louis XV et Louis XVI, ou révélations historiques tirées de manuscrits inédits. pp. ix. 426. *Paris,* 1830. 8°. **12355. bbb. 3.**

—— [For editions and translations of the " Notice sur la vie de Mme Campan " by J. F. Barrière, included in editions of her " Mémoires sur la vie de Marie Antoinette " :] *See* CAMPAN (J. L. H.)

—— Tableaux de genre et d'histoire, peints par différens maitres, ou Morceaux inédits sur la Régence, la jeunesse de Louis XV. et le règne de Louis XVI. Recueillis et publiés par F. Barrière. pp. xvi. 391. *Paris,* 1828. 8°. **9225. b. 4.**

BARRIÈRE (MARCEL) Essai sur l'art du roman. pp. 110. *Paris,* 1931. 8°. **11822. t. 28.**

—— Guillaume II et son temps. [A history of the years 1908–1914. With a portrait.] pp. 316. *Paris,* 1934. 8°. **10709. bb. 2.**

—— Le Mauvais Eros. Chronique des mœurs du Second Empire. Roman inédit. 1923. *See* PERIODICAL PUBLICATIONS.—*Paris.* Les Œuvres libres, *etc.* no. 30. 1921, *etc.* 8°. **12208. ee. 30.**

—— Le Nouveau Don Juan. (L'Éducation d'un contemporain.—Le Roman de l'ambition.—Les Ruines de l'amour.) 3 pt. *Paris,* 1900. 12°. **012550. l. 62.**

—— L'Œuvre de H. de Balzac. Étude littéraire et philosophique sur la Comédie humaine. pp. xxvii. 502. *Paris,* 1890. 8°. **011840. l. 33.**

—— Les Princes d'Orleans, *etc.* [Reminiscences of Louis Philippe Albert, comte de Paris, and of his son Louis Philippe Robert, duc d'Orléans, in 1890–91.] pp. 284. *Paris,* 1933. 8°. **10655. p. 13.**

BARRIÈRE (MARCELLIN) Un Astronome qui s'est instruit lui-même . . . ou Réfutation des principaux systèmes planétaires adoptés par la science astronomique officielle, *etc.* [With a plate.] pp. 16. *Bordeaux,* 1868. 8°. **8561. cc. 33. (6.)**

BARRIÈRE (MARCELLIN THÉOPHILE) Essai sur les tumeurs du voile du palais, confondues sous le nom d'adénomes. Thèse, *etc.* pp. 54. *Montpellier,* 1878. 4°. **7379. l. 13. (1.)**

BARRIÈRE (MICHEL FÉLIX) Dissertation sur la délivrance. Thèse, *etc.* pp. 22. *Montpellier,* 1832. 4°. **1181. f. 8. (16.)**

BARRIÈRE (P.) *Docteur ès lettres.* Alfred de Vigny. Essai d'interprétation littéraire et morale. pp. 303. *Paris; Courtrai* [printed, 1930]. 8°. **11822. s. 7.**

BARRIÈRE (P. B. M.) Avantages de l'allaitement maternel ; thèse, *etc.* pp. 26. *Paris,* 1833. 4°. **1184. e. 11. (12.)**

BARRIÈRE (P. J. L.) *See* COLLECTION. Collection des mémoires sur l'art dramatique, publiés ou traduits par MM. Andrieux, Barrière, *etc.* [1822, *etc.*] 8°. **840. e. 13–19.**

—— *See* DÉSAUGIERS (M. A. M.) and BARRIÈRE (P. J. L.) Le Mari en vacances, comédie-vaudeville, *etc.* 1813. 8°. **11738. d. 6. (7.)**

—— *See* DÉSAUGIERS (M. A. M.) and BARRIÈRE (P. J. L.) Trois pour une . . . comédie-vaudeville, *etc.* 1816. 8°. **11738. d. 8. (1.)**

—— *See* GENTIL DE CHAVAGNAC (M. J.) La Vendange normande . . . vaudeville . . . par Gentil et * * * [i.e. D. A. F. and P. J. L. Barrière], *etc.* 1817. 8°. **11738. f. 27. (6.)**

BARRIÈRE (PIERRE) called LA BARRE. *See* CHÂTEL (J.) Procedure faicte contre J. Chastel . . . Auec l'histoire . . . du . . . parricide attenté contre le Sieur roy Henry quatriesme par P. Barrière, *etc.* 1601. 8°. **860. d. 6. (10.)**

—— *See* DAZÈS ( ) *Abbé.* Les Jésuites ligueurs et complices de Barrière, *etc.* 1827. 8°. [*Documents historiques concernant . . . la Compagnie de Jésus.* tom. 1.] **04785. i. 42.**

—— *See* DAZÈS ( ) *Abbé.* Von den Jesuiten als Liguisten und Mitverschwornen von Barrière, *etc.* 1841. 8°. [*Dokumente zur Geschichte . . . der Gesellschaft Jesu, etc.* pt. 2.] **1367. h. 30.**

BARRIÈRE (Pierre) called La Barre.

—— Auswahl von gliechzeitigen Denckschriften über die Mordthat des Pierre Barrière, *etc.* 1797. *See* Schiller (J. C. F. von) [*Works edited or translated by Schiller.*] Allgemeine Sammlung historischer Memoires vom zwölften Jahrhundert, *etc.* Abt. 2. Bd. 14. 1790, *etc.* 8°. **1432.** h. **9.**

—— Extraict du procez criminel fait a Pierre Barriere dit la Barre, natif d'Orleans. Accusé de l'horrible . . . assassinat . . . attenté contre la personne du roy. pp. 15. *I. Mettayer : Tours*, 1593. 8°. **901.** a. **36.**

—— [Another edition.] Bref discours du procès criminel fait à Pierre Barrière, *etc.* 1837. *See* Cimber (M. L.) *pseud.* Archives curieuses de l'histoire de France. sér. 1. tom. 13. 1834, *etc.* 8°. **805.** b. **5.**

—— Histoire prodigieuse d'vn detestable parricide entrepris en la personne du roy par Pierre Barriere dit La Barre, & comme sa Maieste en fut miraculeusemẽt garentie. [By Étienne Pasquier.] pp. 40. [*Paris ?*] 1594. 8°. **1070.** k. **7.**

BARRIÈRE (Pierre Anne Jean François) Dissertation sur la dysenterie bilieuse, *etc.* pp. 31. *Montpellier*, 1817. 4°. **1180.** h. **9. (29.)**

BARRIÈRE (Pierre Ferdinand)

—— *See* Laval (Pierre de) Les Rimes de Pierre de Laval, 1576. [Edited by P. Barrière.] 1937. 8°. **11474.** d. **9.**

—— L'Académie de Bordeaux. Centre de culture internationale au XVIIIe siècle (1712–1792). [With plates.] pp. xii. 374. *Bordeaux, Paris*, 1951. 8°. **8356.** p. **35.**

—— Un Grand provincial : Charles-Louis de Secondat, baron de La Brède et de Montesquieu. [With plates, including portraits.] pp. xvi. 549. *Bordeaux*, [1946.] 8°. **010665.** i. **104.**

—— La Vie intellectuelle en Périgord, 1550–1800. pp. 587. *Bordeaux*, 1936. 8°. **11859.** bb. **8.**

BARRIÈRE (Théodore) *See* Bayard (J. F. A.) and Barrière (T.) Quand on attend sa belle, vaudeville, *etc.* 1849. 8°. [*Bibliothèque dramatique, etc.* tom. 30.] **2296.** b. **30.**

—— *See* Bourgeois (A. A.) and Barrière (T.) Les Infidèles, comédie, *etc.* 1854. 8°. [*Bibliothèque dramatique, etc.* tom. 70.] **2296.** d. **8.**

—— *See* Bourgeois (A. A.) and Barrière (T.) La Vie d'une comédienne, drame, *etc.* 1854. 8°. [*Bibliothèque dramatique, etc.* tom. 56.] **2296.** c. **25.**

—— —— 1855. fol. [*Théâtre contemporain illustré.* liv. 163, 164.] **2296.** h.

—— *See* Byam (Edwin C.) Théodore Barrière, Dramatist of the Second Empire. [With a portrait and a bibliography.] 1938. 8°. [*Johns Hopkins Studies in Romance Literatures and Languages.* Extra vol. 13.] **Ac. 2689/6.**

—— *See* Decourcelle (A.) Un Roi de la mode ; comédie . . . par MM. Decourcelle, T. Barrière et Barbier. [1851.] 8°. **2296.** c. **7.**

—— *See* Decourcelle (A.) Tambour battant, comédie-vaudeville . . . par MM. A. Decourcelle, T. Barrière et L. Morand. [1851.] 8°. **2296.** c. **8.**

—— *See* Decourcelle (A.) and Barrière (T.) La Petite cousine, comédie vaudeville, *etc.* [1849.] 8°. **2296.** b. **17.**

BARRIÈRE (Théodore)

—— *See* Decourcelle (A.) and Barrière (T.) Les Portraits, comédie, *etc.* 1849. 8°. [*Bibliothèque dramatique, etc.* tom. 13.] **2296.** b. **13.**

—— *See* Decourcelle (A.) and Barrière (T.) Une Vengeance. Comédie-vaudeville, *etc.* 1852. 8°. **11739.** g. **44.**

—— *See* Decourcelle (A.) and Barrière (T.) Un Vilain Monsieur, vaudeville, *etc.* [1848.] 8°. **2296.** b. **16.**

—— —— 1854. fol. [*Théâtre contemporain illustré.* liv. 106, 107.] **2296.** h.

—— *See* Duval (Georges L. J.) *pseud.*, and Barrière (T.) Mon bonnet de nuit, comédie-vaudeville, *etc.* 1835. 8°. [*Magasin théatral, etc.* tom. 9.] **11735.** i. **9. (7.)**

—— *See* Grangé (Eugène) *pseud.* English Exhibition. Comédie-vaudeville . . . par MM. E. Grangé, T. Barrière et Decourcelle. 1851. 8°. **11737.** g. **31. (22.)**

—— *See* Grangé (Eugène) *pseud.* La Tête de Martin, comédie . . . par MM. E. Grangé, Decourcelle et T. Barrière. 1853. fol. [*Théâtre contemporain illustré.* liv. 66, 67.] **2296.** h.

—— —— 1852. 8°. **2296.** c. **13.**

—— *See* Hugelmann (G.) *Journalist.* Toast à Théodore Barrière, *etc.* [1866.] 8°. **12301.** g. **45.**

—— *See* Mirecourt (Eugène de) *pseud.* Histoire contemporaine, *etc.* (no. 92. Théodore Barrière.) 1867, *etc.* 12°. **10661.** aaa. **33.**

—— *See* Pinel-Dumanoir (P. F.) and Barrière (T.) Les Bourgeois gentilshommes, comédie, *etc.* 1857. 8°. [*Bibliothèque dramatique, etc.* tom. 77.] **2296.** d. **15.**

—— —— 1862. fol. [*Théâtre contemporain illustré.* liv. 518, 519.] **2296.** h.

—— *See* Pinel-Dumanoir (P. F.) and Barrière (T.) Les Toilettes tapageuses, comédie, *etc.* 1857. fol. [*Théâtre contemporain illustré.* liv. 250.] **2296.** h.

—— *See* Poujol (A.) *the Younger*, and Barrière (T.) Jeanne de Naples, *etc.* [1861.] 18°. **11739.** a. **46. (5.)**

—— *See* Regnauld de Prébois (A.) and Barrière (T.) Une Pécheresse, drame, *etc.* 1860. 8°. [*Bibliothèque dramatique, etc.* tom. 89.] **2296.** d. **27.**

—— —— 1862. fol. [*Théâtre contemporain illustré.* liv. 503, 504.] **2296.** h.

—— Les Batons dans les roues, vaudeville en un acte, *etc.* pp. 39. *Paris*, 1854. 8°. [*Bibliothèque dramatique, etc.* tom. 60.] **2296.** c. **29.**

—— [Another edition.] pp. 10. 1856. *See* Théâtre. Théâtre contemporain illustré. liv. 231, 232. [1852, *etc.*] fol. **2296.** h.

—— Les Bêtises du coeur. Comédie en trois actes, *etc.* pp. 96. *Paris*, 1871. 8°. **11740.** b. **1. (4.)**

—— La Boîte de Pandore. Opéra-bouffe en 3 actes. pp. viii. 100. *Paris, Bruxelles*, 1871. 8°. **11739.** aa. **55. (6.)**

—— Le Bout de l'an de l'amour. Causerie à deux. pp. 23. *Paris*, 1863. 8°. **11739.** c. **17. (6.)**

—— Les Brebis galeuses. Comédie en quatre actes. pp. 144. *Paris*, 1867. 8°. **11739.** bbb. **16. (1.)**

—— Cendrillon. Comédie en cinq actes, *etc.* pp. 136. *Paris*, 1859. 8°. **11739.** c. **11. (3.)**

BARRIÈRE (Théodore)

—— Le Chemin de Damas. Pièce en trois actes. pp. 110. *Paris*, 1878. 8°. **11740. b. 15. (1.)**

—— Dinah. Comédie en deux actes. pp. 56. *Paris*, 1873. 8°. **11737. b. 24. (2.)**

—— Le Feu au couvent. Comédie en un acte en prose . . . Deuxième édition. pp. 58. *Paris*, 1860. 8°. **11739. bb. 20. (2.)**

—— Laurence. Drame en deux actes par T. Barrière, M. Carré et J. Barbier, *etc.* pp. 40. *Paris*, [1850.] 8°. [*Bibliothèque dramatique, etc.* tom. 25.] **2296. b. 25.**

—— Malheur aux vaincus. Comédie en cinq actes, en prose, avec une préface, *etc.* pp. 160. *Paris*, 1866. 8°. **11739. ff. 8.**

—— [Another edition.] pp. 91. *Paris*, 1870. 8°. **11740. b. 3. (1.)**

—— Un Ménage en ville. Comédie en trois actes. pp. 94. *Paris*, 1865. 8°. **11739. bbb. 13. (1.)**

—— Midi a quatorze heures, comédie-vaudeville en un acte, *etc.* pp. 44. *Paris*, 1854. 8°. [*Bibliothèque dramatique, etc.* tom. 36.] **2296. c. 5.**

—— [Another edition.] pp. 13. 1857. *See* Théâtre. Théâtre contemporain illustré. liv. 23, 24. [1852, *etc.*] fol. **2296. h.**

—— Un Monsieur qui attend des témoins. Comédie en un acte. pp. 32. *Paris*, 1873. 8°. **11737. b. 24. (3.)**

—— Les Parisiens, pièce en trois actes, *etc.* pp. 107. *Paris*, 1855. 8°. [*Bibliothèque dramatique, etc.* tom. 63.] **2296. d. 1.**

—— [Another edition.] pp. 30. 1857. *See* Théâtre. Théâtre contemporain illustré. liv. 243, 244. [1852, *etc.*] fol. **2296. h.**

—— Les Scandales d'hier. Comédie en trois actes. pp. 98. *Paris*, 1878. 8°. **11740. b. 15. (2.)**

—— Théodoros. Drame en cinq actes, *etc.* pp. 23. *Paris*, [1869.] fol. **11737. i. 10.**

BARRIÈRE (Théodore) and **BEAUPLAN** (Arthur de)

—— Le Lys dans la vallée, drame en cinq actes en prose d'après H. de Balzac. pp. 29. 1854. *See* Théâtre. Théâtre contemporain illustré. liv. 108, 109. [1852, *etc*]. fol. **2296. h.**

BARRIÈRE (Théodore) and **BEAUVALLET** (Léon)

—— Le Crime de Faverne. Drame en cinq actes et sept tableaux. pp. 132. *Paris*, 1868. 8°. **11739. cc. 11. (3.)**

BARRIÈRE (Théodore) and **BERNARD** (Victor) *Dramatist.*

—— Les Demoiselles de Montfermeil. Comédie en trois actes. pp. 138. *Paris*, 1878. 8°. **11740. e. 4.**

BARRIÈRE (Théodore) and **CAPENDU** (Ernest)

—— Les Faux bonshommes. Comédie en quatre actes, *etc.* *See* Chefs-d'œuvres. Chefs-d'œuvre du théatre moderne. tom. 1. 1873, *etc.* fol. **11737. i. 4.**

—— Les Faux bonshommes, a comedy . . . Edited, with English notes and notice on Barrière, by . . . Ch. Cassal. pp. xvi. 304. *Trübner & Co.: London*, 1868. 8°. [*Théâtre français moderne.* vol. 6.] **11735. bbb. 2.**

BARRIÈRE (Théodore) and **CAPENDU** (Ernest)

—— *Οἱ Κουτοπονηροι. Κωμωδια εἰς πραξεις τεσσαρας . . . Κατα μεταφρασιν Ἀγγελου Βλαχου.* pp. 264. *Ἐν Ἀθηναις*, 1906. 8°. [*Βιβλιοθηκη Μαρασλη, etc.* no. 328.] **12207. s. 56.**

—— L'Héritage de Monsieur Plumet. Comédie en quatre actes. pp. 147. *Paris*, 1858. 8°. **11739. c. 14. (1.)**

BARRIÈRE (Théodore) and **CARRÉ** (Michel)

—— Un Duel chez Ninon, comédie-vaudeville en un acte, *etc.* pp. 36. *Paris*, 1849. 8°. [*Bibliothèque dramatique, etc.* tom. 21.] **2296. b. 21.**

—— La Plus belle nuit de la vie, vaudeville en un acte, *etc.* pp. 29. *Paris*, 1850. 8°. [*Bibliothèque dramatique, etc.* tom. 31.] **2296. b. 31.**

BARRIÈRE (Théodore) and **CRISAFULLI** (Henri)

—— Le Démon du jeu. Comédie en cinq actes. Deuxième édition. pp. 162. *Paris*, 1864. 8°. **11739. aa. 38.**

BARRIÈRE (Théodore) and **DAVYL** (Louis Poupart)

—— Le Gascon. Drame en cinq actes, *etc.* pp. 159. *Paris*, 1878. 8°. **11740. b. 12. (5.)**

BARRIÈRE (Théodore) and **DECOURCELLE** (Adrien) Les Douze travaux d'Hercule, comédie en deux actes mêlée de chant, *etc.* pp. 72. [*Paris*, 1849.] 8°. [*Bibliothèque dramatique, etc.* tom. 16.] **2296. b. 16.**

—— L'Enseignement mutuel, vaudeville en un acte. pp. 27. *Paris*, 1851. 8°. [*Théâtre choisi des auteurs contemporains.* tom. 3.] **2296. a. 2.**

—— [Another edition.] pp. 10. 1853. *See* France. [*Appendix.—Literature, etc.*] La France dramatique, *etc.* tom. 22. 1841, *etc.* 8°. **2296. f. 22.**

—— Un Monsieur qui suit les femmes, comédie-vaudeville en deux actes. pp. 59. *Paris*, [1850?] [*Bibliothèque dramatique, etc.* tom. 31.] **2296. b. 31.**

—— [Another edition.] pp. 17. 1860. *See* Théâtre. Théâtre contemporain illustré. liv. 64, 65. [1852, *etc.*] fol. **2296. h.**

—— Monsieur mon fils, comédie-vaudeville en deux actes, *etc.* pp. 54. *Paris*, 1854. 8°. [*Bibliothèque dramatique, etc.* tom. 62.] **2296. c. 31.**

—— [Another edition.] pp. 15. 1860. *See* Théâtre. Théâtre contemporain illustré. liv. 401, 402. [1852, *etc.*] fol. **2296. h.**

—— [Un Monsieur qui suit les femmes.] Kensington Gardens, or, "Quite a ladies' man." A comedy . . . Adapted from the French. By R. B. Brough. pp. 35. *London*, [1871?] 12°. [*Lacy's Acting Edition of Plays, etc.* vol. 88.] **2304. g. 6.**

BARRIÈRE (Théodore) and **FAUCHERY** (Antoine)

—— Calino, charge d'atelier, *etc.* [A comedy.] pp. 38. *Paris*, 1856. 8°. [*Bibliothèque dramatique, etc.* tom. 71.] **2296. d. 9.**

BARRIÈRE (Théodore) and **FOURNIER** (Marc)

—— Manon Lescaut, drame en cinq actes mêlé de chants, *etc.* pp. 97. *Paris*, 1854. 8°. [*Bibliothèque dramatique, etc.* tom. 35.] **2296. c. 4.**

—— [Another edition.] pp. 28. 1854. *See* Théâtre. Théâtre contemporain illustré. liv. 118, 119. [1852, *etc.*] fol. **2296. h.**

BARRIÈRE (THÉODORE) and **GONDINET** (EDMOND)

—— A Linnet's Head. Piece in three acts. [From "Tête de linotte," by T. Barrière and E. Gondinet.] pp. 82. [1883.] 8°. *See* LINNET. **11739**. de. **9**. (**4**.)

BARRIÈRE (THÉODORE) and **JAIME** (ADOLPHE)

—— L'Âne mort, drame en 5 actes, *etc.* pp. 84. *Paris*, 1853. 8°. [*Bibliothèque dramatique, etc.* tom. 52.] **2296**. c. **21**.

—— La Boisière, drame en cinq actes, *etc.* pp. 114. *Paris*, 1853. 8°. [*Bibliothèque dramatique, etc.* tom. 49.] **2296**. c. **18**.

—— [Another edition.] pp. 32. 1854. *See* THÉÂTRE. Théâtre contemporain illustré. liv. 136. 137. [1852, *etc.*] fol. **2296**. h.

BARRIÈRE (THÉODORE) and **KOCK** (HENRI DE)

—— Les Grands siècles, pièce en trois actes, *etc.* pp. 42. 1856. *See* THÉÂTRE. Théâtre contemporain illustré. liv. 191, 192. [1852, *etc.*] fol. **2296**. h.

—— L'Histoire de Paris, trois actes, *etc.* pp. 40. 1856. *See* THÉÂTRE. Théâtre contemporain illustré. liv. 186, 187. [1852.] fol. **2296**. h.

—— La Maison du Pont Notre-Dame. Drame en cinq actes *etc.* pp. 117. *Paris*, 1860. 8°. [*Bibliothèque dramatique, etc.* tom. 91.] **2296**. d. **29**.

—— [Another edition.] pp. 34. 1862. *See* THÉÂTRE. Théâtre contemporain illustré. liv. 521, 522. [1852, *etc.*] fol. **2269**. h.

—— The House on the Bridge of Notre Dame. A drama, in three acts. Adapted from the French . . . by Colin Hazlewood. pp. 40. *London*, [1861.] 12°. [*Lacy's Acting Edition of Plays, etc.* vol. 50.] **2304**. e. **24**.

—— The Old House on the Bridge of Notre Dame. A drama in three acts. Adapted from the French. pp. 47. *London*, [1861.] 12°. [*Lacy's Acting Edition of Plays, etc.* vol. 50.] **2304**. e. **24**.

BARRIÈRE (THÉODORE) and **LORIN** (JULES)

—— Le Piano de Berthe, comédie mêlée de chant en un acte, *etc.* pp. 36. *Paris*, 1854. 8°. [*Bibliothèque dramatique, etc.* tom. 41.] **2296**. c. **10**.

—— Quand on veut tuer son chien . . . Proverbe en un acte, *etc.* pp. 40. *Paris*, 1854. 8°. [*Bibliothèque dramatique, etc.* tom. 51.] **2296**. c. **20**.

BARRIÈRE (THÉODORE) and **MURGER** (HENRY)

—— Le Vie de Bohème, pièce en cinq actes, mêlée de chants, *etc.* pp. 116. *Paris*, 1849. 8°. [*Bibliothèque dramatique, etc.* tom. 24.] **2296**. b. **24**.

—— [Another edition.] pp. 32. 1857. *See* THÉÂTRE. Théâtre contemporain illustré. liv. 26. 27. [1852, *etc.*] fol. **2296**. h.

—— [Another edition.] 1873. *See* CHEFS-D'ŒUVRE. Chefs-d'œuvre du théâtre moderne. tom. 2. 1873, *etc.* fol. **11737**. i. **4**.

—— *See* GIACOSA (G.) and ILLICA (L.) La Vie de Bohème. Comédie lyrique . . . d'après Th. Barrière et H. Murger, *etc.* 1898. 12°. **11740**. ee. **32**.

—— Une Petite fille de la Grande Armée. Comédie-vaudeville en deux actes, *etc.* pp. 24. *Paris*, 1852. 8°. **11739**. g. **60**.

BARRIÈRE (THÉODORE) and **PLOUVIER** (ÉDOUARD)

—— L'Ange de minuit. Drame en six actes, *etc.* pp. 27. 1862. *See* THÉÂTRE. Théâtre contemporain illustré. liv. 558, 559. [1852, *etc.*] fol. **2296**. h.

—— The Angel of Midnight. A legend of terror, in three acts. From the French . . . adpated by W. E. Suter and T. H. Lacy. pp. 56. *London*, [1861.] 12°. [*Lacy's Acting Edition of Plays, etc.* vol. 51.] **2304**. e. **25**.

—— L'Outrage. Drame en cinq actes. pp. 103. *Paris*, 1859. 8°. **11739**. b. **25**. (**1**.)

—— [Another edition.] pp. 24. *Paris*, [1859?] fol. **11737**. i. **11**.

BARRIÈRE (THÉODORE) and **SARDOU** (VICTORIEN)

—— Les Gens nerveux. Comédie en trois actes. pp. 116. *Paris*, 1860. 8°. **11739**. aa. **17**.

BARRIÈRE (THÉODORE) and **SÉJOUR** (VICTOR)

—— Les Enfants de la louve. Drame en cinq actes et un prologue. pp. 147. *Paris*, 1865. 8°. **11739**. bb. **20**. (**3**.)

BARRIÈRE (THÉODORE) and **SUPERDAC** (AUGUSTE)

—— Les Métamorphoses de Jeannette, vaudeville en un acte, *etc.* pp. 36. [1850.] 8°. [*Bibliothèque dramatique, etc.* tom. 25.] **2296**. b. **25**.

BARRIÈRE (THÉODORE) and **TAILLADE** ( )

—— Le Château des Ambrières, drame en cinq actes, *etc.* pp. 69. *Paris*, 1857. 8°. [*Bibliothèque dramatique, etc.* tom. 74.] **2296**. d. **12**.

—— [Another edition.] *See* THÉÂTRE. pp. 20. 1857. Théâtre contemporain illustré. liv. 263, 264. [1852, *etc.*] fol. **2296**. h.

BARRIÈRE (THÉODORE) and **THIBOUST** (LAMBERT)

—— Aux crochets d'un gendre. Comédie en quatre actes. pp. 160. *Paris*, 1864. 8°. **11739**. b. **36**.

—— Le Chic. Comédie en trois actes. pp. 95. *Paris*, 1866. 8°. **11737**. bb. **17**.

—— Une Corneille qui abat des noix. Comédie en trois actes. pp. 108. *Paris*, 1862. 8°. **11739**. aaa. **20**. (**1**.)

—— Une Femme dans ma fontaine, vaudeville en un acte, *etc.* pp. 32. *Paris*, 1854. 8°. [*Bibliothèque dramatique, etc.* tom. 50.] **2296**. c. **19**.

—— Les Filles de marbre, drame en cinq actes, *etc.* pp. 76. *Paris*, 1853. 8°. [*Bibliothèque dramatique, etc.* tom. 51.] **2296**. c. **20**.

—— [Another edition.] pp. 21. 1858. *See* THÉÂTRE. Théâtre contemporain illustré. liv. 316, 317. [1852, *etc.*] fol. **2296**. h.

—— The Marble Heart; or, the Sculptor's dream. [Adapted from the French play of Barrière and Thiboust.] By Charles Selby. pp. 54. [1854.] 12°. [*Lacy's Acting Edition of Plays, etc.* vol. 15.] *See* SELBY (Charles) **2304**. d. **19**.

—— [Les Filles de marbre.] Srdce Kamenná. Činohra v pěti jednáních . . . Přeložil A. Pulda. Velbloud. Veselohra . . . Dle anglického vzdělal V. Drost. Přeložila E. Pešková. pp. 80. *v Praze*, [1877.] 8°. [*Divadelní Ochotník . . . Nové sbírký sv.* 153.] **11758**. p. **18**. (**3**.)

BARRIÈRE (THÉODORE) and **THIBOUST** (LAMBERT)

—— L'Infortunée Caroline. Comédie en trois actes, mêlée de couplets. pp. 85. *Paris*, 1864. 8°. **11737. aaa. 40. (1.)**

—— Romantic Caroline. A farcical comedy in one act. Founded upon the three acts comedy of Barrière and Thiboust by Joseph Hatton. pp. 32. *Robson & Sons: London*, [1874.] 8°. **11781. d. 29. (11.)**

—— Les Ivresses, ou la chanson de l'amour. Comédie en quatre actes. pp. 164. *Paris*, 1863. 8°. **11739. aa. 28.**

—— Les Jocrisses de l'amour. Comédie en trois actes. pp. 121. *Paris*, 1865. 8°. **11739. bbb. 13. (2.)**

—— Deuxième édition. pp. 121. *Paris*, 1865. 8°. **11739. bbb. 13. (3.)**

BARRIÈRE-FLAVY (C.) *See* CINTEGABELLE. Cintegabelle au xve siècle. Document inédit. ([Edited by] C. Barrière Flavy.) 1888. 8°. **10105. dd. 5. (2.)**

—— *See* FOIX. Censier du pays de Foix à la fin du XIVe siècle . . . [Edited by] C. Barrière Flavy. 1898. 8°. **010168. ff. 12.**

—— Les Arts industriels des peuples barbares de la Gaule du vme au VIIIme siècle. (Planches et légendes.) 3 tom. *Toulouse, Paris*, 1901. fol. **7702. s. 1.**

—— Le Capitaine Jean Le Comte, gouverneur du château et de la ville de Foix, 1584–1600. Épisode des guerres de la ligue et de religion dans le comté de Foix. Extrait du Bulletin périodique de la Société Ariégeoise des Sciences, Lettres et Arts, *etc.* pp. 63. *Foix*, 1906. 8°. **10600. g. 13. (5.)**

—— Dénombrement du comté de Foix sous Louis XIV, 1670–1674. Étude . . . suivie du texte du dénombrement. pp. xxxvii. 166. *Toulouse*, 1889. 8°. **010171. m. 29.**

—— Histoire de la ville et de la châtellenie de Saverdun . . . Avec . . . des plans, *etc.* pp. xvi. 334. *Toulouse, Paris*, [1891.] 8°. **10174. g. 23.**

BARRIÉS (CARL) Die Cholera morbus. Ueber ihre Entstehung, Ausbildung, Zeugung und Ansteckungsfähigkeit, mit Bezug auf alle übrigen ansteckenden Krankheiten . . . . nebst einem Anhange über die Mängel des Armenwesens, durch welche besonders ansteckende Krankheiten begünstigt . . . werden, *etc.* pp. ix. 238. 36. pl. II. *Hamburg*, 1831. 8°. **1175. h. 18.**

—— Peter Krukenberg . . . Biographische Skizze und Charakteristik seiner Lehrthätigkeit. pp. 59. *Halle*, 1866. 8°. **10707. cc. 40. (7.)**

BARRIÉ Y AGÜERO (JUAN) Biografia del Excmo. Señor Don Manuel de Enna. pp. 154. *Madrid*, 1851. 8°. **10632. bb. 20.**

BARRIFFE (WILLIAM) Mars, his Triumph. Or, the Description of an Exercise performed the XVIII. of October, 1638. in Merchant-Taylors Hall by certain Gentlemen of the Artillery Garden, London. pp. 48. *I. L. [John Legatt] for Ralph Mab: London*, 1639. 4°. **8828. ee. 3.**
A portrait of Major-General Lambert, by B. Moncornet, is inserted.

—— [Another edition.] pp. 24. *John Dawson: London*, 1645. 4°. **9930. f. 61.**
Pt. 2 of an edition, probably the fifth, of "Military Discipline."

—— Military Discipline: or the Yong Artillery Man. Wherein is discoursed and showne the postures both of musket and pike . . . With the way to draw up the Swedish Brigade. The second edition, newly revised and much inlarged. pp. 377. *R. O. [Richard Oulton] for Ralph Mab: London*, 1639. 4°. **8828. ee. 4.**

BARRIFFE (WILLIAM)

—— [Another edition.] Militarie Discipline . . . As also, Mars his triumph. And . . . Some Brief Instructions for the exercising of the Cavalry . . . The sixth edition, newly revised and enlarged. [With plates and folding leaves.] 3 pt. *By Gartrude Dawson: London*, 1661. 4°. **717. g. 34.**

—— The third edition, newly revised and much inlarged. [With a plate and folding leaves.] pp. 421. *By Iohn Dawson, sold by Andrew Crooke: London*, 1643. 4°. **717. g. 33.**

BARRIGA (JOAQUIN MARIA) [For official documents issued by J. M. Barriga as Secretary of War for New Granada.] *See* NEW GRANADA, *Republic of.—Despacho de Guerra.*

BARRIGA (JUAN AGUSTÍN) Discursos literarios y Notas críticas. pp. 278. *Santiago de Chile*, 1915. 8°. **011853. pp. 26.**

BARRIGA (VALERIO FRANCISCO) *See* OBANDO (J. M.) *President of the Republic of New Granada.* Causa de responsabilidad contra el ciudadano presidente de la republica. (Jeneral J. M. Obando i los ex-secretarios de gobierno i de guerra señores A. del Real i V. F. Barriga.) 1855. 8°. **8179. g. 48.**

—— [For official documents issued by V. F. Barriga as Secretary of War for New Granada:] *See* NEW GRANADA, *Republic of.—Despacho de Guerra.*

BARRIGA (VICTOR M.)

—— *See* MANUEL, *Fray, de la Orden de Ntra. Sra. de la Merced de la Provincia de Lima.* Mística flor del sol, *etc.* [Edited by V. M. Barriga.] 1947. 8°. **11453. d. 17.**

—— *See* VALLE GOICOCHEA (L.) Bibliografía de obras y artículos publicados por el M.R.P. Fr. Víctor M. Barriga. 1947. 8°. **11925. g. 26.**

—— Arequipa y sus blasones. [Documents, edited by V. M. Barriga.] pp. 133. *Arequipa*, 1940. 8°. **9918. l. 16.**
Biblioteca "Arequipa." tom. 3.

—— Documentos para la historia de Arequipa. *Arequipa*, 1939– . 8°. **W.P. c. 547.**
Biblioteca "Arequipa." tom. 1, *etc.*

—— Documentos para la historia de la Universidad de Arequipa, 1765–1828. Documentos de las Bibliotecas Nacionales de Madrid y del Perú. (Separata de la "Revista Universitaria".) [Edited by V. M. Barriga.] pp. 303. *Arequipa*, 1953. 8°. **8385. f. 41.**
Biblioteca "Arequipa". tom. 9.

—— Memorias para la historia de Arequipa, *etc.* 4 tom. *Arequipa*, 1941–52. 8°. **10164. f. 20.**
Biblioteca "Arequipa." tom. 4–6, 8.

—— Los Mercedarios en el Perú en el siglo XVI. Documentos inéditos del Archivo General de Indias, *etc.* [Edited by V. M. Barriga.] 5 vol. *Roma*, 1933–54. 8°. **4633. r. 1.**
Vol. 2–5 were published in Arequipa.

—— Mercedarios ilustres en el Perú, *etc.* *Arequipa*, 1943– 8°. **W.P.c.551.**

—— El Templo de la Merced de Lima. Documentos para la historia del arte. [With plates.] pp. 429. *Arequipa*, 1944. 8°. **07822. de. 36.**

—— Los Terremotos en Arequipa, 1582–1868. Documentos de los Archivos de Arequipa y de Sevilla. [Edited by V. M. Barriga.] pp. ix. 426. *Arequipa*, 1951. 8°. **10163. g. 4.**
Biblioteca "Arequipa." tom. 7.

BARRIGA DE MONTVALON (ANDREAS) *See* BARRIGUE DE MONTVALON.

BARRIGA VILLALBA (ANTONIO MARÍA)

—— *See* OTERO MUÑOZ (G.) Esmeraldas de Colombia. (2. Estudio científico. Por el Profesor A. M. Barriga Villalba.) 1948. 8°. **7107**. ee. **32**.

—— Estudio sobre las posibilidades de establecer, con la ayuda oficial, la fabricación de medicinas y drogas que se importan, *etc.* *In:* COLOMBIA. [Republic of Colombia, 1886– .]—*Congreso.* [*Proyectos de Ley.*] Proyecto de ley y exposición de motivos sobre grande y pequeña industria química. 1938. 8°. L.A.S. **381/12**. (**18**.)

BARRIGER (JOHN WALKER) Legislative History of the Subsistence Department of the United States Army from June 16, 1775 to August 15, 1876 . . . Second edition. pp. 113. xv. 1877. 8°. *See* UNITED STATES OF AMERICA.—*Department of War.*—*Office of the Commissary-General of Subsistence.* A.S. **623**.

BARRIGUE DE FONTAINIEU (G. de) *See* TIRUVAḶḶAVAR. Le Livre de l'amour . . . Traduit . . . par G. de Barrigue de Fontainieu. 1889. 8°. **14172**. a. **38**.

BARRIGUE DE MONTVALON (ANDRÉ) [For editions of the "Mémoires présentées au Roi par deux magistrats du Parlement d'Aix," i.e. A. J. B. de Boyer, Marquis d'Aguilles and A. Barrigue de Montvalon, and publications relating thereto :] *See* BOYER (Alexandre J. B. de) *Marquis d'Aguilles.* **4091**. bb. **40**. (**24**.)

—— Epitome juris et legum Romanarum, frequentioris usus juxta seriem Digestorum, cum brevissimis additionibus et notis, tam ex pragmaticis quam ex usu forensi selectis. pp. xii. 537. 61. *Tolosæ*, 1786. 12°. **878**. c. **1**.

—— Traité des successions, conformément au droit romain, et aux ordonnances du royaume . . . Nouvelle édition. 2 tom. *Aix*, 1786. 4°. **496**. f. **15**, **16**.

BARRIKADENKAEMPFER. Die Barikadenkämpfer an die National-Versammlung. [Revolutionary verses.] *Berlin*, 1848. *s. sh.* 8°. **1851**. c. **6**. (**10**.)

BARRIL (JEHAN) À très illustre et puissante Princesse et dame, Madame Margueritte de France, Royne de Nauarre . . . par vng vostre tres hũble seruiteur, Jehan Barril marchant de Thoulouze par vng vray zelle presente, salut & paix. [A book of devotions.] [*N. Viellard ?*]: *Tholose*, 1535. 4°. **8415**. d. **9**.

BARRILI (ANTON GIULIO) *See* HOLST (H. P.) A-ing-fo-hi. Lustspiel . . . Frei nach Holst und Barrili, *etc.* [1881.] 16°. **012207**. f. **13**. (**10**.)

—— *See* HORATIUS FLACCUS (Q.) [*Carmina et Epodi.—Italian, Genoese dialect.*] Odi ed Epodi . . . Con prefazion de A. G. Barrili. 1899. 8°. **11386**. e. **23**.

—— *See* IMPERIALE (G. V.) De' Giornali di Gio. Vincenzo Imperiale . . . Anno primo. Con prefazione e note di A. G. Barrili. 1898. 8°. [*Atti della Società Ligure di Storia Patria.* vol. 29.] Ac. **6510**.

—— *See* IMPERIALE (G. V.) Viaggi di Gian Vincenzo Imperiale. Con prefazione e note di A. G. Barrili. 1898. 8°. [*Atti della Società Ligure di Storia Patria.* vol. 29.] Ac. **6510**.

—— *See* MAMELI DE' MANNELLI (G. R. G.) Scritti editi e inediti . . . Ordinati e publicati . . . a cura di A. G. Barrili. 1902. 8°. **12227**. g. **3**.

—— *See* PERTUSIO (M.) La Vita e gli scritti di Giovanni Ruffini. Con prefazione di A. G. Barrili. 1908. 8°. **10633**. f. **23**.

BARRILI (ANTON GIULIO)

—— *See* VENUS. Studio critico intorno al Pervigilium Veneris con versione di A. G. Barrili, *etc.* 1889. 8°. **11312**. q. **4**. (**2**.)

—— I Tre capolavori giovanili di A. G. Barrili. Capitan Dodèro, Santa Cecilia, Il Libro nero. Seconda edizione . . . preceduta da biografia [by Benedetto Croce] e ritratto dell' autore. pp. xix. 313. *Milano*, 1909. 8°. **12227**. c. **3**.

—— Amori alla macchia. Novella. pp. 342. *Milano*, 1885 [1884]. 8°. **12471**. e. **36**.

—— Amori antichi. Seconda edizione. pp. vii. 412. *Milano*, 1891. 8°. **12471**. e. **42**.

—— L'Anello di Salomone. Racconto. pp. 349. *Milano*, 1883. 8°. **12471**. f. **40**.

—— Arrigo il Savio. Racconto. Seconda edizione. pp. 300. *Milano*, 1886. 8°. **12471**. g. **37**.

—— La Bella Graziana. Romanzo . . . Seconda edizione. pp. 372. *Milano*, 1892. 8°. **12471**. h. **30**.

—— Canzoni al vento. [Edited by Pier Giulio Breschi.] pp. xii. 250. *Milano*, 1911. 8°. **11436**. c. **55**.

—— The Adventures of Captain Dodèro . . . (Capitan Dodèro.) Translated and annotated by H. B. Cotterill. *Ital. & Eng.* pp. 63. *G. G. Harrap & Co.: London; Brentano's: New York*, [1920.] 8°. [*Harrap's Bilingual Series.*] **012901**. e. **2/26**.

—— Casa Polidori. Romanza. Seconda edizione. pp. 358. *Milano*, 1886. 8°. **12471**. d. **24**.

—— Castel Gavone. Storia del secolo XV. pp. 318. *Milano*, 1875. 8°. **12471**. ee. **12**.

—— La Castellana. Romanzo. pp. 350. *Milano*, 1894. 8°. **12470**. d. **33**.

—— Come un sogno. Racconto. (Seconda edizione.) pp. 223. *Milano*, 1875. 8°. **12471**. bbb. **23**.

—— Quarta edizione. pp. 215. *Milano*, 1879. 8°. **12471** c 5.

—— Le Confessioni di Fra Gualberto. Storia del secolo XV. Seconda edizione. pp. 166. *Milano*, 1873. 8°. **12471**. b. 15.

—— La Conquista d'Alessandro. Studio dal vero. pp. 427. *Milano*, 1879. 8°. **12471**. e. 4.

—— Il Conte rosso. Romanzo . . . Seconda edizione. pp. 378. *Milano*, 1884. 8°. **12471**. cc. **38**.

—— Cristoforo Colombo. Orazione, *etc.* pp. 20. *Genova*, 1892. 8°. **10601**. ff. **10**. (**5**.)

—— Cuor di ferro e cuor d'oro. Romanzo . . . Seconda edizione, riveduta, *etc.* pp. 563. *Milano*, 1879. 8°. **12471**. ee. **27**.

—— [Cuor di ferro.] A Noble Kinsman. A novel . . . Translated . . . by H. A. Martin. 2 vol. *T. Fisher Unwin: London*, 1885. 8°. **12471**. g. 26.

—— Da Virgilio a Dante. Lezioni universitarie. pp. 443. *Genova*, 1892. 8°. **011840**. k. **71**.

—— Dalla rupe. Novella. Seconda edizione. pp. 244. *Milano*, 1884. 8°. **12470**. ee. **12**.

—— Il Dantino. Romanzo. pp. 314. *Milano*, 1888. 8°. **12471**. d. 36.

—— Diamante nero. Romanzo. pp. 388. *Milano*, 1897. 8°. **12471**. k. **12**.

—— [Another copy.] **12471**. s. 27.

BARRILI (Anton Giulio)

—— Diana degli Embriaci. Storia del xii secolo. pp. 331. *Milano*, 1877. 8°. **12471**. c. **13**.

—— La Donna di picche. Romanzo. pp. 390. *Milano*, 1880. 8°. **12471**. e. **12**.

—— Le Due Beatrici. pp. viii. 378. *Milano*, 1892. 8°. **12471**. h. **32**.

—— [Another edition.] pp. viii. 378. *Milano*, 1901. 8°. **12470**. s. **6**.

—— I Figli del cielo. Romanzo colombiano. pp. 387. *Milano*, 1893. 8°. **12471**. h. **28**.

—— La Figlia del re. Romanzo. pp. 392. *Roma*, 1894. 8°. **12471**. b. **58**.

—— Fior d'oro. Romanzo colombiano. pp. 339. *Milano*, 1895. 8°. **12471**. i. **13**.

—— Un Giudizio di Dio. Romanzo. pp. 430. *Milano*, 1887. 8°. **12471**. dd. **2**.

—— Giuseppe Verdi. Vita e opere. pp. 156. *Genova*, 1892. 8°. Hirsch **4839**.

—— Giuseppe Verdi, vita e opere. Seconda edizione. pp. 156. *Genova*, 1892. 8°. **10629**. d. **18**.

—— La Legge Oppia. Commedia togata in tre atti. pp. 119. *Genova*, 1873. 8°. **11715**. e. **12**.

—— Il Lettore della principessa. Romanzo . . . Seconda edizione. pp. 366. *Milano*, 1885. 8°. **12471**. c. **45**.

—— The Princess's Private Secretary . . . Translated . . . by . . . Judge Stephen. pp. viii. 335. *Digby, Long & Co.: London*, 1893. 8°. **12471**. ccc. **40**.

—— Monsù Tomè. Racconto. pp. 349. *Milano*, 1885. 18°. **12471**. f. **51**.

—— La Montanara. Racconto. pp. 413. *Milano*, 1886. 8°. **12471**. g. **31**.

—— Napoleone. Conferenza. *See* Italian Life. La Vita italiana durante la Rivoluzione francese, *etc.* 1897. 8°. **9165**. a. **20**.

—— Una Notte d'estate, *etc.* pp. 172. *Roma*, 1897. 8°. **12471**. de. **7**.

—— O tutto o nulla. Romanzo. pp. 376. *Milano*, 1881. 8°. **12471**. e. **26**.

—— Per il xxv. anniversario di Roma capitale, 1895. Con Garibaldi alle porte di Roma, 1867. Ricordi e note. pp. 288. *Milano*, [1895.] 8°. **9150**. a. **35**.

—— Il Prato maledetto. Storia del x. secolo. pp. 353. *Milano*, 1896. 8°. **12471**. i. **26**

—— Il Ponte del Paradiso. Racconto. pp. 335. *Milano*, 1904. 8°. **12471**. t. **11**.

—— Raggio di Dio. Romanzo. pp. 371. *Milano*, 1899. 8°. **12471**. l. **9**.

—— Re di cuori. Romanzo. pp. 270. *Milano*, 1912. 8°. **12470**. ee. **8**.

—— Il Rinnovamento letterario italiano. Lezioni universitarie. pp. 371. *Genova*, 1890. 8°. **011840**. f. **70**.

—— Il Ritratto del diavolo. Romanzo. pp. 313. *Milano*, 1882. 8°. **12471**. bbb. **41**.

—— The Devil's Portrait . . . Translated . . . by E. Wodehouse. 2 vol. *Remington & Co.: London*, 1885. 8°. **12619**. w. **7**.

—— [Another edition.] pp. 312. *W. S. Gottsberger: New York*, 1885. 8°. **12471**. ccc. **34**.

BARRILI (Anton Giulio)

—— Rosa di Gerico. Romanzo. pp. 351. *Milano*, 1891. 8°. **12471**. h. **24**.

—— I Rossi e i Neri. Romanzo . . . Seconda edizione. 2 vol. *Milano*, 1881. 8°. **12470**. ccc. **31**.

—— Scudi e corone. Romanzo. pp. 379. *Milano*, 1890. 8°. **12489**. k. **26**.

—— Semiramide. Racconto babilonese. pp. 381. *Milano*, 1873. 8°. **12471**. bbb. **10**.

—— La Signora Àutari. Storia inverisimile. pp. 271. *Milano*, 1889. 8°. **12470**. ee. **33**.

—— La Sirena. Storia vera. pp. 192. *Roma*, 1883. 8°. **12471**. cc. **37**.

—— Sorrisi di gioventù. Ricordi e note. pp. vii. 296. *Milano*, 1899. 8°. **012357**. de. **17**.

—— La Spada di fuoco. Racconto. pp. 373. *Milano*, 1887. 8°. **12471**. d. **28**.

—— Terra vergine. Romanzo colombiano. pp. 374. *Milano*, 1892. 8°. **12471**. h. **29**.

—— Il Tesoro di Golconda. Racconto. pp. 344. *Milano*, 1879. 8°. **12471**. e. **3**.

—— Tizio Caio Sempronio. Storia mezzo romana . . . Seconda edizione, *etc.* pp. 333. *Milano*, 1879. 8°. **12471**. e. **1**.

—— Tra cielo e terra. Romanzo. pp. 355. *Genova*, 1894. 8°. **12471**. h. **36**.

—— [L'Undecimo comandamento.] The Eleventh Commandment. A romance . . . From the Italian by Clara Bell, *etc.* pp. 377. *W. S. Gottsberger: New York*, 1882. 8°. **12471**. b. **48**.

—— The Eleventh Commandment . . . Authorised translation from the Italian. 2 vol. *Remington & Co.: London*, 1883. 8°. **12471**. f. **44**.

—— Uomini e bestie. Racconti d'estate, *etc.* pp. 317. *Milano*, 1886. 8°. **12471**. d. **29**.

—— Val d'Olivi. Racconto . . . Seconda edizione. pp. 303. *Milano*, 1879. 8°. **12471**. e. **2**.

—— Val d'Olivi . . . Ins Deutsche übertragen von Carl Reissner. pp. 281. *Leipzig*, 1877. 8°. [*Italienische Novellisten, etc.* Bd. 2.] **12471**. cc. **48**.

—— Vittor Hugo. Saggi critici di A. G. Barrili ed E. Panzacchi. Con un' appendice contenente le poesie scelte di Vittor Hugo, *etc.* pp. lx. 145. *Milano*, 1885. 8°. **11483**. cc. **13**.

—— Voci del passato. Discorsi e conferenze . . . 1881–1907. pp. vii. 338. *Milano*, 1909. 8°. **012301**. eee. **5**.

BARRILLEAU (C. Ch.) De l'abus des astringens; thèse, *etc.* pp. 27. *Paris*, 1813. 4°. **1182**. i. **11**. **(26.)**

BARRILLEAU (Georges)

—— *See* Ducrocq (T.) *Professeur à la Faculté de Droit de Paris.* Cours de droit administratif, *etc.* (tom. 6 par T. Ducrocq et G. Barrilleau. 1905.) 1897, *etc.* 8°. **2228**. a. **1**.

BARRILLIET (François Charles Théodore) Faculté de Droit de Paris. Thèse pour la licence. (Jus romanum. De litterarum obligatione et fide instrumentorum.—Droit français. Des effets de commerce.) pp. 90. *Paris*, 1857. 8°. **5406**. aa. **1**. **(21.)**

BARRILLON (François Guillaume) Des systèmes de concession des chemins de fer, dans leurs rapports avec les intérêts de l'état. pp. 64. *Lyon*, 1844. 8°. **1396**. i. 24. (4.)

BARRILLON (François Guillaume)

—— Politique de la France et de l'humanité dans le conflit américain. pp. 40. *Paris*, 1861. 8°. **8177.** e. **31.** (**1.**)

—— Utilité et tracé d'un chemin de fer de Lyon à Genève, Grenoble et Chambéry. Rapport présenté au Conseil municipal de la ville de Lyon, par M. Barrillon, au nom d'une commission spéciale . . . précédé du rapport présenté par M. le maire au Conseil municipal dans la séance du 20 février 1845, sur un projet de chemin de fer de Lyon à Genève, par la vallée du Rhône, avec embranchement sur Grenoble et Chambéry. [With a map and plans.] pp. 42. *Lyon*, 1845. 8°. **1396.** i. **24.** (**5.**)

BARRILLON (G.) Un Drame en Amérique. 2 vol. *Paris*, 1879. 12°. **12517.** aaa. **13.**

BARRILLON (Jean) Journal de Jean Barrillon, Secrétaire du Chancelier Duprat, 1515–1521. Publié pour la première fois . . . par Pierre de Vaissière. 2 tom. 1897, 99. 8°. *See* Paris.—*Société de l'Histoire de France.* Ac. **6884/89.**

BARRILLON (P.) Le Port du Rouen et la Seine maritime en 1921. [With a map.] pp. 62. *Rouen*, 1921. 8°. **08235.** b. **42.**

BARRILLON (Paul) *Marquis de Branges, French Ambassador to England.* *See* Barillon.

BARRILLOT (Anatole) Entretiens ecclésiastiques sur la piété nécessaire au prêtre dans toutes les positions du ministère pastoral, suivis de quelques pieux souvenirs de la tonsure et de chaque ordre. pp. 336. *Paris*, 1848. 12°. **4071.** c. **5.**

BARRILLOT (François) Le Concile œcuménique. Lettre de Jean Populus à Pie ix. Avant-propos par Eugène Chatelain. pp. 36. *Paris*, 1870. 8°. **3900.** e. **3.** (**2.**)

—— Lamartine devant le tribunal du peuple, par un républicain de la veille. pp. 32. *Paris*, [1848.] 8° **8052.** d. **3.**

—— La Mascarde humaine. Satires de mœurs du xixe siècle. [In verse.] pp. 300. *Paris*, 1863. 12°. **11481.** bbb. **4.**

—— Le Myosotis. Drame en un acte, en vers, *etc.* pp. 36. *Paris*, 1861. 12°. **11739.** aaa. **8.** (**12.**)

—— Un Portrait de maître. Comédie en un acte et en vers, *etc.* pp. 36. *Paris*, 1859. 8°. **11739.** c. **14.** (**4.**)

—— Triboulet à Napoleon iii. [A satire in verse.] pp. 32. *Paris*, 1861. 8°. **11481.** f. **37.** (**13.**)

BARRIMORE. *See* Barrymore.

BARRIN (Augustin Félix Élisabeth) *Count de la Galissonnière.*

—— Discours prononcé . . . à l'ouverture de l'Assemblée Générale des Trois États de cette province, le 16 mars 1789. pp. 11. *Angers*, 1789. 8°. **911.** c. **9.** (**2.**)

—— Discours improvisé. [Delivered in the States-General, 6 May 1789, on the verification of the powers of each order.] *See* France. [*Appendix.—History, etc.—Revolution of* 1789.] Collection de pièces intéressantes . . . sur l'histoire de France, *etc.* tom. 9. [1801.] 8°. **1195.** f. **16.**

—— Observations dans la Chambre de la Noblesse, sur la cherté des grains . . . Le 16 juin 1789. pp. 19. *Versailles*, [1789.] 8°. R. **79.** (**1.**)

BARRIN (Augustin Félix Élisabeth) *Count de la Galissonnière.*

—— Observations sur l'établissement proposé d'une milice ou garde-bourgeoise, faites à l'Assemblée nationale . . . juillet 1789. pp. 14. [*Paris*, 1789.] 8°. R. **79.** (**2.**)

—— Vues sur le rapport de M. Mounier, concernant la constitution . . . Juillet 1789. pp. 34. *Versailles*, [1789.] 8°. R. **81.** (**17.**)

—— Motion . . . sur la gabelle. Séance du 16 septembre 1789. pp. 16. *Paris*, [1789.] 8°. R. **79.** (**3.**)

—— Lettre . . . à M. Baudouin. [On the decree of the Assemblée Nationale of 24 Dec. 1789 admitting non-catholics to public appointments.] pp. 3. *Paris*, [1789.] 8°. F.R. **169.** (**6.**)

—— [Another copy.] Lettre . . . à M. Baudouin. *Paris*, [1789.] 8°. R. **79.** (**4.**)

—— Opinion . . . prononcée dans la séance du 14 mars 1790, sur la suppression et le remplacement de la gabelle. pp. 20. [*Paris*, 1790.] 8°. R. **79.** (**5.**)

—— Opinion . . . prononcée, le 20 mai 1790 . . . Sur la question si la nation doit déléguer au Roi, ou au Corps législatif, l'exercice du droit de la guerre et de la paix, ainsi que celui de faire les traités d'alliance et de commerce. pp. 29. *Paris*, [1790.] 8°. R. **79.** (**6.**)

—— Protestation . . . Contre le décret du 19 juin 1790, portant suppression de la noblesse. pp. 11. [*Paris*, 1790.] 8°. R. **79.** (**7.**)

—— Opinion sur les moyens de payer la dette exigible, prononcée . . . le 24 septembre 1790, *etc.* pp. 19. *Paris* [1790.] 8°. R. **79.** (**8.**)

—— Opinion improvisée . . . à l'Assemblée nationale, du 21 octobre 1790. Sur la couleur du pavillon de France. pp. 7. *Paris*, 1790. 8°. R. **79.** (**9.**)

—— Des calomnies politiques. [A reply to an attack by the municipality of Paris on the aristocracy.] pp. 4. [*Paris*, 1791.] 8°. R. **79.** (**24.**)

—— Sur la liberté et la sanction du roi. pp. 8. [*Paris*, 1791.] 8°. R. **79.** (**26.**)

—— Opinion . . . Sur le projet d'organisation de la marine militaire, proposé par le comité de la marine, prononcée le 15 janvier 1791. pp. 14. [*Paris*, 1791.] 8°. R. **79.** (**10.**)

—— [Another issue.] Nouvelle opinion . . . sur le nouveau projet d'organisation de la marine militaire proposé, par le Comité de la marine; prononcée le 14 avril 1791. 1791. *See* France.—*Assemblée Nationale Constituante.* [1789–1791.] Procès-verbal de l'Assemblée . . . Nationale. tom. 52. 1789, *etc.* 8°. **284.** k. **22.**

—— Opinion . . . sur le revenu public produit par la vente du tabac. 12 février 1791. pp. 16. [*Paris*, 1791.] 8°. R. **79.** (**11.**)

—— Opinion . . . sur le projet de loi et le rapport sur la résidence des fonctionnaires publics. Prononcée le 25 février 1791. pp. 16. [*Paris*, 1791.] 8°. R. **79.** (**12.**)

—— Opinion . . . Sur le rapport fait au nom du comité militaire, par M. Dubois de Crancé, sur les invalides. 23 mars 1791. pp. 21. [*Paris*, 1791.] 8°. R. **79.** (**13.**)

—— Déclaration . . . sur les décrets des 28 et 29 mars 1791 (sur la résidence du roi, et sur son abdication présumée), *etc.* pp. 8. [*Paris*, 1791.] 8°. R. **79.** (**15.**)

BARRIN (Augustin Félix Élisabeth) *Count de la Gallissonnière.*

—— Deuxième opinion . . . Sur la résidence des fonctionnaires publics. 28 mars 1791. pp. 16. [*Paris*, 1791.] 8°. R. **79**. (**14**.)

—— Nouvelle opinion . . . sur le nouveau projet de la marine militaire, proposé par le Comité de marine ; prononcée le 14 avril 1791, *etc.* pp. 50. *Paris*, 1791. 8°. R. **79**. (**16**.)

—— Observations improvisées . . . sur l'article XIII qui préjuge la suppression des maîtres-pilotes. Séance du 16 avril 1791. pp. 16. *Paris*, 1791. 8°. R. **79**. (**17**.)

—— Observations sur le rapport des comités, féodal, des domaines, d'agriculture et de commerce concernant le cours des fleuves et des rivières, les isles et alluvions, la pêche, les moulins, usines, bacs, &c. Prononcées . . . le 23 avril 1791. pp. 19. [*Paris*, 1791.] 8°. R. **79**. (**18**.)

—— Opinion . . . sur l'émission proposé de petits assignats de cinq livres. 6 mai 1791. pp. 16. [*Paris*, 1791.] 8°. R. **79**. (**19**.)

—— Opinion . . . sur le droit d'initiative, réclamé par les colonies, pour les loix relatives à l'état des personnes dans les colonies. 13 mai, 1791. pp. 15. [*Paris*, 1791.] 8°. R. **79**. (**20**.)

—— Opinion . . . Sur les baux à convenant, ou domaine congéable de Bretagne, prononcée dans la séance du jeudi 26 mai 1791. pp. 45. [*Paris*, 1791.] 8°. R. **79**. (**21**.)

—— Opinion . . . sur la proposition faite par le comité, de supprimer la faculté d'accorder des lettres de grace, et d'enlever par-là au Roi, la plus belle prérogative de sa couronne. 4 juin, 1791. pp. 8. [*Paris*, 1791.] 8°. R. **79**. (**22**.)

—— Opinion . . . sur la question : Le roi est-il oui ou non, justiciable d'un tribunal quelconque ? 15 juillet 1791. pp. 15. [*Paris*, 1791.] 8°. R. **79**. (**23**.)

—— Réflexions sur le décret rendu en novembre 1791, qui prescrit un serment individuel à tous les prêtres du culte catholique, *etc.* pp. 20. *Paris*, 1791. 8°. R. **79**. (**27**.)

—— Opinion . . . sur l'aliénation proposée des biens domaniaux, ecclésiastiques et autres établissemens de main-morte. [1793 ?] *See* Dugour (A. J.) afterwards Gurov (A. A.) École de politique, *etc.* tom. 12. [1792, *etc.*] 8°. F. **325**.

—— [Another edition.] *See* France. [*Appendix.—History, etc.—Revolution of* 1789.] Collection de pièces intéressantes . . . sur l'histoire de France, *etc.* tom. 12. 1801. 8°. **1195**. f. **17**.

BARRIN (Augustin Félix Élisabeth) *Count de la Gallissonnière*, and **LAPLANCHE** (Jean Guillaume) *Count de Ruillé.*

—— Déclaration sur la constitution françoise. pp. 3. [*Paris*, 1791.] 8°. R. **79**. (**25**.)

BARRIN (Jean) *See* Ovidius Naso (P.) [*Two or more Works.—French.*] Les Épitres amoureues [*sic*] (les Élégies amoureuses) d'Ovide, traduites en françois [by J. Barrin], *etc.* 1702. 8°. **11375**. e. **2**.

—— —— 1704. 12°. **237**. a. **6**.

—— *See* Ovidius Naso (Publius) [*Two or more Works.—French.*] Les Œuvres galantes et amoureuses d'Ovide, contenant . . . Les Epîtres & les Élegies amoureuses [translated by J. Barrin], *etc.* 1763. 12°. **11352**. a. **42**.

BARRIN (Jean)

—— *See* Ovidius Naso (P.) [*Two or more Works.—French.*] Les Œuvres galantes et amoureuses d'Ovide, contenant l'Art d'aimer . . . les Épîtres et les Élégies amoureuses. [The two last translated by J. Barrin.] 1777. 12°. **11355**. a. **5**.

—— *See* Periodical Publications.—*Amsterdam.* Nouvelles de la République des Lettres. [1687–89. By Pierre Bayle, J. Barrin and others.] 1684, *etc.* 12°. P.P. **4261**. h.

—— La Vie de la bienheureuse Françoise d'Amboise, Duchesse de Bretagne. pp. 311. *Rennes*, 1704. 8°. **4864**. bb. **5**.

BARRIN (Roland Michel) *Marquis de la Gallissonnière.*

—— *See* Collection. Collection de pièces originales . . . ou lettres du maréchal de Richelieu . . . du comte de Maillebois et autres, sur l'expédition de Minorque ou de Mahon, en 1756. [1797-98.] 8°. **935**. i. **23**.

—— *See* Duhamel du Monceau (H. L.) Underretning om, hvorledes Træer, perennerende Urter, Fröe, og adskillige andre Naturalier, best kand forsendes til Söes, *etc.* [By H. L. Duhamel du Monceau and R. M. Barrin, but here ascribed to the former alone.] 1760. 8°. B. **654**. (**4**.)

—— *See* Duhamel du Monceau (H. L.) and Barrin (R. M.) Avis pour le transport par mer des arbres. 1753. 12°. **444**. a. **46**.

—— —— 1758. 8°. [*Mémoire instructif sur la manière de rassembler . . . les diverses curiosités, etc.*] **727**. d. **21**.

—— *See* Duhamel du Monceau (H. L.) and Barrin (R. M.) Vorschläge nach welchen der Transport der Bäume . . . über die See zu veranstalten ist, übersetzt [from the work by H. L. Duhamel Du Monceau and R. M. Barrin]. 1756. 8°. B. **628**. (**2**.)

—— *See* Duhamel du Monceau (H. L.) and Barrin (R. M.) Anweisung wie die Bäume . . . und verschiedene andere Seltenheiten der Naturgeschichte über Meer zu verschicken sind. 1761. 8°. [*Jaeger* (*W.*) *Anweisung wie die verschiedenen Seltenheiten der Naturgeschichte . . . zu verschicken sind.*] **973**. i. **2**.

BARRING. Barring o' the Door. The Sea, the Sea. To which is added, March to the battle-field. Go, youth beloved. The Maid of Judah. My wife's dead. Love is like a summer flower. All's well. [Ballads.] *For the Booksellers: Glasgow*, [1830 ?] 16°. **1078**. k. **11**. (**29**.)

—— [Another copy.] **11621**. aaa. **30**. (**22**.)

BARRINGER (Benton Elwood)

—— Student Teaching in Agriculture, *etc.* [A thesis.] pp. xi. 124. *Washington*, 1925. 8°. **08385**. f. **77**.

BARRINGER (Charles Wright) Dissertation sur les systèmes nosologiques et sur la nomenclature médicale. pp. 27. *Paris*, 1860. 4°. [*Collection des thèses soutenues à la Faculté de Médecine de Paris.* An 1860. tom. 1.] **7373**. c. **9**.

BARRINGER (Daniel Moreaux) Meteor Crater, formerly called Coon Mountain or Coon Butte, in Northern Central Arizona. [With maps and illustrations.] pp. 24. pl. XVIII. [1910.] fol. **7105**. i. **22**.

BARRINGER (E. F.) Larkin v Fitzhugh. A mock trial, *etc.* pp. 64. *London, New York*, [1924.] 8°. [*French's Acting Edition.*] **11791**. t. **1**/**20**.

BARRINGER (George A.) Catalogue de l'histoire de l'Amérique. 1903– . fol. *See* Paris.—*Bibliothèque Nationale.* [*Imprimés.*] **11899**. r. **5**.

—— Étude sur l'anglais parlé aux États-Unis. pp. 16. *Paris*, 1874. 8°. [*Actes de la Société Philologique.* tom. 3. no. 6.] Ac. **9808**.

BARRINGER (GEORGE WASHINGTON) Why am I ill? or, Health for a shilling; being an explanation of the Barringerian system of medicine, *etc.* pp. 32. *Prof. Barringer: London*, 1871. 8°. **7391**. df. **38**. (**7**.)

BARRINGER (LESLIE)

—— *See* CORY (Harper) and BARRINGER (L.) Animals All, *etc.* 1940, *etc.* 8°. W.P. **5331**.

—— Gerfalcon. [A novel.] pp. vii. 410 *William Heinemann: London*, 1927. 8°. NN. **12699**

—— Joris of the Rock. pp. 325. *William Heinemann London*, 1928. 8°. NN. **14608**

—— Kay the Left-Handed. pp. 284. *William Heinemann: London, Toronto*, 1935. 8°. NN. **23921**.

—— Know Ye Not Agincourt? . . . Illustrated by C. Walter Hodges. pp. ix. 213. *London*, [1936.] 8°. [*Nelsonian Library*. no. 37.] **12827.aaa.1/37.**

—— The Rose in Splendour. A story of the wars of Lancaster and York . . . Illustrations by Alan Blyth. pp. 160. *Phoenix House: London*, 1953. 8°. [*Pageant Books*.] W.P. A. **505**/3.

—— Shy Leopardess. pp. vii. 392. *Methuen & Co.: London*, 1948. 8°. NN. **38871**.

—— Strange Dwellings Series. Edited by L. Barringer. *T. Nelson & Sons: London*, 1941- . 8°. **012208.c.3.**

BARRINGER (LEWIN BENNITT)

—— Flight without Power. The art of gliding and soaring. [With contributions by Paul and Ernest Schweizer, K. O. Lange and others.] pp. ix. 251. *Pitman Publishing Corporation: New York, Chicago*, [1940.] 8°. **08771**. c. **58**.

BARRINGER (MARIA MASSEY) Dixie Cookery: or, how I managed my table for twelve years. A practical cookbook for Southern housekeepers. pp. 121. *Loring: Boston*, 1867. 8°. **7955**. aaa. **17**.

BARRINGER (MARIE)

—— The Four and Lena . . . Illustrated by Maud & Miska Petersham. pp. 216. *Doubleday, Doran & Co.: New York*, 1938. 8°. **12821**. bb. **22**.

—— Martin the Goose Boy, *etc.* pp. x. 188. *Doubleday, Doran & Co.: Garden City, N.Y.*, 1932. 8°. **12837.de.19.**

BARRINGER (MICHAEL)

—— Inquest! A play in three acts. pp. 93. *London*, [1935.] 8°. [*Year Book Press Series of Plays*.] W.P. **2236**/**100**.

BARRINGER (THOMAS) A Choice Collection of Eighty Four Statute and Common Laws; abstracted from the best records, enquirable and presentable in the Court-Leet, and other petty courts, *etc.* pp. 24. *For the Author: London*, [1750?] 12°. **6281**. a. **2**.
The caption-title reads: " The Charge of the Court-Leet."

BARRINGTON, *Character in Fiction*. Barrington. Przez autorkę " Molly Bawn " [i.e. Margaret W. Argles, afterwards Hungerford]. pp. 30. [*Warsaw*,] 1889. 8°. **12641**. i. **16**. (**3**.)

—— Barrington's Fate. [By Margaret Hunt.] pp. 414. *Roberts Bros.: Boston*, 1883. 8°. [*No Name Series*.] **12209.de.3/4.**

BARRINGTON ASSOCIATES, INC. *See* KILLOUGH (Hugh B.) The Economics of Marketing. By H. B. Killough . . . and Barrington Associates, Inc. 1933. 8°. **08206**. h. **33**.

BARRINGTON ( ) *Mrs.* A Catalogue of the Genuine Collection of Pictures, miniatures . . . of the late Mrs. Barrington . . . and also of William Wilkinson, Esq . . . which . . . will be sold by auction . . . on . . . the 6th of . . . December, 1755. pp. 4. [*London*, 1755.] 4°. **C.119.h.3.(28.)**

BARRINGTON (ALICIA GEORGETTE BARRINGTON) *Lady.* Bible History for Children, and a short history of Christianity after the days of the Apostles, *etc.* pp. vii. 129. *J. Nisbet & Co.: London*, 1889. 8°. **3109**. de. **14**.

BARRINGTON (AMY) *of Dublin.*

—— *See* ENGLAND.—*Exchequer.* [Returns made by parishes, wards and livery companies of the City of London to the Exchequer of persons assessed for payment of the Poll Tax of 1641. Indexed by A. Barrington.] 1934, *etc.* 4°. **Ac.5962.b/46.**

—— *See* WESTMINSTER. The Inhabitants of Westminster in the reign of Charles I . . . Indexed by Miss Amy Barrington. 1935. 4°. **09915**. t. **12**

BARRINGTON (AMY) *of the Galton Eugenics Laboratory.*

—— *See* ELDERTON (Ethel M.) On the Correlation of Fertility with Social Value . . . By E. M. Elderton, A. Barrington, *etc.* 1913. 4°. [*Eugenics Laboratory Memoirs.* no. 18.] Ac. **3820**. i. (**13**.)

—— *See* RISCHBIETH (H.) Dwarfism. [With a bibliography and iconography by A. Barrington.] 1912. 4°. [*Treasury of Human Inheritance.* vol. 1.] Ac. **3820**. i. (**6**.)

—— *See* STOCKS (Percy) Hereditary Disorders of Bone Development . . . By P. Stocks . . . with the assistance of A. Barrington, *etc.* 1925, *etc.* 4°. [*Treasury of Human Inheritance.* vol. 3.] Ac. **3820**. i. (**6**.)

BARRINGTON (AMY) *of the Galton Eugenics Laboratory*, and **PEARSON** (KARL)

—— A First Study of the Inheritance of Vision and of the relative influence of Heredity and Environment on Sight, *etc.* pp. 61. *London*, 1909. 4°. [*Eugenics Laboratory Memoirs.* no. 5.] Ac. **3820**. i. (**5**.)

—— A Preliminary Study of Extreme Alcoholism in Adults. By A. Barrington and K. Pearson . . . With the assistance of David Heron. pp. 55. *London*, 1910. 4°. [*Eugenics Laboratory Memoirs.* no. 14.] Ac. **3820**. i. (**11**.)

BARRINGTON (ANNE) Fugitive Thoughts, *etc.* [Verses.] pp. 26. *Robert Scott: London*, [1928.] 12°. **011644**. de. **129**.

BARRINGTON (ARCHIBALD) Chronological Chart of British Architecture: with the genealogy and armorial bearings of the Sovereigns of England, and parallel tables of the most important events in British and general history. *Thomas Varty: London*, 1843. fol. **Cup.1248.b.10.**

—— Lectures on Heraldry, in which the principles of the science are familiarly explained, and its application shewn to the study of history and architecture, *etc.* [With plates.] pp. xii. 216. *George Bell: London*, 1844. 12°. **607**. c. **19**.

—— Manual for Students of British Architecture: containing a brief description of its characteristic features . . . a table shewing the duration of each style, *etc.* pp. 36. *George Bell: London*, 1843. 12°. **1265**. b. **3**.

BARRINGTON (Archibald)

—— Plain Hints for understanding the Genealogy and Armorial Bearings of the Sovereigns of England, with a description of the different styles of British architecture, *etc.* [With plates.] pp. xii. 146. *Thomas Varty: London*, 1843. 8°. **1265**. b. **6**.

—— Pocket Chart of British Architecture. Chronologically arranged by A. Barrington. (Description of the figures in the Pocket Chart, *etc.*) pp. 24. *George Bell: London*, 1844. 12°. **1265**. b. **4**.

—— Pocket Chart of Foreign Architecture. Chronologically arranged by A. Barrington. (Pocket Manual of Foreign Architecture, *etc.*) pp. 30. *George Bell: London*, 1844. 12°. **1265**. b. **5**.

BARRINGTON (Arthur Harry Manliffe)

—— Forest Administration in the Arakan Forest Division from the 1st July 1902 to the 30th June 1915 . . . With appendices and map. pp. ii. 227. 1917 [1918]. fol. *See* Burma. [*Miscellaneous Public Documents, etc.*] I.S. Bu. **18/3**.

—— Forest Soil and Vegetation in the Hlaing Forest Circle, Burma. pp. ii. 95. pl. 11. *Rangoon*, 1931. fol. [*Burma Forest Bulletin.* no. 25.] I.S. Bu. **18/12**.

BARRINGTON (Boyd C.) The Magna Charta and other great charters of England, with an historical treatise and copious explanatory notes. pp. 342. *W. J. Campbell: Philadelphia*, 1900. 8°. **9510**. cc. **8**.

BARRINGTON (C. J.) A Catalogue of a Miscellaneous Collection of Books . . . on sale . . . by C. J. Barrington, *etc.* pp. 92. *London*, [1824.] 8°. **130**. k. **15**. (**5**.)

BARRINGTON (Cecil Vivian) *See* England.—*Laws and Statutes.*—iv. *Shop Hours.* The Shop Hours Acts, 1892–1904. With the rules issued by the central authorities, extracts from other acts relating to shops, and a note on procedure in regard to early closing. By C. V. Barrington. 1905. 8°. **6325**. de. **47**.

BARRINGTON (Charles George) Seventy Years' Fishing, *etc.* pp. 308. *Smith, Elder & Co.: London*, 1906. 8°. **7913**. dd. **35**

BARRINGTON (Charlotte Mary) *Viscountess Barrington.*

—— Through Eighty Years, 1855–1935. The Reminiscences of Charlotte, Viscountess Barrington. [With plates, including portraits.] pp. ix. 254. *John Murray: London*, 1936. 8°. **010822**. f. **26**.

BARRINGTON (*Hon.* Daines) *See* Engel (S.) Herrn Samuel Engel's . . . Neuer Versuch über die Lage der nördlichen Gegenden von Asien und Amerika, und dem Versuch eines Wegs durch die Nordsee nach Indien; nebst den Schriften so Hr. Daines Barrington zu Behauptung eben dieses herausgegeben, *etc.* 1777. 4°. **571**. h. **28**.

—— *See* Maurelle (F. A.) Voyage of the Sonora in the Second Bucareli Expedition . . . Translated by the Hon. D. Barrington, *etc.* 1920. 4°. **10497**. g. **21**.

—— *See* Orosius (P.) The Anglo-Saxon Version, from the historian Orosius, by Ælfred the Great. Together with an English translation from the Anglo-Saxon [by the editor, the Hon. D. Barrington]. 1773. 8°. **804**. c. **45**.

—— *See* Wynn (*Sir* John) *Bart.* The History of the Gwedir Family. [Edited by the Hon. D. Barrington.] 1770. 8°. **138**. a. **13**.

BARRINGTON (*Hon.* Daines)

—— Miscellanies. [With plates.] pp. viii. 557. *J. Nichols: London*, 1781. 4°. **461**. k. **25**.

—— [Another copy.] **724**. i. **1**.

—— [Another copy.] **92**. g. **14**.

—— [Another copy.] **12271**. h. **9**.
Imperfect; wanting the titlepage, pp. 343–432, *and all after p.* 534.

—— Account of a very Remarkable Young Musician [i.e. Mozart]. In a letter, *etc.* [An extract from the "Philosophical Transactions" of the Royal Society.] *Lockyer Davis: London*, 1771. 8°. Hirsch iv. **1554**a.

—— Instances of Navigators who have reached High Northern Latitudes. Read at a meeting of the Royal Society, *etc.* pp. 8. *Benjamin White: London*, [1774.] 4°. T. **1555**. (**5**.)

—— Observations on the Statutes, chiefly the more ancient, from Magna Charta to the twenty-first of James the First, Ch. xxvii. With an appendix; being a proposal for new modelling the Statutes. [By the Hon. D. Barrington.] pp. xi. 341. 1766. 4°. *See* England. [*Appendix.—Law.*] **6145**. l. **5**.

—— Observations upon the Statutes, chiefly the more ancient, from Magna Charta to the twenty-first of James the First, Ch. xxvii . . . [By the Hon. D. Barrington.] The second edition, with corrections and additions. pp. xi. 428. 1767. 8°. *See* England. [*Appendix.—Law.*] **6147**. aa. **9**.

—— Observations on the more ancient Statutes from Magna Charta to the twenty-first of James i. cap. xxvii. With an appendix, being a proposal for new modelling the Statutes . . . The fourth edition. pp. xii. 578. *W. Bowyer & J. Nichols: London*, 1775. 4°. **518**. l. **8**.

—— [Another copy.] **19**. b. **11**.

—— [Another copy.] G. **15142**.

—— Observations on the more Ancient Statutes . . . The fifth edition. [With a portrait.] pp. xii. 578. *G. Leigh & J. Sotheby: London*, 1796. 4°. **6193**. dd. **1**.

—— Observations on the Practice of Archery in England, *etc.* [Reprinted from "Archæologia."] pp. 23. ms. notes [by Sophia S. Banks]. [*London*, 1785.] 4°. **797**. dd. **13**.
A number of prints and one drawing have been inserted in this copy.

—— The Probability of Reaching the North Pole discussed. pp. 90. *C. Heydinger: London*, 1775. 4°. **462**. .. **10**. (**3**.)

—— [Another copy.] T. **1555**. (**4**.)

—— Additional Instances of Navigators, who have reached High Northern Latitudes, lately received from Holland. (A supplement to The Probability of Reaching the North Pole.) pp. 93–112. *C. Heydinger: London*, 1775. 4°. **462**. e. **10**. (**4**.)
The pagination continues that of the main work.

—— Observations on the Floating Ice which is found in High Northern and Southern Latitudes. To which are added Experiments on the freezing of sea water, by B. Higgins. (A second supplement to The Probability of Reaching the North Pole.) pp. 118–155. *C. Heydinger: London*, 1776. 4°. T. **1555**. (**4***.)
The pagination continues that of the first supplement.

BARRINGTON (*Hon.* Daines)

—— The Possibility of Approaching the North Pole asserted . . . A new edition. With an appendix, containing papers on the same subject and on a North West Passage, by Colonel Beaufoy, F.R.S. Illustrated with a map of the North Pole . . . Second edition. pp. xxiv. 258. *T. & J. Allman: London*, 1818. 8°. **798.** g. **7.**

—— [Another copy.] G. **16020.** *Imperfect; wanting the half-title. At the end are inserted two articles from the Quarterly Review, written by Sir J. Barrow.*

BARRINGTON (E.) *pseud.* [i.e. Eliza Louisa Moresby Beck.] Anne Boleyn. pp. 376. *Cassell & Co.: London*, [1932.] 8°. **N.N.23713.**

—— The Chaste Diana. A romance, *etc.* pp. 325. *Dodd, Mead & Co.: New York*, 1923. 8°. **12602.** tt. **5.**

—— [Another issue.] pp. vi. 325. *John Lane: London*, 1923. 8°. NN. **9284.** *With a different titlepage and different preliminary matter.*

—— Cleopatra, *etc.* pp. 252. *Readers Library Publishing Co.: London*, [1935.] 8°. **012601.** ee. **70.**

—— The Crowned Lovers. The true romance of Charles the First and his queen. [A novel.] pp. 191. *Cassell & Co.: London*, 1935. 8°. NN. **23690.**

—— The Divine Lady: a romance of Nelson and Emma Hamilton. pp. 417. *G. G. Harrap: London*, 1925. 8°. NN. **10578.**

—— [Another edition.] pp. 357. *Hodder & Stoughton: London*, [1929.] 8°. **012601.** bb. **61.**

—— The Duel of the Queens. A romance of Mary, Queen of Scotland. pp. 373. *Cassell & Co.: London*, 1930. 8°. NN. **17295.**

—— The Empress of Hearts. A romance of Marie Antoinette. pp. 286. *G. G. Harrap & Co.: London*, 1928. 8°. NN. **14606.**

—— The Exquisite Perdita. pp. v. 377. *G. G. Harrap & Co.: London*, 1926. 8°. NN. **12261.**

—— [Another edition.] pp. 320. *Hodder & Stoughton: London*, [1929.] 8°. **012601.** bb. **76.**

—— The Gallants. Following according to their wont the Ladies. pp. 308. *G. G. Harrap & Co.: London; printed in U.S.A.*, [1927.] 8°. **12601.** s. **18.**

—— Glorious Apollo. pp. viii. 371. *Dodd, Mead & Co. New York*, 1925. 8°. Ashley 355

—— Glorious Apollo. (Fifth printing.) pp. 371. *Dodd, Mead & Co.: New York*, 1925. 8°. **012643.** tt. **81.** *Imperfect; wanting the table of contents and half title to part* 1.

—— Glorious Apollo. pp. viii. 371. **F.P.** *G. G. Harrap & Co.: London*, 1926. 8°. NN. **11539.**

—— [Another edition.] pp. 320. *Hodder & Stoughton: London*, [1929.] 8°. **012601.** bb. **62.**

—— The Graces. pp. 308. *Cassell & Co.: London*, 1934. 8°. NN. 21674.

—— The Great Romantic: being an interpretation of Mr. Sam[l] Pepys and Elizabeth his wife. pp. 319. *Cassell & Co.: London*, 1933. 8°. NN. **20044.**

—— The Irish Beauties. A romance of the luck of the Gunnings. pp. 319. *Cassell & Co.: London*, 1931. 8°. NN. 18581

BARRINGTON (E.) *pseud.* [i.e. Eliza Louisa Moresby Beck.]

—— "The Ladies!" A shining constellation of wit and beauty . . . Illustrated with portraits. pp. 268. *T. Fisher Unwin: London; printed in U.S.A.*, 1923 [1922]. 8°. **12633.** g. **15.**

—— [A reissue.] *Ernest Benn: London*, 1927. 8°. **12601.** s. **17.**

—— The Laughing Queen. A romance of Cleopatra. pp. 317. *G. G. Harrap & Co.: London*, 1929. 8°. NN. **15647.**

—— The Thunderer. A romance of Napoleon and Josephine. pp. 317. *G. G. Harrap & Co.: London*, 1927. 8°. NN. **13072.**

—— [Another edition.] pp. 320. *Hodder & Stoughton: London*, [1930.] 8°. **012601.** d. **30.**

—— The Wooing of the Queens. pp. 279. *Cassell & Co.: London*, 1934. 8°. NN. 22792.

BARRINGTON (Edward C.)

—— The Human Geography of Guernsey. (Reprinted from the Transactions of La Société Guernesiaise.) [With plates.] *Guernsey*, [1936.] 4°. **010352.** d. **46.**

BARRINGTON (Emilie Isabel) *See* Bagehot (Walter) The Works and Life of Walter Bagehot. Edited by Mrs. R. Barrington. 1915. 8°. **12274.** dd. **2.**

—— *See* Bagehot (Walter) The Love-Letters of Walter Bagehot and Eliza Wilson . . . Edited by their sister Mrs. R. Barrington. 1933. 8°. **010920.** b. **5.**

—— Essays on the Purpose of Art. Past and present creeds of English painters. pp. xix. 421. *Longmans & Co.: London*, 1914. 8°. **07805.** cc. **2.**

—— G. F. Watts. Reminiscences. [With plates.] pp. xx. 210. *George Allen: London*, 1905. 4°. **10827.** h. **22.**

—— Helen's Ordeal. [A novel.] pp. 311. *Osgood, McIlvaine & Co.: London*, 1894. 8°. **012630.** h. **63.**

—— Leighton and John Kyrle, 'the Man of Ross.' pp. 45. *David Douglas: Edinburgh*, 1903. 8°. **10600.** ff. **14.** **(7.)**

—— Lena's Picture. A story of love. 2 vol. *David Douglas: Edinburgh*, 1892. 8°. **012641.** g. **20.**

—— (New edition.) pp. 320. *Osgood, McIlvaine & Co.: London*, 1893. 8°. **012630.** g. **4.**

—— The Life, Letters and Work of Frederic Leighton. [With plates.] 2 vol. *George Allen: London*, 1906. 4°. L.R. **26.** b. **6.**

—— Life of Walter Bagehot . . . With portraits and other illustrations. pp. viii. 478. *Longmans & Co.: London*, 1914. 8°. **010826.** k. **18.**

—— The Reality of the Spiritual Life. pp. 46. *David Douglas: Edinburgh*, 1889. 8°. **4372.** d. **27.** **(3.)**

—— A Retrospect, and other articles. pp. viii. 349. *Osgood, McIlvaine & Co.: London*, 1896. 8°. **012356.** h. **6.**

—— A St. Luke of the Nineteenth Century . . . An old-fashioned story, *etc.* pp. 486. *Longmans & Co.: London*, 1922. 8°. NN. **8291.**

—— The Servant of All. Pages from the . . . life of . . . James Wilson. Twenty years of mid-Victorian life . . . With illustrations [including portraits]. 2 vol. *Longmans & Co.: London*, 1927. 8°. **010855.** h. **5.**

BARRINGTON (Emilie Isabel)

—— Through Greece and Dalmatia. A Diary of impressions recorded by pen & picture. pp. xx. 262. *A. & C. Black: London*, 1912. 8°. **10126**. eee. **24**.

BARRINGTON (F. H.) Kansas Day. Containing a brief history of Kansas, and a collection by Kansas authors, *etc.* pp. 253. *G. W. Crane & Co.: Topeka*, 1892. 8°. **9605**. b. **28**.

BARRINGTON (G. W.) *Writer of Tales.*

—— Bandits of Bald Hill, *etc.* pp. 256. *Hutchinson & Co.: London*, [1934.] 8°. **12709**. i. **14**.

—— Blondy of the Double Star, *etc.* pp. 255. *Hutchinson & Co.: London*, [1933.] 8°. A.N. **1786**

—— Jan. A story of a Dutch barge dog. Written and illustrated by G. W. Barrington. pp. 123. *Hutchinson & Co.: London*, 1951. 8°. **12834**. ee. **10**.

—— Jan, the Dutch barge dog, *etc.* pp. 148. *Longmans, Green & Co.: New York, Toronto*, 1953. 8°. **12836**. d. **2**.

—— Nzwala. The story of an impala antelope. Written and illustrated by G. W. Barrington. pp. 110. *Hutchinson's Books for Young People: London*, [1949.] 8°. [*Chestnut Library.*] W.P. **631/9**.

—— [Nzwala.] Wind Runner, *etc.* pp. 160. *Longmans, Green & Co.: New York, Toronto*, 1951. 8°. **12833**. c. **18**.

—— Outlaws of Badger Hollow, *etc.* pp. 256. *Hutchinson & Co.: London*, [1934.] 8°. **12709**. f. **13**.

—— Red of the Circle G, *etc.* pp. 256. *Hutchinson & Co.: London*, [1934.] 8°. A.N. **1984**.

BARRINGTON (George) *See* Lambert (Richard S.) The Prince of Pickpockets. A study of G. Barrington, *etc.* [With a portrait.] 1930. 8°. **10824**. aaa. **17**.

—— The Frauds and Cheats of London detected . . . With wood cuts, *etc.* pp. 80. *J. Lee: London*, 1802. 12°. Wrongly ascribed to Barrington. **10350**. bbb. **31**.

—— Barrington's New London Spy for 1805, or, the Frauds of London detected; to which is added, an appendix containing a sketch of scenes and characters in a ramble through the metropolis . . . Also, a treatise on the art of boxing, by Mr. Belcher. The fourth edition, considerably enlarged. pp. xii. 140. *Thomas Tegg: London*, [1805?] 12°. Wrongly ascribed to Barrington. **12331**. aa. **38**.
With an additional titlepage, engraved.

—— [Another edition.] The London Spy: or, the Frauds of London described: being a complete disclosure of all the dark transactions in and about that great city. pp. 24. *T. Johnston: Falkirk*, 1809. 12°. **1079**. i. **24**. (**20**.)

—— The History of New Holland, from its first discovery in 1616, to the present time. With a particular account of its produce and inhabitants; and a description of Botany Bay . . . To which is prefixed, an introductory Discourse on Banishment, by the Right Honourable William Eden [reprinted from his "Principles of Penal Law"] . . . The second edition, illustrated with maps. pp. xxxv. 254. *John Stockdale: London*, 1808. 8°. **798**. e. **3**.
Wrongly ascribed to Barrington. The first edition and the real second edition, published in 1787, [of which this is a reissue,] *were anonymous and are entered under the heading* New Holland.

BARRINGTON (George)

—— The History of New South Wales, including Botany Bay, Port Jackson, Pamaratta [*sic*], Sydney, and all its dependancies . . . with the customs and manners of the natives, and an account of the English colony, from its foundation to the present time . . . Enriched with . . . coloured prints. pp. 505. *M. Jones: London*, 1802. 8°. Wrongly ascribed to Barrington. **9781**. c. **12**.

—— (Second edition.) pp. 544. *M. Jones: London*, 1810. 8°. **10491**. e. **2**.

—— A Voyage to Botany Bay, with a description of the country, manners, customs, religion, &c. of the natives, by the celebrated . . . George Barrington. To which is added his life and trial. (A Sequel to Barrington's Voyage to New South Wales, comprising an interesting narrative of the transactions and behaviour of the convicts, *etc.*) 2 pt. *C. Lowndes: London*, [1795?.] 1801. 8°. **10491**. aaa. **10**.

—— [Another edition.] A Voyage to New South Wales; comprising an interesting narrative of the transactions and behaviour of the convicts: the progress of the colony . . . By G. Barrington . . . To which is annexed his life and trial. pp. 184. *John Swain: New-York*, [1803.] 8°. **10492**. d. **4**.

—— [Another edition.] An Account of a Voyage to New South Wales . . . Enriched with . . . colour'd prints. pp. 467. *M. Jones: London*, 1803. 8°. **10491**. d. **1**.

—— [Another edition.] pp. 472. *M. Jones: London*. 1810. 8°. **10491**. e. **1**.

—— Voyage à Botany-Bay, avec une description du pays, des moeurs, des coûtumes et de la religion des natifs . . . Traduit de l'anglais, sur la troisième édition. pp. xv. 192. *Paris*, an VI [1798?]. 8°. **10492**. cc. **23**.

—— The Genuine Life and Trial of George Barrington, from his birth in June, 1755, to the time of his conviction at the Old-Bailey, in September 1790, *etc.* pp. 48. *Robert Barker: London*, 1790. 8°. **10826**. aa. **32**. (**1**.)

—— [Another edition.] Memoirs of George Barrington; from his birth in MDCCLV, to his last conviction at the Old Bailey, on . . . the 17th of September, MDCCXC. pp. 115. *M. Smith: London*, 1790. 8°. **635**. f. **18**. (**2**.)

—— The Life and Extraordinary Adventures of George Barrington, now transported to Botany-Bay, *etc.* pp. 8. *W. A.: Darlington*, [1795?] 12°. **1076**. l. **2**. (**1**.)

—— The Life of George Barrington, containing every remarkable circumstance from his birth to the present time . . . With the whole of his celebrated speeches, taken from the records of King's Bench, Old Bailey, &c. To which is added a copy of a letter from him at Cape of Good-Hope to a gentleman in the County of York, dated 1st July, 1[791]. pp. 42. *For the Booksellers: London*, 1792. 8°. **1202**. c. **39**.
Cropped.

—— The Life, Times and Adventures of George Barrington, the celebrated thief & pickpocket . . . Embellished with beautiful engravings. (Second edition.) pp. 73. *John Wilson: London*, [1820?] 8°. **10826**. aa. **13**.

—— The Memoirs of George Barrington, containing every remarkable circumstance, from his birth to the present time . . . with the whole of his celebrated speeches, *etc.* pp. 40. *J. Bird; Simmonds: London*, [1790.] 8°. **1416**. c. **38**.

BARRINGTON (Greville G.) How to Cure Insomnia. pp. 39. *Lutterworth's: London*, [1926.] 8°. **07660**. f. **15**.

BARRINGTON (HOWARD) *See* STONE (Simon) *pseud.* [i.e. H. Barrington.]

BARRINGTON (JOHN)

—— The Moving Finger. pp. 144. *John Langdon: London,* [1947.] 8°. NN. **37193.**

—— Murder in White Pit. pp. 143. *John Langdon: London,* [1947.] 8°. NN. **37194.**

BARRINGTON (*Right Hon.* JOHN) A Defence of the Conduct of Barbadoes, during the late expedition to Martinique and Guadaloupe. In a letter to the Right Hon. Gen. Barrington. By a native resident in that Island. pp. 88. *R. & J. Dodsley: London,* 1760. 8°. **102.** d. **60.**

BARRINGTON (JOHN H.) *See* HARVEY, afterwards BARRINGTON.

BARRINGTON (JOHN SHREEVE)

—— Anthropometry and Anatomy. [With illustrations.] pp. 111. *Encyclopaedic Press: London,* 1953. fol. Cup. **366.** e. **11.**

—— Art and Anatomy. [With illustrations.] pp. 168. *Neville Woodbury: London,* 1951. 4°. Cup. **366.** e. 4.

BARRINGTON (JOHN SHUTE) *Viscount Barrington. See* MACKEWEN (Robert) A Crown of Righteousness the Reward of Christian Fortitude. A funeral sermon on the late Lord Vis. Barrington, *etc.* 1735. 8°. **1416.** c. **39.**

—— *See* SHERLOCK (Thomas) successively *Bishop of Bangor, of Salisbury* and *of London.* Remarks on the various Interpretations of the more sure word of Prophecy, 2 Pet. I. 19, which have been lately published by the Dean of Chichester [i.e. T. Sherlock], and the author of the Miscellanea Sacra [i.e. Viscount Barrington], *etc.* 1726. 8°. **115.** d. **37.**

—— The Theological Works of the first Viscount Barrington, including the Miscellanea Sacra, the Essay on the Dispensations, and his correspondence with Dr. Lardner, never before published. To which are prefixed, a life of the author, with a brief memoir of his son, Shute Barrington, the late Bishop of Durham, by the Rev. Geo. Townsend. 3 vol. *C. & J. Rivington: London,* 1828. 8°. **1004.** f. **16–18.**

—— An Account of the late Proceedings of the Dissenting Ministers at Salters-Hall . . . In a letter to the Rev^d Dr. Gale. [By Viscount Barrington.] The second edition. pp. 38. 1719. 8°. *See* GALE (John) *D.D.* **698.** i. **10.** (**3.**)

—— An Answer to Some Queries in a paper [by John Sladen], intituled, Reasons offered against pushing for the Repeal of the Corporation and Test Acts. [By Viscount Barrington.] pp. 32. 1732. 8°. *See* ENGLAND.—*Laws and Statutes.*—VIII.—Charles II. T. **1760.** (**7.**)

—— [Another copy.] **116.** e. **4.**

—— *See* ENGLAND.—*Laws and Statutes.*—VIII.—Charles II. Animadversions on a Paper intituled, An Answer to Some Queries. By the author of the Reasons against pushing, *etc.* [i.e. John Sladen.] 1733. 8°. **116.** e. 5.

—— A Discourse of Natural and Revealed Religion: and the relation they bear to each other. [By Viscount Barrington.] pp. 36. 1732. 8°. *See* DISCOURSE. **4136.** b. **51.**

—— [Another copy.] **702.** g. **7.** (**9.**)

BARRINGTON (JOHN SHUTE) *Viscount Barrington.*

—— Dissertatio philosophica inauguralis de theocratia civili, *etc.* pp. 36. *F. Halma: Trajecti ad Rhenum,* 1697. 4°. **523.** g. **52.** (**3.**)

—— A Dissuasive from Jacobitism: shewing in general what the nation is to expect from a Popish king; and in particular, from the Pretender. [By Viscount Barrington.] pp. 42. 1713. 8°. *See* JACOBITISM. **111.** c. **42.**

—— The Second Part of the Dissuasive from Jacobitism: wherein the interest of the Clergy and Universities, with relation to Popery and the Pretender, is consider'd. [By Viscount Barrington.] pp. 40. 1713. 8°. *See* JACOBITISM. **110.** d. **60.**

—— An Essay on the several Dispensations of God to Mankind, in the order, in which they lie in the Bible: or, a short system of the religion of nature and Scripture, *etc.* [By Viscount Barrington.] pp. xxxi. 163. 1728. 8°. *See* ESSAY. **4380.** b. **21.**

—— *See* CLERGYMAN. Remarks upon a Book, intituled, An Essay on the several Dispensations of God to Mankind, *etc.* 1733. 8°. **480.** a. **20.** (**4.**)

—— *See* SEMLER (J. S.) Zusätze zu Lord Barringtons Versuch über das Christenthum und den Deismus [i.e. "An Essay on the several Dispensations of God to Mankind"]. 1783. 8°. **4015.** d. **41.**

—— An Essay on the Teaching and Witness of the Holy Spirit. *See* WATSON (Richard) *Bishop of Llandaff.* A Collection of Theological Tracts. vol. 4. 1785. 8°. **13.** a. **4.**

—— [Another edition.] *See* WATSON (Richard) *Bishop of Llandaff.* A Collection of Theological Tracts. vol. 4. 1791. 8°. **495.** f. **4.**

—— An Essay upon the Interest of England; in respect to Protestants dissenting from the Establish'd Church. [By Viscount Barrington.] pp. 36. 1701. 4°. *See* PROTESTANTS. **698.** i. **31.**

—— A Letter from a Lay-man, in communion with the Church of England, tho' dissenting from her in some points. To the Right Rev^d the Lord Bishop of ——. [By Viscount Barrington.] pp. 28. 1714. 4°. *See* LETTER. T. **1754.** (**12.**)

—— [Another copy.] **116.** d. **7.**

—— The second edition, corrected and enlarged. With a postscript, shewing how far the Bill to prevent the growth of Schism, is inconsistent with the Act of Toleration, and the other laws of this realm. pp. 36. 1714. 8°. *See* LETTER. **698.** g. **27.** (**3.**)

—— The Layman's Letter to the Bishop of Bangor: or, an Examination of his Lordship's Preservative against the Nonjurors; of the Vindication of the Realm and Church of England [by Archbishop Wake]; of the Nonjurors Seperation [*sic*] from Publick Assemblies, examin'd, by Dr. Bennet; and of all other late discourses, occasion'd by the charge of perjury, rebellion and schism, imputed to the body of the people. [By Viscount Barrington.] pp. 44. 1716. 4°. *See* LAYMAN. 698.g.27.(6.)

—— [Another copy.] **109.** e. **6.**

—— The second edition. pp. 44. 1716. 4°. See LAYMAN. **3936.** bb. **23.**

—— The Layman's Second Letter to the Bishop of Bangor: or, an Examination of his Lordship's Sermon before the King, and of Dr. Snape's Letter to his Lordship. [By Viscount Barrington.] pp. 40. 1717. 4°. See LAYMAN. T. **1693.** (**14.**)

—— [Another copy.] **109.** e. **7.**

BARRINGTON (John Shute) *Viscount Barrington.*

—— A Letter to Protestant Dissenters concerning their Conduct in the Ensuing Elections, *etc.* [By Viscount Barrington.] pp. 11. 1733. 4°. *See* Protestant Dissenters. **101.** f. **72.**

—— Miscellanea Sacra: or, a New method of considering so much of the history of the Apostles, as is contained in Scripture, *etc.* [By Viscount Barrington. With a map.] 2 vol. 1725. 8°. *See* Apostles. [*Appendix.*] **1113.** i. **5.**

—— (A new edition, with large additions and corrections.) To which is added, an Essay on the dispensations of God to mankind, as revealed in Scripture; together with a dissertation on Hebr. xii, 22–25, now first published, *etc.* [Edited by the Hon. Shute Barrington. With a portrait.] 3 vol. 1770. 8°. *See* Apostles. [*Appendix.*] **3755.** b. **6.**

—— Oratio, de studio philosophiæ conjungendo cum studio juris romani; habita in inclyta Academia Trajectina, *etc.* pp. 41. *F. Halma: Trajecti ad Rhenum,* 1698. 4°. **491.** b. **17.** (**21.**)

—— Reflexions on the xiith. Query, contain'd in a paper [by John Sladen], entitled, Reasons offer'd against pushing for the Repeal of the Corporation and Test-Acts; and on the Animadversions [also by Sladen] on the Answer to it. In a letter to a friend. [By Viscount Barrington.] pp. 30. 1733. 8°. *See* England.—*Laws and Statutes.*—viii.—Charles ii. **116.** e. 3.

—— The Rights of Protestant Dissenters. In two parts. The first, being the case of the Dissenters review'd. The second, a vindication of their right to an absolute toleration, from the objections of Sir H. Mackworth, in his treatise, intitul'd, Peace at Home. [By Viscount Barrington. The first part only.] pp. xxvii. 78. 1704. 4°. *See* Protestant Dissenters. **698.** i. **10.**

—— The second edition, corrected and enlarg'd. 2 pt. 1705. 4°. *See* Protestant Dissenters. **110.** f. **35.**

—— *See* Protestant Dissenters. A Letter to a Friend: in which the Occasional Conformists are proved to be guilty of schism and hypocrisy. In answer to . . . The Rights of Protestant Dissenters [by Viscount Barrington], *etc.* 1704. 4°. **110.** f. **38.**

—— *See* Protestant Dissenters. The Rights of the Church of England asserted and prov'd, in an answer to a late pamphlet, entitl'd The Rights of the Protestant Dissenters, in a review of their case. 1705. 4°. **110.** f. **37.**

—— A Speech on the Question, that the project call'd the Harburgh Lottery, is an infamous and fraudulent undertaking, *etc.* [By Viscount Barrington.] pp. 32. 1723 [1734]. 4°. *See* Harburg Lottery. E. **2016.** (**13.**)

BARRINGTON (Jonah) *pseud.* [i.e. Cyril Carr Dalmaine.]

—— And Master of None. [Autobiographical reminiscences. With portraits.] pp. 279. *Walter Edwards: London,* [1948.] 8°. **10861.** h. 14.

BARRINGTON (Jonah) *pseud.* [i.e. Cyril Carr Dalmaine], and **FENWICK** ( )

—— Lord Haw-Haw of Zeesen. Being a complete and revealing biography of Germany's no. 1 English radio announcer, *etc.* pp. 128. *Hutchinson & Co.: London,* [1939.] 8°. **12332.** aa. 32.

BARRINGTON (*Sir* Jonah) *See* Battersby (Leslie) Correspondence of the Reverend L. Battersby . . . with Sir J. Barrington . . . on the subject of Family-Money, *etc.* 1810. 8°. **8145.** d. **5.**

BARRINGTON (*Sir* Jonah)

—— Historic Memoirs of Ireland; comprising secret records of the National Convention, the Rebellion, and the Union; with delineations of the principal characters connected with these translations, *etc.* [With portraits and facsimiles.] 2 vol. *R. Bentley, for H. Colburn: London,* 1833 [1809–33]. 4°. **601.** m. **7, 8.**

With an additional titlepage to vol. 1, *engraved, bearing the title " Historic Anecdotes and Secret Memoirs of the Legislative Union between Great Britain and Ireland," and with the imprint " London, Published by G. Robinson . . . 1809." The work was apparently published in parts.*

—— Second edition. 2 vol. *R. Bentley, for H. Colburn: London,* 1833. 4°. **601.** m. **9, 10.**

—— Personal Sketches of his Own Times. By Sir J. Barrington. [With a portrait.] 3 vol. *Henry Colburn; H. Colburn & R. Bentley: London,* 1827–32. 8°. **615.** g. **14–16.**

—— Third edition, with a memoir of the author; an essay on Irish wit and humour; and notes and corrections by Townsend Young. 2 vol. *G. Routledge & Sons: London,* 1869. 8°. **2406.** e. **8.**

—— [Another edition of vol. 1, 2.] pp. x. 498. *Cameron & Ferguson: Glasgow & London,* 1876. 8°. **10826.** aaa. **5.**

—— [Another edition of vol. 1, 2.] Recollections of Jonah Barrington . . . With an introduction by George Birmingham. pp. xx. 485. *Talbot Press: Dublin,* [1918.] 8°. [*Every Irishman's Library.*] **012208.** f. **37/8.**

—— Rise and Fall of the Irish Nation. [With portraits.] pp. 8. xiii. 494. *G. G. Bennis: Paris,* 1833. 8°. **601.** h. **14.**

With an additional titlepage, lithographed.

—— [Another edition.] pp. xix. 26–399. *James Duffy: Dublin,* 1853. 12°. **1325.** f. **7.**

BARRINGTON (Joseph Thomas) England on the Defensive; or, the Problem of invasion critically examined, *etc.* pp. xiv. 328. *Kegan Paul & Co.: London,* 1881. 8°. **8830.** bb. **13.**

BARRINGTON (Judith) *Lady. See* Goodwin (Thomas) *Minister at Southweal.* A Fair Prospect shewing clearly the difference between things that are seen, & things that are not seen, in a sermon at the funeral of Lady J. Barrington. 1658. 12°. **1415.** a. **36.**

BARRINGTON (Lowell)

—— *See* Davis (Owen) *Dramatist,* and Davis (D.) Ethan Frome. A dramatization of Edith Wharton's novel . . . suggested by a dramatization by L. Barrington. [1954.] 8°. **11792.** f. **16.**

BARRINGTON (*Hon.* Lowther John) The Child's Preacher; or, the Gospel taught to children, in very simple language. pp. xi. 159. *Wertheim & Macintosh: London,* 1850. 16°. **3226.** a. **4.**

—— From Ur to Machpelah, the story of Abraham. pp. viii. 324. *Sampson Low & Co.: London,* 1872. 8°. **4823.** c. **5.**

—— The Gain of Death. A sermon preached at Watton . . . on the occasion of the death of Abel Smith, Esq. pp. 52. *Printed for private distribution: Hertford,* 1859. 12°. **4920.** aaa. **4.**

—— " Gathered Lambs." pp. 20. *J. Nisbet & Co.: London,* 1877. 8°. **4407.** de. 5.

BARRINGTON (*Hon.* LOWTHER JOHN)

—— Short and Simple Prayers for Daily Use. pp. 48. *Simpkin, Marshall & Co.; Groombridge & Sons: London; Simson & Groombridge: Hertford,* [1871.] 8°. **3457.** bb. **30.**

—— New and enlarged edition. pp. 52. *Simpkin, Marshall & Co.; Groombridge & Sons: London; Simson & Groombridge: Hertford,* [1874.] 8°. **3457.** b. **43. (4.)**

—— Short Prayers in Simple Words, for daily use . . . New edition. pp. 48. *Simpkin, Marshall & Co.; Groombridge & Sons: London; Simson & Co.: Hertford,* [1880.] 12°. **4422.** aa. **22. (1.)**

—— "The Spiritual House." A sermon, *etc.* pp. 26. *J. Nisbet & Co.: London,* 1852. 16°. **4475.** aa. **78.**

—— The Widow of Nain, and other lectures on various passages of Scripture. pp. viii. 246. *J. Nisbet & Co.: London,* 1846. 12°. **1358.** c. **82.**

BARRINGTON (MARGARET)

—— My Cousin Justin. [A novel.] pp. 288. *Jonathan Cape: London,* 1939. 8°. NN. **30257.**

BARRINGTON (MARY) *See* LEESON (Ida) and BARRINGTON (M.) Bibliography of Captain James Cook, *etc.* 1928. 8°. **11907.** d. **17.**

BARRINGTON (*Sir* MATTHEW) *Bart.* Letter of Sir Matthew Barrington, Bart. to Sir Robert Peel. [Detailing a plan for improving the condition of the agricultural population of Ireland. With an appendix: "Prospectus. The Farmers' Estate Society, Ireland."] pp. 39. *Dublin,* [1848.] 8°. **8145.** d. **81. (6.)**
Printed for private circulation.

—— [Another edition.] Reasons for the Formation of the Farmers' Estate Company in Ireland, suggested in a correspondence of Sir Matthew Barrington, Bart. with the late Sir Robert Peel, Bart. pp. 29. *Browne & Nolan Dublin,* 1852. 8°. **8226.** c. **82. (7.**

BARRINGTON (MAURICE) *pseud.* [i.e. DENIS WILLIAM BROGAN.]

—— Stop on the Green Light! pp. 288. *Hamish Hamilton: London,* 1941. 8°. NN. **32952.**

BARRINGTON (*Sir* MICHAEL) *Bart.*

—— An Address to the Inhabitants of Limerick, on the opening of the Mont de Piété, or Charitable Pawn Office, for the support of Barrington's Hospital, in that city. pp. 28. *William Holden: Dublin,* 1836. 8°. **10923.** ff. **1. (9.)**

BARRINGTON (MICHAEL JOHN)

—— Antagonists of Destiny. (A novel.) [With plates.] pp. xxix. 88. *For the Author:* [*London,*] 1948. 4°. **12643.** s. **13.**

—— Blaye, Roland, Rudel and the Lady of Tripoli. A study in the relations of poetry to life, A.D. 731–1950. [With plates.] pp. xvi. 242. *Bennett Bros.: Salisbury,* 1953. 8°. **11869.** r. **36.**

—— David Arnot. pp. xii. 259. *Crosby Lockwood: London,* 1927. 8°. NN. **12991.**

—— Grahame of Claverhouse, Viscount Dundee. [With illustrations and maps and a bibliography.] pp. xv. 447. *Martin Secker: London,* 1911. 8°. **10855.** h. **13.**

—— The Invisible Army. pp. xxiii. 122. *Press of Shield & Spring: London,* 1949. 8°. **12650.** ee. **4.**

BARRINGTON (MICHAEL JOHN)

—— The King's Fool. A romance. pp. viii. 340. *W. Blackwood & Sons: Edinburgh & London,* 1904. 8°. **012629.** c. **43.**

—— The Knight of the Golden Sword. pp. xii. 337. *Chatto & Windus: London,* 1909. 8°. **012623.** aa. **42.**

—— The Lady of Tripoli. A romance . . . With illustrations adapted from mediaeval MSS. by Celia Martin. pp. xi. 268. *Chatto & Windus: London,* 1910. 8°. **012623.** aaa. **1.**

—— 'The Mercury of Peace, the Mars of War:' Robert Devereux, Earl of Essex, K.G. Reprinted . . . from The Essex Review, *etc.* [With a portrait.] pp. 54. *Benham & Co.: Colchester,* [1952.] 8°. **10863.** bb. **26.**

—— A Mystery to this Day. [With plates.] pp. xvii. 156. *Shield & Spring: London,* 1949. 4°. **012643.** ppp. **45.**
Privately printed.

—— The Reminiscences of Sir Barrington Beaumont, Bart., now, by permission of his great-grandson, published for the first time. [A novel. By M. J. Barrington.] pp. xii. 308. 1902. 8°. *See* BEAUMONT (*Sir* Barrington) *Bart.* **10827.** f. **6.**

BARRINGTON (PAMELA) *pseud.* [i.e. MURIEL VERE BARLING.]

—— Account Rendered. pp. 190. *Arthur Barker: London,* 1953. 8°. NNN. **3999.**

—— Among those present. pp. 206. *Arthur Barker: London,* 1953. 8°. NNN. **4357.**

—— The Changing Heart. pp. 203. *John Long: London,* [1948.] 8°. NN. **38203.**

—— Forty-three Candles for Mr. Beamish. pp. 283. *Evans Bros.: London,* 1950. 8°. NNN. **747.**

—— The Mortimer Story. pp. 191. *Arthur Barker: London,* 1952. 8°. NNN. **3242.**

—— Mr. Hedley's Private Hell. pp. 223. *John Long: London,* [1950.] 8°. NNN. **54.**

—— The Rest is Silence. pp. 253. *Evans Bros.: London,* 1951. 8°. NNN. **1925.**

—— Saga of a Scoundrel. pp. 207. *John Long: London,* [1947.] 8°. NN. **37741.**

—— Space of Heaven. pp. 287. *John Long: London.* [1936.] 8°. NN. **2738.**

—— The Triangle has four Sides. pp. 299. *Evans Bros.: London,* [1949.] 8°. NNN. **35.**

—— White Pierrot. pp. 286. *John Long: London,* [1932.] 8°. NN. **19405.**

BARRINGTON (PATRICK)

—— Songs of a Sub-Man, *etc.* pp. viii. 91. *Methuen & Co.: London,* 1934. 8°. **11654.** aaa. **68.**

BARRINGTON (RICHARD MANLIFFE) *See* ENGLAND.—*British Association for the Advancement of Science.* Report on the Migration of Birds, *etc.* (Returns relating to the Coasts of Ireland, by R. M. Barrington and A. G. More.) 1882, *etc.* 8°. Ac. **1181/47.**

—— The Migration of Birds as observed at Irish lighthouses and lightships, including the original reports from 1888–97 . . . and an analysis of these and of the previously published reports from 1881–87 together with an appendix giving the measurements of about 1600 wings. pp. xxv. 285. 667. *R. H. Porter: London,* [1900.] 8°.
7286.ppp.51.

BARRINGTON (*Mrs.* Russell) *See* Barrington (Emilie I.)

BARRINGTON (Rutland) Rutland Barrington: a record of thirty-five years' experience on the English stage. By himself. With a preface by Sir W. S. Gilbert. With thirty-two illustrations from photographs. pp. 270. *Grant Richards: London,* 1908. 8°. **010854. f. 3.**

—— More Rutland Barrington. By himself. Illustrated. pp. 233. *Grant Richards: London,* 1911. 8°. **10855. df. 22.**

BARRINGTON (*Hon.* Samuel)

—— The Barrington Papers, selected from the letters and papers of Admiral the Hon. S. Barrington and edited by D. Bonner-Smith. [*London,*] 1937– . 8°. [*Publications of the Navy Records Society.* vol. 77, 81, etc. **Ac. 8109.**

BARRINGTON (*Hon.* Shute) successively *Bishop of Llandaff, of Salisbury* and *of Durham. See* Apostles. [*Appendix.*] Miscellanea Sacra, *etc.* [By Viscount Barrington.] A new edition [edited by the Hon. S. Barrington], *etc.* 1770. 8°. **3755. b. 6.**

—— *See* Bowyer (William) *Printer.* Critical Conjectures and Observations on the New Testament . . . The third edition, much enlarged. [With contributions by the Hon. S. Barrington and others.] 1782. 4°. **675. g. 14.**

—— —— 1812. 4°. **6. c. 11.**

—— *See* Gray (Robert) *Bishop of Bristol.* A Sermon, preached in Bishopwearmouth Church . . . on occasion of the death of the Hon. and Right Rev. S. Barrington, Lord Bishop of this Diocese [i.e. the Diocese of Durham]. 1826. 8°. **4920. cc. 46. (2.)**

—— *See* Petitioner. A Letter to . . . Shute, Lord Bishop of Landaff [with reference to his speech on the Dissenters' Bill], from a Petitioner. 1774. 8°. **4105. b. 11. (3.)**

—— *See* Sharp (John) *Sub-Dean and Prebendary of Durham.* The Speech made to the Right Reverend . . . Shute . . . Lord Bishop of Durham . . . with his Lordship's answer. [1791.] 8°. **4105. aaa. 50.**

—— Sermons, Charges, and Tracts, now first collected into a volume. pp. vii. 446. *W. Bulmer & Co.: London,* 1811. 8°. **694. l. 7.**

—— [Another copy.] **224. i. 7.**
Imperfect; wanting the half-title.

—— Vigilance, a counterbalance to past concessions, and a prevention of future prodigality, recommended in two Charges and a Letter to the Clergy of the Diocese of Durham. A new edition, with a preface, in reply to Mr. Lingard's preface . . . To which are added, Two Letters to the author of "Remarks on the Bishop of Durham's Charge, occasioned by the Vindication of those Remarks lately re-published." By a Clergyman of the Diocese of Durham. pp. xiii. 296. *W. Bulmer & Co.: London,* 1813. 8°. **4446. aaa. 12.**

—— Letters between . . . Shute . . . Lord Bishop of Durham . . . and Percival Stockdale, *etc.* [Edited by the latter.] pp. xxix. 67. *J. Ridgway: London,* 1792. 8°. **1416. f. 53.**

—— A Charge delivered to the Clergy of the Diocese of Durham, at the primary visitation of that diocese, in the year mdccxcii. pp. 37. *R. Cruttwell: Bath,* 1792. 4°. **694. h. 10. (2.)**

—— [Another copy.] **114. b. 3. (1.)**

—— [Another edition.] pp. 50. *R. Cruttwell: Bath,* 1792. 8°. **4446. bb. 1. (3.)**

—— The second edition, with an appendix. pp. 61. *T. Rickaby: London,* 1794. 4°. **679. e. 3. (5.)**

—— [Another edition of the appendix.] pp. 32. *T. Rickaby: London,* 1794. 4°. **694. h. 10. (3.)**

BARRINGTON (*Hon.* Shute) successively *Bishop of Llandaff, of Salisbury* and *of Durham.*

—— A Charge delivered to the Clergy of the Diocese of Durham; at the ordinary visitation of that diocese, in the year mdccxcvii. pp. iv. 42. *T. Rickaby: London,* 1797. 4°. **694. i. 24. (15.)**

—— [Another copy.] **114. b. 3. (2.)**

—— [Another copy.] **L.P.** **676. h. 12**

—— [Another edition.] pp. iv. 49. *T. Rickaby: London,* 1797. 8°. **4446. bb. 1. (4.)**

—— A Charge delivered to the Clergy of the Diocese of Durham, at the ordinary visitation of that diocese in July, 1801. pp. 23. *W. Bulmer & Co.: London,* 1802. 4°. **694. h. 10. (4.)**

—— [Another copy.] **114. b. 3. (3.)**
With an errata-slip pasted on the last page.

—— A Charge, delivered to the Clergy of the Diocese of Durham, at the ordinary visitation of that diocese, in the year 1806. pp. 14. *W. Bulmer & Co.: London,* 1807. 4°. **694. h. 10. (5.)**

—— [Another copy.] **114. b. 4.**

—— [Another edition.] The Grounds on which the Church of England separated from the Church of Rome, stated in a Charge delivered to the Clergy of the Diocese of Durham . . . 1806 . . . A new edition. pp. 23. *F. & C. Rivington: London,* 1807. 12°. **701. c. 9. (1.)**

—— *See* Index (Elijah) *pseud.* A Protestant's Reply to the Author [John Lingard] of a Pamphlet, entitled, "Remarks on a Charge delivered to the Clergy of the Diocese of Durham, by Shute, Bishop of Durham, at the ordinary visitation of that diocese in the year 1806." 1807. 12°. **701. c. 9. (4.)**

—— *See* Index (Elijah) *pseud.* A Review of a Pamphlet [signed: Elijah Index] entitled "A Protestant's Reply." [By John Lingard.] 1807. 12°. **3940. de. 22.**

—— *See* Index (Elijah) *pseud.* Reply to the Reviewer of a Pamphlet, entitled, "A Protestant's Reply to the Author of 'Remarks on the Bishop of Durham's Charge,'" *etc.* 1807. 12°. **701. c. 9. (5.)**

—— Remarks on a Charge delivered to the Clergy of the Diocese of Durham, by Shute, Bishop of Durham, at the ordinary visitation of that diocese in the year 1806. Second edition, enlarged and interspersed with a few cursory remarks on his sermon before the Lords, anno 1799. [By John Lingard.] pp. 52. *Keating, Brown & Co.: London,* 1807. 12°. **701. c. 9. (2.)**

—— A Letter to the Author of "Remarks on a Charge delivered by Shute, Bishop of Durham, at the ordinary visitation of that diocese in the year 1806." By a Clergyman of the diocese of Durham [i.e. Henry Phillpotts]. pp. iv. 42. *D. Akenhead & Sons: Newcastle upon Tyne,* 1807. 12°. **701. c. 9. (3.)**

—— A General Vindication of the Remarks on the Charge of the Bishop of Durham. Containing a reply to a Letter from a Clergyman of the diocese of Durham [i.e. Henry Phillpotts], second ed., a reply to the Observations of the Rev. Thos. Le Mesurier . . . a reply to the Strictures of the Rev. G. S. Faber . . . and some observations on the more fashionable methods of interpreting the Apocalypse. [By John Lingard.] *S. Hodgson: Newcastle,* 1808. 12°. **701. c. 9. (8.)**
Imperfect; wanting all after p. 100.

BARRINGTON (*Hon.* SHUTE) successively *Bishop of Llandaff, of Salisbury* and *of Durham.*

—— [Another edition.] A General Vindication of the Catholic's Remarks on the intolerant Charge of Shute Barrington, Bishop of Durham, to the clergy of his diocese, with appropriate animadversions on three illiberal replies attempted to be made by the Rev. T. Le Mesurier, the Rev. George Faber, and an anonymous clergyman [i.e. Henry Phillpotts] in answer to the Catholic's Remarks on the Bishop's charge . . . By a Catholic Divine [i.e. John Lingard]. To this edition are added the Remarks on the Bishop's Charge, alluded to in the above. pp. 97. *R. Coyne: Dublin,* 1808. 8°. **3939. e. 14.**

—— A Second Letter to the Author of Remarks on the Bishop of Durham's Charge, occasioned by the Vindication of those remarks lately republished. By a Clergyman of the diocese of Durham [i.e. Henry Phillpotts]. pp. 72. *D. Akenhead & Sons: Newcastle upon Tyne,* 1808. 12°. **701.** c. **9.** **(6.)**

—— A Letter to a Clergyman of the Diocese of Durham, in answer to his Second Letter to the Author of the Remarks on the Bishop of Durham's Charge. [By John Lingard.] pp. 62. *Preston & Heaton: Newcastle upon Tyne,* 1808. 12°. **701.** c. **9.** **(7.)**

—— A Charge delivered to the Clergy of the Diocese of Sarum at the primary visitation of that diocese, in the year MDCCLXXXIII. pp. 24. *Oxford,* 1783. 4°. **4016.** bb. **35.** **(3.)**

—— [Another copy.] T. **1984.** **(11.)**

—— [Another copy.] **679.** e. **3.** **(2.)**

—— Second edition. pp. 23. *J. Nichols: London,* 1791. 8°. **4446.** e. **6.** **(2.)**

—— [Another copy.] **4446.** bb. **1.** **(2.)**

—— A Letter to . . . Shute, Lord Bishop of Sarum; containing some gentle strictures on his Lordship's charge, delivered to the clergy of that diocese, in the year 1783. From a Lay-Member of the Church of England. pp. 60. *S. Hazard: Bath,* 1784. 8°. **4106.** b. **18.**

—— A Fast Sermon for February the 27th, 1799; from Isaiah, chap. x. ver. 5. [By the Hon. S. Barrington.] pp. 16. 1799. 4°. *See* FAST SERMON. **681.** g. **26.** **(8.)**

—— The Grounds on which the Church of England separated from the Church of Rome reconsidered, in a view of the Romish doctrine of the Eucharist; with an explanation of the antepenultimate answer in the Church Catechism. pp. x. 46. *W. Bulmer & Co.: London,* 1809. 8°. **695.** g. **2.** **(1.)**

—— [Another copy.] **108.** f. **57.**

—— Second edition. pp. 78. *W. Bulmer & Co.: London,* 1809. 8°. **3938.** bb. **79.** **(1.)**

—— Third edition. pp. 78. *W. Bulmer & Co.: London,* 1810. 8°. **3939.** h. **3.** **(2.)**

—— The Church of England Doctrine of the Lord's Supper, being an abstract of the grounds on which the Church of England separated from the Church of Rome. [Extracted from "The Grounds on which the Church of England separated from the Church of Rome reconsidered."] pp. 25. *W. Bulmer & Co.: London,* 1809. 8°. **4372.** df. **1.** **(3.)**

BARRINGTON (*Hon.* SHUTE) successively *Bishop of Llandaff, of Salisbury* and *of Durham.*

—— *See* HOLLINGSWORTH (Nathaniel J.) Three More Pebbles fresh from the Brook; or, the Romish Goliah slain with his own weapon! In three letters, to the Rev. J. Lingard, D.D. author of Remarks on the Bishop . . . of Durham's Charge . . . A new edition, *etc.* 1838. 8°. **3938. e. 64.**

—— Three More Pebbles fresh from the Brook; or, the Romish Goliah slain with his own weapon: being an answer to "Remarks on 'The Grounds on which the Church of England separated from the Church of Rome reconsidered, by Shute, Bishop of Durham'": in three letters to the Remarker [i.e. John Lingard]. By the author of "A Defence of the Doctrine and Worship of the Church of England" [i.e. N. J. Hollingsworth]. pp. x. 109. *Geo. Walker: Durham* [1809?] 12°. **3939.** b. **14**

—— A Letter to the Clergy of the Diocese of Sarum. To which are added, Directions relating to orders, institutions, and licences. pp. 63. *B. C. Collins: Salisbury,* 1789. 8°. **4016.** bb. **35.** **(4.)**

—— Second edition, with additions. pp. 146. *Collins & Easton: Salisbury,* 1790. 8°. **4446.** bb. **1.** **(1.)**

—— The Political Life of William Wildman Viscount Barrington, compiled from original papers by his brother, Shute, Bishop of Durham. [With a portrait.] pp. ii. 207. *W. Bulmer & Co.: London,* 1814. 4°. **435.** k. **8.**

—— [Another copy.] **133.** f. **5.**

—— [Another copy.] G. **1476.**

—— [Another edition.] pp. x. 219. *Payne & Foss; Hatchard: London,* 1815. 8°. **10817.** f. **5.**

—— A Sermon preached before the Incorporated Society for the Propagation of the Gospel in Foreign Parts; at their anniversary meeting . . . on February 17, 1775. (An Abstract of the Charter, and of the Proceedings of the Society . . . from the 18th day of February 1774, to the 17th day of February 1775.—A List of the Members of the Society, *etc.*) pp. xxv. 76. *T. Harrison & S. Brooke: London,* 1775. 4°. T. **2142.** **(1.)**

—— [Another copy.] **686.** f. **23.** **(3.)**

—— A Sermon preached before the Lords spiritual and temporal, in the Abbey Church of Westminster, on . . . January 30, 1772, being the day appointed to be observed as the day of the martyrdom of King Charles I. pp. 18. *W. Bowyer & J. Nichols: London,* 1772. 4°. **694.** i. **19.** **(2.)**

—— [Another copy.] **681.** g. **12.** **(2.)**

—— A Sermon preached before the Lords spiritual and temporal, on Wednesday, February 27, 1799. pp. 24. *T. Rickaby: London,* 1799. 4°. **114.** b. **43.**

—— [Another copy.] **L.P.** **681.** h. **2.**

—— A Copy of a Letter to the Bishop of Durham, from the Black Dwarf in London [i.e. Thomas Jonathan Wooler?], on clerical persecutions in his Diocese. pp. 2. *J. Marshall: Newcastle,* [1822?] *s. sh.* fol. **Cup.1245.a.16.(5.)**

—— The House of Peeresses: or, Female oratory. Containing the debates of several peeresses on the Bishop of Landaff's Bill for the more effectual discouragement of the crime of adultery . . . President, A****a Ba****ss C*****s, late Ma*******ss of C********n [Amelia Baroness Conyers, late Marchioness of Carmarthen]. pp. 56. *G. Kearsly: London,* 1779. 4°. **12332.** dd. **37.**

BARRINGTON (*Hon.* SHUTE) successively *Bishop of Llandaff, of Salisbury* and *of Durham.*

—— The House of Peeresses: or, Female oratory. Containing the debates of several peeresses on the Bishop of Landaff's Bill for the more effectual discouragement of the crime of adultery . . . Second edition. pp. 56. *G. Kearsly: London,* 1779. 4°. **11630.** d. **7.** (**15.**)

—— [Another copy.] **838.** k. **29.**

—— [A reissue.]

The House of Peeresses, *etc.* *London,* 1779. 4°. **8417.** ee. **3.**

—— (Third edition, with considerable additions, and explanatory notes.) pp. 56. *G. Kearsly: London,* 1779. 4°. **1346.** i. **45.**

—— (The fourth edition, improved.) pp. 56. *G. Kearsly: London,* 1779. 4°. **12330.** k. **24.**

—— [Another copy.] **12330.** i. **30.**

—— (The fifth edition, improved.) pp. 56. *G. Kearsly: London,* 1779. 4°. **807.** h. **9.**

BARRINGTON (*Sir* THOMAS) *See* ENGLAND.—*Parliament.—Parliamentary Proceedings.*—II. The Parliaments Resolution concerning the sending of Sir T. Barrington . . . to Colchester, *etc.* [26 August 1642.] 1642. 4°. **601.** d. **67.**

—— *See* ENGLAND.—*Parliament.—Parliamentary Proceedings.* Instructions Agreed upon by the Lords and Commons assembled in Parliament for Sir Thomas Barrington, Sir William Masham [and others] . . . Members of the House of Commons, and Deputie-Lieutenants for the County of Essex . . . to be sent into the same county, *etc.* [5 October 1642.] 1642. 4°. E. **121.** (**1.**)

—— A Letter sent to Mr. Speaker. [Dated: 7 June 1642. Signed by Sir T. Barrington and others.] *See* PARKER (John) *of Upper Wallop.* A Letter sent from one Mr. Parker, *etc.* 1642. 4°. E. **112.** (**18.**)

BARRINGTON (WILLIAM LEADBEATER) The True Origin of the American Rebellion: being a lecture, delivered in the Friends' Institute . . . Dublin, November 26th, 1864. pp. 33. *E. D. Webb & Son: Dublin,* 1865. 8°. **8177.** aaa. **84.** (**7.**)

BARRINGTON (WILLIAM WILDMAN) *Viscount Barrington. See* BARRINGTON (Shute) successively *Bishop of Llandaff, of Salisbury,* and *of Durham.* The Political Life of William Wildman, Viscount Barrington. [With a portrait.] 1814. 4°. **435.** k. **8.**

—— —— 1815. 8°. **10817.** f. **5.**

—— *See* DALRYMPLE (*Sir* John) *Bart., one of the Barons of Exchequer in Scotland.* Three Letters to Viscount Barrington, on his Lordship's official conduct. 1778. 8°. **8132.** e. **20.**

—— —— 1779. 8°. **103.** d. **12.**

—— The Barrington-Bernard Correspondence and illustrative matter, 1760–1770.—Drawn from the "Papers of Sir Francis Bernard" . . . Edited by Edward Channing . . . and Archibald Cary Coolidge. pp. xxiii. 306. 1912. 8°. [*Harvard Historical Studies.* vol. 17.] *See* BERNARD (*Sir* Francis) *Bart.* Ac. **2692/10.**

BARRINGTON-BROWNE (WILLIAM ELLIS) *See* BROWNE (W. E. B.)

BARRINGTON-KENNETT (ELLINOR FRANCES) *See* KENNETT.

BARRINGTON-KENNETT (VINCENT HUNTER) *See* KENNETT.

BARRINGTON-WARD (JOHN GROSVENOR) *See* WARD.

BARRINGTON-WARD (*Sir* LANCELOT EDWARD) *K.C.V.O. See* WARD.

BARRINGTON-WARD (MARK JAMES) *See* WARD.

BARRINGTON-WARD (ROBERT MACGOWAN) *See* WARD.

BARRINTON ( ) Carta al Caballero Barrinton . . . sobre las inscripciones de la Pira del dos de Mayo de la Catedral de México. La escribia J. M. B. [i.e. José Mariano Baristain de Souza Fernandez de Lara.] [1812.] 4°. *See* B., J. M. **9770.** aaa. **14.** (**5.**)

BARRIO (ANDRÉS BRAVO DEL) *See* BRAVO DEL BARRIO.

BARRIO (CRISTINO VALVERDE DEL) *See* VALVERDE DEL BARRIO.

BARRIO (DIEGO MARTÍNEZ) *See* MARTÍNEZ BARRIO.

BARRIO (DOMINGO MARTÍNEZ) *See* MARTÍNEZ BARRIO.

BARRIO (GABRIELE) Gab. Barrii . . . Pro lingua latina libri tres. De æternitate urbis liber unus. De laudibus Italiæ liber unus. pp. 596. MS. NOTES. *In Aedibus Populi Romani: Romæ,* 1571. 8°. **12935.** a. **44.**

—— Gab. Barrii . . . De antiquitate et situ Calabriæ, libri quinque. *See* ITALY. [*Appendix.—History.*] Italiæ illustratæ . . . scriptores varii, *etc.* 1600. fol. **592.** g. **1.**

—— Editio novissima, *etc.* pp. 187. 1723. *See* GRAEVIUS (J. G.) Thesaurus antiquitatum et historiarum Italiæ. tom. 9. pt. 5. 1725 [1704], *etc.* fol **L.R.302.a.2/9.**

—— [Another edition.] *See* JORDANUS (D.) Delectus scriptorum rerum Neapolitanarum, *etc.* 1735. fol. **180.** g. **7.**

—— Gabrielis Barrii De antiquitate, & situ Calabriæ libri quinque. Nunc primum ex authographo restituti, ac per capita distributi. Cum animadversionibus Sertorii Quatrimanni . . . necnon prolegomenis, additionibus, & notis Thomæ Aceti . . . Quibus accedit dissertatio Petri Polidori . . . qua Bruttii a calumnia de inlatis Ieus Christo D. N. tormentis & morte vindicantur. 2 pt. *Romæ,* 1737. fol. **180.** g. [illegible]

—— [Another copy, with a different titlepage.] Thomæ Aceti . . . in Gabrielis Barrii . . . De antiquitate & situ Calabriæ libros quinque, nunc primum ex autographo restitutos ac per capita distributos, prolegomena, additiones & notæ, *etc.* *Romæ,* 1737. fol. **664.** f. **4.**

—— [Another edition.] *See* JORDANUS (D.) Rarissimorum scriptorum rerum Neapolitanarum collectio, *etc.* 1738. fol. **9166.** k. **1.**

—— Gabriel Barrius . . . De laudibus Italiæ. 1725. *See* GRAEVIUS (J. G.) Thesaurus antiquitatum et historiarum Italiæ. tom. 1. pt. 1. fol. 1725 [1704], *etc.* **L.R.302.a.2/1.**

—— Ioachimi Abbatis Vita. (La Vita dell' Abbate Gioachino.) *Lat. & Ital.* *See* JOACHIMUS, *Abbot of Fiore.* Vaticinia, siue prophetiæ, *etc.* 1589. 4°. **C.81.b.23.(1.)**

—— [Another edition.] *See* JOACHIMUS, *Abbot of Fiore.* Profetie ouero vaticinii, *etc.* 1591. 8°. C. **36.** d. **13.**

—— [Another edition.] *See* JOACHIMUS, *Abbot of Fiore.* Vaticinia, siue prophetiæ, *etc.* 1600. 4°. **8610.** b. **24.**

—— Vita dell' Abbate Gioachino. *See* JOACHIMUS, *Abbot of Fiore.* Profetie, *etc.* 1592. 12°. **8632.** aa. **29.**

BARRIO (JOSÉ MARÍA DEL) Panegyrica oratio in solemnibus exequiis . . . Ildefonsi Nugnetii de Haro et Peralta, Mexicanorum Pontíficis, olimque Pro-regis, *etc.* pp. 26. [*Mexico,* 1800.] 4°. **4867.** b. **8.**

BARRIO (José María del)

—— [A reissue.] *See* Nuñez de Haro y Peralta (I.) *Archbishop of Mexico.* Relacion de la fúnebre ceremonia y exêquias del . . . Señor . . . Don Ildefonso Nuñez de Haro y Peralta, *etc.* 1802. 4°. **4986.** bb. **10.**

BARRIO (Josep del)

—— La Tasca dels Militants del P. S. U. en el Sindicat de cara a la Guerra. [With a portrait.] pp. 8. [*Barcelona*, 1937.] 8°. [*Partit Socialista Unificat de Catalunya. Primera Conferència Nacional. Addresses.*] **08042.** bb. **35/2.**

BARRIO (Juan Ventura) *See* Ventura Barrio (J.)

BARRIO (Manuel García del) *See* García del Barrio.

BARRIO (Paulino del) Noticia sobre el terreno carbonífero de Coronel i Lota, i sobre los trabajos de esplotacion en él emprendidos. [With plates and a map.] pp. 107. *Santiago*, 1857. 4°. **7104.** e. **15.**

BARRIO (Pedro del) *See* Minguez (F.) Por F. Minguez, ensayador de la casa de la moneda desta ciudad: F. Beteta: y P. del Barrio Guardas, *etc.* [1660?] fol. **1322.** l. **7.** (**25.**)

BARRIO ANGULO (Gabriel Pérez del) *See* Pérez del Barrio Angulo.

BARRIOBERO (Eduardo) *See* Barriobero y Herrán.

BARRIOBERO Y ARMAS (Juan) *Baron de Río Toría.* Los Consejos de Estado. Contribución al estudio del desenvolvimiento político del gobierno de los pueblos. pp. 44. *Madrid*, 1927. 8°. **8042.** m. **2.**

—— La Nobleza Española. Su estado legal. pp. 173. *Madrid*, 1902. 8°. **9903.** cc. **31.**

BARRIOBERO Y HERRÁN (Eduardo) *See* De Quincey (Thomas) El Asesinato, considerado como una de las bellas artes. Traducción, prólogo y notas de E. Barriobero. [1928.] 8°. **012352.** b. **50.**

—— *See* Fernandez de Velasco y Pimentel (B.) *Duke de Frias.* Deleite de la discreción y fácil escuela de la agudeza . . . Restauración y prólogo de E. Barriobero y Herrán. 1932. 8°. **12356.** p. **40.**

—— *See* Kalyāṇa-Malla. Ananga-Ranga . . . Traducción, prólogo y notas de E. Barriobero y Herrán. 1931. 8°. **14055.** hhh. **1.**

—— *See* Lucian, *of Samosata.* [*Two or more Works.—Spanish.*] Luciano de Samosata. Los Amores—El Banquete . . . Traducción directa, prólogo y notas de E. Barriobero y Herrán. 1931. 8°. **08467.** de. **16.**

—— *See* Mariana (J. de) Del Rey y de la institución de la dignidad real . . . Traducido . . . por E. Barriobero y Herrán. 1930. 8°. **8009.** ccc. **9.**

—— *See* Martinez de Toledo (A.) El Arcipreste de Talavera habla de los vicios de las malas mujeres y complexiones de los hombres . . . Estudio preliminar de E. Barriobero y Herrán. 1931. 8°. **3043.a.2.**

—— *See* Suetonius Tranquillus (C.) [*Vitae XII. Caesarum.*] Roma galante bajo los Césares. Primera versión directa al castellano, con un estudio biográfico-crítico del autor por E. Barriobero y Herrán, *etc.* 1907. 8°. **10606.** b. **53.**

—— Cervantes de levita. Nuestros libros de caballería. Dos ensayos de crítica. pp. 96. *Madrid*, 1905. 8°. **11852.** de. **19.**

BARRIOBERO Y HERRÁN (Eduardo)

—— Los Delitos sexuales en las viejas leyes españolas. Recopilación, prólogo, notas y glosario, por E. Barriobero y Herrán. pp. 203. *Madrid*, 1930. 8°. **05385.** ee. **8.**

BARRIOL (Alfred) Théorie et pratique des opérations financières . . . Quatrième édition, revue, corrigée et augmentée, *etc.* pp. vii. 429. *Paris*, 1931. 8°. **8224.** df. **4.**

BARRIOLA (Ignacio María)

—— La Medicina popular en el país vasco. pp. 166. *San Sebastián*, 1952. 8°. [*Monografías vascongadas.* no. 9.] Ac. **165.** b.

BARRIO LORENZOT (Juan Francisco del) *See* Mexico, *City of.* [*Official Documents.*] Ordenanzas de Gremios de la Nueva España . . . Compendio . . . de la Compilación Nueva de Ordenanzas . . . Hízolo . . . F. del Barrio Lorenzot, *etc.* 1920. 4°. **08282.** dd. **47.**

BARRION (Charles) De l'eau minérale de Coise, Savoie; son analyse, son emploi en thérapeutique. Thèse, *etc.* pp. 57. *Montpellier*, 1867. 4°. **7379.** g. **10.** (**3.**)

BARRION (Désiré) Dissertation sur l'empoisonnement par l'alcool. Thèse, *etc.* pp. 27. *Montpellier*, 1827. 4°. **1181.** d. **13.** (**17.**)

BARRION (Firmin) Essai sur le diagnostic dans les principales affections des poumons et de leurs dépendances; thèse, *etc.* pp. 19. *Paris*, 1833. 4°. **1184.** e. **12.** (**33.**)

BARRION (Gustave) Thèse pour le doctorat en médecine. (Questions sur diverses branches des sciences médicales.) pp. 31. *Paris*, 1839. 4°. [*Collection des thèses soutenues à la Faculté de Médecine de Paris.* An 1839. tom. 1.] **7371.** a. **1.**

BARRIONUEVO (Garcia) *Marquis de Cusano.* Garciæ Barrionueuo . . . Panegyricus ill^{mo} et ex^{mo} Dno. Petro Fernandez à Castro . . . Proregi Neapolitano, et supremi Italiæ consilij Præsidi scriptus. [With plates.] pp. 196. *Ex typographia T. Longi: Neapoli*, 1616. fol. **814.** l. **11.**

BARRIONUEVO (Gaspar Paez de) *See* Paez de Barrionuevo.

BARRIONUEVO (Jeronimo de) *See* Barrionuevo de Peralta.

BARRIONUEVO (José Calvo de) *See* Calvo de Barrionuevo.

BARRIONUEVO (M. Martínez) *See* Martínez Barrionuevo.

BARRIONUEVO (Pedro) Dissertation sur la fièvre adynamique, *etc.* pp. 31. *Paris*, 1825. 4°. **1183.** h. **14.** (**12.**)

BARRIO-NUEVO (Pierre) *See* Barrionuevo (Pedro)

BARRIONUEVO (Rodrigo de) *Begin.* Muy poderoso señor. El padre Rodrigo de Barrionueuo, de la Compañia de Iesus, *etc.* [A memorial to the King of Spain, on the affairs of the Jesuits in Peru, etc.] [1630?] fol. **4783.** f. **7.** (**8.**)

BARRIONUEVO DE PERALTA (Jerónimo)

—— Avisos de D. Jerónimo de Barrionuevo. 1654–1658. Precede una noticia de la vida y escritos del autor por A. Paz y Mélia. 4 tom. *Madrid*, 1892, 93. 8°. **09076.** a. **6.**

—— Por Don Geronimo Barnueuo de Peralta, Cauallero de la Orden de Santiago . . . Contra Don Diego de Silua Marques de Orani . . . En respuesta de su informacion. ff. 12. [*Madrid?* 1630?] **765.** i. **6.** (**28.**)

BARRIONUEVO DE PERALTA (JERÓNIMO)

—— Por Don Geronimo Varrionueuo de Peralta, Cauallero de la Orden de Santiago, Depositario general desta Corte. Contra el Marques de Orani D. Diego de Silua, como padre y legitimo administrador de don Fadrique de Silua su hijo. [A pleading.] ff. 9. [*Madrid*, 1630?] fol. **765**. i. **6**. (**27**.)

BARRIOS (CÁNDIDO) Armas reglamentarias en el ejército y en la armada. 2 vol. *Madrid*, 1877. 8°. [*Biblioteca Militar.* tom. 4, 5.] **8823.g.40.**

BARRIOS (DANIEL LEVI DE) *See* BARRIOS (Miguel de)

BARRIOS (EDUARDO)

—— Cuatro Cuentos. Edited with introduction, notes, exercises, and vocabulary by Seymour Resnick. pp. viii. 158. *Harper & Bros.: New York*, [1951.] 8°. **12944**. h. **3**.

—— El Hermano asno. [A novel.] pp. 167. *Buenos Aires*, 1946. 8°. **12492**. bbb. **4**.
Part of the "Biblioteca contemporánea."

—— Los Hombres del hombre. Novela, *etc.* pp. 317. *Santiago*, 1950. 8°. **12493**. cc. **27**.

—— Tamarugal. Una lejana historia entre dos cuentos que le pertenecen, *etc.* pp. 230. *Santiago*, 1944. 8°. **12489**. w. **41**.

BARRÍOS (GERARDO)

—— *See* SAN SALVADOR, *City of.—Sociedad Cooperativa "Gerardo Barrios 29 de Agosto."* Honenaje [*sic*] tributado a la Memoria del Héroe Capitán General Gerardo Barrios, *etc.* 1928. 8°. **010885**. g. **31**.

—— Recurso de nulidad interpuesto contra la sentencia pronunciada en el juicio arbitral entre el . . . Capitan Jeneral Don G. Barríos, y la representacion de Don E. Wallerstein. pp. 20. *San Salvador*, 1862. 8°. **6784**. aaa. **17**. (**1**.)

BARRIOS (JUAN DE) *Bishop of Río de la Plata. See* BARRIOS Y TOLEDO (J. de los)

BARRIOS (MARÍA ESTHER LLANA) *See* LLANA BARRIOS.

BARRIOS (MARIO LLANA) *See* LLANA BARRIOS.

BARRIOS (MIGUEL) Cristino. [A novel.] pp. 232. *Madrid*, 1882. 8°. **12489**. b. **2**.

BARRIOS (MIGUEL DE) *See* PENSO VEGA (J.) Respuesta panegirica a la carta que escrivio . . . J. Penso Vega al . . . Doctor I. Orobio. Glossala D. L. de Barrios [i.e. M. de Barrios]. [1677.] 8°. **4033**. a. **37**. (**7**.)

—— *See* ROEST (M.) De Opuscula van Daniel Levi—Miguel —de Barrios, *etc.* [1861.] 8°. **C. 57**. c. **21**. (**2**.)

—— *See* SOLOMON BEN JUDAH IBN GĚBHĪRŌL. Dias Penitentiales . . . Acto primero de contricion, del sabio Salomon ben Guebirol, traducido . . . por Don M. de Barrios. (Acto segundo de contricion, por Don M. de Barrios.) [1675?] 8°. **4033**. a. **37**. (**5**.)

—— Atlas Angelico de la Gran Bretaña, declaracion a su Gran Rey Jacobo Segundo, de que Atlante fue Henoch hijo de Jared, antes del Diluvio con la Monarchia Britanica. Y de lo que predixo de ella Isaias cap. 19. Hasta el presente año de 1688. y de lo que ha de ha contecerle hasta que sane de sus interiores heridas. pp. 161. [1688.] 8°. **808**. f. **20**.

—— Breve discurso, politico, sobre las expulsiones, de los Hebreos, en diversos reynos, y provinçias, de Europa, *etc.* [By M. de Barrios?] pp. 14. [1675?] 4°. *See* HEBREWS. **4033**. a. **37**. (**10**.)

BARRIOS (MIGUEL DE)

—— El Canto junto al Encanto, comedia famosa. [In verse.] pp. 42. [1665?] 4°. **11728**. a. **36**.

—— Contra la Verdad no ay Fuerça. [A drama in verse.] Panegirico a los tres bien aventurados martires Abraham Athias, Yahacob Rodriguez Càsares, y Raquel Nuñez Fernandez, que fueron quemados vivos en Córdova, *etc.* *D. de Castro Tartaz: Amsterdam*, [1665?] 8°. **4033**. a. **37**. (**3**.)
Imperfect; wanting pp. 17–32, 81–96.

—— Coro de las Musas, dirigido al Excelentissimo Señor Don Francisco de Melo, *etc.* pp. 648. *B. Vivien: Brusselas*, 1672. 12°. **243**. a. **34**.

—— Descripcion de las islas del mar Athlantico y de America. [In verse.] *See* EXQUEMELIN (A. O.) Piratas de la America, *etc.* 1793. 4°. **1197**. h. **19**.

—— Desembozos de la Verdad contra las Mascaras del Mundo, *etc.* pp. 21. [*Amsterdam*, 1675?] 8°. **4033**. a. **37**. (**6**.)

—— Comedia nueva. El Español de Oràn. Escrita par un Ingenio Militar. [By M. de Barrios.] pp. 45. [1720?] 4°. *See* SPANIARD. **11728**. i. **7**. (**6**.)

—— Estrella de Jacob. Sobre flores de lis. [With other pieces in prose and verse.] pp. 68 [168]. *Amsterdam*, 1686. 8°. **C. 57**. c. **21**. (**1**.)
The pagination is irregular.

—— Flor de Apolo, dirigida al ilustrissimo señor D. Antonio Fernandez de Cordoua, &c. [A collection of poems and plays. With a portrait of Antonio de Cordova and engravings in the text.] 3 pt. *B. Vivien: Bruselas*, 1665. 4°. **1073**. k. **12**.

—— [A reissue.] Las Poësias famosas, y Comedias de Don Miguel de Barrios. Segunda impression enriquescida con . . . estampas. *G. & J. Verdussen: Amberes*, 1674. 4°. **11450**. e. **33**.

—— [Another copy.] **1072**. g. **28**.
This copy contains also the titlepage of the issue of 1665.

—— Imperio de Dios en la harmonía del mundo. [A poem.] pp. 32. [*Brussels*, 1670?] 4°. **640**. l. **18**. (**2**.)
In this copy the engraving on the titlepage is supplied from another source.

—— Imperio de Dios en la harmonía del mundo. (Imperio de Dios. Piedra derribadora de la soñada estatua, desde el año de 1689 al de 1700.) pp. 46. [*Brussels?* 1700?] 4°. **1072**. g. **30**.
A reissue of the preceding, with additional matter in prose, and with an allegorical plate incorporating a portrait of the author.

—— Libre Alvedrio, y harmonia del cuerpo por disposicion del alma, *etc.* [In verse, followed by other works in prose and verse.] pp. 108. *B. Vivien: Brusselas*, 1680. 8°. **4033**. a. **37**. (**1**.)

—— Mediar Estremos. Decada primera en Roshasana, *etc.* pp. 78 [80]. *I. van Velsen: Amsterdam*, 5437 [1677]. 8°. **4033**. a. **37**. (**4**.)

—— Metros Nobles, *etc.* pp. 16. *Amsterdam*, [1675?] 8°. **4033**. a. **37**. (**2**.)
The running title reads: "Alabança a la Ley."

—— [Origen] del Reyno Dinamarques. [By M. de Barrios.] pp. 51–56. [1675?] 8°. *See* DENMARK. **4033**. a. **37**. (**9**.)

BARRIOS (MIGUEL DE)

—— Pedir Favor al Contrario. Comedia famosa. [In verse.] pp. 36. *Sevilla*, [1735?] 4°. **11728. a. 37.**

—— [Another copy.] **11728. i. 7. (7.)**

—— Triumpho del Govierno Popular, y de la Antiguedad Holandesa, *etc.* [With other works.] [*Amsterdam*, 1683.] 8°. **4033. aa. 43.**
This volume consists of several distinct fragmentary pieces in prose and verse, following one another in no apparent order. The pagination is occasionally continuous, but exceedingly irregular throughout. This is " Exemplaar A " in Roest's " De Opuscula van Daniel Levi—Miguel—de Barrios."

—— Trompeta del Juizio contra el Papa y la Inquisicion, satyra. [By M. de Barrios?] [1675?] 8°. *See* POPE. **4033. a. 37. (8.)**

BARRIOS (MODESTO)

—— *See* ARCE (M. J.) *President of the Republic of Central America.* Memoria del General M. J. Arce . . . Comentada por . . . M. Barrios, *etc.* 1947. 8°. **8179. g. 9.**

—— Tratado de Puericultura. pp. 145. *Managua*, 1924. 8°. **8304. ee. 39.**

BARRIOS (RICARDO)

—— *See* SZÉCSY (J. de) Arte barroco en Antigua. (Baroque Art in Antigua.) . . . Versión castellana de Ricardo Barrios. 1953. 8°. **7823. ee. 34.**

BARRIO Y LIMA (LORENZO PHELIPE DE LA TORRE) *See* TORRE BARRIO Y LIMA.

BARRIO Y MIER (MATIAS) Historia General del Derecho Español. Extracto taquigrafico de las explicaciones del Dr. D. M. Barrio y Mier. 3 tom. *Madrid*, [1894.] 8°. **5384. aa. 11.**

BARRIO Y RENGEL (JOSE M. DEL) Sermon predicado por el P. D. Jose M. del Barrio y Rengel . . . en la solemne funcion que el Comercio de México dedicó á Maria Santisima de Guadalupe, *etc.* pp. 52. *México*, 1857. 8°. **4424. aaa. 6.**

BARRIOS Y TOLEDO (JUAN DE LOS) successively *Bishop of Río de la Plata* and *of Santa Marta* and *Archbishop of New Granada.*

—— *See* GANDÍA (E. de) El Primer clérigo y el primer obispo [i.e. J. de los Barrios y Toledo] del Río de la Plata. 1934. 8°. **20010. a. 7.**

BARRIS (CYPRIEN LACAVE LA PLAGNE) *See* LACAVE LA PLAGNE BARRIS.

BARRIS (PIERRE JOSEPH PAUL) *Baron.* Rapport et projet de décret sur la réunion des communes de Saint Antonin et de Feneyrols au district de Montauban présentés . . . le 9 août 1792, *etc.* pp. 4. [*Paris*, 1792.] 8°. **F.R. 111. (26.)**

BARRIS (PIERRE S. PAUL) *Baron. See* BARRIS (Pierre Joseph Paul)

BARRIS (RAFAEL) *See* BARRIS MUÑOZ.

BARRIS (W. H.) Descriptions of some new Blastoids from the Hamilton Group. *See* WACHSMUTH (Charles) On a new genus and species of Blastoids, *etc.* 1883. 4°. **7203. cc. 6.**

BARRISH (JOÁNNE INGRAM) *See* INGRAM-BARRISH (J.)

BARRIS MUÑOZ (RAFAEL) *See* SANCHO (H.) and BARRIS MUÑOZ (R.) El Puerto de Santa María en el descubrimiento de América, *etc.* 1926. 8°. **10161. e. 28.**

BARRIS MUÑOZ (RAFAEL)

—— Notas Crítico-Biográficas de Francisco de Vitoria, *etc.* pp. 64. *Sevilla*, 1928. 8°. **10633. b. 45.**

BARRISTER. *See* also BARRISTER-AT-LAW.

—— *See* BANTING (William) The Rational Cure of Obesity . . . Re-edited . . . by a Barrister [i.e. A. M. Broadley]. 1902. 8°. **7620. aaa. 59.**

—— *See* BEETON (Samuel O.) Beeton's Law Book . . . Revised by a Barrister. [1876.] 8°. **6146. aaa. 3.**

—— —— [1879.] 8°. **6147. f. 21.**

—— *See* CURRAN (*Right Hon.* John P.) Speeches of the Right Honourable J. P. Curran . . . With a Memoir. By a Barrister [i.e. Thomas Osborne Davis]. 1843. 8°. **1205. f. 15.**

—— *See* ENGLAND.—*Laws and Statutes.*—IV. *Elections.* The Election Statutes, including the Corrupt Practices Act, chronologically arranged, with an index . . . Edited by a Barrister. [i.e. W. H. Cooke] 1857. 8°. **1381. b. 29.**

—— *See* ENGLAND.—*Court of Bankruptcy.* The Rules and Orders in Bankruptcy, dated 19th of October, 1852; with the schedule of forms in full, explanatory notes and index. By a Barrister, of the Middle Temple. 1852. 12°. **6405. a. 42. (5.)**

—— Second edition, *etc.* 1852. 12°. **6405. b. 37. (9.)**

—— *See* FONBLANQUE (Albany) *the Younger.* How we are governed . . . The thirteenth edition, revised . . . and considerably enlarged by " a Barrister." [1879.] 8°. **8010. de. 3.**

—— *See* GULLY (Robert) Journals kept by Mr. Gully and Capt. Denham, during a captivity in China, in the year 1842. Edited by a Barrister. 1844. 8°. **1434. f. 6.**

—— *See* JACOB (Giles) The Complete Court-Keeper; or, Land-Steward's assistant . . . Eighth edition, enlarged and corrected . . . by a Barrister. 1819. 8°. **1129. e. 7.**

—— *See* RUSSELL (John) *Earl Russell.* Political Opinions on the Roman Catholic Question, expressed in parliament and in public. By the Rt. Hon. Lord J. Russell . . . compiled . . . by a Barrister. 1850. 8°. **3938. c. 82.**

—— *See* SCOTT (Henry) *Metal-Broker, of Wolverhampton.* The Case of " The Confessional Unmasked " . . . With some prefatory remarks, by a Barrister. 1868. 8°. **6495. aa. 45. (5.)**

—— An Abstract of an Act for the further amendment of the Laws relating to the Poor in England. 7 & 8 Victoria cap. 101. With an analytical index. By a Barrister. pp. 36. *W. M. Clark: London*, 1844. 12°. **1381. b. 18.**

—— An Abstract of the new County Courts and the Employers and Workmen Acts: containing the rules and orders, so far as they apply to the said Acts . . . By a Barrister. pp. 322. *John Heywood: Manchester; Simpkin, Marshall & Co.: London*, [1875.] 8°. **6146. aaa. 1. (3.)**

—— Advocacy in the County Courts. A letter to Sir Alexander Cockburn . . . By a Barrister of the Inner Temple. [Signed: " A Barrister."] pp. 19. *S. Sweet: London*, 1851. 8°. **6146. bbb. 20. (6.)**

—— An Alphabetical Arrangement of Mr Peel's Acts, Lord Lansdowne's Act, &c. &c. . . . and other statutes relating to the criminal law . . . Second edition . . . By a Barrister. [i.e. John Frederick Archbold] pp. xi. 309. *J. & W. T. Clarke: London*, 1830. 12°. **1129. c. 27.**

—— Analysis of the Evidence given before the Select Committees upon the Slave Trade. By a Barrister. pp. 121. *Partridge & Oakey: London*, 1850. 8°. **8155. c. 10.**

—— An Answer to the Speech of the Right Hon. Sir Robert Peel . . . upon the Second Reading of the Jewish Disabilities Bill. By a Barrister. pp. 23. *F. & J. Rivington: London*, 1848. 8°. **4033. d. 16.**

—— Argument on the case of Marshal Ney, with reference to the 12th article of the convention of Paris, and the treaty of the 20th Nov. 1815. In which the reasonings of Messrs. Dupin and Berryer, his Counsel, are considered. With an appendix, containing their argument as published by themselves, the dispatch of the Duke of Wellington inclosing the convention of Paris, and the convention itself. By a Barrister. pp. 51. *Longman & Co.; London*, 1816. 8°. **1059. h. 18. (6.)**

—— The Bacon-Shakespeare Controversy. By a Barrister. [i.e. Howard Bridgewater.] Reprinted from Baconiana, *etc. London*, [1927.] 8°. **11767. g. 3.**

—— The Barrister: or, Strictures on the education proper for the Bar, *etc.* [By Thomas Ruggles.] 2 vol. *J. Deighton: London*, 1792. 8°. **510. a. 35.**

—— A Barrister's Collection of Stories which have been sworn upon oath to be true. 3 ser. *Horace Cox: London*, 1898. 8°. **012613. f. 21.**

—— The Boundary Act, 11th July, 1832, with explanatory notes, and an analysis. By a Barrister. To which is added the Order in Council, altering the dates in the Reform Act. pp. 76. *C. G. Cabban: London*, 1832. 12°. **514. a. 13. (1.)**

—— Capital Punishment from an Utilitarian Point of View. By a Barrister, late Scholar of Trinity College, Cambridge. pp. 36. *R. J. Mitchell & Sons: London*, 1879. 8°. **6146. b. 37. (8.)**

—— The Chemist's Legal Hand-Book. By a Barrister. pp. ii. 244. *The British and Colonial Druggist: London*, 1899. 8°. **6095. de. 19.**

—— Christianity and Common Sense. A plea for the worship of our Heavenly Father, and also for the opening of museums and galleries on Sundays. By a Barrister. pp. iii. iii. 246. *Chapman & Hall: London*, 1883. 8°. **4018. h. 11.**

—— Church and State in the Abstract, and in relation to our National Churches, and to Dissenters. By a Barrister. pp. 3. *William Macintosh: London*, [1873.] 8°. **4405. k. 1. (149*.)**

—— Church of England Patronage and its Consequences. By a Barrister. pp. 8. *S. W. Partridge & Co.: London*, 1879. 8°. **4109. aa. 20. (7.)**

—— A Common-Sense Protest against a Capital Romish Error. By a Barrister. pp. 32. *Protestant Association Office; Wertheim, Macintosh & Hunt: London*, 1859. 8°. **3939. b. 61. (3.)**

—— A Comparative State of the two Rejected Money Bills, in 1692 and 1769. With some observations on Poynings Act, and the explanatory statute of Philip and Mary. By a Barrister [i.e. Richard Power]. pp. 91. *James Williams: Dublin*, 1770. 8°. **8145. bb. 8.**

—— A Complete Abstract of the Debtors Act, 1869; with the rules, and an index. By a Barrister. pp. 20. *A. Heywood & Son: Manchester; Simpkin, Marshall & Co.: London*, 1870. 8°. **6375. a. 43. (6.)**

—— A Complete Abstract of the New Bankruptcy Act; with an index. By a Barrister. (Second edition.) pp. 28. *A. Heywood & Son: Manchester; Simpkin, Marshall & Co.: London*, 1870. 8°. **6375. b. 47. (11.)**

—— Considerations on Divorce a vinculo Matrimonii, in connexion with Holy Scripture. By a Barrister [i.e. Edward Lowth Badeley]. pp. 62. *C. J. Stewart: London*, 1857. 8°. **5176. c. 30.**

—— The Contagious Diseases Acts: the mistake of the advocates, in and out of Parliament, for their repeal: and how to obtain repeal. By a Barrister. pp. 3. *William Macintosh: London*, 1875. 8°. **6146. aaa. 1. (4.)**

—— The Creation of our First Parents according to the Hebrew Scriptures, and as differing from the account in our English version. By a Barrister. pp. 11. *William Macintosh: London*, 1875. 8°. **4422. h. 1. (18.)**

—— Culverwell v. Sidebottom. A letter to Her Majesty's Attorney-General. With a full report of the above extraordinary trial. By a Barrister [i.e. Frederick Lawrence]. pp. 24. *Effingham Wilson: London*, 1857. 8°. **6146. g. 17. (4.)**

—— Gambling. Culverwell v. Sidebottom. A Letter to Her Majesty's Attorney General, with a full report of the above extraordinary trial . . . Second edition. To which are added, the trial of Sidebottom v. Adkins, and Lord Derby's celebrated letter to the Jockey Club. pp. 30. *Effingham Wilson: London*, 1859. 8°. **6405. c. 3.**

—— Dattaka Siromani [by Bharatachandra Ṣiromaṇi], and Dattaka Tilaka. Remarks [on those works] by a Barrister. pp. 15. *J. Wenger: Calcutta*, 1867. 8°. **8023. ee. 9. (2.)**

—— A Digest of the Evidence taken before the Select Committee of the House of Commons on Andover Union; with some introductory remarks. By a Barrister. pp. lxx. 195. *J. Murray: London*, 1846. 8°. **8275. d. 24.**

—— A Digested Index to the nineteen volumes of Mr. Vesey's Reports of cases in the High Court of Chancery . . . By a Barrister. pp. 461. 1822. 8°. *See* ENGLAND.—*Court of Chancery.—Reports of Cases.* Reports of Cases, *etc.* [1789–1816.] 1795, *etc.* fol. & 8°. **22. a. 17.**

—— The Ecclesiastical Legal Guide to Archbishops, Bishops and their Secretaries, the Clergy . . . &c. With forms of the different instruments, and particulars of the ceremonies . . . and cases and opinions from eminent counsel . . . Carefully selected and arranged by a Barrister, *etc.* pt. 1. pp. viii. 472. *J. S. Hodson: London*, 1839. 8°. **1130. k. 16.**

No more published.

—— 1823; or, a New Year's Gift for the true Orangemen of Ireland. By a Barrister. [A condemnation of the practice of painting the Statue of William III on the 4th of November.] pp. 24. *A. O'Neil: Dublin*, 1823. 8°. **8145. c. 4.**

—— An Elementary ABC Guide to the Poor Law. By a Barrister. pp. vii. 32. *Eyre & Spottiswoode: London*, [1895.] 16°. **6345. a. 9.**

—— Essays. By a Barrister [i.e. Sir James Fitz-James Stephen]. Reprinted from the Saturday Review. pp. iv. 335. *Smith, Elder & Co.: London*, 1862. 8°. **8405. h. 16.**

—— Euphrates versus Suez, or, Which is the shortest? Being a reply to a Quarterly Reviewer, of "The Suez and Euphrates Routes to India." By a Barrister. pp. 32. *Effingham Wilson: London*, 1857. 8°. **08235. c. 3. (15.)**

—— Everyday Law . . . By a Barrister. pp. 70. *Iliffe & Son: London,* [1897.] 16°. [*Nutshell Series.*] **012208**. de. **5/11**.

—— Every Man's Own Lawyer: a handy book of the principles of law and equity; comprising the rights and wrongs of individuals . . . By a Barrister. *Lockwood & Co.: London,* 1863- . 12°. **6148**. c. **1**.
Various editions. This set includes a Supplement to the 59th edition.

—— [Another copy of the fourth edition, with a different titlepage.] Every Man his Own Lawyer, *etc.* pp. xii. 384. *Lockwood & Co.: London,* 1865. 12°. **6145**. aa. **13**.

—— [Another issue of the 7th, 8th and 9th editions.] Every Lawyer's Own Book: a handy volume on the general principles and points of practice of the Courts of Law and Equity, with many . . . modern forms and precedents. By a Barrister. Seventh (eighth, ninth) edition, *etc.* 3 vol. *Lockwood & Co.: London,* 1869–72. 8°. **6146**. aa. **7–9**.

—— The Exclusion of the Queen from the Liturgy historically and legally considered. By a Barrister. pp. 40. *H. Butterworth: London,* 1821. 8°. **3475**. b. **45**.

—— [Another copy.] **3475**. b. **14**
Imperfect; wanting the last leaf.

—— The Exclusion of the Queen from the Liturgy . . . considered . . . The second edition, corrected. pp. 40. *H. Butterworth: London,* 1821. 8°. **8140**. e. **38**. **(8.)**

—— The third edition, revised and corrected, *etc.* pp. 40. *H. Butterworth: London,* 1821. 8°. **10807**. ff. **2**. **(15.)**

—— An Exegesis of the Seventh Chapter of St. Paul's Epistle to the Romans. By a Barrister. pp. 44. *Seeley, Jackson & Halliday: London,* 1857. 8°. **3265**. c. **6**.

—— An Exposition of the Hair Powder Act, setting forth its legal operation; with a full abstract of the Act. By a Barrister. pp. 60. *G. G. & J. Robinson: London,* 1795. 8°. **8225**. b. **17**.

—— An Exposure of the Injurious Effects of the Present System of the Bankruptcy Law, in London and in the Country; with suggestions for its improvement . . . By a Barrister. [Reprinted from the "Morning Chronicle."] pp. 60. *J. W. Parker: London,* 1841. 8°. **1380**. f. **33**.

—— Fair Play: being an examination of the rival claims of homœopathy and the chartered schools of medicine and surgery. By a Barrister. pp. 48. *Leath & Ross: London,* 1863. 8°. **7460**. aa. **7**.

—— [Another copy.] **07305**. e. **21**. **(2.)**
Imperfect; wanting pp. 17–32.

—— Faithful Abstracts of the Acts for the Amendment of the Law of Bankruptcy, and for the relief of insolvent debtors. With an index. By a Barrister. pp. 26. *R. Walwyn: London,* 1842. 12°. **1380**. c. **38**.

—— A Few Words on the subject of Canada. By a Barrister [i.e. Charles Clark]. pp. 52. *Longman & Co.: London,* 1837. 8°. T. **2381**. **(3.)**

—— [Another copy.] **1196**. h. **34**

—— Five Hundred Pounds Reward. A novel. By a Barrister [i.e. William Knox Wigram]. 3 vol. *Richard Bentley: London,* 1867. 8°. **12635**. dd. **2**.

—— Five Minutes Examination of an Article in the . . . Edinburgh Review respecting the Judicial Character of Lord Eldon. By a Barrister. pp. 16. *Henry Butterworth: London,* 1823. 8°. C.T.80.(4.)

—— Gambling. Culverwell v. Sidebottom . . . By a Barrister. *See* supra: Culverwell v. Sidebottom.

—— "Go out quickly." Luke xiv. 21. [Signed: A Barrister, i.e. John Macgregor.] pp. 8. *Seeleys, etc.: London,* [1855.] 8°. **4193**. f. **22**.

—— The Grammar of Law: containing the first principles of natural, religious, political, and civil law; together with a synopsis of the common and statute law. To which is added the royal prerogatives, and an explanation of law terms in general use. By a Barrister. pp. xi. 337. *Joseph Rickerby: London,* 1839. 8°. **1129**. a. **27**.

—— Grammar Schools Considered, with reference to a case lately decided by the Lord Chancellor. By a Barrister. 1820. *See* PERIODICAL PUBLICATIONS.—*London.* The Pamphleteer, *etc.* vol. 16. 1813, *etc.* 8°. P.P. **3557**. w.

—— The Gross Abuses of Public Charities pointed out, and the necessity of enacting the Charitable Trusts Bill demonstrated. By a Barrister. pp. 89. *Owen Richards: London,* 1846. 8°. **1392**. e. **10**.

—— A Guide to the Law: for general use. By a Barrister [i.e. Edward Reynolds] . . . Thirteenth edition. pp. iii. 190. *Stevens & Sons: London,* 1870. 8°. **6146**. aa. **10**.

—— Fifteenth edition. pp. iii. 194. *Stevens & Sons: London,* 1871. 8°. **6146**. aa. **11**.

—— Sixteenth edition. pp. iii. 189. *Stevens & Sons: London,* 1871. 8°. **6146**. aaa. **4**.

—— Eighteenth edition. pp. iii. 189. *Stevens & Sons: London,* 1872. 8°. **6145**. aa. **15**.

—— Nineteenth edition. pp. iii. 208. *Stevens & Sons: London,* 1873. 8°. **6145**. aa. **16**.

—— Twenty-third edition. pp. xiii. 305. *Stevens & Sons: London,* 1880. 8°. **6146**. h. **26**.

—— The Handy Guide to the Road Traffic Act, 1930 . . . By a Barrister. pp. 30. *"On & Off Duty" Office: London,* [1931.] 16°. **6427**. de. **9**.

—— Hints on Advocacy . . . By a Barrister [i.e. Richard Harris]. pp. 217. *Waterlow Bros. & Layton: London,* 1879. 8°. **6281**. de. **12**.

—— Second edition, revised and enlarged. pp. 296. *Waterlow Bros. & Layton: London,* 1879. 8°. **6281**. de. **13**.

—— Hints to Students of Law, by a Barrister. pp. 15. *W. Benning & Co.: London,* 1847. 8°. **6005**. d. **5**.

—— Hints to the Public, and the Legislature, on the Nature and Effect of Evangelical Preaching. By a Barrister [i.e. James Sedgwick]. Part the first. pp. 147. *Johnson, etc.: London,* 1808. 8°. T. **206**. **(1*.)**

—— Fourth edition. pp. 139. *Johnson, etc.: London,* 1808. 8°. **4498**. ee. **14**. **(1.)**

—— Hints to the Public . . . Part the second. pp. 198. *Johnson, etc.: London,* 1808. 8°. T. **206**. **(1.)**

—— [Another copy.] **4498**. ee. **14**. **(2.)**

—— Hints to the Public . . . Part the third. pp. 140. *Johnson, etc.: London,* 1809. 8°. T. **86**. **(2.)**

—— Hints to the Public . . . Part the fourth. pp. 159. *Johnson & Co., etc.: London; A. Constable & Co.: Edinburgh,* 1810. 8°. **1103**. k. **61**.

—— Hints to the Public, *etc.* 5 pt. *Sherwood, Neely & Jones: London,* 1812. 8°. **4106**. g. **7**.
A made-up set. Pt. 2 *is of the 4th edition and bears the date* 1815.

—— *See* COLLYER (William B.) An Appeal to the Legislature, and to the public; in answer . . . to the Hints of a Barrister [i.e. James Sedgwick] on the Nature and Effect of Evangelical Preaching, *etc.* 1809. 8°. **4109**. h. **9**. (**2**.)

—— *See* LAYMAN. A Defence of the Principal Doctrines of Evangelical Religion, in a letter to "a Barrister" [i.e. James Sedgwick]; occasioned by his "Hints on the Nature and Effect of Evangelical Preaching." 1808. 8°. **4380**. bbb. **47**. (**1**.)

—— *See* VIGIL, *pseud.* The Legislature alarmed, and the Barrister unmasked! Occasioned by Hints to the Public and the Legislature, *etc.* [1802?] 8°. **4110**. b. **27**.

—— An Appeal to the Legislature and to the Public; in answer to the Hints of a Barrister [i.e. James Sedgwick], on the Nature and Effect of Evangelical Preaching. By an Evangelical Preacher [i.e. William Bengo Collyer]. pp. 55. *J. G. Barnard: London,* 1808. 8°. **4107**. bb. **19**.

—— A Few Words on the Increase of Methodism, occasioned by "Hints of a Barrister" [i.e. James Sedgwick], and the observations [by Sydney Smith] in the Edinburgh Review. pp. 23. *J. Miles & R. Hunter: London,* 1810. 8°. **4139**. d. **11**.

—— Hints to Witnesses in Courts of Justice. By a Barrister [i.e. Barron Field]. pp. 24. *J. Butterworth & Son: London; J. Cooke: Dublin,* 1815. 8°. **6281**. b. **4**.

—— History against Colenso. Examination of the witnesses. By a Barrister. [A reply to Bishop Colenso's work, "The Pentateuch and Book of Joshua critically examined."] 4 pt. pp. 232. *W. Curry & Co.: Dublin; Wertheim, Macintosh & Hunt: London,* 1863–64. 8°. **3155**. cc. **10**.

—— The History of John A——: by a Barrister. pp. 32. *Judd & Glass; Wertheim & Macintosh: London,* 1856. 32°. **4986**. a. **2**.
A later edition entitled "The Pious Cabman" is entered below.

—— I accuse France. By a barrister. pp. 28. *Spanish Press Services: London,* [1937.] 8°. **08052**. c. **77**.

—— Imprisonment for Debt, and Bankruptcy. With a suggestion. By a Barrister. pp. 15. *Butterworths: London,* 1869. 8°. **6405**. bb. **1**.

—— In my Opinion. By a Barrister. Social problems. Part I.—Women and their rights. pp. 22. *R. S. Chrystal: Manchester,* [1902.] 8°. **08275**. h. **62**.
No more published.

—— The Income Tax: its advantages over all other taxation, and answers to gainsayers. By a Barrister. pp. 3. *William Macintosh: London,* 1874. 8°. **8223**. e. **1**. (**172**.)

—— The Independence of Poland. By a Barrister. pp. viii. 74. *W. J. Bradley: London,* 1855. 8°. **8093**. b. **72**. (**1**.)

—— The Juror's, Guide, or, the Spirit of the jury laws; pointing out the qualifications, duties, powers, and liabilities of jurors . . . By a Barrister. pp. vi. 120. *T. Hurst: London,* 1833. 12°. **1129**. b. **19**.

—— Justice in England. By a Barrister. pp. 288. *Victor Gollancz: London,* 1938. 8°. **6190**. de. **31**.

—— Know how to make your Will. How to put your affairs in legal order. By a barrister . . . With many specimen wills and a special section appertaining to Scots law. pp. 128. *W. Foulsham & Co.: New York,* [1953.] 8°. **6356**. a. **6**.

—— Know your Rights in Marriage and Divorce. One hundred and one questions answered by "Barrister." pp. 35. *Warrel-Way Publishers: Ruislip,* [1948.] 12°. [*"Know Your Rights" Books.* no. 1.] **5175**. a. **52**.

—— The Law of Bills of Exchange and Promissory Notes. By a Barrister. pp. viii. 100. *London,* 1840. 12°. [*Tyas' Legal Handbooks.*] **1128**. a. **46**.

—— The Law of Debtor and Creditor . . . By a Barrister. pp. viii. 92. *London,* 1840. 12°. [*Tyas' Legal Handbooks.*] **1128**. a. **42**.

—— Third edition. pp. viii. 92. *London,* [1843?] 12°. [*Tyas' Legal Handbooks.*] **1128**. a. **48**.

—— The Law of Landlord and Tenant. By a Barrister. pp. 120. *W. Foulsham & Co.: London,* [1952.] 8°. **6327**. aa. **10**.

—— The Law of Negotiable Instruments, a handbook of the law on inland & foreign bills of exchange, promissory notes . . . By a Barrister. pp. 56. *T. Pettitt & Co.: London,* [1868.] 8°. **6375**. a. **46**.

—— The Law of Partnership . . . By a Barrister. pp. viii. 74. *London,* 1840. 12°. [*Tyas' Legal Handbooks.*] **1128**. a. **43**.

—— Law Students' and Practitioners' Common Place Book of Law and Equity . . . By a Barrister [i.e. Charles Erdman Petersdorff]. pp. 380. *Butterworths; Simpkin, Marshall & Co.: London,* 1871. 4°. **6145**. m. **1**.

—— Lawyers and Christianity. By a Barrister. pp. 19. *Monthly Tract Society: London,* [1895.] 8°. **4371**. bb. **24**. (**8**.)

—— The Lawyers' Stamp Table. A complete list of all the stamp duties, as amended by the recent acts, with notes of the decided cases. By a Barrister. pp. 181. *Law Times Office: London,* 1864. 12°. **6375**. a. **1**.

—— Lay Thoughts on the Indian Mutiny. By a Barrister. Second edition. pp. 41. *H. Sweet: London,* 1858. 8°. **8023**. d. **3**.

—— A Letter to a Member of Parliament on the Police of the Metropolis. By a Barrister. Second edition. pp. 42. *W. Wright: London,* 1822. 8°. **6055**. b. **3**.

—— A Letter to Benjamin D'Israeli, Esq., M.P. upon the subject of his recent attack upon the Minister [i.e. Sir Robert Peel]. By a Barrister. pp. 15. *William Pickering: London,* 1846. 8°. **8138**. d. **8**.

—— Letter to Joshua Spencer, Esq. occasioned by his Thoughts on an Union. By a Barrister [i.e. William Johnson]. pp. 42. *John Archer: Dublin,* 1798. 8°. **8145**. d. **4**.

—— A Letter to S. C. Cox, Esq. one of the Masters of the Court of Chancery, respecting the practice of that Court, with suggestions for its alteration. By a Barrister. pp. 24. *H. Butterworth: London,* 1824. 8°. C.T.80.(5.)

—— A Letter to the Lord Bishop of London on the Promulgation of the recent Papal Bull. By a Barrister. pp. 66. *J. Ridgway; W. & T. Piper: London,* [1851.] 8°. **3938.** c. **5.**

—— A Letter to the Lord Mayor and Common Council of the City of London. [In reference to their Address to the Queen.] By a Barister [*sic*]. pp. 24. *W. Wright: London,* 1821. 8°. **8135.** bb. **12.**

—— A Letter to the Right Hon. the Earl of Eldon, on the present state of agricultural lessees and their right to relief from the payment of rent. By a Barrister. pp. vii. 48. *Longman & Co., etc.: London,* 1822. 8°. **1027.** b. **22.** (**18.**)

—— Letter to the Right Honorable Lord Lyndhurst, on the appointment of sheriffs in Ireland, under the Earl of Mulgrave, by a Barrister [i.e. Henry Hall Joy?]. pp. 94. *Longman, Orme & Co., etc.: London,* 1838. 8°. T. **2439.** (**2.**)

—— Letters on the Subject of Union, addressed to Messrs. Saurin and Jebb, in which Mr. Jebb's "Reply" is considered. By a Barrister [i.e. Sir William Cusack Smith]. pp. 80. *J. Milliken: Dublin,* 1799. 8°. **1103.** g. **10.** (**1.**)

—— [Another copy.] **117.** h. **17.**

—— [Another edition.] pp. 115. *J. Wright: London,* 1799. 8°. **111.** d. **64.**

—— "Lloyd's" Lawyer. Legal advice for all alphabetically arranged. By a Barrister. pp. 162. *London,* [1910.] 8°. [*Lloyd's Popular Handbooks.* no. 7.] **12199.** e. **1/7.**

—— (New edition with supplement.) pp. 178. *London,* [1912.] 8°. [*Lloyd's Popular Handbooks.* no. 7.] **12199.** e. **1/14.**

—— The Magistracy of England, its abuses, and their remedy in popular election. By a Barrister. pp. 30. *Henry Hooper: London,* 1835. 8°. **6146.** b. **6.**

—— Mr. Ricardo's Anatomy of the Navigation Laws, dissected. By a Barrister. pp. 206. *Chapman & Hall: London,* 1848. 12°. **8245.** c. **5.**

—— Notes on Bishop Magee's Pleadings for Christ. By a Barrister. pp. 53. *Thomas Scott: Ramsgate,* [1871.] 8°. **4017.** e. **3.** (**2.**)

—— Notes on the Investment of Trust Funds in East India Stock. By a Barrister. pp. 16. *Stevens & Sons: London,* 1867. 8°. **6355.** aaa. **2.**

—— Notes on the Reform Bill. By a Barrister [i.e. Sir John Taylor Coleridge]. pp. 58. [*London,* 1831.] 8°. **8138.** c. **8.**

—— Notes on the Reform Bill. By a barrister [i.e. Sir John Taylor Coleridge]. pp. 63. MS. NOTE [by S. T. Coleridge]. *Roake & Varty: London,* 1831. 8°. C. **126.** h. **15.** (**3.**)

—— Second edition, with additions. pp. 70. *Roake & Varty: London,* 1831. 8°. T. **1321.** (**8.**)

—— Notes on the War. By a Barrister. [Signed: H. T. C., i.e. H. T. Cameron.] 1855. 8°. *See* C., H. T. **8821.** c. **16.** (**1.**)

—— Observations on Intimidation at Elections in Ireland, by Mob Violence and Priestly Influence, and the law relating thereto, with suggestions for its amendment. Also, an appendix, containing . . . evidence . . . illustrative of the intimidation statistics of 1852. By a Barrister. pp. 75. *W. Curry & Co.: Dublin; Thomas Hatchard: London,* 1854. 8°. **8145.** b. **11.**

—— Observations on the Doctrine of Rank Modus, laid down in the late case of Morris v. the Duke of Norfolk. By a Barrister (A. B.). 1842. 8°. *See* B., A. **1383.** d. **2.**

—— Observations on the Queen's Case, and particularly on the evidence of Meidge Barbara Kress: in a letter to a friend on the Continent. By a Barrister. pp. 114. *J. Hatchard & Son: London,* 1821. 8°. **1102.** g. **24.** (**13.**)

—— On the Suffrage and Duration of Parliaments. By a Barrister [i.e. Thomas Banister]. Fourth edition. *See* LENNOX (Charles) *3rd Duke of Richmond.* The Right of the People to Universal Suffrage, *etc.* 1859. 8°. **8138.c.74.**

—— The Orator: a treasury of English eloquence, containing selections from the most celebrated speeches of the past and present. Edited, with short explanatory notes and references, by a Barrister. pp. viii. 288. *S. O. Beeton: London,* 1865. 8°. **12301.** h. **20.**

—— Orthodox Theories of Prayer. By a Barrister. pp. 20. *Thomas Scott: London,* [1874.] 8°. **4017.** e. **7.** (**1.**)

—— Our Creed. Being an appeal to the Church of England regarding some doubts about the truth of ecclesiastical Christianity. By a Barrister. pp. viii. 155. *Chapman & Hall: London,* 1877. 8°. **4017.** bb. **9.**

—— Overend, Gurney & Co., Limited. A plain statement of the case. By a Barrister. pp. 19. *James Gilbert: London,* 1867. 8°. **8227.** bbb. **10.**

—— Papal Aggression Considered. By a Barrister. pp. 24. *Charles Dolman: London,* 1850. 8°. **3938.** e. **10.**

—— Parliamentary Elections. An outline of the law and practice. With hints to candidates, agents, speakers, canvassers, and others. By a Barrister. pp. 89. *T. Murby & Co.: London,* [1906.] 8°. **6325.** eee. **6.**

—— The Pious Cabman. By a Barrister. pp. 8. *Wertheim & Macintosh; Judd & Glass: London,* [1858.] 8°. **4986.** b. **10.**

An earlier edition, entitled "The History of John A——" is entered above.

—— A Plain Guide for Suitors in the County Court. By a Barrister. pp. xvii. 193. *Virtue & Co.: London,* 1868. 8°. **6405.** a. **7.**

—— New and revised edition. pp. xvii. 193. *Strahan & Co.: London,* 1870. 12°. **8703.** cc. **7.**

—— The Present Laws relating to Savings Banks in England . . . With explanatory notes, forms, &c. and a copious index. By a Barrister. pp. 89. *S. Sweet, etc.: London,* 1825. 12°. **1129.** d. **15.**

—— The Probable Consequences of a Union impartially considered; by a Barrister. pp. 18. *J. Milliken: Dublin,* 1799. 8°. **117.** h. **39.**

—— [Another copy.] **111.** d. **68.**

—— The Question, as to the admission of Catholics to Parliament, considered, upon the principles of existing laws. With supplemental observations on the coronation oath. By a Barrister [i.e. Sir John Joseph Dillon]. pp. 79. *E. Booker; J. Debrett: London,* 1801. 8°. **8135.** cc. **10.**

—— Questions and Answers on Mercantile Law. By a Barrister. pp. viii. 152. *V. & R. Stevens & J. S. Norton: London; Hodges & Smith: Dublin,* 1848. 12°. **1380.** b. **9.**

—— Questions for the New Year. Prepared by a Barrister. *G. J. Cross: London*, [1873.] 8°. **1891**. d. **1**. **(29.)**

—— A Record of a Record Reign. Compiled by a Barrister. [With reference to the reign of Queen Victoria.] pp. 24. *Simpkin, Marshall & Co.: London*, [1897.] 8°. **9004**. k. **16**. (**5**.)

—— [Another copy.] **10601**. ee. **22**. (**4**.)

—— Reflections on Slavery: in reply to certain passages of a speech recently delivered by Mr. Canning. Addressed to the Right Hon. Lord Dacre. By a Barrister [i.e. Joseph Beldam]. pp. 25. *Hatchard & Son; J. & A. Arch: London*, 1826. 8°. T. **1131**. (**11**.)

—— The Reform Act, June 7th, 1832, with . . . notes and an analysis. By a Barrister. pp. vi. 64. *C. G. Cabban: London*, 1832. 12°. **514**. a. **13**. (**2**.)

—— The Relations between Barristers, Solicitors and the Public; or, Lawyers and their clients. Third edition. pp. viii. 131. By a Barrister. *Effingham Wilson: London*, 1930. 8°. **6190**. de. **19**.

A previous edition, entitled "Lawyers and their Clients" is entered under LAWYERS.

—— Remarks on a late Tract by the Rev. John Keble, M.A., entitled Against profane dealing with Holy Matrimony. By a Barrister. pp. 39. *J. Hatchard & Son: London*, 1849. 8°. **5175**. d. **4**.

—— A Review of the Arguments in favor of the Continuance of Impeachments, notwithstanding a dissolution. By a Barrister [i.e. Spencer Perceval ?]. pp. 123. *W. Clarke; J. Stockdale: London*, 1791. 8°. **517**. k. **20**. (**3**.)

—— A Review of the Principal Facts connected with the Rise, Progress, Conclusion and Character of the recent State Prosecutions in Ireland . . . By a Barrister [i.e. David Leahy]. pp. 352. *Longman & Co.: London*, 1845. 8°. **1384**. f. **8**.

—— Roman Catholicism: being an historical and legal review of its past position and present claims in England. By a Barrister. pp. 75. *Longman & Co.: London*, 1851. 8°. **3938**. c. **4**.

—— Servants and Masters. The law of disputes, rights and remedies in plain language. By a Barrister. pp. vii. 36. *Horace Cox: London*, 1892. 8°. **6325**. aaa. **44**.

—— Second edition. pp. vii. 36. *Horace Cox: London*, 1894. 8°. **6325**. de. **39**.

—— Third edition, edited by His Honour Judge Gye. pp. vii. 36. *Horace Cox: London*, 1904. 8°. **6325**. cccc. **25**.

—— A Short Address to the People of England: upon the important subject of the proposed continuance of the income or property tax. By a Barrister. pp. 23. *F. C. & J. Rivington: London*, 1816. 8°. **104**. d. **24**.

—— A Short Review of the History of the Navigation Laws of England . . . To which are added a note on the present state of the law and an account of the acts and parts of acts proposed to be repealed by the Bill now before Parliament. By a Barrister [i.e. Stafford Henry Northcote, afterwards Earl of Iddesleigh]. pp. 80. *James Ridgway: London*, 1849. 8°. **6146**. h. **1**. (**10**.)

—— Second edition. pp. 83. *James Ridgway: London*, 1849. 8°. **8245**. e. **10**.

—— Sixty Questions upon the Proposed Criminal Code. By a Barrister. pp. 16. *Stevens & Haynes: London*, 1879. 8°. **6485**. df. **2**. (**11**.)

—— A Sketch of Cheap Corn: or, The Wealth of agriculture. By a Barrister. pp. 67. *Hatchard & Sons: London*, 1850. 12°. **8245**. a. **69**. (**4**.)

—— Sophisms of Free-Trade and Popular Political Economy examined. By a Barrister [i.e. Sir John Barnard Byles]. Second edition. pp. xvi. 226. *Seeleys: London*, 1850. 16°. **8205**. a. **18**.

—— Ninth edition, *etc.* pp. xii. 343. *Manchester Reciprocity Association: Manchester; Simpkin Marshall & Co.: London*, 1870. 16°. **8246**. aaa. **30**.

—— *See* PEARSON (Robert) *Wharfinger*. Free Trade. A reply to "Sophisms of Free Trade . . . by a Barrister" [i.e. Sir J. B. Byles]. 1850. 8°. **8245**. b. **56**.

—— Free Trade and its so-called Sophisms: a reply [by Edgar Alfred Bowring and Vere Henry Hobart, Baron Hobart] to "Sophisms of Free Trade, etc., examined by a Barrister" [i.e. Sir J. B. Byles]. Second edition, revised and enlarged. pp. 95. *J. W. Parker: London*, 1850. 12°. **8245**. a. **54**.

—— "The Star" Home Lawyer. First aid in legal difficulties. By a Barrister. pp. 64. *Daily News: London & Manchester*, [1916.] 8°. **6145**. aa. **41**.

—— Strikes and Lock-outs; or, the Law of combination. With a summary of the law of arbitrations of disputes between masters and workmen. By a Barrister. pp. xviii. 78. *William Tegg: London*, 1867. 8°. **6325**. aa. **3**.

—— A Substitute for Official General Registration of Deeds and Transactions inter vivos, affecting titles to land, proposed in a letter to Sir E. B. Sugden, *etc.* [Signed: a Barrister.] pp. 23. *William Walker: London*, 1830. 8°. **6305**. aaa. **2**.

—— Tales, by a Barrister. [By Frederick Liardet] 3 vol. *Chapman & Hall: London*, 1844. 8°. N. **2394**.

—— Thoughts on the Abolition of the Established Church as a means of pacificating Ireland. By a Barrister. pp. 16. *Hodges, Smith & Foster: Dublin*, 1868. 8°. **8145**. ee. **3**. (**3**.)

—— Thoughts on the Study of Prophecy; the duty and the discouragements. To which are added a few words on the twenty-fourth chapter of St. Matthew's Gospel. By a Barrister [i.e. Peter Frederick O'Malley]. pp. 89. *J. J. Guillaume: London*, 1849. 12°. **3185**. a. **3**.

—— A Tour in Quest of Genealogy, through several parts of Wales, Somersetshire, and Wiltshire, in a series of letters . . . interspersed with a description of Stourhead and Stonehenge . . . and curious fragments from a manuscript collection ascribed to Shakespeare. By a Barrister [i.e. Richard Fenton]. [The editor's dedication signed: H. Jones, i.e. R. Fenton himself ?] pp. 338. *Sherwood, Nealy & Jones: London*, 1811. 8°. **195**. c. **11**.

—— [Another copy.] G. **15965**.

—— Shakespeariana. Reprinted from the "Stratford-on-Avon Herald." [A review, extracted by Robert Gibbs from "The European Magazine," of "A Tour in Quest of Genealogy . . . By a Barrister."] pp. 8. *E. Adams: Stratford-on-Avon*, [1864 ?] 8°. **11761**. b. **3**.

—— Two Tracts shewing, that Americans, born before the independence, are, by the law of England, not aliens. First, a discussion, &c. Second, a reply, &c. By a Barrister [i.e. John Reeves]. 2 pt. *Reed & Hunter; J. Hatchard: London*, 1814. 8°. B. **710**. (**4**.)

BARRISTER.

—— The Universal Obligation of Tithes. By a Barrister. pp. vi. 136. *Elliot Stock: London,* 1901. 8°. **4109.** ee. **26.**

—— [Another copy.] **764.** c. **5.**

—— The Vagrant Act, in relation to the liberty of the subject . . . By a Barrister. Second edition. With a postscript. 2 pt. *John Murray: London,* 1824. 8°. T. **1086.** **(10.)**
With this copy is bound up a second copy of the postscript, with a separate titlepage.

—— What have the Whigs done for Ireland ? or, the English Whigs and Irish Famine. By a Barrister. pp. 42. *E. J. Milliken: Dublin; Longman & Co.: London,* 1851. 8°. **8145.** e. **5.**

—— What is Limited Liability ? A plain and practical explanation of the new law, 19 & 20 Vic. c. 47. By a Barrister. pp. 10. *W. & H. S. Warr: London,* 1857. 12°. **8246.** a. **4.**

BARRISTER-AT-LAW. *See* also BARRISTER.

—— The Act relating to Bills of Sale, rendered into plain English, and revised with explanatory notes, by a Barrister-at-Law. pp. 7. *F. E. Longley: London,* [1883.] 8°. **6146.** f. **10.** **(2.)**

—— The Act relating to the Liability of Employers, rendered into plain English, and revised with explanatory notes, by a Barrister-at-Law. pp. 8. *F. E. Longley: London,* [1883.] 8°. **6146.** f. **10.** **(3.)**

—— The Act relating to the Sale of Food and Drugs, rendered into plain English, and revised with explanatory notes, by a Barrister-at-Law. pp. 15. *F. E. Longley: London,* [1883.] 8°. **6146.** f. **10.** **(4.)**

—— An Appeal to the Conscience of a Fanatick : shewing that the King of England, by the fundamental laws of it, is as absolute and independent a monarch, as any of the Kings mentioned in Scripture ; and consequently as free as any of them from any humane, coactive power, to punish, censure, or dethrone him. Whereunto is added a short view of the laws both foreign and domestick, against seditious conventicles. By a Barrister at Law [i.e. Bartholomew Lane]. pp. 28. *J. G. for John Walthoe: London,* 1684. 4°. **8122.** e. **6.**

—— An Argument in favour of the Rights of Cross-Examination. By a Barrister-at-Law. pp. 23. *J. Bickerstaff: London,* 1803. 8°. C.T. **71.** **(2.)**

—— Be Your own Lawyer ; or, the Secrets of the Law Office. Giving . . . the mercantile or business laws of Canada . . . By a Barrister-at-Law. pp. 148. *W. H. Anger: Toronto,* 1896. 8°. **06605.** g. **7.**
A later edition, entitled " Your own Lawyer and Conveyancer " is entered below.

—— The Canadian Lawyer : a handy book of the laws and of legal information . . . Compiled by a Barrister-at-Law. Third edition, revised and enlarged. pp. iv. 348. *Carswell Co. : Toronto,* 1899. 8°. **06605.** h. **6.**

—— Fourth edition, revised and enlarged. pp. iv. 354. *Carswell Co.: Toronto,* 1907. 8°. **06605.** i. **28.**
Subsequent editions are entered under CANADIAN LAWYER.

—— Cassell's Family Lawyer . . . By a Barrister-at-Law. pp. xi. xii. 1128. *London,* 1898. 8°. **6144.** f. **2.**

—— Special edition, *etc.* 3 vol. *London,* [1902.] 8°. **6144.** g. **3.**

BARRISTER-AT-LAW.

—— [A reissue.] Cassell's Lawyer, *etc.* *London,* [1903.] 8°. **6144.** **g.** **7.**

—— Cassell's Family Lawyer . . . New and revised edition. 3 vol. *London,* 1903, 04. 8°. **6144.** **f.** **4.**

—— Revised and enlarged edition. 3 vol. *London,* 1908. 8°. **6145.** h. **15.**

—— A Complete Popular Guide to the Licensing Bill, 1908. By a Barrister-at-Law. pp. 29. *P. S. King & Son: London,* 1908. 8°. **6146.** ee. **8.** **(3.)**

—— Delicate Inquiry ! Prince of Wales. A letter to the Earl of Moira : in which is contained, a review of the libellous pamphlets lately published with intent to defame the character of the Prince of Wales. By a Barrister at Law. pp. 77. *J. F. Hughes : London,* 1806. 8°. **8135.** cc. **59.** **(7.)**

—— [Another copy.] **8135.** bb. **1.** **(5.)**

—— Glebe Lands and the Duties on Land Values. What incumbents have to do. By a Barrister-at-Law. pp. 19. *S.P.C.K.: London,* 1913. 8°. **6006.** a. **23.** **(6.)**

—— The Home Counsellor. By a barrister-at-law. pp. 320. *Odhams Press: London,* [1938.] 8°. **6146.** aaaa. **7.**

—— The Home Lawyer : a practical handbook for the household. By a Barrister-at-Law. pp. xii. 180. *Cassell & Co.: London,* 1905. 8°. **6191.** de. **2.**

—— The Law of Mutual Life Assurance with special reference to the decision of Lord Cairns in the Kent Mutual Society's case. To which is appended . . . a verbatim report of Lord Cairns's judgment. By a Barrister-at-Law . . . Reprinted, with . . . additions from The Review. pp. 36. *The Review: London,* 1872. 8°. **8227.** bb. **47.**

—— The Law of Parliamentary Impeachments. By a Barrister at Law. pp. iv. 39. *T. Whieldon: London,* 1788. 8°. **518.** d. **27.** **(11.)**

—— Meerut Conspiracy Case . . . Specially written by a Barrister- at-Law, *etc.* pp. 16. *Meerut Prisoners' Release Committee: London,* [1933.] 8°. **20017.** c. **20.**

—— My Lawyer. A concise abridgment of and popular guide to the laws of England. By a Barrister-at-Law. pp. xii. 548. *Kegan Paul & Co.: London,* 1887. 8°. **6146.** d. **9.**

—— Second edition. pp. xii. 568. *Kegan Paul & Co.: London,* 1892. 8°. **6146.** f. **27.**

—— New and cheaper edition. pp. xii. 568. *Kegan Paul & Co.: London,* 1894. 8°. **6146.** f. **30.**

—— Fifth edition. pp. xii. 573. *Kegan Paul & Co.: London,* 1897. 8°. **6146.** dd. **1.**
Pp. 561–573 are in duplicate.

—— Seventeenth year of publication. pp. xii. 484. *Effingham Wilson: London,* 1904. 8°. **6146.** dd. **4.**

—— Eighteenth year of publication. pp. xii. 484. *Effingham Wilson: London,* 1905. 8°. **6146.** aa. **47.**

—— Nineteenth edition. pp. xii. 484. *Effingham Wilson: London,* 1906. 8°. **6146.** aa. **49.**

—— Twentieth edition. pp. xii. 484. *Effingham Wilson: London,* 1907. 8°. **6146.** dd. **5.**

—— The Opium Question, as between Nation and Nation. By a Barrister at Law. pp. 52. *James Bain: London,* 1840. 8°. **8005.** g. **7.**

BARRISTER-AT-LAW.

—— A Penny Law Library . . . intended for general use ; reprinted, compiled . . . and condensed by a Barrister at Law, from Blackstone's Commentaries, *etc.* *Fred. Lawrance: London,* [1830?] 8°. [*Penny National Library.* vol. 1.] **1157.** l. **1.**
Imperfect : wanting all after p. 320.

—— Popular Guide to National Insurance. The new act fully analysed and explained. By a Barrister-at-Law. (Second edition revised to date.) pp. 30. "*Daily Chronicle*" : *London,* [1912.] 8°. **6004.** k. **1.** (**6.**)

—— Post-Mortem Talks with Public Men, obtained through trance mediumship by a Barrister-at-law and recorded by him, *etc.* [The communications in Part 1 received through the medium Sara Harris.] pp. xx. 150. *Two Worlds Publishing Co.: Manchester,* 1934. 8°. **8634.** a. **48.**

—— Reflections on the Natural and Acquired Endowments requisite for the Study of the Law, and the means to be used in the pursuit of it. By a Barrister at Law [i.e Joseph Simpson]. pp. viii. 54. *J. Worral; T. Waller: London,* 1764. 8°. **08218.b.16.(8.)**

—— [Another copy.] Reflections on the Natural and Acquired Endowments requisite for the Study of the Law . . . By a Barrister at Law [i.e. Joseph Simpson]. *London,* 1764. 8°. **518.** h. **6.** (**9.**)
Part of the imprint has failed to print.

—— The Rise and Practice of Imprisonment in Personal Actions examined ; and a mode of proceeding offered, reconciling the ancient and modern practice, in aid both of debtor and creditor. By a Barrister at Law [i.e. Thomas Hallie Delamayne]. pp. 104. *J. Wilkie: London,* 1772. 8°. **883.** i. **20.** (**2.**)

—— The Road Murder ; being a complete report and analysis of . . . this mysterious tragedy. By a Barrister-at-Law, *etc.* pp. 63. *London,* [1860.] 8°. **6496.** aaa. **9.**

—— Tolley's Synopsis of Estate Duty . . . Compiled by a Barrister-at-Law. Edited by Kenneth Mines . . . [and] L. E. Feaver. (1950 [*etc.*] edition.) *Chas. H. Tolley & Co.: London,* 1950– . 8°. **W.P. A. 550.**

—— The Tichborne Romance ; its matter-of-fact and moral. By a Barrister-at-Law. pp. iv. 256. *G. Routledge & Sons: London,* 1872. 16°. **6496.** a. **2.**

—— A Treatise on Heresy, as cognizable by the Spiritual Courts. And an examination of the Statute 9th and 10th of William III[d]. c. 32, entitled, an Act for the more effectual suppressing of blasphemy . . . By a Barrister at Law [i.e. Sir Benjamin Hobhouse]. pp. 146. *T. Cadell: London,* 1792. 8°. **518.** k. **20.** (**1.**)

—— A Treatise upon the Law and Proceedings in Cases of High Treason, &c. By a Barrister at Law. [A reprint of the edition of 1793.] pp. 95. *See* KELYNG (*Sir* John) *Lord Chief Justice of the Court of King's Bench.* Sir John Kelyng's Reports of Crown Cases, *etc.* 1873. 8°. **6120.** aaa. **6.**

—— A Vote for Moderate Counsels . . . An ode, by a Barrister at Law. pp. 14. *James Vade: London,* 1681. fol. **11602.** i. **27.** (**2.**)

—— What's the Law ? Law for laymen. By a Barrister-at-Law. pp. 160. *G. Routledge & Sons: London,* [1906.] 16°. **012216.** hh. **3.**
Part of the "Miniature Reference Libary."

BARRISTER-AT-LAW.

—— ? Who am I ? By a Barrister-at-Law. [On heraldry.] pp. 8. [1909.] *obl.* 8°. **9905.** a. **12.**

—— Your own Lawyer and Conveyancer ; or, Treasures of the Law Office. Giving . . . the mercantile or business laws of Canada and Newfoundland . . . Third edition . . . revised and enlarged, by a Barrister-at-Law. *W. H. Anger: Toronto,* 1901. 8°. **06605.** g. **27.**
A previous edition, entitled "Be your own Lawyer" is entered above.

BARRITT (ALFRED TEMPLAR) *See* BARRITT (Wesley) and BARRITT (A. T.) Questions and Answers for Dental Students, *etc.* 1922. 8°. **07611.** de. **1.**

—— *See* BARRITT (Wesley) and BARRITT (A. T.) The Simplex Handbook of Dental Materia Medica and Therapeutics, *etc.* 1914. *obl.* 8°. **7510.** dg. **47.**

—— —— 1923. 8°. **07510.** e. **31.**

BARRITT (E. LLOYD)

—— Captivity. A play in one act. pp. 22. *London,* [1935.] 8°. [*Year Book Press Series of Plays.*] **W.P. 2236/97.**

BARRITT (FRANCES FULLER) Alicia Newcome ; or, the Land Claim. A tale of the Upper Missouri. pp. 123. *E. F. Beadle & Co.: London & New York,* [1862.] 16°. **12706.** a. **32.** (**1.**)

—— The Far West ; or, the Beauty of Willard's Mill. pp. 109. *E. F. Beadle & Co.: London & New York,* [1862.] 16°. **12706.** a. **31.** (**2.**)

BARRITT (JOHN W.) The Care and Operation of Machine Tools. pp. xv. 292. *New York,* 1927. 8°. [*Wiley Trade Series.*] **012208.1.5/7.**

BARRITT (LEON) Engravings. How to estimate their cost. A concise description of the best known methods, with specimen illustrations and prices, *etc.* *Barritt & Burgin: New York,* 1890. 4°. **7858.** t. **25.**

BARRITT (THOMAS) *See* AXON (William E. A.) Lancashire and Cheshire Traditions, illustrated by a manuscript written by T. Barritt. [1876.] 8°. **1881.** c. **16.** (**35.**)

BARRITT (W.) *Artist. See* LOSSING (Benson J.) Pictorial History of the Civil War in the United States of America . . . Illustrated by . . . Lossing and Barritt, *etc.* 1866, *etc.* 8°. **9603.** ee. **7.**

BARRITT (WESLEY) and **BARRITT** (ALFRED TEMPLAR) Questions and Answers for Dental Students. Dental surgery. pp. vii. 177. *Henry Kimpton: London,* 1922. 8°. **07611.** de. **1.**

—— The Simplex Handbook of Dental Materia Medica and Therapeutics, *etc.* pp. xi. 340. *Henry Kimpton: London,* 1914. *obl.* 8°. **7510.** dg. **47.**

—— Second edition, revised and enlarged. pp. xiii. 297. *Henry Kimpton: London,* 1923. 8°. **07510.** e. **31.**

BARRIUS (FRANCISCUS) *See* BARRY (F. de)

BARRIUS (GABRIEL) *See* BARRIO (Gabriele)

BARRIUSO (PATROCINIO GARCÍA) *See* GARCÍA BARRIUSO.

BARRIVE (L.) Общественное движеніе въ царствованіе Александра Второго. Историческіе очерки . . . Съ гравюрами фото-тинто. pp. 154. *Москва,* 1911. 8°. **9476.** h. **41.**
Another edition of "Освободительное движеніе въ царствованіе Александра Второго" published in 1909.

BARRLAY (C. J.) Anleitung zur Erkennung und Prüfung photographischer Chemikalien zum Gebrauch für Photographen. pp. iv. 83. *Köln*, 1864. 12°. **1399. c. 53. (3.)**

BARRO (JEAN DE) *See* BIBLE.—*Liturgical Epistles and Gospels.* [*Latin.*] Les postilles ꝛ expositions des epistres et euuangilles domĩcales, *etc.* [Revised by J. de Barro.] 1492. fol. IB. **43215.**

BARROCIUS (PETRUS) *See* BAROZZI (Pietro) successively *Bishop of Belluno* and *of Padua.*

BARROCO (PLACIDO DE ANDRADE) *See* ANDRADE BARROCO.

BARRODALE (SAMUEL) Code Geometrical Drawing. Suggestions for the use of the Complete-Drawing-Code Ruler, *etc.* *E. Preston & Sons: Birmingham*, [1888.] *s. sh.* fol. **1801. d. 2. (100.)**

—— Barrodale's Code Geometrical Drawing, *etc.* (Third edition.) *T. H. Barrodale: [Birmingham*, 1890.] 4°. **8529. i. 2. (1.)**

BARROERI (GIOVANNI ANTONIO) *See* BOTERO (G.) Ioannis Boterii . . . carmina, a Io. Antonio Barroerio . . . collecta, *etc.* 1615. 8°. **11409. bbb. 2.**

—— Annotationi . . . sopra la Primavera del Signor Giovanni Botero. *See* BOTERO (G.) La Primavera, *etc.* 1607. 4°. **11427. ee. 4.**

BARROERIUS (JOANNES ANTONIUS) *See* BARROERI (Giovanni A.)

BARROETA ALDAMAR (JOAQUÍN) *See* BAROETA Y ALDAMAR.

BARROETAVEÑA (FRANCISCO ANTONIO) *See* GUIDO LAVALLE (R.) El General Don Tomás Guido y el paso de los Andes . . . Con un juicio del Dr. F. A. Barroetaveña. 1917. 8°. **10884. f. 4.**

—— *See* HERRERO (Antonio) El Poeta del Hombre. Almafuerte (P. B. Palacios) . . . Estudio preliminar del Dr. F. A. Barroetaveña, *etc.* 1918. 8°. **011853. tt. 29.**

—— Alemania contra el Mundo . . . Prólogo biográfico por . . . P. B. Palacios. pp. xii. 639. *Buenos Aires*, 1916. 8° **08027. df. 10.**

BARROIL (ÉTIENNE) L'Art équestre. Traité de haute école d'équitation . . . Vignettes, *etc.* 2 pt. *Paris*, 1887, 89. 8°. **7907. f. 35.**

BARROILHET (P.) *of Audignon.*

—— Essai sur les signes que présente la face dans les maladies, *etc.* [A thesis.] pp. 40. *Paris*, 1809. 4°. **1182. h. 6. (31.)**

BARROILHET (PIERRE GABRIEL MARIE) Du catarrhe vésical ; thèse, *etc.* pp. 25. *Paris*, 1834. 4°. **1184. f. 15. (25.)**

BARROIS. *See* LORRAINE AND BAR, *Duchy of.*

BARROIS (AD. LETHIERRY) *See* LETHIERRY-BARROIS.

BARROIS (AUGUSTE) Les Étapes d'un volontaire au Dahomey. Drame en cinq actes, *etc.* pp. 104. *Paris*, 1893. 12°. **11740. cc. 4. (10.)**

—— Le Falot de Diogène. Étude de mœurs parisiennes. pp. 335. *Paris*, 1889. 12°. **012547. h. 63.**

—— Les Héros obscurs. Nouvelles patriotiques. pp. 259. *Paris*, 1889. 18°. **012547. k. 14**

BARROIS (AUGUSTE EUGÈNE) Faculté de Droit de Paris. Thèse pour la licence. (Jus romanum. Commodati vel contra, *etc.*—Droit français. Du contrat de louage.) pp. 58. *Paris*, 1860. 8°. **5406. c. 2. (6.)**

BARROIS (AUGUSTIN GEORGES)

—— *See* THUREAU-DANGIN (F.) Arslan-Tash. Par F. Thureau-Dangin, A. Barrois, *etc.* 1931. 4°. **L.R. 56. a. 1/16.**

—— Manuel d'archéologie biblique. 2 tom. *Paris*, 1939, 53. 8°. **07705.bb.54.**

BARROIS (CHARLES) *See* COTTEAU (G.) Notice sur les échinides urgoniens recueillis par M. Barrois dans le province d'Oviedo, Espagne. [1879.] 8°. **7106. g. 22. (3*.)**

—— *See* CROSS (Charles W.) Études de M. Charles Whitman sur des roches de Bretagne. Analyse de M. C. Barrois. [1881.] 8°. **7106. bbb. 26. (6.)**

—— *See* ZITTEL (C. A.) Traité de paléontologie . . . Traduit par . . . C. Barrois, *etc.* 1883, *etc.* 8°. **7202. dd. 1.**

—— L'Âge de la pierre de Totternhoe. (Extrait des Annales de la Société Géologique du Nord.) [*Lille*, 1876.] 8°. **7106. f. 4. (11.)**

—— L'Âge des couches de Blackdown, Devonshire. (Extrait des Annales de la Société Géologique du Nord.) pp. 8. *Lille*, 1875. 8°. **7108. b. 1. (13.)**

—— L'Âge des "Folkestone beds" du lower green sand. (Extrait des Annales de la Société Géologique du Nord.) *Lille*, [1875.] 8°. **7106. f. 1. (8.)**

—— La Dénudation des Wealds et le Pas-de-Calais. (Extrait des Annales de la Société Géologique du Nord.) *Lille*, [1876.] 8°. **7106. f. 1. (9.)**

—— Description géologique de la craie de l'Île de Wight. pp. 30. 1875. *See* PERIODICAL PUBLICATIONS.—*Paris.* Annales des sciences géologiques, *etc.* tom. 6. 1869, *etc.* 8°. **P.P. 2084. b.**

—— [Another issue.] pp. 30. *Paris*, [1875.] 8°. **7109. c. 3.**

—— [Another edition.] pp. 30. *Paris*, 1875. 8°. [*Bibliothèque de l'École des Hautes Études.* Section des sciences naturelles. tom. 13. no. 2.] **Ac. 8929/5.**

—— *See* WESTLAKE (Ernest) Tabular Index to the Upper Cretaceous Fossils of England and Ireland, cited by Dr. C. Barrois in his "Description géologique de l'Ile de Wight," *etc.* 1888. 4°. **7204. h. 6. (1.)**

—— Description sommaire des terrains qui affleurent sur la carte de Réthel, *etc.* (Extrait des Annales de la Société Géologique du Nord.) [*Lille*, 1881.] 8°. **7202. aaa. 28. (1.)**

—— L'Eocène supérieur des Flandres. (Extrait des Annales de la Société Géologique du Nord.) *Lille*, [1876.] 8°. **7106. f. 7. (9.)**

—— Faune du calcaire d'Erbray, Loire Inférieure, *etc.* pp. 348. pl. XVII. *Lille*, 1889. 4°. [*Mémoires de la Société Géologique du Nord.* tom. 3.] **Ac. 3119.**

—— [A reissue, with the pagination continued to include the descriptions of the plates.] pp. 364. pl. XVII. *Lille*, 1889. 8°. [*Mémoires de la Société d'Amateurs des Sciences et Arts de Lille.* sér. 4. tom. 16.] **Ac. 355/2.**

—— A Geological Sketch of the Boulonnais. (Reprinted from "Proceedings of the Geologists' Association.") pp. 37. [*London*, 1879.] 8°. **7106. f. 11. (18.)**

—— Le Granite de Rostrenen, ses apophyses et ses contacts. (Extrait des Annales de la Société Géologique du Nord.) pp. 119. *Lille*, 1884. 8°. **7106. f. 18. (2.)**

—— Le Marbre griotte des Pyrénées. (Extrait des Annales de la Société Géologique du Nord.) *Lille*, [1879.] 8°. **7106. f. 11. (16.)**

BARROIS (Charles)

—— Mémoire sur le terrain crétacé des Ardennes et des régions voisines. (Extrait des Annales de la Société Géologique du Nord.) *Lille*, 1878. 8°. **7202**. bb. **9**.

—— Mémoire sur le terrain crétacé du bassin d'Oviédo, Espagne. pp. 40. 1879. *See* Periodical Publications.—*Paris*. Annales des sciences géologiques, *etc*. tom. 10. 1869, *etc*. 8°. P.P. **2084**. b.

—— [Another copy, extracted from the "Annales des sciences géologiques."] **7106**. g. **22**. (**3**.)

—— Mémoire sur les éruptions diabasiques siluriennes du Menez-Hom, Finistère. pp. 74. *Paris*, 1889. 8°. [*Bulletin des Services de la Carte géologique de la France*. vol. 1. no. 7.] **7108**. g4.

—— Note préliminaire sur le terrain silurien de l'ouest de la Bretagne. (Extrait des Annales de la Société Géologique du Nord.) pp. 57. *Lille*, [1876.] 8°. **7106**. f. **1**. (**10**.)

—— Note sur le terrain dévonien de la Province de Léon, Espagne. (Association française pour l'avancement des sciences. Congrès du Havre, 1877.) pp. 4. *Paris*, 1877. 8°. **7109**. f. **2**. (**2**.)

—— Note sur le terrain dévonien de la Rade de Brest, *etc*. (Extrait des Annales de la Société Géologique du Nord.) *Lille*, [1877.] 8°. **7106**. f. **6**. (**9**.)

—— Note sur les traces de l'époque glaciaire en quelques points des côtes de la Bretagne. (Extrait des Annales de la Société Géologique du Nord. *Lille*, [1877.] 8°. **7106**. f. **7**. (**10**.)

—— Notes sur les recherches du Dr. J. Lehmann dans la région granulitique de la Saxe. (Extrait des Annales de la Société Géologique du Nord.) [*Lille*, 1883.] 8°. **7106**. cc. **13**. (**2**.)

—— Observations sur le terrain silurien supérieur de la Haute-Garonne. (Extrait des Annales de la Société Géologique du Nord.) [*Lille*,] 1882. 8°. **7202**. aaa. **28**. (**2**.)

—— Recherches sur le terrain crétacé supérieur de l'Angleterre et de l'Irlande. pp. 232. *Lille*, 1876. 4°. [*Mémoires de la Société Géologique du Nord*. tom. 1. pt. 1.] Ac. **3119**.

—— [Another issue.] *Lille*, 1876. 4°. **7109**. dd. **10**.

—— Recherches sur les terrains anciens des Asturies et de la Galice . . . Ouvrage accompagné d'un atlas de 20 planches. pp. 630. *Lille*, 1882. 4°. [*Mémoires de la Société Géologique du Nord*. tom. 2. pt. 1.] Ac. **3119**.

—— [Another issue.] *Lille*, 1882. 4°. **7105**. e. **17**.

—— Les Sables de Sissonne . . . et les alluvions de la vallée de la Souche. (Extrait des Annales de la Société Géologique du Nord.) *Lille*, [1878.] 8°. **7106**. f. **7**. (**13**.)

—— Sur l'étendue du système tertiaire inférieur dans les Ardennes et sur les argiles à silex. (Extrait des Annales de la Société Géologique du Nord.) *Lille*, 1879. 8°. **7106**. f. **11**. (**17**.)

—— Sur le byssacanthus Gosseleti, plagiostome du dévonien de l'Ardenne. (Association française pour l'avancement des sciences. Congrès de Lille, 1874.) pp. 2. *Lille*, [1874.] 8°. **7106**. c. **1**. (**7**.)

—— Sur le terrain silurien supérieur de la presqu'île de Crozon. (Extrait des Annales de la Société Géologique du Nord.) *Lille*, [1880.] 8°. **7106**. f. **13**. (**6**.)

—— Sur les faunes siluriennes de la Haute-Garonne. (Extrait des Annales de la Société Géologique du Nord.) [*Lille*, 1883.] 8°. **7106**. cc. **13**. (**3**.)

BARROIS (Charles)

—— Sur les plages soulevées de la côte occidentale du Finistère. 2e note. (Extrait des Annales de la Société Géologique du Nord.) *Lille*, [1882.] 8°. **7202**. aaa. **28**. (**3**.)

—— La Zone à belemnites plenus. Étude sur le cénomanien et le turonien du bassin de Paris. [Extracted from the "Annales de la Société Géologique du Nord."] *Lille*, 1875. 8°. **7203**. aaa. **1**. (**6**.)

BARROIS (Charles) and GUERNE (Jules de)

—— Description de quelques espèces nouvelles de la craie de l'est du bassin de Paris. (Extrait des Annales de la Société Géologique du Nord.) *Lille*, 1878. 8°. **7106**. f. **7**. (**12**.)

BARROIS (Charles) and OFFRET (Albert)

—— Sur la constitution géologique de la chaîne bétique. [Reprinted from the "Comptes rendus des séances de l'Académie des Sciences."] pp. 8. *Paris*, [1886.] 4°. **7107**. e. **9**. (**2**.)

BARROIS (Étienne) Histoire du mémorable siége de la ville d'Orléans par les Anglois, commencé le 12. d'Octobre 1428. & levé le 8. de May 1429. par la valeur de Jeanne d'Arc . . . Enrichie de la vie de Jean d'Orléans, comte de Dunois, *etc*. pp. xxiii. 95. *Orléans*, 1739. 8°. G. **15232**.

BARROIS (Georges Ferdinand) Des flexions de l'utérus. pp. 50. *Paris*, 1860. 4°. [*Collection des thèses soutenues à la Faculté de Médecine de Paris*. An 1860. tom. 1.] **7373**. c. **9**.

BARROIS (Hippolyte Marie Jules) Essai sur la rougeole. Thèse, *etc*. pp. 23. *Montpellier*, 1836. 4°. **1181**. h. **3***. (**26**.)

BARROIS (Jacques Marie) Catalogue de la bibliothèque de feu M. Falconet, médecin consultant du Roi, *etc*. [By J. M. Barrois.] 2 tom. 1763. 8°. *See* Falconet (C.) **269**. h. **1**, **2**.

—— Catalogue des livres de la bibliothèque de feu M. de Selle, trésorier général de la Marine. [With supplement.] [By J. M. Barrois.] pp. xlviii. 310. 8. 1761. 8°. *See* Selle (de) *Treasurer of the Navy*. **269**. i. **14**. (**1**.)

—— Catalogue des livres de la bibliothèque de feu M. J. B. Denis Guyon, Chev. Seigneur de Sardière, *etc*. [By J. M. Barrois.] pp. xxxvi. 270. 1759. 8°. *See* Guyon (J. B. D.) *Seigneur de Sardière*. **269**. h. **3**. (**2**.)

—— Catalogue des livres de la bibliothèque de feu Monsieur Larchevesque, *etc*. [By J. M. Barrois. With a plate.] pp. iv. 368. 1749. 8°. *See* Larchevesque (A.) **269**. i. **22**. (**1**.)

—— Catalogue des livres de la bibliothèque de feu Monsieur le président Bernard de Rieux. [By J. M. Barrois.] pp. xv. 351. 40. 1747. 8°. *See* Bernard (Gabriel) *Count de Rieux*. **269**. h. **3**. (**1**.)

BARROIS (Joseph)

—— [For the catalogue of the Barrois Manuscripts included in the Historical Manuscripts Commissions report on the manuscripts of the Earl of Ashburnham :] *See* Ashburnham (Bertram) *5th Earl of Ashburnham*.

—— *See* Delisle (L. V.) Les Manuscrits du comte d'Ashburnham. Rapport . . . suivi d'observations . . . sur plusieurs manuscrits du fonds Barrois. 1883. 4°. **11905**. bb. **13**.

—— *See* Delisle (L. V.) Observations sur l'origine de plusieurs manuscrits de la collection de M. Barrois. 1866. 8°. **11904**. g. **1**. (**4**.)

BARROIS (JOSEPH)

—— *See* MACQUEREAU (R.) Histoire générale de l'Europe durant les années 1527, 28, 29 . . . Publiée pour la première fois et sur le manuscrit autographe. [Edited by J. Barrois.] 1841. 8°. **1441. k. 1. (2.)**

—— *See* OGIER, *the Dane*. La Chevalerie. Ogier de Danemarche . . . Poème . . . publié pour la première fois d'après le MS., *etc.* [Edited by J. Barrois.] 1842. 8°. **1464. f. 23.**

—— *See* PHILIP, called *Count d'Artois, etc.* Le Livre du très chevalereux comte d'Artois et de sa femme fille au comte de Boulogne. Publié . . . pour la première fois. [Edited by J. Barrois.] 1837. 4°. **839. i. 19.**

—— Bibliothèque protypographique, ou librairies des fils du roi Jean, Charles v., Jean de Berri, Philippe de Bourgogne, et les siens. pp. xl. 346. *Paris*, 1830. 4°. **619. l. 28.**

—— Dactylologie et langage primitif restitués d'après les monuments. pp. 360. 35. pl. 61. *Paris*, 1850. 4°. **1333. k. 4.**

—— Éléments carlovingiens linguistiques et littéraires. pp. 360. pl. 8. *Paris*, 1846. 4°. **1331. g. 5.**

—— Lecture littérale des hiéroglyphes et des cunéiformes par l'auteur de la Dactylologie [i.e. J. Barrois]. pp. iv. 80. pl. 17. 1853. 4°. *See* LECTURE. **1331. k. 13.**

BARROIS (JULES) Mémoire sur la métamorphose des bryozoaires. pp. 67. *Paris*, 1880. 8°. [*Bibliothèque de l'École des Hautes Études.* Section des sciences naturelles. tom. 21. no. 1.] **Ac. 8929/5.**

—— Mémoire sur l'embryologie des némertes. pp. 232. *Paris*, 1877. 8°. [*Bibliothèque de l'École des Hautes Études.* Section des sciences naturelles. tom. 17. no. 1.] **Ac. 8929/5.**

—— Notice sur le climat du Caire. [With plates.] 1890. *See* ALEXANDRIA.—*Institut Égyptien.* Bulletin, *etc.* sér. 2. no. 10. 1882, *etc.* 8°. **Ac. 10/4.**

—— Recherches sur l'embryologie des bryozoaires. pp. 305. pl. 16. *Lille*, 1877. 4°. [*Travaux de l'Insitut Zoologique de Lille.* fasc. 1.] **Ac. 3554.**

BARROIS (JULIEN) *See* SEMET (L. T.) and BARROIS (J.) Poésies. 1845. 12°. **1161. f. 30.**

—— Poésies. Par J. Barrois et L. T. Semet. pp. 116. *Lille*, 1846. 12°. **1161. f. 31.**

BARROIS (LOUIS THÉOPHILE) Lettre à M. J. Hébrard, au sujet de la brochure qu'il vient de publier sur l'état de la librairie en France en 1847. pp. 4. [*Paris*, 1847.] 8°. **1881. c. 3. (3.)**

—— Mémoire sur cette question : Est-il avantageux au Gouvernement et au commerce de la librairie d'établir un droit de 50 pour cent sur les livres étrangers importés en France ? pp. 6. *Paris*, 1809. 4°. **8228. i. 78.** *Lithographed.*

—— Mémoire sur cette question : Quels seraient les meilleurs moyens à employer pour soulager les souffrances des commerçants et des propriétaires de Paris et de la France ? . . . Par un bourgeois de Paris (L. T. Barrois), *etc.* pp. 8. [*Paris*, 1848.] 8°. **935. i. 39. (4.)**

—— Observations relatives au projet d'un nouveau cercle de la librairie, de l'imprimerie, de la papeterie, *etc.* pp. 4 [*Paris*, 1847 ?] 8°. **1881. c. 3. (2**.)**

BARROIS (THÉODORE) *See* PERIODICAL PUBLICATIONS.—*Lille.* Revue biologique du Nord de la France, publiéf. sous la direction de T. Barrois, *etc.* 1888, *etc.* 8°. **P.P. 3012. be.**

BARROIS (THÉODORE)

—— Recherches sur la faune des eaux douces des Açores. [With 3 plates.] pp. 172. *Paris*, 1896. 8°. [*Mémoires de la Société des Sciences de l'Agriculture et des Arts de Lille.* sér. 5. fasc. 6.] **Ac. 355/2.**

BARROIS (THÉOPHILE) Catalogue des livres et manuscrits arabes et turcs qui se trouvent chez T. Barrois fils, *etc.* pp. 24. [*Paris*,] 1835. 8°. **14598. b. 2. (1*.)**

—— Catalogue des livres italiens qui se trouvent chez Théophile Barrois fils, *etc.* pp. 43. *Paris*, 1813. 8°. S.C. **759. (3.)**

—— Catalogue des livres persans, hindoustanis, malabars, sanskrits, chinois, tartares-mantchous, japonais, malais, géorgiens, kurdes, wolofes, esquimaux, égyptiens, éthiopiens, etc., qui se trouvent à la librairie étrangère de T. Barrois fils, *etc.* pp. 22. *Paris*, 1832. 8°. **14598. b. 2. (1.)**

—— Catalogue d'une collection de tableaux de diverses écoles, provenant du cabinet de M. * * * [identified in a MS. note as — Barrois], dont la vente se fera . . . 5 novembre 1812, *etc.* pp. 15. MS. NOTES AND PRICES. 1812. 8°. *See* CATALOGUES. [MISSING.]

—— Notice d'un cabinet, consistant en tableaux par divers bons maîtres des trois écoles, dont la vente se fera vendredi 26 et samedi 27 février 1813, *etc.* [Catalogue of the collection of T. Barrois.] pp. 13. MS. PRICES. 1813. 8°. **562. e. 29. (11.)**

—— No. 1. Livres hébreux et arabes, nouvellement arrivés à la librairie étrangère et orientale de T. Barrois fils, *etc.* (No. 2. Livres arabes et turcs, persans, hindostanis, malabars et sanskrits, *etc.*—No. 3. Livres sanskrits, chinois, tartares-mantchous, géorgiens, égyptiens, éthiopiens, grecs modernes, *etc.*) 3 pt. [*Paris*,] 1834. 8°. **14598. b. 2. (2.)**

BARROIS D'ENTREMONT (JEAN BAPTISTE) Des accidents qui peuvent survenir pendant les opérations. pp. 43. *Paris*, 1845. 4°. [*Collection des thèses soutenues à la Faculté de Médecine de Paris.* An 1845. tom. 1.] **7371. f. 2.**

BARROLL, *Family of.* *See* BARROLL (Hopewell H.) Barroll in Great Britain and America, *etc.* [With portraits.] 1910. 8°. **09915. e. 7.**

BARROLL (HOPEWELL HORSEY) Barroll in Great Britain and America, 1554–1910. [With plates, including portraits.] pp. viii. 138. *J. H. Saumenig & Co.: Baltimore*, 1910. 8°. **09915. e. 7.**

BARROLL (MARY LOUISE) Around-the-World Cook Book. The culinary gleanings of a naval officer's wife. pp. vii. 360. *Century Co.: New York*, 1913. 8°. **07942. h. 21.**

BARROMEO (CARLI) *See* CHARLES [Borromeo], *Saint, Cardinal, Archbishop of Milan.*

BARRON (A. A.) Auction Bridge . . . for Beginners and others, *etc.* pp. 15. [*The Author: Virginia Water*, 1929.] fol. **7915. e. 38.** *Reproduced from typewriting.*

BARRON (A. L.) and REED (GUILFORD B.)

—— Clostridium Botulinum Type E Toxin and Toxoid. (Reprinted from Canadian Journal of Microbiology.) [1954.] 8°. **1865. c. 20. (71.)**

BARRON (ALEXANDER)

—— Art and Literature. [An introduction to vol. 4 of the I.U.S. Reading Course.] pp. 51. *International University Society: Nottingham*, [1952.] 8°. **12216**. f. 2/4.

BARRON (ALFRED) *See* NOYES (John H.) Home-Talks . . . Edited by A. Barron and G. N. Miller. 1875, *etc.* 8°. **4379**. b. **35**.

—— Footnotes, or Walking as a Fine Art. pp. 330. *Wallingford Printing Co.: Wallingford, Conn.*, 1875. 8°. **12357**. i. **10**.

BARRON (ALICE)

—— The Two Daisy's, and Granny's Story. pp. 16. *A. H. Stockwell: Ilfracombe*, 1945. 8°. **12830**. aa. **40**.

BARRON (ARCHIBALD F.) *See* CHISWICK.—*National Apple Congress*. British Apples. Report of the Committee of the National Apple Congress . . . Compiled . . . by Mr. A. F. Barron. 1884. 8°. **7073**. bb. **1**.

—— Vines and Vine-Culture . . . Reprinted and . . . extended from the Florist and Pomologist, with . . . illustrations, *etc.* pp. xx. 240. "*Journal of Horticulture*": *London*, 1883. 8°. **7078**. df. **39**.

—— Vines and Vine Culture . . . Fourth edition. Revised and enlarged. pp. xvi. 202. viii. "*Journal of Horticulture*" *Office: London*, 1900. 8°. **7080**. aa. **40**.

—— Fifth edition. Revised and enlarged (by W. P. Thomson). pp. xvi. 211. "*Journal of Horticulture*": *London*, 1912. 8°. **07076**. f. **58**.

BARRON (ARTHUR) *of the Inner Temple*.

—— *See* LOVELASS (Peter) The Law's Disposal of a Person's Estate who dies without Will or Testament . . . Twelfth edition . . . enlarged by A. Barron. 1838. 8°. **1130**. f. **11**.

BARRON (ARTHUR) *of the Inner Temple*, and **ARNOLD** (THOMAS JAMES)

—— Reports of Cases of Controverted Elections, before Committees of the House of Commons, in the Fourteenth Parliament of the United Kingdom, and of cases upon appeal from the decisions of revising barristers in the Court of Common Pleas, from Michaelmas Term, 1843, to Easter Term, 1846, *etc.* vol. 1. pp. iv. 825. 1846. 8°. *See* ENGLAND.—*Parliament.—House of Commons.—Proceedings.*—I. **1242**. b. **7**.

BARRON (ARTHUR) *of the Inner Temple*, and **AUSTIN** (ALFRED) *of the Middle Temple, etc.*

—— Reports of Cases of Controverted Elections in the Fourteenth Parliament of the United Kingdom. pp. xvi. 685. 1844. 8°. *See* ENGLAND.—*Parliament.—House of Commons.—Proceedings.*—I. **1242**. b. **6**.

BARRON (ARTHUR) *Publisher*.

—— *See* 'UMAR KHAIYAM. [*English.—Fitzgerald's Version.*] Rubáiyát of Omar Khayyám, *etc.* [The editor's preface signed: A. B., i.e. A. Barron?] 1945. 16°. **11630**. a. **34**.

BARRON (ARTHUR OSWALD)

—— *See* ENGLAND.—*College of Arms.* [*Visitations.—Berkshire.*] The Visitation of Berkshire in 1532 . . . Edited by O. Barron. 1898. 8°. [*The Genealogist.* New series. vol. 14. Supplement.] **2100**. a.

BARRON (ARTHUR OSWALD)

—— *See* LEE, *Kent.* The Register of all the Marriages, Christenings and Burials in the Church of S. Margaret, Lee . . . Edited by L. L. Duncan and A. O. Barron. 1888. 8°. Ac. **5662**. a/**1**.

—— *See* LONDON.—III. *Burlington Fine Arts Club.* Catalogue of a Collection of Objects of British Heraldic Art to the end of the Tudor period. [With an introduction by O. Barron.] 1916. 4°. Ac. **4644/71**.

—— *See* PERIODICAL PUBLICATIONS.—*London.* The Ancestor, *etc.* (Edited by O. Barron.) 1902, *etc.* 8°. P.P. **3869**. cc.

—— Day In and Day Out. [Essays.] By "The Londoner," of The Evening News [i.e. A. O. Barron]. pp. xv. 255. 1924. 8°. *See* LONDONER, *of the Evening News.* **012352**. a. **16**.

—— Heraldry [in Shakespeare's England]. *See* SHAKESPEARE (W.) [*Appendix.—Miscellaneous.*] Shakespeare's England, *etc.* 1916. 8°. **2020.f.**

—— Northamptonshire Families. Edited by O. Barron. [With plates.] 2 vol. pp. xxi. 380. *A. Constable & Co.: London*, 1906. fol. [*Victoria History of the Counties of England.* Northampton. Genealogical volume.] **2063.b.**

—— [Another copy.] Northamptonshire Families, *etc.* *London*, 1906. fol. L.R. **301**. bb. **3**.

BARRON (C. C. N.) New Zealand. Decisions of the Speakers of the House of Representatives . . . Compiled by C. C. N. Barron. pp. vii. 135. 1889. 8°. *See* NEW ZEALAND.—*House of Representatives.* **8154**. a. **11**.

BARRÓN (CÁRLOS) Oda que compuso el abogado Don C. Barron, alabando el carácter, y talento del admirable profesor oculista Eduardo Fitz Geraldo, Irlandes. *México*, 1833. 4°. **11450**. e. **5**. **(15.)**

BARRON (CHARLES) *See* ADAMS (Arthur) *F.L.S., R.N.* A Manual of Natural History for the use of Travellers . . . By A. Adams . . . C. Barron. 1854. 12°. **7002**. aa. **1**.

BARRON (CLARENCE WALKER) The Audacious War. pp. xiv. 192. *Constable & Co.: London; Houghton Mifflin Co.: Boston & New York;* [*printed in U.S.A.*,] 1915. 8°. **9082**. e. **13**.

—— The Mexican Problem . . . With introduction by Talcott Williams. [With plates.] pp. xxiv. 136. *Houghton Mifflin Co.: Boston & New York*, 1917. 8°. **08175**. aaa. **9**.

—— More They Told Barron. *See* infra: They Told Barron.

—— They Told Barron. (More They Told Barron.) Conversations and revelations of an American Pepys in Wall Street. The notes of . . . C. W. Barron, edited and arranged by Arthur Pound and Samuel Taylor Moore. [With portraits.] 2 vol. *Harper & Bros.: New York, London*, 1930, 31. 8°. **10880**. r. **20**.

—— A World Remaking; or, Peace Finance. pp. xiii. 242. *Harper & Bros.: New York & London*, 1920. 8°. **08225**. k. **64**.

BARRON (DANIEL) "The Bargraph." [A circular calculating chart.] *Witherby & Co.: London*, [1911.] **8226**. s. **26**.

BARRON (DAVID) A Book of Remembrance. David Barron 1871–1926. [The editor's preface signed: A. J. With a portrait.] pp. 280. *Kingsgate Press: London*, [1926.] 8°. **012273**. aaa. **54**.

BARRON (DONALD HENRY)

—— The Results of Peripheral Anastomoses between the Fore and Hind Limb Nerves of Albino Rats, *etc.* (Reprinted from the Journal of Comparative Neurology.) *Wistar Institute Press: Philadelphia*, 1934. 8°. **7209.** dd. **10.**

BARRON (DOUGLAS GORDON) *See* URIE, *Barony of.* The Court Book of the Barony of Urie . . . Edited . . . with notes and introduction by . . . D. G. Barron. 1892. 8°. [*Publications of the Scottish History Society.* vol. 12.] Ac. **8256.**

—— The Castle of Dunnottar and its history . . . With a description of the buildings by W. Mackay Mackenzie . . . and G. P. H. Watson. [With plates.] pp. xxxiii. 148. *W. Blackwood & Sons: Edinburgh & London*, 1925. 4°. **10370.** i. **9.**

—— Gleanings. [Verses.] By D. G. B. [i.e. D. G. Barron.] pp. 53. 1929. 8°. *See* B., D. G. **11640.** g. **41.**

—— In Defence of the Regalia, 1651–2 : being selections from the family papers of the Ogilvies of Barras. Edited, with introduction, by Rev. D. G. Barron . . . With photogravure frontispiece and nine illustrations. pp. xvi. 371. *Longmans & Co.: London*, 1910. 8°. **9916.** e. **15.**

—— Jean Charlier de Gerson the Author of the De Imitatione Christi. pp. 118. *W. Blackwood & Sons: Edinburgh & London*, 1936. 8°. **20020.** cc. **69.**

—— Our Lapsed Masses, with some practical suggestions for their reform. pp. 27. *W. Blackwood & Sons: Edinburgh*, 1884. 8°. **8277.** bbb. **55. (12.)**

BARRON (EDITH) Graded Tests in Arithmetic for Senior Girls, *etc.* (Answers.) *Blackie & Son: London & Glasgow*, 1931–34. 8°. Book III.) 4 pt. **010370.b.13/6.**

BARRON (EDNA)

—— Wanderlust, and other poems. pp. 16. *Arthur H. Stockwell: Ilfracombe*, [1954.] 8°. **11659.** e. **68.**

BARRÓN (EDUARDO) Museo Nacional de Pintura y Escultura. Catálogo de la escultura, formado por E. Barrón. (Ilustrado con 92 láminas en fototipia.) pp. 289. 1908. 8°. *See* MADRID.—*Museo Nacional de Pintura y Escultura.* **7856.** de. **49.**

BARRON (EDWARD) The Lost Goddess. [A novel.] pp. iii. 341. *H. Holt & Co.: New York*, 1908. 8°. **012627.** a. **9.**

BARRON (EDWARD EVELYN)

—— The National Benevolent Institution, 1812–1936. A short account of its rise and progress extracted from the minutes. [With plates.] pp. xi. 131. *Spottiswoode, Ballantyne & Co.: London*, 1936. 8°. **8287.** c. **2.**

—— A Short Account of the Founding and Formation of the Law Association. Compiled from the minutes of the Association for its first century. pp. 28. 1921. 8°. See LONDON. - III. Law Association for the Benefit of Widows, etc **6025.** de. **13.**

—— A Short History of the Law Association from its foundation in 1817 to 1938. [A new edition of "A Short Account of the Founding and Formation of the Law Association."] Compiled from the minutes of the Association by E. E. Barron. pp. 40. 1938. 8°. *See* LONDON.—III. *Law Association for the Benefit of Widows, etc.* **6025.** de. **17.**

BARRON (ELIZA MARY) Leaves from an Old Portfolio. pp. 234. *Samuel Tinsley: London*, 1875. 8°. **12618.** cc. **4.**

BARRON (ELWYN ALFRED) *See* BARRETT (Wilson) and BARRON (E. A.) In Old New York. A romance. 1900. 8°. **012641.** dd. **15.**

—— Deeds of Heroism and Daring . . . Edited by E. A. Barron. pp. xiii. 402. *New York & London*, [1920.] 8°. [*Harper's Pictorial Library of the World War.* vol. 10.] **9084.** g. **10/10.**

—— Manders. [A tale.] pp. viii. 328. *J. Macqueen: London*, 1898. 8°. **012643.** aa. **6.**

—— Marcel Levignet. pp. 360. *Duffield & Co.: New York*, 1906. 8°. **012706.** b. **52.**

—— The Triple Scar. (Third impression.) pp. 351. *Sisley's: London*, 1907. 8°. **012627.** b. **1.**

—— The Viking. [A drama in verse.] With preface by L. Barrett. pp. 141. *A. C. McClurg & Co.: Chicago*, 1888. 8°. **11791.** b. **10.**

BARRÓN (EUSTAQUIO) *See* GÓMEZ FARÍAS (B.) Juicio de imprenta. Documentos relativos al promovido por el Sr. D. E. Barron contra B. Gomez Farías. 1856. 4°. **6785.** b. **7. (5.)**

—— *See* PARDO (E.) Informe en estrados que el licenciado D. E. Pardo, como apoderado del Sr. D. E. Barron, pronunció . . . en el incidente promovido sobre competencia de jurisdiccion de la causa criminal promovida al Sr. D. Santos Degollado, por abuso de imprenta. 1857. 8°. **6784.** b. **7. (1.)**

BARRON (EVAN MACLEOD) *See* BARRON (James) *of Inverness.* A Highland Editor. Selected writings of J. Barron . . . edited by . . . E. M. Barron. 1927, *etc.* 8°. W.P. **8078.**

—— The Betrayal of Scotland. An exposure of self-government . . . Reprinted from "The Inverness Courier." pp. 32. *R. Carruthers & Sons: Inverness*, 1932. 8°. **8142.** c. **49.**

—— Inverness and the Macdonalds. pp. 126. *R. Carruthers & Sons: Inverness*, 1930. 8°. **010369.** f. **36.**

—— Inverness in the Fifteenth Century. pp. 129. *R. Carruthers & Sons: Inverness*, 1906. 8°. **10369.** e. **29.**

—— Inverness in the Middle Ages. pp. 70. *R. Carruthers & Sons: Inverness*, 1907. 8°. **010370.** f. **61.**

—— Prince Charlie's Pilot (Donald Macleod). A record of loyalty and devotion. pp. 205. *R. Carruthers & Sons: Inverness*, 1913. 8°. **010827.** k. **35.**

—— The Scottish War of Independence : a critical study. pp. xxviii. 499. *J. Nisbet & Co.: London*, 1914. 8°. **9510.** ccc. **30.**

—— The Scottish War of Independence . . . Second edition, with new introduction. pp. xciv. 526. *R. Carruthers & Sons: Inverness*, 1934. 8°. **2396.** e. **18.**

—— The Truth about the Highlands, *etc.* pp. 16. *R. Carruthers & Sons: Inverness*, 1931. 8°. [*Highland Handbooks.* no. 6.] **10370.b.13/6.**

BARRON (F.) *Writer of Verse.*

—— A Series of Verses on the Royal Mineral Water Hospital. By an In-Patient (F. Barron). pp. 14. *E. R. Blackett: Bath*, 1891. 8°. **11601.** dd. **9. (7.)**

BARRON (FRANK)

—— Personal Soundness in University Graduate Students. An experimental study of young men in the sciences and professions. pp. vi. 31. *University of California Press: Berkeley & Los Angeles*, 1954. 8°. [*University of California Publications. Personality Assessment and Research.* no. 1.] Ac. **2689.** gkd.

BARRON (Harry)

—— Modern Plastics, *etc.* pp. xv. 680. *Chapman & Hall: London*, 1945. 8°. **8772.** f. **11.**

—— Modern Plastics . . . Second edition revised. pp. xx. 779. *Chapman & Hall: London*, 1949. 8°. **8769.** g. **52.**

—— Modern Rubber Chemistry . . . With 70 illustrations. pp. 341. *Hutchinson: London*, 1937. 8°. **8899.** i. **30.**

—— Modern Synthetic Rubbers. pp. viii. 274. *Chapman & Hall: London*, 1942. 8°. **7946.** b. **28.**

—— Modern Synthetic Rubbers . . . Second edition, revised and enlarged. pp. xii. 355. *Chapman & Hall: London*, 1943. 8°. **7946.** b. **44.**

—— Modern Synthetic Rubbers. Third edition, revised and enlarged. pp. xix. 636. *Chapman & Hall: London*, 1949. 8°. **7949.** b. **36.**

BARRON (Hector) Lawn Tennis in Six Lessons, *etc.* pp. vi. 39. *Webster's Publications: London*, [1924.] 8°. **7904.** aa. **48.**

BARRON (*Sir* Henry) *Bart.* Accumulative Bonds. A new form of security, *etc.* (Fifth edition.) pp. 15. *Effingham Wilson & Co.: London*, 1887. 8°. **8248.** d. **27.** (**5.**)

BARRON (Henry Marshall) How to Argue. pp. 55. *Lincoln Williams: London*, [1932.] 8°. **011805.** df. **28.**

—— How to Debate and the Science of Argument. pp. 24. *A. H. Stockwell & Co.: London*, [1933.] 8°. **011805.** g. **58.**

—— Texts for Sermons on various occasions and subjects . . . With a preface by H. Scott Holland. pp. xxviii. 237. *Methuen & Co.: London*, 1900. 8°. **4499.** ee. **14.**

—— Your Parish History: how to discover and write it. pp. 108. *Wells Gardner & Co.: London*, [1930.] 8°. **010360.** aa. **76.**

BARRON (*Sir* Henry Winston) *Bart.* A Few Notes on the Public Schools and Universities of Holland and Germany, taken during a tour in the summer of 1839. pp. 99. *James Ridgway: London*, 1840. 8°. T. **2444.** (**7.**)

—— 1. A Few Notes on the Public Schools and Universities of Holland and Germany . . . By H. W. Barron, *etc.* [A review of this and other works on Dutch and German schools. Signed: W. E. H.] [1840.] 8°. *See* H., W. E. C.T. **235.** (**4.**)

—— Queen Victoria and Italy. pp. 58. *James Ridgway: London*, 1859. 8°. **8032.** d. **8.**

BARRON (J. B.) and **WADDAMS** (Herbert Montague)

—— Communism and the Churches. A documentation. pp. 102. *SCM Press: London*, 1950. 8°. **08008.** aa. **104.**

BARRON (J. B.) *Director of Revenue and Customs, Government of Palestine.*

—— Mohammedan Wakfs in Palestine. pp. 73. *Greek Convent Press: Jerusalem*, 1922. 8°. **05318.** de. **37.**

BARRON (James) *B.D.* *See* Goodwin (Thomas) *D.D.* The Works of T. Goodwin. [With a preface to vol. 1 by T. Owen and J. Barron.] 1681, *etc.* fol. **479.** f. **1–5.**

—— *See* Goodwin (Thomas) *D.D.* A Discourse of the Punishment of Sin in Hell, *etc.* [Edited by T. Owen and J. Barron.] 1680. 8°. **4375.** aaa. **20.**

BARRON (James) *Commodore.* *See* Decatur (Stephen) Correspondence, between the late Commodore S. Decatur and Com. J. Barron, *etc.* 1820. 8°. **1414.** h. **10.** (**2.**)

—— Proceedings of the General Court Martial for the trial of Commodore J. Barron, Captain Charles Gordon, Mr. William Hook, and Captain John Hall, of the United States' Ship Chesapeake . . . Jan., 1808. pp. 496. *Jacob Gideon Jr.: [Washington,]* 1822. 8°. **1245.** b. **38.**

BARRON (James) *Engineer and General Superintendent of the Navigation of the Ribble.*

—— A History of the Ribble Navigation from Preston to the Sea . . . With charts, plans and illustrations. pp. xv. 503. 1938. 4°. *See* Preston.—*Corporation.* Cup. **1247.** i. **12.**

BARRON (James) *of Inverness.* *See* Bain (John) *Master Mariner.* Life of a Scottish Sailor, *etc.* [With a memoir by J. Barron.] [1897.] 8°. **8805.** aaa. **36.**

—— A Highland Editor. Selected writings of James Barron of the "Inverness Courier," edited by his son Evan Macleod Barron. [With a portrait.] *R. Carruthers & Sons: Inverness*, 1927– . 8°. W.P. **8078.**

—— The Northern Highlands in the Nineteenth Century. Newspaper index and annals. vol. 1–3. *R. Carruthers & Sons: Inverness*, 1903–13. 4°. **010370.** h. **17.**
No more published.

BARRON (James) *of Wells Street, Oxford Street.* Modern and Elegant Designs of Cabinet & Upholstery Furniture, *etc.* [Plates.] *W. M. Thiselton: London*, [1820?] fol. **561*.** f. **14.**

BARRON (John) *See* Barronius (Joannes)

BARRON (John Augustus) The Bills of Sale and Chattel Mortgage Acts of the several Provinces of the Dominion of Canada. Being a complete and exhaustive annotation of the revised Statutes of Ont. 1887, chap. cxxv . . . Preceded by an introductory treatise on the law of bills of sale . . . Second edition. pp. liv. 708. *Carswell & Co.: Toronto*, [1888.] 8°. **06605.** ee. **1.**

—— Chattel Mortgages and Bills of Sale . . . A new edition of Barron on Bills of Sale. By J. A. Barron and . . . A. H. O'Brien. pp. xxxii. 534. *Canada Law Journal Co.: Toronto*, 1897. 8°. **06605.** ee. **2.**

—— Barron and O'Brien on Chattel Mortgages . . . Second revised edition. pp. lii. 754. *Canada Law Book Co.: Toronto; Cromarty Law Book Co.: Philadelphia*, 1914 [1913]. 8°. **6605.** d. **6.**

—— The Conditional Sales Acts: being an annotation of the Act respecting Conditional Sales of Chattels . . . and Amendments thereto. To which is appended a complete set of forms . . . Second edition. pp. xxiii. 208. *Carswell Co.: Toronto*, 1907. 8°. **06605.** i. **26.**

BARRON (John Hall)

—— *See* Passer (A.) The Stamps of Turkey . . . Edited . . . by J. H. Barron and J. Simons. 1938. 8°. **20032.** bb. 36.

—— *See* Seymour (J. B.) The Stamps of Great Britain. By J. B. Seymour . . . Edited . . . by J. H. Barron and J. Simons. 1934, *etc.* 8°. **8247.h.1.**

BARRÓN (José Manuel Escandón y) *Marquis de Villavieja.* *See* Escandón y Barrón. **10635.** e. **4.**

BARRON (Joseph Thomas) Elements of Epistemology. pp. 225. *Burns, Oates & Co.: London; printed in U.S.A.*, 1931. 8°. **8459.** s. **13.**

BARRON (Joseph Thomas)

—— The Idea of the Absolute in Modern British Philosophy . . . A dissertation, *etc.* pp. viii. 95. *Washington*, 1929. 8°. [*Catholic University of America. Studies in Sacred Theology.* no. 31.] Ac. **2692.** y/**20.**

BARRON (Juan José) and **BARRERA Y CARRAGAL** (Francisco Xavier de la) Representacion dirigida al Soberano Congreso Constituyente por los Ciudadanos J. J. Barron, y ex-diputado F. J. de la Barrera, pidiendo se declare nula la provision de contador general de lotería hecha en el ex-diputado D. A. Cumplido, por ser contraria à las leyes que prescriben la rigorosa escala en estos empleos. (Segundo ocurso de los ciudadanos Barron y Barrera al . . . Congreso, *etc.*) 2 pt. *Mexico*, 1823. 4°. **9770.** bb. **14.** (**46.**)

BARRON (Leonard) *See* Blanchan (Neltje) The American Flower Garden . . . Planting lists by L. Barron, *etc.* 1909. 4°. **7031.** w. **18.**

—— *See* Correvon (Henry) Rock Garden and Alpine Plants . . . Edited by L. Barron. 1930. 8°. **07028.** b. **28.**

—— *See* Roberts (J. L.) Modern Dahlias . . . Edited by L. Barron. 1938. 8°. **7032.** r. **3.**

—— The Complete Book of Gardening. [By various authors.] Edited and with a foreword by L. Barron. pp. xx. 645. *Doubleday, Doran & Co.: Garden City, N.Y.*, 1936. 8°. **07030.** ff. **64.**

—— Gardening for the Small Place. pp. 95. *Garden City, N.Y.*, 1935. 8°. [*Doubleday Garden Handbooks.* no. 1.] W.P. **11513/1.**

—— Lawns and how to make them, together with the proper keeping of putting greens . . . Illustrated. pp. 174. *Doubleday, Page & Co.: London*, 1906. 8°. [*Garden Library.* no. 3.] **7033.** bb. **1/3.**

BARRÓN (Lope) Cantabria y Logroño. Estudio filológico-histórico. pp. 253. *Málaga*, 1914. 8°. **9181.** b. **22.**

—— Frases Populares, *etc.* pp. 459. 6. *Málaga*, 1897. 8°. **012305.** ee. **7.**

BARRON (Louie) *pseud.* Zerola of Nazareth. pp. v. 160. *C. J. Musson: Toronto*, 1895. 16°. **12705.** aa. **22.**

BARRON (Louis) Autour de Paris. 500 dessins d'après nature par G. Fraipont. pp. 497. *Paris*, [1891.] 4°. **1783.** c. **7.**

—— Les Environs de Paris. Ouvrage illustré de . . . dessins d'après nature par G. Fraipont et accompagné d'une carte, *etc.* pp. 604. *Paris*, [1886.] 4°. **10170.** k. **4.**

—— Les Fleuves de France. La Garonne . . . Ouvrage orné de 153 dessins par A. Chapon. pp. 407. *Paris*, [1891.] 8°. **10169.** d. **4.**

—— Les Fleuves de France. La Loire . . . Ouvrage orné de 134 dessins par A. Chapon. pp. ii. 396. *Paris*, [1888.] 8°. **010171.** h. **15.**

—— Les Fleuves de France. Le Rhône . . . Ouvrage orné de 168 dessins par A. Chapon. pp. 454. *Paris*, [1892.] 8°. **010171.** g. **7.**

—— Les Fleuves de France. La Seine . . . Ouvrage orné de 175 dessins par A. Chapon. pp. 461. *Paris*, [1889.] 8°. **010171.** h. **31.**

—— [Another edition.] pp. 307. *Paris*, [1904.] 8°. **010169.** h. **16.**

BARRON (Louis)

—— Les Jeux. Jeux historiques, jeux nationaux, sports modernes, *etc.* pp. 237. *Paris*, [1892.] 8°. **7912.** cc. **2.**

—— Paris pittoresque. 1800–1900. La vie.—Les moeurs.—Les plaisirs. Ouvrage orné de 500 reproductions d'estampes et de 20 gravures, *etc.* pp. 413. *Paris*, [1899.] 4°. **10173.** h. **24.**

BARRON (Louise) *See* Ephemerides. Almanack for 1862. [By L. Barron.] 1861. 4°. **717.** m. **11.** (**27.**)

BARRON (Margaret) *See* Oliver (John) *Principal of the Western Dairy Institute, Berkeley.* Cheese and Butter Making . . . Parts i. and ii. by J. Oliver. Part iii. by Margaret Barron. [1892.] 8°. **7942.** e. **31.**

BARRON (Maurice)

—— *See* Hayden (Arthur G.) and Barron (M.) The Rigid-Frame Bridge, *etc.* [1950.] 8°. **08773.** c. **1.**

BARRON (Milton Leon)

—— People who intermarry. Intermarriage in a New England industrial community. pp. xii. 389. *Syracuse University Press: [Syracuse]*, 1946. 8°. **8417.** cc. **14.**

BARRON (Norman Simpson)

—— The Dairy Farmer's Veterinary Book. A complete guide to the farm treatment and control of cow diseases. [With plates.] pp. 188. *Dairy Farmer: Ipswich*, 1950. 8°. **07295.** f. **81.**

—— The Dairy Farmer's Veterinary Book, *etc.* (Second edition.) pp. 188. *Dairy Farmer: Ipswich*, 1950. 8°. **07295.** f. **82.**

The date on the verso of the titlepage is 1951.

—— The Pig Farmer's Veterinary Book, *etc.* [With plates.] pp. xiii. 105. *Dairy Farmer (Books): Ipswich*, 1952. 8°. **7295.** pp. **18.**

—— The Pig Farmer's Veterinary Book, *etc.* (Second edition.) pp. xiii. 105. *Dairy Farmer: Ipswich*, 1952. 8°. **7295.** pp. **25.**

BARRON (Olive Cunninghame) Songs of the Rhodesian Bush. [With a portrait.] pp. 80. *Trefoil Publishing Co.: London*, [1931.] 8°. **11640.** e. **36.**

—— Twilight in Rhodesia. A novel, *etc.* [With a portrait.] pp. 254. *Trefoil Publishing Co.: London*, [1930.] 8°. NN. **17494.**

BARRON (Oswald) *See* Barron (Arthur O.)

BARRON (P. A.) The House Desirable . . . With 101 illustrations . . . and 85 plans and elevations. pp. xv. 253. *Methuen & Co.: London*, 1929. 8°. **07815.** i. **50.**

BARRON (Percy) The Hate Flame. pp. 382. *Hodder & Stoughton: London*, 1908. 8°. **012627.** aaa. **13.**

BARRON (Philip F.) *See* Periodical Publications.—*Dublin.* Ancient Ireland. A weekly magazine . . . By P. F. Barron. 1835. 8°. P.P. **6160.**

—— An Irish Primer. no. 1–3. *J. S. Folds: Dublin*, [1836?] 16° & 8°. **829.** b. **1.**

BARRON (Phyllis)

—— A Note on the Block Printing of Cover Papers. *See* Seaby (Allen W.) Colour Printing with Linoleum and Wood Blocks, *etc.* 1928. 8°. **07943.** b. **73.**

BARRON (Richard) *Captain.* Views in India, chiefly among the Neelgherry Hills, taken during a short residence on them in 1835, with notes and descriptive illustrations. By Captain R. Barron . . . Engraved by R. Havell. pl. 6. *Robt. Havell: London,* 1837. fol. **1784**. c. **10**.

BARRON (Richard) *Dissenting Minister.* *See* Bower (Archibald) A Faithful Account of Mr. Archibald Bower's motives for leaving his office of Secretary to the Court of Inquisition, *etc.* [Edited by R. Barron.] 1750. 8º. **699.e.1.(1.)**

—— *See* B - w - r (A - - ch - b - ld) A Faithful Account of Mr. A - - ch - b - ld B - w - r's [i.e. Archibald Bower's] Motives for leaving his office of Secretary to the Court of Inquisition, *etc.* [Edited by R. Barron.] [1750.] 8º. T. **1613**. (**7**.)

—— *See* B - w - r (Archibald) A Faithful Account of Mr. A - ch - b - ld B - w - r's Motives for leaving his office of Secretary to the Court of Inquisition. [Edited by R. Barron.] 1756. 8º. [*A Letter from a Clergyman at London to the . . . inhabitants of Lisbon, etc.*] T. **1620**. (**8**.)

—— *See* Gordon (Thomas) *of Kircudbright.* A Cordial for Low Spirits, *etc.* [Edited by R. Barron.] 1751. 12º. **292**. e. **33, 34**.

—— *See* Milton (John) [*Prose Works.*] The Works of John Milton, historical, political and miscellaneous, *etc.* [Edited by T. Birch and R. Barron.] 1753. 4º. **685**. i. **12, 13**.

—— *See* Milton (John) [*Prose Works.—Eikonoklastes.*] *Εἰκονοκλαστης* . . . Now first published from the author's second edition . . . with many enlargements ; by R. Baron, *etc.* 1756. 4º. **599**. i. **14**.

—— —— 1770. 8º. **8122**. f. **46**.

—— —— 1806. 8º. [*Prose Works of John Milton.* vol. 2.] **2041**. e.

—— *See* Nedham (Marchamont) The Excellencie of a Free State. [Edited by R. Barron.] 1767. 8º. **8006**. c. **27**.

—— The Pillars of Priestcraft and Orthodoxy shaken. [A collection of tracts. Edited by R. Barron.] 2 vol. *R. Griffiths : London,* 1752. 12º. **4103**. aaa. **33**.

—— The second edition. 4 vol. ms. notes [by J. Mitford]. *Mr. Cadell, etc. : London,* 1768. 12º. **4106**. a. **12**.

BARRON (Robert) Memoir of the Rev. William Rogers . . . Minister of Whiteabbey Presbyterian Church, Ireland. pp. viii. 258. *Religious Tract & Book Depôt: Belfast,* 1898. 8º. **4956**. g. **3**.

BARRON (Samuel Benton) The Lone Star Defenders. A chronicle of the Third Texas Cavalry, Ross' Brigade [1861–65. With illustrations]. pp. 276. *Neale Publishing Co.: New York & Washington,* 1908. 8º. **8821**. de. **25**.

BARRON (Samuel L.) *See* Cassel (K. G.) The Theory of Social Economy . . . Translated by S. L. Barron, *etc.* 1932. 8º. **08206**. h. **2**.

BARRON (Seth Lee)

—— *See* Gottlieb (Bernhard) Endodontia. By B. Gottlieb . . . S. L. Barron, *etc.* 1950. 8º. **07612**. bb. **21**.

BARRON (Seth Lee) and **SCHOTT** (Ernst Adolf)

—— Cardiographic Technique. A manual for cardiological technicians. pp. vii. 156. *William Heinemann Medical Books: London,* 1952. 8º. **7617**. b. **33**.

BARRON (Thomas) *F.G.S.* The Topography and Geology of the District between Cairo and Suez. pp. 133. 1907. 8º. *See* Egypt.—*Ministry of Finance.—Survey Department.* **7109**. dd. **24**.

—— The Topography and Geology of the Peninsula of Sinai, Western portion. pp. 241. 1907. 8º. *See* Egypt.—*Ministry of Finance.—Survey Department.* **10076**. ff. **35**.

BARRON (Thomas) *F.G.S.*, and **HUME** (William Fraser)

—— Notes on the Geology of the Eastern Desert of Egypt. pp. 42. *Dulau & Co.: London,* 1902. 8º. **7109**. e. **38**.

—— Topography and Geology of the Eastern Desert of Egypt, Central portion. [With maps and plans.] pp. viii. 331. 1902. 8º. *See* Egypt.—*Ministry of Public Works.—Survey Department.* **7109**. dd. **34**.

BARRON (Tom) A Complete Treatise of the methods used by Tom Barron, England, in producing heavy layers. (A treatise on poultry.) pp. 79. *Tom Barron Publishing Co.: Philadelphia,* [1914.] 8º. **07291**. de. **5**.

BARRON (Tom) and **LEIGH** (J. N.)

—— The Daily Mail Poultry Book . . . Edited by J. W. Hurst. pp. viii. 142. *Associated Newspapers: London,* 1921. 8º. **7286**. e. **23**.

—— The Daily Mail Poultry Book . . . Edited by W. M. Elkington. pp. 172. *Daily Mail Publications: [London,* 1950.] 8º. **7295**. p. **21**.

BARRON (William) *Captain.* Old Whaling Days. pp. x. 211. *Andrews & Co.: Hull,* 1895. 8º. **10460**. aaa. **42**.

BARRON (William) *Head Gardener at Elvaston Castle.* The British Winter Garden : being a practical treatise on evergreens, *etc.* [With plates.] pp. xii. 121. *Bradbury & Evans : London,* 1852. 8º. **7055**. d. **1**.

BARRON (William) *Professor at the University of St. Andrews.* An Essay on the Mechanical Principles of the Plough. [With plates.] pp. 71. *J. Balfour: Edinburgh,* 1774. 8º. **723**. d. **3**. (**1**.)

—— History of the Colonization of the Free States of Antiquity, applied to the present contest between Great Britain and her American Colonies. With reflections concerning the future settlement of these Colonies. [By W. Barron.] pp. vii. 151. 1777. 4º. *See* England. [*Appendix.—History and Politics.*—ii. 1777.] **522**. k. **12**.

—— Histoire de la fondation des colonies des anciennes républiques, adaptée à la dispute présente de la Grande Bretagne avec ses colonies américaines. Traduite de l'anglais [of W. Barron, by Marie Antoine Cérisier], *etc.* pp. 247. 1778. 8º. *See* England. [*Appendix.—History and Politics.*—ii. 1777.] **8154**. aaa. **5**.

—— *See* Symonds (John) *LL.D.* Remarks upon an Essay [by W. Barron] intituled, The History of the Colonization of the Free States of Antiquity, *etc.* 1778. 8º. T. **917**. (**9**.)

—— History of the Political Connection between England and Ireland, from the reign of Henry ii. to the present time. [By W. Barron.] pp. x. 200. 32. 1780. 4º. *See* England. [*Appendix.—History and Politics.*—i.] **600**. i. **22**.

—— [Another copy.] **189**. c. **18**.

—— [Another copy.] G. **4752**.

—— Lectures on Belles Lettres and Logic. 2 vol. *Longman & Co.: London ; Bell & Bradfute: Edinburgh,* 1806. 8º. **1086**. d. **23, 24**.

BARRONI, afterwards **PAOLI** (MARIANNA) Nuova e distinta relazione della gran giustizia seguita in Trento il giorno 21. Febraro 1767 di due donne (M. Barroni e Margarita Cersari), e otto capi di assassini da strada, *etc.* *Trento*, [1767.] 4°. **811**. h. **18**. (**26**.)

BARRONIUS (JOANNES) Theses aliquot philosophicæ, quas . . . adolescentes ex inclyto Collegio Salvatoriano . . . propugnabunt Andreapoli, *etc.* *Praes.* J. Barronius. [The dedicatory epistle in the name of the Candidates signed: A. L. M. C.] *Iohannes Wreittoun: Edinburgi*, 1627. 8°. **527**. c. **28**.

BARROS (FLEURY DE) *See* FLEURY DE BARROS.

BARROS (ADHEMAR PEREIRA DE) *See* PEREIRA DE BARROS (A.)

BARROS (ALONSO DE) Desengaño de Cortesanos . . . Le desabus des courtisans . . . Traduit en françois par Sebastien Hardy, *etc.* *Span. & Fr.* pp. 277. *F. Huby: Paris*, 1617. 8°. **11451**. b. **14**.

—— Proverbios Morales, *etc.* [In verse.] pp. 60. *L. Sanchez: Madrid*, 1598. 8°. **12305**. aaa. **33**.

—— [Another edition.] pp. 60. *A. Martin: Madrid*, 1608. 8°. **12304**. aaa. **35**.
Slightly cropped.

—— [Another edition.] pp. 42. *S. de Cormellas: Barcelona*, 1619. 8°. **9930**. aa. **5**. (**2**.)

—— [Another edition.] 1857. *See* ARIBAU (B. C.) Biblioteca de autores Españoles. tom. 42. 1849, *etc.* 8°. **12232.f.1/42.**

—— [Another edition.] pp. 113. *Madrid*, 1874. 16°. **12314**. a. **13**.

—— Proverbios. [Extracts from "Proverbios morales."] *In:* MELO (A. de) Libro de varios sonetos, *etc.* pp. 17–25. 1955. 8°. **11454**. c. **14**.

—— Proverbi Morali . . . Tradotti in Italiano dal Signor Alessandro Adimari. Col testo spagniolo a rincontro, *etc.* pp. 171. *Z. Pignoni: Firenze*, 1622. 12°. **12304**. aa. **16**.

—— Prouebios [*sic*] Morales, Heraclito de A. de Varros, concordados por el Maestro Bartolome Ximenes Paton. *Span. & Lat.* pp. 78. *P. de la Cuesta: Baeça*, 1615. 4°. **1074**. l. **25**.

—— [Another edition.] *Span. & Lat.* pp. 78. *P. Craesbeeck: Lisboa*, 1617. 4°. **1070**. h. **10**.

—— Perla de los Proverbios Morales de A. de Barros. pp. 54. *I. Rodriguez: Lisboa*, 1617. 8°. **1075**. b. **15**.

BARROS (ÁLVARO) Confirmacion de la defensa del Teniente-Coronel Don Ricardo Mendez. pp. 32. *Buenos Aires*, 1874. 8°. **6784**. h. **2**. (**13**.)

BARROS (ANDRÉ DE) Vida do apostolico padre Antonio Vieyra da Companhia de Jesus, *etc.* [With a portrait.] pp. 686. *Lisboa*, 1746. fol. **689.eee.22.**

—— [Another edition.] pp. xiii. 415. 1857. *See* VIEIRA (Antonio) *Jesuit.* Obras, *etc.* 1854, *etc.* 8°. **3678**. cc. **9**.

—— Vozes Saudosas, da eloquencia, do espirito, do zelo, e eminente sabedoria do padre Antonio Vieira . . . acompanhadas com hum fidelissimo echo, que sonoramente resulta do interior da obra Clavis prophetarum, *etc.* [A biography of A. Vieira, with several of his writings, various epitaphs and encomiums, etc.] pp. 135 [315]. *Lisboa Occidental*, 1736. 8°. **1112**. g. **16**.

BARROS (ANTONIO ORREGO) *See* ORREGO BARROS.

BARROS (BRÁS DE) *See* BRÁS, *de Braga, Frei.*

BARROS (DOMINGO BORGES DE) *Baron de Pedra Branca.* *See* BORGES DE BARROS.

BARROS (DULCE QUEIROZ DE) *See* QUEIROZ DE BARROS.

BARROS (EUGENIO DE) *See* PERIODICAL PUBLICATIONS. *Coimbra.* O Phosphoro. Publicaçao quinzenal litteraria . . . Redactores A. B. Cerqueira Lobo . . . E. de Barros, *etc.* 1860, *etc.* 4°. P.P. **4128**. h.

BARROS (FRANCISCO DE) O Morgado de S. Cosme. Chronica da Aldeia. Primeira edição. 2ª série. pp. 316. *Porto*, 1888. 8°. **12489**. bb. **19**.

BARROS (GIOVANNI DI) *See* BARROS (João de)

BARROS (GUILLERMO MONCKEBERG) *See* MONCKEBERG BARROS.

BARROS (HENRIQUE DA GAMA) *See* GAMA BARROS.

BARROS (HENRIQUE DO REGO) *See* REGO BARROS.

BARROS (J. C. DE)

—— *See* CAINE (*Sir* Thomas H. H.) *K.B.E.* [The Scapegoat.] A Expiação. Tradução de J. C. de Barros, *etc.* 1942. 8°. **12650**. de. **20**.

—— *See* DELL (Ethel M.) Os Rochedos de Valpré. Tradução de J. C. de Barros. [1935?] 8°. **012641**. pp. **39**.

BARROS (JAGY REGO) *See* REGO BARROS (J.)

BARROS (JOÃO DE) *Historian.*

ASIA.

—— Asia de Joam de Barros, dos fectos que os Portugueses fizeram no descobrimento ⁊ conquista dos mares ⁊ terras do Oriente. (Primeira decada.—Segunda decada da Asia, *etc.*) **G. L.** 2 pt. *G. Galharde: Lisboa*, 1552, 53. fol. **150**. i. **4**.

—— [Another copy.] G. **6637**.
Imperfect; wanting the two leaves of errata, following the titlepage.

—— Terceira decada da Asia, *etc.* ff. 266. *J. de Barreira: Lisboa*, 1563. fol. G. **6593**.

—— Quarta Decada da Asia de J. de Barros . . . Reformada accrescentada e illustrada com notas e taboas geographicas, por João Baptista Lavanha. pp. 711. *A. Falorsi: Madrid*, 1615. fol. **582**. i. **12**.
With an additional titlepage, engraved.

—— [Another copy.] C. **79**. c. **11**.

—— [Another copy.] **148**. e. **14**.

—— [Another copy.] G. **6600**.

—— Decada primeira (segunda—terceira) da Asia, *etc.* 3 vol. *I. Rodriguez: Lisboa*, 1628. fol. **582**. i. **9–11**.

—— [Another copy.] **148**. e. **11–13**

—— [Another copy.] G. **6799–6801**.

—— [Another copy.] C. **79**. c. **10**.
Each volume of this copy contains an engraved titlepage altered with a pen from that of the edition of the fourth Decade published at Madrid in 1615. This copy differs from the preceding in containing no taxation of price.

BARROS (JOÃO DE) *Historian.*

—— Da Asia de João de Barros e de Diogo de Couto. Nova edição, *etc.* [With portraits.] 24 vol.

Da Asia de J. de Barros . . . Decada primeira(—quarta). [Decada quarta edited by João B. Lavanha.] 8 vol. 1778, 77. **978.** c. **1–8.** Vida de João de Barros. Por Manoel Severim de Faria e indice geral das quatro decadas da sua Asia. pp. lxxiv. 258. 1778. **978.** c. **9.**

Da Asia de Diogo de Couto . . . Decada quarta(—decima; decada undecima da Asia . . . supprindo a que falta de D. de Couto; decada duodecima). 14 tom. 1778–88. **978.** c. **10–23.** Indice geral das decadas de Couto. pp. 1–386. [1788.] **978.** c. **24.**

Lisboa, 1778, 1777–[88]. 12°. 978. c. 1–24.

Imperfect; wanting the portrait of Alfonso de Albuquerque in Decada segunda, pt. 1; *the portrait of Diogo do Couto in Decada quarta, pt.* 1; *all but the first leaf of D. do Couto's letter to Philip* II, *King of Portugal, prefixed to Decada oitava; and the preliminary matter of the last volume, containing the titlepage, and the life of D. do Couto.*

—— [Another copy.] Da Asia de João de Barros e de Diogo de Couto, *etc.* *Lisboa*, 1778, 77–[88]. 8°. **9196.** ff. **4.** *Imperfect; wanting the map in Decada quarta, pt.* 2, *and the preliminary matter of the last volume, containing the titlepage and the life of D. do Couto.*

—— [Another copy of vol. 1–17.] **148.** a. **7–23.**

—— Primera década da Ásia. pp. xci. 254. *Paris, Lisboa; Lisbôa* [printed], 1920. 8°. [*Antologia portuguesa.*] **12232.** b. **10.**

—— Ásia . . . Segunda década. Sexta edição, actualizada na ortografia e anotada por Hernani Cidade. Notas históricas finais por Manuel Múrias. pp. 471. 1945. 8°. *See* PORTUGAL.—*Ministério do Ultramar.* —*Agência Geral do Ultramar.* 10055. w. 22.

—— L'Asie de Barros, ou l'histoire des conquestes des Portugais aux Indes Orientales. Partie première. pp. 1–16. *See* THEVENOT (M.) Relations de divers voyages, *etc.* tom. 2. 1696. fol. **566.** k. **5.**

—— Die Asia des Joao de Barros in wortgetreuer Uebertragung von Dr. E. Feust. Bd. 1. Hälfte 1. pp. xiv. 191. *Nürnberg*, 1844. 4°. **1312.** k. **8.** *No more published.*

—— Della historia del Signor Giovan de Barros della prima deca dell' Asia, *etc.* *See* RAMUSIO (G. B.) Primo [*etc.*] volume . . . delle nauigatione et viaggi, *etc.* vol. 1. 1554, *etc.* fol. **566.** k. **1.**

—— L'Asia del Sig. Giovanni di Barros . . . Nuouamente di lingua Portoghese tradotta. Dal S. Alfonso Ulloa. (Deca prima.—La seconda deca.) 2 vol. *V. Valgrisio: Venetia*, 1562. 4°. **280.** k. **16.**

—— Libro nono de la tercera decada de la Assia de Juan de Barros, de los hechos de los Portugueses, en el descubrimiẽto y cõquista de los mares y tierras del Oriẽte. Traduzido de Portugues en Castellano [by F. de Menezes, Count da Ericeira]. Contiene las cosas que se hizieron en el tiempo que don Enrique de Meneses las governò. (Govierno y hechos de don Enrique de Meneses.) ff. 103. *I. Delgado: Madrid*, 1628. 4°. G. **2728.**

Selections and Extracts.

—— Aphorismos y Exemplos politicos, y militares, sacados de la primera Decada de Iuan de Barros por don Fernando Ulvia de Castro, *etc.* pp. 97. *P. Craesbeeck: Lisboa*, 1621. 4°. **521.** f. **7.**

—— Extractos da Asia, *etc.* (Extracts from Da Asia.) *Port. & Eng.* 1900. *See* THEAL (George M.) Records of South-Eastern Africa, *etc.* vol. 6. 1898, *etc.* 8°. **09061.** aa.

BARROS (JOÃO DE) *Historian.* [ASIA.—*Selections and Extracts.*]

—— The History of Ceylon, from the earliest times to 1600 A.D., as related by Joãn [*sic*] de Barros and Diogo do Couto. Translated and edited by Donald Ferguson. pp. 445. *Colombo*, 1909. 8°. [*Journal of the Ceylon Branch of the Royal Asiatic Society.* vol. 20. no. 60.] Ac. **8830.**

—— Aanzienelyke scheeps-togt door . . . Vasco da Gamma als ammiraal ter Zee en Onder-Konink van Indien . . . in't jaar 1524, *etc.* pp. 138. *See* AA (Pieter van der) *Bookseller.* Naaukeurige versameling der gedenkwaardigste zee en land reysen, *etc.* dl. 40. 1707. 8°. **979.** e. **11.** (**2.**)

—— [Another edition.] pp. 74. *See* AA (Pieter van der) *Bookseller.* De Aanmerkenswaardigste . . . zee- en landreizen der Portugeezen, *etc.* dl. 1. 1727. fol. **566.** l. **5.**

—— De Alder-eerste scheepstogten der Portugysen . . . in het jaar 1419 . . . beginnende met het vinden van de Caap Non en Bojador, tot de Caap de Bon Esperance, *etc.* pp. 6. 149. *See* AA (Pieter van der) *Bookseller.* Naaukeurige versameling der gedenk-waardigste zee en land reysen, *etc.* dl. 3. 1707. 8°. **979.** e. **1.** (**4.**)

—— [Another edition.] pp. 82. *See* AA (Pieter van der) *Bookseller.* De Aanmerkenswaardigste . . . zee- en landreizen der Portugeezen, *etc.* dl. 1. 1727. fol. **566.** l. **5.**

—— Bloedige scheeps-togt van den Maarschalk Don Fernando Coutinho na Oost Indien . . . in't jaar 1509, *etc.* pp. 23. *See* AA (Pieter van der) *Bookseller.* Naaukeurige versameling der gedenk-waardigste zee en land reysen, *etc.* dl. 23. 1707. 8°. **979.** e. **6.** (**2.**)

—— [Another edition.] pp. 26. *See* AA (Pieter van der) *Bookseller.* Aanmerkenswaardigste . . . zee- en landreizen der Portugeezen, *etc.* dl. 1. 1727. fol. **566.** l. **5.**

—— Eerste scheeps-togt van Vasco da Gamma tot ontdekking van de Indien in het jaar 1497, *etc.* pp. 40. *See* AA (Pieter van der) *Bookseller.* Naaukeurige versameling der gedenk-waardigste zee en land reysen, *etc.* dl. 6. 1707. 8°. **979.** e. **2.** (**3.**)

—— [Another edition.] pp. 22. *See* AA (Pieter van der) *Bookseller.* De Aanmerkenswaardigste . . . zee- en landreizen der Portugeezen, *etc.* dl. 1. 1727. fol. **566.** l. **5.**

—— Held-dadige scheeps-togt van Alfonso d'Albuquerque na de Roode Zee in het jaar 1506, *etc.* pp. 517. *See* AA (Pieter van der) *Bookseller.* Naaukeurige versameling der gedenk-waardigste zee en land reysen, *etc.* dl. 20. 1707. 8°. **979.** e. **5.** (**1.**)

—— [Another edition.] pp. 276. *See* AA (Pieter van der) *Bookseller.* De Aanmerkenswaardigste . . . zee- en landreizen der Portugeezen, *etc.* dl. 1. 1727. fol. **566.** l. **5.**

—— Ongemeene scheeps-togten en manhafte krygs-bedryven te water en land door Diego Lopez Sequeira . . . in de Oost-Indien . . . in't jaar 1518, *etc.* pp. 384. *See* AA (Pieter van der) *Bookseller.* Naaukeurige versameling der gedenk-waardigste zee en land reysen, *etc.* dl. 37. 1707. 8°. **979.** e. **8.** (**1.**)

—— [Another edition.] pp. 204. *See* AA (Pieter van der) *Bookseller.* De Aanmerkenswaardigste . . . zee- en landreizen der Portugeezen, *etc.* dl. 1. 1727. fol. **566.** l. **5.**

—— Roem-rugte scheeps-togt van Francisco d'Almeida na Oost-Indien . . . in't jaar 1505, *etc.* pp. 240. *See* Aa (Pieter van der) *Bookseller.* Naaukeurige versameling der gedenk-waardigste zee en land reysen, *etc.* dl. 16. 1707. 8°. **979. e. 4. (2.)**

—— [Another edition.] pp. 132. *See* Aa (Pieter van der) *Bookseller.* De Aanmerkenswaardigste . . . zee- en landreizen der Portugeezen, *etc.* dl. 1. 1727. fol. **566. l. 5.**

—— Roemwaardige scheeps-togten en dappere krygs-bedryven ter zee en te land onder't bestuur van Duarte de Menezes als . . . gouverneur van Oost-Indien : ter aflossing van . . . Diego Lopez de Sequeira . . . in't jaar 1521. pp. 179. *See* Aa (Pieter van der) *Bookseller.* Naaukeurige versameling der gedenkwaardigste zee en land reysen, *etc.* dl. 35. 1707. 8°. **979. e. 9. (3.)**

—— [Another edition.] pp. 96. *See* Aa (Pieter van der) *Bookseller.* De Aanmerkenswaardigste . . . zee- en landreizen der Portugeezen, *etc.* dl. 1. 1727. fol. **566. l. 5.**

—— Scheeps-togt gedaan door Fernando Perez d'Andrade . . . van Malacca afgezonden na de Golf van Bengale en Kusten van China in 't jaar 1516, *etc.* pp. 47. *See* Aa (Pieter van der) *Bookseller.* Naaukeurige versameling der gedenk-waardigste zee en land reysen, *etc.* dl. 29. 1707. 8°. **979. e. 7. (3.)**

—— [Another edition.] pp. 30. *See* Aa (Pieter van der) *Bookseller.* De Aanmerkenswaardigste . . . zee- en landreizen der Portugeezen, *etc.* dl. 1. 1727. fol. **566. l. 5.**

—— Scheeps-togt van Pedro da Nhaya na Oost-Indien . . . in't jaar 1505, *etc.* pp. 41. *See* Aa (Pieter van der) *Bookseller.* Naaukeurige versameling der gedenk-waardigste zee en land reysen, *etc.* dl. 17. 1707. 8°. **979. e. 4. (3.)**

—— [Another edition.] pp. 24. *See* Aa (Pieter van der) *Bookseller.* De Aanmerkenswaardigste . . . zee- en landreizen der Portugeezen, *etc.* dl. 1. 1727. fol. **566. l. 5.**

—— Scheeps-togt van Tristano d'Acunha na Oost-Indien . . . in het jaar 1506, *etc.* pp. 48. *See* Aa (Pieter van der) *Bookseller.* Naaukeurige versameling der gedenk-waardigste zee en land reysen, *etc.* dl. 19. 1707. 8°. **979. e. 4. (5.)**

—— [Another edition.] pp. 26. *See* Aa (Pieter van der) *Bookseller.* De Aanmerkenswaardigste . . . zee- en landreizen der Portugeezen, *etc.* dl. 1. 1727. fol. **566. l. 5.**

—— Scheeps-togten en manhafte krygs-bedryven te water en te land gedaan door Lopo Soares d'Albegeria : uit last des Konings Don Manuel van Portugaal, als kapetein generaal en gouverneur der Oost-Indien, in't jaar 1515, *etc.* pp. 126. *See* Aa (Pieter van der) *Bookseller.* Naaukeurige versameling der gedenk-waardigste zee en land reysen, *etc.* dl. 28. 1707. 8°. **979. e. 7. (2.)**

—— [Another edition.] pp. 70. *See* Aa (Pieter van der) *Bookseller.* De Aanmerkenswaardigste . . . zee- en Landreizen der Portugeezen, *etc.* dl. 1. 1727. fol. **566. l. 5.**

—— Staat-zugtige scheeps-togten en krygs-bedryven . . . in Oost Indien, door Don Lopo Vaz de Sampayo, gedaan in't jaar 1526, *etc.* pp. 192. *See* Aa (Pieter van der) *Bookseller.* Naaukeurige versameling der gedenk-waardigste zee en land reysen, *etc.* dl. 44. 1707. 8°. **979. e. 12. (2.)**

—— [Another edition.] pp. 104. *See* Aa (Pieter van der) *Bookseller.* De Aanmerkenswaardigste . . . zee- en landreizen der Portugeezen, *etc.* dl. 1. 1727. fol. **566. l. 5.**

—— Tien-jaarige scheeps-togten en heldhaftige krygs-bedryven te water en te land, door Nuno da Cunha . . . in Oost Indien ; in't jaar 1528 en vervolgens. pp. 421. *See* Aa (Pieter van der) *Bookseller.* Naaukeurige versameling der gedenk-waardigste zee en land reysen, *etc.* dl. 45. 1707. 8°. **979. e. 13. (1.)**

—— [Another edition.] pp. 224. *See* Aa (Pieter van der) *Bookseller.* De Aanmerkenswaardigste . . . zee- en landreizen der Portugeezen, *etc.* dl. 1. 1727. fol. **566. l. 5.**

—— Twee bysondere scheeps-togten na Oost-Indien van Francisco d'Albuquerque, in het jaar 1503. En Lopo Soares in het jaar 1504, *etc.* pp. 40. *See* Aa (Pieter van der) *Bookseller.* Naaukeurige versameling der gedenk-waardigste zee en land reysen, *etc.* dl. 14. 1707. 8°. **979. e. 3. (6.)**

—— [Another edition.] pp. 22. *See* Aa (Pieter van der) *Bookseller.* De Aanmerkenswaardigste . . . zee- en landreizen der Portugeezen, *etc.* dl. 1. 1727. fol. **566. l. 5.**

—— Twee bysondere scheeps-togten na Oost-Indien van Gonsalo de Sequeira in het jaar 1510. En Garcia de Noronha in het jaar 1511, *etc.* pp. 47. *See* Aa (Pieter van der) *Bookseller.* Naaukeurige versameling der gedenk-waardigste zee en land reysen, *etc.* dl. 25. 1707. 8°. **979. e. 6. (4.)**

—— [Another edition.] pp. 26. *See* Aa (Pieter van der) *Bookseller.* De Aanmerkenswaardigste . . . zee- en landreizen, *etc.* dl. 1. 1727. fol. **566. l. 5.**

—— Twee bysondere scheeps-togten na Oost-Indien, van Pedralvarez Cabral in het jaar 1500. En Joan da Nova, in het jaar 1501, *etc.* pp. 38. *See* Aa (Pieter van der) *Bookseller.* Naaukeurige versameling der gedenk-waardigste zee en land reysen, *etc.* dl. 9. 1707. 8°. **979. e. 3. (1.)**

—— [Another edition.] pp. 22. *See* Aa (Pieter van der) *Bookseller.* De Aanmerkenswaardigste . . . zee- en landreizen der Portugeezen, *etc.* dl. 1. 1727. fol. **566. l. 5.**

—— Twee ongelukkige scheeps-togten na Oost-Indien, van Jorge de Mello in het jaar 1507. En Jorge d'Aguiar in het jaar 1508, *etc.* pp. 45. *See* Aa (Pieter van der) *Bookseller.* Naaukeurige versameling der gedenk-waardigste zee en land reysen, *etc.* dl. 21. 1707. 8°. **979. e. 5. (2.)**

—— [Another edition.] pp. 26. *See* Aa (Pieter van der) *Bookseller.* De Aanmerkenswaardigste . . . zee- en landreizen der Portugeezen, *etc.* dl. 1. 1727. fol. **566. l. 5.**

—— Tweede scheeps-togt van Don Vasco da Gamma, zee-voogd van Arabien, Persien, Indien en het geheele Oosten, na Oost-Indien . . . in het jaar 1502, *etc.* pp. 33. *See* Aa (Pieter van der) *Bookseller.* Naaukeurige versameling der gedenk-waardigste zee en land reysen, *etc.* dl. 12. 1707. 8°. **979. e. 3. (4.)**

—— [Another edition.] pp. 19. *See* Aa (Pieter van der) *Bookseller.* De Aanmerkenswaardigste . . . zee- en landreizen der Portugeezen, *etc.* dl. 1. 1727. fol. **566. l. 5.**

BARROS (JOÃO DE) *Historian.* [ASIA.—*Selections and Extracts.*]

—— Vervolg der tien-jaarige scheeps-togten en manhafte krigs-bedryven door Nuno da Cunha . . . in Oost-Indien, zederd het jaar 1536 tot aan zyn dood. pp. 431. *See* AA (Pieter van der) *Bookseller.* Naaukeurige versameling der gedenk-waardigste zee en land reysen, *etc.* dl. 46. 1707. 8°. **979.** e. **13.** (**2.**)

—— [Another edition.] pp. 230. *See* AA (Pieter van der) *Bookseller.* De Aanmerkenswaardigste . . . zee- en landreizen der Portugeezen, *etc.* dl. 1. 1727. fol. **566.** l. **5.**

Appendix.

—— [For separate editions of the continuation of the Asia by Diego do Couto :] *See* COUTO (D. do)

—— *See* MACCLYMONT (James R.) The Discoveries made by Pedraluarez Cabral and his captains. An attempt to harmonise the narrations of the voyage set forth by Barros and by Correa. 1909. 8°. **010057.** k. **33.**

—— *See* RIBEIRO (João) *Capitano.* Ribeiro's History of Ceilão. With a summary of De Barros, *etc.* 1909. 8°. **09057.** bb. **36.**

OTHER WORKS.

—— Chronica do Emperador Clarimundo, donde os Reys de Portugal descendem, tirada de linguagem Ungara por Joaõ de Barros [or rather, written by him] . . . e agora novamente accrescentada com a vida deste escritor [by M. S. de Faria]. Quarta impressaõ. pp. 509. 1742. fol. *See* CLARIMUNDO, *Emperador.* **12403.** i. **9.**

—— Quinta impressaõ, *etc.* 3 tom. 1791. 8°. *See* CLARIMUNDO, *Emperador.* **1458.** a. **3–5.**

—— A primeira parte da Cronica do Emperador Clarimundo, *etc.* ff. 211. 1601. fol. *See* CLARIMUNDO, *Emperador.* G. **10239.**

—— Mercadoria espiritual. *See* infra : Ropica pnefma.

—— Panegyricos do grande J. de Barros . . . Reimpressos conforme a sua antiga linguagem . . . anno 1533. Por Joaquin Francisco Monteiro de Campos Coelho, e Soiza. pp. v. 326. *Lisboa,* 1791. 8°. **1201.** b. **1.**

—— [Ropica pnefma de Joã de Barros.] *Begin.* Joam de barros : ao senhor Duarte đ Resende paz: ꝛ saude enuia. *End.* Acabouse dempremir esta mercadoria espiritual, *etc.* G.L. *G. Galharde: Lixboa,* 1532. 4°. C. **25.** e. **30.** *Imperfect; wanting the titlepage which has been supplied in facsimile.*

APPENDIX.

—— *See* CAMPOS (A.) O Insigne Viziense João de Barros. 1897. 8°. **9006.** i. **12.** (**3.**)

BARROS (JOÃO DE) *Translator.*

—— *See* JEROME (Jerome K.) [They and I.] Os Meus Filhos e Eu . . . Tradução de J. de Barros e Dulce Queiroz de Barros. [1943.] 8°. **12650.** de. **14.**

—— *See* RIO (J. do) Homenagem a João do Rio. Discursos de L. Teixeira e J. de Barros, *etc.* 1950. 8°. [*Ocidente.* Suplemento.] P.P. **4123.** bc/1. (**22.**)

—— *See* ROBERTS (Cecil E. M.) Vitória Quatro e Meia . . . Tradução . . . por J. de Barros e Dulce Queiroz de Barros. [1940?] 8°. **12650.** de. **8.**

BARROS (JOÃO ALBERTO LINS DE) *See* LINS DE BARROS (J. A.)

BARROS (JOÃO DO REGO) *See* REGO BARROS.

BARROS (JOAQUIM SERGIO DE)

—— Faculdade de Medicina do Rio de Janeiro. These apresentada . . . pelo Dr. J. S. de Barros . . . Hygiene escolar, *etc.* pp. 97. *Rio de Janeiro,* 1903. 4°. **7379.** n. **4.** (**8.**)

BÁRROS (JOSÉ ANTONIO) *See* ROYO (J. M.) Instruccion moral i relijiosa para las escuelas de la Republica [of New Granada]. Nociones importantes, tomadas del Frances, *etc.* (Editor, J. A. Barros.) 1857. 12°. **3506.** b. **21.**

BARROS (JOSÉ BARBOZA DE) *See* BARBOZA DE BARROS.

BARROS (JOSÉ JOAQUIM SOARES DE) *See* SOARES DE BARROS E VASCONCELLOS.

BARROS (JOSÉ MARÍA) Sentencia pronunciada el dia 28 de Mayo por el juez 2°. de lo Civil Lic. Don J. M. Barros, en el juicio posesorio promovido por el Dr. D. A. Fernandez Monjardin, contra D. J. Ibes Limantour. pp. 61. *México,* 1863. 4°. **6785.** b. **4.** (**11.**)

BARROS (JOSÉ MAURICE FERNANDES PEREIRA DE) *See* FERNANDES PEREIRA DE BARROS.

BARROS (JOSÉ RAMÓN DEL FRANCO) *See* FRANCO BARROS.

BARROS (JUAN MARTÍNEZ DE) *See* MARTÍNEZ DE BARROS.

BARROS (JULIO ZENTENO) *See* ZENTENO BARROS.

BARROS (MANOEL JOAQUIM FERNANDES DE) *See* FERNANDES DE BARROS.

BARROS (MIGUEL ANTONIO DE) Poesias de Miguel Antonio de Barros, *etc.* pp. 48. *Lisboa,* 1825. 8°. **11452.** aaa. **58.** (**4.**)

BARROS (PEDRO IGNACIO DE GASTRO Y) *See* GASTRO Y BARROS.

BARROS (PRUDENTE JOSÉ DE MORAES) *See* MORAES BARROS.

BARROS (TOMÁS DE) Copia de vna carta que escriuio el padre T. de Barros de la Compañia de Jesus, en Junio de 622, al Padre general, en que declara lo que los de la Compañia hizieron en el imperio de Etiopia, en el dicho año de 622. pp. 14. [1624?] fol. **4783.** f. **7.** (**4.**)

—— Relatione della missione fatta da' Padri della Compagnia di Giesu nell' Etiopia, gl'anni 1621. 1622. e 1623. *See* JESUITS. [*Letters from Missions.*] Lettere annue d'Etiopia, Malabar, Brasil, e Goa, *etc.* 1627. 8°. **4766.** aaa. **8.** (**2.**)

—— Relation de la mission faite par les pères de la Compagnie de Jésus en Éthiopie és années 1621, 1622 & 1623. *See* JESUITS. [*Letters from Missions.*] Histoire de ce qui s'est passé en Éthiopie, Malabar, Brasil, et és Indes Orientales, *etc.* 1628. 8°. **867.** d. **18.**

BARROS ARANA (DIEGO)

—— *See* ÁLVAREZ DE TOLEDO (Fernando) *Poet.* Puren indomito. Poema . . . Publicado bajo la dirección de Don D. Barros Arana. 1862. 8°. **12296.** dd. **2/1.**

—— *See* CHIAPPA (V. M.) Bibliografía de Don Diego Barros Arana, *etc.* 1907. 8°. **11906.** k. **11.** (**4.**)

—— *See* CHILI. Coleccion de historiadores de Chile y documentos relativos a la historia nacional. (tom. 5. Hechos de Don Gargia Hurtado de Mendoza . . . por Suarez de Figueroa. Hechos de Don A. de Sotomayor, por Caro de Torres. Guerras de Chile, por Tesilllo [*sic*]. [With introductions by D. Barros Arana.] 1861, *etc.* 4°. **20090.a.**

BARROS ARANA (Diego)

—— See Chili.—*Real Tribunal de Minas*. Informe anual que presenta la Secretaria de este Real Tribunal, en el cual con arreglo a las reales ordenanzas i disposiciones de la Junta Jeneral de Electores se da razon del resultado de las visitas practicadas por los diputados jenerales i territoriales de todo el Reino : de los minerales, minas i trapiches que comprende . . . Toda para el año de 1803. [With an introduction by D. Barros Arana.] 1894. 4°. **7107**. ee. **29**. (**1**.)

—— See Donoso (R.) Barros Arana, *etc.* 1931. 8°. **10880**. tt. **14**.

—— See García (José) *S.J.* Diario del viaje i navegación hechos por el padre J. García . . . desde su mision de Cailin . . . hacia el sur, *etc.* [With an introduction signed: D. B. A., i.e. D. Barros Arana.] 1889. 8°. [*Documentos para la Historia de la Náutica en Chile.*] **8806**. g. **24**.

—— See Jufré del Águila (M.) Compendio historial del descubrimiento i conquista del reino de Chile, *etc.* [With a biography of the author by D. Barros Arana.] 1897. 8°. **9770**. f. **9**.

—— See Montebruno López (J.) Sobre Don Diego Barros Arana, *etc.* [1946.] 8°. **10891**. b. **4**.

—— See Moraleda i Montero (J. de) Esploraciones jeográficas . . . Precedidas de una introduccion por Don D. Barros Arana, *etc.* 1888. 8°. **10480**. eee. **28**.

—— See Nuñez de Pineda y Bascuñan (Francisco) Cautiverio Feliz, y razon de las guerras dilatadas de Chile. [With an introduction by D. Barros Arana.] 1863. 4°. [*Coleccion de historiadores de Chile.* tom. 3.] **20090.a.**

—— See Olivares (M. de) Historia de la Compañia de Jesus en Chile, 1593–1736 . . . Con una introduccion biográfica i notas por D. D. Barros Arana. 1874. 8°. [*Coleccion de historiadores de Chile.* tom. 7.] **20090.a.**

—— See Periodical Publications.—*Santiago*. Revista Chilena, publicada bajo la direccion de M. L. Amunátegui i . . . D. Barros Arana. 1875, *etc.* 8°. P.P. **4095**. d.

—— See Stevenson (William B.) Memorias . . . sobre las campañas de San Martín y Cochrane en el Perú . . . Noticia sobre Stevenson por D. Barros Arana. [1917.] 8°. [*Biblioteca Ayacucho.* vol. 15.] **9774.a.1/15.**

—— See Torrente (M.) Historia de la Revolucion de Chile, 1810–1828, *etc.* [With a biography of the author by D. Barros Arana.] 1900. 8°. [*Coleccion de historiadores i de documentos relativos a la independencia de Chile.* tom. 3.] **9774**. d. **1/3**.

—— See Tribaldos de Toledo (L.) Vista jeneral de las continuadas guerras, dificil conquista del gran reino Provincias de Chile. [With an introduction by D. Barros Arana.] 1863. 4°. [*Coleccion de historiadores de Chile.* tom. 4.] **20090.a.**

—— Biblioteca Americana. Collection d'ouvrages inédits ou rares sur l'Amérique. [Edited by D. Barros Arana.] 3 vol. *Leipzig & Paris*, 1861–64. 8°. **12296**. dd. **2**.

—— Las Campañas de Chiloé, 1820–1826. Memoria histórica, *etc.* pp. xii. 215. *Santiago*, 1856. 8°. **9772**. bbb. **6**.

—— Compendio de historia de América. 4 pt. *Santiago*, 1865. 8°. **9602**. bbb. **15**.

—— [Another copy.] **9781**. d. **28**.

—— Courcelle Seneuil. Article nécrologique . . . Extrait des Annales de l'Université du Chili . . . Traduit de l'espagnol par Mme C. de Huici. pp. 22. *Paris*, [1892.] 8°. **10601**. d. **27**. (**8**.)

—— La Cuestion de limites entre Chile i la República Arjentina. pp. 57. *Santiago de Chile*, 1895. 8°. **8180**. k. **10**. (**8**.)

—— [Another edition.] [With a map.] pp. viii. 128. *Santiago de Chile*, 1898. 8°. **8180**. k. **15**.

—— Un Decenio de la Historia de Chile, 1841–1851. 2 tom. *Santiago de Chile*, 1905, 06. 8°. **9770**. l. **9**.

—— El Doctor Don Rodolfo Amando Philippi, su vida i sus obras. pp. vii. 248. *Santiago de Chile*, 1904. 8°. **10630**. ff. **48**.

—— Don Claudio Gay, su vida i sus obras. Estudio biográfico i crítico, *etc.* pp. viii. 235. *Santiago de Chile*, 1876. 4°. **10882**. i. **5**.

—— Don Miguel Luis Amunátegui, 1828–1888. (Biografía.) [By D. Barros Arana. With a portrait.] pp. iii. 346. [1889.] 8°. See Amunátegui (M. L.) **010882**. m. **8**.

—— Don Miguel Luis Amunátegui, candidato á la Presidencia de la Republica, *etc.* pp. 230. *Santiago*, 1875. 8°. **8179**. a. **3**.

—— Elementos de jeografía física . . . Segunda edicion, revisada i completada. pp. xx. 362. *Santiago*, 1874. 8°. **10002**. dd. **3**.

—— Esposición de los derechos de Chile en el litijo de límites sometido al fallo arbitral de S. M. B. pp. 128. *Santiago de Chile*, 1899. 8°. **8180**. h. **48**.

—— Historia de la guerra del Pacifico, 1879–1880 (1880–1881) . . . Illustrada con mapas i planos. 2 tom. *Santiago*, 1880, 81. 8°. **9771**. f. **5**.

—— Histoire de la guerre du Pacifique, 1879–1880 (1880–1881). 2 pt. *Paris*, 1881, 82. 8°. **9772**. ee. **6**.

—— [Another copy.] **9772**. ee. **8**.

—— Historia de la independencia de Chile durante los años 1811 i 1812. See Vicuña Mackenna (B.) Historia jeneral de la Republica de Chile, *etc.* tom. 1. 1866, *etc.* 8°. **9781**. e. **20**.

—— Historia jeneral de Chile. 16 tom. *Santiago*, 1884–1902. 8°. **9781**. g. **9**.

—— Historia jeneral de la independencia de Chile. tom. 1. pp. iii. 325. *Santiago*, 1854. 8°. **9772**. c. **15**.

—— El Jeneral Freire. pp. v. 124. *Santiago*, 1852. 16°. **10883**. a. **29**.

The titlepage is mutilated.

—— Jeografía etnográfica. Apuntes sobre la etnografia de Chile. See Chili. Estudios jeográficos sobre Chile, *etc.* 1875. 8°. **10481**. ff. **2**.

—— Lecturas populares. I. Los Antiguos habitantes de Chile. pp. 23. *Santiago*, 1874. 12°. **9772**. a. **2**.

—— Notas para una bibliografía de obras anonimas i seudonimas sobre la historia, la jeografía i la literatura de America. pp. 171. *Santiago de Chile*, 1882. 4°. **11905**. aa. **34**.

—— Orígenes de Chile. 2 tom. *Santiago, Chile*, 1934. 8°. **9770**. pp. **10**.

BARROS ARANA (DIEGO)

—— Proceso de Pedro de Valdivia i otros documentos ineditos concernientes a este conquistador, reunidos i anotados por D. Barros Arana. pp. 392. *Santiago*, 1873. 8°. **6785. g. 1.**

—— Vida i viajes de Hernando de Magallanes. pp. vi. 155. *Santiago de Chile*, 1864. 8°. **10632. dd. 5.**

—— [Another copy.] **10632. dd. 6.**

—— Vida e viagens de Fernão de Magalhães . . . Traducção . . . de Fernando de Magalhães Villas-Boas . . . Com um appendice original. pp. 192. *Lisboa*, 1881. 8°. **10632. eee. 12.**

BARROS BARRETO (JOÃO DE) Dissertação cadeira de hygiene e historia da medicina. Estudo hygienico dos esgotos da cidade do Rio de Janeiro. Proposições tres sobre uma das cadeiras da Faculdade, *etc.* pp. 187. *Rio de Janeiro*, 1889. 8°. **7686. dd. 6.**

BARROS BARRETO (M. DE) Memoria sobre o melhoramento do porto de Pernambuco. [With two plates.] pp. 30. *Recife*, 1865. 8°. **10481. dd. 28. (2.)**

BARROS BASTO (ARTUR CARLOS DE)

—— *See* JEWS.—*Service Books.*—*Daily Prayers.*—*Portuguese Rite.* Birkath ha-Mazon. Graças após a refeição . . . Arranjo e tradução por A. C. de Barros Basto. 1940. 8°. **1974. b. 23. (1.)**

—— *See* JEWS.—*Service Books.*—*Daily Prayers.*—*Portuguese Rite.* Oração antes de deitar . . . Arranjo e tradução por A. C. de Barros Basto. 1940. 8°. **1974. b. 23. (2.)**

—— *See* JEWS.—*Service Books.*—*Feastday Prayers.*—*Portuguese Rite.* Hallel . . . Arranjo e tradução por A. C. de Barros Basto. 1940. 8°. **1974. b. 23. (4.)**

—— *See* JEWS.—*Service Books.*—*Feastday Prayers.*—*Portuguese Rite.* Nehilah ou encerramento de Kipur . . . Arranjo e tradução por A. C. de Barros Basto. 1929. 8°. **1974. b. 23. (6.)**

—— *See* JEWS.—*Service Books.*—*Feastday Prayers.*—*Portuguese Rite.* A Noite de Kipur . . . Arranjo e tradução por A. C. de Barros Basto. 1929. 8°. **1974. b. 23. (5.)**

—— *See* JEWS.—*Service Books.*—*Feastday Prayers.*—*Portuguese Rite.* As Noites de Hanukah ou da Festa dos Macabeus. Arranjo por A. C. de Barros Basto. 1943. 8°. **1974. b. 34.**

—— *See* JEWS.—*Service Books.*—*Sabbath Prayers.*—*Portuguese Rite.* Oração matinal de Shabbath . . . Arranjo e tradução por A. C. de Barros Basto. 1939. 8°. **1974. b. 23. (7.)**

—— *See* JEWS.—*Service Books.*—*Sabbath Prayers.*—*Portuguese Rite.* Saída de Shabbath . . . Arranjo e tradução por A. C. de Barros Basto. 1929. 8°. **1974. b. 23. (3.)**

—— *See* MANASSEH, *ben Joseph, ben Israel.* Memorial de preceitos israelitas. (Adaptação do "Tesouro dos Dinim," do Rabbi Menasseh Ben-Israel [by A. C. de Barros Basto].) 1931, 32. 8°. **01959. a. 50**

—— Don Yahia Ben-Yahia. O 1°. Rabi-mór de Portugal. pp. 29. *Pôrto*, 1944. 8°. **10635. c. 50.**

—— H'ad Gadiah. Influências hebraicas no folclore português. (Separata da Rev. de est. históricos.) pp. 27. *Pôrto*, 1928. 8°. **11869. p. 15.**

—— Judeus e prosélitos. Colectânea organizada por A. C. de Barros Basto. pp. 45. *Porto*, 1946. 8°. **04034. pp. 22.**

BARROS BORGOÑO (LUIS)

—— *See* CHILE.—*Caja de Ahorros de Empleados Públicos.* Don Luis Barros Borgoño. Homenaje, *etc.* [With a portrait.] 1944. 8°. **12358. g. 22.**

—— *See* EDWARDS (Agustín) Elogio de Don Eliodoro Yáñez . . . Discurso . . . y respuesta de Don L. Barros Borgoño. 1933. 8°. **11858. b. 39.**

—— El Convenio de la Liga de las Naciones, *etc.* pp. 134. *Santiago de Chile*, 1920. 8°. **08028. de. 96.**

—— La Mision del vicario apostólico Don Juan Muzi. Notas para la historia de Chile, 1823–1825. pp. x. 363. *Santiago*, 1883. 8°. **4744. g. 1.**

—— The Problem of the Pacific and the New Policies of Bolivia . . . Together with two juridical reports by John W. Davis. pp. vii. 191. *Sun Job Printing Office: Baltimore*, 1924. 8°. **8180. d. 14.**

—— Don Luis Barros Borgoño. Apuntes para su biografía. pp. 52. [1919?] 12°. **10633. b. 23.**

BARROS DE VALLADARES (JOSÉ MARIA) Repertorio bibliographico das obras que tratam da India e possue a Bibliotheca Nacional de Nova Goa. pp. x. 37. *Nova Goa*, 1905. 8°. **11908. r. 16. (3.)**

BARROS E COSTA (MANOEL DE) Summa breve dos casos reservados do Arcebispado de Braga . . . accrescentado [*sic*] com o Aviso & exame de confessores. *J. Ferreyra: Coimbra*, 1681. 8°. **506. a. 21. (2.)**
Imperfect; wanting "O Aviso & exame de confessores."

BARROS E CUNHA (JOÃO GUALBERTO DE) Os Factos. [On the financial and political condition of Portugal.] pp. 56. *Lisboa*, 1870. 8°. **8225. cc. 6.**

—— Historia da liberdade em Portugal. pp. 334. *Lisboa*, 1869. 8°. **9195. c. 10.**

BARROS ERRÁZURIZ (ALFREDO)

—— *See* CHILE.—*Ministerio del Interior.* Recopilacion de todas las leyes, decretos i demas disposiciones de interes jeneral del Ministerio del Interior. [Compiled by G. Pérez Valdivieso and A. Barros Errázuriz.] 1897. 8°. **L.A.S. 315/8.**

BARROS E SOUSA DE MESQUITA DE MACEDO LEITÃO E CARVALHOSA (MANUEL FRANCISCO DE) *Viscount de Santarem.* *See* EANNES (G.) *de Zurara.* Chronica do descobrimento e conquista de Guiné . . . precedida de uma introducção e illustrada com algumas notas pelo Visconde de Santarem. 1841. 4°. **804. h. 16.**

—— *See* EDWARD, *King of Portugal.* Leal conselheiro . . . precedido d'uma introducção . . . e publicado debaixo dos auspicios do . . . Visconde de Santarem. 1842. 4°. **721. l. 9.**

—— *See* FREITAS (J. A. de) O 2. Visconde de Santarem e os seus Atlas Geographicos, *etc.* 1909. 8°. **10003. w. 2.**

—— *See* PERIODICAL PUBLICATIONS.—*Paris.* Annales des voyages. (Nouvelles annales des voyages.) [sér. 4, 5 edited by the Viscount de Santarem and others.] 1808, *etc.* 8°. **P.P. 3905.**

—— Opusculos e Esparsos. Colligidos e coordenados por Jordão de Freitas, e novamente publicados pelo 3°. Visconde de Santarem. 2 vol. *Lisboa*, 1910. 4°. **12226. i. 11.**

—— Inéditos. (Miscellanea.) Colligidos, coordenados e annotados por Jordão de Freitas . . . e trazidos á publicidade pelo 3° Visconde de Santarem. pp. vii. 580. *Lisboa*, 1914. 4°. **12231. s. 1.**

BARROS E SOUSA DE MESQUITA DE MACEDO LEITÃO E CARVALHOSA (Manuel Francisco de) *Viscount de Santarem.*

—— Corpo diplomatico Portuguez, contendo todos os tratados . . . entre a Corõa de Portugal e as diversas potencias do mundo . . . até aos nossos dias. Tomo primeiro. Portugal e Hespanha. pp. lii. 589. 1846. 8°. *See* Portugal. [*Collections of Laws, etc.*] **6915**. bb. **3**.

—— Demonstração dos direitos que tem a Coroa de Portugal sobre os territorios situados na costa occidental d'Africa entre o 5° grau e 12 minutos e o 8° de latitude meridional e por conseguinte aos territorios de Molembo, Cabinda e Ambriz. pp. 40. *Lisboa*, 1855. 8°. **8155**. cc. **48**. (**3**.)

—— A Statement of Facts, proving the right of the crown of Portugal to the territories situated on the Western Coast of Africa, laying [*sic*] between the fifth degree and twelve minutes, and the eighth degree of south latitude . . . Translated into English from the . . . Portuguese of Viscount de Santarem. pp. 44. *J. C. Bridgewater: London*, 1856. 8°. **8023**. b. **31**.

—— [Another copy.] **F.P.** **8023**. b. **32**.

—— [Another edition.] Also a translation of the despatch & memorandum by . . . J. de Andrade Corvo on the above subject, extracted from the Portuguese White Book, *etc.* pp. 67. *H. J. Fitch: London*, 1877. 8°. **010097**. g. **21**.

—— Essai sur l'histoire de la cosmographie et de la cartographie pendant le moyen âge, et sur les progrès de la géographie après les grandes découvertes du xve siècle, pour servir d'introduction et d'explication à l'Atlas composé de mappemondes et de portulans . . . depuis le vi^e^ siècle, *etc.* 3 tom. *Paris*, 1849–52. 8°. Maps **29**. a. **45**.

—— Atlas, *etc.* 3 pt. *Paris*, 1849. fol. Maps **93**. e. **12**.

—— Memoria sobre a prioridade dos descobrimentos portuguezes na costa d'Africa Occidental, para servir de illustração á Chronica da Conquista de Guiné por Azurara. pp. viii. 245. *Pariz*, 1841. 8°. **804**. d. **28**.

—— Memoria sobre o estabelecimento de Macau, escripta pelo Visconde de Santarem. Abreviada relação da embaixada que El-Rei D. João v. mandou ao imperador da China e Tartaria (pelo seu embaixador A. Metello de Sousa Menezes). Relatorio de Francisco de Assis Pacheco de Sampaio a El-Rei D. José i dando conta dos successos da embaixada a que fôra mandado á côrte de Pekim no anno de 1752. Publicação feita por Julio Firmino Judice Biker. pp. 108. *Lisboa*, 1879. 8°. **9056**. ff. **1**.

—— Memorias para a historia, e theoria das Cortes Geraes, que em Portugal se celebrárão pelos tres estados do reino ordenadas, e compostas no anno de 1824. 2 pt. *Lisboa*, 1828. 4°. 1444. h. 8.

—— Memórias e alguns documentos para a história e teoria das Côrtes Geraes que em Portugal se celebraram pelos três Estados do Reino . . . Nova edição publicado pelo 3° Visconde de Santarém . . . precedida dum estudo de A. Sardinha. 5 pt. *Lisboa*, 1924. 8°. **9195**. k. **17**.

—— Noticia dos manuscriptos perteneentes ao direito publico externo diplomatico de Portugal, e á historia, e litteratura do mesmo paiz, que existem na bibliotheca R. de Paris, e outras da mesma capital, e nos archivos de França examinados, e colligidos pelo segundo Visconde de Santarem. pp. 105. *Lisboa*, 1827. 4°. **1444**. g. 3.

BARROS E SOUSA DE MESQUITA DE MACEDO LEITÃO E CARVALHOSA (Manuel Francisco de) *Viscount de Santarem.*

—— Quadro elementar das relações politicas e diplomaticas de Portugal com as diversas potencias do mundo, desde o principio da monarchia Portugueza até aos nossos dias. [tom. 9–11, 16–18. By L. A. Rebello da Silva. tom. 12, 13. By J. da Silva Mendes Leal.] tom. 1–18. *Pariz, Lisboa*, 1842–60. 8°. **1445**. e. **2–10**.

—— Tableau élémentaire des relations politiques et diplomatiques du Portugal avec les différentes puissances du monde . . . Traduit en français par F. L. Alvarèz d'Andrada. [The introduction only.] pp. 56. *Orléans*, 1829. 8°. **1444**. h. **6**.

—— [Another copy.] **8042**. bb. **30**.

—— [Another copy.] **595**. e. **19**.

—— Recherches historiques, critiques et bibliographiques sur Americ Vespuce et ses voyages. pp. xvi. 284. *Paris*, [1842.] 8°. **615**. h. **29**.

—— Researches respecting Americus Vespucius, and his Voyages . . . Translated by E. V. Childe. pp. 221. *C. C. Little & J. Brown: Boston*, 1850. 8°. **1452**. b. **42**.

—— [Another copy.] **10408**. b. **29**.

—— Recherches sur la priorité de la découverte des pays situés sur la côte occidentale d'Afrique, au-dela du Cap Bojador, et sur les progrès de la science géographique, après les navigations des Portugais, au xve siècle. Accompagnées d'un Atlas composé de mappemondes et de cartes pour la plupart inédites, dressées depuis le xie jusqu'au xviie siècle. pp. cxiv. 335. *Paris*, 1842. 8°. **1298**. c. **14**.

—— Atlas. fol. Maps **93**. e. **17**.

BARROS E VASCONCELLOS (José Joaquim Soares de) *See* Soares de Barros e Vasconcellos.

BARROS FERREIRA ( )

—— *See* Dickens (Charles) [*Christmas Books.*] Carlos Dickens: O Grilo da Lareira. Chateaubriand: Átala, *etc.* (Tradução de Barros Ferreira.) 1937. 12°. **12638**. a. **84**.

—— *See* Scott (*Sir* Walter) *Bart.* [*Ivanhoe.*] Ivanhoé, ou o Cavaleiro Negro. Adaptação de Barros Ferreira, *etc.* 1942. 8°. **12649**. d. **17**.

BARROS FRANCO (José Miguel)

—— Apuntes para la historia diplomática de Chile. El caso del "Baltimore." [A thesis.] pp. 157. *Santiago de Chile*, 1950. 8°. **9770**. w. **5**.

BARROS GOMES (H. de) *Translator.*

—— *See* Ferro (A.) Salazar . . . Translated by H. de Barros Gomes and J. Gibbons, *etc.* 1939. 8°. **10635**. d. **21**.

BARROS GOMES (Henrique de) A Navegação do Zambeze. Discursos proferidos . . . na Camara dos Deputados na sessão de 19 de maio de 1888. pp. 14. *Lisboa*, 1888. 8°. **8028**. ff. **16**. (**4**.)

—— As Negociações com a Inglaterra no periodo de 1886 a 1889. Discurso proferido na Camara dos Dignos Pares do Reino em sessão de 10 de junho de 1891. pp. 59. *Lisboa*, 1891. 8°. **8042**. dd. **9**. (**7**.)

BARROS GOMES (HENRIQUE DE)

—— O Padroado da Corôa de Portugal nas Indias orientaes e a Concordata de 23 de junho de 1886. Discursos proferidos na Camara dos Senhores Deputados nas sessões de 5, 6 e 7 de maio de 1887. pp. 107. *Lisboa*, 1887. 8°. **4530. b. 1.**

—— A Questão de Tungue e o tratado com a China. Discurso proferido na Camara dos Pares nas sessões de 25 e 26 de junho de 1888. pp. 39. *Lisboa*, 1888. 8°. **8023. ee. 21. (2.)**

BARROS GREZ (DANIEL) Fábulas originales. Ensayos. Segunda edicion, correjida i aumentada. [In verse.] pp. 95. *Santiago*, 1862. 12°. **12305. aa. 50. (4.)**

—— Pipiolos i Pelucones, *etc.* [A sequel to the author's "Huérfano."] 2 tom. *Santiago de Chile*, 1876. 8°. **12489. m. 1.**

BARROS JARPA (ERNESTO) Hacia la solución. Apuntaciones al margen de la negociación chileno-peruana de 1921. pp. 363. *Santiago*, 1922. 8°. **8180. dd. 42.**

BARROS LEITÃO E CARVALHOZA (JOÃO DIOGO DE) *Viscount de Santarem. See* CLAUDIO, *da Conceição.* Oraçao funebre recitada nas . . . exequias do . . . Visconde de Santarem J. D. de Barros Leitão e Carvalhoza, *etc.* 1818. 8°. **4864. aa. 48.**

BARROS LOBO (ED. DE) Viagens no chiado. Apontamentos de jornada de um lisboeta atravez de Lisboa. Por Beldemonio (Ed. de Barros Lobo). pp. xvi. 311. *Porto*, 1887. 8°. **10161. bb. 19.**

BARROS MACHADO (ANTONIO DE)

—— Generalidades acerca da Lunda e da sua exploração biológica. [With illustrations.] pp. 107. *Lisboa*, 1952. fol. [*Publicações Culturais da Companhia de Diamantes de Angola.* no. 12.] **W.P.14366/12.**

—— Ochyroceratidae—Araneae—de l'Angola. pp. 88. *Lisboa*, 1951. fol. [*Publicações culturais da Companhia de Diamantes de Angola.* no. 8.] W.P. **14366/8.**

—— Révision systématique des glossines du groupe palpalis—Diptera. pp. 189. *Lisboa*, 1954. fol. [*Publicações culturais da Companhia de Diamantes de Angola.* no. 22.] W.P. **14366/22**

BARROSO (AGUSTÍN) *See* CRESPO Y MARTÍNEZ (G.) and BARROSO (A.) Estudio sobre la Crísis Mercantil y la depreciacion de la plata, *etc.* 1886. 8°. **L.A.S.518/14.**

BARROSO (ANTONIO) Ardides dobles de amor, comedia en tres actos y en verso. pp. 62. *Madrid*, 1847. 8°. **11726. d. 1. (3.)**
Part of "La España Dramática."

—— Ensayos sobre el arte de la declamacion. pp. 218. *Madrid*, 1845. 8°. **11805. e. 14.**

—— El Ultimo Amor, drama en tres actos y en verso. pp. 14. *Madrid*, 1847. 4°. **1343. n. 11. (5.)**
Part of "La Biblioteca Dramática."

BARROSO (ANTONIO) and **ALBA** (JUAN DE)

—— La Calderona, drama en cuatro actos. [In verse.] pp. 22. *Madrid*, 1847. 4°. **1343. n. 11. (2.)**
Part of "La Biblioteca Dramática."

BARROSO (CARLOS) Cervantes e Portugal. Curiosidade litteraria, *etc.* pp. 10. *Lisboa*, [1872.] 8°. Cerv. **593.**

BARROSO (FRANCISCO DÍEZ) *See* DÍEZ BARROSO.

BARROSO (GUSTAVO)

—— *See* LIMA (H. de) and BARROSO (G.) Pequeno dicionário brasileiro da língua portuguesa, *etc.* 1949. 8°. **12978.p.45.**

—— *See* NILUS (S. A.) Os Protocolos dos Sábios de Sião . . . Texto completo e apostilado por G. Barroso. 1936. 8°. **Cup.700.c.7.**

—— Espirito do seculo XX. pp. 290. *Rio de Janeiro*, 1936. 8°. **12359. b. 25.**

—— Historia Secreta do Brasil, *etc.* *S. Paulo*, 1937-38. 8°.
Imperfect; wanting pt. 4. pt. 1-3. **9088.1.53.**

—— Integralismo e catolicismo, *etc.* pp. 286. *Rio de Janeiro*, 1937. 8°. **20013. h. 18.**

—— Mapirunga. Translated and with explanatory preface by R. B. Cunninghame Graham. pp. 39. *Wm. Heinemann: London*, 1924. 8°. **12489. p. 49.**

—— Mythes, contes at légendes des Indiens. Folk-lore brésilien. [With plates.] pp. iii. 179. *Paris*, 1930. 8°. **12450. p. 19.**

—— O Quarto imperio. (A sintese economica-politica-espiritual.) pp. 177. *Rio de Janeiro*, 1935. 8°. [*Problemas politicos contemporaneos.* no. 9.] W.P. **12071/9.**

—— A Senhora de Pangim, *etc.* pp. 203. *Rio*, 1932. 8°. **12492. e. 10.**

—— Terra de Sol. Naturezza e costumes do Norte. pp. 274. *Rio de Janeiro*, 1912. 8°. **12359. b. 29.**

BARROSO (JOSÉ LIBERATO) A Instrucção Publica no Brasil. pp. xv. 265. *Rio de Janeiro*, 1867. 8°. **8305. ee. 17.**

BARROSO (JOSÉ MARZELINO ORTIZ) *See* ORTIZ BARROSO.

BARROSO (MANUEL GERÓNIMO) Briozoos de la Estación de Biología marítima de Santander, *etc.* pp. 63. *Madrid*, 1912. 8°. [*Trabajos del Museo de Ciencias Naturales.* Serie zoológica. no. 3.] Ac. **2828/2.**

BARROSO (MATEO HERNÁNDEZ) *See* HERNÁNDEZ BARROSO.

BARROSO NUNES (SEBASTIÃO)

—— Faculdade de Medicina do Rio de Janeiro. These apresentada . . . pelo Dr. S. Barroso Nunes . . . Hematologia nas psychoses e cerebro-psychoses, *etc.* pp. 69. pl. 6. *Rio de Janeiro*, 1904. 4°. **7380. a. 8. (5.)**

BARROS PAIVA (TANCREDO DE)

—— Achêgas a um Diccionario de Pseudonymos, Iniciaes, Abreviaturas e Obras Anonymas de Auctores Brasileiros e de Estrangeiros, sobre o Brasil ou no mesmo impressas. pp. 248. *Rio de Janeiro*, 1929. 8°. **11860. c. 6.**

BARROS PENA (JUAN GARCÍA) *See* GARCÍA BARROS PENA.

BARROS PIMENTEL (FRANCISCO DE)

—— Faculdade de Medicina do Rio de Janeiro. These apresentada . . . por F. de Barros Pimentel . . . Da lithiase biliar, *etc.* pp. 110. *Rio de Janeiro*, 1902. 4°. **7379. n. 4. (7.)**
The date on the wrapper is 1903.

BARROS PRADO (EDUARDO)

—— [Yo vi el Amazonas.] Eu vi o Amazonas . . . Traduçao feita do espanhol [by A. A. Botelho de Mogalhães]. [With plates and a portrait.] pp. 475. *Rio de Janeiro*, 1952. 8°. [*Conselho Nacional de Proteção aos Índios. Publicação.* no. 109.] L.A.S. **170.**

BARROS TERRA (ANTONIO DE)

—— Faculdade de Medicina do Rio de Janeiro. These apresentada . . . pelo Dr. A. de Barros Terra . . . Da segunda bulha cardiaca, *etc.* pp. 91. *Rio de Janeiro*, 1904. 4°. **7380.** a. **8.** (**7.**)

BARROS VIDAL ( )

—— Um Destino a serviço do Brasil. [On President Vargas of Brazil. With plates, including a portrait.] pp. 331. *Rio*, 1945. 8°. **10899.** ee. **24.**

BARROS Y GÓMEZ (BERNARDO G.) Discursos pronunciados en la sesión solemne celebrada . . . a la memoria del . . . Sr. B. G. Barros y Gómez, *etc.* [Including his "Discurso de ingreso."] pp. 36. 1924. 8°. *See* HAVANNA.—*Academia Nacional de Artes y Letras.* Ac. **1908/4.** (**3.**)

BARROS Y SOUSA (MANUEL FRANCISCO DE) *Viscount de Santarem. See* BARROS E SOUSA DE MESQUITA DE MACEDO LEITÃO E CARVALHOSA.

BARROT (ADOLPHE) Piezas oficiales relativas a los acontecimientos de Cartajena, en julio i agosto del presente año, conexionados con la persona del Señor A. Barrot consul francés en aquella plaza. [With supplement]. 2 pt. FEW MS. NOTES. *Bogotá*, 1833, 34. 4°. **1446.** i. **17.**

BARROT (CAMILLE HYACINTHE ODILON) *See* BOCHER (P. H. E.) Décrets du 22 janvier. Biens de la Maison d'Orléans. Distribution des écrits destinés à la défense. Explications de M. Bocher et plaidoiries de M. O. Barrot. 1852. 8°. **8052.** e. **11.**

—— *See* COMPAGNIE UNIVERSELLE DU CANAL MARITIME DE SUEZ. Mémoire à consulter sur la consultation de Mes O. Barrot, Dufaure . . . en date du 30 novembre 1863. 1864. 4°. **8776.** g. **30.**

—— *See* FRANCE. [*Laws, etc.* – I.] Bulletin annoté des lois . . . Avec des notices par O. Barrot, Vatimesnil, *etc.* 1834, *etc.* 8°. P.P. **1363.**

—— *See* LEBEY (A.) Louis Napoléon Bonaparte et le ministère Odilon Barrot, 1849. 1912. 8°. **10658.** v. **18.**

—— *See* LEFEBVRE DE VATIMESNIL (A. F. H.) Mémoire à consulter et consultation par MM. Vatimesnil . . . Odilon Barrot [and others] sur les décrets du 22 janvier 1852 relatifs aux biens de la famille d'Orléans. 1852. 8°. **8052.** f. **36.**

—— *See* MIRECOURT (E. de) *pseud.* Les Contemporains. (pt. 55. Odilon Barrot. [With a portrait.]) 1855, *etc.* 16°. **10662.** a. **28.**

—— *See* MIRECOURT (E. de) *pseud.* Histoire contemporaine, *etc.* (no. 7. Odilon Barrot. [With a portrait.]) 1867, *etc.* 8°. **10661.** aaa. **20.**

—— *See* NAPOLEON III., *Emperor of the French.* [*Biography.* —I.] Histoire complète de Louis N. Bonaparte . . . Contenant des lettres de Chateaubriand, O. Barrot, *etc.* 1848. 12°. **10660.** a. **40.**

—— *See* PARIS.—*Salle Barthélemy.* Conférences littéraires de la Salle Barthélemy. (Discours d'adieu. Par M. O. Barrot.) sér. 2. 1864. 12°. **12237.** bb. **3.**

BARROT (CAMILLE HYACINTHE ODILON)

—— *See* PLOCQUE (A.) Consultation de MM. les bâtonniers de l'ordre des avocats du barreau de Paris en réponse aux questions posées par M. le comte d'Haussonville, suivie des adhésions motivées de MM. O. Barrot et Hébert, *etc.* 1860. 8°. **5425.** b. **33.**

—— Consultation pour . . . Mohammed Saïd Pacha Vice-roi d'Égypte [defining his position with regard to the Suez Canal Company] délibérée par Me O. Barrot, MM[es] Dufaure et Jules Favre. pp. 38. [*Paris*, 1860.] 4°. **8022.** f. **5.**

—— De l'organisation judiciaire en France. pp. 247. *Paris*, 1872. 12°. **5423.** aaa. **5.**

—— De la centralisation et de ses effets. pp. 247. *Paris*, 1861. 12°. **8026.** b. **32.**

—— [Another copy.] De la centralisation et de ses effets. *Paris*, 1861. 12°. C.T. **51.**

—— Mémoires posthumes. [Edited by P. Duvergier de Hauranne, —— Corbin, and —— Graugnard, with a preface by Duvergier de Hauranne.] Deuxième édition. 4 tom. *Paris*, 1875, 76. 8°. **10661.** ff. **11.**
Tom. 1 *only is of the second edition.*

—— Notice sur l'Assemblée Constituante. [Reprinted from Lepec's Bulletin annoté des lois.] pp. xvii. [*Paris*, 1834.] 8°. R. **66.** (**6.**)

—— Nouvelle consultation pour . . . Ismaïl Pacha, Vice-roi d'Égypte, délibérée par Me O. Barrot, MM[es] Dufaure et J. Favre. Note explicative sur le travail & le salaire des ouvriers égyptiens requis pour la Compagnie du Canal de Suez. pp. 24. [*Paris*, 1863.] 4°. **8027.** i. **11.** (**1.**)

BARROT (ÉMILE) De l'anémie. Thèse, *etc.* pp. 54. *Montpellier*, 1863. 4°. **7379.** f. **2.** (**3.**)

BARROT (FERDINAND) Réponse . . . à M. le comte de Chambrun [i.e. to his "Mémoire sur les élections de la Lozère]. pp. 14. *Paris*, 1863. 8°. **8050.** dd. **16.**

BARROT (GEORGIANA M.) Account of a Voyage to Manilla, in a series of letters from the lady of the consul-general of France to all India, M. Adolphe Barrot, to her uncle, *etc.* pp. 58. *For private circulation: Yarmouth*, 1842. 8°. **1425.** e. **16.**

BARROT (JACQUES) *See* DAMAS DE MARILLAC (C. C. de) *Viscount.* Outrage fait à l'uniforme national par M. Damas, gouverneur de la Martinique, sur MM. Blauzel et Barrot de Moissac, passagers sur le navire la Françoise Désirée, mouillé en la rade de Saint-Pierre, *etc.* [1790.] 8°. F. **721.** (**12.**)

BARROT (JEAN ANDRÉ) Convention Nationale. Observations sur quelques moyens à prendre pour faire prospérer la république. pp. 46. *Paris*, an 3 [1795]. 8°. F. **1265.** (**4.**)

—— Corps Législatif. Conseil des Anciens. Rapport . . . sur la résolution relative à des biens soumissionnés par les citoyens Bacot & Denoroy. pp. 15. *Paris*, an 5 [1797]. 8°. F. **737.** (**19.**)

—— Opinion . . . sur le jugement de Louis XVI. pp. 24. [*Paris*,] 1793. 8°. F. **912.** (**19.**)

BARROT (ODILON) *See* BARROT (Camille H. O.)

BARROTTI (GIOVANNI ANDREA) *See* BAROTTI.

BARROUGH (PHILIP) The Methode of Phisicke, conteyning the causes, signes, and cures of inward diseases in mans body . . . Whereunto is added, the forme and rule of making remedies and medicines, *etc.* pp. 303. *Thomas Vautroullier: London*, 1583. fol. C. **54.** k. **11.**

—— [Another edition.] pp. 392. *Richard Field: London*, 1590. 4°. **1166.** e. **24.**

BARROUGH (PHILIP)

—— The third edition corrected and augmented, with two other bookes newly added by the author. pp. 484. *Richard Field: London*, 1596. 4°. **7320. e. 1.**

—— The fourth edition, corrected and amended. pp. 477. *Richard Field: London*, 1610. 4°. **775. e. 31.**

—— The fifth edition, corrected, *etc.* pp. 479. *Richard Field: London*, 1617. 4°. **774. h. 1.**

—— The sixth edition. pp. 479. *Richard Field: London*, 1624. 4°. **774. g. 1.**

—— The seventh edition. pp. 477. *George Miller: London*, 1634. 4°. **773. e. 23.**

—— [Another edition.] pp. 477. *Abraham Miller; sold by J. Blague & S. Howes: London*, 1652. 4°. **1039. h. 5.**

BARROUQUÈRE-CLARET (C.) Settat, centre historique de la Chaouïa (Maroc), *etc.* [With plates.] pp. 201. *Paris*, 1919. 8°. **010094. e. 13.**

BARROUX (ANDRÉ)

—— *See* CLÉMENT (J. B.) Ville de Saint-Denis. 1836–1936 . . . Inédits et chansons diverses de J. B. Clément. Réunis par A. Barroux. 1936. 8°. **20012. ee. 11.**

BARROUX (MARIUS)

—— *See* BALTEAU (J.) Dictionnaire de biographie française. Sous la direction de J. Balteau . . . M. Barroux, *etc.* 1933, *etc.* 8°. **W.P. 2345.**

—— *See* PARIS.—*Archives de la Seine.* Ville de Paris. Inventaire sommaire des Archives de la Seine. Partie municipale. Période révolutionnaire . . . Fonds de l'Administration générale de la Commune . . . (série D) analysés par M. M. Barroux. 1892. 4°. **S. 148. e. 2.**

—— Les Dons et les achats aux Archives de la Seine de 1896 à 1902; état sommaire. pp. 54. *Paris*, 1903. 8°. **10171. g. 18.**

—— Essai de bibliographie critique des généralités de l'histoire de Paris. pp. vi. 153. *Paris*, 1908. 8°. **11904. d. 9.**

—— L'Hôtel de l'Administration départementale de la Seine de 1791 à 1803. pp. 18. *Paris*, 1905. 8°. **10171. g. 33.**

—— Les Sources de l'ancien état civil parisien. Répertoire critique. pp. vii. 136. *Paris*, 1898. 8°. **09915. a. 10.**

BARROUX (R.)

—— Dagobert, roi des Francs. pp. 218. *Paris*, 1938. 8°. **09200. e. 22.**

BARROVIAN. The Barrovian. The King William's College Magazine. *See* CASTLETOWN. —*King William's College.*

—— The Barrovian. The magazine of the Secondary School for Boys, Barrow-in-Furness. *See* BARROW-IN-FURNESS. —*Municipal Secondary School for Boys.*

BARROW, *Cheshire.—Women's Institute.*

—— The Book of Barrow, Cheshire. Produced in 1952 from the scrapbook which was compiled in 1951 by the Barrow Women's Institute, *etc.* [With a map.] ff. 139. [*Barrow*, 1952.] 4°. **010368. bb. 30.**
Reproduced from typewriting.

BARROW, *River.* The River Barrow. Leatherum Lankum. The Pearl of the Irish Nation. Murueen na Gruaga Bawne. [Ballads.] pp. 8. *W. Goggin: Limerick*, [1810?] 8°. **11622. df. 51. (5.)**
Imperfect; wanting pp. 5, 6.

BARROW DIGGERS. The Barrow Diggers. A dialogue in imitation of the Grave Diggers in Hamlet; with numerous explanatory notes. [By Charles Woolls.] pp. 112. pl. 11. *Whittaker & Co.: London*, 1839. 4°. **811. k. 9.**

BARROW-DIGGING. Barrow-Digging. By a Barrow-Knight [i.e. S. Isaacson], *etc.* *See* BARROW-KNIGHT.

BARROW-IN-FURNESS.

—— The "Borough" Guide to Barrow-in-Furness and the Lake District. pp. 40. *E. J. Burrow & Co.: Cheltenham*, [1919.] 8°. **10354. a. 72.**

—— Barrow-in-Furness, Lancashire, *etc.* [A new edition of The "Borough" Guide to Barrow-in-Furness and the Lake District.] pp. 48. *E. J. Burrow & Co.: Cheltenham*, [1920.] 8°. **10354. a. 73.**

—— The County Borough of Barrow-in-Furness Official Handbook . . . Second edition. [etc.] *Ed. J. Burrow & Co.: Cheltenham & London*, [1954–] 4°. **010368. bb. 35.**

—— The Official Guide to Barrow-in-Furness. pp. 74. [*Barrow-in-Furness*, 1924.] 8°. **010360. a. 11.**

—— *Barrow Naturalists' Field Club.* Annual Report and Proceedings for . . . 1877 [*etc.*]. *Barrow*, 1877– . 8°. **Ac. 3003.**
Imperfect; wanting pp. 9–20 *of the report for* 1877.

—— *Barrow Port and District Development Committee.* The Port of Barrow. Harbour and dock dues, labourage rates, industries, &c., &c. Compiled and arranged by H. N. Appleby. Published jointly by the London, Midland & Scottish Railway Company and the Barrow Port & District Development Committee. pp. 118. [1924.] 8°. *See* LONDON MIDLAND AND SCOTTISH RAILWAY. **010368. g. 9.**

—— *Free Public Library.* The First(—Eighteenth) Annual Report. *Barrow-in-Furness*, 1883–1901. 8°. **A.R.65.**

—— Catalogue of the Books in the Reference and Lending Departments. Compiled by John Frowde. [With supplements.] 3 pt. *Barrow-in-Furness*, 1885–89. 8°. **11900.b.55.**

—— [Another edition.] pp. 214. *Barrow-in-Furness*, 1892. 8°. **11900 f.45.**

—— Catalogue of the Books in the Juvenile Lending Department. Compiled by J. Frowde. pp. 35. *Barrow-in-Furness*, 1886. 8°. **11904. a. 31. (10.)**

—— *Library and Museum Committee.*

—— Barrow and District. An illustrated history . . . Compiled by F. Barnes. [With maps.] pp. 144. *Barrow-in-Furness*, 1951. 8°. **010368. pp. 51.**

—— *Municipal Secondary School for Boys.* The 'Barrovian.' The magazine of the Secondary School for Boys, Barrow-in-Furness. With which is incorporated "The Gradian." *Barrow-in-Furness*, 1908– . 4°. **P.P. 6145. bo.**

BARROW-IN-FURNESS, CAMPBELL WEST, *Bishop of.* *See* WATSON.

——, HENRY, *Bishop of.* *See* WARE.

BARROW-IN-FURNESS DIRECTORY. *See* DIRECTORIES.—*Barrow-in-Furness.*

BARROW-KNIGHT. Barrow-Digging. By a Barrow-Knight [i.e. Stephen Isaacson]. In six fyttes. With notes by an Esquire. pp. 82. *John Ollivier: London,* 1845. 8°. **11607.** g. **28.**

BARROW NATURALISTS' FIELD CLUB. *See* BARROW-IN-FURNESS.

BARROW PILOT. The Barrow Pilot; or, a Tale of the Irish Sea. pp. 1–16. *Barrow,* [1870.] 8°. **12621.** h. **33.**
Chap. 1 *only; "presented with the Barrow Times."*

BARROW, *Family of.*

—— *See* CARLTON (William J.) The Barrows of Bristol, *etc.* 1951. 8°. [STAPLES (*Leslie C.*) *The Dickens Ancestry.*] **9918.** a. **42.**

BARROW (ALBERT STEWART) *See* also SABRETACHE, *pseud.* [i.e. A. S. Barrow.]

—— Snapshots of War, Love, and Sport. pp. 192. *Walbrook & Co.: London,* [1916.] 8°. **012613.** f. **34.**

BARROW (ALFRED HENRY) Fifty Years in Western Africa. Being a record of the work of the West Indian Church on the banks of the Rio Pongo, *etc.* pp. 157. *S.P.C.K.: London,* 1900. 8°. **04420.** i. **2.**

BARROW (BENNET HILLIARD)

—— Plantation Life in the Florida Parishes of Louisiana, 1836–1846, as reflected in the diary of Bennet H. Barrow. By Edwin Adams Davis, *etc.* [With plates, including a portrait.] pp. xvi. 457. *Columbia University Press: New York,* 1943. 8°. [*Columbia University Studies in the History of American Agriculture.* no. 9.] **Ac.2688/36.**

BARROW (C.) A Letter to . . . the Marquis of Chandos . . . on the affairs of the West Indies. pp. 16. COPIOUS MS. NOTES [by the author]. *Richard Clay: London,* 1830. 8°. **8156.** b. **8.**

BARROW (CECIL MONTEFIORE) *See* CHAUCER (G.) [*Canterbury Tales.—Clerk's Tale.*] Chaucer's The Clerkes Tale. With introduction, notes, and questions by C. M. Barrow. 1900. 8°. **11626.** bbb. **28.**

—— *See* DE QUINCEY (T.) De Quincey's Revolt of the Tartars and the English Mail-Coach. With introduction and notes by C. M. Barrow, *etc.* 1895. 8°. **012272.aaaa.1/16.**

—— *See* MACAULAY (T. B.) *Baron Macaulay.* [*Essays.—Lord Clive.*] Macaulay's Life of Clive. With introduction and notes by C. M. Barrow. 1895. 8°. **012272.aaaa.1/30.**

—— *See* PERIODICAL PUBLICATIONS.—*Madras.* Madras Educational Calendar . . . Edited by C. M. Barrow. 1889, *etc.* 8°. P.P. **2566.** l.

—— *See* PERIODICAL PUBLICATIONS.—*Madras.* The New Asiatic Review. C. M. Barrow, J. Collyer Adam, editors. 1907, *etc.* 8°. P.P. **3778.** c.

—— F. A. Examination of 1880 [in the University of Madras] . . . The Early Empire of Rome, from the death of Julius Caesar to the death of Domitian. Edited by C. M. Barrow. pp. 413. *Addison & Co.: Madras,* 1879. 12°. **9040.** bb. **3.**

—— The Poetical Selections prescribed for the Matriculation Examination of the University of Madras, to be held in December, 1872. Edited by C. M. Barrow. pp. 96. *C. Stolz: Mangalore,* 1871. 8°. **8356.** b. **46.**

BARROW (CHARLES C.)

—— A Short History of the Parish Church of S. Nicolas, Newport, Salop. pp. 16. *British Publishing Co.: Gloucester,* [1938.] 8°. **07822.** aa. **3.**

BARROW (CHARLES C.)

—— A Short History of the Parish Church of S. Nicholas, Newport, Salop . . . 2nd edition, revised. pp. 24. *British Publishing Co.: Gloucester,* 1946. 8°. **07822.** aa. **85.**

BARROW (CLAUDE L.) *See* FITZGERALD (Edward A.) Climbs in the New Zealand Alps . . . With contributions by Sir M. Conway . . . C. L. Barrow, *etc.* 1896. 8°. K.T.C. **32.** a. **4.**

BARROW (DAVID CRENSHAW)

—— *See* REED (Thomas W.) David Crenshaw Barrow. [With portraits.] [1935.] 8°. **010886.** e. **35.**

BARROW (*Sir* EDMUND GEORGE) *G.C.B.* The Growth of Europe through the Dark Ages, A.D. 401–1100, *etc.* pp. 356. *H. F. & G. Witherby: London,* 1927. 8°. **09073.** d. **26.**

—— Infantry Fire Tactics. Three short lectures for native officers . . . Translated by Havildar Ajab Khan. pp. 13. *Noronha & Co.: Hongkong,* 1895. 8°. **8822.** cc. **18.** **(1.)**

—— The Life of General Sir Charles Carmichael Munro, *etc.* [With plates, including portraits.] pp. 287. *Hutchinson & Co.: London,* 1931. 8°. **010815.** i. **23.**

—— The Sepoy Officer's Manual, *etc.* pp. 134. *Thacker, Spink & Co.: Calcutta,* 1880. 16°. **8831.** a. **55.**

—— Third edition. Revised and brought up to date by . . . A. H. Bingley. pp. xiv. 168. *Thacker, Spink & Co.: Calcutta,* 1895. 8°. **8831.** ee. **24.**

—— Barrow's Sepoy Officer's Manual . . . Fifth edition. Revised and brought up to date by Capt. F. Etheridge. pp. xviii. 267. *Thacker, Spink & Co.: Calcutta & Simla,* 1914. 8°. **8824.** aaa. **48.**

—— Sixth edition, revised and brought up to date by Lieut. W. Brooke-Tindall. pp. xvi. 297. *Thacker, Spink & Co.: Calcutta,* 1917. 16°. **8824.** aaa. **67.**

—— Seventh edition. Revised and brought up to date by Capt. W. Brooke-Tindall. pp. xix. 279. *Thacker, Spink & Co.: Calcutta & Simla,* 1918. 16°. **8823.** aa. **47.**

BARROW (EDWARD GRANT)

—— My Fifty Years in Baseball. By E. G. Barrow, with James M. Kahn. [With plates, including portraits.] pp. viii. 216. *Coward-McCann: New York,* [1951.] 8°. **7921.** b. **15.**

BARROW (EDWIN PINDER) A Beetle on his Back. By a Looker-on [i.e. E. P. Barrow]. pp. 16. 1886. 8°. *See* LOOKER-ON. **12331.** g. **27.** **(8.)**

—— Fireside Fables. pp. xi. 88. *Elliot Stock: London,* 1902. 8°. **012305.** h. **12.**

—— Second edition. pp. xvi. 176. *J. M. Dent & Sons: London,* 1910. 8°. **012305.** h. **31.**

—— Follow Thou. A scripture play. E. P. B. [i.e. E. P. Barrow.] pp. 42. 1911. 8°. *See* B., E. P. **11773.** ee. **4.** **(1.)**

—— More Fireside Fables. pp. x. 62. *Elliot Stock: London,* 1903. 8°. **012305.** ee. **18.**

—— My Heresy. By an Undenominational Christian. [The preface signed: E. P. B., i.e. E. P. Barrow.] pp. 48. 1894. 8°. *See* B., E. P. **4371.** aaaa. **23.** **(4.)**

—— Regni Evangelium. A survey of the teaching of Jesus Christ. pp. ix. 272. *Williams & Norgate: London,* 1892. 8°. **3227.** df. **37.**

BARROW (Edwin Pinder)

—— Stray Links. Fifty short studies for sermons and meditations. pp. x. 50. *Skeffington & Son: London,* 1888. 8°. **4478. c. 126.**

—— The Way not a Sect, and other sermons. pp. 195. *J. M. Dent & Sons: London,* 1911. 8°. **4466.** ee. **36.**

BARROW (Elfrida de Renne)

—— *See* Anderson (Mary S.) Georgia . . . By M. S. Anderson, E. de R. Barrow, *etc.* 1933. 8°. **9616.** f. **6.**

BARROW (Frances Elizabeth) *See* Fanny, *Aunt, pseud.* [i.e. F. E. Barrow.]

BARROW (Francis) *Captain in the Strood and Frindsburg Volunteers.* A Minute Detail of the Proceedings of the Court of Enquiry, on the conduct of Captain Francis Barrow and Lieutenant John Gibbs of the Strood and Frindsburg Volunteers. pp. 62. *G. Woodfall: London,* 1804. 8°. **10368.** e. **7. (15.)**

BARROW (Francis) *Rev.* A Sermon, preached in the parish church of St. Mary, Ashford, May 12, 1843, before the . . . Archdeacon of Maidstone . . . on the occasion of the archdeacon's visitation. pp. 23. *J. G. F. & J. Rivington: London,* 1843. 8°. **701.** k. **9. (15.)**

BARROW (Frank) An Indian District (Gonda, Oudh). By a District Officer [i.e. F. Barrow]. Compiled from official and other sources. pp. iii. viii. 97. 1895. 8°. *See* Gonda, *Oudh.* **8023.** aaa. **17.**

—— 2nd edition. pp. iii. viii. 97. 1898. 8°. *See* Gonda, *Oudh.* **8023.** aaa. **20.**

BARROW (Frank Leslie)

—— *See* Pippard (Alfred J. S.) and Barrow (F. L.) The Stress Analysis of Bow Girders. 1926. 8°. [*Building Research Board. Technical Paper.* no. 1.] B.S. **38.** a/**2.**

—— Building Science, *etc.* pp. vii. 235. *Longmans & Co.: London,* 1932. 8°. **07815.** e. **77.**

—— Plumbing in America. A report on a visit to U.S.A. and Canada on plumbing. pp. iv. 24. *London,* 1948. 8°. [*National Building Studies.* Special Report. no. 2.] B.S. **38**a/**13.**

BARROW (George) and **WILLS** (Leonard Johnston)

—— Records of London Wells. pp. iv. 215. pl. iii. *London,* 1913. 8°. [*Memoirs of the Geological Survey.*] **B.S.38.Ga/6.(11.)**

BARROW (George) *Geologist.*

—— *See* Strangways (Charles E. F.) The Geology of Eskdale . . . By C. Fox-Strangways . . . C. Reid . . . and G. Barrow. 1889. 8°. **B.S.38.Ga/4.(65.)**

—— *See* Strangways (C. E. F.) The Geology of the Country around Northallerton and Thirsk . . . By C. Fox-Strangways . . . A. G. Cameron. and G. Barrow. 1886. 8°. **B.S.38.Ga/4.(66.)**

—— *See* Strangways (C. E. F.) and Barrow (G.) The Geology of the Country between Whitby and Scarborough, *etc.* 1882. 8°. **B.S.38.Ga/4.(64.)**

—— The Geology of North Cleveland. pp. iv. 101. *London,* 1888. 8°. [*Memoirs of the Geological Survey.*] **B.S.38.Ga/4.(73.)**

BARROW (*Sir* George) *Bart.* Ceylon: past and present. pp. 196. *John Murray: London,* 1857. 8°. **10056.** b. **18.**

BARROW (*Sir* George de Symons) *G.C.B.*

—— 'David.' Shepherd, poet, warrior, king. [With plate.] pp. 128. *Skeffington & Son: London,* [1946.] 8°. **4809.** b. **4.**

—— The Fire of Life . . . With 25 illustrations. [An autobiography.] pp. viii. 256. *Hutchinson & Co.: London,* [1942.] 8°. **10859.** v. **13.**

—— India, our Finest Monument. pp. 139. *King Bros. & Potts: St. Leonards-on-Sea,* [1950.] 8°. **09059.** i. **3.**

BARROW (George Forster) A Few Private Prayers, chiefly for those who have been confirmed, *etc.* pp. 8. *Parsons & Cousins: Rye & Hastings,* [1871.] 8°. **3457.** aaa. **31.**

—— Why I did not have my Child baptized; or, a Little conversation on Infant Baptism. pp. 16. *William Macintosh: London,* [1871.] 16°. **4257.** aa. **26.**

BARROW (George L.) Fiji for the Fijians. A protest and a plea. pp. 13. *Perth, W.A.,* [1921.] 8°. **08157.** e. **9.**

BARROW (George Neale)

—— Sincerity in Worship. [A sermon.] *See* John, *the Baptist, Saint, Church of, at Bedminster, Bristol.* Five Sermons, preached in Bedminster Parish Church, *etc.* 1855. 8°. **4463.** g. **4.**

BARROW (George Staunton) The Mystery of Christ, being an examination of the doctrine contained in the first three chapters of the Epistle . . . to the Ephesians. pp. xii. 206. *Rivingtons: London,* 1876. 8°. **4224.** bb. **35.**

BARROW (Grace M.) Lady Jane Grey. A tragedy, in five acts. [In verse.] pp. 32. *Grellier: [London,* 1881.] 12°. **11781.** bb. **33.**

BARROW (Harold T.)

—— Guarding the Crown Jewels. A message to boys and young men. [With plates.] pp. 30. *Uplift Books: Croydon,* 1947. 8°. **4397.** aaa. **38.**

—— Youth and Christian Experience. pp. 94. *Uplift Books: Croydon,* 1947. 8°. **4194.** aa. **62.**

—— Youth and Vital Religion. Messages to young men and women of to-day. pp. 93. *Uplift Books: Croydon,* [1946.] 8°. **4398.** b. **70.**

BARROW (Henry)

—— *See* Gifford (George) *Minister at Malden.* A Short Reply vnto the Last Printed Books of Henry Barrow and Ihon Greenwood, the chiefe ringleaders of our Donatists in England, *etc.* 1591. 4°. **4103.** aaa. **42.**

—— *See* Powicke (Frederick J.) Henry Barrow . . . and the exiled Church of Amsterdam, *etc.* 1900. 8°. **4902.** h. **3.**

—— *See* Some (Robert) A Godly Treatise, wherein are examined and confuted many execrable fancies, giuen out . . . partly by H. Barrow, *etc.* 1589. 4°. **4139.** bbb. **17.**

—— *See* Wall (Thomas) *Author of "Baptism Anatomized."* More Work for the Dean. In a brief answer to some scandalous reports published by Dr. Stillingfleet . . . against . . . H. Barrow [and others], *etc.* 1681. 4°. **T. 1030. (10.)**

BARROW (Henry)

—— A Brief Discouerie of the False Church. pp. 263. [*Dort ?*] 1590. 4°. C. **37**. f. **18**.

—— [Another edition.] Done from an authentick manuscript written in the reign of Queen Elizabeth. pp. 391. *London*, 1707. 8°. **873**. k. 3.

—— *See* Christian Church. The Spirit of Libertinism display'd, in a brief collection and confutation of the blasphemous . . . notions vented by the betrayers of The Rights of the Christian Church. With some . . . reflections on his vindicator, in a pretended Discovery of False Churches [i.e. the work by Henry Barrow]. 1709. 8°. **4105**. aa. **21**.

—— A Collection of certain Letters and Conferences lately passed betwixt certaine Preachers & two Prisoners in the Fleet (Henry Barrow, Ihon Greenwood). pp. 70. [*Dort ?*] 1590. 4°. **4107**. aa. **71**.

—— A Collection of certaine Sclaunderous Articles gyuen out by the Bisshops against such faithful Christians as they now vniustly deteyne in their prisons, togeather with the answeare of the saide prisoners thereunto. Also the some of certaine conferences had in the Fleete, according to the Bisshops bloudie mandate with two prisoners there [J. Greenwood and H. Barrow]. [*Dort ?*] 1590. 4°. T. **1013**. (**10**.)
The titlepage is mutilated.

—— The Examinations of Henry Barrowe, Iohn Grenewood and Iohn Penrie, before the high commissioners, and Lordes of the Counsel, penned by the prisoners themselves before their deathes. **B.L.** [*Dort ?* 1593 ?] 4°. T. **804**. (**1**.)

—— [Another copy.] C. **27**. c. **29**.

—— [Another edition.] pp. 48. *William Marshall: London*, [1690 ?] 4°. **105**. c. **45**.

—— [Another edition.] 1745. *See* Harleian Miscellany. The Harleian Miscellany, *etc.* vol. 4. 1744, *etc.* 4°. **185**. a. **8**.

—— [Another edition.] 1809. *See* Harleian Miscellany. The Harleian Miscellany, *etc.* vol. 4. 1808, *etc.* 4°. 2072.g.

—— Mr. H. Barrowes Platform. Which may serve as a preparative to purge away prelatisme with some other parts of poperie. Made ready to be sent from Miles Mickle-bound to Much-beloved England. Together with some other memorable things, *etc.* [*London ?*] 1611. 8°. **698**. a. **35**. (**2**.)

—— A Petition directed to her most excellent Maiestie, wherein is deliuered 1. A meane howe to compound the ciuill dissention in the church of England. 2. A proofe that they who write for Reformation, doe not offend against the stat. of 23. Eliz. c.[2], *etc.* [By H. Barrow.] pp. 83. [1590 ?] 4°. *See* Elizabeth, *Queen of England.* **4106**. aaa. 3.

—— [Another copy.] **108**. b. 2.

—— A Plaine Refutation of M. Giffards booke, intituled, A short treatise gainst the Donatistes of England . . . Here also is prefixed a summe of the causes of our separation . . . which M. Giffard hath twise sought to confute, and hath now twise receiued answer, by H. Barrowe. Here is furder inserted a brief refutation of M. Giff. supposed consimilitude betwixt the Donatistes & vs . . . By J. Greenwood. Here are also annexed a few observations of M. Giff. his last Reply, *etc.* pp. 260. [*London ?* 1605.] 4°. T. **804**. (**3**.)

BARROW (Henry)

—— The Pollution of Universitie Learning, or Sciences—falsely so Called, *etc.* (Extracted out of Mr. H. Barrow's booke [" A plaine refutation of M. Giffards booke, intituled, A short treatise gainst the Donatistes of England "].) pp. 12. *London*, 1642. 4°. **702**. d. **8**. (**13**.)

—— Relics of the Puritan Martyrs, 1593. Four Principall and Waighty Causes for Separation by Henry Barrowe. A Pastoral Letter, written from Prison, and part of a Controversial Epistle by John Greenwood. Edited from a contemporary ms. by T. G. Crippen. pp. 30. 1906. 8°. *See* London.—iii. *Congregational Historical Society.* Ac. **2067**/2. (3.)

—— A True Description out of the Word of God, of the Visible Church. [By H. Barrow.] 4°. 1589 *See* Bible.—*Appendix.* [*Miscellaneous.*] **4103**. c. **53**. (**2**.)

—— [Another edition.] 1613. 4°. [*Lawne* (*C.*) *Brownisme turned the inside out-ward.*] *See* Bible.—*Appendix.* [*Miscellaneous.*] **4103**. c. **35**.

BARROW (Humphrey) The Relief of the Poore: and Advancement of Learning: proposed. pp. 13. *William Larner: London*, 1656. 4°. **1027**. i. **16**. (**6**.)

BARROW (Isaac) *D.D.*

COLLECTIONS.

—— The Works of the learned Isaac Barrow, D.D. . . . Published by the Reverend Dr. Tillotson. [The theological works, English and Latin, with " Some Account of the Life of Dr. Isaac Barrow," signed: A. H., i.e. Abraham Hill.] 4 vol. *M. Flesher for Brabazon Aylmer: London*, 1683–87. fol. **676**. g. **8–11**.

—— [Another edition.] The Theological Works of Isaac Barrow, D.D. 8 vol. *University Press: Oxford*, 1830. 8°. **3753**. cc. **3**.

—— [Another edition.] Edited . . . by the Rev. Alexander Napier. [With " Some Account of the Life of Dr. Isaac Barrow," by Abraham Hill, and " A Notice of Barrow's Life and Academical Times," by W. Whewell.] 9 vol. *University Press: Cambridge*, 1859. 8°. **3752**. c. **2**.

—— The Works of the learned Isaac Barrow, D.D. . . . Being all his English works . . . Published by His Grace, Dr. John Tillotson. [With " Some Account of the Life of Dr. Isaac Barrow," signed: A. H., i.e. Abraham Hill.] 3 vol. *Brabazon Aylmer: London*, 1700. fol. G. **20256–7**.
Vol. 2 *is of the second edition, vol.* 3 *of the third.*

—— [Another edition.] 3 vol. *James Round: London*, 1716. fol. **17**. g. **9, 10**.

—— [Another edition.] 3 vol. *Robert Knaplock: London*, 1722. fol. L.16.a.7.
Vol. 2 *is of the fourth edition, vol.* 3 *of the fifth.*

—— The fifth edition corrected. 3 vol. *A. Millar; J. & R. Tonson: London*, 1741. fol. **479**. g. **1, 2**.

—— The Sermons of the learned Dr. Isaac Barrow . . . Published by Archbishop Tillotson. 6 vol. *G. Hamilton & J. Balfour: Edinburgh*, 1751. 12°. G. **20093–8**.

—— The Theological Works of Isaac Barrow, D.D., *etc.* [The English works.] 6 vol. *Clarendon Press: Oxford*, 1818. 8°. **492**. d. **13–18**.

—— [Another edition.] The Works of Dr. Isaac Barrow. With some account of his life, summary of each discourse, notes, &c. by the Rev. T. S. Hughes. 7 vol. *A. J. Valpy: London*, 1830, 31. 12°. **492**. a. **6–12**.

BARROW (ISAAC) *D.D.*

—— [Another edition.] The Works of Isaac Barrow, D.D. With a life of the author, by the Rev. James Hamilton. A new edition . . . with the entire notes and references, carefully revised. 3 vol. *Thomas Nelson: Edinburgh*, 1841, 42. 8°. **2204. b. 1.**

—— The Mathematical Works of Isaac Barrow, D.D. . . . Edited for Trinity College by W. Whewell. *Lat.* 3 pt. *University Press: Cambridge*, 1860. 8°. **8506. dd. 6.**

—— Sermons and Fragments attributed to Isaac Barrow, D.D. . . . To which are added, two dissertations, on the duration of future punishments, and on dissenters. Now first collected and edited from the MSS. in the University and Trinity College libraries, Cambridge. By the Rev. J. P. Lee. pp. viii. 248. *B. Fellowes: London*, 1834. 8°. **1021. c. 23.**

—— Sermons, on various subjects. 5 vol. *Ogles, Duncan & Co.: London*, 1820, 21. 8°. **4453. fff. 4.**

TWO OR MORE WORKS.

—— A Brief Exposition on the Creed, the Lord's-Prayer, and Ten Commandments. To which is added The Doctrine of the Sacraments, *etc.* [With a portrait.] pp. 459. *J. H. for Brabazon Aylmer: London*, 1697. 8°. **1018. e. 20.**

—— Extracts from the Works of Dr. Isaac Barrow. [Ten sermons.] 1754. *See* WESLEY (John) A Christian Library, *etc.* vol. 35. 1749, *etc.* 12°. **3605. aa.**

—— The Christian, the Pagan, the Mahometan, and the Jewish Religions compared.—Of the Excellency of the Christian Religion. 1795. *See* FAMILY LECTURES. Family Lectures, *etc.* vol. 2. 1791, *etc.* 8°. **224. k. 3.**

—— Twenty Two Sermons on Various Subjects, selected from the works of the Rev. I. Barrow. pp. viii. 469. *Clarendon Press: Oxford*, 1798. 8°. **677. c. 9.**

—— Sermons selected from the Works of the Rev. Isaac Barrow. 2 vol. *Clarendon Press: Oxford*, 1810. 8°. **4455. e. 7.**

Vol. 1 is another edition of the preceding.

—— Extracts from the Works of Dr. Isaac Barrow. [Ten sermons.] 1825. *See* WESLEY (John) A Christian Library, *etc.* vol. 21. 1819, *etc.* 8°. **495. e. 11.**

—— [Twenty-one sermons.] *See* WORDSWORTH (Christopher) *Master of Trinity College, Cambridge.* Christian Institutes, *etc.* vol. 2. 1837. 8°. **495. f. 23.**

—— On the Eucharist.—On Faith.—On the Love of our Neighbour.—Against Foolish Talking and Jesting.—Of Industry in our particular Calling as Scholars.—An Exposition of the Lord's Prayer. *See* BROGDEN (James) *M.A., Vicar of Deddington.* Illustrations of the Liturgy and Ritual of the United Church of England and Ireland, *etc.* vol. 2. 1842. 12°. **1219. g. 5.**

LETTERS.

—— [Correspondence with John Collins.] *See* RIGAUD (Stephen P.) Correspondence of Scientific Men of the Seventeenth Century, *etc.* 1841, *etc.* 8°. **1209. h. 20.**

SINGLE WORKS.

—— A Brief Exposition of the Lord's Prayer and the Decalogue. To which is added The Doctrine of the Sacraments. [Edited by Archbishop Tillotson.] pp. 269. *M. Flesher, for Brabazon Aylmer: London*, 1681. 8°. **3225. a. 6.**

—— A Brief State of the Socinian Controversy. Concerning a Trinity in Unity. pp. 23. *Brabazon Aylmer: London*, 1698. 12°. **4224. a. 12.**

—— The Crucifixion of Christ. [A sermon.] *See* FISH (Henry C.) History and Repository of Pulpit Eloquence, *etc.* vol. 1. 1857. 8°. **4426. g. 2.**

—— [Another edition.] 1857. *See* SERMONS. The Great Sermons of the Great Preachers, *etc.* 1858, *etc.* 8°. **4463. g. 24.**

—— A Defence of the B. Trinity, *etc.* pp. 97. *B. Aylmer: London*, 1697. 8°. **4381. e. 4.**

—— A Discourse concerning the Unity of the Church. 1850. *See* GIBSON (Edmund) successively *Bishop of Lincoln* and *of London.* Supplement to Gibson's Preservative from Popery, *etc.* vol. 8. 1849, *etc.* 8° **3940.k.7/8.**

—— The Doctrine of the Sacraments. pp. iv. 27. *J. & J. Fletcher: Oxford*, [1780?] 12°. **4372. d. 8. (3.)**

Previously published with "A Brief Exposition of the Lord's Prayer and the Decalogue."

—— The third edition. pp. iv. 27. *J. & J. Fletcher: Oxford*, 1781. 12°. **4327. b. 6.**

—— The fourth edition. pp. iv. 24. *See* ENGLAND.—*Church of England.—Society for Promoting Christian Knowledge.* Religious Tracts, dispersed by the Society for Promoting Christian Knowledge. vol. 2. 1800. 12°. **224. c. 24.**

—— Fifth edition. pp. iv. 24. *F. & C. Rivington: London*, 1806. 12°. **4372. d. 15. (3.)**

—— [A reissue.] *See* ENGLAND.—*Church of England.—Society for Promoting Christian Knowledge.* Religious Tracts, dispersed by the Society for Promoting Christian Knowledge. vol. 2. 1807. 12°. **863. l. 2.**

—— On Baptism. [Extracted from "The Doctrine of the Sacraments."] *See* BROGDEN (James) *M.A., Vicar of Deddington.* Illustrations of the Liturgy and Ritual of the United Church of England and Ireland, *etc.* vol. 1. 1842. 12°. **1219. g. 4.**

—— The Duty and Reward of Bounty to the Poor: in a sermon preached at the Spittal upon Wednesday in Easter Week, Anno Dom. MDCLXXI. pp. 230. *Andrew Clark for Brabazon Aylmer: London*, 1671. 8°. **4454. aa. 8.**

—— The third edition. [With a portrait.] pp. 176. *M. F. [Flesher] for Brabazon Aylmer : London*, 1680. 8°. **4474. b. 104. (1.)**

—— [Another copy.] **1359. a. 51. (1.)**

Imperfect; wanting the portrait.

—— Lectiones Geometricæ: in quibus, præsertim, generalia curvarum linearum symptomata declarantur. pp. 147. *Typis Gulielmi Godbid: Londini*, 1670. 4°. **8533. b. 20.**

—— Geometrical Lectures: explaining the generation, nature and properties of curve lines . . . Translated from the Latin edition, revised, corrected and amended by the late Sir Isaac Newton [and John Collins]. By Edmund Stone. pp. 209 [309]. pl. XI. *Stephen Austen: London*, 1735. 8°. **52. f. 4.**

—— The Geometrical Lectures of Isaac Barrow. Translated, with notes and proofs, and a discussion on the advance made therein on the work of his predecessors in the infinitesimal calculus, by J. M. Child. pp. xiv. 218. *Open Court Publishing Co.: Chicago & London*, 1916. 8°. [*Open Court Series of Classics of Science and Philosophy.* no. 3.] **8708. a. 37/3.**

—— Isaaci Barrow . . . Lectiones habitæ in Scholis publicis Academiæ Cantabrigiensis. Annis Domini 1664, 1665, 1666. Et ultimæ quatuor incerti tempor . 2 pt. *J. Playford, pro Georgio Wells: Londini*, 1684. 8°. **529. a. 12.**

—— [A reissue.] Isaaci Barrow Lectiones Mathematicæ XXIII; in quibus principia matheseôs generalia exponuntur: habitæ Cantabrigiæ A.D. 1664, 1665, 1666. Accesserunt ejusdem lectiones IV. In quibus theoremata & problemata Archimedis de sphærâ & cylindro, methodo analyticâ eruuntur. *Londini*, 1685. 8°. **8529. aa. 16.**
With the addition of a leaf containing the dedication.

—— The Usefulness of Mathematical Learning Explained and Demonstrated: being mathematical lectures read in the Publick Schools at the University of Cambridge . . . To which is prefixed, the oratorical preface of our learned author spoke before the University on his being elected the Lucasian Professor of the Mathematics. Translated by the Revd John Kirkby. [With a portrait.] pp. xxxii. 440. *Stephen Austen: London*, 1734. 8°. **51. d. 17.**

—— Lectiones XVIII, Cantabrigiæ in Scholis publicis habitæ; in quibus opticorum phænomenωn genuinæ rationes investigantur, ac exponuntur. Annexæ sunt Lectiones aliquot Geometricæ. [Edited by Sir Isaac Newton and John Collins.] *Typis Gulielmi Godbid: Londini*, 1669. 4°. **8715. aaa. 55.**
Imperfect; wanting the "Lectiones Geometricae."

—— [Another edition.] Lectiones Opticæ & Geometricæ, *etc.* 2 pt. *Typis Guilielmi Godbid: Londini*, 1674. 4°. **537. f. 6.**

—— Of Contentment, Patience and Resignation to the Will of God. Several sermons, *etc.* [Edited by Thomas Barrow. With a portrait.] pp. 269. *Brabazon Aylmer: London*, 1685. 8°. **1021. a. 8.**

—— [Another copy, with a different titlepage.] *M. Flesher, for Brabazon Aylmer: London*, 1685. 8°. **C. 72. b. 5.**

—— [Another edition.] pp. 244. *J. Round: London*, 1714. 12°. **4452. aaa. 8.**

—— Directions how to be Content. Being an extract out of his Sermons of Contentment, in his own words. By I. Barrow. *See* H., J. A New-Year's Gift, *etc.* 1704. 12°. **4404. b. 85.**

—— Of Industry, in five discourses: viz. In general. In our general calling, as Christians. In our particular calling, as gentlemen. In our particular calling, as scholars . . . Published by His Grace, John, Lord Arch-bishop of Canterbury. [With a portrait.] pp. 188. *J. H. for Brab. Aylmer: London*, 1693. 8°. **852. d. 20.**

—— [Another edition.] pp. 188. *W. B. for Brab. Aylmer: London*, 1700. 8°. **8405. aaa. 21.**

—— [Another edition.] The Duty and Rewards of Industry Considered. pp. vii. 184. *Wetton & Jarvis: London*, 1822. 12°. **4453. df. 9.**

—— Four Sermons on Obedience to our Spiritual Guides and Governors. [The sermon "Of Obedience to our Spiritual Guides and Governors," divided into four parts.] pp. 73. *Gilbert & Rivington: London*, 1840. 12°. **4475. de. 4. (13.)**

—— Practical Discourses upon the Consideration of our Latter End; and the danger and mischief of delaying repentance, *etc.* [With a portrait.] pp. 176. *J. H. for B. Aylmer: London*, 1694. 8°. **1021. a. 9.**

—— A Sermon preached on the Fifth of November, MDCLXXIII. pp. 36. *J. D. for Brabazon Aylmer: London*, 1679. 4°. **4473. c. 1. (5.)**

—— A Sermon upon the Passion of our Blessed Saviour: preached at Guild-Hall Chappel on Good Friday, the 13th day of April, 1677. pp. 43. *Brabazon Aylmer: London*, 1677. 4°. **694. g. 13. (10.)**

—— [Another copy.] **226. h. 18. (17.)**

—— [Another edition.] pp. 97. *Brabazon Aylmer: London*, 1678. 12°. **4474. b. 104. (2.)**

—— [Another edition.] pp. 97. *M. Flesher, for Brabazon Aylmer: London*, 1682. 8°. **1359. a. 51. (2.)**

—— Sermons preached upon Several Occasions. [Edited by Archbishop Tillotson.] pp. 519. *E. Flesher, for Brabazon Aylmer: London*, 1678. 8°. **1021. a. 6.**

—— [Another copy.] **C. 69. aa. 3.**
With an engraved portrait inserted.

—— The Accession. A sermon on the King's happy return. [Extracted from "Sermons preached upon Several Occasions."] *See* Brogden (James) *M.A., Vicar of Deddington.* Illustrations of the Liturgy and Ritual of the United Church of England and Ireland, *etc.* vol. 3. 1842. 12°. **1219. g. 6.**

—— Several Sermons against Evil-Speaking. [Edited by Archbishop Tillotson. With a portrait.] pp. 140. 2pt. *Brabazon Aylmer: London*, 1678. 8°. **1021. a. 7.**

—— [Another edition.] Sermons on Evil-Speaking. pp. 192. *London*, 1887. 16°. [*Cassell's National Library.* vol. 60.] **12208.bb.15/60.**

—— Spiritus sanctus est persona distincta, Patri Filioque coëssentialis, & ab utroque procedens.—Episcopo Romano nulla in Ecclesiam Anglicanam jurisdictis competit. [Theses, in verse.] [*Cambridge*, 1670.] *s. sh.* fol. **11409. i. 10. (11.)**

—— A Treatise of the Pope's Supremacy. To which is added A Discourse concerning the Unity of the Church. [Edited by Archbishop Tillotson. With a portrait.] 2 pt. *Miles Flesher, for Brabazon Aylmer: London*, 1680. 4°. **491. c. 5.**

—— [Another copy.] **855. d. 20.**

—— [Another edition.] pp. iv. 476. 1836. *See* Cardwell (Edward) *D.D.* Enchiridion theologicum anti-Romanum, *etc.* vol. 2. 1836, *etc.* 8°. **1119. f. 25.**

—— A new edition, corrected. [Edited by Frederick Field. With a portrait.] pp. xiii. 561. *S.P.C.K.: London*, 1851. 8°. **3940. f. 60.**

—— [Another edition.] Edited, with introduction and notes, by Thomas M'Crie. pp. xlii. 418. *Johnstone & Hunter: Edinburgh*, 1852. 8°. **3936. g. 8.**

—— Barrow on the Pope's Supremacy. (Carefully revised and edited by the Rev. John Cumming.) pp. vii. 448. *British Society for Promoting the Religious Principles of the Reformation: London*, 1849. 8°. [*Gibson (Edmund) Supplement to Gibson's Preservative from Popery.* vol. 1.] **3940.k.7/1.**

—— Reasons for Renouncing the Pope. (Extracted from Barrow's Treatise on the Pope's Supremacy.) pp. 27. *Nisbet, etc.: London*, 1849. 12°. **3939. d. 57. (2.)**

—— Holy Scripture and the Pope's Supremacy Contrasted . . . (Taken from Dr. Barrow's Treatise of the Pope's Supremacy.) Edited by James Brogden. pp. 23. *S.P.C.K.: London*, 1850. 12°. **3940. d. 71. (2.)**

—— Reasons for Renouncing the Pope. (Extracted from Barrow's Treatise on the Pope's Supremacy.) pp. 28. *London*, 1851. 12°. [*British Society for Promoting the Religious Principles of the Reformation. Tracts.* no. 26.] **3939. b. 2.**
Previous edition, 1849.

—— *See* Baxter (Richard) An Answer to Mr. Dodwell and Dr. Sherlocke; confuting an universal humane church-supremacy, aristocratical and monarchical; as church-tyranny and popery: and defending Dr. I. Barrow's treatise against it, *etc.* 1682. 4°. **4135**. c. **8**.

SELECTIONS.

—— Selections from Dr. Barrow. *See* Montagu (Basil) Selections from the Works of Taylor, Hooker, Milton, Hall, Barrow, and Bacon, *etc.* vol. 2. 1807. 12°. **8407**. c. **20**.

—— [Another edition.] *See* Montagu (Basil) Selections from the Works of Taylor . . . Barrow, *etc.* 1829. 8°. **716**. c. **21**.

—— [Another edition.] *See* Montagu (Basil) Selections from the Works of Taylor . . . Barrow, *etc.* 1839. 8° **12295**. aa. **25**.

—— The Beauties of Isaac Barrow, D.D. Selected from all his sermons and devotional writings, with a biographical notice of the author. By B. S. Esq., Barrister at Law [i.e. Bartholomew Stritch]. pp. xiv. 274. *T. C. Newby: London,* 1846. 12°. **1358**. c. **17**.

—— Selections from the Writings of Isaac Barrow, D.D. With a memoir. pp. 304. *R.T.S.: London,* [1866.] 8°. [*Wisdom of our Fathers.*] **4419**. h. **42/1**.

WORKS EDITED OR WITH CONTRIBUTIONS BY BARROW.

—— *See* Archimedes. [*Works.*] Archimedis opera . . . Methodo nova illustrata & succincte demonstrata per I. Barrow. 1675. 4°. **529**. f. **14**.

—— *See* Euclid. [*Data.*] Euclidis Data succinctè demonstrata: unà cum emendationibus quibusdam & additionibus ad Elementa Euclidis nuper edita. Operâ Mrl I. Barrow. 1657. 12°. **530**. b. **6**. (**2**.)

—— —— 1659. 12°. 717.b.9.

—— —— 1676. 12°. 8532.aaa.12.

—— —— 1778. 12°. 530.b.7.

—— *See* Euclid. [*Elementa.*] Euclidis Elementorum libri xv. breviter demonstrati, operâ I. Barrow. 1655. 12°. **530**. b. **6**. (**1**.)

—— *See* Euclid. [*Elementa.*] Euclidis Elementorum libri xv. breviter demonstrati, opera I. Barrow. 1659. 8°. **717**. b. **9**.

—— —— 1676, *etc.* 8°. **8532**. aaa. **12**.

—— *See* Euclid. [*Elementa.*] Euclidis Elementorum libri xv. breviter demonstrati, operâ I. Barrow, *etc.* (Lectio . . . Isaaci Barrow . . . in qua theoremata Archimedis de sphæra & cylindro, per methodum indivisibilium investigata, ac breviter demonstrata exhibentur.) 1678. 12°. **530**. b. **7**.

—— *See* Euclid. [*Elementa.*] Euclide's Elements; the whole fifteen books compendiously demonstrated by Mr. I. Barrow . . . And translated out of the Latin. 1660. 8°. **8529**. a. **22**.

—— *See* Euclid. [*Elementa.*] Euclide's Elements; the whole fifteen books compendiously demonstrated. With Archimedes theorems of the sphere and cylinder, investigated by the method of indivisibles. By I. Barrow, *etc.* 1714. 8°. **8535**. aaa. **15**.

—— —— 1722. 8°. **52**. a. **11**.

—— —— 1751. 8°. **8529**. bb. **17**.

—— *See* Hale (*Sir* Matthew) The Judgment of the late Lord Chief Justice Sir Matthew Hale, of the Nature of True Religion . . . To which is annexed the judgment of Sir Francis Bacon . . . And somewhat of Dr. I. Barrows on the same subject. 1684. 4°. **698**. e. **3**. (**11**.)

—— —— 1832. 8°. **908**. d. **14**. (**4**.)

APPENDIX.

—— *See* Osmond (Percy H.) Isaac Barrow: his life and times. [With a portrait.] 1944. 8°. **10860**. b. **30**.

—— *See* Wace (Henry) *Dean of Canterbury.* Barrow, the exhaustive preacher. 1877. 8°. [*Kempe (John E.) The Classic Preachers of the English Church, etc.* ser. 1.] **4464**. i. **12**.

BARROW (Isaac) *Socialist.* A Standard lifted for the People. A Sermon delivered on Castle Hill, Hindley, on Sunday, August 4, 1839. pp. 14. *Samuel Gardner: Bolton,* 1839. 8°. **4477**. bb. **6**.

BARROW (J.) *M.D.* Membrorum principalium apostasia: or, a Short view of those many diseases . . . which proceed from a defection . . . of the principal . . . parts of the body from the performance of their . . . functions; together with their cures by the matchless Tinctura Cælestis, *etc.* pp. 1–4. [*London?* 1670?] 4°. **1166**. h. **6**. (**4**.)

Mutilated, and imperfect at the end.

BARROW (J. R.) Language and Literature. [On the methods of teaching English in Bengal.] Reprinted from the "Dacca Review," *etc.* pp. 98. *Longmans & Co.: Calcutta,* [1917.] 8°. **8365**. a. **52**.

BARROW (J. W.) A Brief History of the Bloemfontein Mission, South Africa, *etc.* (Part i. . . . by . . . J. W. Barrow.—Part ii. . . . By an Associate of the Mission.) pp. 24. *J. T. Hayes: London,* 1876. 8°. **4767**. bb. **18**. (**8**.)

BARROW (James) *Minister of Zoar Chapel, Hoxton.* Redemption Hymns, or Songs of Zion. [With supplement.] pp. ii. 137. *H. Fenwick: London,* 1766, [79.] 8°. **3434**. e. **37**.

—— Third edition. pp. iv. 190. *J. Wayte: London,* 1803. 12°. **3437**. a. **39**.

BARROW (James) *of St. Olave's, Southwark.* *See* Barrow (John) *of St. Olave's, Southwark.* The Lord's Arm stretched out in answer to prayer: or, a true relation of the deliverance of James Barrow, who was oppressed with evil spirits near two years, *etc.* 1664. 4°. **873**. e. **124**.

BARROW (Joe Louis) *See* Louis (Joe)

BARROW (John) *Canon of Windsor.* A Sermon preached at the triennial Visitation of Seth Lord Bishop of Sarum, held at Reading . . . 1683. pp. 35. *Ralph Holt for John Gellibrand: London,* 1683. 4°. **693**. f. **1**. (**7**.)

—— [Another copy.] **226**. i. **12**. (**3**.)

BARROW (John) *Civil Engineer.* Facts relating to North-Eastern Texas, condensed from notes made during a tour through that portion of the United States of America, for the purpose of examining the country as a field for emigration. pp. 68. *Simpkin, Marshall & Co.: London,* 1849. 8°. **10410**. c. **4**.

BARROW (John) *D.D.* *See* Bible.—*John, Gospel of.* [*English.*] The Gospel according to St. John . . . compared with the original Greek, and revised, by five Clergymen [i.e. J. Barrow and others]. 1857. 8°. **3051**. d. **7**.

—— *See* Bible.—*John, Gospel of.* [*English.*] The Gospel according to S. John . . . with notes on every one of the alterations proposed by the five Clergymen in their revised version of this Gospel, published in mdccclvii., *etc.* 1862. 4°. **3051**. e. **4**.

BARROW (JOHN) *D.D.*

—— *See* BIBLE.—*Romans.* [*English.*] The Epistle of St. Paul to the Romans . . . newly compared with the original Greek, and revised by five Clergymen [i.e. J. Barrow and others]. 1858. 8°. **3051.** d. **8.**

See BIBLE.— Corinthians. [English.]

—— The Epistles of St. Paul to the Corinthians . . . Newly compared with the original Greek, and revised, by five Clergymen [i.e. J. Barrow and others]. 1858. 8°. **3051.** d. **9.**

—— *See* HICKES (George) *Dean of Worcester.* Two Treatises on the Christian Priesthood, *etc.* [The editor's advertisement signed: I. B., i.e. J. Barrow.] 1847, *etc.* 8°. **2204.** d. **10.**

—— *See* JOHN, *Chrysostom, Saint, etc.* [*Homilies.—On Parts of the Bible.*] The Homilies of S. John Chrysostom . . . on the Epistle . . . to the Hebrews. [The translation revised by J. Barrow.] 1877. 8°. [*PUSEY* (*E. B.*) *A Library of Fathers, etc.*] **3628.de.1.**

—— *See* TAYLOR (Jeremy) *Bishop of Down and Connor,* and *of Dromore.* On the Reverence due to the Altar . . . Edited by J. Barrow. 1848. 4°. **3475.** b. **18.**

—— *See* WADE (Thomas) *Rev., M.A.* Notes on the Gospel of St. John, as translated by "Five Clergymen" [i.e. J. Barrow and others]. 1857. 8°. **3051.** e. **1.**

—— The Case of Queen's College, Oxford; in a letter . . . to the Rt. Hon. W. E. Gladstone. pp. 59. *J. H. Parker: Oxford & London,* 1854. 8°. **8364.** e. **8.**

—— *See* THOMSON (William) successively *Bishop of Gloucester* and *Archbishop of York.* An Open College best for all. A reply to the Case of Queen's College by . . . J. Barrow, *etc.* 1854. 8°. **8364.** e. **26.**

—— Life of St. Ninian, *etc.* [By J. Barrow.] pp. vi. 148. 1845. 8°. *See* NINIAN, *Saint, Bishop of Galloway.* **1370.** b. **1.**

—— Life of St. Ninian, *etc.* [Here attributed to Mark Pattison, but in fact by J. Barrow.] 1901. 8°. [*The Lives of the English Saints.* vol. 5.] *See* PATTISON (Mark) **4828.** ee. **1.**

BARROW (JOHN) *F.R.S.* *See* COATS (William) The Geography of Hudson's Bay . . . Edited by J. Barrow. 1852. 8°. Ac. **6172/11.**

—— *See* COOK (James) *the Circumnavigator.* [*Compilations.*] Captain Cook's Voyages of Discovery. Edited by J. Barrow. 1860. 8°. **10026.** b. **15.**

—— —— 1904. 8°. **010028.** f. **4.**

—— *See* COOK (James) *the Circumnavigator.* [*Logs and Journals.—Abridgments and Adaptations.*] Captain Cook's Voyages of Discovery. [The abridgment of J. Barrow.] [1906.] 8°. **12206.** p. **1/93.**

—— —— 1908. 8°. **012206.** de. **1/65.**

—— *See* STAUNTON (*Sir* George T.) *Bart.* Memoir of Sir J. Barrow, *etc.* [The editor's preface signed: J. B., i.e. John Barrow.] [1852.] 8°. **10825.** c. **26.**

—— Excursions in the North of Europe, through parts of Russia, Finland, Sweden, Germany, and Norway in 1830 and 1833. pp. 380. *John Murray: London,* 1834. 12°. **1048.** c. **2.**

—— Expeditions on the Glaciers: including an ascent of Mont Blanc, Monte Rosa, Col du Géant, and Mont Buét. By a Private of the thirty-eighth Artists', and Member of the Alpine Club [i.e. J. Barrow], *etc.* pp. 126. 1864. 8°. *See* EXPEDITIONS. **10195.** b. **25.**

BARROW (JOHN) *F.R.S.*

—— A Family Tour through South Holland; up the Rhine; and across the Netherlands, to Ostend.] By J. Barrow. With illustrations by R. Batty.] pp. viii. 295. 1831. 8°. *See* NETHERLANDS. [Appendix.-Topography and Travels.] **12200.** g. **8.** (**1.**)

—— The Life and Correspondence of Admiral Sir William Sidney Smith. [With portraits and plans.] 2 vol. *Richard Bentley: London,* 1848. 8°. **1452.** g. **1.**

—— The Life, Voyages, and Exploits of Admiral Sir Francis Drake . . . with numerous original letters. pp. xv. 428. *John Murray: London,* 1843. 8°. **1203.** f. **5.**

—— Second edition, abridged. pp. xii. 187. *John Murray: London,* 1844. 16°. **1155.** b. **2.** (**2.**)

—— Memoirs of the Naval Worthies of Queen Elizabeth's Reign. pp. xvi. 495. *John Murray: London,* 1845. 8°. **1203.** f. **16.**

—— [Another copy.] G. **13122.**

—— Mountain Ascents in Westmoreland and Cumberland. pp. vii. 208. *Sampson Low & Co.: London,* 1886. 8°. **10352.** bbb. **32.**

—— A Private Memoir of the Life and Services of the late William Barrow . . . Commander, Royal Navy. pp. ix. 170. *For private circulation:* [*London,*] 1850. 8°. **10817.** i. **24.**

—— Summer Tours in Central Europe. 1853–54. 3 pt. *W. H. Dalton: London,* 1855–57. 8°. **10106.** e. **27.**

—— Tour in Austrian Lombardy, the Northern Tyrol, and Bavaria, in 1840. pp. xv. 375. *John Murray: London,* 1841. 12°. **791.** i. **17.**

—— Tour on the Continent by Rail and Road in the summer of 1852. pp. 126. *Longman & Co.: London,* 1853. 8°. [*Traveller's Library.* vol. 2.] **1156.** h. **8.**

—— A Tour round Ireland, through the sea-coast counties, in the autumn of 1835. pp. xi. 379. 38. *John Murray: London,* 1836. 8°. **567.** c. **25.**

—— A Visit to Iceland by way of Tronyem, in the summer of 1834. pp. xxiv. 320. *John Murray: London,* 1835. 12°. **791.** e. **3.**

—— Ein Besuch auf der Insel Island über Tronyem im Sommer 1834. pp. xiv. 186. *Stuttgart & Tübingen,* 1836. 8°. [*WIDENMANN* (*E.*) *and HAUFF* (*W.*) *Reisen und Länderbeschreibungen, etc.* Lfg. 8.] **1294.** c. **2.**

BARROW (JOHN) *Jeweller.* Original Poems, selected from one hundred and fifty . . . With a short sketch of the author's life, and a likeness drawn and engraved by himself. pp. 108. *R. Menzies: Edinburgh,* 1813. 18°. **993.** b. **3.**

BARROW (JOHN) *of St. Olave's, Southwark.* The Lord's Arm stretched out in an answer of prayer: or, a True relation of the wonderful deliverance of James Barrow, who was possessed with evil spirits near two years . . . Published by me, John Barrow. pp. 20. *London,* 1664. 4°. **873.** e. **124.**
Cropped.

BARROW (JOHN) *of Upton, Barbadoes.* A Declaration of the Inhabitants of Barbados respecting the demolition of the Methodist Chapel. With an appendix. [Signed by J. Barrow, R. Hamden and others.] "*The Barbadian*": *Barbados,* 1826. 8°. **8156.** b. **9.**

BARROW (JOHN) *Teacher of Mathematics. See* ENCYCLOPAEDIAS. Dictionarium Polygraphicum, *etc.* [Edited by J. Barrow.] 1735. 8°. **1044**. g. **4, 5.**

—— —— 1758. 8°. **1400**. d. **25, 26.**

—— *See* EUCLID. [*Elementa.*] Euclide's Elements . . . To which is now added an Appendix, containing the nature, construction and application of logarithms, by J. Barrow, *etc.* 1751. 8°. **8529**. bb. **17.**

—— *See* MATHER (William) *of Bedford, Schoolmaster.* The Young Man's Companion . . . The twenty-first edition, with . . . additions and improvements, by J. Barrow. 1761. 12°. **012224**. aa. **2.**

—— *See* PUFENDORF (S. von) *Baron.* The Law of Nature and of Nations . . . To which are now added . . . the . . . notes of Mr. Barbeyrac, translated [by the editor J. Barrow] from his fourth edition, *etc.* 1749. fol. **496**. i. **17.**

—— A Collection of Authentic, Useful, and Entertaining Voyages and Discoveries, digested in a chronological series, *etc.* [With plates, including maps.] 3 vol. *J. Knox: London,* 1765. 12°. **10026**. p. **20.**

—— Dictionarium medicum universale: or, a New medical dictionary. Containing an explanation of all the terms used in physic, anatomy . . . chymistry, *etc.* *T. Longman & C. Hitch; A. Miller: London,* 1749. 8°. **777**. d. **34.**

—— Navigatio Britannica: or, a Complete system of navigation, *etc.* pp. xvi. 296. 128. *W. & J. Mount and T. Page: London,* 1750. 4°. G. **16215.**

—— A New and Universal Dictionary of Arts and Sciences . . . With an introductory preface, tracing the progress of literature from the earliest ages . . . Illustrated with . . . copper-plates, *etc.* *For the Proprietors; sold by John Hinton: London,* 1751. fol. **715**. l. **6.**

—— A Supplement to the New and Universal Dictionary of Arts and Sciences. *For the Proprietors; sold by John Hinton: London,* 1754. fol. **715**. l. **7.**

—— Tables calculated for the use of all who are concerned in trade and business, *etc.* *See* GENTLEMAN. The Gentleman, Tradesman and Traveller's Pocket Library, *etc.* pt. 2. 1753. 12°. **794**. d. **35.**

BARROW (*Sir* JOHN) *Bart. See* CLAPPERTON (Hugh) Journal of a Second Expedition into the Interior of Africa, *etc.* [With an introduction, signed: J. B., i.e. Sir J. Barrow.] 1829. 4°. **567**. h. **11.**

—— *See* CLAPPERTON (Hugh) Journal of an Excursion (from Kouka to Sackatoo), etc. etc. [Edited by Sir J. Barrow.] 1826. 4°. [DENHAM (*Dixon*) *Narrative of Travels and Discoveries in Northern and Central Africa, etc.*] **792**. l. **21.**

—— —— 1826. 8°. **792**. i. **25.**

—— —— 1828. 8°. **10096**. cc. **19.**

—— —— 1831. 16°. **1051**. b. **25.**

—— *See* DANIELL (Samuel) *Artist.* Sketches representing the Native Tribes, Animals, and Scenery of Southern Africa, *etc.* [With descriptive letterpress by W. Somerville and Sir J. Barrow.] 1820. 4°. **562***. e. **13.**

—— *See* REICHENBACH (A. B.) Die Völker der Erde nach ihrer Eigenthümlichkeit in Regierungsform . . . durch Wort und Bild geschildert nach den Werken eines Barrow, H. Barth, *etc.* 1859, *etc.* 8°. **10003**. d. **13.**

BARROW (*Sir* JOHN) *Bart.*

—— *See* STAUNTON (*Sir* George T.) *Bart.* Memoir of Sir John Barrow, Bart., and description of the Barrow Monument, *etc.* [1852.] 8°. **10825**. c. **26.**

—— *See* TUCKEY (James H.) Narrative of an Expedition to explore the River Zaire, *etc.* [Edited by Sir J. Barrow.] 1818. 4°. **982**. i. **10.**

—— An Account of Travels into the Interior of Southern Africa, in the years 1797 and 1798, including observations on the geology & geography, the natural history . . . and sketches of the various tribes surrounding the Cape of Good Hope. To which is annexed a description of the present state . . . of that colony. With a map constructed from actual observations made in the course of the travels. [With maps.] 2 vol. *T. Cadell & W. Davies: London,* 1801, 04. 4°. **984**. e. **20, 21.**

—— [Another copy.] **146**. e. **19, 20.**

—— [Another copy.] G. **7184–5.**

—— Travels into the Interior of South Africa . . . The second edition, with additions and alterations. Illustrated, *etc.* 2 vol. *T. Cadell & W. Davies: London,* 1806. 4°. **10094**. g. **10.**

—— [Another copy.] **10094**. g. **8.**
Imperfect; wanting the General Chart in vol. 1 *and the Chart of Algoa Bay in vol.* 2. *Pp.* 421, 2 *in vol.* 1 *mutilated.*

—— An Auto-biographical Memoir of Sir John Barrow . . . including reflections, observations and reminiscences at home and abroad, from early life to advanced age. [With a portrait.] pp. xi. 515. *John Murray: London,* 1847. 8°. **1453**. h. **1.**

—— A Chronological History of Voyages into the Arctic Regions; undertaken chiefly for the purpose of discovering a North-East, North-West, or Polar Passage between the Atlantic and Pacific; from the earliest periods of Scandinavian navigation to the departure of the recent expeditions under the orders of Captain Ross and Buchan. pp. 379. 48. *John Murray: London,* 1818. 8°. **978**. l. **1.**

—— [Another copy.] **303**. i. **4.**

—— [Another copy.] C. **60**. i. **16.**
With numerous autograph signatures of Arctic explorers and others, and an autograph letter to Col. John Barrow, son of the author, from Fridtjof Nansen.

—— [Another copy.] G. **7180.**

—— Fac-simile copy of letter dated 5th Aug. 1816 from . . . Sir J. Barrow to . . . Sir F. Ronalds . . . relative to the electric telegraph. [1881?] *s. sh.* 4°. **1881**. c. **16. (68*.)**

—— The Eventful History of the Mutiny . . . of H.M.S. Bounty; its cause and consequences. [By Sir J. Barrow.] pp. xi. 356. 1831. 8°. *See* BOUNTY, *H.M.S.* **12200.gg.13.**

—— The Eventful History of the Mutiny and Piratical Seizure of H.M.S. Bounty . . . [By Sir John Barrow.] Illustrated by six etchings from original drawings by Lieut.-Colonel Batty. Second edition. pp. xi. 356. 1835. 8°. *See* BOUNTY, *H.M.S.* **09525**. de. **51.**

—— [Another edition.] A Description of Pitcairn's Island and its Inhabitants. With an authentic account of the mutiny of the ship Bounty, *etc.* pp. 303. 1845. 12°. *See* PITCAIRN'S ISLAND. **12205**. b. **23.**

—— [Another edition.] The Mutiny and Piratical Seizure of H.M.S. Bounty, *etc.* pp. vi. 392. *William Tegg: London,* [1876.] 8°. **10492**. bb. **2.**

—— [A reissue.] *G. Routledge & Sons: London,* 1883 [1882]. 8°. **10491**. bb. **12.**

—— [Another edition.] The Mutiny of the Bounty and the Pitcairn Islanders . . . With an introduction by . . . H. R. Haweis. pp. 160. *London*, 1886. 16°. [*Routledge's World Library.*] **12207. ee. 22.**

—— [Another edition.] The Mutiny & Piratical Seizure of H.M.S. Bounty . . . With an introduction by Admiral Sir Cyprian Bridge. pp. xxiii. 376. *Humphrey Milford: London*, 1914. 8°. [*World's Classics.*] **012209. df. 106.**

—— *See* BOUNTY, *H.M.S.* The Mutiny of the Bounty, *etc.* [Abridged from the accounts of William Bligh and Sir J. Barrow.] 1885. 8°. **12354. aaa. 49.**

—— The Life of George Lord Anson. [With a portrait.] pp. xxxiv. 484. *John Murray: London*, 1839. 8°. **615. f. 12.**

—— The Life of Richard Earl Howe, K.G., Admiral of the Fleet, and General of Marines. [With a portrait.] pp. xvi. 432. *John Murray: London*, 1838. 8°. **615. f. 13.**

—— [Another copy.] MS. NOTES [transcribed from those of Sir E. Codrington]. **C. 45. d. 27.**
With pp. 11–40 of the proof-sheets of the "Memoir of the Life of Sir Edmund Codrington," edited by Lady Bourchier, inset.

—— A Memoir of the Life of Peter the Great. [By Sir J. Barrow.] pp. xvi. 366. 1832. 12°. *See* PETER, called *the Great, Emperor of Russia.* **12200. gg. 3. (2.)**

—— [Another edition.] pp. 320. *Harper & Bros.: New York*, 1845. 12°. **12205. b. 69.**

—— The Life of Peter the Great . . . New edition, with notes. Illustrated. pp. xvi. 414. *William Tegg: London*, [1874.] 8°. **10790. aaa. 34.**

—— [A reissue.] *W. P. Nimmo & Co.: Edinburgh*, 1883. 8°. **10790. aaa. 15.**

—— Sketches of the Royal Society, and Royal Society Club. pp. vi. 212. *John Murray: London*, 1849. 8°. **740. d. 1.**

—— Some Account of the Public Life, and a Selection from the unpublished Writings, of the Earl of Macartney, the latter consisting of extracts from an account of the Russian Empire; a sketch of the political history of Ireland; and a journal of an embassy from the King of Great Britain to the Emperor of China, with an appendix to each volume. [With a portrait.] 2 vol. *T. Cadell & W. Davies: London*, 1807. 4°. **1321. f. 10.**

—— [Another copy.] **134. b. 6.**

—— [Another copy.] **G. 1971.**

—— Travels in China: containing descriptions, observations and comparisons made and collected in the course of a short residence at the Imperial Palace of Yuen-min-yuen, and on a subsequent journey from Pekin to Canton. pp. x. 632. *T. Cadell & W. Davies: London*, 1804. 4°. **981. f. 16.**

—— [Another copy.] **G. 7186.**

—— [Another copy.]
[Travels in China, *etc.* *London*, 1804. 4°. **146. e. 21.**
Imperfect; wanting the frontispiece, the titlepage, and all before p. vii, which are supplied in photostat facsimile.

—— First American edition. pp. 422. *W. E. M'Laughlin: Philadelphia*, 1805. 8°. **1425. h. 22.**

—— Travels in China . . . In which it is attempted to appreciate the rank that this extraordinary empire may be considered to hold in the scale of civilised nations . . . Illustrated with several engravings. The second edition. pp. x. 632. *T. Cadell & W. Davies: London*, 1806. 4°. **10057. v. 12.**

—— Voyage en Chine, formant le complément du voyage de Lord Macartney; contenant des observations et des descriptions faites pendant le séjour de l'auteur dans le palais impérial de Yuen Min-Yuen, et en traversant l'empire Chinois, de Peking à Canton. Suivi de la relation de l'ambassade envoyée en 1719, a Peking, par Pierre premier, empereur de Russie. Traduits de l'anglais, avec des notes, par J. Castéra. 3 tom. *Paris*, an XIII [1805]. 8°. **566. d. 10, 11.**

—— Collection des planches. 4°. **566. i. 21.**

—— Voyage en Chine et en Tartarie de l'ambassade de Lord Macartney . . . Traduit de l'anglais avec des notes. [An abridgment by Count A. Mahé de la Bourdonnais of J. H. Castéra's translation of "Travels in China," by Sir J. Barrow, Bart.] Suivi de la Guerre sino-japonaise . . . par le comte A. Mahé de la Bourdonnais, *etc.* 2 tom. [1896.] 8°. *See* CHINA. **010057. f. 38.**

—— Johann Barrow's . . . Reise durch China von Peking nach Canton . . . Aus dem Englischen übersetzt und mit einigen Anmerkungen begleitet von Johann Christian Hüttner . . . Mit Kupfern. 2 Tl. *Weimar*, 1804. 8°. **1298. e. 26.**

—— *See* PROUDFOOT (W. J.) "Barrow's Travels in China." An investigation into the origin . . . of the "Facts and observations" related in a work entitled "Travels in China, by J. Barrow," *etc.* 1861. 8°. **10056. bb. 26.**

—— A Voyage to Cochin China, in the years 1792, and 1793: containing a general view of the productions, and political importance of this kingdom; and also of such European settlements as were visited on the voyage, with sketches of the manners, character, and condition of their inhabitants. To which is annexed an account of a journey, made in the years 1801 and 1802, to the residence of the chief of the Booshuana nation . . . from a manuscript journal [by —— Truter] with a chart of the route, *etc.* 2 pt. pp. xviii. 447. *T. Cadell & W. Davies: London*, 1806. 4°. **982. i. 15.**

—— [Another copy.] **146. f. 14.**

—— [Another copy.] **G. 7187.**

—— Voyage à la Cochinchine . . . Traduit de l'anglais, avec des notes et additions, par Malte-Brun. 2 tom. *Paris*, 1807. 8°. **1294. d. 3.**

—— Atlas. fol. **1294. d. 4.**

—— Voyages of Discovery and Research within the Arctic Regions, from . . . 1818 to the present time: under the command of the several naval officers employed by sea and land in search of a North West Passage from the Atlantic to the Pacific . . . Abridged and arranged from the official narratives, with occasional remarks. With portrait and maps. pp. xiv. 530. *John Murray: London*, 1846. 8°. **10460. c. 2.**

—— [Another copy.] **G. 16017.**

—— *See* ROSS (*Sir* John) Observations on a Work, entitled: "Voyages of Discovery and Research within the Arctic Regions," by Sir J. Barrow. 1846. 8°. **10460. e. 25. (1.)**

BARROW (*Sir* JOHN CROKER) *Bart.* *See* P., J. A Letter of Remonstrance, addressed to . . . J. C. Barrow. [Being a reply to his pamphlet entitled: "A Few Words to his friends and former flock in Kensington"], *etc.* 1859. 8°. **3940. cc. 79. (4.)**

—— Poems. pp. vii. 257. *Longmans & Co.: London*, 1876. 8°. **11652. bb. 13.**

—— Arden. A poem. pp. 75. *Saunders & Otley: London*, 1856. 8°. **11648. a. 69.**

BARROW (*Sir* JOHN CROKER) *Bart.*

—— " Mary of Nazareth ": a legendary poem, *etc.* 3 pt. *Burns & Oates: London,* [1889, 90.] 8°. **011653.** e. **69.**

—— The Seven Cities of the Dead, and other poems, lyrics, and sonnets. pp. viii. 136. *Longmans & Co.: London,* 1893. 8°. **011653.** m. **99.**

—— ' Towards the Truth.' Thoughts in verse. pp. 70. *Longmans & Co.: London,* 1885. 8°. **11653.** e. **42.**

—— The Valley of Tears. A poem. pp. 154. *Longmans & Co.: London,* 1865. 8°. **11647.** aaa. **12.**

BARROW (JOHN GANE)

—— [Letters to myself.] Digression. (Personal records of travel.) [With plates, including a portrait.] pp. 254. *Skeffington & Son: London,* 1931. 8°. **010028.** ee. **30.**

BARROW (JOHN GRAVES)

—— A Bibliography of Bibliographies in Religion. pp. xi. 489. *Edwards Bros.: Ann Arbor,* [1955.] 4°. BB.A. f. **10.**

—— [Another copy.]
A Bibliography of Bibliographies in Religion. Ann Arbor, [1955.] 4°. **2726.ab.4.**

BARROW (JOHN HENRY) *Esq.* *See* PERIODICAL PUBLICATIONS.—*London.* The Mirror of Parliament . . . for the session commencing 29th January 1828 [*etc.*]. Edited by J. H. Barrow, *etc.* 1828, *etc.* fol. **8137.b.1.**

—— Characteristic Sketches of Animals, principally in the Zoological Gardens, Regent's Park, drawn from the life and engraved by Thomas Landseer: with descriptive . . . notices by J. H. Barrow. *Moon & Co.: London,* 1832. fol. **445.** g. **11.**

—— Emir Malek, Prince of the Assassins. An historical novel of the thirteenth century. [The advertisement signed: J. B., i.e. J. H. Barrow.] 3 vol. 1827. 12°. *See* B., J. N. **467.**

—— [For " The Exquisites: a farce," attributed to J. H. Barrow:] *See* EXQUISITES.

—— [For " King Glumpus: an interlude," attributed to J. H. Barrow:] *See* GLUMPUS, *King.*

BARROW (JOHN HENRY) *Independent Minister.* Apostolic Succession considered and rejected. A letter to the Rev. A. J. Pigott, *etc.* pp. 4. *J. Dinnis: [London,* 1843.] 8°. **908.** d. 2. (9.)

—— Report of the public discussion, held . . . between Mr. J. H. Barrow . . . and Dr. F. R. Lees . . . on the question " is teetotalism in harmony with the divine word ? " Published from the short-hand notes of Mr. J. B. Hewitt, *etc.* pp. 40. *F. R. Lees: Leeds,* 1845. 8°. **8435.** aa. **85.** (1.)

—— Temperance and Tee-Totalism. Being a candid enquiry into the lawfulness or unlawfulness of using distilled and fermented liquors, *etc.* pp. 40. *John Snow: London,* 1845. 12°. **1388.** c. **14.**

BARROW (JOSEPH CHARLES) [Sixteen plates from drawings by J. C. Barrow, engraved by G. J. Parkins, of views of churches and other buildings, with descriptive letter-press.] *J. C. Barrow: London,* 1790–93. fol. **199.** i. **3.**

—— [Another copy.] **558*.** g. **14.** (**1.**)
Twelve plates only.

BARROW (KATHERINE MARY) Three Years in Tristan da Cunha . . . With thirty-seven original illustrations from photographs, and a map. pp. xii. 280. *Skeffington & Son: London,* 1910. 8°. **010095.** f. **43.**

BARROW (KATHLEEN MARION) Brushwood. A novel. pp. 319. *William Heinemann: London,* 1922. 8°. NN. **7880.**

—— Rosewood and Mahogany. pp. 288. *Stanley Paul & Co.: London,* [1929.] 8°. NN. **15475.**

—— Sarah Herring. pp. 283. *A. M. Philpot: London,* [1924.] 8°. NN. **10143.**

—— The Singing Heart. pp. 284. *A. M. Philpot: London,* [1923.] 8°. NN. **9252.**

BARROW (KATHLEEN MARION) and **CUNYNGHAME** (ANNA B. DE M.)

—— How Women can help the Wounded, *etc.* pp. 96. *Hodder & Stoughton: London,* 1914. 8°. [" *The Standard* " *How to Help Series.*] **08027.** de. **40/3.**

BARROW (KNAPP) Mid-Channel Telegraphs. pp. 11. [1869.] fol. **8757.** m. **3.**

BARROW (LOUIS)

—— *See* BRIDGES (Shirley) Fladbury and its Mills and the Lower Avon Navigation. [Based on the notes of L. Barrow.] 1949. 8°. **010360.** p. **33.**

BARROW (M. E.) A Menology, or Record of departed friends. pp. viii. 296. *Parker & Co.: London,* 1888. 16°. **3129.** df. **53.**

BARROW (NORMAN)

—— The High Priest. [A novel.] pp. 320. *Faber & Faber: London,* 1947. 8°. NN. **36980.**

BARROW (PERCY JAMES) The Battle of Cressy. pp. 20. *London, New York,* [1927.] 8°. [*French's Plays for Schoolgirls.* no. 12.] W.P. **7004/12.**

—— Cornered. [A novel] . . . Illustrated by A. Talbot Smith. pp. vii. 221. *Wells Gardner & Co.: London,* 1910. 8°. **012808.** aaa. **4.**

—— The Man who Went Back. pp. 288. *T. Fisher Unwin: London,* 1925. 8°. NN. **10430.**

BARROW (R.) *M.A., LL.D.,* and **DAWSON** (JOHN HERBERT) Honourable Service: a vade mecum prècis [*sic*] of citizenship. pp. 44. *Dawson & Watson: Manchester,* [1907.] 8°. [" *Register* " *Technical Handbooks.* no. 1.] **012202.** e. **12.**

BARROW (REGINALD HAYNES)

—— *See* AUGUSTINE, *Saint, Bishop of Hippo.* [*Single Works.—De Civitate Dei.—Selections and Extracts.*] Introduction to St. Augustine, the City of God . . . Translation and running commentary by R. H. Barrow. 1950. 8°. **3670.** bb. **36.**

—— *See* WELLS (Joseph) *Warden of Wadham College, Oxford,* and BARROW (R. H.) A Short History of the Roman Empire to the Death of Marcus Aurelius, *etc.* 1931. 8°. **9042.** a. **19.**

—— The Romans. pp. 224. *Penguin Books: Harmondsworth,* 1949. 8°. [*Pelican Books.* A. 196.] **012209.** d. **4/196.**

—— A Selection of Latin Inscriptions. pp. vi. 91. *Clarendon Press: Oxford,* 1934. 8°. **07704.** de. 55.

—— Slavery in the Roman Empire . . . With twelve illustrations. pp. xvi. 259. *Methuen & Co.: London,* 1928. 8°. **08157.** f. **42.**

BARROW (RICHARD BRIDGMAN) *See* THOM (Adam) Barrow in Furnace, *etc.* [An attack on R. B. Barrow, with reference to the affairs of Overend, Gurney & Co.] 1869. 8°. **1414.** h. **10.** (**7.**)

BARROW (ROBERT) [For editions and translations of Jonathan Dickenson's "God's Protecting Providence, Man's Surest Help and Defence, in times of the greatest difficulty, and most eminent danger. Evidenced in the remarkable deliverance of Robert Barrow, with divers other persons, from the devouring waves of the sea, *etc.*":] *See* DICKINSON (Jonathan) of Jamaica.

—— *See* PEARSON (John) *Member of the Society of Friends.* Antichristian Treachery Discovered, *etc.* [By J. Pearson, R. Barrow, and others.] [1686?] fol. **4151**. h. **2**.

BARROW (S.) *pseud.* [i.e. *Sir* RICHARD PHILLIPS.] Five Hundred Questions on the New Testament . . . Eighty-eighth edition. Revised and improved. pp. 72. *Whittaker & Co.: London,* [1840?] 12°. **4372**. aa. **6**. **(3.)**

—— The Tutor's Key to Barrow's 500 Questions on the New Testament. *Whittaker & Co.: London,* [1840?] 12°. **3129**. df. **58**. **(1.)**

—— Five Hundred Questions on the Old Testament . . . Second edition. pp. 69. *Richard Phillips: London,* 1819. 12°. **3149**. a. **13**.

—— Tenth edition. pp. 69. *Sir R. Phillips & Co.: London,* 1823. 12°. **3129**. a. **14**.

—— Sixtieth edition. Revised and improved. pp. 72. *Whittaker & Co.: London,* [1833.] 12°. **3149**. a. **14**.

—— A Popular Dictionary of Facts and Knowledge, for the use of schools and students, with several hundred engravings in wood. pp. iv. 232. *Poole & Edwards: London,* 1827. 12°. **1136**. f. **16**.

—— The Schoolmaster's Register. Applicable to the studies and pursuits of boys' schools. *W. Edwards: London,* [1840?] 8°. **712**. f. **13**.

—— Sermons, adapted to the use of schools . . . selected from the works of celebrated preachers. By the Rev. S. Barrow . . . Second edition. pp. vi. 496. *Longman & Co.: London,* 1814. 12°. **4452**. aaa. **3**.

—— Fourth edition. pp. vi. 496. *Longman & Co.: London,* 1817. 12°. **1021**. a. **10**.

—— The Young Britons' Catechism of their Social Rights and Duties, *etc.* [With "Sir Richard Phillip's Golden Rules for Jurymen."] pp. 32. *J. Souter: London,* 1816. 12°. **692**. a. **30**.

BARROW (SARAH FIELD) *See* ANTICHRIST. [Ludus de Antichristo.] Antichrist and Adam . . . Translated . . by S. F. Barrow . . . and W. H. Hulme, *etc.* 1925. 8°. **11707**. d. **40**.

—— The Medieval Society Romances. pp. 141. *New York,* 1924. 8°. [*Columbia University Studies in English and Comparative Literature.*] Ac. **2688/16**. **(38.)**

BARROW (THOMAS) *Esq.* The Case of Thomas Barrow, Esq; Susannah his Wife, and Alice Hare her Sister. [Against a bill promoted by Lady Hare for settling the estate of Sir Ralph Hare.] [*London,* 1697?] *s. sh.* fol. **816**. m. **5**. **(12.)**

BARROW (THOMAS) *Father of Isaac Barrow.* *See* BARROW (Isaac) *D.D.* Of Contentment, Patience and Resignation to the Will of God, *etc.* [Edited by T. Barrow.] 1685. 8°. **1021**. a. **8**.

—— —— 1714. 12°. **4452**. aaa. **8**.

BARROW (THOMAS HENRY) The Horse and Stable Companion . . . Edited by . . . W. Johnston. pp. 159. *T. A. J. Waddington: York,* [1905.] 16°. **7294**. a. **14**.

—— 8th edition. pp. 167. *T. A. J. Waddington: York,* [1919.] 16°. **07293**. e. **9**.

BARROW (THOMAS PATEMAN) Bradlaugh's Bunkum, a new and popular comic song, *etc.* [1884.] *s. sh.* 8°. **1871**. e. **1**. **(124*.)**

—— A Month in Her Majesty's Prison, Leicester, and how I got it . . . Sixth thousand. pp. 16. [*Leicester,* 1882.] 8°. **6146**. f. **1**. **(5.)**

—— Queen Victoria's Jubilee. National hymn. [*Leicester,*] 1886. *s. sh.* fol. **1871**. e. **1**. **(139.)**

BARROW (WALTER) *See* MUIRHEAD (John H.) Birmingham Institutions, *etc.* (The Town and its Industries. By W. Barrow.) 1911. 8°. **010352**. f. **15**.

BARROW (WILL)

—— Rhymes of a Countryman. pp. 105. *Chaterson: London,* 1953. 8°. **11659**. b. **42**.

BARROW (WILLIAM) *A.M.* *See* DUMAS (Alexandre) *the Elder.* [*Isabel de Bavière.*] Isabel of Bavaria . . . Translated . . . by W. Barrow. 1846. 8°. **12410**. e. **35**.

—— *See* DUMAS (Alexandre) *the Elder.* [*Les Trois Mousquetaires.*] The Three Musketeers . . . Translated . . . by W. Barrow. 1846. 8°. **12410**. e. **32**.

—— *See* DUMAS (Alexandre) *the Elder.* [*Les Trois Mousquetaires.*] The Three Musketeers, *etc.* (From the translation by W. Barrow.) 1952. 8°. **12519**. f. **6**.

—— *See* DUMAS (Alexandre) *the Elder.* [*Vingt ans après.*] Twenty Years After . . . Translated . . . by W. Barrow. 1846. 8°. **12410**. e. **33**.

BARROW (WILLIAM) *Commander, R.N.* *See* BARROW (John) *F.R.S.* A Private Memoir of the Life and Services of the late William Barrow . . . Commander, Royal Navy. 1850. 8°. **10817**. i. **24**.

BARROW (WILLIAM) *M.D.* *See* BAYLE (G. L.) Researches on Pulmonary Phthisis. From the French of G. L. Bayle. By W. Barrow. 1815. 8°. **1187**. f. **8**.

BARROW (WILLIAM) *Playwright.*

—— Four in Hand. A collection of one-act plays for young people. pp. 90. *Blackie & Son: London & Glasgow,* 1951. 8°. [*Troubadour Plays.*] W.P. **1969/28**.

BARROW (WILLIAM) *Rev., LL.D.* Consecration of Colours. A sermon, preached in the Collegiate Church of Southwell . . . before the Southwell Loyal Volunteers, *etc.* pp. 17. *S. & I. Ridge: Newark,* 1804. 4°. **4476**. i. **31**. **(4.)**

—— Eight Sermons preached before the University of Oxford, in the year 1799, at the Lecture founded by the Rev. John Bampton. pp. xvi. 412. *F. & C. Rivington: London,* 1799. 8°. **226**. d. **9**. **(2.)**

—— An Essay on Education; in which are particularly considered the merits and the defects of the discipline and instruction in our academies. 2 vol. *F. & C. Rivington: London,* 1802. 12°. **1030**. f. **14**.

—— The second edition, corrected and enlarged. 2 vol. *F. & C. Rivington: London,* 1804. 12°. **8309**. aaa. **36**.

—— The Expediency of Translating our Scriptures into several of the Oriental Languages, and the means of rendering those translations useful, in an attempt to convert the nations of India to the Christian faith. A sermon, *etc.* pp. 29. *University Press: Oxford,* 1808. 4°. **582**. h. **6**. **(7.)**

Printed for the author.

—— *See* BUCHANAN (Claudius) A Vindication of the Hindoos from the Aspersions of the Reverend Claudius Buchanan, *etc.* (pt. 2. In reply to the observations of The Christian Observer . . . With remarks on a sermon preached at Oxford, by the Rev. Dr. Barrow, On the expediency of introducing Christianity among the Natives of India.) 1808. 8°. T. **1152**. **(1, 8.)**

BARROW (William) *Rev., LL.D.*

—— Familiar Dissertations on Theological and Moral Subjects. pp. vi. 420. *F. C. & J. Rivington: London,* 1819. 8°. **1115. h. 11.**

—— Familiar Sermons, on several of the Doctrines and Duties of the Christian Religion. 3 vol. *F. C. & J. Rivington: London,* 1818, 21. 8°. **4453. e. 3.**

—— [Another copy of vol. 3.] **1021. c. 24.**

—— Pecuniary Contributions for the Diffusion of Religious Knowledge. A sermon, *etc. G. Stretton, etc.: Nottingham,* 1815. 4°. **T. 1984. (5.)**

—— The Right of Resisting Foreign Invasion. A sermon preached at the Collegiate Church of Southwell . . . before the Southwell Loyal Volunteers, *etc.* pp. 22. *S. & I. Ridge: Newark,* 1803. 4°. **4476. i. 31. (3.)**

BARROWBY (William) *See* also Pierce (Dod) *M.S., pseud.* [i.e. W. Barrowby, James Kilpatrick, afterwards Kirkpatrick, and Isaac Schomberg?]

—— *See* Astruc (J.) A Treatise of the Venereal Disease . . . Translated into English by W. Barrowby. 1737. 8°. **1174. g. 43.**

BARROW (William J.)

—— Black Writing Ink of the Colonial Period . . . Reprinted from The American Archivist, *etc.* [1948.] 8°. **7949. m. 4.**

BARROWCLIFF (Marmaduke) and **CARR** (Francis Howard) Organic Medicinal Chemicals, synthetic and natural. pp. xiii. 331. *Baillière & Co.: London,* 1921. 8°. [*Industrial Chemistry.*] **8711. bb. 1/10.**

BARROWCLIFFE (A. J.) *pseud.* [i.e. Albert Julius Mott.] Amberhill. [A novel.] 2 vol. *Smith, Elder & Co.: London,* 1856. 8°. **12630. c. 4.**

—— Amberhill: or, Guilty Peace. A new edition. pp. 290. *Smith, Elder & Co.: London,* 1862. 8°. **12602. b. 26.**

—— Normanton. pp. iv. 340. *Smith, Elder & Co.: London,* 1862. 8°. **12631. cc. 2.**

—— [Another edition.] pp. 263. *Smith, Elder & Co.: London,* 1865. 8°. **12602. b. 3.**

—— Trust for Trust. 3 vol. *Smith, Elder & Co.: London,* 1859. 8°. **12635. d. 2.**

BARROWE (Henry) *See* Barrow.

BARROWE (Humphrey) *See* Barrow.

BARROWFORD.

—— Barrowford Urban District, Lancashire. The official guide, [1953–.] 8°. *See* Pike (Leslie E.) **10353. g. 39.**

BARROWMAN (Jean Ethel)

—— Happy Release, and other stories. pp. 59. *Arthur H. Stockwell: Ilfracombe,* 1955. 8°. **NNN. 7406.**

BARROWS (Alice)

—— Assistance on School Plant Problems as a Function of State Departments of Education. (Studies of State Departments of Education. no. 4.) pp. vi. 92. *Washington,* 1941. 8°. [*U.S. Office of Education. Bulletin.* 1940. no. 6. pt. 4.] **A.S. 202.**

—— Functional Planning of Elementary School Buildings. pp. viii. 83. *Washington,* 1937. 4°. [*U.S. Office of Education.* Bulletin 1936. no. 19.] **A.S. 202.**

BARROWS (Alice)

—— The School Building Situation and Needs. pp. 62. *Washington,* 1938. 8°. [*U.S. Office of Education. Bulletin.* 1937. no. 35.] **A.S. 202.**

—— The School Plant: trends, present situation and needs. pp. iv. 47. *Washington,* 1945. 8°. [*Biennial Survey of Education in the United States.* 1938–40. vol. 1. chap. 9.] **A.S. 202/22.**

BARROWS (Alice) and **SIMONSON** (Lee)

—— The School Auditorium as a Theater. pp. v. 51. *Washington,* 1939. 8°. [*U.S. Department of the Interior. Office of Education. Bulletin.* 1939. no. 4.] **A.S. 202.**

BARROWS (Anna) Eggs. Facts and fancies about them. pp. 159. *D. Lothrop Co.: Boston,* [1890.] 8°. **7285. a. 46.**

—— Principles of Cookery. pp. iv. 200. *American School of Home Economics: Chicago,* 1907. 8°. [*Library of Home Economics.* vol. 5.] **7955. de. 14.**

BARROWS (Charles D.) The Expulsion of the Chinese. What is a reasonable policy for the times? A sermon, *etc.* pp. 19. *S. Carson & Co.: San Francisco,* 1886. 8°. **8177. df. 16. (5.)**

BARROWS (Charles Henry) Alsace-Lorraine; or, the Struggle of 2000 years as pointing to a new basis for peace among nations. pp. 34. *Printed for private circulation: Springfield, Mass.,* 1918. 8°. **8425. h. 55.**

—— An Historical Address delivered before the citizens of Springfield in Massachusetts at the public celebration, May 26, 1911, of the two hundred and seventy-fifth anniversary of the settlement, *etc.* pp. 100. 1916. 8°. *See* Springfield, *Mass.—Connecticut Valley Historical Society.* **10409. r. 10.**

—— The History of Springfield in Massachusetts for the Young. Being also in some part the history of other towns and cities in the County of Hampden. [With illustrations.] pp. 166. 1909. 8°. *See* Springfield, *Mass.—Connecticut Valley Historical Society.* **10410. pp. 10.**

—— The Personality of Jesus. pp. viii. 252. *J. Clarke & Co.: London; Cambridge, Mass.,* printed, 1906. 8°. **4227. i. 35.**

—— The Poets and Poetry of Springfield in Massachusetts, from early times to the end of the nineteenth century. [An anthology compiled by C. H. Barrows.] pp. 166. *Springfield,* 1907. 8°. [*Papers and Proceedings of the Connecticut Valley Historical Society.* vol. 3.] **Ac. 8401. t.**

BARROWS (Charles M.) Acts and Anecdotes of Authors, *etc.* pp. iv. 481. *New England Publishing Co.: Boston,* 1887. 8°. **011840. f. 8.**

BARROWS (Chester Leonard)

—— William M. Evarts, Lawyer, Diplomat, Statesman. [With a portrait.] pp. x. 587. *University of North Carolina Press: Chapel Hill,* [1941.] 8°. **10889. cc. 6.**

BARROWS (Comfort Edwin) *See* Comer (John) The Diary of John Comer. Edited with notes by C. E. Barrows, *etc.* 1893. 8°. [*Collections of the Rhode Island Historical Society.* vol. 8.] **Ac. 8490.**

—— The Development of Baptist Principles in Rhode Island. pp. 104. *American Baptist Publication Society: Philadelphia,* 1877. 12°. **4182. a. 5.**

BARROWS (David Prescott) *See* Berkeley, *California.* —*University of California.* University of California Publications: Bureau of International Relations. (University of California Publications in International Relations . . . Editors: D. P. Barrows [and others].) 1923, *etc.* 8°. Ac. **2689**. g/**35**.

—— *See* Sait (Edward M.) and Barrows (D. P.) British Politics in Transition. 1925. 8°. 8012.aaa.1/8.

—— Berbers and Blacks. Impressions of Morocco, Timbuktu, and the Western Sudan, *etc.* [With plates.] pp. xvi. 251. *Century Co.: New York & London,* [1927.] 8°. **10094**. c. **8**.

—— A Decade of American Government in the Philippines, 1903–1913. pp. 66. *World Book Co.: Yonkers-on-Hudson,* 1914. 8°. **09057**. aa. **32**.

—— The Ethno-Botany of the Coahuilla Indians of Southern California. A dissertation, *etc.* pp. 82. *University of Chicago Press: Chicago,* 1900. 8°. **010006**. h. **48**.

—— A History of the Philippines. pp. 332. *American Book Co.: New York,* [1905.] 8°. **09057**. aa. **12**.

—— Revised edition. pp. viii. 406. *World Book Co.: Yonkers-on-Hudson,* 1924. 8°. **9058**. a. **10**.

BARROWS (David Prescott) and **BARROWS** (Thomas N.)

—— Government in California. pp. vii. 61. *World Book Co.: Yonkers-on-Hudson,* 1925. 8°. **08175**. aaa. **30**.

BARROWS (David Prescott) and **REED** (Thomas Harrison)

—— Government Handbooks. (Edited by D. P. Barrows and T. H. Reed.) 9vol. *World Book Co.: Yonkers-on-Hudson; G. G. Harrap & Co.: London,* 1915–32. 8°. 8012. aaa. 1.

BARROWS (E. Fletcher)

—— Modification of the Dominance of Agouti to Non-Agouti in the Mouse . . . From "Journal of Genetics." *Cambridge,* [1934.] 8°. **7209**. c. **30**.

BARROWS (Edmund John)

—— Industrial High Voltage Distribution and Public Supply. pp. v. 126. *Sir Isaac Pitman & Sons: London,* 1946. 8°. **08756**. c. **70**.

BARROWS (Edward M.)

—— The Great Commodore. The exploits of Matthew Calbraith Perry . . . Illustrated. [With a portrait.] pp. 397. *Bobbs-Merrill Co.: Indianapolis, New York,* [1935.] 8°. **010886**. eee. **6**.

BARROWS (Elijah Porter) The Advancement of Biblical Knowledge . . . From the Biblical Repository. *See* Christian Ministry. Essays on the Christian Ministry, *etc.* [1841.] 8°. **1126**. k. **15**. (**2**.)

—— Biblical Geography and Antiquities . . . With numerous maps and plans, *etc.* (Reprinted, with revision and additional matter, from the original edition of the American Tract Society.) pp. x. 628. *R.T.S.: London,* [1872.] 8°. **10077**. d. **19**.

—— [Another copy.] **4430**. ee. **8**.

—— The Manners and Customs of the Jews . . . [Extracted from "Biblical Geography and Antiquities."] Carefully revised and with many illustrations. pp. xii. 176. *R.T.S.: London,* [1884.] 8°. **4033**. df. **39**.

BARROWS (Elijah Porter)

—— The Claims of Home Missions. A sermon preached before the Synod of the Western Reserve, *etc.* pp. 24. *Charles Aikin: Hudson,* 1843. 8°. **4486**. f. **3**. (**15**.)

—— Companion to the Bible. pp. 668. pl. v. *American Tract Society: New York,* [1867.] 8°. **3149**. ccc. **17**.

—— [Another edition.] A New Introduction to the Study of the Bible. pp. viii. 568. *R.T.S.: London,* [1869.] 8°. **04419**. i. **7**.

—— [Another copy.] **4430**. ee. **7**.

—— The Harmony of Creation: and the subordination of the physical part of it to the moral. An address delivered before the Trustees, Faculty, and Students of the Medical Department of the Western Reserve College, *etc.* pp. 22. *Observer Press: Hudson,* 1847. 8°. **7680**. aaa. **58**. (**5**.)

—— Memoir of Everton Judson. [With a portrait.] pp. 212. *Crocker & Brewster: Boston,* 1852. 8°. **4985**. c. **12**.

—— The Scriptural Method of Reform. A sermon. pp. 16. *Observer Press: Hudson,* 1847. 8°. **4486**. aaa. **92**. (**16**.)

BARROWS (Florence Louise)

—— Propagation of Lycopodium. I. Spores, cuttings, and bulbils. II. Endophytic fungus in gametophyte and sporophyte . . . Reprinted . . . from Contributions from Boyce Thompson Institute, *etc.* [A thesis.] *New York,* 1935. 8°. **07076**. dd. **42**.

BARROWS (Frank Wilson) Practical Pattern-Making . . . Fully illustrated, *etc.* pp. 326. *C. Lockwood & Son: London; N. W. Henley Publishing Co.: New York,* 1906. 8°. **07943**. m. **48**.

BARROWS (Harlan Harland) *See* Blackwelder (Eliot) and Barrows (H. H.) Elements of Geology. [1911.] 8°. **07107**. e. **29**.

—— *See* Salisbury (Rollin D.) and Barrows (H. H.) The Environment of Camp Grant. 1918. 8°. [*Illinois State Geological Survey. Bulletin.* no. 39.] A.S.I.26.

—— Geography of the Middle Illinois Valley. pp. xii. 128. pl. 16. *Urbana,* 1910. 8°. [*Illinois State Geological Survey. Bulletin.* no. 15.] A.S.I.26.

BARROWS (Harold Kilbreth)

—— Floods. Their hydrology and control. [With maps.] pp. vii. 132. *McGraw-Hill Book Co.: New York,* 1948. 8°. **08777**. b. **54**.

—— Water Power Engineering. pp. ix. 734. *McGraw-Hill Book Co.: New York,* 1927. 8°. **08776**. cc. **28**.

—— Water Power Engineering . . . Second edition. pp. ix. 762. *McGraw-Hill Book Co.: New York & London,* 1934. 8°. **2246**. f. **11**.

—— Water Power Engineering . . . Third edition. pp. ix. 791. *McGraw-Hill Book Co.: New York & London,* 1943. 8°. **08777**. c. **26**.

BARROWS (Harold Kilbreth) and **BABB** (Cyrus Cates)

—— Water Resources of the Penobscot River Basin, Maine, *etc.* [With maps.] pp. 285. *Washington,* 1912. 8°. [*U.S. Geological Survey. Water-Supply Paper.* no. 279.] A.S. **212**.

BARROWS (HAROLD KILBRETH) and **HORTON** (ROBERT ELMER)

—— Determination of Stream Flow during the Frozen Season. pp. 93. *Washington*, 1907. 8°. [*U.S.A. Geological Survey. Water-Supply and Irrigation Paper.* no. 187.] A.S. **212.**

BARROWS (HAROLD MURDOCK) *See* LEWIS (Gerald C.) and BARROWS (H. M.) The Prevention of Cruelty to Children Act, 1894, *etc.* 1894. 8°. **6485.** aa. **28.**

BARROWS (HARRY PERCY) Development of Agricultural Instruction in Secondary Schools. pp. 108. *Washington*, 1920. 8°. [*U.S. Bureau of Education. Bulletin.* 1919. no. 85.] A.S. **202.**

BARROWS (HENRY D.) International Bi-Metallism. An essay, *etc.* pp. 55. *Stoll & Thayer: Los Angeles*, 1891. 8°. **08227.** ee. **48.** (4.)

BARROWS (ISABEL CHAPIN) *See* LAKE MOHONK. First Mohonk Conference on the Negro Question . . . Reported and edited by I. C. Barrows. 1890. 8°. **8156.** e. **16.**

—— *See* LAKE MOHONK. Proceedings of the Eighth Annual Meeting of the Lake Mohonk Conference of Friends of the Indian, 1890. Edited by I. C. Barrows. 1890. 8°. **8156.** ee. **12.**

BARROWS (JACK)

—— Mating Call. [On marriage.] pp. 70. *Arthur H. Stockwell: Ilfracombe*, 1954. 8°. **8418.** b. **21.**

BARROWS (JOHN HENRY) Henry Ward Beecher, the Shakespeare of the pulpit. [With a portrait.] pp. xvi. 541. *Funk & Wagnalls Co.: New York*, 1893. 8°. [*American Reformers.*] **10883.** bbb. **10.**

—— Results of the Parliament of Religions. (Reprinted from "The Forum.") pp. 14. *New York*, 1894. 8°. **4183.** f. **29.** (3.)

—— Seven Lectures on the Credibility of the Gospel Histories, *etc.* pp. 146. *D. Lothrop Co.: Boston*, [1891.] 8°. **3226.** de. **19.**

The title on the cover and the running title is "The Gospels are True Histories."

—— The World's Parliament of Religions. An illustrated and popular story of the World's first Parliament of Religions, held in Chicago in connection with the Columbian Exposition of 1893. 2 vol. See CONGRESSES.—World's Parliament of Religions. 1893. 8°. **4182.** ff. **1.**

—— [Another copy, with a different titlepage.] "*Review* See CONGRESSES.—World's Parliament of Religions. 1893. 8°. **4182.** e. **31.**

—— Dr. J. H. Barrows on the Claims of Christianity: a criticism. Reprinted from "The Hindu." pp. ii. 52. *National Press: Madras*, 1897. 8°. **4371.** f. **17.** (3.)

BARROWS (JOHN OTIS) On Horseback in Cappadocia; or, a Missionary Tour, *etc.* pp. 333. *Congregational Sunday-School & Publishing Society: Boston*, [1884.] 8°. **4766.** bb. **36.**

BARROWS (L. D.) *See* HOLYOAKE (George J.) Rudiments of Public Speaking . . . Revised by L. D. Barrows. 1861. 8°. **11805.** cc. **25.**

—— Distinctive Feature of Methodism. pp. 44. *Nelson & Phillips: New York*, [1877.] 8°. **4182.** aa. **30.**

—— The Substance of an Anti-Slavery Address, delivered on the annual fast of 1844, before the congregation of the M. E. Church of Nashua and Nashville. pp. 16. *Murray & Kimball: Nashua*, 1844. 8°. **8156.** aaa. **82.** (6.)

BARROWS (MARJORIE) The Child Life Story Book. Compiled by M. Barrows. *Rand, MacNally & Co.: New York*, [1932.] 4°. **12807.** i. **81.**

—— Fraidy Cat, *etc.* *Rand McNally & Co.: Chicago*, [1942.] 4°. **012826.** ee. **20.**

—— The Picture Book of Poetry. Compiled by M. Barrows. *Rand, McNally & Co.: New York*, [1932.] 4°. **11602.** i. **30.**

—— The Pirate of Pooh and other plays for children. pp. 192. *Rand McNally & Co.: New York*, [1936.] 8°. **20029.** ee. **17.**

—— Snuggles. Photographs by Harry Whittier Frees. Story by M. Barrows. *Rand McNally & Co.: New York*, [1935.] 8°. **20054.** g. **36.**

—— Whiskers. Photographs by Harry Whittier Frees. Story by M. Barrows. *Rand McNally & Co.: Chicago*, [1937.] 4°. **20059.** d. **23.**

BARROWS (MARY MINERVA) The Value of Cheerfulness. [An anthology.] Edited by M. M. Barrows. pp. 84. *Siegle, Hill & Co.: London; printed in America*, [1912.] 8°. **8410.** ee. **43.**

—— The Value of Contentment. Edited by M. M. Barrows. pp. 84. *Siegle, Hill & Co.: London; Boston* printed. [1913.] 8°. **08408.** eee. **73.**

—— The Value of Happiness. Edited by M. M. Barrows. pp. 98. *Siegle, Hill & Co.: London; printed in America*, [1912.] 8°. **8411.** ee. **20.**

—— The Value of Sincerity and Character. Edited by M. M. Barrows. *Siegle, Hill & Co.: London; printed in America*, [1912.] 8°. **8410.** ee. **57.**

BARROWS (NATHANIEL A.)

—— Blow All Ballast! The story of the "Squalus." [With plates.] pp. 244. *G. G. Harrap & Co.: London*, 1940. 8°. **10497.** aa. **38.**

BARROWS (SAMUEL JUNE) *See* ABBOT (Ezra) *the Younger*. Ezra Abbot. [Biographical notices and addresses. With a preface by S. J. Barrows.] 1884. 8°. **4985.** df. **29.**

—— *See* LORD (Eliot) The Italian in America . . . By E. Lord . . . S. J. Barrows. 1905. 8°. **08275.** b. **17.**

—— *See* PARKER (Theodore) West Roxbury Sermons, *etc.* [With an introduction by S. J. Barrows.] 1892. 8°. **4487.** a. **42.**

—— *See* PRATĀPACHANDRA MAJUMDĀR. Heart-Beats . . . With a biographical sketch of the author by S. J. Barrows. 1894. 16°. **4371.** aaaa. **47.**

—— *See* PRATĀPACHANDRA MAJUMDĀR. Heart-beats . . . With a biographical sketch of the author by S. J. Barrows. 1935. 8°. **04374.** e. 5.

—— [For reports prepared for the International Prison Commission by S. J. Barrows:] *See* INTERNATIONAL PENAL AND PENITENTIARY COMMISSION.

—— A Baptist Meeting-House: the staircase to the old faith, the open door to the new. pp. 221. *American Unitarian Association: Boston*, 1885. 8°. **4417.** k. **1.**

—— The Church's Missions as affected by Race Problems in the United States. pp. 8. *Society for Promoting Christian Knowledge: London*, 1908. 8°. [*Pan-Anglican Papers.* S.E. 3c.] **4108.** cc. **35.**

BARROWS (SAMUEL JUNE)

—— The Criminal Insane in the United States and in foreign countries. Report. pp. 81. [*U.S. Senate Documents.* 55th Congress. 2nd Session. vol. 22. no. 273.] 1898. 8°. *See* UNITED STATES OF AMERICA.—*Department of State.* A.S. **10**/4.

—— The Doom of the Majority of Mankind. pp. vi. 154. *American Unitarian Association: Boston,* 1883. 8°. **4257**. k. **26**.

—— [Another copy.] **4257**. h. **31**.

—— The Evolution of the Afric-American. *D. Appleton & Co.: New York,* 1892. 8°. [*Evolution Series.* no. 28.] **7006**. bbb. **43**.

—— L'Influence des idées humanitaires sur les doctrines théologiques. (Extrait des actes du troisième Congrès International du Christianisme libéral et progressif.) *Genève,* 1905. 8°. **4378**. k. **5**. (**5**.)

—— The Isles and Shrines of Greece . . . Illustrated. pp. xii. 389. *Sampson Low & Co.: London; Cambridge, U.S.A.* printed, 1898. 8°. **10126**. eee. **2**.

—— Jesus as a Penologist, *etc.* pp. 12. *Industrial School Gem: Louisville, Ky.,* 1902. 8°. **4374**. m. **12**. (**2**.)

—— Mythical and Legendary Elements in the New Testament . . . Reprinted from "The New World," *etc.* pp. 28. [1899.] 8°. **03128**. i. **41**. (**4**.)

—— New Legislation concerning Crimes, Misdemeanors, and Penalties. Compiled from the laws of the fifty-fifth Congress and from the session laws of the states and territories for 1897 and 1898. By S. J. Barrows. pp. xxiv. 480. *Washington,* 1900. 8°. [*U.S. Senate Documents.* 56th Congress. 1st session. no. 283.] A.S. **10**/4.

—— The Sixth International Prison Congress held at Brussels, Belgium, August, 1900. Report of its proceedings and conclusions. pp. 90. 1903. 8°. [*U.S. House Documents.* 57th Congress. 2nd Session. no. 374.] *See* INTERNATIONAL PENAL AND PENITENTIARY CONGRESS. [Brussels, 1908.] A.S. **10**.

BARROWS (SARAH TRACY) *See* SPYRI (J.) Was der Grossmütter Lehre bewirkt . . . Edited with exercises, notes, and vocabulary by S. T. Barrows. [1911.] 8°. **12213**. a. **1**/**73**.

BARROWS (THOMAS) *See* NICHOLSON (Kenyon) and BARROWS (T.) Two Weeks Off, *etc.* [1927.] 8°. **011781**. g. **1**/**155**.

BARROWS (THOMAS N.) *See* BARROWS (David P.) and BARROWS (T. N.) Government in California. 1925. 8°. **08175**. aaa. **30**.

—— *See* CARMAN (Harry J.) Columbia Research Bureau American History Test. By H. J. Carman . . . T. N. Barrows, *etc.* [1926, *etc.*] 8°. 9617.ee.2.

—— *See* OTIS (Arthur S.) Otis Classification Tests. [By A. S. Otis, in collaboration with T. N. Barrows.] [1922, *etc.*] 4°. **8309**. h. **34**.

BARROWS (WALTER BRADFORD) The Common Crow of the United States. By W. B. Barrows and E. A. Schwarz, *etc.* pp. 98. *Washington,* 1895. 8°. [*U.S. Dept. of Agriculture. Division of Ornithology and Mammalogy. Bulletin.* no. 6.] A.S. **811**.

—— The English Sparrow—Passer domesticus—in North America, especially in its relations to agriculture. Prepared under the direction of Dr. C. Hart Merriam . . . by W. B. Barrows. [With a map.] pp. 405. *Washington,* 1889. 8°. [*U.S. Dept. of Agriculture. Division of Economic Ornithology and Mammalogy. Bulletin.* no. 1.] A.S. **811**.

BARROWS (WILLIAM) *See* PERIODICAL PUBLICATIONS.—*Boston, Mass.* The Boston Review (The Congregational Review), *etc.* [vol. 5–7. Edited by W. Barrows and others.] 1861, *etc.* 8°. P.P. **907**. d.

—— Future Punishment Constitutional. A sermon. pp. 23. *Chas. Hamilton: Worcester, Mass.,* 1852. 8°. **4486**. bb. **63**. (**4**.)

The imprint on the wrapper is: S. K. Whipple & Co.: Boston.

—— The Indian's Side of the Indian Question. pp. 206. *D. Lothrop Co.: Boston,* [1888.] 8°. **8175**. a. **2**.

—— Ministerial Freedom. A sermon delivered before the Orthodox Congregational Church and Society at Norton, Mass., *etc.* pp. 31. *G. C. Rand: Boston,* 1850. 8°. **4486**. bb. **63**. (**1**.)

—— Oregon. The struggle for possession. [With a map.] pp. viii. 363. *Houghton, Mifflin & Co.: Boston,* 1884. 8°. [*American Commonwealths.*] **9603**. aaa. **13**.

—— Purgatory; doctrinally, practically, and historically opened, *etc.* pp. ix. 228. *American Tract Society: New York,* 1882. 12°. **4257**. k. **21**.

—— Shall we Legislate? Alcohol and the commonwealth. The question argued. pp. 42. *Perkins & Whipple: Boston,* 1851. 8°. **8435**. cc. **10**.

—— The United States of Yesterday and of To-morrow. pp. 432. *Roberts Bros.: Boston,* 1888. 8°. **10409**. bb. **31**.

BARROWS (WILLIAM EDWARD) Light, Photometry and Illuminating Engineering. Embodying a . . . revision of "Light, Photometry and Illumination." pp. x. 412. *McGraw-Hill Book Co.: New York,* 1925. 8°. **8716**. h. **3**.

—— Light, Photometry and Illuminating Engineering . . . Second edition. pp. x. 445. *McGraw-Hill Book Co.: New York & London,* 1938. 8°. **08715**. dd. **22**.

—— Light, Photometry, and Illuminating Engineering . . . Third edition. pp. ix. 415. *McGraw-Hill Book Co.: New York,* 1951. 8°. **8717**. b. **13**.

BARROWS (WILLIAM MORTON) Laboratory Exercises in Zoölogy, *etc.* pp. vi. 103. *World Book Co.: Yonkers-on-Hudson,* 1930. 8°. [*New-World Science Series.*] **08710**. b. **1**/**22**.

—— Science of Animal Life. An introduction to zoölogy . . . Illustrated. pp. ix. 389. *World Book Co.: Yonkers-on-Hudson,* 1927. 8°. [*New-World Science Series.*] **08710**. b. **1**/**17**.

BARROWS (WINIFRED) The Flower Child of Ravenna, Isolde of Ireland, and Melisande: three mediæval romances. pp. 70. *Dryden Publishing Co.: London,* 1916. 8°. **12403**. de. **16**.

—— Golden Memories in the Land of the Saints. [Travel sketches of Italy. With plates.] pp. 45. *A. H. Stockwell: London,* [1929.] 8°. **010151**. df. **34**.

—— Meanderings of a Mole . . . [A tale.] With drawings in line by Joan McConnell. pp. 23. *Alexander Moring: London,* [1938.] 8°. **12820**. f. **5**.

—— St. George of Merrie England. A play. pp. 38. *Mitre Press: London,* [1929.] 8°. **011781**. de. **111**.

BARROZZIO DE VIGNOLE (JACQUES) *See* BAROZZI (Giacomo) called IL VIGNOLA.

BARRS (Burton)

—— East Florida in the American Revolution. [With portraits.] pp. 42. *Guild Press: Jacksonville*, 1932. 8°. **09555**. d. **24**.

BARRS (Charles Edward)

—— The Determination of Cadmium in Spelter and Zinc Ores. (Reprinted from the Journal of the Society of Chemical Industry.) pp. 4. *London*, 1924. 8°. **8900**. e. **18**.

—— The Influence of Impurities in Lead on its Behaviour when Heated with Concentrated Sulphuric Acid. (Reprinted from the Journal of the Society of Chemical Industry.) pp. 7. *London*, 1919. 8°. **8900**. e. **19**.

BARRS (Frederick William George) A Letter on the subject of the Proposal for transferring the assessing and collecting of the Assessed Taxes to the Excise, *etc.* pp. 16. *M. Billing, Son & Co.: Birmingham*, [1869.] 8°. **8227**. bbb. **11**.

BARRS (Henry Hollier Hood) Married Women and their Debts . . . Being reports of the hitherto unreported cases of . . . Cox v. Bennett . . . Hood Barrs v. Cathcart, *etc.* pp. iv. 35. *W. Clowes & Sons: London*, 1895. 8°. **6146**. k. **13**. (**5**.)

BARRUCAND (Victor) *See* Banville (T. de) Critiques. Choix et préface de V. Barrucand. 1917. 8°. **011853**. pp. **41**.

—— *See* Choudieu (P. R.) Mémoires et notes de Choudieu . . . Publiés . . . par V. Barrucand. 1897. 8°. **010663**. k. **28**.

—— *See* Circassian Woman, and Barrucand (V.) Adilé Sultane. Roman. 1911. 8°. **012548**. c. **13**.

—— *See* Eberhardt (I.W.M.) Notes de route. Maroc, Algérie, Tunisie. Publiées avec une préface par V. Barrucand, *etc.* 1908. 8°. **010097**. e. **69**.

—— *See* Eberhardt (I.W.M.) Pages d'Islam . . . Avec une préface et des notes par V. Barrucand. 1920. 8°. **010094**. e. **16**.

—— *See* Eberhardt (I.W.M.) Trimardeur . . . Terminé et publié . . . par V. Barrucand. 1922. 8°. **012547**. bb. **15**.

—— *See* Eberhardt (I.W.M.) and Barrucand (V.) Dans l'ombre chaude de l'Islam, *etc.* 1908. 8°. **010097**. k. **5**.

—— *See* Grabinski (G.) *Count.* La Vie véritable du citoyen Jean Rossignol . . . par V. Barrucand. [A review.] [1896.] 8°. **011852**. i. **17**. (**7**.)

—— *See* Rossignol (J. A.) La Vie véritable du citoyen Jean Rossignol . . . Publiée . . . par V. Barrucand. 1896. 18°. **010664**. ee. **3**.

—— *See* Rossignol (Jean Antoine) *General.* La Vie véritable du citoyen Jean Rossignol, *etc.* [Edited, with an introduction, by V. Barrucand.] [1933.] 8°. **10655**. pp. **22**.

—— Le Pain gratuit. Avec des articles de H. Rochefort, G. Clémenceau, *etc.* pp. 250. *Paris*, 1896. 12°. **8277**. aa. **24**.

—— Une Partie d'échecs. Poème scénique. pp. 44. *Paris*, 1889. 8°. **11740**. e. **27**. (**2**.)

—— Pour le roi. (Drame.) pp. 64. *Paris*, 1897. 8°. **11740**. ee. **12**.

BARRUCCABÀ. *See* Baruccabà.

BARRUÉ (Pierre) La Sténographie apprise sans professeur. Phonographie Isaac Pitman appropriée à la langue française . . . par P. Barrué. *Paris*, 1881. 8°. **12991**. c. **43**. (**1**.)

BARRUÉ (Prudent) Un Concordat. Solution catholique et libérale de la question romaine. pp. 32. *Paris*, 1861. 8°. **8033**. c. **36**. (**7**.)

—— Zéphyrin Bunon. Histoire d'un parvenu. pp. 384. *Paris*, 1867. 12°. **12516**. c. **1**.

BARRUÉ (Sylvestre Victor) Législation et dictionnaire des patentes, contenant un résumé complet des instructions, circulaires et décisions en vigueur, *etc.* 2 tom. *Aurillac*, 1863. 8°. **5425**. dd. **8**.

BARRUEL (Augustin) *See* Boscovich (R. G.) Les Eclipses ; poème . . . traduit en françois par M. l'abbé de Barruel. 1779. 4°. **640**. k. **11**.

—— *See* Chasteaugiron (J. M. de) Examen impartial et paisible des objections proposées à l'auteur des Éclaircissemens. (Correspondance avec l'Abbé Barruel.) 1802. 8°. **203**. a. **18**.

—— *See* Giraud-Soulavie (J. L.) Pièces relatives à l'Histoire naturelle de la France méridionale. Mémoire . . . contre Me Barruel . . . auteur du libelle intitulé : Genêse, selon M. Soulavie. [1784.] 8°. F.R. **451**. (**9**.)

—— *See* Giraud-Soulavie (J. L.) Suite des pièces relatives à l'histoire naturelle de la France méridionale . . . Consultation pour l'abbé Giraud-Soulavie . . . contre l'abbé Barruel . . . auteur . . . du libelle intitulé : Genèse, selon M. Soulavie. [1785 ?] 8°. F. **1024**. (**15**.)

—— *See* Payson (S.) Proofs of the Real Existence and Dangers of Illuminism. Containing an abstract of . . . what Dr. Robison and the Abbé Barruel have published on this subject, *etc.* 1802. 12°. **4183**. b. **7**.

—— A l'anonyme auteur [i.e. H. B. J. Bethisy] du soi-disant véritable état de la question de la promesse de fidélité, l'Abbé Barruel. pp. 9. *A. Dulau & Co.: Londres*, 1800. 12°. **3901**. aa. **6**.

—— Collection ecclésiastique, ou Recueil complet des ouvrages faits depuis l'ouverture des États-généraux, relativement au clergé, a sa constitution civile, décrétée par l'Assemblée Nationale, sanctionnée par le roi. Dirigée par M. l'abbé Barruel [and M. N. S. Guillon]. 14 vol. tom. 1—tom. 6. pt. 1. *Paris*, 1791–93. 8°. **935**. d. **1–14**.

—— Conduite du Pape [Pius vi.] dans les circonstances présentes. *See* Narbonne-Lara (F. de) successively *Bishop of Gap* and *of Évreux*. Lettre pastorale, *etc.* 1792. 8°. F. **164**. (**3**.)

—— De la conduite des curés dans les circonstances présentes, ou bien Lettre d'un curé de campagne à son confrère, député à l'assemblée nationale, sur la conduite à tenir par les pasteurs des âmes, dans les affaires du jour. [Signed: C . . . ., Curé de * * *, i.e. Augustin Barruel.] pp. 16. 1790. 8°. *See* C . . . ., *Curé de* * * *. F.R. **138**. (**1**.)

—— [Another copy.] F. **114**. (**10**.)

—— Détail des raisons péremptoires qui ont déterminé le clergé de Paris, et d'autres diocèses, à faire la déclaration de fidélité exigé par la République. (Extrait d'une lettre adressée à M. l'abbé Barruel.—Note de l'abbé Barruel en envoyant la lettre précédente.) pp. 23. *A. Dulau & Co.: Londres*, 1800. 12°. **3901**. aa. **7**.

—— *See* Lambert (Pierre T.) Lettre . . . à M. l'abbé Barruel [in answer to his " Détail des raisons," *etc.*]. 1800. 12°. **3901**. aa. **39**.

—— Réponse . . . à une lettre de M. l'abbé Lambert [entitled "Lettre . . . à M. l'abbé Barruel," in answer to his "Détail des raisons," *etc.*]. pp. 11. *A. Dulau & Co.: Londres*, 1800. 12°. **3901**. aa. **8**.

—— Développement du serment exigé des prêtres en fonction par l'Assemblée générale. Extrait du Journal Ecclésiastique, *etc.* pp. 16. [*Paris*, 1790?] 8°. F. **1057**. (**4**.)

—— Du Pape et de ses droits religieux à l'occasion du Concordat. 2 tom. *Paris*, 1803. 8°. **1123**. i. **5, 6**.
Imperfect; wanting pp. 81–96 *of tom.* 1.

—— Du principe et de l'obstination des Jacobins, en réponse au sénateur Grégoire [i.e. to his pamphlet: "De la constitution française de l'an 1814"]. pp. 16. MS. NOTE [in Russian]. [1814.] 8°. **8052**. k. **5**. (**5**.)

—— L'Évangile et le clergé françois sur la soumission des pasteurs dans les révolutions des empires. pp. 87. MS. NOTE. *A. Dulau & Co.: Londres*, 1800. 12°. **3901**. cc. **4**.
The MS. *note consists of* 66 *pages in reply to the above, entitled "De la soumission passive, ou Réponse à l'ouvrage qui a pour titre: L'Évangile et le clergé françois."*

—— Les Helviennes, ou Lettres provinciales philosophiques . . . Septième édition. 4 tom. *Paris*, 1830. 12°. **1133**. a. **2, 3**.

—— Histoire du clergé pendant la Révolution françoise, *etc.* pp. ix. 601. *J. P. Coghlan: Londres*, 1793. 8°. **4633**. i. **18**.

—— Histoire du clergé pendant la Révolution française . . . Édition augmentée. 2 tom. *Baylis: Londres*, 1801. 12°. **1126**. b. **7**.

—— The History of the Clergy during the French Revolution, *etc.* 3 pt. *J. P. Coghlan, etc.: London*, 1794. 8°. **4630**. aaa. **1**.

—— Geschichte der Klerisey in Frankreich während der Revolution . . . Aus dem Frantzösischen übersetzt und mit einem Anhange vermehret von Kanonikus Collinet. 3 Tl. *Frankfurt & Leipzig*, 1794. 8°. **4629**. aaa. **7**.

—— Lettres sur le divorce, à un député de l'Assemblée Nationale . . . Ou bien, Réfutation d'un ouvrage [by A. J. U. Hennet] ayant pour titre: Du divorce. 2 pt. *Paris*, 1789. 8°. F.R. **207**. (**1**.)

—— Mémoires pour servir à l'histoire du Jacobinisme. [With "Observations sur quelques articles du Monthly Review relatifs aux Mémoires."] 4 pt. *P. Le Boussonier & Co.: Londres*, 1797, 98. 8°. **671**. d. **14–17**.

—— [Another copy.] **285**. l. **18–21**.

—— [Another copy.] Mémoires pour servir à l'histoire du jacobinisme, *etc.* *Paris*, 1912. 8°. **4786**. df. **16**.

—— [Another edition.] 5 tom. *Hambourg*, 1798, 99. 8°. **9220**. c. **17**.

—— Abrégé des Mémoires pour servir à l'histoire du Jacobinisme . . . reduits en un volume par l'auteur. Nouvelle édition conforme à la copie imprimée à Londres. pp. viii. 315. *Luxembourg*, 1800. 8°. **671**. d. **18**.

—— Mémoires pour servir à l'histoire du Jacobinisme. Abrégé par E. Perrenet. pp. x. 408. *Paris*, 1911. 8°. **04785**. h. **42**.

—— Memoirs, illustrating the History of Jacobinism. A translation from the French [by the Hon. Robert Clifford]. 4 vol. *The Author: London*, 1797, 98. 8°. **8010**. bbb. **7**.

—— Second edition. 4 pt. *The Translator: London*, 1798. 8°. **1442**. i. **2, 3**.

—— A Segredo revelado, ou manifestaçaõ do systema dos Pedreiros-livres e Illuminados e sua influencia na fatal revolução Franceza, obra extrahida das memorias para a historia do Jacobinismo do Abbade Barruel, e publicada em Portuguez por J. A. de Macedo. Segunda edição. 6 pt. *Lisboa*, 1810–12. 8°. **1369**. b. **1**.

—— *See* CLOWES (John) Letters to a Member of Parliament on the character and writings of Baron Swedenborg, containing a . . . refutation of all the Abbé Barruel's calumnies [in his "Memoirs of Jacobinism"], *etc.* 1822. 8°. **3716**. d. **10**.

—— *See* FREEMASONS. [*Appendix.*] Free Masonry. Its pretensions exposed . . . its dangerous tendency exhibited in extracts from the Abbé Barruel [i.e. from the "Memoirs of Jacobinism"], *etc.* 1828. 8°. **1369**. i. **16**.

—— Application of Barruel's Memoirs of Jacobinism to the Secret Societies of Ireland and Great Britain. By the translator of that work [i.e. Hon. Robert Clifford]. pp. xxii. 50. *E. Booker: London*, 1798. 8°. E. **2175**. (**6**.)

—— [Another copy.] **4165**. b. **106**. (**4**.)

—— Remarks on the Assertions of the Author of the Memoirs of Jacobinism (the Abbé Barruel) respecting the Character of Emanuel Swedenborg and the tendency of his writings. (Chiefly extracted from . . . Letters to a Member of Parliament on the Character . . . of Baron Swedenborg [by John Clowes].) pt. 1. pp. 37. *John Ormrod: Philadelphia*, 1800. 8°. **4887**. aaa. **44**.

—— Ode sur le glorieux avénement de Louis Auguste au trône, présentée à la reine, *etc.* pp. 11. *Paris*, 1774. 8°. F. **883**. (**11**.)

—— Le Patriote véridique, ou Discours sur les vrais causes de la révolution actuelle. pp. 132. *Paris*, 1789. 12°. F.R. **134**. (**5**.)

—— Le Plagiat du comité—soi disant ecclésiastique—de l'Assemblée nationale, ou décret de Julien l'apostat, formant les bases de la constitution civile du clergé françois, *etc.* [A political satire by A. Barruel.] pp. 24. 1790. 8°. *See* FRANCE.—*Assemblée Nationale Constituante.*—[1789–1791.]—*Comité Ecclésiastique.* F. **466**. (**3**.)

—— Préjugés légitimes, sur la Constitution civile du clergé . . . Extrait du Journal Ecclésiast., *etc.* [By A. Barruel.] pp. 16. [1791.] 8°. *See* FRANCE.—*Constitutional Church.*—*Appendix.* F.R. **161**. (**24**.)

—— Prône d'un bon curé sur le serment civique, *etc.* [By A. Barruel.] pp. 15. 1791. 8°. *See* FRANCE.—*Constitutional Church.*—*Appendix.* F.R. **162**. (**8**.)

—— Question décisive sur les pouvoirs ou la jurisdiction des nouveaux pasteurs. [Reprinted from the "Journal Ecclésiastique."] *Paris*, 1791. 12°. F.R. **150**. (**20**.)

—— Réplique pacifique aux trois avocats de M. le sénateur Grégoire. [A reply to a pamphlet entitled: "Lettre amicale" on the question of a constitution for France in 1814.] pp. 22. *Paris*, 1814. 8°. **8052**. k. **6**. (**4**.)

—— Lettres d'un voyageur à l'abbé Barruel, ou nouveaux documens pour ses Mémoires, *etc.* pp. 191. [*London*,] 1800. 8°. **1201**. g. **31**.
Probably written by Barruel himself.

BARRUEL (Ernest) *See* Henry (Étienne O.) and Barruel (E.) Notice sur Chabetout et ses sources minérales, *etc.* 1858. 8°. **7470. e. 67. (9.)**

BARRUEL (Étienne)

—— Observations sur l'instruction publique, et particulièrement sur les écoles centrales. pp. 86. *Paris*, an 8 [1800]. 8°. F.R. **595. (2.)**

—— Plan d'instruction publique considérée sous le rapport des livres élémentaires . . . Seconde édition. [With a table.] pp. 315. *Paris*, 1791. 8°. **1126. c. 24. (1.)**

BARRUEL (Jean Pierre) Notice sur le fossile humain trouvé près Moret, département de Seine-et-Marne. pp. 8. *Paris*, 1824. 8°. **T. 2050. (4.)**

—— *See* Huot (J. J. N.) Notice géologique sur le prétendu fossile humain trouvé près de Moret. [In reply to J. P. Barruel.] 1824. 8°. **T. 2050. (5.)**

—— Réponse aux principaux écrits qui ont paru sur le fossile humain trouvé dans le mois de septembre 1823, au Long-Rocher de Montigny, près Moret, Département de Seine-et-Marne. pp. 40. *Paris*, 1824. 8°. **T. 2050. (3.)**

—— *See* Payen (Anselme) Encore un mot sur le fossile, ou examen de la réponse de M. Barruel, *etc.* 1824. 8°. **T. 2050. (6.)**

BARRUEL (M. G.) Traité de chimie technique appliquée aux arts et à l'industrie, *etc.* 7 tom. *Paris*, 1856–63. 8°. **8906. b. 1.**

—— [Another copy of tom. 1–5.] **8906. b. 2.**

—— Traité élémentaire de géologie, minéralogie et géognosie. *See* Gasc (J. P.) Cours d'études rationnelles, *etc.* 1839. 8°. **1135. k. 19.**

BARRUEL (Paul)

—— [Vie et mœurs des oiseaux.] Birds of the World: their life and habits. Translated by Phyllis Barclay-Smith. [With illustrations.] pp. 204. *George G. Harrap & Co.: London; Paris* printed, 1954. 4°. **7288. dd. 11.**

BARRUEL-BEAUVERT (Antoine Joseph de) *Count.* Actes des apôtres. (Actes des apôtres et des martyrs.) [By A. J. de Barruel-Beauvert.] 4 tom. 1796, 97. *See* Periodical Publications.—*Paris.* [Lettre à un rentier.] **F. 1485, 86.**

—— Adresse d'un proscrit par la Convention, à l'Assemblée Législative. pp. 16. *Paris*, [1795.] 8°. **F. 1031. (11.)**

—— Au peuple françois. [Recommending moderation and unity of action in the States General.] pp. 14. *Paris*, 1789. 8°. **F.R. 14. (2.)**

—— La Fille naturelle, ou l'Abus de l'indépendance, drame historique en trois actes et en vers. Par M. de B. [i.e. A. J. de Barruel-Beauvert.] pp. 84. 1803. 8°. *See* B., M. de. **11738. aa. 21. (2.)**

—— La Lanterne magique républicaine. [By A. J. de Barruel-Beauvert.] pp. 106. 1799. 8°. *See* Lanterne. **F. 1484. (6.)**

—— Lettres sur quelques particularités secrètes de l'histoire, pendant l'interrègne des Bourbons, à M. le comte Armand de * * *, *etc.* 3 tom. *Paris*, 1815. 8°. **283. h. 28–30.**

—— Le Major du régiment de Forez, ou le Chevalier de Barruel-Beauvert. Drame historique en un acte, en prose. [By A. J. de Barruel-Beauvert.] pp. 46. *Genève*, 1804. 8°. **11738. aa. 21. (3.)**

—— Pensées et observations modestes de M. le Comte de B * * * [i.e. Count A. J. de Barruel-Beauvert.] pp. viii. 159. 1785. 8°. *See* B., *M. le Comte de.* **721. d. 35.**

BARRUEL-BEAUVERT (Antoine Joseph de) *Count.*

—— Premier cri contre Albion. pp. 14. *Paris*, 1803. 8°. **F. 557. (1.)**

—— Première (—cinquième) lettre à un rentier habitant une solitude au bord de la mer, *etc.* pp. 151. 1796. 8°. *See* Periodical Publications.—*Paris.* [Lettre à un rentier.] **F. 1484. (1.)**

—— Reflexions sur quelques ouvrages modernes, et particulièrement sur la Religion considérée comme l'unqiue base du bonheur & de la vraie philosophie, par Mme. la Marquise de Sillery . . . Par M. le comte de B * * * [i.e. Count A. J. de Barruel-Beauvert.] pp. vi. 102. 1788. 8°. *See* B * * *, *M. le Comte de.* **4375. aaa. 1.**

—— Vie de J. J. Rousseau; précédée de quelques lettres relatives au même sujet. pp. 431. *Londres* [*Paris ?*], 1789. 8°. **275. g. 2.**

BARRUEL-BEAUVERT (Joseph de) *Count.* *See* Barruel-Beauvert (A. J. de)

BARRUEL-BEAUVERT (Philippe Auguste de) Lettre du délégué de la population française de Grey-Town, Amérique centrale, *etc.* (Bombardement et entière destruction de Grey-Town. 2me lettre du délégué, *etc.*) 2 pt. *Paris*, 1856. 8°. **8180. g. 51. (6.)**

BARRUFALDI (Girolamo) *See* Baruffaldi.

BARRUNDIA (José Francisco) *See* America, *South.* Sobre las Turbaciones de Sur-América. Publicado en Londres en 1830. y traducido por J. Barrundia. 1831. 4°. **8180. cc. 2. (8.)**

—— *See* Filisola (V.) El Ciudadano General de Brigada Vicente Filisola à J. F. Barrundia . . . en contestacion à su libelo, *etc.* 1824. 16°. **8179. a. 21.**

—— *See* Filisola (V.) Notas que . . . dió á luz . . . V. Filisola, en contestacion al libelo que contra él publicó . . . J. F. Barrundia, *etc.* 1824. 8°. **9770. a. 1.**

—— *See* Filisola (V.) La Cooperación de México en la independencia de Centro América. [A reprint of "El Ciudadano General de Brigada Vicente Filisola á José Francisco Barrundia," and "Notas que se citan en el cuaderno que dió á luz . . . V. Filisola, en contestación al libelo que contra él publicó . . . J. F. Barrundia."] 1911. 8°. [*Documentos inéditos ó muy raros para la historia de México.* tom. 35.] **9772.cc.13.**

—— *See* Guatemalan. Observaciones críticas con motivo de la impresion de una correspondencia entre el Jefe del Estado y el Señor J. Barrundia. Por un Guatemalteco. [1837.] 4°. **8180. cc. 2. (12.)**

BARRUNDIA (José Martín) *See* C., A. B. Contestacion á "El Universal" de Méjico [in its comments on a pamphlet by J. M. Barrundia.] 1890. 8°. **8180. e. 20. (4.)**

—— Mensaje presentado al Congreso Federal, *etc.* [1830.] fol. pp. 18. *See* America, *Central.* [*Republic of Central America.*] **8180. i. 29. (7.)**

BARRUOL (Jean)

—— *See* Brunon (J.) and Barruol (J.) Les Français en Italie sous Henri II, *etc.* [1952.] fol. L.R. **301. i. 8.**

—— La Contre-Révolution en Provence et dans le Comtat, d'après des documents inédits. pp. 320. *Cavaillon*, 1928. 8°. **10167. d. 25.**

BARRUS, *Saint, Bishop of Cork.* *See* Barr.

BARRUS (CLARA) John Burroughs, boy and man, *etc.* [With portraits.] pp. ix. 385. *Doubleday, Page & Co.: Garden City, N.Y., & Toronto,* 1921. 8°. **10884.** bb. **12.**

—— The Life and Letters of John Burroughs . . . With illustrations. 2 vol. *Houghton Mifflin Co.: Boston & New York,* 1925. 8°. **010883.** h. **45.**

—— Nursing the Insane. pp. x. 409. *Macmillan Co.: New York,* 1908. 8°. **07660.** h. **31.**

—— Our Friend John Burroughs . . . Including autobiographical sketches by Mr. Burroughs, *etc.* [With plates, including portraits.] pp. vii. 286. *Houghton Mifflin Co.: Boston & New York,* 1914. 8°. **10889.** e. **38.**

—— Whitman and Burroughs, Comrades . . . With illustrations [including portraits]. pp. xxx. 392. *Houghton Mifflin Co.: Boston & New York,* 1931. 8°. **10881.** v. **2.**

BARRUS (MORTIER FRANKLIN)

—— *See* GILBERT (Arthur W.) The Potato. By A. W. Gilbert . . . assisted by M. F. Barrus, *etc.* 1917. 8°. **07073.** i. **1/39.**

—— Bean Anthracnose. *Ithaca, N.Y.,* 1921. 8°. [*Cornell University Agricultural Experiment Station.* Memoir 42.] Ac. **2692.** h/2.

BARRUS (MORTIER FRANKLIN) and **CHUPP** (CHARLES)

—— Potato Diseases and their Control. pp. 123. *Ithaca,* 1926. 8°. [*Cornell Extension Bulletin.* no. 135.] Ac. **2692.** ha/2.

BARRUS (MORTIER FRANKLIN) and **CROSBY** (CYRUS RICHARD)

—— Control of Diseases and Insect Pests of Potatoes in Up-State New York. pp. 29. *Ithaca,* 1932. 8°. [*Cornell Extension Bulletin.* no. 238.] Ac. **2692.** ha/2.

—— Control of Diseases and Insect Pests of Potatoes on Long Island. pp. 26. *Ithaca,* 1934. 8°. [*Cornell Extension Bulletin.* no. 288.] Ac. **2692.** ha/2.

BARRY. Illustrated Guide to Barry, South Wales. pp. 72. [*Barry,* 1897.] 8°. **010347.** g. **1.** (**9.**)

—— The Official Guide to Barry, Glamorgan, *etc.* [With a map.] pp. 78. *E. J. Burrow & Co.: Cheltenham,* [1923.] 8°. **10354.** a. **74.**

Barry Camera Club.

—— Invitation Coronation and Centenary Exhibition of Pictorial Photography. Memorial Hall, Barry, 11th–18th July, 1953, *etc.* [A catalogue.] *Barry,* [1953.] 8°. **7960.** df. **61.**

Corporation.

—— The Municipal Tenants' Handbook; issued by the Mayor and Corporation for the guidance and information of all tenants of the Corporation estates of the Borough of Barry. *British Publishing Co.: Gloucester,* [1951–] 8°. *Various editions.* **8289.** ee. **66.**

—— *Cymdeithas Cymrodorion y Barri.* Adroddiad y Pwyllgor, am 1911–1912 (1912–1913). 2 pt. [*Barry,* 1912, 13.] 8°. **872.** d. **63.**

—— Cân Filwriaethus y Gymdeithas gan Garn [i.e. R. Garn Adams?]. Canwyd hi am y waith gyntaf hos Fercher. Hyd. 8fed. 1913. Alaw: " Rhyfelgyrch Capten Morgan." [*Barry,* 1913.] *s. sh.* 8°. **1875.** d. (**126.**)

—— Syllabus of Instruction in Welsh. Chiefly for Elementary Schools where English is the predominant language. pp. 16. *Barry,* 1912. 8°. **12978.** d. **16.**

BARRY.—*Public Libraries.*

—— Barry. Free Libraries. Annual Report. 1902-1903 (—1916-1917). 15 pt. *Barry Docks,* 1903–17. 8°. A.R. **981.**

—— Report on a Visit of Inspection to the Free Public Libraries of Birmingham, Bristol, Kingston-on-Thames, Leeds, Liverpool, London & Manchester. By John Roch, Librarian. pp. 11. [*Barry,* 1911?] 8°. **11900.bb.75.**

BARRY, *the Soldier.* Barry, the Soldier; or, " Try Christ." pp. 8. *R.T.S.:* [*London,* 1867.] 32°. **4411.** a. **50.** (**2.**)

BARRY CAMERA CLUB. *See* BARRY.

BARRY DOCK TIDE TABLE AND YEAR BOOK. *See* PERIODICAL PUBLICATIONS.—*Barry Dock Town.*

BARRY, DU BARRY & CO.

—— The Curability of Stomach, Pulmonary, Nervous, Bilious and Liver Complaints, demonstrated by numerous authenticated cases . . . By a remedy which saves fifty times its cost in other means of cure! (Hundred-and-second edition.) [A pamphlet advertising Du Barry's Revalenta Arabica.] pp. 31. *Barry, Du Barry & Co.: London,* 1855. 8°. **1190.** i. **43.**

BARRY, *Family of, of County Cork.*

—— *See* BARRY (Edmond) Barrymore. Records of the Barrys of County Cork, *etc.* 1902. 8°. **9906.** pp. **23.**

BARRY, *Family of, of Eynsham. See* BARRY (Stanley L.) The Pedigree of the Barrys of Eynsham, Oxon. 1928. 4°. **09915.** g. **9.**

BARRY, *Family of, of Manorbeer.*

—— *See* BARRY (*Sir* John W.) *K.C.B.* Notes on Barry Genealogy in England and Wales . . . With . . . genealogical tree. 1906. fol. **9918.** k. **2.**

—— *See* DUCKETT (*Sir* George F.) *Bart.* Evidences of the Barri Family of Manorbeer, *etc.* [1891.] 8°. **9904.** cc. **49.** (**6.**)

BARRY ( ) *Citoyen,* and **CORNISSET** ( ) Mémoire pour les Cns Barry et Cornisset frères, marchands de bois pour l'approvisionnement de Paris. pp. 22. *Paris,* [1799?] 8°. **F. 1021.** (**8.**)

BARRY ( ) *Mrs.* The Family Doctor, or, Mrs. Barry and her Bourbon. [A tale.] pp. 384. *Henry Hoyt: Boston.* [1870.] 16°. **11622.** g. **15.**

BARRY ( ) *Mrs., Author of " The Amorous Merchant." See* GRAHAM, afterwards BARRY ( )

BARRY ( ) *Volontaire du Bataillon de Nôtre Dame.* Réclamation de trois citoyens, volontaires du bataillon de Nôtre Dame. [Signed by Barry, Bertrand and Maillard. Against a resolution to dismiss them from the battalion.] pp. 4. [*Paris,* 1790?] 4°. **F. 12*.** (**40.**)

BARRY ( ) *Writer of Verse.* The City of the West; a fragment. [In verse. Signed: B——, i.e. —— Barry.] pp. 161. 1834. 8°. *See* B——. **11644.** ccc. **34.**

BARRY (DE) *See* LE BRETON (F.) *Agricultural Writer.* Traité sur les propriétés . . . du sucre. Suivi de l'extrait d'un mémoire de M. de Barry, sur les fourmis des cannes à sucre. 1789. 12°. **450.** d. **28.**

BARRY (ADA LOOMIS) Yunini's Story of the Tail of Tears. A . . . general accounting of the history of the American Indian since the coming of De Sota, and the specific history of the tribe of Cherokees. . . Embellished with original illustrations by Howard Harmon Arens. [With plates.] pp. 230. *Fudge & Co.: London,* [1932.] 4°. **010007.** k. **48.**

BARRY (ALBERT) *See* MUIRCHU, *Maccu Mactheni.* Life of Saint Patrick . . . Translated and edited by Rev. A. Barry. 1895. 8°. **4829.** ccc. **7.**

—— *See* SARNELLI (G. M.) The Holy Rosary . . . Translated by Rev. A. Barry. 1890. 8°. **4372.** f. **41.** **(9.)**

—— Life of Blessed Margaret Mary Alacoque, *etc.* pp. 192. *Burns & Oates: London,* [1889.] 8°. **4829.** a. **49.**

—— The Life of Count Moore, compiled from materials supplied by his family. pp. xiii. 301. *M. H. Gill & Son: Dublin,* 1905. 8°. **10854.** dd. **4.**

—— Lives of Irish Saints . . . Third edition. pp. 91. *M. H. Gill & Son: Dublin,* 1908. 32°. **4824.** a. **48.**

BARRY (ALDA M. MILNER)

—— Lessons on the Apostles' Creed and the Lord's Prayer. Junior classes. Prepared for use in South Africa. Edited [or rather, written] by A. M. Milner-Barry. pp. xiv. 245. *S.P.C.K.: London,* 1939. 8°. **03504.** ff. **91.**

BARRY (ALDA M. MILNER) and **ALLSUP** (DOROTHY)

—— Forms of Prayer and Praise for use in Sunday School . . . Compiled by Alda Milner-Barry . . . and Dorothy Allsup . . . New edition with alterations and additions. pp. 64. *National Society; S.P.C.K.:* [*London,* 1946.] 8°. **3458.** aaa. **60.**

BARRY (ALEXANDER) *See* BOSTOCK (John) *M.D.* Syllabus of a Course of Chemical Lectures delivered . . . by J. Bostock . . . A. Aikin . . . A. Barry. 1827. 8°. **1035.** l. **35.**

BARRY (ALEXANDRE) *See* BARRY (Marie A.)

BARRY (ALFRED) *Bishop of Sydney. See* BAINES (Edward) *Vicar of Yalding.* Sermons . . . Edited, with . . . memoir, by A. Barry. 1883. 8°. **4466.** f. **24.**

—— *See* BARRY (Edward M.) Lectures on Architecture . . . Edited . . . by A. Barry, *etc.* 1881. 8°. **2261.** e. **8.**

—— *See* BIBLE.—*Old Testament.* [*English.*] An Old Testament Commentary, *etc.* (vol. 3. I. Kings. By the Rev. A. Barry.) 1882, *etc.* 8°. **3054.c.2.**

—— *See* BIBLE.—*New Testament.* [*English.*] The New Testament Commentary for Schools. Edited by C. J. Ellicott, *etc.* (Ephesians and Philippians.—Colossians.—Philemon. With commentary by the Rev. A. Barry.) [1879, *etc.*] 8°. **3103.** b. **11.**

—— *See* HYMNALS. [*English.*] Hymns for the Use of Cheltenham College. [The preface signed: A. B., i.e. A. Barry.] [1865?] 32°. **3433.** de. **48.**

—— *See* LITURGIES.—*Church of England.—Common Prayer.* The Teacher's Prayer-Book; being the Book of Common Prayer, with introductions . . . and notes, by A. Barry. [1882.] 8°. **3408.** aaaa. **23.**

—— —— [1884.] 16°. **3408.** aaa. **27.**

—— —— [1900.] 16°. **3405.** aaaa. **29.**

—— *See* LITURGIES.—*Church of England.—Common Prayer.—Catechism.* [*English.*] Notes on the Catechism . . . By . . . A. Barry. 1867. 16°. **3504.** b. **65.**

—— *See* PUGIN (Edward W.) Notes on the Reply of the Rev. A. Barry . . . to the "Infatuated Statements" made by E. W. Pugin, on the Houses of Parliament, *etc.* 1868. 8°. **07822.g.33.**

BARRY (ALFRED) *Bishop of Sydney.*

—— *See* WORDSWORTH (John) *Bishop of Salisbury.* A Representative Church Council. Speeches by J. Wordsworth . . . and A. Barry, *etc.* 1903. 8°. **04429.dd.17/75.**

—— The Adaptation of Christianity to the requirements of human society. *See* CHRISTIANITY. Credentials of Christianity. 1876. 8°. **04018.** g. **45/5.**

—— The Adaptation of Christianity to the Requirements of Human Society. *See* CHRISTIANITY. Credentials of Christianity, *etc.* 1880. 8°. **4017.** dg. **6/3.**

—— The Anglican Communion: its position and prospects. Sermons . . . by the Bishop of Kentucky [T. U. Dudley], the Archbishop of Rupert's Land [R. Machray], the Archbishop of Sydney [W. S. Smith], the Bishop of Calcutta [E. R. Johnson], the Archbishop of Capetown [W. W. Jones]. [Edited by Bishop Barry.] pp. 110. *S.P.C.K.: London,* 1897. 8°. **4430.** bbb. **15.**

—— The Architect of the new Palace at Westminster. A reply to a pamphlet by E. W. Pugin, Esq., entitled Who was the Art-Architect of the Houses of Parliament?" pp. iv. 120. *John Murray: London,* 1868. 8°. [A defence of the claims of Sir Charles Barry.] **7814.** c. **4.**

—— Second edition. pp. iv. 129. *John Murray: London,* 1868. 8°. **7814.** c. **5.**

—— The Atonement of Christ. Six lectures, *etc.* pp. xi. 111. *Macmillan & Co.: London & New York,* 1871. 8°. **4462.** aaa. **8.**

—— "Christ in the midst of us." A sermon, *etc.* pp. 16. *C. Kemplay: Leeds,* 1862. 8°. **10347.** f. **14.** **(22.)**

—— The Christian Sunday: its history, its sacredness and its blessing. Four lectures. pp. 125. *S.P.C.K.: London,* 1905. 8°. **04429.** ccc. **28.**

—— The "Christian Year" [of John Keble]. 1876. *See* KEMPE (John E.) The St. James's Lectures, *etc.* ser. 2. 1875, *etc.* 8°. **4464.** i. **1.**

—— [Another edition.] *See* KEMPE (John E.) Companions for the Devout Life, *etc.* 1877. 8°. **4466.** a. **12.**

—— The Church and Education. *See* WEIR (Archibald) and MACLAGAN (W. D.) The Church and the Age, *etc.* ser. 1. 1870, *etc.* 8°. **4108.** f. **10.**

—— Church and State. A paper read . . . at the Church Congress . . . 1890, *etc.* pp. 11. *Church Defence Institution: London,* 1891. 8°. [*Church Defence Handy Volume, etc.*] **4109.** c. **21.**

—— The Church Questions of the Day. An address delivered at the Annual Meeting of the Halifax Church Institute. pp. 28. *Longmans & Co.: London; Whitley & Booth: Halifax,* 1868. 8°. **4108.** b. **103.** **(6.)**

—— Church Unity and Lay Help. A sermon, *etc.* pp. 19. *R. Jackson: Leeds,* [1882.] 8°. **4473.** g. **13.** **(16.)**

—— Clergy and Laity in the Church. A sermon, *etc.* pp. 16. *G. Bell & Sons: London,* 1877. 8°. **4473.** b. **11.** **(18.)**

—— Discourse I . . . on the Christian Doctrine of Prayer. (Discourse II. Is Prayer needless?—Discourse III. Is Prayer useless?) 3 pt. *H. W. Stacey: Norwich,* [1876.] 12°. [*Norwich Cathedral Argumentative Discourses, etc.* ser. 8.] **4462.** a. **28.**

—— Do we Believe? The Law of Faith perfected in Christ. Four lectures delivered in St. George's, Windsor. pp. 141. *S.P.C.K.: London,* 1908. 8°. **04429.** a. **122.**

—— The Doctrine of the Cross. Six sermons, *etc.* pp. 96. *Dyson: Hereford; Simpkin, Marshall & Co.: London,* [1868.] 8°. **4464.** aaa. **4.**

BARRY (Alfred) *Bishop of Sydney.*

—— The Doctrine of the Spirit: three sermons, *etc.* pp. 96. *Deighton, Bell & Co.: Cambridge,* 1867. 12°. **4463. aa. 6.**

—— The Ecclesiastical Expansion of England in the growth of the Anglican Communion. The Hulsean Lectures for 1894–95. pp. xi. 387. *Macmillan & Co.: London,* 1895. 8°. **4460.** b. **1.**

—— England's Mission to India. Some impressions from a recent visit. pp. 214. *S.P.C.K.: London,* 1895. 8°. **4429.** a. **103.**

—— English Christianity Today. *See* Gwatkin (Henry M.) The Church past and present, *etc.* 1900. 8°. **4533.** eee. **6.**

—— First Words in Australia. Sermons, *etc.* pp. 207. *Macmillan & Co.: London; Melbourne* [printed], 1884. 8°. **4466.** c. **18.**

—— The Higher Education of Women. Inaugural lecture, *etc.* pp. 27. *Bell & Daldy: London,* 1871. 8°. **8309.** c. **52. (12.)**

—— The Influence of the Spiritual Life of the Minister of Christ on his Pastoral Work, an address . . . and Preaching, its substance and method, a paper, *etc.* pp. 16. *J. Parker & Co.: Oxford & London,* 1875. 8°. **4479.** bbb. **4. (2.)**

—— Introduction to the Study of the Old Testament. pt. 1. pp. xvi. 272. *J. W. Parker & Son: London,* 1856. 8°. **3128.** f. **35.**

No more published.

—— Is it Nothing to you? A plea for support of the Church Temperance Society, *etc.* pp. 30. *Church of England Temperance Society: London,* [1899.] 8°. **8435.** eee. **2. (4.)**

—— Jeremy Taylor, the English Chrysostom. [A lecture.] 1878. *See* Kempe (John S.) The Classic Preachers of the English Church, *etc.* ser. 2. 1877, *etc.* 8°. **4464.** i. **12.**

—— The Labourer worthy of his Hire. A sermon, *etc.* pp. 16. *W. Macintosh: London,* 1869. 8°. **4478.** bb. **3.**

—— The Law of Independence & the Law of Help. A sermon, *etc.* pp. 12. *London,* [1872.] 8°. [*Miscellaneous Papers of the Society for Organising Charitable Relief.*] **8277.** dd. **33. (3.)**

—— Lectures on Christianity and Socialism, *etc.* pp. xvi. 167. *Cassell & Co.: London,* 1890. 8°. **8275.** ee. **35.**

—— The Lessons of the War and the Duties of the Peace. A sermon, *etc.* pp. 19. *Thomas Harrison: Leeds,* 1856. 8°. **4477.** c. **9.**

—— Life and Times of St. Ambrose. *See* Lefroy (William) *Dean of Norwich.* Lectures on Ecclesiastical History, *etc.* 1896. 8°. **4535.** bb. **19.**

—— The Life and Works of Sir Charles Barry. [With a portrait.] pp. xiii. 407. pl. 39. *John Murray: London,* 1867. 8°. **10826.** h. **5.**

—— Memoir of the Life and Works of Sir Charles Barry . . . Second edition. With portrait and illustrations. pp. xvi. 407. *John Murray: London,* 1870. 8°. **10826.** h. **6.**

—— The Manifold Witness for Christ . . . Being the Boyle Lectures for 1877 and 1878. pp. 22. 400. *John Murray: London,* 1880. 8°. **4463.** gg. **18.**

BARRY (Alfred) *Bishop of Sydney.*

—— Masters in English Theology; being the King's College Lectures for 1877. Edited, with a historical preface, by A. Barry. pp. xxiv. 240. *John Murray: London,* 1877. 8°. **4707.** aaaa. **17.**

—— The Meaning of Church Restoration. *See* Lake (William C.) *Dean of Durham.* Sermons at the Reopening of Durham Cathedral, *etc.* 1877. 8°. **4479.** d. **1.**

—— Not that we would be unclothed, but clothed upon. The motto for the Christian, the Minister and the Church. An ordination sermon . . . With a note on the present ecclesiastical position. pp. 30. *Rivingtons: London,* 1877. 8°. **4479.** cc. **15. (8.)**

—— Notes on Greek Accents, drawn up originally for the use of Cheltenham College. pp. 15. *George Bell & Sons: London,* 1889. 8°. **012924.** bb. **43.**

—— The Office of Art in the Glorification of God. A sermon, *etc.* pp. 15. *See* Halifax.—*All Souls' Church.* Some of the Sermons preached during the Octave of the dedication of All Souls' Church, Halifax, *etc.* [1859.] 12°. **4463.** a. **26.**

—— The Old which is ever New. A sermon, *etc.* pp. 15. *Macmillan & Bowes: Cambridge,* 1889. 8°. **4473.** cc. **23. (7.)**

—— On Some of the Present Needs of the Church of England. A lecture, *etc.* pp. 48. *Macmillan & Co.: London,* 1867. 8°. **4108.** aa. **90. (11.)**

—— On the Ways in which Non-abstainers can help the Temperance Cause. Address, *etc.* pp. 12. *Church of England Temperance Society: London,* [1902.] 8°. **8436.** h. **9. (4.)**

—— The Parables of the Old Testament. pp. vii. 264. *S.P.C.K.: London,* [1889.] 8°. **4422.** n. **37.**

—— The Perfection of the Human Character of Jesus Christ. A lecture, *etc.* pp. 25. *Hodder & Stoughton: London,* 1873. 8°. **4017.** g. **1. (2.)**

—— [Another edition.]
The Perfection of the Human Character of Jesus Christ. *See* Objections. Popular Objections to Revealed Truth, *etc.* 1873. 8°. **4017.** g. **5.**

—— The Perfection of the Human Character of Jesus Christ. *See* Objections. Popular Objections to Revealed Truth, *etc.* 1880. 8°. **4017.** dg. **6/4.**

—— [Another edition.] See Objections. Popular Objections to Revealed Truth. 1874. 8°. **04018.g.45/3.**

—— The Position of the Laity in the Church. pp. ix. 155. 1903. *Elliot Stock: London,* 1903. 8°. [*The Church's Outlook for the Twentieth Century.*] **4109.** ee. **47/1.**

—— The Present Duty of Churchmen towards National Education . . . A paper, *etc.* pp. 16. *National Education Union: Manchester & London,* [1871.] 8°. **8304.** bb. **20. (10.)**

—— The Preservation of Body and Soul and Spirit. A sermon, *etc.* pp. 18. *Rivingtons: London,* 1881. 8°. **4473.** f. **20. (19.)**

—— The Relations of Technical to General Education. A lecture, *etc.* pp. 32. *R. Clay, Sons & Taylor: London,* 1869. 8°. **8311.** eee. **18.**

—— Religion for Every Day. Lectures to men. pp. 128. *S.P.C.K.: London,* [1873.] 12°. **4402.** i. **30.**

BARRY (Alfred) *Bishop of Sydney.*

—— The Religious Duty of Thought. A sermon. *See* Sermons. Sermons to Young Men. [1891.] 8°. **4429.** aa. **67.**

—— Revelation and Inspiration. *See* Bible.—*Appendix.* [*Miscellaneous.*] Six Sermons on the Bible, *etc.* 1892. 8°. **4429.** c. **20.**

—— Richard Hooker. *See* supra: Masters in English Theology . . . Lectures, *etc.* 1877. 8°. **4707.** aaaa. **17.**

—— Sermons for Boys; or, Memorials of Cheltenham Sundays. pp. vii. 286. *Cassell & Co.: London,* [1869.] 8°. **4463.** a. **4.**

—— Sermons for Passion-Tide and Easter, preached in Worcester Cathedral, *etc.* pp. 155. *Simpkin, Marshall & Co.: London,* [1881.] 8°. **4466.** b. **34.**

—— Sermons preached at Westminster Abbey. pp. 354. *Cassell & Co.: London,* 1884. 8°. **4466.** c. **4.**

—— Sermons preached in the Chapel of Cheltenham College. pp. xiii. 432. *Bell & Daldy: London,* 1865. 8°. **4464.** bbb. **2.**

—— Society. [A sermon.] *See* Kempe (John E.) "The Use and Abuse of the World," *etc.* 1873. 8°. **4465.** b. **18.**

—— [Another edition.] *See* Kempe (John E.) "The Use and Abuse of the World," *etc.* ser. 1. 1877. 8°. **4420.** c. **6.**

—— Some Lights of Science on the Faith. Eight lectures preached before the University of Oxford . . . 1892 on the foundation of . . . John Bampton. pp. xvi. 348. *Longmans & Co.: London,* 1892. 8°. **4453.** f. **23.**

—— Study in its bearing on Preaching. *See* Ellicott (Charles J.) *Bishop of Gloucester and Bristol.* Homiletical and Pastoral Lectures, *etc.* 1879. 8°. **4499.** cc. **8.**

—— The Suffering of one Member the Suffering of all. A village sermon, *etc.* pp. 16. *Hatchards: London,* 1870. 8°. **4476.** d. **4.**

—— Three Sermons preached at the Leeds Free Grammar School . . . With a preface on school services. pp. 54. *F. & J. Rivington: London,* 1855. 8°. **4462.** g. **2.**

—— True Christian Temperance. A sermon, *etc.* pp. 12. *Church of England Temperance Society: London,* [1894.] 8°. **4476.** df. **6.** **(8.)**

—— Unity and Wisdom in God. Two sermons, *etc.* pp. 32. *Bell & Daldy: London,* 1868. 8°. **4477.** dd. **26.** **(4.)**

—— The Universal Kingdom of Christ. A sermon, *etc.* pp. 20. *Crossley & Clarke: Leicester; Hamilton & Co.: London,* 1873. 8°. **4479.** bbb. **1.** **(1.)**

—— What is Natural Theology? An attempt to estimate the cumulative evidence of many witnesses to God. (Boyle Lectures, 1876.) pp. viii. 327. *S.P.C.K.: London,* [1877.] 8°. **4017.** df. **43.**

—— The Witness of the Truth. An ordination sermon. pp. 18. *J. Parker & Co.: Oxford & London,* 1870. 8°. **4479.** cc. **1.** **(6.)**

—— The Work of the Church in London. The St. James's Lectures of 1896. [Edited by Bishop Barry] . . . With an introductory lecture by the Lord Bishop of London. pp. 16. 224. *John Murray: London,* 1896. 8°. **4192.** bbb. **49.**

BARRY (Alice Frances)

—— Armchair Reflections. Reminiscences of an old lady. (Articles re-printed from the "Mid-Sussex Times" and the "British Weekly.') pp. 165. *Southern Publishing Co.: Brighton,* [c. 1950.] 8°. **12362.** a. **15.**

—— Arrows. A collection of songs and verses. pp. viii. 126. *Simpkin, Marshall & Co.: London,* 1901. 8°. **011651.** eee. **75.**

—— Last Poems. [Edited by Vera I. Arlett.] pp. 31. *Hove,* 1952. 8°. **11657.** h. **55.**

BARRY (Aristide) De l'emploi de l'ophthalmoscope en chirurgie et en médecine. pp. 92. *Paris,* 1872. 4°. [*Collection des thèses soutenues à la Faculté de Médecine de Paris.* An 1872. tom. 1.] **7373.** n. **7.**

BARRY (Armstrong) Laurel and Myrtle. Poems. pp. 78. *W. Hodge & Co.: Glasgow & Edinburgh,* [1918.] 8°. **011648.** eee. **55.**

BARRY (Arthur John) Railway Expansion in China and the Influence of Foreign Powers on its Development. pp. 27. *London,* 1910. 8°. [*Proceedings of the Central Asian Society.*] **8026.** i. **1.** **(28.)**

BARRY (C.) *Ex-Superintendent of Telegraphs.* A List of twenty-five hundred and forty-one—2541—Words, selected from the English Language, and carefully tested by the telegraph alphabet to prevent conflict in transmission. pp. 7. *T. Brakell: Liverpool,* [1868.] 4°. **1801.** d. **2.** **(7.)**

—— The Telegraph Detector, based on the English and Morse systems. *T. Brakell: Liverpool,* 1874. fol. **8756.** g. **19.**

BARRY (Catharine) Epilogue spoken by Mrs. Barry, April the 7th, 1709, at a representation of Love for Love; for the benefit of Mr. Betterton, at his leaving the stage. pp. 6. *E. Sanger & E. Curll: London,* 1709. 8°. **11643.** bbb. **13.** **(1.)**

BARRY (Cecil Charles Stewart) Clinical Lectures on Abdominal Gynæcological Operations. pp. 185. *Superintendent, Government Printing: Rangoon,* 1915. 8°. **07580.** bb. **43.**

—— The Treatment of Gonorrhoea and its Complications in Women. pp. 28. *Superintendent, Government Printing:* [*Rangoon,*] 1920. 8°. **07580.** bb. **44.**

—— When and how to perform a few Minor Gynæcological Operations. pp. 110. *Superintendent, Government Printing:* [*Rangoon,*] 1918. 8°. **07580.** bb. **42.**

BARRY (Charles) *Artist.*

—— South African Animal Studies. [Drawings.] [*Johannesburg,*] 1946. fol. Cup. **1252.** a. **30.**

—— South African Native Studies. [Drawings.] [*Johannesburg,*] 1946. fol. Cup. **1252.** a. **31.**

BARRY (Charles) *of Toulouse. See* Baltazar (Jean) Histoire de la guerre de Guyenne . . . Réimpression textuelle . . . accompagnée d'une notice, et de notes par M. C. Barry. 1876. 8°. **9220.** eee. **8.**

BARRY (Charles) *pseud.* [i.e. Charles Bryson.] *See* Savi (Ethel W.) Mixed Cargo. Stories . . . By E. W. Savi and C. Barry. [1932.] 8°. NN. **18864.**

—— The Avenging Ikon. pp. vi. 248. *Methuen & Co.: London,* 1930. 8°. NN. **16798.**

BARRY (CHARLES) *pseud.* [i.e. CHARLES BRYSON.]

—— The Boat Train Mystery. pp. 256. *Hurst & Blackett: London*, [1938.] 8°. **NN. 29707.**

—— A Case Dead and Buried. A Gilmartin story. pp. 255. *Hurst & Blackett: London*, 1938. 8°. NN. **28500.**

—— The Case for Tressider. pp. 128. *Hodder & Stoughton: London*, 1937. 8°. [*New at Ninepence Illustrated Thrillers.*] W.P. **11929/2.**

—— The Clue of the Clot. pp. 288. *Hutchinson & Co.: London*, [1928.] 8°. NN. **14246.**

—— The Clue of the Clot. pp. 256. *Philip Allan: London*, [1936.] 8°. NN. **26705.**

—— The Corpse on the Bridge. pp. 248. *Methuen & Co.: London*, 1927. 8°. NN. **13247.**

—— The Dead Have No Mouths. pp. 224. *Hurst & Blackett: London*, 1940. 8°. NN. **32092.**

—— Death in Darkness. pp. 286. *Hurst & Blackett: London*, [1933.] 8°. NN. **20390.**

—— Death of a First Mate. pp. 287. *Hurst & Blackett: London*, [1935.] 8°. NN. **24312.**

—— Death Overseas. pp. 288. *Hurst & Blackett: London*, [1937.] 8°. NN. **27688.**

—— The Detective's Holiday. pp. 223. *Methuen & Co.: London*, 1926. 8°. NN. **11529.**

—— The Ghost of a Clue. pp. viii. 278. *Methuen & Co.: London*, 1931. 8°. NN. **17492.**

—— The Mouls House Mystery. pp. 240. *Methuen & Co.: London*, 1926. 8°. NN. **12253.**

—— Murder on Monday . . . ? pp. viii. 270. *Eyre & Spottiswoode: London*, 1932. 8°. NN. **19296.**

—— Nicholas Lattermole's Case. pp. 255. *Hurst & Blackett: London*, [1939.] 8°. NN. **30350.**

—— Poison in Public. pp. 286. *Hurst & Blackett: London*, 1936. 8°. NN. **26327.**

—— Envenenado em Público. Tradução de Edmundo Paula Rosa. pp. 329. *Lisboa*, [1940?] 8°. **12650.** e. **26.**

—— The Red Star Mystery, *etc.* pp. 160. *Mellifont Press: London*, [1933.] 8°. **012603.** a. **48.**

—— Secrecy at Sandhurst. pp. 208. *Hurst & Blackett: London*, 1951. 8°. NNN. **1411.**

—— The Shot from the Door. pp. 228. *Hurst & Blackett: London*, [1934.] 8°. **NN.22594.**

—— The Smaller Penny. pp. 280. *R. Holden & Co.: London*, [1925.] 8°. NN. **10436.**

—— The Thirteenth House. pp. 64. *Mellifont Press: London; Dublin* printed, [1935.] 8°. **12626.** s. **3.**

—— The Thirteenth House. (Second edition.) pp. 64. *Mellifont Press: London; Dublin* printed, [1940.] 8°. **012641.** n. **52.**

—— Unsought Adventure. [Autobiographical reminiscences.] pp. 287. *Hurst & Blackett: London*, [1939.] 8°. **10859.** bb. **3.**

—— The Witness at the Window. pp. 246. *Methuen & Co.: London*, 1927. 8°. NN. **12877.**

BARRY (CHARLES) *pseud.* [i.e. CHARLES BRYSON.]

—— The Wrong Murder Mystery. pp. 287. *Hurst & Blackett: London*, [1933.] 8°. NN. **21419.**

BARRY (*Sir* CHARLES) *See* BARRY (Alfred) *Bishop of Sydney.* The Life and Works of Sir Charles Barry. [With a portrait.] 1867. 8°. **10826.** h. **5.**

—— —— 1870. 8°. **10826.** h. **6.**

—— *See* BARRY (Alfred) *Bishop of Sydney.* The Architect of the New Palace at Westminster, *etc.* [A defence of the claims of Sir Charles Barry.] 1868. 8°. **7814.** c. **4.**

—— —— 1868. 8°. **7814.** c. **5.**

—— *See* HILTORFF (J. J.) Notice historique et biographique sur la vie et les œuvres de Sir C. Barry, *etc.* 1860. 4°. **10855.** g. **5.**

—— *See* PUGIN (Edward W.) Who was the Architect of the Houses of Parliament? A statement of facts, founded on the letters of Sir C. Barry, *etc.* 1867. 8°. **7814.** b. **35.**

—— *See* WHIFFEN (Marcus) The Architecture of Sir Charles Barry in Manchester and Neighbourhood. 1950. 8°. [*Swinnerton Research Essay.*] Ac. **4663.** (1.)

—— *See* WYATT (*Sir* Matthew D.) On the Architectural Career of Sir Charles Barry. [1860.] 4°. **10825.** f. **14.**

—— The Travellers' Club House . . . Illustrated by drawings made by Mr. Hewitt . . . Accompanied by an essay on the present state of architectural study . . . by W. H. Leeds. pp. viii. 35. pl. 10. *John Weale: London*, 1839. fol. **788.** g. **27.**

BARRY (CHARLES A.) *Phrenologist.* What shall we do with our Children? How to find their true natures and the best way to educate them. pp. 35. *Occult Publishing Co.: Boston*, 1891. 8°. **8310.** a. **30.**

BARRY (CHARLES AINSLIE) *See* WAGNER (Wilhelm R.) [*Die Meistersinger von Nürnberg.*] The Mastersingers of Nuremberg, *etc.* [With a preface by C. A. Barry.] [1909.] 8°. **11748.** de. **16.**

BARRY (CHARLES ALFRED) The First Principles of the Church. Essays and notes. pp. xiv. 220. *Longmans & Co.: London*, 1913. 8°. **4107.** eee. **11.**

BARRY (CHARLES BISSELL)

—— The Rates of Food Consumption by Zamindars in the Tallagang Tahsil of the Attock District, *etc.* pp. ix. 16. *Lahore*, 1925. 8°. [*Board of Economic Inquiry, Punjab. Rural Section. Publication.* no. 6.] W.P. **5983/6.**

BARRY (CHARLES ÉTIENNE GUILLAUME) Dissertation sur la propriété contagieuse de la pourriture d'hôpital; thèse, *etc.* pp. 15. *Paris*, 1828. 4°. **1184.** c. **8.** (21.)

BARRY (CHARLES JAMES) The Beginnings of Christianity in Britain. A study for young people. pp. 54. *Congregational Union of England & Wales: London*, [1921.] 8°. **04705.** a. **31.**

—— The Blurred Mirror, and other sermons. pp. 154. *A. H. Stockwell: London*, [1918.] 8°. **04478.** df. **30.**

—— How the Gospel came to Britain. Stories of the early Church in Britain retold for children. pp. 48. *Congregational Union of England & Wales: London*, [1921.] 8°. **04705.** a. **30.**

BARRY (CHARLES PATRICK)

—— *See* ENCYCLOPAEDIAS. Collier's Encyclopedia . . . C. P. Barry, editor-in-chief, *etc.* [1949, *etc.*] 8°. **012221.d.2.**

BARRY (CHARLES PATRICK)

—— *See* ENCYCLOPAEDIAS. Collier's Encyclopedia . . . C. P. Barry, editor-in-chief. [1950.] 4°. **12214. e. 2.**

—— *See* ENCYCLOPAEDIAS. Collier's Encyclopedia . . . C. P. Barry, editor in chief, *etc.* [1952.] 8°. **012224. d. 4.**

BARRY (*Right Hon.* CHARLES ROBERT) Speeches. pp. 58. *W. B. Kelly: Dublin,* 1868. 8°. **8145. bbb. 10.**

—— Union Rating, Ireland. Speech . . . June 13, 1866, on moving the second reading of the Poor-Law—Ireland—Amendment Bill . . . With notes, statistical and otherwise, by Joseph Fisher, *etc.* pp. 48. *Longmans & Co.: London,* 1866. 8°. **6503. bb. 21.**

BARRY (COLLIS) Legal Medicine in India and Toxicology . . . Illustrated by plates. 2 vol. *Thacker & Co.: Bombay,* [1902, 03.] 8°. **6095. ee. 12.**

—— Second edition. vol. 1. pp. xxii. 600. pl. XII. *Thacker & Co.: Bombay,* [1904.] 8°. **6095. ee. 14.**

BARRY (COLMAN JAMES)

—— The Catholic Church and German Americans. A dissertation, *etc.* pp. xii. 348. *Catholic University of America Press: Washington,* 1953. 8°. [*Catholic University of America. Studies in American Church History.* vol. 40.] **Ac. 2692. y/19.**

BARRY (CONSTANT ÉTIENNE ALFRED EDWARD) *See* CÉNAC-MONCAUT (J. E. M.) Lettres à MM. G. Paris et Barry sur les Celtes, *etc.* 1869. 8°. **11852. i. 18. (4.)**

—— *See* VIC (C. de) and VAISSETE (J. J.) Histoire générale de Languedoc, *etc.* (Édition . . . annotée par E. Mabille, E. Barry, *etc.*) 1872, *etc.* 4°. **9230. i–k.**

—— Inscriptions inédites des Pyrénées. 1866. *See* PARIS.—*Comité des Travaux historiques et Scientifiques.* Mémoires . . . Archéologie. 1863, *etc.* 8°. **Ac. 440/2.**

—— Nemausus Arecomicorum. Notes de M. E. Barry extraites du livre II de la nouvelle édition de l'Histoire générale de Languedoc. pp. 106. *Toulouse,* 1872. 8° **7704. b. 36. (6.)**

—— Recueil des inscriptions antiques de la province de Languedoc préparé par E. Barry . . . E. Germer-Durand . . . publié par MM. A. Lebègue . . . F. Germer-Durand . . . A. Allmer, *etc.* pp. xlv. 24. 1251. *Toulouse,* 1893. 4°. [*Histoire générale de Languedoc, etc.* tom. 15.] **9230. k.**

—— Souvenirs d'une collection de Province. (Les lampes de bronze.) Dessins de M. Bruno Dusan. pp. 36. pl. 5. *Toulouse,* 1861. 4°. **7707. f. 4.**

—— Thèse de littérature sur les vicissitudes et les transformations du cycle populaire de Robin Hood. pp. 102. *Paris,* 1832. 8°. **T. 1510. (1.)**

BARRY (CRYSTAL)

—— The Tale of Papa Whiskers and Mr. Watson's Lettuces . . . Illustrated by Mary Smith. *H. A. & W. L. Pitkin: Manchester,* [1944.] 8°. **12828. b. 22.**

—— Toy Town Tales . . . Illustrations by Mary Smith, *etc.* pp. 24. *H. A. & W. L. Pitkin: Manchester,* [1943.] 8°. **12812. e. 57.**

BARRY (DAVID) *Rev.* The Absolution of Recidivi and of Occasionarii. pp. 72. *M. H. Gill & Son: Dublin,* 1914. 8°. **4109. de. 52.**

—— My Neighbour's Character. pp. 24. *"Irish Messenger": Dublin,* [1933.] 8°. **08408. eee. 56.**

BARRY (DAVID) *Surgeon to the Forces.* *See* CHERVIN (N.) Documens recueillis par MM. Chervin, Louis et Trousseau, membres de la Commission envoyée à Gibraltar pour observer l'épidémie de 1828 ; et par le Dr. Barry, *etc.* 1830. 8°. **1168. h. 30.**

—— *See* JENCKEN (Ferdinand) *Dr.* Cholera Morbus . . . With the treatment of the Cholera Morbus by Dr. Russell and Dr. Barry. 1832. 8°. **T. 1381. (19.)**

—— Dissertation sur le passage du sang à travers le cœur, thèse, *etc.* pp. 21. *Paris,* 1827. 4°. **1183. i. 11. (9.)**

—— Experimental Researches on the Influence exercised by Atmospheric Pressure upon the Progression of the Blood in the Veins, upon . . . absorption, and upon the prevention and cure of the symptoms caused by the bites of rabid or venomous animals . . . With an appendix, containing the original reports of Baron Cuvier . . . Dumeril, and Laennec, *etc.* [With a plate.] pp. xv. 175. *T. & G. Underwood: London,* 1826. 8°. **783. f. 28.**

—— *See* SEARLE (Henry) A Critical Analysis of the Memoir read by Dr. Barry . . . on Atmospheric Pressure, *etc.* 1827. 8°. **783. f. 29.**

BARRY (DAVID) *Traveller in South America.* *See* JUAN Y SANTACILLA (J.) and ULLOA (A. de) Noticias secretas de America . . . Sacadas a luz . . . por D. Barry. 1826. 4°. **798. cc. 3.**

—— —— 1918. 8°. **9774.a.1/31,32.**

BARRY (DAVID FITZ-DAVID) *Earl of Barrymore.* *See* BOYLE (Richard) 1*st Earl of Cork.* A Letter of the Earle of Corke . . . Wherein is shewed the barbarous cruelty the Rebels have lately used . . . and how my Lord Barrimoore burned and spoiled their country, *etc.* 1642. 4°. **E. 146. (12.)**

BARRY (DAVID S.) Forty Years in Washington . . . With illustrations. pp. xi. 349. *Little, Brown & Co.: Boston,* 1924. 8°. **010880. g. 36.**

BARRY (DAVID THOMAS)

—— Psalms and Hymns for the Church, School, and Home. Compiled by Rev. D. T. Barry . . . Fourth edition. pp. 346. 1865. 24°. *See* BIBLE.—*Psalms.—Selections.* [*English.*] **3435. aa. 44.**

—— Psalms and Hymns for the Church, School and Home. Edited by Rev. D. T. Barry . . . Fifth edition. pp. v. 326. 1866. 24°. *See* BIBLE.—*Psalms.—Selections.* [*English.*] **3091. a. 25.**

—— Psalms and Hymns for the church, school, and home . . . Seventh edition. pp. viii. 376. 1867. 8°. *See* BIBLE.—*Psalms.—Selections.* [*English.*] **3440. pp. 2.**

—— [Psalms and Hymns for the Church, *etc.*] The Parish Hymn Book for the Church, School, and Home . . . Edition B., *etc.* [The introductory note signed: D. T. B., i.e. D. T. Barry.] pp. viii. 304. [1871.] 32°. *See* BIBLE.—*Psalms.—Selections.* [*English.*] **3440. a. 5.**

BARRY (DAVID W.)

—— *See* PARKER (Everett C.) The Television-Radio Audience and Religion. [By] E. C. Parker, D. W. Barry, *etc.* [1955.] 8°. **W.P. 3419 1.**

BARRY (DENNIS)

—— Woodheap Cats . . . [A tale.] With illustrations by William Wood. pp. 205. *Peter Lunn: London,* 1947. 8°. **12831. aa. 37.**

BARRY (DERMOT) Tom Creagan. A novel. pp. 188. *Hamish Hamilton: London,* 1931. 8°. **012614. d. 15.**

BARRY (Dermot)

—— [Tom Creagan.] Tomás Ó Créagáin. Riobárd Ó Faracáin d'aistriġ go Gaeilge. pp. 143. Oifig an tSoláṫair: Baile Áṫa Cliaṫ. 1954. 8°. **12699**. aa. **51**.

BARRY (E.) *Sergeant-Major, 2nd Middlesex Artillery Volunteers.* Artillery Volunteers Vade mecum, *etc.* pp. 112. *Simpkin, Marshall & Co.: London,* 1880. 16°. **8831. a. 32.**

BARRY (E. S. B.) *See* Barry (James) *Curate of Bratton Clovelly, Devonshire.* Elijah, or the Baalim in Israel, *etc.* [With a preface by E. S. B. Barry.] 1869. 8°. **11781.** aaa. **7.**

BARRY (Edmond)

—— Barrymore. Records of the Barrys of County Cork from the earliest to the present time. With pedigrees . . . Reprinted from the Journal of the Cork Historical and Archæological Society. pp. 214. *Guy & Co.: Cork,* 1902. 8°. **9906.** pp. **23.**

BARRY (Eduardo) *See* Jachin. Jachin y Boaz, ó una llave auténtica para la puerta de Framosonería . . . Traducida . . . por E. Barry. 1822. 12°. **4785.** cc. **21.**

—— *See* Ramsay (David) *M.D., of South Carolina.* La Vida de Jorge Washington . . . Traducida . . . por E. Barry. 1826. 12°. **10882.** aaa. **26.**

BARRY (Edward) *D.D. See* Reban (J.) Strictures on a Sermon preached by the Rev. E. Barry, D.D. . . . at the Visitation at Abingdon, *etc.* 1809. 8°. **4475. f. 54. (3.)**

—— Twelve Sermons preached on particular occasions. pp. 216. *The Author: London,* 1789. 8°. **4455.** bb. **1.**

—— Sermons, preached on public occasions . . . The third edition, *etc.* [With a portrait.] pp. iv. 380. *Smart & Cowslade: Reading,* 1805. 4°. **4465.** h. **22.**

—— Theological, Philosophical, and Moral Essays . . . To these are added, a letter, addressed to the King . . . on the brutal practice of boxing . . . A new edition. pp. xxiv. 300. *H. D. Symonds: London,* 1799. 8°. **4374.** d. **18.**

—— Theological, Philosophical and Moral Essays . . . To these are added, A letter . . . addressed to the King, Lords and Commons, on the brutal practice of boxing. pp. xxiv. 300. *Printed for the Author: London,* [c. 1795.] 8°. 4383. b. 14.

—— The second edition. pp. xxiv. 300. *The Author: London,* [1800?] 8°. **8405.** k. **4.**

—— The Anniversary Sermon preached before . . . the Royal Humane Society, *etc.* pp. 22. *The Society: London,* 1820. 12°. **1026. h. 30. (7.)**

—— Bull Baiting! A sermon, on barbarity to God's dumb creation, *etc.* pp. vi. 13. *Smart & Cowslade: Reading,* [1802.] 4°. **T. 27. (2.)**

—— A Discourse, delivered to the young gentlemen of the Grammar-school, Reading . . . on a mournful occasion. pp. 21. *Smart & Cowslade: Reading,* [1799.] 8°. **4477.** aa. **136. (5.)**

—— A Dispassionate Address to the Subjects of Great Britain. pp. 28. *H. D. Symonds, etc.: London,* [1793?] 8°. **8135.** b. **30. (6.)**

—— Essays on the following subjects; Celibacy, Wedlock, Seduction, Pride, Duelling, *etc.* pp. 190. *Smart & Cowslade: Reading,* 1806. 8°. **1387.** h. **31.**

BARRY (Edward) *D.D.*

—— The Friendly Call of Truth and Reason to a new species of Dissenters. pp. 142. *Smart & Cowslade: Reading,* 1799. 8°. **4135.** e. **5. (3.)**

—— The Friendly Call of Truth and Reason . . . To which are prefixed, a few observations on the expediency of Parliamentary interposition duly to explain and . . . amend the Act of William and Mary commonly called "The Toleration Act" . . . Third edition. pp. iv. 148. *Smart & Cowslade: Reading,* 1806. 8°. **T. 132. (6*.)**

—— Fourth edition. pp. v. 179. *M. Cowslade & Co.: Reading,* [1815.] 8°. **1200.** cc. **22.**

—— A Letter on the Practice of Boxing, addressed to the King, Lords, and Commons. pp. 34. *The Author: London,* 1789. 8°. **7912.** g. **36.**

—— On the Necessity of adopting some Measures to reduce the present Number of Dogs; with a short account of hydrophobia, *etc.* pp. 37. *Richardson: London,* [1796?] 8°. **7293.** i. **8.**

—— A Sermon preached before the Ancient and Honourable Society of Free and Accepted Masons of England, *etc.* pp. 23. *T. Harper: London,* 1808. 4°. **4476.** dd. **5.**

—— A Sermon preached . . . before the Royal Grand Modern Order of Jerusalem Sols, *etc.* pp. 17. *J. Denew: London,* 1788. 8°. **1112. e. 18. (9.)**

—— A Sermon preached . . . for . . . the Royal Humane Society, *etc.* [With the directions of the Society in cases of suspended animation.] pp. viii. 28. *Royal Humane Society: London,* 1804. 8°. **T. 195. (3.)**

—— [Another copy.] **1026.** h. **29. (5.)**

—— A Sermon preached to the Convicts under sentence of death, in Newgate, *etc.* pp. 20. *J. Denew: London,* 1788. 4°. **694.** b. **1. (3.)**

—— A Token of Esteem to departed Worth! Or, an Epistle of sincere condolence, to the inhabitants of Bristol at large, but to the parishioners of Temple in particular; occasioned by the death of their pastor, the Rev. Joseph Easterbrook. pp. 16. *The Author: London,* 1791. 8°. **4906.** aa. **26.**

BARRY (Edward) *Professor of History at Toulouse. See* Barry (Constant E. A. E.)

BARRY (Edward) *Writer of Verse.* The Call to Action, and other poems. pp. 16. *A. H. Stockwell: London,* [1929.] 8°. **011644.** g. **37.**

BARRY (*Sir* Edward) *Bart.* Dissertatio medica inauguralis de nutritione, *etc.* pp. 19. *Lugduni Batavorum,* 1719. 4°. **1185.** h. **14. (12.)**

—— Observations historical, critical, and medical, on the Wines of the Ancients, and the analogy between them and modern wines. With general observations on the principles and qualities of water, and in particular on those of Bath. pp. xii. 479. *T. Cadell: London,* 1775. 4°. **449.** i. **9.**

—— [Another copy.] **41.** h. **11.**

—— [Another copy.] G. **19285.**

—— A Treatise on a Consumption of the Lungs. With a previous account of nutrition, and of the structure and use of the lungs . . . The second edition, with additions. pp. 276. *W. & J. Innys: London,* 1727. 8°. **1187.** e. **8.**

—— A Treatise on the three different Digestions, and Discharges of the Human Body. And the diseases of their principal organs. pp. xvi. 434. *A. Millar: London,* 1759. 8°. **42.** e. **6.**

BARRY (Edward Leopold Milner) *See* Hacklaender (F. W.) Der geheime Agent . . . Edited . . . by E. L. Milner-Barry. 1894. 8º. **2322**. d. **18**.

—— *See* Scheffel (J. V. von) Der Trompeter von Säkkingen . . . Edited by E. L. Milner-Barry, *etc.* 1903. 8º. **012202**. ff. **8/15**.

BARRY (Edward Leopold Milner) and **RIPPMANN** (Walter)

—— Passages from Standard Authors for translation into modern languages. Advanced texts. pp. viii. 59. *Hachette & Co.: London,* 1897. 8º. **12274**. aaa. **37**.

BARRY (Edward Middleton) *See* London.—iii. Royal Institute of British Architects, ~~etc.~~ Royal Institute of British Architects. Case of Mr. E. M. Barry, R.A., and the Office of Works, *etc.* 1870. 4º. **1865**. c. **18**. **(54.)**

—— Lectures on Architecture delivered at the Royal Academy . . . Edited, with introductory memoir, by Alfred Barry . . . With portrait and illustrations. pp. 71. 433. *John Murray: London,* 1881. 8º. **2261**. e. **8**.

—— New Law Courts. Letter . . . to the Secretary of the Treasury on the appointment of the architect to the new building. pp. 5. *Privately printed: London,* [1868.] 8º. **906**. k. **12**. **(11.)**

—— The New Law Courts, and the National Gallery. Facts relating to the late competitions, with a reply to portions of Mr. Street's recent pamphlet. pp. 24. *Macmillan & Co.: London,* 1872. 8º. **7820**. bbb. **51**. **(5.)**

BARRY (Edward William)

—— In Memoriam: Edward William Barry. [With a portrait.] pp. 89. *Issued for private circulation: London,* [1909?] 8º. **10860**. aa. **25**.

BARRY (Edwin) *See* Gedge (Sydney) Barnabas, the Son of Consolation. A sermon preached . . . on the occasion of the death of . . . E. Barry. 1869. 8º. **4905**. dd. **10**. **(10.)**

BARRY (Elizabeth) *See* Wither (George) Divine Poems, by way of paraphrase, on the Ten Commandments, *etc.* [The editor's preface signed: E. B., i.e. Elizabeth Barry, his daughter.] 1688. 8º. **1076**. d. **35**.

BARRY, afterwards **NEWBY** (Emma) *See* Newby.

BARRY (Ernest F.)

—— *See* Morgan (J. J. M. de) The History of the Armenian People . . . Translated by E. F. Barry. [1949.] 8º. **09136**. bb. **30**.

BARRY (Étienne) Discours prononcé à la fête du deux pluviôse, an 5me répub. avant la prestation du serment de haine à la royauté & à l'anarchie, et de fidélité à la Constitution de l'an 3me. *Toulon,* [1797.] *s. sh.* 4º. **936**. f. **7**. **(20.)**

—— Discours sur l'origine des institutions religieuses. *See* Paris.—*Section de la Place Louis XIV.* Section Guillaume Tell. Assemblée générale. Séance du 20 frimaire, l'an 2e, *etc.* [1793.] 8º. F. **619**. **(35.)**

—— Précis de la fête du 10 août célébrée dans la commune de Toulon . . . le 7 fructidor l'an 4eme . . . à laquelle a été jointe la rejouissance pour les nouvelles & éclatantes victoires des armées républicaines, en Italie & en Allemagne. pp. 19. *A bord de l'Orient, de l'imprimerie de l'Armée Navale,* [1796.] 4º. **935**. b. **7**. **(16.)**

BARRY (F.) *Abbé.* Étienne Delcher, évêque constitutionnel de la Haute-Loire. Étude religieuse sur la Révolution. [With plates.] pp. xiii. 361. *Paris,* 1925. 8º. **4863**. g. **6**.

BARRY (F.) *of Trieste.* *See* Littrow (H. von) Dialoghi nautici . . . recati nelle lingue inglese e francese dai rispettivi P.O.P., L. Schor e F. Barry. 1861. 8º. **12901**. bb. **14**.

BARRY (F. Booth) *See* Periodical Publications.—*Leicester.* The Midland Counties Constitutional Magazine . . . Edited by F. Booth-Barry. [1887, *etc.*] 8º. P.P. **3558**. m.

—— The Primrose League: its aims, object & work. (Second edition.) pp. 16. *Iliffe & Son: Coventry,* [1889.] 8º. **8138**. bbb. **135**. **(2.)**

BARRY (Fanny) *See* Story. Now for a Story! A collection of short original stories for children. By F. Barry [and others], *etc.* 1893. 8º. **012807**. ff. **16**.

—— The Fox Family. *See* Stories. Stories jolly: stories new, *etc.* 1889. 8º. **12807**. t. **7**.

—— Peter. *See* Stories. Stories jolly: stories new, *etc.* 1889. 8º. **12807**. t. **7**.

—— Soap-Bubble Stories. For children. pp. x. 214. *Skeffington & Son: London,* 1892. 8º. **012807**. ee. **3**.

BARRY (Florence Valentine) *See* Edgeworth (Maria) Maria Edgeworth: Chosen Letters. With an introduction by F. V. Barry. 1931. 8º. **10906**. aaa. **27**.

—— *See* Taylor (Jane) *of Ongar.* Jane Taylor. Prose and poetry. With an introduction by F. V. Barry. 1925. 8º. **012274**. a. **5**.

—— A Century of Children's Books. pp. vii. 257. *Methuen & Co.: London,* 1922. 8º. **011850**. aa. **26**.

BARRY (Francis James)

—— Who, a Stranger, *etc.* [A poem.] *Dolmen Press: Dublin,* 1953. 8º. **Cup.510.ah.5.**

BARRY (Franciscus de) De successionibus testati ac intestati opus, *etc.* 2 tom. *P. Roussin: Lugduni,* 1617. fol. C. **18**. c. **7**.

—— [Another edition.] Opus de successionibus testati ac intestati, *etc.* pp. 824. *Apud I. Wildium: Francofurti,* 1653. fol. **5255**. f. **14**.

BARRY (Françoise)

—— Les Droits de la reine sous la monarchie française jusqu'en 1789. pp. 212. *Paris,* 1932. 8º. **5408**. aa. **29**.

BARRY (Frank Russell) *Bishop of Southwell.*

—— *See* Anglo-Catholicism. Anglo-Catholicism of To-day . . . [By] Lord Hugh Cecil . . . F. R. Barry, *etc.* 1934. 8º. **4106**. cc. **27**.

—— *See* Dearmer (Percy) and Barry (F. R.) Westminster Prayers. 1936. 8º. **3455**. i. **35**.

—— *See* Stirling (John) The Study Bible, *etc.* (St. Luke . . . With new studies by . . . F. R. Barry.) 1926, *etc.* 8º. **03126.h.2/3.**

—— Christ in University Life. Addresses given in St. Mary-the-Virgin, Oxford . . . 1930. [By F. R. Barry, and others, and edited by him.] pp. 160. *Hodder & Stoughton: London,* 1931. 8º. **04478**. g. **67**.

—— Christianity & Psychology. Lectures towards an introduction. pp. vii. 195. *Student Christian Movement: London,* 1923. 8º. **4016**. de. **21**.

—— [Another edition.] pp. 290. *Student Christian Movement: London,* 1933. 8º. [*Torch Library.*] **3606.aa.7/1.**

BARRY (FRANK RUSSELL) *Bishop of Southwell.*

—— Church and Leadership. pp. 154. *S.C.M. Press: London,* 1945. 8°. **4105. df. 36.**

—— Convictions. Some thoughts for a time of crisis. pp. xv. 103. *Nisbet & Co.: London,* 1939. 8°. **04402. f. 86.**

—— Faith in Dark Ages. pp. 96. *Student Christian Movement Press: London,* 1940. 8°. **04374. h. 56.**

—— I Heard a Voice. (Four sermons.) pp. 47. *Christophers: London,* [1940.] 8°. **4480. de. 25.**

—— " One Clear Call." An appeal to the Church of England. pp. 28. *W. Heffer & Sons: Cambridge,* 1922. 8°. **4106. ee. 48.**

—— A Philosophy from Prison. A study of the Epistle to the Ephesians. pp. 155. *Student Christian Movement: London,* 1926. 8°. **03265. ee. 39.**

—— A Philosophy from Prison. A study of the Epistle to the Ephesians. (Second impression) pp. 123. *Student Christian Movement Press: London,* 1940. 8°. **03265. de. 41.**

—— Recovery of Man. pp. viii. 109. *Nisbet & Co.: London,* 1948. 8°. **4380. k. 39.**

—— The Relevance of Christianity. An approach to Christian ethics. pp. xvi. 317. *Nisbet & Co.: London,* 1931. 8°. [*Library of Constructive Theology.*] **03605.h.20/6.**

—— Third edition. pp. xvi. 323. *Nisbet & Co.: London,* 1932. 8°. [*Library of Constructive Theology.*] **03605.h.20/7.**

—— The Relevance of the Church. pp. 235. *Nisbet & Co.: London,* 1935. 8°. **4105. cc. 33.**

—— Religion and the War. pp. xiii. 92. *Methuen & Co.: London,* 1915. 8°. **4017. dg. 13.**

—— Right Marriage. By F. R. Barry . . . Claud Mullins . . . Douglas White. pp. 29. *Student Christian Movement Press: London,* 1934. 8°. **08416. bb. 51.**

—— Right Marriage. By F. R. Barry . . . Claud Mullins . . . and Douglas White. (Second revised edition.) pp. 30. *Student Christian Movement Press: London,* 1935. 8°. **08416. aa. 75.**

—— St. Paul and Social Psychology. An introduction to the Epistle to the Ephesians. pp. v. 122. *Humphrey Milford: London,* 1923. 8°. **03265. f. 69.**

—— The War and Christian Ethics. pp. 23. *B. H. Blackwell: Oxford,* 1914. 8°. **04376. ee. 37.**

—— What has Christianity to say? pp. 191. *Student Christian Movement Press: London,* 1937. 8°. **04374. g. 40.**

BARRY (FRED) What has been said. A dictionary of quotations on Tariff Reform, *etc.* pp. 162. *W. H. Maisey: London,* 1906. 8°. **08228. g. 87.**

BARRY (FREDERICK)

—— *See* PASCAL (B.) [Traitez de l'équilibre des liqueurs et de la pesanteur de l'air.] The Physical Treatises of Pascal. The Equilibrium of Liquids and the Weight of the Mass of the Air . . . With introduction and notes by F. Barry. 1937. 8°. [*Records of Civilization.* no. 28.] **Ac.2688/45.(28.)**

BARRY (FREDERICK)

—— The Scientific Habit of Thought. An informal discussion of the source and character of dependable knowledge. pp. xiii. 358. *Columbia University Press: New York,* 1927. 8°. **08465. h. 35.**

BARRY (GARRETT FRANCIS)

—— Violation of the Cloister. An historical synopsis and commentary . . . A dissertation, *etc.* pp. xii. 260. *Catholic University of America Press: Washington,* 1942. 8°. [*Catholic University of America. Canon Law Studies.* no. 148.] **Ac. 2692. y/21.**

BARRY (GEORGE) The History of the Orkney Islands: in which is comprehended an account of their present as well as their ancient state . . . With plates, *etc.* pp. viii. 509. *The Author: Edinburgh,* 1805. 4°. **983. e. 24.**

—— [Another copy.] **G. 5421.**

—— The second edition, with corrections and additions by . . . James Headrick. pp. xvi. 512. *Longman & Co.: London,* 1808. 4°. **10370. f. 11.**

—— [Another edition.] With a prefatory account of the agricultural progress and present state of the islands. pp. xxxix. 457. *W. Peace: Kirkwall,* 1867. 8°. **10369. cc. 4.**

BARRY (GEORGE DUNCAN) The Inspiration and Authority of Holy Scripture: a study in the literature of the first five centuries. pp. 146. *S.P.C.K.: London,* 1919. 8°. [*Handbooks of Christian Literature.*] **20047.aaa.6/1.**

—— The Transfiguration of our Lord. [With the narratives from the New Testament.] pp. viii. 131. *Longmans & Co.: London,* 1911. 8°. **4223. df. 36.**

BARRY (GEORGE SMITH)

—— The Highway Engineers' Association of Scotland, 1884–1936. A brief historical record. pp. 39. *Surrey Fine Art Press: Redhill,* [1936.] 4°. **20029. d. 36.**

BARRY (*Sir* GERALD REID)

—— Report on Greece. pp. 16. *"News Chronicle" Publications Dept.: London,* [1945.] 8°. **8029. e. 43.**

—— This England. The Englishman in print. Edited by Gerald Barry. pp. xiii. 190. *Geoffrey Bles: London,* 1933. 8°. **010352. bb. 24.**

—— The 'Week-end' Calendar. Edited by G. Barry. With decorations by John Armstrong. pp. vi. 319. *Geoffrey Bles: London,* 1932. 8°. **12298. df. 13.**

BARRY (GERARD) Dissertatio medica inauguralis de colica Pictorum, *etc.* pp. 20. *C. Stewart: Edinburgh,* 1814. 8°. **1184. b. 19. (10.)**

BARRY (GERRAT) A Discourse of Military Discipline . . . declaringe the parte and sufficiencie ordained in a private souldier, and in each officer . . . and . . . treatinge of fire-wourckes . . . as alsoe of firtifasions. pp. 211. *By the Widowe of Jhon Mommart: Bruxells,* 1634. fol. **719. l. 17.**

With an additional titlepage, engraved.

—— [Another copy.] A Discourse of Military Discipline, *etc.* *Bruxells,* 1634. fol. **G. 2430.**

—— The Seige of Breda, by the armes of Phillip the Fourt, under the government of Isabella atchived by the conduct of Ambr. Spinola. [With plates.] pp. 157. *Ex officina Hastenii: Lovanii,* 1627. fol. **591. f. 21.**

The titlepage is engraved. The date in the colophon is 1628.

BARRY (Giraldus de) *Cambrensis. See* Giraldus [de Barry], *Cambrensis, etc.*

BARRY (Gonzaga) name in religion of Mary Barry.

—— *See* Oliver (Mary) *I.B.V.M.* Love is a Light Burden. The life of Mother Mary Gonzaga Barry, I.B.V.M. [With a portrait.] 1950. 8º. **4956.** k. **43.**

BARRY (H.) *Writer of Verse.* They Live, and other verses. pp. 19. *A. H. Stockwell: London,* [1931.] 8º. **11640.** de. **46.**

BARRY (Henry) *Baron Santry.* To the Honourable Master Henry Barry, son to . . . Lord Santry, on his birth-day. By one of his school-fellows. [A poem.] [*Dublin?* 1725?] *s. sh.* fol. C.121.g.8.(131.)

BARRY (Henry) *Late Fellow of Queen's College, Oxford.* Cæsar and the Britons. pp. 174. *Baldwin & Cradock: London,* 1831. 8º. **807.** b. **1.**

—— Letter to Lord Wharncliffe, on innovations in the services of the Church. pp. 20. *J. Vincent: Oxford,* 1845. 8º. **908.** d. **2.** (**10.**)

—— The Manual of Happiness. By . . . H. Barry. Edited by his daughter [Emma Newby]. pp. 277. *T. C. Newby: London,* 1862. 12º. **8407.** bb. **25.**

—— A Sermon preached in the parish church of Chippenham, *etc.* pp. 20. *J. M. Coombs: Chippenham,* 1820. 8º. **4477.** f. **76.** (**9.**)

BARRY (Henry) *Lieutenant.* The Advantages which America derives from her commerce, connexion and dependence on Britain. Addressed to the people of America. [By Lieut. H. Barry.] pp. 16. 1775. 8º. *See* America. **1061.** h. **29.** (**10.**)

—— The Strictures [by Charles Lee] on the Friendly Address [i.e. " A Friendly Address to all reasonable Americans," attributed to Myles Cooper, but more probably by Thomas B. Chandler] examined, and a refutation of its principles attempted, *etc.* [By H. Barry.] pp. 14. 1775. 8º. *See* Americans. **1061.** h. **29.** (**12.**)

BARRY (Henry Boothby) The Advantages and Disadvantages of the Feudal System. A prize essay read in the Sheldonian Theatre, Oxford. pp. 57. *J. Vincent: Oxford,* 1843. 8º. **9004.** gg. **16.** (**1.**)

—— Thoughts on the Renovation of Cathedral Institutions. pp. 20. *James Ridgway: London,* 1852. 8º. **4107.** e. **5.**

BARRY (Herbert) Ivan at Home; or, Pictures of Russian life, *etc.* [With plates.] pp. xv. 322. *Publishing Co.: London,* 1872. 8º. **10290.** dd. **15.**

—— Russia in 1870. pp. xii. 418. *Wyman & Sons: London,* 1871. 8º. **10292.** c. **26.**

—— Russian Metallurgical Works, iron, copper, and gold, concisely described. pp. 71. *Effingham Wilson: London,* 1870. 8º. **7104.** a. **5.**

BARRY (Hilary)

—— " No Greater Love." A Passion play. pp. 34. [*The Author: Belfast,* 1954.] 8º. **011781.** i. **145.**

BARRY (Hugh Desmond)

—— *See* Tattersall (William R.) and Barry (H. D.) The Dentist's Handbook on Law and Ethics, *etc.* 1953. 8º. **6429.** bb. **69.**

—— Superannuation for the General Medical Practitioner in the National Health Service in England, Scotland and Wales. pp. 21. *William Heinemann Medical Books:* [*London,* 1955.] 8º. **7682.** b. **67.**

BARRY (I. D.) Reminiscences of Italy. *See* Swellendam.—*Literary Institute.* Literary Recreations: a selection of lectures, *etc.* 1862. 8º. **12272.** d. **2.**

BARRY (Ian) Speculation in Economics, *etc.* pp. v. 160. *Williams & Norgate: London,* 1925. 8º. **8207.** tt. **19.**

—— The World's Scandalous Directorship. An investigation of unrest. pp. 149. *E. J. Burrow & Co.: London,* 1937. 8º. **08008.** cc. **42.**

BARRY (Iris)

—— *See* Bardèche (M.) and Brasillach (R.) History of the Film . . . Translated and edited by I. Barry. 1938. 8º. **11797.** d. **14.**

—— *See* Pilkington (Laetitia) Memoirs of Mrs. Letitia Pilkington . . . With an introduction by I. Barry. 1928. 8º. W.P. **6666/2.**

—— Here is Thy Victory. pp. 256. *E. Mathews & Marrot: London,* 1930. 8º. NN. **16584.**

—— The Last Enemy. pp. 320. *Bobbs-Merrill Co.: Indianapolis,* [1929.] 8º. NN. **23299.**

—— Let's go to the Pictures. [With plates.] pp. xv. 270. *Chatto & Windus: London,* 1926. 8º. **011795.** h. **73.**

—— Portrait of Lady Mary Wortley Montagu. [With portraits.] pp. 294. *Ernest Benn: London,* 1928 [1927]. 8º. **010855.** b. **67.**

—— [Another edition.] pp. 336. *Bobbs-Merrill Co.: Indianapolis,* [1928.] 8º. **010855.** eee. **40.**

—— Splashing into Society. [A humorous tale.] pp. 111. *Constable & Co.: London,* 1923. 8º. **012628.** i. **60.**

BARRY (J. C.)

—— *See* Greatheed (Bertie) An Englishman in Paris: 1803 . . . Edited by J. P. T. Bury and J. C. Barry. 1953. 8º. **10175.** ff. **39.**

BARRY (J. J.) *See* Roselly de Lorgues (A. F. F.) *Count.* The Life of Christopher Columbus . . . Compiled . . . by J. J. Barry. 1869. 8º. **10629.** dd. **28.**

BARRY (J. Neilson) and **BARR** (Hy Max) Redskin and Pioneer. Brave tales of the great Northwest, *etc.* pp. 244. *Rand, McNally & Co.: Chicago,* [1932.] 8º. [*American Life Series.*] W.P. **4942/7.**

BARRY (Jacobus) Disputatio medica inauguralis de merocele vel hernia crurali, *etc.* pp. 40. *C. Stewart: Edinburgi,* 1812. 8º. T. **183.** (**9.**)

BARRY (James) *Baron Santry, Chief Justice of the King's Bench in Ireland.* The Case of Tenures upon the commission of Defective Titles argued by all the Judges of Ireland, with their resolution and the reasons of their resolution. pp. 56. *Society of Stationers: Dublin,* 1637. fol. **518.** l. **1.**

—— [A reissue.] *Society of Stationers: Dublin,* 1639. 8º. **515.** k. **21.** (**1.**)

—— [Another edition.] *See* Molyneux (William) *of Dublin, the Elder.* The Case of Ireland's being bound by Acts of Parliament in England, *etc.* pt. 2. 1720. 8º. **884.** h. **12.** (**1.**)

—— [Another edition.] *See* Molyneux (William) *of Dublin, the Elder.* The Case of Ireland's being bound by Acts of Parliament in England, *etc.* 1725. 12º. **1384.** a. **1.**

BARRY (James) *Curate of Bratton Clovelly, Devonshire.* Elijah, or the Baalim in Israel: a metrical libretto, in four parts, dedicated in . . . 1838 . . . to her late Royal Highness, the Duchess of Kent. [With a preface by E. L. B. Barry.] pp. viii. 55. *J. Parker & Co.: Oxford & London,* 1869. 8º. **11781.** aaa. **7.**

BARRY (JAMES) *Curate of Kelvedon Hatch.* A Sermon on the Offertory, *etc.* pp. 12. *T. S. Richardson: Ongar,* 1843. 12°. **4475**. de. **8**. **(19.)**

BARRY (JAMES) *of Durham. See* ATHERTON (William) *Wesleyan Minister.* Memoir of James Barry of Durham. 1830. 8°. **4906**. cc. **52**. **(5.)**

BARRY (JAMES) *R.A. See* BURROUGHS (Francis) A Poetical Epistle to J. Barry, Esq., containing strictures upon some of the works of that . . . artist, *etc.* 1805. 8°. C.116.e.4.

—— *See* WOOD (*Sir* Henry T.) A Note on the Pictures by J. Barry in the Great Room of the Society of Arts. 1880. 8°. **7807**. f. **13**. **(6.)**

—— The Works of James Barry . . . containing his correspondence from France and Italy with Mr. Burke [and with William Burke], his lectures on painting [and other works] (now first published from manuscripts, and illustrated by engravings, from sketches left by the author) . . . and his inquiry into the causes, which have obstructed the progress of the fine arts in England . . . To which is prefixed some account of the life and writings of the author. [With a portrait.] 2 vol. *T. Cadell & W. Davies: London,* 1809. 4°. **561***. d. **9**, **10**.

—— [Another copy.] G. **2181**.

—— An Account of a Series of Pictures, in the Great Room of the Society of Arts . . . at the Adelphi. pp. 249. *The Author: London,* 1783. 8°. B. **506**. **(2.)**

—— [Another copy.] **58**. g. **20**.

—— Catalogue of a Series of Pictures upon the subject of Human Culture, painted for the Society for the Encouragement of Arts . . . by J. Barry. [Drawn up by J. Barry.] pp. 4. [1783.] 4°. S.C. **1070**. **(12.)**

—— A Description of the Series of Pictures painted by James Barry . . . preserved in the Great Room of the Society for the Encouragement of Arts, *etc.* [Abridged from "The Account of a series of pictures," *etc.*] pp. 29. *T. Spilsbury & Son: London,* 1792. 8°. **7854**. e. **26**. **(1.)**

—— [Another edition.] pp. 16. *C. Whittingham: London,* 1803. 8°. **7856**. c. **34**. **(1.)**

—— [Another edition.] pp. 16. *T. Woodfall: London,* 1817. 8°. T. **1606**. **(5.)**

—— [Another copy.] **7856**. aaa. **42**. **(15.)**

—— An Inquiry into the Real and Imaginary Obstructions to the Acquisition of the Arts in England. pp. vii. 227. *T. Becket: London,* 1775. 8°. **62**. a. **27**.

—— The Lectures of James Barry. *See* WORNUM (Ralph N.) Lectures on Painting. By the Royal Academicians, *etc.* 1848. 8°. [*Bohn's Scientific Library.*] **2502**. h. **9**.

—— A Letter to the Dilettanti Society respecting the obtention of certain matters essentially necessary for the improvement of public taste, and for accomplishing the original views of the Royal Academy of Great Britain. pp. 76. *J. Walker: London,* 1798. 4°. **561***. d. **8**. **(7.)**

—— [Another copy.] MS. CORRECTIONS. **679**. e. **10**. **(2.)**

—— [Another copy.] MS. CORRECTIONS. **128**. e. **3**. *With a portrait and plates inset.*

—— [Another edition.] Reflections on the present state of the Art of Painting in England . . . in a Letter to the Dilletanti Society. *See* PILKINGTON (Matthew) *Vicar of Donabate, Dublin.* The Gentleman's and Connoisseur's Dictionary of Painters, *etc.* 1798. 4°. **132**. f. **13**.

BARRY (JAMES) *R.A.*

—— A Letter to the Dilettanti Society . . . The second edition; with an appendix, respecting the matters lately agitated between the Academy and the Professor of Painting. pp. 292. *J. Walker: London,* 1799. 8°. **274**. k. **15**.

—— A Letter to the Right Honourable the President . . . of the Society for the Encouragement of Arts, Manufactures, and Commerce. pp. 101. *The Author: London,* 1793. 8°. **272**. g. **18**.

—— A Series of Etchings by James Barry . . . from his original . . . paintings, in the Great Room of the Society of Arts, Manufactures and Commerce, Adelphi. [With illustrative letterpress, compiled from Barry's account.] *Colnaghi: London,* 1808. fol. **1752**. d. **4**.

BARRY (JAMES) *Rev. See* HUNGTINGTON (William) *S.S.* A Few Fragments of the Life and Death of the Rev. J. Barry, intended as a supplement to the Coal-heaver's Cousin. 1789. 8°. **4905**. aaa. **21**.

—— A Brief and Plain Discovery of the Falseness and Unscripturalness of Anabaptism: as the same is now practis'd by those of that perswasion . . . To which are added, some remarks on a nameless author; and a postscript, occasion'd by Mr. Stennet's reply to Russen . . . The third edition. pp. 193. *The Author: London,* 1715. 12°. **4323**. a. **6**. *Imperfect; wanting pp.* 61–72, *and* 153–172.

—— [A new edition, by William Huntington?] pp. 184. *E. Huntington: London,* 1815. 8°. **3756**. e. **4**. **(5.)**

—— [Another copy.] **4326**. g. **10**.

—— [Another edition.] pp. 173. *E. Palmer & Son: London,* 1848. 12°. **4326**. aa. **10**.

—— A Help to Prayer: or, a Serious and impartial discourse of right prayer, *etc.* pp. 149. *John Marshall: London,* 1701. 12°. **1223**. a. **22**.

—— Barry on Election. Revised by William Huntington . . . Second edition. pp. 104. *T. Bensley: London,* 1802. 8°. **3756**. e. **4**. **(2.)** *There is a second titlepage reading: "The Doctrine of Particular Election," etc.* 1715.

—— [Another copy.] **4256**. c. **4**.

—— Third edition. pp. 102. *E. Huntington: London,* 1814. 8°. **4256**. c. **6**.

—— [Another edition.] Barry on Particular Election, *etc. See* HUNTINGTON (William) *S.S.* Forty Shipes save none for Satan, *etc.* 1855. 16°. **3751**. a. **7**.

—— The Only Refuge of a Troubled Soul in times of affliction. Or, the Mystery of the apple-tree. In two sermons . . . Revised by William Huntington . . . Second edition. pp. 126. *T. Bensley: London,* 1802. 8°. **3756**. e. **4**. **(3.)**

—— [Another copy.] **4256**. c. **5**.

—— [Another edition.] pp. 125. *E. Huntington: London,* 1814. 8°. **4256**. c. **7**.

—— [Another edition.] pp. 84. *E. Palmer & Son: London,* 1856. 12°. **4477**. a. **7**.

—— A Reviving Cordial for a Sin-sick Despairing Soul, in the time of temptation . . . By an unworthy Minister of the Gospel [i.e. J. Barry]. pp. 133. 1699. 12°. *See* CORDIAL. **4401**. bbb. **26**.

BARRY (James) *Rev.*

—— [Another edition.] The Coal-heaver's Cousin rescued from the Bats; and his incomparable cordials recovered. [Edited by William Huntington.] pp. 130. *G. Terry & J. David: London*, 1788. 8°. **3756.** e. **4.** (**1.**)
With an additional titlepage, reprinted from the edition of 1699.

—— [Another edition.] pp. 138. *E. Huntington: London*, 1814. 8°. **4902.** f. **12.**

—— [Another edition.] pp. 143. *T. Bensley: London*, 1802. 8°. **4902.** f. **11.**

—— The Spirit of Prayer, the Infallible Character of a Heaven-born Soul; or, a Serious and impartial discourse of right prayer, *etc.* pp. 174. *London*, 1702. 12°. **4405.** bb. **37.**

—— [Another edition. Edited by William Hungtington.] pp. 134. *E. Huntington: London*, 1807. 8°. **3756.** e. **4.** (**4.**)

—— [Another edition.] pp. 130. *E. Huntington: London*, 1814. 8°. **3478.** d. **29.**

BARRY (James Grene) The Cromwellian Settlement of the County of Limerick. (Reprint from Limerick Field Club Journal.) 9 pt. *Guy & Co.: Limerick*, 1909 [1900–09]. 8°. **09004.** bb. **17.** (**4.**)

—— Sir John Bourke of Brittas, Martyr. *See* O'Connell (Mary A.) For Faith and Fatherland, *etc.* 1888. 8°. **4956.** a. **15.**

BARRY (James William) *See* Church (George E.) Explorations made in the Valley of the River Madeira, *etc.* (Exploration of the rivers and lakes of the Department of the Beni, Bolivia, by J. A. Palacios, from 1844 to 1847 . . . Translated from Spanish by J. W. Barry.—New fluvial outlet for Bolivia. By . . . Y. Arauz. Translated from Spanish by J. W. Barry.—Voyage made from the city of the Gram Pará to the mouth of the river Madeira by the expedition which ascended the river to the mines of Mato Grosso . . . in . . . 1749 . . . Translated from Portuguese by J. W. Barry.) 1875. 8°. **10481.** cc. **2.**

BARRY (Jean) *of Tonnerre.* Mémoire historique des événemens qui se sont passés à Tonnerre pendant le cours de la Révolution. [Signed by J. Barry and others.] pp. 19. *Paris*, [1793?] 4°. **F. 57*.** (**10.**)

BARRY (Jean) *Pasteur, of Codognan. See* Guimard (F.) À tout le monde en général, à M. le Pasteur Barry en particulier. [Concerning his address to the Protestants of La Vaunage.] 1868. 12°. **3900.** b. **19.** (**3.**)

—— *See* Guimard (F.) Un Petit mot à M. le Pasteur Barry au sujet de ses réflexions sur la brochure [entitled: "Quelques réflexions sur les Protestants"] de M. l'Abbé Prouvèze. 1868. 12°. **3900.** b. **19.** (**2.**)

—— L'Apostacie, de l'Église Romaine dévoilée à M. l'Abbé Prouvèze. [In reply to his "Quelques refléxions sur les Protestants."] pp. 35. *Nîmes*, 1868. 8°. **3900.** f. **1.** (**3.**)

—— Aux Protestants de La Vaunage. Quelques réflexions sur la brochure de M. l'Abbé Prouvèze [entitled: "Quelques réflexions sur les Protestants"]. pp. 28. *Nîmes*, 1868. 8°. **3902.** c. **13.**

BARRY (Jerome)

—— Lady of Night. pp. 172. *T. V. Boardman & Co.: London, New York*, 1945. 8°. **12729.** aa. **6.**

BARRY (Jerome)

—— Leopard Cat's Cradle. pp. 186. *T. V. Boardman & Co.: London, New York*, 1943. 8°. **12727.** c. **40.**

—— Leopard Cat's Cradle. pp. 160. *T. V. Boardman & Co.: London*, 1948. 8°. **012635.** b. **47.**
Boardman Books. no. 48.

—— Murder with your Malted. [A novel.] pp. 160. *T. V. Boardman & Co.: London, New York*, 1942. 8°. **012646.** aaa. **71.**

BARRY (John) *Adventurer.*

—— Cards on the Table. [Autobiographical reminiscences.] pp. 212. *Sampson Low & Co.: London*, [1939.] 8°. **10858.** f. **16.**

BARRY (John) *Commodore.*

—— *See* Clark (William B.) Gallant John Barry, *etc.* [With a portrait.] 1938. 8°. **010885.** eee. **76.**

—— *See* Griffin (M. I. J.) The History of Commodore John Barry. [With a portrait.] 1897. 8°. **010881.** ee. **16.**

—— —— 1903. 8°. **010882.** m. **38.**

—— *See* Gurn (Joseph) Commodore John Barry, Father of the American Navy. [With portraits.] [1933.] 8°. **010885.** eee. **34.**

—— *See* Hannon (Bryan) Three American Commodores, *etc.* [With portraits.] 1936. 8°. **010886.** g. **37.**

BARRY (John) *D.D.* Statement of Accounts of St. Patrick's College, from June 1, 1859, to Dec. 31, 1861. [With an account by J. Barry of his administration of the College.] pp. 15. [1862.] 8°. *See* Melbourne.—*College of St. Patrick.* **8356.** bb. **26.**

BARRY (John) *Malefactor.* A Short Narrative of the Behaviour, &c. of John Barry, while under sentence of death, who was executed May 16th, 1746 . . . for causing . . . to be falsely made . . . the last will and testament of James Barry, *etc.* [*London*, 1746.] *s. sh.* fol. **1890.** e. **3.** (**12.**)

BARRY (John) *Rev., M.A.*

—— Public Worship Explained. pp. 24. 1944. 8°. *See* Down, Connor and Dromore, *Diocese of.—Diocesan Council of Youth.* **3479.** a. **9.**

BARRY (John) *Soldier in Ireland.* The Most Blessed . . . Newes from Ireland, shewing the fortunate successe of the Protestants, and Gods just vengeance on the Rebels, *etc.* pp. 8. *For T. W. & G. H.: London*, 1642. 4°. G. **4157.** (**29*.**)

BARRY (John) *Wesleyan Missionary to Jamaica.* Letter addressed to the Right Hon. Sir George Murray . . . occasioned by certain remarks contained in a pamphlet, by A. Barclay, Esq.; of Jamaica, entitled, "Effects of the late colonial policy of Great Britain," &c. involving the characters of the missionaries in that island. pp. 30. *John Mason: London*, 1830. 8°. **8155.** de. **2.** (**2.**)

BARRY (John A.) *Lieutenant-Colonel. See* Beudant (E.) Horse Training, *etc.* [Translated by J. A. Barry.] 1931. 8°. **7916.** b. **3.**

BARRY (John Arthur) Against the Tides of Fate. pp. 331. *Duckworth & Co.: London*, 1899. 8°. **012643.** g. **21.**

—— In the Great Deep. Sea stories. pp. 320. *Methuen & Co.: London*, 1896. 8°. **012626.** ee. **41.**

BARRY (JOHN ARTHUR)

—— The Luck of the Native-Born. pp. 319. *J. Macqueen: London*, 1898. 8°. **012643. b. 42.**

—— Red Lion and Blue Star, with other stories. pp. 312. *Hutchinson & Co.: London*, 1902. 8°. **012638. aa. 8.**

—— Sea Yarns . . . With eight coloured illustrations by Charles Pears. pp. 300. *W. & R. Chambers: London, Edinburgh*, 1910. 8°. **012808. aa. 9.**

—— A Son of the Sea. pp. viii. 352. *Duckworth & Co.: London*, 1899. 8°. **012642. b. 16.**

—— South Sea Shipmates. Being the matter-of-fact adventures of two Australian sailormen in various seas, and on ships of varying degrees of maritime iniquity. pp. 304. *T. Werner Laurie: London*, [1913.] 8°. **NN. 1502.**

—— Steve Brown's Bunyip, and other stories . . . With introductory verses by Rudyard Kipling. Fifth edition. pp. 297. *Remington & Co.: London*, 1893. 8°. **012630. f. 6.**

—— [Another copy.] Steve Brown's Bunyip, and other stories . . . Fifth edition. *London*, 1893. 8°. File **165.**

BARRY (JOHN COOPER) Ideals and Principles of Church Reform . . . With introductory note by James Denney. pp. xvi. 205. *T. & T. Clark: Edinburgh*, 1910. 8°. **4107. de. 35.**

BARRY (JOHN D. UNDERWOOD)

—— Venus through the Lens. Photographed, arranged and presented by J. d. U. Barry professionally known as "Dubarry." [Plates, with an explanatory introduction.] *Thorsons: London*, [1942.] 4°. **Cup.804.m.6.**

BARRY (JOHN DANIEL) A Daughter of Thespis. A novel. pp. 347. *Chapman & Hall: London; Boston* printed, 1903. 8°. **012638. dd. 49.**

—— The Intriguers. A novel. pp. 295. *D. Appleton & Co.: New York*, 1896. 8°. **012706. ee. 60.**

—— Intimations. A collection of brief essays dealing mainly with aspects of everyday living, *etc.* pp. xiv. 196. *Paul Elder & Co.: San Francisco*, [1913.] 8°. **012355. i. 57.**

—— Mademoiselle Blanche. A novel. pp. 330. *Stone & Kimball: New York*, 1896. 8°. **012706. m. 36.**

—— [Another edition.] The Acrobat, or, Mademoiselle Blanche. A novel. pp. 330. *John Lane: London*, 1900. 8°. **012641. c. 51.**

BARRY (JOHN EVARTS)

—— Skeleton in Concrete. pp. 256. *John Gifford: [London,]* 1952. 8°. **12731. i. 18.**

—— The Uranium Murders. [A novel.] pp. 192. *John Long: London*, 1951. 8°. **12731. de. 29.**

BARRY (JOHN JOSEPH) How to Make Etchings. pp. 64. *John Lane: London; printed in U.S.A.*, [1930.] 8°. **7853. r. 14.**

BARRY (JOHN MAXWELL) *Baron Farnham.* Lord Farnham's Speech at the Reformation meeting at Cavan, *etc.* pp. 12. *W. Curry, jun. & Co.: Dublin*, [1827.] 12°. **3939. aa. 5. (3.)**

—— A Few Philosophical Reasons against Catholic Emancipation; a letter to . . . Lord Farnham. pp. 32. *J. Robins: London*, 1827. 8°. **8275. ee. 24. (3.)**

BARRY (JOHN PATRICK) At the Gates of the East. A book of travel among historic wonderlands . . . With 33 illustrations. pp. xvi. 261. *Longmans & Co.: London*, 1906. 8°. **10027. dd. 13.**

BARRY (JOHN STETSON) A Genealogical and Biographical Sketch of the Name and Family of Stetson from the year 1634 to the year 1847. pp. 116. *The Author: Boston*, 1847. 8°. **9917. e. 15.**

—— A Historical Sketch of the Town of Hanover, Mass., with family genealogies. pp. 448. pl. 40. *The Author: Boston*, 1853. 8°. **10412. f. 7.**

—— The History of Massachusetts. 3 vol. *Phillips, Sampson & Co.: Boston*, 1855–57. 8°. **9602. d. 3.**

BARRY (*Sir* JOHN VINCENT WILLIAM) and **PATON** (*Sir* GEORGE WHITECROSS)

—— An Introduction to the Criminal Law in Australia. By J. V. Barry . . . and G. W. Paton . . . assisted by G. Sawer, *etc.* pp. x. 128. *Macmillan & Co.: London*, 1948. 8°. [*English Studies in Criminal Science.* vol. 6.] W.P. **10/6.**

BARRY (JOHN WARREN) Studies in Corsica, sylvan and social. pp. xvi. 302. *Sampson Low & Co.: London*, 1893. 8°. **10131. ee. 6.**

BARRY (*Sir* JOHN WOLFE) *K.C.B.* See WELCH (Charles) *F.S.A.* History of the Tower Bridge . . . With a description of the Tower Bridge, by J. W. Barry, *etc.* 1894. 4°. **10349. i. 18.**

—— *See* WELCH (Charles) *F.S.A.* A Short Account of the Tower Bridge . . . With a description of its construction, by J. W. Barry, *etc.* 1894. 8°. **10350. bb. 44.**

—— Address on the Streets & Traffic of London. Delivered at the opening meeting of the session, 1898–9, of the Society of Arts, *etc.* [With a map.] pp. 44. *William Trounce: London*, 1899. 8°. **12302. aaa. 51. (1.)**
The half-title reads "Streets and Traffic of London."

—— Address on the Streets & Traffic of London. Delivered at the opening meeting of the session, 1899–1900, of the Society of Arts, *etc.* pp. 15. pl. VI. *William Trounce: London*, 1899. 8°. **12302. aaa. 51. (2.)**
The half-title reads "Streets and Traffic of London, Part II."

—— Notes on Barry Genealogy in England and Wales . . . With appendices and genealogical tree. [With plates.] pp. iii. 89. *Printed for private circulation: London*, 1906. fol. **9918. k. 2.**

—— Railway Appliances. A description of details of railway construction subsequent to the completion of the earthworks and structures, *etc.* pp. xiii. 299. *Longmans & Co.: London*, 1876. 8°. [*Text-books of Science.*] **8707. bb. 6.**

—— Sixth edition with an appendix. pp. xiii. 331. *Longmans & Co.: London*, 1890. 8°. [*Text-Books of Science.*] **2244. a. 7.**

—— Railways and Locomotives. Lectures delivered at the School of Military Engineering at Chatham in 1877. By J. W. Barry . . . and F. J. Bramwell. pp. ix. 429. *Longmans & Co.: London*, 1882. 8°. **8767. c. 23.**

BARRY (JOSEPH AMBER)

—— Left Bank, Right Bank. Paris and Parisians. pp. 224. *William Kimber: London*, 1952. 8°. **10175. bb. 37.**

—— Libraries in Need. [With illustrations.] pp. 23. 1949. 8°. *See* UNITED NATIONS EDUCATIONAL, SCIENTIFIC AND CULTURAL ORGANIZATION. **U.N.L.112/93.**

BARRY (KATHARINE V.)

—— Towards the Light. A play in three acts, for children. Based on the records of the Chartist Rising, Newport, November 4th, 1839. pp. 35. 1939. 8°. *See* NEWPORT, *Monmouthshire.—Chartist Centenary Committee.* **11782. b. 68.**

BARRY (KEITH)

—— Stories from French Classics. Chosen and translated by K. Barry. pp. 191. *Collins: Glasgow*, 1938. 8º. [*Laurel and Gold Series*. vol. 71.] **012208.ccc.1/78.**

—— Writing for Profit. A ten lesson course in journalism and short story writing. pp. 100. *Thorsons: London*, [1948.] 8º. **11868. aa. 26.**

BARRY (LÉON) *See* RIOU (G.) Épitaphe pour un homme oublié (L. Barry), *etc.* 1926. 8º. **011824. cc. 20.**

—— L'Aïeul . . . Dessins de Jos. Jullien. pp. 30. *Saint-Félicien-en-Vivarais, Paris*, 1928. 8º. [*Collection du Pigeonnier*. no. 19.] **012202. eee. 2/19.**

—— Au delà du bonheur. Roman. pp. 395. *Paris*, [1912.] 8º. **12550. ppp. 28.**

BARRY (LIAM)

—— Our Legacy from Burke. A survey of some of his works; and a broad analysis from the literary aspect. pp. 235. *Paramount Printing House: Cork*, 1952. 8º. **11869. aa. 15.**

BARRY (LILY EMILY FRANCES) In the Paths of Peace . . . With illustrations. pp. vii. 310. *Canada Engraving & Litho. Co.: Montreal*, 1901. 8º. **04402. eee. 8.**

BARRY (LODOWICK) *See* BARRY (Lording)

BARRY (LORDING)

—— *See* EWEN (Cecil H. L'E.) Lording Barry, Poet and Pirate. 1938. 8º. **10857. bb. 11.**

—— Ram-Alley; or, Merrie-Trickes. A comedy, *etc.* [In verse.] *G. Eld, for Robert Wilson: London*, 1611. 4º. **644. b. 1.**
Imperfect; wanting B2. and B3. which are supplied in facsimile.

—— [Another edition.] *John Norton for Robert Wilson: London*, 1636. 4º. **644. b. 2.**

—— [Another copy.] **161. g. 23.**

—— [Another edition.] *See* DODSLEY (Robert) A Select Collection of Old Plays. vol. 5. 1780. 8º. **82. a. 13.**

—— [Another edition.] *See* BRITISH DRAMA. The Ancient British Drama. vol. 2. 1810. 8º **11773.i.24.**

—— [Another edition.] 1825. *See* DODSLEY (Robert) A Select Collection of Old Plays. vol. 5. 1825, *etc.* 8º. **642. h. 11.**

—— [Another edition.] 1875. *See* DODSLEY (Robert) A Select Collection of Old English Plays, *etc.* vol. 10. 1874, *etc.* 8º. **2302. e.**

—— [Another edition.] *Privately printed: [London,]* 1913. 8º. [*Tudor Facsimile Texts*.] Tab. **579. a. 13.**

BARRY (LOUIS) Dissertation sur la hernie de naissance ou congénitale, *etc.* pp. 29. *Montpellier*, [1806.] 4º. **1180. f. 3. (4.)**

BARRY (M. L.) Hard Realities. [Tales.] pp. 256. *J. & R. Maxwell: London*, [1884.] 8º. **12624. g. 37.**

BARRY (MAE HOWLEY)

—— Frankincense and Myrtle. A one-act comedy, *etc.* pp. 35. *Samuel French: New York*, [1941.] 8º. **011791. aaa. 20.**

—— Second Blooming. [A one-act play.] pp. 29. *Samuel French: New York*, [1941.] 8º. **011791. aa. 67.**

BARRY (MALTMAN) The Catechism of the Eastern Question: being an historical retrospect from 1710 to 1878. pp. 23. *Effingham Wilson: London*, 1880. 8º. **8028. de. 16. (6.)**

BARRY (MARGARET ALICE)

—— A Floristic and Ecologic Study of Coal Mine Ridge. [With illustrations.] pp. 40. *Stanford University*, 1940. 8º. [*Contributions from the Dudley Herbarium*. vol. 3. no. 1.] **Ac. 2692. ng.**

BARRY (MARIE ALEXANDRE) Souvenirs des grands jours. [In verse.] pp. vi. 225. *Toulouse*, 1863. 8º. **11481. i. 16.**

BARRY (MARTIN) *See* BISCHOFF (T. L. W. von) Bestätigung des von . . . Dr. Barry bei den Kaninchen behaupteten Eindringens der Spermatozoiden in das Ei. 1854. 4º. **7407. g. 36. (2.)**

—— *See* KEBER (G. A. F.) Mikroskopische Untersuchungen über die Porosität der Körper. Nebst einer Abhandlung über den Eintritt der Samenzellen in das Ei . . . Mit Zusätzen von M. Barry, *etc.* 1854. 4º. **7407. h. 17. (3.)**

—— Ascent to the Summit of Mont Blanc, 16th–18th of . . . Sept^r^, 1834. pp. 40. MS. NOTE. *H. Teape & Son: London*, [1835.] 8º. **10195. cc. 3.**

—— [Another edition.] [With a panorama.] pp. ii. 119. *W. Blackwood & Sons: Edinburgh; T. Cadell: London*, 1836. 8º. **1048. f. 29.**

—— Martin Barry's Bestätigung einiger neuern mikroskopischen Beobachtungen. Aus dem Englischen übersetzt und mit Zusätzen versehen von F. Keber. pp. 54. *Königsberg*, 1855. 8º. **7005. e. 4.**

—— Neue Untersuchungen über die schraubenförmige Beschaffenheit der Elementarfasern der Muskeln nebst Beobachtungen über die muskulöse Natur der Flimmerhärchen. Aus dem Manuscripte des englischen Originals übersetzt von Prof. Purkinje. Mit vier Kupfertafeln. (Besonderer Abdruck aus Müller's Archiv.) pp. 68. *Berlin*, 1851. 8º. **7406. b. 6.**

—— On the Unity of Structure in the Animal Kingdom . . . From the Edinburgh New Philosophical Journal, *etc.* pp. 26. [*Edinburgh*, 1837.] 8º. **7204. c. 16. (1.)**

—— Researches in Embryology . . . From the Philosophical Transactions. 1838(–40). [With plates.] 3 ser. *R. & J. E. Taylor: London*, 1838–40. 4º. **7406. h. 8.**
Copy presented by the author to Alexander von Humboldt.

—— Observations in reply to T. Wharton Jones's Strictures [on the author's "First series of researches in Embryology"] . . . From the London Medical Gazette, *etc.* pp. 7. *London*, 1839. 8º. **7680. aaa. 19.**

BARRY (MARY) *See* BARRY (Gonzaga) name in religion of MARY BARRY.

BARRY (MARY ELIZABETH) and **GOETZ** (DELIA)

—— Children of the other Americas. A guide to materials in English on the other Americas suitable for the elementary and junior high school grades. Prepared by M. Elizabeth Barry and Delia Goetz, with the assistance of Dorothy Conzelman, under the supervision of the Division of Intellectual Cooperation of the Pan American Union. pp. ix. 172. 1942. 8º. *See* UNITED STATES OF AMERICA.—*Office of Inter-American Affairs.* **A.S. 779/2.**

BARRY (MARY ELIZABETH) and **HANNA** (PAUL ROBERT) Wonder Flights of Long Ago. Edited by M. E. Barry and P. R. Hanna, *etc.* pp. vii. 218. *D. Appleton & Co.: New York*, [1930.] 8º. **012403. df. 52.**

BARRY (MARY INVIOLATA)

—— *See* DEFERRARI (Roy J.) A Concordance of Ovid. By R. J. Deferrari . . . M. I. Barry, *etc.* 1939. 4º. **2049.h.**

BARRY (Mary Inviolata)

—— *See* Deferrari (Roy J.) and Barry (M. I.) A Lexicon of St. Thomas Aquinas, based on the Summa Theologica and selected passages of his other works, *etc.* [1948, *etc.*] 4°. **3671.g.1.**

BARRY (Mary Martin)

—— An Analysis of the Prosodic Structure of Selected Poems of T. S. Eliot. A dissertation, *etc.* pp. x. 135. *Catholic University of America Press: Washington,* 1948. 8°. **11870.** c. **41.**

BARRY (Michael) *See* Stirling (John) *D.D.* A Handbook of Rhetoric . . . Revised . . . by . . . Professor Barry. 1864. 12°. **11805.** b. **1.**

—— Orators and Elocution: a class book on public speaking. pp. xiv. 479. *J. F. Fowler: Dublin,* 1862. 8°. **11824.** bbb. **21.**

BARRY (Michael Joseph) *See* also Bouillon de Garçon, *pseud.* [i.e. M. J. Barry.]

—— Heinrich and Leonore, an Alpine story. Correggio: and some miscellaneous verse, original and translated. pp. viii. 95. *Hodges, Figgis & Co.: Dublin,* 1886. 8°. **11641.** bbb. **57.**

—— Ireland as she was, as she is, and as she shall be. pp. 112. *James Duffy: Dublin,* 1845. 8°. [*Loyal National Repeal Association of Ireland. Repeal Prize Essays.*] **8146.** bbb. **50.**

—— Lays of the War, and Miscellaneous Lyrics. (Third edition.) pp. viii. 134. xvii. *Longman & Co.: London,* 1856. 8°. **11649.** c. **32.**

—— The Pope and the Romagna. pp. 67. *Hodges, Smith & Co.: Dublin,* 1860. 8°. **8032.** d. **9.**

—— The Songs of Ireland. Edited by M. J. Barry. pp. 238. *James Duffy: Dublin,* 1845. 12°. **1156.** a. **8.** (**3.**)

—— [Another edition.] [With " Essay on Irish Songs. By Thomas Davis, M.R.I.A."] pp. 252. *James Duffy: Dublin,* 1860. 12°. **11622.** bbb. **19.**

—— A Waterloo Commemoration for 1854. [In verse.] pp. 36. *W. S. Orr & Co.: London,* [1854.] 8°. **11647.** e. **45.**

BARRY (Michael Joseph) and **KEOGH** (*Right Hon.* William N.)

—— A Treatise on the Practice of the High Court of Chancery of Ireland. 2 pt. pp. xxviii. xxxv. 568. *Hodges & Smith: Dublin,* 1840, 42. 8°. **1130.** h. **7.**

BARRY (Mona)

—— Diary of a Grass Widow. Illustrated by Joyce Dennys. pp. 223. *Michael Joseph: London,* 1939. 8°. **012331.** n. **11.**

BARRY (Octavia) The Lady Victoria Tylney Long Wellesley. A memoir. By her eldest god-daughter (Octavia Barry). With portraits and illustrations. pp. xii. 194. *Skeffington & Son: London,* 1899. 8°. **10827.** de. **9.**

BARRY (Pascal) Dissertation sur le catarrhe aigu de la vessie. Thèse, *etc.* pp. 23. *Montpellier,* 1835. 4°. **1181.** g. **13.** (**23.**)

BARRY (Patrick) *Author of " Dockyard Economy," etc.* Dockyard Economy and Naval Power. [With plates.] pp. xxiii. ii. 312. *Sampson Low & Co.: London,* 1863. 8°. **8806.** e. **15.**

BARRY (Patrick) *Author of " Dockyard Economy," etc.*

—— The Dockyards and the Private Shipyards of the Kingdom. pp. 71. *T. Danks: London,* 1863. 8°. **8806.** d. **20.**

—— The Dockyards, Shipyards, and Marine of France, *etc.* pp. v. 257. *Simpkin, Marshall & Co.: London,* 1864. 8°. **8806.** ee. **12.**

—— No Rates, but Equal Local Government Taxation throughout the Kingdom. pp. 18. *Simpkin, Marshall & Co.: London,* [1906.] 8°. **8229.** df. **42.** (**3.**)

—— Over the Atlantic and Great Western Railway. [With a map.] pp. xiv. 146. *Sampson Low & Co.: London,* 1866. 8°. **8235.** aaa. **24.**

—— Shoeburyness and the Guns: a philosophical discourse. pp. xix. 262. *Sampson Low & Co.: London,* 1865. 8°. **8828.** cc. **33.**

—— The Theory and Practice of the International Trade of the United States and England, and of the trade of the United States and Canada; with tables of federal currency, *etc.* pp. 161. *D. B. Cooke & Co.: Chicago,* 1858. 8°. **8247.** ee. **25.**

—— Wealth and Poverty considered. pp. vi. 232. *Longmans & Co.: London,* 1870 [1869]. 8°. **8226.** aaa. **22.**

—— Second edition. pp. vi. 232. *Longmans & Co.: London,* 1871. 8°. **8282.** bb. **38.**

—— The Workman's Wrongs, and the Workman's Rights. A plea for the people, *etc.* pp. viii. 146. *Longmans & Co.: London,* 1871. 8°. **8282.** bb. **39.**

BARRY (Patrick) *O.S.B.*

—— Handwriting Sheets, *etc.* *James Barrie: London,* 1954. 8°. **7950.** bb. **22.**

BARRY (Patrick) *of New York. See* Periodical Publications.—*Albany.* The Horticulturist, and Journal of Rural Art . . . Edited by A. J. Downing (P. Barry). [1846, *etc.*] 4° & 8°. P.P. **2182.** b.

—— The Fruit Garden; a treatise intended to explain and illustrate the physiology of fruit-trees, *etc.* pp. xiv. 398. *Charles Scribner: New York,* 1851. 8°. **7055.** d. **2.**

—— Barry's Fruit Garden . . . New edition, revised . . . by the author, *etc.* pp. 516. *Orange Judd Co.: New York,* 1883. 12°. **7054.** c. **11.**

BARRY (Patrick J.) Die Zustände im Wiener Schottenkloster vor der Reform des Jahres 1418. pp. 106. *Aichach,* 1927. 8°. **04784.** h. **14.**

BARRY (Patrick J.) *Novelist.* Brennon's Revenge. A story of New York underworld, and of Irish life during the Anglo-Irish war. pp. 238. *A. H. Stockwell: London,* [1930.] 8°. NN. **17294.**

BARRY (*Sir* Patrick Redmond)

—— *See* England. [*Laws and Statutes.*—iv. *Public Health.*] Glen's Public Health Act, 1936 . . . Edited by the Hon. Sir P. R. Barry . . . and H. A. P. Fisher. 1952. 8°. **6429.** c. **37.**

BARRY (Paul de) Les Cent illustres de la Maison de Dieu en toute sorte de profession, *etc.* pp. 582. *P. Borde: Lyon,* 1660. 8°. **4864.** de. **1.**

—— Livre de pensez-i bien. Contenant le moien court, facile & assuré de se sauver. Dédié à la jeunesse, & à tous ceux qui désirent de jouir de l'heureuse éternité. Augmenté de quatre beaux mots, & de la filosofie du vrai crétien. Traduxion nouvelle, *etc.* [By P. de Barry.] pp. 255. 1681. 12°. *See* Livre. **1471.** c. **38.**

BARRY (PAUL DE)

—— Le Paradis ouvert à Philagie par cent dévotions à la mère de Dieu . . . Vingtième réimpression améliorée, et précédée d'une introduction critique par Jean Darche. pp. 432. *Paris*, 1868. 8°. **3455**. cc. **37**.

—— Pensez-y bien, ou réflexions sur les quatre fins dernières, *etc.* [By P. de Barry.] pp. 311. 1810. 12°. *See* RÉFLEXIONS. **4400**. e. **3**.

—— Solitudo Hagiophilæ: sive Instructio ad annua octo vel decem dierum exercitia spiritualia . . . peragenda . . . Gallicè conscripta, interprete R. P. Michaele Cuvelier . . . Editio quarta, emendatior, *etc.* pp. 708. *Apud J. W. Friessem: Coloniae*, 1680. 24°. **4401**. f. **15**.

BARRY (PHILIP) *See* REIZENSTEIN, afterwards RICE (Elmer L.) and BARRY (P.) Cock Robin, *etc.* 1929. 8°. **11791**. aa. **49**.

—— —— [1933.] 8°. **11791**. tt. **1/232**.

—— The Animal Kingdom. A comedy. pp. 198. *Samuel French: New York*, 1932. 8°. **11791**. s. **6**.

—— Here Come the Clowns. A play in three acts. pp. 192. *Coward-McCann: New York*, [1939.] 8°. **11792**. bb. **9**.

—— Holiday. A comedy in three acts. pp. 205. *Samuel French: New York*, 1929. 8°. **11791**. aa. **42**.

—— Hotel Universe. A play. pp. 166. *Samuel French: New York*, 1930. 8°. **11791**. p. **51**.

—— In a Garden. A comedy in three acts. pp. 88. *New York, London*, [1926.] 8°. [*French's Standard Library Edition.*] **011781**. g. **1/135**.

—— [Another edition.] pp. 133. *Samuel French: New York*, 1929. 8°. **11791**. aa. **39**.

—— John. A play. pp. 173. *Samuel French: New York*, 1929. 8°. **11791**. aa. **44**.

—— The Joyous Season. A play. pp. 168. *Samuel French: New York*, 1934. 8°. **20018**. aa. **22**.

—— Liberty Jones. A play with music for city children. pp. 167. *Coward-McCann: New York*, [1941.] 8°. **11792**. bb. **12**.

—— Paris Bound. A comedy. [With musical notes.] pp. 193. *Samuel French: New York*, 1929. 8°. **11791**. aa. **43**.

—— The Philadelphia Story. A comedy in three acts. pp. 206. *Coward-McCann: New York*, [1940.] 8°. **2303**. f. **19**.

—— The Philadelphia Story, *etc.* pp. 141. *Samuel French: New York*, [1942.] 8°. [*French's Standard Library Edition.*] **011781**. g. **1/489**.

—— Spring Dance. A comedy in three acts . . . Adapted from an original play by Eleanor Golden and Eloise Barrangon, *etc.* pp. 116. *New York*, [1936.] 8°. [*French's Standard Library Edition.*] **011781**. g. **1/416**.

—— Tomorrow and Tomorrow. A play. pp. 173. *Samuel French: New York*, 1931. 8°. **11791**. r. **27**.

—— War in Heaven. [A novel.] pp. 250. *Coward McCann: New York*, [1938.] 8°. **12718**. dd. **7**.

—— White Wings. A comedy in four acts. pp. 107. *New York, London*, [1928.] 8°. [*French's Standard Library Edition.*] **011781**. g. **1/187**.

—— [Another edition.] pp. 149. *Samuel French: New York*, 1929. 8°. **11791**. aa. **40**.

BARRY (PHILIP)

—— Without Love. A comedy in three acts. [With the music of the songs.] pp. 206. *Coward-McCann: New York*, 1943. 8°. **11792**. b. **32**.

—— Without Love. A comedy in three acts. (Revised and rewritten. Acting edition.) pp. 117. *Samuel French: New York*, [1949.] 8°. **11792**. e. **8**.

—— You and I. A comedy in three acts. pp. 110. *New York, London*, [1925.] 8°. [*French's Standard Library Edition.*] **011781**. g. **1/87**.

—— [Another edition.] pp. 160. *Samuel French: New York*, 1929. 8°. **11791**. aa. **38**.

—— The Youngest. A comedy in three acts. [With plates.] pp. 126. *New York, London*, [1925.] 8°. [*French's Standard Library Edition.*] **011781**. g. **1/91**.

—— [Another edition.] pp. 162. *Samuel French: New York*, 1929. 8°. **11791**. aa. **41**.

BARRY (PHILIP BEAUFOY) Amateur Acting from a New Angle. pp. 128. *Ernest Benn: London*, 1928. 8°. **011805**. h. **60**.

—— Back-Stage . . . Sketches . . . contributed . . . to the London "Evening News" . . . Illustrated by Bert Thomas, *etc.* pp. 32. *Pictorial Art: [London*, 1947.] 8°. **11795**. de. **51**.

—— How to Succeed as a Playwright. pp. 160. *Hutchinson & Co.: London*, [1928.] 8°. **011805**. i. **40**.

—— How to Succeed as a Writer, *etc.* pp. 126. *Hutchinson & Co.: London*, [1928.] 8°. **011824**. cc. **33**.

—— How to Succeed on the Stage, *etc.* pp. 86. *G. Allen & Unwin: London*, 1927. 8°. **11795**. aaa. **41**.

—— The Mystery of the Blue Diamond. pp. 94. *T. Nelson & Sons: London*, [1928.] 8°. [*Captain Series.*] 012826.a.1/8.

—— [A reissue.] The Mystery of the Blue Diamond. *London*, [1954.] 8°. **12836**. ff. **17**.

—— 99 Points, for Amateur Actors. pp. 63. *Samuel French: London*, [1936.] 8°. **011794**. a. **11**.

—— The Secret Power . . . A handbook to the art of living. pp. 79. *London*, [1927.] 8°. [*Rider's Mind and Body Handbooks.* vol. 17.] **7409**. a. **30/13**.

—— Sinners Down the Centuries, *etc.* [With portraits.] pp. 281. *Jarrolds: London*, [1929.] 8°. **010603**. f. **12**.

—— Twelve Monstrous Criminals, from Nero to Rasputin . . . With 8 illustrations. pp. xii. 275. *Hutchinson & Co.: London*, [1928.] 8°. **06055**. ee. **17**.

—— [Another edition.] pp. 127. *Rich & Cowan: London*, [1933.] 8°. [*True Crime Series.* no. 5.] 20039.aa.3/5.

—— Twenty Human Monsters, in purple and in rags, from Caligula to Landru, *etc.* [With plates.] pp. 286. *Jarrolds: London*, [1929.] 8°. **010603**. d. **12**.

BARRY (PHILIP FRANCIS GOULD) A Book of Christmas Verses. pp. 78. *J. Walch & Sons: Hobart Town*, 1865. 16°. **11651**. a. **30**.

BARRY (PHILIP MAURICE)

—— No Cross, No Victory. Addresses for the three hours' devotion. pp. 48. *A. R. Mowbray & Co.: London & Oxford*, 1947. 8°. **4397**. aaa. **21**.

—— A Present for the Vicar. A handbook on the technique of ordering services, choir, and congregation. pp. 76. *A. R. Mowbray & Co.: London & Oxford*, 1945. 8°. **3479**. aa. **20**.

BARRY (PHILIP MAURICE)

—— A Present for the Vicar, *etc.* (Second and revised edition.) pp. 91. *A. R. Mowbray & Co.: London & Oxford*, 1947. 8°. **3479**. aa. **35**.

—— Some Adventures of Faith. pp. vii. 92. *W. Heffer & Sons: Cambridge*, 1934. 8°. **04413**. g. **61**.

BARRY (PHILLIPS)

—— *See* FLANDERS (Helen H.) The New Green Mountain Songster . . . Collected, transcribed, & edited by H. H. Flanders . . . P. Barry. 1939. 8°. **11689**. dd. **9**.

—— British Ballads from Maine . . . With texts and airs. By P. Barry, Fannie Hardy Eckstorm, Mary Winslow Smith, *etc.* pp. xlvi. 535. *Yale University Press: New Haven; Oxford University Press: London*, 1929. 8°. **011604**. k. **54**.

BARRY (R. MILNER) Bayreuth and Franconian Switzerland. pp. 214. *S. Sonnenschein & Co.: London*, 1887. 8°. **10235**. b. **30**.

BARRY (REDMOND) Barry appellant, Jephson respondent. The respondents case. pp. 3. [*London*, 1720.] fol. **19**. h. **1**. **(177.)**

BARRY (*Sir* REDMOND) *K.C.M.G.* *See* A'BECKETT (T. T.) A Comparative View of Court Fees . . . in reply to the letter of the Acting Chief Justice . . . in reference thereto . . . To which are appended the letter of His Honor, *etc.* [1854.] 8°. **6605**. b. **22**.

—— *See* MELBOURNE.—*Intercolonial Exhibition of Australasia*, 1866–67. Intercolonial Exhibition, 1866. Vocabulary of dialects spoken by aboriginal natives, *etc.* [Edited by Sir R. Barry.] 1867. 8°. **12907**. bb. **21**.

—— *See* MELBOURNE.—*Intercolonial Exhibition, etc.* Exposition Intercoloniale. Vocabulaire des dialectes des aborigènes, *etc.* [Edited by Sir R. Barry.] 1867. 8°. **12901**. ccc. **15**. **(4.)**

—— *See* MELBOURNE.—*Public Library.* The Catalogue of the Public Library of Victoria . . . Preface by the President [Sir R. Barry]. 1880. 8°. **11906**. e. **75**.

—— An Address delivered by his Honor Sir Redmond Barry . . . before the University Forensic Society; and an address also delivered by him, on the opening of the Circuit Court at Portland, *etc.* pp. 54. *Lucas: Melbourne*, [1860.] 8°. **6605**. b. **26**.

—— Address on the Opening of the Free Public Library of Ballarat East. pp. 30. "*The Star*": *Ballarat*, 1869. 12°. **11902**. b. **8**.

—— Address on the Opening of the School of Mines, at Ballarat, Victoria. Delivered . . . on Wednesday, October 26th, A.D. 1870. pp. 23. *Mason, Firth & M'Cutcheon: Melbourne*, 1870. 8°. **07104**. e. **44**.

—— Address to the workmen employed in building the Great Hall of the Melbourne Public Library and Museum, in Melbourne, Victoria. Delivered . . . September 8, A.D. 1866. pp. 40. *Wilson & Mackinnon: Melbourne*, 1866. 8°. **7814**. bb. **34**. **(9.)**

—— Architecture, Sculpture and Painting. (Lecture . . . delivered at the Melbourne Mechanics' Institution, on the 8th September, 1847.) pp. 38. *Mason, Firth & M'Cutcheon: Melbourne*, 1876. 8°. **07805**. g. **57**.

—— Inaugural Address delivered before the members of the Victorian Institute on Friday, the 21st of September, 1854. pp. 15. *Lucas Bros.: Melbourne*, 1854. 8°. **8704**. bbb. **29**. **(1.)**

BARRY (*Sir* REDMOND) *K.C.M.G.*

—— Music and Poetry. (Lecture . . . delivered at the Melbourne Mechanics' Institution on Wednesday, October 24th, 1849.) pp. 44. *Mason, Firth & M'Cutcheon: Melbourne*, 1872. 8°. **7807**. f. **13**. **(4.)**

—— [Another copy.] **L.P.** **7894**. t. **5**. *Without the wrapper.*

BARRY (RENÉ) *See* BARY.

BARRY (RICHARD)

—— Signalling Simplified for L.S.F. & L.D.F. Mallow District Command Area. [*Mallow*, 1941.] 32°. **8838**. a. **7**. *Reproduced from typewriting.*

BARRY (RICHARD) *Earl of Barrymore.* *See* CHANCELLOR (Edwin B.) The Lives of the Rakes. (vol. 5. 'Old Q' and Barrymore.) 1924, *etc.* 8°. **010603**. d. **15/5**.

—— *See* PASQUIN (Anthony) *pseud.* [i.e. John Williams.] The Life of the late Earl of Barrymore, *etc.* 1793. 8°. **12330**. aaa. **3**. **(4.)**

—— *See* PASQUIN (Anthony) *pseud.* [i.e. JOHN WILLIAMS.] The Life of the Late Earl of Barrymore, *etc.* [With a portrait.] 1793. 8°. **641**. g. **28**. **(5.)**

—— *See* PASQUIN (Anthony) *pseud.* [i.e. John Williams.] The Life of the Late Earl of Barrymore . . . Third edition, *etc.* 1793. 8°. **T. 1091**. **(5.)**

—— *See* PASQUIN (Anthony) *pseud.* [i.e. John Williams.] The Life of the Late Earl of Barrymore . . . A new edition, *etc.* [With a portrait.] 1793. 8°. **641**. g. **28**. **(6.)**

—— Truth opposed to Fiction. Or, an impartial review of the life of the late . . . Earl of Barrymore . . . By a personal observer, the author of several popular publications. pp. vii. 121. *C. & G. Kearsley: London*, 1793. 8°. **1416**. c. **41**.

BARRY (RICHARD HAYES)

—— The Events Man: being an account of the adventures of Stanley Washburn, American War Correspondent [in the dispatch boat "Fawan" during the Russo-Japanese war], *etc.* pp. 294. *Moffat, Yard & Co.: New York*, 1907. 8°. **09055**. aaa. **19**.

—— Fruit of the Desert, *etc.* pp. vi. 245. *Curtis Brown: London; Garden City, N.Y.*, printed, 1920. 8°. A.N. **2226**.

—— Mr. Rutledge of South Carolina. [With a portrait.] pp. ix. 430. *Duell, Sloan & Pearce: New York*, [1942.] 8°. **10890**. bb. **3**.

—— Port Arthur: a monster heroism . . . Illustrations from photographs, *etc.* pp. 344. *Moffat, Yard & Co.: New York*, 1905. 8°. **09055**. b. **14**.

—— Sandy from the Sierras . . . Illustrated by Fletcher C. Ransom. pp. 318. *B. F. Steven & Brown: London* [*New York* printed], 1906. 8°. **012706**. b. **27**.

BARRY (RICHARD VON) Zwei Fahrten in das nördliche Eismeer nach Spitzbergen und Novaja Zemlja unternommen von Sr. kön. Hoheit Prinz Heinrich von Bourbon, Graf von Bardi . . . in den Jahren 1891 und 1892 geschildert von R. von Barry, *etc.* pp. viii. 169. *Pola*, 1894. 8°. **10470**. h. **34**.

BARRY (ROBERT BRUÈRE OTTER) *See* AYSCOUGH (H. G. C. P.) and BARRY (R. B. O.) With the Russians in Mongolia, *etc.* 1914. 8°. **010075**. e. **18**.

BARRY (S.) *Writer of Plays.* The Dutchman's Ghost; or, All right. An original farce, in one act, *etc.* pp. 16. *Samuel French: New York,* [1868?] 12°. **11770.** bb. **4.**

BARRY (S. F.) *See* BENTON (C.) and BARRY (S. F.) A Statistical View of the Number of Sheep in the several towns and counties in Maine, New Hampshire, *etc.* 1837. 12°. **7294.** d. **2.**

BARRY (SPRANGER) *See* DUBLIN.—*Crow Street Theatre.* An Estimate of the Theatrical Merits of the two tragedians of Crow Street [S. Barry and Henry Mossop], *etc.* 1760. 8°. **11795.** e. **16.**

—— *See* J., T. A Letter of Compliment to the ingenious author of a Treatise on the passions . . . with a critical enquiry into the theatrical merit of Mr. G—k, Mr. Q—n and Mr. B—y [i.e. S. Barry]. [1747.] 8°. **641.** f. **8.** (**2.**)

—— *See* TREATISE. A Treatise on the Passions . . . with a critical inquiry into the theatrical merit of . . . Mr. B —— y [i.e. S. Barry], *etc.* [1760?] 8°. **641.** f. **8.** (**1.**)

—— An Answer, in behalf of S. Barry . . . to the Case and Petition of T. Sheridan, manager and lessee of the united Theatres of Aungier-Street and Smock-Alley, and also to the Petition of two of the Proprietors of said united theatres, *etc.* [*Dublin?* 1756?] *s. sh.* fol. **1890.** e. **5.** (**147.**)

BARRY (STANLEY LEONARD) The Pedigree of the Barrys of Eynsham, Oxon. pp. 48. *Dean & Son: London,* 1928. 4°. **09915.** g. **9.**

BARRY (T. D.) *See* PAYEN (A.) Industrial Chemistry . . . based upon a translation, partly by . . . T. D. Barry . . . of Payen's Précis de chimie industrielle, *etc.* 1878. 8°. **08909.** i. **9.**

BARRY (THOMAS) *Compiler of Guide Books.*

—— The "Borough" Pocket Guide to Halstead, *etc.* pp. 36. *E. J. Burrow: Cheltenham,* [1919.] 8°. **10354.** a. **361.**

BARRY (THOMAS) *of the Convent of S. Iacopo sopr' Arno, Florence.*

—— Lettera sopra la cicisbeatura scritta dal Sig. T. B. Irlandese [i.e. T. Barry] all'illustrissima Signora N. N. Con un accordo di cicisbeatura in dieci articoli. Edizione seconda . . . accresciuta con copiose aggiunte, *etc.* pp. lxxii. 1770. 8°. *See* B., T., *Irlandese.* **8415.** cc. **16.** (**1.**)

BARRY (THOMAS HEDLEY) *See* DANIELS (Richard G.) Nitro Cellulose Lacquer Manufacture . . . Sectional editor T. H. Barry. [1933.] 8°. W.P. **994/2.**

—— *See* MORRELL (Robert S.) Synthetic Resins and Allied Plastics. Edited by R. S. Morrell . . . in collaboration with T. H. Barry, *etc.* 1937. 8°. **8899.** i. **33.**

—— *See* MYDDLETON (William W.) and BARRY (T. H.) Fats, *etc.* 1924. 4°. **8903.** cc. **26.**

—— The Chemistry of the Natural & Synthetic Resins. By T. H. Barry . . . Alan A. Drummond . . . R. S. Morrell. pp. vii. 196. *Ernest Benn: London,* 1926. 8°. [*Oil & Colour Chemistry Monographs.*] **8896.g.15/5.**

—— How to Photograph Buildings, *etc.* [With plates.] pp. 30. *Fountain Press: London,* 1927. 8°. **8904.** aa. **20.**

—— Natural Varnish Resins. pp. xii. 294. *Ernest Benn: London,* 1932. 8°. **07942.** bb. **42.**

BARRY (TOM) Courage. A comedy. pp. 119. *Samuel French: New York,* 1929. 8°. **11791.** p. **19.**

BARRY (TOM B.)

—— Guerilla Days in Ireland. [Autobiographical reminiscences.] pp. 228. *Irish Press: Dublin,* 1949. 8°. **9508.** eee. **5.**

BARRY (V. D.) *See* MARTINET (Antoine) A Salve for the Bite of the Black Viper . . . Translated . . . by V. D. Barry. 1852. 8°. **3900.** a. **49.**

BARRY (VINCENT CHRISTOPHER)

—— *See* DILLON (Thomas P.) and BARRY (V. C.) Ceimic. 1950. 8°. **08909.** a. **68.**

—— Antitubercular Substances, *etc.* [By V. C. Barry, Dermot Twomey and Laurence O'Rourke, Joan E. McCormick and P. W. D. Mitchell and others.] *Hodges, Figgis & Co.: Dublin; Williams & Norgate: London,* 1947– . 8°. [*Proceedings of the Royal Irish Academy.* vol. 51. sec. B. no. 7–9, 14, 15; vol. 53. sec. B. no. 7, 8; vol. 57. sec. B. no. 3, 4, *etc.* Vol. 62. Sec. B. no. 12, etc.] Ac. **1540/4.**

—— Nótaí cleaċtta ar an g-ceimioċt, maille le cláir anailíse do luċt na céad-bliadna, *etc.* pp. 43. Oifig an tSoláṫair: Baile Áṫa Cliaṫ, 1942. 8°. **08900.** a. **25.**

—— Studies in the Chemotherapy of Tuberculosis. pp. 10. *London,* 1952. 8°. [*Royal Institute of Chemistry. Lectures, Monographs and Reports.* 1952. no. 2.] Ac. **3921/32.**

BARRY (WILLIAM) *Artist.* Ben Nevis. An artist's experience. pp. 34. *Northern Counties Printing & Publishing Co.: Inverness,* [1896.] *obl.* 8°. **10369.** a. **48.**

BARRY (WILLIAM) *B.A., London.* *See* SHAKESPEARE (W.) [*Smaller Collections of Plays.*] Blackie's Junior School Shakespeare. [Edited by W. Barry and others.] 1893, *etc.* 8°. **11761.** ee.

—— *See* SHAKESPEARE (W.) [*King Henry v.*] Shakespeare's Play of King Henry v. With . . . notes by W. Barry. 1892. 16°. **12200.** c. **15/26.**

BARRY (WILLIAM) *C.E.* Venezuela: a visit to the gold mines of Guyana, and voyage up the river Orinoco during 1886, *etc.* pp. 159. lxxviii. *Marshall Bros.: London,* 1886. 8°. **10481.** aaa. **28**

BARRY (WILLIAM) *of Sloane Street, London.* Moorland and Stream. With notes and prose idyls on shooting and trout fishing. pp. iv. 299. *Tinsley Bros.: London,* 1871. 8°. **7906.** de. **7.**

—— Sporting Rambles and Holiday Papers. pp. iv. 262. *G. Routledge & Sons: London & New York,* [1873.] 8°. **7905.** aaa. **6.**

BARRY (WILLIAM) *Pastor of the First Church in Framingham.* A History of Framingham, Massachusetts, including the plantation, from 1640 to the present time, with an appendix, containing a notice of Sudbury and its first proprietors; also, a register of the inhabitants of Framingham before 1800, with genealogical sketches. pp. iv. 456. *J. Munroe & Co.: Boston,* 1847. 8°. **10410.** e. **3.**

—— The Rights and Duties of Neighboring Churches. Two sermons, *etc.* pp. 43. *B. H. Greene: Boston,* 1844. 8°. **4486.** c. **34.** (**7.**)

BARRY (William E.) Chronicles of Kennebunk: being scenes and episodes in an old Maine village & vicinity. With illustrations, *etc.* pp. 86. *Redfield-Kendrick-Odell Co.: New York*, 1923. *obl.* 4°. **Cup.1247.m.40.**

BARRY (William Edwin) The Jade God. A mystery play in three acts . . . Dramatized from a novel of the same name by Alan Sullivan. pp. 77. *New York, London*, [1930.] 8°. [*French's Standard Library Edition.*] **011781**. g. **1/244**.

BARRY (William Farquhar) *See* Barnard (Jonathan G.) and Barry (W. F.) Report of the Engineer and Artillery Operations of the army of the Potomac from its organization to the close of the Peninsular Campaign, *etc.* 1863. 8°. **9604**. cc. **2**.

—— *See* United States of America.—*Department of War.* Instruction for Field Artillery. Prepared by . . . W. F. Barry [and others], *etc.* 1864. 8°. **8828**. bb. **29**.

BARRY (William Francis)

—— *See* Burke (C. E.) The Structure of Life . . . With a preface by Rev. W. Barry, *etc.* 1899. 8°. **8410**. f. **45**.

—— Arden Massiter. [A novel.] pp. viii. 344. *T. Fisher Unwin: London*, 1900. 8°. **012641**. aaa. **1**.

—— Catholic Europe. *See* Acton (J. E. E. D.) *Baron Acton.* The Cambridge Modern History, *etc.* vol. 1. The Renaissance. 1902, *etc.* 8°. **2070.g.**

—— The Coming Age and the Catholic Church. A forecast. pp. vi. 246. *Cassell & Co.: London*, 1929. 8°. **3942**. eee. **51**.

—— The Dayspring. [A novel.] pp. viii. 405. *T. Fisher Unwin: London*, 1903. 8°. **012638**. bb. **48**.

—— Ernest Renan. [With plates, including portraits.] pp. viii. 288. *Hodder & Stoughton: London*, 1905. 8°. [*Literary Lives.*] **10600**. cc. **15/2**.

—— Four Centuries of Luther. (Reprinted from The Tablet.) pp. 12. *Catholic Truth Society: London*, 1917. 8°. **3943**. aa. **332**.

—— Freemasons in France. (Reprinted from the National Review.) pp. 23. *Catholic Truth Society: London*, [1906.] 8°. **3943**. aa. **403**. (**2**.)

—— Heralds of Revolt. Studies in modern literature and dogma. pp. xv. 383. *Hodder & Stoughton: London*, 1904. 8°. **011853**. i. **14**.

—— New edition, revised and enlarged. pp. xlviii. 383. *Hodder & Stoughton: London*, 1909. 8°. **011851**. ee. **86**.

—— John Henry, Cardinal Newman. (Reprinted with additions, from The Tablet.) *See* Newman (J. H.) *Cardinal.* Eight Lectures on the position of Catholics in England, *etc.* 1890. 8°. **3940**. cc. **6**.

—— Cardinal Newman. [A revised edition of "John Henry, Cardinal Newman."] pp. 32. *Catholic Truth Society: London*, [1894.] 8°. **3943**. aa. **364**.

—— The King's Highway of the Holy Cross. pp. 14. *Burns & Oates: London*, [1905.] 16°. **04420**. de. **24**. (**1**.)

—— The Knights of the Red Cross. A sermon preached at the requiem for fallen Catholic soldiers & sailors belonging to the Catholic missions of Birmingham, *etc.* pp. 16. *Burns & Oates: London*, [1915.] 8°. **4473**. h. **39**.

—— The Layman in the Church. *See* Gasquet (Francis A.) *Cardinal.* The Layman in the Pre-Reformation Parish, *etc.* [1900.] 8°. **3943**. aa. **333**.

BARRY (William Francis)

—— Literature. The word of life or of death. pp. 71. *Cassell & Co.: London*, 1912. 8°. [*New Tracts for the Times.*] **12205**. cc. **29/8**.

—— Memories and Opinions. [With plates, including a portrait.] pp. xiii. 302. *G. P. Putnam's Sons: London & New York*, 1926. 8°. **4920**. k. **8**.

—— The New Antigone. A romance. [By W. Barry.] 1887. 8°. *See* Antigone. **012639**. m. **19**.

—— Newman. pp. vi. 288. *Hodder & Stoughton: London*, 1904. 8°. [*Literary Lives.*] **10600**. cc. **15/1**.

—— Cardinal Newman. (Revised edition.) pp. 254. *Hodder & Stoughton: London*, [1927.] 8°. [Hodder & Stoughton's People's Library.] **12211.c.1/40.**

—— The Papacy and Modern Times. A political sketch, 1303–1870. pp. 256. *Williams & Norgate: London*, [1911.] 8°. [*Home University Library of Modern Knowledge.*] **12199**. p. **1/2**.

—— The Papal Monarchy from St. Gregory the Great to Boniface viii. 590–1303. pp. xxviii. 435. *T. Fisher Unwin: London*, 1902. 8°. [*Story of the Nations.* vol. 58.] **9012.a.1/58.**

—— The Place of Dreams. Four stories. pp. vi. 274. *Catholic Truth Society: London*, 1893. 8°. **4399**. eee. **2**.

—— [Another edition.] pp. xi. 274. *Sands & Co.: London*, 1901. 8°. **012637**. a. **31**.

—— The Prospects of Catholicism. (Reprinted from the National Review.) pp. 24. *Catholic Truth Society: London*, [1901.] 8°. **3943**. aa. **365**. (**1**.)

—— Roma sacra. Essays on Christian Rome. pp. vi. 250. *Longmans & Co.: London*, 1927. 8°. **04530**. g. **18**.

—— Thoughts for Freethinkers. An appeal to young men. pp. 32. *Catholic Truth Society: London*, [1905.] 8°. **3938.gg.19.(4.)**

—— The Tradition of Scripture: its origin, authority and interpretation. pp. xxv. 278. *Longmans & Co.: London*, 1906. 8°. [*Westminster Library.*] **2206**. a. **9/1**.

—— Second edition, revised. pp. xxix. 278. *Longmans & Co.: London*, 1908. 8°. [*Westminster Library.*] **2206**. a. **9/5**.

—— The Triumph of Life; or, Science and the soul. pp. xi. 247. *Longmans & Co.: London*, 1928. 8°. **04375**. ee. **27**.

—— The Turks, Cardinal Newman, and the Council of Ten . . . Reprinted . . . from The Nineteenth Century and After, *etc.* pp. 15. *Spottiswoode, Ballantyne & Co.: London*, 1919. 8°. **08028**. i. **4**.

—— The Turks, Cardinal Newman, and the Council of Ten, *etc.* pp. 15. [*London*,] 1920. 8°. [*Publications of the Anglo-Hellenic League.* no. 40.] **8027.b.65/40.**

—— The Two Standards. [A tale.] pp. viii. 530. *T. Fisher Unwin: London*, 1898. 8°. **012642**. aaa. **1**.

—— The Wizard's Knot. (Second impression.) pp. viii. 376. *T. Fisher Unwin: London*, 1901. 8°. **012629**. d. **49**.

—— The World's Debate. An historical defence of the Allies. pp. xx. 332. *Hodder & Stoughton: London*, 1917. 8°. **09007**. bb. **1**.

BARRY (WILLIAM FREDERICK) *See* AGABEG (A.) and BARRY (W. F.) The Bills of Exchange Act, 1882, *etc.* 1883. 8°. **6375**. h. **17**.

—— —— 1884. 8°. **6376**. t. **13**.

—— *See* ENGLAND.—*Supreme Court of Judicature.—High Court of Justice.—King's Bench Division.—[Reports.]* The Law Reports. Queen's (King's) Bench Division, *etc.* [1908–1921. Reported by W. F. Barry and others.] 1876, *etc.* 8°. Bar. A. **9**.

—— *See* LONDON.—III. *Council of Law Reporting.* The Law Reports . . . Compilers . . . W. F. Barry, *etc.* 1892. 8°. **5807.a.16.**

BARRY (WILLIAM JACKSON) Up and Down; or, Fifty years colonial experiences . . . Being the life history of Captain W. J. Barry. Written by himself . . . With portrait, *etc.* pp. xii. 307. *Sampson Low & Co.: London,* 1879. 8°. **10827**. b. **10**.

BARRY (WILLIAM JAMES) The Sacramentals of the Holy Catholic Church; or, Flowers from the garden of the liturgy. pp. 264. *J. P. Walsh: Cincinnati,* 1858. 8°. **3476**. c. **71**.

—— [Another edition.] pp. xv. 214. *T. Richardson & Sons: London & Derby,* 1879. 16°. **3478**. aaa. **13**.

BARRY (WILLIAM TAYLOR) Address . . . to the People of the United States. pp. 24. *F. P. Blair: Washington,* 1834. 8°. **8246**. ff. **3**.

—— Letter . . . to the House of Representatives . . . reviewing the report of the Select Committee of that House appointed to investigate affairs of the Post Office Department, March 2 1835. pp. 30. *Blair & Rives: Washington,* 1835. 8°. **8307**. ee. **15**.

BARRY (WILLIAM WHITMORE OTTER) *See* WELFORD (Alfred W. B.) and BARRY (W. W. O.) The Law relating to Fire Insurance. 1911. 8°. **6144**. s. **9**.

—— —— 1921. 8°. **6144**. ss. **1**.

—— —— 1932. 8°. **6145**. r. **8**.

—— *See* WELFORD (Alfred W. B.) and BARRY (W. W. O.) The Law relating to Fire Insurance, *etc.* 1948. 4°. **8233**. bb. **55**.

BARRY (WILLIAM WHITTAKER) Forms and Precedents in Conveyancing, with introduction and practical notes. pp. xxiv. 456. *Simpkin, Marshall & Co.: London,* 1872. 8°. **6305**. aaa. **3**.

—— A Treatise on the Law and Practice of Benefit Building and Freehold Land Societies; with an appendix of rules and forms. pp. xx. 189. *Horace Cox: London,* 1866. 8°. **6375**. aaa. **3**.

—— A Treatise on the Practice of Conveyancing. pp. xxx. 515. *Butterworths: London,* 1865. 8°. **6305**. bb. **2**.

—— A Treatise on the Statutory Jurisdiction of the Court of Chancery, with an appendix of precedents. pp. l. 411. *V. & R. Stevens & Sons: London,* 1861. 8°. **6190**. d. **1**.

—— A Walking Tour in Normandy. By the author of "All Round Ireland on Foot" [i.e. W. W. Barry]. pp. xii. 252. 1868. 8°. *See* NORMANDY. **10169**. b. **9**.

—— A Walking Tour round Ireland in 1865. By an Englishman [i.e. W. W. Barry]. pp. xix. 406. 1867. 8°. *See* ENGLISHMAN. **10390**. dd. **4**.

BARRYMORE, *Earls of. See* ROBINSON (John R.) *Writer of Memoirs.* The Last Earls of Barrymore. 1769–1824. 1894. 8°. **10817**. dd. **14**.

BARRYMORE, DAVID, *1st Earl of. See* BARRY.

——, RICHARD, *7th Earl of. See* BARRY.

BARRYMORE (EDWARD J.) The Pilgrim of Einsiedeln . . . and other poems. pp. 24. *A. H. Stockwell: London,* [1923.] 8°. **11644**. dd. **52**.

BARRYMORE (ETHEL) [ETHEL BLYTHE.]

—— *See* BARRYMORE (John) We Three. Ethel—Lionel—John, *etc.* [With portraits.] [1935.] 16°. **10883**. a. **41**.

—— Memories. An autobiography . . . Illustrated. [With portraits.] pp. x. 310. *Harper & Bros.: New York,* [1955.] 8°. **10892**. bb. **31**.

BARRYMORE (JOHN) [JOHN BLYTHE.]

—— *See* FOWLER (Gene) Good Night, Sweet Prince. The life and times of J. Barrymore. 1947. 8°. **10890**. a. **7**.

—— *See* FOWLER (Gene) Good Night, Sweet Prince. [With portraits.] 1949. 8°. **10889**. de. **5**.

—— *See* WATERS (Alma P.) John Barrymore, *etc.* [With a portrait.] [1942.] 8°. **10889**. bb. **16**.

—— Confessions of an Actor . . . Illustrated. *Bobbs-Merrill Co.: Indianapolis,* [1926.] 8°. **10884**. b. **24**.

—— [Another edition.] pp. 128. *R. Holden & Co.: London,* 1926. 8°. **010884**. ee. **20**.

—— We Three. Ethel—Lionel—John, *etc.* [With portraits.] *Saalfield Publishing Co.: Akron, New York,* [1935.] 16°. **10883**. a. **41**.

BARRYMORE (LIONEL) [LIONEL BLYTHE.]

—— *See* BARRYMORE (John) We Three. Ethel—Lionel—John, *etc.* [With portraits.] [1935.] 16°. **10883**. a. **41**.

—— We Barrymores. By Lionel Barrymore as told to Cameron Shipp, *etc.* [With plates, including portraits.] pp. viii. 244. *Peter Davies: London,* 1951. 8°. **10889**. e. **28**.

BARRYMORE (WILLIAM) The Blood Red Knight! or, the Fatal Bridge. A melo-dramatic romance, in two acts, *etc.* pp. 20. *London,* [1850?] 12°. [*Duncombe's Edition of the British Theatre.* vol. 66.] **2304**. b. **3**.

—— The Fatal Snow Storm: or, Lowina of Tobolski! A melo-drama, in two acts, *etc.* pp. 34. *London,* [1831.] 12°. [*Richardson's New Minor Drama.* vol. 4.] **643**. a. **15**.

—— [Another edition.] pp. 34. *London,* [1837?] 12°. [*Cumberland's Minor Theatre, etc.* vol. 13.] **643**. a. **7**.

—— The Forest of Bondy; or, Dog of Montargis. A drama, in three acts [translated and adapted from R. C. Guilbert de Pixérécourt's "Le Chien de Montargis." By W. Barrymore?]; adapted to Hodgson's theatrical characters and scenes in the same. pp. 24. [c. 1825.] 8°. *See* BONDY, *Forest of.* **11779**. aa. **40**. (**2**.)

—— The Forest of Bondy . . . A melo drama, *etc.* [Translated and adapted from R. C. Guilbert de Pixérécourt's "Le Chien de Montargis." By W. Barrymore?] pp. 36. [c. 1830.] 12°. *See* BONDY, *Forest of.* **2304**. a. **2**.

BARRYMORE (WILLIAM)

—— Gilderoy; or, the bonnie boy: a melo-drama, in two acts, *etc.* pp. viii. 54. *London,* [1829.] 12°. [*Richardson's New Minor Drama.* vol. 2.] **643**. a. **14**.

—— [Another edition.] pp. 54. *London,* [1834.] 12°. [*Cumberland's Minor Theatre, etc.* vol. 8.] **643**. a. **4**.

—— El Hyder: the chief of the Ghaut Mountains. A grand eastern melo-dramatic spectacle, in two acts. pp. 25. *London,* [1852.] 12°. [*Lacy's Acting Edition of Plays.* vol. 6.] **2304**. d. **10**.

—— El Hyder; the chief of the Ghaut Mountains. A grand eastern melodramatic spectacle, in two acts. 1871. *See* BRITISH DRAMA. The British Drama. Illustrated. vol. 6. 1864, *etc.* 8°. **11770**. bbb. **12**. (**23**.)

—— [Another edition.] pp. 12. *London,* [1875?] 8° [*Dicks' Standard Plays.* no. 140.] 11770.bbb.4.
A reissue of the edition of 1871.

—— The Man in the Moon; or, the Harlequin Dog-Star. An entirely new comic pantomime, *etc.* pp. 19. *J. Tabby: London,* 1826. 8°. **11778**. aaa. **16**. (**2**.)

—— Manfredi the mysterious Hermit; a romantic melodrama in two acts. pp. 46. *T. H. Lacy: London,* [1854.] 12°. **11771**. aa. **18**.

—— Meg Murnock, the hag of the glen. A melodrama. pp. 32. *T. H. Lacy: London,* [1854.] 12°. **11771**. aa. **23**.

—— The Secret. A farce, in one act. Adapted from the French. pp. 19. *T. H. Lacy: London,* [1854.] 12°. **11771**. aa. **26**.

—— [Another edition.] pp. 19. *London,* [1860?] 12°. [*Lacy's Acting Edition of Plays.* vol. 48.] **2304**. e. **22**.

—— [Another edition.] pp. 7. *London,* [1879?] 8°. [*Dick's Standard Plays.* no. 262.] 11770.bbb.4.

—— Trial by Battle; or, Heaven defend the right: a melodramatic spectacle in two acts, *etc.* pp. 24. *London,* [1831?] 12°. [*Duncombe's Edition of the British Theatre.*] **2304**. a. **4**.

—— [Another edition.] pp. 24. *T. H. Lacey: London.* [1854.] 12°. **11771**. aa. **13**.

—— The Two Swindlers; or, There he goes! A farce, in one act, *etc.* *See* DICKENS (Charles) [*Pickwick Papers.*] "Bardell v. Pickwick," *etc.* [1885.] 8°. [*Dicks' Standard Plays.* no. 636.] **11770**. bbb. **4**.

—— Wallace: the Hero of Scotland. A romantic historical drama, in three acts. pp. 36. *London,* [1867?] 12°. [*Lacy's Acting Edition of Plays.* vol. 73.] **2304**. f. **18**.

—— Wallace, the Hero of Scotland, *etc.* pp. 15. *London,* [1888.] 8°. [*Dicks' Standard Plays.* no. 953.] **11770**. bbb. **4**.

BARRY TAILLEBOIS (   ) Parallèle de la conduite des évêques de France lors du formulaire & de la constitution unigenitus, & à l'égard de la nouvelle constitution civile du clergé. pp. 43. *Carcassonne,* [1790?] 8°. **F.R. 149**. (**1**.)

BARS. Behind the Bars. [On the treatment of the insane. By Adeline T. Lunt.] pp. 356. *Lee & Shepard: Boston,* 1871. 16°. **7660**. de. **27**.

—— The Two Bars: a tale of rescue. By the author of "Found on the dark mountains," *etc.* [i.e. Mary Kennion]. pp. 96. *Partridge & Co.: London,* [1882.] 16°. **4421**. ee. **47**.

BARSA, *Saint and Martyr, Bishop of Edessa. See* BARSIMAEUS.

BARSAC (LOUIS) *pseud.* [i.e. ERNEST JAMES OLDMEADOW.] Shadows and Fireflies: a book of verse. (Second edition.) pp. 88. *Unicorn Press: London,* 1898. 16°. [*Unicorn Books of Verse.* no. 1.] **11607**. aaa. **25/1**.

BARSACQ (ANDRÉ)

—— *See* GOGOL' (N. V.) [*Ревизор.*] Le Revizor . . . Adaptation d'André Barsacq, *etc.* 1949. 8°. [*France Illustration. Supplément théâtral et littéraire.* no. 32.] **P.P. 4283**. m. (**1**.)

BARSALI (E.) Bibliografia epaticologica italiana. pp. 37. *Pisa,* 1902. 8°. **11899**. h. **23**. (**3**.)

BARSALI (SCIPIONE) Gesù, Messia, Redentore, Dio fatto carne. Dimostrazione storico-filosofica compilata . . in opposizione ai sofisti neganti la divinità di Gesù Cristo. pp. 382. *S. Miniato,* 1866. 8°. **3902**. bb. **20**.

BARSALIBI (DIONYSIUS) *Bishop of Amida. See* DIONYSIUS, *bar Ṣalībī, etc.*

BARSALOU FROMENTY (GUSTAVE) Études sur le passé et sur l'avenir des travailleurs industriels. pp. 171. *Agen,* 1848. 8°. **8275**. a. **16**.

—— La Philosophie terrestre. pp. 488. *Genève,* 1876. 8°. **4380**. cc. **8**.

BARSALOUX (ELSA) The Priscilla Cluny Crochet Book . . . By E. Barsaloux and others. pp. 32. *Priscilla Publishing Co.: Boston,* [1920.] 8°. **7742**. pp. **4**.

—— The Priscilla Sweater Book, including hats, caps, and other accessories, with directions for working. 2 no. *Priscilla Publishing Co.: Boston,* 1917, 20. 8°. **7743**. ee. **36**.

—— The Priscilla War Work Book, including directions for knitted garments and comfort kits from the American Red Cross, and knitted garments for the boy scout. pp. 32. *Priscilla Publishing Co.: Boston,* [1917.] 4°. **7742**. r. **1**.

BARSAMA, *Saint and Martyr, Bishop of Edessa. See* BARSIMAEUS.

BÂRSAN (ZAHARIA)

—— Domnul de rouă. Poem dramatic in trei acte în versuri. pp. 184. *Bucureşti,* [1938.] 8°. **11758**. v. **29**.

—— Trandafirii roşii. Poem dramatic în trei acte, în versuri. Ediţia v. pp. 175. *Bucureşti,* [1938.] 8°. **11758**. v. **30**.

BARSANTI (A.) *See* MORGAN (Jacques J.M. de) Kom Ombos . . . Par J. de Morgan . . . A. Barsanti. 1895, *etc.* fol. [*Catalogue des monuments et inscriptions de l'Égypte antique.* sér. 1. tom. 2.] **7710**. t. **2**.

BARSANTI (A.) and **MASPERO** (*Sir* GASTON) *K.C.M.G.*

—— Fouilles autour de la pyramide d'Ounas. pp. 98. *Le Caire,* 1900. 8°. Dept. of Egyptian & Assyrian Antiquities.

BARSANTI (EUGENIO) I Processi di Dante. pp. 103. ii. *Firenze,* 1908. 8°. **011420**. cc. **7**. (**2**.)

BARSANTI (EZIO) L'Inquisitorato alle revisioni e appuntature nell'antica repubblica di Venezia. pp. x. 113. *Livorno,* 1898. 8°. **8223**. bb. **56**. (**4**.)

BARSANTI (GIOVANNI CARLO) De balneis oratio. 1770. *See* CALOGIERÀ (A.) Nuova raccolta d'opuscoli scientifici, *etc.* tom. 20. 1755, *etc.* 12°. **247**. a. **20**.

BARSANTI (Joannes Carolus) *See* Barsanti (Giovanni C.)

BARSANTI (Leopoldo) Le Piante nella Divina Commedia. pp. 5. *Pisa*, 1901. 8°. **11422**. g. **25**. (**6**.)

BARSANTI (Ottavio) Lecture on the Legitimacy of the Papal Sovereignty. pp. 34. *T. Verga: Melbourne*, 1870. 8°. **8032**. c. **7**. (**1**.)

—— I Protestanti tra i selvaggi della Nuova Zelanda, ossia Storia del Pai Marire. pp. 283. *Torino*, 1868. 8°. **4745**. aa. **28**.

—— St. Patrick's Apostleship. A lecture, *etc.* pp. 31. v. *T. Verga: Melbourne*, 1871. 8°. **4823**. e. **2**. (**1**.)

—— I Selvaggi dell' Australia dinazi alla scienza e al protestantismo. pp. xix. 259. *Roma, Torino*, 1868. 8°. **4745**. aa. **29**.

BARSANTI (Paolo) Il Pubblico insegnamento in Lucca dal secolo xiv. alla fine del secolo xviii. Contributo alla storia della cultura nazionale. (Saggio di bibliografia storica delle scuole italiane.) pp. viii. 259. *Lucca*, 1905. 8°. **08355**. k. **19**.

BARSANTI (Pietro Vincenzo) Della storia del padre Girolamo Savonarola libri quattro, *etc.* [By P. V. Barsanti.] pp. xxiv. 345. 1782. 4°. *See* Savonarola (G.) [*Appendix.*] **3901**. h. **14**. (**1**.)

BARSANTI (Pio) Il Diritto criminale e il progresso. Prolusione, *etc.* pp. 21. *Macerata*, 1882. 8°. **5373**. g. **8**. (**3**.)

BARSANTI (Rocco Maria) successively *Bishop of Fossombrone* and *of Pesaro. See* Rome, *Church of.*—Pius vi., *Pope.* Pius P. P. Sextus venerabili fratri Roccho Maria, *etc.* [A letter of commendation, dated 15 July 1778.] 1778. *s. sh.* 4°. T. **24***. (**49**.)

BARSANUPHIUS, *a Monk of Palestine. Του ἁγιου Βαρσανουφιου . . . Διδασκαλια περι των 'Ωριγενους, Εὐαγριου και Διδυμου φρονηματων.* Sancti Barsanuphii . . . Doctrina circa opiniones Origenis, Evagrij et Didymi. *Gr. & Lat.* 1860. *See* Migne (J. P.) Patrologiæ cursus completus . . . Series Græca. tom. 86. 1857, *etc.* 4°. **2001**. f.

BARSAS (Isabel de) Isabel de Barsas; a tradition of the twelfth century. 3 vol. *Baldwin, Cradock & Joy: London*, 1823. 12°. N. **124**.

BÄRSCH. [For the German surname of this form:] *See* Baersch.

BARSCHAK (Erna)

—— The Innocent Empress. An intimate study of Eugénie . . . Illustrated with photographs. pp. 346. *E. P. Dutton & Co.: New York*, 1943. 8°. **10656**. h. **32**.

BARSCHALL (Emil Charles) *See* Hogarth (William) Die Werke von W. Hogarth. Nach den Original-Platten auf 118 Blättern photolithographirt . . . Bearbeitet von E. C. Barschall. 1878. fol. **1756**. d. **1**.

BARSCHERUS (Anne) *See* Barskier.

BARSE ( ) *Citoyen.* Les Patriotes déportés de la Guadeloupe par les Anglais, aux membres de la Convention nationale, composant la commission des Colonies. [Signed by Barse and others, denouncing the former government and certain inhabitants as having given up the island to the English.] pp. 19. [*Paris*, 1794.] 8°. F. **690**. (**6**.)

BARSE (Jules) *See* Aguilhon (J. J. H.) and Barse (J.) Observations sur la préparation et les effets du chloroforme. 1848. 8°. **7460**. c. **1**.

—— *See* Chevallier (Jean B. A.) and Barse (J.) Manuel pratique de l'appareil de Marsh, ou guide de l'expert toxicologiste, *etc.* 1843. 8°. **7460**. aaa. **7**.

—— *See* Chevallier (Jean B. A.) and Barse (I.) Monographie générale de l'empoisonnement par l'acide sulfurique, *etc.* 1846. 8°. **7510**. aaa. **29**. (**10**.)

—— Manuel de la Cour d'Assises dans les questions d'empoisonnement . . . ou Recueil des principes de la toxicologie ramenés à des formalités judiciaires . . . Contenant des travaux inédits sur plusieurs points de la science par M. Orfila. pp. xx. 404. *Paris*, 1845. 12°. **6095**. aa. **2**.

BARSE (Louis) *See* Sylvester ii., *Pope.* Lettres et discours de Gerbert, traduits . . . et publiés . . . par M. L. Barse. 1847. 12°. **4855**. a. **36**.

BARSE (Mary Emma) *See* Blain (Mary E.) *pseud.* [i.e. M. E. Barse.]

BÂRSEAN (Andreiŭ) *See* Bârseanŭ.

BÂRSEANU (Andreiŭ) *See* Jarník (J. U.) Glossaire des chansons populaires roumaines de Transylvanie. Collection Bârsean-Jarník, *etc.* 1885. 8°. **12942**. aaa. **39**.

—— *See* Jarník (J. U.) and Bârseanu (A.) Doine şi strigăturĭ din Ardeal, date la iveală de Dr. J. U. Iarnik şi A. Bârseanu, *etc.* (Glossaire.) 1885. 8°. Ac. **743/6**.

—— *See* Radulescu-Motru (C.) Andrei Bârseanu şi naţionalismul, *etc.* 1924. 8°. [*Academia Română. Discursuri de recepţiune.* no. 58.] Ac. **743**. b.

BARSEGAPÈ (Pietro da) Poemetto inedito. *See* Biondelli (B.) Studii linguistici. 1856. 8°. **12901**. g. **16**.

—— [Another edition.] *See* Biondelli (B.) Poesie Lombarde inedite, *etc.* 1856. 8°. **11431**. g. **7**.

—— Die Reimpredigt des Pietro da Barsegapè. Kritischer Text mit Einleitung, Grammatik und Glossar herausgegeben von E. Keller. *Ital.* pp. viii. 96. *Frauenfeld*, 1901. 4°. **11422**. h. **17**.

BARSEGOV (A. A.)

—— *See* Modzolevsky (I. V.) and Barsegov (A. A.) Общий курс железных дорог, *etc.* 1951. 8°. **8236**. h. **8**.

BARSEWISCH (von) *Hauptmann im* 1. *Bad. Leib-Grenadier-Regiment No.* 109. Geschichte des Grossherzoglich Badischen Leib-Grenadier-Regiments, 1803–1871. i. Theil. Geschichte . . . 1803–1869, verfasst durch von Barsewisch. (ii. Theil. Das 1. Grossherzoglich Badische Leib-Grenadier-Regiment im Feldzuge 1870–71 . . . Zusammengestellt und bearbeitet . . . von Major von Trapp-Ehrenschild. Zweite Auflage.) 2 pt. *Karlsruhe*, 1893. 8°. **8829**. k. **40**.

BARSEWISCH (C. F. R. von) Meine Kriegs-Erlebnisse während des Siebenjährigen Krieges 1757–1763. Wortgetreuer Abdruck aus dem Tagebuche des Kgl. Preuss. General-Quartiermeister-Lieutenants C. F. R. von Barsewisch. Zweite Auflage. pp. 213. *Berlin*, 1863. 8°. **9385**. bb. **5**.

BARSEWISCH (Julius von) *See* Angelus (A.) Einiges von den alten Städten, Fürsten und dem Adel der Mark Brandenburg . . . zusammengestellt aus den Annales . . . von M. A. Angelus durch J. von Barsewisch. 1864. 8°. **9904**. b. **22**.

BARSI (József) *See* Vargha (Gy.) *Member of the Hungarian Academy.* Barsi József emlékezete 1810–1893. 1897. 8°. **010790. e. 7. (3.)**

—— Az emberi öntudat jelen fokáról, *etc.* pp. 27. *Pest,* 1870. 8°. [*Magyar Tudományos Akadémia. Értekezések a társadalmi tudományok köréből.* köt. 2. sz. 2.] Ac. **825/46.**

—— Magyarország felső tanintézetei és középtanodai 1870–1872-ben. Szerkesztette Dr. Barsi J. pp. 336 [386]. *Budapesten,* 1874. 4°. [*Hivatalos statistikai közlemények.* évf. 7. füz. 3.] S. **460.**

—— Magyarország közoktatási statistikaja 186$\frac{4}{5}$–186$\frac{7}{8}$-ban . . . Szerkeztette Dr. Barsi J. pp. xvii. 297. *Pest,* 1868 [1869]. 4°. [*Hivatalos statistikai közlemények.* évf. 1. füz. 5.] S. **460.**

—— A szerelemről és házasságról . . . Irta Barsi J. . . . Kiadta Horváth D. pp. 89. *Kecskeméten,* 1861. 12°. **8415.** bb. **43. (1.)**

—— Utazás ismeretlen állomás felé, 1849–1856. pp. 414. *Budapest,* 1890. 16°. [*Olcsó könyvtár.* sz. 278.] **12215.a.1/278.**

—— [Another copy.] Utazás ismeretlen állomás felé 1849–1856. *Budapest,* 1890. 16°. **010795.** bb. **104.**

BARSI (Niccolò)

—— Le Voyage de Niccolò Barsi en Moldavie, 1633. (Nuova e vera relatione del viaggio fatto da Nicolò Barsi da Lucca. [Edited by C. C. Giurescu.]) *See* Paris.—*École Roumaine en France.* Mélanges, *etc.* 1925. pt. 1. 1923, *etc.* 8°. Ac. **743.** g.

BARSICKOW (Hermann Christian August) Zwei Familien mit Lipomatosis musculorum progressiva . . . Inaugural-Dissertation, *etc.* pp. 35. *Halle,* 1872. 8°. **7386.c.16.(2.)**

BARSICKOW (Max) Über das sekundäre Dickenwachstum der Palmen in den Tropen. 1901. *See* Wurzburg.—*Physikalisch-Medicinishe Gesellschaft.* Verhandlungen, *etc.* N.F. Bd. 34. no. 8. 1869, *etc.* 8°. Ac. **3763/3.**

BARSIMAEUS, *Saint and Martyr, Bishop of Edessa. See* Moesinger (G.) Acta S.S. Martyrum Edessenorum Sarbelii, Barsimati, *etc.* 1874, *etc.* 8°. **4827.** dd. **21.**

BARSIMSON (Jacob) *See* Oppenheim (Samuel) *of New York.* More about Jacob Barsimson, the first Jewish settler in New York, *etc.* [1925.] 8°. **010760.** i. **13.**

BARSINGHAUSEN, *Monastery at.* Archiv des Klosters Barsinghausen. *See* Hodenberg (W. von) *Baron.* Calenberger Urkundenbuch. Abt. 1. [1855, *etc.*] 4°. **10260.** f. **10.**

BARSI RONÁY (Jenő) *See* Ronáy (J. J.) *Barsi, Count.*

BARSIS, *Saint and Martyr, Bishop of Edessa. See* Barsimaeus.

BARSIS (Max)

—— Bottoms up. An unreliable handbook for skiers. [Cartoons.] *Stephen Daye Press: Brattleboro,* [1939.] 8°. **12332.** d. **58.**

BARSISIUS (Christophorus) *See* Barzizius.

BARSIUS (Vincentius) Veneran. Carmelitani F. V. Barsii Mantuani . . . De Betigallico cōflictu libellus. [In verse.] *In ædibus C. Achillini: Bononiæ,* 1526. 4°. **11408.** bb. **23.**

BARSIUS (Vincentius)

—— Insubria Venerandi Carmelitani Vincentii Barsii Mantuani Philosophi. (Elegiarū Libellus.) *per Hieronymū de Benedictis: Bononię,* 1524. 8°. **1477.** a. **14.**

BARSKAYA (B. Prilezhaeva) *See* Prilezhaeva-Barskaya (B.)

BARSKAYA (N.)

—— Заслуженный артист РСФСР Евгений Валерианович Самойлов. [With portraits.] pp. 25. *Москва,* 1951. 8°. [*Мастера советского кино.*] W.P. **11/10.**

BARSKETT (*Sir* James) *See* Justin (M. P.) Histoire politique et statistique de l'Île d'Hayti . . . écrite sur des documents officiels et des notes communiquées par Sir J. Barskett, *etc.* 1826. 8°. **9555.** cc. **22.**

BARSKIER (Anne Hans)

—— Kiøge Huuskors; en original Dansk Folke-Roman . . . hvori fortaelles alle de Begivenheder der ved Trolddomskunster skal vaere passeret i et Huus i Kiøge. Samlet af Quindens [i.e. A. Barskier's] egne Skrifter . . . af Johan Bruunsmand . . . Ny Udgave. pp. 63. *Kiøbenhavn,* 1820. 8°. **9425.** a. **40. (10.)**

—— Køge huskors. [Edited by Johan Brunsmand.] Med indledning og noter ved Anders Bæksted. pp. 320. *København,* 1953. 8°. [*Danmarks folkeminder.* no. 61.] **10281.** r. **6/61.**

—— Energumeni Coagienses, sive Admirabilis historia, de horrenda Cacodæmonis tentatione, quacum in Selandia Daniæ, eiusque urbe Coagia familia civis . . . est conflictata . . . Nunc verò . . . Latinè interpretata editaque studio & cura Johannis Brunsmanni. pp. 82. *H. à Damme: Lugd. Batavorum,* 1693. 12°. **719.** a. **5.**

—— Editio altera, *etc.* pp. 156. *Ex officina J. Melchioris: Lipsiæ,* 1695. 12°. **8632.** aa. **2.**
With an additional titlepage, reading " *J. Brunsmanni energumeni coagienses, etc.*"

BARSKOV (Yakov Lazarevich)

—— *See* Catherine ii, *Empress of Russia.* Сочиненія . . . съ объяснительными примѣчаніями . . . А. Н. Пыпина. [Tom. 12 edited by Ya. Barskov.] 1901, *etc.* 8°. Ac. **1125/77.**

—— *See* Radishchev (A. N.) Путешествие из Петербурга в Москву . . . Том. 2. Материалы к изучению "Путешествия." (Статьи Я. Л. Барскова и М. В. Жижки. Описание рукописей и печатных изданий "Путешествия" Я. Л. Барскова. Комментарии его же.) 1935. 8°. **010291.** f. **36.**

—— Списокъ трудовъ . . . А. Н. Пыпина 1853–1903. pp. 122. 1903. 8°. *See* Russia.—*Академия Наук СССР. Отдѣленіе Русскаго Языка и Словесности.* Ac. **1125.** e.

BARSKY (Arthur Joseph)

—— Plastic Surgery . . . With 432 illustrations. pp. 355. *W. B. Saunders Co.: Philadelphia & London,* 1938. 8°. **07481.** d. **28.**

—— Principles and Practice of Plastic Surgery. pp. 499. *Baillière, Tindall & Cox: London; Baltimore* printed, 1950. 8°. **7483.** dd. **2.**

BARSKY-PLAKA-ALBOV (Vasily Grigor'evich Grigorovich) *See* Grigorovich-Barsky-Plaka-Albov.

BARSLEY (Michael Henry)

—— Alice in Wunderground, and other blits and pieces . . . Illustrated by the author. pp. 48. *John Murray: London,* 1940. 8°. **12332.** f. **1.**

—— Common Man and Colonel Bogus . . . Illustrated by the author. pp. 113. *Pilot Press: London,* 1944. 8°. **012331.** m. **164.**

—— Grabberwocky and other Fights of Fancy . . . Illustrated by Osbert Lancaster. pp. 43. *John Murray: London,* 1939. 8°. **11657.** d. **3.**

—— The Intimate Papers of Colonel Bogus . . . Copiously and curiously illustrated by the author. (Reprinted.) pp. xii. 122. *Pilot Press: London,* 1943. 8°. **012331.** m. **158.**

—— Modern American Humour. Selected by M. Barsley. pp. xx. 143. *Pilot Press: London,* 1942. 8°. **012316.e.64.**

—— The Phoenix Book of Wit and Humour. Edited by M. Barsley. pp. 255. *Phoenix House: London,* 1949. 8°. **12332.** bb. **39.**

—— Ritzkrieg. The old guard's private war . . . Copiously and curiously illustrated by the author. pp. 96. *Pilot Press: London,* 1940. 8°. **012331.** m. **127.**

—— This England, 1940–1946. Selected by Michael Barsley. Nicolas Bentley drew the pictures. pp. 80. *New Statesman & Nation: London,* [1946.] 8°. **12332.** f. **6.**

—— The Wolf at the Door. [Autobiographical reminiscences.] Illustrated by the author. pp. 208. *Michael Joseph: London,* 1946. 8°. **10861.** aa. **33.**

BARSOBIA. *See* Warsaw.

BARSOCCHINI (Domenico)

—— *See* Bertini (D.) Raccolta di documenti per servire alla storia ecclesiastica lucchese. [Begun under the editorship of D. Bertini, continued under that of D. Barsocchini.] 1818, *etc.* 4°. [*Memorie e documenti per servire all'istoria del principato lucchese.* tom. 4. pt. 1, 2 ; tom. 5. pt. 1–3.] **574.** l. **18.**

—— *See* Mansi (G. D.) *Archbishop of Lucca.* Diario sacro delle chiese di Lucca . . . accresciuto di molte notizie . . . dall' Ab. D. Barsocchini. 1836. 8°. **4605.** cc. **11.**

—— *See* Pieri (P.) Della vita e delle opere dell' abbate D. Barsocchini, *etc.* 1873. 8°. **4867.** ee. **40.**

—— Ragionamento cronologico intorno ai Rè ed Imperatori che ressero l'Italia dall' anno 700 al 1000.—Raccolta di documenti per servire alla storia ecclesiastica Lucchese. 1837. *See* Lucca.—*Accademia Lucchese.* Memorie e documenti per servire all' istoria del principato Lucchese. tom. 5. 1813, *etc.* 4°. **574.** l. **18.**

—— Ragionamento sopra il Volto Santo di Lucca. pp. 99. *Lucca,* 1844. 4°. **3902.** i. **6. (16.)**
A dedication in ms. *by the author is attached to the leaf preceding the titlepage.*

BARSOMA, *Bishop of Nisibis.*

—— *See* Vööbus (A.) Les Messalliens et les réformes de Barçauma de Nisibe dans l'église perse. 1947. 8°. [*Contributions of Baltic University.* no. 34.] Ac. **2631.**

BARSON (Georgius) *See* Bársony.

BARSON (Wilfred A.) Electric Overhead Travelling Crane Design. [With diagrams.] pp. vii. 120. *C. Lockwood & Son: London,* 1930. 8°. **08755.** b. **49.**

BARSONY (Elemér) *See* Baradlai (J.) A magyarországi gyógyszerészet története az ősidőktől a mai napig. Írták: Dr. Baradlai J. és Bársony E. 1930. 8°. **8901.** dd. **18.**

BARSONY (Georgius) successively *Bishop of Grosswardein* and *of Erlau.* Veritas toti mundo declarata: Sacram Cæsaream Regiamq; Majestatem non obligari ad tolerandos in Ungaria Lutheranos & Calvinistas. Authore primum . . . G. Barsony . . . Impugnata deinde ab hæretico quodam Protestantium fautore, sed præsenti scripto vindicata per Catholicum pacis, patriæ . . . studiosum. pp. 152. *M. Srnensky: [Tyrnau,]* 1681. 8°. **1020.** h. **16.**

—— [Another edition.] pp. 99. *Tyrnaviæ,* 1706. 12°. **5107.** aa. **12.**

—— [Another edition.] pp. 224. [*Tyrnau?* 1720?] 8°. **9315.** aa. **34. (4.)**

BÁRSONY (István) *See* Hungary.—*Magyar Királyi Államvasutak.* Ungarn . . . Unter Mitwirkung von Stefan Bársony [and others] . . . redigiert von A. Krain. 1909. fol. **1783.** cc. **8.**

—— A boszorkány, és más elbeszélések. pp. 158. *Budapest,* 1911. 8°. **012590.** aaa. **62.**

—— Dobogó szivek. [A novel.] pp. 159. *Budapest,* 1891. 8°. [*Szépirodalmi könyvtár.* no. 12.] **012264.** ee. **4.**

—— Ecce homo. [Short stories.] pp. 176. *Budapest,* 1897. 8°. **012591.** g. **31.**

—— Élőképek. [Short stories.] pp. 163. *Budapest,* [1902.] 8°. **012590.** cc. **9.**

—— Erdőn, mezőn. Természeti és vadászati képek . . . Spányi B. . . . és más művészek eredeti rajzaival. pp. 207. *Budapest,* 1894. 4°. **7912.** k. **13.**

—— Igaz mesék. pp. 158. *Budapest,* [1903.] 8°. **012590.** dd. **13.**

—— Ingovány. Regény . . . Második kiadás. pp. 188. *Budapest,* [1912.] 8°. **12590.** f. **34.**

—— A kaméleon-leány és más elbeszélések. [Short stories.] pp. 160. *Budapest,* [1899.] 8°. **12591.** k. **1.**

—— A királytigris. Regény. pp. 158. *Budapest,* [1903.] 8°. **012590.** aa. **28.**

—— Magyar természeti és vadászati képek . . . Képekkel díszítette Neogrády A. pp. 178. *Budapest,* 1900. 8°. **7907.** dd. **24.**

—— A napsütötte férfi, és más elbeszélések. pp. 160. *Budapest,* 1904. 8°. **012590.** m. **59.**

—— A rab király szabadon. Fantasztikus állatregény . . . Mühlbeck K. rajzaival. pp. 183. *Budapesten,* [1903.] 8°. **012590.** bb. **3.**

—— A róna és az erdő. Állatjellemek, hangulatok, vadász emlékek és arczképek gyüjteménye. Képekkel díszítette: Olgyay F. pp. 293. *Budapest,* 1902. 8°. **12591.** h. **40.**

—— A szabad ég alatt. [Short sketches.] pp. 149. *Budapest,* 1888. 8°. **7006.** aaa. **12.**

—— Tarka mesék. Elbeszélések. pp. 240. *Budapest,* 1908. 8°. **012589.** i. **2.**

—— Tréfás történetek. [Short stories.] pp. 287. *Budapest,* 1905. 8°. **12555.** s. **6.**

BÁRSONY (ISTVÁN)

—— Vadász-történetek. pp. 65. *Budapest*, 1898. 16°. *Magyar könyvtár.* no. 28. **012590**. de. **43**.

—— Vig világ. Mulattató történetek, kalandok, adomák, a vadász-, erdész- és gazdaéletből, a falu és a puszta világából. Huszonöt műmelléklettel. Illusztrálta Garad A. és Neogrády A. pp. 149. *Budapest*, [1898.] 4°. **1874**. c. **14**.

—— Visszhang. Elbeszélések . . . Neogrády A. és Goró L. rajzaival. pp. 165. *Budapest*, 1903. 8°. **012590**. aa. **27**.

BARSOR (JEAN) *pseud.* [i.e. J. B. ARTIGES.] Rimes de fête. pp. 30. *A Cyclopolis* [*Brussels*, 1897.] 8°. **011483**. ee. 5. (6.)

BARSOTTI (DIVO)

—— Il Dio di Abramo. L'esperienza di Dio nella Genesi. pp. 414. *Firenze*, 1952. 8°. **3156**. aa. **43**. *Deificum lumen.* vol. 7.

BARSOTTI (GIOVANNI CARLO FILIPPO) *See* VERACINI (T.) Vita del venerabil sacerdote il dottore Giovancarlo F. Barsotti, *etc.* 1771. 4°. **1232**. d. **1**.

—— Vita del servo di Dio Gaetano Pratesi . . . pubblicata dal dottor T. Veracini, *etc.* pp. xvi. 200. *Firenze*, 1756. 4°. **1231**. e. **21**.

BARSOTTI (GIUSEPPE) *See* LAMPRECHT (J. F.) Vita del sig. Barone Goffredo Guglielmo di Leibnitz . . . tradotta . . . da G. Barsotti. 1787. 8°. **612**. e. **9**.

BARSOTTI (MATTEO) La Coronatione della miracolosissima imagine di Maria Vergine detta del Sasso nella chiesa di S. Agostino di Lucca. Con una breve narratione della solenne festa fatta nella medesima chiesa per la canonizatione di S. Gio. da S. Facondo, e la vita elogiastica dell'istesso santo [by Raffaello Nuccorini]. pp. 236. *I Marescandoli: Lucca*, 1693. 4°. **1124**. g. **25**.

BARSOTTI (MICHELE) Il Mercenario del Papa-Re. Racconto. pp. 291. *Lucca*, 1886. 8°. **12470**. aaa. **32**.

BARSOTTI (ONORIO AMBRAGIO) Il Giglio della purità conservato con varii mezzi e specialmente con la divozione del sacro cingolo dell' angelico dottore San Tommaso d'Aquino coll' aggiunta di una istruzione del padre Lorenzo Scupoli. Quarta edizione. pp. 93. *Roma*, 1842. 16°. **1360**. a. **18**.

BARSOTTINI (GEREMIA) *See* EVANGELISTI (A.) Giosuè Carducci col suo maestro (G. Barsottini), *etc.* 1924. 8°. **10634**. bbb. **4**.

—— Poesie italiane. [With an introduction by Cesare Maggi.] pp. xxxi. 528. *Prato*, 1891. 8°. **11429**. e. **28**.

BARSOV (ANTON) *See* CELLARIUS (C.) *the Elder*. Краткая латинская грамматика . . . съ нѣмецкаго на россійской языкъ переведена . . . А. Барсовымъ. 1762. 8°. **12933**. bbb. **29**.

BARSOV (EL'PIDIFOR VASIL'EVICH) Богатырское слово въ спискѣ начала XVII вѣка, открытое Е. В. Барсовымъ, *etc.* pp. 27. *Санктпетербургъ*, 1881. 8°. [*Записки Имп. Академіи Наукъ.* том. 40. прил. no. 5.] Ac. **1125/48**.

—— [Another issue.] [*Сборникъ Отдѣленія Русскаго Языка и Словесности Императорской Академіи Наукъ.* том. 28. no. 3.] Ac. **1125/39**.

—— Петръ Великій въ народныхъ преданіяхъ Сѣвернаго края, собранныхъ Е. В. Барсовымъ. pp. 17. *Москва*, 1872. 8°. **10795**. f. **41**. (8.)

BARSOV (EL'PIDIFOR VASIL'EVICH)

—— Причитанья Сѣвернаго края, собранныя Е. В. Барсовымъ. част. 1. Плачи похоронные, надгробные и надмогильные, *etc.* (Сѣверно-русскій словарь съ общими замѣчаніями о языкѣ причитаній.) pp. xxxi. 327. xxxiii. *Москва*, 1872. 8°. **11585**. l. **23**.

BARSOV (NIKOLAI IVANOVICH) Матеріалы для біографіи Иннокентія Борисова, Архіепископа Херсонскаго и Таврическаго. Собралъ и издалъ . . . Н. Барсовъ. 2 вып. *С.-Петербургъ*, 1884, 88. 8°. **4886**. h. **33**.

—— Русскій простонародный мистицизмъ. Сообщеніе, *etc.* pp. 64. *Санктпетербургъ*, 1869. 8°. **8468**. dd. **35**. (**1**.)

BARSOV (NIKOLAI PAVLOVICH) *See* NECHAEV (M. G.) Путешествіе . . . М. Г. Нечаева въ Іерусалимъ . . . Издано подъ редакціею Н. П. Барсова. 1875. 8°. **10077**. h. **26**. (**1**.)

—— Народныя школы въ Юго-Западномъ краѣ, очеркъ ихъ учрежденія, устройства и современнаго состоянія. Составилъ Н. Барсовъ. pp. 103. [*Saint Petersburg?* 1864.] 8°. **8355**. eee. **2**. (**3**.)

—— Отчетъ о поѣздкѣ съ педагогическою цѣлю по Волыни и Подоліи. pp. 45. *Санктпетербургъ*, 1863. 8°. **8355**. eee. **2**. (**1**.)

—— Очерки русской исторической географіи. Географія начальной — несторовой — лѣтописи. Изслѣдованіе Н. П. Варсова . . . Изданіе второе, исправленное и дополненное, *etc.* pp. iv. 371. *Варшава*, 1885. 8°. **9456**. e. **3**.

—— Школы на Волыни и Подоліи въ 1862 году. (Очеркъ изъ современнаго состоянія.) [Signed: Н. Барсовъ.] pp. 156. *Санктпетербургъ*, 1863. 8°. **8355**. eee. **2**. (**2**.)

—— Славянскій вопросъ и его отношеніе къ Россіи . . . Посвящается друзьямъ славянства. pp. 25. *Вильна*, 1867. 8°. **8093**. aaa. **42**. (**3**.)

BARSOV (TIMOTHEI VASIL'EVICH) Константинопольскій патріархъ и его власть надъ русскою церковію. pp. viii. iv. 578. v. *С.-Петербургъ*, 1878. 8°. **3926**. k. **4**.

—— Святѣйшій сvнодъ въ его прошломъ. pp. iv. 446. *С.-Петербургъ*, 1896. 8°. **4685**. g. **31**.

BARSOVA (VALERIYA VLADIMIROVNA)

—— *See* POLYANOVSKY (G.) Барсова. [A biography. With portraits.] 1941. 8°. **10797**. a. **20**.

BARSS (FRANCISZEK) *See* KRAUSHAR (A.) Barss, Palestrant Warszawski, jego misya polityczna we Francyi, 1793–1800. 1903. 8°. **9476**. ddd. **12**.

BARSS (JOHN EDMUND) *See* CICERO (M. T.) [*Selections.—Latin.*] Orations of Cicero, with a selection from his Letters. Edited by . . . F. G. Moore and J. E. Barss. [1929.] 8°. **11396**. de. **10**.

—— *See* NEPOS (C.) Cornelius Nepos. Twenty lives. Edited by J. E. Barss. 1900. 8°. **11305**. c. **39/1**.

—— *See* SALLUSTIUS CRISPUS (C.) [*Selections.*] Third Year Latin for sight reading. Selections from Sallust and Cicero. By J. E. Barss. [1911.] 8°. **12934**. dd. **32**.

—— Writing Latin. 2 vol. *D. C. Heath & Co.: London*, 1908. 8°. [*Gildersleeve-Lodge Latin Series.*] **12934**. dd. **39**.

BARSS (W. M.)

—— A High Speed Pen Recorder and its Amplifier. pp. 5. pl. 4. *Harwell*, 1950. fol. [*A.E.R.E. Memoranda.* no. G/M 76.] B.S. **62**/**38**.

BARSS (W. R.) Note on Measurements of Radio-activity by means of Alpha Rays. (From the "American Journal of Science.") [*New Haven, Conn.*, 1912.] 8°. **08709**. cc. **4**. **(2.)**

BARSTAD (ANVOR) *See* SCOTT (Gabriel) Kari . . . Translated by A. Barstad, *etc.* 1931. 8°. **12583**. r. **28**.

BARSTAD (HANS JACOB) Bergens Forsvar 1801 og 1807–1814 . . . Med Kart over Bergen i 1801. pp. xxxii. 504. *Bergen*, 1887. 8°. **9424**. i. **9**.

—— Norges landforsvar, 1604–1643 . . . Med 2 karter, *etc.* pp. iv. 211. pl. IV. *Christiania*, 1905. 8°. [*Skrifter udgivne af Videnskabs-Selskabet i Christiania.* Hist.-fil. Klasse. 1905. no. 3.] Ac. **1054/5**.

BARSTAD (SVERRE)

—— Menighetsblad i Norge. pp. 117. *Flisa*, 1935. 8°. **11858**. a. **18**.

BARSTOW (BEATRICE) *See* FAGUET (E.) The Cult of Incompetence . . . Translated . . . by B. Barstow, *etc.* 1911. 8°. **8006**. i. **16**.

—— *See* KEROPHILAS (K.) Eleftherios Venizelos, his life and work . . . Translated by B. Barstow. 1915. 8°. **010795**. a. **5**.

—— *See* VERGNET (P.) France in Danger . . . Translated by B. Barstow. 1915. 8°. **08026**. aa. **19**.

BARSTOW (BENJAMIN) Speech . . . on the Abolition Propensities of Caleb Cushing, *etc.* pp. 16. *National Democrat: Boston*, 1853. 8°. **8156**. bb. **15**.

BARSTOW (CHARLES H.) Angels Unawares, *etc.* pp. 128. *F. Warne & Co.: London*, [1895.] 8°. **4399**. l. **16**.

—— Natty's Violin, *etc.* pp. 188. *F. Warne & Co.: London & New York*, [1897.] 8°. **012806**. ee. **4**.

—— Old Ransom; or, Light after darkness. A story of street life, *etc.* pp. viii. 85. *F. Warne & Co.: London*, [1884.] 8°. **4417**. de. **32**.

—— Through Deep Waters, *etc.* pp. 185. *F. Warne & Co.: London & New York*, [1898.] 8°. **012806**. l. **38**.

BARSTOW (CHARLES LESTER) Famous Pictures. Noted paintings described with anecdotes of the painters . . . Illustrated. New and revised edition. pp. vii. 252. *Century Co.: New York, London*, [1930.] 8°. **7853**. r. **23**.

—— Famous Sculpture . . . New and revised edition. pp. 257. *D. Appleton-Century Co.: New York, London*, [1932.] 8°. **7877**. b. **5**.

—— Famous Sculpture. pp. 249. *Century Co.: New York*, 1916. 8°. **7875**. dg. **21**.

BARSTOW (D.) A Secular Diary for ascertaining any day of the week or month in either the old or new style, commencing 1601, and continued up to the year 1900. [*London ?*], 1836. *s. sh.* fol. **9005**. a. **3**.

BARSTOW (GEORGE) The History of New Hampshire, from its discovery, in 1614, to the passage of the Toleration Act, in 1819. [With plates.] pp. iv. 456. *I. S. Boyd: Concord*, 1842. 8°. **1447**. f. **15**.

—— Second edition. pp. iv. 456. *Little & Brown: Boston; G. P. Putnam & Co.: New York*, 1853. 8°. **9602**. e. **6**.

BARSTOW (GEORGE EAMES) The Effect of Psychology on Americanism. pp. 27. *Society of Applied Psychology: New York & London*, 1920. 8°. **08463**. de. **25**.

BARSTOW (HENRY CLEMENTS) *See* SULTĀN JAHĀN BĒGAM, *Nawab of Bhopal*. The Tāj-ul Ikbāl Tārikh Bhopal . . . Translated by H. C. Barstow. 1876. 8°. **14109**. a. **41**.

BARSTOW (JAMES) A Letter to the Revd Mr Hall of Leicester, in answer to his attack on West-Indian proprietors, with some observations on the general question as to the abolition of West Indian slavery. pp. 61. *J. Hearne & J. M. Richardson: London*, 1824. 8°. T. **1139**. **(4.)**

BARSTOW (JOHN MONTAGU ORCZY) *See* BLAKENEY (John) *pseud.* [i.e. J. M. O. Barstow.]

BARSTOW (MARJORIE LATTA) Memories. (Yale University Prize Poem, 1914.) pp. 19. *Yale University Press: [New Haven,]* 1914. 8°. **11686**. ee. **44**.

—— Wordsworth's Theory of Poetic Diction. A study of the historical and personal background of the Lyrical Ballads . . . A dissertation, *etc.* pp. xv. 187. *New Haven*, 1917. 8°. [*Yale Studies in English.* no. 57.] Ac. **2692**. ma/**3**.

BARSTOW (ROBBINS WOLCOTT) Getting acquainted with God. A book of devotions, *etc.* pp. 115. *Macmillan Co.: New York*, 1928. 8°. **04402**. h. **82**.

BARSTOW (WILLIAM) *M.D.* Sulphurets: what they are . . . With a chapter on the blow-pipe assay of minerals. pp. 114. *A. Roman & Co.: San Francisco, New York*, 1867. 12°. **7104**. a. **6**.

BARSTOW (WILLIAM AUGUSTUS) *See* BASHFORD (Coles) The Trial in the Supreme Court . . . on the relation of C. Bashford vs. W. A. Barstow, contesting the right to the office of Governor of Wisconsin. 1856. 8°. **6778**. c. **4**.

BARSTOW (ZEDEKIAH S.)

—— The Ministers of Christ should not be Afraid. A sermon preached at the installation of Rev. Salmon Bennet . . . as Collegiate Pastor . . . of the First Congregational Church in Boscawen. pp. 24. *Morril & Chadwick: Concord*, 1833. 8°. **4485**. g. **4**.

—— The Committees vindicated: an examination of the Rev. Mr. Barstow's "Remarks on the preliminary history of two discourses by Rev. Aaron Bancroft." pp. 22. *Keene, N.H.*, 1822. 8°. **1414**. i. **21**.

BARSUKOV (ALEKSANDR PLATONOVICH)

—— *See* VITTE (S. YU.) *Count.* Автографы извѣстныхъ и замѣчательныхъ людей, *etc.* [Edited by A. P. Barsukov.] 1905. 8°. [*Старина и Новизна.* кн. 9.] Ac. **7888**.

—— Обзоръ источниковъ и литературы русскаго родословія, по поводу книги П. Н. Петрова, "Исторія русскаго дворянства," А. Барсукова, *etc.* pp. 96. *Санктпетербургъ*, 1887. 8°. [*Записки Императорской Академіи Наукъ.* том. 54. прил. no. 4.] Ac. **1125/48**.

—— Родъ Шереметевыхъ. кн. 1–4. *Санктпетербургъ*, 1881–84. 4°. **9902**. k. **18**.
Imperfect; wanting кн. 5.

—— Списки городовыхъ воеводъ и другихъ лицъ воеводскаго управленія Московскаго государства XVII столѣтія . . . Составилъ А. Барсуковъ. pp. ix. 611. *С.-Петербургъ*, 1902. 8°. **8824**. g. **21**.

—— Шкловскіе авантюристы. 1778–1783 гг. [Signed: А. Барсуковъ.] pp. 32. 1872. *See* RUSSIA. [*Appendix.—History and Politics.*] Памятники новой русской исторіи, *etc.* том. 2. отд. 1. 1871, *etc.* 8°. **9455**. e. **22**.

BARSUKOV (EVGENY ZAKHAROVICH)

—— *See* MANIKOVSKY (A. A.) Боевое снабжение русской армии в мировую войну. Издание второе переработал и дополнил Е. З. Барсуков, *etc.* 1930. 8°. **9087.c.5.**

BARSUKOV (EVGENY ZAKHAROVICH)

—— Русская артиллерия в мировую войну. Том первый. pp. 395. *Москва*, 1938. 8°. **9087. bbb. 21.**
Imperfect; wanting том. 2.

BARSUKOV (IVAN PLATONOVICH) *See* INNOKENTY, successively *Bishop and Archbishop of Kamtchatka* and *Metropolitan of Moscow.* Творенія . . . Собраны И. Барсуковымъ. 1886, *etc.* 8°. **12265. k. 4.**

—— Графъ Николай Николаевичъ Муравьевъ-Амурскій по его письмамъ . . . и печатнымъ источникамъ . . . Матеріалы для біографіи. [With a portrait.] 2 кн. *Москва*, 1891. 8°. **10795. h. 33.**

—— Иннокентій, Митрополитъ Московскій и Коломенскій по его сочиненіямъ, письмамъ и разсказамъ современниковъ. [A biography. With a facsimile and portraits of Innokenty.] pp. viii. 769. 14. xiv. *Москва*, 1883. 8°. **10795. i. 5.**

—— Жизнь и подвиги Иннокентія, проповѣдника евангелія на Алеутскихъ Островахъ. Составлено Е. А. Сысоевой по книгѣ И. Барсукова: "Иннокентій, митрополитъ Московскій и Коломенскій." Съ портретомъ и одной картинкой. pp. 92. *С.-Петербургъ*, 1892. 8°. **4804. f. 2. (2.)**

—— Памятники Діонисія, епископа Якутскаго, *etc.* [With a portrait.] pp. 147. 76. *С.-Петербургъ*, 1902. 8°. **4887. g. 19.**

BARSUKOV (M. I.)

—— *See* RUSSIA.—*Всесоюзная Конференція по Планированію Здравоохраненія и Рабочего Отдыха.* Здравоохранение и рабочий отдых во второй пятилетке, *etc.* (Ответственный редактор М. Барсуков.) 1933. 8°. S. N. **84/6.**

BARSUKOV (NIKOLAI PLATONOVICH) *See* BRIKNER (A. G.) Объ изданіи дневника Храповицкаго. [A reply to the strictures of N. P. Barsukov.] 1876. 8°. **011850. k. 15. (3.)**

—— *See* DMITRIEV (I. I.) *Poet.* Письма . . . къ князю П. А. Вяземскому. (Съ предисловіемъ и примѣчаніями Н. П. Барсукова.) 1898. 8°. [*Старина и Новизна.* кн. 2.] Ac. **7888.**

—— *See* FILARET, successively *Bishop of Riga, Archbishop of Kharkov, etc.* [D. G. Gumilevsky.] Письма . . . къ Н. Н. Шереметевой, *etc.* (Съ предисловіемъ и примѣчаніями Н. П. Барсукова.) 1900. 8°. [*Старина и Новизна.* кн. 3.] Ac. **7888.**

—— *See* GRIGOROVICH-BARSKY-PLAKA-ALBOV (V. G.) Странствованія . . . по святымъ мѣстамъ востока . . . Подъ редакціею Н. Барсукова. 1885, *etc.* 8°. **010077. n. 4.**

—— *See* IOAKIM, *Patriarch of Russia.* Житіе и завѣщаніе . . . Патріарха Московскаго Іоакима. [With a preface by N. P. Barsukov.] 1879. 4°. Ac. **9086/28.**

—— *See* KARAMZIN (N. M.) Письма . . . къ князю П. А. Вяземскому, *etc.* (Съ предисловіемъ и примѣчаніями Н. П. Барсукова.) 1897. 8°. [*Старина и Новизна.* кн. 1.] Ac. **7888.**

—— *See* KHRAPOVITSKY (A. V.) Дневникъ А. В. Храповицкаго. 1782–1793 . . . съ біографическою статьею . . . Н. Барсукова. 1874. 8°. **10790. g. 1.**

—— *See* STROEV (P. M.) Описаніе рукописей монастырей Волоколамскаго, Новый Іерусалимъ . . . Съ предисловіемъ . . . Н. Барсукова. 1891. 8°. Ac. **9086/61.**

BARSUKOV (NIKOLAI PLATONOVICH)

—— Жизнь и труды М. П. Погодина . . . Изданіе А. Д. и П. Д. Погодиныхъ. [With a portrait.] 22 кн. *С.-Петербургъ*, 1888–1910. 8°. **010795. k. 1.**

—— Жизнь и труды П. М. Строева. pp. iii. v. 668. *Санктпетербургъ*, 1878. 8°. **10795. h. 6.**

—— [Another copy.] **10790. f. 4.**

—— Жизнь и труды В. Г. Барскаго, *etc.* pp. 72. *Санктпетербургъ*, 1885. 8°. **010795. g. 9. (3.)**

—— Источники русской агіографіи. pp. xi. 308. 8. 1882. 8°. *See* LENINGRAD. —*Общество Любителей Древней Письменности.* Ac. **9086/40.**

—— Письма М. П. Погодина, С. П. Шевырева и М. А. Максимовича къ князю П. А. Вяземскому. Съ предисловіемъ и примѣчаніями Н. П. Барсукова [and edited by him]. 1901. *See* LENINGRAD. —*Общество Ревнителей Русскаго Историческаго Просвѣщенія, etc.* Старина и Новизна, *etc.* кн. 4. 1897, *etc.* 8°. Ac. **7888.**

BARSUKOVA (LIDIYA EVGEN'EVNA)

—— Герцен, Огарев и их окружение. Рукописи, переписка и документы. [A bibliography.] Составили . . . Л. Е. Барсукова, А. В. Давыдов [and others] . . . Редакция Б. П. Козьмина. [With plates, including portraits and facsimiles.] pp. xvi. 438. *Москва*, 1940. 8°. [*Бюллетени Государственного Литературного Музея.* no. 5.] Ac. **9657.** f.

BARSY (E.)

—— *See* APOSTLES' CREED. [*Hungarian.*] Hiszek egy Istenben, *etc.* [With illustrations by E. Barsy.] [1933.] 8°. **03504. i. 6.**

BARSZCZEWSKI (JAN) Proza i wiersze. cz. 1. pp. 194. *Kijów*, 1849. 12°. **12265. bb. 8.**
No more published.

—— Szlachcic zawalnia czyli Białoruś w fantastycznych opowiadaniach przez J. Barszczewskiego. Poprzedzone krytycznym rzutem oka na literaturę białoruską przez R. Podbereskiego. Z ryciną R. Żukowskiego, *etc.* (Wydał Jan Eynerling.) 4 tomik. *Petersburg*, 1844–46. 8°. **12590. d. 12.**

BARSZCZEWSKI (S.) *See* CARNEGIE (A.) [The Empire of Business.] Państwo Interesu . . . Przełożył S. Barszczewski. 1904. 8°. **08226. a. 9.**